Directory of Grant Making Trusts

2010/11
21ST EDITION

RESEARCH TEAM

TOM TRAYNOR
CATRIONA CHRONNELL
ALAN FRENCH
JOHN SMYTH
JESSICA CARVER
SARAH JOHNSTON
DENISE LILLYA

DIRECTORY OF SOCIAL CHANGE

Published by
Directory of Social Change
24 Stephenson Way
London NW1 2DP
Tel: 08450 77 77 07; Fax: 020 7391 4804
email publications@dsc.org.uk
www.dsc.org.uk
from whom further copies and a full publications catalogue are available.

Directory of Social Change Northern Office
Federation House, Hope Street, Liverpool L1 9BW
Policy & Research 0151 708 0136; email: research@dsc.org.uk

Directory of Social Change is a Registered Charity no. 800517

First published by Charities Aid Foundation 1968
Second edition 1971
Third edition 1974
Fourth edition 1975
Fifth edition 1977
Sixth edition 1978
Seventh edition 1981
Eighth edition 1983
Ninth edition 1985
Tenth edition 1987
Eleventh edition 1989
Twelfth edition 1991
Thirteenth edition 1993
Fourteenth edition 1995
Fifteenth edition 1997
Sixteenth edition 1999
Seventeenth edition published by Directory of Social Change 2001
Eighteenth edition 2003
Nineteenth edition 2005
Twentieth edition 2007
Twenty-first edition 2010

ISBN 978 1 906294 34 2

British Library Cataloguing in Publication Data
A catalogue record for this book is available from the British Library

Cover design by Kate Bass
Text designed by Eugenie Dodd Typographics, London
Typeset by Marlinzo Services, Frome
Printed and bound by Antony Rowe, Chippenham

Contents

Foreword

Today, more than ever, the *Directory of Grant Making Trusts* (DGMT) plays a vital role in enabling the work of the voluntary sector. The last year saw unprecedented change amongst funders, with some well-known players temporarily or permanently changing focus or even ceasing operations, and others facing uncertainty of income going forward. This is overlaid on an exceptionally difficult environment for raising charitable funds.

There will always be debate about the role of charities in our society, but it is increasingly clear that in the present economic environment a harsh dichotomy is at play: the services of charities are needed more than ever, yet funds available are being squeezed from all sides. While disasters very rightly receive high profile attention and corresponding donations, many of the day-to-day services that do so much to improve life for so many are at risk. Donations from the public are under pressure, and severe cuts to local authority funding seem inevitable.

Against this backdrop, the DGMT is an enabler. Charities are resourceful – if they aren't they don't survive – and the DGMT quickly and easily helps them consider funding options and prioritise applications. But as well as assisting charities to target their efforts to greatest effect, let's not forget that it also helps grantmakers. By helping to ensure applications received fit their criteria, funders can spend their time more usefully in assessing applications which have a greater potential of being supported. This win-win effect means that the DGMT continues to play an essential role for both charities and funders.

Mary E Craig OBE FCIBS FRSA
Chief Executive, Lloyds TSB Foundation for Scotland

Introduction

This book covers the largest 2,500 grant-making trusts in the UK that give grants to organisations. The amounts given by individual funders range from £25,000 in total each year up to £598 million. The combined giving of all these trusts totals over £3.6 billion a year. The top 150 are listed at the end of this introduction and include the Big Lottery Fund and Awards for All, as well as more 'traditional' grant-making trusts.

Charities Aid Foundation published the first edition of the *Directory of Grant Making Trusts* (DGMT) in 1968 and it has been researched and published by the Directory of Social Change since 2001. Over this time the title has gained a notable reputation as a comprehensive guide to UK grant-making trusts and their funding policies. It is designed to provide a bridge between the foundation and fundraising communities in the UK. Today it is hard to imagine the difficulties which must have been encountered in trying to obtain funds from trusts before the DGMT brought together so many of them in one place.

The DGMT is a key source of information on how trusts see themselves and their grantmaking. Each entry aims to reflect the trust's own view of its policies, priorities and exclusions. Other guides include independent, sometimes critical comment on and analysis of trust activities. The DGMT does not. Rather, it is the trusts' guide to grant-making trusts.

The research carried out has resulted in over 200 trusts appearing in this edition for the first time. On average it appears that about 100 relevant new trusts are established each year that at a later date make it into this directory.

Since the last edition of this book was published we have experienced a global recession which few saw coming. As a result there have been many casualties in the world of grant-making trusts. Some high profile, such as the Lloyds TSB Foundation for Scotland which suspended its grantmaking due to unsuccessful negotiations with the Lloyds Banking Group about future funding arrangements. It would also appear that the future of the foundation itself is now uncertain (which means that the foundation does not feature here).

Potential fundraisers should, however, remain optimistic. While many trusts have disappeared from this edition for one reason or another, as stated above, there are over 200 trusts new to this edition; so the money is still out there. The funders in this edition have also given several hundred million pounds more than was described in the last edition. While most of this is due to a few large funders increasing their grantmaking since last time, other funders have also increased their giving. It must be said, however, that the full impact of the recession on grant-making trusts may not be revealed until the next edition.

We value the opinions of our readers on all aspects of this directory. We are always looking to improve the guide and would welcome any feedback – positive or negative – which could be useful for future editions. Please contact us at Research Team, Directory of Social Change, Federation House, Hope Street, Liverpool L1 9BW, telephone 0151 708 0136 or email us at: research@dsc.org.uk with any comments you would like to make.

The trusts we have listed This directory aims to include the majority of UK-based trusts capable of giving at least £25,000 a year to organisations. Every trust was sent a questionnaire giving them the opportunity to update key information about how they operate.

Many of the trusts are extremely helpful and provide comprehensive information on their current policies via their websites and published material. However, not all trusts are so open. Where a trust does not make this information available, their details have been updated where possible using the information on file at the Charity Commission or the Office of the Scottish Charity Regulator, where appropriate. In addition all contact details were checked. Trusts have been included in the index under the relevant headings according to their own published guidelines. We have placed those trusts for which we do not have such information available under what we believe are the most suitable categories based on the information in their annual reports and accounts.

Some trusts continue to state their wish not to be included in this book. However, we believe that trust directories provide an invaluable bridge between the trust community and the rest of the voluntary sector, and that trusts in receipt of public funds through tax relief should not attempt to draw a veil of secrecy over their activities. Consequently, we have declined requests from trusts to be excluded from this directory.

In general we have included:

■ trusts with a grant-making capacity of at least £25,000 per year which make grants to charities and voluntary organisations, including Big Lottery Fund and Awards for All.

We have excluded:

■ trusts which fund individuals only

■ trusts which fund one organisation exclusively

■ trusts which have a grant-making capacity or an income of less than £25,000 (smaller local trusts are included on www.trustfunding.org.uk)

■ trusts which have ceased to exist or are being wound down with remaining funds fully committed.

We continue to include trusts which state that they do not respond to unsolicited applications. We believe their inclusion benefits fundraisers by giving a broader overview of the grant-making community, and that the information could be important in supporting relationship fundraising activity. We feel it benefits the trusts in helping them to communicate that they do not wish to receive applications, which fundraisers might not know if they identified the trust through other avenues. In this way we are working towards achieving one of our Great Giving campaign goals of reducing the number of ineligible applications that are submitted to trusts.

Acknowledgements

We would like to thank Mary Craig, Chief Executive of the Lloyds TSB Foundation for Scotland, for contributing the foreword to this edition.

We would also like to thank all those trusts who make their information openly available, and all those who replied to our questionnaire.

How to use the DGMT

The directory starts with three indexes:

- trusts by geographical area
- trusts by field of interest and type of beneficiary
- trusts by grant type.

There is a listing of the top 150 trusts by grant total at the end of this introduction. All of these lists are in alphabetical order.

Using these indexes, users should end up with a shortlist of trusts whose funding policies match their needs.

Trusts by geographical area

This index enables you to see which trusts will consider applications from a charity or project in a particular geographical area. It contains two separate listings:

LIST OF GEOGRAPHICAL AREA HEADINGS

This is a complete list of all the geographical area headings used in the DGMT. The page numbers relate to the second listing.

LIST OF TRUSTS BY GEOGRAPHICAL AREA

These pages list trusts under the geographical areas from which they will consider applications for funding.

Trusts by field of interest and type of beneficiary

This index enables you to see which trusts are likely to fund projects doing a particular type of work to benefit a particular type of person. It lists trusts according to:

- the type of activity or work they are willing to fund – their 'fields of interest';
- who they want to benefit – their preferred 'beneficiaries'.

These pages contain two separate listings:

CATEGORISATION OF FIELDS OF INTEREST AND TYPES OF BENEFICIARY

This lists all of the headings used in the DGMT to categorise fields of interest and types of beneficiary. This listing should help you match your project with one – or more – of the categories used. The page numbers relate to the second listing.

LIST OF TRUSTS BY FIELD OF INTEREST AND TYPE OF BENEFICIARY

These pages list trusts under the fields of interest and types of beneficiary they have indicated they have a preference for or might be willing to support.

The index is structured hierarchically. This means that the general heading comes first, followed by more specific subject areas. For example, *Education and training* is split into eight sub-headings, including *Higher education*; *Informal, continuing and adult education*; *Primary and secondary school education*; and so on. Some of these are then split further. For example, *Primary and secondary school education* contains a further four categories including *Faith schools* and *Special needs schools*.

So, if your project falls under a specific heading such as *Special needs schools*, it may also be worth looking at the trusts which have expressed a general interest in funding primary and secondary education and, above that, education and training.

Trusts by type of grant

This index enables you to see which trusts will consider making the types of grant you are looking for. Trusts are listed under the types of grant that they have indicated they are willing to make. These pages contain two separate listings:

LIST OF GRANT TYPES

This lists all of the headings used in the DGMT to categorise grant types. Page numbers relate to the second listing.

LIST OF TRUSTS BY GRANT TYPE

These pages list trusts under the types of grant that they are willing to make.

The largest trusts

At the end of these sections, we have listed the largest 150 trusts by grant total in alphabetical order. Between them they account for around £3 billion, or about 83% of the funds available in the book. Please do not use this simply as a mailing list: these trusts cover a wide range of specialist interests and many of them will never fund your work.

We recommend that you read each entry carefully and compile your own list of major trusts relevant to you. You can then set this list alongside the other lists generated from the other indexes in the directory. We believe this is the most effective way of ensuring that you do not omit any major trusts.

How to use the DGMT
Key steps

STEP 1

Define the project, programme or work for which you are seeking funding.

▼

STEP 2

Geographical area: find the area most local to your requirements. Note down the names of the trusts listed here.

▼

STEP 3

Field of interest and type of beneficiary: identify the categories that match your project. Note down the names of the trusts listed here.

▼

STEP 4

Type of grant: identify the type of grant you are looking for. Note down the names of the trusts listed here.

▼

STEP 5

Compare the three lists of trusts to produce a list of those whose funding policies most closely match the characteristics of the project for which you are seeking funding.

▼

STEP 6

If your trust list is **too short** you could include trusts that have a general interest in funding your area.

▼

STEP 7

Look up entries for the trusts identified, study their details carefully and pay close attention to 'What is funded' and 'What is not funded'.

▼

STEP 8

Look at the list of the **top 150 trusts**. Look up entries for the trusts identified, study their details carefully and again pay close attention to 'What is funded' and 'What is not funded'.

Checklist

STEP 1 The following checklist will help you assemble the information you need.

- What is the geographical location of the people who will benefit from any funding received?
- What facilities or services will the funding provide?
- What are the characteristics which best describe the people who will benefit from any funding received?
- What type of grant are you looking for?

EXAMPLE *Funding is being sought for a project in Merseyside to enable unemployed young people to take part in an employment training scheme.*

- *The geographical location is: England → North West → **Merseyside***
- *The service to be provided is: **Vocational training***
- *The key characteristic of the people to benefit is that they are: **Unemployed***
- *The type of grant being sought is: **Project support***

STEP 2 Look up the area where your project is based in the list of geographical area headings on page 2.

- Turn to the relevant pages in the list of trusts by geographical area and note down the names of the trusts which have stated that they will consider funding projects in your area.

EXAMPLE *Look up the area most local to your requirements (Merseyside) in the list of geographical area headings. Then turn to the relevant page in the list of trusts by geographical area and look up the names of the trusts listed under Merseyside. You may want to look at the trusts listed under the broader region (North West) as well. Note down the names so that they can be compared with the lists through the indexes by type of grant and by field of interest and type of beneficiary.*

It is also worth looking at trusts listed under England, as a trust listed under a more general heading may be just as willing to fund activity in a specific region as another which states that it has a specific interest in that region.

STEP 3 **Using the 'Field of interest and type of beneficiary' category on page 44, identify all the categories that match the project, programme or work for which you are seeking funding.**

Turn to the relevant pages in the list of trusts by field of interest and type of beneficiary and look up the headings identified.

Note down the names of the trusts that appear under these headings so that you can compare them with the names identified through the indexes by geographical area and by type of grant.

EXAMPLE *With a project to provide training for work, you will probably look first under the main heading 'Education and training'. Under this heading you will find the sub-heading 'Informal, continuing and adult education' and under this you will find the heading 'Vocational education and training'. Note down the page numbers beside 'Informal, continuing and adult education' and 'Vocational education and training'. Trusts that have expressed an interest in funding vocational training may represent your best prospects, but trusts with a more general interest in funding informal education and training might be worth approaching – particularly if they like to fund projects in your area.*

If you look under 'Beneficial groups' you will find 'People who are poor, on low incomes', which is under 'Social and economic circumstances' and 'Disadvantaged and socially excluded people'. Note down this page number too.

STEP 4 **Look up the type of grant that you are seeking in 'Trusts by type of grant' on page 150.**

Turn to the relevant pages in the list of trusts by type of grant and note down the names of the trusts which will consider giving the type of grant that you are seeking. Compare these names with those that you identified through the indexes by geographical area and by field of interest and type of beneficiary.

EXAMPLE *Look up the type of grant you are seeking in the list of grant types (in this case 'Project support'). Then turn to the relevant page of the list of trusts by type of grant and look at the names of the trusts listed under 'Project support'. Note down the names of all these trusts.*

STEP 5 **Compare the lists of trust names produced via steps 2, 3 and 4, and make a list of all the trusts which appear on more than one list. This will produce a list of trusts whose funding policies most closely match the characteristics of the project for which you are seeking funding.**

STEP 6 If the list turns out to be too short it can easily be adjusted.

EXAMPLE *You find that you have ended up with a list of five trusts. Going back to step 3, you could include the trusts which come under 'Education and training', or, going back to step 2, you could include trusts which will consider funding projects in the North West.*

STEP 7 Look up the entries for the trusts identified and study their details carefully, paying particular attention to 'Where funding can be given', 'What is funded' and 'What is not funded'.

If you feel that there is a good match between the characteristics of the project for which you require support and the funding policies of the trust identified, you could submit an application.

STEP 8 Look at the list of the top 150 trusts.

Check that you have not missed any of the major funders because you have made your search too specific. Some of the largest foundations give to a wide range of organisations and projects, and they tend to give the largest grants. They are also the most over-subscribed.

Look up the entries for each trust and study their details carefully, paying particular attention to 'Where funding can be given', 'What is funded' and 'What is not funded'. If you feel that there is a good match between the characteristics of the project for which you require support and the funding policies of the trust identified, you could submit an application.

However, make sure that there is a good reason for writing to any trust that you select: do not just send off indiscriminate applications to the whole list!

A typical trust entry

A complete entry should contain information under the headings listed below. An explanation of the information which should appear in these fields is given alongside.

WHERE FUNDING CAN BE GIVEN
The village, town, borough, parish or other geographical area the trust is prepared to fund

WHAT IS FUNDED
Details of the types of project or activity the trust plans to fund

WHAT IS NOT FUNDED
The types of projects or causes the trust will definitely not fund, e.g. expeditions, scholarships

SAMPLE GRANTS
The main grants given by the trust in the last financial year

TRUSTEES
Names of the trustees

PUBLICATIONS
Titles of publications the trust has produced which are of interest to grant seekers

WHO TO APPLY TO
The name and address of the person to whom applications should be sent

CC NO
Charity registration number

■ The Fictitious Trust

WHERE FUNDING CAN BE GIVEN UK.
WHO CAN BENEFIT Charities benefiting children.
WHAT IS FUNDED Education and training.
WHAT IS NOT FUNDED No grants to individuals.
TYPE OF GRANT One-off, capital, running costs.
RANGE OF GRANTS £250–£5,000.
SAMPLE GRANTS A school (£5,000); a university (£1,000); a school library (£800); a school (£600); a grammar school, a further education college and for classroom equipment (£500 each); a university appeal (£400); and a wheelchair ramp (£250).
FINANCES *Year* 2008 *Income* £55,000 *Grants* £50,000 *Assets* £800,000
TRUSTEES Peter Brown, Chair; Mrs Mary Brown; Alistair Johnson; Lord Great; Lady Good.
PUBLICATIONS *The Fictitious Trust – The First 20 Years.*
OTHER INFORMATION This trust recently merged with the Fictional Trust.
HOW TO APPLY In writing to the address below. An sae should be enclosed if an acknowledgement is required.
WHO TO APPLY TO A Grant, Secretary, The Old Barn, Main Street, New Town ZC48 2QQ *Tel* 020 7123 4567 *Fax* 020 7123 4567 *email* trust@abc.co.uk *Website* www.abc.co.uk
CC NO 123456　　　　**ESTABLISHED** 1993

WHO CAN BENEFIT
The kinds of people, animals, etc., the trust wishes to ultimately benefit

TYPE OF GRANT
The types of grant or loan the trust is prepared to give, e.g. one-off, recurring, running costs

RANGE OF GRANTS
The smallest, largest and typical size of grant normally given

FINANCES
The most recent financial information, including the total amount of grants given

OTHER INFORMATION
Any other information which might be useful to grant seekers

HOW TO APPLY
Useful information to those preparing their grant application

ESTABLISHED
Year established

A list of the top 150 trusts by grant total

This is a list of the largest 150 trusts by grant total in alphabetical order. Between them they account for around £3 billion, or about 83% of the funds available in the book. Please do not use this simply as a mailing list: these trusts cover a wide range of specialist interests and many of them will never fund your work.

We recommend that you read each entry carefully and compile your own list of major trusts relevant to you. You can then set this list alongside the other lists generated from the other indexes in the directory. We believe this is the most effective way of ensuring that you do not omit any major trusts.

The 29th May 1961 Charitable Trust

Abbey Charitable Trust

Achisomoch Aid Company Limited

Action Medical Research

Aid to the Church in Need (UK)

The Alice Trust

Allchurches Trust Ltd

Arcadia (formerly the Lisbet Rausing Charitable Fund)

The John Armitage Charitable Trust

The Army Benevolent Fund

Arthritis Research Campaign

Arts Council England

The Arts Council of Northern Ireland

The Arts Council of Wales

AW Charitable Trust

Awards for All

The Baily Thomas Charitable Fund

David and Frederick Barclay Foundation

The Baring Foundation

BBC Children in Need

The Big Lottery Fund

The Birmingham Community Foundation

The Barrow Cadbury Trust and the Barrow Cadbury Fund

CAFOD

Capital Community Foundation

The Childwick Trust

CHK Charities Limited

Christian Aid

The City Bridge Trust (formerly Bridge House Trust)

The City Parochial Foundation

The Clore Duffield Foundation

The Clothworkers' Foundation

Clydpride Ltd

The Coalfields Regeneration Trust

Comic Relief

The Community Foundation for Greater Manchester

The Community Foundation for Northern Ireland

The Peter Cruddas Foundation

Peter De Haan Charitable Trust

Diabetes UK

The Diana, Princess of Wales Memorial Fund

The DM Charitable Trust

The Dulverton Trust

The Dunhill Medical Trust

The James Dyson Foundation

The John Ellerman Foundation

The Eranda Foundation

Euro Charity Trust

The Eveson Charitable Trust

Esmée Fairbairn Foundation

Allan and Nesta Ferguson Charitable Settlement

The Fidelity UK Foundation

The Football Foundation

The Foyle Foundation

The Freemasons' Grand Charity

The Gatsby Charitable Foundation

J Paul Getty Jr Charitable Trust

The Goldsmiths' Company Charity

GrantScape

The M and R Gross Charities Limited

Paul Hamlyn Foundation

The Helen Hamlyn Trust

Help the Aged

The Helping Foundation

The Hintze Family Charitable Foundation

Hobson Charity Limited

HSBC Global Education Trust

The Hunter Foundation

Investream Charitable Trust

The ITF Seafarers Trust

The Elton John Aids Foundation

Kent Community Foundation

Keren Association

The Kirby Laing Foundation

The Lancaster Foundation

The Lancaster-Taylor Charitable Trust

The LankellyChase Foundation

Leukaemia Research Fund

The Leverhulme Trust

The Linbury Trust

Liverpool Charity and Voluntary Services

Lloyds TSB Foundation for England and Wales

The Lord's Taverners

John Lyon's Charity

Man Group plc Charitable Trust

Mayfair Charities Ltd

The Mercers' Charitable Foundation

Community Foundation for Merseyside

The Monument Trust

The Peter Moores Foundation

Muslim Hands

The National Art Collections Fund

Asthma UK

The Northern Rock Foundation

Nottinghamshire Community Foundation

The Nuffield Foundation

Oxfam (GB)

The P F Charitable Trust

The Parthenon Trust

The Pears Foundation

The Jack Petchey Foundation

The Prince's Charities Foundation

Private Equity Foundation

Quartet Community Foundation (formerly the Greater Bristol Foundation)

The R D Crusaders Foundation

Rachel Charitable Trust

The Rank Foundation

The Sigrid Rausing Trust

The Robertson Trust

The Roddick Foundation

The Joseph Rowntree Charitable Trust

The Joseph Rowntree Foundation

Royal British Legion

Royal Masonic Trust for Girls and Boys

The Rufford Maurice Laing Foundation

S F Foundation

The Scottish Arts Council

The Scottish Community Foundation

Seafarers UK (formerly King George's Fund for Sailors)

The Samuel Sebba Charitable Trust

The Shetland Charitable Trust

Shlomo Memorial Fund Limited

The Henry Smith Charity

The Sobell Foundation

The Souter Charitable Trust

St James's Place Foundation

The Stewards' Company Limited (incorporating the J W Laing Trust and the J W Laing Biblical Scholarship Trust)

The Bernard Sunley Charitable Foundation

The Sutton Trust

Tearfund

The Sir Jules Thorn Charitable Trust

The True Colours Trust

The Tubney Charitable Trust

The Tudor Trust

Community Foundation Serving Tyne and Wear and Northumberland

'v'

The Vardy Foundation

The Vodafone (Group) Foundation

The Volant Charitable Trust

Wales Council for Voluntary Action

The Waterloo Foundation

The Wates Foundation

The Wellcome Trust

The Garfield Weston Foundation

The Maurice Wohl Charitable Foundation

The Charles Wolfson Charitable Trust

The Wolfson Family Charitable Trust

The Wolfson Foundation

The South Yorkshire Community Foundation

Youth Music

Other publications and resources

The following publications and resources may also be of interest to readers of the DGMT. They are all available directly from the Directory of Social Change by ringing 08450 77 77 07 or visiting our website at www.dsc.org.uk.

The Guide to Grants for Individuals in Need
Directory of Social Change

This best-selling funding guide gives details of a wide range of funds and other support available for the relief of individual poverty and hardship. It remains a key reference book for social workers, as well as the individuals themselves and those concerned with their welfare.

- Details on national and local charitable trusts which collectively give over £300 million a year towards the relief of individual poverty and hardship.
- Essential advice on applications for each source: eligibility; types of grants given; annual grant total; contact details.
- An example of how to make an effective application, and advice on finding the right sources to apply to.

The Educational Grants Directory
Directory of Social Change

This best-selling guide gives details on a wide range of funds and other support available to schoolchildren and students in need, up to and including first degree level. It is a key reference book for educational social workers, student welfare officers, teachers and advice agencies, and the individuals themselves and their families. It includes:

- Sources of funding for children and students up to and including first degree level from trusts that collectively give around £50 million each year.
- Essential advice and information on applications for each source including eligibility, types of grants given, annual grant total and contact details.
- An example of how to make an effective application, and advice on finding the right sources to apply to.

The Guide to UK Company Giving
Directory of Social Change

This invaluable guide includes details of over 500 companies in the UK that give a combined total of around £360 million in cash donations to voluntary and community organisations. It contains:

- Essential information on who to contact with each company.
- Details information on cash donations, sponsorship, staff volunteering and gifts in kind.

The Guide to the Major Trusts Volumes 1 & 2
Directory of Social Change

The in-depth research and independent comment that these flagship titles offer has made them an essential reference guide for all fundraisers. These guides are the only source of independent critical analysis of trusts in practice.

Volume 1: concentrates on the 400 largest trusts that give over £300,000 a year.

Volume 2: complements volume 1 to provide a further 1,200 trusts that give between £30,000 and £300,000 each year.

www.trustfunding.org.uk

Packed with information on more than 4,500 UK grant-making trusts, this successful and popular tool for fundraisers lists trusts that collectively give over £3.6 billion each year.

■ Search by geographical area, name of trust, type of grant or by keyword search.

■ Choose to receive notification when information on a particular trust or trusts are updated.

■ Receive monthly bulletins that keep you informed of news and updates.

www.grantsfor individuals.org.uk

A Guide to Grants for Individuals in Need and *The Educational Grants Directory* come together in this database. It contains over 3,500 trusts and foundations that give to individuals for educational and welfare purposes. Collectively they give over £350 million each year.

■ Search by geographical area, name of trust, type of grant or by keyword search.

■ Choose to receive notification when information on a particular trust or trusts is updated.

■ Receive monthly bulletins that keep you informed of news and updates.

www.companygiving. org.uk

This database contains all those companies in *The Guide to UK Company Giving*, as well as newly discovered company giving and support. Over 500 companies are featured, giving over £360 million in cash donations. Entries contain full details on the various giving methods (cash donations, in-kind support, employee-led support, sponsorship and commercially-led support), and describe both what the company is prepared to fund and the organisations it has supported in the past.

■ Search by geographical area, name of company, type of grant or keyword.

■ Choose to receive notification when information on a particular company or companies is updated.

■ Receive monthly bulletins that keep you informed of news and updates.

www.government funding.org.uk

This database is an essential tool for anyone looking for information on statutory funding. Continually updated, it provides details on over £2.3 billion of funding from local, regional, national and European sources.

- Receive notification of funding rounds before they open.
- Use funder ratings for an independent and unique insight into what to expect from over 200 local, regional, national and European sources.
- Search by type of grant, e.g. small grants, loans and contracts.

DSC also offers a range of specialist funding guides. These guides provide essential tailored reference points for fundraisers working in specific areas.

They include:

The Youth Funding Guide
The Sports Funding Guide
The Environmental Funding Guide
The Government Funding Guide

And, finally, a trusted source of fundraising advice.
The Complete Fundraising Handbook

Trusts by geographical area

This index contains two separate listings:

Geographical area headings: This lists all of the geographical area headings used in the DGMT.

Trusts by geographical area: This lists the trusts appearing in the DGMT under the geographical area for which they have expressed a funding preference.

Trusts by geographical area

The index contains two separate listings:

Geographical area headings
This lists all of the geographical area headings used in DGMT.

Trusts by geographical area
This lists the trusts appearing in the DGMT under the geographical areas for which they have expressed a funding preference

Type of place

■ Developing world

The A B Charitable Trust
Abbey Charitable Trust
Access Sport
The Alchemy Foundation
The Pat Allsop Charitable Trust
Viscount Amory's Charitable
    Trust
Anglo American Group
    Foundation
The Anson Charitable Trust
The Archer Trust
The Ardwick Trust
The AS Charitable Trust
AstonMansfield Charitable
    Trust
The Avon and Somerset Police
    Community Trust
Veta Bailey Charitable Trust
The Austin Bailey Trust
The Balmore Trust
The Barbour Trust
The Baring Foundation
The Bartlett Taylor Charitable
    Trust
The Bay Tree Charitable Trust
The John Beckwith Charitable
    Trust
The Bellinger Donnay Trust
Bergqvist Charitable Trust
The Body Shop Foundation
H E and E L Botteley
    Charitable Trust
P G and N J Boulton Trust
The Bower Trust
John and Susan Bowers Fund
The Harold and Alice Bridges
    Charity
Bristol Archdeaconry Charity
Buckland Charitable Trust
The Burden Trust
Burdens Charitable Foundation
The Audrey and Stanley Burton
    1960 Charitable Trust
The Arnold Burton 1998
    Charitable Trust
Henry T and Lucy B Cadbury
    Charitable Trust
The Calpe Trust
The Canning Trust
The Casey Trust
Christadelphian Samaritan
    Fund
Christian Aid
The Church Urban Fund
Stephen Clark 1957
    Charitable Trust
John Coldman Charitable Trust
The E Alec Colman Charitable
    Fund Ltd
The Coltstaple Trust
The Conscience Trust

The Gershon Coren Charitable
    Foundation
Michael Cornish Charitable
    Trust
The Evan Cornish Foundation
The Cotton Trust
The Cray Trust
The Cumber Family Charitable
    Trust
The Hamilton Davies Trust
The Digbeth Trust
The Dorfred Charitable Trust
The Drapers' Charitable Fund
The Dulverton Trust
The Eagle Charity Trust
The Gilbert and Eileen Edgar
    Foundation
The Ellerdale Trust
The Ellis Campbell Foundation
The Elmgrant Trust
The Ericson Trust
Euro Charity Trust
Samuel William Farmer's Trust
The Farmers' Company
    Charitable Fund
The A M Fenton Trust
Allan and Nesta Ferguson
    Charitable Settlement
The Earl Fitzwilliam Charitable
    Trust
The Football Association
    National Sports Centre
    Trust
The Forest Hill Charitable Trust
The Donald Forrester Trust
The Anna Rosa Forster
    Charitable Trust
Four Acre Trust
The Four Winds Trust
Sydney E Franklin Deceased's
    New Second Charity
The Jill Franklin Trust
The Hugh Fraser Foundation
The Fulmer Charitable Trust
The Fuserna Foundation
The Galanthus Trust
The Angela Gallagher Memorial
    Fund
Global Care
Gloucestershire Community
    Foundation
The Constance Green
    Foundation
The Gulbenkian Foundation
H C D Memorial Fund
The Alfred Haines Charitable
    Trust
The Haramead Trust
Miss K M Harbinson's
    Charitable Trust
The Peter Harrison Foundation
Hasluck Charitable Trust
The Headley Trust
The Heart of England
    Community Foundation
Help the Aged

Philip Henman Trust
The Joanna Herbert-Stepney
    Charitable Settlement (also
    known as The Paget
    Charitable Trust)
The Heritage of London Trust
    Ltd
The Hilden Charitable Fund
The Horne Trust
The Hunter Foundation
The Worshipful Company of
    Innholders General Charity
    Fund
The Innocent Foundation
The Jephcott Charitable Trust
The Joffe Charitable Trust
The Cyril and Eve Jumbo
    Charitable Trust
The Soli and Leah Kelaty Trust
    Fund
The Kiawah Charitable Trust
The Kirby Laing Foundation
The Beatrice Laing Trust
The Langley Charitable Trust
The William Leech Charity
The Leonard Trust
The Linbury Trust
The Enid Linder Foundation
The Marie Helen Luen
    Charitable Trust
Paul Lunn-Rockliffe Charitable
    Trust
The Lyndhurst Trust
The Lynn Foundation
Mahavir Trust (also known as
    the K S Mehta Charitable
    Trust)
The Marchday Charitable Fund
Mariapolis Limited
Marr-Munning Trust
The Methodist Relief and
    Development Fund
The Millhouses Charitable
    Trust
The Mirianog Trust
The Morel Charitable Trust
Muslim Hands
Nazareth Trust Fund
Network for Social Change
Mr and Mrs F E F Newman
    Charitable Trust
Alice Noakes Memorial
    Charitable Trust
The Norda Trust
The Northern Rock Foundation
The Father O'Mahoney
    Memorial Trust
The Odin Charitable Trust
The Parthenon Trust
The Pears Foundation
The Pilkington Charities Fund
The Col W W Pilkington Will
    Trusts The General Charity
    Fund
The David and Elaine Potter
    Foundation

Prairie Trust
The W L Pratt Charitable Trust
The Bishop Radford Trust
Ranworth Trust
The Eleanor Rathbone
    Charitable Trust
The Reed Foundation
The Rhododendron Trust
The Ripple Effect Foundation
The River Farm Foundation
The Rivers Charitable Trust
Robyn Charitable Trust
The Rock Foundation
The Roddick Foundation
The Sir James Roll Charitable
    Trust
The Rothera Charitable
    Settlement
The Rowan Charitable Trust
The RRAF Charitable Trust
The Rufford Maurice Laing
    Foundation
The Rufford Small Grants
    Foundation
Ryklow Charitable Trust 1992
    (also known as A B
    Williamson Charitable Trust)
The J S and E C Rymer
    Charitable Trust
The Saga Charitable Trust
The Alan and Babette
    Sainsbury Charitable Fund
The Shanti Charitable Trust
Rita and David Slowe
    Charitable Trust
The SMB Charitable Trust
The W F Southall Trust
St Francis's Leprosy Guild
St Mark's Overseas Aid Trust
    (SMOAT)
The Peter Stebbings Memorial
    Charity
The Stone Family Foundation
The Gay and Keith Talbot Trust
The Lady Tangye Charitable
    Trust
C B and H H Taylor 1984 Trust
Tearfund
The Loke Wan Tho Memorial
    Foundation
The Tinsley Foundation
The Tisbury Telegraph Trust
The Tolkien Trust
The Tresillian Trust
Ulting Overseas Trust
The Unite Foundation (The
    Amicus Foundation)
The United Society for the
    Propagation of the Gospel
The Valentine Charitable Trust
The Van Neste Foundation
The Vardy Foundation
The Verdon-Smith Family
    Charitable Settlement
The Vodafone (Group)
    Foundation

War on Want
The Westcroft Trust
The Harold Hyam Wingate
    Foundation
The Wood Family Trust
The Matthews Wrightson
    Charity Trust
The Wyndham Charitable Trust
Zephyr Charitable Trust

....

■ Areas of social deprivation

The 29th May 1961 Charitable
    Trust
Abbey Charitable Trust
Access Sport
The Alchemy Foundation
The Pat Allsop Charitable Trust
Viscount Amory's Charitable
    Trust
The Anson Charitable Trust
The Archer Trust
AstonMansfield Charitable
    Trust
The Avon and Somerset Police
    Community Trust
The Austin Bailey Trust
The Barbour Trust
The Bartlett Taylor Charitable
    Trust
The Bay Tree Charitable Trust
The John Beckwith Charitable
    Trust
The Bellinger Donnay Trust
Bergqvist Charitable Trust
P G and N J Boulton Trust
John and Susan Bowers Fund
The Harold and Alice Bridges
    Charity
Bristol Archdeaconry Charity
The Burden Trust
The Arnold Burton 1998
    Charitable Trust
The Calpe Trust
Christian Aid
The Church Urban Fund
Stephen Clark 1957
    Charitable Trust
John Coldman Charitable Trust
The E Alec Colman Charitable
    Fund Ltd
The Coltstaple Trust
The Cotton Trust
The Cray Trust
The Hamilton Davies Trust
The Digbeth Trust
The Drapers' Charitable Fund
The Dulverton Trust
The Ellis Campbell Foundation
The Elmgrant Trust
Samuel William Farmer's Trust
The Farmers' Company
    Charitable Fund
The A M Fenton Trust

The Earl Fitzwilliam Charitable
    Trust
The Football Association
    National Sports Centre
    Trust
The Forest Hill Charitable Trust
The Forte Charitable Trust
Four Acre Trust
The Hugh Fraser Foundation
Gloucestershire Community
    Foundation
The Gulbenkian Foundation
The Alfred Haines Charitable
    Trust
The Peter Harrison Foundation
The Heart of England
    Community Foundation
Help the Aged
The Heritage of London Trust
    Ltd
The Hilden Charitable Fund
The Horne Trust
The Hunter Foundation
The Worshipful Company of
    Innholders General Charity
    Fund
The Jephcott Charitable Trust
The Soli and Leah Kelaty Trust
    Fund
The Kiawah Charitable Trust
The William Leech Charity
The Marie Helen Luen
    Charitable Trust
The Lynn Foundation
Marr-Munning Trust
Millennium Stadium Charitable
    Trust
The Millhouses Charitable
    Trust
The Morel Charitable Trust
Muslim Hands
Nazareth Trust Fund
The Norda Trust
The Northern Rock Foundation
The Odin Charitable Trust
The David and Elaine Potter
    Foundation
The Bishop Radford Trust
The Ripple Effect Foundation
Mrs L D Rope Third Charitable
    Settlement
The Rufford Maurice Laing
    Foundation
The J S and E C Rymer
    Charitable Trust
The SMB Charitable Trust
St Mark's Overseas Aid Trust
    (SMOAT)
The Lady Tangye Charitable
    Trust
The Westcroft Trust
The Harold Hyam Wingate
    Foundation
The Wood Family Trust
The Matthews Wrightson
    Charity Trust

The Wyndham Charitable Trust

....

■ Urban areas, inner cities

Abbey Charitable Trust
Access Sport
The Alchemy Foundation
The Pat Allsop Charitable Trust
Viscount Amory's Charitable Trust
The Anson Charitable Trust
The Archer Trust
AstonMansfield Charitable Trust
The Avon and Somerset Police Community Trust
The Austin Bailey Trust
The Barbour Trust
The Bartlett Taylor Charitable Trust
The Bay Tree Charitable Trust
The John Beckwith Charitable Trust
The Bellinger Donnay Trust
Bergqvist Charitable Trust
The Oliver Borthwick Memorial Trust
P G and N J Boulton Trust
John and Susan Bowers Fund
The Harold and Alice Bridges Charity
Bristol Archdeaconry Charity
The Burden Trust
The Arnold Burton 1998 Charitable Trust
The Calpe Trust
Christian Aid
The Church Urban Fund
Stephen Clark 1957 Charitable Trust
John Coldman Charitable Trust
The E Alec Colman Charitable Fund Ltd
The Coltstaple Trust
The Cotton Trust
The Cray Trust
The Hamilton Davies Trust
The Digbeth Trust
The Drapers' Charitable Fund
The Dulverton Trust
The Ellis Campbell Foundation
The Elmgrant Trust
Samuel William Farmer's Trust
The Farmers' Company Charitable Fund
The A M Fenton Trust
The Earl Fitzwilliam Charitable Trust
The Football Association National Sports Centre Trust
The Forest Hill Charitable Trust
The Forte Charitable Trust
Four Acre Trust
The Hugh Fraser Foundation

Gloucestershire Community Foundation
The Gulbenkian Foundation
The Alfred Haines Charitable Trust
The Peter Harrison Foundation
The Heart of England Community Foundation
Help the Aged
The Heritage of London Trust Ltd
The Hilden Charitable Fund
The Horne Trust
The Hunter Foundation
The Worshipful Company of Innholders General Charity Fund
The Jephcott Charitable Trust
The Soli and Leah Kelaty Trust Fund
The Kiawah Charitable Trust
The William Leech Charity
The Marie Helen Luen Charitable Trust
The Lynn Foundation
Marr-Munning Trust
The Millhouses Charitable Trust
The Morel Charitable Trust
Muslim Hands
Nazareth Trust Fund
The Norda Trust
The Northern Rock Foundation
The Odin Charitable Trust
The David and Elaine Potter Foundation
The Bishop Radford Trust
The Ripple Effect Foundation
The Rufford Maurice Laing Foundation
The J S and E C Rymer Charitable Trust
The SMB Charitable Trust
St Mark's Overseas Aid Trust (SMOAT)
The Lady Tangye Charitable Trust
The Westcroft Trust
The Harold Hyam Wingate Foundation
The Wood Family Trust
The Matthews Wrightson Charity Trust
The Wyndham Charitable Trust

....

■ Rural areas

Abbey Charitable Trust
Access Sport
The Alchemy Foundation
The Pat Allsop Charitable Trust
Viscount Amory's Charitable Trust
The Anson Charitable Trust
The Archer Trust

AstonMansfield Charitable Trust
The Avon and Somerset Police Community Trust
The Austin Bailey Trust
The Barbour Trust
The Bartlett Taylor Charitable Trust
The Bay Tree Charitable Trust
The John Beckwith Charitable Trust
The Bellinger Donnay Trust
Bergqvist Charitable Trust
P G and N J Boulton Trust
John and Susan Bowers Fund
The Harold and Alice Bridges Charity
Bristol Archdeaconry Charity
The Burden Trust
The Arnold Burton 1998 Charitable Trust
The Calpe Trust
Christian Aid
The Church Urban Fund
Stephen Clark 1957 Charitable Trust
The Coalfields Regeneration Trust
John Coldman Charitable Trust
The E Alec Colman Charitable Fund Ltd
The Coltstaple Trust
The Cotton Trust
The Cray Trust
The Hamilton Davies Trust
The Digbeth Trust
The Drapers' Charitable Fund
The Dulverton Trust
The Ellis Campbell Foundation
The Elmgrant Trust
Samuel William Farmer's Trust
The Farmers' Company Charitable Fund
The A M Fenton Trust
The Earl Fitzwilliam Charitable Trust
The Football Association National Sports Centre Trust
The Forest Hill Charitable Trust
The Forte Charitable Trust
Four Acre Trust
The Hugh Fraser Foundation
The Angela Gallagher Memorial Fund
Gloucestershire Community Foundation
The Gulbenkian Foundation
The Alfred Haines Charitable Trust
The Peter Harrison Foundation
The Heart of England Community Foundation
Help the Aged
The Heritage of London Trust Ltd

The Hilden Charitable Fund
The Horne Trust
The Hunter Foundation
The Worshipful Company of
Innholders General Charity
Fund
The Jephcott Charitable Trust
The Soli and Leah Kelaty Trust
Fund
The Kiawah Charitable Trust
The William Leech Charity
The Marie Helen Luen
Charitable Trust
The Lynn Foundation
Marr-Munning Trust
The Millhouses Charitable
Trust
The Morel Charitable Trust
Muslim Hands
Nazareth Trust Fund
The Norda Trust
The Northern Rock Foundation
The Odin Charitable Trust
The David and Elaine Potter
Foundation
The Bishop Radford Trust
The Ripple Effect Foundation
The Rufford Maurice Laing
Foundation
The J S and E C Rymer
Charitable Trust
Schroder Charity Trust
The SMB Charitable Trust
St Mark's Overseas Aid Trust
(SMOAT)
The Lady Tangye Charitable
Trust
The Westcroft Trust
The Harold Hyam Wingate
Foundation
The Wood Family Trust
The Matthews Wrightson
Charity Trust
The Wyndham Charitable Trust

Worldwide

Achisomoch Aid Company
Limited
Adenfirst Ltd
The Ajahma Charitable Trust
The Alborada Trust
The Alexis Trust
Altamont Ltd
AM Charitable Trust
The Amalur Foundation Limited
Andor Charitable Trust
The Henry Angest Foundation
Anglo American Group
Foundation
Arcadia (formerly the Lisbet
Rausing Charitable Fund)
The Archbishop of
Canterbury's Charitable
Trust
The John M Archer Charitable
Trust
The Archer Trust
The Armenian Relief Society of
Great Britain Trust
The Ove Arup Foundation
Astellas European Foundation
The Bagri Foundation
The Baker Charitable Trust
The Batchworth Trust
Bay Charitable Trust
The Bay Tree Charitable Trust
The Beacon Trust
Bear Mordechai Ltd
Beauland Ltd
The Becker Family Charitable
Trust
The John Beckwith Charitable
Trust
The Ruth Berkowitz Charitable
Trust
The Bisgood Charitable Trust
(registered as Miss Jeanne
Bisgood's Charitable Trust)
The Neville and Elaine Blond
Charitable Trust
The Boltons Trust
Salo Bordon Charitable Trust
The Boshier-Hinton Foundation
P G and N J Boulton Trust
The A H and E Boulton Trust
The Bromley Trust
The Rory and Elizabeth Brooks
Foundation
Buckingham Trust
Buckland Charitable Trust
The Bulldog Trust Limited
The Clara E Burgess Charity
The Arnold Burton 1998
Charitable Trust
The Derek Butler Trust
P H G Cadbury Charitable
Trust
The G W Cadbury Charitable
Trust
Calleva Foundation
The Calpe Trust

Carlee Ltd
The Casey Trust
The Elizabeth Casson Trust
Catholic Foreign Missions
The Worshipful Company of
Chartered Accountants
General Charitable Trust
(also known as CALC)
Childs Charitable Trust
The Cobalt Trust
The Bernard Coleman
Charitable Trust
The E Alec Colman Charitable
Fund Ltd
The Coltstaple Trust
The Cookson Charitable Trust
Michael Cornish Charitable
Trust
The Evan Cornish Foundation
The Cumber Family Charitable
Trust
Itzchok Meyer Cymerman Trust
Ltd
Oizer Dalim Trust
The De Laszlo Foundation
The Diana, Princess of Wales
Memorial Fund
The Dorfred Charitable Trust
Double 'O' Charity Ltd
The Duis Charitable Trust
The Charles Dunstone
Charitable Trust
Mildred Duveen Charitable
Trust
Edupoor Limited
The Emilienne Charitable Trust
Entindale Ltd
The Esfandi Charitable
Foundation
The Matthew Eyton Animal
Welfare Trust
The Fairstead Trust
Allan and Nesta Ferguson
Charitable Settlement
Fisherbeck Charitable Trust
The Follett Trust
The Forest Hill Charitable Trust
The Donald Forrester Trust
The Anna Rosa Forster
Charitable Trust
The Forte Charitable Trust
Four Acre Trust
The Four Winds Trust
Sydney E Franklin Deceased's
New Second Charity
The Jill Franklin Trust
Friends of Boyan Trust
Maurice Fry Charitable Trust
The Fuserna Foundation
The G D Charitable Trust
The Galanthus Trust
The Angela Gallagher Memorial
Fund
Generations Charitable Trust
Global Care
Golubovich Foundation

H and T Clients Charitable
Trust
H C D Memorial Fund
The Doughty Hanson
Charitable Foundation
The Haramead Trust
Miss K M Harbinson's
Charitable Trust
The Hargrave Foundation
The Charlotte Heber-Percy
Charitable Trust
Philip Henman Trust
Hinduja Foundation
The Holbeck Charitable Trust
Sir Harold Hood's Charitable
Trust
The Hope Trust
HSBC Global Education Trust
The Hutton Foundation
The Innocent Foundation
International Spinal Research
Trust
Irshad Trust
Jay Education Trust
The Joffe Charitable Trust
The Cyril and Eve Jumbo
Charitable Trust
Jusaca Charitable Trust
The Soli and Leah Kelaty Trust
Fund
Ernest Kleinwort Charitable
Trust
Kollel and Co. Limited
The K P Ladd Charitable Trust
Maurice and Hilda Laing
Charitable Trust
The David Laing Foundation
The Kirby Laing Foundation
The Martin Laing Foundation
The Beatrice Laing Trust
The Lancaster-Taylor
Charitable Trust
The Langdale Trust
The Langley Charitable Trust
Laslett's (Hinton) Charity
Mrs F B Laurence Charitable
Trust
The Law Society Charity
The Leigh Trust
The Lennox and Wyfold
Foundation
Lifeline 4 Kids
The Limbourne Trust
The Linbury Trust
Lindale Educational
Foundation
The Enid Linder Foundation
The Charles Lloyd Foundation
The Lolev Charitable Trust
The Lotus Foundation
Henry Lumley Charitable Trust
Paul Lunn-Rockliffe Charitable
Trust
Lord and Lady Lurgan Trust
The Madeline Mabey Trust
The Mactaggart Third Fund

The Brian Maguire Charitable
Trust
Mahavir Trust (also known as
the K S Mehta Charitable
Trust)
Malbin Trust
The Mallinckrodt Foundation
The Manoukian Charitable
Foundation
Marchig Animal Welfare Trust
Mariapolis Limited
Michael Marks Charitable
Trust
Brian Mercer Charitable Trust
Mercury Phoenix Trust
The Methodist Relief and
Development Fund
T and J Meyer Family
Foundation Limited
The Millward Charitable Trust
The Minos Trust
Minton Charitable Trust
Diana and Allan Morgenthau
Charitable Trust
Vyoel Moshe Charitable Trust
Brian and Jill Moss Charitable
Trust
The Mountbatten Memorial
Trust
The Edwina Mountbatten Trust
The Naggar Charitable Trust
Nathan Charitable Trust
Network for Social Change
Alice Noakes Memorial
Charitable Trust
The Northampton Queen's
Institute Relief in Sickness
Fund
The Northcott Devon
Foundation
The Northmoor Trust
The Norton Rose Charitable
Foundation
The Nottingham Gordon
Memorial Trust for Boys
and Girls
The Sir Peter O'Sullevan
Charitable Trust
The Oakdale Trust
The Ogle Christian Trust
The Oikonomia Trust
Old Possum's Practical Trust
The Olga Charitable Trust
Onaway Trust
Panahpur Charitable Trust
Panton Trust
The Paphitis Charitable Trust
The Paragon Trust
The Park House Charitable
Trust
The Parthenon Trust
The Pears Foundation
The Persson Charitable Trust
(formerly Highmoore Hall
Charitable Trust)

The Austin and Hope
Pilkington Trust
Polden-Puckham Charitable
Foundation
The Polehanger Trust
The J S F Pollitzer Charitable
Settlement
Edith and Ferdinand Porjes
Charitable Trust
The J E Posnansky Charitable
Trust
The David and Elaine Potter
Foundation
Prairie Trust
Premierquote Ltd
Premishlaner Charitable Trust
The Puebla Charitable Trust
The Pyne Charitable Trust
The Queen Anne's Gate
Foundation
Quothquan Trust
The R D Crusaders Foundation
The Ragdoll Foundation
The Rainford Trust
Ranworth Trust
The Eleanor Rathbone
Charitable Trust
The Sigrid Rausing Trust
The Eva Reckitt Trust Fund
Reuben Brothers Foundation
The Rhododendron Trust
The Rock Foundation
The Roddick Foundation
Romeera Foundation
The Gerald Ronson Foundation
Joshua and Michelle Rowe
Charitable Trust
The Rowland Family
Foundation
The RRAF Charitable Trust
The Rubin Foundation
The Rufford Maurice Laing
Foundation
The Rufford Small Grants
Foundation
Ryklow Charitable Trust 1992
(also known as A B
Williamson Charitable Trust)
S F Foundation
The Michael Sacher Charitable
Trust
The Michael Harry Sacher
Trust
Erach and Roshan Sadri
Foundation
The Saga Charitable Trust
The Alan and Babette
Sainsbury Charitable Fund
The Sammermar Trust
The Hon. M J Samuel
Charitable Trust
The Sandhu Charitable
Foundation
The Annie Schiff Charitable
Trust

The Schmidt-Bodner Charitable
Trust
Schroder Charity Trust
The Schroder Foundation
Scott (Eredine) Charitable
Trust
The Seedfield Trust
The Ayrton Senna Foundation
The Shanley Charitable Trust
The Barnett and Sylvia Shine
No 2 Charitable Trust
Shlomo Memorial Fund Limited
The Simpson Education and
Conservation Trust
Rita and David Slowe
Charitable Trust
Ruth Smart Foundation
The SMB Charitable Trust
The N Smith Charitable
Settlement
The Stanley Smith UK
Horticultural Trust
R H Southern Trust
Spears-Stutz Charitable Trust
St Francis's Leprosy Guild
C E K Stern Charitable Trust
The Sigmund Sternberg
Charitable Foundation
The Stewards' Company
Limited (incorporating the J
W Laing Trust and the J W
Laing Biblical Scholarship
Trust)
The Andy Stewart Charitable
Foundation
The Stone Family Foundation
The Strawberry Charitable
Trust
Sueberry Ltd
The Suva Foundation Limited
The Tabeel Trust
The Gay and Keith Talbot Trust
Tearfund
Thackray Medical Research
Trust
The Loke Wan Tho Memorial
Foundation
The Thornton Trust
The Three Oaks Trust
The Tinsley Foundation
The Tory Family Foundation
The Tresillian Trust
The TUUT Charitable Trust
Ulting Overseas Trust
The Ulverscroft Foundation
The Unite Foundation (The
Amicus Foundation)
The David Uri Memorial Trust
War on Want
Weatherley Charitable Trust
The Weinberg Foundation
The Weinstein Foundation
The Weinstock Fund
The Wessex Youth Trust
The Westcroft Trust
The Westminster Foundation

The Melanie White Foundation
Limited
The Williams Family Charitable
Trust
Dame Violet Wills Charitable
Trust
The Winton Charitable
Foundation
Women's World Day of Prayer
Woodlands Green Ltd
Wychdale Ltd
Yankov Charitable Trust
The Dennis Alan Yardy
Charitable Trust
The John Young Charitable
Settlement
Zephyr Charitable Trust

....

■ Europe (outside UK)

Aid to the Church in Need (UK)
Armenian General Benevolent
Union London Trust
The Arts Council of Northern
Ireland
British Institute at Ankara
British Ornithologists' Union
The William A Cadbury
Charitable Trust
The Catholic Charitable Trust
Christian Response to Eastern
Europe
Church of Ireland Priorities
Fund
The Community Foundation for
Northern Ireland
The Edith Maud Ellis 1985
Charitable Trust
The Ericson Trust
The February Foundation
Feed the Minds
The Fidelity UK Foundation
The Gulbenkian Foundation
The Headley Trust
The Hospital Saturday Fund
The Reta Lila Howard
Foundation
The Huxham Charitable Trust
The Inland Waterways
Association
The Ireland Fund of Great
Britain
The Irish Youth Foundation
(UK) Ltd (incorporating The
Lawlor Foundation)
The Elton John Aids
Foundation
The Kennedy Charitable
Foundation
Lauchentilly Charitable
Foundation 1988
The Leverhulme Trust
The Lyras Family Charitable
Trust
Marr-Munning Trust
The Esme Mitchell Trust

The Henry Moore Foundation
The Eleni Nakou Foundation
Nazareth Trust Fund
Mr and Mrs F E F Newman
Charitable Trust
Novi Most International
The Father O'Mahoney
Memorial Trust
The Old Broad Street Charity
Trust
Open Gate
The Ouseley Trust
Oxfam (GB)
Rachel Charitable Trust
The Peggy Ramsay Foundation
The Joseph Rank Trust
Relief Fund for Romania
Limited
The Joseph Rowntree
Charitable Trust
William Arthur Rudd Memorial
Trust
Saint Sarkis Charity Trust
The Scott Bader
Commonwealth Ltd
St Mark's Overseas Aid Trust
(SMOAT)
The Sylvanus Charitable Trust
C B and H H Taylor 1984 Trust
Veneziana Fund
Webb Memorial Trust
The H D H Wills 1965
Charitable Trust

....

■ Republic of Ireland

The Arts Council of Northern
Ireland
The William A Cadbury
Charitable Trust
Church of Ireland Priorities
Fund
The Community Foundation for
Northern Ireland
The Edith Maud Ellis 1985
Charitable Trust
The Gulbenkian Foundation
The Hospital Saturday Fund
The Reta Lila Howard
Foundation
The Inland Waterways
Association
The Ireland Fund of Great
Britain
The Irish Youth Foundation
(UK) Ltd (incorporating The
Lawlor Foundation)
The Elton John Aids
Foundation
The Kennedy Charitable
Foundation
Lauchentilly Charitable
Foundation 1988
The Esme Mitchell Trust
Mr and Mrs F E F Newman
Charitable Trust

The Ouseley Trust
The Peggy Ramsay Foundation
The Joseph Rank Trust
C B and H H Taylor 1984 Trust
The H D H Wills 1965
   Charitable Trust

....

■ Asia

4 Charity Foundation
The Acacia Charitable Trust
Achiezer Association Ltd
The Sylvia Adams Charitable
   Trust
Aid to the Church in Need (UK)
The Altajir Trust
Ambika Paul Foundation
The Ardwick Trust
BHST
BibleLands
The Bertie Black Foundation
British Institute at Ankara
The Britto Foundation
Mrs E E Brown Charitable
   Settlement
The CH (1980) Charitable
   Trust
Chasdei Tovim Me'oros
Closehelm Ltd
The Vivienne and Samuel
   Cohen Charitable Trust
Col-Reno Ltd
The Craps Charitable Trust
The Daiwa Anglo-Japanese
   Foundation
The Wilfrid Bruce Davis
   Charitable Trust
The Debmar Benevolent Trust
The Djanogly Foundation
The DM Charitable Trust
The Dollond Charitable Trust
The Doughty Charity Trust
Dushinsky Trust Ltd
Euro Charity Trust
The Family Rich Charities Trust
The February Foundation
Federation of Jewish Relief
   Organisations
Feed the Minds
Mejer and Gertrude Miriam
   Frydman Foundation
The Everard and Mina
   Goodman Charitable
   Foundation
The Great Britain Sasakawa
   Foundation
Paul Hamlyn Foundation
The Helen Hamlyn Trust
The Daniel Howard Trust
The Humanitarian Trust
Investream Charitable Trust
The Isaacs Charitable Trust
JCA Charitable Foundation
The Norman Joels Charitable
   Trust

The Elton John Aids
   Foundation
The J E Joseph Charitable
   Fund
The Josh Charitable Trust
The Bernard Kahn Charitable
   Trust
The Ian Karten Charitable
   Trust
The Kasner Charitable Trust
The Kiawah Charitable Trust
The Neil Kreitman Foundation
Kupath Gemach Chaim
   Bechesed Viznitz Trust
The Lambert Charitable Trust
Largsmount Ltd
The Lauffer Family Charitable
   Foundation
The Kennedy Leigh Charitable
   Trust
The Leverhulme Trust
The Joseph Levy Charitable
   Foundation
Lewis Family Charitable Trust
Jack Livingstone Charitable
   Trust
The Locker Foundation
The Sir Jack Lyons Charitable
   Trust
Marbeh Torah Trust
The Hilda and Samuel Marks
   Foundation
Marr-Munning Trust
Melodor Ltd
Melow Charitable Trust
Mercaz Torah Vechesed
   Limited
MYR Charitable Trust
Nazareth Trust Fund
Ner Foundation
NJD Charitable Trust
The Father O'Mahoney
   Memorial Trust
Open Gate
Oxfam (GB)
The Payne Charitable Trust
Peltz Trust
The Pestalozzi Overseas
   Children's Trust
The John Porter Charitable
   Trust
The Porter Foundation
The Puri Foundation
The Rayne Trust
The Rehoboth Trust
Rowanville Ltd
The Ruzin Sadagora Trust
The Scotshill Trust
The Scott Bader
   Commonwealth Ltd
The Helene Sebba Charitable
   Trust
The Samuel Sebba Charitable
   Trust
SEM Charitable Trust

The Archie Sherman Cardiff
   Foundation
Sino-British Fellowship Trust
The Sobell Foundation
The Solo Charitable
   Settlement
Songdale Ltd
St Mark's Overseas Aid Trust
   (SMOAT)
The Cyril and Betty Stein
   Charitable Trust
Tadlus Limited
The Tajtelbaum Charitable
   Trust
Trustees of Tzedakah
The Vail Foundation
The Witzenfeld Foundation
The Maurice Wohl Charitable
   Foundation
The Charles Wolfson
   Charitable Trust
The Wolfson Family Charitable
   Trust
The Wolfson Foundation
Woodlands Foundation Limited

....

■ Africa

The Sylvia Adams Charitable
   Trust
Aid to the Church in Need (UK)
The Beit Trust
British Ornithologists' Union
The Childwick Trust
Comic Relief
The Dugdale Charitable Trust
The Dulverton Trust
The Estelle Trust
Euro Charity Trust
The February Foundation
Feed the Minds
The Gatsby Charitable
   Foundation
Philip and Judith Green Trust
The Headley Trust
The Elton John Aids
   Foundation
The Kiawah Charitable Trust
The Lauffer Family Charitable
   Foundation
The Leverhulme Trust
Marr-Munning Trust
Nazareth Trust Fund
The Nchima Trust
The Noel Buxton Trust
The Father O'Mahoney
   Memorial Trust
Open Gate
Oxfam (GB)
The Pestalozzi Overseas
   Children's Trust
The Scotshill Trust
The Scott Bader
   Commonwealth Ltd
SEM Charitable Trust

The Archie Sherman Cardiff
Foundation
St Mark's Overseas Aid Trust
(SMOAT)
The Sir Halley Stewart Trust
Mrs R P Tindall's Charitable
Trust
The True Colours Trust
The Trust for Education
The Tudor Trust
The Scurrah Wainwright Charity
The Zochonis Charitable Trust

■ Americas and the West Indies

Aid to the Church in Need (UK)
The Beaverbrook Foundation
British Ornithologists' Union
The Catholic Charitable Trust
Feed the Minds
The Christina Mary Hendrie
Trust for Scottish and
Canadian Charities
The Neil Kreitman Foundation
The Lauffer Family Charitable
Foundation
The Leverhulme Trust
Marr-Munning Trust
The Henry Moore Foundation
The Peter Moores Foundation
MYR Charitable Trust
Nazareth Trust Fund
The Father O'Mahoney
Memorial Trust
Open Gate
Oxfam (GB)
The Scott Bader
Commonwealth Ltd
The Helene Sebba Charitable
Trust
The Archie Sherman Cardiff
Foundation
St James' Trust Settlement
St Mark's Overseas Aid Trust
(SMOAT)
The Sylvanus Charitable Trust
G R Waters Charitable Trust
2000
The Worwin UK Foundation

■ Australasia

The C Alma Baker Trust
The Lauffer Family Charitable
Foundation
The Mount Everest Foundation
Open Gate
The Archie Sherman Cardiff
Foundation
St Mark's Overseas Aid Trust
(SMOAT)

United Kingdom

The 1989 Willan Charitable
Trust
The 29th May 1961 Charitable
Trust
4 Charity Foundation
The A B Charitable Trust
Abbey Charitable Trust
Aberbrothock Charitable Trust
The Aberdeen Endowments
Trust
The Aberdeenshire Educational
Trust Scheme
Brian Abrams Charitable Trust
Eric Abrams Charitable Trust
The Acacia Charitable Trust
Access Sport
Achiezer Association Ltd
The ACT Foundation
Action Medical Research
The Company of Actuaries'
Charitable Trust Fund
The Sylvia Adams Charitable
Trust
The Adamson Trust
The Victor Adda Foundation
The Adint Charitable Trust
The Adnams Charity
AF Trust Company
Age Concern Scotland Grants
The AIM Foundation
The Green and Lilian F M
Ainsworth and Family
Benevolent Fund
The Sylvia Aitken Charitable
Trust
The Alabaster Trust
Alba Charitable Trust
D G Albright Charitable Trust
The Alchemy Foundation
Alcohol Education and
Research Council
Aldgate and All Hallows'
Barking Exhibition
Foundation
The Aldgate Freedom
Foundation
Alexandra Rose Charities
The Alice Trust
All Saints Educational Trust
Allchurches Trust Ltd
The H B Allen Charitable Trust
The Rita Allen Charitable Trust
The Alliance Family Foundation
Angus Allnatt Charitable
Foundation
The Pat Allsop Charitable Trust
The Almond Trust
Almondsbury Charity
The Altajir Trust
Alvor Charitable Trust
Amabrill Limited
Ambika Paul Foundation
The Ammco Trust
Sir John and Lady Amory's
Charitable Trust

Viscount Amory's Charitable
Trust
The Ampelos Trust
The AMW Charitable Trust
The Anchor Foundation
The Andrew Anderson Trust
The André Christian Trust
Anguish's Educational
Foundation
The Animal Defence Trust
The Eric Anker-Petersen
Charity
The Annandale Charitable
Trust
The Anson Charitable Trust
The Apax Foundation
Ambrose and Ann Appelbe
Trust
The Appletree Trust
The John Apthorp Charitable
Trust
The Milly Apthorp Charitable
Trust
The Arbib Foundation
Archbishop of Wales' Fund for
Children
The Architectural Heritage
Fund
The Ardwick Trust
The Argentarius Foundation
The Argus Appeal
Armenian General Benevolent
Union London Trust
The John Armitage Charitable
Trust
The Armourers' and Brasiers'
Gauntlet Trust
The Army Benevolent Fund
The Arnold Foundation
Arsenal Charitable Trust
The Artemis Charitable Trust
Arthritis Research Campaign
The Arts and Entertainment
Charitable Trust
Arts Council England
The Arts Council of Wales
The AS Charitable Trust
Ashburnham Thanksgiving
Trust
A J H Ashby Will Trust
The Ashden Trust
The Ashendene Trust
The Laura Ashley Foundation
The Norman C Ashton
Foundation
The Ashworth Charitable Trust
The Ian Askew Charitable Trust
The Associated Country
Women of the World
(ACWW)
The Association of Colleges
Charitable Trust
The Association of Friends of
Essex Churches
AstonMansfield Charitable
Trust

The Astor Foundation
The Astor of Hever Trust
The Aurelius Charitable Trust
The Lord Austin Trust
The Avenue Charitable Trust
The John Avins Trustees
The Avon and Somerset Police
   Community Trust
AW Charitable Trust
Awards for All
The Aylesford Family
   Charitable Trust
The BAA Communities Trust
Harry Bacon Foundation
The BACTA Charitable Trust
Veta Bailey Charitable Trust
The Austin Bailey Trust
The Baily Thomas Charitable
   Fund
The Baird Trust
The Roy and Pixie Baker
   Charitable Trust
The Balcombe Charitable Trust
The Balint Family Charitable
   Trusts
The Albert Casanova Ballard
   Deceased Trust
The Ballinger Charitable Trust
Balmain Charitable Trust
The Balmore Trust
The Balney Charitable Trust
The Baltic Charitable Fund
The Bamford Charitable
   Foundation
The Banbury Charities
William P Bancroft (No 2)
   Charitable Trust and
   Jenepher Gillett Trust
The Band Trust
The Barbers' Company General
   Charities
The Barbour Trust
The Barcapel Foundation
Barchester Healthcare
   Foundation
David and Frederick Barclay
   Foundation
The Baring Foundation
Peter Barker-Mill Memorial
   Charity
Barleycorn Trust
The Barnabas Trust
Lord Barnby's Foundation
Barnes Workhouse Fund
The Barnsbury Charitable Trust
The Barnstaple Bridge Trust
The Barnwood House Trust
The Misses Barrie Charitable
   Trust
Barrington Family Charitable
   Trust
The Charity of William Barrow
Stephen J Barry Charitable
   Trust
The Bartlett Taylor Charitable
   Trust

The Worshipful Company of
   Basketmakers' Charitable
   Trust
The Paul Bassham Charitable
   Trust
D H and L H Baylin Charitable
   Trust
The Louis Baylis (Maidenhead
   Advertiser) Charitable Trust
BBC Children in Need
B-CH 1971 Charitable Trust
The Bearder Charity
The James Beattie Charitable
   Trust
The Beaufort House Trust
   Limited
The Beaverbrook Foundation
The Beccles Town Lands
   Charity
The Becketts and Sargeants
   Educational Foundation
The Victoria and David
   Beckham Children's Charity
The Peter Beckwith Charitable
   Trust
The Bedford Charity (The
   Harpur Trust)
The Bedfordshire and
   Hertfordshire Historic
   Churches Trust
The Bedfordshire and Luton
   Community Foundation
The David and Ruth Behrend
   Fund
The Bellahouston Bequest
   Fund
Bellasis Trust
The Bellhouse Foundation
The Bellinger Donnay Trust
Belljoe Tzedoko Ltd
The Benfield Motors Charitable
   Trust
The Benham Charitable
   Settlement
The Hervey Benham Charitable
   Trust
Maurice and Jacqueline
   Bennett Charitable Trust
Michael and Leslie Bennett
   Charitable Trust
The Gerald Bentall Charitable
   Trust
Bergqvist Charitable Trust
The Berkshire Community
   Foundation
The Bestway Foundation
The Betterware Foundation
Thomas Betton's Charity for
   Pensions and Relief-in-Need
BHST
The Mason Bibby 1981 Trust
The Bideford Bridge Trust
The Big Lottery Fund
The Billmeir Charitable Trust
Percy Bilton Charity
The Bingham Trust

The Bintaub Charitable Trust
The Birmingham Community
   Foundation
The Birmingham District
   Nursing Charitable Trust
The Birmingham Hospital
   Saturday Fund Medical
   Charity and Welfare Trust
Birmingham International
   Airport Community Trust
The Lord Mayor of
   Birmingham's Charity
Birthday House Trust
The Michael Bishop
   Foundation
The Bishop's Development
   Fund
The Sydney Black Charitable
   Trust
The Bertie Black Foundation
Sir Alec Black's Charity
Isabel Blackman Foundation
The BlackRock (UK) Charitable
   Trust
The Herbert and Peter
   Blagrave Charitable Trust
The Blair Foundation
Blakes Benevolent Trust
The Blanchminster Trust
The Sir Victor Blank Charitable
   Settlement
Blatchington Court Trust
The Blueberry Charitable Trust
The Bluston Charitable
   Settlement
Enid Blyton Trust for Children
The Nicholas Boas Charitable
   Trust
The Body Shop Foundation
The Bonamy Charitable Trust
The John and Celia Bonham
   Christie Charitable Trust
The Charlotte Bonham-Carter
   Charitable Trust
Bonhomie United Charity
   Society
BOOST Charitable Trust
The Booth Charities
The Boots Charitable Trust
The Bordon and Liphook
   Charity
The Oliver Borthwick Memorial
   Trust
The Bothwell Charitable Trust
H E and E L Botteley
   Charitable Trust
The Harry Bottom Charitable
   Trust
Sir Clive Bourne Family Trust
The Anthony Bourne
   Foundation
Bourneheights Limited
Community Foundation for
   Bournemouth, Dorset and
   Poole
The Bower Trust

The Bowerman Charitable
Trust
John and Susan Bowers Fund
The Bowland Charitable Trust
The William Brake Charitable
Trust
The Tony Bramall Charitable
Trust
The Bransford Trust
The Breast Cancer Research
Trust
The Brewers' Company
General Charitable Trust
The Harold and Alice Bridges
Charity
Briggs Animal Welfare Trust
The Brighton District Nursing
Association Trust
Bristol Archdeaconry Charity
The Bristol Charities
John Bristow and Thomas
Mason Trust
Britannia Foundation
The British Council for
Prevention of Blindness
The British Dietetic
Association General and
Education Trust Fund
The British Gas (Scottish Gas)
Energy Trust
British Heart Foundation
British Humane Association
British Institute at Ankara
British Record Industry Trust
The Britten-Pears Foundation
The Britto Foundation
The J and M Britton Charitable
Trust
The Charles and Edna
Broadhurst Charitable Trust
The Roger Brooke Charitable
Trust
The David Brooke Charity
The Charles Brotherton Trust
Joseph Brough Charitable
Trust
The Swinfen Broun Charitable
Trust
Mrs E E Brown Charitable
Settlement
Bill Brown's Charitable
Settlement
R S Brownless Charitable
Trust
Brownsword Charitable
Foundation
T B H Brunner's Charitable
Settlement
The Jack Brunton Charitable
Trust
Brushmill Ltd
The Bryant Trust
The Buckinghamshire
Foundation
The Buckinghamshire Historic
Churches Trust

The Buckinghamshire Masonic
Centenary Fund
The Buffini Chao Foundation
The Rosemary Bugden
Charitable Trust
The E F Bulmer Benevolent
Fund
The BUPA Foundation
The Burden Trust
Burdens Charitable Foundation
The Burdett Trust for Nursing
The Burry Charitable Trust
The Audrey and Stanley Burton
1960 Charitable Trust
The Burton Breweries
Charitable Trust
The Geoffrey Burton Charitable
Trust
Consolidated Charity of Burton
upon Trent
Butchers' Company General
Charities
The Bill Butlin Charity Trust
Ann Byrne Charitable Trust
C and F Charitable Trust
C J Cadbury Charitable Trust
Edward Cadbury Charitable
Trust
Henry T and Lucy B Cadbury
Charitable Trust
The Christopher Cadbury
Charitable Trust
The Richard Cadbury
Charitable Trust
The William A Cadbury
Charitable Trust
The Cadbury Foundation
The Edward and Dorothy
Cadbury Trust
The George Cadbury Trust
The Barrow Cadbury Trust and
the Barrow Cadbury Fund
The Cadogan Charity
CAF (Charities Aid Foundation)
CAFOD
The Callander Charitable Trust
Calypso Browning Trust
The Cambridgeshire
Community Foundation
The Cambridgeshire Historic
Churches Trust
The Camelia Trust
The Campden Charities
The Frederick and Phyllis Cann
Trust
The Canning Trust
M R Cannon 1998 Charitable
Trust
H and L Cantor Trust
Capital Community Foundation
Cardy Beaver Foundation
The Carew Pole Charitable
Trust
The D W T Cargill Fund
Caring for Kids (Radio Tay)

The Carlsson Family
Foundation
The Carlton House Charitable
Trust
The Worshipful Company of
Carmen Benevolent Trust
The Richard Carne Trust
The Carnegie Dunfermline
Trust
The Carnegie Trust for the
Universities of Scotland
The Carpenter Charitable Trust
The Carpenters' Company
Charitable Trust
The Carr-Gregory Trust
The Carrington Charitable
Trust
The Carron Charitable Trust
The Leslie Mary Carter
Charitable Trust
Carter's Educational
Foundation
The Carvill Trust
Cash for Kids Radio Clyde
Sir John Cass's Foundation
The Castang Foundation
The Catalyst Charitable Trust
(formerly the Buckle Family
Charitable Trust)
The Catholic Trust for England
and Wales
The Cattanach Charitable Trust
The Joseph and Annie Cattle
Trust
The Thomas Sivewright Catto
Charitable Settlement
The Wilfrid and Constance
Cave Foundation
The Cayo Foundation
Elizabeth Cayzer Charitable
Trust
The B G S Cayzer Charitable
Trust
The Cazenove Charitable Trust
Celtic Charity Fund
The Cemlyn-Jones Trust
CfBT Education Trust
The CH (1980) Charitable
Trust
R E Chadwick Charitable Trust
The Amelia Chadwick Trust
The Pamela Champion
Foundation
Champneys Charitable
Foundation
The Chapman Charitable Trust
John William Chapman's
Charitable Trust
The Charities Advisory Trust
Charitworth Limited
The Charter 600 Charity
The Chasah Trust
Chasdei Tovim Me'oros
The Chelsea Building Society
Charitable Foundation

The Chelsea Square 1994 Trust

The Cheruby Trust

The Cheshire Provincial Fund of Benevolence

Chest, Heart and Stroke Scotland

The Chetwode Foundation

The Malcolm Chick Charity

Child Growth Foundation

Children's Liver Disease Foundation

The Children's Research Fund

The Childwick Trust

The Chippenham Borough Lands Charity

The Chipping Sodbury Town Lands Charity

CHK Charities Limited

The Chownes Foundation

The Chrimes Family Charitable Trust

The Christabella Charitable Trust

Christadelphian Samaritan Fund

Christian Aid

The Church and Community Fund

The Church Burgesses Educational Foundation

Church Burgesses Trust

Church Lands and John Johnson's Estate Charities

Church of Ireland Priorities Fund

The Church Urban Fund

City and County of Swansea Welsh Church Act Fund

The City Bridge Trust (formerly known as Bridge House Trust)

The City Educational Trust Fund

The City Parochial Foundation

CLA Charitable Trust

Stephen Clark 1957 Charitable Trust

J A Clark Charitable Trust

The Hilda and Alice Clark Charitable Trust

The Roger and Sarah Bancroft Clark Charitable Trust

The Clarke Charitable Settlement

The Cleary Foundation

The Cleopatra Trust

Lord Clinton's Charitable Trust

The Clore Duffield Foundation

Miss V L Clore's 1967 Charitable Trust

Closehelm Ltd

The Clothworkers' Foundation

Richard Cloudesley's Charity

The Clover Trust

The Robert Clutterbuck Charitable Trust

Clydpride Ltd

The Francis Coales Charitable Foundation

The Coalfields Regeneration Trust

The John Coates Charitable Trust

Coats Foundation Trust

The Cobtree Charity Trust Ltd

The Denise Cohen Charitable Trust

The Vivienne and Samuel Cohen Charitable Trust

The R and S Cohen Fondation

The John S Cohen Foundation

The Colchester Catalyst Charity

John Coldman Charitable Trust

The Cole Charitable Trust

The Colefax Charitable Trust

The John and Freda Coleman Charitable Trust

The George Henry Collins Charity

The Sir Jeremiah Colman Gift Trust

Col-Reno Ltd

The Colt Foundation

Colwinston Charitable Trust

Colyer-Fergusson Charitable Trust

Comic Relief

The Comino Foundation

Community Foundation for Calderdale

The Community Foundation for Greater Manchester

The Community Foundation for Northern Ireland

The Company of Tobacco Pipe Makers' and Tobacco Blenders' Benevolent Fund

The Compton Charitable Trust

The Douglas Compton James Charitable Trust

The Congleton Inclosure Trust

The Congregational and General Charitable Trust

The Conscience Trust

The Conservation Foundation

The Consolidated Charities for the Infirm Merchant Taylors' Company

The Construction Industry Trust for Youth

The Cook and Wolstenholme Charitable Trust

Gordon Cook Foundation

The Ernest Cook Trust

The Cooks Charity

The Catherine Cookson Charitable Trust

Harold and Daphne Cooper Charitable Trust

Mabel Cooper Charity

The Alice Ellen Cooper Dean Charitable Foundation

The Co-operative Foundation

The Marjorie Coote Animal Charity Trust

The Marjorie Coote Old People's Charity

The Helen Jean Cope Trust

The J Reginald Corah Foundation Fund

The Gershon Coren Charitable Foundation

The Corinthian Trust

Edwin Cornforth 1983 Charity Trust

Cornwall Community Foundation

The Cornwall Historic Churches Trust

The Duke of Cornwall's Benevolent Fund

The Cornwell Charitable Trust

The Sidney and Elizabeth Corob Charitable Trust

The Corona Charitable Trust

The Costa Family Charitable Trust (formerly the Morgan Williams Charitable Trust)

The Cotton Industry War Memorial Trust

The Cotton Trust

Country Houses Foundation

County Durham Foundation

The Augustine Courtauld Trust

Coutts Charitable Trust

The General Charities of the City of Coventry

Coventry Building Society Charitable Foundation

The John Cowan Foundation

The Sir Tom Cowie Charitable Trust

Cowley Charitable Foundation

The Sir William Coxen Trust Fund

The Lord Cozens-Hardy Trust

The Craignish Trust

The Craps Charitable Trust

Michael Crawford Children's Charity

The Cray Trust

The Crescent Trust

Criffel Charitable Trust

Cripplegate Foundation

The Violet and Milo Cripps Charitable Trust

The Cromarty Trust

The Harry Crook Foundation

The Cross Trust

The Cross Trust

The Croydon Relief in Need Charities

The Mayor of Croydon's Charity Fund

The Peter Cruddas Foundation

Cruden Foundation Ltd
The Ronald Cruickshanks' Foundation
Cuby Charitable Trust
Cullum Family Trust
The Culra Charitable Trust
Cumberland Building Society Charitable Foundation
Cumbria Community Foundation
The Cunningham Trust
The Harry Cureton Charitable Trust
The D J H Currie Memorial Trust
The Dennis Curry Charitable Trust
The Raymond Curtis Charitable Trust
The Manny Cussins Foundation
The Cutler Trust (the Worshipful Company of Makers of Playing Cards)
The Cwmbran Trust
The D'Oyly Carte Charitable Trust
The Roald Dahl Foundation
The Daily Prayer Union Charitable Trust Ltd
The Daiwa Anglo-Japanese Foundation
The Dr and Mrs A Darlington Charitable Trust
Baron Davenport's Charity
The Davidson (Nairn) Charitable Trust
Davidson Charitable Trust
The Alderman Joe Davidson Memorial Trust
Michael Davies Charitable Settlement
The Gwendoline and Margaret Davies Charity
The Hamilton Davies Trust
The Wilfrid Bruce Davis Charitable Trust
Davis-Rubens Charitable Trust
The Dawe Charitable Trust
The De Clermont Charitable Company Ltd
The Helen and Geoffrey De Freitas Charitable Trust
Peter De Haan Charitable Trust
The Leopold De Rothschild Charitable Trust
The Deakin Charitable Trust
William Dean Countryside and Educational Trust
The Debmar Benevolent Trust
The Delfont Foundation
The Delius Trust
The Dellal Foundation
The Delves Charitable Trust
The Demigryphon Trust

The Denman Charitable Trust
The Denton Charitable Trust
The Denton Wilde Sapte Charitable Trust
The Earl of Derby's Charitable Trust
The Derbyshire Churches and Chapels Preservation Trust
Derbyshire Community Foundation
The J N Derbyshire Trust
Devon Community Foundation
The Devon Educational Trust
The Devon Historic Churches Trust
The Duke of Devonshire's Charitable Trust
The Sandy Dewhirst Charitable Trust
DG Charitable Settlement
The Laduma Dhamecha Charitable Trust
Diabetes UK
Alan and Sheila Diamond Charitable Trust
The Dibden Allotments Charity
The Gillian Dickinson Trust
The Dickon Trust
The Digbeth Trust
The Dinwoodie Settlement
Disability Aid Fund (The Roger and Jean Jefcoate Trust)
Dischma Charitable Trust
The Djanogly Foundation
The DLA Piper Charitable Trust (previously known as the DLA Charitable Trust)
The DLM Charitable Trust
The DM Charitable Trust
Louise Dobson Charitable Trust
The Derek and Eileen Dodgson Foundation
The Dollond Charitable Trust
Domepride Ltd
The Dorcas Trust
The Dorema Charitable Trust
The Dorset Historic Churches Trust
The Dorus Trust
The Doughty Charity Trust
The R M Douglas Charitable Trust
The Drapers' Charitable Fund
The Drayson Foundation
Dromintee Trust
The Dugdale Charitable Trust
The Dulverton Trust
The P B Dumbell Charitable Trust
The Dumbreck Charity
Dunard Fund
Ronald Duncan Literary Foundation
The Dunhill Medical Trust

The Harry Dunn Charitable Trust
The Houghton Dunn Charitable Trust
The W E Dunn Trust
Annette Duvollet Charitable Trust
The Dwek Family Charitable Trust
The Dyers' Company Charitable Trust
The James Dyson Foundation
EAGA Partnership Charitable Trust
The Eagle Charity Trust
Audrey Earle Charitable Trust
The Earley Charity
Earls Colne and Halstead Educational Charity
The Earmark Trust
East Kent Provincial Charities
East London Community Foundation
Eastern Counties Educational Trust Limited
The Sir John Eastwood Foundation
The Ebenezer Trust
The EBM Charitable Trust
The Ecology Trust
Eden Arts Trust
EDF Energy Trust (EDFET)
The Gilbert and Eileen Edgar Foundation
Gilbert Edgar Trust
Edinburgh Children's Holiday Fund
The Edinburgh Trust, No 2 Account
Edinburgh Voluntary Organisations' Trust Funds
Educational Foundation of Alderman John Norman
The W G Edwards Charitable Foundation
The William Edwards Educational Charity
Dr Edwards' and Bishop King's Fulham Endowment Fund
The Elephant Trust
The George Elias Charitable Trust
The Gerald Palmer Eling Trust Company
The Elizabeth Frankland Moore and Star Foundation
The Wilfred and Elsie Elkes Charity Fund
The Maud Elkington Charitable Trust
Ellador Ltd
The Ellerdale Trust
The John Ellerman Foundation
The Ellinson Foundation Ltd
The Edith Maud Ellis 1985 Charitable Trust

The Ellis Campbell Foundation
James Ellis Charitable Trust
The Elm House Trust
The Elmgrant Trust
The Elmley Foundation
Elshore Ltd
The Vernon N Ely Charitable Trust
The Embleton Trust
The Emerton-Christie Charity
EMI Music Sound Foundation
The Emmandjay Charitable Trust
The Worshipful Company of Engineers Charitable Trust Fund
The Englefield Charitable Trust
The English Schools' Football Association
The Enkalon Foundation
The Epigoni Trust
Epilepsy Research UK
The Equitable Charitable Trust
The Equity Trust Fund
The Eranda Foundation
The Ericson Trust
The Ernest Hecht Charitable Foundation
The Erskine Cunningham Hill Trust
Essex Community Foundation
The Essex Fairway Charitable Trust
The Essex Heritage Trust
Essex Provincial Charity Fund
The Essex Youth Trust
The Estelle Trust
Euro Charity Trust
The Evangelical Covenants Trust
The Alan Evans Memorial Trust
Sir John Evelyn's Charity
The Eventhall Family Charitable Trust
The Everard Foundation
The Eveson Charitable Trust
The Beryl Evetts and Robert Luff Animal Welfare Trust
The Execution Charitable Trust
The Mayor of Exeter's Appeal Fund
The Exilarch's Foundation
Extonglen Limited
F C Charitable Trust
The F P Limited Charitable Trust
The Faber Charitable Trust
Esmée Fairbairn Foundation
The Fairway Trust
Faisaltex Charitable Trust
The Family Foundations Trust (also known as Mintz Family Foundation)
Famos Foundation Trust
The Lord Faringdon Charitable Trust

Samuel William Farmer's Trust
The Farmers' Company Charitable Fund
The Thomas Farr Charitable Trust
Walter Farthing (Trust) Limited
Farthing Trust
The Fassnidge Memorial Trust
Joseph Fattorini Charitable Trust 'B' Account
The Fawcett Charitable Trust
The February Foundation
The John Feeney Charitable Bequest
The George Fentham Birmingham Charity
The A M Fenton Trust
Elizabeth Ferguson Charitable Trust Fund
The Fidelity UK Foundation
The Bluff Field Charitable Trust
The Doris Field Charitable Trust
Fife Council/Common Good Funds and Trusts
The Fifty Fund
Dixie Rose Findlay Charitable Trust
Finnart House School Trust
Gerald Finzi Charitable Trust
Firtree Trust
The Sir John Fisher Foundation
The Fishmongers' Company's Charitable Trust
Marc Fitch Fund
The Fitton Trust
The Earl Fitzwilliam Charitable Trust
Bud Flanagan Leukaemia Fund
The Rose Flatau Charitable Trust
The Ian Fleming Charitable Trust
The Joyce Fletcher Charitable Trust
The Roy Fletcher Charitable Trust
Florence's Charitable Trust
The Florian Charitable Trust
The Flow Foundation
The Gerald Fogel Charitable Trust
The Football Association National Sports Centre Trust
The Football Association Youth Trust
The Football Foundation
The Forbes Charitable Foundation
Forbesville Limited
The Forces Trust
Ford Britain Trust
The Oliver Ford Charitable Trust
Fordeve Ltd

The Lady Forester Trust
The Foresters' Fund for Children
The Foresters' Charity Stewards UK Trust
Gwyneth Forrester Trust
Lord Forte Foundation
Foundation for Management Education
The Fowler, Smith and Jones Charitable Trust
The Foyle Foundation
The Isaac and Freda Frankel Memorial Charitable Trust
The Gordon Fraser Charitable Trust
The Hugh Fraser Foundation
The Joseph Strong Frazer Trust
The Louis and Valerie Freedman Charitable Settlement
The Freemasons' Grand Charity
The Thomas Freke and Lady Norton Charity
The Charles S French Charitable Trust
The Anne French Memorial Trust
The Freshfield Foundation
The Freshgate Trust Foundation
The Friarsgate Trust
The Friends Hall Farm Street Trust
Friends of Biala Ltd
The Friends of Kent Churches
Friends of Muir Group
Friends of Wiznitz Limited
Friends Provident Charitable Foundation
The Frognal Trust
T F C Frost Charitable Trust
The Patrick Frost Foundation
Mejer and Gertrude Miriam Frydman Foundation
The Fulmer Charitable Trust
Worshipful Company of Furniture Makers Charitable Fund
Gableholt Limited
The Galbraith Trust
The Gale Family Charitable Trust
The Gamlen Charitable Trust
The Gamma Trust
The Gannochy Trust
The Ganzoni Charitable Trust
The Worshipful Company of Gardeners of London
The Samuel Gardner Memorial Trust
The Garnett Charitable Trust
Garrick Charitable Trust
Garvan Limited

Gatwick Airport Community Trust

The Robert Gavron Charitable Trust

Jacqueline and Michael Gee Charitable Trust

The General Nursing Council for England and Wales Trust

J Paul Getty Jr Charitable Trust

The Gibbs Charitable Trust

Simon Gibson Charitable Trust

The G C Gibson Charitable Trust

The Harvey and Hilary Gilbert Charitable Trust

The Girdlers' Company Charitable Trust

The B and P Glasser Charitable Trust

The Glass-House Trust

The Glastonbury Trust Limited

Global Charities (formally GCap Charities)

Gloucestershire Community Foundation

The Gloucestershire Historic Churches Trust

Worshipful Company of Glovers of London Charity Fund

GMC Trust

The GNC Trust

The Mrs Godfrey-Payton Trust

The Meir Golda Trust

The Sydney and Phyllis Goldberg Memorial Charitable Trust

The Golden Bottle Trust

Golden Charitable Trust

The Jack Goldhill Charitable Trust

The Goldmark Trust

The Goldsmiths' Arts Trust Fund

The Goldsmiths' Company Charity

The Golsoncott Foundation

The Good Neighbours Trust

Goodfund

Nicholas and Judith Goodison's Charitable Settlement

The Everard and Mina Goodman Charitable Foundation

The Goodman Foundation

Mike Gooley Trailfinders Charity

Leonard Gordon Charitable Trust

The Gosling Foundation Limited

The Gough Charitable Trust

The Gould Charitable Trust

The Grace Charitable Trust

A B Grace Trust

The Graff Foundation

The Grahame Charitable Foundation Limited

Grampian Police Diced Cap Charitable Fund

The Granada Foundation

Grand Charitable Trust of the Order of Women Freemasons

The Grand Order of Water Rats' Charities Fund

The Grange Farm Centre Trust

Grantham Yorke Trust

GrantScape

The J G Graves Charitable Trust

The Gray Trust

The Great Britain Sasakawa Foundation

The Great Stone Bridge Trust of Edenbridge

The Great Torrington Town Lands Charity

The Constance Green Foundation

The Barry Green Memorial Fund

The Philip Green Memorial Trust

Philip and Judith Green Trust

Mrs H R Greene Charitable Settlement

Greenham Common Community Trust Limited

Naomi and Jeffrey Greenwood Charitable Trust

Greggs Foundation (formerly Greggs Trust)

The Greys Charitable Trust

Grimmitt Trust

The Grocers' Charity

The M and R Gross Charities Limited

The Grove Charitable Trust

The GRP Charitable Trust

The David and Marie Grumitt Foundation

The Bishop of Guildford's Foundation

The Guildry Incorporation of Perth

The Walter Guinness Charitable Trust

The Gulbenkian Foundation

The Gunter Charitable Trust

The Gur Trust

Gurunanak

Dr Guthrie's Association

The H and J Spack Charitable Trust

The H and M Charitable Trust

The H P Charitable Trust

The Hackney Parochial Charities

The Hadfield Trust

The Hadley Trust

The Hadrian Trust

The Alfred Haines Charitable Trust

The Hale Trust

E F and M G Hall Charitable Trust

The Edith Winifred Hall Charitable Trust

Robert Hall Charity

The Hamamelis Trust

Hamilton Wallace Trust

Paul Hamlyn Foundation

Sue Hammerson's Charitable Trust

The Hammonds Charitable Trust

The Hampshire and Islands Historic Churches Trust

Hampshire and Isle of Wight Community Foundation

The Hampstead Wells and Campden Trust

Hampton Fuel Allotment Charity

The W A Handley Charitable Trust

Beatrice Hankey Foundation Ltd

The Hanley Trust

The Hanlye Charitable Trust

The Kathleen Hannay Memorial Charity

Lord Hanson Foundation

Harbo Charities Limited

The Harborne Parish Lands Charity

The Harbour Charitable Trust

The Harbour Foundation

The Harding Trust

William Harding's Charity

The Hare of Steep Charitable Trust

The Harebell Centenary Fund

The Kenneth Hargreaves Charitable Trust

The Harris Charitable Trust

The Harris Charity

The Harris Family Charitable Trust

The Harrison and Potter Trust

The John Harrison Charitable Trust

The Peter Harrison Foundation

The Spencer Hart Charitable Trust

The Hartley Charitable Trust

The N and P Hartley Memorial Trust

The Alfred And Peggy Harvey Charitable Trust

William Geoffrey Harvey's Discretionary Settlement

The Edward Harvist Trust Fund

Haskel Family Foundation

Hasluck Charitable Trust

The Hathaway Trust
The Maurice Hatter Foundation
The M A Hawe Settlement
The Hawthorne Charitable Trust
The Dorothy Hay-Bolton Charitable Trust
The Haydan Charitable Trust
The Haymills Charitable Trust
The Charles Hayward Foundation
Headley-Pitt Charitable Trust
Heagerty Charitable Trust
The Heald Charitable Trust
Healthsure Group Ltd
May Hearnshaw's Charity
The Heart of England Community Foundation
The Heathcoat Trust
Heathside Charitable Trust
Percy Hedley 1990 Charitable Trust
The Hedley Denton Charitable Trust
The Hedley Foundation
The H J Heinz Company Limited Charitable Trust
The Hellenic Foundation
The Michael and Morven Heller Charitable Foundation
The Simon Heller Charitable Settlement
Help the Aged
Help the Homeless
Help the Hospices
The Helping Foundation
The Hemby Trust
The Christina Mary Hendrie Trust for Scottish and Canadian Charities
The Henley Educational Charity
The Tim Henman Charitable Foundation
Esther Hennell Charitable Trust
The G D Herbert Charitable Trust
The Joanna Herbert-Stepney Charitable Settlement (also known as The Paget Charitable Trust)
The Anne Herd Memorial Trust
The Herefordshire Community Foundation
The Herefordshire Historic Churches Trust
The Heritage of London Trust Ltd
The Hertfordshire Community Foundation
The Hesed Trust
The Hesslewood Children's Trust (Hull Seamen's and General Orphanage)
The Bernhard Heuberger Charitable Trust

Hexham and Newcastle Diocesan Trust (1947)
The P and C Hickinbotham Charitable Trust
The Rosalind Hicks Charitable Trust
The Higgs Charitable Trust
Alan Edward Higgs Charity
The High Sheriff's Police Trust for the County of West Midlands
Highcroft Charitable Trust
The Hilden Charitable Fund
The Joseph and Mary Hiley Trust
The Holly Hill Charitable Trust
The Derek Hill Foundation
The Charles Littlewood Hill Trust
The Hillingdon Community Trust
The Hillingdon Partnership Trust
R G Hills Charitable Trust
Hinchley Charitable Trust
Lady Hind Trust
Stuart Hine Trust
The Hinrichsen Foundation
The Hintze Family Charitable Foundation
The Hitchin Educational Foundation
The Henry C Hoare Charitable Trust
The Eleemosynary Charity of William Hobbayne
Hobson Charity Limited
Hockerill Educational Foundation
Matthew Hodder Charitable Trust
The Sir Julian Hodge Charitable Trust
The Jane Hodge Foundation
The J G Hogg Charitable Trust
The Holden Charitable Trust
John Holford's Charity
The Hollands-Warren Fund
The Hollick Family Charitable Trust
The Holliday Foundation
The Dorothy Holmes Charitable Trust
The Holst Foundation
P H Holt Foundation
The Edward Holt Trust
The Holywood Trust
The Homelands Charitable Trust
The Homestead Charitable Trust
Mary Homfray Charitable Trust
HopMarket Charity
The Cuthbert Horn Trust
The Antony Hornby Charitable Trust

The Horne Foundation
The Horne Trust
The Worshipful Company of Horners' Charitable Trusts
The Hornsey Parochial Charities
The Hospital of God at Greatham
The Hospital Saturday Fund
The Sir Joseph Hotung Charitable Settlement
Houblon-Norman/George Fund
The House of Industry Estate
The Reta Lila Howard Foundation
The Daniel Howard Trust
The Clifford Howarth Charity Settlement
The Huddersfield Medical Trust Fund
The Hudson Foundation
The Huggard Charitable Trust
The Geoffrey C Hughes Charitable Trust
The Hull and East Riding Charitable Trust
Hulme Trust Estates (Educational)
The Humanitarian Trust
The Humberside Charitable Health Trust
The Michael and Shirley Hunt Charitable Trust
The Albert Hunt Trust
The Hunter Foundation
Miss Agnes H Hunter's Trust
The Huntingdon Foundation
Huntingdon Freemen's Charity
John Huntingdon's Charity
Hurdale Charity Limited
The Nani Huyu Charitable Trust
The P Y N and B Hyams Trust
The Hyde Charitable Trust – Youth Plus
The Idlewild Trust
The Iliffe Family Charitable Trust
Impetus Trust
The Indigo Trust
The Ingram Trust
The Inland Waterways Association
The Inlight Trust
The Inman Charity
The Inner London Magistrates Court Poor Box Charity and Feeder Charity
The Worshipful Company of Innholders General Charity Fund
The International Bankers Charitable Trust (The Worshipful Compnay of Interntional Bankers)
The Inverforth Charitable Trust
Investream Charitable Trust

The Ireland Fund of Great
  Britain
The Irish Youth Foundation
  (UK) Ltd (incorporating The
  Lawlor Foundation)
The Ironmongers' Foundation
The Charles Irving Charitable
  Trust
Irwin Trust
The ISA Charity
The Isaacs Charitable Trust
The Island Health Trust
The Isle of Anglesey Charitable
  Trust
Isle of Dogs Community
  Foundation
The ITF Seafarers Trust
J A R Charitable Trust
J I Charitable Trust
The J J Charitable Trust
The J R S S T Charitable Trust
Elizabeth Jackson Charitable
  Trust
Jacobs Charitable Trust
The Ruth and Lionel Jacobson
  Trust (Second Fund) No 2
Jaffe Family Relief Fund
John James Bristol Foundation
The Susan and Stephen
  James Charitable
  Settlement (also known as
  the Stephen James
  Charitable Trust)
The James Trust
The Jarman Charitable Trust
The John Jarrold Trust
The Jeffrey Charitable Trust
Rees Jeffreys Road Fund
The Jenour Foundation
The Jephcott Charitable Trust
The Jerusalem Trust
Jerwood Charitable Foundation
Jesus Hospital Charity
Jewish Child's Day
The Jewish Youth Fund
The JMK Charitable Trust
The Joanies Trust
The Harold Joels Charitable
  Trust
The Jonathan Joels Charitable
  Trust
The Nicholas Joels Charitable
  Trust
The Norman Joels Charitable
  Trust
The Elton John Aids
  Foundation
The Michael John Trust
The Lillie Johnson Charitable
  Trust
The Johnson Group Cleaners
  Charity
The Johnnie Johnson Trust
The Johnson Wax Ltd
  Charitable Trust
The Joicey Trust

The Jones 1986 Charitable
  Trust
Dezna Robins Jones Charitable
  Foundation
The Marjorie and Geoffrey
  Jones Charitable Trust
The Jordan Charitable
  Foundation
The Joron Charitable Trust
The J E Joseph Charitable
  Fund
The Lady Eileen Joseph
  Foundation
The Josh Charitable Trust
JTH Charitable Trust
The Judith Trust
The Anton Jurgens Charitable
  Trust
The Bernard Kahn Charitable
  Trust
The Stanley Kalms Foundation
The Karenza Foundation
The Boris Karloff Charitable
  Foundation
The Ian Karten Charitable
  Trust
The Kasner Charitable Trust
The Kass Charitable Trust
The Kathleen Trust
The Michael and Ilse Katz
  Foundation
The Katzauer Charitable
  Settlement
The C S Kaufman Charitable
  Trust
The Geoffrey John Kaye
  Charitable Foundation
The Emmanuel Kaye
  Foundation
The Caron Keating Foundation
Kelsick's Educational
  Foundation
The KempWelch Charitable
  Trust
The Kay Kendall Leukaemia
  Fund
William Kendall's Charity (Wax
  Chandlers' Company)
The Kennel Club Charitable
  Trust
Kent Community Foundation
The Nancy Kenyon Charitable
  Trust
Keren Association
Kermaville Ltd
E and E Kernkraut Charities
  Limited
The Peter Kershaw Trust
The Kessler Foundation
Keswick Hall Charity
The Ursula Keyes Trust
The Robert Kiln Charitable
  Trust
The King Henry VIII Endowed
  Trust Warwick

The King/Cullimore Charitable
  Trust
The King's Fund
The Mary Kinross Charitable
  Trust
Kinsurdy Charitable Trust
Kirkley Poor's Lands Estate
The Richard Kirkman
  Charitable Trust
Kirschel Foundation
Robert Kitchin (Saddlers'
  Company)
The Marina Kleinwort
  Charitable Trust
The Sir James Knott Trust
The Kobler Trust
The Kohn Foundation
The KPMG Foundation
The Kreditor Charitable Trust
The Kreitman Foundation
The Neil Kreitman Foundation
The Heinz, Anna and Carol
  Kroch Foundation
Kupath Gemach Chaim
  Bechesed Viznitz Trust
The Kyte Charitable Trust
Lacims-Maclis Charitable Trust
The Late Sir Pierce Lacy
  Charity Trust
John Laing Charitable Trust
The Laing Family Foundations
The Christopher Laing
  Foundation
The Lambert Charitable Trust
Community Foundation for
  Lancashire
Lancashire Environmental
  Fund
Duchy of Lancaster Benevolent
  Fund
The Lancaster Foundation
LandAid Charitable Trust
The Jack Lane Charitable Trust
The Allen Lane Foundation
The Langtree Trust
The LankellyChase Foundation
The Lanvern Foundation
The R J Larg Family Charitable
  Trust
Largsmount Ltd
The Lark Trust
Lauchentilly Charitable
  Foundation 1988
Laufer Charitable Trust
The Lauffer Family Charitable
  Foundation
The Kathleen Laurence Trust
The Edgar E Lawley Foundation
The Herd Lawson and Muriel
  Lawson Charitable Trust
The Lawson Beckman
  Charitable Trust
The Raymond and Blanche
  Lawson Charitable Trust
The Carole and Geoffrey
  Lawson Foundation

The Mason Le Page Charitable
Trust
The Leach Fourteenth Trust
The David Lean Foundation
The Leathersellers' Company
Charitable Fund
The Leche Trust
The Arnold Lee Charitable
Trust
The William Leech Charity
The Lord Mayor of Leeds
Appeal Fund
Leeds Building Society
Charitable Foundation
The Leeds Community
Foundation
Leicester Charity Link (formerly
The Leicester Charity
Organisation Society)
Leicestershire Historic
Churches Trust
The Kennedy Leigh Charitable
Trust
Morris Leigh Foundation
Mrs Vera Leigh's Charity
The P Leigh-Bramwell Trust 'E'
The Erica Leonard Trust
The Leonard Trust
The Mark Leonard Trust
Lesley Lesley and Mutter Trust
Leukaemia Research Fund
The Leverhulme Trade
Charities Trust
The Leverhulme Trust
Lord Leverhulme's Charitable
Trust
The Joseph Levy Charitable
Foundation
Lewis Family Charitable Trust
The John Spedan Lewis
Foundation
The Sir Edward Lewis
Foundation
John Lewis Partnership
General Community Fund
The Lewis Ward Trust
Lichfield Conduit Lands
The Thomas Lilley Memorial
Trust
Limoges Charitable Trust
Lincolnshire Community
Foundation
The Lincolnshire Old Churches
Trust
The Lind Trust
The Linden Charitable Trust
The Linmardon Trust
The Ruth and Stuart Lipton
Charitable Trust
The Lister Charitable Trust
Frank Litchfield Charitable
Trust
The Andrew and Mary
Elizabeth Little Charitable
Trust

The Second Joseph Aaron
Littman Foundation
The George John and Sheilah
Livanos Charitable Trust
Liverpool Charity and Voluntary
Services
The Liverpool One Foundation
Liverpool Sailors' Home Trust
The Elaine and Angus Lloyd
Charitable Trust
The Lloyd Fund
Lloyd's Charities Trust
The Lloyd-Everett Trust
Lloyds TSB Foundation for
England and Wales
Lloyds TSB Foundation for
Northern Ireland
Lloyds TSB Foundation for the
Channel Islands
Llysdinam Charitable Trust
Localtrent Ltd
The Loftus Charitable Trust
London Catalyst (formerly The
Metropolitan Hospital-
Sunday Fund)
The London Law Trust
London Legal Support Trust
The London Marathon
Charitable Trust
London Masonic Charitable
Trust
The William and Katherine
Longman Trust
The Lord's Taverners
The Loseley and Guildway
Charitable Trust
The Lowy Mitchell Foundation
The C L Loyd Charitable Trust
LSA Charitable Trust
The Marie Helen Luen
Charitable Trust
Robert Luff Foundation Ltd
Lady Lumley's Educational
Foundation
C F Lunoe Trust Fund
The Ruth and Jack Lunzer
Charitable Trust
The Lyndhurst Trust
The Lynn Foundation
The Lynwood Trust
John Lyon's Charity
The Lyons Charitable Trust
The Sir Jack Lyons Charitable
Trust
Malcolm Lyons Foundation
Sylvanus Lyson's Charity
The M and C Trust
The M D and S Charitable
Trust
The M K Charitable Trust
(formerly the Mendel
Kaufman Charitable Trust)
The E M MacAndrew Trust
The R S Macdonald Charitable
Trust

Macdonald-Buchanan
Charitable Trust
The Macfarlane Walker Trust
The Mackay and Brewer
Charitable Trust
The Mackintosh Foundation
The MacRobert Trust
Ian Mactaggart Trust
James Madison Trust
The Magdalen and Lasher
Charity
Magdalen Hospital Trust
The Magen Charitable Trust
Mageni Trust
The Makin Charitable Trust
Man Group plc Charitable
Trust
Manchester Airport Community
Trust Fund
The Manchester Guardian
Society Charitable Trust
Manchester Kids
Lord Mayor of Manchester's
Charity Appeal Trust
Mandeville Trust
The Manifold Charitable Trust
W M Mann Foundation
R W Mann Trust
The Leslie and Lilian Manning
Trust
Maranatha Christian Trust
Marbeh Torah Trust
The Marchday Charitable Fund
The Stella and Alexander
Margulies Charitable Trust
Market Harborough and The
Bowdens Charity
The Ann and David Marks
Foundation
The Hilda and Samuel Marks
Foundation
J P Marland Charitable Trust
The Michael Marsh Charitable
Trust
The Marsh Christian Trust
The Charlotte Marshall
Charitable Trust
The Jim Marshall Charitable
Trust
The D G Marshall of
Cambridge Trust
Marshall's Charity
Marshgate Charitable
Settlement
Sir George Martin Trust
John Martin's Charity
The Mason Porter Charitable
Trust
The Nancie Massey Charitable
Trust
The Mathew Trust
Matliwala Family Charitable
Trust
The Matt 6.3 Charitable Trust
The Violet Mauray Charitable
Trust

The Maxell Educational Trust
The Maxwell Family Foundation
Evelyn May Trust
Mayfair Charities Ltd
The Mayfield Valley Arts Trust
Mazars Charitable Trust
The Robert McAlpine
    Foundation
The McDougall Trust
The A M McGreevy No 5
    Charitable Settlement
The McKenna Charitable Trust
Martin McLaren Memorial
    Trust
The Helen Isabella McMorran
    Charitable Foundation
D D McPhail Charitable
    Settlement
The James Frederick and Ethel
    Anne Measures Charity
Medical Research Council
The Medlock Charitable Trust
The Anthony and Elizabeth
    Mellows Charitable
    Settlement
Melow Charitable Trust
Meningitis Trust
Menuchar Ltd
Mercaz Torah Vechesed
    Limited
The Mercers' Charitable
    Foundation
The Merchant Taylors'
    Company Charities Fund
The Merchant Venturers'
    Charity
The Merchants' House of
    Glasgow
The Mersey Docks and
    Harbour Company
    Charitable Fund
Community Foundation for
    Merseyside
The Zachary Merton and
    George Woofindin
    Convalescent Trust
The Tony Metherell Charitable
    Trust
The Metropolitan Drinking
    Fountain and Cattle Trough
    Association
Mickleham Charitable Trust
Gerald Micklem Charitable
    Trust
The Masonic Province of
    Middlesex Charitable Trust
Midhurst Pensions Trust
The Migraine Trust
Miles Trust for the Putney and
    Roehampton Community
Millennium Stadium Charitable
    Trust
The Hugh and Mary Miller
    Bequest Trust
The Miller Foundation
The Millfield House Foundation

The Millfield Trust
The Millhouses Charitable
    Trust
The Millichope Foundation
The Mills Charity
The Clare Milne Trust
Milton Keynes Community
    Foundation
The Edgar Milward Charity
The Keith and Joan
    Mindelsohn Charitable
    Trust
The Peter Minet Trust
Minge's Gift and the Pooled
    Trusts
The Mirfield Educational
    Charity
The Mirianog Trust
The Laurence Misener
    Charitable Trust
The Mishcon Family Charitable
    Trust
The Misselbrook Trust
The Brian Mitchell Charitable
    Settlement
The Mitchell Charitable Trust
The Esme Mitchell Trust
Keren Mitzvah Trust
The Mizpah Trust
The Mobbs Memorial Trust Ltd
The Modiano Charitable Trust
The Moette Charitable Trust
The Mole Charitable Trust
The D C Moncrieff Charitable
    Trust
Monmouthshire County Council
    Welsh Church Act Fund
The Montague Thompson
    Coon Charitable Trust
The Colin Montgomerie
    Charitable Foundation
The Monument Trust
Moody Charitable Trust
George A Moore Foundation
The Henry Moore Foundation
The Nigel Moores Family
    Charitable Trust
John Moores Foundation
The Peter Moores Foundation
The Morel Charitable Trust
The Morgan Charitable
    Foundation
The Mr and Mrs J T Morgan
    Foundation
The J P Morgan Foundations
The Oliver Morland Charitable
    Trust
S C and M E Morland's
    Charitable Trust
The Morris Charitable Trust
The Willie and Mabel Morris
    Charitable Trust
The Peter Morrison Charitable
    Foundation
G M Morrison Charitable Trust

The Stanley Morrison
    Charitable Trust
Moshal Charitable Trust
The Moshulu Charitable Trust
The Moss Charitable Trust
The Robert and Margaret
    Moss Charitable Trust
Moss Family Charitable Trust
The Mothercare Charitable
    Foundation
Moto in the Community Trust
J P Moulton Charitable
    Foundation
The Mount Everest Foundation
Mountbatten Festival of Music
The Mugdock Children's Trust
The F H Muirhead Charitable
    Trust
The Mulberry Trust
The Edith Murphy Foundation
Murphy-Neumann Charity
    Company Limited
The John R Murray Charitable
    Trust
The Mushroom Fund
The Music Sales Charitable
    Trust
The Mutual Trust Group
MYA Charitable Trust
MYR Charitable Trust
The Kitty and Daniel Nabarro
    Charitable Trust
The Nadezhda Charitable Trust
The Willie Nagel Charitable
    Trust
The Janet Nash Charitable
    Settlement
The National Art Collections
    Fund
Asthma UK
The National Churches Trust
    (formerly the Historic
    Churches Preservation
    Trust with the Incorporated
    Church Building Society)
The National Manuscripts
    Conservation Trust
The Nationwide Foundation
Nazareth Trust Fund
Needham Market and Barking
    Welfare Charities
The Worshipful Company of
    Needlemakers' Charitable
    Fund
The Neighbourly Charitable
    Trust
The James Neill Trust Fund
Nemoral Ltd
Ner Foundation
Nesswall Ltd
Nestle Rowntree Employees
    Community Fund
The New Appeals Organisation
    for the City and County of
    Nottingham
New Court Charitable Trust

Newby Trust Limited
The Newcomen Collett
   Foundation
The Richard Newitt Fund
Mr and Mrs F E F Newman
   Charitable Trust
The Frances and Augustus
   Newman Foundation
Newpier Charity Ltd
Alderman Newton's
   Educational Foundation
The NFU Mutual Charitable
   Trust
The Chevras Ezras Nitzrochim
   Trust
NJD Charitable Trust
The Noel Buxton Trust
The Noon Foundation
The Norda Trust
Norie Charitable Trust
Normalyn Charitable Trust
The Norman Family Charitable
   Trust
The Duncan Norman Trust
   Fund
The Normanby Charitable Trust
The North British Hotel Trust
The North West Cancer
   Research Fund
North West London Community
   Foundation
The Northampton Municipal
   Church Charities
The Earl of Northampton's
   Charity
The Northcott Devon Medical
   Foundation
The Northern Rock Foundation
The Northumberland Village
   Homes Trust
The Northumbria Historic
   Churches Trust
The Northwood Charitable
   Trust
The Norton Foundation
The Norwich Church of England
   Young Men's Society
The Norwich Historic Churches
   Trust Ltd
The Norwich Town Close
   Estate Charity
The Norwood and Newton
   Settlement
The Noswad Charity
The Notgrove Trust
The Nottingham General
   Dispensary
Nottinghamshire Community
   Foundation
The Nottinghamshire Historic
   Churches Trust
The Nottinghamshire Miners'
   Welfare Trust Fund
The Nuffield Foundation
The Oak Trust
The Oakley Charitable Trust

The Oakmoor Charitable Trust
The Odin Charitable Trust
Ogilvie Charities Deed No.2
   (including the Charity of
   Mary Catherine Ford Smith)
Oglesby Charitable Trust
The Oizer Charitable Trust
The Old Broad Street Charity
   Trust
The Old Enfield Charitable
   Trust
The John Oldacre Foundation
The Oldham Foundation
Open Gate
The Ormsby Charitable Trust
Orrin Charitable Trust
The Ouseley Trust
The Owen Family Trust
Oxfam (GB)
City of Oxford Charity
The Oxfordshire Community
   Foundation
The P F Charitable Trust
The Doris Pacey Charitable
   Foundation
Padwa Charitable Foundation
The Pallant Charitable Trust
The Palmer Foundation
Eleanor Palmer Trust
The Panacea Society
The James Pantyfedwen
   Foundation
The Park Charitable Trust
The Frank Parkinson
   Agricultural Trust
The Samuel and Freda
   Parkinson Charitable Trust
Arthur James Paterson
   Charitable Trust
The Constance Paterson
   Charitable Trust
Miss M E Swinton Paterson's
   Charitable Trust
The Patrick Charitable Trust
The Jack Patston Charitable
   Trust
Paycare Charity Trust
   (previously known as
   Patients' Aid Association
   Hospital and Medical
   Charities Trust)
The Payne Charitable Trust
The Harry Payne Trust
The Peacock Charitable Trust
The Susanna Peake Charitable
   Trust
The David Pearlman Charitable
   Foundation
Pearson's Holiday Fund
The Pedmore Sporting Club
   Trust Fund
The Dowager Countess
   Eleanor Peel Trust
Pegasus (Stanley) Trust
Peltz Trust
The Pennycress Trust

The Performing Right Society
   Foundation
B E Perl Charitable Trust
The Persula Foundation
The Jack Petchey Foundation
The Petplan Charitable Trust
The Philips and Rubens
   Charitable Trust
The Phillips Charitable Trust
The Phillips Family Charitable
   Trust
Philological Foundation
The David Pickford Charitable
   Foundation
The Bernard Piggott Trust
The Claude and Margaret Pike
   Charity
The Pilgrim Trust
The Cecil Pilkington Charitable
   Trust
The Pilkington Charities Fund
The Sir Harry Pilkington Trust
The Col W W Pilkington Will
   Trusts The General Charity
   Fund
Miss A M Pilkington's
   Charitable Trust
Mrs Pilkington's Charitable
   Trust
The Platinum Trust
G S Plaut Charitable Trust
   Limited
The Poling Charitable Trust
The George and Esme Pollitzer
   Charitable Settlement
The Pollywally Charitable Trust
The Ponton House Trust
The Mayor of Poole's Appeal
   Fund
The John Porter Charitable
   Trust
The Porter Foundation
Porticus UK
The Portishead Nautical Trust
The Portrack Charitable Trust
The Mary Potter Convent
   Hospital Trust
The Powell Foundation
The W L Pratt Charitable Trust
The Douglas Prestwich
   Charitable Trust
The William Price Charitable
   Trust
The Lucy Price Relief-in-Need
   Charity
Sir John Priestman Charity
   Trust
The Primrose Trust
The Prince's Charities
   Foundation
Princess Anne's Charities
The Priory Foundation
Prison Service Charity Fund
Private Equity Foundation
The Privy Purse Charitable
   Trust

The Proven Family Trust
The Provincial Grand Charity of the Province of Derbyshire
PSA Peugeot Citroen Charity Trust
The Richard and Christine Purchas Charitable Trust
The Puri Foundation
Mr and Mrs J A Pye's Charitable Settlement
Quartet Community Foundation (formerly the Greater Bristol Foundation)
Queen Mary's Roehampton Trust
The Queen's Silver Jubilee Trust
Quercus Trust
R S Charitable Trust
The R V W Trust
The Monica Rabagliati Charitable Trust
Rachel Charitable Trust
The Mr and Mrs Philip Rackham Charitable Trust
Richard Radcliffe Charitable Trust
The Radcliffe Trust
The Bishop Radford Trust
Radio City Charity Foundation
The Peggy Ramsay Foundation
The Rank Foundation
The Joseph Rank Trust
The Fanny Rapaport Charitable Settlement
The Ratcliff Foundation
The Ratcliff Pension Charity
The Ratcliffe Charitable Trust
The E L Rathbone Charitable Trust
The Ravensdale Trust
The Rayden Charitable Trust
The Roger Raymond Charitable Trust
The Rayne Foundation
The Rayne Trust
The John Rayner Charitable Trust
The Albert Reckitt Charitable Trust
The Sir James Reckitt Charity
The Red Arrows Trust
Red Hill Charitable Trust
The Red Rose Charitable Trust
The C A Redfern Charitable Foundation
Redfern Charitable Trust
The Reed Foundation
Richard Reeve's Foundation
The Rehoboth Trust
The Max Reinhardt Charitable Trust
REMEDI
The Rest Harrow Trust
The Joan K Reynell Charitable Trust

The Nathaniel Reyner Trust Fund
The Rhondda Cynon Taff Welsh Church Acts Fund
Daisie Rich Trust
The Sir Cliff Richard Charitable Trust
C B Richard Ellis Charitable Trust
The Clive Richards Charity
The Violet M Richards Charity
The Richmond Parish Lands Charity
The Muriel Edith Rickman Trust
Ridgesave Limited
The Ripple Effect Foundation
The Sir John Ritblat Family Foundation
The River Farm Foundation
The River Trust
The Rivers Charitable Trust
Riverside Charitable Trust Limited
The Daniel Rivlin Charitable Trust
Rix-Thompson-Rothenburg Foundation
Thomas Roberts Trust
The Alex Roberts-Miller Foundation
The Robertson Trust
Edwin George Robinson Charitable Trust
Robyn Charitable Trust
The Rochester Bridge Trust
The Rock Solid Trust
The Rofeh Trust
Richard Rogers Charitable Settlement
Rokach Family Charitable Trust
The Helen Roll Charitable Trust
The Sir James Roll Charitable Trust
The Roman Research Trust
The C A Rookes Charitable Trust
Mrs L D Rope Third Charitable Settlement
Rosa – the UK fund for women and girls
The Rosca Trust
The Rose Foundation
The Cecil Rosen Foundation
Rosetrees Trust
The Rothera Charitable Settlement
The Rothermere Foundation
The Rotherwick Foundation
The Rothley Trust
The Rothschild Foundation
The Roughley Charitable Trust
Mrs Gladys Row Fogo Charitable Trust
The Rowan Charitable Trust

Rowanville Ltd
The Christopher Rowbotham Charitable Trust
The Rowing Foundation
The Rowlands Trust
The Joseph Rowntree Charitable Trust
The Joseph Rowntree Foundation
Joseph Rowntree Reform Trust Limited
Royal Artillery Charitable Fund
Royal British Legion
Royal Docks Trust (London)
Royal Masonic Trust for Girls and Boys
The Royal Scots Benevolent Society
The Alfred and Frances Rubens Charitable Trust
William Arthur Rudd Memorial Trust
The Rugby Group Benevolent Fund Limited
The Russell Trust
The J S and E C Rymer Charitable Trust
S O Charitable Trust
Dr Mortimer and Theresa Sackler Foundation
The Raymond and Beverley Sackler Foundation
The Ruzin Sadagora Trust
The Saddlers' Company Charitable Fund
The Jean Sainsbury Animal Welfare Trust
Saint Luke's College Foundation
The Saintbury Trust
The Saints and Sinners Trust
The Salamander Charitable Trust
The Salt Foundation
The Salt Trust
The Salters' Charities
The Andrew Salvesen Charitable Trust
Basil Samuel Charitable Trust
Coral Samuel Charitable Trust
The Peter Samuel Charitable Trust
The Camilla Samuel Fund
The Samworth Foundation
The Sandra Charitable Trust
Jimmy Savile Charitable Trust
The Scarfe Charitable Trust
The Schapira Charitable Trust
The R H Scholes Charitable Trust
The Schreib Trust
The Schreiber Charitable Trust
The Scotshill Trust
The Scott Bader Commonwealth Ltd

The Francis C Scott Charitable Trust

The Frieda Scott Charitable Trust

Sir Samuel Scott of Yews Trust

The Sir James and Lady Scott Trust

The Scott Trust Foundation

The Storrow Scott Will Trust

The Scottish Arts Council

Scottish Churches' Community Trust

Scottish Coal Industry Special Welfare Fund

The Scottish Community Foundation

The Scottish International Education Trust

The Scouloudi Foundation

Seafarers UK (King George's Fund for Sailors)

Seamen's Hospital Society

The Searchlight Electric Charitable Trust

The Searle Charitable Trust

The Helene Sebba Charitable Trust

The Samuel Sebba Charitable Trust

Leslie Sell Charitable Trust

Sellata Ltd

SEM Charitable Trust

The Seven Fifty Trust

The Severn Trent Water Charitable Trust Fund

sfgroup Charitable Fund for Disabled People

SFIA Educational Trust Limited

The Cyril Shack Trust

Peter Shalson Family Charitable Trust

The Jean Shanks Foundation

The Shanti Charitable Trust

ShareGift (The Orr Mackintosh Foundation)

The Linley Shaw Foundation

The Sheepdrove Trust

The Sheffield and District Hospital Services Charitable Fund

The Sheldon Trust

The P and D Shepherd Charitable Trust

The Sylvia and Colin Shepherd Charitable Trust

The Archie Sherman Cardiff Foundation

The Archie Sherman Charitable Trust

The R C Sherriff Trust

The Shetland Charitable Trust

SHINE (Support and Help in Education)

The Bassil Shippam and Alsford Trust

The Shipwrights' Company Charitable Fund

The Shirley Foundation

The Shoe Zone Trust

The J A Shone Memorial Trust

The Charles Shorto Charitable Trust

The Barbara A Shuttleworth Memorial Trust

The Mary Elizabeth Siebel Charity

David and Jennifer Sieff Charitable Trust

The Julius Silman Charitable Trust

The Leslie Silver Charitable Trust

The Simpson Foundation

The Huntly and Margery Sinclair Charitable Trust

Sino-British Fellowship Trust

The Skelton Bounty

The Charles Skey Charitable Trust

Skipton Building Society Charitable Foundation

The John Slater Foundation

Sloane Robinson Foundation

The Mrs Smith and Mount Trust

The Amanda Smith Charitable Trust

The E H Smith Charitable Trust

The Smith Charitable Trust

The Henry Smith Charity

The Leslie Smith Foundation

The Martin Smith Foundation

Stanley Smith General Charitable Trust

Philip Smith's Charitable Trust

The R C Snelling Charitable Trust

The Snowball Trust

The Sobell Foundation

Solev Co Ltd

Solihull Community Foundation

The Solo Charitable Settlement

David Solomons Charitable Trust

Friends of Somerset Churches and Chapels

Songdale Ltd

The E C Sosnow Charitable Trust

The Souter Charitable Trust

The South Square Trust

The Stephen R and Philippa H Southall Charitable Trust

The W F Southall Trust

The Southdown Trust

The Southover Manor General Education Trust

The Southwold Trust

The Sovereign Health Care Charitable Trust

Spar Charitable Fund

Sparks Charity (Sport Aiding Medical Research For Kids)

Sparquote Limited

The Spear Charitable Trust

The Worshipful Company of Spectacle Makers' Charity

The Jessie Spencer Trust

The Ralph and Irma Sperring Charity

The Moss Spiro Will Charitable Foundation

Split Infinitive Trust

W W Spooner Charitable Trust

Stanley Spooner Deceased Charitable Trust

The Spoore, Merry and Rixman Foundation

The Spring Harvest Charitable Trust

Rosalyn and Nicholas Springer Charitable Trust

Springfields Employees' Medical Research and Charity Trust Fund

Springrule Ltd

The Spurrell Charitable Trust

The Geoff and Fiona Squire Foundation

St Andrew Animal Fund

St Andrew's Conservation Trust

St Christopher's College Educational Trust

St Gabriel's Trust

St Hilda's Trust

St James' Trust Settlement

St James's Place Foundation

Sir Walter St John's Educational Charity

St Katharine and Shadwell Trust

The St Laurence Relief In Need Trust

St Michael's and All Saints' Charities

St Monica Trust Community Fund

The Late St Patrick White Charitable Trust

St Teilo's Trust

The Stafford Trust

Miss Doreen Stanford Trust

The Stanley Foundation Ltd

The Stanton Ballard Charitable Trust

The Staples Trust

The Star Charitable Trust

The Starfish Trust

The Peter Stebbings Memorial Charity

The Steel Charitable Trust

The Cyril and Betty Stein Charitable Trust

The Steinberg Family Charitable Trust

The Hugh Stenhouse Foundation

Stervon Ltd

The Stevenage Community Trust

The June Stevens Foundation

Stevenson Family's Charitable Trust

The Steventon Allotments and Relief-in-Need Charity

The Stewards' Charitable Trust

The Sir Halley Stewart Trust

The Leonard Laity Stoate Charitable Trust

The Stobart Newlands Charitable Trust

The Edward Stocks-Massey Bequest Fund

The Stokenchurch Educational Charity

The Stoller Charitable Trust

The M J C Stone Charitable Trust

The Stone-Mallabar Charitable Foundation

The Samuel Storey Family Charitable Trust

Peter Stormonth Darling Charitable Trust

Peter Storrs Trust

The Strangward Trust

The Strasser Foundation

Stratford upon Avon Town Trust

Strathclyde Police Benevolent Fund

The W O Street Charitable Foundation

The A B Strom and R Strom Charitable Trust

The Sudborough Foundation

The Suffolk Foundation

The Suffolk Historic Churches Trust

The Alan Sugar Foundation

The Summerfield Charitable Trust

The Bernard Sunley Charitable Foundation

Surrey Community Foundation

The Surrey Historic Buildings Trust Ltd

Sussex Community Foundation

The Sussex Historic Churches Trust

The Adrienne and Leslie Sussman Charitable Trust

The Sutasoma Trust

Sutton Coldfield Municipal Charities

The Sutton Nursing Association

The Sutton Trust

Swan Mountain Trust

The Swan Trust

Swansea and Brecon Diocesan Board of Finance Limited

The John Swire (1989) Charitable Trust

The Swire Charitable Trust

The Hugh and Ruby Sykes Charitable Trust

The Charles and Elsie Sykes Trust

The Sylvanus Charitable Trust

The Stella Symons Charitable Trust

T and S Trust Fund

Tadlus Limited

The Tajtelbaum Charitable Trust

The Talbot Trusts

The Talbot Village Trust

Tallow Chandlers Benevolent Fund

Talteg Ltd

The Tangent Charitable Trust

The Lady Tangye Charitable Trust

The David Tannen Charitable Trust

The Tanner Trust

The Lili Tapper Charitable Foundation

The Mrs A Lacy Tate Trust

The Tay Charitable Trust

C B and H H Taylor 1984 Trust

Humphrey Richardson Taylor Charitable Trust

The A R Taylor Charitable Trust

The Connie and Albert Taylor Charitable Trust

The Cyril Taylor Charitable Trust

The Taylor Family Foundation

A P Taylor Trust

Rosanna Taylor's 1987 Charity Trust

The Tedworth Charitable Trust

Tees Valley Community Foundation

Tegham Limited

The Templeton Goodwill Trust

Tesco Charity Trust

Thames Community Foundation

The Thames Wharf Charity

The Thistle Trust

The David Thomas Charitable Trust

The Thomas Wall Trust

The Arthur and Margaret Thompson Charitable Trust

The Maurice and Vivien Thompson Charitable Trust

The Thompson Family Charitable Trust

The Len Thomson Charitable Trust

The Sue Thomson Foundation

The Sir Jules Thorn Charitable Trust

The Thornton Foundation

The Three Guineas Trust

The Thriplow Charitable Trust

The Tillett Trust

Mrs R P Tindall's Charitable Trust

The Tisbury Telegraph Trust

TJH Foundation

The Tolkien Trust

Tollemache (Buckminster) Charitable Trust

Tomchei Torah Charitable Trust

The Tompkins Foundation

Toni and Guy Charitable Foundation Limited

The Torah Temimah Trust

Toras Chesed (London) Trust

Tottenham Grammar School Foundation

The Tower Hill Trust

The Towry Law Charitable Trust (also known as the Castle Educational Trust)

The Toy Trust

The Mayor of Trafford's Charity Fund

Annie Tranmer Charitable Trust

Anthony Travis Charitable Trust

The Constance Travis Charitable Trust

The Treeside Trust

The Triangle Trust (1949) Fund

The True Colours Trust

Truedene Co. Ltd

The Truemark Trust

Truemart Limited

Trumros Limited

The Trust for Education

Trust for London

Trust Sixty Three

The Trusthouse Charitable Foundation

The Tubney Charitable Trust

The James Tudor Foundation

Tudor Rose Ltd

The Tudor Trust

The Tufton Charitable Trust

The R D Turner Charitable Trust

The Douglas Turner Trust

The Florence Turner Trust

Miss S M Tutton Charitable Trust

Community Foundation Serving Tyne and Wear and Northumberland

Trustees of Tzedakah

UKI Charitable Foundation

Ulster Garden Villages Ltd

Ultach Trust

Ulverston Town Lands Charity

The Underwood Trust

The Union of Orthodox Hebrew Congregation
United Trusts
United Utilities Trust Fund
The Michael Uren Foundation
Uxbridge United Welfare Trust
'v'
The Vail Foundation
Vale of Glamorgan – Welsh Church Fund
The Valentine Charitable Trust
The Albert Van Den Bergh Charitable Trust
John and Lucille van Geest Foundation
The Van Neste Foundation
Mrs Maud Van Norden's Charitable Foundation
The Vandervell Foundation
The Vardy Foundation
The Variety Club Children's Charity
Veneziana Fund
The William and Patricia Venton Charitable Trust
The Verdon-Smith Family Charitable Settlement
Roger Vere Foundation
Victoria Homes Trust
Viking Cares (For the Kids)
The Nigel Vinson Charitable Trust
The William and Ellen Vinten Trust
The Vintners' Company Charitable Foundation
Vintners' Gifts Charity
Vision Charity
Vivdale Ltd
The Viznitz Foundation
The Vodafone (Group) Foundation
The Volant Charitable Trust
Voluntary Action Fund
Wade's Charity
The Scurrah Wainwright Charity
The Wakefield and Tetley Trust
Wakeham Trust
The Community Foundation in Wales
Wales Council for Voluntary Action
Robert and Felicity Waley-Cohen Charitable Trust
The Walker Trust
Wallace and Gromit's Children's Foundation
Wallington Missionary Mart and Auctions
The F J Wallis Charitable Settlement
Walton on Thames Charity
Sir Siegmund Warburg's Voluntary Settlement
The Ward Blenkinsop Trust

The George Ward Charitable Trust
The Barbara Ward Children's Foundation
The John Warren Foundation
The Waterloo Foundation
G R Waters Charitable Trust 2000
The Waterways Trust
The Wates Foundation
Blyth Watson Charitable Trust
The Howard Watson Symington Memorial Charity
John Watson's Trust
The Weavers' Company Benevolent Fund
Webb Memorial Trust
The David Webster Charitable Trust
The William Webster Charitable Trust
The James Weir Foundation
The Barbara Welby Trust
The Weldon UK Charitable Trust
The Wellcome Trust
Welsh Church Fund Dyfed area (Carmarthenshire, Ceredigion and Pembrokeshire)
The Welton Foundation
Wessex Cancer Trust
The West Derby Wastelands Charity
West London Synagogue Charitable Fund
The West Yorkshire Police Community Fund
Mrs S K West's Charitable Trust
The Garfield Weston Foundation
The Barbara Whatmore Charitable Trust
The Whitaker Charitable Trust
The Colonel W H Whitbread Charitable Trust
The Simon Whitbread Charitable Trust
White Rose Children's Aid International Charity
The Whitecourt Charitable Trust
A H and B C Whiteley Charitable Trust
The Norman Whiteley Trust
The Whitley Animal Protection Trust
The Whittlesey Charity
The Lionel Wigram Memorial Trust
The Richard Wilcox Welfare Charity
The Felicity Wilde Charitable Trust

The Wilkinson Charitable Foundation
The Will Charitable Trust
The Kay Williams Charitable Foundation
The Williams Charitable Trust
Williams Serendipity Trust
The H D H Wills 1965 Charitable Trust
The Dame Violet Wills Will Trust
The Wilmcote Charitrust
The John Wilson Bequest Fund
Sumner Wilson Charitable Trust
David Wilson Foundation
The Wilson Foundation
J and J R Wilson Trust
The Community Foundation for Wiltshire and Swindon
The Benjamin Winegarten Charitable Trust
The Harold Hyam Wingate Foundation
The Francis Winham Foundation
Anona Winn Charitable Trust
Wirral Mayor's Charity
WISCM
The Witzenfeld Foundation
The Michael and Anna Wix Charitable Trust
The Wixamtree Trust
The Woburn 1986 Charitable Trust
The Maurice Wohl Charitable Foundation
The Charles Wolfson Charitable Trust
The Wolfson Family Charitable Trust
The Wolfson Foundation
The Wolseley Charitable Trust
Women Caring Trust
The James Wood Bequest Fund
The Wood Family Trust
The Woodcock Charitable Trust
The F Glenister Woodger Trust
Woodlands Foundation Limited
Woodlands Trust
The Woodroffe Benton Foundation
The Geoffrey Woods Charitable Foundation
The Woodward Charitable Trust
The A and R Woolf Charitable Trust
The Woolnoth Society Charitable Trust
Worcester Municipal Charities (incorporating Worcester Consolidated Municipal Charity and Worcester

Municipal Exhibitions
Foundation)
The Worcestershire and
Dudley Historic Churches
Trust
The Fred and Della Worms
Charitable Trust
The Worwin UK Foundation
The Wragge and Co. Charitable
Trust
The Diana Edgson Wright
Charitable Trust
The Matthews Wrightson
Charity Trust
Miss E B Wrightson's
Charitable Settlement
Wychville Ltd
The Wyndham Charitable Trust
The Wyseliot Charitable Trust
The Xerox (UK) Trust
The Yapp Charitable Trust
The Yardley Great Trust
The W Wing Yip and Brothers
Foundation
York and North Yorkshire
Community Foundation
The York Children's Trust
Yorkshire Agricultural Society
Yorkshire Building Society
Charitable Foundation
The South Yorkshire
Community Foundation
The Yorkshire Dales
Millennium Trust
The Yorkshire Historic
Churches Trust
The William Allen Young
Charitable Trust
The John K Young Endowment
Fund
The Young Foundation
Youth Music
Elizabeth and Prince Zaiger
Trust
The Marjorie and Arnold Ziff
Charitable Foundation
Stephen Zimmerman
Charitable Trust
The Zochonis Charitable Trust
Zurich Community Trust (UK)
Limited

UK excluding Channel Islands

England

AF Trust Company
The John Armitage Charitable
Trust
Arts Council England
Barchester Healthcare
Foundation
The Baring Foundation
Birthday House Trust
The Bothwell Charitable Trust
H E and E L Botteley
Charitable Trust
The British Gas (Scottish Gas)
Energy Trust
The Catholic Trust for England
and Wales
The Malcolm Chick Charity
The Church and Community
Fund
The Church Urban Fund
CLA Charitable Trust
Country Houses Foundation
The Sir William Coxen Trust
Fund
The DM Charitable Trust
The Doughty Charity Trust
The James Dyson Foundation
The English Schools' Football
Association
The Ernest Hecht Charitable
Foundation
The Football Foundation
Gwyneth Forrester Trust
The Joseph Strong Frazer Trust
The Freemasons' Grand
Charity
The General Nursing Council
for England and Wales
Trust
The Goodman Foundation
Leonard Gordon Charitable
Trust
Lady Hind Trust
The Hintze Family Charitable
Foundation
J I Charitable Trust
The Ian Karten Charitable
Trust
Lloyds TSB Foundation for
England and Wales
Marshall's Charity
Marshgate Charitable
Settlement
The McKenna Charitable Trust
Moss Family Charitable Trust
Moto in the Community Trust
MYR Charitable Trust
The National Churches Trust
(formerly the Historic
Churches Preservation
Trust with the Incorporated
Church Building Society)

The Noon Foundation
The Norwood and Newton
Settlement
The Ouseley Trust
The John Rayner Charitable
Trust
Royal British Legion
The Raymond and Beverley
Sackler Foundation
The R H Scholes Charitable
Trust
The Severn Trent Water
Charitable Trust Fund
Skipton Building Society
Charitable Foundation
The Sobell Foundation
The Leonard Laity Stoate
Charitable Trust
TJH Foundation
Toni and Guy Charitable
Foundation Limited
'v'
The Barbara Ward Children's
Foundation
The Waterways Trust
A H and B C Whiteley
Charitable Trust
The Francis Winham
Foundation
The Yapp Charitable Trust
Youth Music

....

■ Greater London

Arsenal Charitable Trust
The Ashendene Trust
The Bellinger Donnay Trust
Bergqvist Charitable Trust
Butchers' Company General
Charities
Capital Community Foundation
The Chapman Charitable Trust
The City Bridge Trust (formerly
known as Bridge House
Trust)
The City Parochial Foundation
The Consolidated Charities for
the Infirm Merchant
Taylors' Company
Coutts Charitable Trust
The Charles S French
Charitable Trust
The Worshipful Company of
Gardeners of London
The Goldsmiths' Company
Charity
The Grange Farm Centre Trust
The Hale Trust
The Helping Foundation
The Heritage of London Trust
Ltd
The Antony Hornby Charitable
Trust
The Worshipful Company of
Horners' Charitable Trusts

The Inner London Magistrates
    Court Poor Box Charity and
    Feeder Charity
The J E Joseph Charitable
    Fund
William Kendall's Charity (Wax
    Chandlers' Company)
The King's Fund
Robert Kitchin (Saddlers'
    Company)
The Mason Le Page Charitable
    Trust
London Catalyst (formerly The
    Metropolitan Hospital-
    Sunday Fund)
London Legal Support Trust
The London Marathon
    Charitable Trust
London Masonic Charitable
    Trust
Man Group plc Charitable
    Trust
The Masonic Province of
    Middlesex Charitable Trust
The Peter Minet Trust
The Music Sales Charitable
    Trust
The Earl of Northampton's
    Charity
Ogilvie Charities Deed No.2
    (including the Charity of
    Mary Catherine Ford Smith)
The David Pickford Charitable
    Foundation
SHINE (Support and Help in
    Education)
The Mrs Smith and Mount
    Trust
T and S Trust Fund
Tallow Chandlers Benevolent
    Fund
The Cyril Taylor Charitable
    Trust
The Taylor Family Foundation
Trust for London
The Vintners' Company
    Charitable Foundation
Vintners' Gifts Charity
The Wates Foundation
Woodlands Trust
The Woolnoth Society
    Charitable Trust

■ **Barking and Dagenham**

The Association of Friends of
    Essex Churches
East London Community
    Foundation
Ford Britain Trust
The Jack Petchey Foundation

■ **Barnet**

The Milly Apthorp Charitable
    Trust

Maurice and Jacqueline
    Bennett Charitable Trust
The Bintaub Charitable Trust
Brushmill Ltd
Elshore Ltd
Finnart House School Trust
Forbesville Limited
The Grove Charitable Trust
The Edward Harvist Trust Fund
The Bernhard Heuberger
    Charitable Trust
Highcroft Charitable Trust
Jesus Hospital Charity
Jewish Child's Day
The Jonathan Joels Charitable
    Trust
The Laing Family Foundations
John Lyon's Charity
North West London Community
    Foundation
Eleanor Palmer Trust
Sparquote Limited

■ **Bexley**

Ford Britain Trust

■ **Brent**

The Edward Harvist Trust Fund
The Maurice Hatter Foundation
John Lyon's Charity
North West London Community
    Foundation
The W Wing Yip and Brothers
    Foundation

■ **Camden**

The British Council for
    Prevention of Blindness
Sir John Cass's Foundation
Michael Crawford Children's
    Charity
The Foyle Foundation
The Grahame Charitable
    Foundation Limited
The Hampstead Wells and
    Campden Trust
The Edward Harvist Trust Fund
J A R Charitable Trust
The Harold Joels Charitable
    Trust
The Lowy Mitchell Foundation
John Lyon's Charity
Mayfair Charities Ltd
The Nuffield Foundation
Philological Foundation
Richard Reeve's Foundation
Sparquote Limited
The Will Charitable Trust

■ **City of London**

Aldgate and All Hallows'
    Barking Exhibition
    Foundation
The Aldgate Freedom
    Foundation
Sir John Cass's Foundation
The Company of Tobacco Pipe
    Makers' and Tobacco
    Blenders' Benevolent Fund
The Denton Wilde Sapte
    Charitable Trust
The Girdlers' Company
    Charitable Trust
The B and P Glasser
    Charitable Trust
The Spencer Hart Charitable
    Trust
The Sir Joseph Hotung
    Charitable Settlement
John Lyon's Charity
The Modiano Charitable Trust
The Worshipful Company of
    Needlemakers' Charitable
    Fund
Richard Reeve's Foundation
St Katharine and Shadwell
    Trust
The Wakefield and Tetley Trust
The Geoffrey Woods Charitable
    Foundation

■ **City of Westminster**

The Associated Country
    Women of the World
    (ACWW)
The Avenue Charitable Trust
The Nicholas Boas Charitable
    Trust
Sir John Cass's Foundation
The R and S Cohen Fondation
Dischma Charitable Trust
The Edinburgh Trust, No 2
    Account
The Glass-House Trust
The Graff Foundation
The M and R Gross Charities
    Limited
The H and J Spack Charitable
    Trust
The Edward Harvist Trust Fund
The Simon Heller Charitable
    Settlement
The Hollick Family Charitable
    Trust
The P Y N and B Hyams Trust
The J J Charitable Trust
Jacobs Charitable Trust
The Jerusalem Trust
The Nicholas Joels Charitable
    Trust
The Stanley Kalms Foundation
The Boris Karloff Charitable
    Foundation
Largsmount Ltd

The Ruth and Stuart Lipton
Charitable Trust
John Lyon's Charity
Medical Research Council
Nemoral Ltd
Philological Foundation
Basil Samuel Charitable Trust
Seafarers UK (King George's
Fund for Sailors)
ShareGift (The Orr Mackintosh
Foundation)
Sparquote Limited
The Woodward Charitable
Trust

■ Croydon

The Croydon Relief in Need
Charities
The Mayor of Croydon's
Charity Fund
The W Wing Yip and Brothers
Foundation

■ Ealing

The Eleemosynary Charity of
William Hobbayne
John Lyon's Charity
North West London Community
Foundation
Sparquote Limited

■ Enfield

North West London Community
Foundation
The Old Enfield Charitable
Trust
Sparquote Limited

■ Greenwich

Sir John Cass's Foundation
Sir John Evelyn's Charity
Ford Britain Trust

■ Hackney

Sir John Cass's Foundation
East London Community
Foundation
Friends of Wiznitz Limited
The Gur Trust
The Hackney Parochial
Charities
The Harbour Foundation
The Hornsey Parochial
Charities
Hurdale Charity Limited
MYA Charitable Trust
The Jack Petchey Foundation
St Katharine and Shadwell
Trust

■ Hammersmith and Fulham

Sir John Cass's Foundation
Dr Edwards' and Bishop King's
Fulham Endowment Fund
The Girdlers' Company
Charitable Trust
John Lyon's Charity
Sparquote Limited

■ Haringey

The Hornsey Parochial
Charities
North West London Community
Foundation
Sparquote Limited
Tottenham Grammar School
Foundation

■ Harrow

The Samuel Gardner Memorial
Trust
The Edward Harvist Trust Fund
The Geoffrey John Kaye
Charitable Foundation
John Lyon's Charity
North West London Community
Foundation

■ Havering

The Association of Friends of
Essex Churches
East London Community
Foundation
Ford Britain Trust
The Jack Petchey Foundation

■ Hillingdon

The Fassnidge Memorial Trust
The Hillingdon Community
Trust
The Hillingdon Partnership
Trust
North West London Community
Foundation
A P Taylor Trust
Uxbridge United Welfare Trust

■ Hounslow

Thames Community
Foundation

■ Islington

Sir John Cass's Foundation
Richard Cloudesley's Charity
Cripplegate Foundation
Richard Reeve's Foundation
Sparquote Limited

■ Kensington and Chelsea

The Army Benevolent Fund
The Campden Charities
Sir John Cass's Foundation
Grand Charitable Trust of the
Order of Women
Freemasons
Lord Hanson Foundation
John Lyon's Charity
Sparquote Limited

■ Kingston upon Thames

Thames Community
Foundation

■ Lambeth

Sir John Cass's Foundation
Sir Walter St John's
Educational Charity

■ Lewisham

Sir John Cass's Foundation
Sir John Evelyn's Charity

■ Merton

The Vernon N Ely Charitable
Trust

■ Newham

The Association of Friends of
Essex Churches
AstonMansfield Charitable
Trust
Sir John Cass's Foundation
East London Community
Foundation
Ford Britain Trust
The Island Health Trust
The Jack Petchey Foundation
Royal Docks Trust (London)
St Katharine and Shadwell
Trust

■ Redbridge

The Association of Friends of
Essex Churches
East London Community
Foundation
Ford Britain Trust
The Jack Petchey Foundation

■ Richmond upon Thames

Barnes Workhouse Fund
Hampton Fuel Allotment
Charity
The Richmond Parish Lands
Charity
Thames Community
Foundation

Southwark

The Sir Victor Blank Charitable
Settlement
Sir John Cass's Foundation
The Girdlers' Company
Charitable Trust
The ITF Seafarers Trust
The McDougall Trust
The Newcomen Collett
Foundation
The Wakefield and Tetley Trust

Sutton

Barleycorn Trust
Firtree Trust
The Lynwood Trust
The Sutton Nursing
Association
Humphrey Richardson Taylor
Charitable Trust
Wallington Missionary Mart
and Auctions

Tower Hamlets

Aldgate and All Hallows'
Barking Exhibition
Foundation
Sir John Cass's Foundation
East London Community
Foundation
The Girdlers' Company
Charitable Trust
The Island Health Trust
Isle of Dogs Community
Foundation
The Palmer Foundation
The Jack Petchey Foundation
The Ratcliff Pension Charity
St Katharine and Shadwell
Trust
The Tower Hill Trust
The Wakefield and Tetley Trust

Waltham Forest

The Association of Friends of
Essex Churches
East London Community
Foundation
The Jack Petchey Foundation

Wandsworth

Sir John Cass's Foundation
Miles Trust for the Putney and
Roehampton Community
Sir Walter St John's
Educational Charity

South Eastern England

The Ammco Trust
The Bellinger Donnay Trust
The Chapman Charitable Trust
The Chelsea Square 1994
Trust
The Essex Fairway Charitable
Trust
The GNC Trust
E F and M G Hall Charitable
Trust
The Dorothy Hay-Bolton
Charitable Trust
The Antony Hornby Charitable
Trust
The Leach Fourteenth Trust
The Earl of Northampton's
Charity
Red Hill Charitable Trust
The Mrs Smith and Mount
Trust
The Taylor Family Foundation

Berkshire

The Ashendene Trust
The Louis Baylis (Maidenhead
Advertiser) Charitable Trust
Bergqvist Charitable Trust
The Berkshire Community
Foundation
The Herbert and Peter
Blagrave Charitable Trust
Church Lands and John
Johnson's Estate Charities
The Colefax Charitable Trust
The Earley Charity
The Gilbert and Eileen Edgar
Foundation
The Gerald Palmer Eling Trust
Company
Greenham Common
Community Trust Limited
The Henley Educational Charity
The Iliffe Family Charitable
Trust
The JMK Charitable Trust
The Johnson Wax Ltd
Charitable Trust
The Spoore, Merry and Rixman
Foundation
The St Laurence Relief In
Need Trust
The Vodafone (Group)
Foundation
The Wates Foundation

Buckinghamshire

The Alice Trust
The Louis Baylis (Maidenhead
Advertiser) Charitable Trust
Bergqvist Charitable Trust
The Buckinghamshire
Foundation
The Buckinghamshire Historic
Churches Trust
The Buckinghamshire Masonic
Centenary Fund
William Harding's Charity
London Legal Support Trust
Milton Keynes Community
Foundation
The Mobbs Memorial Trust Ltd
The Powell Foundation
The Stokenchurch Educational
Charity
The Wates Foundation

East Sussex

The Argus Appeal
The Brighton District Nursing
Association Trust
The Derek and Eileen Dodgson
Foundation
Gatwick Airport Community
Trust
The Hale Trust
Stuart Hine Trust
The Magdalen and Lasher
Charity
The Moss Charitable Trust
The Poling Charitable Trust
The Rotherwick Foundation
The Southover Manor General
Education Trust
Sussex Community Foundation
The Sussex Historic Churches
Trust
The Mrs A Lacy Tate Trust
The Wates Foundation

Hampshire

The BAA Communities Trust
The Herbert and Peter
Blagrave Charitable Trust
Bonhomie United Charity
Society
The Bordon and Liphook
Charity
The Colefax Charitable Trust
The John and Freda Coleman
Charitable Trust
The Dibden Allotments Charity
The Dugdale Charitable Trust
The Ellis Campbell Foundation
Ford Britain Trust
Greenham Common
Community Trust Limited
The Walter Guinness
Charitable Trust
The Hampshire and Islands
Historic Churches Trust
Hampshire and Isle of Wight
Community Foundation
The James Trust

The Johnson Wax Ltd
  Charitable Trust
The Emmanuel Kaye
  Foundation
The Leonard Trust
Gerald Micklem Charitable
  Trust
The Moss Charitable Trust
The William Price Charitable
  Trust
The Rotherwick Foundation
Wessex Cancer Trust

■ Isle of Wight

Hampshire and Isle of Wight
  Community Foundation
Wessex Cancer Trust

■ Kent

The Charity of William Barrow
The Coalfields Regeneration
  Trust
The Cobtree Charity Trust Ltd
The Cole Charitable Trust
Colyer-Fergusson Charitable
  Trust
The Cromarty Trust
The Friends of Kent Churches
Gatwick Airport Community
  Trust
The Great Stone Bridge Trust
  of Edenbridge
The Hale Trust
R G Hills Charitable Trust
Matthew Hodder Charitable
  Trust
The Hollands-Warren Fund
Kent Community Foundation
London Legal Support Trust
The David Pickford Charitable
  Foundation
The Rochester Bridge Trust
The Rothermere Foundation

■ Oxfordshire

The Arbib Foundation
The Ashendene Trust
The Banbury Charities
The Louis Baylis (Maidenhead
  Advertiser) Charitable Trust
Bergqvist Charitable Trust
The Henley Educational Charity
Elizabeth Jackson Charitable
  Trust
The Robert and Margaret
  Moss Charitable Trust
City of Oxford Charity
The Oxfordshire Community
  Foundation
St Michael's and All Saints'
  Charities
The Stanton Ballard Charitable
  Trust

The Steventon Allotments and
  Relief-in-Need Charity
The Vodafone (Group)
  Foundation
Robert and Felicity Waley-
  Cohen Charitable Trust
The Wates Foundation

■ Surrey

John Bristow and Thomas
  Mason Trust
The John and Freda Coleman
  Charitable Trust
The John Cowan Foundation
T F C Frost Charitable Trust
Gatwick Airport Community
  Trust
The Bishop of Guildford's
  Foundation
The Hale Trust
The Ingram Trust
The Johnson Wax Ltd
  Charitable Trust
The Erica Leonard Trust
London Legal Support Trust
The Masonic Province of
  Middlesex Charitable Trust
The R C Sherriff Trust
Surrey Community Foundation
The Surrey Historic Buildings
  Trust Ltd
Humphrey Richardson Taylor
  Charitable Trust
Walton on Thames Charity
The Wates Foundation

■ West Sussex

The Argus Appeal
The BAA Communities Trust
The Derek and Eileen Dodgson
  Foundation
The Dugdale Charitable Trust
Gatwick Airport Community
  Trust
The Hale Trust
The Michael and Shirley Hunt
  Charitable Trust
The Moss Charitable Trust
The Poling Charitable Trust
The Southover Manor General
  Education Trust
Sussex Community Foundation
The Sussex Historic Churches
  Trust
The Wates Foundation
The F Glenister Woodger Trust

....

■ South Western
  England

The Chelsea Square 1994
  Trust
The Cornwell Charitable Trust

The Joyce Fletcher Charitable
  Trust
The Garnett Charitable Trust
The GNC Trust
The Leach Fourteenth Trust
The Norman Family Charitable
  Trust
The Oldham Foundation
The Verdon-Smith Family
  Charitable Settlement

■ Avon

Almondsbury Charity
The Avon and Somerset Police
  Community Trust
Bristol Archdeaconry Charity
The Bristol Charities
The J and M Britton Charitable
  Trust
M R Cannon 1998 Charitable
  Trust
The Chipping Sodbury Town
  Lands Charity
The Harry Crook Foundation
The Denman Charitable Trust
John James Bristol Foundation
The Merchant Venturers'
  Charity
The Portishead Nautical Trust
Quartet Community Foundation
  (formerly the Greater Bristol
  Foundation)
The Rock Solid Trust
The Ralph and Irma Sperring
  Charity
The Starfish Trust
The Wates Foundation
The Dame Violet Wills Will
  Trust

■ Cornwall and Scilly Isles

The Blanchminster Trust
Cornwall Community
  Foundation
The Cornwall Historic
  Churches Trust
The Heathcoat Trust
The Michael and Ilse Katz
  Foundation
The Clare Milne Trust

■ Devon

The H B Allen Charitable Trust
The Albert Casanova Ballard
  Deceased Trust
The Barnstaple Bridge Trust
The Bideford Bridge Trust
Lord Clinton's Charitable Trust
The Dr and Mrs A Darlington
  Charitable Trust
Devon Community Foundation
The Devon Educational Trust

The Devon Historic Churches
    Trust
The Mayor of Exeter's Appeal
    Fund
The Great Torrington Town
    Lands Charity
The Heathcoat Trust
The Rosalind Hicks Charitable
    Trust
Lesley Lesley and Mutter Trust
The Clare Milne Trust
The Northcott Devon Medical
    Foundation
The Claude and Margaret Pike
    Charity
Saint Luke's College
    Foundation
The Dame Violet Wills Will
    Trust

■ Dorset

Community Foundation for
    Bournemouth, Dorset and
    Poole
The Dorset Historic Churches
    Trust
The Moss Charitable Trust
The Mayor of Poole's Appeal
    Fund
The Talbot Village Trust
Mrs R P Tindall's Charitable
    Trust
The Valentine Charitable Trust
The Wates Foundation
Wessex Cancer Trust

■ Gloucestershire

The Barnwood House Trust
Gloucestershire Community
    Foundation
The Gloucestershire Historic
    Churches Trust
The Charles Irving Charitable
    Trust
Elizabeth Jackson Charitable
    Trust
The Jack Lane Charitable Trust
The Langtree Trust
Sylvanus Lyson's Charity
The Notgrove Trust
Quartet Community Foundation
    (formerly the Greater Bristol
    Foundation)
St Monica Trust Community
    Fund
The Summerfield Charitable
    Trust
The Wates Foundation

■ Somerset

The Avon and Somerset Police
    Community Trust

The Hilda and Alice Clark
    Charitable Trust
Quartet Community Foundation
    (formerly the Greater Bristol
    Foundation)
Friends of Somerset Churches
    and Chapels
St Monica Trust Community
    Fund
The Wates Foundation

■ Wiltshire

The Bellinger Donnay Trust
The Herbert and Peter
    Blagrave Charitable Trust
The Chippenham Borough
    Lands Charity
The Thomas Freke and Lady
    Norton Charity
The Fulmer Charitable Trust
The Walter Guinness
    Charitable Trust
The Jack Lane Charitable Trust
St Monica Trust Community
    Fund
Mrs R P Tindall's Charitable
    Trust
The Vodafone (Group)
    Foundation
Wessex Cancer Trust
The Community Foundation for
    Wiltshire and Swindon

....

■ West Midlands
region

The Lord Mayor of
    Birmingham's Charity
The Michael Bishop
    Foundation
The Bransford Trust
The E F Bulmer Benevolent
    Fund
The Coalfields Regeneration
    Trust
Coventry Building Society
    Charitable Foundation
The W E Dunn Trust
The GNC Trust
The Pedmore Sporting Club
    Trust Fund
The Rugby Group Benevolent
    Fund Limited
The Connie and Albert Taylor
    Charitable Trust
The Wilmcote Charitrust
The Yardley Great Trust

■ Herefordshire

The Elmley Foundation
The Eveson Charitable Trust
The Herefordshire Community
    Foundation

The Herefordshire Historic
    Churches Trust
The Jordan Charitable
    Foundation

■ Shropshire

Baron Davenport's Charity
The P B Dumbell Charitable
    Trust
The Roy Fletcher Charitable
    Trust
The Lady Forester Trust
The Maxell Educational Trust
Pegasus (Stanley) Trust
The Walker Trust

■ Staffordshire

The Bamford Charitable
    Foundation
Britannia Foundation
The Swinfen Broun Charitable
    Trust
The Burton Breweries
    Charitable Trust
Consolidated Charity of Burton
    upon Trent
The Clarke Charitable
    Settlement
Baron Davenport's Charity
The Wilfred and Elsie Elkes
    Charity Fund
The Alfred Haines Charitable
    Trust
Lichfield Conduit Lands
The Michael Marsh Charitable
    Trust
Open Gate
The Strasser Foundation
The Vodafone (Group)
    Foundation

■ Warwickshire

The Aylesford Family
    Charitable Trust
Birmingham International
    Airport Community Trust
Baron Davenport's Charity
The Dumbreck Charity
The William Edwards
    Educational Charity
Ford Britain Trust
The Mrs Godfrey-Payton Trust
The Alfred Haines Charitable
    Trust
The Heart of England
    Community Foundation
Alan Edward Higgs Charity
Elizabeth Jackson Charitable
    Trust
The King Henry VIII Endowed
    Trust Warwick
The Michael Marsh Charitable
    Trust

The Harry Payne Trust
The Lucy Price Relief-in-Need
   Charity
PSA Peugeot Citroen Charity
   Trust
The C A Rookes Charitable
   Trust
The Snowball Trust
Stratford upon Avon Town
   Trust
Robert and Felicity Waley-
   Cohen Charitable Trust
Woodlands Trust

■ **West Midlands**

The Lord Austin Trust
The John Avins Trustees
The Aylesford Family
   Charitable Trust
The James Beattie Charitable
   Trust
The Birmingham Community
   Foundation
The Birmingham District
   Nursing Charitable Trust
Birmingham International
   Airport Community Trust
The Charles Brotherton Trust
The Bryant Trust
The William A Cadbury
   Charitable Trust
Christadelphian Samaritan
   Fund
The Cole Charitable Trust
The George Henry Collins
   Charity
The Cook and Wolstenholme
   Charitable Trust
The General Charities of the
   City of Coventry
Baron Davenport's Charity
The Digbeth Trust
The P B Dumbell Charitable
   Trust
The Dumbreck Charity
The Eveson Charitable Trust
The John Feeney Charitable
   Bequest
The George Fentham
   Birmingham Charity
The Friends Hall Farm Street
   Trust
Grantham Yorke Trust
Grimmitt Trust
The Alfred Haines Charitable
   Trust
The Harborne Parish Lands
   Charity
The Heart of England
   Community Foundation
Alan Edward Higgs Charity
The High Sheriff's Police Trust
   for the County of West
   Midlands

Elizabeth Jackson Charitable
   Trust
The Jarman Charitable Trust
The London Marathon
   Charitable Trust
The Michael Marsh Charitable
   Trust
The James Frederick and Ethel
   Anne Measures Charity
The Keith and Joan
   Mindelsohn Charitable
   Trust
The Payne Charitable Trust
The Harry Payne Trust
The Bernard Piggott Trust
PSA Peugeot Citroen Charity
   Trust
The Roughley Charitable Trust
The Sheldon Trust
The Snowball Trust
Solihull Community Foundation
Sutton Coldfield Municipal
   Charities
C B and H H Taylor 1984 Trust
Woodlands Trust
The W Wing Yip and Brothers
   Foundation

■ **Worcestershire**

Baron Davenport's Charity
The Dumbreck Charity
The Elmley Foundation
The Eveson Charitable Trust
HopMarket Charity
The Michael Marsh Charitable
   Trust
John Martin's Charity
The Harry Payne Trust
Worcester Municipal Charities
   (incorporating Worcester
   Consolidated Municipal
   Charity and Worcester
   Municipal Exhibitions
   Foundation)
The Worcestershire and
   Dudley Historic Churches
   Trust

....

■ **East Midlands**

The Bamford Charitable
   Foundation
The Becketts and Sargeants
   Educational Foundation
Bergqvist Charitable Trust
The Bingham Trust
The Michael Bishop
   Foundation
The Boots Charitable Trust
Britannia Foundation
The Burton Breweries
   Charitable Trust
The Frederick and Phyllis Cann
   Trust

Carter's Educational
   Foundation
The Clarke Charitable
   Settlement
The Coalfields Regeneration
   Trust
The Compton Charitable Trust
The Douglas Compton James
   Charitable Trust
The Helen Jean Cope Trust
The J Reginald Corah
   Foundation Fund
Coventry Building Society
   Charitable Foundation
The Derbyshire Churches and
   Chapels Preservation Trust
Derbyshire Community
   Foundation
The J N Derbyshire Trust
Dromintee Trust
The W E Dunn Trust
The Maud Elkington Charitable
   Trust
The Everard Foundation
The Fifty Fund
Ford Britain Trust
The GNC Trust
The Gray Trust
The Hartley Charitable Trust
Healthsure Group Ltd
The Joanna Herbert-Stepney
   Charitable Settlement (also
   known as The Paget
   Charitable Trust)
The Hesed Trust
Elizabeth Jackson Charitable
   Trust
Leicester Charity Link (formerly
   The Leicester Charity
   Organisation Society)
Leicestershire Historic
   Churches Trust
Lincolnshire Community
   Foundation
The Lincolnshire Old Churches
   Trust
The London Marathon
   Charitable Trust
Market Harborough and The
   Bowdens Charity
The New Appeals Organisation
   for the City and County of
   Nottingham
Alderman Newton's
   Educational Foundation
The Northampton Municipal
   Church Charities
The Nottingham General
   Dispensary
Nottinghamshire Community
   Foundation
The Nottinghamshire Historic
   Churches Trust
The Nottinghamshire Miners'
   Welfare Trust Fund
Open Gate

....

The Jack Patston Charitable Trust

The Mary Potter Convent Hospital Trust

The Provincial Grand Charity of the Province of Derbyshire

The Puri Foundation

The Rugby Group Benevolent Fund Limited

The Samworth Foundation

The Shoe Zone Trust

The Mary Elizabeth Siebel Charity

The Strangward Trust

Viking Cares (For the Kids)

The Vodafone (Group) Foundation

The George Ward Charitable Trust

The John Warren Foundation

The Wates Foundation

The Howard Watson Symington Memorial Charity

The Wilmcote Charitrust

David Wilson Foundation

The Wilson Foundation

■ Derbyshire

The Bamford Charitable Foundation

The Bingham Trust

Britannia Foundation

The Burton Breweries Charitable Trust

The Clarke Charitable Settlement

The Helen Jean Cope Trust

The Derbyshire Churches and Chapels Preservation Trust

Derbyshire Community Foundation

Open Gate

The Provincial Grand Charity of the Province of Derbyshire

The Samworth Foundation

■ Leicestershire

The Burton Breweries Charitable Trust

The Helen Jean Cope Trust

The J Reginald Corah Foundation Fund

Dromintee Trust

The Maud Elkington Charitable Trust

The Everard Foundation

The Joanna Herbert-Stepney Charitable Settlement (also known as The Paget Charitable Trust)

The Hesed Trust

Leicester Charity Link (formerly The Leicester Charity Organisation Society)

Leicestershire Historic Churches Trust

Market Harborough and The Bowdens Charity

Alderman Newton's Educational Foundation

Open Gate

The Jack Patston Charitable Trust

The Samworth Foundation

The Shoe Zone Trust

The George Ward Charitable Trust

The Howard Watson Symington Memorial Charity

David Wilson Foundation

■ Lincolnshire

Lincolnshire Community Foundation

The Lincolnshire Old Churches Trust

Viking Cares (For the Kids)

The John Warren Foundation

■ Northamptonshire

The Becketts and Sargeants Educational Foundation

Bergqvist Charitable Trust

The Frederick and Phyllis Cann Trust

The Compton Charitable Trust

The Douglas Compton James Charitable Trust

The Maud Elkington Charitable Trust

Ford Britain Trust

Healthsure Group Ltd

Elizabeth Jackson Charitable Trust

The London Marathon Charitable Trust

The Northampton Municipal Church Charities

The John Warren Foundation

The Wilson Foundation

■ Nottinghamshire

The Boots Charitable Trust

Carter's Educational Foundation

The Helen Jean Cope Trust

The J N Derbyshire Trust

The Fifty Fund

The Gray Trust

The Hartley Charitable Trust

The New Appeals Organisation for the City and County of Nottingham

The Nottingham General Dispensary

Nottinghamshire Community Foundation

The Nottinghamshire Historic Churches Trust

The Nottinghamshire Miners' Welfare Trust Fund

Open Gate

The Mary Potter Convent Hospital Trust

The Puri Foundation

The Samworth Foundation

The Mary Elizabeth Siebel Charity

The Vodafone (Group) Foundation

The John Warren Foundation

The Wates Foundation

■ Eastern

The Adnams Charity

Anguish's Educational Foundation

The Association of Friends of Essex Churches

The BAA Communities Trust

The Beccles Town Lands Charity

The Bedford Charity (The Harpur Trust)

The Bedfordshire and Hertfordshire Historic Churches Trust

The Bedfordshire and Luton Community Foundation

The Hervey Benham Charitable Trust

Bergqvist Charitable Trust

Ann Byrne Charitable Trust

The Cambridgeshire Community Foundation

The Cambridgeshire Historic Churches Trust

The Chapman Charitable Trust

The Christabella Charitable Trust

The Colchester Catalyst Charity

The Cole Charitable Trust

The Harry Cureton Charitable Trust

The D J H Currie Memorial Trust

Earls Colne and Halstead Educational Charity

The Ebenezer Trust

Educational Foundation of Alderman John Norman

Essex Community Foundation

The Essex Heritage Trust

Essex Provincial Charity Fund

The Essex Youth Trust

Walter Farthing (Trust) Limited

Farthing Trust

Ford Britain Trust

The Charles S French Charitable Trust

The Anne French Memorial
Trust
The GNC Trust
The Grange Farm Centre Trust
Robert Hall Charity
Healthsure Group Ltd
The Hertfordshire Community
Foundation
Hinchley Charitable Trust
The Hitchin Educational
Foundation
The House of Industry Estate
Huntingdon Freemen's Charity
John Huntingdon's Charity
The John Jarrold Trust
Keswick Hall Charity
Kirkley Poor's Lands Estate
London Legal Support Trust
The D G Marshall of
Cambridge Trust
The Masonic Province of
Middlesex Charitable Trust
The Mills Charity
The D C Moncrieff Charitable
Trust
The Mothercare Charitable
Foundation
The Music Sales Charitable
Trust
Needham Market and Barking
Welfare Charities
The Neighbourly Charitable
Trust
The Norwich Historic Churches
Trust Ltd
The Norwich Town Close
Estate Charity
Ogilvie Charities Deed No.2
(including the Charity of
Mary Catherine Ford Smith)
The Jack Patston Charitable
Trust
The Jack Petchey Foundation
The Mr and Mrs Philip
Rackham Charitable Trust
Red Hill Charitable Trust
The Rosca Trust
The R C Snelling Charitable
Trust
The Southwold Trust
The Stevenage Community
Trust
The Strangward Trust
The Suffolk Foundation
The Suffolk Historic Churches
Trust
Trust Sixty Three
The John Warren Foundation
The Whittlesey Charity
The A and R Woolf Charitable
Trust

■ Bedfordshire

The Bedford Charity (The
Harpur Trust)

The Bedfordshire and
Hertfordshire Historic
Churches Trust
The Bedfordshire and Luton
Community Foundation
Bergqvist Charitable Trust
The Hitchin Educational
Foundation
The House of Industry Estate
The Neighbourly Charitable
Trust
Trust Sixty Three
The John Warren Foundation

■ Cambridgeshire

The Cambridgeshire
Community Foundation
The Cambridgeshire Historic
Churches Trust
The Cole Charitable Trust
The Harry Cureton Charitable
Trust
Farthing Trust
Robert Hall Charity
Hinchley Charitable Trust
Huntingdon Freemen's Charity
John Huntingdon's Charity
The D G Marshall of
Cambridge Trust
The Jack Patston Charitable
Trust
The Whittlesey Charity

■ Essex

The Association of Friends of
Essex Churches
The BAA Communities Trust
The Hervey Benham Charitable
Trust
The Christabella Charitable
Trust
The Colchester Catalyst
Charity
The D J H Currie Memorial
Trust
Earls Colne and Halstead
Educational Charity
The Ebenezer Trust
Essex Community Foundation
The Essex Heritage Trust
Essex Provincial Charity Fund
The Essex Youth Trust
Walter Farthing (Trust) Limited
Ford Britain Trust
The Charles S French
Charitable Trust
The Grange Farm Centre Trust
London Legal Support Trust
Ogilvie Charities Deed No.2
(including the Charity of
Mary Catherine Ford Smith)
The Jack Petchey Foundation
The Rosca Trust

■ Hertfordshire

The Bedfordshire and
Hertfordshire Historic
Churches Trust
Bergqvist Charitable Trust
The Hertfordshire Community
Foundation
The Hitchin Educational
Foundation
London Legal Support Trust
The Masonic Province of
Middlesex Charitable Trust
The Mothercare Charitable
Foundation
The Stevenage Community
Trust
Trust Sixty Three
The A and R Woolf Charitable
Trust

■ Norfolk

Anguish's Educational
Foundation
Ann Byrne Charitable Trust
Educational Foundation of
Alderman John Norman
The Anne French Memorial
Trust
Healthsure Group Ltd
The John Jarrold Trust
Keswick Hall Charity
The D C Moncrieff Charitable
Trust
The Norwich Historic Churches
Trust Ltd
The Norwich Town Close
Estate Charity
The Mr and Mrs Philip
Rackham Charitable Trust
The R C Snelling Charitable
Trust

■ Suffolk

The Adnams Charity
The Beccles Town Lands
Charity
The Anne French Memorial
Trust
Kirkley Poor's Lands Estate
The Mills Charity
The D C Moncrieff Charitable
Trust
The Music Sales Charitable
Trust
Needham Market and Barking
Welfare Charities
Ogilvie Charities Deed No.2
(including the Charity of
Mary Catherine Ford Smith)
The Southwold Trust
The Suffolk Foundation
The Suffolk Historic Churches
Trust

■ North West

The Mason Bibby 1981 Trust
The Booth Charities
The Bowland Charitable Trust
The Harold and Alice Bridges
    Charity
Britannia Foundation
The Charles and Edna
    Broadhurst Charitable Trust
The Charles Brotherton Trust
The Camelia Trust
The Cheshire Provincial Fund
    of Benevolence
The Chrimes Family Charitable
    Trust
The Coalfields Regeneration
    Trust
The Community Foundation for
    Greater Manchester
The Congleton Inclosure Trust
Cumberland Building Society
    Charitable Foundation
Cumbria Community
    Foundation
The Hamilton Davies Trust
The Earl of Derby's Charitable
    Trust
EAGA Partnership Charitable
    Trust
Eden Arts Trust
The Ellerdale Trust
The Eventhall Family
    Charitable Trust
The Fairway Trust
Faisaltex Charitable Trust
Famos Foundation Trust
The Galbraith Trust
The GNC Trust
A B Grace Trust
The Granada Foundation
Gurunanak
The Hadfield Trust
The Harris Charity
The N and P Hartley Memorial
    Trust
Healthsure Group Ltd
The Helping Foundation
The Hemby Trust
John Holford's Charity
The Edward Holt Trust
Hulme Trust Estates
    (Educational)
The Johnson Group Cleaners
    Charity
The J E Joseph Charitable
    Fund
Kelsick's Educational
    Foundation
The Peter Kershaw Trust
The Ursula Keyes Trust
Community Foundation for
    Lancashire
Duchy of Lancaster Benevolent
    Fund
The Herd Lawson and Muriel
    Lawson Charitable Trust

Liverpool Charity and Voluntary
    Services
The Liverpool One Foundation
Liverpool Sailors' Home Trust
The Makin Charitable Trust
Manchester Airport Community
    Trust Fund
The Manchester Guardian
    Society Charitable Trust
Manchester Kids
Lord Mayor of Manchester's
    Charity Appeal Trust
The Ann and David Marks
    Foundation
Matliwala Family Charitable
    Trust
The Mersey Docks and
    Harbour Company
    Charitable Fund
Community Foundation for
    Merseyside
John Moores Foundation
The Mushroom Fund
The North West Cancer
    Research Fund
The Northern Rock Foundation
Oglesby Charitable Trust
The Oldham Foundation
The Payne Charitable Trust
The Pilkington Charities Fund
The Proven Family Trust
Radio City Charity Foundation
The Fanny Rapaport Charitable
    Settlement
The Ravensdale Trust
The Nathaniel Reyner Trust
    Fund
The Rowan Charitable Trust
The Christopher Rowbotham
    Charitable Trust
The Francis C Scott Charitable
    Trust
The Frieda Scott Charitable
    Trust
The Sir James and Lady Scott
    Trust
The P and D Shepherd
    Charitable Trust
SHINE (Support and Help in
    Education)
The J A Shone Memorial Trust
The Skelton Bounty
Springfields Employees'
    Medical Research and
    Charity Trust Fund
The Edward Stocks-Massey
    Bequest Fund
T and S Trust Fund
The Mayor of Trafford's Charity
    Fund
Ulverston Town Lands Charity
United Utilities Trust Fund
The Vodafone (Group)
    Foundation
The West Derby Wastelands
    Charity

The Norman Whiteley Trust
Wirral Mayor's Charity
The W Wing Yip and Brothers
    Foundation
The Yorkshire Dales
    Millennium Trust
The Zochonis Charitable Trust

■ Cheshire

Britannia Foundation
The Cheshire Provincial Fund
    of Benevolence
The Congleton Inclosure Trust
The Hamilton Davies Trust
John Holford's Charity
The Ursula Keyes Trust
Manchester Airport Community
    Trust Fund
John Moores Foundation
The Proven Family Trust
The Christopher Rowbotham
    Charitable Trust
The Vodafone (Group)
    Foundation

■ Cumbria

The Harold and Alice Bridges
    Charity
Cumberland Building Society
    Charitable Foundation
Cumbria Community
    Foundation
EAGA Partnership Charitable
    Trust
Eden Arts Trust
The Hadfield Trust
Kelsick's Educational
    Foundation
The Herd Lawson and Muriel
    Lawson Charitable Trust
The Northern Rock Foundation
The Payne Charitable Trust
The Proven Family Trust
The Francis C Scott Charitable
    Trust
The Frieda Scott Charitable
    Trust
Ulverston Town Lands Charity
The Norman Whiteley Trust
The Yorkshire Dales
    Millennium Trust

■ Greater Manchester

The Booth Charities
The Camelia Trust
The Cheshire Provincial Fund
    of Benevolence
The Community Foundation for
    Greater Manchester
The Hamilton Davies Trust
Famos Foundation Trust
The Helping Foundation
The Edward Holt Trust

Hulme Trust Estates
(Educational)
The J E Joseph Charitable
Fund
The Peter Kershaw Trust
Duchy of Lancaster Benevolent
Fund
Manchester Airport Community
Trust Fund
The Manchester Guardian
Society Charitable Trust
Manchester Kids
Lord Mayor of Manchester's
Charity Appeal Trust
The Ann and David Marks
Foundation
The Christopher Rowbotham
Charitable Trust
The Sir James and Lady Scott
Trust
SHINE (Support and Help in
Education)
The Skelton Bounty
T and S Trust Fund
The Mayor of Trafford's Charity
Fund
The W Wing Yip and Brothers
Foundation
The Zochonis Charitable Trust

■ Lancashire

The Harold and Alice Bridges
Charity
Cumberland Building Society
Charitable Foundation
Faisaltex Charitable Trust
The Galbraith Trust
A B Grace Trust
The Harris Charity
Community Foundation for
Lancashire
Duchy of Lancaster Benevolent
Fund
Matliwala Family Charitable
Trust
Community Foundation for
Merseyside
John Moores Foundation
The Christopher Rowbotham
Charitable Trust
The Francis C Scott Charitable
Trust
The Skelton Bounty
Springfields Employees'
Medical Research and
Charity Trust Fund
The Edward Stocks-Massey
Bequest Fund
The Yorkshire Dales
Millennium Trust

■ Merseyside

The Mason Bibby 1981 Trust
The Charles and Edna
Broadhurst Charitable Trust
The Charles Brotherton Trust
The Camelia Trust
The Cheshire Provincial Fund
of Benevolence
The Chrimes Family Charitable
Trust
The Ellerdale Trust
The Hemby Trust
The Johnson Group Cleaners
Charity
Duchy of Lancaster Benevolent
Fund
Liverpool Charity and Voluntary
Services
The Liverpool One Foundation
Liverpool Sailors' Home Trust
The Makin Charitable Trust
The Mersey Docks and
Harbour Company
Charitable Fund
Community Foundation for
Merseyside
John Moores Foundation
The Mushroom Fund
The Pilkington Charities Fund
The Proven Family Trust
Radio City Charity Foundation
The Ravensdale Trust
The Nathaniel Reyner Trust
Fund
The Rowan Charitable Trust
The J A Shone Memorial Trust
The Skelton Bounty
The West Derby Wastelands
Charity
Wirral Mayor's Charity

....

■ Yorkshire & the Humber

The Norman C Ashton
Foundation
The Bearder Charity
The Benfield Motors Charitable
Trust
The Bishop's Development
Fund
The Charles Brotherton Trust
The Jack Brunton Charitable
Trust
The Audrey and Stanley Burton
1960 Charitable Trust
M R Cannon 1998 Charitable
Trust
The Joseph and Annie Cattle
Trust
John William Chapman's
Charitable Trust
The Church Burgesses
Educational Foundation
Church Burgesses Trust

The Coalfields Regeneration
Trust
Community Foundation for
Calderdale
The Marjorie Coote Animal
Charity Trust
The Marjorie Coote Old
People's Charity
The Elm House Trust
The A M Fenton Trust
The Freshgate Trust
Foundation
The GNC Trust
The Constance Green
Foundation
The Harrison and Potter Trust
The Hartley Charitable Trust
The N and P Hartley Memorial
Trust
The Hesslewood Children's
Trust (Hull Seamen's and
General Orphanage)
The Joseph and Mary Hiley
Trust
The Huddersfield Medical Trust
Fund
The Hull and East Riding
Charitable Trust
The Humberside Charitable
Health Trust
Duchy of Lancaster Benevolent
Fund
The Lord Mayor of Leeds
Appeal Fund
The Leeds Community
Foundation
The Lincolnshire Old Churches
Trust
Lady Lumley's Educational
Foundation
The Mayfield Valley Arts Trust
The Mirfield Educational
Charity
The James Neill Trust Fund
Nestle Rowntree Employees
Community Fund
Open Gate
Sir John Priestman Charity
Trust
The J S and E C Rymer
Charitable Trust
The Salt Foundation
The P and D Shepherd
Charitable Trust
The Sylvia and Colin Shepherd
Charitable Trust
Split Infinitive Trust
The Talbot Trusts
Viking Cares (For the Kids)
Wade's Charity
The Scurrah Wainwright Charity
The West Yorkshire Police
Community Fund
York and North Yorkshire
Community Foundation
The York Children's Trust

Yorkshire Agricultural Society
The South Yorkshire
  Community Foundation
The Yorkshire Dales
  Millennium Trust
The Yorkshire Historic
  Churches Trust

■ **Humberside, East Riding**

The Joseph and Annie Cattle
  Trust
The Hesslewood Children's
  Trust (Hull Seamen's and
  General Orphanage)
The Hull and East Riding
  Charitable Trust
The Humberside Charitable
  Health Trust
The Lincolnshire Old Churches
  Trust
The J S and E C Rymer
  Charitable Trust
Viking Cares (For the Kids)

■ **North Yorkshire**

The Charles Brotherton Trust
The Jack Brunton Charitable
  Trust
M R Cannon 1998 Charitable
  Trust
The Marjorie Coote Animal
  Charity Trust
The Elm House Trust
Lady Lumley's Educational
  Foundation
Nestle Rowntree Employees
  Community Fund
Sir John Priestman Charity
  Trust
The Sylvia and Colin Shepherd
  Charitable Trust
Viking Cares (For the Kids)
York and North Yorkshire
  Community Foundation
The York Children's Trust
The Yorkshire Dales
  Millennium Trust

■ **South Yorkshire**

John William Chapman's
  Charitable Trust
The Church Burgesses
  Educational Foundation
Church Burgesses Trust
The Marjorie Coote Old
  People's Charity
The Freshgate Trust
  Foundation
The Mayfield Valley Arts Trust
The James Neill Trust Fund
Open Gate
The Talbot Trusts
Viking Cares (For the Kids)

The South Yorkshire
  Community Foundation

■ **West Yorkshire**

Community Foundation for
  Calderdale
Duchy of Lancaster Benevolent
  Fund
The Audrey and Stanley Burton
  1960 Charitable Trust
The Bearder Charity
The Benfield Motors Charitable
  Trust
The Bishop's Development
  Fund
The Charles Brotherton Trust
The Constance Green
  Foundation
The Harrison and Potter Trust
The Huddersfield Medical Trust
  Fund
The Joseph and Mary Hiley
  Trust
The Leeds Community
  Foundation
The Lord Mayor of Leeds
  Appeal Fund
The Mirfield Educational
  Charity
The Norman C Ashton
  Foundation
The Salt Foundation
The West Yorkshire Police
  Community Fund
Wade's Charity

....

■ **North East**

The 1989 Willan Charitable
  Trust
The Roy and Pixie Baker
  Charitable Trust
The Ballinger Charitable Trust
The Barbour Trust
The Benfield Motors Charitable
  Trust
Joseph Brough Charitable
  Trust
M R Cannon 1998 Charitable
  Trust
The Coalfields Regeneration
  Trust
The Catherine Cookson
  Charitable Trust
County Durham Foundation
The Sir Tom Cowie Charitable
  Trust
Cumberland Building Society
  Charitable Foundation
The Gillian Dickinson Trust
The Dickon Trust
The Ellinson Foundation Ltd
The Elm House Trust
The GNC Trust
Goodfund

Greggs Foundation (formerly
  Greggs Trust)
The Hadrian Trust
The W A Handley Charitable
  Trust
The N and P Hartley Memorial
  Trust
The Hedley Denton Charitable
  Trust
Hexham and Newcastle
  Diocesan Trust (1947)
The Hospital of God at
  Greatham
The Sir James Knott Trust
The William Leech Charity
The Leslie and Lilian Manning
  Trust
The Millfield House Foundation
The Northern Rock Foundation
The Northumberland Village
  Homes Trust
The Northumbria Historic
  Churches Trust
Sir John Priestman Charity
  Trust
The Rothley Trust
The Christopher Rowbotham
  Charitable Trust
S O Charitable Trust
The Storrow Scott Will Trust
The P and D Shepherd
  Charitable Trust
The Sylvia and Colin Shepherd
  Charitable Trust
St Hilda's Trust
T and S Trust Fund
Tees Valley Community
  Foundation
Community Foundation Serving
  Tyne and Wear and
  Northumberland
The William Webster
  Charitable Trust
Yorkshire Agricultural Society

■ **Cleveland**

The Barbour Trust
The Hadrian Trust
Hexham and Newcastle
  Diocesan Trust (1947)
The Hospital of God at
  Greatham
The Sir James Knott Trust
The Northern Rock Foundation
The Northumbria Historic
  Churches Trust
Tees Valley Community
  Foundation
Yorkshire Agricultural Society

■ **Durham County**

The Barbour Trust
Joseph Brough Charitable
  Trust

M R Cannon 1998 Charitable
Trust
County Durham Foundation
The Sir Tom Cowie Charitable
Trust
The Gillian Dickinson Trust
The Hadrian Trust
Hexham and Newcastle
Diocesan Trust (1947)
The Hospital of God at
Greatham
The Sir James Knott Trust
The William Leech Charity
The Northern Rock Foundation
The Northumbria Historic
Churches Trust
Sir John Priestman Charity
Trust
Yorkshire Agricultural Society

■ Northumberland

The Barbour Trust
Joseph Brough Charitable
Trust
Cumberland Building Society
Charitable Foundation
The Gillian Dickinson Trust
The Hadrian Trust
The W A Handley Charitable
Trust
Hexham and Newcastle
Diocesan Trust (1947)
The Hospital of God at
Greatham
The Sir James Knott Trust
The William Leech Charity
The Northern Rock Foundation
The Northumbria Historic
Churches Trust
The Christopher Rowbotham
Charitable Trust
St Hilda's Trust
Community Foundation Serving
Tyne and Wear and
Northumberland
Yorkshire Agricultural Society

■ Tyne & Wear

The Barbour Trust
Joseph Brough Charitable
Trust
The Sir Tom Cowie Charitable
Trust
The Gillian Dickinson Trust
The Ellinson Foundation Ltd
The Hadrian Trust
The W A Handley Charitable
Trust
Hexham and Newcastle
Diocesan Trust (1947)
The Hospital of God at
Greatham
The Sir James Knott Trust
The William Leech Charity

The Northern Rock Foundation
The Northumbria Historic
Churches Trust
Sir John Priestman Charity
Trust
The Christopher Rowbotham
Charitable Trust
S O Charitable Trust
St Hilda's Trust
T and S Trust Fund
Community Foundation Serving
Tyne and Wear and
Northumberland

Northern Ireland

Church of Ireland Priorities
Fund
The Community Foundation for
Northern Ireland
The Enkalon Foundation
The Garnett Charitable Trust
The GNC Trust
The Goodman Foundation
Lloyds TSB Foundation for
Northern Ireland
The Esmé Mitchell Trust
John Moores Foundation
Royal British Legion
Ulster Garden Villages Ltd
Ultach Trust
Victoria Homes Trust
The Vodafone (Group)
Foundation
Women Caring Trust

Scotland

Aberbrothock Charitable Trust
The Aberdeen Endowments
Trust
The Aberdeenshire Educational
Trust Scheme
Age Concern Scotland Grants
The AMW Charitable Trust
The BAA Communities Trust
The Baird Trust
Barchester Healthcare
Foundation
The Bellahouston Bequest
Fund
The Benfield Motors Charitable
Trust
The British Gas (Scottish Gas)
Energy Fund
The Callander Charitable Trust
Caring for Kids (Radio Tay)
The Carnegie Dunfermline
Trust
The Carnegie Trust for the
Universities of Scotland
Cash for Kids Radio Clyde
The Cattanach Charitable Trust
Chest, Heart and Stroke
Scotland

The Coalfields Regeneration
Trust
The Craignish Trust
The Cray Trust
The Cromarty Trust
The Cross Trust
Cumberland Building Society
Charitable Foundation
The Cunningham Trust
The Davidson (Nairn)
Charitable Trust
The Dickon Trust
Edinburgh Children's Holiday
Fund
Edinburgh Voluntary
Organisations' Trust Funds
The Ellis Campbell Foundation
The Erskine Cunningham Hill
Trust
Fife Council/Common Good
Funds and Trusts
The Gannochy Trust
The GNC Trust
Grampian Police Diced Cap
Charitable Fund
The Guildry Incorporation of
Perth
Dr Guthrie's Association
The Christina Mary Hendrie
Trust for Scottish and
Canadian Charities
The Anne Herd Memorial Trust
The Holywood Trust
Miss Agnes H Hunter's Trust
The Jeffrey Charitable Trust
The Jordan Charitable
Foundation
JTH Charitable Trust
The Ian Karten Charitable
Trust
The Late Sir Pierce Lacy
Charity Trust
The Andrew and Mary
Elizabeth Little Charitable
Trust
The R S Macdonald Charitable
Trust
The Mackintosh Foundation
W M Mann Foundation
The Nancie Massey Charitable
Trust
The Mathew Trust
The Merchants' House of
Glasgow
The Stanley Morrison
Charitable Trust
Moto in the Community Trust
The Mugdock Children's Trust
The North British Hotel Trust
The Northwood Charitable
Trust
Miss M E Swinton Paterson's
Charitable Trust
The Ponton House Trust
The Robertson Trust

Mrs Gladys Row Fogo
    Charitable Trust
The Scottish Arts Council
Scottish Churches' Community
    Trust
Scottish Coal Industry Special
    Welfare Fund
The Scottish Community
    Foundation
The Scottish International
    Education Trust
The P and D Shepherd
    Charitable Trust
The Shetland Charitable Trust
The Hugh Stenhouse
    Foundation
Strathclyde Police Benevolent
    Fund
The Templeton Goodwill Trust
The Arthur and Margaret
    Thompson Charitable Trust
The Len Thomson Charitable
    Trust
Voluntary Action Fund
John Watson's Trust
A H and B C Whiteley
    Charitable Trust
The John Wilson Bequest Fund
J and J R Wilson Trust
The James Wood Bequest
    Fund
The John K Young Endowment
    Fund

■ **Central**

The Callander Charitable Trust
Mrs Gladys Row Fogo
    Charitable Trust
The James Wood Bequest
    Fund

■ **Grampian Region**

Aberbrothock Charitable Trust
The Aberdeen Endowments
    Trust
The Aberdeenshire Educational
    Trust Scheme
The BAA Communities Trust
Grampian Police Diced Cap
    Charitable Fund

■ **Highlands & Islands**

The Cromarty Trust
The Davidson (Nairn)
    Charitable Trust
The Jordan Charitable
    Foundation
The Mackintosh Foundation
The Shetland Charitable Trust

■ **Lothians Region**

The BAA Communities Trust
The Benfield Motors Charitable
    Trust
Edinburgh Children's Holiday
    Fund
Edinburgh Voluntary
    Organisations' Trust Funds
The Ponton House Trust
Mrs Gladys Row Fogo
    Charitable Trust
The John Wilson Bequest Fund
The John K Young Endowment
    Fund

■ **Southern Scotland**

The Callander Charitable Trust
Cumberland Building Society
    Charitable Foundation
The Holywood Trust

■ **Strathclyde**

The BAA Communities Trust
The Bellahouston Bequest
    Fund
Cash for Kids Radio Clyde
The Andrew and Mary
    Elizabeth Little Charitable
    Trust
The Merchants' House of
    Glasgow
The Stanley Morrison
    Charitable Trust
Strathclyde Police Benevolent
    Fund
The Templeton Goodwill Trust
The James Wood Bequest
    Fund

■ **Tayside & Fife**

Aberbrothock Charitable Trust
Caring for Kids (Radio Tay)
The Carnegie Dunfermline
    Trust
The Ellis Campbell Foundation
Fife Council/Common Good
    Funds and Trusts
The Guildry Incorporation of
    Perth
The Late Sir Pierce Lacy
    Charity Trust
The Mathew Trust
The Northwood Charitable
    Trust
The Arthur and Margaret
    Thompson Charitable Trust

Wales

Archbishop of Wales' Fund for
    Children

The John Armitage Charitable
    Trust
The Arts Council of Wales
The Laura Ashley Foundation
The Austin Bailey Trust
Barchester Healthcare
    Foundation
The Baring Foundation
Birthday House Trust
H E and E L Botteley
    Charitable Trust
The Bower Trust
The British Gas (Scottish Gas)
    Energy Trust
The Catholic Trust for England
    and Wales
The Cemlyn-Jones Trust
The Chapman Charitable Trust
The Chrimes Family Charitable
    Trust
The Church and Community
    Fund
City and County of Swansea
    Welsh Church Act Fund
CLA Charitable Trust
The Coalfields Regeneration
    Trust
Colwinston Charitable Trust
The Cwmbran Trust
The DM Charitable Trust
The James Dyson Foundation
The Ernest Hecht Charitable
    Foundation
Ford Britain Trust
Gwyneth Forrester Trust
The Joseph Strong Frazer Trust
The Freemasons' Grand
    Charity
The General Nursing Council
    for England and Wales
    Trust
The GNC Trust
The Goodman Foundation
Leonard Gordon Charitable
    Trust
Lady Hind Trust
The Hintze Family Charitable
    Foundation
The Jane Hodge Foundation
The Isle of Anglesey Charitable
    Trust
J I Charitable Trust
Dezna Robins Jones Charitable
    Foundation
The Ian Karten Charitable
    Trust
Lloyds TSB Foundation for
    England and Wales
Llysdinam Charitable Trust
Marshall's Charity
Marshgate Charitable
    Settlement
The McKenna Charitable Trust
Millennium Stadium Charitable
    Trust

Monmouthshire County Council
Welsh Church Act Fund
The Mr and Mrs J T Morgan
Foundation
Moto in the Community Trust
The National Churches Trust
(formerly the Historic
Churches Preservation
Trust with the Incorporated
Church Building Society)
The Noon Foundation
The North West Cancer
Research Fund
The Norwood and Newton
Settlement
The Ouseley Trust
The James Pantyfedwen
Foundation
The Payne Charitable Trust
The Bernard Piggott Trust
Radio City Charity Foundation
The Rhondda Cynon Taff
Welsh Church Acts Fund
Royal British Legion
The Severn Trent Water
Charitable Trust Fund
Skipton Building Society
Charitable Foundation
The Sobell Foundation
St Teilo's Trust
The Leonard Laity Stoate
Charitable Trust
Swansea and Brecon Diocesan
Board of Finance Limited
TJH Foundation
Toni and Guy Charitable
Foundation Limited
Vale of Glamorgan – Welsh
Church Fund
The Community Foundation in
Wales
Wales Council for Voluntary
Action
The Barbara Ward Children's
Foundation
The Waterways Trust
Welsh Church Fund Dyfed
area (Carmarthenshire,
Ceredigion and
Pembrokeshire)
A H and B C Whiteley
Charitable Trust
The Yapp Charitable Trust

■ North Wales

The Cemlyn-Jones Trust
The Chrimes Family Charitable
Trust
The Isle of Anglesey Charitable
Trust
The North West Cancer
Research Fund
The Payne Charitable Trust
The Bernard Piggott Trust
Radio City Charity Foundation

■ Mid and West Wales

The North West Cancer
Research Fund
Swansea and Brecon Diocesan
Board of Finance Limited
Welsh Church Fund Dyfed
area (Carmarthenshire,
Ceredigion and
Pembrokeshire)

■ South Wales

The Austin Bailey Trust
City and County of Swansea
Welsh Church Act Fund
The Cwmbran Trust
Ford Britain Trust
Monmouthshire County Council
Welsh Church Act Fund
The Rhondda Cynon Taff
Welsh Church Acts Fund
Swansea and Brecon Diocesan
Board of Finance Limited
Vale of Glamorgan – Welsh
Church Fund

Channel Islands

The Hampshire and Islands
Historic Churches Trust
Lloyds TSB Foundation for the
Channel Islands
Wessex Cancer Trust

Trusts by field of interest and type of beneficiary

This index contains two separate listings:

Categorisation of fields of interest and type of beneficiary: This lists all of the headings used in the DGMT to categorise fields of interest and types of beneficiary.

Trusts by field of interest and type of beneficiary: This lists trusts under the fields of interest and types of beneficiary for which they have expressed a funding preference.

Trusts by field of interest and type of beneficiary

These pages contain two separate listings:

Categorisation of fields of interest and type of beneficiary
This lists all of the headings used in the DGMT to categorise fields of interest and types of beneficiary

Trusts by field of interest and type of beneficiary
This lists trusts under the fields of interest and types of beneficiary for which they have expressed a funding preference

Arts, culture, sport and recreation 49

Arts and culture 52

■ **Access to the arts 54**

■ **Amateur and community arts 54**
Community arts 54
Eisteddfodau 55
Participation in the arts 55

■ **Arts and culture of specific communities 55**
Greek art and culture 55
Japanese art and culture 55
Portugese art and culture 55
Scottish and Gaelic art and culture 55

■ **Arts management, policy and planning 55**

■ **Combined arts 55**

■ **Crafts 55**

■ **Disability arts 55**

■ **Libraries 55**

■ **Literature 55**

■ **Museums and gallaries 55**

■ **Performing arts 55**
Music 56
Dance 56
Theatre 56

■ **Visual arts 56**
Design 56
Fine arts 56
Public art/sculpture 57

Heritage and the built environment 57

■ **Arts and the environment 58**
Architecture 58
Landscape 58

■ **Heritage 58**

■ **Maintenance and preservation of buildings 58**
Religious buildings 59

■ **Restoration and maintenance of inland waterways 60**

■ **Built environment – education and research 60**

Humanities 60

■ **Archaeology 60**

■ **History 60**

■ **International understanding 60**

■ **Philosophy and ethics 60**

Media and communications 60

Recreation and sport 60

- Parks and open spaces 61
- Recreation facilities 61
- Sport for people with a disability 61
- Sports 61

Development, housing and employment 62

Community and economic development 63

Housing 63

Specific industries 64

Education and training 64

Higher education 69

Informal, continuing and adult education 69

- Vocational education and training 69

Integrated education 69

Management of schools 70

Particular subjects, curriculum development 70

- Arts education and training 70
- Business education 70
- Citizenship, personal and social education 71
- Construction industry education 71
- Domestic/lifeskills education 71
- Hospitality education 71
- Literacy education 71
- Religious education 71
- Science education 71
- Sports education 71
- Technology, engineering and computer education 71

Pre-school education, nursery schools 71

Primary and secondary school education 71

- Faith schools 72
- Public and independent schools 72
- Special needs schools 72
- State schools 73

Teacher training and development 73

Environment and animals 73

Agriculture and fishing 75

- Farming and food production 75
- Fishing and fisheries 75
- Forestry 75
- Horticulture 76

Animal care 76

Animal conservation 76

Countryside 76

Environmental education and research 77

Natural environment 77

■ Flora and fauna 78

■ Water resources 78

■ Wild places, wilderness 78

Pollution abatement and control 78

Sustainable environment 78

■ Energy issues 78

■ Loss of environment 78

Transport 78

General charitable purposes 79
Health 87
Alternative, complementary medicine 92

Health care 92

■ Health training 93

■ Medical equipment 93

■ Medical institutions 93

■ Nursing 94

■ Primary health care 94

■ Therapy 94

Health education/ prevention/ development 94

■ Health promotion 94

History of medicine 94

Medical research and clinical treatment 94

Philanthropy and the voluntary sector 97
Voluntarism 97

■ Community participation 97

Voluntary sector capacity building 97

Religious activities 97
Christianity 102

■ Christian causes, work 104
Christian churches 104
Christian social thought 105
Ecumenicalism 105
Missionary work, evangelism 105

Hinduism 106

Inter-faith activities 106

Islam 106

Judaism 106

■ Jewish causes, work 108

■ Orthodox Judaism 108

Religious understanding 109

Rights, law and conflict 109
Citizen participation 109

Conflict resolution 110

Legal advice and services 110

Rights, equality and justice 110

■ Civil liberties 110

■ Cultural equity 110

■ Disability rights 110

■ Economic justice 110

■ Human rights 110

Arts, culture, sport and recreation

The 29th May 1961 Charitable Trust
The A B Charitable Trust
Access Sport
The Victor Adda Foundation
The Alice Trust
Allchurches Trust Ltd
Angus Allnatt Charitable Foundation
The Ammco Trust
The AMW Charitable Trust
Andor Charitable Trust
The Eric Anker-Petersen Charity
Arcadia
The Architectural Heritage Fund
The Armourers' and Brasiers' Gauntlet Trust
Arsenal Charitable Trust
Arts Council England
The Arts Council of Northern Ireland
The Arts Council of Wales
The Ove Arup Foundation
A J H Ashby Will Trust
The Ashden Trust
The Ashendene Trust
The Laura Ashley Foundation
The Association of Friends of Essex Churches
The Astor Foundation
The Astor of Hever Trust
The Aurelius Charitable Trust
The Baird Trust
The Roy and Pixie Baker Charitable Trust
The Ballinger Charitable Trust
The Barcapel Foundation
The Baring Foundation
Barrington Family Charitable Trust
The John Beckwith Charitable Trust
The Bedford Charity (The Harpur Trust)
The Bedfordshire and Hertfordshire Historic Churches Trust
The Bellahouston Bequest Fund
The Hervey Benham Charitable Trust
Bergqvist Charitable Trust
The Big Lottery Fund
Birmingham International Airport Community Trust
The Nicholas Boas Charitable Trust
BOOST Charitable Trust
The Boshier-Hinton Foundation
The Bowerman Charitable Trust
John and Susan Bowers Fund

British Institute at Ankara
The Britten-Pears Foundation
The Rory and Elizabeth Brooks Foundation
T B H Brunner's Charitable Settlement
The Buckinghamshire Historic Churches Trust
The Rosemary Bugden Charitable Trust
The Audrey and Stanley Burton 1960 Charitable Trust
The Arnold Burton 1998 Charitable Trust
The Derek Butler Trust
Edward Cadbury Charitable Trust
P H G Cadbury Charitable Trust
The William A Cadbury Charitable Trust
The Edward and Dorothy Cadbury Trust
The Barrow Cadbury Trust and the Barrow Cadbury Fund
The Cambridgeshire Historic Churches Trust
The Carnegie Dunfermline Trust
The Carpenters' Company Charitable Trust
The Carr-Gregory Trust
Carter's Educational Foundation
Elizabeth Cayzer Charitable Trust
The Cemlyn-Jones Trust
The Chipping Sodbury Town Lands Charity
Stephen Clark 1957 Charitable Trust
J A Clark Charitable Trust
The Clore Duffield Foundation
Miss V L Clore's 1967 Charitable Trust
The Robert Clutterbuck Charitable Trust
The Francis Coales Charitable Foundation
The John Coates Charitable Trust
The Denise Cohen Charitable Trust
The R and S Cohen Fondation
The John S Cohen Foundation
The Bernard Coleman Charitable Trust
Colwinston Charitable Trust
Colyer-Fergusson Charitable Trust
The Congleton Inclosure Trust
The Ernest Cook Trust
Country Houses Foundation
The Craignish Trust
The Crescent Trust
The Cromarty Trust
The Cross Trust

Cruden Foundation Ltd
The D J H Currie Memorial Trust
The D'Oyly Carte Charitable Trust
The Daiwa Anglo-Japanese Foundation
The Gwendoline and Margaret Davies Charity
The Hamilton Davies Trust
The Helen and Geoffrey De Freitas Charitable Trust
Peter De Haan Charitable Trust
The De Laszlo Foundation
The Leopold De Rothschild Charitable Trust
The Deakin Charitable Trust
The Delius Trust
The Denton Wilde Sapte Charitable Trust
The Derbyshire Churches and Chapels Preservation Trust
The Devon Historic Churches Trust
The Gillian Dickinson Trust
Dischma Charitable Trust
The Djanogly Foundation
The Dorset Historic Churches Trust
The Drapers' Charitable Fund
The Duis Charitable Trust
The Dulverton Trust
Dunard Fund
Ronald Duncan Literary Foundation
The Houghton Dunn Charitable Trust
The Dyers' Company Charitable Trust
The Earmark Trust
Eden Arts Trust
The Gilbert and Eileen Edgar Foundation
The Edinburgh Trust, No 2 Account
The Elephant Trust
The John Ellerman Foundation
The Ellis Campbell Foundation
The Elmgrant Trust
The Elmley Foundation
The English Schools' Football Association
The Equity Trust Fund
The Eranda Foundation
The Ericson Trust
The Essex Heritage Trust
The Alan Evans Memorial Trust
Esmée Fairbairn Foundation
The Fairway Trust
The Family Rich Charities Trust
The Lord Faringdon Charitable Trust
Samuel William Farmer's Trust
The February Foundation
The John Feeney Charitable Bequest

Fife Council/Common Good
  Funds and Trusts
Gerald Finzi Charitable Trust
The Sir John Fisher Foundation
Fisherbeck Charitable Trust
The Fishmongers' Company's
  Charitable Trust
Marc Fitch Fund
The Joyce Fletcher Charitable
  Trust
The Follett Trust
The Football Association
  National Sports Centre
  Trust
The Football Association Youth
  Trust
The Football Foundation
Ford Britain Trust
The Donald Forrester Trust
The Foyle Foundation
The Jill Franklin Trust
The Gordon Fraser Charitable
  Trust
The Hugh Fraser Foundation
The Joseph Strong Frazer Trust
The Thomas Freke and Lady
  Norton Charity
The Freshgate Trust
  Foundation
The Friends of Kent Churches
Friends of Muir Group
The Frognal Trust
The Galanthus Trust
The Gannochy Trust
The Samuel Gardner Memorial
  Trust
The Garnett Charitable Trust
Garrick Charitable Trust
The Gatsby Charitable
  Foundation
ntoring-style support brings
  benefits
Gatwick Airport Community
  Trust
The Robert Gavron Charitable
  Trust
Jacqueline and Michael Gee
  Charitable Trust
J Paul Getty Jr Charitable Trust
The Gibbs Charitable Trust
Simon Gibson Charitable Trust
The Girdlers' Company
  Charitable Trust
The Glass-House Trust
The Gloucestershire Historic
  Churches Trust
Golden Charitable Trust
The Jack Goldhill Charitable
  Trust
The Goldsmiths' Arts Trust
  Fund
The Goldsmiths' Company
  Charity
The Golsoncott Foundation
Golubovich Foundation

Nicholas and Judith
  Goodison's Charitable
  Settlement
The Gosling Foundation
  Limited
The Granada Foundation
The Grand Order of Water
  Rats' Charities Fund
The Grange Farm Centre Trust
The J G Graves Charitable
  Trust
The Great Britain Sasakawa
  Foundation
The Greys Charitable Trust
Grimmitt Trust
The Grocers' Charity
The Gulbenkian Foundation
The Hadfield Trust
The Hadrian Trust
The Hale Trust
Robert Hall Charity
Paul Hamlyn Foundation
The Helen Hamlyn Trust
The Hampshire and Islands
  Historic Churches Trust
The W A Handley Charitable
  Trust
The Harding Trust
William Harding's Charity
The Kenneth Hargreaves
  Charitable Trust
The Harris Charitable Trust
The Peter Harrison Foundation
Haskel Family Foundation
The Dorothy Hay-Bolton
  Charitable Trust
The Charles Hayward
  Foundation
The Headley Trust
The Hellenic Foundation
The Hemby Trust
The Henley Educational Charity
The Herefordshire Historic
  Churches Trust
The Heritage of London Trust
  Ltd
The Derek Hill Foundation
The Hinrichsen Foundation
The Hintze Family Charitable
  Foundation
Hobson Charity Limited
Matthew Hodder Charitable
  Trust
The Holbeck Charitable Trust
The Holst Foundation
The Homestead Charitable
  Trust
The Horne Foundation
The Reta Lila Howard
  Foundation
The Geoffrey C Hughes
  Charitable Trust
Human Relief Foundation
Huntingdon Freemen's Charity
The Idlewild Trust
The Iliffe Family Charitable
  Trust

The Inland Waterways
  Association
The Inlight Trust
The Ireland Fund of Great
  Britain
The Irish Youth Foundation
  (UK) Ltd (incorporating The
  Lawlor Foundation)
Jacobs Charitable Trust
The John Jarrold Trust
Jerwood Charitable Foundation
The JMK Charitable Trust
The Joanies Trust
The Johnnie Johnson Trust
The Johnson Wax Ltd
  Charitable Trust
Jusaca Charitable Trust
The Stanley Kalms Foundation
The Boris Karloff Charitable
  Foundation
The Kathleen Trust
The Michael and Ilse Katz
  Foundation
The Robert Kiln Charitable
  Trust
The Marina Kleinwort
  Charitable Trust
The Sir James Knott Trust
The Kobler Trust
The Kohn Foundation
The Neil Kreitman Foundation
The Christopher Laing
  Foundation
The David Laing Foundation
Lancashire Environmental
  Fund
The LankellyChase Foundation
The R J Larg Family Charitable
  Trust
The Lark Trust
Laslett's (Hinton) Charity
The Lawson Beckman
  Charitable Trust
The Raymond and Blanche
  Lawson Charitable Trust
The Carole and Geoffrey
  Lawson Foundation
The David Lean Foundation
The Leathersellers' Company
  Charitable Fund
The Leche Trust
Leeds Building Society
  Charitable Foundation
Leicestershire Historic
  Churches Trust
Lord Leverhulme's Charitable
  Trust
The Joseph Levy Charitable
  Foundation
John Lewis Partnership
  General Community Fund
The Limbourne Trust
The Linbury Trust
The Lincolnshire Old Churches
  Trust
The Linden Charitable Trust
The Lister Charitable Trust

The George John and Sheilah Livanos Charitable Trust
The Charles Lloyd Foundation
Lloyds TSB Foundation for Northern Ireland
The London Marathon Charitable Trust
The William and Katherine Longman Trust
The Lord's Taverners
Lady Lumley's Educational Foundation
The Ruth and Jack Lunzer Charitable Trust
Lord and Lady Lurgan Trust
John Lyon's Charity
The Sir Jack Lyons Charitable Trust
The Mackintosh Foundation
The MacRobert Trust
Ian Mactaggart Trust
Mageni Trust
Man Group plc Charitable Trust
Manchester Airport Community Trust Fund
The Manifold Charitable Trust
W M Mann Foundation
The Manoukian Charitable Foundation
Market Harborough and The Bowdens Charity
Michael Marks Charitable Trust
The Marsh Christian Trust
Marshall's Charity
Sir George Martin Trust
John Martin's Charity
The Nancie Massey Charitable Trust
The Mayfield Valley Arts Trust
The Anthony and Elizabeth Mellows Charitable Settlement
The Mercers' Charitable Foundation
The Merchant Venturers' Charity
The Merchants' House of Glasgow
The Metropolitan Drinking Fountain and Cattle Trough Association
Gerald Micklem Charitable Trust
Miles Trust for the Putney and Roehampton Community
Millennium Stadium Charitable Trust
The Miller Foundation
The Millichope Foundation
The Millward Charitable Trust
Milton Keynes Community Foundation
The Peter Minet Trust
The Esmé Mitchell Trust
The Modiano Charitable Trust

Monmouthshire County Council Welsh Church Act Fund
The Monument Trust
The Henry Moore Foundation
The Nigel Moores Family Charitable Trust
The Peter Moores Foundation
The Morel Charitable Trust
The Stanley Morrison Charitable Trust
The Mount Everest Foundation
The Mugdock Children's Trust
The John R Murray Charitable Trust
The Kitty and Daniel Nabarro Charitable Trust
The Eleni Nakou Foundation
The National Art Collections Fund
The National Churches Trust
The National Manuscripts Conservation Trust
Network for Social Change
The Normanby Charitable Trust
The Northern Rock Foundation
The Northumbria Historic Churches Trust
The Northwood Charitable Trust
The Norton Foundation
The Norwich Church of England Young Men's Society
The Norwich Historic Churches Trust Ltd
The Noswad Charity
The Nottinghamshire Historic Churches Trust
The Oakdale Trust
The Oakley Charitable Trust
The Old Broad Street Charity Trust
Old Possum's Practical Trust
The Oldham Foundation
Orrin Charitable Trust
The Ouseley Trust
The Owen Family Trust
The Pallant Charitable Trust
The James Pantyfedwen Foundation
The Parthenon Trust
Miss M E Swinton Paterson's Charitable Trust
The Jack Patston Charitable Trust
The Pedmore Sporting Club Trust Fund
Peltz Trust
The Performing Right Society Foundation
The Bernard Piggott Trust
The Pilgrim Trust
The Austin and Hope Pilkington Trust
The Col W W Pilkington Will Trusts The General Charity Fund

Polden-Puckham Charitable Foundation
The John Porter Charitable Trust
The Porter Foundation
The Prince's Charities Foundation
PSA Peugeot Citroen Charity Trust
The Puri Foundation
Mr and Mrs J A Pye's Charitable Settlement
Quercus Trust
The R V W Trust
The Radcliffe Trust
The Ragdoll Foundation
The Peggy Ramsay Foundation
The Sigrid Rausing Trust
The Ravensdale Trust
The Rayne Foundation
The Reed Foundation
The Max Reinhardt Charitable Trust
The Rhododendron Trust
The Rhondda Cynon Taff Welsh Church Acts Fund
The Sir Cliff Richard Charitable Trust
The Clive Richards Charity
The Richmond Parish Lands Charity
Rix-Thompson-Rothenburg Foundation
The Alex Roberts-Miller Foundation
The Robertson Trust
The Rock Solid Trust
The Roman Research Trust
Mrs L D Rope Third Charitable Settlement
The Rose Foundation
The Rothley Trust
The Rothschild Foundation
The Roughley Charitable Trust
The Rowing Foundation
The Rowlands Trust
The Joseph Rowntree Charitable Trust
Royal Docks Trust (London)
The J S and E C Rymer Charitable Trust
The Michael Sacher Charitable Trust
The Michael Harry Sacher Trust
Dr Mortimer and Theresa Sackler Foundation
The Raymond and Beverley Sackler Foundation
The Saddlers' Company Charitable Fund
The Alan and Babette Sainsbury Charitable Fund
The Saintbury Trust
The Andrew Salvesen Charitable Trust
Coral Samuel Charitable Trust

The Peter Samuel Charitable Trust

The Scarfe Charitable Trust

Schroder Charity Trust

The Scotshill Trust

The Frieda Scott Charitable Trust

The Scottish Arts Council

Scottish Coal Industry Special Welfare Fund

The Scottish International Education Trust

The Scouloudi Foundation

The Searle Charitable Trust

The Samuel Sebba Charitable Trust

The Archie Sherman Charitable Trust

The R C Sherriff Trust

The Shetland Charitable Trust

The Shipwrights' Company Charitable Fund

The N Smith Charitable Settlement

The Martin Smith Foundation

The Stanley Smith UK Horticultural Trust

Friends of Somerset Churches and Chapels

The E C Sosnow Charitable Trust

Spears-Stutz Charitable Trust

Split Infinitive Trust

St Andrew's Conservation Trust

The Steel Charitable Trust

Stevenson Family's Charitable Trust

The Stewards' Charitable Trust

Peter Stormonth Darling Charitable Trust

The Suffolk Historic Churches Trust

The Summerfield Charitable Trust

The Surrey Historic Buildings Trust Ltd

The Sussex Historic Churches Trust

Sutton Coldfield Municipal Charities

The Swan Trust

The Connie and Albert Taylor Charitable Trust

A P Taylor Trust

The Thistle Trust

The Tillett Trust

The Tinsley Foundation

Miss S M Tutton Charitable Trust

The Underwood Trust

Vale of Glamorgan – Welsh Church Fund

Veneziana Fund

Robert and Felicity Waley-Cohen Charitable Trust

Sir Siegmund Warburg's Voluntary Settlement

The Ward Blenkinsop Trust

The John Warren Foundation

The Waterways Trust

The Howard Watson Symington Memorial Charity

Welsh Church Fund Dyfed area (Carmarthenshire, Ceredigion and Pembrokeshire)

The Westcroft Trust

The Barbara Whatmore Charitable Trust

The Whitaker Charitable Trust

The Colonel W H Whitbread Charitable Trust

A H and B C Whiteley Charitable Trust

The Williams Charitable Trust

The Harold Hyam Wingate Foundation

The Winton Charitable Foundation

The Wixamtree Trust

The Maurice Wohl Charitable Foundation

The Wolfson Foundation

The Woodward Charitable Trust

The Worcestershire and Dudley Historic Churches Trust

The Fred and Della Worms Charitable Trust

The Worwin UK Foundation

Miss E B Wrightson's Charitable Settlement

The Wyseliot Charitable Trust

The W Wing Yip and Brothers Foundation

York and North Yorkshire Community Foundation

The York Children's Trust

The Yorkshire Dales Millennium Trust

The Yorkshire Historic Churches Trust

Youth Music

The Marjorie and Arnold Ziff Charitable Foundation

The Zochonis Charitable Trust

Arts and culture

The A B Charitable Trust

The Victor Adda Foundation

Angus Allnatt Charitable Foundation

The AMW Charitable Trust

Andor Charitable Trust

The Eric Anker-Petersen Charity

The Armourers' and Brasiers' Gauntlet Trust

Arts Council England

The Arts Council of Northern Ireland

The Arts Council of Wales

The Ashden Trust

The Ashendene Trust

The Laura Ashley Foundation

The Aurelius Charitable Trust

The Ballinger Charitable Trust

The Baring Foundation

Barrington Family Charitable Trust

The Hervey Benham Charitable Trust

Bergqvist Charitable Trust

The Nicholas Boas Charitable Trust

The Bowerman Charitable Trust

John and Susan Bowers Fund

British Institute at Ankara

The Britten-Pears Foundation

The Rory and Elizabeth Brooks Foundation

T B H Brunner's Charitable Settlement

The Rosemary Bugden Charitable Trust

The Audrey and Stanley Burton 1960 Charitable Trust

The Derek Butler Trust

Edward Cadbury Charitable Trust

P H G Cadbury Charitable Trust

The William A Cadbury Charitable Trust

The Edward and Dorothy Cadbury Trust

The Carnegie Dunfermline Trust

Elizabeth Cayzer Charitable Trust

J A Clark Charitable Trust

The Clore Duffield Foundation

Miss V L Clore's 1967 Charitable Trust

The Francis Coales Charitable Foundation

The John Coates Charitable Trust

The Denise Cohen Charitable Trust

The R and S Cohen Fondation

The John S Cohen Foundation

Colwinston Charitable Trust

Colyer-Fergusson Charitable Trust

The Ernest Cook Trust

The Craignish Trust

The Crescent Trust

The Cross Trust

The D'Oyly Carte Charitable Trust

The Daiwa Anglo-Japanese Foundation

The Gwendoline and Margaret Davies Charity

Peter De Haan Charitable
  Trust
The Leopold De Rothschild
  Charitable Trust
The Deakin Charitable Trust
The Delius Trust
The Denton Wilde Sapte
  Charitable Trust
Dischma Charitable Trust
The Djanogly Foundation
The Drapers' Charitable Fund
The Duis Charitable Trust
Dunard Fund
Ronald Duncan Literary
  Foundation
The Dyers' Company
  Charitable Trust
The Earmark Trust
Eden Arts Trust
The Gilbert and Eileen Edgar
  Foundation
The Elephant Trust
The John Ellerman Foundation
The Elmgrant Trust
The Elmley Foundation
The Equity Trust Fund
The Eranda Foundation
The Ericson Trust
Esmée Fairbairn Foundation
The Family Rich Charities Trust
The Lord Faringdon Charitable
  Trust
The John Feeney Charitable
  Bequest
Fife Council/Common Good
  Funds and Trusts
Gerald Finzi Charitable Trust
The Sir John Fisher Foundation
The Joyce Fletcher Charitable
  Trust
The Follett Trust
Ford Britain Trust
The Foyle Foundation
The Gordon Fraser Charitable
  Trust
The Hugh Fraser Foundation
The Freshgate Trust
  Foundation
The Samuel Gardner Memorial
  Trust
The Garnett Charitable Trust
Garrick Charitable Trust
The Gatsby Charitable
  Foundation
Gatwick Airport Community
  Trust
The Robert Gavron Charitable
  Trust
Jacqueline and Michael Gee
  Charitable Trust
J Paul Getty Jr Charitable Trust
The Gibbs Charitable Trust
Simon Gibson Charitable Trust
The Girdlers' Company
  Charitable Trust
The Glass-House Trust
Golden Charitable Trust

The Jack Goldhill Charitable
  Trust
The Goldsmiths' Arts Trust
  Fund
The Goldsmiths' Company
  Charity
The Golsoncott Foundation
Golubovich Foundation
Nicholas and Judith
  Goodison's Charitable
  Settlement
The Granada Foundation
The Grand Order of Water
  Rats' Charities Fund
The J G Graves Charitable
  Trust
The Great Britain Sasakawa
  Foundation
The Greys Charitable Trust
Grimmitt Trust
The Grocers' Charity
The Gulbenkian Foundation
The Hadfield Trust
The Hadrian Trust
Paul Hamlyn Foundation
The W A Handley Charitable
  Trust
The Harding Trust
The Kenneth Hargreaves
  Charitable Trust
The Harris Charitable Trust
Haskel Family Foundation
The Headley Trust
The Hellenic Foundation
The Hemby Trust
The Henley Educational Charity
The Heritage of London Trust
  Ltd
The Derek Hill Foundation
The Hinrichsen Foundation
The Hintze Family Charitable
  Foundation
Hobson Charity Limited
Matthew Hodder Charitable
  Trust
The Holst Foundation
The Homestead Charitable
  Trust
The Horne Foundation
The Reta Lila Howard
  Foundation
The Geoffrey C Hughes
  Charitable Trust
Human Relief Foundation
The Idlewild Trust
The Ireland Fund of Great
  Britain
Jacobs Charitable Trust
The John Jarrold Trust
Jerwood Charitable Foundation
The Joanies Trust
The Stanley Kalms Foundation
The Boris Karloff Charitable
  Foundation
The Kathleen Trust
The Michael and Ilse Katz
  Foundation

The Robert Kiln Charitable
  Trust
The Marina Kleinwort
  Charitable Trust
The Kobler Trust
The Kohn Foundation
The Christopher Laing
  Foundation
The David Laing Foundation
The LankellyChase Foundation
The R J Larg Family Charitable
  Trust
The Lark Trust
The Lawson Beckman
  Charitable Trust
The Carole and Geoffrey
  Lawson Foundation
The Leathersellers' Company
  Charitable Fund
The Leche Trust
Leeds Building Society
  Charitable Foundation
Lord Leverhulme's Charitable
  Trust
The Joseph Levy Charitable
  Foundation
The Limbourne Trust
The Linbury Trust
The Linden Charitable Trust
The Charles Lloyd Foundation
Lloyds TSB Foundation for
  Northern Ireland
The London Marathon
  Charitable Trust
The William and Katherine
  Longman Trust
The Ruth and Jack Lunzer
  Charitable Trust
Lord and Lady Lurgan Trust
John Lyon's Charity
The Sir Jack Lyons Charitable
  Trust
The Mackintosh Foundation
The MacRobert Trust
Ian Mactaggart Trust
Mageni Trust
Man Group plc Charitable
  Trust
The Manifold Charitable Trust
W M Mann Foundation
Market Harborough and The
  Bowdens Charity
Michael Marks Charitable
  Trust
The Marsh Christian Trust
Sir George Martin Trust
John Martin's Charity
The Nancie Massey Charitable
  Trust
The Mayfield Valley Arts Trust
The Anthony and Elizabeth
  Mellows Charitable
  Settlement
The Mercers' Charitable
  Foundation
The Merchants' House of
  Glasgow

Miles Trust for the Putney and Roehampton Community
Millennium Stadium Charitable Trust
The Millward Charitable Trust
The Peter Minet Trust
The Esmé Mitchell Trust
The Modiano Charitable Trust
Monmouthshire County Council Welsh Church Act Fund
The Monument Trust
The Henry Moore Foundation
The Nigel Moores Family Charitable Trust
The Peter Moores Foundation
The Morel Charitable Trust
The John R Murray Charitable Trust
The Eleni Nakou Foundation
The National Art Collections Fund
The National Manuscripts Conservation Trust
Network for Social Change
The Normanby Charitable Trust
The Northwood Charitable Trust
The Noswad Charity
The Oakdale Trust
The Oakley Charitable Trust
The Old Broad Street Charity Trust
Old Possum's Practical Trust
The Oldham Foundation
Orrin Charitable Trust
The Ouseley Trust
The Owen Family Trust
The Pallant Charitable Trust
The James Pantyfedwen Foundation
The Parthenon Trust
Peltz Trust
The Performing Right Society Foundation
The Bernard Piggott Trust
The Pilgrim Trust
The Austin and Hope Pilkington Trust
The Col W W Pilkington Will Trusts The General Charity Fund
The John Porter Charitable Trust
The Porter Foundation
The Prince's Charities Foundation
Mr and Mrs J A Pye's Charitable Settlement
Quercus Trust
The R V W Trust
The Radcliffe Trust
The Ragdoll Foundation
The Peggy Ramsay Foundation
The Sigrid Rausing Trust
The Ravensdale Trust
The Rayne Foundation

The Max Reinhardt Charitable Trust
The Rhododendron Trust
The Rhondda Cynon Taff Welsh Church Acts Fund
The Clive Richards Charity
Rix-Thompson-Rothenburg Foundation
The Robertson Trust
The Rose Foundation
The Rothschild Foundation
The Roughley Charitable Trust
The Rowlands Trust
Royal Docks Trust (London)
The Michael Sacher Charitable Trust
The Michael Harry Sacher Trust
Dr Mortimer and Theresa Sackler Foundation
The Raymond and Beverley Sackler Foundation
The Alan and Babette Sainsbury Charitable Fund
The Andrew Salvesen Charitable Trust
Coral Samuel Charitable Trust
The Scarfe Charitable Trust
Schroder Charity Trust
The Frieda Scott Charitable Trust
The Scottish Arts Council
The Scottish International Education Trust
The Archie Sherman Charitable Trust
The R C Sherriff Trust
The Shetland Charitable Trust
The N Smith Charitable Settlement
The Martin Smith Foundation
The E C Sosnow Charitable Trust
Spears-Stutz Charitable Trust
Stevenson Family's Charitable Trust
The Summerfield Charitable Trust
The Swan Trust
A P Taylor Trust
The Thistle Trust
The Tillett Trust
Miss S M Tutton Charitable Trust
Veneziana Fund
Robert and Felicity Waley-Cohen Charitable Trust
Sir Siegmund Warburg's Voluntary Settlement
The Ward Blenkinsop Trust
The Barbara Whatmore Charitable Trust
The Whitaker Charitable Trust
A H and B C Whiteley Charitable Trust
The Williams Charitable Trust

The Harold Hyam Wingate Foundation
The Maurice Wohl Charitable Foundation
The Wolfson Foundation
The Woodward Charitable Trust
The Fred and Della Worms Charitable Trust
The Worwin UK Foundation
The Wyseliot Charitable Trust
The York Children's Trust
Youth Music
The Marjorie and Arnold Ziff Charitable Foundation
The Zochonis Charitable Trust

....

■ Access to the arts

The Robert Gavron Charitable Trust
Paul Hamlyn Foundation
The Linbury Trust
Lloyds TSB Foundation for Northern Ireland
Miles Trust for the Putney and Roehampton Community
The Alan and Babette Sainsbury Charitable Fund

....

■ Amateur and community arts

The Ashden Trust
Colyer-Fergusson Charitable Trust
Eden Arts Trust
The Ericson Trust
The Joyce Fletcher Charitable Trust
The Robert Gavron Charitable Trust
The Gulbenkian Foundation
The Horne Foundation
The Joanies Trust
The R J Larg Family Charitable Trust
The Joseph Levy Charitable Foundation
John Martin's Charity
The Monument Trust
The Oakdale Trust
The James Pantyfedwen Foundation
The Ragdoll Foundation
The Woodward Charitable Trust

■ Community arts

The Ashden Trust
Colyer-Fergusson Charitable Trust
Eden Arts Trust
The Ericson Trust

The Monument Trust
The Scottish Arts Council

■ Eisteddfodau

The Oakdale Trust
The James Pantyfedwen
  Foundation

■ Participation in the arts

Eden Arts Trust
The Robert Gavron Charitable
  Trust
The Horne Foundation
The Ragdoll Foundation
The Woodward Charitable
  Trust

**■ Arts and culture of
  specific
  communities**

The Baring Foundation
The Daiwa Anglo-Japanese
  Foundation
The Great Britain Sasakawa
  Foundation
The Gulbenkian Foundation
The Hellenic Foundation
Miles Trust for the Putney and
  Roehampton Community
The Eleni Nakou Foundation

■ Greek art and culture

The Hellenic Foundation

■ Japanese art and culture

The Daiwa Anglo-Japanese
  Foundation
The Great Britain Sasakawa
  Foundation

**■ Portugese art and
  culture**

The Gulbenkian Foundation

**■ Scottish and Gaelic art
  and culture**

The Scottish Arts Council

**■ Arts management,
  policy and planning**

The Eric Anker-Petersen
  Charity
Esmée Fairbairn Foundation
Miles Trust for the Putney and
  Roehampton Community

The Peter Moores Foundation

■ Combined arts

The Earmark Trust
The Elephant Trust
The Joyce Fletcher Charitable
  Trust

■ Crafts

The Ernest Cook Trust
The Girdlers' Company
  Charitable Trust
The Radcliffe Trust

■ Disability arts

The A B Charitable Trust
The Robert Gavron Charitable
  Trust
Lloyds TSB Foundation for
  Northern Ireland
Rix-Thompson-Rothenburg
  Foundation

■ Libraries

The Francis Coales Charitable
  Foundation
Colwinston Charitable Trust
The J G Graves Charitable
  Trust
Paul Hamlyn Foundation
The Headley Trust
The Heritage of London Trust
  Ltd
The Mercers' Charitable
  Foundation
The John R Murray Charitable
  Trust
The Pilgrim Trust

■ Literature

The Elmgrant Trust
The Joyce Fletcher Charitable
  Trust
The Follett Trust
Garrick Charitable Trust
Matthew Hodder Charitable
  Trust
The Limbourne Trust
The John R Murray Charitable
  Trust

**■ Museums and
  gallaries**

The Victor Adda Foundation
The Armourers' and Brasiers'
  Gauntlet Trust
The Aurelius Charitable Trust

The Clore Duffield Foundation
The Francis Coales Charitable
  Foundation
The Crescent Trust
The Djanogly Foundation
The Duis Charitable Trust
The Joyce Fletcher Charitable
  Trust
J Paul Getty Jr Charitable Trust
The Girdlers' Company
  Charitable Trust
Golden Charitable Trust
The J G Graves Charitable
  Trust
The W A Handley Charitable
  Trust
The Headley Trust
The Heritage of London Trust
  Ltd
The Idlewild Trust
The Leche Trust
The Linbury Trust
The Manifold Charitable Trust
Michael Marks Charitable
  Trust
The Marsh Christian Trust
Sir George Martin Trust
The Mercers' Charitable
  Foundation
The Henry Moore Foundation
The Peter Moores Foundation
The National Art Collections
  Fund
The National Manuscripts
  Conservation Trust
Orrin Charitable Trust
The Pilgrim Trust
The Radcliffe Trust
The Sigrid Rausing Trust
The Raymond and Beverley
  Sackler Foundation
Spears-Stutz Charitable Trust
The Summerfield Charitable
  Trust

■ Performing arts

Angus Allnatt Charitable
  Foundation
The Eric Anker-Petersen
  Charity
The Hervey Benham Charitable
  Trust
The Britten-Pears Foundation
The Rosemary Bugden
  Charitable Trust
Colwinston Charitable Trust
The Cross Trust
The Deakin Charitable Trust
The Delius Trust
The Duis Charitable Trust
Dunard Fund
The Equity Trust Fund
Esmée Fairbairn Foundation
The Family Rich Charities Trust

The John Feeney Charitable
  Bequest
Gerald Finzi Charitable Trust
The Sir John Fisher Foundation
The Joyce Fletcher Charitable
  Trust
The Gordon Fraser Charitable
  Trust
The Hugh Fraser Foundation
The Freshgate Trust
  Foundation
Garrick Charitable Trust
The Gatsby Charitable
  Foundation
The Gibbs Charitable Trust
The Girdlers' Company
  Charitable Trust
The Grand Order of Water
  Rats' Charities Fund
The Harding Trust
The Harris Charitable Trust
The Headley Trust
The Henley Educational Charity
The Hinrichsen Foundation
The Holst Foundation
The Geoffrey C Hughes
  Charitable Trust
The Idlewild Trust
Jerwood Charitable Foundation
The Boris Karloff Charitable
  Foundation
The Kathleen Trust
The Michael and Ilse Katz
  Foundation
The Robert Kiln Charitable
  Trust
The Kohn Foundation
The Leche Trust
The Limbourne Trust
The Linbury Trust
The Charles Lloyd Foundation
The Mackintosh Foundation
The MacRobert Trust
The Manifold Charitable Trust
W M Mann Foundation
Sir George Martin Trust
John Martin's Charity
The Mayfield Valley Arts Trust
The Mercers' Charitable
  Foundation
The Merchants' House of
  Glasgow
Miles Trust for the Putney and
  Roehampton Community
The Millward Charitable Trust
The Peter Moores Foundation
The Morel Charitable Trust
The Northwood Charitable
  Trust
The Oakdale Trust
The Ouseley Trust
The Pallant Charitable Trust
The Performing Right Society
  Foundation
The Bernard Piggott Trust
Mr and Mrs J A Pye's
  Charitable Settlement

The R V W Trust
The Radcliffe Trust
The Rhondda Cynon Taff
  Welsh Church Acts Fund
The Rowlands Trust
The Tillett Trust
Miss S M Tutton Charitable
  Trust
The Whitaker Charitable Trust
The Williams Charitable Trust
Youth Music

■ Music

Angus Allnatt Charitable
  Foundation
The Hervey Benham Charitable
  Trust
The Britten-Pears Foundation
The Rosemary Bugden
  Charitable Trust
The Cross Trust
The Deakin Charitable Trust
The Delius Trust
Dunard Fund
Esmée Fairbairn Foundation
The Family Rich Charities Trust
The John Feeney Charitable
  Bequest
Gerald Finzi Charitable Trust
The Sir John Fisher Foundation
The Joyce Fletcher Charitable
  Trust
The Hugh Fraser Foundation
The Freshgate Trust
  Foundation
The Gatsby Charitable
  Foundation
The Harding Trust
The Harris Charitable Trust
The Hinrichsen Foundation
The Holst Foundation
The Kathleen Trust
The Michael and Ilse Katz
  Foundation
The Robert Kiln Charitable
  Trust
The Kohn Foundation
The Leche Trust
The Charles Lloyd Foundation
The Mackintosh Foundation
The MacRobert Trust
The Manifold Charitable Trust
W M Mann Foundation
Sir George Martin Trust
John Martin's Charity
The Mayfield Valley Arts Trust
The Peter Moores Foundation
The Oakdale Trust
The Ouseley Trust
The Pallant Charitable Trust
The Performing Right Society
  Foundation
The R V W Trust
The Radcliffe Trust
The Rhondda Cynon Taff
  Welsh Church Acts Fund

The Rowlands Trust
The Tillett Trust
Miss S M Tutton Charitable
  Trust
The Whitaker Charitable Trust
Youth Music

■ Dance

The Girdlers' Company
  Charitable Trust

■ Theatre

The Eric Anker-Petersen
  Charity
The Cross Trust
The Equity Trust Fund
Esmée Fairbairn Foundation
The Sir John Fisher Foundation
The Gatsby Charitable
  Foundation
The Gibbs Charitable Trust
The Grand Order of Water
  Rats' Charities Fund
The Headley Trust
The Leche Trust
The Mackintosh Foundation
The Peter Moores Foundation
The Morel Charitable Trust
The Bernard Piggott Trust
The Williams Charitable Trust

■ Visual arts

The Laura Ashley Foundation
Colwinston Charitable Trust
The Duis Charitable Trust
Dunard Fund
The Elephant Trust
The Joyce Fletcher Charitable
  Trust
The Gordon Fraser Charitable
  Trust
Jerwood Charitable Foundation
John Martin's Charity
The Mercers' Charitable
  Foundation
The Henry Moore Foundation
The Peter Moores Foundation
The National Art Collections
  Fund
The Max Reinhardt Charitable
  Trust
Robert and Felicity Waley-
  Cohen Charitable Trust

■ Design

The Mercers' Charitable
  Foundation

■ Fine arts

The Mercers' Charitable
  Foundation

The Henry Moore Foundation
The Peter Moores Foundation
The National Art Collections
Fund
The Max Reinhardt Charitable
Trust
Robert and Felicity Waley-
Cohen Charitable Trust

■ **Public art/sculpture**

The Henry Moore Foundation

Heritage and the built environment

The Alice Trust
Allchurches Trust Ltd
The Architectural Heritage
Fund
The Ove Arup Foundation
A J H Ashby Will Trust
The Association of Friends of
Essex Churches
The Baird Trust
The Barcapel Foundation
The Bedfordshire and
Hertfordshire Historic
Churches Trust
The Bellahouston Bequest
Fund
The Hervey Benham Charitable
Trust
Birmingham International
Airport Community Trust
T B H Brunner's Charitable
Settlement
The Buckinghamshire Historic
Churches Trust
The Arnold Burton 1998
Charitable Trust
The Cambridgeshire Historic
Churches Trust
The Carpenters' Company
Charitable Trust
Stephen Clark 1957
Charitable Trust
The Francis Coales Charitable
Foundation
Colyer-Fergusson Charitable
Trust
Country Houses Foundation
The Cromarty Trust
The Helen and Geoffrey De
Freitas Charitable Trust
The Derbyshire Churches and
Chapels Preservation Trust
The Devon Historic Churches
Trust
The Dorset Historic Churches
Trust
The Drapers' Charitable Fund
The Dulverton Trust
The Houghton Dunn Charitable
Trust

The Gilbert and Eileen Edgar
Foundation
The Edinburgh Trust, No 2
Account
The Ellis Campbell Foundation
The Elmgrant Trust
The Essex Heritage Trust
The Alan Evans Memorial Trust
Esmée Fairbairn Foundation
The Fairway Trust
The February Foundation
Fife Council/Common Good
Funds and Trusts
Fisherbeck Charitable Trust
The Fishmongers' Company's
Charitable Trust
Marc Fitch Fund
The Jill Franklin Trust
The Freshgate Trust
Foundation
The Friends of Kent Churches
The Frognal Trust
The Galanthus Trust
The Gannochy Trust
The Samuel Gardner Memorial
Trust
Gatwick Airport Community
Trust
J Paul Getty Jr Charitable Trust
The Girdlers' Company
Charitable Trust
The Glass-House Trust
The Gloucestershire Historic
Churches Trust
The Goldsmiths' Company
Charity
The Golsoncott Foundation
The Gosling Foundation
Limited
The Greys Charitable Trust
The Grocers' Charity
The Hadrian Trust
The Hampshire and Islands
Historic Churches Trust
The W A Handley Charitable
Trust
The Kenneth Hargreaves
Charitable Trust
The Dorothy Hay-Bolton
Charitable Trust
The Charles Hayward
Foundation
The Headley Trust
The Hemby Trust
The Herefordshire Historic
Churches Trust
The Heritage of London Trust
Ltd
The Holbeck Charitable Trust
The Idlewild Trust
The Iliffe Family Charitable
Trust
The Inland Waterways
Association
The Johnnie Johnson Trust
The LankellyChase Foundation
Laslett's (Hinton) Charity

The Raymond and Blanche
Lawson Charitable Trust
The Leche Trust
Leeds Building Society
Charitable Foundation
Leicestershire Historic
Churches Trust
The Linbury Trust
The Lincolnshire Old Churches
Trust
The Charles Lloyd Foundation
Manchester Airport Community
Trust Fund
The Manifold Charitable Trust
Market Harborough and The
Bowdens Charity
The Marsh Christian Trust
Marshall's Charity
The Anthony and Elizabeth
Mellows Charitable
Settlement
The Mercers' Charitable
Foundation
The Metropolitan Drinking
Fountain and Cattle Trough
Association
Gerald Micklem Charitable
Trust
Miles Trust for the Putney and
Roehampton Community
The Esmé Mitchell Trust
Monmouthshire County Council
Welsh Church Act Fund
The Monument Trust
The Peter Moores Foundation
The National Churches Trust
The Normanby Charitable Trust
The Northern Rock Foundation
The Northumbria Historic
Churches Trust
The Norwich Historic Churches
Trust Ltd
The Nottinghamshire Historic
Churches Trust
The Owen Family Trust
The James Pantyfedwen
Foundation
Miss M E Swinton Paterson's
Charitable Trust
The Jack Patston Charitable
Trust
The Pilgrim Trust
The Prince's Charities
Foundation
The Rhondda Cynon Taff
Welsh Church Acts Fund
The Robertson Trust
The Rock Solid Trust
Mrs L D Rope Third Charitable
Settlement
The Rothschild Foundation
The Roughley Charitable Trust
Royal Docks Trust (London)
The J S and E C Rymer
Charitable Trust
The Peter Samuel Charitable
Trust

The Frieda Scott Charitable
    Trust
The Shetland Charitable Trust
The Stanley Smith UK
    Horticultural Trust
Friends of Somerset Churches
    and Chapels
St Andrew's Conservation
    Trust
Stevenson Family's Charitable
    Trust
Peter Stormonth Darling
    Charitable Trust
The Suffolk Historic Churches
    Trust
The Surrey Historic Buildings
    Trust Ltd
The Sussex Historic Churches
    Trust
The Connie and Albert Taylor
    Charitable Trust
Vale of Glamorgan – Welsh
    Church Fund
Veneziana Fund
The John Warren Foundation
The Waterways Trust
Welsh Church Fund Dyfed
    area (Carmarthenshire,
    Ceredigion and
    Pembrokeshire)
The Colonel W H Whitbread
    Charitable Trust
The Wolfson Foundation
The Worcestershire and
    Dudley Historic Churches
    Trust
The Yorkshire Dales
    Millennium Trust
The Yorkshire Historic
    Churches Trust
The Marjorie and Arnold Ziff
    Charitable Foundation

....

■ **Arts and the
environment**

The Carpenters' Company
    Charitable Trust
The Samuel Gardner Memorial
    Trust
J Paul Getty Jr Charitable Trust
The Glass-House Trust
The Headley Trust
The Heritage of London Trust
    Ltd
Leeds Building Society
    Charitable Foundation
Manchester Airport Community
    Trust Fund
The Metropolitan Drinking
    Fountain and Cattle Trough
    Association
Monmouthshire County Council
    Welsh Church Act Fund
The Monument Trust
The Shetland Charitable Trust

The Stanley Smith UK
    Horticultural Trust
The Marjorie and Arnold Ziff
    Charitable Foundation

■ **Architecture**

The Glass-House Trust
The Heritage of London Trust
    Ltd
Monmouthshire County Council
    Welsh Church Act Fund

■ **Landscape**

The Samuel Gardner Memorial
    Trust
J Paul Getty Jr Charitable Trust
Manchester Airport Community
    Trust Fund
The Metropolitan Drinking
    Fountain and Cattle Trough
    Association
The Stanley Smith UK
    Horticultural Trust
The Marjorie and Arnold Ziff
    Charitable Foundation

....

■ **Heritage**

The Architectural Heritage
    Fund
A J H Ashby Will Trust
The Hervey Benham Charitable
    Trust
Birmingham International
    Airport Community Trust
T B H Brunner's Charitable
    Settlement
The Arnold Burton 1998
    Charitable Trust
The Carpenters' Company
    Charitable Trust
The Francis Coales Charitable
    Foundation
The Helen and Geoffrey De
    Freitas Charitable Trust
The Houghton Dunn Charitable
    Trust
The Gilbert and Eileen Edgar
    Foundation
The Essex Heritage Trust
Esmée Fairbairn Foundation
The Fairway Trust
The Fishmongers' Company's
    Charitable Trust
Marc Fitch Fund
The Freshgate Trust
    Foundation
The Frognal Trust
The Samuel Gardner Memorial
    Trust
J Paul Getty Jr Charitable Trust
The Goldsmiths' Company
    Charity

The Gosling Foundation
    Limited
The Grocers' Charity
The W A Handley Charitable
    Trust
The Headley Trust
The Heritage of London Trust
    Ltd
Leeds Building Society
    Charitable Foundation
The Linbury Trust
The Manifold Charitable Trust
Market Harborough and The
    Bowdens Charity
The Marsh Christian Trust
The Anthony and Elizabeth
    Mellows Charitable
    Settlement
The Mercers' Charitable
    Foundation
Gerald Micklem Charitable
    Trust
Miles Trust for the Putney and
    Roehampton Community
The Esmé Mitchell Trust
Monmouthshire County Council
    Welsh Church Act Fund
The Monument Trust
The Peter Moores Foundation
The Normanby Charitable Trust
The Northern Rock Foundation
The Owen Family Trust
Miss M E Swinton Paterson's
    Charitable Trust
The Pilgrim Trust
The Robertson Trust
Mrs L D Rope Third Charitable
    Settlement
The Rothschild Foundation
The Peter Samuel Charitable
    Trust
St Andrew's Conservation
    Trust
Peter Stormonth Darling
    Charitable Trust
The Surrey Historic Buildings
    Trust Ltd
The Connie and Albert Taylor
    Charitable Trust
Veneziana Fund
The Wolfson Foundation

....

■ **Maintenance and
preservation of
buildings**

The Alice Trust
Allchurches Trust Ltd
The Architectural Heritage
    Fund
The Association of Friends of
    Essex Churches
The Baird Trust
The Bedfordshire and
    Hertfordshire Historic
    Churches Trust

The Bellahouston Bequest
Fund

The Buckinghamshire Historic
Churches Trust

The Cambridgeshire Historic
Churches Trust

The Carpenters' Company
Charitable Trust

Stephen Clark 1957
Charitable Trust

The Francis Coales Charitable
Foundation

Colyer-Fergusson Charitable
Trust

The Cromarty Trust

The Derbyshire Churches and
Chapels Preservation Trust

The Devon Historic Churches
Trust

The Dorset Historic Churches
Trust

The Dulverton Trust

The Edinburgh Trust, No 2
Account

The Ellis Campbell Foundation

The Essex Heritage Trust

The Alan Evans Memorial Trust

Esmée Fairbairn Foundation

The Fairway Trust

Fife Council/Common Good
Funds and Trusts

The Fishmongers' Company's
Charitable Trust

The Jill Franklin Trust

The Friends of Kent Churches

The Girdlers' Company
Charitable Trust

The Gloucestershire Historic
Churches Trust

The Greys Charitable Trust

The Grocers' Charity

The Hadrian Trust

The Hampshire and Islands
Historic Churches Trust

The Dorothy Hay-Bolton
Charitable Trust

The Headley Trust

The Hemby Trust

The Herefordshire Historic
Churches Trust

The Heritage of London Trust
Ltd

The Idlewild Trust

The LankellyChase Foundation

Laslett's (Hinton) Charity

The Raymond and Blanche
Lawson Charitable Trust

The Leche Trust

Leicestershire Historic
Churches Trust

The Lincolnshire Old Churches
Trust

The Charles Lloyd Foundation

Manchester Airport Community
Trust Fund

The Manifold Charitable Trust

Marshall's Charity

Miles Trust for the Putney and
Roehampton Community

Monmouthshire County Council
Welsh Church Act Fund

The Monument Trust

The National Churches Trust

The Northumbria Historic
Churches Trust

The Norwich Historic Churches
Trust Ltd

The Nottinghamshire Historic
Churches Trust

The James Pantyfedwen
Foundation

The Jack Patston Charitable
Trust

The Pilgrim Trust

The Prince's Charities
Foundation

The Rhondda Cynon Taff
Welsh Church Acts Fund

The Rock Solid Trust

Royal Docks Trust (London)

The Frieda Scott Charitable
Trust

Friends of Somerset Churches
and Chapels

The Suffolk Historic Churches
Trust

The Surrey Historic Buildings
Trust Ltd

The Sussex Historic Churches
Trust

The Connie and Albert Taylor
Charitable Trust

Vale of Glamorgan – Welsh
Church Fund

The John Warren Foundation

Welsh Church Fund Dyfed
area (Carmarthenshire,
Ceredigion and
Pembrokeshire)

The Worcestershire and
Dudley Historic Churches
Trust

The Yorkshire Historic
Churches Trust

■ Religious buildings

Allchurches Trust Ltd

The Architectural Heritage
Fund

The Association of Friends of
Essex Churches

The Bedfordshire and
Hertfordshire Historic
Churches Trust

The Bellahouston Bequest
Fund

The Buckinghamshire Historic
Churches Trust

The Cambridgeshire Historic
Churches Trust

Stephen Clark 1957
Charitable Trust

The Francis Coales Charitable
Foundation

Colyer-Fergusson Charitable
Trust

The Derbyshire Churches and
Chapels Preservation Trust

The Devon Historic Churches
Trust

The Dorset Historic Churches
Trust

The Alan Evans Memorial Trust

The Fishmongers' Company's
Charitable Trust

The Jill Franklin Trust

The Friends of Kent Churches

The Girdlers' Company
Charitable Trust

The Gloucestershire Historic
Churches Trust

The Grocers' Charity

The Hadrian Trust

The Hampshire and Islands
Historic Churches Trust

The Dorothy Hay-Bolton
Charitable Trust

The Headley Trust

The Hemby Trust

The Herefordshire Historic
Churches Trust

The Heritage of London Trust
Ltd

The LankellyChase Foundation

Laslett's (Hinton) Charity

The Leche Trust

Leicestershire Historic
Churches Trust

The Lincolnshire Old Churches
Trust

The Charles Lloyd Foundation

The Manifold Charitable Trust

Marshall's Charity

Miles Trust for the Putney and
Roehampton Community

Monmouthshire County Council
Welsh Church Act Fund

The Monument Trust

The National Churches Trust

The Northumbria Historic
Churches Trust

The Norwich Historic Churches
Trust Ltd

The Nottinghamshire Historic
Churches Trust

The James Pantyfedwen
Foundation

The Jack Patston Charitable
Trust

The Pilgrim Trust

The Prince's Charities
Foundation

The Rhondda Cynon Taff
Welsh Church Acts Fund

The Rock Solid Trust

The Frieda Scott Charitable
Trust

Friends of Somerset Churches
and Chapels

The Suffolk Historic Churches
  Trust
The Sussex Historic Churches
  Trust
Vale of Glamorgan – Welsh
  Church Fund
The John Warren Foundation
Welsh Church Fund Dyfed
  area (Carmarthenshire,
  Ceredigion and
  Pembrokeshire)
The Worcestershire and
  Dudley Historic Churches
  Trust
The Yorkshire Historic
  Churches Trust

■ Restoration and maintenance of inland waterways

The Carpenters' Company
  Charitable Trust
The Inland Waterways
  Association
Leeds Building Society
  Charitable Foundation
Gerald Micklem Charitable
  Trust
The Waterways Trust

■ Built environment – education and research

The Ove Arup Foundation
The Carpenters' Company
  Charitable Trust
The Gannochy Trust
Leeds Building Society
  Charitable Foundation

Humanities

The Aurelius Charitable Trust
British Institute at Ankara
The Barrow Cadbury Trust and
  the Barrow Cadbury Fund
The Cemlyn-Jones Trust
The Francis Coales Charitable
  Foundation
The Denise Cohen Charitable
  Trust
The Cromarty Trust
The Daiwa Anglo-Japanese
  Foundation
The Edinburgh Trust, No 2
  Account
The Elmgrant Trust
Marc Fitch Fund
The Golsoncott Foundation
The Great Britain Sasakawa
  Foundation
The Gulbenkian Foundation

The Inlight Trust
The Robert Kiln Charitable
  Trust
The Neil Kreitman Foundation
The Lawson Beckman
  Charitable Trust
Leeds Building Society
  Charitable Foundation
The Mount Everest Foundation
The Kitty and Daniel Nabarro
  Charitable Trust
The Eleni Nakou Foundation
Peltz Trust
Polden-Puckham Charitable
  Foundation
The Sir Cliff Richard Charitable
  Trust
The Roman Research Trust
Mrs L D Rope Third Charitable
  Settlement
The Rothley Trust
The Joseph Rowntree
  Charitable Trust
The Scouloudi Foundation
The Tinsley Foundation
The Westcroft Trust
The W Wing Yip and Brothers
  Foundation
The York Children's Trust

■ Archaeology

Marc Fitch Fund
The Robert Kiln Charitable
  Trust
The Roman Research Trust

■ History

The Cemlyn-Jones Trust
The Francis Coales Charitable
  Foundation
The Cromarty Trust
Marc Fitch Fund
The Neil Kreitman Foundation
The Roman Research Trust
The Scouloudi Foundation

■ International understanding

The Barrow Cadbury Trust and
  the Barrow Cadbury Fund
The Daiwa Anglo-Japanese
  Foundation
The Edinburgh Trust, No 2
  Account
The Great Britain Sasakawa
  Foundation
The Gulbenkian Foundation
The Mount Everest Foundation
The Kitty and Daniel Nabarro
  Charitable Trust
The Eleni Nakou Foundation
The Rothley Trust

The Tinsley Foundation
The Westcroft Trust
The W Wing Yip and Brothers
  Foundation
The York Children's Trust

■ Philosophy and ethics

The Inlight Trust
Polden-Puckham Charitable
  Foundation
The Sir Cliff Richard Charitable
  Trust
Mrs L D Rope Third Charitable
  Settlement
The Joseph Rowntree
  Charitable Trust

Media and communications

The Eric Anker-Petersen
  Charity
The Follett Trust
Paul Hamlyn Foundation
The David Lean Foundation
Leeds Building Society
  Charitable Foundation

Recreation and sport

Access Sport
Angus Allnatt Charitable
  Foundation
Arsenal Charitable Trust
The John Beckwith Charitable
  Trust
The Bedford Charity (The
  Harpur Trust)
The Bellahouston Bequest
  Fund
The Big Lottery Fund
Birmingham International
  Airport Community Trust
BOOST Charitable Trust
The Carnegie Dunfermline
  Trust
Carter's Educational
  Foundation
The Chipping Sodbury Town
  Lands Charity
The Robert Clutterbuck
  Charitable Trust
The Bernard Coleman
  Charitable Trust
The Congleton Inclosure Trust
The D J H Currie Memorial
  Trust
The Hamilton Davies Trust
The Gilbert and Eileen Edgar
  Foundation

The English Schools' Football Association

Samuel William Farmer's Trust

The February Foundation

The John Feeney Charitable Bequest

Fife Council/Common Good Funds and Trusts

The Football Association National Sports Centre Trust

The Football Association Youth Trust

The Football Foundation

The Joseph Strong Frazer Trust

The Thomas Freke and Lady Norton Charity

Gatwick Airport Community Trust

The Girdlers' Company Charitable Trust

The Granada Foundation

The Grange Farm Centre Trust

The J G Graves Charitable Trust

The Hale Trust

Robert Hall Charity

William Harding's Charity

The Kenneth Hargreaves Charitable Trust

The Peter Harrison Foundation

The Dorothy Hay-Bolton Charitable Trust

The Henley Educational Charity

The Heritage of London Trust Ltd

Huntingdon Freemen's Charity

Lancashire Environmental Fund

Leeds Building Society Charitable Foundation

The Joseph Levy Charitable Foundation

The Lister Charitable Trust

The George John and Sheilah Livanos Charitable Trust

The London Marathon Charitable Trust

The Lord's Taverners

Lady Lumley's Educational Foundation

John Lyon's Charity

Manchester Airport Community Trust Fund

The Merchant Venturers' Charity

Gerald Micklem Charitable Trust

Millennium Stadium Charitable Trust

The Peter Minet Trust

Monmouthshire County Council Welsh Church Act Fund

The Morel Charitable Trust

The Stanley Morrison Charitable Trust

The Mugdock Children's Trust

The Northern Rock Foundation

The Norwich Church of England Young Men's Society

The Pedmore Sporting Club Trust Fund

PSA Peugeot Citroen Charity Trust

The Puri Foundation

Mr and Mrs J A Pye's Charitable Settlement

The Richmond Parish Lands Charity

The Alex Roberts-Miller Foundation

The Robertson Trust

The Rowing Foundation

Royal Docks Trust (London)

The Saddlers' Company Charitable Fund

Scottish Coal Industry Special Welfare Fund

The Searle Charitable Trust

The Shetland Charitable Trust

The Shipwrights' Company Charitable Fund

The Martin Smith Foundation

The Stewards' Charitable Trust

Peter Stormonth Darling Charitable Trust

The Connie and Albert Taylor Charitable Trust

The Howard Watson Symington Memorial Charity

The Winton Charitable Foundation

Miss E B Wrightson's Charitable Settlement

The York Children's Trust

■ Parks and open spaces

The John Feeney Charitable Bequest

The J G Graves Charitable Trust

The Heritage of London Trust Ltd

The Merchant Venturers' Charity

■ Recreation facilities

The Carnegie Dunfermline Trust

Carter's Educational Foundation

The Chipping Sodbury Town Lands Charity

Samuel William Farmer's Trust

The Football Association National Sports Centre Trust

The Thomas Freke and Lady Norton Charity

The Granada Foundation

The Hale Trust

William Harding's Charity

The Peter Harrison Foundation

Lancashire Environmental Fund

The Joseph Levy Charitable Foundation

Lady Lumley's Educational Foundation

The Northern Rock Foundation

■ Sport for people with a disability

BOOST Charitable Trust

The Football Association National Sports Centre Trust

The Kenneth Hargreaves Charitable Trust

The Peter Harrison Foundation

The Dorothy Hay-Bolton Charitable Trust

The Henley Educational Charity

The Joseph Levy Charitable Foundation

The London Marathon Charitable Trust

The Lord's Taverners

Gerald Micklem Charitable Trust

Mr and Mrs J A Pye's Charitable Settlement

The Rowing Foundation

■ Sports

Access Sport

Angus Allnatt Charitable Foundation

The John Beckwith Charitable Trust

BOOST Charitable Trust

The D J H Currie Memorial Trust

The English Schools' Football Association

The Football Association National Sports Centre Trust

The Football Association Youth Trust

The Football Foundation

The Peter Harrison Foundation

The Henley Educational Charity

The Joseph Levy Charitable Foundation

The George John and Sheilah Livanos Charitable Trust

The London Marathon Charitable Trust

The Lord's Taverners

Millennium Stadium Charitable
    Trust
The Peter Minet Trust
The Richmond Parish Lands
    Charity
The Alex Roberts-Miller
    Foundation
The Rowing Foundation
The Saddlers' Company
    Charitable Fund
The Searle Charitable Trust
The Shipwrights' Company
    Charitable Fund
The Martin Smith Foundation
The Stewards' Charitable Trust
Peter Stormonth Darling
    Charitable Trust
The York Children's Trust

Development, housing and employment

The ACT Foundation
The AIM Foundation
The Ajahma Charitable Trust
The Ashden Trust
The Laura Ashley Foundation
The BAA Communities Trust
The Balmore Trust
The Big Lottery Fund
Birmingham International
    Airport Community Trust
The Boots Charitable Trust
The Oliver Borthwick Memorial
    Trust
The Boshier-Hinton Foundation
R S Brownless Charitable
    Trust
The Buckinghamshire
    Foundation
Henry T and Lucy B Cadbury
    Charitable Trust
The Cadbury Foundation
The Barrow Cadbury Trust and
    the Barrow Cadbury Fund
CAFOD
Calypso Browning Trust
Capital Community Foundation
The Chelsea Building Society
    Charitable Foundation
The Coalfields Regeneration
    Trust
The Community Foundation for
    Northern Ireland
The Consolidated Charities for
    the Infirm Merchant
    Taylors' Company
The Cooks Charity
Cumbria Community
    Foundation
Baron Davenport's Charity
The Helen and Geoffrey De
    Freitas Charitable Trust
The Digbeth Trust
The Drapers' Charitable Fund
The Duis Charitable Trust
The Dulverton Trust
The Dyers' Company
    Charitable Trust
The Emmandjay Charitable
    Trust
Esmée Fairbairn Foundation
Allan and Nesta Ferguson
    Charitable Settlement
The Sir John Fisher Foundation
The Football Association
    National Sports Centre
    Trust
The Football Foundation
The Oliver Ford Charitable
    Trust
The Donald Forrester Trust
Friends Provident Charitable
    Foundation

Worshipful Company of
    Furniture Makers Charitable
    Fund
The Gatsby Charitable
    Foundation
Gatwick Airport Community
    Trust
Jacqueline and Michael Gee
    Charitable Trust
J Paul Getty Jr Charitable Trust
The Girdlers' Company
    Charitable Trust
The Glass-House Trust
Gloucestershire Community
    Foundation
The Grocers' Charity
The Gulbenkian Foundation
The Hadfield Trust
Hampton Fuel Allotment
    Charity
The W A Handley Charitable
    Trust
The Harbour Foundation
The Haymills Charitable Trust
The Charles Hayward
    Foundation
Help the Homeless
The Hemby Trust
Matthew Hodder Charitable
    Trust
The Horne Trust
The Worshipful Company of
    Horners' Charitable Trusts
The Hyde Charitable Trust –
    Youth Plus
Impetus Trust
The Irish Youth Foundation
    (UK) Ltd (incorporating The
    Lawlor Foundation)
Isle of Dogs Community
    Foundation
Jusaca Charitable Trust
The Peter Kershaw Trust
The Mary Kinross Charitable
    Trust
LandAid Charitable Trust
The Allen Lane Foundation
Laslett's (Hinton) Charity
The Leathersellers' Company
    Charitable Fund
Leeds Building Society
    Charitable Foundation
Liverpool Sailors' Home Trust
Lloyds TSB Foundation for
    Northern Ireland
The Lotus Foundation
C F Lunoe Trust Fund
John Lyon's Charity
Magdalen Hospital Trust
The Charlotte Marshall
    Charitable Trust
The Mathew Trust
The Merchant Venturers'
    Charity
The Merchants' House of
    Glasgow

Community Foundation for
  Merseyside
The Methodist Relief and
  Development Fund
Miles Trust for the Putney and
  Roehampton Community
The Millfield House Foundation
Monmouthshire County Council
  Welsh Church Act Fund
The Monument Trust
John Moores Foundation
The J P Morgan Foundations
The Kitty and Daniel Nabarro
  Charitable Trust
The Nadezhda Charitable Trust
The Nationwide Foundation
The Worshipful Company of
  Needlemakers' Charitable
  Fund
The Noon Foundation
The Norda Trust
North West London Community
  Foundation
The Northern Rock Foundation
The Norton Foundation
The Nottinghamshire Miners'
  Welfare Trust Fund
Novi Most International
The Oldham Foundation
The Phillips Charitable Trust
The Pilgrim Trust
The Plaisterers' Company
  Charitable Trust
The Puebla Charitable Trust
Mr and Mrs J A Pye's
  Charitable Settlement
The Sigrid Rausing Trust
The Rayne Foundation
The Robertson Trust
The Rowan Charitable Trust
The Joseph Rowntree
  Charitable Trust
Royal Docks Trust (London)
The Saddlers' Company
  Charitable Fund
Scottish Churches' Community
  Trust
The Scottish Community
  Foundation
The Scottish International
  Education Trust
The Searle Charitable Trust
The Shanti Charitable Trust
The Sheldon Trust
Dr Richard Solomon's
  Charitable Trust
The Stokenchurch Educational
  Charity
Sutton Coldfield Municipal
  Charities
The Hugh and Ruby Sykes
  Charitable Trust
Ulster Garden Villages Ltd
The Nigel Vinson Charitable
  Trust
The Scurrah Wainwright Charity
Wakeham Trust

Wales Council for Voluntary
  Action
War on Want
The Waterloo Foundation
The Wixamtree Trust
The Wood Family Trust
Woodlands Trust

Community and economic development

The AIM Foundation
The Ashden Trust
The Laura Ashley Foundation
The BAA Communities Trust
The Balmore Trust
The Big Lottery Fund
Birmingham International
  Airport Community Trust
The Boots Charitable Trust
The Buckinghamshire
  Foundation
The Cadbury Foundation
The Barrow Cadbury Trust and
  the Barrow Cadbury Fund
Capital Community Foundation
The Coalfields Regeneration
  Trust
The Community Foundation for
  Northern Ireland
Cumbria Community
  Foundation
The Helen and Geoffrey De
  Freitas Charitable Trust
The Digbeth Trust
The Dulverton Trust
Esmée Fairbairn Foundation
Allan and Nesta Ferguson
  Charitable Settlement
The Football Association
  National Sports Centre
  Trust
The Football Foundation
Friends Provident Charitable
  Foundation
The Gatsby Charitable
  Foundation
Gatwick Airport Community
  Trust
J Paul Getty Jr Charitable Trust
The Glass-House Trust
Gloucestershire Community
  Foundation
The Grocers' Charity
The Gulbenkian Foundation
The Hadfield Trust
The Harbour Foundation
The Haymills Charitable Trust
The Hyde Charitable Trust –
  Youth Plus
Isle of Dogs Community
  Foundation
The Mary Kinross Charitable
  Trust

LandAid Charitable Trust
The Allen Lane Foundation
Leeds Building Society
  Charitable Foundation
The Lotus Foundation
The Mathew Trust
The Merchant Venturers'
  Charity
Community Foundation for
  Merseyside
The Methodist Relief and
  Development Fund
Miles Trust for the Putney and
  Roehampton Community
The Millfield House Foundation
Monmouthshire County Council
  Welsh Church Act Fund
John Moores Foundation
The J P Morgan Foundations
The Kitty and Daniel Nabarro
  Charitable Trust
The Noon Foundation
The Norda Trust
North West London Community
  Foundation
The Northern Rock Foundation
Novi Most International
The Puebla Charitable Trust
The Sigrid Rausing Trust
The Robertson Trust
The Rowan Charitable Trust
The Joseph Rowntree
  Charitable Trust
Royal Docks Trust (London)
Scottish Churches' Community
  Trust
The Scottish Community
  Foundation
The Scottish International
  Education Trust
The Shanti Charitable Trust
The Sheldon Trust
Dr Richard Solomon's
  Charitable Trust
The Stokenchurch Educational
  Charity
Sutton Coldfield Municipal
  Charities
The Hugh and Ruby Sykes
  Charitable Trust
The Scurrah Wainwright Charity
Wakeham Trust
Wales Council for Voluntary
  Action
The Wixamtree Trust
Woodlands Trust

Housing

The Oliver Borthwick Memorial
  Trust
Henry T and Lucy B Cadbury
  Charitable Trust
Calypso Browning Trust
The Chelsea Building Society
  Charitable Foundation

The Consolidated Charities for the Infirm Merchant Taylors' Company
Baron Davenport's Charity
The Duis Charitable Trust
The Emmandjay Charitable Trust
The Oliver Ford Charitable Trust
The Girdlers' Company Charitable Trust
The Glass-House Trust
Hampton Fuel Allotment Charity
The W A Handley Charitable Trust
The Charles Hayward Foundation
Help the Homeless
The Hemby Trust
The Horne Trust
The Hyde Charitable Trust – Youth Plus
The Irish Youth Foundation (UK) Ltd (incorporating The Lawlor Foundation)
Jusaca Charitable Trust
The Peter Kershaw Trust
LandAid Charitable Trust
Laslett's (Hinton) Charity
Leeds Building Society Charitable Foundation
Lloyds TSB Foundation for Northern Ireland
John Lyon's Charity
Magdalen Hospital Trust
The Charlotte Marshall Charitable Trust
The Monument Trust
The Nadezhda Charitable Trust
The Nationwide Foundation
The Norton Foundation
The Oldham Foundation
The Pilgrim Trust
Mr and Mrs J A Pye's Charitable Settlement
The Rayne Foundation
The Rowan Charitable Trust
Ulster Garden Villages Ltd
Woodlands Trust

Specific industries

The Cooks Charity
Cumbria Community Foundation
The Drapers' Charitable Fund
The Dyers' Company Charitable Trust
The Sir John Fisher Foundation
The Oliver Ford Charitable Trust
Worshipful Company of Furniture Makers Charitable Fund

The W A Handley Charitable Trust
Matthew Hodder Charitable Trust
The Worshipful Company of Horners' Charitable Trusts
The Leathersellers' Company Charitable Fund
Liverpool Sailors' Home Trust
C F Lunoe Trust Fund
The Merchants' House of Glasgow
The Worshipful Company of Needlemakers' Charitable Fund
The Phillips Charitable Trust
The Plaisterers' Company Charitable Trust
The Saddlers' Company Charitable Fund
The Searle Charitable Trust

Education and training

The 1989 Willan Charitable Trust
The Aberdeen Endowments Trust
The Aberdeenshire Educational Trust Scheme
The Acacia Charitable Trust
AF Trust Company
Aldgate and All Hallows' Barking Exhibition Foundation
All Saints Educational Trust
The Alliance Family Foundation
Angus Allnatt Charitable Foundation
The Pat Allsop Charitable Trust
Almondsbury Charity
Ambika Paul Foundation
The Ammco Trust
Viscount Amory's Charitable Trust
The AMW Charitable Trust
Anglo American Group Foundation
Anguish's Educational Foundation
The Apax Foundation
Ambrose and Ann Appelbe Trust
The John Armitage Charitable Trust
The Armourers' and Brasiers' Gauntlet Trust
The Arts Council of Wales
A J H Ashby Will Trust
The Norman C Ashton Foundation
The Association of Colleges Charitable Trust
The Astor of Hever Trust
The Lord Austin Trust
The BAA Communities Trust
The Baily Thomas Charitable Fund
The Roy and Pixie Baker Charitable Trust
The Balcombe Charitable Trust
The Balint Family Charitable Trusts
The Bamford Charitable Foundation
The Banbury Charities
The Charity of William Barrow
The Beaufort House Trust Limited
The Becketts and Sargeants Educational Foundation
The Bedford Charity (The Harpur Trust)
The Beit Trust
The Bellahouston Bequest Fund
The Bestway Foundation
BibleLands

The Big Lottery Fund
The Blanchminster Trust
Blatchington Court Trust
The Nicholas Boas Charitable
Trust
The Boltons Trust
The Booth Charities
The Boots Charitable Trust
The Boshier-Hinton Foundation
The Harry Bottom Charitable
Trust
The Bowland Charitable Trust
The Bristol Charities
John Bristow and Thomas
Mason Trust
Britannia Foundation
British Record Industry Trust
The J and M Britton Charitable
Trust
The Rory and Elizabeth Brooks
Foundation
The Charles Brotherton Trust
Brushmill Ltd
The Buffini Chao Foundation
The Rosemary Bugden
Charitable Trust
The BUPA Foundation
The Audrey and Stanley Burton
1960 Charitable Trust
The Arnold Burton 1998
Charitable Trust
Edward Cadbury Charitable
Trust
The William A Cadbury
Charitable Trust
The Cadbury Foundation
The Edward and Dorothy
Cadbury Trust
The Campden Charities
The Carlton House Charitable
Trust
The Richard Carne Trust
The Carnegie Trust for the
Universities of Scotland
The Carpenters' Company
Charitable Trust
The Carr-Gregory Trust
The Carron Charitable Trust
Carter's Educational
Foundation
Sir John Cass's Foundation
The Cemlyn-Jones Trust
CfBT Education Trust
The Worshipful Company of
Chartered Accountants
General Charitable Trust
The Cheruby Trust
The Childwick Trust
The Chipping Sodbury Town
Lands Charity
The Chrimes Family Charitable
Trust
The Church Burgesses
Educational Foundation
Church Burgesses Trust
The City Educational Trust
Fund

J A Clark Charitable Trust
The Clore Duffield Foundation
The Coalfields Regeneration
Trust
Coats Foundation Trust
The Denise Cohen Charitable
Trust
The Vivienne and Samuel
Cohen Charitable Trust
The R and S Cohen Fondation
The John S Cohen Foundation
The John and Freda Coleman
Charitable Trust
The Coltstaple Trust
The Comino Foundation
The Company of Tobacco Pipe
Makers' and Tobacco
Blenders' Benevolent Fund
The Douglas Compton James
Charitable Trust
The Congleton Inclosure Trust
The Construction Industry
Trust for Youth
Gordon Cook Foundation
The Lord Cozens-Hardy Trust
The Craignish Trust
The Cromarty Trust
The Harry Crook Foundation
The Cross Trust
The Peter Cruddas Foundation
Cruden Foundation Ltd
The Ronald Cruickshanks'
Foundation
Cullum Family Trust
The Cutler Trust (the
Worshipful Company of
Makers of Playing Cards)
The Daiwa Anglo-Japanese
Foundation
The Hamilton Davies Trust
The Deakin Charitable Trust
The Demigryphon Trust
The Devon Educational Trust
The Dibden Allotments Charity
Dischma Charitable Trust
The Djanogly Foundation
The Dorcas Trust
The Dorema Charitable Trust
Double 'O' Charity Ltd
The Drapers' Charitable Fund
Dromintee Trust
The Duis Charitable Trust
The Dyers' Company
Charitable Trust
The James Dyson Foundation
Earls Colne and Halstead
Educational Charity
East Kent Provincial Charities
Eastern Counties Educational
Trust Limited
The Sir John Eastwood
Foundation
The Gilbert and Eileen Edgar
Foundation
The Edinburgh Trust, No 2
Account

Educational Foundation of
Alderman John Norman
Edupoor Limited
The William Edwards
Educational Charity
The Ellinson Foundation Ltd
The Edith Maud Ellis 1985
Charitable Trust
The Ellis Campbell Foundation
The Elm House Trust
The Elmgrant Trust
EMI Music Sound Foundation
The Emilienne Charitable Trust
The Emmandjay Charitable
Trust
The Worshipful Company of
Engineers Charitable Trust
Fund
The Equitable Charitable Trust
The Eranda Foundation
The Ernest Hecht Charitable
Foundation
The Essex Youth Trust
Euro Charity Trust
The F P Limited Charitable
Trust
Esmée Fairbairn Foundation
The Fairway Trust
Faisaltex Charitable Trust
The Lord Faringdon Charitable
Trust
Samuel William Farmer's Trust
Farthing Trust
The February Foundation
The George Fentham
Birmingham Charity
Allan and Nesta Ferguson
Charitable Settlement
Fife Council/Common Good
Funds and Trusts
Fisherbeck Charitable Trust
The Fishmongers' Company's
Charitable Trust
The Ian Fleming Charitable
Trust
The Joyce Fletcher Charitable
Trust
Florence's Charitable Trust
The Flow Foundation
The Follett Trust
The Football Association
National Sports Centre
Trust
The Football Foundation
Forbesville Limited
Ford Britain Trust
The Donald Forrester Trust
Lord Forte Foundation
Foundation for Management
Education
Four Acre Trust
The Foyle Foundation
The Hugh Fraser Foundation
The Joseph Strong Frazer Trust
The Louis and Valerie
Freedman Charitable
Settlement

The Freemasons' Grand
  Charity
The Thomas Freke and Lady
  Norton Charity
The Freshgate Trust
  Foundation
The Friarsgate Trust
Friends of Muir Group
Friends of Wiznitz Limited
Mejer and Gertrude Miriam
  Frydman Foundation
The Angela Gallagher Memorial
  Fund
The Samuel Gardner Memorial
  Trust
The Garnett Charitable Trust
The Gatsby Charitable
  Foundation
Gatwick Airport Community
  Trust
The Robert Gavron Charitable
  Trust
Jacqueline and Michael Gee
  Charitable Trust
The Girdlers' Company
  Charitable Trust
The Glastonbury Trust Limited
The Golden Bottle Trust
The Goldsmiths' Company
  Charity
The Golsoncott Foundation
Nicholas and Judith
  Goodison's Charitable
  Settlement
The Everard and Mina
  Goodman Charitable
  Foundation
The Granada Foundation
The J G Graves Charitable
  Trust
The Great Britain Sasakawa
  Foundation
The Great Stone Bridge Trust
  of Edenbridge
Greggs Foundation
Grimmitt Trust
The Grocers' Charity
The Guildry Incorporation of
  Perth
The Gulbenkian Foundation
The H and M Charitable Trust
H C D Memorial Fund
The Hadrian Trust
The Hale Trust
Paul Hamlyn Foundation
The Helen Hamlyn Trust
Sue Hammerson's Charitable
  Trust
Hampton Fuel Allotment
  Charity
The Hanlye Charitable Trust
The Kathleen Hannay
  Memorial Charity
The Haramead Trust
Harbo Charities Limited
The Harbour Charitable Trust
The Harbour Foundation

William Harding's Charity
The Harebell Centenary Fund
The Kenneth Hargreaves
  Charitable Trust
The Harris Charity
Haskel Family Foundation
The Maurice Hatter Foundation
The Dorothy Hay-Bolton
  Charitable Trust
The Haymills Charitable Trust
The Headley Trust
May Hearnshaw's Charity
The Heathcoat Trust
The Hedley Foundation
The Michael and Morven Heller
  Charitable Foundation
The Simon Heller Charitable
  Settlement
The Hemby Trust
The Henley Educational Charity
Philip Henman Trust
The Charles Littlewood Hill
  Trust
Hinduja Foundation
The Hintze Family Charitable
  Foundation
The Hitchin Educational
  Foundation
Hobson Charity Limited
Hockerill Educational
  Foundation
Matthew Hodder Charitable
  Trust
The Sir Julian Hodge
  Charitable Trust
The Jane Hodge Foundation
The Holbeck Charitable Trust
John Holford's Charity
The Hope Trust
The Antony Hornby Charitable
  Trust
The Horne Foundation
The Hornsey Parochial
  Charities
The Reta Lila Howard
  Foundation
HSBC Global Education Trust
Hulme Trust Estates
  (Educational)
Human Relief Foundation
The Humanitarian Trust
The Hunter Foundation
Miss Agnes H Hunter's Trust
The Hyde Charitable Trust –
  Youth Plus
The Iliffe Family Charitable
  Trust
The International Bankers
  Charitable Trust (The
  Worshipful Compnay of
  Interntional Bankers)
The Ireland Fund of Great
  Britain
The Irish Youth Foundation
  (UK) Ltd (incorporating The
  Lawlor Foundation)

Isle of Dogs Community
  Foundation
J A R Charitable Trust
The J J Charitable Trust
The Ruth and Lionel Jacobson
  Trust (Second Fund) No 2
John James Bristol Foundation
The Jerusalem Trust
Jerwood Charitable Foundation
The Joanies Trust
The Michael John Trust
The Johnson Wax Ltd
  Charitable Trust
The Joron Charitable Trust
The Ian Karten Charitable
  Trust
The Kass Charitable Trust
The Soli and Leah Kelaty Trust
  Fund
Kelsick's Educational
  Foundation
The KempWelch Charitable
  Trust
E and E Kernkraut Charities
  Limited
The Peter Kershaw Trust
Keswick Hall Charity
The Robert Kiln Charitable
  Trust
Robert Kitchin (Saddlers'
  Company)
The Sir James Knott Trust
The Kohn Foundation
The KPMG Foundation
The Kreditor Charitable Trust
The Kreitman Foundation
The Neil Kreitman Foundation
John Laing Charitable Trust
Maurice and Hilda Laing
  Charitable Trust
The David Laing Foundation
The Lambert Charitable Trust
Duchy of Lancaster Benevolent
  Fund
The Lancaster-Taylor
  Charitable Trust
The Allen Lane Foundation
The Lanvern Foundation
The Lawson Beckman
  Charitable Trust
The Carole and Geoffrey
  Lawson Foundation
The Leathersellers' Company
  Charitable Fund
The Leche Trust
The Arnold Lee Charitable
  Trust
Leeds Building Society
  Charitable Foundation
The Kennedy Leigh Charitable
  Trust
The Leigh Trust
The P Leigh-Bramwell Trust 'E'
The Mark Leonard Trust
The Leverhulme Trade
  Charities Trust
The Leverhulme Trust

Lord Leverhulme's Charitable Trust
The Joseph Levy Charitable Foundation
Lewis Family Charitable Trust
John Lewis Partnership General Community Fund
The Lewis Ward Trust
Lichfield Conduit Lands
The Linbury Trust
The Liverpool One Foundation
Lloyds TSB Foundation for Northern Ireland
Localtrent Ltd
The Loftus Charitable Trust
The Lord's Taverners
The C L Loyd Charitable Trust
The Marie Helen Luen Charitable Trust
Henry Lumley Charitable Trust
Lady Lumley's Educational Foundation
The Ruth and Jack Lunzer Charitable Trust
Lord and Lady Lurgan Trust
John Lyon's Charity
The Sir Jack Lyons Charitable Trust
Malcolm Lyons Foundation
The Madeline Mabey Trust
The Mackintosh Foundation
The MacRobert Trust
Ian Mactaggart Trust
James Madison Trust
Magdalen Hospital Trust
The Magen Charitable Trust
Man Group plc Charitable Trust
The Manifold Charitable Trust
W M Mann Foundation
The Manoukian Charitable Foundation
Maranatha Christian Trust
The Marchday Charitable Fund
The Hilda and Samuel Marks Foundation
The Michael Marsh Charitable Trust
The Marsh Christian Trust
The Charlotte Marshall Charitable Trust
Marshgate Charitable Settlement
Sir George Martin Trust
John Martin's Charity
The Nancie Massey Charitable Trust
The Mathew Trust
The Maxell Educational Trust
The Maxwell Family Foundation
The McKenna Charitable Trust
The Medlock Charitable Trust
Melodor Ltd
Melow Charitable Trust
The Mercers' Charitable Foundation

The Merchant Taylors' Company Charities Fund
The Merchant Venturers' Charity
The Merchants' House of Glasgow
The Methodist Relief and Development Fund
T and J Meyer Family Foundation Limited
Gerald Micklem Charitable Trust
Miles Trust for the Putney and Roehampton Community
The Miller Foundation
The Millichope Foundation
The Edgar Milward Charity
The Peter Minet Trust
Minge's Gift and the Pooled Trusts
The Mirfield Educational Charity
The Moette Charitable Trust
Monmouthshire County Council Welsh Church Act Fund
The Colin Montgomerie Charitable Foundation
John Moores Foundation
The Peter Moores Foundation
The Morel Charitable Trust
The Mr and Mrs J T Morgan Foundation
The J P Morgan Foundations
The Morris Charitable Trust
G M Morrison Charitable Trust
The Stanley Morrison Charitable Trust
Vyoel Moshe Charitable Trust
The Moss Charitable Trust
The Robert and Margaret Moss Charitable Trust
Moto in the Community Trust
J P Moulton Charitable Foundation
The Music Sales Charitable Trust
Muslim Hands
The Mutual Trust Group
The Kitty and Daniel Nabarro Charitable Trust
The Eleni Nakou Foundation
The Nchima Trust
The Worshipful Company of Needlemakers' Charitable Fund
New Court Charitable Trust
The Newcomen Collett Foundation
The Richard Newitt Fund
Alderman Newton's Educational Foundation
The Noon Foundation
The Normanby Charitable Trust
The North British Hotel Trust
The Northampton Municipal Church Charities

The Northumberland Village Homes Trust
The Northwood Charitable Trust
The Norton Foundation
The Norton Rose Charitable Foundation
The Norwich Town Close Estate Charity
The Nottingham Gordon Memorial Trust for Boys and Girls
The Nottinghamshire Miners' Welfare Trust Fund
The Nuffield Foundation
The Father O'Mahoney Memorial Trust
The Oakley Charitable Trust
The Oizer Charitable Trust
Old Possum's Practical Trust
Open Gate
The Owen Family Trust
City of Oxford Charity
Padwa Charitable Foundation
The Palmer Foundation
The James Pantyfedwen Foundation
The Park House Charitable Trust
The Parthenon Trust
The Dowager Countess Eleanor Peel Trust
Peltz Trust
The Performing Right Society Foundation
The Pestalozzi Overseas Children's Trust
The Jack Petchey Foundation
Philological Foundation
The Bernard Piggott Trust
The Pilgrim Trust
The Plaisterers' Company Charitable Trust
The Pollywally Charitable Trust
The Ponton House Trust
The John Porter Charitable Trust
The Porter Foundation
Porticus UK
The David and Elaine Potter Foundation
The William Price Charitable Trust
The Lucy Price Relief-in-Need Charity
Sir John Priestman Charity Trust
The Prince's Charities Foundation
Private Equity Foundation
PSA Peugeot Citroen Charity Trust
The Puri Foundation
Mr and Mrs J A Pye's Charitable Settlement
Quartet Community Foundation

The Queen Anne's Gate
  Foundation
The Queen's Silver Jubilee
  Trust
Richard Radcliffe Charitable
  Trust
The Radcliffe Trust
The Peggy Ramsay Foundation
The Rank Foundation
The Ravensdale Trust
The Roger Raymond Charitable
  Trust
The Rayne Foundation
The Eva Reckitt Trust Fund
The Reed Foundation
Richard Reeve's Foundation
Relief Fund for Romania
  Limited
Reuben Brothers Foundation
The Clive Richards Charity
The Violet M Richards Charity
The Richmond Parish Lands
  Charity
The Muriel Edith Rickman
  Trust
Ridgesave Limited
The River Farm Foundation
Riverside Charitable Trust
  Limited
Rix-Thompson-Rothenburg
  Foundation
The Alex Roberts-Miller
  Foundation
The Robertson Trust
The Roddick Foundation
The Sir James Roll Charitable
  Trust
The Rose Foundation
The Rothermere Foundation
The Rotherwick Foundation
The Rothley Trust
The Rowan Charitable Trust
The Christopher Rowbotham
  Charitable Trust
The Rowland Family
  Foundation
The Rowlands Trust
Royal Docks Trust (London)
Royal Masonic Trust for Girls
  and Boys
Ryklow Charitable Trust 1992
The J S and E C Rymer
  Charitable Trust
The Michael Harry Sacher
  Trust
The Saddlers' Company
  Charitable Fund
Erach and Roshan Sadri
  Foundation
Saint Luke's College
  Foundation
The Saintbury Trust
The Salt Foundation
The Andrew Salvesen
  Charitable Trust
Coral Samuel Charitable Trust
The Samworth Foundation

Santander UK Foundation
  Limited
Schroder Charity Trust
The Scott Bader
  Commonwealth Ltd
The Scott Trust Foundation
The Scottish Arts Council
The Scottish International
  Education Trust
The Samuel Sebba Charitable
  Trust
SEM Charitable Trust
The Ayrton Senna Foundation
SFIA Educational Trust Limited
The Jean Shanks Foundation
The Sheepdrove Trust
The Archie Sherman Cardiff
  Foundation
The Archie Sherman Charitable
  Trust
SHINE (Support and Help in
  Education)
The Bassil Shippam and
  Alsford Trust
The Shoe Zone Trust
Sino-British Fellowship Trust
Sloane Robinson Foundation
The Leslie Smith Foundation
The Martin Smith Foundation
The R C Snelling Charitable
  Trust
The E C Sosnow Charitable
  Trust
The South Square Trust
The Stephen R and Philippa H
  Southall Charitable Trust
The Southdown Trust
R H Southern Trust
The Southover Manor General
  Education Trust
Split Infinitive Trust
The Spoore, Merry and Rixman
  Foundation
Rosalyn and Nicholas Springer
  Charitable Trust
St Christopher's College
  Educational Trust
St Gabriel's Trust
St James's Place Foundation
Sir Walter St John's
  Educational Charity
The Stanley Foundation Ltd
Stevenson Family's Charitable
  Trust
The Stokenchurch Educational
  Charity
The Stone-Mallabar Charitable
  Foundation
Peter Storrs Trust
Stratford upon Avon Town
  Trust
The W O Street Charitable
  Foundation
The Sudborough Foundation
Sueberry Ltd
The Summerfield Charitable
  Trust

Sussex Community Foundation
The Sutasoma Trust
Sutton Coldfield Municipal
  Charities
The Sutton Trust
The Hugh and Ruby Sykes
  Charitable Trust
Tallow Chandlers Benevolent
  Fund
The Mrs A Lacy Tate Trust
Humphrey Richardson Taylor
  Charitable Trust
The A R Taylor Charitable Trust
The Connie and Albert Taylor
  Charitable Trust
The Cyril Taylor Charitable
  Trust
Tesco Charity Trust
The Thomas Wall Trust
The Thompson Family
  Charitable Trust
The Thornton Trust
The Thriplow Charitable Trust
Mrs R P Tindall's Charitable
  Trust
The Tolkien Trust
The Tory Family Foundation
Tottenham Grammar School
  Foundation
The Towry Law Charitable Trust
The Triangle Trust (1949) Fund
The Trust for Education
Ultach Trust
The Unite Foundation (The
  Amicus Foundation)
Uxbridge United Welfare Trust
Vale of Glamorgan – Welsh
  Church Fund
The Vardy Foundation
The William and Ellen Vinten
  Trust
The Vintners' Company
  Charitable Foundation
Wakeham Trust
Robert and Felicity Waley-
  Cohen Charitable Trust
The Walker Trust
The Ward Blenkinsop Trust
The Howard Watson Symington
  Memorial Charity
John Watson's Trust
Webb Memorial Trust
The James Weir Foundation
The Weldon UK Charitable
  Trust
The Westminster Foundation
The Whitaker Charitable Trust
The Colonel W H Whitbread
  Charitable Trust
The Simon Whitbread
  Charitable Trust
The Whittlesey Charity
The Williams Charitable Trust
Williams Serendipity Trust
The Wilson Foundation
The Harold Hyam Wingate
  Foundation

The Winton Charitable Foundation
The Michael and Anna Wix Charitable Trust
The Wixamtree Trust
The Charles Wolfson Charitable Trust
The Wolfson Foundation
Women Caring Trust
The Wood Family Trust
The Woodroffe Benton Foundation
Worcester Municipal Charities
The Fred and Della Worms Charitable Trust
The Worwin UK Foundation
Miss E B Wrightson's Charitable Settlement
The Yapp Charitable Trust
The W Wing Yip and Brothers Foundation
The York Children's Trust
The Young Foundation
Youth Music
Elizabeth and Prince Zaiger Trust
The Marjorie and Arnold Ziff Charitable Foundation
The Zochonis Charitable Trust

Higher education

AF Trust Company
The Alliance Family Foundation
The Beit Trust
The Harry Bottom Charitable Trust
The Rory and Elizabeth Brooks Foundation
The BUPA Foundation
The Carlton House Charitable Trust
The Carnegie Trust for the Universities of Scotland
The Elmgrant Trust
The Essex Youth Trust
The Fairway Trust
The February Foundation
The Football Association National Sports Centre Trust
The Hugh Fraser Foundation
The Joseph Strong Frazer Trust
The Gatsby Charitable Foundation
Paul Hamlyn Foundation
The Haymills Charitable Trust
The Henley Educational Charity
The Ian Karten Charitable Trust
Kelsick's Educational Foundation
Keswick Hall Charity
The Kreitman Foundation
The Leche Trust

The Leverhulme Trade Charities Trust
The Loftus Charitable Trust
John Lyon's Charity
The Sir Jack Lyons Charitable Trust
James Madison Trust
Miles Trust for the Putney and Roehampton Community
Monmouthshire County Council Welsh Church Act Fund
The Peter Moores Foundation
J P Moulton Charitable Foundation
The Eleni Nakou Foundation
The Richard Newitt Fund
The Northwood Charitable Trust
Mr and Mrs J A Pye's Charitable Settlement
Richard Reeve's Foundation
The Robertson Trust
Sloane Robinson Foundation
The South Square Trust
Stevenson Family's Charitable Trust
The Thriplow Charitable Trust
Webb Memorial Trust
The Wilson Foundation
The Winton Charitable Foundation

Informal, continuing and adult education

The Association of Colleges Charitable Trust
The Beit Trust
The Big Lottery Fund
The Boots Charitable Trust
The Cadbury Foundation
The John and Freda Coleman Charitable Trust
The Duis Charitable Trust
The Elmgrant Trust
The Essex Youth Trust
The Fairway Trust
The Hugh Fraser Foundation
The Freemasons' Grand Charity
The Gatsby Charitable Foundation
Gatwick Airport Community Trust
The Girdlers' Company Charitable Trust
Greggs Foundation
Paul Hamlyn Foundation
The Haymills Charitable Trust
The Hyde Charitable Trust – Youth Plus
Isle of Dogs Community Foundation
Jerwood Charitable Foundation

Kelsick's Educational Foundation
John Laing Charitable Trust
The Allen Lane Foundation
John Lyon's Charity
Magdalen Hospital Trust
The Mathew Trust
The Merchant Venturers' Charity
The Methodist Relief and Development Fund
Miles Trust for the Putney and Roehampton Community
The Millichope Foundation
The Peter Minet Trust
Monmouthshire County Council Welsh Church Act Fund
John Moores Foundation
The Nuffield Foundation
Mr and Mrs J A Pye's Charitable Settlement
Richard Reeve's Foundation
The Christopher Rowbotham Charitable Trust
Sloane Robinson Foundation
The Trust for Education
The Wilson Foundation
The Yapp Charitable Trust

■ Vocational education and training

The John and Freda Coleman Charitable Trust
The Hugh Fraser Foundation
The Freemasons' Grand Charity
The Gatsby Charitable Foundation
The Girdlers' Company Charitable Trust
The Haymills Charitable Trust
The Hyde Charitable Trust – Youth Plus
Isle of Dogs Community Foundation
Jerwood Charitable Foundation
Kelsick's Educational Foundation
The Allen Lane Foundation
John Lyon's Charity
Magdalen Hospital Trust
The Nuffield Foundation
The Christopher Rowbotham Charitable Trust

Integrated education

The Beit Trust
The Essex Youth Trust
HSBC Global Education Trust
Sloane Robinson Foundation
Women Caring Trust

Management of schools

CfBT Education Trust
The Gulbenkian Foundation
Monmouthshire County Council
    Welsh Church Act Fund
The Kitty and Daniel Nabarro
    Charitable Trust
The Nuffield Foundation
Sloane Robinson Foundation

Particular subjects, curriculum development

All Saints Educational Trust
Angus Allnatt Charitable
    Foundation
The Arts Council of Wales
The Beit Trust
The Big Lottery Fund
British Record Industry Trust
The Richard Carne Trust
The Cemlyn-Jones Trust
CfBT Education Trust
Church Burgesses Trust
The Clore Duffield Foundation
Coats Foundation Trust
The Construction Industry
    Trust for Youth
The Deakin Charitable Trust
The Duis Charitable Trust
The James Dyson Foundation
The Ellis Campbell Foundation
The Elmgrant Trust
EMI Music Sound Foundation
The Worshipful Company of
    Engineers Charitable Trust
    Fund
The Ian Fleming Charitable
    Trust
The Joyce Fletcher Charitable
    Trust
Lord Forte Foundation
Foundation for Management
    Education
The Foyle Foundation
The Samuel Gardner Memorial
    Trust
The Gatsby Charitable
    Foundation
The Girdlers' Company
    Charitable Trust
The Glastonbury Trust Limited
The Golsoncott Foundation
Nicholas and Judith
    Goodison's Charitable
    Settlement
The J G Graves Charitable
    Trust
The Gulbenkian Foundation
Paul Hamlyn Foundation
The Harbour Foundation

The Headley Trust
The Michael and Morven Heller
    Charitable Foundation
Matthew Hodder Charitable
    Trust
The Hope Trust
HSBC Global Education Trust
The Hyde Charitable Trust –
    Youth Plus
The International Bankers
    Charitable Trust (The
    Worshipful Compnay of
    Interntional Bankers)
The J J Charitable Trust
The Ruth and Lionel Jacobson
    Trust (Second Fund) No 2
The Jerusalem Trust
The Joanies Trust
Keswick Hall Charity
The Robert Kiln Charitable
    Trust
Maurice and Hilda Laing
    Charitable Trust
The Leverhulme Trust
The Joseph Levy Charitable
    Foundation
The Linbury Trust
Magdalen Hospital Trust
The Maxell Educational Trust
The Methodist Relief and
    Development Fund
Miles Trust for the Putney and
    Roehampton Community
The Peter Moores Foundation
The Music Sales Charitable
    Trust
The Kitty and Daniel Nabarro
    Charitable Trust
The Nuffield Foundation
Old Possum's Practical Trust
The Performing Right Society
    Foundation
The Pilgrim Trust
Sir John Priestman Charity
    Trust
Richard Radcliffe Charitable
    Trust
The Radcliffe Trust
The Peggy Ramsay Foundation
The Sir James Roll Charitable
    Trust
Saint Luke's College
    Foundation
The Scottish Arts Council
Sloane Robinson Foundation
The South Square Trust
Split Infinitive Trust
St Christopher's College
    Educational Trust
St Gabriel's Trust
Humphrey Richardson Taylor
    Charitable Trust
Ultach Trust
The William and Ellen Vinten
    Trust
Miss E B Wrightson's
    Charitable Settlement

Youth Music

....

■ Arts education and training

Angus Allnatt Charitable
    Foundation
The Arts Council of Wales
British Record Industry Trust
The Richard Carne Trust
The Cemlyn-Jones Trust
The Clore Duffield Foundation
Coats Foundation Trust
The Deakin Charitable Trust
The Duis Charitable Trust
The James Dyson Foundation
The Elmgrant Trust
EMI Music Sound Foundation
The Ian Fleming Charitable
    Trust
The Joyce Fletcher Charitable
    Trust
The Samuel Gardner Memorial
    Trust
The Golsoncott Foundation
Nicholas and Judith
    Goodison's Charitable
    Settlement
The Gulbenkian Foundation
Paul Hamlyn Foundation
The Headley Trust
Matthew Hodder Charitable
    Trust
The Joanies Trust
The Robert Kiln Charitable
    Trust
The Linbury Trust
Miles Trust for the Putney and
    Roehampton Community
The Peter Moores Foundation
The Music Sales Charitable
    Trust
The Performing Right Society
    Foundation
The Pilgrim Trust
The Radcliffe Trust
The Peggy Ramsay Foundation
The Scottish Arts Council
The South Square Trust
Split Infinitive Trust
Humphrey Richardson Taylor
    Charitable Trust
Miss E B Wrightson's
    Charitable Settlement
Youth Music

....

■ Business education

The Ellis Campbell Foundation
Foundation for Management
    Education
The Gatsby Charitable
    Foundation
The International Bankers
    Charitable Trust (The

Worshipful Compnay of
Interntional Bankers)
The Nuffield Foundation

■ Citizenship, personal and social education

The Big Lottery Fund
The Elmgrant Trust
The Methodist Relief and
Development Fund
The Kitty and Daniel Nabarro
Charitable Trust

■ Construction industry education

The Construction Industry
Trust for Youth

■ Domestic/lifeskills education

All Saints Educational Trust
The Duis Charitable Trust
The Girdlers' Company
Charitable Trust
The Methodist Relief and
Development Fund
Miles Trust for the Putney and
Roehampton Community

■ Hospitality education

Lord Forte Foundation

■ Literacy education

CfBT Education Trust
The Duis Charitable Trust
The Elmgrant Trust
The Foyle Foundation
The Headley Trust
Matthew Hodder Charitable
Trust
The Hyde Charitable Trust –
Youth Plus
The J J Charitable Trust
The Methodist Relief and
Development Fund
Miles Trust for the Putney and
Roehampton Community
The Kitty and Daniel Nabarro
Charitable Trust
Old Possum's Practical Trust
Ultach Trust

■ Religious education

Church Burgesses Trust
The Girdlers' Company
Charitable Trust
The Glastonbury Trust Limited
The Hope Trust
The Ruth and Lionel Jacobson
Trust (Second Fund) No 2
The Jerusalem Trust
Keswick Hall Charity
Maurice and Hilda Laing
Charitable Trust
The Joseph Levy Charitable
Foundation
Miles Trust for the Putney and
Roehampton Community
Sir John Priestman Charity
Trust
Saint Luke's College
Foundation
St Christopher's College
Educational Trust
St Gabriel's Trust

■ Science education

The Gatsby Charitable
Foundation
The J G Graves Charitable
Trust
The Michael and Morven Heller
Charitable Foundation
The Kitty and Daniel Nabarro
Charitable Trust
The Nuffield Foundation
The William and Ellen Vinten
Trust

■ Sports education

The Girdlers' Company
Charitable Trust

■ Technology, engineering and computer education

The James Dyson Foundation
The Worshipful Company of
Engineers Charitable Trust
Fund
The Gatsby Charitable
Foundation
The Harbour Foundation
The Headley Trust
The Michael and Morven Heller
Charitable Foundation
Magdalen Hospital Trust
The Maxell Educational Trust
The Kitty and Daniel Nabarro
Charitable Trust
Richard Radcliffe Charitable
Trust

The Sir James Roll Charitable
Trust
The William and Ellen Vinten
Trust

Pre-school education, nursery schools

Carter's Educational
Foundation
The Elmgrant Trust
Samuel William Farmer's Trust
The Football Association
National Sports Centre
Trust
The Thomas Freke and Lady
Norton Charity
The Angela Gallagher Memorial
Fund
Gatwick Airport Community
Trust
The Hale Trust
The Hemby Trust
The Henley Educational Charity
HSBC Global Education Trust
John Lyon's Charity
The Madeline Mabey Trust
Miles Trust for the Putney and
Roehampton Community
Monmouthshire County Council
Welsh Church Act Fund
Mr and Mrs J A Pye's
Charitable Settlement
Richard Reeve's Foundation

Primary and secondary school education

The Alliance Family Foundation
The Ammco Trust
A J H Ashby Will Trust
The BAA Communities Trust
The Baily Thomas Charitable
Fund
The Charity of William Barrow
The Harry Bottom Charitable
Trust
The Bristol Charities
The Cadbury Foundation
Carter's Educational
Foundation
The Congleton Inclosure Trust
The Daiwa Anglo-Japanese
Foundation
The Hamilton Davies Trust
The Deakin Charitable Trust
The Dibden Allotments Charity
Earls Colne and Halstead
Educational Charity
Eastern Counties Educational
Trust Limited

The William Edwards
  Educational Charity
The Ellis Campbell Foundation
The Elmgrant Trust
The Equitable Charitable Trust
The Fairway Trust
Faisaltex Charitable Trust
Samuel William Farmer's Trust
The February Foundation
The Joyce Fletcher Charitable
  Trust
The Football Association
  National Sports Centre
  Trust
Ford Britain Trust
The Joseph Strong Frazer Trust
The Thomas Freke and Lady
  Norton Charity
Mejer and Gertrude Miriam
  Frydman Foundation
The Angela Gallagher Memorial
  Fund
The Gatsby Charitable
  Foundation
Gatwick Airport Community
  Trust
The Robert Gavron Charitable
  Trust
The Girdlers' Company
  Charitable Trust
The Gulbenkian Foundation
The Hale Trust
Paul Hamlyn Foundation
Hampton Fuel Allotment
  Charity
The Hanlye Charitable Trust
The Harris Charity
The Haymills Charitable Trust
The Headley Trust
The Hedley Foundation
The Henley Educational Charity
The Charles Littlewood Hill
  Trust
John Holford's Charity
The Horne Foundation
The Hornsey Parochial
  Charities
HSBC Global Education Trust
Hulme Trust Estates
  (Educational)
The J J Charitable Trust
The Ruth and Lionel Jacobson
  Trust (Second Fund) No 2
The Ian Karten Charitable
  Trust
Kelsick's Educational
  Foundation
The Peter Kershaw Trust
The Leche Trust
Leeds Building Society
  Charitable Foundation
The Mark Leonard Trust
The Leverhulme Trust
The Joseph Levy Charitable
  Foundation
The Lord's Taverners
John Lyon's Charity

Malcolm Lyons Foundation
The Madeline Mabey Trust
The Charlotte Marshall
  Charitable Trust
Sir George Martin Trust
The Maxell Educational Trust
The Medlock Charitable Trust
The Mercers' Charitable
  Foundation
Gerald Micklem Charitable
  Trust
Miles Trust for the Putney and
  Roehampton Community
The Mirfield Educational
  Charity
Monmouthshire County Council
  Welsh Church Act Fund
The Kitty and Daniel Nabarro
  Charitable Trust
The Newcomen Collett
  Foundation
The North British Hotel Trust
The Nuffield Foundation
The Owen Family Trust
City of Oxford Charity
The Pestalozzi Overseas
  Children's Trust
The Jack Petchey Foundation
Philological Foundation
PSA Peugeot Citroen Charity
  Trust
Mr and Mrs J A Pye's
  Charitable Settlement
Richard Reeve's Foundation
Relief Fund for Romania
  Limited
Rix-Thompson-Rothenburg
  Foundation
The Robertson Trust
The Salt Foundation
Sloane Robinson Foundation
The Leslie Smith Foundation
The South Square Trust
St James's Place Foundation
The A R Taylor Charitable Trust
John Watson's Trust
The Colonel W H Whitbread
  Charitable Trust
The Wilson Foundation
The Wixamtree Trust

....

■ **Faith schools**

The Alliance Family Foundation
Faisaltex Charitable Trust
Mejer and Gertrude Miriam
  Frydman Foundation
Miles Trust for the Putney and
  Roehampton Community
The Owen Family Trust

....

■ **Public and
independent
schools**

The Daiwa Anglo-Japanese
  Foundation
The Elmgrant Trust
The Equitable Charitable Trust
The Fairway Trust
Samuel William Farmer's Trust
The Hale Trust
The Headley Trust
The Peter Kershaw Trust
The Leche Trust
The Leverhulme Trust
Sir George Martin Trust
The Mercers' Charitable
  Foundation
The Nuffield Foundation
The Owen Family Trust
The A R Taylor Charitable Trust

....

■ **Special needs
schools**

The Ammco Trust
The Baily Thomas Charitable
  Fund
Eastern Counties Educational
  Trust Limited
The Ellis Campbell Foundation
The Elmgrant Trust
The Equitable Charitable Trust
Samuel William Farmer's Trust
The Joyce Fletcher Charitable
  Trust
Ford Britain Trust
The Thomas Freke and Lady
  Norton Charity
The Angela Gallagher Memorial
  Fund
The Girdlers' Company
  Charitable Trust
The Hale Trust
The J J Charitable Trust
The Ruth and Lionel Jacobson
  Trust (Second Fund) No 2
The Ian Karten Charitable
  Trust
Kelsick's Educational
  Foundation
Leeds Building Society
  Charitable Foundation
The Joseph Levy Charitable
  Foundation
The Lord's Taverners
Gerald Micklem Charitable
  Trust
Miles Trust for the Putney and
  Roehampton Community
The Kitty and Daniel Nabarro
  Charitable Trust
The North British Hotel Trust
Relief Fund for Romania
  Limited

Rix-Thompson-Rothenburg
Foundation
St James's Place Foundation
John Watson's Trust

....

■ State schools

The Deakin Charitable Trust
The Mark Leonard Trust
Richard Reeve's Foundation

Teacher training and development

The Methodist Relief and
Development Fund
Monmouthshire County Council
Welsh Church Act Fund

Environment and animals

Aberbrothock Charitable Trust
The AIM Foundation
The Alborada Trust
Anglo American Group
Foundation
The Animal Defence Trust
Arcadia (formerly the Lisbet
Rausing Charitable Fund)
A J H Ashby Will Trust
The Ashden Trust
The Ashendene Trust
The Associated Country
Women of the World
(ACWW)
The Astor Foundation
The Astor of Hever Trust
The BAA Communities Trust
Harry Bacon Foundation
The C Alma Baker Trust
The Balcombe Charitable Trust
The Balney Charitable Trust
The Beit Trust
The Bellahouston Bequest
Fund
The Hervey Benham Charitable
Trust
The Big Lottery Fund
Birmingham International
Airport Community Trust
The Blair Foundation
The Body Shop Foundation
The Boshier-Hinton Foundation
The Bothwell Charitable Trust
John and Susan Bowers Fund
Briggs Animal Welfare Trust
The Bromley Trust
C J Cadbury Charitable Trust
Edward Cadbury Charitable
Trust
The Christopher Cadbury
Charitable Trust
The G W Cadbury Charitable
Trust
The William A Cadbury
Charitable Trust
The Cadbury Foundation
The Edward and Dorothy
Cadbury Trust
CAFOD
Calypso Browning Trust
M R Cannon 1998 Charitable
Trust
The Carron Charitable Trust
The Leslie Mary Carter
Charitable Trust
The Wilfrid and Constance
Cave Foundation
The Cemlyn-Jones Trust
The Chelsea Square 1994
Trust
J A Clark Charitable Trust
The Cleopatra Trust
The Robert Clutterbuck
Charitable Trust

The John Coates Charitable
Trust
The John S Cohen Foundation
Colyer-Fergusson Charitable
Trust
The Conscience Trust
The Conservation Foundation
The Ernest Cook Trust
The Marjorie Coote Animal
Charity Trust
The Craignish Trust
The Cromarty Trust
The D J H Currie Memorial
Trust
The Dennis Curry Charitable
Trust
The D'Oyly Carte Charitable
Trust
The Dr and Mrs A Darlington
Charitable Trust
The Helen and Geoffrey De
Freitas Charitable Trust
Peter De Haan Charitable
Trust
William Dean Countryside and
Educational Trust
The Delves Charitable Trust
Dischma Charitable Trust
The Dorus Trust
The Duis Charitable Trust
The Dulverton Trust
The Dumbreck Charity
Dunard Fund
The Houghton Dunn Charitable
Trust
The Dunn Family Charitable
Trust
Audrey Earle Charitable Trust
The EBM Charitable Trust
The Ecology Trust
The Edinburgh Trust, No 2
Account
The John Ellerman Foundation
The Ellis Campbell Foundation
The Elmgrant Trust
The Ericson Trust
The Alan Evans Memorial Trust
The Beryl Evetts and Robert
Luff Animal Welfare Trust
The Matthew Eyton Animal
Welfare Trust
Esmée Fairbairn Foundation
Samuel William Farmer's Trust
The Farmers' Company
Charitable Fund
The February Foundation
Fife Council/Common Good
Funds and Trusts
The Fishmongers' Company's
Charitable Trust
The Flow Foundation
Ford Britain Trust
The Oliver Ford Charitable
Trust
The Donald Forrester Trust
The Anna Rosa Forster
Charitable Trust

Sydney E Franklin Deceased's
New Second Charity
The Gordon Fraser Charitable
Trust
The Hugh Fraser Foundation
The Freshfield Foundation
Maurice Fry Charitable Trust
The Fuellers Charitable Trust
Fund
The G D Charitable Trust
The Galanthus Trust
The Gannochy Trust
The Worshipful Company of
Gardeners of London
The Garnett Charitable Trust
The Gatsby Charitable
Foundation
Gatwick Airport Community
Trust
J Paul Getty Jr Charitable Trust
The G C Gibson Charitable
Trust
The Girdlers' Company
Charitable Trust
The Glastonbury Trust Limited
The GNC Trust
Goodfund
The Gosling Foundation
Limited
The Gough Charitable Trust
GrantScape
The Barry Green Memorial
Fund
The Gulbenkian Foundation
The Gunter Charitable Trust
H C D Memorial Fund
The Hadfield Trust
The Hadrian Trust
The Hamamelis Trust
The Hanlye Charitable Trust
The Harebell Centenary Fund
The Kenneth Hargreaves
Charitable Trust
The N and P Hartley Memorial
Trust
William Geoffrey Harvey's
Discretionary Settlement
The Headley Trust
The G D Herbert Charitable
Trust
The Joanna Herbert-Stepney
Charitable Settlement
The Holly Hill Charitable Trust
The J G Hogg Charitable Trust
The Homestead Charitable
Trust
The Cuthbert Horn Trust
The Reta Lila Howard
Foundation
The Geoffrey C Hughes
Charitable Trust
The Michael and Shirley Hunt
Charitable Trust
Miss Agnes H Hunter's Trust
The Idlewild Trust
The J J Charitable Trust
The John Jarrold Trust

Rees Jeffreys Road Fund
The Johnson Wax Ltd
Charitable Trust
The Kennel Club Charitable
Trust
The Robert Kiln Charitable
Trust
Ernest Kleinwort Charitable
Trust
The Kreitman Foundation
John Laing Charitable Trust
The Christopher Laing
Foundation
The Martin Laing Foundation
Lancashire Environmental
Fund
Mrs F B Laurence Charitable
Trust
The Leach Fourteenth Trust
The Leathersellers' Company
Charitable Fund
The Mark Leonard Trust
Lord Leverhulme's Charitable
Trust
The John Spedan Lewis
Foundation
John Lewis Partnership
General Community Fund
The Limbourne Trust
Limoges Charitable Trust
The Linbury Trust
The William and Katherine
Longman Trust
The Lotus Foundation
LSA Charitable Trust
The Lyons Charitable Trust
The R S Macdonald Charitable
Trust
The Mackintosh Foundation
The MacRobert Trust
Manchester Airport Community
Trust Fund
The Manifold Charitable Trust
Marchig Animal Welfare Trust
Market Harborough and The
Bowdens Charity
Michael Marks Charitable
Trust
The Marsh Christian Trust
Sir George Martin Trust
The Maxwell Family Foundation
The Mercers' Charitable
Foundation
The Mersey Docks and
Harbour Company
Charitable Fund
The Methodist Relief and
Development Fund
The Metropolitan Drinking
Fountain and Cattle Trough
Association
T and J Meyer Family
Foundation Limited
Millennium Stadium Charitable
Trust
The Miller Foundation
The Millichope Foundation

The Millward Charitable Trust
The Peter Minet Trust
The Minos Trust
The D C Moncrieff Charitable
Trust
The Monument Trust
The Morel Charitable Trust
Moto in the Community Trust
The Edith Murphy Foundation
The Kitty and Daniel Nabarro
Charitable Trust
The Nchima Trust
Network for Social Change
The NFU Mutual Charitable
Trust
Alice Noakes Memorial
Charitable Trust
The Nottinghamshire Miners'
Welfare Trust Fund
The Sir Peter O'Sullevan
Charitable Trust
The Oakdale Trust
The Oakley Charitable Trust
Old Possum's Practical Trust
The John Oldacre Foundation
The Oldham Foundation
Onaway Trust
Open Gate
Orrin Charitable Trust
The Owen Family Trust
Panton Trust
The Frank Parkinson
Agricultural Trust
The Jack Patston Charitable
Trust
The Peacock Charitable Trust
The Persula Foundation
The Petplan Charitable Trust
The Phillips Charitable Trust
The Pilgrim Trust
The Cecil Pilkington Charitable
Trust
The Col W W Pilkington Will
Trusts The General Charity
Fund
Mrs Pilkington's Charitable
Trust
Polden-Puckham Charitable
Foundation
The John Porter Charitable
Trust
The Porter Foundation
Prairie Trust
The Prince's Charities
Foundation
Princess Anne's Charities
Mr and Mrs J A Pye's
Charitable Settlement
Quartet Community Foundation
The Sigrid Rausing Trust
The Rhododendron Trust
The Ripple Effect Foundation
The Robertson Trust
The Rochester Bridge Trust
The Roddick Foundation
The Rothera Charitable
Settlement

The Rothschild Foundation
The Roughley Charitable Trust
The Rowan Charitable Trust
The Rowlands Trust
Royal Docks Trust (London)
The Rufford Maurice Laing Foundation
The Rufford Small Grants Foundation
Ryklow Charitable Trust 1992
The Michael Harry Sacher Trust
The Jean Sainsbury Animal Welfare Trust
The Saintbury Trust
The Salters' Charities
The Hon. M J Samuel Charitable Trust
The Peter Samuel Charitable Trust
The Sandra Charitable Trust
The Scarfe Charitable Trust
Schroder Charity Trust
The Scotshill Trust
The Scott Bader Commonwealth Ltd
The Scouloudi Foundation
Seafarers UK (King George's Fund for Sailors)
The Linley Shaw Foundation
The Sheepdrove Trust
The Sylvia and Colin Shepherd Charitable Trust
The Shetland Charitable Trust
The Shipwrights' Company Charitable Fund
The Simpson Education and Conservation Trust
The John Slater Foundation
Ruth Smart Foundation
The SMB Charitable Trust
The N Smith Charitable Settlement
The Stanley Smith UK Horticultural Trust
The R C Snelling Charitable Trust
The South Square Trust
The Stephen R and Philippa H Southall Charitable Trust
The W F Southall Trust
R H Southern Trust
St Andrew Animal Fund
The Stafford Trust
The Staples Trust
The Steel Charitable Trust
The June Stevens Foundation
Stevenson Family's Charitable Trust
The Sylvanus Charitable Trust
The Mrs A Lacy Tate Trust
The Connie and Albert Taylor Charitable Trust
Tearfund
The Loke Wan Tho Memorial Foundation
The Tubney Charitable Trust

The Underwood Trust
The Valentine Charitable Trust
The William and Patricia Venton Charitable Trust
Wales Council for Voluntary Action
The Waterloo Foundation
The David Webster Charitable Trust
The Westminster Foundation
The Whitaker Charitable Trust
The Colonel W H Whitbread Charitable Trust
The Simon Whitbread Charitable Trust
A H and B C Whiteley Charitable Trust
The Whitley Animal Protection Trust
The Richard Wilcox Welfare Charity
The Will Charitable Trust
The H D H Wills 1965 Charitable Trust
J and J R Wilson Trust
The Wixamtree Trust
Woodlands Trust
The Woodroffe Benton Foundation
The Woodward Charitable Trust
The A and R Woolf Charitable Trust
The Diana Edgson Wright Charitable Trust
Yorkshire Agricultural Society
The Yorkshire Dales Millennium Trust
Elizabeth and Prince Zaiger Trust
Zephyr Charitable Trust

Agriculture and fishing

The C Alma Baker Trust
The Ecology Trust
The John Ellerman Foundation
Esmée Fairbairn Foundation
The Farmers' Company Charitable Fund
The Fishmongers' Company's Charitable Trust
The Oliver Ford Charitable Trust
The Worshipful Company of Gardeners of London
The Gatsby Charitable Foundation
The G C Gibson Charitable Trust
The Headley Trust
The J J Charitable Trust
The John Spedan Lewis Foundation
The Limbourne Trust

LSA Charitable Trust
The MacRobert Trust
Manchester Airport Community Trust Fund
Marchig Animal Welfare Trust
The Methodist Relief and Development Fund
The NFU Mutual Charitable Trust
The John Oldacre Foundation
The Frank Parkinson Agricultural Trust
The Cecil Pilkington Charitable Trust
Prairie Trust
Mr and Mrs J A Pye's Charitable Settlement
Quartet Community Foundation (formerly the Greater Bristol Foundation)
The Peter Samuel Charitable Trust
Seafarers UK (King George's Fund for Sailors)
The Stanley Smith UK Horticultural Trust
Yorkshire Agricultural Society

■ Farming and food production

Esmée Fairbairn Foundation
The Farmers' Company Charitable Fund
The Gatsby Charitable Foundation
The J J Charitable Trust
The Limbourne Trust
Mr and Mrs J A Pye's Charitable Settlement

■ Fishing and fisheries

The Fishmongers' Company's Charitable Trust
The John Spedan Lewis Foundation
Seafarers UK (King George's Fund for Sailors)

■ Forestry

The Headley Trust
Manchester Airport Community Trust Fund
Mr and Mrs J A Pye's Charitable Settlement
The Peter Samuel Charitable Trust

■ Horticulture

The Oliver Ford Charitable Trust
The Worshipful Company of Gardeners of London
The Gatsby Charitable Foundation
The John Spedan Lewis Foundation
LSA Charitable Trust
The MacRobert Trust
The Stanley Smith UK Horticultural Trust

Animal care

The Alborada Trust
The Animal Defence Trust
The Astor Foundation
Harry Bacon Foundation
The Bellahouston Bequest Fund
Briggs Animal Welfare Trust
Calypso Browning Trust
The Wilfrid and Constance Cave Foundation
The Cemlyn-Jones Trust
The Chelsea Square 1994 Trust
The Robert Clutterbuck Charitable Trust
The Marjorie Coote Animal Charity Trust
The Dumbreck Charity
The EBM Charitable Trust
The Beryl Evetts and Robert Luff Animal Welfare Trust
The Matthew Eyton Animal Welfare Trust
The Anna Rosa Forster Charitable Trust
The GNC Trust
The Barry Green Memorial Fund
The Hanlye Charitable Trust
William Geoffrey Harvey's Discretionary Settlement
The Joanna Herbert-Stepney Charitable Settlement
The J G Hogg Charitable Trust
The Homestead Charitable Trust
The Michael and Shirley Hunt Charitable Trust
The Kennel Club Charitable Trust
Limoges Charitable Trust
The William and Katherine Longman Trust
The Lyons Charitable Trust
The R S Macdonald Charitable Trust
Marchig Animal Welfare Trust
The Millward Charitable Trust
The Edith Murphy Foundation

Alice Noakes Memorial Charitable Trust
The Sir Peter O'Sullevan Charitable Trust
Old Possum's Practical Trust
The Oldham Foundation
Open Gate
The Persula Foundation
The Petplan Charitable Trust
The Phillips Charitable Trust
Mrs Pilkington's Charitable Trust
The Rothschild Foundation
The Jean Sainsbury Animal Welfare Trust
The Sandra Charitable Trust
The Scotshill Trust
The John Slater Foundation
Ruth Smart Foundation
St Andrew Animal Fund
The Sylvanus Charitable Trust
The Tubney Charitable Trust
The William and Patricia Venton Charitable Trust
The Richard Wilcox Welfare Charity
The H D H Wills 1965 Charitable Trust
J and J R Wilson Trust
The Wixamtree Trust

Animal conservation

A J H Ashby Will Trust
Birmingham International Airport Community Trust
The Body Shop Foundation
The Carron Charitable Trust
The Wilfrid and Constance Cave Foundation
The Cemlyn-Jones Trust
The Robert Clutterbuck Charitable Trust
The Marjorie Coote Animal Charity Trust
The Dr and Mrs A Darlington Charitable Trust
William Dean Countryside and Educational Trust
The Dumbreck Charity
The John Ellerman Foundation
Samuel William Farmer's Trust
Sydney E Franklin Deceased's New Second Charity
Maurice Fry Charitable Trust
The GNC Trust
William Geoffrey Harvey's Discretionary Settlement
The Joanna Herbert-Stepney Charitable Settlement
The Holly Hill Charitable Trust
The Kreitman Foundation
The John Spedan Lewis Foundation
The Lotus Foundation

Marchig Animal Welfare Trust
The Oakdale Trust
Old Possum's Practical Trust
The Owen Family Trust
The Jack Patston Charitable Trust
Mr and Mrs J A Pye's Charitable Settlement
The Rhododendron Trust
The Rothschild Foundation
The Rufford Small Grants Foundation
Ryklow Charitable Trust 1992
The Michael Harry Sacher Trust
The Jean Sainsbury Animal Welfare Trust
The Simpson Education and Conservation Trust
St Andrew Animal Fund
The Tubney Charitable Trust
The David Webster Charitable Trust
The Whitley Animal Protection Trust
The H D H Wills 1965 Charitable Trust
The Diana Edgson Wright Charitable Trust

Countryside

Aberbrothock Charitable Trust
The Astor Foundation
The BAA Communities Trust
The Big Lottery Fund
The Blair Foundation
The Bothwell Charitable Trust
The Bromley Trust
The Cadbury Foundation
M R Cannon 1998 Charitable Trust
Colyer-Fergusson Charitable Trust
The Ernest Cook Trust
The D J H Currie Memorial Trust
The D'Oyly Carte Charitable Trust
The Dr and Mrs A Darlington Charitable Trust
The Helen and Geoffrey De Freitas Charitable Trust
The Dunn Family Charitable Trust
The John Ellerman Foundation
The Ellis Campbell Foundation
The Alan Evans Memorial Trust
Samuel William Farmer's Trust
The Freshfield Foundation
Maurice Fry Charitable Trust
The Galanthus Trust
The Gannochy Trust
Gatwick Airport Community Trust
J Paul Getty Jr Charitable Trust

The Girdlers' Company
Charitable Trust
The GNC Trust
The Gough Charitable Trust
The Idlewild Trust
The John Spedan Lewis
Foundation
Manchester Airport Community
Trust Fund
Sir George Martin Trust
The Kitty and Daniel Nabarro
Charitable Trust
The Pilgrim Trust
The Cecil Pilkington Charitable
Trust
Prairie Trust
Quartet Community Foundation
(formerly the Greater Bristol
Foundation)
The Rufford Maurice Laing
Foundation
The Rufford Small Grants
Foundation
Ryklow Charitable Trust 1992
The Linley Shaw Foundation
The Connie and Albert Taylor
Charitable Trust
The Valentine Charitable Trust
The David Webster Charitable
Trust
The Whitaker Charitable Trust
The Colonel W H Whitbread
Charitable Trust
The Simon Whitbread
Charitable Trust
The Will Charitable Trust
The Woodroffe Benton
Foundation
Zephyr Charitable Trust

Environmental education and research

The BAA Communities Trust
The Big Lottery Fund
Birmingham International
Airport Community Trust
The Body Shop Foundation
The Cadbury Foundation
The Ernest Cook Trust
The Helen and Geoffrey De
Freitas Charitable Trust
William Dean Countryside and
Educational Trust
The Duis Charitable Trust
The Dulverton Trust
The Dunn Family Charitable
Trust
The John Ellerman Foundation
Gatwick Airport Community
Trust
The Holly Hill Charitable Trust
The J J Charitable Trust
The Mark Leonard Trust

The John Spedan Lewis
Foundation
The Limbourne Trust
Manchester Airport Community
Trust Fund
Marchig Animal Welfare Trust
The Kitty and Daniel Nabarro
Charitable Trust
Network for Social Change
The Cecil Pilkington Charitable
Trust
The Porter Foundation
Prairie Trust
Quartet Community Foundation
(formerly the Greater Bristol
Foundation)
The Rufford Small Grants
Foundation
The Saintbury Trust
The Stanley Smith UK
Horticultural Trust
The Staples Trust
The Woodward Charitable
Trust

Natural environment

A J H Ashby Will Trust
The Ashendene Trust
The BAA Communities Trust
The Balney Charitable Trust
The Blair Foundation
The Bromley Trust
The Christopher Cadbury
Charitable Trust
The Cadbury Foundation
The Carron Charitable Trust
The Robert Clutterbuck
Charitable Trust
The Conscience Trust
The Conservation Foundation
The Ernest Cook Trust
The Cromarty Trust
The D'Oyly Carte Charitable
Trust
The Dr and Mrs A Darlington
Charitable Trust
The Helen and Geoffrey De
Freitas Charitable Trust
William Dean Countryside and
Educational Trust
The Dulverton Trust
The Houghton Dunn Charitable
Trust
The Dunn Family Charitable
Trust
The John Ellerman Foundation
The Elmgrant Trust
The Ericson Trust
Samuel William Farmer's Trust
Maurice Fry Charitable Trust
The Galanthus Trust
The Gannochy Trust
Gatwick Airport Community
Trust

J Paul Getty Jr Charitable Trust
The Girdlers' Company
Charitable Trust
The Glastonbury Trust Limited
The Headley Trust
The J J Charitable Trust
The John Spedan Lewis
Foundation
The Limbourne Trust
Manchester Airport Community
Trust Fund
Marchig Animal Welfare Trust
The Marsh Christian Trust
The Mercers' Charitable
Foundation
The Mersey Docks and
Harbour Company
Charitable Fund
The Methodist Relief and
Development Fund
The Metropolitan Drinking
Fountain and Cattle Trough
Association
T and J Meyer Family
Foundation Limited
Millennium Stadium Charitable
Trust
The Peter Minet Trust
The Nchima Trust
The Oakdale Trust
The Owen Family Trust
The Jack Patston Charitable
Trust
The Cecil Pilkington Charitable
Trust
Polden-Puckham Charitable
Foundation
Prairie Trust
Mr and Mrs J A Pye's
Charitable Settlement
Quartet Community Foundation
(formerly the Greater Bristol
Foundation)
The Sigrid Rausing Trust
The Rhododendron Trust
The Rufford Small Grants
Foundation
Ryklow Charitable Trust 1992
The Saintbury Trust
The Hon. M J Samuel
Charitable Trust
The Peter Samuel Charitable
Trust
Schroder Charity Trust
The Simpson Education and
Conservation Trust
The Stanley Smith UK
Horticultural Trust
Stevenson Family's Charitable
Trust
The Tubney Charitable Trust
The Valentine Charitable Trust
The David Webster Charitable
Trust
The Will Charitable Trust
The H D H Wills 1965
Charitable Trust

The Woodroffe Benton
Foundation
Zephyr Charitable Trust

■ **Flora and fauna**

A J H Ashby Will Trust
The Ashendene Trust
The Balney Charitable Trust
The Blair Foundation
The Ernest Cook Trust
The Cromarty Trust
The Dulverton Trust
The Houghton Dunn Charitable
Trust
The J J Charitable Trust
Manchester Airport Community
Trust Fund
Marchig Animal Welfare Trust
The Marsh Christian Trust
The Mercers' Charitable
Foundation
The Methodist Relief and
Development Fund
The Jack Patston Charitable
Trust
Mr and Mrs J A Pye's
Charitable Settlement
The Peter Samuel Charitable
Trust
The Simpson Education and
Conservation Trust
The Stanley Smith UK
Horticultural Trust
The Valentine Charitable Trust
The Will Charitable Trust
The H D H Wills 1965
Charitable Trust

■ **Water resources**

The Headley Trust
The Mersey Docks and
Harbour Company
Charitable Fund
The Methodist Relief and
Development Fund
The Metropolitan Drinking
Fountain and Cattle Trough
Association
The Nchima Trust
Mr and Mrs J A Pye's
Charitable Settlement

■ **Wild places,
wilderness**

The Dulverton Trust
J Paul Getty Jr Charitable Trust
The Girdlers' Company
Charitable Trust

Pollution abatement and control

The John Ellerman Foundation
Gatwick Airport Community
Trust
Lancashire Environmental
Fund
The Limbourne Trust
Prairie Trust
Quartet Community Foundation
(formerly the Greater Bristol
Foundation)
The Sigrid Rausing Trust
The Saintbury Trust
The Valentine Charitable Trust
The Woodroffe Benton
Foundation
Zephyr Charitable Trust

Sustainable environment

The AIM Foundation
The Associated Country
Women of the World
(ACWW)
The BAA Communities Trust
The Body Shop Foundation
The Bromley Trust
The Cadbury Foundation
J A Clark Charitable Trust
The Conscience Trust
The Dunn Family Charitable
Trust
The Ecology Trust
The John Ellerman Foundation
The Freshfield Foundation
The Fuellers Charitable Trust
Fund
The Gannochy Trust
Gatwick Airport Community
Trust
The Glastonbury Trust Limited
The Gulbenkian Foundation
John Laing Charitable Trust
Lancashire Environmental
Fund
The Mark Leonard Trust
The Limbourne Trust
Manchester Airport Community
Trust Fund
The Methodist Relief and
Development Fund
Open Gate
Polden-Puckham Charitable
Foundation
Prairie Trust
Quartet Community Foundation
(formerly the Greater Bristol
Foundation)
The Sigrid Rausing Trust
The Rowan Charitable Trust

The Rufford Maurice Laing
Foundation
The Rufford Small Grants
Foundation
The Saintbury Trust
The Staples Trust
The David Webster Charitable
Trust
The Woodroffe Benton
Foundation
Zephyr Charitable Trust

■ **Energy issues**

The BAA Communities Trust
The Fuellers Charitable Trust
Fund
The Mark Leonard Trust
The Methodist Relief and
Development Fund

■ **Loss of environment**

The Bromley Trust
The Rufford Small Grants
Foundation

Transport

The John Ellerman Foundation
Gatwick Airport Community
Trust
The Gosling Foundation
Limited
The J J Charitable Trust
Rees Jeffreys Road Fund
Prairie Trust
Quartet Community Foundation
(formerly the Greater Bristol
Foundation)
The Rochester Bridge Trust
Seafarers UK (King George's
Fund for Sailors)
The Shipwrights' Company
Charitable Fund

General charitable purposes

The 1989 Willan Charitable Trust

The 29th May 1961 Charitable Trust

The Acacia Charitable Trust

The Adnams Charity

The Green and Lilian F M Ainsworth and Family Benevolent Fund

The Sylvia Aitken Charitable Trust

D G Albright Charitable Trust

Allchurches Trust Ltd

The H B Allen Charitable Trust

The Rita Allen Charitable Trust

The Alliance Family Foundation

Almondsbury Charity

AM Charitable Trust

The Amalur Foundation Limited

Sir John and Lady Amory's Charitable Trust

The Ampelos Trust

Andor Charitable Trust

The Henry Angest Foundation

The Annandale Charitable Trust

The Anson Charitable Trust

Ambrose and Ann Appelbe Trust

The John Apthorp Charitable Trust

The Arbib Foundation

The John M Archer Charitable Trust

The Ardwick Trust

The Argentarius Foundation

The Armourers' and Brasiers' Gauntlet Trust

The Arnold Foundation

Arsenal Charitable Trust

The Ashendene Trust

The Ashworth Charitable Trust

The Ian Askew Charitable Trust

The Astor Foundation

The Avenue Charitable Trust

AW Charitable Trust

Awards for All

The Aylesford Family Charitable Trust

The BACTA Charitable Trust

The Bagri Foundation

The Balint Family Charitable Trusts

The Albert Casanova Ballard Deceased Trust

Balmain Charitable Trust

The Bamford Charitable Foundation

The Banbury Charities

The Band Trust

Peter Barker-Mill Memorial Charity

Lord Barnby's Foundation

The Barnsbury Charitable Trust

The Barnstaple Bridge Trust

The Misses Barrie Charitable Trust

Stephen J Barry Charitable Trust

The Bartlett Taylor Charitable Trust

The Worshipful Company of Basketmakers' Charitable Trust

The Paul Bassham Charitable Trust

The Batchworth Trust

The Bay Tree Charitable Trust

D H and L H Baylin Charitable Trust

The Louis Baylis (Maidenhead Advertiser) Charitable Trust

The Bearder Charity

The James Beattie Charitable Trust

The Beaverbrook Foundation

The Beccles Town Lands Charity

The Becker Family Charitable Trust

The Victoria and David Beckham Children's Charity

The Peter Beckwith Charitable Trust

The Bedfordshire and Luton Community Foundation

The David and Ruth Behrend Fund

Bellasis Trust

The Bellinger Donnay Trust

The Benfield Motors Charitable Trust

The Benham Charitable Settlement

Maurice and Jacqueline Bennett Charitable Trust

The Gerald Bentall Charitable Trust

The Berkshire Community Foundation

The Bideford Bridge Trust

The Billmeir Charitable Trust

The Bingham Trust

The Birmingham Community Foundation

The Lord Mayor of Birmingham's Charity

Birthday House Trust

The Michael Bishop Foundation

The Bertie Black Foundation

Isabel Blackman Foundation

The BlackRock (UK) Charitable Trust

The Blair Foundation

Blakes Benevolent Trust

The Sir Victor Blank Charitable Settlement

The Neville and Elaine Blond Charitable Trust

The Bluston Charitable Settlement

The Bonamy Charitable Trust

The John and Celia Bonham Christie Charitable Trust

The Charlotte Bonham-Carter Charitable Trust

The Bordon and Liphook Charity

The Boshier-Hinton Foundation

H E and E L Botteley Charitable Trust

Community Foundation for Bournemouth, Dorset and Poole

The Bower Trust

The William Brake Charitable Trust

The Bransford Trust

The Brewers' Company General Charitable Trust

The Britto Foundation

The J and M Britton Charitable Trust

The Charles and Edna Broadhurst Charitable Trust

The Roger Brooke Charitable Trust

Joseph Brough Charitable Trust

The Swinfen Broun Charitable Trust

Mrs E E Brown Charitable Settlement

Brownsword Charitable Foundation

T B H Brunner's Charitable Settlement

The Jack Brunton Charitable Trust

The Bryant Trust

The Buckinghamshire Masonic Centenary Fund

Buckland Charitable Trust

The Buffini Chao Foundation

The Bulldog Trust Limited

The Burden Trust

Burdens Charitable Foundation

The Geoffrey Burton Charitable Trust

Consolidated Charity of Burton upon Trent

The Derek Butler Trust

The Bill Butlin Charity Trust

Edward Cadbury Charitable Trust

P H G Cadbury Charitable Trust

The Christopher Cadbury Charitable Trust

The G W Cadbury Charitable Trust

The Richard Cadbury Charitable Trust

The Edward and Dorothy Cadbury Trust

The George Cadbury Trust

The Cadogan Charity
The Callander Charitable Trust
Calleva Foundation
The Camelia Trust
The Frederick and Phyllis Cann
Trust
The Canning Trust
H and L Cantor Trust
Capital Community Foundation
Cardy Beaver Foundation
The Carew Pole Charitable
Trust
The D W T Cargill Fund
The Carlton House Charitable
Trust
The Carpenters' Company
Charitable Trust
The Carrington Charitable
Trust
The Carvill Trust
The Catalyst Charitable Trust
The Joseph and Annie Cattle
Trust
The Thomas Sivewright Catto
Charitable Settlement
The Wilfrid and Constance
Cave Foundation
The Cayo Foundation
The B G S Cayzer Charitable
Trust
The Cazenove Charitable Trust
R E Chadwick Charitable Trust
The Amelia Chadwick Trust
The Pamela Champion
Foundation
The Chapman Charitable Trust
The Charities Advisory Trust
The Charter 600 Charity
The Worshipful Company of
Chartered Accountants
General Charitable Trust
The Cheruby Trust
The Cheshire Provincial Fund
of Benevolence
The Chetwode Foundation
The Malcolm Chick Charity
The Chippenham Borough
Lands Charity
CHK Charities Limited
The Chownes Foundation
Christian Aid
Church Burgesses Trust
City and County of Swansea
Welsh Church Act Fund
The Hilda and Alice Clark
Charitable Trust
The Roger and Sarah Bancroft
Clark Charitable Trust
The Cleary Foundation
Lord Clinton's Charitable Trust
Closehelm Ltd
The Clothworkers' Foundation
Clydpride Ltd
The Coalfields Regeneration
Trust
The John Coates Charitable
Trust

The Cobalt Trust
The Cobtree Charity Trust Ltd
The John S Cohen Foundation
John Coldman Charitable Trust
The Cole Charitable Trust
The Colefax Charitable Trust
The George Henry Collins
Charity
The Sir Jeremiah Colman Gift
Trust
Community Foundation for
Calderdale
The Community Foundation for
Greater Manchester
The Compton Charitable Trust
The Douglas Compton James
Charitable Trust
The Congleton Inclosure Trust
The Cook and Wolstenholme
Charitable Trust
The Catherine Cookson
Charitable Trust
The Cookson Charitable Trust
Mabel Cooper Charity
The Alice Ellen Cooper Dean
Charitable Foundation
The Helen Jean Cope Trust
The Gershon Coren Charitable
Foundation
Michael Cornish Charitable
Trust
The Evan Cornish Foundation
Cornwall Community
Foundation
The Duke of Cornwall's
Benevolent Fund
The Cornwell Charitable Trust
The Sidney and Elizabeth
Corob Charitable Trust
County Durham Foundation
The Augustine Courtauld Trust
Coutts Charitable Trust
The General Charities of the
City of Coventry
Coventry Building Society
Charitable Foundation
The Sir Tom Cowie Charitable
Trust
Cowley Charitable Foundation
The Lord Cozens-Hardy Trust
The Craignish Trust
The Craps Charitable Trust
The Cray Trust
Cripplegate Foundation
The Croydon Relief in Need
Charities
The Mayor of Croydon's
Charity Fund
Cruden Foundation Ltd
The Ronald Cruickshanks'
Foundation
Cullum Family Trust
The Culra Charitable Trust
The Cumber Family Charitable
Trust
Cumberland Building Society
Charitable Foundation

The Dennis Curry Charitable
Trust
The Raymond Curtis Charitable
Trust
The Manny Cussins
Foundation
The Cutler Trust (the
Worshipful Company of
Makers of Playing Cards)
The Cwmbran Trust
The Daisy Trust
The Alderman Joe Davidson
Memorial Trust
Michael Davies Charitable
Settlement
The Gwendoline and Margaret
Davies Charity
Davis-Rubens Charitable Trust
The De Clermont Charitable
Company Ltd
Peter De Haan Charitable
Trust
The De Laszlo Foundation
The Leopold De Rothschild
Charitable Trust
The Delfont Foundation
The Dellal Foundation
The Delves Charitable Trust
The Demigryphon Trust
The Denton Wilde Sapte
Charitable Trust
The Earl of Derby's Charitable
Trust
Derbyshire Community
Foundation
Devon Community Foundation
The Duke of Devonshire's
Charitable Trust
The Sandy Dewhirst Charitable
Trust
DG Charitable Settlement
The Laduma Dhamecha
Charitable Trust
Alan and Sheila Diamond
Charitable Trust
The Dibden Allotments Charity
The Gillian Dickinson Trust
The Dickon Trust
Dischma Charitable Trust
The Djanogly Foundation
The DLA Piper Charitable Trust
The DLM Charitable Trust
The DM Charitable Trust
Louise Dobson Charitable
Trust
The Dollond Charitable Trust
The Dorus Trust
Double 'O' Charity Ltd
The R M Douglas Charitable
Trust
The Drapers' Charitable Fund
Dromintee Trust
The Dulverton Trust
The P B Dumbell Charitable
Trust
The Dumbreck Charity

Ronald Duncan Literary
Foundation
The Dunn Family Charitable
Trust
The Charles Dunstone
Charitable Trust
Mildred Duveen Charitable
Trust
Annette Duvollet Charitable
Trust
The Dwek Family Charitable
Trust
The Dyers' Company
Charitable Trust
The James Dyson Foundation
The Eagle Charity Trust
Audrey Earle Charitable Trust
The Earley Charity
The Earmark Trust
East London Community
Foundation
The Gilbert and Eileen Edgar
Foundation
The Edinburgh Trust, No 2
Account
Edinburgh Voluntary
Organisations' Trust Funds
The George Elias Charitable
Trust
The Elizabeth Frankland Moore
and Star Foundation
The Wilfred and Elsie Elkes
Charity Fund
The Maud Elkington Charitable
Trust
The Ellerdale Trust
The Edith Maud Ellis 1985
Charitable Trust
The Elm House Trust
The Elmgrant Trust
The Emerton-Christie Charity
The Englefield Charitable Trust
The Epigoni Trust
The Erskine Cunningham Hill
Trust
Essex Community Foundation
The Essex Fairway Charitable
Trust
Essex Provincial Charity Fund
The Eventhall Family
Charitable Trust
The Everard Foundation
The Mayor of Exeter's Appeal
Fund
The Faber Charitable Trust
The Fairstead Trust
The Fairway Trust
The Family Foundations Trust
The Lord Faringdon Charitable
Trust
The Thomas Farr Charitable
Trust
Walter Farthing (Trust) Limited
Farthing Trust
The Fassnidge Memorial Trust
The Fawcett Charitable Trust

The John Feeney Charitable
Bequest
The A M Fenton Trust
The Fidelity UK Foundation
The Bluff Field Charitable Trust
The Doris Field Charitable
Trust
Fife Council/Common Good
Funds and Trusts
The Sir John Fisher Foundation
Fisherbeck Charitable Trust
The Earl Fitzwilliam Charitable
Trust
The Rose Flatau Charitable
Trust
Florence's Charitable Trust
The Florian Charitable Trust
The Gerald Fogel Charitable
Trust
Fordeve Ltd
The Foresters' Charity
Stewards UK Trust
Gwyneth Forrester Trust
The Donald Forrester Trust
Four Acre Trust
The Isaac and Freda Frankel
Memorial Charitable Trust
The Gordon Fraser Charitable
Trust
The Hugh Fraser Foundation
The Joseph Strong Frazer Trust
The Louis and Valerie
Freedman Charitable
Settlement
The Freemasons' Grand
Charity
The Charles S French
Charitable Trust
The Anne French Memorial
Trust
The Freshgate Trust
Foundation
The Friarsgate Trust
Friends of Wiznitz Limited
The Patrick Frost Foundation
The Fuellers Charitable Trust
Fund
Worshipful Company of
Furniture Makers Charitable
Fund
The Galbraith Trust
The Gale Family Charitable
Trust
The Gamlen Charitable Trust
The Gamma Trust
The Ganzoni Charitable Trust
The Gatsby Charitable
Foundation
ntoring-style support brings
benefits
The Robert Gavron Charitable
Trust
Simon Gibson Charitable Trust
The G C Gibson Charitable
Trust
The Harvey and Hilary Gilbert
Charitable Trust

Global Charities (formally
GCap Charities)
Worshipful Company of
Glovers of London Charity
Fund
GMC Trust
The GNC Trust
The Mrs Godfrey-Payton Trust
The Golden Bottle Trust
The Goldmark Trust
The Goldsmiths' Company
Charity
The Everard and Mina
Goodman Charitable
Foundation
Mike Gooley Trailfinders
Charity
The Gosling Foundation
Limited
The Gough Charitable Trust
The Gould Charitable Trust
A B Grace Trust
The Graff Foundation
Grampian Police Diced Cap
Charitable Fund
Grand Charitable Trust of the
Order of Women
Freemasons
Grantham Yorke Trust
GrantScape
The J G Graves Charitable
Trust
The Gray Trust
The Great Stone Bridge Trust
of Edenbridge
The Great Torrington Town
Lands Charity
The Constance Green
Foundation
The Philip Green Memorial
Trust
Mrs H R Greene Charitable
Settlement
Greenham Common
Community Trust Limited
Greggs Foundation
Grimmitt Trust
The Grocers' Charity
The GRP Charitable Trust
The Bishop of Guildford's
Foundation
The Walter Guinness
Charitable Trust
The Gunter Charitable Trust
Gurunanak
The H and J Spack Charitable
Trust
H and T Clients Charitable
Trust
The Edith Winifred Hall
Charitable Trust
Robert Hall Charity
Hamilton Wallace Trust
Sue Hammerson's Charitable
Trust
The Hammonds Charitable
Trust

Hampshire and Isle of Wight
Community Foundation
The Hampstead Wells and
Campden Trust
Hampton Fuel Allotment
Charity
The W A Handley Charitable
Trust
The Kathleen Hannay
Memorial Charity
The Doughty Hanson
Charitable Foundation
Lord Hanson Foundation
The Haramead Trust
Harbo Charities Limited
The Harbour Charitable Trust
The Harbour Foundation
The Hare of Steep Charitable
Trust
The Harebell Centenary Fund
The Hargrave Foundation
The Spencer Hart Charitable
Trust
The Hartley Charitable Trust
The N and P Hartley Memorial
Trust
The Edward Harvist Trust Fund
The Maurice Hatter Foundation
The M A Hawe Settlement
The Hawthorne Charitable
Trust
The Haydan Charitable Trust
Headley-Pitt Charitable Trust
Heagerty Charitable Trust
May Hearnshaw's Charity
The Heart of England
Community Foundation
The Heathcoat Trust
Heathside Charitable Trust
The Charlotte Heber-Percy
Charitable Trust
Percy Hedley 1990 Charitable
Trust
The Hedley Denton Charitable
Trust
The Hemby Trust
The Christina Mary Hendrie
Trust for Scottish and
Canadian Charities
The Tim Henman Charitable
Foundation
Esther Hennell Charitable
Trust
The Joanna Herbert-Stepney
Charitable Settlement
The Herefordshire Community
Foundation
The Hertfordshire Community
Foundation
The Rosalind Hicks Charitable
Trust
The Higgs Charitable Trust
The Hilden Charitable Fund
The Joseph and Mary Hiley
Trust
The Hillingdon Partnership
Trust

R G Hills Charitable Trust
Lady Hind Trust
The Henry C Hoare Charitable
Trust
The Eleemosynary Charity of
William Hobbayne
The Sir Julian Hodge
Charitable Trust
The Jane Hodge Foundation
The J G Hogg Charitable Trust
The Hollick Family Charitable
Trust
The Holliday Foundation
The Dorothy Holmes Charitable
Trust
P H Holt Foundation
Mary Homfray Charitable Trust
The Antony Hornby Charitable
Trust
The Worshipful Company of
Horners' Charitable Trusts
The Hornsey Parochial
Charities
The Hospital of God at
Greatham
The Sir Joseph Hotung
Charitable Settlement
The House of Industry Estate
The Daniel Howard Trust
The Clifford Howarth Charity
Trust
The Hudson Foundation
The Huggard Charitable Trust
The Hull and East Riding
Charitable Trust
The P Y N and B Hyams Trust
The Iliffe Family Charitable
Trust
Impetus Trust
The Ingram Trust
The Inman Charity
The Worshipful Company of
Innholders General Charity
Fund
The Inverforth Charitable Trust
The Ironmongers' Foundation
The Charles Irving Charitable
Trust
Irwin Trust
The ISA Charity
The Isaacs Charitable Trust
The J Isaacs Charitable Trust
The Isle of Anglesey Charitable
Trust
Isle of Dogs Community
Foundation
Elizabeth Jackson Charitable
Trust
John James Bristol Foundation
The Jenour Foundation
The Jephcott Charitable Trust
The Jonathan Joels Charitable
Trust
The Norman Joels Charitable
Trust
The Johnson Group Cleaners
Charity

The Joicey Trust
The Jones 1986 Charitable
Trust
Dezna Robins Jones Charitable
Foundation
The Marjorie and Geoffrey
Jones Charitable Trust
The Jordan Charitable
Foundation
The Joron Charitable Trust
The Lady Eileen Joseph
Foundation
The Josh Charitable Trust
JTH Charitable Trust
The Anton Jurgens Charitable
Trust
The Stanley Kalms Foundation
The Karenza Foundation
The Boris Karloff Charitable
Foundation
The Michael and Ilse Katz
Foundation
The Geoffrey John Kaye
Charitable Foundation
The Soli and Leah Kelaty Trust
Fund
The Kennedy Charitable
Foundation
The Nancy Kenyon Charitable
Trust
Keren Association
E and E Kernkraut Charities
Limited
The Kessler Foundation
The Ursula Keyes Trust
The King Henry VIII Endowed
Trust Warwick
The King/Cullimore Charitable
Trust
Kinsurdy Charitable Trust
The Richard Kirkman
Charitable Trust
Robert Kitchin (Saddlers'
Company)
Ernest Kleinwort Charitable
Trust
The Sir James Knott Trust
Lacims-Maclis Charitable Trust
The Late Sir Pierce Lacy
Charity Trust
John Laing Charitable Trust
The Laing Family Foundations
The Christopher Laing
Foundation
The David Laing Foundation
The Kirby Laing Foundation
The Martin Laing Foundation
Duchy of Lancaster Benevolent
Fund
The Jack Lane Charitable Trust
The Langdale Trust
The Langley Charitable Trust
The Langtree Trust
Lauchentilly Charitable
Foundation 1988
The Lauffer Family Charitable
Foundation

The Kathleen Laurence Trust
The Lawson Beckman
   Charitable Trust
The Raymond and Blanche
   Lawson Charitable Trust
The Leach Fourteenth Trust
The Leathersellers' Company
   Charitable Fund
The Lord Mayor of Leeds
   Appeal Fund
Leeds Building Society
   Charitable Foundation
Leicester Charity Link
The Kennedy Leigh Charitable
   Trust
Morris Leigh Foundation
Mrs Vera Leigh's Charity
The P Leigh-Bramwell Trust 'E'
The Lennox and Wyfold
   Foundation
The Erica Leonard Trust
The Mark Leonard Trust
Lord Leverhulme's Charitable
   Trust
The Sir Edward Lewis
   Foundation
Lichfield Conduit Lands
The Thomas Lilley Memorial
   Trust
Limoges Charitable Trust
The Linbury Trust
Lincolnshire Community
   Foundation
The Linden Charitable Trust
The Enid Linder Foundation
The Linmardon Trust
The Ruth and Stuart Lipton
   Charitable Trust
The Second Joseph Aaron
   Littman Foundation
The George John and Sheilah
   Livanos Charitable Trust
Liverpool Charity and Voluntary
   Services
Jack Livingstone Charitable
   Trust
The Elaine and Angus Lloyd
   Charitable Trust
The Lloyd Fund
Lloyd's Charities Trust
The Lloyd-Everett Trust
Lloyds TSB Foundation for
   Northern Ireland
Lloyds TSB Foundation for the
   Channel Islands
Llysdinam Charitable Trust
London Masonic Charitable
   Trust
The William and Katherine
   Longman Trust
The Loseley and Guildway
   Charitable Trust
The Lowy Mitchell Foundation
The C L Loyd Charitable Trust
Henry Lumley Charitable Trust
Paul Lunn-Rockliffe Charitable
   Trust

The Lynn Foundation
The Lyras Family Charitable
   Trust
The M D and S Charitable
   Trust
The E M MacAndrew Trust
Macdonald-Buchanan
   Charitable Trust
The Macfarlane Walker Trust
The Mackay and Brewer
   Charitable Trust
The Mackintosh Foundation
The MacRobert Trust
The Mactaggart Third Fund
Magdalen Hospital Trust
The Brian Maguire Charitable
   Trust
Mahavir Trust
The Makin Charitable Trust
Malbin Trust
The Mallinckrodt Foundation
Man Group plc Charitable
   Trust
The Manchester Guardian
   Society Charitable Trust
Lord Mayor of Manchester's
   Charity Appeal Trust
Mandeville Trust
The Manifold Charitable Trust
W M Mann Foundation
R W Mann Trust
The Stella and Alexander
   Margulies Charitable Trust
Market Harborough and The
   Bowdens Charity
The Ann and David Marks
   Foundation
The Hilda and Samuel Marks
   Foundation
J P Marland Charitable Trust
The Marsh Christian Trust
The Charlotte Marshall
   Charitable Trust
The Jim Marshall Charitable
   Trust
The D G Marshall of
   Cambridge Trust
Sir George Martin Trust
John Martin's Charity
The Violet Mauray Charitable
   Trust
The Maxell Educational Trust
The Maxwell Family Foundation
Evelyn May Trust
Mazars Charitable Trust
The A M McGreevy No 5
   Charitable Settlement
The McKenna Charitable Trust
Martin McLaren Memorial
   Trust
The Helen Isabella McMorran
   Charitable Foundation
The James Frederick and Ethel
   Anne Measures Charity
The Medlock Charitable Trust
Melodor Ltd

The Mercers' Charitable
   Foundation
The Merchant Venturers'
   Charity
The Merchants' House of
   Glasgow
Mercury Phoenix Trust
The Mersey Docks and
   Harbour Company
   Charitable Fund
Community Foundation for
   Merseyside
Gerald Micklem Charitable
   Trust
The Masonic Province of
   Middlesex Charitable Trust
Midhurst Pensions Trust
The Hugh and Mary Miller
   Bequest Trust
The Miller Foundation
The Millhouses Charitable
   Trust
The Millichope Foundation
The Mills Charity
Milton Keynes Community
   Foundation
The Edgar Milward Charity
The Keith and Joan
   Mindelsohn Charitable
   Trust
The Minos Trust
Minton Charitable Trust
The Mirianog Trust
The Laurence Misener
   Charitable Trust
The Misselbrook Trust
The Brian Mitchell Charitable
   Settlement
The Esme Mitchell Trust
Keren Mitzvah Trust
The Mizpah Trust
The Mobbs Memorial Trust Ltd
The Modiano Charitable Trust
The Mole Charitable Trust
The D C Moncrieff Charitable
   Trust
The Montague Thompson
   Coon Charitable Trust
The Colin Montgomerie
   Charitable Foundation
The Monument Trust
Moody Charitable Trust
George A Moore Foundation
The Morgan Charitable
   Foundation
The Mr and Mrs J T Morgan
   Foundation
The Oliver Morland Charitable
   Trust
The Willie and Mabel Morris
   Charitable Trust
The Peter Morrison Charitable
   Foundation
The Stanley Morrison
   Charitable Trust
Vyoel Moshe Charitable Trust
The Mulberry Trust

The Mushroom Fund
The Kitty and Daniel Nabarro Charitable Trust
The Willie Nagel Charitable Trust
The Naggar Charitable Trust
The Janet Nash Charitable Settlement
Needham Market and Barking Welfare Charities
The Worshipful Company of Needlemakers' Charitable Fund
The James Neill Trust Fund
Nestle Rowntree Employees Community Fund
New Court Charitable Trust
Newpier Charity Ltd
The Noon Foundation
Norie Charitable Trust
The Norman Family Charitable Trust
The Duncan Norman Trust Fund
The Normanby Charitable Trust
The Northwood Charitable Trust
The Notgrove Trust
Nottinghamshire Community Foundation
The Nottinghamshire Miners' Welfare Trust Fund
The Oak Trust
The Oakdale Trust
The Oakmoor Charitable Trust
The Odin Charitable Trust
Oglesby Charitable Trust
The Old Broad Street Charity Trust
Old Possum's Practical Trust
Onaway Trust
The Ormsby Charitable Trust
Orrin Charitable Trust
The Oxfordshire Community Foundation
The P F Charitable Trust
Padwa Charitable Foundation
Panahpur Charitable Trust
The James Pantyfedwen Foundation
The Paphitis Charitable Trust
The Paragon Trust
The Samuel and Freda Parkinson Charitable Trust
Miss M E Swinton Paterson's Charitable Trust
The Patrick Charitable Trust
The Peacock Charitable Trust
The Susanna Peake Charitable Trust
The Dowager Countess Eleanor Peel Trust
Pegasus (Stanley) Trust
The Pennycress Trust
The Philips and Rubens Charitable Trust

The Phillips Family Charitable Trust
The David Pickford Charitable Foundation
The Bernard Piggott Trust
The Claude and Margaret Pike Charity
The Cecil Pilkington Charitable Trust
The Sir Harry Pilkington Trust
Miss A M Pilkington's Charitable Trust
The Plaisterers' Company Charitable Trust
G S Plaut Charitable Trust Limited
The Poling Charitable Trust
The George and Esme Pollitzer Charitable Settlement
The J S F Pollitzer Charitable Settlement
The Mayor of Poole's Appeal Fund
Edith and Ferdinand Porjes Charitable Trust
The John Porter Charitable Trust
The Porter Foundation
The Portrack Charitable Trust
The David and Elaine Potter Foundation
The W L Pratt Charitable Trust
Premierquote Ltd
The Primrose Trust
Princess Anne's Charities
Prison Service Charity Fund
The Privy Purse Charitable Trust
The Proven Family Trust
The Provincial Grand Charity of the Province of Derbyshire
PSA Peugeot Citroen Charity Trust
Quartet Community Foundation
The Queen's Silver Jubilee Trust
The R D Crusaders Foundation
R J M Charitable Trust
The Monica Rabagliati Charitable Trust
Rachel Charitable Trust
The Mr and Mrs Philip Rackham Charitable Trust
The Rainford Trust
The Joseph and Lena Randall Charitable Trust
The Rank Foundation
The Joseph Rank Trust
Ranworth Trust
The Ratcliff Foundation
The Ratcliffe Charitable Trust
The Ravensdale Trust
The John Rayner Charitable Trust
The Albert Reckitt Charitable Trust
The Sir James Reckitt Charity

The Red Arrows Trust
The C A Redfern Charitable Foundation
Redfern Charitable Trust
The Reed Foundation
Relief Fund for Romania Limited
The Rest Harrow Trust
Reuben Brothers Foundation
The Joan K Reynell Charitable Trust
The Nathaniel Reyner Trust Fund
The Rhododendron Trust
The Rhondda Cynon Taff Welsh Church Acts Fund
Daisie Rich Trust
C B Richard Ellis Charitable Trust
The Clive Richards Charity
The Richmond Parish Lands Charity
Ridgesave Limited
The Ripple Effect Foundation
The Sir John Ritblat Family Foundation
The River Farm Foundation
The Rivers Charitable Trust
Riverside Charitable Trust Limited
The Robertson Trust
Robyn Charitable Trust
The Rochester Bridge Trust
The Rofeh Trust
Richard Rogers Charitable Settlement
Rokach Family Charitable Trust
The Helen Roll Charitable Trust
The Sir James Roll Charitable Trust
Romeera Foundation
The Gerald Ronson Foundation
The C A Rookes Charitable Trust
Mrs L D Rope Third Charitable Settlement
The Rose Foundation
The Rothermere Foundation
The Rothley Trust
The Rothschild Foundation
The Roughley Charitable Trust
The Rowan Charitable Trust
The Rowlands Trust
Royal Artillery Charitable Fund
The RRAF Charitable Trust
The Alfred and Frances Rubens Charitable Trust
The Rubin Foundation
William Arthur Rudd Memorial Trust
The Rufford Maurice Laing Foundation
The Rugby Group Benevolent Fund Limited
The Russell Trust

The J S and E C Rymer Charitable Trust

The Michael Sacher Charitable Trust

The Michael Harry Sacher Trust

Dr Mortimer and Theresa Sackler Foundation

The Saddlers' Company Charitable Fund

The Alan and Babette Sainsbury Charitable Fund

The Saintbury Trust

The Salamander Charitable Trust

The Salt Trust

The Salters' Charities

The Andrew Salvesen Charitable Trust

The Sammermar Trust

Basil Samuel Charitable Trust

Coral Samuel Charitable Trust

The Samworth Foundation

The Sandhu Charitable Foundation

Jimmy Savile Charitable Trust

The Schmidt-Bodner Charitable Trust

The R H Scholes Charitable Trust

The Schreib Trust

The Schroder Foundation

The Scotshill Trust

The Scott Bader Commonwealth Ltd

The Frieda Scott Charitable Trust

The Storrow Scott Will Trust

The Scottish Community Foundation

The Scouloudi Foundation

The Searchlight Electric Charitable Trust

The Samuel Sebba Charitable Trust

SEM Charitable Trust

The Cyril Shack Trust

Peter Shalson Family Charitable Trust

The Shanti Charitable Trust

ShareGift (The Orr Mackintosh Foundation)

The Sheepdrove Trust

The Sheldon Trust

The P and D Shepherd Charitable Trust

The Sylvia and Colin Shepherd Charitable Trust

The Archie Sherman Charitable Trust

The Barnett and Sylvia Shine No 2 Charitable Trust

The Charles Shorto Charitable Trust

David and Jennifer Sieff Charitable Trust

The Julius Silman Charitable Trust

The Leslie Silver Charitable Trust

The Huntly and Margery Sinclair Charitable Trust

The Charles Skey Charitable Trust

Skipton Building Society Charitable Foundation

The John Slater Foundation

Rita and David Slowe Charitable Trust

The SMB Charitable Trust

The N Smith Charitable Settlement

The Amanda Smith Charitable Trust

The E H Smith Charitable Trust

The Smith Charitable Trust

The Leslie Smith Foundation

Solihull Community Foundation

The Solo Charitable Settlement

Dr Richard Solomon's Charitable Trust

The South Square Trust

The Stephen R and Philippa H Southall Charitable Trust

The W F Southall Trust

The Southwold Trust

Spar Charitable Fund

The Spear Charitable Trust

The Worshipful Company of Spectacle Makers' Charity

The Jessie Spencer Trust

The Ralph and Irma Sperring Charity

W W Spooner Charitable Trust

Stanley Spooner Deceased Charitable Trust

Rosalyn and Nicholas Springer Charitable Trust

The Spurrell Charitable Trust

The Geoff and Fiona Squire Foundation

St James' Trust Settlement

St Mark's Overseas Aid Trust (SMOAT)

The Late St Patrick White Charitable Trust

Miss Doreen Stanford Trust

The Stanton Ballard Charitable Trust

The Star Charitable Trust

The Peter Stebbings Memorial Charity

The Steel Charitable Trust

The Hugh Stenhouse Foundation

The Sigmund Sternberg Charitable Foundation

The Stevenage Community Trust

The June Stevens Foundation

Stevenson Family's Charitable Trust

The Steventon Allotments and Relief-in-Need Charity

The Andy Stewart Charitable Foundation

The Leonard Laity Stoate Charitable Trust

The Edward Stocks-Massey Bequest Fund

The Stoller Charitable Trust

The M J C Stone Charitable Trust

The Samuel Storey Family Charitable Trust

The Strangward Trust

The Strasser Foundation

Stratford upon Avon Town Trust

Strathclyde Police Benevolent Fund

The A B Strom and R Strom Charitable Trust

The Sudborough Foundation

The Suffolk Foundation

The Alan Sugar Foundation

The Bernard Sunley Charitable Foundation

Surrey Community Foundation

Sussex Community Foundation

The Adrienne and Leslie Sussman Charitable Trust

The Sutasoma Trust

Sutton Coldfield Municipal Charities

The Swan Trust

Swansea and Brecon Diocesan Board of Finance Limited

The John Swire (1989) Charitable Trust

The Swire Charitable Trust

The Hugh and Ruby Sykes Charitable Trust

The Charles and Elsie Sykes Trust

The Stella Symons Charitable Trust

The Talbot Village Trust

Tallow Chandlers Benevolent Fund

The Tangent Charitable Trust

The Lady Tangye Charitable Trust

The Tanner Trust

The Mrs A Lacy Tate Trust

The Tay Charitable Trust

C B and H H Taylor 1984 Trust

The A R Taylor Charitable Trust

Rosanna Taylor's 1987 Charity Trust

The Tedworth Charitable Trust

Tees Valley Community Foundation

The Templeton Goodwill Trust

Thames Community Foundation

The Thames Wharf Charity

The David Thomas Charitable Trust

The Arthur and Margaret
Thompson Charitable Trust
The Maurice and Vivien
Thompson Charitable Trust
The Thompson Family
Charitable Trust
The Thornton Foundation
The Tisbury Telegraph Trust
The Tolkien Trust
Tollemache (Buckminster)
Charitable Trust
Toni and Guy Charitable
Foundation Limited
The Tower Hill Trust
The Mayor of Trafford's Charity
Fund
Annie Tranmer Charitable Trust
Anthony Travis Charitable Trust
The Constance Travis
Charitable Trust
The Treeside Trust
The Triangle Trust (1949) Fund
The Truemark Trust
Truemart Limited
Trust Sixty Three
The Trusthouse Charitable
Foundation
The Tudor Trust
The R D Turner Charitable
Trust
The Douglas Turner Trust
The Florence Turner Trust
The TUUT Charitable Trust
Community Foundation Serving
Tyne and Wear and
Northumberland
UKI Charitable Foundation
Ulverston Town Lands Charity
The Underwood Trust
United Trusts
The Michael Uren Foundation
The David Uri Memorial Trust
The Albert Van Den Bergh
Charitable Trust
John and Lucille van Geest
Foundation
Mrs Maud Van Norden's
Charitable Foundation
The Vandervell Foundation
The Vardy Foundation
The Verdon-Smith Family
Charitable Settlement
Roger Vere Foundation
Victoria Homes Trust
Viking Cares (For the Kids)
The Nigel Vinson Charitable
Trust
Voluntary Action Fund
Wade's Charity
The Wakefield and Tetley Trust
The F J Wallis Charitable
Settlement
The Ward Blenkinsop Trust
The George Ward Charitable
Trust
G R Waters Charitable Trust
2000

Weatherley Charitable Trust
The William Webster
Charitable Trust
The Weinberg Foundation
The Weinstock Fund
The James Weir Foundation
The Barbara Welby Trust
Welsh Church Fund Dyfed
area (Carmarthenshire,
Ceredigion and
Pembrokeshire)
The Welton Foundation
The Wessex Youth Trust
The West Derby Wastelands
Charity
West London Synagogue
Charitable Fund
Mrs S K West's Charitable
Trust
The Garfield Weston
Foundation
The Melanie White Foundation
Limited
The Whitecourt Charitable
Trust
A H and B C Whiteley
Charitable Trust
The Whittlesey Charity
The Lionel Wigram Memorial
Trust
The Kay Williams Charitable
Foundation
The Williams Charitable Trust
Williams Serendipity Trust
The H D H Wills 1965
Charitable Trust
The Dame Violet Wills Will
Trust
The Wilmcote Charitrust
Sumner Wilson Charitable
Trust
David Wilson Foundation
The Community Foundation for
Wiltshire and Swindon
The Harold Hyam Wingate
Foundation
Wirral Mayor's Charity
The Witzenfeld Foundation
The Wixamtree Trust
The Woburn 1986 Charitable
Trust
The Charles Wolfson
Charitable Trust
The Wolseley Charitable Trust
The James Wood Bequest
Fund
The Woodcock Charitable Trust
The F Glenister Woodger Trust
The Geoffrey Woods Charitable
Foundation
The Woodward Charitable
Trust
The A and R Woolf Charitable
Trust
The Woolnoth Society
Charitable Trust
The Worwin UK Foundation

The Wragge and Co. Charitable
Trust
The Diana Edgson Wright
Charitable Trust
The Matthews Wrightson
Charity Trust
Wychville Ltd
The Wyndham Charitable Trust
The Yardley Great Trust
The Dennis Alan Yardy
Charitable Trust
Yorkshire Building Society
Charitable Foundation
The South Yorkshire
Community Foundation
The John Young Charitable
Settlement
The William Allen Young
Charitable Trust
Elizabeth and Prince Zaiger
Trust
The Marjorie and Arnold Ziff
Charitable Foundation
The Zochonis Charitable Trust
Zurich Community Trust (UK)
Limited

Health

The 1989 Willan Charitable Trust
Aberbrothock Charitable Trust
The ACT Foundation
Action Medical Research
The Company of Actuaries' Charitable Trust Fund
The Adamson Trust
The Adint Charitable Trust
The AIM Foundation
The Green and Lilian F M Ainsworth and Family Benevolent Fund
The Sylvia Aitken Charitable Trust
The Ajahma Charitable Trust
The Alchemy Foundation
Alcohol Education and Research Council
The Alliance Family Foundation
The Pat Allsop Charitable Trust
Almondsbury Charity
The Ammco Trust
Andor Charitable Trust
Anglo American Group Foundation
The Milly Apthorp Charitable Trust
The John Armitage Charitable Trust
The Armourers' and Brasiers' Gauntlet Trust
The Artemis Charitable Trust
Arthritis Research Campaign
The Arts and Entertainment Charitable Trust
The Norman C Ashton Foundation
Astellas European Foundation
The Astor Foundation
The Astor of Hever Trust
The Lord Austin Trust
The John Avins Trustees
Harry Bacon Foundation
Veta Bailey Charitable Trust
The Baker Charitable Trust
The Roy and Pixie Baker Charitable Trust
The Balcombe Charitable Trust
The Balint Family Charitable Trusts
The Albert Casanova Ballard Deceased Trust
The Band Trust
The Barbers' Company General Charities
The Barbour Trust
The Barcapel Foundation
Barchester Healthcare Foundation
David and Frederick Barclay Foundation
The Barnwood House Trust
The Misses Barrie Charitable Trust

The Batchworth Trust
B-CH 1971 Charitable Trust
The John Beckwith Charitable Trust
The Peter Beckwith Charitable Trust
The Bellahouston Bequest Fund
The Bellhouse Foundation
Bergqvist Charitable Trust
The Ruth Berkowitz Charitable Trust
The Bestway Foundation
The Mason Bibby 1981 Trust
BibleLands
The Big Lottery Fund
The Billmeir Charitable Trust
The Bintaub Charitable Trust
The Birmingham District Nursing Charitable Trust
The Birmingham Hospital Saturday Fund Medical Charity and Welfare Trust
Sir Alec Black's Charity
The Herbert and Peter Blagrave Charitable Trust
The Boltons Trust
The Booth Charities
The Boots Charitable Trust
The Boshier-Hinton Foundation
The Bothwell Charitable Trust
The Harry Bottom Charitable Trust
Sir Clive Bourne Family Trust
The Bowerman Charitable Trust
The Tony Bramall Charitable Trust
The Breast Cancer Research Trust
The Brighton District Nursing Association Trust
The British Council for Prevention of Blindness
The British Dietetic Association General and Education Trust Fund
British Heart Foundation
The David Brooke Charity
The Rory and Elizabeth Brooks Foundation
The Charles Brotherton Trust
Bill Brown's Charitable Settlement
R S Brownless Charitable Trust
Buckland Charitable Trust
The BUPA Foundation
The Burden Trust
The Burdett Trust for Nursing
The Burry Charitable Trust
The Audrey and Stanley Burton 1960 Charitable Trust
The Arnold Burton 1998 Charitable Trust
The Derek Butler Trust

Henry T and Lucy B Cadbury Charitable Trust
P H G Cadbury Charitable Trust
The William A Cadbury Charitable Trust
The Cadbury Foundation
The Edward and Dorothy Cadbury Trust
M R Cannon 1998 Charitable Trust
The Carr-Gregory Trust
The Carron Charitable Trust
The Elizabeth Casson Trust
The Castang Foundation
The Wilfrid and Constance Cave Foundation
The Cayo Foundation
Celtic Charity Fund
The Cemlyn-Jones Trust
Champneys Charitable Foundation
The Charities Advisory Trust
Chest, Heart and Stroke Scotland
Child Growth Foundation
Children's Liver Disease Foundation
The Children's Research Fund
The Childwick Trust
The Chrimes Family Charitable Trust
J A Clark Charitable Trust
The Clarke Charitable Settlement
The Cleopatra Trust
Miss V L Clore's 1967 Charitable Trust
Richard Cloudesley's Charity
The Clover Trust
The Coalfields Regeneration Trust
The John Coates Charitable Trust
The Denise Cohen Charitable Trust
The Vivienne and Samuel Cohen Charitable Trust
The Colchester Catalyst Charity
The Bernard Coleman Charitable Trust
The Colt Foundation
The Coltstaple Trust
The Congleton Inclosure Trust
The Consolidated Charities for the Infirm Merchant Taylors' Company
Harold and Daphne Cooper Charitable Trust
The J Reginald Corah Foundation Fund
Michael Cornish Charitable Trust
The Cotton Trust
The John Cowan Foundation

The Sir William Coxen Trust Fund
The Lord Cozens-Hardy Trust
Michael Crawford Children's Charity
The Crescent Trust
Criffel Charitable Trust
The Peter Cruddas Foundation
Cruden Foundation Ltd
The Cunningham Trust
The Harry Cureton Charitable Trust
The Manny Cussins Foundation
The D'Oyly Carte Charitable Trust
The Roald Dahl Foundation
The Dr and Mrs A Darlington Charitable Trust
Baron Davenport's Charity
The Wilfrid Bruce Davis Charitable Trust
The De Clermont Charitable Company Ltd
The Deakin Charitable Trust
The Delves Charitable Trust
The Demigryphon Trust
The Denman Charitable Trust
The Denton Charitable Trust
The Denton Wilde Sapte Charitable Trust
The J N Derbyshire Trust
Diabetes UK
The Dinwoodie Settlement
Disability Aid Fund (The Roger and Jean Jefcoate Trust)
The Djanogly Foundation
The Derek and Eileen Dodgson Foundation
The Dorema Charitable Trust
The Dorus Trust
The Drayson Foundation
Dromintee Trust
The Duis Charitable Trust
The Dumbreck Charity
The Dunhill Medical Trust
The Houghton Dunn Charitable Trust
The Dunn Family Charitable Trust
The W E Dunn Trust
The Dyers' Company Charitable Trust
The James Dyson Foundation
The Earmark Trust
The Sir John Eastwood Foundation
The EBM Charitable Trust
The Gilbert and Eileen Edgar Foundation
Gilbert Edgar Trust
The Edinburgh Trust, No 2 Account
The Gerald Palmer Eling Trust Company
The John Ellerman Foundation
James Ellis Charitable Trust

The Emerton-Christie Charity
The Emmandjay Charitable Trust
The Englefield Charitable Trust
The Epigoni Trust
Epilepsy Research UK
The Eranda Foundation
Essex Provincial Charity Fund
The Eveson Charitable Trust
The F P Limited Charitable Trust
Faisaltex Charitable Trust
The Family Rich Charities Trust
Samuel William Farmer's Trust
Joseph Fattorini Charitable Trust 'B' Account
The February Foundation
Elizabeth Ferguson Charitable Trust Fund
Fife Council/Common Good Funds and Trusts
Dixie Rose Findlay Charitable Trust
The Sir John Fisher Foundation
The Fishmongers' Company's Charitable Trust
The Fitton Trust
Bud Flanagan Leukaemia Fund
The Ian Fleming Charitable Trust
Florence's Charitable Trust
The Florian Charitable Trust
The Flow Foundation
The Follett Trust
Ford Britain Trust
The Lady Forester Trust
The Foresters' Charity Stewards UK Trust
The Donald Forrester Trust
The Anna Rosa Forster Charitable Trust
The Forte Charitable Trust
The Hugh Fraser Foundation
The Joseph Strong Frazer Trust
The Louis and Valerie Freedman Charitable Settlement
The Freemasons' Grand Charity
The Freshfield Foundation
The Freshgate Trust Foundation
The Friarsgate Trust
The Frognal Trust
T F C Frost Charitable Trust
Maurice Fry Charitable Trust
The Fuserna Foundation
The Galanthus Trust
The Ganzoni Charitable Trust
The Garnett Charitable Trust
The Gatsby Charitable Foundation
Gatwick Airport Community Trust
The Robert Gavron Charitable Trust

Jacqueline and Michael Gee Charitable Trust
The General Nursing Council for England and Wales Trust
J Paul Getty Jr Charitable Trust
Simon Gibson Charitable Trust
The G C Gibson Charitable Trust
The Girdlers' Company Charitable Trust
The B and P Glasser Charitable Trust
GMC Trust
The Meir Golda Trust
The Sydney and Phyllis Goldberg Memorial Charitable Trust
The Golden Bottle Trust
Golden Charitable Trust
The Jack Goldhill Charitable Trust
The Goldsmiths' Company Charity
The Everard and Mina Goodman Charitable Foundation
Mike Gooley Trailfinders Charity
The Grand Order of Water Rats' Charities Fund
Grantham Yorke Trust
The Constance Green Foundation
Grimmitt Trust
The Grocers' Charity
The Gunter Charitable Trust
H C D Memorial Fund
E F and M G Hall Charitable Trust
Robert Hall Charity
The Hamamelis Trust
Hamilton Wallace Trust
The Helen Hamlyn Trust
Sue Hammerson's Charitable Trust
Hampton Fuel Allotment Charity
The W A Handley Charitable Trust
The Hanlye Charitable Trust
The Kathleen Hannay Memorial Charity
The Haramead Trust
The Harbour Charitable Trust
The Harebell Centenary Fund
The Hargrave Foundation
The Kenneth Hargreaves Charitable Trust
The Harris Charitable Trust
The Harris Family Charitable Trust
The John Harrison Charitable Trust
The N and P Hartley Memorial Trust

The Alfred And Peggy Harvey
Charitable Trust
Hasluck Charitable Trust
The Maurice Hatter Foundation
The Haymills Charitable Trust
The Charles Hayward
Foundation
The Headley Trust
Healthsure Group Ltd
The Hedley Foundation
The Michael and Morven Heller
Charitable Foundation
The Simon Heller Charitable
Settlement
Help the Hospices
The Hemby Trust
The Christina Mary Hendrie
Trust for Scottish and
Canadian Charities
The G D Herbert Charitable
Trust
The Joanna Herbert-Stepney
Charitable Settlement
The Charles Littlewood Hill
Trust
Lady Hind Trust
Hinduja Foundation
The Hintze Family Charitable
Foundation
The Sir Julian Hodge
Charitable Trust
The Jane Hodge Foundation
The Holbeck Charitable Trust
The Hollands-Warren Fund
The Edward Holt Trust
The Homelands Charitable
Trust
The Homestead Charitable
Trust
The Antony Hornby Charitable
Trust
The Horne Trust
The Hospital Saturday Fund
The Huddersfield Medical Trust
Fund
Human Relief Foundation
The Humanitarian Trust
The Humberside Charitable
Health Trust
The Albert Hunt Trust
Miss Agnes H Hunter's Trust
Huntingdon Freemen's Charity
The Nani Huyu Charitable Trust
The Iliffe Family Charitable
Trust
International Spinal Research
Trust
The Isaacs Charitable Trust
The Island Health Trust
The Ruth and Lionel Jacobson
Trust (Second Fund) No 2
John James Bristol Foundation
The Jarman Charitable Trust
The John Jarrold Trust
The Jeffrey Charitable Trust
The Nicholas Joels Charitable
Trust

The Elton John Aids
Foundation
The Michael John Trust
The Lillie Johnson Charitable
Trust
The Johnson Wax Ltd
Charitable Trust
The Jones 1986 Charitable
Trust
Dezna Robins Jones Charitable
Foundation
The Joron Charitable Trust
The Judith Trust
The Ian Karten Charitable
Trust
The Michael and Ilse Katz
Foundation
The Emmanuel Kaye
Foundation
The Caron Keating Foundation
The KempWelch Charitable
Trust
The Kay Kendall Leukaemia
Fund
The Kennedy Charitable
Foundation
The Peter Kershaw Trust
The Ursula Keyes Trust
The King's Fund
The Kingsbury Charity
The Mary Kinross Charitable
Trust
Kirschel Foundation
Ernest Kleinwort Charitable
Trust
The Kobler Trust
The Kohn Foundation
The KPMG Foundation
The Kreditor Charitable Trust
The Kreitman Foundation
The Heinz, Anna and Carol
Kroch Foundation
The Kyte Charitable Trust
Maurice and Hilda Laing
Charitable Trust
The Christopher Laing
Foundation
The David Laing Foundation
The Beatrice Laing Trust
The Lambert Charitable Trust
The Langdale Trust
The Langley Charitable Trust
The LankellyChase Foundation
The Lanvern Foundation
The R J Larg Family Charitable
Trust
Laslett's (Hinton) Charity
Mrs F B Laurence Charitable
Trust
The Kathleen Laurence Trust
The Edgar E Lawley Foundation
The Lawson Beckman
Charitable Trust
The Raymond and Blanche
Lawson Charitable Trust
The Mason Le Page Charitable
Trust

The Leathersellers' Company
Charitable Fund
The Arnold Lee Charitable
Trust
The William Leech Charity
Leeds Building Society
Charitable Foundation
The Leigh Trust
Lesley Lesley and Mutter Trust
Leukaemia Research Fund
The Joseph Levy Charitable
Foundation
Lewis Family Charitable Trust
John Lewis Partnership
General Community Fund
The Lewis Ward Trust
Lifeline 4 Kids
The Linbury Trust
The Linden Charitable Trust
The Enid Linder Foundation
Frank Litchfield Charitable
Trust
The Andrew and Mary
Elizabeth Little Charitable
Trust
The George John and Sheilah
Livanos Charitable Trust
The Liverpool One Foundation
The Elaine and Angus Lloyd
Charitable Trust
Lloyds TSB Foundation for
Northern Ireland
Lloyds TSB Foundation for the
Channel Islands
London Catalyst
The London Law Trust
The Lord's Taverners
The Lotus Foundation
The C L Loyd Charitable Trust
The Marie Helen Luen
Charitable Trust
Robert Luff Foundation Ltd
Henry Lumley Charitable Trust
Lord and Lady Lurgan Trust
The Lyons Charitable Trust
The Lyras Family Charitable
Trust
The Madeline Mabey Trust
The E M MacAndrew Trust
The R S Macdonald Charitable
Trust
Macdonald-Buchanan
Charitable Trust
The Mackintosh Foundation
The MacRobert Trust
Mandeville Trust
R W Mann Trust
The Leslie and Lilian Manning
Trust
The Manoukian Charitable
Foundation
The Marchday Charitable Fund
Market Harborough and The
Bowdens Charity
The Hilda and Samuel Marks
Foundation

The Michael Marsh Charitable Trust
The Marsh Christian Trust
The Charlotte Marshall Charitable Trust
Marshgate Charitable Settlement
Sir George Martin Trust
John Martin's Charity
The Nancie Massey Charitable Trust
The Violet Mauray Charitable Trust
The Maxwell Family Foundation
Evelyn May Trust
The Robert McAlpine Foundation
The McKenna Charitable Trust
D D McPhail Charitable Settlement
Medical Research Council
The Medlock Charitable Trust
The Anthony and Elizabeth Mellows Charitable Settlement
Meningitis Trust
Brian Mercer Charitable Trust
The Mercers' Charitable Foundation
The Merchant Taylors' Company Charities Fund
Mercury Phoenix Trust
The Tony Metherell Charitable Trust
The Methodist Relief and Development Fund
T and J Meyer Family Foundation Limited
Gerald Micklem Charitable Trust
The Migraine Trust
Miles Trust for the Putney and Roehampton Community
The Hugh and Mary Miller Bequest Trust
The Miller Foundation
The Millichope Foundation
The Millward Charitable Trust
The Peter Minet Trust
Minge's Gift and the Pooled Trusts
The Mishcon Family Charitable Trust
The Mitchell Charitable Trust
Monmouthshire County Council Welsh Church Act Fund
The Monument Trust
The Peter Moores Foundation
The Morel Charitable Trust
The Morgan Charitable Foundation
The Morris Charitable Trust
The Willie and Mabel Morris Charitable Trust
G M Morrison Charitable Trust
Brian and Jill Moss Charitable Trust

The Moss Charitable Trust
The Robert and Margaret Moss Charitable Trust
The Mothercare Charitable Foundation
J P Moulton Charitable Foundation
The Edwina Mountbatten Trust
The F H Muirhead Charitable Trust
The Edith Murphy Foundation
Murphy-Neumann Charity Company Limited
The Janet Nash Charitable Settlement
Asthma UK
The Nchima Trust
The Neighbourly Charitable Trust
Nestle Rowntree Employees Community Fund
Network for Social Change
New Court Charitable Trust
The Frances and Augustus Newman Foundation
The Normanby Charitable Trust
The North British Hotel Trust
The North West Cancer Research Fund
North West London Community Foundation
The Northampton Queen's Institute Relief in Sickness Fund
The Northcott Devon Medical Foundation
The Northwood Charitable Trust
The Norton Foundation
The Norton Rose Charitable Foundation
The Nottingham General Dispensary
The Nottinghamshire Miners' Welfare Trust Fund
The Nuffield Foundation
The Father O'Mahoney Memorial Trust
The Oakdale Trust
The Oakley Charitable Trust
Old Possum's Practical Trust
The Olga Charitable Trust
The Owen Family Trust
The Park Charitable Trust
The Parthenon Trust
Arthur James Paterson Charitable Trust
The Constance Paterson Charitable Trust
Paycare Charity Trust (previously known as Patients' Aid Association Hospital and Medical Charities Trust)
The Harry Payne Trust
The Peacock Charitable Trust

The Pedmore Sporting Club Trust Fund
The Dowager Countess Eleanor Peel Trust
Peltz Trust
The Persula Foundation
The Bernard Piggott Trust
The Cecil Pilkington Charitable Trust
The Pilkington Charities Fund
The Austin and Hope Pilkington Trust
The Col W W Pilkington Will Trusts The General Charity Fund
G S Plaut Charitable Trust Limited
The John Porter Charitable Trust
The Porter Foundation
The J E Posnansky Charitable Trust
The Mary Potter Convent Hospital Trust
The Douglas Prestwich Charitable Trust
Sir John Priestman Charity Trust
The Prince's Charities Foundation
Princess Anne's Charities
The Priory Foundation
The Richard and Christine Purchas Charitable Trust
Mr and Mrs J A Pye's Charitable Settlement
The Pyne Charitable Trust
The Queen Anne's Gate Foundation
The Monica Rabagliati Charitable Trust
The Mr and Mrs Philip Rackham Charitable Trust
Richard Radcliffe Charitable Trust
The Rank Foundation
The Fanny Rapaport Charitable Settlement
The Ravensdale Trust
The Roger Raymond Charitable Trust
The Rayne Foundation
The C A Redfern Charitable Foundation
The Reed Foundation
The Max Reinhardt Charitable Trust
Relief Fund for Romania Limited
REMEDI
Reuben Brothers Foundation
The Violet M Richards Charity
The Richmond Parish Lands Charity
The Muriel Edith Rickman Trust
The River Farm Foundation

Riverside Charitable Trust Limited

Thomas Roberts Trust

The Robertson Trust

Edwin George Robinson Charitable Trust

The Roddick Foundation

The Rosca Trust

The Rose Foundation

Rosetrees Trust

The Rothera Charitable Settlement

The Rotherwick Foundation

The Rothley Trust

The Rothschild Foundation

Mrs Gladys Row Fogo Charitable Trust

The Rowan Charitable Trust

The Christopher Rowbotham Charitable Trust

The Rowlands Trust

The RRAF Charitable Trust

The Rufford Maurice Laing Foundation

Ryklow Charitable Trust 1992

The J S and E C Rymer Charitable Trust

The Michael Sacher Charitable Trust

The Michael Harry Sacher Trust

Dr Mortimer and Theresa Sackler Foundation

The Raymond and Beverley Sackler Foundation

The Alan and Babette Sainsbury Charitable Fund

The Saintbury Trust

The Saints and Sinners Trust

The Salters' Charities

The Andrew Salvesen Charitable Trust

Basil Samuel Charitable Trust

The Peter Samuel Charitable Trust

The Camilla Samuel Fund

The Sandra Charitable Trust

The Scarfe Charitable Trust

Schroder Charity Trust

The Scotshill Trust

Scott (Eredine) Charitable Trust

Sir Samuel Scott of Yews Trust

The Sir James and Lady Scott Trust

The Scouloudi Foundation

The Helene Sebba Charitable Trust

The Samuel Sebba Charitable Trust

The Ayrton Senna Foundation

The Jean Shanks Foundation

The Sheepdrove Trust

The Sheffield and District Hospital Services Charitable Fund

The Sylvia and Colin Shepherd Charitable Trust

The Archie Sherman Cardiff Foundation

The Bassil Shippam and Alsford Trust

The Barbara A Shuttleworth Memorial Trust

The Simpson Education and Conservation Trust

The Huntly and Margery Sinclair Charitable Trust

The John Slater Foundation

The SMB Charitable Trust

The N Smith Charitable Settlement

The Henry Smith Charity

The R C Snelling Charitable Trust

The Sobell Foundation

The E C Sosnow Charitable Trust

The South Square Trust

The Sovereign Health Care Charitable Trust

Sparks Charity (Sport Aiding Medical Research For Kids)

The Worshipful Company of Spectacle Makers' Charity

Springfields Employees' Medical Research and Charity Trust Fund

St Francis's Leprosy Guild

St Michael's and All Saints' Charities

St Monica Trust Community Fund

The Stanley Foundation Ltd

The Starfish Trust

The Peter Stebbings Memorial Charity

The Steel Charitable Trust

The Steinberg Family Charitable Trust

Stevenson Family's Charitable Trust

The Andy Stewart Charitable Foundation

The Sir Halley Stewart Trust

The Stoller Charitable Trust

The Stone-Mallabar Charitable Foundation

Peter Stormonth Darling Charitable Trust

The Strangward Trust

The W O Street Charitable Foundation

Sueberry Ltd

Sussex Community Foundation

The Sutton Nursing Association

The Hugh and Ruby Sykes Charitable Trust

The Charles and Elsie Sykes Trust

The Tajtelbaum Charitable Trust

The Gay and Keith Talbot Trust

The Talbot Trusts

Tallow Chandlers Benevolent Fund

The A R Taylor Charitable Trust

The Connie and Albert Taylor Charitable Trust

Thackray Medical Research Trust

The Loke Wan Tho Memorial Foundation

The Thompson Family Charitable Trust

The Len Thomson Charitable Trust

The Sue Thomson Foundation

The Sir Jules Thorn Charitable Trust

TJH Foundation

The Tolkien Trust

The Tompkins Foundation

The Tory Family Foundation

The Towry Law Charitable Trust

The True Colours Trust

The James Tudor Foundation

UKI Charitable Foundation

The Ulverscroft Foundation

The Underwood Trust

The Unite Foundation (The Amicus Foundation)

The Albert Van Den Bergh Charitable Trust

John and Lucille van Geest Foundation

The Vintners' Company Charitable Foundation

The Volant Charitable Trust

The Wakefield and Tetley Trust

Robert and Felicity Waley-Cohen Charitable Trust

The Walker Trust

Wallace and Gromit's Children's Foundation

The Ward Blenkinsop Trust

The Waterloo Foundation

Blyth Watson Charitable Trust

The Weinstein Foundation

The Wellcome Trust

The Welton Foundation

Wessex Cancer Trust

The Westcroft Trust

The Simon Whitbread Charitable Trust

The Richard Wilcox Welfare Charity

The Felicity Wilde Charitable Trust

The Will Charitable Trust

The Kay Williams Charitable Foundation

The Williams Charitable Trust

Williams Serendipity Trust

The Harold Hyam Wingate Foundation

Anona Winn Charitable Trust

The Michael and Anna Wix Charitable Trust

The Wixamtree Trust
The Maurice Wohl Charitable
Foundation
The Charles Wolfson
Charitable Trust
The Wolfson Foundation
The Wood Family Trust
The Woodroffe Benton
Foundation
The Woodward Charitable
Trust
The A and R Woolf Charitable
Trust
The Fred and Della Worms
Charitable Trust
The Worwin UK Foundation
The Wragge and Co. Charitable
Trust
Miss E B Wrightson's
Charitable Settlement
The Wyseliot Charitable Trust
The York Children's Trust
The William Allen Young
Charitable Trust
The John K Young Endowment
Fund
The Young Foundation
Zephyr Charitable Trust
The Marjorie and Arnold Ziff
Charitable Foundation
The Zochonis Charitable Trust
Zurich Community Trust (UK)
Limited

Alternative, complementary medicine

The AIM Foundation
The Sir John Fisher Foundation
The Joanna Herbert-Stepney
Charitable Settlement
London Catalyst
Mr and Mrs J A Pye's
Charitable Settlement
The Simon Whitbread
Charitable Trust

Health care

Aberbrothock Charitable Trust
The ACT Foundation
Almondsbury Charity
The Milly Apthorp Charitable
Trust
The Artemis Charitable Trust
The Norman C Ashton
Foundation
Veta Bailey Charitable Trust
The Barbers' Company General
Charities
David and Frederick Barclay
Foundation
The Barnwood House Trust

The Birmingham District
Nursing Charitable Trust
Sir Alec Black's Charity
The Harry Bottom Charitable
Trust
The Tony Bramall Charitable
Trust
The Burdett Trust for Nursing
The William A Cadbury
Charitable Trust
The Cadbury Foundation
The Carron Charitable Trust
The Elizabeth Casson Trust
Chest, Heart and Stroke
Scotland
The Clarke Charitable
Settlement
The Congleton Inclosure Trust
The John Cowan Foundation
The Sir William Coxen Trust
Fund
The Manny Cussins
Foundation
The D'Oyly Carte Charitable
Trust
Baron Davenport's Charity
The Deakin Charitable Trust
The Denton Wilde Sapte
Charitable Trust
The Dinwoodie Settlement
Disability Aid Fund (The Roger
and Jean Jefcoate Trust)
The Duis Charitable Trust
The Dunhill Medical Trust
Gilbert Edgar Trust
James Ellis Charitable Trust
The Emmandjay Charitable
Trust
The Eranda Foundation
The Eveson Charitable Trust
The Family Rich Charities Trust
Samuel William Farmer's Trust
Joseph Fattorini Charitable
Trust 'B' Account
Elizabeth Ferguson Charitable
Trust Fund
Fife Council/Common Good
Funds and Trusts
Ford Britain Trust
The Lady Forester Trust
The Forte Charitable Trust
The Hugh Fraser Foundation
The Freemasons' Grand
Charity
The Freshfield Foundation
The Freshgate Trust
Foundation
Maurice Fry Charitable Trust
The Ganzoni Charitable Trust
The Gatsby Charitable
Foundation
Gatwick Airport Community
Trust
The General Nursing Council
for England and Wales
Trust
Simon Gibson Charitable Trust

The Girdlers' Company
Charitable Trust
GMC Trust
The Goldsmiths' Company
Charity
The Grand Order of Water
Rats' Charities Fund
The Constance Green
Foundation
Robert Hall Charity
Hampton Fuel Allotment
Charity
The W A Handley Charitable
Trust
The Hanlye Charitable Trust
The Kenneth Hargreaves
Charitable Trust
The Harris Family Charitable
Trust
The Haymills Charitable Trust
The Charles Hayward
Foundation
Healthsure Group Ltd
The Hedley Foundation
The Michael and Morven Heller
Charitable Foundation
Help the Hospices
The Hemby Trust
The Joanna Herbert-Stepney
Charitable Settlement
The Charles Littlewood Hill
Trust
The Hintze Family Charitable
Foundation
The Hollands-Warren Fund
The Homelands Charitable
Trust
The Horne Trust
The Hospital Saturday Fund
The Huddersfield Medical Trust
Fund
Human Relief Foundation
The Humanitarian Trust
Huntingdon Freemen's Charity
The Island Health Trust
The Ruth and Lionel Jacobson
Trust (Second Fund) No 2
The Jarman Charitable Trust
The Ian Karten Charitable
Trust
The Kennedy Charitable
Foundation
The Peter Kershaw Trust
The King's Fund
Ernest Kleinwort Charitable
Trust
The Langdale Trust
The LankellyChase Foundation
Laslett's (Hinton) Charity
The Raymond and Blanche
Lawson Charitable Trust
Leeds Building Society
Charitable Foundation
Lesley Lesley and Mutter Trust
The Joseph Levy Charitable
Foundation

John Lewis Partnership
General Community Fund
Lifeline 4 Kids
The Andrew and Mary
Elizabeth Little Charitable
Trust
Lloyds TSB Foundation for
Northern Ireland
London Catalyst
The Lord's Taverners
Lord and Lady Lurgan Trust
The MacRobert Trust
Market Harborough and The
Bowdens Charity
The Marsh Christian Trust
Sir George Martin Trust
John Martin's Charity
Evelyn May Trust
The Robert McAlpine
Foundation
The Medlock Charitable Trust
The Anthony and Elizabeth
Mellows Charitable
Settlement
The Tony Metherell Charitable
Trust
The Methodist Relief and
Development Fund
Gerald Micklem Charitable
Trust
Miles Trust for the Putney and
Roehampton Community
Monmouthshire County Council
Welsh Church Act Fund
The Monument Trust
The Morgan Charitable
Foundation
Brian and Jill Moss Charitable
Trust
The Edwina Mountbatten Trust
The Frances and Augustus
Newman Foundation
The North British Hotel Trust
The Northampton Queen's
Institute Relief in Sickness
Fund
The Nottingham General
Dispensary
The Owen Family Trust
The Park Charitable Trust
The Constance Paterson
Charitable Trust
Paycare Charity Trust
(previously known as
Patients' Aid Association
Hospital and Medical
Charities Trust)
The Mary Potter Convent
Hospital Trust
The Douglas Prestwich
Charitable Trust
Sir John Priestman Charity
Trust
The Prince's Charities
Foundation
The Richard and Christine
Purchas Charitable Trust

Richard Radcliffe Charitable
Trust
The Rayne Foundation
Relief Fund for Romania
Limited
Reuben Brothers Foundation
The Violet M Richards Charity
Riverside Charitable Trust
Limited
Thomas Roberts Trust
The Rose Foundation
The Rotherwick Foundation
The Christopher Rowbotham
Charitable Trust
Dr Mortimer and Theresa
Sackler Foundation
The Saintbury Trust
The Sheepdrove Trust
The Sheffield and District
Hospital Services
Charitable Fund
The Sylvia and Colin Shepherd
Charitable Trust
The E C Sosnow Charitable
Trust
The South Square Trust
Stevenson Family's Charitable
Trust
The Tajtelbaum Charitable
Trust
The A R Taylor Charitable Trust
The Connie and Albert Taylor
Charitable Trust
The True Colours Trust
John and Lucille van Geest
Foundation
Wallace and Gromit's
Children's Foundation
Blyth Watson Charitable Trust
The Westcroft Trust
Anona Winn Charitable Trust
The Charles Wolfson
Charitable Trust

....

■ **Health training**

Veta Bailey Charitable Trust
The Barbers' Company General
Charities
The Dinwoodie Settlement
The Methodist Relief and
Development Fund

....

■ **Medical equipment**

The Barnwood House Trust
Disability Aid Fund (The Roger
and Jean Jefcoate Trust)
Samuel William Farmer's Trust
The Grand Order of Water
Rats' Charities Fund
The Constance Green
Foundation
The Hedley Foundation
The Ian Karten Charitable
Trust

The Joseph Levy Charitable
Foundation
Lifeline 4 Kids
London Catalyst
The Lord's Taverners
The Frances and Augustus
Newman Foundation
The North British Hotel Trust
Paycare Charity Trust
(previously known as
Patients' Aid Association
Hospital and Medical
Charities Trust)
The Sylvia and Colin Shepherd
Charitable Trust

....

■ **Medical institutions**

Aberbrothock Charitable Trust
The Barnwood House Trust
The Birmingham District
Nursing Charitable Trust
Sir Alec Black's Charity
The Harry Bottom Charitable
Trust
Chest, Heart and Stroke
Scotland
The Clarke Charitable
Settlement
The John Cowan Foundation
The Sir William Coxen Trust
Fund
Baron Davenport's Charity
The Deakin Charitable Trust
The Duis Charitable Trust
The Dunhill Medical Trust
Gilbert Edgar Trust
The Emmandjay Charitable
Trust
The Eveson Charitable Trust
Samuel William Farmer's Trust
Joseph Fattorini Charitable
Trust 'B' Account
Elizabeth Ferguson Charitable
Trust Fund
Fife Council/Common Good
Funds and Trusts
Ford Britain Trust
The Hugh Fraser Foundation
The Freemasons' Grand
Charity
The Ganzoni Charitable Trust
Gatwick Airport Community
Trust
The Girdlers' Company
Charitable Trust
The Constance Green
Foundation
Robert Hall Charity
Hampton Fuel Allotment
Charity
The Haymills Charitable Trust
The Charles Hayward
Foundation
Healthsure Group Ltd
The Hedley Foundation

The Michael and Morven Heller
  Charitable Foundation
Help the Hospices
The Homelands Charitable
  Trust
The Horne Trust
The Hospital Saturday Fund
The Huddersfield Medical Trust
  Fund
The Ruth and Lionel Jacobson
  Trust (Second Fund) No 2
The Jarman Charitable Trust
The Kennedy Charitable
  Foundation
The Peter Kershaw Trust
Ernest Kleinwort Charitable
  Trust
The LankellyChase Foundation
The Raymond and Blanche
  Lawson Charitable Trust
Leeds Building Society
  Charitable Foundation
The Joseph Levy Charitable
  Foundation
Lloyds TSB Foundation for
  Northern Ireland
Lord and Lady Lurgan Trust
The Marsh Christian Trust
Sir George Martin Trust
Evelyn May Trust
The Robert McAlpine
  Foundation
The Medlock Charitable Trust
The Anthony and Elizabeth
  Mellows Charitable
  Settlement
The Tony Metherell Charitable
  Trust
Gerald Micklem Charitable
  Trust
Miles Trust for the Putney and
  Roehampton Community
Monmouthshire County Council
  Welsh Church Act Fund
The Monument Trust
The Morgan Charitable
  Foundation
The North British Hotel Trust
The Northampton Queen's
  Institute Relief in Sickness
  Fund
The Nottingham General
  Dispensary
The Owen Family Trust
The Park Charitable Trust
Paycare Charity Trust
  (previously known as
  Patients' Aid Association
  Hospital and Medical
  Charities Trust)
The Douglas Prestwich
  Charitable Trust
Sir John Priestman Charity
  Trust
The Prince's Charities
  Foundation

Richard Radcliffe Charitable
  Trust
The Rayne Foundation
The Rose Foundation
Dr Mortimer and Theresa
  Sackler Foundation
The Sheffield and District
  Hospital Services
  Charitable Fund
The Tajtelbaum Charitable
  Trust
The A R Taylor Charitable Trust
The Connie and Albert Taylor
  Charitable Trust
Wallace and Gromit's
  Children's Foundation
Blyth Watson Charitable Trust

....

■ **Nursing**

The Barbers' Company General
  Charities
The Birmingham District
  Nursing Charitable Trust
The General Nursing Council
  for England and Wales
  Trust
The Hedley Foundation
The Ruth and Lionel Jacobson
  Trust (Second Fund) No 2
The Joseph Levy Charitable
  Foundation
The Edwina Mountbatten Trust

....

■ **Primary health care**

The Island Health Trust
The Ruth and Lionel Jacobson
  Trust (Second Fund) No 2
The Methodist Relief and
  Development Fund

....

■ **Therapy**

The Artemis Charitable Trust
The Elizabeth Casson Trust

Health education/ prevention/ development

The AIM Foundation
The Big Lottery Fund
The Tony Bramall Charitable
  Trust
The British Dietetic
  Association General and
  Education Trust Fund
Henry T and Lucy B Cadbury
  Charitable Trust
Chest, Heart and Stroke
  Scotland
The Colt Foundation
The Cotton Trust

Gilbert Edgar Trust
The John Ellerman Foundation
J Paul Getty Jr Charitable Trust
The Haramead Trust
The Joanna Herbert-Stepney
  Charitable Settlement
Human Relief Foundation
The King's Fund
Lloyds TSB Foundation for
  Northern Ireland
London Catalyst
The Methodist Relief and
  Development Fund
Monmouthshire County Council
  Welsh Church Act Fund
The Robert and Margaret
  Moss Charitable Trust
The Richard and Christine
  Purchas Charitable Trust
Mr and Mrs J A Pye's
  Charitable Settlement
Relief Fund for Romania
  Limited
The Violet M Richards Charity
The Rosca Trust
The Rowan Charitable Trust
The York Children's Trust

....

■ **Health promotion**

Chest, Heart and Stroke
  Scotland
The Big Lottery Fund
The British Dietetic
  Association General and
  Education Trust Fund
The Robert and Margaret
  Moss Charitable Trust

History of medicine

The Joanna Herbert-Stepney
  Charitable Settlement
Thackray Medical Research
  Trust
The Wellcome Trust

Medical research and clinical treatment

The 1989 Willan Charitable
  Trust
Aberbrothock Charitable Trust
Action Medical Research
The Company of Actuaries'
  Charitable Trust Fund
The Adamson Trust
The Green and Lilian F M
  Ainsworth and Family
  Benevolent Fund
The Sylvia Aitken Charitable
  Trust

Alcohol Education and Research Council
The Alliance Family Foundation
The Pat Allsop Charitable Trust
Anglo American Group Foundation
The Armourers' and Brasiers' Gauntlet Trust
Arthritis Research Campaign
Astellas European Foundation
The Astor Foundation
The Astor of Hever Trust
The Baker Charitable Trust
The Balint Family Charitable Trusts
The Barbers' Company General Charities
David and Frederick Barclay Foundation
The Barnwood House Trust
The John Beckwith Charitable Trust
The Bellhouse Foundation
Bergqvist Charitable Trust
The Ruth Berkowitz Charitable Trust
The Herbert and Peter Blagrave Charitable Trust
The Breast Cancer Research Trust
The British Council for Prevention of Blindness
British Heart Foundation
The Charles Brotherton Trust
Buckland Charitable Trust
The BUPA Foundation
The Burden Trust
The Burry Charitable Trust
The Arnold Burton 1998 Charitable Trust
P H G Cadbury Charitable Trust
The Castang Foundation
The Cayo Foundation
Celtic Charity Fund
The Cemlyn-Jones Trust
The Charities Advisory Trust
Chest, Heart and Stroke Scotland
Child Growth Foundation
Children's Liver Disease Foundation
The Children's Research Fund
The Childwick Trust
The Clarke Charitable Settlement
The Cleopatra Trust
The Bernard Coleman Charitable Trust
The Colt Foundation
The Cotton Trust
The John Cowan Foundation
The Sir William Coxen Trust Fund
Cruden Foundation Ltd
The Cunningham Trust
The Roald Dahl Foundation

The De Clermont Charitable Company Ltd
The Denman Charitable Trust
The Denton Charitable Trust
Diabetes UK
The Dinwoodie Settlement
The Dorus Trust
The Dunhill Medical Trust
The Dunn Family Charitable Trust
The James Dyson Foundation
The Earmark Trust
The EBM Charitable Trust
The Gilbert and Eileen Edgar Foundation
Gilbert Edgar Trust
The John Ellerman Foundation
James Ellis Charitable Trust
The Emmandjay Charitable Trust
Epilepsy Research UK
The Eranda Foundation
Essex Provincial Charity Fund
The Eveson Charitable Trust
The Family Rich Charities Trust
Samuel William Farmer's Trust
Elizabeth Ferguson Charitable Trust Fund
The Fishmongers' Company's Charitable Trust
Bud Flanagan Leukaemia Fund
The Ian Fleming Charitable Trust
The Follett Trust
The Donald Forrester Trust
The Anna Rosa Forster Charitable Trust
The Hugh Fraser Foundation
The Joseph Strong Frazer Trust
The Freemasons' Grand Charity
The Frognal Trust
T F C Frost Charitable Trust
Maurice Fry Charitable Trust
The Garnett Charitable Trust
The Gatsby Charitable Foundation
The Girdlers' Company Charitable Trust
GMC Trust
The Sydney and Phyllis Goldberg Memorial Charitable Trust
Golden Charitable Trust
Mike Gooley Trailfinders Charity
The Gunter Charitable Trust
The Hamamelis Trust
Hamilton Wallace Trust
The W A Handley Charitable Trust
The Harbour Charitable Trust
The Harebell Centenary Fund
The Kenneth Hargreaves Charitable Trust
The Harris Charitable Trust

The John Harrison Charitable Trust
The N and P Hartley Memorial Trust
The Alfred And Peggy Harvey Charitable Trust
The Haymills Charitable Trust
The Hedley Foundation
The Michael and Morven Heller Charitable Foundation
The Simon Heller Charitable Settlement
The Christina Mary Hendrie Trust for Scottish and Canadian Charities
The Sir Julian Hodge Charitable Trust
The Jane Hodge Foundation
The Holbeck Charitable Trust
The Edward Holt Trust
The Homelands Charitable Trust
The Homestead Charitable Trust
The Antony Hornby Charitable Trust
Miss Agnes H Hunter's Trust
International Spinal Research Trust
The John Jarrold Trust
The Jeffrey Charitable Trust
The Elton John Aids Foundation
The Jones 1986 Charitable Trust
The Emmanuel Kaye Foundation
The Caron Keating Foundation
The KempWelch Charitable Trust
The Kay Kendall Leukaemia Fund
The Peter Kershaw Trust
The Mary Kinross Charitable Trust
Ernest Kleinwort Charitable Trust
The Kohn Foundation
The Heinz, Anna and Carol Kroch Foundation
The Kyte Charitable Trust
The R J Larg Family Charitable Trust
The Kathleen Laurence Trust
The Edgar E Lawley Foundation
The William Leech Charity
The Leigh Trust
Leukaemia Research Fund
The Joseph Levy Charitable Foundation
Lewis Family Charitable Trust
The Linbury Trust
Frank Litchfield Charitable Trust
The George John and Sheilah Livanos Charitable Trust
The London Law Trust

The Lotus Foundation
The Marie Helen Luen
    Charitable Trust
Robert Luff Foundation Ltd
Lord and Lady Lurgan Trust
The Madeline Mabey Trust
The R S Macdonald Charitable
    Trust
Macdonald-Buchanan
    Charitable Trust
The Mackintosh Foundation
Mandeville Trust
The Manoukian Charitable
    Foundation
Marshgate Charitable
    Settlement
The Nancie Massey Charitable
    Trust
Evelyn May Trust
The Robert McAlpine
    Foundation
D D McPhail Charitable
    Settlement
Medical Research Council
The Medlock Charitable Trust
Meningitis Trust
Brian Mercer Charitable Trust
The Mercers' Charitable
    Foundation
The Tony Metherell Charitable
    Trust
Gerald Micklem Charitable
    Trust
The Migraine Trust
The Millward Charitable Trust
Monmouthshire County Council
    Welsh Church Act Fund
The Monument Trust
The Peter Moores Foundation
The Willie and Mabel Morris
    Charitable Trust
G M Morrison Charitable Trust
The Robert and Margaret
    Moss Charitable Trust
The Mothercare Charitable
    Foundation
J P Moulton Charitable
    Foundation
The F H Muirhead Charitable
    Trust
Asthma UK
Nestle Rowntree Employees
    Community Fund
The Frances and Augustus
    Newman Foundation
The North British Hotel Trust
The North West Cancer
    Research Fund
The Northcott Devon Medical
    Foundation
The Northwood Charitable
    Trust
The Nottingham General
    Dispensary
The Nuffield Foundation
The Oakdale Trust
Old Possum's Practical Trust

The Owen Family Trust
The Parthenon Trust
Arthur James Paterson
    Charitable Trust
The Constance Paterson
    Charitable Trust
Paycare Charity Trust
    (previously known as
    Patients' Aid Association
    Hospital and Medical
    Charities Trust)
The Harry Payne Trust
The Dowager Countess
    Eleanor Peel Trust
The Persula Foundation
The Cecil Pilkington Charitable
    Trust
The Pilkington Charities Fund
The Col W W Pilkington Will
    Trusts The General Charity
    Fund
The Richard and Christine
    Purchas Charitable Trust
Mr and Mrs J A Pye's
    Charitable Settlement
The Monica Rabagliati
    Charitable Trust
The Mr and Mrs Philip
    Rackham Charitable Trust
The Rank Foundation
The Rayne Foundation
The Max Reinhardt Charitable
    Trust
REMEDI
The Violet M Richards Charity
The Muriel Edith Rickman
    Trust
The Robertson Trust
Edwin George Robinson
    Charitable Trust
Rosetrees Trust
Mrs Gladys Row Fogo
    Charitable Trust
The Rowlands Trust
Ryklow Charitable Trust 1992
The Raymond and Beverley
    Sackler Foundation
The Alan and Babette
    Sainsbury Charitable Fund
The Peter Samuel Charitable
    Trust
The Camilla Samuel Fund
The Scarfe Charitable Trust
Sir Samuel Scott of Yews
    Trust
The Jean Shanks Foundation
The Sheepdrove Trust
The Simpson Education and
    Conservation Trust
The SMB Charitable Trust
The N Smith Charitable
    Settlement
The Henry Smith Charity
The South Square Trust
Sparks Charity (Sport Aiding
    Medical Research For Kids)

The Worshipful Company of
    Spectacle Makers' Charity
St Francis's Leprosy Guild
The Sir Halley Stewart Trust
Peter Stormonth Darling
    Charitable Trust
The Charles and Elsie Sykes
    Trust
Tallow Chandlers Benevolent
    Fund
The Connie and Albert Taylor
    Charitable Trust
The Len Thomson Charitable
    Trust
The Sir Jules Thorn Charitable
    Trust
The Towry Law Charitable Trust
The Ulverscroft Foundation
John and Lucille van Geest
    Foundation
The Vintners' Company
    Charitable Foundation
The Wellcome Trust
The Welton Foundation
Wessex Cancer Trust
The Felicity Wilde Charitable
    Trust
The Will Charitable Trust
The Kay Williams Charitable
    Foundation
The Williams Charitable Trust
The Harold Hyam Wingate
    Foundation
The Charles Wolfson
    Charitable Trust
The Wolfson Foundation
The Woodroffe Benton
    Foundation
The Worwin UK Foundation
Miss E B Wrightson's
    Charitable Settlement
The Wyseliot Charitable Trust
The John K Young Endowment
    Fund

Philanthropy and the voluntary sector

Almondsbury Charity
The Baring Foundation
The Big Lottery Fund
The Boshier-Hinton Foundation
The Edward and Dorothy
　　Cadbury Trust
CAF (Charities Aid Foundation)
The Digbeth Trust
Samuel William Farmer's Trust
Gatwick Airport Community
　　Trust
The Gulbenkian Foundation
The Hadrian Trust
Paul Hamlyn Foundation
The Kenneth Hargreaves
　　Charitable Trust
The Hemby Trust
Impetus Trust
The William Leech Charity
The Mark Leonard Trust
Lloyds TSB Foundation for
　　Northern Ireland
Lloyds TSB Foundation for the
　　Channel Islands
The London Law Trust
The Medlock Charitable Trust
The Millfield House Foundation
John Moores Foundation
The Northern Rock Foundation
The Pears Foundation
The Jack Petchey Foundation
Mrs L D Rope Third Charitable
　　Settlement
The Joseph Rowntree
　　Charitable Trust
'v'
Voluntary Action Fund
Wakeham Trust
Wales Council for Voluntary
　　Action
York and North Yorkshire
　　Community Foundation

Voluntarism

The Big Lottery Fund
The Gulbenkian Foundation
The Hemby Trust
The William Leech Charity
The Mark Leonard Trust
Lloyds TSB Foundation for
　　Northern Ireland
The London Law Trust
The Jack Petchey Foundation
Mrs L D Rope Third Charitable
　　Settlement
'v'
Wakeham Trust
Wales Council for Voluntary
　　Action

■ Community participation

The Big Lottery Fund
The Gulbenkian Foundation
The Hemby Trust
The Mark Leonard Trust
The London Law Trust
The Jack Petchey Foundation
Wakeham Trust

Voluntary sector capacity building

Almondsbury Charity
The Baring Foundation
CAF (Charities Aid Foundation)
The Digbeth Trust
Gatwick Airport Community
　　Trust
The Hadrian Trust
Paul Hamlyn Foundation
The Northern Rock Foundation
Voluntary Action Fund

Religious activities

4 Charity Foundation
Brian Abrams Charitable Trust
Eric Abrams Charitable Trust
The Acacia Charitable Trust
Achiezer Association Ltd
Achisomoch Aid Company
　　Limited
Adenfirst Ltd
Aid to the Church in Need (UK)
The Alabaster Trust
Alba Charitable Trust
The Alexis Trust
All Saints Educational Trust
The Alliance Family Foundation
The Almond Trust
Almondsbury Charity
The Altajir Trust
Altamont Ltd
Alvor Charitable Trust
AM Charitable Trust
Amabrill Limited
Viscount Amory's Charitable
　　Trust
The Anchor Foundation
The Andrew Anderson Trust
Andor Charitable Trust
The Andre Christian Trust
The Archbishop of
　　Canterbury's Charitable
　　Trust
The Archer Trust
The Ardwick Trust
The John Armitage Charitable
　　Trust
The Armourers' and Brasiers'
　　Gauntlet Trust
The AS Charitable Trust
Ashburnham Thanksgiving
　　Trust
The Ashendene Trust
The Astor of Hever Trust
AW Charitable Trust
The Austin Bailey Trust
The Baird Trust
The Baker Charitable Trust
The Balint Family Charitable
　　Trusts
The Balney Charitable Trust
William P Bancroft (No 2)
　　Charitable Trust and
　　Jenepher Gillett Trust
David and Frederick Barclay
　　Foundation
Barleycorn Trust
The Barnabas Trust
Bay Charitable Trust
The Beacon Trust
Bear Mordechai Ltd
The Beaufort House Trust
　　Limited
Beauland Ltd
The Becker Family Charitable
　　Trust

The Bellahouston Bequest Fund

Belljoe Tzedoko Ltd

Maurice and Jacqueline Bennett Charitable Trust

Michael and Leslie Bennett Charitable Trust

The Ruth Berkowitz Charitable Trust

BHST

The Bintaub Charitable Trust

The Bisgood Charitable Trust (registered as Miss Jeanne Bisgood's Charitable Trust)

The Bishop's Development Fund

The Sydney Black Charitable Trust

The Bertie Black Foundation

The Sir Victor Blank Charitable Settlement

The Neville and Elaine Blond Charitable Trust

The Blueberry Charitable Trust

The Bluston Charitable Settlement

The Bonamy Charitable Trust

Salo Bordon Charitable Trust

The Boshier-Hinton Foundation

H E and E L Botteley Charitable Trust

The Harry Bottom Charitable Trust

P G and N J Boulton Trust

The A H and E Boulton Trust

Sir Clive Bourne Family Trust

Bourneheights Limited

The Bowerman Charitable Trust

The Bowland Charitable Trust

Bristol Archdeaconry Charity

Mrs E E Brown Charitable Settlement

T B H Brunner's Charitable Settlement

Brushmill Ltd

Buckingham Trust

The Burden Trust

The Audrey and Stanley Burton 1960 Charitable Trust

The Arnold Burton 1998 Charitable Trust

C and F Charitable Trust

Edward Cadbury Charitable Trust

Henry T and Lucy B Cadbury Charitable Trust

The William A Cadbury Charitable Trust

The Cambridgeshire Historic Churches Trust

H and L Cantor Trust

Carlee Ltd

The Carlton House Charitable Trust

The Carpenter Charitable Trust

The Carpenters' Company Charitable Trust

The Catholic Charitable Trust

Catholic Foreign Missions

The Catholic Trust for England and Wales

The Cemlyn-Jones Trust

The CH (1980) Charitable Trust

Charitworth Limited

The Chasah Trust

Chasdei Tovim Me'oros

Childs Charitable Trust

The Childwick Trust

The Christabella Charitable Trust

Christian Response to Eastern Europe

The Church and Community Fund

Church Burgesses Trust

Church of Ireland Priorities Fund

The Church Urban Fund

The Hilda and Alice Clark Charitable Trust

The Roger and Sarah Bancroft Clark Charitable Trust

The Clarke Charitable Settlement

The Clore Duffield Foundation

Miss V L Clore's 1967 Charitable Trust

Closehelm Ltd

Richard Cloudesley's Charity

Clydpride Ltd

The Denise Cohen Charitable Trust

The Vivienne and Samuel Cohen Charitable Trust

John Coldman Charitable Trust

The E Alec Colman Charitable Fund Ltd

Col-Reno Ltd

The Congregational and General Charitable Trust

Harold and Daphne Cooper Charitable Trust

The Gershon Coren Charitable Foundation

The Corinthian Trust

Edwin Cornforth 1983 Charity Trust

The Cornwall Historic Churches Trust

The Sidney and Elizabeth Corob Charitable Trust

The Corona Charitable Trust

The Costa Family Charitable Trust

The Craps Charitable Trust

Criffel Charitable Trust

The Cross Trust

Cuby Charitable Trust

The Manny Cussins Foundation

Itzchok Meyer Cymerman Trust Ltd

The Daily Prayer Union Charitable Trust Ltd

Oizer Dalim Trust

Davidson Charitable Trust

The Alderman Joe Davidson Memorial Trust

Davis-Rubens Charitable Trust

The Leopold De Rothschild Charitable Trust

The Deakin Charitable Trust

The Debmar Benevolent Trust

The Dellal Foundation

Alan and Sheila Diamond Charitable Trust

The Djanogly Foundation

The Dollond Charitable Trust

Domepride Ltd

The Dorcas Trust

The Dorema Charitable Trust

The Doughty Charity Trust

The Dugdale Charitable Trust

The Duis Charitable Trust

The Dulverton Trust

The Houghton Dunn Charitable Trust

Dushinsky Trust Ltd

The Dyers' Company Charitable Trust

The Earmark Trust

The Ebenezer Trust

The Gilbert and Eileen Edgar Foundation

The George Elias Charitable Trust

The Gerald Palmer Eling Trust Company

Ellador Ltd

The Ellinson Foundation Ltd

The Edith Maud Ellis 1985 Charitable Trust

The Elmgrant Trust

Elshore Ltd

The Vernon N Ely Charitable Trust

The Emmandjay Charitable Trust

The Englefield Charitable Trust

Entindale Ltd

The Ernest Hecht Charitable Foundation

The Erskine Cunningham Hill Trust

The Esfandi Charitable Foundation

The Evangelical Covenants Trust

The Exilarch's Foundation

Extonglen Limited

F C Charitable Trust

The F P Limited Charitable Trust

The Faber Charitable Trust

The Fairway Trust

The Family Foundations Trust

Famos Foundation Trust

Farthing Trust
Joseph Fattorini Charitable
Trust 'B' Account
Federation of Jewish Relief
Organisations
Feed the Minds
Finnart House School Trust
Firtree Trust
Fisherbeck Charitable Trust
The Rose Flatau Charitable
Trust
The Flow Foundation
The Gerald Fogel Charitable
Trust
Forbesville Limited
Fordeve Ltd
The Forest Hill Charitable Trust
The Donald Forrester Trust
The Forte Charitable Trust
The Four Winds Trust
The Fowler, Smith and Jones
Charitable Trust
The Isaac and Freda Frankel
Memorial Charitable Trust
The Hugh Fraser Foundation
The Joseph Strong Frazer Trust
The Thomas Freke and Lady
Norton Charity
The Anne French Memorial
Trust
The Friends Hall Farm Street
Trust
Friends of Biala Ltd
Friends of Boyan Trust
Mejer and Gertrude Miriam
Frydman Foundation
The Fulmer Charitable Trust
Gableholt Limited
The Gale Family Charitable
Trust
The Angela Gallagher Memorial
Fund
The Ganzoni Charitable Trust
Garvan Limited
Jacqueline and Michael Gee
Charitable Trust
The Gibbs Charitable Trust
The Girdlers' Company
Charitable Trust
The B and P Glasser
Charitable Trust
Global Care
The Meir Golda Trust
Golden Charitable Trust
The Jack Goldhill Charitable
Trust
The Everard and Mina
Goodman Charitable
Foundation
Leonard Gordon Charitable
Trust
The Gough Charitable Trust
The Grace Charitable Trust
The Grahame Charitable
Foundation Limited
Philip and Judith Green Trust

Naomi and Jeffrey Greenwood
Charitable Trust
The Greys Charitable Trust
The M and R Gross Charities
Limited
The Grove Charitable Trust
The GRP Charitable Trust
The Gur Trust
The H and J Spack Charitable
Trust
The H P Charitable Trust
E F and M G Hall Charitable
Trust
Sue Hammerson's Charitable
Trust
The W A Handley Charitable
Trust
Beatrice Hankey Foundation
Ltd
The Kathleen Hannay
Memorial Charity
Harbo Charities Limited
The Harbour Foundation
The Harris Charitable Trust
Haskel Family Foundation
The Hathaway Trust
The Maurice Hatter Foundation
The Haydan Charitable Trust
Headley-Pitt Charitable Trust
Heagerty Charitable Trust
May Hearnshaw's Charity
Heathside Charitable Trust
The Helping Foundation
The Joanna Herbert-Stepney
Charitable Settlement
The Hesed Trust
The Bernhard Heuberger
Charitable Trust
Hexham and Newcastle
Diocesan Trust (1947)
The P and C Hickinbotham
Charitable Trust
Highcroft Charitable Trust
Hinchley Charitable Trust
Hinduja Foundation
Stuart Hine Trust
Hockerill Educational
Foundation
Matthew Hodder Charitable
Trust
The Sir Julian Hodge
Charitable Trust
The Jane Hodge Foundation
The Holbeck Charitable Trust
The Holden Charitable Trust
The Homelands Charitable
Trust
The Homestead Charitable
Trust
Sir Harold Hood's Charitable
Trust
The Hope Trust
The Daniel Howard Trust
The Humanitarian Trust
The Huntingdon Foundation
Hurdale Charity Limited
The Hutton Foundation

The Huxham Charitable Trust
The P Y N and B Hyams Trust
The Inlight Trust
Investream Charitable Trust
Irshad Trust
Irwin Trust
The Isaacs Charitable Trust
J A R Charitable Trust
Jacobs Charitable Trust
The Ruth and Lionel Jacobson
Trust (Second Fund) No 2
The Susan and Stephen
James Charitable
Settlement
The James Trust
The Jarman Charitable Trust
Jay Education Trust
JCA Charitable Foundation
The Jerusalem Trust
Jewish Child's Day
The Jewish Youth Fund
The JMK Charitable Trust
The Harold Joels Charitable
Trust
The Nicholas Joels Charitable
Trust
The Norman Joels Charitable
Trust
The Joron Charitable Trust
The J E Joseph Charitable
Fund
Jusaca Charitable Trust
The Bernard Kahn Charitable
Trust
The Stanley Kalms Foundation
The Kasner Charitable Trust
The Kass Charitable Trust
The Michael and Ilse Katz
Foundation
The Katzauer Charitable
Settlement
The C S Kaufman Charitable
Trust
The Geoffrey John Kaye
Charitable Foundation
The Emmanuel Kaye
Foundation
The Soli and Leah Kelaty Trust
Fund
The KempWelch Charitable
Trust
The Kennedy Charitable
Foundation
Keren Association
Kermaville Ltd
E and E Kernkraut Charities
Limited
The Kessler Foundation
Keswick Hall Charity
The King Henry VIII Endowed
Trust Warwick
Kirschel Foundation
The Kobler Trust
The Kohn Foundation
Kollel and Co. Limited
The Kreditor Charitable Trust
The Neil Kreitman Foundation

Kupath Gemach Chaim
  Bechesed Viznitz Trust
The Late Sir Pierce Lacy
  Charity Trust
The K P Ladd Charitable Trust
Maurice and Hilda Laing
  Charitable Trust
The Beatrice Laing Trust
The Lambert Charitable Trust
Duchy of Lancaster Benevolent
  Fund
The Lancaster Foundation
The Langdale Trust
The Langley Charitable Trust
Largsmount Ltd
Laslett's (Hinton) Charity
Laufer Charitable Trust
The Lauffer Family Charitable
  Foundation
The Lawson Beckman
  Charitable Trust
The Carole and Geoffrey
  Lawson Foundation
The Leathersellers' Company
  Charitable Fund
The Arnold Lee Charitable
  Trust
The William Leech Charity
The Kennedy Leigh Charitable
  Trust
Morris Leigh Foundation
The P Leigh-Bramwell Trust 'E'
The Leonard Trust
The Joseph Levy Charitable
  Foundation
Lewis Family Charitable Trust
The Lind Trust
Lindale Educational
  Foundation
The Ruth and Stuart Lipton
  Charitable Trust
Jack Livingstone Charitable
  Trust
The Elaine and Angus Lloyd
  Charitable Trust
The Charles Lloyd Foundation
Localtrent Ltd
The Locker Foundation
The Loftus Charitable Trust
The Lolev Charitable Trust
The Lowy Mitchell Foundation
The C L Loyd Charitable Trust
Paul Lunn-Rockliffe Charitable
  Trust
The Ruth and Jack Lunzer
  Charitable Trust
The Lyndhurst Trust
The Lynwood Trust
The Sir Jack Lyons Charitable
  Trust
Malcolm Lyons Foundation
The Lyras Family Charitable
  Trust
Sylvanus Lyson's Charity
The M and C Trust
The M D and S Charitable
  Trust

The M K Charitable Trust
The Magen Charitable Trust
Malbin Trust
Maranatha Christian Trust
Marbeh Torah Trust
The Stella and Alexander
  Margulies Charitable Trust
Mariapolis Limited
The Ann and David Marks
  Foundation
The Michael Marsh Charitable
  Trust
The Marsh Christian Trust
The Charlotte Marshall
  Charitable Trust
Marshall's Charity
Marshgate Charitable
  Settlement
Sir George Martin Trust
John Martin's Charity
The Mason Porter Charitable
  Trust
Matliwala Family Charitable
  Trust
The Matt 6.3 Charitable Trust
The Violet Mauray Charitable
  Trust
Mayfair Charities Ltd
Mazars Charitable Trust
The Anthony and Elizabeth
  Mellows Charitable
  Settlement
Melodor Ltd
Melow Charitable Trust
Menuchar Ltd
Mercaz Torah Vechesed
  Limited
The Mercers' Charitable
  Foundation
The Merchant Taylors'
  Company Charities Fund
Miles Trust for the Putney and
  Roehampton Community
The Miller Foundation
The Millfield Trust
The Millhouses Charitable
  Trust
The Edgar Milward Charity
The Minos Trust
The Laurence Misener
  Charitable Trust
The Mishcon Family Charitable
  Trust
The Mitchell Charitable Trust
The Modiano Charitable Trust
The Mole Charitable Trust
Monmouthshire County Council
  Welsh Church Act Fund
The Colin Montgomerie
  Charitable Foundation
The Peter Moores Foundation
The Mr and Mrs J T Morgan
  Foundation
Diana and Allan Morgenthau
  Charitable Trust
The Oliver Morland Charitable
  Trust

S C and M E Morland's
  Charitable Trust
The Peter Morrison Charitable
  Foundation
Moshal Charitable Trust
The Moshulu Charitable Trust
Brian and Jill Moss Charitable
  Trust
The Moss Charitable Trust
Moss Family Charitable Trust
Muslim Hands
MYA Charitable Trust
MYR Charitable Trust
The Nadezhda Charitable Trust
The Willie Nagel Charitable
  Trust
The Naggar Charitable Trust
Nathan Charitable Trust
Nazareth Trust Fund
The Worshipful Company of
  Needlemakers' Charitable
  Fund
Nemoral Ltd
Ner Foundation
Nesswall Ltd
Mr and Mrs F E F Newman
  Charitable Trust
Newpier Charity Ltd
The Chevras Ezras Nitzrochim
  Trust
NJD Charitable Trust
Normalyn Charitable Trust
The Norman Family Charitable
  Trust
The Northumbria Historic
  Churches Trust
The Norwich Church of England
  Young Men's Society
The Norwood and Newton
  Settlement
The Nottinghamshire Historic
  Churches Trust
The Ogle Christian Trust
The Oikonomia Trust
The Oizer Charitable Trust
The Owen Family Trust
The Doris Pacey Charitable
  Foundation
Padwa Charitable Foundation
The Panacea Society
Panahpur Charitable Trust
The James Pantyfedwen
  Foundation
The Park Charitable Trust
The Park House Charitable
  Trust
Miss M E Swinton Paterson's
  Charitable Trust
The Jack Patston Charitable
  Trust
The Payne Charitable Trust
The Harry Payne Trust
The David Pearlman Charitable
  Foundation
The Pears Foundation
Peltz Trust
B E Perl Charitable Trust

The Persson Charitable Trust
The Philips and Rubens
  Charitable Trust
The Phillips Family Charitable
  Trust
The David Pickford Charitable
  Foundation
The Bernard Piggott Trust
G S Plaut Charitable Trust
  Limited
The Polehanger Trust
The George and Esme Pollitzer
  Charitable Settlement
The Pollywally Charitable Trust
Edith and Ferdinand Porjes
  Charitable Trust
The John Porter Charitable
  Trust
Porticus UK
The J E Posnansky Charitable
  Trust
Premierquote Ltd
Premishlaner Charitable Trust
Sir John Priestman Charity
  Trust
The Pyne Charitable Trust
Quothquan Trust
R J M Charitable Trust
R S Charitable Trust
Rachel Charitable Trust
The Bishop Radford Trust
The Rank Foundation
The Joseph Rank Trust
The Fanny Rapaport Charitable
  Settlement
The Ravensdale Trust
The Rayden Charitable Trust
The Rayne Trust
The Sir James Reckitt Charity
The Rehoboth Trust
The Rest Harrow Trust
The Nathaniel Reyner Trust
  Fund
The Sir Cliff Richard Charitable
  Trust
The Clive Richards Charity
Ridgesave Limited
The Sir John Ritblat Family
  Foundation
The River Trust
The Daniel Rivlin Charitable
  Trust
The Rock Foundation
The Rock Solid Trust
The Rofeh Trust
Rokach Family Charitable Trust
The Sir James Roll Charitable
  Trust
The Gerald Ronson Foundation
Mrs L D Rope Third Charitable
  Settlement
The Rotherwick Foundation
Rowanville Ltd
The Rowland Family
  Foundation
The Joseph Rowntree
  Charitable Trust

The RRAF Charitable Trust
The Alfred and Frances
  Rubens Charitable Trust
The Rubin Foundation
S F Foundation
S O Charitable Trust
The Michael Sacher Charitable
  Trust
The Michael Harry Sacher
  Trust
The Ruzin Sadagora Trust
Saint Sarkis Charity Trust
The Salamander Charitable
  Trust
The Salters' Charities
The Hon. M J Samuel
  Charitable Trust
The Peter Samuel Charitable
  Trust
The Scarfe Charitable Trust
The Schapira Charitable Trust
The Annie Schiff Charitable
  Trust
The Schmidt-Bodner Charitable
  Trust
The Schreib Trust
The Schreiber Charitable Trust
Scottish Churches' Community
  Trust
The Helene Sebba Charitable
  Trust
The Samuel Sebba Charitable
  Trust
The Seedfield Trust
Sellata Ltd
SEM Charitable Trust
The Seven Fifty Trust
The Cyril Shack Trust
The Shanti Charitable Trust
The Archie Sherman Cardiff
  Foundation
The Archie Sherman Charitable
  Trust
The Bassil Shippam and
  Alsford Trust
Shlomo Memorial Fund Limited
The J A Shone Memorial Trust
The Julius Silman Charitable
  Trust
The Leslie Silver Charitable
  Trust
The Simpson Foundation
The SMB Charitable Trust
The R C Snelling Charitable
  Trust
The Sobell Foundation
Solev Co Ltd
The Solo Charitable
  Settlement
Songdale Ltd
The Souter Charitable Trust
The W F Southall Trust
Sparquote Limited
Spears-Stutz Charitable Trust
The Moss Spiro Will Charitable
  Foundation

The Spring Harvest Charitable
  Trust
Rosalyn and Nicholas Springer
  Charitable Trust
Springrule Ltd
St Teilo's Trust
The Steel Charitable Trust
The Cyril and Betty Stein
  Charitable Trust
The Steinberg Family
  Charitable Trust
C E K Stern Charitable Trust
The Sigmund Sternberg
  Charitable Foundation
Stervon Ltd
The Stewards' Company
  Limited (incorporating the J
  W Laing Trust and the J W
  Laing Biblical Scholarship
  Trust)
The Sir Halley Stewart Trust
The Leonard Laity Stoate
  Charitable Trust
The Stobart Newlands
  Charitable Trust
The Strawberry Charitable
  Trust
The A B Strom and R Strom
  Charitable Trust
Sueberry Ltd
The Alan Sugar Foundation
The Adrienne and Leslie
  Sussman Charitable Trust
Sutton Coldfield Municipal
  Charities
The Sylvanus Charitable Trust
T and S Trust Fund
The Tabeel Trust
Tadlus Limited
The Tajtelbaum Charitable
  Trust
Talteg Ltd
The Tangent Charitable Trust
The Lady Tangye Charitable
  Trust
The David Tannen Charitable
  Trust
The Lili Tapper Charitable
  Foundation
C B and H H Taylor 1984 Trust
Tearfund
Tegham Limited
The Thornton Trust
Mrs R P Tindall's Charitable
  Trust
The Tisbury Telegraph Trust
The Tolkien Trust
Tomchei Torah Charitable
  Trust
The Torah Temimah Trust
Toras Chesed (London) Trust
The Tory Family Foundation
Truedene Co. Ltd
Truemart Limited
Trumros Limited
Tudor Rose Ltd
The Tufton Charitable Trust

Trustees of Tzedakah
UKI Charitable Foundation
Ulting Overseas Trust
The Union of Orthodox Hebrew
  Congregation
The United Society for the
  Propagation of the Gospel
The David Uri Memorial Trust
The Vail Foundation
The Van Neste Foundation
The Vardy Foundation
Vivdale Ltd
The Viznitz Foundation
Robert and Felicity Waley-
  Cohen Charitable Trust
Wallington Missionary Mart
  and Auctions
The Weinstein Foundation
West London Synagogue
  Charitable Fund
The Westcroft Trust
The Westminster Foundation
The Whitecourt Charitable
  Trust
The Norman Whiteley Trust
The Williams Family Charitable
  Trust
Dame Violet Wills Charitable
  Trust
The Benjamin Winegarten
  Charitable Trust
The Harold Hyam Wingate
  Foundation
The Michael and Anna Wix
  Charitable Trust
The Wixamtree Trust
The Maurice Wohl Charitable
  Foundation
The Charles Wolfson
  Charitable Trust
The Wolfson Family Charitable
  Trust
Women's World Day of Prayer
The James Wood Bequest
  Fund
Woodlands Foundation Limited
Woodlands Green Ltd
The A and R Woolf Charitable
  Trust
The Worcestershire and
  Dudley Historic Churches
  Trust
The Fred and Della Worms
  Charitable Trust
Wychdale Ltd
Wychville Ltd
Yankov Charitable Trust
The Yorkshire Historic
  Churches Trust
The Marjorie and Arnold Ziff
  Charitable Foundation
Stephen Zimmerman
  Charitable Trust

Christianity

Aid to the Church in Need (UK)
The Alabaster Trust
The Alexis Trust
The Almond Trust
Almondsbury Charity
Alvor Charitable Trust
Viscount Amory's Charitable
  Trust
The Anchor Foundation
The Andrew Anderson Trust
The Andre Christian Trust
The Archbishop of
  Canterbury's Charitable
  Trust
The Archer Trust
The Armourers' and Brasiers'
  Gauntlet Trust
The AS Charitable Trust
Ashburnham Thanksgiving
  Trust
The Ashendene Trust
The Baird Trust
The Balney Charitable Trust
William P Bancroft (No 2)
  Charitable Trust and
  Jenepher Gillett Trust
Barleycorn Trust
The Barnabas Trust
The Beacon Trust
The Beaufort House Trust
  Limited
The Bisgood Charitable Trust
  (registered as Miss Jeanne
  Bisgood's Charitable Trust)
The Bishop's Development
  Fund
The Sydney Black Charitable
  Trust
H E and E L Botteley
  Charitable Trust
The Harry Bottom Charitable
  Trust
P G and N J Boulton Trust
The A H and E Boulton Trust
The Bowland Charitable Trust
Bristol Archdeaconry Charity
T B H Brunner's Charitable
  Settlement
Buckingham Trust
The Burden Trust
Henry T and Lucy B Cadbury
  Charitable Trust
The William A Cadbury
  Charitable Trust
The Cambridgeshire Historic
  Churches Trust
The Carpenter Charitable Trust
The Carpenters' Company
  Charitable Trust
The Catholic Charitable Trust
Catholic Foreign Missions
The Catholic Trust for England
  and Wales
The Chasah Trust
Childs Charitable Trust

The Christabella Charitable
  Trust
Christian Response to Eastern
  Europe
The Church and Community
  Fund
Church Burgesses Trust
The Church Urban Fund
The Hilda and Alice Clark
  Charitable Trust
The Roger and Sarah Bancroft
  Clark Charitable Trust
The Clarke Charitable
  Settlement
Richard Cloudesley's Charity
John Coldman Charitable Trust
The Congregational and
  General Charitable Trust
The Corinthian Trust
Edwin Cornforth 1983 Charity
  Trust
The Cornwall Historic
  Churches Trust
The Costa Family Charitable
  Trust
Criffel Charitable Trust
The Cross Trust
The Daily Prayer Union
  Charitable Trust Ltd
The Dorcas Trust
The Dugdale Charitable Trust
The Dulverton Trust
The Houghton Dunn Charitable
  Trust
The Dyers' Company
  Charitable Trust
The Earmark Trust
The Ebenezer Trust
The Edith Maud Ellis 1985
  Charitable Trust
The Vernon N Ely Charitable
  Trust
The Emmandjay Charitable
  Trust
The Englefield Charitable Trust
The Erskine Cunningham Hill
  Trust
The Evangelical Covenants
  Trust
F C Charitable Trust
The Fairway Trust
Farthing Trust
Joseph Fattorini Charitable
  Trust 'B' Account
Feed the Minds
Firtree Trust
Fisherbeck Charitable Trust
The Forest Hill Charitable Trust
The Forte Charitable Trust
The Four Winds Trust
The Fowler, Smith and Jones
  Charitable Trust
The Thomas Freke and Lady
  Norton Charity
The Anne French Memorial
  Trust

The Friends Hall Farm Street
  Trust
The Fulmer Charitable Trust
The Gale Family Charitable
  Trust
The Angela Gallagher Memorial
  Fund
The Ganzoni Charitable Trust
The Gibbs Charitable Trust
The Girdlers' Company
  Charitable Trust
Global Care
Golden Charitable Trust
The Gough Charitable Trust
The Grace Charitable Trust
Philip and Judith Green Trust
The Greys Charitable Trust
E F and M G Hall Charitable
  Trust
The W A Handley Charitable
  Trust
Beatrice Hankey Foundation
  Ltd
The Kathleen Hannay
  Memorial Charity
The Harris Charitable Trust
Headley-Pitt Charitable Trust
Heagerty Charitable Trust
May Hearnshaw's Charity
The Joanna Herbert-Stepney
  Charitable Settlement
The Hesed Trust
Hexham and Newcastle
  Diocesan Trust (1947)
The P and C Hickinbotham
  Charitable Trust
Hinchley Charitable Trust
Stuart Hine Trust
Hockerill Educational
  Foundation
Matthew Hodder Charitable
  Trust
The Jane Hodge Foundation
The Holbeck Charitable Trust
The Homelands Charitable
  Trust
The Homestead Charitable
  Trust
Sir Harold Hood's Charitable
  Trust
The Hope Trust
The Hutton Foundation
The Huxham Charitable Trust
Irwin Trust
J A R Charitable Trust
The James Trust
The Jarman Charitable Trust
The Jerusalem Trust
The KempWelch Charitable
  Trust
The Kennedy Charitable
  Foundation
The King Henry VIII Endowed
  Trust Warwick
The Late Sir Pierce Lacy
  Charity Trust
The K P Ladd Charitable Trust

Maurice and Hilda Laing
  Charitable Trust
The Beatrice Laing Trust
Duchy of Lancaster Benevolent
  Fund
The Lancaster Foundation
The Langdale Trust
The Langley Charitable Trust
Laslett's (Hinton) Charity
The Leathersellers' Company
  Charitable Fund
The William Leech Charity
The P Leigh-Bramwell Trust 'E'
The Leonard Trust
The Lind Trust
Lindale Educational
  Foundation
The Elaine and Angus Lloyd
  Charitable Trust
The Charles Lloyd Foundation
Paul Lunn-Rockliffe Charitable
  Trust
The Lyndhurst Trust
The Lynwood Trust
Sylvanus Lyson's Charity
Maranatha Christian Trust
Mariapolis Limited
The Marsh Christian Trust
The Charlotte Marshall
  Charitable Trust
Marshall's Charity
Marshgate Charitable
  Settlement
Sir George Martin Trust
John Martin's Charity
The Mason Porter Charitable
  Trust
The Matt 6.3 Charitable Trust
Mazars Charitable Trust
The Anthony and Elizabeth
  Mellows Charitable
  Settlement
The Mercers' Charitable
  Foundation
The Merchant Taylors'
  Company Charities Fund
Miles Trust for the Putney and
  Roehampton Community
The Millfield Trust
The Millhouses Charitable
  Trust
The Edgar Milward Charity
The Minos Trust
Monmouthshire County Council
  Welsh Church Act Fund
The Peter Moores Foundation
The Mr and Mrs J T Morgan
  Foundation
The Oliver Morland Charitable
  Trust
S C and M E Morland's
  Charitable Trust
The Moshulu Charitable Trust
The Moss Charitable Trust
The Nadezhda Charitable Trust
Nathan Charitable Trust
Nazareth Trust Fund

Mr and Mrs F E F Newman
  Charitable Trust
The Norman Family Charitable
  Trust
The Northumbria Historic
  Churches Trust
The Norwich Church of England
  Young Men's Society
The Norwood and Newton
  Settlement
The Nottinghamshire Historic
  Churches Trust
The Ogle Christian Trust
The Oikonomia Trust
The Owen Family Trust
The Panacea Society
Panahpur Charitable Trust
The James Pantyfedwen
  Foundation
The Park House Charitable
  Trust
Miss M E Swinton Paterson's
  Charitable Trust
The Jack Patston Charitable
  Trust
The Payne Charitable Trust
The Persson Charitable Trust
The David Pickford Charitable
  Foundation
The Bernard Piggott Trust
G S Plaut Charitable Trust
  Limited
The Polehanger Trust
Sir John Priestman Charity
  Trust
The Pyne Charitable Trust
Quothquan Trust
The Bishop Radford Trust
The Rank Foundation
The Ravensdale Trust
The Sir James Reckitt Charity
The Rehoboth Trust
The Nathaniel Reyner Trust
  Fund
The Sir Cliff Richard Charitable
  Trust
The Clive Richards Charity
The River Trust
The Rock Foundation
The Rock Solid Trust
Mrs L D Rope Third Charitable
  Settlement
The Rotherwick Foundation
The Joseph Rowntree
  Charitable Trust
Saint Sarkis Charity Trust
The Salamander Charitable
  Trust
The Salters' Charities
The Scarfe Charitable Trust
Scottish Churches' Community
  Trust
The Seedfield Trust
The Seven Fifty Trust
The Shanti Charitable Trust
The Bassil Shippam and
  Alsford Trust

The J A Shone Memorial Trust
The Simpson Foundation
The SMB Charitable Trust
The Souter Charitable Trust
The W F Southall Trust
The Spring Harvest Charitable
 Trust
St Teilo's Trust
The Stewards' Company
 Limited (incorporating the J
 W Laing Trust and the J W
 Laing Biblical Scholarship
 Trust)
The Sir Halley Stewart Trust
The Leonard Laity Stoate
 Charitable Trust
The Stobart Newlands
 Charitable Trust
The Sylvanus Charitable Trust
The Tabeel Trust
The Lady Tangye Charitable
 Trust
C B and H H Taylor 1984 Trust
Tearfund
The Thornton Trust
Mrs R P Tindall's Charitable
 Trust
The Tisbury Telegraph Trust
The Tolkien Trust
The Tory Family Foundation
The Tufton Charitable Trust
Ulting Overseas Trust
The United Society for the
 Propagation of the Gospel
The Van Neste Foundation
The Vardy Foundation
Wallington Missionary Mart
 and Auctions
The Westcroft Trust
The Westminster Foundation
The Whitecourt Charitable
 Trust
The Norman Whiteley Trust
Dame Violet Wills Charitable
 Trust
The Wixamtree Trust
Women's World Day of Prayer
The James Wood Bequest
 Fund
The Worcestershire and
 Dudley Historic Churches
 Trust
The Yorkshire Historic
 Churches Trust

■ Christian causes, work

The Alexis Trust
The Almond Trust
Alvor Charitable Trust
The Andrew Anderson Trust
The Archbishop of
 Canterbury's Charitable
 Trust
The Archer Trust

Ashburnham Thanksgiving
 Trust
Barleycorn Trust
H E and E L Botteley
 Charitable Trust
Bristol Archdeaconry Charity
The Carpenter Charitable Trust
The Carpenters' Company
 Charitable Trust
Church Burgesses Trust
The Church Urban Fund
The Cross Trust
The Englefield Charitable Trust
Farthing Trust
Firtree Trust
The Forest Hill Charitable Trust
The Forte Charitable Trust
The Four Winds Trust
The Fowler, Smith and Jones
 Charitable Trust
The Anne French Memorial
 Trust
The Friends Hall Farm Street
 Trust
The Angela Gallagher Memorial
 Fund
The Gibbs Charitable Trust
The Girdlers' Company
 Charitable Trust
Global Care
The Joanna Herbert-Stepney
 Charitable Settlement
Matthew Hodder Charitable
 Trust
The Jerusalem Trust
The KempWelch Charitable
 Trust
The Langdale Trust
The William Leech Charity
The Marsh Christian Trust
Sir George Martin Trust
Mazars Charitable Trust
The Mercers' Charitable
 Foundation
Miles Trust for the Putney and
 Roehampton Community
Nathan Charitable Trust
Nazareth Trust Fund
The Norman Family Charitable
 Trust
The Norwood and Newton
 Settlement
The Owen Family Trust
The Panacea Society
The Park House Charitable
 Trust
The Payne Charitable Trust
Quothquan Trust
The Sir Cliff Richard Charitable
 Trust
The River Trust
The Rock Solid Trust
The Salamander Charitable
 Trust
The Salters' Charities
The Seedfield Trust
The Shanti Charitable Trust

The J A Shone Memorial Trust
The Spring Harvest Charitable
 Trust
The Stewards' Company
 Limited (incorporating the J
 W Laing Trust and the J W
 Laing Biblical Scholarship
 Trust)
The Stobart Newlands
 Charitable Trust
Tearfund
Mrs R P Tindall's Charitable
 Trust
The Tufton Charitable Trust
The Vardy Foundation
The Whitecourt Charitable
 Trust

■ Christian churches

Aid to the Church in Need (UK)
The Alabaster Trust
Almondsbury Charity
Viscount Amory's Charitable
 Trust
The Ashendene Trust
The Baird Trust
The Balney Charitable Trust
William P Bancroft (No 2)
 Charitable Trust and
 Jenepher Gillett Trust
The Bisgood Charitable Trust
 (registered as Miss Jeanne
 Bisgood's Charitable Trust)
The Bishop's Development
 Fund
The Sydney Black Charitable
 Trust
The A H and E Boulton Trust
T B H Brunner's Charitable
 Settlement
Henry T and Lucy B Cadbury
 Charitable Trust
The William A Cadbury
 Charitable Trust
The Cambridgeshire Historic
 Churches Trust
The Catholic Charitable Trust
Catholic Foreign Missions
The Catholic Trust for England
 and Wales
The Church and Community
 Fund
Church Burgesses Trust
The Hilda and Alice Clark
 Charitable Trust
The Roger and Sarah Bancroft
 Clark Charitable Trust
Richard Cloudesley's Charity
The Congregational and
 General Charitable Trust
The Corinthian Trust
Edwin Cornforth 1983 Charity
 Trust
The Cornwall Historic
 Churches Trust
The Dugdale Charitable Trust

The Houghton Dunn Charitable
Trust
The Ebenezer Trust
The Edith Maud Ellis 1985
Charitable Trust
The Emmandjay Charitable
Trust
The Erskine Cunningham Hill
Trust
Joseph Fattorini Charitable
Trust 'B' Account
The Thomas Freke and Lady
Norton Charity
The Anne French Memorial
Trust
The Friends Hall Farm Street
Trust
The Gale Family Charitable
Trust
The Angela Gallagher Memorial
Fund
The Gibbs Charitable Trust
The Girdlers' Company
Charitable Trust
The Gough Charitable Trust
The Greys Charitable Trust
E F and M G Hall Charitable
Trust
The W A Handley Charitable
Trust
The Harris Charitable Trust
Headley-Pitt Charitable Trust
Heagerty Charitable Trust
Hexham and Newcastle
Diocesan Trust (1947)
The P and C Hickinbotham
Charitable Trust
The Jane Hodge Foundation
The Homelands Charitable
Trust
Sir Harold Hood's Charitable
Trust
The Hope Trust
The Huxham Charitable Trust
J A R Charitable Trust
The Jarman Charitable Trust
The Kennedy Charitable
Foundation
The King Henry VIII Endowed
Trust Warwick
Laslett's (Hinton) Charity
The P Leigh-Bramwell Trust 'E'
Lindale Educational
Foundation
The Charles Lloyd Foundation
Sylvanus Lyson's Charity
The Charlotte Marshall
Charitable Trust
Marshall's Charity
The Anthony and Elizabeth
Mellows Charitable
Settlement
Monmouthshire County Council
Welsh Church Act Fund
The Oliver Morland Charitable
Trust

S C and M E Morland's
Charitable Trust
Nazareth Trust Fund
The Northumbria Historic
Churches Trust
The Norwood and Newton
Settlement
The Nottinghamshire Historic
Churches Trust
The Ogle Christian Trust
The Owen Family Trust
Miss M E Swinton Paterson's
Charitable Trust
The Bernard Piggott Trust
Sir John Priestman Charity
Trust
The Bishop Radford Trust
The Sir James Reckitt Charity
The Nathaniel Reyner Trust
Fund
The Clive Richards Charity
Mrs L D Rope Third Charitable
Settlement
The Rotherwick Foundation
The Joseph Rowntree
Charitable Trust
Saint Sarkis Charity Trust
The Simpson Foundation
The W F Southall Trust
St Teilo's Trust
The Leonard Laity Stoate
Charitable Trust
The Sylvanus Charitable Trust
The Lady Tangye Charitable
Trust
C B and H H Taylor 1984 Trust
The Thornton Trust
The Tolkien Trust
The Westcroft Trust
The Westminster Foundation
The Norman Whiteley Trust
The Wixamtree Trust
The James Wood Bequest
Fund
The Worcestershire and
Dudley Historic Churches
Trust
The Yorkshire Historic
Churches Trust

■ **Christian social thought**

The Carpenters' Company
Charitable Trust
The Jerusalem Trust
The Norman Family Charitable
Trust
The Sir Halley Stewart Trust

■ **Ecumenicalism**

The Carpenters' Company
Charitable Trust
The Gibbs Charitable Trust
Mariapolis Limited
The Norman Family Charitable
Trust

Mrs L D Rope Third Charitable
Settlement

■ **Missionary work,
evangelism**

The Armourers' and Brasiers'
Gauntlet Trust
Barleycorn Trust
The Barnabas Trust
The Beacon Trust
P G and N J Boulton Trust
The A H and E Boulton Trust
The Carpenters' Company
Charitable Trust
The Chasah Trust
The Daily Prayer Union
Charitable Trust Ltd
The Dugdale Charitable Trust
The Evangelical Covenants
Trust
The Fairway Trust
Farthing Trust
Feed the Minds
Philip and Judith Green Trust
Beatrice Hankey Foundation
Ltd
The Hesed Trust
Hinchley Charitable Trust
Stuart Hine Trust
Hockerill Educational
Foundation
The Hope Trust
The Huxham Charitable Trust
The Jerusalem Trust
Maurice and Hilda Laing
Charitable Trust
The Beatrice Laing Trust
The Lancaster Foundation
The Langley Charitable Trust
Paul Lunn-Rockliffe Charitable
Trust
The Lyndhurst Trust
Maranatha Christian Trust
The Millhouses Charitable
Trust
The Moshulu Charitable Trust
Nathan Charitable Trust
Nazareth Trust Fund
The Norman Family Charitable
Trust
The Ogle Christian Trust
The Owen Family Trust
Panahpur Charitable Trust
The Payne Charitable Trust
The Persson Charitable Trust
Quothquan Trust
The Rank Foundation
The Sir Cliff Richard Charitable
Trust
The Rock Foundation
The Seedfield Trust
The J A Shone Memorial Trust
The Spring Harvest Charitable
Trust
St Teilo's Trust

The Stewards' Company
Limited (incorporating the J
W Laing Trust and the J W
Laing Biblical Scholarship
Trust)
The Tabeel Trust
The Thornton Trust
Ulting Overseas Trust
The United Society for the
Propagation of the Gospel
Wallington Missionary Mart
and Auctions
The Norman Whiteley Trust
Dame Violet Wills Charitable
Trust
Women's World Day of Prayer

Hinduism

The Carpenters' Company
Charitable Trust
The Norman Family Charitable
Trust

Inter-faith activities

The Carpenters' Company
Charitable Trust
The Duis Charitable Trust
The Elmgrant Trust
The Anne French Memorial
Trust
Hinduja Foundation
The Joseph Levy Charitable
Foundation
The Norman Family Charitable
Trust
The Sir James Roll Charitable
Trust
Scottish Churches' Community
Trust
The Sigmund Sternberg
Charitable Foundation
The Sir Halley Stewart Trust
West London Synagogue
Charitable Fund

Islam

The Altajir Trust
The Carpenters' Company
Charitable Trust
Irshad Trust
Matliwala Family Charitable
Trust
Muslim Hands
The Norman Family Charitable
Trust

Judaism

4 Charity Foundation
Brian Abrams Charitable Trust
Eric Abrams Charitable Trust
The Acacia Charitable Trust
Achiezer Association Ltd
Achisomoch Aid Company
Limited
Adenfirst Ltd
Alba Charitable Trust
The Alliance Family Foundation
Altamont Ltd
AM Charitable Trust
Amabrill Limited
Andor Charitable Trust
The Ardwick Trust
AW Charitable Trust
The Baker Charitable Trust
The Balint Family Charitable
Trusts
Bay Charitable Trust
Bear Mordechai Ltd
Beauland Ltd
The Becker Family Charitable
Trust
Belljoe Tzedoko Ltd
Maurice and Jacqueline
Bennett Charitable Trust
Michael and Leslie Bennett
Charitable Trust
The Ruth Berkowitz Charitable
Trust
BHST
The Bintaub Charitable Trust
The Bertie Black Foundation
The Sir Victor Blank Charitable
Settlement
The Neville and Elaine Blond
Charitable Trust
The Blueberry Charitable Trust
The Bluston Charitable
Settlement
The Bonamy Charitable Trust
Salo Bordon Charitable Trust
Sir Clive Bourne Family Trust
Bourneheights Limited
Mrs E E Brown Charitable
Settlement
Brushmill Ltd
The Audrey and Stanley Burton
1960 Charitable Trust
The Arnold Burton 1998
Charitable Trust
C and F Charitable Trust
H and L Cantor Trust
Carlee Ltd
The Carlton House Charitable
Trust
The Carpenters' Company
Charitable Trust
The CH (1980) Charitable
Trust
Charitworth Limited
Chasdei Tovim Me'oros
The Childwick Trust
The Clore Duffield Foundation

Miss V L Clore's 1967
Charitable Trust
Closehelm Ltd
Clydpride Ltd
The Denise Cohen Charitable
Trust
The Vivienne and Samuel
Cohen Charitable Trust
The E Alec Colman Charitable
Fund Ltd
Col-Reno Ltd
Harold and Daphne Cooper
Charitable Trust
The Gershon Coren Charitable
Foundation
The Sidney and Elizabeth
Corob Charitable Trust
The Corona Charitable Trust
The Craps Charitable Trust
Cuby Charitable Trust
The Manny Cussins
Foundation
Itzchok Meyer Cymerman Trust
Ltd
Oizer Dalim Trust
Davidson Charitable Trust
The Alderman Joe Davidson
Memorial Trust
Davis-Rubens Charitable Trust
The Leopold De Rothschild
Charitable Trust
The Debmar Benevolent Trust
The Dellal Foundation
Alan and Sheila Diamond
Charitable Trust
The Djanogly Foundation
The Dollond Charitable Trust
Domepride Ltd
The Doughty Charity Trust
The Duis Charitable Trust
Dushinsky Trust Ltd
The George Elias Charitable
Trust
Ellador Ltd
The Ellinson Foundation Ltd
Elshore Ltd
Entindale Ltd
The Esfandi Charitable
Foundation
The Exilarch's Foundation
Extonglen Limited
The Faber Charitable Trust
The Family Foundations Trust
Famos Foundation Trust
Federation of Jewish Relief
Organisations
Finnart House School Trust
The Rose Flatau Charitable
Trust
The Flow Foundation
The Gerald Fogel Charitable
Trust
Forbesville Limited
Fordeve Ltd
The Isaac and Freda Frankel
Memorial Charitable Trust
Friends of Biala Ltd

Friends of Boyan Trust
Mejer and Gertrude Miriam Frydman Foundation
Gableholt Limited
Garvan Limited
Jacqueline and Michael Gee Charitable Trust
The B and P Glasser Charitable Trust
The Meir Golda Trust
Golden Charitable Trust
The Jack Goldhill Charitable Trust
The Everard and Mina Goodman Charitable Foundation
Leonard Gordon Charitable Trust
The Grahame Charitable Foundation Limited
Naomi and Jeffrey Greenwood Charitable Trust
The M and R Gross Charities Limited
The Grove Charitable Trust
The GRP Charitable Trust
The Gur Trust
The H and J Spack Charitable Trust
The H P Charitable Trust
The Harbour Foundation
Haskel Family Foundation
The Hathaway Trust
The Maurice Hatter Foundation
The Haydan Charitable Trust
Heathside Charitable Trust
The Helping Foundation
The Bernhard Heuberger Charitable Trust
Highcroft Charitable Trust
The Holden Charitable Trust
The Daniel Howard Trust
The Humanitarian Trust
The Huntingdon Foundation
Hurdale Charity Limited
The P Y N and B Hyams Trust
Investream Charitable Trust
The Isaacs Charitable Trust
Jacobs Charitable Trust
The Ruth and Lionel Jacobson Trust (Second Fund) No 2
The Susan and Stephen James Charitable Settlement
Jay Education Trust
JCA Charitable Foundation
Jewish Child's Day
The Jewish Youth Fund
The Harold Joels Charitable Trust
The Nicholas Joels Charitable Trust
The Norman Joels Charitable Trust
The Joron Charitable Trust
The J E Joseph Charitable Fund

Jusaca Charitable Trust
The Bernard Kahn Charitable Trust
The Stanley Kalms Foundation
The Kasner Charitable Trust
The Kass Charitable Trust
The Michael and Ilse Katz Foundation
The Katzauer Charitable Settlement
The C S Kaufman Charitable Trust
The Geoffrey John Kaye Charitable Foundation
The Emmanuel Kaye Foundation
Keren Association
Kermaville Ltd
E and E Kernkraut Charities Limited
The Kessler Foundation
Kirschel Foundation
The Kobler Trust
The Kohn Foundation
Kollel and Co. Limited
The Kreditor Charitable Trust
The Neil Kreitman Foundation
Kupath Gemach Chaim Bechesed Viznitz Trust
The Lambert Charitable Trust
Largsmount Ltd
Laufer Charitable Trust
The Lauffer Family Charitable Foundation
The Lawson Beckman Charitable Trust
The Carole and Geoffrey Lawson Foundation
The Arnold Lee Charitable Trust
The Kennedy Leigh Charitable Trust
Morris Leigh Foundation
The Joseph Levy Charitable Foundation
Lewis Family Charitable Trust
The Ruth and Stuart Lipton Charitable Trust
Jack Livingstone Charitable Trust
Localtrent Ltd
The Locker Foundation
The Loftus Charitable Trust
The Lolev Charitable Trust
The Lowy Mitchell Foundation
The Ruth and Jack Lunzer Charitable Trust
The Sir Jack Lyons Charitable Trust
Malcolm Lyons Foundation
The M and C Trust
The M D and S Charitable Trust
The M K Charitable Trust
The Magen Charitable Trust
Malbin Trust
Marbeh Torah Trust

The Stella and Alexander Margulies Charitable Trust
The Ann and David Marks Foundation
The Violet Mauray Charitable Trust
Mayfair Charities Ltd
Melodor Ltd
Melow Charitable Trust
Menuchar Ltd
Mercaz Torah Vechesed Limited
The Laurence Misener Charitable Trust
The Mishcon Family Charitable Trust
The Mitchell Charitable Trust
The Modiano Charitable Trust
The Mole Charitable Trust
Diana and Allan Morgenthau Charitable Trust
The Peter Morrison Charitable Foundation
Moshal Charitable Trust
Brian and Jill Moss Charitable Trust
Moss Family Charitable Trust
MYA Charitable Trust
MYR Charitable Trust
The Willie Nagel Charitable Trust
The Naggar Charitable Trust
Nemoral Ltd
Ner Foundation
Nesswall Ltd
Newpier Charity Ltd
The Chevras Ezras Nitzrochim Trust
NJD Charitable Trust
Normalyn Charitable Trust
The Norman Family Charitable Trust
The Oizer Charitable Trust
The Doris Pacey Charitable Foundation
The Park Charitable Trust
The David Pearlman Charitable Foundation
The Pears Foundation
Peltz Trust
B E Perl Charitable Trust
The Philips and Rubens Charitable Trust
The Phillips Family Charitable Trust
G S Plaut Charitable Trust Limited
The George and Esme Pollitzer Charitable Settlement
The Pollywally Charitable Trust
Edith and Ferdinand Porjes Charitable Trust
The John Porter Charitable Trust
The J E Posnansky Charitable Trust
Premierquote Ltd

Premishlaner Charitable Trust
R J M Charitable Trust
R S Charitable Trust
Rachel Charitable Trust
The Fanny Rapaport Charitable
  Settlement
The Rayden Charitable Trust
The Rayne Trust
The Rest Harrow Trust
Ridgesave Limited
The Sir John Ritblat Family
  Foundation
The Daniel Rivlin Charitable
  Trust
Rokach Family Charitable Trust
The Gerald Ronson Foundation
Rowanville Ltd
The Alfred and Frances
  Rubens Charitable Trust
The Rubin Foundation
S F Foundation
S O Charitable Trust
The Ruzin Sadagora Trust
The Hon. M J Samuel
  Charitable Trust
The Peter Samuel Charitable
  Trust
The Schapira Charitable Trust
The Annie Schiff Charitable
  Trust
The Schmidt-Bodner Charitable
  Trust
The Schreib Trust
The Schreiber Charitable Trust
The Helene Sebba Charitable
  Trust
The Samuel Sebba Charitable
  Trust
Sellata Ltd
SEM Charitable Trust
The Cyril Shack Trust
The Archie Sherman Cardiff
  Foundation
The Archie Sherman Charitable
  Trust
Shlomo Memorial Fund Limited
The Julius Silman Charitable
  Trust
The Leslie Silver Charitable
  Trust
The Sobell Foundation
Solev Co Ltd
The Solo Charitable
  Settlement
Songdale Ltd
Sparquote Limited
Spears-Stutz Charitable Trust
The Moss Spiro Will Charitable
  Foundation
Rosalyn and Nicholas Springer
  Charitable Trust
Springrule Ltd
The Cyril and Betty Stein
  Charitable Trust
The Steinberg Family
  Charitable Trust
C E K Stern Charitable Trust

The Sigmund Sternberg
  Charitable Foundation
Stervon Ltd
The Strawberry Charitable
  Trust
The A B Strom and R Strom
  Charitable Trust
Sueberry Ltd
The Alan Sugar Foundation
The Adrienne and Leslie
  Sussman Charitable Trust
T and S Trust Fund
Tadlus Limited
The Tajtelbaum Charitable
  Trust
Talteg Ltd
The Tangent Charitable Trust
The David Tannen Charitable
  Trust
The Lili Tapper Charitable
  Foundation
Tegham Limited
Tomchei Torah Charitable
  Trust
The Torah Temimah Trust
Toras Chesed (London) Trust
Truedene Co. Ltd
Truemart Limited
Trumros Limited
Tudor Rose Ltd
Trustees of Tzedakah
The Union of Orthodox Hebrew
  Congregation
The David Uri Memorial Trust
The Vail Foundation
Vivdale Ltd
The Viznitz Foundation
Robert and Felicity Waley-
  Cohen Charitable Trust
The Weinstein Foundation
West London Synagogue
  Charitable Fund
The Williams Family Charitable
  Trust
The Benjamin Winegarten
  Charitable Trust
The Harold Hyam Wingate
  Foundation
The Michael and Anna Wix
  Charitable Trust
The Maurice Wohl Charitable
  Foundation
The Charles Wolfson
  Charitable Trust
The Wolfson Family Charitable
  Trust
Woodlands Foundation Limited
Woodlands Green Ltd
The A and R Woolf Charitable
  Trust
The Fred and Della Worms
  Charitable Trust
Wychdale Ltd
Wychville Ltd
Yankov Charitable Trust
The Marjorie and Arnold Ziff
  Charitable Foundation

Stephen Zimmerman
  Charitable Trust

....

■ Jewish causes, work

Altamont Ltd
The Audrey and Stanley Burton
  1960 Charitable Trust
The Arnold Burton 1998
  Charitable Trust
Miss V L Clore's 1967
  Charitable Trust
The Duis Charitable Trust
Ellador Ltd
The Faber Charitable Trust
Leonard Gordon Charitable
  Trust
Naomi and Jeffrey Greenwood
  Charitable Trust
The Hathaway Trust
The Susan and Stephen
  James Charitable
  Settlement
The Lambert Charitable Trust
Malbin Trust
The Modiano Charitable Trust
Moss Family Charitable Trust
Normalyn Charitable Trust
The Pears Foundation
Peltz Trust
B E Perl Charitable Trust
The Pollywally Charitable Trust
Sellata Ltd
Sparquote Limited
The Moss Spiro Will Charitable
  Foundation
Rosalyn and Nicholas Springer
  Charitable Trust
The Tangent Charitable Trust
The Wolfson Family Charitable
  Trust

....

■ Orthodox Judaism

Achisomoch Aid Company
  Limited
Amabrill Limited
The Becker Family Charitable
  Trust
Belljoe Tzedoko Ltd
Bourneheights Limited
C and F Charitable Trust
The Doughty Charity Trust
Extonglen Limited
Friends of Boyan Trust
The H P Charitable Trust
The Helping Foundation
The Lolev Charitable Trust
Mayfair Charities Ltd
Mercaz Torah Vechesed
  Limited
Nemoral Ltd
Newpier Charity Ltd
Rowanville Ltd
C E K Stern Charitable Trust

T and S Trust Fund
Tadlus Limited
Tegham Limited
The Torah Temimah Trust
Vivdale Ltd

Religious understanding

The Carpenters' Company
    Charitable Trust
The Doughty Charity Trust
The Gilbert and Eileen Edgar
    Foundation
The Elmgrant Trust
The Anne French Memorial
    Trust
Keswick Hall Charity
The Kennedy Leigh Charitable
    Trust
The Joseph Levy Charitable
    Foundation
The Norman Family Charitable
    Trust
Quothquan Trust

Rights, law and conflict

The A B Charitable Trust
The Ajahma Charitable Trust
The AS Charitable Trust
The Body Shop Foundation
The Boshier-Hinton Foundation
John and Susan Bowers Fund
Britannia Foundation
The British Gas (Scottish Gas)
    Energy Trust
The Bromley Trust
The Barrow Cadbury Trust and
    the Barrow Cadbury Fund
Celtic Charity Fund
The Charities Advisory Trust
The Chelsea Building Society
    Charitable Foundation
J A Clark Charitable Trust
The Community Foundation for
    Northern Ireland
The Daiwa Anglo-Japanese
    Foundation
The Denton Wilde Sapte
    Charitable Trust
The Dorus Trust
The Duis Charitable Trust
The Dulverton Trust
EDF Energy Trust (EDFET)
The Edith Maud Ellis 1985
    Charitable Trust
The Embleton Trust
The Emmandjay Charitable
    Trust
Allan and Nesta Ferguson
    Charitable Settlement
Ford Britain Trust
Sydney E Franklin Deceased's
    New Second Charity
Friends Provident Charitable
    Foundation
Maurice Fry Charitable Trust
The G D Charitable Trust
The Gamlen Charitable Trust
J Paul Getty Jr Charitable Trust
Greggs Foundation
The Gulbenkian Foundation
Paul Hamlyn Foundation
The Helen Hamlyn Trust
The Hilden Charitable Fund
The Ireland Fund of Great
    Britain
The J R S S T Charitable Trust
The Joffe Charitable Trust
The Allen Lane Foundation
The Law Society Charity
The Leigh Trust
The Mark Leonard Trust
The Joseph Levy Charitable
    Foundation
Lloyds TSB Foundation for
    Northern Ireland
London Legal Support Trust
Mariapolis Limited
The Methodist Relief and
    Development Fund

The Millfield House Foundation
John Moores Foundation
The Peter Moores Foundation
S C and M E Morland's
    Charitable Trust
The Kitty and Daniel Nabarro
    Charitable Trust
The Nadezhda Charitable Trust
Network for Social Change
Newby Trust Limited
The Noon Foundation
The Northern Rock Foundation
Novi Most International
The Nuffield Foundation
The Harry Payne Trust
The Persula Foundation
Polden-Puckham Charitable
    Foundation
The David and Elaine Potter
    Foundation
Prairie Trust
The Monica Rabagliati
    Charitable Trust
The Eleanor Rathbone
    Charitable Trust
The Sigrid Rausing Trust
The Roddick Foundation
Rosa – the UK fund for women
    and girls
The Rowan Charitable Trust
The Joseph Rowntree
    Charitable Trust
Joseph Rowntree Reform Trust
    Limited
The Alan and Babette
    Sainsbury Charitable Fund
Santander UK Foundation
    Limited
The Scott Bader
    Commonwealth Ltd
The Severn Trent Water
    Charitable Trust Fund
The W F Southall Trust
The Staples Trust
The Tinsley Foundation
United Utilities Trust Fund
The Scurrah Wainwright Charity
War on Want
Women Caring Trust
Worcester Municipal Charities
    (incorporating Worcester
    Consolidated Municipal
    Charity and Worcester
    Municipal Exhibitions
    Foundation)
The Xerox (UK) Trust
The York Children's Trust

Citizen participation

The Barrow Cadbury Trust and
    the Barrow Cadbury Fund
The Methodist Relief and
    Development Fund
The Nuffield Foundation

The Joseph Rowntree
Charitable Trust
Joseph Rowntree Reform Trust
Limited
The Tinsley Foundation

Conflict resolution

The AS Charitable Trust
The Barrow Cadbury Trust and
the Barrow Cadbury Fund
The Charities Advisory Trust
J A Clark Charitable Trust
The Daiwa Anglo-Japanese
Foundation
The Dulverton Trust
The Edith Maud Ellis 1985
Charitable Trust
Allan and Nesta Ferguson
Charitable Settlement
J Paul Getty Jr Charitable Trust
The Gulbenkian Foundation
The Ireland Fund of Great
Britain
The Joffe Charitable Trust
The Allen Lane Foundation
Mariapolis Limited
S C and M E Morland's
Charitable Trust
The Kitty and Daniel Nabarro
Charitable Trust
Novi Most International
The Harry Payne Trust
Polden-Puckham Charitable
Foundation
Prairie Trust
The Joseph Rowntree
Charitable Trust
The Scott Bader
Commonwealth Ltd
The W F Southall Trust
Women Caring Trust

Legal advice and services

Britannia Foundation
The British Gas (Scottish Gas)
Energy Trust
The Chelsea Building Society
Charitable Foundation
The Denton Wilde Sapte
Charitable Trust
EDF Energy Trust (EDFET)
The Embleton Trust
The Emmandjay Charitable
Trust
Friends Provident Charitable
Foundation
The Law Society Charity
Lloyds TSB Foundation for
Northern Ireland
London Legal Support Trust
John Moores Foundation
The Northern Rock Foundation

The Nuffield Foundation
The Rowan Charitable Trust
Santander UK Foundation
Limited
The Severn Trent Water
Charitable Trust Fund
United Utilities Trust Fund
Worcester Municipal Charities
(incorporating Worcester
Consolidated Municipal
Charity and Worcester
Municipal Exhibitions
Foundation)

Rights, equality and justice

The A B Charitable Trust
The Ajahma Charitable Trust
The Body Shop Foundation
John and Susan Bowers Fund
The Bromley Trust
The Barrow Cadbury Trust and
the Barrow Cadbury Fund
Celtic Charity Fund
The Dorus Trust
The Duis Charitable Trust
Allan and Nesta Ferguson
Charitable Settlement
Ford Britain Trust
Sydney E Franklin Deceased's
New Second Charity
The G D Charitable Trust
Greggs Foundation
The Gulbenkian Foundation
Paul Hamlyn Foundation
The Helen Hamlyn Trust
The Hilden Charitable Fund
The J R S S T Charitable Trust
The Joffe Charitable Trust
The Allen Lane Foundation
The Law Society Charity
The Leigh Trust
The Mark Leonard Trust
The Joseph Levy Charitable
Foundation
The Methodist Relief and
Development Fund
The Millfield House Foundation
John Moores Foundation
The Peter Moores Foundation
The Kitty and Daniel Nabarro
Charitable Trust
The Nadezhda Charitable Trust
Network for Social Change
Newby Trust Limited
The Noon Foundation
The Nuffield Foundation
The Persula Foundation
Polden-Puckham Charitable
Foundation
The Monica Rabagliati
Charitable Trust
The Eleanor Rathbone
Charitable Trust
The Sigrid Rausing Trust

The Roddick Foundation
Rosa – the UK fund for women
and girls
The Rowan Charitable Trust
The Joseph Rowntree
Charitable Trust
Joseph Rowntree Reform Trust
Limited
The Alan and Babette
Sainsbury Charitable Fund
The Staples Trust
The Tinsley Foundation
The Scurrah Wainwright Charity
The Xerox (UK) Trust
The York Children's Trust

■ Civil liberties

The Barrow Cadbury Trust and
the Barrow Cadbury Fund
The Joseph Rowntree
Charitable Trust
Joseph Rowntree Reform Trust
Limited
The Tinsley Foundation

■ Cultural equity

Greggs Foundation
The Gulbenkian Foundation
Paul Hamlyn Foundation
The Kitty and Daniel Nabarro
Charitable Trust

■ Disability rights

The Dorus Trust
The G D Charitable Trust
The Gulbenkian Foundation
John Moores Foundation
Newby Trust Limited
The Rowan Charitable Trust
The Xerox (UK) Trust

■ Economic justice

Allan and Nesta Ferguson
Charitable Settlement
The Millfield House Foundation
The Sigrid Rausing Trust
The Joseph Rowntree
Charitable Trust
The Tinsley Foundation

■ Human rights

The A B Charitable Trust
The Ajahma Charitable Trust
The Body Shop Foundation
The Bromley Trust
The Barrow Cadbury Trust and
the Barrow Cadbury Fund
The Helen Hamlyn Trust

The Methodist Relief and
   Development Fund
The Persula Foundation
Polden-Puckham Charitable
   Foundation
The Monica Rabagliati
   Charitable Trust
The Sigrid Rausing Trust
The Roddick Foundation
The Rowan Charitable Trust
The Tinsley Foundation

....

■ Racial justice

The Barrow Cadbury Trust and
   the Barrow Cadbury Fund
Celtic Charity Fund
The Duis Charitable Trust
Ford Britain Trust
The Hilden Charitable Fund
The Leigh Trust
The Joseph Levy Charitable
   Foundation
John Moores Foundation
The Peter Moores Foundation
The Noon Foundation
The Joseph Rowntree
   Charitable Trust
The Tinsley Foundation

....

■ Social justice

John and Susan Bowers Fund
The Duis Charitable Trust
The Methodist Relief and
   Development Fund
Network for Social Change
Joseph Rowntree Reform Trust
   Limited
The Tinsley Foundation
The Scurrah Wainwright Charity
The Xerox (UK) Trust

....

■ Women's rights

The Duis Charitable Trust
The Methodist Relief and
   Development Fund
John Moores Foundation
Polden-Puckham Charitable
   Foundation
The Eleanor Rathbone
   Charitable Trust
The Sigrid Rausing Trust
Rosa – the UK fund for women
   and girls
The Rowan Charitable Trust
The Staples Trust

....

■ Young people's rights

The Duis Charitable Trust
The Gulbenkian Foundation

The Mark Leonard Trust
The Nadezhda Charitable Trust
The Nuffield Foundation
The Rowan Charitable Trust
The Xerox (UK) Trust
The York Children's Trust

Science and technology

The Armourers' and Brasiers'
   Gauntlet Trust
Astellas European Foundation
The Big Lottery Fund
The Boshier-Hinton Foundation
British Ornithologists' Union
The Ernest Cook Trust
The Crescent Trust
William Dean Countryside and
   Educational Trust
The Dunn Family Charitable
   Trust
The James Dyson Foundation
The Beryl Evetts and Robert
   Luff Animal Welfare Trust
The Gatsby Charitable
   Foundation
The Granada Foundation
Paul Hamlyn Foundation
The Simon Heller Charitable
   Settlement
The Michael John Trust
The Kohn Foundation
The Leathersellers' Company
   Charitable Fund
The John Spedan Lewis
   Foundation
The MacRobert Trust
The Miller Foundation
The Mountbatten Memorial
   Trust
The Kitty and Daniel Nabarro
   Charitable Trust
The Nuffield Foundation
Open Gate
The Petplan Charitable Trust
The David and Elaine Potter
   Foundation
Mrs L D Rope Third Charitable
   Settlement
The Rowlands Trust
The Michael Sacher Charitable
   Trust
Dr Mortimer and Theresa
   Sackler Foundation
The Raymond and Beverley
   Sackler Foundation
The Alan and Babette
   Sainsbury Charitable Fund
The Andrew Salvesen
   Charitable Trust
The Simpson Education and
   Conservation Trust
The Thompson Family
   Charitable Trust
The Wellcome Trust
The Wilkinson Charitable
   Foundation
The Wolfson Foundation
The John K Young Endowment
   Fund

Engineering/ technology

The Armourers' and Brasiers' Gauntlet Trust
The Ernest Cook Trust
The James Dyson Foundation
Paul Hamlyn Foundation
The Mountbatten Memorial Trust
The Kitty and Daniel Nabarro Charitable Trust
Open Gate

....

■ Life sciences

The Big Lottery Fund
British Ornithologists' Union
The Ernest Cook Trust
The Crescent Trust
William Dean Countryside and Educational Trust
The Dunn Family Charitable Trust
The Beryl Evetts and Robert Luff Animal Welfare Trust
The Gatsby Charitable Foundation
The John Spedan Lewis Foundation
The Petplan Charitable Trust
The Andrew Salvesen Charitable Trust
The Simpson Education and Conservation Trust
The Thompson Family Charitable Trust
The Wellcome Trust

....

■ Physical/earth sciences

The Armourers' and Brasiers' Gauntlet Trust
Mrs L D Rope Third Charitable Settlement
The John K Young Endowment Fund

Social sciences, policy and research

The Boshier-Hinton Foundation
British Institute at Ankara
CAF (Charities Aid Foundation)
CfBT Education Trust
EAGA Partnership Charitable Trust
The Elmgrant Trust
Esmée Fairbairn Foundation
The Gatsby Charitable Foundation
The Robert Gavron Charitable Trust
The Kenneth Hargreaves Charitable Trust
Haskel Family Foundation
Houblon-Norman/George Fund
The Joffe Charitable Trust
The Allen Lane Foundation
The Leverhulme Trust
The Joseph Levy Charitable Foundation
James Madison Trust
The McDougall Trust
The Kitty and Daniel Nabarro Charitable Trust
The Eleni Nakou Foundation
The Nuffield Foundation
Prairie Trust
The Joseph Rowntree Charitable Trust
The Joseph Rowntree Foundation
The Steel Charitable Trust
The Sir Halley Stewart Trust
The Nigel Vinson Charitable Trust
War on Want
Webb Memorial Trust

Economics

CAF (Charities Aid Foundation)
Houblon-Norman/George Fund

Political science

Esmée Fairbairn Foundation
The Gatsby Charitable Foundation
The Joffe Charitable Trust
The Allen Lane Foundation
The Leverhulme Trust
James Madison Trust
The McDougall Trust
The Eleni Nakou Foundation
The Joseph Rowntree Charitable Trust
The Joseph Rowntree Foundation
Webb Memorial Trust

Social policy

CfBT Education Trust
The Gatsby Charitable Foundation
The Robert Gavron Charitable Trust
The Kenneth Hargreaves Charitable Trust
Haskel Family Foundation
The Joseph Levy Charitable Foundation
The Kitty and Daniel Nabarro Charitable Trust
Prairie Trust
The Joseph Rowntree Foundation
The Sir Halley Stewart Trust
Webb Memorial Trust

Social welfare

The 1989 Willan Charitable Trust
The 29th May 1961 Charitable Trust
The Acacia Charitable Trust
The ACT Foundation
The Company of Actuaries' Charitable Trust Fund
The Sylvia Adams Charitable Trust
The Adint Charitable Trust
Age Concern Scotland Grants
The Green and Lilian F M Ainsworth and Family Benevolent Fund
The Sylvia Aitken Charitable Trust
The Ajahma Charitable Trust
The Alborada Trust
The Alchemy Foundation
Alexandra Rose Charities
The Rita Allen Charitable Trust
Almondsbury Charity
The Ammco Trust
Viscount Amory's Charitable Trust
The AMW Charitable Trust
The Andrew Anderson Trust
The Apax Foundation
The Appletree Trust
The Archbishop of Canterbury's Charitable Trust
Archbishop of Wales' Fund for Children
The Archer Trust
The Ardwick Trust
The Argus Appeal
The John Armitage Charitable Trust
The Armourers' and Brasiers' Gauntlet Trust
The Artemis Charitable Trust
The Arts and Entertainment Charitable Trust
The Ashendene Trust
The Ashworth Charitable Trust
The Associated Country Women of the World (ACWW)
AstonMansfield Charitable Trust
The Astor Foundation
The Lord Austin Trust
The Avon and Somerset Police Community Trust
Awards for All
The Roy and Pixie Baker Charitable Trust
The Balcombe Charitable Trust
The Balint Family Charitable Trusts
The Albert Casanova Ballard Deceased Trust
The Ballinger Charitable Trust

The Balmore Trust
The Balney Charitable Trust
The Band Trust
The Barbour Trust
Barchester Healthcare Foundation
David and Frederick Barclay Foundation
Barnes Workhouse Fund
The Charity of William Barrow
The Batchworth Trust
BBC Children in Need
The Victoria and David Beckham Children's Charity
The John Beckwith Charitable Trust
The Peter Beckwith Charitable Trust
The Bedford Charity (The Harpur Trust)
The Bedfordshire and Luton Community Foundation
The Beit Trust
The Bellahouston Bequest Fund
Bergqvist Charitable Trust
The Bestway Foundation
The Mason Bibby 1981 Trust
The Big Lottery Fund
The Birmingham District Nursing Charitable Trust
The Sydney Black Charitable Trust
The Blanchminster Trust
The Blueberry Charitable Trust
The Boltons Trust
The Booth Charities
The Boots Charitable Trust
Salo Bordon Charitable Trust
The Boshier-Hinton Foundation
The Anthony Bourne Foundation
Community Foundation for Bournemouth, Dorset and Poole
The Bristol Charities
John Bristow and Thomas Mason Trust
Britannia Foundation
British Humane Association
The Bromley Trust
The David Brooke Charity
The Rory and Elizabeth Brooks Foundation
Bill Brown's Charitable Settlement
Brushmill Ltd
Buckland Charitable Trust
The Burden Trust
The Audrey and Stanley Burton 1960 Charitable Trust
The Arnold Burton 1998 Charitable Trust
The Burton Breweries Charitable Trust
Butchers' Company General Charities

Ann Byrne Charitable Trust
Edward Cadbury Charitable Trust
The G W Cadbury Charitable Trust
The William A Cadbury Charitable Trust
The Edward and Dorothy Cadbury Trust
The Barrow Cadbury Trust and the Barrow Cadbury Fund
The Calpe Trust
The Cambridgeshire Community Foundation
The Campden Charities
Capital Community Foundation
The Carpenter Charitable Trust
The Carr-Gregory Trust
The Leslie Mary Carter Charitable Trust
Carter's Educational Foundation
The Cattanach Charitable Trust
The Wilfrid and Constance Cave Foundation
The Cayo Foundation
The Chapman Charitable Trust
John William Chapman's Charitable Trust
The Chelsea Square 1994 Trust
The Cheruby Trust
The Chipping Sodbury Town Lands Charity
The Chrimes Family Charitable Trust
Christadelphian Samaritan Fund
Christian Response to Eastern Europe
The Church and Community Fund
Church Lands and John Johnson's Estate Charities
The Church Urban Fund
The City Bridge Trust
The City Parochial Foundation
The Cleopatra Trust
Miss V L Clore's 1967 Charitable Trust
The Clothworkers' Foundation
Richard Cloudesley's Charity
The Clover Trust
The Robert Clutterbuck Charitable Trust
The Coalfields Regeneration Trust
The Denise Cohen Charitable Trust
The Vivienne and Samuel Cohen Charitable Trust
The R and S Cohen Fondation
The E Alec Colman Charitable Fund Ltd
The Coltstaple Trust
Colyer-Fergusson Charitable Trust

Comic Relief
The Community Foundation for Greater Manchester
The Community Foundation for Northern Ireland
The Douglas Compton James Charitable Trust
The Congleton Inclosure Trust
The Consolidated Charities for the Infirm Merchant Taylors' Company
The Cook and Wolstenholme Charitable Trust
The Cooks Charity
The Co-operative Foundation
The J Reginald Corah Foundation Fund
The Gershon Coren Charitable Foundation
Michael Cornish Charitable Trust
Cornwall Community Foundation
County Durham Foundation
Coutts Charitable Trust
The John Cowan Foundation
Michael Crawford Children's Charity
Criffel Charitable Trust
The Violet and Milo Cripps Charitable Trust
The Croydon Relief in Need Charities
Cruden Foundation Ltd
The Ronald Cruickshanks' Foundation
Cullum Family Trust
Cumbria Community Foundation
The D J H Currie Memorial Trust
The Dr and Mrs A Darlington Charitable Trust
Baron Davenport's Charity
The Davidson (Nairn) Charitable Trust
The Hamilton Davies Trust
Peter De Haan Charitable Trust
The Denman Charitable Trust
The Denton Charitable Trust
Derbyshire Community Foundation
The J N Derbyshire Trust
The Dibden Allotments Charity
Dischma Charitable Trust
The Djanogly Foundation
The Derek and Eileen Dodgson Foundation
The Dorcas Trust
The Dorema Charitable Trust
The Dorus Trust
Double 'O' Charity Ltd
The R M Douglas Charitable Trust
The Drapers' Charitable Fund
The Dulverton Trust

The Dumbreck Charity
The Houghton Dunn Charitable Trust
The W E Dunn Trust
The Dyers' Company Charitable Trust
The James Dyson Foundation
The Eagle Charity Trust
East Kent Provincial Charities
East London Community Foundation
Eastern Counties Educational Trust Limited
The Sir John Eastwood Foundation
The Ebenezer Trust
The EBM Charitable Trust
Gilbert Edgar Trust
Edinburgh Children's Holiday Fund
The Edinburgh Trust, No 2 Account
Edinburgh Voluntary Organisations' Trust Funds
Edupoor Limited
Dr Edwards' and Bishop King's Fulham Endowment Fund
The Gerald Palmer Eling Trust Company
The Maud Elkington Charitable Trust
The Ellerdale Trust
The Edith Maud Ellis 1985 Charitable Trust
The Vernon N Ely Charitable Trust
The Emerton-Christie Charity
The Emilienne Charitable Trust
The Emmandjay Charitable Trust
The Englefield Charitable Trust
The Enkalon Foundation
The Epigoni Trust
The Eranda Foundation
The Ericson Trust
The Ernest Hecht Charitable Foundation
Essex Community Foundation
Euro Charity Trust
Sir John Evelyn's Charity
The Eveson Charitable Trust
The Execution Charitable Trust
F C Charitable Trust
Esmee Fairbairn Foundation
The Fairway Trust
The Family Rich Charities Trust
Samuel William Farmer's Trust
The Fassnidge Memorial Trust
The Fawcett Charitable Trust
The February Foundation
The John Feeney Charitable Bequest
The George Fentham Birmingham Charity
Elizabeth Ferguson Charitable Trust Fund

Fife Council/Common Good Funds and Trusts
The Sir John Fisher Foundation
Fisherbeck Charitable Trust
The Fishmongers' Company's Charitable Trust
The Fitton Trust
Florence's Charitable Trust
The Flow Foundation
The Football Association National Sports Centre Trust
The Forces Trust
Ford Britain Trust
The Oliver Ford Charitable Trust
The Forest Hill Charitable Trust
The Lady Forester Trust
The Foresters' Fund for Children
The Foresters' Charity Stewards UK Trust
The Donald Forrester Trust
Four Acre Trust
The Fowler, Smith and Jones Charitable Trust
Sydney E Franklin Deceased's New Second Charity
The Jill Franklin Trust
The Gordon Fraser Charitable Trust
The Hugh Fraser Foundation
The Joseph Strong Frazer Trust
The Louis and Valerie Freedman Charitable Settlement
The Freemasons' Grand Charity
The Thomas Freke and Lady Norton Charity
The Freshgate Trust Foundation
Friends of Muir Group
The Frognal Trust
Maurice Fry Charitable Trust
The Fuserna Foundation
The Angela Gallagher Memorial Fund
The Gannochy Trust
The Ganzoni Charitable Trust
The Gatsby Charitable Foundation
Gatwick Airport Community Trust
The Robert Gavron Charitable Trust
J Paul Getty Jr Charitable Trust
The Gibbs Charitable Trust
Simon Gibson Charitable Trust
The Girdlers' Company Charitable Trust
The B and P Glasser Charitable Trust
The Glass-House Trust
The Sydney and Phyllis Goldberg Memorial Charitable Trust

The Jack Goldhill Charitable Trust

The Goldsmiths' Company Charity

Goodfund

The Goodman Foundation

Mike Gooley Trailfinders Charity

The Gosling Foundation Limited

The Gough Charitable Trust

Grantham Yorke Trust

The Constance Green Foundation

Greggs Foundation

Grimmitt Trust

The Bishop of Guildford's Foundation

The Guildry Incorporation of Perth

The Gulbenkian Foundation

The Gunter Charitable Trust

Gurunanak

Dr Guthrie's Association

The H and M Charitable Trust

H C D Memorial Fund

The Hackney Parochial Charities

The Hadfield Trust

The Hadley Trust

The Hadrian Trust

The Alfred Haines Charitable Trust

The Hale Trust

E F and M G Hall Charitable Trust

Robert Hall Charity

Sue Hammerson's Charitable Trust

Hampshire and Isle of Wight Community Foundation

The Hampstead Wells and Campden Trust

Hampton Fuel Allotment Charity

The W A Handley Charitable Trust

The Hanley Trust

The Hanlye Charitable Trust

The Kathleen Hannay Memorial Charity

The Haramead Trust

Miss K M Harbinson's Charitable Trust

The Harborne Parish Lands Charity

The Harbour Charitable Trust

The Harding Trust

William Harding's Charity

The Hargrave Foundation

The Kenneth Hargreaves Charitable Trust

The Harris Charitable Trust

The Harris Charity

The Harrison and Potter Trust

Hasluck Charitable Trust

The Dorothy Hay-Bolton Charitable Trust

The Charles Hayward Foundation

The Headley Trust

The Heald Charitable Trust

Healthsure Group Ltd

May Hearnshaw's Charity

The Heathcoat Trust

The Hedley Foundation

The H J Heinz Company Limited Charitable Trust

The Hemby Trust

The Christina Mary Hendrie Trust for Scottish and Canadian Charities

The Henley Educational Charity

Philip Henman Trust

The G D Herbert Charitable Trust

The Joanna Herbert-Stepney Charitable Settlement

The Hertfordshire Community Foundation

The Hesslewood Children's Trust (Hull Seamen's and General Orphanage)

The P and C Hickinbotham Charitable Trust

The High Sheriff's Police Trust for the County of West Midlands

The Hilden Charitable Fund

The Charles Littlewood Hill Trust

Hinduja Foundation

Hobson Charity Limited

The J G Hogg Charitable Trust

John Holford's Charity

The Edward Holt Trust

The Holywood Trust

The Homelands Charitable Trust

The Homestead Charitable Trust

HopMarket Charity

The Horne Foundation

The Horne Trust

The Hornsey Parochial Charities

The Reta Lila Howard Foundation

Human Relief Foundation

The Humanitarian Trust

The Albert Hunt Trust

Miss Agnes H Hunter's Trust

Huntingdon Freemen's Charity

John Huntingdon's Charity

The Nani Huyu Charitable Trust

The Hyde Charitable Trust – Youth Plus

Impetus Trust

The Indigo Trust

The Inner London Magistrates Court Poor Box Charity and Feeder Charity

The Ireland Fund of Great Britain

The Irish Youth Foundation (UK) Ltd (incorporating The Lawlor Foundation)

The ITF Seafarers Trust

J A R Charitable Trust

The Ruth and Lionel Jacobson Trust (Second Fund) No 2

Jaffe Family Relief Fund

The Jarman Charitable Trust

The John Jarrold Trust

The Jeffrey Charitable Trust

Jesus Hospital Charity

The Nicholas Joels Charitable Trust

The Lillie Johnson Charitable Trust

The Johnnie Johnson Trust

The Johnson Wax Ltd Charitable Trust

The Jones 1986 Charitable Trust

The Cyril and Eve Jumbo Charitable Trust

The Anton Jurgens Charitable Trust

The Kass Charitable Trust

The Emmanuel Kaye Foundation

Kelsick's Educational Foundation

The KempWelch Charitable Trust

William Kendall's Charity (Wax Chandlers' Company)

Kent Community Foundation

The Peter Kershaw Trust

The King's Fund

The Kingsbury Charity

The Mary Kinross Charitable Trust

Kirkley Poor's Lands Estate

Ernest Kleinwort Charitable Trust

The Sir James Knott Trust

The KPMG Foundation

The Kreditor Charitable Trust

The Kreitman Foundation

The Neil Kreitman Foundation

The Kyte Charitable Trust

John Laing Charitable Trust

The Christopher Laing Foundation

The David Laing Foundation

The Beatrice Laing Trust

The Lambert Charitable Trust

Community Foundation for Lancashire

Lancashire Environmental Fund

Duchy of Lancaster Benevolent Fund

The Allen Lane Foundation

The Langdale Trust

The Langley Charitable Trust

The LankellyChase Foundation

The R J Larg Family Charitable Trust
The Lark Trust
Laslett's (Hinton) Charity
Mrs F B Laurence Charitable Trust
The Kathleen Laurence Trust
The Edgar E Lawley Foundation
The Lawson Beckman Charitable Trust
The Raymond and Blanche Lawson Charitable Trust
The Carole and Geoffrey Lawson Foundation
The Leach Fourteenth Trust
The William Leech Charity
Leeds Building Society Charitable Foundation
The Leeds Community Foundation
The Leigh Trust
The Mark Leonard Trust
The Leverhulme Trade Charities Trust
Lord Leverhulme's Charitable Trust
The Joseph Levy Charitable Foundation
John Lewis Partnership General Community Fund
The Limbourne Trust
The Linbury Trust
The Enid Linder Foundation
The Lister Charitable Trust
The Andrew and Mary Elizabeth Little Charitable Trust
The Liverpool One Foundation
The Elaine and Angus Lloyd Charitable Trust
Lloyds TSB Foundation for England and Wales
Lloyds TSB Foundation for Northern Ireland
Lloyds TSB Foundation for the Channel Islands
Localtrent Ltd
London Catalyst
The Lotus Foundation
The C L Loyd Charitable Trust
The Marie Helen Luen Charitable Trust
Henry Lumley Charitable Trust
Lady Lumley's Educational Foundation
The Lynwood Trust
John Lyon's Charity
Malcolm Lyons Foundation
The M and C Trust
The R S Macdonald Charitable Trust
The MacRobert Trust
Ian Mactaggart Trust
The Magdalen and Lasher Charity
Magdalen Hospital Trust
Manchester Kids

The Manifold Charitable Trust
R W Mann Trust
The Leslie and Lilian Manning Trust
The Manoukian Charitable Foundation
The Marchday Charitable Fund
Market Harborough and The Bowdens Charity
The Hilda and Samuel Marks Foundation
Marr-Munning Trust
The Michael Marsh Charitable Trust
The Marsh Christian Trust
The Charlotte Marshall Charitable Trust
Sir George Martin Trust
John Martin's Charity
The Maxwell Family Foundation
The Robert McAlpine Foundation
The Medlock Charitable Trust
Melow Charitable Trust
Brian Mercer Charitable Trust
The Mercers' Charitable Foundation
The Merchant Taylors' Company Charities Fund
The Merchants' House of Glasgow
Community Foundation for Merseyside
The Zachary Merton and George Woofindin Convalescent Trust
The Tony Metherell Charitable Trust
The Methodist Relief and Development Fund
Mickleham Charitable Trust
Gerald Micklem Charitable Trust
Miles Trust for the Putney and Roehampton Community
Millennium Stadium Charitable Trust
The Miller Foundation
The Mills Charity
The Millward Charitable Trust
Milton Keynes Community Foundation
The Peter Minet Trust
The Mirfield Educational Charity
The Mishcon Family Charitable Trust
The Mitchell Charitable Trust
The Modiano Charitable Trust
The D C Moncrieff Charitable Trust
Monmouthshire County Council Welsh Church Act Fund
The Monument Trust
John Moores Foundation
The Morel Charitable Trust

The Morgan Charitable Foundation
S C and M E Morland's Charitable Trust
The Morris Charitable Trust
G M Morrison Charitable Trust
Vyoel Moshe Charitable Trust
The Moss Charitable Trust
The Robert and Margaret Moss Charitable Trust
Moto in the Community Trust
Mountbatten Festival of Music
The Mugdock Children's Trust
The Edith Murphy Foundation
Murphy-Neumann Charity Company Limited
The Kitty and Daniel Nabarro Charitable Trust
The Nadezhda Charitable Trust
The Nationwide Foundation
The Nchima Trust
The Worshipful Company of Needlemakers' Charitable Fund
Nestle Rowntree Employees Community Fund
The New Appeals Organisation for the City and County of Nottingham
New Court Charitable Trust
Newby Trust Limited
The Noel Buxton Trust
The Norda Trust
The Normanby Charitable Trust
The North British Hotel Trust
North West London Community Foundation
The Northampton Municipal Church Charities
The Northampton Queen's Institute Relief in Sickness Fund
The Earl of Northampton's Charity
The Northcott Devon Foundation
The Northern Rock Foundation
The Northmoor Trust
The Northumberland Village Homes Trust
The Norton Foundation
The Norton Rose Charitable Foundation
The Norwich Town Close Estate Charity
The Nottingham General Dispensary
The Nottingham Gordon Memorial Trust for Boys and Girls
The Nottinghamshire Miners' Welfare Trust Fund
The Nuffield Foundation
The Father O'Mahoney Memorial Trust
The Oakdale Trust
The Oakley Charitable Trust

Ogilvie Charities Deed No.2
(including the Charity of
Mary Catherine Ford Smith)
The Old Enfield Charitable
Trust
Old Possum's Practical Trust
The Oldham Foundation
The Olga Charitable Trust
The Owen Family Trust
Eleanor Palmer Trust
The Panacea Society
The Paphitis Charitable Trust
The Park House Charitable
Trust
The Constance Paterson
Charitable Trust
Miss M E Swinton Paterson's
Charitable Trust
The Harry Payne Trust
The Peacock Charitable Trust
The Pears Foundation
Pearson's Holiday Fund
The Pedmore Sporting Club
Trust Fund
The Persula Foundation
The Pestalozzi Overseas
Children's Trust
The Jack Petchey Foundation
The Phillips Family Charitable
Trust
The Bernard Piggott Trust
The Pilgrim Trust
The Pilkington Charities Fund
The Austin and Hope
Pilkington Trust
The Col W W Pilkington Will
Trusts The General Charity
Fund
Mrs Pilkington's Charitable
Trust
G S Plaut Charitable Trust
Limited
The Pollywally Charitable Trust
The John Porter Charitable
Trust
The Porter Foundation
Porticus UK
The Portishead Nautical Trust
The J E Posnansky Charitable
Trust
The Mary Potter Convent
Hospital Trust
The Lucy Price Relief-in-Need
Charity
Sir John Priestman Charity
Trust
Princess Anne's Charities
The Priory Foundation
PSA Peugeot Citroen Charity
Trust
The Puri Foundation
Quartet Community Foundation
Queen Mary's Roehampton
Trust
The Queen's Silver Jubilee
Trust
R S Charitable Trust

The Monica Rabagliati
Charitable Trust
Radio City Charity Foundation
The Rainford Trust
The Rank Foundation
The Joseph Rank Trust
The Fanny Rapaport Charitable
Settlement
The Ratcliff Pension Charity
The E L Rathbone Charitable
Trust
The Eleanor Rathbone
Charitable Trust
The Sigrid Rausing Trust
The Ravensdale Trust
The Rayne Foundation
The Sir James Reckitt Charity
The Eva Reckitt Trust Fund
The C A Redfern Charitable
Foundation
The Reed Foundation
Relief Fund for Romania
Limited
The Rhododendron Trust
The Rhondda Cynon Taff
Welsh Church Acts Fund
The Sir Cliff Richard Charitable
Trust
The Richmond Parish Lands
Charity
The Ripple Effect Foundation
The River Farm Foundation
Riverside Charitable Trust
Limited
Rix-Thompson-Rothenburg
Foundation
Thomas Roberts Trust
The Robertson Trust
The Roddick Foundation
The Sir James Roll Charitable
Trust
The C A Rookes Charitable
Trust
Mrs L D Rope Third Charitable
Settlement
The Rosca Trust
The Cecil Rosen Foundation
The Rothera Charitable
Settlement
The Rothley Trust
The Rothschild Foundation
The Rowan Charitable Trust
The Christopher Rowbotham
Charitable Trust
The Rowland Family
Foundation
The Rowlands Trust
The Joseph Rowntree
Foundation
Royal British Legion
Royal Docks Trust (London)
Royal Masonic Trust for Girls
and Boys
The Royal Scots Benevolent
Society
The RRAF Charitable Trust

The Rufford Maurice Laing
Foundation
Ryklow Charitable Trust 1992
The Michael Harry Sacher
Trust
Erach and Roshan Sadri
Foundation
The Saga Charitable Trust
Saint Sarkis Charity Trust
The Saintbury Trust
The Saints and Sinners Trust
The Salters' Charities
The Andrew Salvesen
Charitable Trust
Coral Samuel Charitable Trust
The Peter Samuel Charitable
Trust
The Sandra Charitable Trust
Schroder Charity Trust
The Scotshill Trust
Scott (Eredine) Charitable
Trust
The Scott Bader
Commonwealth Ltd
The Francis C Scott Charitable
Trust
The Frieda Scott Charitable
Trust
The Sir James and Lady Scott
Trust
Scottish Churches' Community
Trust
Scottish Coal Industry Special
Welfare Fund
The Scottish Community
Foundation
The Scottish International
Education Trust
The Scouloudi Foundation
Seafarers UK (King George's
Fund for Sailors)
The Searle Charitable Trust
The Samuel Sebba Charitable
Trust
Leslie Sell Charitable Trust
Sellata Ltd
The Shanley Charitable Trust
The Sheffield and District
Hospital Services
Charitable Fund
The Sheldon Trust
The Sylvia and Colin Shepherd
Charitable Trust
The Archie Sherman Cardiff
Foundation
The Archie Sherman Charitable
Trust
The Shetland Charitable Trust
The Shipwrights' Company
Charitable Fund
The Shoe Zone Trust
The J A Shone Memorial Trust
The Mary Elizabeth Siebel
Charity
The Skelton Bounty
The SMB Charitable Trust

The Mrs Smith and Mount Trust
The N Smith Charitable Settlement
The Henry Smith Charity
The Leslie Smith Foundation
Philip Smith's Charitable Trust
The Snowball Trust
The Sobell Foundation
The E C Sosnow Charitable Trust
The Souter Charitable Trust
The South Square Trust
The W F Southall Trust
Spears-Stutz Charitable Trust
Split Infinitive Trust
Rosalyn and Nicholas Springer Charitable Trust
Springfields Employees' Medical Research and Charity Trust Fund
St James's Place Foundation
St Katharine and Shadwell Trust
St Michael's and All Saints' Charities
St Monica Trust Community Fund
The Stafford Trust
The Stanley Foundation Ltd
The Peter Stebbings Memorial Charity
The Steel Charitable Trust
The Stokenchurch Educational Charity
The Stone Family Foundation
The Strangward Trust
Stratford upon Avon Town Trust
The W O Street Charitable Foundation
Sueberry Ltd
The Suffolk Foundation
The Summerfield Charitable Trust
Surrey Community Foundation
Sussex Community Foundation
Sutton Coldfield Municipal Charities
Swan Mountain Trust
The Gay and Keith Talbot Trust
Talteg Ltd
The Lady Tangye Charitable Trust
The Tanner Trust
The A R Taylor Charitable Trust
The Connie and Albert Taylor Charitable Trust
The Taylor Family Foundation
The Tedworth Charitable Trust
Tesco Charity Trust
Thames Community Foundation
The Thomas Wall Trust
The Len Thomson Charitable Trust
The Sue Thomson Foundation

The Three Oaks Trust
Mrs R P Tindall's Charitable Trust
The Tisbury Telegraph Trust
TJH Foundation
The Tolkien Trust
The Tompkins Foundation
The Tory Family Foundation
The Towry Law Charitable Trust
The Triangle Trust (1949) Fund
The True Colours Trust
Truemart Limited
Trust for London
Trust Sixty Three
The Tudor Trust
Community Foundation Serving Tyne and Wear and Northumberland
Trustees of Tzedakah
Ulster Garden Villages Ltd
The Underwood Trust
The Valentine Charitable Trust
The Albert Van Den Bergh Charitable Trust
The Van Neste Foundation
The William and Patricia Venton Charitable Trust
Vintners' Gifts Charity
The Vodafone (Group) Foundation
The Volant Charitable Trust
Voluntary Action Fund
Wade's Charity
The Wakefield and Tetley Trust
Wakeham Trust
The Community Foundation in Wales
Wales Council for Voluntary Action
Walton on Thames Charity
The Ward Blenkinsop Trust
The Waterloo Foundation
The Wates Foundation
Blyth Watson Charitable Trust
The Howard Watson Symington Memorial Charity
John Watson's Trust
The Weavers' Company Benevolent Fund
The Weinstein Foundation
The James Weir Foundation
The Weldon UK Charitable Trust
The West Yorkshire Police Community Fund
The Westcroft Trust
The Westminster Foundation
The Simon Whitbread Charitable Trust
White Rose Children's Aid International Charity
The Whittlesey Charity
Williams Serendipity Trust
The Wilson Foundation
J and J R Wilson Trust
The Community Foundation for Wiltshire and Swindon

The Francis Winham Foundation
Anona Winn Charitable Trust
WISCM
The Michael and Anna Wix Charitable Trust
The Wixamtree Trust
The Maurice Wohl Charitable Foundation
The Wolfson Foundation
Women Caring Trust
The Wood Family Trust
Woodlands Trust
The Woodroffe Benton Foundation
The Woodward Charitable Trust
The Woolnoth Society Charitable Trust
Worcester Municipal Charities
The Fred and Della Worms Charitable Trust
The Wragge and Co. Charitable Trust
The Diana Edgson Wright Charitable Trust
Miss E B Wrightson's Charitable Settlement
The Wyseliot Charitable Trust
York and North Yorkshire Community Foundation
The York Children's Trust
The Yorkshire Dales Millennium Trust
The William Allen Young Charitable Trust
Zephyr Charitable Trust
The Marjorie and Arnold Ziff Charitable Foundation
The Zochonis Charitable Trust
Zurich Community Trust (UK) Limited

Community care services

The 1989 Willan Charitable Trust
The Company of Actuaries' Charitable Trust Fund
Age Concern Scotland Grants
The Green and Lilian F M Ainsworth and Family Benevolent Fund
The Appletree Trust
Archbishop of Wales' Fund for Children
The Archer Trust
The Artemis Charitable Trust
The Astor Foundation
The Avon and Somerset Police Community Trust
The Ballinger Charitable Trust
The Victoria and David Beckham Children's Charity
The Big Lottery Fund

The Birmingham District Nursing Charitable Trust
The Anthony Bourne Foundation
John Bristow and Thomas Mason Trust
The David Brooke Charity
The Rory and Elizabeth Brooks Foundation
The Burton Breweries Charitable Trust
Carter's Educational Foundation
The Cattanach Charitable Trust
The Clover Trust
The Cook and Wolstenholme Charitable Trust
The J Reginald Corah Foundation Fund
The John Cowan Foundation
The D J H Currie Memorial Trust
Baron Davenport's Charity
The Hamilton Davies Trust
The Dorus Trust
The Dulverton Trust
The Dumbreck Charity
East Kent Provincial Charities
Gilbert Edgar Trust
Edinburgh Children's Holiday Fund
The Edinburgh Trust, No 2 Account
The Emerton-Christie Charity
The Emmandjay Charitable Trust
The Eveson Charitable Trust
Esmée Fairbairn Foundation
The Fairway Trust
The Family Rich Charities Trust
Samuel William Farmer's Trust
The Fassnidge Memorial Trust
The February Foundation
The John Feeney Charitable Bequest
Elizabeth Ferguson Charitable Trust Fund
Ford Britain Trust
The Oliver Ford Charitable Trust
The Foresters' Fund for Children
Four Acre Trust
The Jill Franklin Trust
The Gordon Fraser Charitable Trust
The Louis and Valerie Freedman Charitable Settlement
The Freshgate Trust Foundation
The Frognal Trust
The Angela Gallagher Memorial Fund
The Ganzoni Charitable Trust
The Gatsby Charitable Foundation

Gatwick Airport Community Trust
J Paul Getty Jr Charitable Trust
The Girdlers' Company Charitable Trust
The Glass-House Trust
The Gosling Foundation Limited
The Gough Charitable Trust
Grantham Yorke Trust
The Constance Green Foundation
Grimmitt Trust
The Gulbenkian Foundation
Dr Guthrie's Association
The Hadrian Trust
The Alfred Haines Charitable Trust
The Hale Trust
Robert Hall Charity
Hampton Fuel Allotment Charity
The W A Handley Charitable Trust
The Haramead Trust
The Harbour Charitable Trust
The Kenneth Hargreaves Charitable Trust
The Harris Charitable Trust
The Harris Charity
The Charles Hayward Foundation
The Headley Trust
Healthsure Group Ltd
May Hearnshaw's Charity
The H J Heinz Company Limited Charitable Trust
The Hemby Trust
The Christina Mary Hendrie Trust for Scottish and Canadian Charities
The Henley Educational Charity
Philip Henman Trust
The Joanna Herbert-Stepney Charitable Settlement
The Hesslewood Children's Trust (Hull Seamen's and General Orphanage)
The High Sheriff's Police Trust for the County of West Midlands
The Hilden Charitable Fund
The Charles Littlewood Hill Trust
The Holywood Trust
The Horne Trust
The Reta Lila Howard Foundation
Miss Agnes H Hunter's Trust
Huntingdon Freemen's Charity
The Hyde Charitable Trust – Youth Plus
The Irish Youth Foundation (UK) Ltd (incorporating The Lawlor Foundation)
The Ruth and Lionel Jacobson Trust (Second Fund) No 2

The Jarman Charitable Trust
The Jeffrey Charitable Trust
The Lillie Johnson Charitable Trust
The Johnnie Johnson Trust
The Jones 1986 Charitable Trust
Kelsick's Educational Foundation
The KempWelch Charitable Trust
The Peter Kershaw Trust
The King's Fund
The Mary Kinross Charitable Trust
The KPMG Foundation
John Laing Charitable Trust
The Lambert Charitable Trust
Duchy of Lancaster Benevolent Fund
The Allen Lane Foundation
The R J Larg Family Charitable Trust
The Lark Trust
The Edgar E Lawley Foundation
The Raymond and Blanche Lawson Charitable Trust
The Carole and Geoffrey Lawson Foundation
The Leach Fourteenth Trust
The William Leech Charity
Leeds Building Society Charitable Foundation
The Mark Leonard Trust
Lord Leverhulme's Charitable Trust
The Joseph Levy Charitable Foundation
Lloyds TSB Foundation for Northern Ireland
Lloyds TSB Foundation for the Channel Islands
London Catalyst
The Lotus Foundation
Lady Lumley's Educational Foundation
John Lyon's Charity
The R S Macdonald Charitable Trust
The MacRobert Trust
Magdalen Hospital Trust
Manchester Kids
Market Harborough and The Bowdens Charity
Sir George Martin Trust
The Mercers' Charitable Foundation
The Merchants' House of Glasgow
The Zachary Merton and George Woofindin Convalescent Trust
The Methodist Relief and Development Fund
Gerald Micklem Charitable Trust

Miles Trust for the Putney and Roehampton Community
The Peter Minet Trust
The Mirfield Educational Charity
Monmouthshire County Council Welsh Church Act Fund
The Monument Trust
John Moores Foundation
The Mugdock Children's Trust
The Kitty and Daniel Nabarro Charitable Trust
The Nadezhda Charitable Trust
The Nationwide Foundation
The Nchima Trust
Nestle Rowntree Employees Community Fund
Newby Trust Limited
The Noel Buxton Trust
The North British Hotel Trust
The Northcott Devon Foundation
The Northern Rock Foundation
The Nottingham General Dispensary
The Nottingham Gordon Memorial Trust for Boys and Girls
The Nuffield Foundation
Old Possum's Practical Trust
The Panacea Society
The Paphitis Charitable Trust
The Constance Paterson Charitable Trust
Miss M E Swinton Paterson's Charitable Trust
The Pears Foundation
Pearson's Holiday Fund
The Persula Foundation
The Pestalozzi Overseas Children's Trust
The Jack Petchey Foundation
The Bernard Piggott Trust
The Pilkington Charities Fund
G S Plaut Charitable Trust Limited
The Portishead Nautical Trust
The Mary Potter Convent Hospital Trust
The Lucy Price Relief-in-Need Charity
Sir John Priestman Charity Trust
PSA Peugeot Citroen Charity Trust
The Monica Rabagliati Charitable Trust
Radio City Charity Foundation
The Rank Foundation
The Rayne Foundation
The Reed Foundation
Relief Fund for Romania Limited
The Rhondda Cynon Taff Welsh Church Acts Fund
The Richmond Parish Lands Charity

Rix-Thompson-Rothenburg Foundation
The Robertson Trust
The C A Rookes Charitable Trust
Mrs L D Rope Third Charitable Settlement
The Rothley Trust
The Rowan Charitable Trust
The Rowlands Trust
Ryklow Charitable Trust 1992
The Michael Harry Sacher Trust
The Saintbury Trust
The Andrew Salvesen Charitable Trust
The Sandra Charitable Trust
The Francis C Scott Charitable Trust
Scottish Coal Industry Special Welfare Fund
Seafarers UK (King George's Fund for Sailors)
The Searle Charitable Trust
Leslie Sell Charitable Trust
The Sheldon Trust
The Sylvia and Colin Shepherd Charitable Trust
The Shipwrights' Company Charitable Fund
The Mary Elizabeth Siebel Charity
The Mrs Smith and Mount Trust
The Leslie Smith Foundation
The Snowball Trust
St Monica Trust Community Fund
The Connie and Albert Taylor Charitable Trust
The Taylor Family Foundation
The Tedworth Charitable Trust
The Sue Thomson Foundation
The True Colours Trust
The Albert Van Den Bergh Charitable Trust
The William and Patricia Venton Charitable Trust
Wade's Charity
Wakeham Trust
The Wates Foundation
John Watson's Trust
The Weavers' Company Benevolent Fund
The Simon Whitbread Charitable Trust
Williams Serendipity Trust
The Wilson Foundation
J and J R Wilson Trust
The Francis Winham Foundation
WISCM
Women Caring Trust
Woodlands Trust
The Woodward Charitable Trust

The Wragge and Co. Charitable Trust
The York Children's Trust
The Marjorie and Arnold Ziff Charitable Foundation

....

■ Services for and about children and young people

The 1989 Willan Charitable Trust
The Company of Actuaries' Charitable Trust Fund
The Green and Lilian F M Ainsworth and Family Benevolent Fund
Archbishop of Wales' Fund for Children
The Artemis Charitable Trust
The Victoria and David Beckham Children's Charity
The Big Lottery Fund
The Anthony Bourne Foundation
The David Brooke Charity
The Burton Breweries Charitable Trust
Carter's Educational Foundation
The Cattanach Charitable Trust
The Clover Trust
The Cook and Wolstenholme Charitable Trust
The J Reginald Corah Foundation Fund
The John Cowan Foundation
Baron Davenport's Charity
The Dulverton Trust
The Dumbreck Charity
Gilbert Edgar Trust
Edinburgh Children's Holiday Fund
The Edinburgh Trust, No 2 Account
The Emmandjay Charitable Trust
The Eveson Charitable Trust
Esmée Fairbairn Foundation
The Fairway Trust
Samuel William Farmer's Trust
The John Feeney Charitable Bequest
Elizabeth Ferguson Charitable Trust Fund
Ford Britain Trust
The Foresters' Fund for Children
The Gordon Fraser Charitable Trust
The Louis and Valerie Freedman Charitable Settlement
The Freshgate Trust Foundation
The Frognal Trust

The Angela Gallagher Memorial
Fund
The Ganzoni Charitable Trust
The Gatsby Charitable
Foundation
Gatwick Airport Community
Trust
J Paul Getty Jr Charitable Trust
The Girdlers' Company
Charitable Trust
The Glass-House Trust
The Gosling Foundation
Limited
The Gough Charitable Trust
Grantham Yorke Trust
The Constance Green
Foundation
Grimmitt Trust
The Gulbenkian Foundation
Dr Guthrie's Association
The Alfred Haines Charitable
Trust
The Hale Trust
Robert Hall Charity
Hampton Fuel Allotment
Charity
The W A Handley Charitable
Trust
The Haramead Trust
The Harbour Charitable Trust
The Harris Charitable Trust
The Harris Charity
The Headley Trust
May Hearnshaw's Charity
The H J Heinz Company
Limited Charitable Trust
The Hemby Trust
The Christina Mary Hendrie
Trust for Scottish and
Canadian Charities
The Henley Educational Charity
Philip Henman Trust
The Joanna Herbert-Stepney
Charitable Settlement
The Hesslewood Children's
Trust (Hull Seamen's and
General Orphanage)
The High Sheriff's Police Trust
for the County of West
Midlands
The Hilden Charitable Fund
The Charles Littlewood Hill
Trust
The Holywood Trust
The Reta Lila Howard
Foundation
Miss Agnes H Hunter's Trust
The Hyde Charitable Trust –
Youth Plus
The Irish Youth Foundation
(UK) Ltd (incorporating The
Lawlor Foundation)
The Ruth and Lionel Jacobson
Trust (Second Fund) No 2
The Jarman Charitable Trust
The Jeffrey Charitable Trust

The Lillie Johnson Charitable
Trust
The Johnnie Johnson Trust
Kelsick's Educational
Foundation
The KempWelch Charitable
Trust
The Peter Kershaw Trust
The Mary Kinross Charitable
Trust
The KPMG Foundation
John Laing Charitable Trust
Duchy of Lancaster Benevolent
Fund
The R J Larg Family Charitable
Trust
The Edgar E Lawley Foundation
The Carole and Geoffrey
Lawson Foundation
The William Leech Charity
Leeds Building Society
Charitable Foundation
The Mark Leonard Trust
Lord Leverhulme's Charitable
Trust
The Lotus Foundation
Lady Lumley's Educational
Foundation
John Lyon's Charity
The R S Macdonald Charitable
Trust
The MacRobert Trust
Magdalen Hospital Trust
Manchester Kids
The Merchants' House of
Glasgow
Gerald Micklem Charitable
Trust
Miles Trust for the Putney and
Roehampton Community
The Peter Minet Trust
The Mirfield Educational
Charity
John Moores Foundation
The Mugdock Children's Trust
The Nadezhda Charitable Trust
Newby Trust Limited
The Noel Buxton Trust
The North British Hotel Trust
The Northern Rock Foundation
The Nottingham Gordon
Memorial Trust for Boys
and Girls
The Nuffield Foundation
Old Possum's Practical Trust
The Paphitis Charitable Trust
The Constance Paterson
Charitable Trust
Miss M E Swinton Paterson's
Charitable Trust
The Pears Foundation
Pearson's Holiday Fund
The Persula Foundation
The Pestalozzi Overseas
Children's Trust
The Jack Petchey Foundation
The Bernard Piggott Trust

The Pilkington Charities Fund
The Portishead Nautical Trust
The Lucy Price Relief-in-Need
Charity
PSA Peugeot Citroen Charity
Trust
The Monica Rabagliati
Charitable Trust
Radio City Charity Foundation
The Rank Foundation
Relief Fund for Romania
Limited
The Rhondda Cynon Taff
Welsh Church Acts Fund
The Richmond Parish Lands
Charity
The Rothley Trust
Ryklow Charitable Trust 1992
The Andrew Salvesen
Charitable Trust
The Sandra Charitable Trust
The Francis C Scott Charitable
Trust
Scottish Coal Industry Special
Welfare Fund
Seafarers UK (King George's
Fund for Sailors)
The Searle Charitable Trust
Leslie Sell Charitable Trust
The Sylvia and Colin Shepherd
Charitable Trust
The Shipwrights' Company
Charitable Fund
The Mrs Smith and Mount
Trust
The Leslie Smith Foundation
The Snowball Trust
The Connie and Albert Taylor
Charitable Trust
The Taylor Family Foundation
The Tedworth Charitable Trust
Wade's Charity
The Wates Foundation
John Watson's Trust
The Weavers' Company
Benevolent Fund
The Simon Whitbread
Charitable Trust
Williams Serendipity Trust
The Wilson Foundation
WISCM
Women Caring Trust
The York Children's Trust
The Marjorie and Arnold Ziff
Charitable Foundation

....

■ Services for and
about older people

The Company of Actuaries'
Charitable Trust Fund
Age Concern Scotland Grants
The Birmingham District
Nursing Charitable Trust
The Clover Trust

The Cook and Wolstenholme
  Charitable Trust
The John Cowan Foundation
The D J H Currie Memorial
  Trust
Baron Davenport's Charity
The Dumbreck Charity
The Eveson Charitable Trust
Samuel William Farmer's Trust
The Fassnidge Memorial Trust
Gatwick Airport Community
  Trust
The Girdlers' Company
  Charitable Trust
The Constance Green
  Foundation
Grimmitt Trust
The Alfred Haines Charitable
  Trust
The W A Handley Charitable
  Trust
The Charles Hayward
  Foundation
The Hemby Trust
The Christina Mary Hendrie
  Trust for Scottish and
  Canadian Charities
The KempWelch Charitable
  Trust
The Lambert Charitable Trust
The Edgar E Lawley Foundation
The Joseph Levy Charitable
  Foundation
Sir George Martin Trust
The Mercers' Charitable
  Foundation
The Merchants' House of
  Glasgow
The Methodist Relief and
  Development Fund
The North British Hotel Trust
The Pilkington Charities Fund
G S Plaut Charitable Trust
  Limited
PSA Peugeot Citroen Charity
  Trust
Relief Fund for Romania
  Limited
The C A Rookes Charitable
  Trust
The Rowlands Trust
The Andrew Salvesen
  Charitable Trust
Scottish Coal Industry Special
  Welfare Fund
Seafarers UK (King George's
  Fund for Sailors)
The Sylvia and Colin Shepherd
  Charitable Trust
The Mary Elizabeth Siebel
  Charity
The Connie and Albert Taylor
  Charitable Trust
The William and Patricia
  Venton Charitable Trust
J and J R Wilson Trust

The Francis Winham
  Foundation

....

■ Services for and about vulnerable people/people who are ill

The 1989 Willan Charitable
  Trust
The Company of Actuaries'
  Charitable Trust Fund
The Green and Lilian F M
  Ainsworth and Family
  Benevolent Fund
The Appletree Trust
The Archer Trust
The Artemis Charitable Trust
The Birmingham District
  Nursing Charitable Trust
The Dumbreck Charity
The Family Rich Charities Trust
Samuel William Farmer's Trust
The John Feeney Charitable
  Bequest
Ford Britain Trust
The Oliver Ford Charitable
  Trust
The Jill Franklin Trust
The Freshgate Trust
  Foundation
The Angela Gallagher Memorial
  Fund
Gatwick Airport Community
  Trust
J Paul Getty Jr Charitable Trust
The Girdlers' Company
  Charitable Trust
The Constance Green
  Foundation
The Hadrian Trust
The W A Handley Charitable
  Trust
Healthsure Group Ltd
May Hearnshaw's Charity
The Hemby Trust
The Horne Trust
Huntingdon Freemen's Charity
The Ruth and Lionel Jacobson
  Trust (Second Fund) No 2
The Jeffrey Charitable Trust
The Peter Kershaw Trust
The Allen Lane Foundation
The Lark Trust
Leeds Building Society
  Charitable Foundation
The Joseph Levy Charitable
  Foundation
London Catalyst
John Lyon's Charity
Magdalen Hospital Trust
Market Harborough and The
  Bowdens Charity
The Zachary Merton and
  George Woofindin
  Convalescent Trust

The Peter Minet Trust
John Moores Foundation
The Mugdock Children's Trust
The Kitty and Daniel Nabarro
  Charitable Trust
The Nchima Trust
Nestle Rowntree Employees
  Community Fund
Newby Trust Limited
The North British Hotel Trust
The Northcott Devon
  Foundation
The Nottingham General
  Dispensary
The Panacea Society
The Pilkington Charities Fund
G S Plaut Charitable Trust
  Limited
The Portishead Nautical Trust
The Mary Potter Convent
  Hospital Trust
Sir John Priestman Charity
  Trust
The Rothley Trust
The Rowan Charitable Trust
The Rowlands Trust
The Andrew Salvesen
  Charitable Trust
The Sylvia and Colin Shepherd
  Charitable Trust
The Leslie Smith Foundation
The Snowball Trust
The Connie and Albert Taylor
  Charitable Trust
The Sue Thomson Foundation
The True Colours Trust
Woodlands Trust
The Wragge and Co. Charitable
  Trust

....

■ Service for carers

The Astor Foundation
The Emerton-Christie Charity
The Eveson Charitable Trust
The Angela Gallagher Memorial
  Fund
Gatwick Airport Community
  Trust
The Girdlers' Company
  Charitable Trust
The Harris Charitable Trust
The Headley Trust
The Hemby Trust
The Ruth and Lionel Jacobson
  Trust (Second Fund) No 2
The Peter Kershaw Trust
The Joseph Levy Charitable
  Foundation
London Catalyst
Gerald Micklem Charitable
  Trust
The North British Hotel Trust
The Northern Rock Foundation
Rix-Thompson-Rothenburg
  Foundation

■ Services for women

The Lotus Foundation
The Northern Rock Foundation
The Reed Foundation
The Woodward Charitable
  Trust

Community centres and activities

The Ballinger Charitable Trust
The Big Lottery Fund
John Bristow and Thomas
  Mason Trust
Colyer-Fergusson Charitable
  Trust
The Co-operative Foundation
The John Cowan Foundation
The Hamilton Davies Trust
Eastern Counties Educational
  Trust Limited
Dr Edwards' and Bishop King's
  Fulham Endowment Fund
The Emmandjay Charitable
  Trust
Samuel William Farmer's Trust
The George Fentham
  Birmingham Charity
The Football Association
  National Sports Centre
  Trust
Ford Britain Trust
Four Acre Trust
The Thomas Freke and Lady
  Norton Charity
The Angela Gallagher Memorial
  Fund
The Gannochy Trust
Gatwick Airport Community
  Trust
Mike Gooley Trailfinders
  Charity
Grantham Yorke Trust
Greggs Foundation
The Alfred Haines Charitable
  Trust
The W A Handley Charitable
  Trust
The Kenneth Hargreaves
  Charitable Trust
The Hedley Foundation
The Hemby Trust
The Horne Foundation
The Hornsey Parochial
  Charities
The Hyde Charitable Trust –
  Youth Plus
The Jones 1986 Charitable
  Trust
Lancashire Environmental
  Fund
Duchy of Lancaster Benevolent
  Fund

Lord Leverhulme's Charitable
  Trust
Lloyds TSB Foundation for
  Northern Ireland
Lloyds TSB Foundation for the
  Channel Islands
John Lyon's Charity
Magdalen Hospital Trust
The Michael Marsh Charitable
  Trust
John Martin's Charity
The Methodist Relief and
  Development Fund
Gerald Micklem Charitable
  Trust
The Peter Minet Trust
Monmouthshire County Council
  Welsh Church Act Fund
The Nationwide Foundation
The North British Hotel Trust
The Northern Rock Foundation
Ogilvie Charities Deed No.2
  (including the Charity of
  Mary Catherine Ford Smith)
The Owen Family Trust
Pearson's Holiday Fund
The Rhododendron Trust
The Richmond Parish Lands
  Charity
The Ripple Effect Foundation
The Robertson Trust
The Sir James Roll Charitable
  Trust
The Rothley Trust
Royal Docks Trust (London)
The Saga Charitable Trust
The Saintbury Trust
The Frieda Scott Charitable
  Trust
Scottish Churches' Community
  Trust
The Scottish Community
  Foundation
The Sheldon Trust
The Sylvia and Colin Shepherd
  Charitable Trust
The Archie Sherman Cardiff
  Foundation
The Stokenchurch Educational
  Charity
The Summerfield Charitable
  Trust
The Len Thomson Charitable
  Trust
Wade's Charity
Wakeham Trust
The Westcroft Trust
The Yorkshire Dales
  Millennium Trust

■ Community and social centres

John Bristow and Thomas
  Mason Trust
The Co-operative Foundation

The John Cowan Foundation
Samuel William Farmer's Trust
The Thomas Freke and Lady
  Norton Charity
The Kenneth Hargreaves
  Charitable Trust
The Hedley Foundation
The Horne Foundation
Lancashire Environmental
  Fund
John Lyon's Charity
Magdalen Hospital Trust
The Methodist Relief and
  Development Fund
Gerald Micklem Charitable
  Trust
Monmouthshire County Council
  Welsh Church Act Fund
The Northern Rock Foundation
The Owen Family Trust
The Rhododendron Trust
The Frieda Scott Charitable
  Trust
The Summerfield Charitable
  Trust
Wakeham Trust

■ Community organisations

The Big Lottery Fund
John Bristow and Thomas
  Mason Trust
The Emmandjay Charitable
  Trust
Ford Britain Trust
The Hornsey Parochial
  Charities
Duchy of Lancaster Benevolent
  Fund
The Rothley Trust
The Saga Charitable Trust
Scottish Churches' Community
  Trust
The Scottish Community
  Foundation
The Len Thomson Charitable
  Trust
Wakeham Trust

■ Community centres and outings

The Big Lottery Fund
The Angela Gallagher Memorial
  Fund
The Alfred Haines Charitable
  Trust
Magdalen Hospital Trust
The Peter Minet Trust
Ogilvie Charities Deed No.2
  (including the Charity of
  Mary Catherine Ford Smith)
Pearson's Holiday Fund
Wakeham Trust

Emergency response

The Balney Charitable Trust
Bergqvist Charitable Trust
The Calpe Trust
The Carpenter Charitable Trust
Christadelphian Samaritan Fund
Christian Response to Eastern Europe
The Robert Clutterbuck Charitable Trust
The Dulverton Trust
The Dyers' Company Charitable Trust
The Edinburgh Trust, No 2 Account
The Emmandjay Charitable Trust
The Family Rich Charities Trust
The Sir John Fisher Foundation
The Forces Trust
The Forest Hill Charitable Trust
Sydney E Franklin Deceased's New Second Charity
The Gibbs Charitable Trust
The Gosling Foundation Limited
The Alfred Haines Charitable Trust
The W A Handley Charitable Trust
Miss K M Harbinson's Charitable Trust
The Kenneth Hargreaves Charitable Trust
The Charles Littlewood Hill Trust
The Horne Trust
Lloyds TSB Foundation for Northern Ireland
The MacRobert Trust
Magdalen Hospital Trust
Marr-Munning Trust
The Modiano Charitable Trust
Monmouthshire County Council Welsh Church Act Fund
John Moores Foundation
Mountbatten Festival of Music
The Father O'Mahoney Memorial Trust
The Pilkington Charities Fund
Queen Mary's Roehampton Trust
The Sigrid Rausing Trust
The Rhododendron Trust
The Robertson Trust
The Sir James Roll Charitable Trust
The Rothley Trust
The Rowlands Trust
Royal British Legion
The Royal Scots Benevolent Society
The SMB Charitable Trust
The E C Sosnow Charitable Trust
The Gay and Keith Talbot Trust
The Lady Tangye Charitable Trust
The Tisbury Telegraph Trust
Trust Sixty Three
The Woodroffe Benton Foundation
Miss E B Wrightson's Charitable Settlement

■ Armed forces

The Balney Charitable Trust
The Robert Clutterbuck Charitable Trust
The Dyers' Company Charitable Trust
The Edinburgh Trust, No 2 Account
The Sir John Fisher Foundation
The Forces Trust
The Gosling Foundation Limited
The W A Handley Charitable Trust
The Charles Littlewood Hill Trust
Mountbatten Festival of Music
Queen Mary's Roehampton Trust
The Rowlands Trust
Royal British Legion
The Royal Scots Benevolent Society

■ Relief assistance

Bergqvist Charitable Trust
The Calpe Trust
The Carpenter Charitable Trust
Christadelphian Samaritan Fund
Christian Response to Eastern Europe
The Dulverton Trust
The Emmandjay Charitable Trust
The Forest Hill Charitable Trust
Sydney E Franklin Deceased's New Second Charity
The Gibbs Charitable Trust
The Alfred Haines Charitable Trust
The W A Handley Charitable Trust
Miss K M Harbinson's Charitable Trust
Magdalen Hospital Trust
Marr-Munning Trust
The Modiano Charitable Trust
John Moores Foundation
The Father O'Mahoney Memorial Trust
The Pilkington Charities Fund

The Sigrid Rausing Trust
The Rhododendron Trust
The Rothley Trust
The SMB Charitable Trust
The Gay and Keith Talbot Trust
The Lady Tangye Charitable Trust
The Tisbury Telegraph Trust
Trust Sixty Three

Socially preventatative schemes

The Ashendene Trust
The Avon and Somerset Police Community Trust
The Ballinger Charitable Trust
Britannia Foundation
The Bromley Trust
The G W Cadbury Charitable Trust
The Barrow Cadbury Trust and the Barrow Cadbury Fund
The Cayo Foundation
The Violet and Milo Cripps Charitable Trust
The Hamilton Davies Trust
The Emilienne Charitable Trust
The Ericson Trust
Gatwick Airport Community Trust
J Paul Getty Jr Charitable Trust
The Kenneth Hargreaves Charitable Trust
The Charles Hayward Foundation
The Hemby Trust
The High Sheriff's Police Trust for the County of West Midlands
The Hilden Charitable Fund
The Hyde Charitable Trust – Youth Plus
The Indigo Trust
The Irish Youth Foundation (UK) Ltd (incorporating The Lawlor Foundation)
The Mary Kinross Charitable Trust
The Leigh Trust
The Joseph Levy Charitable Foundation
The Lister Charitable Trust
Lloyds TSB Foundation for Northern Ireland
The Lotus Foundation
Magdalen Hospital Trust
The Charlotte Marshall Charitable Trust
The Mercers' Charitable Foundation
The Merchant Taylors' Company Charities Fund

The Kitty and Daniel Nabarro Charitable Trust
The Nadezhda Charitable Trust
The Noel Buxton Trust
The Norda Trust
The Nuffield Foundation
The Oakdale Trust
The Persula Foundation
The Pilgrim Trust
The Portishead Nautical Trust
The Ripple Effect Foundation
The Robertson Trust
Saint Sarkis Charity Trust
The Saintbury Trust
Swan Mountain Trust
The Weavers' Company Benevolent Fund
The West Yorkshire Police Community Fund
The Woodward Charitable Trust

■ Crime prevention

Britannia Foundation
The Barrow Cadbury Trust and the Barrow Cadbury Fund
The Cayo Foundation
Gatwick Airport Community Trust
The Kenneth Hargreaves Charitable Trust
The Hemby Trust
The High Sheriff's Police Trust for the County of West Midlands
The Hyde Charitable Trust – Youth Plus
The Joseph Levy Charitable Foundation
Lloyds TSB Foundation for Northern Ireland
Magdalen Hospital Trust

■ Family justice

The Charles Hayward Foundation
The Nuffield Foundation

■ Family planning and sex education

The G W Cadbury Charitable Trust
The Kitty and Daniel Nabarro Charitable Trust

■ Prisons and penal reform

The Bromley Trust
The Barrow Cadbury Trust and the Barrow Cadbury Fund

The Violet and Milo Cripps Charitable Trust
The Ericson Trust
J Paul Getty Jr Charitable Trust
The Charles Hayward Foundation
The Hilden Charitable Fund
The Indigo Trust
The Mary Kinross Charitable Trust
The Leigh Trust
The Mercers' Charitable Foundation
The Noel Buxton Trust
The Oakdale Trust
The Persula Foundation
The Pilgrim Trust
Saint Sarkis Charity Trust
Swan Mountain Trust
The Woodward Charitable Trust

■ Substance abuse education

The Ashendene Trust
The Emilienne Charitable Trust
The Lister Charitable Trust
The Lotus Foundation
The Charlotte Marshall Charitable Trust
The Merchant Taylors' Company Charities Fund
The Portishead Nautical Trust
The Robertson Trust
The Woodward Charitable Trust

Beneficial groups

Age

■ Babies

The 1989 Willan Charitable Trust
The Victoria and David Beckham Children's Charity
The W E Dunn Trust
The Edwina Mountbatten Trust
The River Farm Foundation
The Francis C Scott Charitable Trust
Viking Cares (For the Kids)

■ Children (up to 11)

The 1989 Willan Charitable Trust
The Adamson Trust
The Pat Allsop Charitable Trust
The Betterware Foundation
BibleLands
Enid Blyton Trust for Children
The Clara E Burgess Charity
Cash for Kids Radio Clyde
The Cattanach Charitable Trust
Celtic Charity Fund
The Cleopatra Trust
The John Coates Charitable Trust
The D J H Currie Memorial Trust
The Raymond Curtis Charitable Trust
The Manny Cussins Foundation
The Demigryphon Trust
The Dorus Trust
The Dumbreck Charity
The W E Dunn Trust
Edinburgh Children's Holiday Fund
The Wilfred and Elsie Elkes Charity Fund
The Maud Elkington Charitable Trust
The English Schools' Football Association
The Epigoni Trust
Samuel William Farmer's Trust
Elizabeth Ferguson Charitable Trust Fund
Dixie Rose Findlay Charitable Trust
The Joyce Fletcher Charitable Trust
The Frognal Trust
The Angela Gallagher Memorial Fund
The Girdlers' Company Charitable Trust
Global Care

The Gosling Foundation Limited

E F and M G Hall Charitable Trust

The Haramead Trust

The Harebell Centenary Fund

The Harris Charitable Trust

The Heald Charitable Trust

The Joanna Herbert-Stepney Charitable Settlement

The Charles Littlewood Hill Trust

The Reta Lila Howard Foundation

The Albert Hunt Trust

The Hunter Foundation

Jewish Child's Day

The Lanvern Foundation

The Edgar E Lawley Foundation

The Carole and Geoffrey Lawson Foundation

Lifeline 4 Kids

The Lyons Charitable Trust

The Madeline Mabey Trust

The R S Macdonald Charitable Trust

The Mackintosh Foundation

The Maxell Educational Trust

Evelyn May Trust

The Mugdock Children's Trust

Murphy-Neumann Charity Company Limited

The Noel Buxton Trust

The Nuffield Foundation

Arthur James Paterson Charitable Trust

The Constance Paterson Charitable Trust

Pearson's Holiday Fund

The Pilkington Charities Fund

Sir John Priestman Charity Trust

The Priory Foundation

The Ragdoll Foundation

The Sylvia and Colin Shepherd Charitable Trust

The Bassil Shippam and Alsford Trust

Stanley Smith General Charitable Trust

Philip Smith's Charitable Trust

Stanley Spooner Deceased Charitable Trust

The Stoller Charitable Trust

The Tedworth Charitable Trust

Tesco Charity Trust

Thames Community Foundation

The Sue Thomson Foundation

The Toy Trust

The Variety Club Children's Charity

Viking Cares (For the Kids)

The Barbara Ward Children's Foundation

The Wates Foundation

Women Caring Trust

The Yapp Charitable Trust

The Zochonis Charitable Trust

....

■ Young people (12–25)

The Adamson Trust

The Green and Lilian F M Ainsworth and Family Benevolent Fund

Angus Allnatt Charitable Foundation

The AMW Charitable Trust

The Milly Apthorp Charitable Trust

The Beit Trust

The Big Lottery Fund

The David Brooke Charity

The Charles Brotherton Trust

The Burton Breweries Charitable Trust

Cash for Kids Radio Clyde

The Church Burgesses Educational Foundation

Lord Clinton's Charitable Trust

The Clover Trust

The Coalfields Regeneration Trust

The Cray Trust

The Cross Trust

The Raymond Curtis Charitable Trust

Peter De Haan Charitable Trust

The Djanogly Foundation

The Dulverton Trust

The Dyers' Company Charitable Trust

The Sir John Eastwood Foundation

Edinburgh Children's Holiday Fund

The Edinburgh Trust, No 2 Account

The Wilfred and Elsie Elkes Charity Fund

EMI Music Sound Foundation

The Emmandjay Charitable Trust

The English Schools' Football Association

The Essex Youth Trust

Esmée Fairbairn Foundation

The George Fentham Birmingham Charity

Dixie Rose Findlay Charitable Trust

Ford Britain Trust

The Hugh Fraser Foundation

The Frognal Trust

The Gannochy Trust

J Paul Getty Jr Charitable Trust

The Girdlers' Company Charitable Trust

The Glass-House Trust

The Gough Charitable Trust

Grantham Yorke Trust

The Grocers' Charity

The Hadfield Trust

The Hadrian Trust

The Alfred Haines Charitable Trust

The Harris Charitable Trust

The Hawthorne Charitable Trust

The Haymills Charitable Trust

The Heald Charitable Trust

The Hedley Foundation

The Christina Mary Hendrie Trust for Scottish and Canadian Charities

The Charles Littlewood Hill Trust

The Holywood Trust

The Horne Foundation

The Reta Lila Howard Foundation

The Humanitarian Trust

The Hunter Foundation

The Worshipful Company of Innholders General Charity Fund

The James Trust

The Mary Kinross Charitable Trust

Ernest Kleinwort Charitable Trust

The Lanvern Foundation

The R J Larg Family Charitable Trust

The Mark Leonard Trust

The Enid Linder Foundation

Paul Lunn-Rockliffe Charitable Trust

The R S Macdonald Charitable Trust

The MacRobert Trust

The Marsh Christian Trust

Sir George Martin Trust

The Nancie Massey Charitable Trust

The Maxell Educational Trust

The Mercers' Charitable Foundation

The Peter Moores Foundation

The Stanley Morrison Charitable Trust

The Mugdock Children's Trust

Newby Trust Limited

The Richard Newitt Fund

The Northcott Devon Foundation

The Norwich Church of England Young Men's Society

Miss M E Swinton Paterson's Charitable Trust

The Peacock Charitable Trust

Pearson's Holiday Fund

The Pestalozzi Overseas Children's Trust

The Jack Petchey Foundation

The Ponton House Trust

The Priory Foundation

The Rank Foundation
The Ratcliff Pension Charity
Richard Reeve's Foundation
The Rhondda Cynon Taff
   Welsh Church Acts Fund
The Richmond Parish Lands
   Charity
The Robertson Trust
Mrs L D Rope Third Charitable
   Settlement
The Rotherwick Foundation
The Andrew Salvesen
   Charitable Trust
The Sandra Charitable Trust
The Searle Charitable Trust
The Bassil Shippam and
   Alsford Trust
The Shipwrights' Company
   Charitable Fund
The Southdown Trust
The Southover Manor General
   Education Trust
St Hilda's Trust
Sir Walter St John's
   Educational Charity
The W O Street Charitable
   Foundation
The Summerfield Charitable
   Trust
The Len Thomson Charitable
   Trust
The Sue Thomson Foundation
Annie Tranmer Charitable Trust
Victoria Homes Trust
Viking Cares (For the Kids)
The Vodafone (Group)
   Foundation
The Barbara Ward Children's
   Foundation
The Wates Foundation
The Wilson Foundation
WISCM
Woodlands Trust
The Xerox (UK) Trust
The Yapp Charitable Trust
The John K Young Endowment
   Fund
The Marjorie and Arnold Ziff
   Charitable Foundation

....

■ **Older people**

The A B Charitable Trust
The Company of Actuaries'
   Charitable Trust Fund
Age Concern Scotland Grants
The Green and Lilian F M
   Ainsworth and Family
   Benevolent Fund
Viscount Amory's Charitable
   Trust
The Milly Apthorp Charitable
   Trust
The Argus Appeal
The Lord Austin Trust
The Baker Charitable Trust

The Balint Family Charitable
   Trusts
The Ballinger Charitable Trust
The Band Trust
Barchester Healthcare
   Foundation
David and Frederick Barclay
   Foundation
The Louis Baylis (Maidenhead
   Advertiser) Charitable Trust
The Benfield Motors Charitable
   Trust
The Gerald Bentall Charitable
   Trust
The Mason Bibby 1981 Trust
Percy Bilton Charity
The Bisgood Charitable Trust
   (registered as Miss Jeanne
   Bisgood's Charitable Trust)
The Herbert and Peter
   Blagrave Charitable Trust
The Bothwell Charitable Trust
P G and N J Boulton Trust
The Harold and Alice Bridges
   Charity
The Charles Brotherton Trust
Bill Brown's Charitable
   Settlement
The Joseph and Annie Cattle
   Trust
The Chelsea Building Society
   Charitable Foundation
The Chelsea Square 1994
   Trust
Lord Clinton's Charitable Trust
The Clore Duffield Foundation
The Clothworkers' Foundation
The Clover Trust
The Coalfields Regeneration
   Trust
Comic Relief
The Consolidated Charities for
   the Infirm Merchant
   Taylors' Company
The Cook and Wolstenholme
   Charitable Trust
The Marjorie Coote Old
   People's Charity
Cumbria Community
   Foundation
The Raymond Curtis Charitable
   Trust
The Manny Cussins
   Foundation
The Dr and Mrs A Darlington
   Charitable Trust
The Denton Charitable Trust
The Djanogly Foundation
The Derek and Eileen Dodgson
   Foundation
The Drapers' Charitable Fund
The Dulverton Trust
The P B Dumbell Charitable
   Trust
The Dumbreck Charity
The Dunhill Medical Trust
The W E Dunn Trust

East Kent Provincial Charities
The Sir John Eastwood
   Foundation
The Gilbert and Eileen Edgar
   Foundation
The W G Edwards Charitable
   Foundation
The Wilfred and Elsie Elkes
   Charity Fund
The Maud Elkington Charitable
   Trust
The John Ellerman Foundation
The Ericson Trust
The Erskine Cunningham Hill
   Trust
The Eveson Charitable Trust
Esmee Fairbairn Foundation
The Fairway Trust
The Lord Faringdon Charitable
   Trust
Samuel William Farmer's Trust
The Fassnidge Memorial Trust
Joseph Fattorini Charitable
   Trust 'B' Account
The Roy Fletcher Charitable
   Trust
The Football Association
   National Sports Centre
   Trust
The Donald Forrester Trust
The Hugh Fraser Foundation
The Joseph Strong Frazer Trust
The Freemasons' Grand
   Charity
The Friarsgate Trust
Friends of Muir Group
The Frognal Trust
The Fuserna Foundation
The Girdlers' Company
   Charitable Trust
The Mrs Godfrey-Payton Trust
The Gosling Foundation
   Limited
The Constance Green
   Foundation
The Philip Green Memorial
   Trust
Greggs Foundation
Grimmitt Trust
The Grocers' Charity
The Bishop of Guildford's
   Foundation
The Guildry Incorporation of
   Perth
The Hadfield Trust
The Hadrian Trust
The Alfred Haines Charitable
   Trust
E F and M G Hall Charitable
   Trust
The Helen Hamlyn Trust
The W A Handley Charitable
   Trust
William Harding's Charity
The Harebell Centenary Fund
The Kenneth Hargreaves
   Charitable Trust

The Harrison and Potter Trust
The N and P Hartley Memorial Trust
The Alfred And Peggy Harvey Charitable Trust
The Dorothy Hay-Bolton Charitable Trust
The Charles Hayward Foundation
The Headley Trust
Headley-Pitt Charitable Trust
The Heart of England Community Foundation
Help the Aged
The Hemby Trust
The Christina Mary Hendrie Trust for Scottish and Canadian Charities
The Sir Julian Hodge Charitable Trust
The Edward Holt Trust
The Cuthbert Horn Trust
The Hospital of God at Greatham
The Hudson Foundation
The Albert Hunt Trust
Miss Agnes H Hunter's Trust
Huntingdon Freemen's Charity
The Worshipful Company of Innholders General Charity Fund
The Charles Irving Charitable Trust
The Ruth and Lionel Jacobson Trust (Second Fund) No 2
John James Bristol Foundation
The Jones 1986 Charitable Trust
The Cyril and Eve Jumbo Charitable Trust
The Anton Jurgens Charitable Trust
The KempWelch Charitable Trust
Ernest Kleinwort Charitable Trust
The Sir James Knott Trust
The Martin Laing Foundation
The Beatrice Laing Trust
The Lambert Charitable Trust
Duchy of Lancaster Benevolent Fund
The Allen Lane Foundation
The Edgar E Lawley Foundation
The Herd Lawson and Muriel Lawson Charitable Trust
The Joseph Levy Charitable Foundation
The Linbury Trust
Lincolnshire Community Foundation
The Linden Charitable Trust
Jack Livingstone Charitable Trust
Lloyds TSB Foundation for England and Wales
Lord and Lady Lurgan Trust

The M and C Trust
The E M MacAndrew Trust
Macdonald-Buchanan Charitable Trust
The Macfarlane Walker Trust
The Marchday Charitable Fund
The Ann and David Marks Foundation
The Michael Marsh Charitable Trust
The Marsh Christian Trust
The Charlotte Marshall Charitable Trust
Sir George Martin Trust
The Nancie Massey Charitable Trust
The Violet Mauray Charitable Trust
The Maxwell Family Foundation
Evelyn May Trust
The Robert McAlpine Foundation
D D McPhail Charitable Settlement
The Mercers' Charitable Foundation
The Merchant Taylors' Company Charities Fund
The Merchant Venturers' Charity
The Zachary Merton and George Woofindin Convalescent Trust
The Tony Metherell Charitable Trust
Miles Trust for the Putney and Roehampton Community
Milton Keynes Community Foundation
The Peter Minet Trust
The Mitchell Charitable Trust
Monmouthshire County Council Welsh Church Act Fund
The Peter Moores Foundation
The Morris Charitable Trust
The Peter Morrison Charitable Foundation
The Edith Murphy Foundation
Murphy-Neumann Charity Company Limited
The Nationwide Foundation
The North British Hotel Trust
The Northampton Queen's Institute Relief in Sickness Fund
The Northern Rock Foundation
The Northwood Charitable Trust
The Nuffield Foundation
The Oakley Charitable Trust
Ogilvie Charities Deed No.2 (including the Charity of Mary Catherine Ford Smith)
The Oldham Foundation
Arthur James Paterson Charitable Trust

The Constance Paterson Charitable Trust
Paycare Charity Trust
The Harry Payne Trust
The Pedmore Sporting Club Trust Fund
The Dowager Countess Eleanor Peel Trust
The Pilkington Charities Fund
The Austin and Hope Pilkington Trust
Mrs Pilkington's Charitable Trust
G S Plaut Charitable Trust Limited
The Ponton House Trust
The Powell Foundation
The Douglas Prestwich Charitable Trust
Sir John Priestman Charity Trust
The Proven Family Trust
The Provincial Grand Charity of the Province of Derbyshire
PSA Peugeot Citroen Charity Trust
The Puri Foundation
Mr and Mrs J A Pye's Charitable Settlement
The Queen's Silver Jubilee Trust
The Rank Foundation
The Joseph Rank Trust
The Ratcliff Pension Charity
The Ravensdale Trust
The Roger Raymond Charitable Trust
The Rayne Foundation
The Rayne Trust
The Sir James Reckitt Charity
The Red Rose Charitable Trust
Relief Fund for Romania Limited
The Violet M Richards Charity
The Richmond Parish Lands Charity
Riverside Charitable Trust Limited
The Robertson Trust
The C A Rookes Charitable Trust
The Rosca Trust
The Cecil Rosen Foundation
Mrs Gladys Row Fogo Charitable Trust
The Rowlands Trust
The RRAF Charitable Trust
The Andrew Salvesen Charitable Trust
The Helene Sebba Charitable Trust
The Sylvia and Colin Shepherd Charitable Trust
The Shetland Charitable Trust
The Bassil Shippam and Alsford Trust

The Mary Elizabeth Siebel
Charity
The Henry Smith Charity
Stanley Smith General
Charitable Trust
Philip Smith's Charitable Trust
The R C Snelling Charitable
Trust
The Sovereign Health Care
Charitable Trust
St Monica Trust Community
Fund
The Stafford Trust
The Stanley Foundation Ltd
The Stanton Ballard Charitable
Trust
The June Stevens Foundation
The Summerfield Charitable
Trust
A P Taylor Trust
Tesco Charity Trust
The Tolkien Trust
John and Lucille van Geest
Foundation
The Van Neste Foundation
The William and Patricia
Venton Charitable Trust
The Wakefield and Tetley Trust
J and J R Wilson Trust
The Francis Winham
Foundation
The Michael and Anna Wix
Charitable Trust
The Wixamtree Trust
Woodlands Trust
The Yapp Charitable Trust
Yorkshire Building Society
Charitable Foundation
Elizabeth and Prince Zaiger
Trust
The Marjorie and Arnold Ziff
Charitable Foundation

Class, group, occupation or former occupation

■ Armed forces

Alexandra Rose Charities
The Ammco Trust
The Armourers' and Brasiers'
Gauntlet Trust
The Army Benevolent Fund
The Balney Charitable Trust
The Baltic Charitable Fund
The Robert Clutterbuck
Charitable Trust
The De Clermont Charitable
Company Ltd
The Dulverton Trust
The Edinburgh Trust, No 2
Account
The Erskine Cunningham Hill
Trust

The Donald Forrester Trust
The Girdlers' Company
Charitable Trust
Mike Gooley Trailfinders
Charity
The W A Handley Charitable
Trust
The Charles Littlewood Hill
Trust
The Sir James Knott Trust
The Beatrice Laing Trust
The Raymond and Blanche
Lawson Charitable Trust
Limoges Charitable Trust
The MacRobert Trust
Mountbatten Festival of Music
The Noswad Charity
The Prince's Charities
Foundation
Princess Anne's Charities
Queen Mary's Roehampton
Trust
The Red Arrows Trust
The Rowlands Trust
Royal Artillery Charitable Fund
Royal British Legion
The Royal Scots Benevolent
Society
The Salters' Charities
Scott (Eredine) Charitable
Trust
Seafarers UK (King George's
Fund for Sailors)
The Leslie Smith Foundation
The Stafford Trust
The A R Taylor Charitable Trust
The Westminster Foundation

■ Art, culture, sports and recreation

The Arts Council of Wales
The Richard Carne Trust
The Equity Trust Fund
The John Feeney Charitable
Bequest
The Follett Trust
Maurice Fry Charitable Trust
Paul Hamlyn Foundation
The Derek Hill Foundation
The Hinrichsen Foundation
The Horne Foundation
The Boris Karloff Charitable
Foundation
The Kathleen Trust
The Anthony and Elizabeth
Mellows Charitable
Settlement
The R V W Trust
The Peggy Ramsay Foundation
The Rayne Foundation
The Tillett Trust
Miss S M Tutton Charitable
Trust

■ The environment, agriculture

The C Alma Baker Trust
Samuel William Farmer's Trust
The Farmers' Company
Charitable Fund
The Fishmongers' Company's
Charitable Trust
The Girdlers' Company
Charitable Trust
The Joicey Trust
Frank Litchfield Charitable
Trust
The NFU Mutual Charitable
Trust
Yorkshire Agricultural Society
The Yorkshire Dales
Millennium Trust

■ Fishermen

The Fishmongers' Company's
Charitable Trust
The Joicey Trust

■ Law, mediation and advice services

The Law Society Charity

■ Manufacturing and service industries

The Arts Council of Wales
The Clothworkers' Foundation
Coats Foundation Trust
The Cotton Industry War
Memorial Trust
Worshipful Company of
Glovers of London Charity
Fund
The Worshipful Company of
Innholders General Charity
Fund
The Leverhulme Trade
Charities Trust
Riverside Charitable Trust
Limited

■ Medicine and health

The John Avins Trustees
Veta Bailey Charitable Trust
B-CH 1971 Charitable Trust
The British Dietetic
Association General and
Education Trust Fund
British Heart Foundation
The Carron Charitable Trust
The Dinwoodie Settlement
Gilbert Edgar Trust
Maurice Fry Charitable Trust

The General Nursing Council for England and Wales Trust

The Kenneth Hargreaves Charitable Trust

The Michael and Morven Heller Charitable Foundation

John Lewis Partnership General Community Fund

Evelyn May Trust

The Northcott Devon Medical Foundation

The Rayne Foundation

The Sandra Charitable Trust

■ Religion

All Saints Educational Trust

Ashburnham Thanksgiving Trust

The Barnabas Trust

The Corinthian Trust

The Anne French Memorial Trust

The Hesed Trust

The Hope Trust

The James Trust

The Jerusalem Trust

The Langley Charitable Trust

The Lyndhurst Trust

Sylvanus Lyson's Charity

Marshall's Charity

The Bishop Radford Trust

The Rehoboth Trust

St Teilo's Trust

Ulting Overseas Trust

Wallington Missionary Mart and Auctions

The James Wood Bequest Fund

■ Science, technology and engineering

The Colt Foundation

Maurice Fry Charitable Trust

The Michael and Morven Heller Charitable Foundation

The Leverhulme Trade Charities Trust

The Kitty and Daniel Nabarro Charitable Trust

The Nottinghamshire Miners' Welfare Trust Fund

Scottish Coal Industry Special Welfare Fund

■ Sporting or social clubs (including Masons)

Essex Provincial Charity Fund

The Freemasons' Grand Charity

Grand Charitable Trust of the Order of Women Freemasons

The Provincial Grand Charity of the Province of Derbyshire

■ Textile workers and designers

The Arts Council of Wales

Coats Foundation Trust

The Cotton Industry War Memorial Trust

■ Transport

The Baltic Charitable Fund

The Worshipful Company of Carmen Benevolent Trust

The Erskine Cunningham Hill Trust

Dixie Rose Findlay Charitable Trust

The Gosling Foundation Limited

The H and M Charitable Trust

The W A Handley Charitable Trust

P H Holt Foundation

The ITF Seafarers Trust

The Joicey Trust

The George John and Sheilah Livanos Charitable Trust

The Merchants' House of Glasgow

The Mersey Docks and Harbour Company Charitable Fund

The Phillips Charitable Trust

Seafarers UK (King George's Fund for Sailors)

Seamen's Hospital Society

The Shipwrights' Company Charitable Fund

Disability

■ People with a mental impairment

The 1989 Willan Charitable Trust

Aberbrothock Charitable Trust

The Sylvia Adams Charitable Trust

The Adamson Trust

The Green and Lilian F M Ainsworth and Family Benevolent Fund

The Archer Trust

The Baily Thomas Charitable Fund

The Herbert and Peter Blagrave Charitable Trust

The Joseph and Annie Cattle Trust

The Chelsea Building Society Charitable Foundation

The J Reginald Corah Foundation Fund

The Drapers' Charitable Fund

The Dumbreck Charity

The W E Dunn Trust

Eastern Counties Educational Trust Limited

The EBM Charitable Trust

The John Ellerman Foundation

James Ellis Charitable Trust

The Emmandjay Charitable Trust

The Eveson Charitable Trust

Esmée Fairbairn Foundation

Samuel William Farmer's Trust

The Roy Fletcher Charitable Trust

The Forbes Charitable Foundation

Ford Britain Trust

The Oliver Ford Charitable Trust

The Jill Franklin Trust

The Hugh Fraser Foundation

The Joseph Strong Frazer Trust

The Freemasons' Grand Charity

The Gatsby Charitable Foundation

The Robert Gavron Charitable Trust

J Paul Getty Jr Charitable Trust

Simon Gibson Charitable Trust

The Girdlers' Company Charitable Trust

The Good Neighbours Trust

The Gosling Foundation Limited

The Constance Green Foundation

Greggs Foundation (formerly Greggs Trust)

Grimmitt Trust

The Grocers' Charity

The Alfred Haines Charitable Trust

Hampton Fuel Allotment Charity

The W A Handley Charitable Trust

The Hawthorne Charitable Trust

The Headley Trust

Healthsure Group Ltd

The Hedley Foundation

The Charles Littlewood Hill Trust

The Hull and East Riding Charitable Trust

The Iliffe Family Charitable Trust

The J J Charitable Trust

The Jeffrey Charitable Trust

The Jones 1986 Charitable
   Trust
The Judith Trust
The Ian Karten Charitable
   Trust
The Sir James Knott Trust
The KPMG Foundation
The Kirby Laing Foundation
The Beatrice Laing Trust
Duchy of Lancaster Benevolent
   Fund
The Leach Fourteenth Trust
The Linbury Trust
The Enid Linder Foundation
Lloyds TSB Foundation for
   England and Wales
Lloyds TSB Foundation for
   Northern Ireland
London Catalyst (formerly The
   Metropolitan Hospital-
   Sunday Fund)
The Lord's Taverners
The MacRobert Trust
Ian Mactaggart Trust
Magdalen Hospital Trust
The Marchday Charitable Fund
The Michael Marsh Charitable
   Trust
The Marsh Christian Trust
The Jim Marshall Charitable
   Trust
The Robert McAlpine
   Foundation
The McKenna Charitable Trust
The Tony Metherell Charitable
   Trust
Miles Trust for the Putney and
   Roehampton Community
The Hugh and Mary Miller
   Bequest Trust
The Peter Minet Trust
John Moores Foundation
Murphy-Neumann Charity
   Company Limited
The Kitty and Daniel Nabarro
   Charitable Trust
The Neighbourly Charitable
   Trust
Nestle Rowntree Employees
   Community Fund
The Normanby Charitable Trust
The Northern Rock Foundation
The Noswad Charity
The Nottingham General
   Dispensary
The Nuffield Foundation
The Parthenon Trust
The Susanna Peake Charitable
   Trust
The Persula Foundation
The Pilkington Charities Fund
The Platinum Trust
The Ponton House Trust
The Douglas Prestwich
   Charitable Trust
The Red Rose Charitable Trust

Relief Fund for Romania
   Limited
The Clive Richards Charity
The Richmond Parish Lands
   Charity
Rix-Thompson-Rothenburg
   Foundation
The Robertson Trust
The Cecil Rosen Foundation
The Rowlands Trust
The Saddlers' Company
   Charitable Fund
SFIA Educational Trust Limited
The Sylvia and Colin Shepherd
   Charitable Trust
The Shirley Foundation
The Mrs Smith and Mount
   Trust
David Solomons Charitable
   Trust
St James's Place Foundation
The Strangward Trust
The Summerfield Charitable
   Trust
Thames Community
   Foundation
The Three Guineas Trust
John and Lucille van Geest
   Foundation
Vision Charity
John Watson's Trust
The Will Charitable Trust
Woodlands Trust
The Woodward Charitable
   Trust
The Xerox (UK) Trust
The York Children's Trust
Elizabeth and Prince Zaiger
   Trust

■ People with autism

The Girdlers' Company
   Charitable Trust
The Headley Trust
Magdalen Hospital Trust
Nestle Rowntree Employees
   Community Fund
The Shirley Foundation
The Three Guineas Trust

■ People who have suffered brain damage

The Girdlers' Company
   Charitable Trust
John and Lucille van Geest
   Foundation

■ People with dyslexia

The Joseph and Annie Cattle
   Trust
The J J Charitable Trust
The KPMG Foundation
The Linbury Trust
Vision Charity

■ People with learning difficulties

Aberbrothock Charitable Trust
The Sylvia Adams Charitable
   Trust
The Green and Lilian F M
   Ainsworth and Family
   Benevolent Fund
The Baily Thomas Charitable
   Fund
The Herbert and Peter
   Blagrave Charitable Trust
The Chelsea Building Society
   Charitable Foundation
The J Reginald Corah
   Foundation Fund
The Drapers' Charitable Fund
The Dumbreck Charity
The W E Dunn Trust
Eastern Counties Educational
   Trust Limited
The EBM Charitable Trust
The John Ellerman Foundation
James Ellis Charitable Trust
The Emmandjay Charitable
   Trust
The Eveson Charitable Trust
Esmée Fairbairn Foundation
The Roy Fletcher Charitable
   Trust
The Forbes Charitable
   Foundation
Ford Britain Trust
The Oliver Ford Charitable
   Trust
The Jill Franklin Trust
The Hugh Fraser Foundation
The Joseph Strong Frazer Trust
The Freemasons' Grand
   Charity
The Gatsby Charitable
   Foundation
The Robert Gavron Charitable
   Trust
J Paul Getty Jr Charitable Trust
Simon Gibson Charitable Trust
The Good Neighbours Trust
The Gosling Foundation
   Limited
The Constance Green
   Foundation
Greggs Foundation (formerly
   Greggs Trust)
Grimmitt Trust
The Grocers' Charity
The Alfred Haines Charitable
   Trust
Hampton Fuel Allotment
   Charity
The W A Handley Charitable
   Trust
The Hawthorne Charitable
   Trust
Healthsure Group Ltd
The Hedley Foundation
The Charles Littlewood Hill
   Trust

The Hull and East Riding
Charitable Trust
The Iliffe Family Charitable
Trust
The Jeffrey Charitable Trust
The Jones 1986 Charitable
Trust
The Judith Trust
The Ian Karten Charitable
Trust
The Sir James Knott Trust
The Kirby Laing Foundation
Duchy of Lancaster Benevolent
Fund
The Leach Fourteenth Trust
The Enid Linder Foundation
Lloyds TSB Foundation for
England and Wales
Lloyds TSB Foundation for
Northern Ireland
London Catalyst (formerly The
Metropolitan Hospital-
Sunday Fund)
The Lord's Taverners
The MacRobert Trust
Ian Mactaggart Trust
Magdalen Hospital Trust
The Marchday Charitable Fund
The Michael Marsh Charitable
Trust
The Marsh Christian Trust
The Jim Marshall Charitable
Trust
The Robert McAlpine
Foundation
The Tony Metherell Charitable
Trust
Miles Trust for the Putney and
Roehampton Community
The Hugh and Mary Miller
Bequest Trust
The Peter Minet Trust
John Moores Foundation
Murphy-Neumann Charity
Company Limited
The Kitty and Daniel Nabarro
Charitable Trust
The Neighbourly Charitable
Trust
Nestle Rowntree Employees
Community Fund
The Normanby Charitable Trust
The Northern Rock Foundation
The Noswad Charity
The Nottingham General
Dispensary
The Nuffield Foundation
The Parthenon Trust
The Susanna Peake Charitable
Trust
The Persula Foundation
The Pilkington Charities Fund
The Platinum Trust
The Ponton House Trust
The Douglas Prestwich
Charitable Trust

Relief Fund for Romania
Limited
The Clive Richards Charity
The Richmond Parish Lands
Charity
Rix-Thompson-Rothenburg
Foundation
The Robertson Trust
The Cecil Rosen Foundation
The Rowlands Trust
The Saddlers' Company
Charitable Fund
SFIA Educational Trust Limited
The Sylvia and Colin Shepherd
Charitable Trust
The Mrs Smith and Mount
Trust
St James's Place Foundation
The Strangward Trust
The Summerfield Charitable
Trust
Thames Community
Foundation
The Will Charitable Trust
Woodlands Trust
The Woodward Charitable
Trust
The Xerox (UK) Trust
The York Children's Trust
Elizabeth and Prince Zaiger
Trust

....

■ People with a physical impairment

The 1989 Willan Charitable
Trust
Aberbrothock Charitable Trust
The Sylvia Adams Charitable
Trust
The Adamson Trust
The Green and Lilian F M
Ainsworth and Family
Benevolent Fund
The Ajahma Charitable Trust
The Ammco Trust
The Cleopatra Trust
The Dibden Allotments Charity
The Dorus Trust
The Drapers' Charitable Fund
The Dumbreck Charity
The W E Dunn Trust
The Sir John Eastwood
Foundation
The EBM Charitable Trust
The John Ellerman Foundation
James Ellis Charitable Trust
The Emerton-Christie Charity
The Emmandjay Charitable
Trust
The Epigoni Trust
The Eveson Charitable Trust
Esmée Fairbairn Foundation
Samuel William Farmer's Trust
The Roy Fletcher Charitable
Trust

The Follett Trust
Ford Britain Trust
The Donald Forrester Trust
The Jill Franklin Trust
The Hugh Fraser Foundation
The Freemasons' Grand
Charity
The Frognal Trust
The Gatsby Charitable
Foundation
The Robert Gavron Charitable
Trust
J Paul Getty Jr Charitable Trust
Simon Gibson Charitable Trust
The Girdlers' Company
Charitable Trust
The Good Neighbours Trust
The Gosling Foundation
Limited
The Constance Green
Foundation
Greggs Foundation (formerly
Greggs Trust)
Grimmitt Trust
The Grocers' Charity
H C D Memorial Fund
The Hadley Trust
The Hadrian Trust
The Alfred Haines Charitable
Trust
Hampton Fuel Allotment
Charity
The W A Handley Charitable
Trust
The Peter Harrison Foundation
The N and P Hartley Memorial
Trust
The Hawthorne Charitable
Trust
The Headley Trust
Healthsure Group Ltd
The Hedley Foundation
The Charles Littlewood Hill
Trust
The Hospital Saturday Fund
The Hull and East Riding
Charitable Trust
Miss Agnes H Hunter's Trust
The Iliffe Family Charitable
Trust
The Jones 1986 Charitable
Trust
The Anton Jurgens Charitable
Trust
The Ian Karten Charitable
Trust
The Sir James Knott Trust
The Kirby Laing Foundation
The Beatrice Laing Trust
Duchy of Lancaster Benevolent
Fund
Mrs F B Laurence Charitable
Trust
The Leach Fourteenth Trust
Lifeline 4 Kids
The Enid Linder Foundation

Lloyds TSB Foundation for
England and Wales
Lloyds TSB Foundation for
Northern Ireland
London Catalyst (formerly The
Metropolitan Hospital-
Sunday Fund)
The Lord's Taverners
The R S Macdonald Charitable
Trust
The MacRobert Trust
Ian Mactaggart Trust
The Marchday Charitable Fund
The Michael Marsh Charitable
Trust
The Marsh Christian Trust
The Jim Marshall Charitable
Trust
The McKenna Charitable Trust
The Mercers' Charitable
Foundation
The Tony Metherell Charitable
Trust
Miles Trust for the Putney and
Roehampton Community
The Hugh and Mary Miller
Bequest Trust
Milton Keynes Community
Foundation
The Peter Minet Trust
John Moores Foundation
Murphy-Neumann Charity
Company Limited
The Neighbourly Charitable
Trust
Nestle Rowntree Employees
Community Fund
Newby Trust Limited
The Normanby Charitable Trust
The Northern Rock Foundation
The Noswad Charity
The Nottingham General
Dispensary
The Parthenon Trust
The Peacock Charitable Trust
The Susanna Peake Charitable
Trust
The Dowager Countess
Eleanor Peel Trust
The Persula Foundation
The Pilkington Charities Fund
The Platinum Trust
The Ponton House Trust
The Douglas Prestwich
Charitable Trust
Richard Radcliffe Charitable
Trust
The Red Rose Charitable Trust
Relief Fund for Romania
Limited
The Clive Richards Charity
The Richmond Parish Lands
Charity
The Muriel Edith Rickman
Trust
The Robertson Trust

Mrs L D Rope Third Charitable
Settlement
The Cecil Rosen Foundation
The Rowlands Trust
Royal Docks Trust (London)
The Saddlers' Company
Charitable Fund
SFIA Educational Trust Limited
The Sylvia and Colin Shepherd
Charitable Trust
Stanley Smith General
Charitable Trust
St James's Place Foundation
The Strangward Trust
The Summerfield Charitable
Trust
Thames Community
Foundation
The Wixamtree Trust
Woodlands Trust
The Woodward Charitable
Trust
The Xerox (UK) Trust
The York Children's Trust
Elizabeth and Prince Zaiger
Trust

....

■ People with a sensory impairment

Blatchington Court Trust
The British Council for
Prevention of Blindness
The Charities Advisory Trust
The John Cowan Foundation
The Wilfred and Elsie Elkes
Charity Fund
James Ellis Charitable Trust
The Eveson Charitable Trust
Samuel William Farmer's Trust
Dixie Rose Findlay Charitable
Trust
The Joseph Strong Frazer Trust
The Frognal Trust
The Girdlers' Company
Charitable Trust
The Dorothy Hay-Bolton
Charitable Trust
The Anne Herd Memorial Trust
Miss Agnes H Hunter's Trust
The Lillie Johnson Charitable
Trust
The Anton Jurgens Charitable
Trust
The Raymond and Blanche
Lawson Charitable Trust
The John Spedan Lewis
Foundation
The R S Macdonald Charitable
Trust
The Tony Metherell Charitable
Trust
Mickleham Charitable Trust
Gerald Micklem Charitable
Trust

Nestle Rowntree Employees
Community Fund
The Northwood Charitable
Trust
The Persula Foundation
Richard Radcliffe Charitable
Trust
The Max Reinhardt Charitable
Trust
The Worshipful Company of
Spectacle Makers' Charity
The Ulverscroft Foundation
John and Lucille van Geest
Foundation
Vision Charity
The Will Charitable Trust
The York Children's Trust

■ Hearing loss

The Wilfred and Elsie Elkes
Charity Fund
The Eveson Charitable Trust
Samuel William Farmer's Trust
The Joseph Strong Frazer Trust
The Girdlers' Company
Charitable Trust
The Northwood Charitable
Trust
The Persula Foundation
The Max Reinhardt Charitable
Trust
John and Lucille van Geest
Foundation

■ Sight loss

Blatchington Court Trust
The British Council for
Prevention of Blindness
The John Cowan Foundation
The Wilfred and Elsie Elkes
Charity Fund
The Eveson Charitable Trust
Samuel William Farmer's Trust
Dixie Rose Findlay Charitable
Trust
The Joseph Strong Frazer Trust
The Frognal Trust
The Girdlers' Company
Charitable Trust
The Anne Herd Memorial Trust
Miss Agnes H Hunter's Trust
The Raymond and Blanche
Lawson Charitable Trust
The R S Macdonald Charitable
Trust
Mickleham Charitable Trust
The Persula Foundation
The Worshipful Company of
Spectacle Makers' Charity
The Ulverscroft Foundation
John and Lucille van Geest
Foundation
Vision Charity
The Will Charitable Trust

Ethnicity

The BACTA Charitable Trust
The Big Lottery Fund
The Bintaub Charitable Trust
The City Parochial Foundation
The Football Association
National Sports Centre
Trust
Greggs Foundation
The Hadrian Trust
The Hilden Charitable Fund
The Hospital of God at
Greatham
The LankellyChase Foundation
The Joseph Levy Charitable
Foundation
Lincolnshire Community
Foundation
Lloyds TSB Foundation for
England and Wales
The Ann and David Marks
Foundation
John Moores Foundation
The Northern Rock Foundation
The Jack Petchey Foundation
The Sigrid Rausing Trust
The Alan and Babette
Sainsbury Charitable Fund
Trust for London

Faith

4 Charity Foundation
Brian Abrams Charitable Trust
Eric Abrams Charitable Trust
The Acacia Charitable Trust
Achisomoch Aid Company
Limited
Adenfirst Ltd
Aid to the Church in Need (UK)
Alba Charitable Trust
The Alexis Trust
All Saints Educational Trust
The Alliance Family Foundation
The Almond Trust
Alvor Charitable Trust
Amabrill Limited
The AMW Charitable Trust
The Anchor Foundation
The Andrew Anderson Trust
Ashburnham Thanksgiving
Trust
AW Charitable Trust
The BACTA Charitable Trust
The Baker Charitable Trust
The Balint Family Charitable
Trusts
William P Bancroft (No 2)
Charitable Trust and
Jenepher Gillett Trust
The Barnabas Trust
Bay Charitable Trust
Beauland Ltd
Belljoe Tzedoko Ltd

The Ruth Berkowitz Charitable
Trust
The Bintaub Charitable Trust
The Sir Victor Blank Charitable
Settlement
The Neville and Elaine Blond
Charitable Trust
The Bonamy Charitable Trust
P G and N J Boulton Trust
Sir Clive Bourne Family Trust
Bristol Archdeaconry Charity
Mrs E E Brown Charitable
Settlement
Buckingham Trust
The Audrey and Stanley Burton
1960 Charitable Trust
The Arnold Burton 1998
Charitable Trust
C and F Charitable Trust
Henry T and Lucy B Cadbury
Charitable Trust
The William A Cadbury
Charitable Trust
H and L Cantor Trust
Carlee Ltd
The CH (1980) Charitable
Trust
Charitworth Limited
Chasdei Tovim Me'oros
The Christabella Charitable
Trust
The Roger and Sarah Bancroft
Clark Charitable Trust
Closehelm Ltd
The Clover Trust
Clydpride Ltd
The E Alec Colman Charitable
Fund Ltd
Col-Reno Ltd
The Gershon Coren Charitable
Foundation
Edwin Cornforth 1983 Charity
Trust
The Sidney and Elizabeth
Corob Charitable Trust
The Corona Charitable Trust
The Costa Family Charitable
Trust
The Cross Trust
The Manny Cussins
Foundation
Itzchok Meyer Cymerman Trust
Ltd
Oizer Dalim Trust
Davidson Charitable Trust
Davis-Rubens Charitable Trust
The Debmar Benevolent Trust
The Dellal Foundation
The Djanogly Foundation
The DM Charitable Trust
Domepride Ltd
The Doughty Charity Trust
The P B Dumbell Charitable
Trust
Dushinsky Trust Ltd
The George Elias Charitable
Trust

Ellador Ltd
The Ellinson Foundation Ltd
The Edith Maud Ellis 1985
Charitable Trust
Elshore Ltd
Entindale Ltd
The Esfandi Charitable
Foundation
The Exilarch's Foundation
The Family Foundations Trust
Joseph Fattorini Charitable
Trust 'B' Account
Federation of Jewish Relief
Organisations
Finnart House School Trust
The Gerald Fogel Charitable
Trust
Forbesville Limited
Fordeve Ltd
The Forte Charitable Trust
The Isaac and Freda Frankel
Memorial Charitable Trust
The Thomas Freke and Lady
Norton Charity
The Friends Hall Farm Street
Trust
Friends of Biala Ltd
Friends of Boyan Trust
Mejer and Gertrude Miriam
Frydman Foundation
The Angela Gallagher Memorial
Fund
Garvan Limited
Global Care
The Meir Golda Trust
The Grahame Charitable
Foundation Limited
The M and R Gross Charities
Limited
The Grove Charitable Trust
The Gur Trust
The H P Charitable Trust
Beatrice Hankey Foundation
Ltd
The Harbour Foundation
Haskel Family Foundation
The Haydan Charitable Trust
Heagerty Charitable Trust
The Helping Foundation
Hexham and Newcastle
Diocesan Trust (1947)
Highcroft Charitable Trust
Hinchley Charitable Trust
The Holden Charitable Trust
The Hope Trust
The Daniel Howard Trust
The Humanitarian Trust
The Huntingdon Foundation
Hurdale Charity Limited
The P Y N and B Hyams Trust
The Isaacs Charitable Trust
Jacobs Charitable Trust
The Susan and Stephen
James Charitable
Settlement
The James Trust
Jay Education Trust

JCA Charitable Foundation
Jewish Child's Day
The Jewish Youth Fund
The JMK Charitable Trust
The Harold Joels Charitable Trust
The Nicholas Joels Charitable Trust
The Norman Joels Charitable Trust
The J E Joseph Charitable Fund
The Judith Trust
The Bernard Kahn Charitable Trust
The Stanley Kalms Foundation
The Kasner Charitable Trust
The Katzauer Charitable Settlement
The C S Kaufman Charitable Trust
The Geoffrey John Kaye Charitable Foundation
The Emmanuel Kaye Foundation
Keren Association
Kermaville Ltd
The Kessler Foundation
Kirschel Foundation
The Kohn Foundation
Kollel and Co. Limited
Kupath Gemach Chaim Bechesed Viznitz Trust
The Late Sir Pierce Lacy Charity Trust
Laufer Charitable Trust
The Lauffer Family Charitable Foundation
The Herd Lawson and Muriel Lawson Charitable Trust
The Arnold Lee Charitable Trust
Morris Leigh Foundation
Lewis Family Charitable Trust
The Lind Trust
The Ruth and Stuart Lipton Charitable Trust
The Second Joseph Aaron Littman Foundation
Jack Livingstone Charitable Trust
The Charles Lloyd Foundation
Localtrent Ltd
The Locker Foundation
The Loftus Charitable Trust
The Lolev Charitable Trust
The Lowy Mitchell Foundation
The Ruth and Jack Lunzer Charitable Trust
The Sir Jack Lyons Charitable Trust
Malcolm Lyons Foundation
Sylvanus Lyson's Charity
The M and C Trust
The M K Charitable Trust
Macdonald-Buchanan Charitable Trust

The Magen Charitable Trust
Malbin Trust
The Mallinckrodt Foundation
Marbeh Torah Trust
The Stella and Alexander Margulies Charitable Trust
The Ann and David Marks Foundation
The Hilda and Samuel Marks Foundation
The Mason Porter Charitable Trust
The Violet Mauray Charitable Trust
Mayfair Charities Ltd
Melodor Ltd
Melow Charitable Trust
Menuchar Ltd
Mercaz Torah Vechesed Limited
Miles Trust for the Putney and Roehampton Community
The Minos Trust
The Mishcon Family Charitable Trust
The Mitchell Charitable Trust
Keren Mitzvah Trust
The Modiano Charitable Trust
The Moette Charitable Trust
The Mole Charitable Trust
The Morgan Charitable Foundation
The Oliver Morland Charitable Trust
S C and M E Morland's Charitable Trust
The Peter Morrison Charitable Foundation
Moshal Charitable Trust
Brian and Jill Moss Charitable Trust
The Mutual Trust Group
MYA Charitable Trust
MYR Charitable Trust
The Nadezhda Charitable Trust
The Naggar Charitable Trust
Nathan Charitable Trust
Nemoral Ltd
Ner Foundation
Nesswall Ltd
NJD Charitable Trust
The Northampton Municipal Church Charities
The Norwood and Newton Settlement
The Ogle Christian Trust
The Oizer Charitable Trust
Open Gate
The Owen Family Trust
The Doris Pacey Charitable Foundation
The Payne Charitable Trust
The David Pearlman Charitable Foundation
The Persson Charitable Trust
The Phillips Family Charitable Trust

The David Pickford Charitable Foundation
The Pollywally Charitable Trust
Porticus UK
The J E Posnansky Charitable Trust
Premishlaner Charitable Trust
Sir John Priestman Charity Trust
Quothquan Trust
R J M Charitable Trust
R S Charitable Trust
The Bishop Radford Trust
The Joseph Rank Trust
The Fanny Rapaport Charitable Settlement
The Ravensdale Trust
The Rayden Charitable Trust
The Rayne Trust
The Albert Reckitt Charitable Trust
The Sir James Reckitt Charity
The Rehoboth Trust
The Rest Harrow Trust
The Rhondda Cynon Taff Welsh Church Acts Fund
The Clive Richards Charity
The Sir John Ritblat Family Foundation
The Rock Solid Trust
The Gerald Ronson Foundation
Rowanville Ltd
S F Foundation
S O Charitable Trust
The Ruzin Sadagora Trust
Saint Luke's College Foundation
The Hon. M J Samuel Charitable Trust
The Annie Schiff Charitable Trust
The Schmidt-Bodner Charitable Trust
The Schreiber Charitable Trust
The Samuel Sebba Charitable Trust
Sellata Ltd
The Cyril Shack Trust
Shlomo Memorial Fund Limited
The Leslie Silver Charitable Trust
The Simpson Foundation
The Moss Spiro Will Charitable Foundation
Springrule Ltd
St Christopher's College Educational Trust
C E K Stern Charitable Trust
The Strawberry Charitable Trust
The A B Strom and R Strom Charitable Trust
T and S Trust Fund
Tadlus Limited
The Tajtelbaum Charitable Trust

The David Tannen Charitable Trust
The Lili Tapper Charitable Foundation
C B and H H Taylor 1984 Trust
The Torah Temimah Trust
Toras Chesed (London) Trust
Truemart Limited
Trustees of Tzedakah
The Union of Orthodox Hebrew Congregation
The Vail Foundation
Vivdale Ltd
The John Warren Foundation
The Weinstein Foundation
The Benjamin Winegarten Charitable Trust
The Maurice Wohl Charitable Foundation
The Wolfson Family Charitable Trust
Woodlands Foundation Limited
Wychville Ltd
Yankov Charitable Trust
The Marjorie and Arnold Ziff Charitable Foundation
Stephen Zimmerman Charitable Trust

....

■ Christians

Aid to the Church in Need (UK)
The Alexis Trust
All Saints Educational Trust
The Almond Trust
Alvor Charitable Trust
The AMW Charitable Trust
The Anchor Foundation
The Andrew Anderson Trust
Ashburnham Thanksgiving Trust
William P Bancroft (No 2) Charitable Trust and Jenepher Gillett Trust
The Barnabas Trust
P G and N J Boulton Trust
Bristol Archdeaconry Charity
Buckingham Trust
Henry T and Lucy B Cadbury Charitable Trust
The William A Cadbury Charitable Trust
The Christabella Charitable Trust
The Roger and Sarah Bancroft Clark Charitable Trust
The Clover Trust
The Costa Family Charitable Trust
The Cross Trust
The P B Dumbell Charitable Trust
The Edith Maud Ellis 1985 Charitable Trust
Joseph Fattorini Charitable Trust 'B' Account

The Forte Charitable Trust
The Thomas Freke and Lady Norton Charity
The Friends Hall Farm Street Trust
The Angela Gallagher Memorial Fund
Global Care
Beatrice Hankey Foundation Ltd
Heagerty Charitable Trust
Hexham and Newcastle Diocesan Trust (1947)
Hinchley Charitable Trust
The Hope Trust
The James Trust
The Late Sir Pierce Lacy Charity Trust
The Herd Lawson and Muriel Lawson Charitable Trust
The Lind Trust
The Charles Lloyd Foundation
Sylvanus Lyson's Charity
Macdonald-Buchanan Charitable Trust
The Mallinckrodt Foundation
The Mason Porter Charitable Trust
Miles Trust for the Putney and Roehampton Community
The Minos Trust
The Oliver Morland Charitable Trust
S C and M E Morland's Charitable Trust
The Nadezhda Charitable Trust
Nathan Charitable Trust
The Norwood and Newton Settlement
The Ogle Christian Trust
Open Gate
The Owen Family Trust
The Payne Charitable Trust
The Persson Charitable Trust
The David Pickford Charitable Foundation
Sir John Priestman Charity Trust
Quothquan Trust
The Bishop Radford Trust
The Joseph Rank Trust
The Ravensdale Trust
The Albert Reckitt Charitable Trust
The Sir James Reckitt Charity
The Rehoboth Trust
The Rhondda Cynon Taff Welsh Church Acts Fund
The Clive Richards Charity
The Rock Solid Trust
The Simpson Foundation
St Christopher's College Educational Trust
C B and H H Taylor 1984 Trust
The John Warren Foundation

....

■ People of the Jewish faith

4 Charity Foundation
Brian Abrams Charitable Trust
Eric Abrams Charitable Trust
The Acacia Charitable Trust
Achisomoch Aid Company Limited
Adenfirst Ltd
Alba Charitable Trust
The Alliance Family Foundation
Amabrill Limited
AW Charitable Trust
The Baker Charitable Trust
The Balint Family Charitable Trusts
Bay Charitable Trust
Beauland Ltd
Belljoe Tzedoko Ltd
The Ruth Berkowitz Charitable Trust
The Sir Victor Blank Charitable Settlement
The Neville and Elaine Blond Charitable Trust
The Bonamy Charitable Trust
Sir Clive Bourne Family Trust
Mrs E E Brown Charitable Settlement
The Audrey and Stanley Burton 1960 Charitable Trust
The Arnold Burton 1998 Charitable Trust
C and F Charitable Trust
H and L Cantor Trust
Carlee Ltd
The CH (1980) Charitable Trust
Charitworth Limited
Chasdei Tovim Me'oros
Closehelm Ltd
Clydpride Ltd
The E Alec Colman Charitable Fund Ltd
Col-Reno Ltd
The Gershon Coren Charitable Foundation
The Sidney and Elizabeth Corob Charitable Trust
The Corona Charitable Trust
The Manny Cussins Foundation
Itzchok Meyer Cymerman Trust Ltd
Oizer Dalim Trust
Davidson Charitable Trust
Davis-Rubens Charitable Trust
The Debmar Benevolent Trust
The Dellal Foundation
The Djanogly Foundation
The DM Charitable Trust
Domepride Ltd
The Doughty Charity Trust
Dushinsky Trust Ltd
The George Elias Charitable Trust

Ellador Ltd
The Ellinson Foundation Ltd
Elshore Ltd
Entindale Ltd
The Esfandi Charitable
Foundation
The Exilarch's Foundation
The Family Foundations Trust
Federation of Jewish Relief
Organisations
Finnart House School Trust
The Gerald Fogel Charitable
Trust
Forbesville Limited
Fordeve Ltd
The Isaac and Freda Frankel
Memorial Charitable Trust
Friends of Biala Ltd
Friends of Boyan Trust
Mejer and Gertrude Miriam
Frydman Foundation
Garvan Limited
The Meir Golda Trust
The Grahame Charitable
Foundation Limited
The M and R Gross Charities
Limited
The Grove Charitable Trust
The Gur Trust
The H P Charitable Trust
The Harbour Foundation
Haskel Family Foundation
The Haydan Charitable Trust
The Helping Foundation
Highcroft Charitable Trust
The Holden Charitable Trust
The Daniel Howard Trust
The Humanitarian Trust
The Huntingdon Foundation
Hurdale Charity Limited
The P Y N and B Hyams Trust
The Isaacs Charitable Trust
Jacobs Charitable Trust
The Susan and Stephen
James Charitable
Settlement
Jay Education Trust
JCA Charitable Foundation
Jewish Child's Day
The Jewish Youth Fund
The Harold Joels Charitable
Trust
The Nicholas Joels Charitable
Trust
The Norman Joels Charitable
Trust
The J E Joseph Charitable
Fund
The Judith Trust
The Bernard Kahn Charitable
Trust
The Stanley Kalms Foundation
The Kasner Charitable Trust
The Katzauer Charitable
Settlement
The C S Kaufman Charitable
Trust

The Geoffrey John Kaye
Charitable Foundation
The Emmanuel Kaye
Foundation
Keren Association
Kermaville Ltd
The Kessler Foundation
Kirschel Foundation
The Kohn Foundation
Kollel and Co. Limited
Kupath Gemach Chaim
Bechesed Viznitz Trust
Laufer Charitable Trust
The Lauffer Family Charitable
Foundation
The Arnold Lee Charitable
Trust
Morris Leigh Foundation
Lewis Family Charitable Trust
The Ruth and Stuart Lipton
Charitable Trust
The Second Joseph Aaron
Littman Foundation
Jack Livingstone Charitable
Trust
Localtrent Ltd
The Locker Foundation
The Loftus Charitable Trust
The Lolev Charitable Trust
The Lowy Mitchell Foundation
The Ruth and Jack Lunzer
Charitable Trust
The Sir Jack Lyons Charitable
Trust
Malcolm Lyons Foundation
The M and C Trust
The M K Charitable Trust
The Magen Charitable Trust
Malbin Trust
Marbeh Torah Trust
The Stella and Alexander
Margulies Charitable Trust
The Ann and David Marks
Foundation
The Hilda and Samuel Marks
Foundation
The Violet Mauray Charitable
Trust
Mayfair Charities Ltd
Melodor Ltd
Melow Charitable Trust
Menuchar Ltd
Mercaz Torah Vechesed
Limited
The Mishcon Family Charitable
Trust
The Mitchell Charitable Trust
Keren Mitzvah Trust
The Modiano Charitable Trust
The Moette Charitable Trust
The Mole Charitable Trust
The Morgan Charitable
Foundation
The Peter Morrison Charitable
Foundation
Moshal Charitable Trust

Brian and Jill Moss Charitable
Trust
The Mutual Trust Group
MYA Charitable Trust
MYR Charitable Trust
The Naggar Charitable Trust
Nemoral Ltd
Ner Foundation
Nesswall Ltd
NJD Charitable Trust
The Oizer Charitable Trust
The Doris Pacey Charitable
Foundation
The David Pearlman Charitable
Foundation
The Phillips Family Charitable
Trust
The Pollywally Charitable Trust
The J E Posnansky Charitable
Trust
Premishlaner Charitable Trust
R J M Charitable Trust
R S Charitable Trust
The Fanny Rapaport Charitable
Settlement
The Rayden Charitable Trust
The Rayne Trust
The Rest Harrow Trust
The Sir John Ritblat Family
Foundation
The Gerald Ronson Foundation
Rowanville Ltd
S F Foundation
S O Charitable Trust
The Ruzin Sadagora Trust
The Hon. M J Samuel
Charitable Trust
The Annie Schiff Charitable
Trust
The Schmidt-Bodner Charitable
Trust
The Schreiber Charitable Trust
The Samuel Sebba Charitable
Trust
Sellata Ltd
The Cyril Shack Trust
Shlomo Memorial Fund Limited
The Leslie Silver Charitable
Trust
The Moss Spiro Will Charitable
Foundation
Springrule Ltd
C E K Stern Charitable Trust
The Strawberry Charitable
Trust
The A B Strom and R Strom
Charitable Trust
T and S Trust Fund
Tadlus Limited
The Tajtelbaum Charitable
Trust
The David Tannen Charitable
Trust
The Lili Tapper Charitable
Foundation
The Torah Temimah Trust
Toras Chesed (London) Trust

Truemart Limited
Trustees of Tzedakah
The Union of Orthodox Hebrew
　Congregation
The Vail Foundation
Vivdale Ltd
The Weinstein Foundation
The Benjamin Winegarten
　Charitable Trust
The Maurice Wohl Charitable
　Foundation
The Wolfson Family Charitable
　Trust
Woodlands Foundation Limited
Wychville Ltd
Yankov Charitable Trust
The Marjorie and Arnold Ziff
　Charitable Foundation
Stephen Zimmerman
　Charitable Trust

Gender and relationships

■ Adopted or fostered children

The Girdlers' Company
　Charitable Trust
The Hemby Trust
The Hospital of God at
　Greatham
The Clifford Howarth Charity
　Trust
The Hyde Charitable Trust –
　Youth Plus
The Anton Jurgens Charitable
　Trust
John Lyon's Charity
The Marchday Charitable Fund

■ Bereaved

Alexandra Rose Charities
Baron Davenport's Charity
The Hemby Trust
The Hospital of God at
　Greatham
The Clifford Howarth Charity
　Trust

■ Carers

The Alchemy Foundation
The Dulverton Trust
Esmée Fairbairn Foundation
The Fishmongers' Company's
　Charitable Trust
The Hugh Fraser Foundation
The Girdlers' Company
　Charitable Trust
The Harris Charitable Trust
The Headley Trust

The Heart of England
　Community Foundation
Help the Aged
The Hemby Trust
The Hospital of God at
　Greatham
The Clifford Howarth Charity
　Trust
The Anton Jurgens Charitable
　Trust
The King's Fund
Lloyds TSB Foundation for
　England and Wales
London Catalyst
John Lyon's Charity
The Marchday Charitable Fund
The Zachary Merton and
　George Woofindin
　Convalescent Trust
John Moores Foundation
The Olga Charitable Trust
Mr and Mrs J A Pye's
　Charitable Settlement
Rix-Thompson-Rothenburg
　Foundation
The True Colours Trust

■ Families

The Carlsson Family
　Foundation
The Leverhulme Trade
　Charities Trust
The Limbourne Trust
Lloyds TSB Foundation for
　England and Wales
Mariapolis Limited
The Charlotte Marshall
　Charitable Trust
Porticus UK
Quothquan Trust
Relief Fund for Romania
　Limited
Ryklow Charitable Trust 1992

■ Lesbians and gay men

The Heart of England
　Community Foundation
The Hospital of God at
　Greatham
The King's Fund
The Allen Lane Foundation

■ Orphans

The Girdlers' Company
　Charitable Trust
The Hospital of God at
　Greatham
Muslim Hands
Stanley Smith General
　Charitable Trust

■ Parents

The Carlsson Family
　Foundation
The Girdlers' Company
　Charitable Trust
The Glass-House Trust
Greggs Foundation
The Alfred Haines Charitable
　Trust
The Heart of England
　Community Foundation
The Hemby Trust
The Hospital of God at
　Greatham
The Clifford Howarth Charity
　Trust
The Hyde Charitable Trust –
　Youth Plus
Lloyds TSB Foundation for
　England and Wales
Lloyds TSB Foundation for
　Northern Ireland
John Lyon's Charity
The Marchday Charitable Fund
The Mothercare Charitable
　Foundation
Quothquan Trust
The Tedworth Charitable Trust

■ Lone parents

The Carlsson Family
　Foundation
The Girdlers' Company
　Charitable Trust
The Alfred Haines Charitable
　Trust
The Heart of England
　Community Foundation
The Hemby Trust
The Hospital of God at
　Greatham
The Clifford Howarth Charity
　Trust
The Hyde Charitable Trust –
　Youth Plus
John Lyon's Charity
The Marchday Charitable Fund
Quothquan Trust

■ Women

The A B Charitable Trust
The Ajahma Charitable Trust
The Associated Country
　Women of the World
　(ACWW)
The Balmore Trust
The Freemasons' Grand
　Charity
J Paul Getty Jr Charitable Trust
Greggs Foundation
The Hadrian Trust
The Heart of England
　Community Foundation

The Hospital of God at
　Greatham
The Judith Trust
The Allen Lane Foundation
The Lotus Foundation
R W Mann Trust
John Moores Foundation
The J P Morgan Foundations
The Eleanor Rathbone
　Charitable Trust
The Sigrid Rausing Trust
The Reed Foundation
Rosa – the UK fund for women
　and girls
The Staples Trust
The Volant Charitable Trust

Ill health

The A B Charitable Trust
Aberbrothock Charitable Trust
The Sylvia Adams Charitable
　Trust
The AMW Charitable Trust
Anglo American Group
　Foundation
The Appletree Trust
The Milly Apthorp Charitable
　Trust
Arthritis Research Campaign
The BACTA Charitable Trust
The Baker Charitable Trust
B-CH 1971 Charitable Trust
The Benfield Motors Charitable
　Trust
The Bintaub Charitable Trust
The Herbert and Peter
　Blagrave Charitable Trust
The Tony Bramall Charitable
　Trust
British Heart Foundation
The Charles Brotherton Trust
R S Brownless Charitable
　Trust
Buckingham Trust
The E F Bulmer Benevolent
　Fund
The BUPA Foundation
P H G Cadbury Charitable
　Trust
Celtic Charity Fund
Champneys Charitable
　Foundation
The Chelsea Building Society
　Charitable Foundation
Child Growth Foundation
The Cleopatra Trust
The Consolidated Charities for
　the Infirm Merchant
　Taylors' Company
The John Cowan Foundation
Criffel Charitable Trust
The Denton Charitable Trust
Diabetes UK
The Diana, Princess of Wales
　Memorial Fund

The Dorus Trust
Dromintee Trust
The W E Dunn Trust
Eastern Counties Educational
　Trust Limited
The Sir John Eastwood
　Foundation
The Wilfred and Elsie Elkes
　Charity Fund
The John Ellerman Foundation
The Emmandjay Charitable
　Trust
The Epigoni Trust
Epilepsy Research UK
Esmée Fairbairn Foundation
The Family Rich Charities Trust
Samuel William Farmer's Trust
The February Foundation
Dixie Rose Findlay Charitable
　Trust
Bud Flanagan Leukaemia Fund
Florence's Charitable Trust
The Follett Trust
The Forte Charitable Trust
Four Acre Trust
The Jill Franklin Trust
The Hugh Fraser Foundation
The Fuserna Foundation
The Gatsby Charitable
　Foundation
Generations Charitable Trust
J Paul Getty Jr Charitable Trust
The Girdlers' Company
　Charitable Trust
The Gosling Foundation
　Limited
The J G Graves Charitable
　Trust
The Constance Green
　Foundation
Grimmitt Trust
The Bishop of Guildford's
　Foundation
The Hadley Trust
Hampton Fuel Allotment
　Charity
The W A Handley Charitable
　Trust
The Hanlye Charitable Trust
The Harborne Parish Lands
　Charity
The Kenneth Hargreaves
　Charitable Trust
The Harris Family Charitable
　Trust
The John Harrison Charitable
　Trust
The Peter Harrison Foundation
The N and P Hartley Memorial
　Trust
Healthsure Group Ltd
May Hearnshaw's Charity
The Heart of England
　Community Foundation
The Hedley Foundation
The Hemby Trust

The Christina Mary Hendrie
　Trust for Scottish and
　Canadian Charities
The High Sheriff's Police Trust
　for the County of West
　Midlands
The Hintze Family Charitable
　Foundation
The Hospital of God at
　Greatham
The Clifford Howarth Charity
　Trust
The Huddersfield Medical Trust
　Fund
The Hull and East Riding
　Charitable Trust
Human Relief Foundation
The Humanitarian Trust
Miss Agnes H Hunter's Trust
Huntingdon Freemen's Charity
The Iliffe Family Charitable
　Trust
Impetus Trust
The Charles Irving Charitable
　Trust
The Ruth and Lionel Jacobson
　Trust (Second Fund) No 2
The Elton John Aids
　Foundation
The Jones 1986 Charitable
　Trust
The Judith Trust
The Anton Jurgens Charitable
　Trust
The Ian Karten Charitable
　Trust
The Caron Keating Foundation
The Mary Kinross Charitable
　Trust
The Kohn Foundation
The Heinz, Anna and Carol
　Kroch Foundation
The Kirby Laing Foundation
The Beatrice Laing Trust
The Allen Lane Foundation
The LankellyChase Foundation
The R J Larg Family Charitable
　Trust
The Kathleen Laurence Trust
The Mason Le Page Charitable
　Trust
The Leigh Trust
Leukaemia Research Fund
The Joseph Levy Charitable
　Foundation
The Lewis Ward Trust
The Linbury Trust
Lincolnshire Community
　Foundation
The Linden Charitable Trust
Lloyds TSB Foundation for
　Northern Ireland
The Loftus Charitable Trust
John Lyon's Charity
The Mackintosh Foundation
Ian Mactaggart Trust
Magdalen Hospital Trust

The Marchday Charitable Fund
The Marsh Christian Trust
The Charlotte Marshall
    Charitable Trust
The Maxwell Family Foundation
The Mercers' Charitable
    Foundation
The Merchants' House of
    Glasgow
Mercury Phoenix Trust
The Zachary Merton and
    George Woofindin
    Convalescent Trust
The Tony Metherell Charitable
    Trust
The Methodist Relief and
    Development Fund
Gerald Micklem Charitable
    Trust
The Miller Foundation
The Monument Trust
John Moores Foundation
The Peter Morrison Charitable
    Foundation
The Mugdock Children's Trust
Asthma UK
Nestle Rowntree Employees
    Community Fund
The Northampton Queen's
    Institute Relief in Sickness
    Fund
The Northern Rock Foundation
The Northwood Charitable
    Trust
The Owen Family Trust
The Panacea Society
The Park Charitable Trust
The Constance Paterson
    Charitable Trust
Paycare Charity Trust
The Pedmore Sporting Club
    Trust Fund
The Pilgrim Trust
G S Plaut Charitable Trust
    Limited
The Pollywally Charitable Trust
The Mary Potter Convent
    Hospital Trust
Sir John Priestman Charity
    Trust
The Provincial Grand Charity of
    the Province of Derbyshire
Mr and Mrs J A Pye's
    Charitable Settlement
Richard Radcliffe Charitable
    Trust
The Ravensdale Trust
Relief Fund for Romania
    Limited
Riverside Charitable Trust
    Limited
Thomas Roberts Trust
The Robertson Trust
The Christopher Rowbotham
    Charitable Trust
The Rowlands Trust

The Andrew Salvesen
    Charitable Trust
The Hon. M J Samuel
    Charitable Trust
The Snowball Trust
The Sovereign Health Care
    Charitable Trust
Split Infinitive Trust
St Francis's Leprosy Guild
The Starfish Trust
The Sutton Nursing
    Association
Swan Mountain Trust
The Talbot Trusts
The Connie and Albert Taylor
    Charitable Trust
Thames Community
    Foundation
The Thornton Trust
The True Colours Trust
The James Tudor Foundation
John and Lucille van Geest
    Foundation
The Vintners' Company
    Charitable Foundation
The Lionel Wigram Memorial
    Trust
The Will Charitable Trust
Woodlands Trust
The Woodward Charitable
    Trust
The Xerox (UK) Trust

....

■ People with specific conditions

■ People with cardiovascular disorders

British Heart Foundation
The John Cowan Foundation
The Girdlers' Company
    Charitable Trust
The Kathleen Laurence Trust
Gerald Micklem Charitable
    Trust
The Park Charitable Trust
John and Lucille van Geest
    Foundation

■ People with glandular and endocrine disorders

Child Growth Foundation
The Cleopatra Trust
Diabetes UK
The Dorus Trust
The Epigoni Trust
The Girdlers' Company
    Charitable Trust

■ People with immune system disorders

Anglo American Group
    Foundation

The Elton John Aids
    Foundation
Lloyds TSB Foundation for
    Northern Ireland
The Mackintosh Foundation
Magdalen Hospital Trust
The Marchday Charitable Fund
Mercury Phoenix Trust
The Methodist Relief and
    Development Fund
Gerald Micklem Charitable
    Trust
The Monument Trust
John Moores Foundation
The True Colours Trust

■ People with a mental impairment

The A B Charitable Trust
The Sylvia Adams Charitable
    Trust
The Chelsea Building Society
    Charitable Foundation
The Dorus Trust
Eastern Counties Educational
    Trust Limited
The Sir John Eastwood
    Foundation
The John Ellerman Foundation
The Hugh Fraser Foundation
The Fuserna Foundation
The Gatsby Charitable
    Foundation
J Paul Getty Jr Charitable Trust
The Girdlers' Company
    Charitable Trust
The Hadley Trust
Hampton Fuel Allotment
    Charity
The Peter Harrison Foundation
Miss Agnes H Hunter's Trust
The Iliffe Family Charitable
    Trust
The Charles Irving Charitable
    Trust
The Judith Trust
The Ian Karten Charitable
    Trust
The Mary Kinross Charitable
    Trust
The Kohn Foundation
The Kirby Laing Foundation
The Beatrice Laing Trust
The Allen Lane Foundation
The LankellyChase Foundation
John Lyon's Charity
The Mercers' Charitable
    Foundation
The Northern Rock Foundation
The Pilgrim Trust
Relief Fund for Romania
    Limited
The Hon. M J Samuel
    Charitable Trust
Swan Mountain Trust
The Will Charitable Trust

Woodlands Trust

■ People with musculoskeletal disorders

Arthritis Research Campaign
The John Cowan Foundation
Miss Agnes H Hunter's Trust
The Kathleen Laurence Trust

■ People with nuerological disorders

The John Cowan Foundation
The Wilfred and Elsie Elkes Charity Fund
Epilepsy Research UK
Dixie Rose Findlay Charitable Trust
The Forte Charitable Trust
The Girdlers' Company Charitable Trust
The John Harrison Charitable Trust
The Hospital of God at Greatham
The Marchday Charitable Fund
Gerald Micklem Charitable Trust
The Owen Family Trust

■ People with oncological disorders

P H G Cadbury Charitable Trust
The Cleopatra Trust
The John Cowan Foundation
The Denton Charitable Trust
The Dorus Trust
Bud Flanagan Leukaemia Fund
The Girdlers' Company Charitable Trust
The Christina Mary Hendrie Trust for Scottish and Canadian Charities
Miss Agnes H Hunter's Trust
The Caron Keating Foundation
The R J Larg Family Charitable Trust
Leukaemia Research Fund
The Tony Metherell Charitable Trust
The Owen Family Trust
The Park Charitable Trust
John and Lucille van Geest Foundation
The Will Charitable Trust

■ People with respiritory disorders

The Girdlers' Company Charitable Trust
Miss Agnes H Hunter's Trust

Relief Fund for Romania Limited
John and Lucille van Geest Foundation

■ People with skin disorders

The Lewis Ward Trust
St Francis's Leprosy Guild

■ People who are substance misusers

Celtic Charity Fund
The Cleopatra Trust
The Dorus Trust
The John Ellerman Foundation
The Epigoni Trust
Esmée Fairbairn Foundation
J Paul Getty Jr Charitable Trust
The High Sheriff's Police Trust for the County of West Midlands
The Leigh Trust
The Linbury Trust
John Lyon's Charity
The Marsh Christian Trust
The Mercers' Charitable Foundation
John Moores Foundation
The Northern Rock Foundation
The Pilgrim Trust
The Robertson Trust
Thames Community Foundation
The Vintners' Company Charitable Foundation
Woodlands Trust
The Woodward Charitable Trust

■ Palliative care

P H G Cadbury Charitable Trust
The John Cowan Foundation
The Diana, Princess of Wales Memorial Fund
The Emmandjay Charitable Trust
The Girdlers' Company Charitable Trust
The Constance Green Foundation
The Hanlye Charitable Trust
The Peter Harrison Foundation
The N and P Hartley Memorial Trust
Healthsure Group Ltd
The Hedley Foundation
The Caron Keating Foundation
The Marchday Charitable Fund
The Marsh Christian Trust

The Zachary Merton and George Woofindin Convalescent Trust
The Mugdock Children's Trust
Richard Radcliffe Charitable Trust
The Connie and Albert Taylor Charitable Trust
The True Colours Trust
John and Lucille van Geest Foundation
The Xerox (UK) Trust

Nationality

■ Asian

Matliwala Family Charitable Trust
The W Wing Yip and Brothers Foundation

■ European

■ Eastern European

Armenian General Benevolent Union London Trust
The Armenian Relief Society of Great Britain Trust
The Manoukian Charitable Foundation
Saint Sarkis Charity Trust

■ Southern European

The Gulbenkian Foundation
The Lyras Family Charitable Trust

■ Western European

■ Irish

The Ireland Fund of Great Britain
The Irish Youth Foundation (UK) Ltd (incorporating The Lawlor Foundation)

Social or economic circumstances

The 1989 Willan Charitable Trust
The 29th May 1961 Charitable Trust
The A B Charitable Trust
The ACT Foundation
The Company of Actuaries' Charitable Trust Fund
The Sylvia Adams Charitable Trust

The Green and Lilian F M Ainsworth and Family Benevolent Fund
The Ajahma Charitable Trust
The Alchemy Foundation
The Aldgate Freedom Foundation
The Alliance Family Foundation
The Pat Allsop Charitable Trust
The Appletree Trust
The Archer Trust
The Ashden Trust
The Ashendene Trust
AstonMansfield Charitable Trust
Awards for All
The BACTA Charitable Trust
The Balint Family Charitable Trusts
The Band Trust
The Bedford Charity (The Harpur Trust)
The Beit Trust
The Bellahouston Bequest Fund
The Benfield Motors Charitable Trust
Bergqvist Charitable Trust
The Big Lottery Fund
Percy Bilton Charity
The Bintaub Charitable Trust
The Oliver Borthwick Memorial Trust
P G and N J Boulton Trust
John Bristow and Thomas Mason Trust
Britannia Foundation
R S Brownless Charitable Trust
Buckingham Trust
The E F Bulmer Benevolent Fund
Consolidated Charity of Burton upon Trent
Butchers' Company General Charities
Ann Byrne Charitable Trust
Henry T and Lucy B Cadbury Charitable Trust
The Barrow Cadbury Trust and the Barrow Cadbury Fund
CAFOD
The Calpe Trust
Calypso Browning Trust
The Campden Charities
The Charities Advisory Trust
The Chelsea Building Society Charitable Foundation
The Chrimes Family Charitable Trust
Christadelphian Samaritan Fund
Christian Aid
The Church Urban Fund
The City Parochial Foundation
CLA Charitable Trust
The Cleopatra Trust

The Clore Duffield Foundation
Closehelm Ltd
Richard Cloudesley's Charity
The R and S Cohen Fondation
The Coltstaple Trust
Colyer-Fergusson Charitable Trust
Comic Relief
The Consolidated Charities for the Infirm Merchant Taylors' Company
The Cotton Trust
Michael Crawford Children's Charity
The Violet and Milo Cripps Charitable Trust
Cumbria Community Foundation
The Dawe Charitable Trust
The Diana, Princess of Wales Memorial Fund
The Dorfred Charitable Trust
The Dorus Trust
Double 'O' Charity Ltd
The Doughty Charity Trust
The Drapers' Charitable Fund
Dromintee Trust
The Duis Charitable Trust
The P B Dumbell Charitable Trust
Eastern Counties Educational Trust Limited
The EBM Charitable Trust
Gilbert Edgar Trust
Dr Edwards' and Bishop King's Fulham Endowment Fund
The Wilfred and Elsie Elkes Charity Fund
The John Ellerman Foundation
The Ellinson Foundation Ltd
The Ellis Campbell Foundation
The Emmandjay Charitable Trust
The Enkalon Foundation
The Epigoni Trust
The Ericson Trust
Euro Charity Trust
The Eveson Charitable Trust
The Execution Charitable Trust
Esmée Fairbairn Foundation
Faisaltex Charitable Trust
The George Fentham Birmingham Charity
The Doris Field Charitable Trust
The Fifty Fund
Fisherbeck Charitable Trust
The Fishmongers' Company's Charitable Trust
The Roy Fletcher Charitable Trust
The Follett Trust
The Donald Forrester Trust
The Anna Rosa Forster Charitable Trust
Four Acre Trust

Sydney E Franklin Deceased's New Second Charity
The Hugh Fraser Foundation
The Freemasons' Grand Charity
Friends Provident Charitable Foundation
Maurice Fry Charitable Trust
The G D Charitable Trust
The Angela Gallagher Memorial Fund
The Gannochy Trust
The Gatsby Charitable Foundation
The Robert Gavron Charitable Trust
Jacqueline and Michael Gee Charitable Trust
Generations Charitable Trust
J Paul Getty Jr Charitable Trust
The Girdlers' Company Charitable Trust
Global Care
Global Charities
Goodfund
The Everard and Mina Goodman Charitable Foundation
The J G Graves Charitable Trust
The Constance Green Foundation
The Philip Green Memorial Trust
Mrs H R Greene Charitable Settlement
Greggs Foundation
The Grocers' Charity
The David and Marie Grumitt Foundation
The Bishop of Guildford's Foundation
Gurunanak
H C D Memorial Fund
The Hackney Parochial Charities
The Hadley Trust
The Alfred Haines Charitable Trust
The Hale Trust
Paul Hamlyn Foundation
Hampton Fuel Allotment Charity
The Hanlye Charitable Trust
The Haramead Trust
The Harbour Foundation
William Harding's Charity
The Kenneth Hargreaves Charitable Trust
The Harrison and Potter Trust
The Peter Harrison Foundation
The Charles Hayward Foundation
May Hearnshaw's Charity
The Heart of England Community Foundation
Help the Aged

Help the Homeless
The Hemby Trust
The Henley Educational Charity
The High Sheriff's Police Trust
for the County of West
Midlands
Highcroft Charitable Trust
The Hilden Charitable Fund
The Holbeck Charitable Trust
The Horne Foundation
The Horne Trust
The Hornsey Parochial
Charities
The Hospital of God at
Greatham
The Clifford Howarth Charity
Trust
Human Relief Foundation
The Humanitarian Trust
The Michael and Shirley Hunt
Charitable Trust
The Albert Hunt Trust
The Hunter Foundation
Miss Agnes H Hunter's Trust
The Hyde Charitable Trust –
Youth Plus
Impetus Trust
The Indigo Trust
The Worshipful Company of
Innholders General Charity
Fund
The Ireland Fund of Great
Britain
The Irish Youth Foundation
(UK) Ltd (incorporating The
Lawlor Foundation)
The Charles Irving Charitable
Trust
The J J Charitable Trust
The Jephcott Charitable Trust
The Joffe Charitable Trust
The Jones 1986 Charitable
Trust
The Lady Eileen Joseph
Foundation
The King's Fund
The Mary Kinross Charitable
Trust
The Kohn Foundation
The KPMG Foundation
The Heinz, Anna and Carol
Kroch Foundation
The Kyte Charitable Trust
John Laing Charitable Trust
Maurice and Hilda Laing
Charitable Trust
The Martin Laing Foundation
The Beatrice Laing Trust
LandAid Charitable Trust
The Allen Lane Foundation
The LankellyChase Foundation
Mrs F B Laurence Charitable
Trust
The Law Society Charity
The Leathersellers' Company
Charitable Fund
The William Leech Charity

The Leigh Trust
The Leonard Trust
The Mark Leonard Trust
The Joseph Levy Charitable
Foundation
John Lewis Partnership
General Community Fund
The Limbourne Trust
The Linbury Trust
Lincolnshire Community
Foundation
The Enid Linder Foundation
The Andrew and Mary
Elizabeth Little Charitable
Trust
The Elaine and Angus Lloyd
Charitable Trust
Lloyds TSB Foundation for
England and Wales
Lloyds TSB Foundation for
Northern Ireland
Localtrent Ltd
The Loftus Charitable Trust
The Loseley and Guildway
Charitable Trust
The Lotus Foundation
The C L Loyd Charitable Trust
LSA Charitable Trust
The Marie Helen Luen
Charitable Trust
Paul Lunn-Rockliffe Charitable
Trust
John Lyon's Charity
The Mackintosh Foundation
Ian Mactaggart Trust
Magdalen Hospital Trust
Mahavir Trust
Manchester Kids
R W Mann Trust
The Marchday Charitable Fund
The Michael Marsh Charitable
Trust
The Marsh Christian Trust
The Charlotte Marshall
Charitable Trust
The Mathew Trust
Evelyn May Trust
The McKenna Charitable Trust
The Mercers' Charitable
Foundation
The Merchant Taylors'
Company Charities Fund
The Merchant Venturers'
Charity
The Methodist Relief and
Development Fund
Gerald Micklem Charitable
Trust
Miles Trust for the Putney and
Roehampton Community
The Millfield House Foundation
Milton Keynes Community
Foundation
The Peter Minet Trust
Minge's Gift and the Pooled
Trusts

Monmouthshire County Council
Welsh Church Act Fund
The Colin Montgomerie
Charitable Foundation
John Moores Foundation
The Morel Charitable Trust
The Moss Charitable Trust
The Robert and Margaret
Moss Charitable Trust
The Edith Murphy Foundation
Muslim Hands
The Kitty and Daniel Nabarro
Charitable Trust
The Nationwide Foundation
Nestle Rowntree Employees
Community Fund
Network for Social Change
The Noel Buxton Trust
The Norda Trust
The North British Hotel Trust
North West London Community
Foundation
The Northcott Devon
Foundation
The Northern Rock Foundation
The Northmoor Trust
The Norton Foundation
Novi Most International
The Nuffield Foundation
The Odin Charitable Trust
Ogilvie Charities Deed No.2
(including the Charity of
Mary Catherine Ford Smith)
The Olga Charitable Trust
Onaway Trust
Oxfam (GB)
The Palmer Foundation
The Parthenon Trust
Paycare Charity Trust
The Harry Payne Trust
Pearson's Holiday Fund
The Persula Foundation
The Pilgrim Trust
The Pilkington Charities Fund
Mrs Pilkington's Charitable
Trust
The Pollywally Charitable Trust
The Portishead Nautical Trust
The W L Pratt Charitable Trust
Sir John Priestman Charity
Trust
The Puebla Charitable Trust
The Puri Foundation
Mr and Mrs J A Pye's
Charitable Settlement
The Queen Anne's Gate
Foundation
Quothquan Trust
Radio City Charity Foundation
The Ravensdale Trust
The Rayne Foundation
The Rayne Trust
The Sir James Reckitt Charity
The Eva Reckitt Trust Fund
Relief Fund for Romania
Limited

The Rhondda Cynon Taff
Welsh Church Acts Fund
The Clive Richards Charity
The Richmond Parish Lands
Charity
Riverside Charitable Trust
Limited
Thomas Roberts Trust
The Alex Roberts-Miller
Foundation
The Robertson Trust
Mrs L D Rope Third Charitable
Settlement
The Rowan Charitable Trust
The Rowland Family
Foundation
The Rowlands Trust
The Joseph Rowntree
Charitable Trust
Royal Docks Trust (London)
Ryklow Charitable Trust 1992
Erach and Roshan Sadri
Foundation
The Alan and Babette
Sainsbury Charitable Fund
Saint Sarkis Charity Trust
The Sandra Charitable Trust
Santander UK Foundation
Limited
The Scott Bader
Commonwealth Ltd
Scottish Coal Industry Special
Welfare Fund
The Seedfield Trust
The Severn Trent Water
Charitable Trust Fund
SFIA Educational Trust Limited
The Shanley Charitable Trust
The Charles Shorto Charitable
Trust
The Mrs Smith and Mount
Trust
The E C Sosnow Charitable
Trust
R H Southern Trust
The Sovereign Health Care
Charitable Trust
Spears-Stutz Charitable Trust
Split Infinitive Trust
The Stone Family Foundation
The Summerfield Charitable
Trust
Sutton Coldfield Municipal
Charities
Tegham Limited
The Thornton Trust
The Tinsley Foundation
The Tolkien Trust
The Tresillian Trust
Trust for London
Trust Sixty Three
UKI Charitable Foundation
The Unite Foundation (The
Amicus Foundation)
The United Society for the
Propagation of the Gospel
Uxbridge United Welfare Trust

The Scurrah Wainwright Charity
The Wakefield and Tetley Trust
Wakeham Trust
The Wates Foundation
John Watson's Trust
The Weavers' Company
Benevolent Fund
The Barbara Whatmore
Charitable Trust
The Michael and Anna Wix
Charitable Trust
The Wood Family Trust
Woodlands Trust
The Woodroffe Benton
Foundation
The Woodward Charitable
Trust
The Woolnoth Society
Charitable Trust
The Worwin UK Foundation
The Yapp Charitable Trust
Zurich Community Trust (UK)
Limited

....

■ Disadvantaged and socially excluded people

■ People with alternative lifestyles (inc. travellers)

The Allen Lane Foundation
The Odin Charitable Trust
The Woodward Charitable
Trust

■ People who are educationally disadvantaged

The Big Lottery Fund
Eastern Counties Educational
Trust Limited
The Ellis Campbell Foundation
The Girdlers' Company
Charitable Trust
Global Care
H C D Memorial Fund
The Hadley Trust
Human Relief Foundation
Miss Agnes H Hunter's Trust
The KPMG Foundation
John Lyon's Charity
The Michael Marsh Charitable
Trust

■ People who are homeless

The 29th May 1961 Charitable
Trust
The A B Charitable Trust
The Sylvia Adams Charitable
Trust
The Aldgate Freedom
Foundation

The Ashden Trust
The Bedford Charity (The
Harpur Trust)
The Beit Trust
The Oliver Borthwick Memorial
Trust
Britannia Foundation
Henry T and Lucy B Cadbury
Charitable Trust
Calypso Browning Trust
The Charities Advisory Trust
The Chelsea Building Society
Charitable Foundation
Christian Aid
The Cleopatra Trust
The Coltstaple Trust
The Dawe Charitable Trust
The Dorus Trust
The Drapers' Charitable Fund
Gilbert Edgar Trust
The Wilfred and Elsie Elkes
Charity Fund
The John Ellerman Foundation
The Ellinson Foundation Ltd
The Emmandjay Charitable
Trust
The Epigoni Trust
The Ericson Trust
The Eveson Charitable Trust
Esmée Fairbairn Foundation
Fisherbeck Charitable Trust
The Fishmongers' Company's
Charitable Trust
The Donald Forrester Trust
The Hugh Fraser Foundation
The Freemasons' Grand
Charity
The G D Charitable Trust
J Paul Getty Jr Charitable Trust
The Girdlers' Company
Charitable Trust
Global Care
The Constance Green
Foundation
Greggs Foundation
The David and Marie Grumitt
Foundation
The Bishop of Guildford's
Foundation
The Alfred Haines Charitable
Trust
Hampton Fuel Allotment
Charity
The Harbour Foundation
The Kenneth Hargreaves
Charitable Trust
The Harrison and Potter Trust
The Peter Harrison Foundation
Help the Aged
Help the Homeless
The Hemby Trust
The Hilden Charitable Fund
The Horne Foundation
The Horne Trust
The Hospital of God at
Greatham
Miss Agnes H Hunter's Trust

The Hyde Charitable Trust –
Youth Plus
The Irish Youth Foundation
(UK) Ltd (incorporating The
Lawlor Foundation)
The Charles Irving Charitable
Trust
The King's Fund
John Laing Charitable Trust
Maurice and Hilda Laing
Charitable Trust
The Beatrice Laing Trust
LandAid Charitable Trust
The Joseph Levy Charitable
Foundation
The Marie Helen Luen
Charitable Trust
John Lyon's Charity
The Mackintosh Foundation
The Marchday Charitable Fund
The Marsh Christian Trust
Miles Trust for the Putney and
Roehampton Community
The Peter Minet Trust
John Moores Foundation
The Kitty and Daniel Nabarro
Charitable Trust
Nestle Rowntree Employees
Community Fund
Network for Social Change
The Odin Charitable Trust
The Persula Foundation
The Pilgrim Trust
The Portishead Nautical Trust
Relief Fund for Romania
Limited
The Robertson Trust
Mrs L D Rope Third Charitable
Settlement
Erach and Roshan Sadri
Foundation
The Mrs Smith and Mount
Trust
The Summerfield Charitable
Trust
Woodlands Trust
The Woodward Charitable
Trust
The Woolnoth Society
Charitable Trust

■ **People who are
housebound**

Paycare Charity Trust
Mrs Pilkington's Charitable
Trust

■ **People who are
disadvantaged by
location**

Mrs H R Greene Charitable
Settlement
Relief Fund for Romania
Limited

The Woolnoth Society
Charitable Trust

■ **Migrants**

The 29th May 1961 Charitable
Trust
The Barrow Cadbury Trust and
the Barrow Cadbury Fund

■ **Offenders**

The 29th May 1961 Charitable
Trust
The A B Charitable Trust
The Alchemy Foundation
The Ashendene Trust
The Big Lottery Fund
The Barrow Cadbury Trust and
the Barrow Cadbury Fund
The Violet and Milo Cripps
Charitable Trust
The Diana, Princess of Wales
Memorial Fund
The Drapers' Charitable Fund
The Emmandjay Charitable
Trust
Esmée Fairbairn Foundation
The Gatsby Charitable
Foundation
The Robert Gavron Charitable
Trust
J Paul Getty Jr Charitable Trust
The Girdlers' Company
Charitable Trust
Mrs H R Greene Charitable
Settlement
Greggs Foundation
H C D Memorial Fund
Paul Hamlyn Foundation
The Charles Hayward
Foundation
The Hemby Trust
The High Sheriff's Police Trust
for the County of West
Midlands
The Hilden Charitable Fund
The Michael and Shirley Hunt
Charitable Trust
The Indigo Trust
The J J Charitable Trust
The Mary Kinross Charitable
Trust
The KPMG Foundation
The Allen Lane Foundation
The LankellyChase Foundation
The Mark Leonard Trust
The Linbury Trust
John Lyon's Charity
The Marchday Charitable Fund
The Mercers' Charitable
Foundation
The Noel Buxton Trust
The Norda Trust
The Nuffield Foundation
The Odin Charitable Trust
The Pilgrim Trust

The Portishead Nautical Trust
Mr and Mrs J A Pye's
Charitable Settlement
The Rhondda Cynon Taff
Welsh Church Acts Fund
Saint Sarkis Charity Trust
The Weavers' Company
Benevolent Fund
Woodlands Trust

■ **Ex-offenders**

The 29th May 1961 Charitable
Trust
The Ashendene Trust
Esmée Fairbairn Foundation
J Paul Getty Jr Charitable Trust
The Girdlers' Company
Charitable Trust
Greggs Foundation
Paul Hamlyn Foundation
The Hemby Trust
The Michael and Shirley Hunt
Charitable Trust
The J J Charitable Trust
The Allen Lane Foundation
The Linbury Trust
John Lyon's Charity
The Marchday Charitable Fund
The Mercers' Charitable
Foundation
The Norda Trust
The Odin Charitable Trust
Mr and Mrs J A Pye's
Charitable Settlement
The Weavers' Company
Benevolent Fund

■ **People on probation**

The Emmandjay Charitable
Trust

■ **Prisoners and their
families**

The A B Charitable Trust
The Michael and Shirley Hunt
Charitable Trust
The Noel Buxton Trust
The Norda Trust
The Odin Charitable Trust
The Weavers' Company
Benevolent Fund

■ **Young people at risk
of offending**

The Big Lottery Fund
The Gatsby Charitable
Foundation
J Paul Getty Jr Charitable Trust
Mrs H R Greene Charitable
Settlement
Paul Hamlyn Foundation
The Hemby Trust

The High Sheriff's Police Trust for the County of West Midlands

The J J Charitable Trust

The Mary Kinross Charitable Trust

The KPMG Foundation

The Mark Leonard Trust

The Nuffield Foundation

The Portishead Nautical Trust

The Rhondda Cynon Taff Welsh Church Acts Fund

The Weavers' Company Benevolent Fund

Woodlands Trust

■ People who are poor, on low incomes

The 1989 Willan Charitable Trust

The 29th May 1961 Charitable Trust

The Sylvia Adams Charitable Trust

The Ajahma Charitable Trust

The Aldgate Freedom Foundation

The Alliance Family Foundation

The Pat Allsop Charitable Trust

The Appletree Trust

The Archer Trust

AstonMansfield Charitable Trust

The Balint Family Charitable Trusts

The Bellahouston Bequest Fund

The Benfield Motors Charitable Trust

P G and N J Boulton Trust

John Bristow and Thomas Mason Trust

Buckingham Trust

The E F Bulmer Benevolent Fund

Butchers' Company General Charities

CAFOD

The Chrimes Family Charitable Trust

Christian Aid

The Church Urban Fund

CLA Charitable Trust

Closehelm Ltd

The R and S Cohen Fondation

Michael Crawford Children's Charity

Double 'O' Charity Ltd

The Doughty Charity Trust

The Drapers' Charitable Fund

Eastern Counties Educational Trust Limited

The EBM Charitable Trust

Euro Charity Trust

The Eveson Charitable Trust

The George Fentham Birmingham Charity

The Fifty Fund

The Fishmongers' Company's Charitable Trust

Sydney E Franklin Deceased's New Second Charity

The Hugh Fraser Foundation

Maurice Fry Charitable Trust

The Angela Gallagher Memorial Fund

The Girdlers' Company Charitable Trust

Global Care

Goodfund

The Everard and Mina Goodman Charitable Foundation

The J G Graves Charitable Trust

Mrs H R Greene Charitable Settlement

Greggs Foundation

The Grocers' Charity

The Bishop of Guildford's Foundation

Gurunanak

H C D Memorial Fund

The Hadley Trust

The Hale Trust

Hampton Fuel Allotment Charity

The Haramead Trust

May Hearnshaw's Charity

Help the Aged

The Hemby Trust

The Henley Educational Charity

Highcroft Charitable Trust

The Hornsey Parochial Charities

The Hospital of God at Greatham

Human Relief Foundation

The Albert Hunt Trust

The Hunter Foundation

The Hyde Charitable Trust – Youth Plus

The Ireland Fund of Great Britain

The Jephcott Charitable Trust

The Jones 1986 Charitable Trust

The Lady Eileen Joseph Foundation

The Kohn Foundation

The Heinz, Anna and Carol Kroch Foundation

Maurice and Hilda Laing Charitable Trust

The Beatrice Laing Trust

LandAid Charitable Trust

The Leathersellers' Company Charitable Fund

John Lewis Partnership General Community Fund

The Enid Linder Foundation

The Andrew and Mary Elizabeth Little Charitable Trust

Localtrent Ltd

LSA Charitable Trust

The Marie Helen Luen Charitable Trust

Paul Lunn-Rockliffe Charitable Trust

Ian Mactaggart Trust

Magdalen Hospital Trust

Mahavir Trust

The Marchday Charitable Fund

The Michael Marsh Charitable Trust

The McKenna Charitable Trust

The Methodist Relief and Development Fund

Gerald Micklem Charitable Trust

Miles Trust for the Putney and Roehampton Community

Monmouthshire County Council Welsh Church Act Fund

The Colin Montgomerie Charitable Foundation

The Morel Charitable Trust

The Moss Charitable Trust

The Robert and Margaret Moss Charitable Trust

The Edith Murphy Foundation

Muslim Hands

The Kitty and Daniel Nabarro Charitable Trust

Nestle Rowntree Employees Community Fund

The Northmoor Trust

The Odin Charitable Trust

The Olga Charitable Trust

Oxfam (GB)

Mrs Pilkington's Charitable Trust

The Pollywally Charitable Trust

The Portishead Nautical Trust

Sir John Priestman Charity Trust

The Puebla Charitable Trust

The Puri Foundation

Mr and Mrs J A Pye's Charitable Settlement

Quothquan Trust

Radio City Charity Foundation

The Rhondda Cynon Taff Welsh Church Acts Fund

The Clive Richards Charity

The Richmond Parish Lands Charity

Riverside Charitable Trust Limited

Mrs L D Rope Third Charitable Settlement

The Rowland Family Foundation

The Rowlands Trust

The Joseph Rowntree Charitable Trust

Royal Docks Trust (London)

The Sandra Charitable Trust
Scottish Coal Industry Special
Welfare Fund
The Seedfield Trust
The Severn Trent Water
Charitable Trust Fund
The Shanley Charitable Trust
R H Southern Trust
Spears-Stutz Charitable Trust
The Summerfield Charitable
Trust
Tegham Limited
The Thornton Trust
The Tinsley Foundation
UKI Charitable Foundation
Uxbridge United Welfare Trust
The Barbara Whatmore
Charitable Trust
The Woolnoth Society
Charitable Trust
The Worwin UK Foundation

■ Prostitutes, sex workers

The LankellyChase Foundation

■ Refugees and asylum seekers

The 29th May 1961 Charitable
Trust
The A B Charitable Trust
The Barrow Cadbury Trust and
the Barrow Cadbury Fund
The Charities Advisory Trust
The Diana, Princess of Wales
Memorial Fund
The Ericson Trust
Maurice Fry Charitable Trust
H C D Memorial Fund
The Harbour Foundation
The Hilden Charitable Fund
The King's Fund
The KPMG Foundation
The Allen Lane Foundation
The LankellyChase Foundation
The Leigh Trust
The Mackintosh Foundation
The Marchday Charitable Fund
John Moores Foundation
Network for Social Change
The Norda Trust
The Odin Charitable Trust
The Pilgrim Trust
The Pilkington Charities Fund
Mr and Mrs J A Pye's
Charitable Settlement
The Alan and Babette
Sainsbury Charitable Fund
The Woodward Charitable
Trust

....
■ Victims, oppressed people

The Alchemy Foundation
Bergqvist Charitable Trust
The Barrow Cadbury Trust and
the Barrow Cadbury Fund
CAFOD
The Charities Advisory Trust
Christadelphian Samaritan
Fund
Christian Aid
The Coltstaple Trust
The Diana, Princess of Wales
Memorial Fund
The Dorfred Charitable Trust
The Follett Trust
The Anna Rosa Forster
Charitable Trust
Sydney E Franklin Deceased's
New Second Charity
The Freemasons' Grand
Charity
Maurice Fry Charitable Trust
The Angela Gallagher Memorial
Fund
J Paul Getty Jr Charitable Trust
The Girdlers' Company
Charitable Trust
Global Care
Greggs Foundation
The Charles Hayward
Foundation
The Heart of England
Community Foundation
The Hemby Trust
The Hilden Charitable Fund
The Horne Trust
The Hospital of God at
Greatham
Human Relief Foundation
The Hyde Charitable Trust –
Youth Plus
The Charles Irving Charitable
Trust
The Heinz, Anna and Carol
Kroch Foundation
The Allen Lane Foundation
The LankellyChase Foundation
The Law Society Charity
The Leathersellers' Company
Charitable Fund
The William Leech Charity
The Leigh Trust
The Leonard Trust
The Joseph Levy Charitable
Foundation
The Loseley and Guildway
Charitable Trust
The Lotus Foundation
The Marchday Charitable Fund
Evelyn May Trust
Monmouthshire County Council
Welsh Church Act Fund
The Morel Charitable Trust
Muslim Hands
The Nationwide Foundation

Network for Social Change
Novi Most International
Oxfam (GB)
The Parthenon Trust
The Pilkington Charities Fund
The Portishead Nautical Trust
The W L Pratt Charitable Trust
Mr and Mrs J A Pye's
Charitable Settlement
The Sir James Reckitt Charity
The Eva Reckitt Trust Fund
The Joseph Rowntree
Charitable Trust
Ryklow Charitable Trust 1992
The Tinsley Foundation
The Tresillian Trust
Trust Sixty Three
The Unite Foundation (The
Amicus Foundation)
The Woodroffe Benton
Foundation
The Woodward Charitable
Trust

■ People who have suffered abuse, violence or torture

The Angela Gallagher Memorial
Fund
J Paul Getty Jr Charitable Trust
The Girdlers' Company
Charitable Trust
Global Care
Greggs Foundation
The Charles Hayward
Foundation
The Hemby Trust
The Hospital of God at
Greatham
The Hyde Charitable Trust –
Youth Plus
The Charles Irving Charitable
Trust
The Heinz, Anna and Carol
Kroch Foundation
The Allen Lane Foundation
The LankellyChase Foundation
The Lotus Foundation
The Marchday Charitable Fund
The Nationwide Foundation
The Portishead Nautical Trust
Mr and Mrs J A Pye's
Charitable Settlement
Ryklow Charitable Trust 1992
The Woodward Charitable
Trust

■ Victims of crime

The Girdlers' Company
Charitable Trust
The Hemby Trust
The Charles Irving Charitable
Trust
The Heinz, Anna and Carol
Kroch Foundation

Ryklow Charitable Trust 1992

■ Victims of disasters

Bergqvist Charitable Trust
*Christadelphian Samaritan
    Fund*
Christian Aid
The Dorfred Charitable Trust
The Follett Trust
*Sydney E Franklin Deceased's
    New Second Charity*
*The Freemasons' Grand
    Charity*
Maurice Fry Charitable Trust
*The Angela Gallagher Memorial
    Fund*
Human Relief Foundation
*The Leathersellers' Company
    Charitable Fund*
The William Leech Charity
The Leonard Trust
*The Loseley and Guildway
    Charitable Trust*
Evelyn May Trust
*Monmouthshire County Council
    Welsh Church Act Fund*
Muslim Hands
Oxfam (GB)
The Parthenon Trust
The Pilkington Charities Fund
The W L Pratt Charitable Trust
The Sir James Reckitt Charity
*The Unite Foundation (The
    Amicus Foundation)*
*The Woodroffe Benton
    Foundation*

■ People suffering from
    famine

The Alchemy Foundation
Bergqvist Charitable Trust
CAFOD
*Christadelphian Samaritan
    Fund*
The Coltstaple Trust
The Dorfred Charitable Trust
*The Anna Rosa Forster
    Charitable Trust*
*Sydney E Franklin Deceased's
    New Second Charity*
Maurice Fry Charitable Trust
*The Angela Gallagher Memorial
    Fund*
Global Care
The Leonard Trust
*The Joseph Levy Charitable
    Foundation*
The Morel Charitable Trust
Oxfam (GB)
The Parthenon Trust
Ryklow Charitable Trust 1992
Trust Sixty Three

■ People suffering
    injustice

The Charities Advisory Trust
*Sydney E Franklin Deceased's
    New Second Charity*
Global Care
The Law Society Charity
The Leigh Trust
Network for Social Change
*The Joseph Rowntree
    Charitable Trust*

■ Victims of war or conflict

CAFOD
*The Diana, Princess of Wales
    Memorial Fund*
The Dorfred Charitable Trust
Maurice Fry Charitable Trust
Global Care
Human Relief Foundation
*The Heinz, Anna and Carol
    Kroch Foundation*
Muslim Hands
Novi Most International
Oxfam (GB)
The Pilkington Charities Fund
The Eva Reckitt Trust Fund

Trusts by type
of grant

This index contains two separate listings:

List of types of grant: This lists all the headings used in the DGMT to categorise types of grant.

Trusts by type of grant: This lists trusts under the types of grant for which they have expressed a funding preference.

Trusts by type of grants

These pages contain two separate listings

List of type of grants
This lists all of the headings used in the DGMT to categorise types of grants

Trusts by type of grants
This lists trusts under the types of grants for which they have expressed a funding preference

Type of support

Capital support 151

■ **Building/renovation 151**

....

■ **Collections and acquisitions 165**

....

■ **Computer systems and equipment 180**

....

■ **Equipment 195**

....

■ **Vehicles 210**

Core support 225

■ **Development funding 225**

....

■ **Strategic funding 241**

Project support 258

■ **Full project funding 258**

....

■ **Project funding (excluding overheads) 273**

....

■ **Seed funding 288**

Campaigning 303

Loan finance 304

Duration of grant

Trusts listed here have expressly stated on a questionniare used as part of the research for this book that they give grants for the specified time period. Other trusts in this book which did not respond to the questionnaire may also give grants as stated below.

....

■ **One-off grant 305**

....

■ **Two years 308**

....

■ **Three years 309**

....

■ **Longer than three years 311**

Type of support

Capital support

■ Building/renovation

The 1989 Willan Charitable
　Trust
The 29th May 1961 Charitable
　Trust
Aberbrothock Charitable Trust
The Aberdeen Endowments
　Trust
The Aberdeenshire Educational
　Trust Scheme
Achiezer Association Ltd
Achisomoch Aid Company
　Limited
The ACT Foundation
Action Medical Research
The Sylvia Adams Charitable
　Trust
The Victor Adda Foundation
The Adint Charitable Trust
The Adnams Charity
AF Trust Company
Aid to the Church in Need (UK)
The AIM Foundation
The Sylvia Aitken Charitable
　Trust
Alcohol Education and
　Research Council
The Aldgate Freedom
　Foundation
Alexandra Rose Charities
Allchurches Trust Ltd
The H B Allen Charitable Trust
The Rita Allen Charitable Trust
The Alliance Family Foundation
Angus Allnatt Charitable
　Foundation
The Pat Allsop Charitable Trust
The Almond Trust
Almondsbury Charity
The Altajir Trust
Altamont Ltd
Alvor Charitable Trust
AM Charitable Trust
Ambika Paul Foundation
The Ammco Trust
Sir John and Lady Amory's
　Charitable Trust
Viscount Amory's Charitable
　Trust
The Ampelos Trust
The AMW Charitable Trust
The Andrew Anderson Trust
The Andre Christian Trust
Anguish's Educational
　Foundation
The Animal Defence Trust
The Eric Anker-Petersen
　Charity
The Annandale Charitable
　Trust
The Appletree Trust

The John Apthorp Charitable
　Trust
The Milly Apthorp Charitable
　Trust
The Arbib Foundation
The Archbishop of
　Canterbury's Charitable
　Trust
The John M Archer Charitable
　Trust
The Archer Trust
The Architectural Heritage
　Fund
The Ardwick Trust
The Argus Appeal
Armenian General Benevolent
　Union London Trust
The Armenian Relief Society of
　Great Britain Trust
The Army Benevolent Fund
Arsenal Charitable Trust
The Artemis Charitable Trust
The Arts and Entertainment
　Charitable Trust
Arts Council England
The Arts Council of Northern
　Ireland
The Arts Council of Wales
The Ove Arup Foundation
The AS Charitable Trust
A J H Ashby Will Trust
The Ashden Trust
The Ashendene Trust
The Norman C Ashton
　Foundation
The Ashworth Charitable Trust
The Ian Askew Charitable Trust
The Associated Country
　Women of the World
　(ACWW)
The Association of Colleges
　Charitable Trust
The Association of Friends of
　Essex Churches
Astellas European Foundation
AstonMansfield Charitable
　Trust
The Astor Foundation
The Astor of Hever Trust
The Aurelius Charitable Trust
The Avenue Charitable Trust
The John Avins Trustees
AW Charitable Trust
The Aylesford Family
　Charitable Trust
The BAA Communities Trust
Harry Bacon Foundation
The BACTA Charitable Trust
The Bagri Foundation
Veta Bailey Charitable Trust
The Austin Bailey Trust
The Baily Thomas Charitable
　Fund
The Baird Trust
The Baker Charitable Trust
The Balcombe Charitable Trust

The Balint Family Charitable
　Trusts
The Albert Casanova Ballard
　Deceased Trust
The Ballinger Charitable Trust
Balmain Charitable Trust
The Balmore Trust
The Balney Charitable Trust
The Baltic Charitable Fund
The Bamford Charitable
　Foundation
The Banbury Charities
William P Bancroft (No 2)
　Charitable Trust and
　Jenepher Gillett Trust
The Band Trust
The Barbers' Company General
　Charities
Barchester Healthcare
　Foundation
David and Frederick Barclay
　Foundation
The Baring Foundation
Peter Barker-Mill Memorial
　Charity
Barleycorn Trust
Lord Barnby's Foundation
Barnes Workhouse Fund
The Barnsbury Charitable Trust
The Barnstaple Bridge Trust
The Misses Barrie Charitable
　Trust
Barrington Family Charitable
　Trust
The Charity of William Barrow
Stephen J Barry Charitable
　Trust
The Bartlett Taylor Charitable
　Trust
The Paul Bassham Charitable
　Trust
The Batchworth Trust
The Bay Tree Charitable Trust
D H and L H Baylin Charitable
　Trust
The Louis Baylis (Maidenhead
　Advertiser) Charitable Trust
BBC Children in Need
B-CH 1971 Charitable Trust
The Beacon Trust
Bear Mordechai Ltd
The Bearder Charity
The James Beattie Charitable
　Trust
The Beaufort House Trust
　Limited
Beauland Ltd
The Beaverbrook Foundation
The Beccles Town Lands
　Charity
The Becker Family Charitable
　Trust
The Becketts and Sargeants
　Educational Foundation
The John Beckwith Charitable
　Trust

The Peter Beckwith Charitable
Trust
The Bedford Charity (The
Harpur Trust)
The Bedfordshire and
Hertfordshire Historic
Churches Trust
The David and Ruth Behrend
Fund
The Beit Trust
The Bellahouston Bequest
Fund
Bellasis Trust
The Bellinger Donnay Trust
Belljoe Tzedoko Ltd
The Benfield Motors Charitable
Trust
The Benham Charitable
Settlement
The Hervey Benham Charitable
Trust
Maurice and Jacqueline
Bennett Charitable Trust
Michael and Leslie Bennett
Charitable Trust
The Gerald Bentall Charitable
Trust
Bergqvist Charitable Trust
The Berkshire Community
Foundation
The Bestway Foundation
The Betterware Foundation
Thomas Betton's Charity for
Pensions and Relief-in-Need
BHST
The Mason Bibby 1981 Trust
BibleLands
The Bideford Bridge Trust
The Big Lottery Fund
The Billmeir Charitable Trust
Percy Bilton Charity
The Bingham Trust
The Bintaub Charitable Trust
The Birmingham Community
Foundation
The Birmingham District
Nursing Charitable Trust
The Birmingham Hospital
Saturday Fund Medical
Charity and Welfare Trust
Birmingham International
Airport Community Trust
The Lord Mayor of
Birmingham's Charity
Birthday House Trust
The Bisgood Charitable Trust
(registered as Miss Jeanne
Bisgood's Charitable Trust)
The Michael Bishop
Foundation
The Bishop's Development
Fund
The Sydney Black Charitable
Trust
The Bertie Black Foundation
Isabel Blackman Foundation

The Herbert and Peter
Blagrave Charitable Trust
The Blair Foundation
Blakes Benevolent Trust
The Blanchminster Trust
The Sir Victor Blank Charitable
Settlement
Blatchington Court Trust
The Neville and Elaine Blond
Charitable Trust
The Bluston Charitable
Settlement
Enid Blyton Trust for Children
The Body Shop Foundation
The Boltons Trust
The Bonamy Charitable Trust
The John and Celia Bonham
Christie Charitable Trust
The Charlotte Bonham-Carter
Charitable Trust
Bonhomie United Charity
Society
The Booth Charities
The Boots Charitable Trust
The Bordon and Liphook
Charity
Salo Bordon Charitable Trust
The Oliver Borthwick Memorial
Trust
The Bothwell Charitable Trust
H E and E L Botteley
Charitable Trust
The Harry Bottom Charitable
Trust
P G and N J Boulton Trust
The A H and E Boulton Trust
Sir Clive Bourne Family Trust
The Anthony Bourne
Foundation
The Bower Trust
The Bowerman Charitable
Trust
John and Susan Bowers Fund
The Bowland Charitable Trust
The William Brake Charitable
Trust
The Tony Bramall Charitable
Trust
The Brewers' Company
General Charitable Trust
The Harold and Alice Bridges
Charity
Briggs Animal Welfare Trust
The Brighton District Nursing
Association Trust
Bristol Archdeaconry Charity
John Bristow and Thomas
Mason Trust
Britannia Foundation
The British Council for
Prevention of Blindness
The British Dietetic
Association General and
Education Trust Fund
The British Gas (Scottish Gas)
Energy Trust

British Heart Foundation
British Humane Association
British Institute at Ankara
British Ornithologists' Union
British Record Industry Trust
The Britto Foundation
The J and M Britton Charitable
Trust
The Charles and Edna
Broadhurst Charitable Trust
The Bromley Trust
The Roger Brooke Charitable
Trust
The David Brooke Charity
The Charles Brotherton Trust
Joseph Brough Charitable
Trust
The Swinfen Broun Charitable
Trust
Mrs E E Brown Charitable
Settlement
Bill Brown's Charitable
Settlement
R S Brownless Charitable
Trust
T B H Brunner's Charitable
Settlement
The Jack Brunton Charitable
Trust
Brushmill Ltd
The Bryant Trust
Buckingham Trust
The Buckinghamshire
Foundation
The Buckinghamshire Historic
Churches Trust
The Buckinghamshire Masonic
Centenary Fund
Buckland Charitable Trust
The Rosemary Bugden
Charitable Trust
The Bulldog Trust Limited
The E F Bulmer Benevolent
Fund
Burdens Charitable Foundation
The Clara E Burgess Charity
The Burry Charitable Trust
The Audrey and Stanley Burton
1960 Charitable Trust
The Arnold Burton 1998
Charitable Trust
The Burton Breweries
Charitable Trust
The Geoffrey Burton Charitable
Trust
Consolidated Charity of Burton
upon Trent
Butchers' Company General
Charities
The Bill Butlin Charity Trust
C and F Charitable Trust
C J Cadbury Charitable Trust
Edward Cadbury Charitable
Trust
Henry T and Lucy B Cadbury
Charitable Trust

P H G Cadbury Charitable Trust

The Christopher Cadbury Charitable Trust

The G W Cadbury Charitable Trust

The Richard Cadbury Charitable Trust

The William A Cadbury Charitable Trust

The Edward and Dorothy Cadbury Trust

The George Cadbury Trust

The Barrow Cadbury Trust and the Barrow Cadbury Fund

The Cadogan Charity

CAFOD

The Callander Charitable Trust

Calleva Foundation

The Calpe Trust

Calypso Browning Trust

The Cambridgeshire Historic Churches Trust

The Campden Charities

The Canning Trust

H and L Cantor Trust

Capital Community Foundation

Cardy Beaver Foundation

The Carew Pole Charitable Trust

The D W T Cargill Fund

Caring for Kids (Radio Tay)

Carlee Ltd

The Carlton House Charitable Trust

The Worshipful Company of Carmen Benevolent Trust

The Carnegie Dunfermline Trust

The Carnegie Trust for the Universities of Scotland

The Carpenter Charitable Trust

The Carpenters' Company Charitable Trust

The Carrington Charitable Trust

The Carron Charitable Settlement

The Leslie Mary Carter Charitable Trust

The Carvill Trust

The Casey Trust

Cash for Kids Radio Clyde

The Elizabeth Casson Trust

The Castang Foundation

The Catalyst Charitable Trust

The Catholic Charitable Trust

Catholic Foreign Missions

The Catholic Trust for England and Wales

The Joseph and Annie Cattle Trust

The Thomas Sivewright Catto Charitable Settlement

The Wilfrid and Constance Cave Foundation

The Cayo Foundation

Elizabeth Cayzer Charitable Trust

The B G S Cayzer Charitable Trust

The Cazenove Charitable Trust

Celtic Charity Fund

The Cemlyn-Jones Trust

The Amelia Chadwick Trust

The Pamela Champion Foundation

The Chapman Charitable Trust

John William Chapman's Charitable Trust

The Charities Advisory Trust

Charitworth Limited

The Charter 600 Charity

The Worshipful Company of Chartered Accountants General Charitable Trust

The Chelsea Square 1994 Trust

The Cheruby Trust

The Cheshire Provincial Fund of Benevolence

The Chetwode Foundation

The Malcolm Chick Charity

Child Growth Foundation

Children's Liver Disease Foundation

Childs Charitable Trust

The Childwick Trust

The Chippenham Borough Lands Charity

The Chipping Sodbury Town Lands Charity

CHK Charities Limited

The Chownes Foundation

The Chrimes Family Charitable Trust

Christadelphian Samaritan Fund

Christian Aid

Christian Response to Eastern Europe

The Church and Community Fund

The Church Burgesses Educational Foundation

Church Burgesses Trust

Church Lands and John Johnson's Estate Charities

City and County of Swansea Welsh Church Act Fund

The City Bridge Trust

The City Educational Trust Fund

CLA Charitable Trust

Stephen Clark 1957 Charitable Trust

The Hilda and Alice Clark Charitable Trust

The Roger and Sarah Bancroft Clark Charitable Trust

The Clarke Charitable Settlement

The Cleary Foundation

The Cleopatra Trust

Lord Clinton's Charitable Trust

The Clore Duffield Foundation

Miss V L Clore's 1967 Charitable Trust

Closehelm Ltd

The Clothworkers' Foundation

Richard Cloudesley's Charity

The Clover Trust

The Robert Clutterbuck Charitable Trust

Clydpride Ltd

The Francis Coales Charitable Foundation

The Coalfields Regeneration Trust

The John Coates Charitable Trust

Coats Foundation Trust

The Cobtree Charity Trust Ltd

The Denise Cohen Charitable Trust

The Vivienne and Samuel Cohen Charitable Trust

The R and S Cohen Fondation

The John S Cohen Foundation

The Colchester Catalyst Charity

John Coldman Charitable Trust

The Cole Charitable Trust

The Colefax Charitable Trust

The John and Freda Coleman Charitable Trust

The George Henry Collins Charity

The E Alec Colman Charitable Fund Ltd

The Sir Jeremiah Colman Gift Trust

Col-Reno Ltd

The Colt Foundation

The Coltstaple Trust

Colwinston Charitable Trust

Colyer-Fergusson Charitable Trust

The Comino Foundation

Community Foundation for Calderdale

The Community Foundation for Northern Ireland

The Company of Tobacco Pipe Makers' and Tobacco Blenders' Benevolent Fund

The Compton Charitable Trust

The Congleton Inclosure Trust

The Congregational and General Charitable Trust

The Conservation Foundation

The Consolidated Charities for the Infirm Merchant Taylors' Company

The Construction Industry Trust for Youth

Gordon Cook Foundation

The Cooks Charity

The Catherine Cookson
    Charitable Trust
Harold and Daphne Cooper
    Charitable Trust
Mabel Cooper Charity
The Alice Ellen Cooper Dean
    Charitable Foundation
The Co-operative Foundation
The Marjorie Coote Animal
    Charity Trust
The Marjorie Coote Old
    People's Charity
The Helen Jean Cope Trust
The J Reginald Corah
    Foundation Fund
The Gershon Coren Charitable
    Foundation
The Corinthian Trust
Edwin Cornforth 1983 Charity
    Trust
The Cornwall Historic
    Churches Trust
The Duke of Cornwall's
    Benevolent Fund
The Cornwell Charitable Trust
The Sidney and Elizabeth
    Corob Charitable Trust
The Corona Charitable Trust
The Costa Family Charitable
    Trust
The Cotton Industry War
    Memorial Trust
Country Houses Foundation
County Durham Foundation
Coutts Charitable Trust
The General Charities of the
    City of Coventry
Coventry Building Society
    Charitable Foundation
The John Cowan Foundation
Cowley Charitable Foundation
The Sir William Coxen Trust
    Fund
The Lord Cozens-Hardy Trust
The Craignish Trust
The Craps Charitable Trust
Michael Crawford Children's
    Charity
The Cray Trust
The Crescent Trust
Criffel Charitable Trust
Cripplegate Foundation
The Violet and Milo Cripps
    Charitable Trust
The Cromarty Trust
The Harry Crook Foundation
The Cross Trust
The Cross Trust
The Croydon Relief in Need
    Charities
The Mayor of Croydon's
    Charity Fund
Cruden Foundation Ltd
The Ronald Cruickshanks'
    Foundation
Cuby Charitable Trust

The Culra Charitable Trust
The Cumber Family Charitable
    Trust
Cumberland Building Society
    Charitable Foundation
Cumbria Community
    Foundation
The D J H Currie Memorial
    Trust
The Dennis Curry Charitable
    Trust
The Raymond Curtis Charitable
    Trust
The Manny Cussins
    Foundation
The Cwmbran Trust
Itzchok Meyer Cymerman Trust
    Ltd
The D'Oyly Carte Charitable
    Trust
The Roald Dahl Foundation
The Daisy Trust
The Daiwa Anglo-Japanese
    Foundation
Oizer Dalim Trust
The Dr and Mrs A Darlington
    Charitable Trust
Baron Davenport's Charity
The Davidson (Nairn)
    Charitable Trust
Davidson Charitable Trust
The Alderman Joe Davidson
    Memorial Trust
Michael Davies Charitable
    Settlement
The Gwendoline and Margaret
    Davies Charity
The Wilfrid Bruce Davis
    Charitable Trust
Davis-Rubens Charitable Trust
The Dawe Charitable Trust
The De Clermont Charitable
    Company Ltd
Peter De Haan Charitable
    Trust
The Leopold De Rothschild
    Charitable Trust
The Deakin Charitable Trust
William Dean Countryside and
    Educational Trust
The Debmar Benevolent Trust
The Delfont Foundation
The Dellal Foundation
The Delves Charitable Trust
The Demigryphon Trust
The Denman Charitable Trust
The Denton Charitable Trust
The Denton Wilde Sapte
    Charitable Trust
The Earl of Derby's Charitable
    Trust
The Derbyshire Churches and
    Chapels Preservation Trust
Derbyshire Community
    Foundation
The J N Derbyshire Trust

Devon Community Foundation
The Devon Educational Trust
The Devon Historic Churches
    Trust
The Duke of Devonshire's
    Charitable Trust
The Sandy Dewhirst Charitable
    Trust
DG Charitable Settlement
The Laduma Dhamecha
    Charitable Trust
Alan and Sheila Diamond
    Charitable Trust
The Dibden Allotments Charity
The Dickon Trust
The Digbeth Trust
The Dinwoodie Settlement
Dischma Charitable Trust
The DLA Piper Charitable Trust
The DLM Charitable Trust
Louise Dobson Charitable
    Trust
The Derek and Eileen Dodgson
    Foundation
The Dollond Charitable Trust
Domepride Ltd
The Dorcas Trust
The Dorema Charitable Trust
The Dorset Historic Churches
    Trust
The Dorus Trust
Double 'O' Charity Ltd
The Doughty Charity Trust
The R M Douglas Charitable
    Trust
The Drapers' Charitable Fund
Dromintee Trust
The Dugdale Charitable Trust
The Duis Charitable Trust
The Dulverton Trust
The P B Dumbell Charitable
    Trust
The Dumbreck Charity
Dunard Fund
Ronald Duncan Literary
    Foundation
The Dunhill Medical Trust
The Houghton Dunn Charitable
    Trust
The Dunn Family Charitable
    Trust
The W E Dunn Trust
Dushinsky Trust Ltd
Mildred Duveen Charitable
    Trust
The Dwek Family Charitable
    Trust
The Dyers' Company
    Charitable Trust
EAGA Partnership Charitable
    Trust
The Eagle Charity Trust
Audrey Earle Charitable Trust
The Earley Charity
Earls Colne and Halstead
    Educational Charity

The Earmark Trust
East Kent Provincial Charities
East London Community
    Foundation
Eastern Counties Educational
    Trust Limited
The Sir John Eastwood
    Foundation
The Ebenezer Trust
The EBM Charitable Trust
Eden Arts Trust
EDF Energy Trust (EDFET)
The Gilbert and Eileen Edgar
    Foundation
Gilbert Edgar Trust
Edinburgh Children's Holiday
    Fund
The Edinburgh Trust, No 2
    Account
Educational Foundation of
    Alderman John Norman
The W G Edwards Charitable
    Foundation
The William Edwards
    Educational Charity
The Elephant Trust
The George Elias Charitable
    Trust
The Gerald Palmer Eling Trust
    Company
The Elizabeth Frankland Moore
    and Star Foundation
The Wilfred and Elsie Elkes
    Charity Fund
The Maud Elkington Charitable
    Trust
Ellador Ltd
The Ellerdale Trust
The John Ellerman Foundation
The Ellinson Foundation Ltd
The Edith Maud Ellis 1985
    Charitable Trust
The Ellis Campbell Foundation
James Ellis Charitable Trust
The Elmgrant Trust
The Elmley Foundation
Elshore Ltd
The Vernon N Ely Charitable
    Trust
The Embleton Trust
The Emerton-Christie Charity
The Emmandjay Charitable
    Trust
The Worshipful Company of
    Engineers Charitable Trust
    Fund
The Englefield Charitable Trust
The English Schools' Football
    Association
The Enkalon Foundation
Entindale Ltd
The Epigoni Trust
Epilepsy Research UK
The Equitable Charitable Trust
The Equity Trust Fund
The Ericson Trust

The Erskine Cunningham Hill
    Trust
Essex Community Foundation
The Essex Fairway Charitable
    Trust
The Essex Heritage Trust
Essex Provincial Charity Fund
The Essex Youth Trust
Euro Charity Trust
The Evangelical Covenants
    Trust
Sir John Evelyn's Charity
The Eventhall Family
    Charitable Trust
The Everard Foundation
The Eveson Charitable Trust
The Beryl Evetts and Robert
    Luff Animal Welfare Trust
The Execution Charitable Trust
The Mayor of Exeter's Appeal
    Fund
The Exilarch's Foundation
F C Charitable Trust
The F P Limited Charitable
    Trust
The Faber Charitable Trust
Esmée Fairbairn Foundation
The Fairway Trust
Faisaltex Charitable Trust
The Family Foundations Trust
The Family Rich Charities Trust
Famos Foundation Trust
The Lord Faringdon Charitable
    Trust
Samuel William Farmer's Trust
The Farmers' Company
    Charitable Fund
The Thomas Farr Charitable
    Trust
Walter Farthing (Trust) Limited
Farthing Trust
The Fassnidge Memorial Trust
Joseph Fattorini Charitable
    Trust 'B' Account
The Fawcett Charitable Trust
Federation of Jewish Relief
    Organisations
Feed the Minds
The John Feeney Charitable
    Bequest
The George Fentham
    Birmingham Charity
The A M Fenton Trust
Allan and Nesta Ferguson
    Charitable Settlement
Elizabeth Ferguson Charitable
    Trust Fund
The Fidelity UK Foundation
The Bluff Field Charitable Trust
The Doris Field Charitable
    Trust
Fife Council/Common Good
    Funds and Trusts
Dixie Rose Findlay Charitable
    Trust
Gerald Finzi Charitable Trust

Firtree Trust
The Sir John Fisher Foundation
The Fishmongers' Company's
    Charitable Trust
Marc Fitch Fund
The Fitton Trust
The Earl Fitzwilliam Charitable
    Trust
Bud Flanagan Leukaemia Fund
The Rose Flatau Charitable
    Trust
The Ian Fleming Charitable
    Trust
The Joyce Fletcher Charitable
    Trust
Florence's Charitable Trust
The Florian Charitable Trust
The Flow Foundation
The Gerald Fogel Charitable
    Trust
The Follett Trust
The Football Association
    National Sports Centre
    Trust
The Football Association Youth
    Trust
The Football Foundation
The Forbes Charitable
    Foundation
Forbesville Limited
The Forces Trust
Ford Britain Trust
The Oliver Ford Charitable
    Trust
Fordeve Ltd
The Forest Hill Charitable Trust
The Foresters' Charity
    Stewards UK Trust
Gwyneth Forrester Trust
The Forte Charitable Trust
Lord Forte Foundation
Foundation for Management
    Education
Four Acre Trust
The Four Winds Trust
The Fowler, Smith and Jones
    Charitable Trust
The Foyle Foundation
The Isaac and Freda Frankel
    Memorial Charitable Trust
Sydney E Franklin Deceased's
    New Second Charity
The Gordon Fraser Charitable
    Trust
The Hugh Fraser Foundation
The Joseph Strong Frazer Trust
The Louis and Valerie
    Freedman Charitable
    Settlement
The Thomas Freke and Lady
    Norton Charity
The Charles S French
    Charitable Trust
The Anne French Memorial
    Trust
The Freshfield Foundation

The Freshgate Trust
Foundation
The Friarsgate Trust
The Friends Hall Farm Street
Trust
Friends of Biala Ltd
The Friends of Kent Churches
Friends of Wiznitz Limited
Friends Provident Charitable
Foundation
The Frognal Trust
T F C Frost Charitable Trust
The Patrick Frost Foundation
Maurice Fry Charitable Trust
Mejer and Gertrude Miriam
Frydman Foundation
The Fuellers Charitable Trust
Fund
The Fulmer Charitable Trust
Worshipful Company of
Furniture Makers Charitable
Fund
Gableholt Limited
The Galbraith Trust
The Gale Family Charitable
Trust
The Gamlen Charitable Trust
The Gamma Trust
The Gannochy Trust
The Ganzoni Charitable Trust
The Worshipful Company of
Gardeners of London
The Samuel Gardner Memorial
Trust
The Garnett Charitable Trust
Garrick Charitable Trust
Garvan Limited
The Gatsby Charitable
Foundation
Gatwick Airport Community
Trust
The Robert Gavron Charitable
Trust
Jacqueline and Michael Gee
Charitable Trust
J Paul Getty Jr Charitable Trust
The Gibbs Charitable Trust
Simon Gibson Charitable Trust
The G C Gibson Charitable
Trust
The Harvey and Hilary Gilbert
Charitable Trust
The Girdlers' Company
Charitable Trust
The B and P Glasser
Charitable Trust
The Glass-House Trust
Global Care
Global Charities (formally
GCap Charities)
Gloucestershire Community
Foundation
The Gloucestershire Historic
Churches Trust

Worshipful Company of
Glovers of London Charity
Fund
GMC Trust
The GNC Trust
The Meir Golda Trust
The Sydney and Phyllis
Goldberg Memorial
Charitable Trust
The Golden Bottle Trust
Golden Charitable Trust
The Jack Goldhill Charitable
Trust
The Goldsmiths' Arts Trust
Fund
The Goldsmiths' Company
Charity
The Golsoncott Foundation
Nicholas and Judith
Goodison's Charitable
Settlement
The Everard and Mina
Goodman Charitable
Foundation
Mike Gooley Trailfinders
Charity
Leonard Gordon Charitable
Trust
The Gosling Foundation
Limited
The Gough Charitable Trust
The Gould Charitable Trust
The Grace Charitable Trust
A B Grace Trust
The Graff Foundation
The Grahame Charitable
Foundation Limited
Grampian Police Diced Cap
Charitable Fund
The Granada Foundation
Grand Charitable Trust of the
Order of Women
Freemasons
The Grand Order of Water
Rats' Charities Fund
The Grange Farm Centre Trust
Grantham Yorke Trust
The J G Graves Charitable
Trust
The Gray Trust
The Great Stone Bridge Trust
of Edenbridge
The Great Torrington Town
Lands Charity
The Constance Green
Foundation
The Barry Green Memorial
Fund
The Philip Green Memorial
Trust
Mrs H R Greene Charitable
Settlement
Greenham Common
Community Trust Limited
Naomi and Jeffrey Greenwood
Charitable Trust

Greggs Foundation
Grimmitt Trust
The Grocers' Charity
The M and R Gross Charities
Limited
The Grove Charitable Trust
The GRP Charitable Trust
The David and Marie Grumitt
Foundation
The Bishop of Guildford's
Foundation
The Guildry Incorporation of
Perth
The Walter Guinness
Charitable Trust
The Gunter Charitable Trust
The Gur Trust
Gurunanak
Dr Guthrie's Association
The H and M Charitable Trust
H C D Memorial Fund
The H P Charitable Trust
The Hackney Parochial
Charities
The Hadfield Trust
The Hadley Trust
The Hadrian Trust
The Hale Trust
E F and M G Hall Charitable
Trust
The Edith Winifred Hall
Charitable Trust
Robert Hall Charity
The Hamamelis Trust
Hamilton Wallace Trust
Sue Hammerson's Charitable
Trust
The Hammonds Charitable
Trust
The Hampshire and Islands
Historic Churches Trust
Hampton Fuel Allotment
Charity
The W A Handley Charitable
Trust
Beatrice Hankey Foundation
Ltd
The Hanley Trust
The Kathleen Hannay
Memorial Charity
The Doughty Hanson
Charitable Foundation
Lord Hanson Foundation
The Haramead Trust
Miss K M Harbinson's
Charitable Trust
Harbo Charities Limited
The Harborne Parish Lands
Charity
The Harbour Charitable Trust
The Harbour Foundation
The Harding Trust
William Harding's Charity
The Hare of Steep Charitable
Trust
The Harebell Centenary Fund

The Kenneth Hargreaves
Charitable Trust
The Harris Charitable Trust
The Harris Charity
The Harrison and Potter Trust
The John Harrison Charitable
Trust
The Peter Harrison Foundation
The Spencer Hart Charitable
Trust
The Hartley Charitable Trust
The N and P Hartley Memorial
Trust
William Geoffrey Harvey's
Discretionary Settlement
The Edward Harvist Trust Fund
Haskel Family Foundation
The Hathaway Trust
The Maurice Hatter Foundation
The M A Hawe Settlement
The Hawthorne Charitable
Trust
The Dorothy Hay-Bolton
Charitable Trust
The Haydan Charitable Trust
The Haymills Charitable Trust
The Headley Trust
Headley-Pitt Charitable Trust
Heagerty Charitable Trust
The Heald Charitable Trust
Healthsure Group Ltd
May Hearnshaw's Charity
The Heart of England
Community Foundation
The Heathcoat Trust
Heathside Charitable Trust
The Charlotte Heber-Percy
Charitable Trust
Percy Hedley 1990 Charitable
Trust
The Hedley Denton Charitable
Trust
The Hedley Foundation
The H J Heinz Company
Limited Charitable Trust
The Hellenic Foundation
The Michael and Morven Heller
Charitable Foundation
The Simon Heller Charitable
Settlement
Help the Aged
Help the Homeless
Help the Hospices
The Hemby Trust
The Christina Mary Hendrie
Trust for Scottish and
Canadian Charities
The Henley Educational Charity
Philip Henman Trust
Esther Hennell Charitable
Trust
The G D Herbert Charitable
Trust
The Joanna Herbert-Stepney
Charitable Settlement
The Anne Herd Memorial Trust

The Herefordshire Historic
Churches Trust
The Heritage of London Trust
Ltd
The Hertfordshire Community
Foundation
The Hesed Trust
The Hesslewood Children's
Trust (Hull Seamen's and
General Orphanage)
The Bernhard Heuberger
Charitable Trust
Hexham and Newcastle
Diocesan Trust (1947)
The P and C Hickinbotham
Charitable Trust
The Higgs Charitable Trust
Alan Edward Higgs Charity
The High Sheriff's Police Trust
for the County of West
Midlands
Highcroft Charitable Trust
The Hilden Charitable Fund
The Joseph and Mary Hiley
Trust
The Holly Hill Charitable Trust
The Charles Littlewood Hill
Trust
The Hillingdon Partnership
Trust
R G Hills Charitable Trust
Hinchley Charitable Trust
Lady Hind Trust
Stuart Hine Trust
The Hinrichsen Foundation
The Hitchin Educational
Foundation
The Eleemosynary Charity of
William Hobbayne
Hobson Charity Limited
Matthew Hodder Charitable
Trust
The Sir Julian Hodge
Charitable Trust
The Jane Hodge Foundation
The J G Hogg Charitable Trust
The Holden Charitable Trust
John Holford's Charity
The Hollick Family Charitable
Trust
The Dorothy Holmes Charitable
Trust
P H Holt Foundation
The Edward Holt Trust
The Holywood Trust
The Homelands Charitable
Trust
The Homestead Charitable
Trust
Mary Homfray Charitable Trust
Sir Harold Hood's Charitable
Trust
HopMarket Charity
The Cuthbert Horn Trust
The Antony Hornby Charitable
Trust

The Horne Foundation
The Horne Trust
The Worshipful Company of
Horners' Charitable Trusts
The Hornsey Parochial
Charities
The Hospital Saturday Fund
Houblon-Norman/George Fund
The House of Industry Estate
The Reta Lila Howard
Foundation
The Daniel Howard Trust
The Clifford Howarth Charity
Trust
The Huddersfield Medical Trust
Fund
The Hudson Foundation
The Huggard Charitable Trust
The Geoffrey C Hughes
Charitable Trust
The Hull and East Riding
Charitable Trust
Hulme Trust Estates
(Educational)
Human Relief Foundation
The Humanitarian Trust
The Michael and Shirley Hunt
Charitable Trust
The Albert Hunt Trust
The Hunter Foundation
Miss Agnes H Hunter's Trust
The Huntingdon Foundation
Huntingdon Freemen's Charity
John Huntingdon's Charity
Hurdale Charity Limited
The Nani Huyu Charitable Trust
The P Y N and B Hyams Trust
The Hyde Charitable Trust –
Youth Plus
The Idlewild Trust
The Iliffe Family Charitable
Trust
The Indigo Trust
The Ingram Trust
The Inland Waterways
Association
The Inman Charity
The Inner London Magistrates
Court Poor Box Charity and
Feeder Charity
The Worshipful Company of
Innholders General Charity
Fund
The Ireland Fund of Great
Britain
The Irish Youth Foundation
(UK) Ltd
The Ironmongers' Foundation
Irshad Trust
The Charles Irving Charitable
Trust
Irwin Trust
The ISA Charity
The Isaacs Charitable Trust
The J Isaacs Charitable Trust
The Island Health Trust

The Isle of Anglesey Charitable Trust
Isle of Dogs Community Foundation
The ITF Seafarers Trust
J A R Charitable Trust
The J J Charitable Trust
The J R S S T Charitable Trust
Elizabeth Jackson Charitable Trust
Jacobs Charitable Trust
The Ruth and Lionel Jacobson Trust (Second Fund) No 2
Jaffe Family Relief Fund
John James Bristol Foundation
The Susan and Stephen James Charitable Settlement
The James Trust
The John Jarrold Trust
JCA Charitable Foundation
The Jeffrey Charitable Trust
Rees Jeffreys Road Fund
The Jenour Foundation
The Jephcott Charitable Trust
The Jerusalem Trust
Jesus Hospital Charity
The Jewish Youth Fund
The JMK Charitable Trust
The Joanies Trust
The Harold Joels Charitable Trust
The Jonathan Joels Charitable Trust
The Nicholas Joels Charitable Trust
The Norman Joels Charitable Trust
The Joffe Charitable Trust
The Lillie Johnson Charitable Trust
The Johnson Group Cleaners Charity
The Johnnie Johnson Trust
The Johnson Wax Ltd Charitable Trust
The Joicey Trust
The Jones 1986 Charitable Trust
The Marjorie and Geoffrey Jones Charitable Trust
The Jordan Charitable Foundation
The J E Joseph Charitable Fund
The Lady Eileen Joseph Foundation
JTH Charitable Trust
The Judith Trust
The Anton Jurgens Charitable Trust
The Bernard Kahn Charitable Trust
The Stanley Kalms Foundation
The Karenza Foundation

The Boris Karloff Charitable Foundation
The Ian Karten Charitable Trust
The Kasner Charitable Trust
The Kass Charitable Trust
The Kathleen Trust
The Michael and Ilse Katz Foundation
The Katzauer Charitable Settlement
The C S Kaufman Charitable Trust
The Geoffrey John Kaye Charitable Foundation
The Emmanuel Kaye Foundation
Kelsick's Educational Foundation
The KempWelch Charitable Trust
The Kay Kendall Leukaemia Fund
The Kennedy Charitable Foundation
The Nancy Kenyon Charitable Trust
Keren Association
Kermaville Ltd
E and E Kernkraut Charities Limited
The Kessler Foundation
The Ursula Keyes Trust
The Robert Kiln Charitable Trust
The King Henry VIII Endowed Trust Warwick
The King/Cullimore Charitable Trust
The Kingsbury Charity
The Mary Kinross Charitable Trust
Kinsurdy Charitable Trust
Kirkley Poor's Lands Estate
The Richard Kirkman Charitable Trust
Kirschel Foundation
Robert Kitchin (Saddlers' Company)
Ernest Kleinwort Charitable Trust
The Marina Kleinwort Charitable Trust
The Sir James Knott Trust
The Kobler Trust
The Kohn Foundation
The Kreditor Charitable Trust
The Kreitman Foundation
The Neil Kreitman Foundation
The Heinz, Anna and Carol Kroch Foundation
The Kyte Charitable Trust
Lacims-Maclis Charitable Trust
The Late Sir Pierce Lacy Charity Trust
John Laing Charitable Trust

Maurice and Hilda Laing Charitable Trust
The Laing Family Foundations
The Christopher Laing Foundation
The Kirby Laing Foundation
The Martin Laing Foundation
The Beatrice Laing Trust
The Lambert Charitable Trust
Lancashire Environmental Fund
Duchy of Lancaster Benevolent Fund
The Lancaster Foundation
LandAid Charitable Trust
The Langdale Trust
The Langley Charitable Trust
The Langtree Trust
The LankellyChase Foundation
The Lanvern Foundation
The R J Larg Family Charitable Trust
Largsmount Ltd
The Lark Trust
Laslett's (Hinton) Charity
Lauchentilly Charitable Foundation 1988
Laufer Charitable Trust
The Lauffer Family Charitable Foundation
Mrs F B Laurence Charitable Trust
The Kathleen Laurence Trust
The Edgar E Lawley Foundation
The Herd Lawson and Muriel Lawson Charitable Trust
The Lawson Beckman Charitable Trust
The Raymond and Blanche Lawson Charitable Trust
The Carole and Geoffrey Lawson Foundation
The Mason Le Page Charitable Trust
The Leach Fourteenth Trust
The David Lean Foundation
The Leathersellers' Company Charitable Fund
The Leche Trust
The Arnold Lee Charitable Trust
The William Leech Charity
The Lord Mayor of Leeds Appeal Fund
Leicester Charity Link
Leicestershire Historic Churches Trust
The Kennedy Leigh Charitable Trust
Morris Leigh Foundation
The Leigh Trust
Mrs Vera Leigh's Charity
The P Leigh-Bramwell Trust 'E'
The Lennox and Wyfold Foundation
The Erica Leonard Trust

The Leonard Trust
The Mark Leonard Trust
Lesley Lesley and Mutter Trust
The Leverhulme Trade
Charities Trust
Lord Leverhulme's Charitable
Trust
The Joseph Levy Charitable
Foundation
Lewis Family Charitable Trust
The Sir Edward Lewis
Foundation
John Lewis Partnership
General Community Fund
Lichfield Conduit Lands
Lifeline 4 Kids
The Thomas Lilley Memorial
Trust
Limoges Charitable Trust
The Linbury Trust
The Lincolnshire Old Churches
Trust
The Lind Trust
Lindale Educational
Foundation
The Linden Charitable Trust
The Enid Linder Foundation
The Linmardon Trust
The Ruth and Stuart Lipton
Charitable Trust
The Lister Charitable Trust
Frank Litchfield Charitable
Trust
The Andrew and Mary
Elizabeth Little Charitable
Trust
The Second Joseph Aaron
Littman Foundation
The George John and Sheilah
Livanos Charitable Trust
Liverpool Charity and Voluntary
Services
Liverpool Sailors' Home Trust
Jack Livingstone Charitable
Trust
The Elaine and Angus Lloyd
Charitable Trust
The Charles Lloyd Foundation
The Lloyd Fund
Lloyd's Charities Trust
The Lloyd-Everett Trust
Lloyds TSB Foundation for
Northern Ireland
Lloyds TSB Foundation for the
Channel Islands
Llysdinam Charitable Trust
Localtrent Ltd
The Locker Foundation
The Loftus Charitable Trust
The Lolev Charitable Trust
London Catalyst
The London Law Trust
The London Marathon
Charitable Trust
The William and Katherine
Longman Trust

The Loseley and Guildway
Charitable Trust
The Lotus Foundation
The C L Loyd Charitable Trust
The Marie Helen Luen
Charitable Trust
Robert Luff Foundation Ltd
Henry Lumley Charitable Trust
Lady Lumley's Educational
Foundation
Paul Lunn-Rockliffe Charitable
Trust
C F Lunoe Trust Fund
The Ruth and Jack Lunzer
Charitable Trust
Lord and Lady Lurgan Trust
The Lynn Foundation
The Lynwood Trust
John Lyon's Charity
The Lyons Charitable Trust
The Sir Jack Lyons Charitable
Trust
Malcolm Lyons Foundation
The Lyras Family Charitable
Trust
The M and C Trust
The M D and S Charitable
Trust
The M K Charitable Trust
The Madeline Mabey Trust
The E M MacAndrew Trust
The R S Macdonald Charitable
Trust
Macdonald-Buchanan
Charitable Trust
The Macfarlane Walker Trust
The Mackay and Brewer
Charitable Trust
The Mackintosh Foundation
The MacRobert Trust
Ian Mactaggart Trust
The Magdalen and Lasher
Charity
Magdalen Hospital Trust
The Magen Charitable Trust
Mageni Trust
Mahavir Trust
Man Group plc Charitable
Trust
The Manchester Guardian
Society Charitable Trust
Manchester Kids
Lord Mayor of Manchester's
Charity Appeal Trust
Mandeville Trust
The Manifold Charitable Trust
W M Mann Foundation
The Leslie and Lilian Manning
Trust
Maranatha Christian Trust
Marbeh Torah Trust
Marchig Animal Welfare Trust
The Stella and Alexander
Margulies Charitable Trust
Mariapolis Limited

Market Harborough and The
Bowdens Charity
Michael Marks Charitable
Trust
The Ann and David Marks
Foundation
The Hilda and Samuel Marks
Foundation
J P Marland Charitable Trust
Marr-Munning Trust
The Michael Marsh Charitable
Trust
The Charlotte Marshall
Charitable Trust
The Jim Marshall Charitable
Trust
The D G Marshall of
Cambridge Trust
Marshall's Charity
Marshgate Charitable
Settlement
Sir George Martin Trust
John Martin's Charity
The Mason Porter Charitable
Trust
The Nancie Massey Charitable
Trust
The Mathew Trust
Matliwala Family Charitable
Trust
The Matt 6.3 Charitable Trust
The Violet Mauray Charitable
Trust
The Maxell Educational Trust
The Maxwell Family Foundation
Evelyn May Trust
Mayfair Charities Ltd
The Mayfield Valley Arts Trust
Mazars Charitable Trust
The Robert McAlpine
Foundation
The McDougall Trust
The A M McGreevy No 5
Charitable Settlement
The McKenna Charitable Trust
Martin McLaren Memorial
Trust
The Helen Isabella McMorran
Charitable Foundation
D D McPhail Charitable
Settlement
The James Frederick and Ethel
Anne Measures Charity
Medical Research Council
The Medlock Charitable Trust
The Anthony and Elizabeth
Mellows Charitable
Settlement
Melodor Ltd
Melow Charitable Trust
Meningitis Trust
Menuchar Ltd
Brian Mercer Charitable Trust
The Mercers' Charitable
Foundation

The Merchant Taylors'
   Company Charities Fund
The Merchant Venturers'
   Charity
The Merchants' House of
   Glasgow
Mercury Phoenix Trust
The Mersey Docks and
   Harbour Company
   Charitable Fund
Community Foundation for
   Merseyside
The Zachary Merton and
   George Woofindin
   Convalescent Trust
The Tony Metherell Charitable
   Trust
The Methodist Relief and
   Development Fund
The Metropolitan Drinking
   Fountain and Cattle Trough
   Association
Gerald Micklem Charitable
   Trust
Midhurst Pensions Trust
The Migraine Trust
Miles Trust for the Putney and
   Roehampton Community
Millennium Stadium Charitable
   Trust
The Hugh and Mary Miller
   Bequest Trust
The Miller Foundation
The Millfield Trust
The Millhouses Charitable
   Trust
The Millichope Foundation
The Mills Charity
The Millward Charitable Trust
The Clare Milne Trust
Milton Keynes Community
   Foundation
The Edgar Milward Charity
The Keith and Joan
   Mindelsohn Charitable
   Trust
The Peter Minet Trust
Minge's Gift and the Pooled
   Trusts
The Minos Trust
The Mirfield Educational
   Charity
The Laurence Misener
   Charitable Trust
The Mishcon Family Charitable
   Trust
The Misselbrook Trust
The Mitchell Charitable Trust
The Esme Mitchell Trust
Keren Mitzvah Trust
The Mizpah Trust
The Mobbs Memorial Trust Ltd
The Modiano Charitable Trust
The Moette Charitable Trust
The Mole Charitable Trust

The D C Moncrieff Charitable
   Trust
Monmouthshire County Council
   Welsh Church Act Fund
The Montague Thompson
   Coon Charitable Trust
The Colin Montgomerie
   Charitable Foundation
The Monument Trust
Moody Charitable Trust
George A Moore Foundation
The Nigel Moores Family
   Charitable Trust
John Moores Foundation
The Peter Moores Foundation
The Morel Charitable Trust
The Morgan Charitable
   Foundation
The Mr and Mrs J T Morgan
   Foundation
Diana and Allan Morgenthau
   Charitable Trust
The Oliver Morland Charitable
   Trust
S C and M E Morland's
   Charitable Trust
The Morris Charitable Trust
The Willie and Mabel Morris
   Charitable Trust
The Peter Morrison Charitable
   Foundation
The Stanley Morrison
   Charitable Trust
Moshal Charitable Trust
Vyoel Moshe Charitable Trust
The Moss Charitable Trust
The Robert and Margaret
   Moss Charitable Trust
Moss Family Charitable Trust
The Mount Everest Foundation
Mountbatten Festival of Music
The Mountbatten Memorial
   Trust
The Edwina Mountbatten Trust
The Mugdock Children's Trust
The F H Muirhead Charitable
   Trust
The Mulberry Trust
The Edith Murphy Foundation
Murphy-Neumann Charity
   Company Limited
The Mushroom Fund
The Music Sales Charitable
   Trust
Muslim Hands
The Mutual Trust Group
MYA Charitable Trust
The Kitty and Daniel Nabarro
   Charitable Trust
The Nadezhda Charitable Trust
The Willie Nagel Charitable
   Trust
The Naggar Charitable Trust
The Eleni Nakou Foundation
The Janet Nash Charitable
   Settlement

Nathan Charitable Trust
Asthma UK
The National Manuscripts
   Conservation Trust
Nazareth Trust Fund
The Nchima Trust
Needham Market and Barking
   Welfare Charities
The Worshipful Company of
   Needlemakers' Charitable
   Fund
The Neighbourly Charitable
   Trust
The James Neill Trust Fund
Nemoral Ltd
Nesswall Ltd
Network for Social Change
Newby Trust Limited
The Newcomen Collett
   Foundation
The Richard Newitt Fund
Mr and Mrs F E F Newman
   Charitable Trust
The Frances and Augustus
   Newman Foundation
Newpier Charity Ltd
Alderman Newton's
   Educational Foundation
The Chevras Ezras Nitzrochim
   Trust
The Noon Foundation
The Norda Trust
Norie Charitable Trust
Normalyn Charitable Trust
The Norman Family Charitable
   Trust
The Duncan Norman Trust
   Fund
The Normanby Charitable Trust
The North British Hotel Trust
The Northampton Municipal
   Church Charities
The Northampton Queen's
   Institute Relief in Sickness
   Fund
The Earl of Northampton's
   Charity
The Northcott Devon
   Foundation
The Northcott Devon Medical
   Foundation
The Northmoor Trust
The Northumberland Village
   Homes Trust
The Northumbria Historic
   Churches Trust
The Northwood Charitable
   Trust
The Norton Foundation
The Norwich Church of England
   Young Men's Society
The Norwich Historic Churches
   Trust Ltd
The Norwich Town Close
   Estate Charity

The Norwood and Newton
Settlement
The Noswad Charity
The Notgrove Trust
The Nottingham General
Dispensary
The Nottingham Gordon
Memorial Trust for Boys
and Girls
Nottinghamshire Community
Foundation
The Nottinghamshire Historic
Churches Trust
The Nottinghamshire Miners'
Welfare Trust Fund
Novi Most International
The Father O'Mahoney
Memorial Trust
The Sir Peter O'Sullevan
Charitable Trust
The Oak Trust
The Oakdale Trust
The Oakley Charitable Trust
The Oakmoor Charitable Trust
The Odin Charitable Trust
Ogilvie Charities Deed No.2
(including the Charity of
Mary Catherine Ford Smith)
Oglesby Charitable Trust
The Oikonomia Trust
The Oizer Charitable Trust
The Old Broad Street Charity
Trust
The Old Enfield Charitable
Trust
Old Possum's Practical Trust
The John Oldacre Foundation
The Oldham Foundation
Onaway Trust
Open Gate
The Ormsby Charitable Trust
Orrin Charitable Trust
The Owen Family Trust
Oxfam (GB)
The Oxfordshire Community
Foundation
The P F Charitable Trust
Padwa Charitable Foundation
The Pallant Charitable Trust
The Palmer Foundation
Eleanor Palmer Trust
The Panacea Society
Panahpur Charitable Trust
Panton Trust
The James Pantyfedwen
Foundation
The Paragon Trust
The Park House Charitable
Trust
The Frank Parkinson
Agricultural Trust
The Samuel and Freda
Parkinson Charitable Trust
The Parthenon Trust
Arthur James Paterson
Charitable Trust

The Constance Paterson
Charitable Trust
Miss M E Swinton Paterson's
Charitable Trust
The Patrick Charitable Trust
The Jack Patston Charitable
Trust
Paycare Charity Trust
The Harry Payne Trust
The Susanna Peake Charitable
Trust
The Pedmore Sporting Club
Trust Fund
The Dowager Countess
Eleanor Peel Trust
Peltz Trust
The Pennycress Trust
The Performing Right Society
Foundation
B E Perl Charitable Trust
The Persson Charitable Trust
The Pestalozzi Overseas
Children's Trust
The Jack Petchey Foundation
The Petplan Charitable Trust
The Philips and Rubens
Charitable Trust
The Phillips Charitable Trust
The Phillips Family Charitable
Trust
Philological Foundation
The Bernard Piggott Trust
The Claude and Margaret Pike
Charity
The Pilgrim Trust
The Cecil Pilkington Charitable
Trust
The Pilkington Charities Fund
The Austin and Hope
Pilkington Trust
The Sir Harry Pilkington Trust
The Col W W Pilkington Will
Trusts The General Charity
Fund
Miss A M Pilkington's
Charitable Trust
Mrs Pilkington's Charitable
Trust
The Plaisterers' Company
Charitable Trust
The Platinum Trust
G S Plaut Charitable Trust
Limited
The Poling Charitable Trust
The George and Esme Pollitzer
Charitable Settlement
The J S F Pollitzer Charitable
Settlement
The Ponton House Trust
The Mayor of Poole's Appeal
Fund
Edith and Ferdinand Porjes
Charitable Trust
The John Porter Charitable
Trust
The Porter Foundation

The Portishead Nautical Trust
The Portrack Charitable Trust
The J E Posnansky Charitable
Trust
The Powell Foundation
Premierquote Ltd
Premishlaner Charitable Trust
The William Price Charitable
Trust
The Lucy Price Relief-in-Need
Charity
Sir John Priestman Charity
Trust
The Primrose Trust
The Prince's Charities
Foundation
Princess Anne's Charities
The Priory Foundation
Prison Service Charity Fund
The Privy Purse Charitable
Trust
The Proven Family Trust
The Provincial Grand Charity of
the Province of Derbyshire
PSA Peugeot Citroen Charity
Trust
The Puebla Charitable Trust
The Richard and Christine
Purchas Charitable Trust
The Puri Foundation
Mr and Mrs J A Pye's
Charitable Settlement
Quartet Community Foundation
Queen Mary's Roehampton
Trust
The Queen's Silver Jubilee
Trust
Quercus Trust
The R D Crusaders Foundation
R J M Charitable Trust
R S Charitable Trust
The Monica Rabagliati
Charitable Trust
Rachel Charitable Trust
The Mr and Mrs Philip
Rackham Charitable Trust
Richard Radcliffe Charitable
Trust
The Radcliffe Trust
The Ragdoll Foundation
The Rainford Trust
The Peggy Ramsay Foundation
The Joseph and Lena Randall
Charitable Trust
The Rank Foundation
Ranworth Trust
The Fanny Rapaport Charitable
Settlement
The Ratcliff Foundation
The Ratcliff Pension Charity
The Ratcliffe Charitable Trust
The Eleanor Rathbone
Charitable Trust
The Sigrid Rausing Trust
The Ravensdale Trust
The Rayden Charitable Trust

The Roger Raymond Charitable
Trust
The Rayne Foundation
The Rayne Trust
The John Rayner Charitable
Trust
The Albert Reckitt Charitable
Trust
The Sir James Reckitt Charity
The Red Arrows Trust
Red Hill Charitable Trust
The Red Rose Charitable Trust
The C A Redfern Charitable
Foundation
The Reed Foundation
Richard Reeve's Foundation
The Max Reinhardt Charitable
Trust
Relief Fund for Romania
Limited
REMEDI
The Rest Harrow Trust
Reuben Brothers Foundation
The Joan K Reynell Charitable
Trust
The Nathaniel Reyner Trust
Fund
The Rhododendron Trust
Daisie Rich Trust
The Sir Cliff Richard Charitable
Trust
C B Richard Ellis Charitable
Trust
The Clive Richards Charity
The Richmond Parish Lands
Charity
The Muriel Edith Rickman
Trust
Ridgesave Limited
The Ripple Effect Foundation
The Sir John Ritblat Family
Foundation
Riverside Charitable Trust
Limited
The Daniel Rivlin Charitable
Trust
Thomas Roberts Trust
The Alex Roberts-Miller
Foundation
The Robertson Trust
Edwin George Robinson
Charitable Trust
Robyn Charitable Trust
The Rochester Bridge Trust
The Rock Foundation
The Rock Solid Trust
The Rofeh Trust
Richard Rogers Charitable
Settlement
Rokach Family Charitable Trust
The Helen Roll Charitable
Trust
The Sir James Roll Charitable
Trust
The Roman Research Trust
Romeera Foundation

The C A Rookes Charitable
Trust
The Rosca Trust
The Rose Foundation
The Cecil Rosen Foundation
The Rothermere Foundation
The Rotherwick Foundation
The Rothley Trust
The Rothschild Foundation
The Roughley Charitable Trust
Mrs Gladys Row Fogo
Charitable Trust
Rowanville Ltd
The Rowing Foundation
The Rowlands Trust
Royal Artillery Charitable Fund
Royal British Legion
Royal Docks Trust (London)
Royal Masonic Trust for Girls
and Boys
The Royal Scots Benevolent
Society
The Alfred and Frances
Rubens Charitable Trust
The Rubin Foundation
William Arthur Rudd Memorial
Trust
The Russell Trust
Ryklow Charitable Trust 1992
The J S and E C Rymer
Charitable Trust
S O Charitable Trust
The Michael Sacher Charitable
Trust
The Michael Harry Sacher
Trust
Dr Mortimer and Theresa
Sackler Foundation
The Raymond and Beverley
Sackler Foundation
The Ruzin Sadagora Trust
The Saddlers' Company
Charitable Fund
The Saga Charitable Trust
The Jean Sainsbury Animal
Welfare Trust
The Alan and Babette
Sainsbury Charitable Fund
Saint Sarkis Charity Trust
The Saintbury Trust
The Saints and Sinners Trust
The Salamander Charitable
Trust
The Salt Foundation
The Salt Trust
The Salters' Charities
The Andrew Salvesen
Charitable Trust
The Sammermar Trust
Basil Samuel Charitable Trust
Coral Samuel Charitable Trust
The Hon. M J Samuel
Charitable Trust
The Peter Samuel Charitable
Trust
The Camilla Samuel Fund

The Samworth Foundation
The Sandra Charitable Trust
Jimmy Savile Charitable Trust
The Scarfe Charitable Trust
The Schapira Charitable Trust
The Annie Schiff Charitable
Trust
The Schmidt-Bodner Charitable
Trust
The R H Scholes Charitable
Trust
The Schreib Trust
The Schreiber Charitable Trust
Schroder Charity Trust
The Scott Bader
Commonwealth Ltd
The Francis C Scott Charitable
Trust
The Frieda Scott Charitable
Trust
The Sir James and Lady Scott
Trust
The Scott Trust Foundation
The Storrow Scott Will Trust
The Scottish Arts Council
Scottish Churches' Community
Trust
Scottish Coal Industry Special
Welfare Fund
The Scottish Community
Foundation
The Scouloudi Foundation
Seafarers UK (King George's
Fund for Sailors)
Seamen's Hospital Society
The Searchlight Electric
Charitable Trust
The Searle Charitable Trust
The Helene Sebba Charitable
Trust
The Samuel Sebba Charitable
Trust
The Seedfield Trust
Leslie Sell Charitable Trust
Sellata Ltd
SEM Charitable Trust
The Ayrton Senna Foundation
The Seven Fifty Trust
The Severn Trent Water
Charitable Trust Fund
SFIA Educational Trust Limited
The Cyril Shack Trust
The Shanti Charitable Trust
ShareGift (The Orr Mackintosh
Foundation)
The Linley Shaw Foundation
The Sheffield and District
Hospital Services
Charitable Fund
The P and D Shepherd
Charitable Trust
The Sylvia and Colin Shepherd
Charitable Trust
The Archie Sherman Cardiff
Foundation

The Archie Sherman Charitable
Trust
The R C Sherriff Trust
The Shetland Charitable Trust
SHINE (Support and Help in
Education)
The Barnett and Sylvia Shine
No 2 Charitable Trust
The Bassil Shippam and
Alsford Trust
The Shipwrights' Company
Charitable Fund
The Shirley Foundation
Shlomo Memorial Fund Limited
The J A Shone Memorial Trust
The Charles Shorto Charitable
Trust
The Barbara A Shuttleworth
Memorial Trust
The Mary Elizabeth Siebel
Charity
David and Jennifer Sieff
Charitable Trust
The Julius Silman Charitable
Trust
The Leslie Silver Charitable
Trust
The Simpson Education and
Conservation Trust
The Simpson Foundation
The Huntly and Margery
Sinclair Charitable Trust
Sino-British Fellowship Trust
The Skelton Bounty
The Charles Skey Charitable
Trust
The John Slater Foundation
Rita and David Slowe
Charitable Trust
The SMB Charitable Trust
The Mrs Smith and Mount
Trust
The N Smith Charitable
Settlement
The Amanda Smith Charitable
Trust
The E H Smith Charitable Trust
The Smith Charitable Trust
The Henry Smith Charity
The Leslie Smith Foundation
The Martin Smith Foundation
Stanley Smith General
Charitable Trust
The Stanley Smith UK
Horticultural Trust
Philip Smith's Charitable Trust
The Snowball Trust
The Sobell Foundation
Solev Co Ltd
Solihull Community Foundation
The Solo Charitable
Settlement
Dr Richard Solomon's
Charitable Trust
Friends of Somerset Churches
and Chapels

Songdale Ltd
The E C Sosnow Charitable
Trust
The South Square Trust
The Stephen R and Philippa H
Southall Charitable Trust
The W F Southall Trust
The Southdown Trust
R H Southern Trust
The Southover Manor General
Education Trust
The Southwold Trust
The Sovereign Health Care
Charitable Trust
Spar Charitable Fund
Sparks Charity (Sport Aiding
Medical Research For Kids)
Sparquote Limited
The Spear Charitable Trust
Spears-Stutz Charitable Trust
The Worshipful Company of
Spectacle Makers' Charity
The Jessie Spencer Trust
The Ralph and Irma Sperring
Charity
The Moss Spiro Will Charitable
Foundation
W W Spooner Charitable Trust
Stanley Spooner Deceased
Charitable Trust
The Spoore, Merry and Rixman
Foundation
The Spring Harvest Charitable
Trust
Rosalyn and Nicholas Springer
Charitable Trust
Springfields Employees'
Medical Research and
Charity Trust Fund
Springrule Ltd
The Spurrell Charitable Trust
The Geoff and Fiona Squire
Foundation
St Andrew Animal Fund
St Andrew's Conservation
Trust
St Francis's Leprosy Guild
St Gabriel's Trust
St James' Trust Settlement
St James's Place Foundation
St Mark's Overseas Aid Trust
(SMOAT)
St Michael's and All Saints'
Charities
The Late St Patrick White
Charitable Trust
St Teilo's Trust
Miss Doreen Stanford Trust
The Stanley Foundation Ltd
The Stanton Ballard Charitable
Trust
The Staples Trust
The Star Charitable Trust
The Starfish Trust
The Steel Charitable Trust

The Cyril and Betty Stein
Charitable Trust
The Steinberg Family
Charitable Trust
The Hugh Stenhouse
Foundation
The Sigmund Sternberg
Charitable Foundation
Stervon Ltd
The Stevenage Community
Trust
The June Stevens Foundation
Stevenson Family's Charitable
Trust
The Steventon Allotments and
Relief-in-Need Charity
The Stewards' Company
Limited
The Leonard Laity Stoate
Charitable Trust
The Stobart Newlands
Charitable Trust
The Edward Stocks-Massey
Bequest Fund
The Stokenchurch Educational
Charity
The Stoller Charitable Trust
The M J C Stone Charitable
Trust
The Stone-Mallabar Charitable
Foundation
The Samuel Storey Family
Charitable Trust
Peter Stormonth Darling
Charitable Trust
Peter Storrs Trust
The Strangward Trust
The Strasser Foundation
Stratford upon Avon Town
Trust
Strathclyde Police Benevolent
Fund
The W O Street Charitable
Foundation
The A B Strom and R Strom
Charitable Trust
The Sudborough Foundation
Sueberry Ltd
The Suffolk Historic Churches
Trust
The Alan Sugar Foundation
The Summerfield Charitable
Trust
The Bernard Sunley Charitable
Foundation
The Surrey Historic Buildings
Trust Ltd
The Sussex Historic Churches
Trust
The Adrienne and Leslie
Sussman Charitable Trust
The Sutasoma Trust
Sutton Coldfield Municipal
Charities
The Sutton Nursing
Association

Swan Mountain Trust
The Swan Trust
Swansea and Brecon Diocesan
   Board of Finance Limited
The John Swire (1989)
   Charitable Trust
The Swire Charitable Trust
The Hugh and Ruby Sykes
   Charitable Trust
The Charles and Elsie Sykes
   Trust
The Sylvanus Charitable Trust
The Stella Symons Charitable
   Trust
The Tabeel Trust
The Tajtelbaum Charitable
   Trust
The Talbot Trusts
The Talbot Village Trust
Tallow Chandlers Benevolent
   Fund
Talteg Ltd
The Tangent Charitable Trust
The Lady Tangye Charitable
   Trust
The David Tannen Charitable
   Trust
The Tanner Trust
The Lili Tapper Charitable
   Foundation
The Mrs A Lacy Tate Trust
The Tay Charitable Trust
C B and H H Taylor 1984 Trust
Humphrey Richardson Taylor
   Charitable Trust
The Connie and Albert Taylor
   Charitable Trust
The Cyril Taylor Charitable
   Trust
A P Taylor Trust
Rosanna Taylor's 1987 Charity
   Trust
Tearfund
The Tedworth Charitable Trust
Tees Valley Community
   Foundation
Tegham Limited
The Templeton Goodwill Trust
Tesco Charity Trust
Thackray Medical Research
   Trust
Thames Community
   Foundation
The Thames Wharf Charity
The Thistle Trust
The Loke Wan Tho Memorial
   Foundation
The Arthur and Margaret
   Thompson Charitable Trust
The Thompson Family
   Charitable Trust
The Len Thomson Charitable
   Trust
The Sue Thomson Foundation
The Sir Jules Thorn Charitable
   Trust

The Thornton Foundation
The Thornton Trust
The Three Guineas Trust
The Three Oaks Trust
The Thriplow Charitable Trust
The Tinsley Foundation
The Tisbury Telegraph Trust
TJH Foundation
The Tolkien Trust
Tollemache (Buckminster)
   Charitable Trust
Tomchei Torah Charitable
   Trust
The Tompkins Foundation
The Tory Family Foundation
Tottenham Grammar School
   Foundation
The Tower Hill Trust
The Towry Law Charitable Trust
The Toy Trust
The Mayor of Trafford's Charity
   Fund
Annie Tranmer Charitable Trust
The Constance Travis
   Charitable Trust
The Treeside Trust
The Triangle Trust (1949) Fund
The True Colours Trust
Truedene Co. Ltd
The Truemark Trust
Truemart Limited
Trumros Limited
Trust for London
Trust Sixty Three
The Trusthouse Charitable
   Foundation
The Tubney Charitable Trust
Tudor Rose Ltd
The Tudor Trust
The Tufton Charitable Trust
The R D Turner Charitable
   Trust
The Douglas Turner Trust
The Florence Turner Trust
Miss S M Tutton Charitable
   Trust
The TUUT Charitable Trust
Community Foundation Serving
   Tyne and Wear and
   Northumberland
Trustees of Tzedakah
Ulster Garden Villages Ltd
Ultach Trust
Ulting Overseas Trust
The Ulverscroft Foundation
Ulverston Town Lands Charity
The Underwood Trust
The Union of Orthodox Hebrew
   Congregation
The United Society for the
   Propagation of the Gospel
United Trusts
The David Uri Memorial Trust
Uxbridge United Welfare Trust
Vale of Glamorgan – Welsh
   Church Fund

The Valentine Charitable Trust
The Albert Van Den Bergh
   Charitable Trust
John and Lucille van Geest
   Foundation
The Van Neste Foundation
Mrs Maud Van Norden's
   Charitable Foundation
The Vandervell Foundation
The Vardy Foundation
The Variety Club Children's
   Charity
Veneziana Fund
The Verdon-Smith Family
   Charitable Settlement
Roger Vere Foundation
Victoria Homes Trust
Viking Cares (For the Kids)
The Nigel Vinson Charitable
   Trust
The William and Ellen Vinten
   Trust
The Vintners' Company
   Charitable Foundation
Vintners' Gifts Charity
Vision Charity
Vivdale Ltd
The Viznitz Foundation
Wade's Charity
The Community Foundation in
   Wales
Wales Council for Voluntary
   Action
Robert and Felicity Waley-
   Cohen Charitable Trust
The Walker Trust
Wallington Missionary Mart
   and Auctions
The F J Wallis Charitable
   Settlement
War on Want
Sir Siegmund Warburg's
   Voluntary Settlement
The Ward Blenkinsop Trust
The George Ward Charitable
   Trust
The Barbara Ward Children's
   Foundation
The John Warren Foundation
G R Waters Charitable Trust
   2000
The Waterways Trust
Blyth Watson Charitable Trust
John Watson's Trust
Weatherley Charitable Trust
The Weavers' Company
   Benevolent Fund
The William Webster
   Charitable Trust
The Weinberg Foundation
The Weinstein Foundation
The Weinstock Fund
The James Weir Foundation
The Barbara Welby Trust
The Weldon UK Charitable
   Trust

The Wellcome Trust
Welsh Church Fund Dyfed area (Carmarthenshire, Ceredigion and Pembrokeshire)
The Welton Foundation
Wessex Cancer Trust
The Wessex Youth Trust
The West Derby Wastelands Charity
West London Synagogue Charitable Fund
The West Yorkshire Police Community Fund
Mrs S K West's Charitable Trust
The Westminster Foundation
The Garfield Weston Foundation
The Colonel W H Whitbread Charitable Trust
The Simon Whitbread Charitable Trust
White Rose Children's Aid International Charity
The Whitecourt Charitable Trust
A H and B C Whiteley Charitable Trust
The Norman Whiteley Trust
The Whitley Animal Protection Trust
The Whittlesey Charity
The Lionel Wigram Memorial Trust
The Felicity Wilde Charitable Trust
The Wilkinson Charitable Foundation
The Will Charitable Trust
The Kay Williams Charitable Foundation
The Williams Family Charitable Trust
The H D H Wills 1965 Charitable Trust
Dame Violet Wills Charitable Trust
The Dame Violet Wills Will Trust
The Wilmcote Charitrust
Sumner Wilson Charitable Trust
David Wilson Foundation
The Wilson Foundation
J and J R Wilson Trust
The Community Foundation for Wiltshire and Swindon
The Benjamin Winegarten Charitable Trust
The Harold Hyam Wingate Foundation
The Francis Winham Foundation
Anona Winn Charitable Trust
Wirral Mayor's Charity

The Michael and Anna Wix Charitable Trust
The Wixamtree Trust
The Woburn 1986 Charitable Trust
The Maurice Wohl Charitable Foundation
The Charles Wolfson Charitable Trust
The Wolfson Family Charitable Trust
The Wolfson Foundation
Women Caring Trust
The James Wood Bequest Fund
Woodlands Green Ltd
Woodlands Trust
The Geoffrey Woods Charitable Foundation
The Woodward Charitable Trust
The A and R Woolf Charitable Trust
The Woolnoth Society Charitable Trust
Worcester Municipal Charities
The Worcestershire and Dudley Historic Churches Trust
The Fred and Della Worms Charitable Trust
The Worwin UK Foundation
The Wragge and Co. Charitable Trust
The Diana Edgson Wright Charitable Trust
The Matthews Wrightson Charity Trust
Miss E B Wrightson's Charitable Settlement
Wychdale Ltd
Wychville Ltd
The Wyndham Charitable Trust
The Wyseliot Charitable Trust
The Xerox (UK) Trust
The Yardley Great Trust
The Dennis Alan Yardy Charitable Trust
The W Wing Yip and Brothers Foundation
The York Children's Trust
Yorkshire Agricultural Society
Yorkshire Building Society Charitable Foundation
The South Yorkshire Community Foundation
The Yorkshire Dales Millennium Trust
The Yorkshire Historic Churches Trust
The John Young Charitable Settlement
The William Allen Young Charitable Trust
The John K Young Endowment Fund

Youth Music
Elizabeth and Prince Zaiger Trust
Zephyr Charitable Trust
The Marjorie and Arnold Ziff Charitable Foundation
Stephen Zimmerman Charitable Trust
The Zochonis Charitable Trust
Zurich Community Trust (UK) Limited

....

■ Collections and acquisitions

The 1989 Willan Charitable Trust
The 29th May 1961 Charitable Trust
Aberbrothock Charitable Trust
The Aberdeen Endowments Trust
The Aberdeenshire Educational Trust Scheme
Achiezer Association Ltd
Achisomoch Aid Company Limited
The ACT Foundation
Action Medical Research
The Company of Actuaries' Charitable Trust Fund
The Sylvia Adams Charitable Trust
The Victor Adda Foundation
The Adint Charitable Trust
The Adnams Charity
AF Trust Company
Age Concern Scotland Grants
Aid to the Church in Need (UK)
The AIM Foundation
The Sylvia Aitken Charitable Trust
The Ajahma Charitable Trust
Alcohol Education and Research Council
Aldgate and All Hallows' Barking Exhibition Foundation
The Aldgate Freedom Foundation
Alexandra Rose Charities
The Alexis Trust
All Saints Educational Trust
Allchurches Trust Ltd
The H B Allen Charitable Trust
The Rita Allen Charitable Trust
The Alliance Family Foundation
Angus Allnatt Charitable Foundation
The Pat Allsop Charitable Trust
The Almond Trust
Almondsbury Charity
The Altajir Trust
Altamont Ltd
Alvor Charitable Trust
AM Charitable Trust

....

Ambika Paul Foundation
The Ammco Trust
Sir John and Lady Amory's
    Charitable Trust
Viscount Amory's Charitable
    Trust
The Ampelos Trust
The AMW Charitable Trust
The Anchor Foundation
The Andrew Anderson Trust
The Andŕe Christian Trust
Anguish's Educational
    Foundation
The Animal Defence Trust
The Eric Anker-Petersen
    Charity
The Annandale Charitable
    Trust
Ambrose and Ann Appelbe
    Trust
The Appletree Trust
The John Apthorp Charitable
    Trust
The Milly Apthorp Charitable
    Trust
The Arbib Foundation
The Archbishop of
    Canterbury's Charitable
    Trust
The John M Archer Charitable
    Trust
The Archer Trust
The Ardwick Trust
The Argus Appeal
Armenian General Benevolent
    Union London Trust
The Armenian Relief Society of
    Great Britain Trust
The Armourers' and Brasiers'
    Gauntlet Trust
The Army Benevolent Fund
Arsenal Charitable Trust
The Arts and Entertainment
    Charitable Trust
Arts Council England
The Arts Council of Northern
    Ireland
The Arts Council of Wales
The Ove Arup Foundation
The AS Charitable Trust
Ashburnham Thanksgiving
    Trust
A J H Ashby Will Trust
The Ashden Trust
The Ashendene Trust
The Laura Ashley Foundation
The Norman C Ashton
    Foundation
The Ashworth Charitable Trust
The Ian Askew Charitable Trust
The Associated Country
    Women of the World
    (ACWW)
The Association of Colleges
    Charitable Trust
Astellas European Foundation

AstonMansfield Charitable
    Trust
The Astor Foundation
The Astor of Hever Trust
The Aurelius Charitable Trust
The Avenue Charitable Trust
The John Avins Trustees
The Avon and Somerset Police
    Community Trust
AW Charitable Trust
The Aylesford Family
    Charitable Trust
The BAA Communities Trust
Harry Bacon Foundation
The BACTA Charitable Trust
The Bagri Foundation
Veta Bailey Charitable Trust
The Austin Bailey Trust
The Baird Trust
The Baker Charitable Trust
The Balcombe Charitable Trust
The Balint Family Charitable
    Trusts
The Albert Casanova Ballard
    Deceased Trust
The Ballinger Charitable Trust
Balmain Charitable Trust
The Balmore Trust
The Balney Charitable Trust
The Baltic Charitable Fund
The Bamford Charitable
    Foundation
The Banbury Charities
William P Bancroft (No 2)
    Charitable Trust and
    Jenepher Gillett Trust
The Band Trust
The Barbers' Company General
    Charities
The Barbour Trust
Barchester Healthcare
    Foundation
David and Frederick Barclay
    Foundation
Peter Barker-Mill Memorial
    Charity
Barleycorn Trust
The Barnabas Trust
Lord Barnby's Foundation
Barnes Workhouse Fund
The Barnsbury Charitable Trust
The Barnstaple Bridge Trust
The Misses Barrie Charitable
    Trust
Barrington Family Charitable
    Trust
The Charity of William Barrow
Stephen J Barry Charitable
    Trust
The Bartlett Taylor Charitable
    Trust
The Paul Bassham Charitable
    Trust
The Batchworth Trust
The Bay Tree Charitable Trust

D H and L H Baylin Charitable
    Trust
The Louis Baylis (Maidenhead
    Advertiser) Charitable Trust
B-CH 1971 Charitable Trust
The Beacon Trust
Bear Mordechai Ltd
The Bearder Charity
The James Beattie Charitable
    Trust
The Beaufort House Trust
    Limited
Beauland Ltd
The Beaverbrook Foundation
The Beccles Town Lands
    Charity
The Becker Family Charitable
    Trust
The Becketts and Sargeants
    Educational Foundation
The Peter Beckwith Charitable
    Trust
The David and Ruth Behrend
    Fund
The Beit Trust
The Bellahouston Bequest
    Fund
Bellasis Trust
The Bellinger Donnay Trust
Belljoe Tzedoko Ltd
The Benfield Motors Charitable
    Trust
The Benham Charitable
    Settlement
Maurice and Jacqueline
    Bennett Charitable Trust
Michael and Leslie Bennett
    Charitable Trust
The Gerald Bentall Charitable
    Trust
Bergqvist Charitable Trust
The Berkshire Community
    Foundation
The Bestway Foundation
The Betterware Foundation
Thomas Betton's Charity for
    Pensions and Relief-in-Need
BHST
The Mason Bibby 1981 Trust
BibleLands
The Bideford Bridge Trust
The Big Lottery Fund
The Billmeir Charitable Trust
The Bingham Trust
The Bintaub Charitable Trust
The Birmingham Community
    Foundation
The Birmingham District
    Nursing Charitable Trust
The Birmingham Hospital
    Saturday Fund Medical
    Charity and Welfare Trust
Birmingham International
    Airport Community Trust
The Lord Mayor of
    Birmingham's Charity

Birthday House Trust

The Bisgood Charitable Trust (registered as Miss Jeanne Bisgood's Charitable Trust)

The Michael Bishop Foundation

The Bishop's Development Fund

The Sydney Black Charitable Trust

The Bertie Black Foundation

Isabel Blackman Foundation

The Herbert and Peter Blagrave Charitable Trust

The Blair Foundation

Blakes Benevolent Trust

The Blanchminster Trust

The Sir Victor Blank Charitable Settlement

Blatchington Court Trust

The Neville and Elaine Blond Charitable Trust

The Bluston Charitable Settlement

Enid Blyton Trust for Children

The Body Shop Foundation

The Bonamy Charitable Trust

The John and Celia Bonham Christie Charitable Trust

The Charlotte Bonham-Carter Charitable Trust

Bonhomie United Charity Society

The Boots Charitable Trust

The Bordon and Liphook Charity

Salo Bordon Charitable Trust

The Oliver Borthwick Memorial Trust

The Bothwell Charitable Trust

H E and E L Botteley Charitable Trust

The Harry Bottom Charitable Trust

P G and N J Boulton Trust

The A H and E Boulton Trust

Sir Clive Bourne Family Trust

The Anthony Bourne Foundation

The Bower Trust

The Bowerman Charitable Trust

John and Susan Bowers Fund

The Bowland Charitable Trust

The William Brake Charitable Trust

The Tony Bramall Charitable Trust

The Brewers' Company General Charitable Trust

The Harold and Alice Bridges Charity

Briggs Animal Welfare Trust

The Brighton District Nursing Association Trust

Bristol Archdeaconry Charity

John Bristow and Thomas Mason Trust

Britannia Foundation

The British Council for Prevention of Blindness

The British Dietetic Association General and Education Trust Fund

The British Gas (Scottish Gas) Energy Trust

British Heart Foundation

British Humane Association

British Institute at Ankara

British Ornithologists' Union

British Record Industry Trust

The Britto Foundation

The J and M Britton Charitable Trust

The Charles and Edna Broadhurst Charitable Trust

The Bromley Trust

The Roger Brooke Charitable Trust

The David Brooke Charity

The Charles Brotherton Trust

Joseph Brough Charitable Trust

The Swinfen Broun Charitable Trust

Mrs E E Brown Charitable Settlement

Bill Brown's Charitable Settlement

R S Brownless Charitable Trust

T B H Brunner's Charitable Settlement

The Jack Brunton Charitable Trust

Brushmill Ltd

The Bryant Trust

Buckingham Trust

The Buckinghamshire Foundation

The Buckinghamshire Masonic Centenary Fund

Buckland Charitable Trust

The Rosemary Bugden Charitable Trust

The Bulldog Trust Limited

The E F Bulmer Benevolent Fund

Burdens Charitable Foundation

The Burdett Trust for Nursing

The Clara E Burgess Charity

The Burry Charitable Trust

The Audrey and Stanley Burton 1960 Charitable Trust

The Arnold Burton 1998 Charitable Trust

The Burton Breweries Charitable Trust

The Geoffrey Burton Charitable Trust

Consolidated Charity of Burton upon Trent

Butchers' Company General Charities

The Bill Butlin Charity Trust

C and F Charitable Trust

C J Cadbury Charitable Trust

Henry T and Lucy B Cadbury Charitable Trust

P H G Cadbury Charitable Trust

The Christopher Cadbury Charitable Trust

The G W Cadbury Charitable Trust

The Richard Cadbury Charitable Trust

The Edward and Dorothy Cadbury Trust

The George Cadbury Trust

The Cadogan Charity

CAFOD

The Callander Charitable Trust

The Calpe Trust

Calypso Browning Trust

The Canning Trust

H and L Cantor Trust

Capital Community Foundation

Cardy Beaver Foundation

The Carew Pole Charitable Trust

The D W T Cargill Fund

Caring for Kids (Radio Tay)

Carlee Ltd

The Carlton House Charitable Trust

The Worshipful Company of Carmen Benevolent Trust

The Carnegie Dunfermline Trust

The Carnegie Trust for the Universities of Scotland

The Carpenter Charitable Trust

The Carpenters' Company Charitable Trust

The Carrington Charitable Trust

The Carron Charitable Settlement

The Leslie Mary Carter Charitable Trust

The Carvill Trust

The Casey Trust

The Elizabeth Casson Trust

The Castang Foundation

The Catalyst Charitable Trust

The Catholic Charitable Trust

Catholic Foreign Missions

The Catholic Trust for England and Wales

The Joseph and Annie Cattle Trust

The Thomas Sivewright Catto Charitable Settlement

The Wilfrid and Constance Cave Foundation

The Cayo Foundation

Elizabeth Cayzer Charitable
    Trust
The B G S Cayzer Charitable
    Trust
The Cazenove Charitable Trust
Celtic Charity Fund
The Cemlyn-Jones Trust
The Amelia Chadwick Trust
The Pamela Champion
    Foundation
The Chapman Charitable Trust
John William Chapman's
    Charitable Trust
The Charities Advisory Trust
Charitworth Limited
The Charter 600 Charity
The Worshipful Company of
    Chartered Accountants
    General Charitable Trust
The Chasah Trust
The Chelsea Building Society
    Charitable Foundation
The Chelsea Square 1994
    Trust
The Cheruby Trust
The Cheshire Provincial Fund
    of Benevolence
The Chetwode Foundation
The Malcolm Chick Charity
Child Growth Foundation
Children's Liver Disease
    Foundation
Childs Charitable Trust
The Childwick Trust
The Chippenham Borough
    Lands Charity
The Chipping Sodbury Town
    Lands Charity
CHK Charities Limited
The Chownes Foundation
The Chrimes Family Charitable
    Trust
The Christabella Charitable
    Trust
Christadelphian Samaritan
    Fund
Christian Aid
Christian Response to Eastern
    Europe
The Church and Community
    Fund
The Church Burgesses
    Educational Foundation
Church Burgesses Trust
Church Lands and John
    Johnson's Estate Charities
Church of Ireland Priorities
    Fund
City and County of Swansea
    Welsh Church Act Fund
The City Educational Trust
    Fund
The City Parochial Foundation
CLA Charitable Trust
Stephen Clark 1957
    Charitable Trust

J A Clark Charitable Trust
The Hilda and Alice Clark
    Charitable Trust
The Roger and Sarah Bancroft
    Clark Charitable Trust
The Clarke Charitable
    Settlement
The Cleary Foundation
The Cleopatra Trust
Lord Clinton's Charitable Trust
The Clore Duffield Foundation
Miss V L Clore's 1967
    Charitable Trust
Closehelm Ltd
The Clothworkers' Foundation
The Clover Trust
The Robert Clutterbuck
    Charitable Trust
Clydpride Ltd
The John Coates Charitable
    Trust
Coats Foundation Trust
The Cobtree Charity Trust Ltd
The Denise Cohen Charitable
    Trust
The Vivienne and Samuel
    Cohen Charitable Trust
The R and S Cohen Fondation
The John S Cohen Foundation
The Colchester Catalyst
    Charity
John Coldman Charitable Trust
The Cole Charitable Trust
The Colefax Charitable Trust
The John and Freda Coleman
    Charitable Trust
The George Henry Collins
    Charity
The E Alec Colman Charitable
    Fund Ltd
The Sir Jeremiah Colman Gift
    Trust
Col-Reno Ltd
The Colt Foundation
The Coltstaple Trust
Colwinston Charitable Trust
Colyer-Fergusson Charitable
    Trust
The Comino Foundation
Community Foundation for
    Calderdale
The Community Foundation for
    Greater Manchester
The Company of Tobacco Pipe
    Makers' and Tobacco
    Blenders' Benevolent Fund
The Compton Charitable Trust
The Congleton Inclosure Trust
The Conservation Foundation
The Consolidated Charities for
    the Infirm Merchant
    Taylors' Company
The Construction Industry
    Trust for Youth
Gordon Cook Foundation
The Cooks Charity

The Catherine Cookson
    Charitable Trust
Harold and Daphne Cooper
    Charitable Trust
Mabel Cooper Charity
The Alice Ellen Cooper Dean
    Charitable Foundation
The Co-operative Foundation
The Marjorie Coote Animal
    Charity Trust
The Marjorie Coote Old
    People's Charity
The Helen Jean Cope Trust
The J Reginald Corah
    Foundation Fund
The Gershon Coren Charitable
    Foundation
The Corinthian Trust
Edwin Cornforth 1983 Charity
    Trust
The Duke of Cornwall's
    Benevolent Fund
The Cornwell Charitable Trust
The Sidney and Elizabeth
    Corob Charitable Trust
The Corona Charitable Trust
The Costa Family Charitable
    Trust
The Cotton Industry War
    Memorial Trust
The Cotton Trust
County Durham Foundation
The Augustine Courtauld Trust
Coutts Charitable Trust
The General Charities of the
    City of Coventry
Coventry Building Society
    Charitable Foundation
The John Cowan Foundation
Cowley Charitable Foundation
The Sir William Coxen Trust
    Fund
The Lord Cozens-Hardy Trust
The Craignish Trust
The Craps Charitable Trust
Michael Crawford Children's
    Charity
The Cray Trust
The Crescent Trust
Criffel Charitable Trust
The Violet and Milo Cripps
    Charitable Trust
The Cromarty Trust
The Harry Crook Foundation
The Cross Trust
The Cross Trust
The Croydon Relief in Need
    Charities
The Mayor of Croydon's
    Charity Fund
Cruden Foundation Ltd
The Ronald Cruickshanks'
    Foundation
Cuby Charitable Trust
The Culra Charitable Trust

The Cumber Family Charitable Trust

Cumberland Building Society Charitable Foundation

Cumbria Community Foundation

The D J H Currie Memorial Trust

The Dennis Curry Charitable Trust

The Raymond Curtis Charitable Trust

The Manny Cussins Foundation

The Cwmbran Trust

Itzchok Meyer Cymerman Trust Ltd

The D'Oyly Carte Charitable Trust

The Daily Prayer Union Charitable Trust Ltd

The Daisy Trust

The Daiwa Anglo-Japanese Foundation

Oizer Dalim Trust

The Dr and Mrs A Darlington Charitable Trust

The Davidson (Nairn) Charitable Trust

Davidson Charitable Trust

The Alderman Joe Davidson Memorial Trust

Michael Davies Charitable Settlement

The Gwendoline and Margaret Davies Charity

The Wilfrid Bruce Davis Charitable Trust

Davis-Rubens Charitable Trust

The Dawe Charitable Trust

The De Clermont Charitable Company Ltd

Peter De Haan Charitable Trust

The Leopold De Rothschild Charitable Trust

The Deakin Charitable Trust

William Dean Countryside and Educational Trust

The Debmar Benevolent Trust

The Delfont Foundation

The Delius Trust

The Dellal Foundation

The Delves Charitable Trust

The Demigryphon Trust

The Denman Charitable Trust

The Denton Charitable Trust

The Denton Wilde Sapte Charitable Trust

The Earl of Derby's Charitable Trust

Derbyshire Community Foundation

The J N Derbyshire Trust

Devon Community Foundation

The Devon Educational Trust

The Duke of Devonshire's Charitable Trust

The Sandy Dewhirst Charitable Trust

DG Charitable Settlement

The Laduma Dhamecha Charitable Trust

Alan and Sheila Diamond Charitable Trust

The Dibden Allotments Charity

The Dickon Trust

The Digbeth Trust

The Dinwoodie Settlement

Dischma Charitable Trust

The DLA Piper Charitable Trust

The DLM Charitable Trust

Louise Dobson Charitable Trust

The Derek and Eileen Dodgson Foundation

The Dollond Charitable Trust

Domepride Ltd

The Dorcas Trust

The Dorema Charitable Trust

The Dorus Trust

Double 'O' Charity Ltd

The Doughty Charity Trust

The R M Douglas Charitable Trust

The Drapers' Charitable Fund

Dromintee Trust

The Dugdale Charitable Trust

The Duis Charitable Trust

The P B Dumbell Charitable Trust

The Dumbreck Charity

Dunard Fund

Ronald Duncan Literary Foundation

The Houghton Dunn Charitable Trust

The Dunn Family Charitable Trust

The W E Dunn Trust

Dushinsky Trust Ltd

Mildred Duveen Charitable Trust

The Dwek Family Charitable Trust

The Dyers' Company Charitable Trust

EAGA Partnership Charitable Trust

The Eagle Charity Trust

Audrey Earle Charitable Trust

The Earley Charity

Earls Colne and Halstead Educational Charity

The Earmark Trust

East Kent Provincial Charities

East London Community Foundation

Eastern Counties Educational Trust Limited

The Ebenezer Trust

The EBM Charitable Trust

Eden Arts Trust

EDF Energy Trust (EDFET)

The Gilbert and Eileen Edgar Foundation

Gilbert Edgar Trust

Edinburgh Children's Holiday Fund

The Edinburgh Trust, No 2 Account

Edinburgh Voluntary Organisations' Trust Funds

Educational Foundation of Alderman John Norman

The W G Edwards Charitable Foundation

The William Edwards Educational Charity

The Elephant Trust

The George Elias Charitable Trust

The Gerald Palmer Eling Trust Company

The Elizabeth Frankland Moore and Star Foundation

The Wilfred and Elsie Elkes Charity Fund

Ellador Ltd

The Ellerdale Trust

The John Ellerman Foundation

The Ellinson Foundation Ltd

The Edith Maud Ellis 1985 Charitable Trust

The Ellis Campbell Foundation

James Ellis Charitable Trust

The Elmgrant Trust

The Elmley Foundation

Elshore Ltd

The Vernon N Ely Charitable Trust

The Embleton Trust

The Emerton-Christie Charity

EMI Music Sound Foundation

The Emmandjay Charitable Trust

The Worshipful Company of Engineers Charitable Trust Fund

The Englefield Charitable Trust

The English Schools' Football Association

The Enkalon Foundation

Entindale Ltd

The Epigoni Trust

Epilepsy Research UK

The Equity Trust Fund

The Ericson Trust

The Erskine Cunningham Hill Trust

Essex Community Foundation

The Essex Fairway Charitable Trust

The Essex Heritage Trust

Essex Provincial Charity Fund

The Essex Youth Trust

Euro Charity Trust

The Evangelical Covenants Trust

The Alan Evans Memorial Trust

Sir John Evelyn's Charity

The Eventhall Family Charitable Trust

The Everard Foundation

The Beryl Evetts and Robert Luff Animal Welfare Trust

The Execution Charitable Trust

The Mayor of Exeter's Appeal Fund

The Exilarch's Foundation

F C Charitable Trust

The F P Limited Charitable Trust

The Faber Charitable Trust

The Fairway Trust

Faisaltex Charitable Trust

The Family Foundations Trust

The Family Rich Charities Trust

Famos Foundation Trust

The Lord Faringdon Charitable Trust

Samuel William Farmer's Trust

The Farmers' Company Charitable Fund

The Thomas Farr Charitable Trust

Walter Farthing (Trust) Limited

Farthing Trust

The Fassnidge Memorial Trust

Joseph Fattorini Charitable Trust 'B' Account

The Fawcett Charitable Trust

Federation of Jewish Relief Organisations

Feed the Minds

The John Feeney Charitable Bequest

The George Fentham Birmingham Charity

The A M Fenton Trust

Allan and Nesta Ferguson Charitable Settlement

Elizabeth Ferguson Charitable Trust Fund

The Fidelity UK Foundation

The Bluff Field Charitable Trust

The Doris Field Charitable Trust

Fife Council/Common Good Funds and Trusts

Dixie Rose Findlay Charitable Trust

Gerald Finzi Charitable Trust

Firtree Trust

The Sir John Fisher Foundation

Marc Fitch Fund

The Fitton Trust

The Earl Fitzwilliam Charitable Trust

Bud Flanagan Leukaemia Fund

The Rose Flatau Charitable Trust

The Ian Fleming Charitable Trust

The Joyce Fletcher Charitable Trust

The Roy Fletcher Charitable Trust

Florence's Charitable Trust

The Florian Charitable Trust

The Flow Foundation

The Gerald Fogel Charitable Trust

The Follett Trust

The Football Association National Sports Centre Trust

The Football Association Youth Trust

The Football Foundation

The Forbes Charitable Foundation

Forbesville Limited

The Forces Trust

Ford Britain Trust

The Oliver Ford Charitable Trust

Fordeve Ltd

The Forest Hill Charitable Trust

The Foresters' Charity Stewards UK Trust

Gwyneth Forrester Trust

The Forte Charitable Trust

Lord Forte Foundation

Foundation for Management Education

Four Acre Trust

The Four Winds Trust

The Fowler, Smith and Jones Charitable Trust

The Foyle Foundation

The Isaac and Freda Frankel Memorial Charitable Trust

Sydney E Franklin Deceased's New Second Charity

The Jill Franklin Trust

The Gordon Fraser Charitable Trust

The Hugh Fraser Foundation

The Joseph Strong Frazer Trust

The Louis and Valerie Freedman Charitable Settlement

The Thomas Freke and Lady Norton Charity

The Charles S French Charitable Trust

The Anne French Memorial Trust

The Freshfield Foundation

The Freshgate Trust Foundation

The Friarsgate Trust

The Friends Hall Farm Street Trust

Friends of Biala Ltd

Friends of Wiznitz Limited

Friends Provident Charitable Foundation

The Frognal Trust

T F C Frost Charitable Trust

The Patrick Frost Foundation

Maurice Fry Charitable Trust

Mejer and Gertrude Miriam Frydman Foundation

The Fuellers Charitable Fund

The Fulmer Charitable Trust

Worshipful Company of Furniture Makers Charitable Fund

Gableholt Limited

The Galbraith Trust

The Gale Family Charitable Trust

The Angela Gallagher Memorial Fund

The Gamlen Charitable Trust

The Gamma Trust

The Gannochy Trust

The Ganzoni Charitable Trust

The Worshipful Company of Gardeners of London

The Samuel Gardner Memorial Trust

The Garnett Charitable Trust

Garrick Charitable Trust

Garvan Limited

The Gatsby Charitable Foundation

Gatwick Airport Community Trust

The Robert Gavron Charitable Trust

Jacqueline and Michael Gee Charitable Trust

The Gibbs Charitable Trust

Simon Gibson Charitable Trust

The G C Gibson Charitable Trust

The Harvey and Hilary Gilbert Charitable Trust

The Girdlers' Company Charitable Trust

The B and P Glasser Charitable Trust

The Glass-House Trust

Global Care

Global Charities (formally GCap Charities)

Gloucestershire Community Foundation

Worshipful Company of Glovers of London Charity Fund

GMC Trust

The GNC Trust

The Mrs Godfrey-Payton Trust

The Meir Golda Trust

The Sydney and Phyllis Goldberg Memorial Charitable Trust

The Golden Bottle Trust

Golden Charitable Trust
The Jack Goldhill Charitable Trust
The Goldsmiths' Arts Trust Fund
The Goldsmiths' Company Charity
The Good Neighbours Trust
Nicholas and Judith Goodison's Charitable Settlement
The Everard and Mina Goodman Charitable Foundation
Mike Gooley Trailfinders Charity
Leonard Gordon Charitable Trust
The Gosling Foundation Limited
The Gough Charitable Trust
The Gould Charitable Trust
The Grace Charitable Trust
A B Grace Trust
The Graff Foundation
The Grahame Charitable Foundation Limited
Grampian Police Diced Cap Charitable Fund
The Granada Foundation
Grand Charitable Trust of the Order of Women Freemasons
The Grand Order of Water Rats' Charities Fund
The Grange Farm Centre Trust
Grantham Yorke Trust
The J G Graves Charitable Trust
The Gray Trust
The Great Stone Bridge Trust of Edenbridge
The Great Torrington Town Lands Charity
The Barry Green Memorial Fund
The Philip Green Memorial Trust
Mrs H R Greene Charitable Settlement
Greenham Common Community Trust Limited
Naomi and Jeffrey Greenwood Charitable Trust
Grimmitt Trust
The Grocers' Charity
The M and R Gross Charities Limited
The Grove Charitable Trust
The GRP Charitable Trust
The David and Marie Grumitt Foundation
The Bishop of Guildford's Foundation
The Guildry Incorporation of Perth

The Walter Guinness Charitable Trust
The Gunter Charitable Trust
The Gur Trust
Gurunanak
Dr Guthrie's Association
The H and M Charitable Trust
H C D Memorial Fund
The H P Charitable Trust
The Hackney Parochial Charities
The Hadfield Trust
The Hadrian Trust
The Alfred Haines Charitable Trust
The Hale Trust
E F and M G Hall Charitable Trust
The Edith Winifred Hall Charitable Trust
Robert Hall Charity
The Hamamelis Trust
Hamilton Wallace Trust
Paul Hamlyn Foundation
Sue Hammerson's Charitable Trust
The Hammonds Charitable Trust
The Hampshire and Islands Historic Churches Trust
The W A Handley Charitable Trust
Beatrice Hankey Foundation Ltd
The Hanley Trust
The Kathleen Hannay Memorial Charity
The Doughty Hanson Charitable Foundation
Lord Hanson Foundation
The Haramead Trust
Miss K M Harbinson's Charitable Trust
Harbo Charities Limited
The Harborne Parish Lands Charity
The Harbour Charitable Trust
The Harbour Foundation
The Harding Trust
William Harding's Charity
The Hare of Steep Charitable Trust
The Harebell Centenary Fund
The Kenneth Hargreaves Charitable Trust
The Harris Charitable Trust
The Harris Charity
The Harrison and Potter Trust
The John Harrison Charitable Trust
The Spencer Hart Charitable Trust
The Hartley Charitable Trust
The N and P Hartley Memorial Trust

William Geoffrey Harvey's Discretionary Settlement
The Edward Harvist Trust Fund
Haskel Family Foundation
The Hathaway Trust
The M A Hawe Settlement
The Hawthorne Charitable Trust
The Dorothy Hay-Bolton Charitable Trust
The Haydan Charitable Trust
The Haymills Charitable Trust
The Headley Trust
Headley-Pitt Charitable Trust
Heagerty Charitable Trust
The Heald Charitable Trust
Healthsure Group Ltd
May Hearnshaw's Charity
The Heart of England Community Foundation
The Heathcoat Trust
Heathside Charitable Trust
The Charlotte Heber-Percy Charitable Trust
Percy Hedley 1990 Charitable Trust
The Hedley Denton Charitable Trust
The Hedley Foundation
The H J Heinz Company Limited Charitable Trust
The Hellenic Foundation
The Michael and Morven Heller Charitable Foundation
The Simon Heller Charitable Settlement
Help the Homeless
Help the Hospices
The Hemby Trust
The Christina Mary Hendrie Trust for Scottish and Canadian Charities
The Henley Educational Charity
Philip Henman Trust
Esther Hennell Charitable Trust
The G D Herbert Charitable Trust
The Joanna Herbert-Stepney Charitable Settlement
The Anne Herd Memorial Trust
The Herefordshire Historic Churches Trust
The Heritage of London Trust Ltd
The Hertfordshire Community Foundation
The Hesed Trust
The Hesslewood Children's Trust (Hull Seamen's and General Orphanage)
The Bernhard Heuberger Charitable Trust
Hexham and Newcastle Diocesan Trust (1947)

The P and C Hickinbotham
Charitable Trust
The Higgs Charitable Trust
The High Sheriff's Police Trust
for the County of West
Midlands
Highcroft Charitable Trust
The Joseph and Mary Hiley
Trust
The Holly Hill Charitable Trust
The Charles Littlewood Hill
Trust
The Hillingdon Partnership
Trust
R G Hills Charitable Trust
Hinchley Charitable Trust
Lady Hind Trust
Stuart Hine Trust
The Hinrichsen Foundation
The Hitchin Educational
Foundation
The Eleemosynary Charity of
William Hobbayne
Hobson Charity Limited
Hockerill Educational
Foundation
Matthew Hodder Charitable
Trust
The Sir Julian Hodge
Charitable Trust
The J G Hogg Charitable Trust
The Holden Charitable Trust
John Holford's Charity
The Hollick Family Charitable
Trust
The Dorothy Holmes Charitable
Trust
P H Holt Foundation
The Edward Holt Trust
The Holywood Trust
The Homelands Charitable
Trust
The Homestead Charitable
Trust
Mary Homfray Charitable Trust
Sir Harold Hood's Charitable
Trust
The Hope Trust
HopMarket Charity
The Cuthbert Horn Trust
The Antony Hornby Charitable
Trust
The Horne Trust
The Worshipful Company of
Horners' Charitable Trusts
The Hornsey Parochial
Charities
The Hospital of God at
Greatham
The Hospital Saturday Fund
Houblon-Norman/George Fund
The House of Industry Estate
The Reta Lila Howard
Foundation
The Daniel Howard Trust

The Huddersfield Medical Trust
Fund
The Hudson Foundation
The Huggard Charitable Trust
The Geoffrey C Hughes
Charitable Trust
The Hull and East Riding
Charitable Trust
Hulme Trust Estates
(Educational)
Human Relief Foundation
The Humanitarian Trust
The Michael and Shirley Hunt
Charitable Trust
The Hunter Foundation
Miss Agnes H Hunter's Trust
The Huntingdon Foundation
Huntingdon Freemen's Charity
John Huntingdon's Charity
Hurdale Charity Limited
The Nani Huyu Charitable Trust
The P Y N and B Hyams Trust
The Hyde Charitable Trust –
Youth Plus
The Idlewild Trust
The Iliffe Family Charitable
Trust
The Indigo Trust
The Ingram Trust
The Inland Waterways
Association
The Inlight Trust
The Inman Charity
The Inner London Magistrates
Court Poor Box Charity and
Feeder Charity
The Worshipful Company of
Innholders General Charity
Fund
The Ireland Fund of Great
Britain
The Irish Youth Foundation
(UK) Ltd
The Ironmongers' Foundation
Irshad Trust
The Charles Irving Charitable
Trust
Irwin Trust
The ISA Charity
The Isaacs Charitable Trust
The J Isaacs Charitable Trust
The Island Health Trust
The ITF Seafarers Trust
J A R Charitable Trust
The J R S S T Charitable Trust
Elizabeth Jackson Charitable
Trust
Jacobs Charitable Trust
The Ruth and Lionel Jacobson
Trust (Second Fund) No 2
Jaffe Family Relief Fund
John James Bristol Foundation
The Susan and Stephen
James Charitable
Settlement
The James Trust

The Jarman Charitable Trust
The John Jarrold Trust
JCA Charitable Foundation
The Jeffrey Charitable Trust
Rees Jeffreys Road Fund
The Jenour Foundation
The Jephcott Charitable Trust
Jerwood Charitable Foundation
Jesus Hospital Charity
Jewish Child's Day
The Jewish Youth Fund
The JMK Charitable Trust
The Joanies Trust
The Harold Joels Charitable
Trust
The Jonathan Joels Charitable
Trust
The Nicholas Joels Charitable
Trust
The Norman Joels Charitable
Trust
The Lillie Johnson Charitable
Trust
The Johnson Group Cleaners
Charity
The Johnnie Johnson Trust
The Johnson Wax Ltd
Charitable Trust
The Joicey Trust
The Jones 1986 Charitable
Trust
The Marjorie and Geoffrey
Jones Charitable Trust
The Jordan Charitable
Foundation
The J E Joseph Charitable
Fund
The Lady Eileen Joseph
Foundation
JTH Charitable Trust
The Judith Trust
The Anton Jurgens Charitable
Trust
The Bernard Kahn Charitable
Trust
The Stanley Kalms Foundation
The Karenza Foundation
The Boris Karloff Charitable
Foundation
The Kasner Charitable Trust
The Kass Charitable Trust
The Kathleen Trust
The Michael and Ilse Katz
Foundation
The Katzauer Charitable
Settlement
The C S Kaufman Charitable
Trust
The Geoffrey John Kaye
Charitable Foundation
The Emmanuel Kaye
Foundation
Kelsick's Educational
Foundation
The KempWelch Charitable
Trust

William Kendall's Charity (Wax
　Chandlers' Company)
The Kennel Club Charitable
　Trust
The Nancy Kenyon Charitable
　Trust
Keren Association
Kermaville Ltd
E and E Kernkraut Charities
　Limited
The Peter Kershaw Trust
The Kessler Foundation
Keswick Hall Charity
The Ursula Keyes Trust
The Robert Kiln Charitable
　Trust
The King Henry VIII Endowed
　Trust Warwick
The King/Cullimore Charitable
　Trust
The Kingsbury Charity
Kinsurdy Charitable Trust
Kirkley Poor's Lands Estate
The Richard Kirkman
　Charitable Trust
Kirschel Foundation
Robert Kitchin (Saddlers'
　Company)
Ernest Kleinwort Charitable
　Trust
The Marina Kleinwort
　Charitable Trust
The Kobler Trust
The Kohn Foundation
The Kreditor Charitable Trust
The Kreitman Foundation
The Neil Kreitman Foundation
The Heinz, Anna and Carol
　Kroch Foundation
The Kyte Charitable Trust
Lacims-Maclis Charitable Trust
The Late Sir Pierce Lacy
　Charity Trust
The Laing Family Foundations
The Christopher Laing
　Foundation
The Martin Laing Foundation
The Lambert Charitable Trust
Lancashire Environmental
　Fund
Duchy of Lancaster Benevolent
　Fund
LandAid Charitable Trust
The Langdale Trust
The Langley Charitable Trust
The Langtree Trust
The LankellyChase Foundation
The Lanvern Foundation
The R J Larg Family Charitable
　Trust
Largsmount Ltd
The Lark Trust
Laslett's (Hinton) Charity
Lauchentilly Charitable
　Foundation 1988
Laufer Charitable Trust

The Lauffer Family Charitable
　Foundation
Mrs F B Laurence Charitable
　Trust
The Kathleen Laurence Trust
The Edgar E Lawley Foundation
The Herd Lawson and Muriel
　Lawson Charitable Trust
The Lawson Beckman
　Charitable Trust
The Raymond and Blanche
　Lawson Charitable Trust
The Carole and Geoffrey
　Lawson Foundation
The Mason Le Page Charitable
　Trust
The Leach Fourteenth Trust
The David Lean Foundation
The Leche Trust
The Arnold Lee Charitable
　Trust
The Lord Mayor of Leeds
　Appeal Fund
Leeds Building Society
　Charitable Foundation
Leicester Charity Link
The Kennedy Leigh Charitable
　Trust
Morris Leigh Foundation
The Leigh Trust
Mrs Vera Leigh's Charity
The P Leigh-Bramwell Trust 'E'
The Lennox and Wyfold
　Foundation
The Erica Leonard Trust
The Leonard Trust
The Mark Leonard Trust
Lesley Lesley and Mutter Trust
The Joseph Levy Charitable
　Foundation
The John Spedan Lewis
　Foundation
The Sir Edward Lewis
　Foundation
John Lewis Partnership
　General Community Fund
Lichfield Conduit Lands
Lifeline 4 Kids
The Thomas Lilley Memorial
　Trust
Limoges Charitable Trust
The Linbury Trust
The Lind Trust
Lindale Educational
　Foundation
The Linden Charitable Trust
The Linmardon Trust
The Ruth and Stuart Lipton
　Charitable Trust
The Lister Charitable Trust
Frank Litchfield Charitable
　Trust
The Andrew and Mary
　Elizabeth Little Charitable
　Trust

The Second Joseph Aaron
　Littman Foundation
Liverpool Charity and Voluntary
　Services
Liverpool Sailors' Home Trust
Jack Livingstone Charitable
　Trust
The Elaine and Angus Lloyd
　Charitable Trust
The Charles Lloyd Foundation
The Lloyd Fund
Lloyd's Charities Trust
The Lloyd-Everett Trust
Lloyds TSB Foundation for the
　Channel Islands
Llysdinam Charitable Trust
Localtrent Ltd
The Locker Foundation
The Loftus Charitable Trust
The Lolev Charitable Trust
London Catalyst
The London Law Trust
The London Marathon
　Charitable Trust
The William and Katherine
　Longman Trust
The Loseley and Guildway
　Charitable Trust
The Lotus Foundation
The C L Loyd Charitable Trust
The Marie Helen Luen
　Charitable Trust
Robert Luff Foundation Ltd
Henry Lumley Charitable Trust
Lady Lumley's Educational
　Foundation
Paul Lunn-Rockliffe Charitable
　Trust
C F Lunoe Trust Fund
The Ruth and Jack Lunzer
　Charitable Trust
Lord and Lady Lurgan Trust
The Lyndhurst Trust
The Lynn Foundation
The Lynwood Trust
John Lyon's Charity
The Lyons Charitable Trust
The Sir Jack Lyons Charitable
　Trust
Malcolm Lyons Foundation
The Lyras Family Charitable
　Trust
Sylvanus Lyson's Charity
The M and C Trust
The M D and S Charitable
　Trust
The M K Charitable Trust
The Madeline Mabey Trust
The E M MacAndrew Trust
The R S Macdonald Charitable
　Trust
Macdonald-Buchanan
　Charitable Trust
The Macfarlane Walker Trust
The Mackay and Brewer
　Charitable Trust

The Mackintosh Foundation
The MacRobert Trust
Ian Mactaggart Trust
The Magdalen and Lasher
Charity
Magdalen Hospital Trust
The Magen Charitable Trust
Mageni Trust
Mahavir Trust
Man Group plc Charitable
Trust
The Manchester Guardian
Society Charitable Trust
Manchester Kids
Lord Mayor of Manchester's
Charity Appeal Trust
Mandeville Trust
The Manifold Charitable Trust
W M Mann Foundation
The Leslie and Lilian Manning
Trust
Maranatha Christian Trust
Marbeh Torah Trust
The Marchday Charitable Fund
Marchig Animal Welfare Trust
The Stella and Alexander
Margulies Charitable Trust
Market Harborough and The
Bowdens Charity
Michael Marks Charitable
Trust
The Ann and David Marks
Foundation
The Hilda and Samuel Marks
Foundation
J P Marland Charitable Trust
Marr-Munning Trust
The Michael Marsh Charitable
Trust
The Marsh Christian Trust
The Charlotte Marshall
Charitable Trust
The Jim Marshall Charitable
Trust
The D G Marshall of
Cambridge Trust
Marshall's Charity
Marshgate Charitable
Settlement
Sir George Martin Trust
John Martin's Charity
The Mason Porter Charitable
Trust
The Nancie Massey Charitable
Trust
The Mathew Trust
Matliwala Family Charitable
Trust
The Matt 6.3 Charitable Trust
The Violet Mauray Charitable
Trust
The Maxell Educational Trust
The Maxwell Family Foundation
Evelyn May Trust
Mayfair Charities Ltd
The Mayfield Valley Arts Trust

Mazars Charitable Trust
The Robert McAlpine
Foundation
The McDougall Trust
The A M McGreevy No 5
Charitable Settlement
The McKenna Charitable Trust
Martin McLaren Memorial
Trust
The Helen Isabella McMorran
Charitable Foundation
D D McPhail Charitable
Settlement
The James Frederick and Ethel
Anne Measures Charity
Medical Research Council
The Anthony and Elizabeth
Mellows Charitable
Settlement
Melodor Ltd
Melow Charitable Trust
Meningitis Trust
Menuchar Ltd
Brian Mercer Charitable Trust
The Mercers' Charitable
Foundation
The Merchant Taylors'
Company Charities Fund
The Merchant Venturers'
Charity
The Merchants' House of
Glasgow
Mercury Phoenix Trust
The Mersey Docks and
Harbour Company
Charitable Fund
Community Foundation for
Merseyside
The Zachary Merton and
George Woofindin
Convalescent Trust
The Tony Metherell Charitable
Trust
The Methodist Relief and
Development Fund
The Metropolitan Drinking
Fountain and Cattle Trough
Association
Gerald Micklem Charitable
Trust
Midhurst Pensions Trust
The Migraine Trust
Miles Trust for the Putney and
Roehampton Community
The Hugh and Mary Miller
Bequest Trust
The Miller Foundation
The Millfield Trust
The Millhouses Charitable
Trust
The Millichope Foundation
The Mills Charity
The Millward Charitable Trust
The Clare Milne Trust
Milton Keynes Community
Foundation

The Edgar Milward Charity
The Keith and Joan
Mindelsohn Charitable
Trust
The Peter Minet Trust
Minge's Gift and the Pooled
Trusts
The Minos Trust
The Mirfield Educational
Charity
The Laurence Misener
Charitable Trust
The Mishcon Family Charitable
Trust
The Misselbrook Trust
The Mitchell Charitable Trust
The Esmé Mitchell Trust
Keren Mitzvah Trust
The Mizpah Trust
The Mobbs Memorial Trust Ltd
The Modiano Charitable Trust
The Moette Charitable Trust
The Mole Charitable Trust
The D C Moncrieff Charitable
Trust
Monmouthshire County Council
Welsh Church Act Fund
The Montague Thompson
Coon Charitable Trust
The Colin Montgomerie
Charitable Foundation
The Monument Trust
Moody Charitable Trust
George A Moore Foundation
The Henry Moore Foundation
The Nigel Moores Family
Charitable Trust
The Peter Moores Foundation
The Morel Charitable Trust
The Morgan Charitable
Foundation
The Mr and Mrs J T Morgan
Foundation
The J P Morgan Foundations
Diana and Allan Morgenthau
Charitable Trust
The Oliver Morland Charitable
Trust
S C and M E Morland's
Charitable Trust
The Morris Charitable Trust
The Willie and Mabel Morris
Charitable Trust
The Peter Morrison Charitable
Foundation
The Stanley Morrison
Charitable Trust
Moshal Charitable Trust
Vyoel Moshe Charitable Trust
The Moss Charitable Trust
The Robert and Margaret
Moss Charitable Trust
Moss Family Charitable Trust
The Mount Everest Foundation
Mountbatten Festival of Music

The Mountbatten Memorial
Trust
The Edwina Mountbatten Trust
The Mugdock Children's Trust
The F H Muirhead Charitable
Trust
The Mulberry Trust
The Edith Murphy Foundation
Murphy-Neumann Charity
Company Limited
The Mushroom Fund
The Music Sales Charitable
Trust
Muslim Hands
The Mutual Trust Group
MYA Charitable Trust
The Kitty and Daniel Nabarro
Charitable Trust
The Nadezhda Charitable Trust
The Willie Nagel Charitable
Trust
The Naggar Charitable Trust
The Eleni Nakou Foundation
The Janet Nash Charitable
Settlement
Nathan Charitable Trust
The National Art Collections
Fund
Asthma UK
The National Churches Trust
The National Manuscripts
Conservation Trust
Nazareth Trust Fund
The Nchima Trust
Needham Market and Barking
Welfare Charities
The Worshipful Company of
Needlemakers' Charitable
Fund
The Neighbourly Charitable
Trust
The James Neill Trust Fund
Nemoral Ltd
Nesswall Ltd
Nestle Rowntree Employees
Community Fund
Network for Social Change
The New Appeals Organisation
for the City and County of
Nottingham
New Court Charitable Trust
Newby Trust Limited
The Newcomen Collett
Foundation
The Richard Newitt Fund
Mr and Mrs F E F Newman
Charitable Trust
Newpier Charity Ltd
Alderman Newton's
Educational Foundation
The Chevras Ezras Nitzrochim
Trust
The Noel Buxton Trust
The Noon Foundation
The Norda Trust
Norie Charitable Trust

Normalyn Charitable Trust
The Norman Family Charitable
Trust
The Duncan Norman Trust
Fund
The Normanby Charitable Trust
The North West Cancer
Research Fund
The Northampton Municipal
Church Charities
The Northampton Queen's
Institute Relief in Sickness
Fund
The Earl of Northampton's
Charity
The Northcott Devon
Foundation
The Northcott Devon Medical
Foundation
The Northmoor Trust
The Northumberland Village
Homes Trust
The Northumbria Historic
Churches Trust
The Northwood Charitable
Trust
The Norton Foundation
The Norwich Church of England
Young Men's Society
The Norwich Historic Churches
Trust Ltd
The Norwich Town Close
Estate Charity
The Norwood and Newton
Settlement
The Noswad Charity
The Notgrove Trust
The Nottingham General
Dispensary
The Nottingham Gordon
Memorial Trust for Boys
and Girls
Nottinghamshire Community
Foundation
The Nottinghamshire Historic
Churches Trust
The Nottinghamshire Miners'
Welfare Trust Fund
Novi Most International
The Father O'Mahoney
Memorial Trust
The Sir Peter O'Sullevan
Charitable Trust
The Oak Trust
The Oakdale Trust
The Oakley Charitable Trust
The Oakmoor Charitable Trust
The Odin Charitable Trust
Ogilvie Charities Deed No.2
(including the Charity of
Mary Catherine Ford Smith)
The Ogle Christian Trust
Oglesby Charitable Trust
The Oikonomia Trust
The Oizer Charitable Trust

The Old Broad Street Charity
Trust
The Old Enfield Charitable
Trust
Old Possum's Practical Trust
The John Oldacre Foundation
The Oldham Foundation
Onaway Trust
Open Gate
The Ormsby Charitable Trust
Orrin Charitable Trust
The Ouseley Trust
The Owen Family Trust
Oxfam (GB)
The Oxfordshire Community
Foundation
The P F Charitable Trust
Padwa Charitable Foundation
The Pallant Charitable Trust
The Palmer Foundation
Eleanor Palmer Trust
The Panacea Society
Panahpur Charitable Trust
Panton Trust
The James Pantyfedwen
Foundation
The Paragon Trust
The Park House Charitable
Trust
The Frank Parkinson
Agricultural Trust
The Samuel and Freda
Parkinson Charitable Trust
The Parthenon Trust
Arthur James Paterson
Charitable Trust
The Constance Paterson
Charitable Trust
Miss M E Swinton Paterson's
Charitable Trust
The Patrick Charitable Trust
The Jack Patston Charitable
Trust
Paycare Charity Trust
The Payne Charitable Trust
The Harry Payne Trust
The Susanna Peake Charitable
Trust
The Pedmore Sporting Club
Trust Fund
Peltz Trust
The Pennycress Trust
The Performing Right Society
Foundation
B E Perl Charitable Trust
The Persson Charitable Trust
The Persula Foundation
The Pestalozzi Overseas
Children's Trust
The Jack Petchey Foundation
The Petplan Charitable Trust
The Philips and Rubens
Charitable Trust
The Phillips Charitable Trust
The Phillips Family Charitable
Trust

Philological Foundation
The David Pickford Charitable
  Foundation
The Bernard Piggott Trust
The Claude and Margaret Pike
  Charity
The Pilgrim Trust
The Cecil Pilkington Charitable
  Trust
The Austin and Hope
  Pilkington Trust
The Sir Harry Pilkington Trust
The Col W W Pilkington Will
  Trusts The General Charity
  Fund
Miss A M Pilkington's
  Charitable Trust
Mrs Pilkington's Charitable
  Trust
The Plaisterers' Company
  Charitable Trust
The Platinum Trust
G S Plaut Charitable Trust
  Limited
The Poling Charitable Trust
The George and Esme Pollitzer
  Charitable Settlement
The J S F Pollitzer Charitable
  Settlement
The Ponton House Trust
The Mayor of Poole's Appeal
  Fund
Edith and Ferdinand Porjes
  Charitable Trust
The John Porter Charitable
  Trust
The Porter Foundation
The Portishead Nautical Trust
The Portrack Charitable Trust
The J E Posnansky Charitable
  Trust
The Powell Foundation
Prairie Trust
The W L Pratt Charitable Trust
Premierquote Ltd
Premishlaner Charitable Trust
The William Price Charitable
  Trust
The Lucy Price Relief-in-Need
  Charity
Sir John Priestman Charity
  Trust
The Primrose Trust
The Prince's Charities
  Foundation
Princess Anne's Charities
The Priory Foundation
Prison Service Charity Fund
The Privy Purse Charitable
  Trust
The Proven Family Trust
The Provincial Grand Charity of
  the Province of Derbyshire
PSA Peugeot Citroen Charity
  Trust
The Puebla Charitable Trust

The Richard and Christine
  Purchas Charitable Trust
The Puri Foundation
The Queen's Silver Jubilee
  Trust
Quercus Trust
The R D Crusaders Foundation
R J M Charitable Trust
R S Charitable Trust
The R V W Trust
The Monica Rabagliati
  Charitable Trust
Rachel Charitable Trust
The Mr and Mrs Philip
  Rackham Charitable Trust
Richard Radcliffe Charitable
  Trust
The Radcliffe Trust
The Ragdoll Foundation
The Rainford Trust
The Peggy Ramsay Foundation
The Joseph and Lena Randall
  Charitable Trust
Ranworth Trust
The Fanny Rapaport Charitable
  Settlement
The Ratcliff Foundation
The Ratcliff Pension Charity
The Ratcliffe Charitable Trust
The Eleanor Rathbone
  Charitable Trust
The Sigrid Rausing Trust
The Ravensdale Trust
The Rayden Charitable Trust
The Roger Raymond Charitable
  Trust
The Rayne Foundation
The Rayne Trust
The John Rayner Charitable
  Trust
The Albert Reckitt Charitable
  Trust
The Sir James Reckitt Charity
The Red Arrows Trust
Red Hill Charitable Trust
The Red Rose Charitable Trust
The C A Redfern Charitable
  Foundation
The Reed Foundation
Richard Reeve's Foundation
The Max Reinhardt Charitable
  Trust
Relief Fund for Romania
  Limited
REMEDI
The Rest Harrow Trust
Reuben Brothers Foundation
The Joan K Reynell Charitable
  Trust
The Nathaniel Reyner Trust
  Fund
The Rhododendron Trust
The Rhondda Cynon Taff
  Welsh Church Acts Fund
Daisie Rich Trust

The Sir Cliff Richard Charitable
  Trust
C B Richard Ellis Charitable
  Trust
The Clive Richards Charity
The Richmond Parish Lands
  Charity
The Muriel Edith Rickman
  Trust
Ridgesave Limited
The Ripple Effect Foundation
The Sir John Ritblat Family
  Foundation
The River Trust
Riverside Charitable Trust
  Limited
The Daniel Rivlin Charitable
  Trust
Thomas Roberts Trust
The Alex Roberts-Miller
  Foundation
The Robertson Trust
Edwin George Robinson
  Charitable Trust
Robyn Charitable Trust
The Rochester Bridge Trust
The Rock Foundation
The Rock Solid Trust
The Rofeh Trust
Richard Rogers Charitable
  Settlement
Rokach Family Charitable Trust
The Helen Roll Charitable
  Trust
The Sir James Roll Charitable
  Trust
The Roman Research Trust
Romeera Foundation
The C A Rookes Charitable
  Trust
The Rosca Trust
The Cecil Rosen Foundation
The Rothermere Foundation
The Rotherwick Foundation
The Rothley Trust
The Rothschild Foundation
The Roughley Charitable Trust
Mrs Gladys Row Fogo
  Charitable Trust
Rowanville Ltd
The Christopher Rowbotham
  Charitable Trust
The Rowing Foundation
The Rowlands Trust
Royal Artillery Charitable Fund
Royal British Legion
Royal Docks Trust (London)
Royal Masonic Trust for Girls
  and Boys
The Royal Scots Benevolent
  Society
The Alfred and Frances
  Rubens Charitable Trust
The Rubin Foundation
William Arthur Rudd Memorial
  Trust

The Russell Trust
Ryklow Charitable Trust 1992
The J S and E C Rymer Charitable Trust
S O Charitable Trust
The Michael Sacher Charitable Trust
The Michael Harry Sacher Trust
Dr Mortimer and Theresa Sackler Foundation
The Raymond and Beverley Sackler Foundation
The Ruzin Sadagora Trust
The Saddlers' Company Charitable Fund
The Saga Charitable Trust
The Jean Sainsbury Animal Welfare Trust
The Alan and Babette Sainsbury Charitable Fund
Saint Sarkis Charity Trust
The Saintbury Trust
The Saints and Sinners Trust
The Salamander Charitable Trust
The Salt Foundation
The Salt Trust
The Salters' Charities
The Andrew Salvesen Charitable Trust
The Sammermar Trust
Basil Samuel Charitable Trust
Coral Samuel Charitable Trust
The Hon. M J Samuel Charitable Trust
The Peter Samuel Charitable Trust
The Camilla Samuel Fund
The Samworth Foundation
The Sandra Charitable Trust
Jimmy Savile Charitable Trust
The Scarfe Charitable Trust
The Schapira Charitable Trust
The Annie Schiff Charitable Trust
The Schmidt-Bodner Charitable Trust
The R H Scholes Charitable Trust
The Schreib Trust
The Schreiber Charitable Trust
Schroder Charity Trust
The Francis C Scott Charitable Trust
The Frieda Scott Charitable Trust
The Sir James and Lady Scott Trust
The Scott Trust Foundation
The Storrow Scott Will Trust
The Scottish Arts Council
Scottish Churches' Community Trust
Scottish Coal Industry Special Welfare Fund

The Scottish Community Foundation
The Scottish International Education Trust
The Scouloudi Foundation
Seamen's Hospital Society
The Searchlight Electric Charitable Trust
The Searle Charitable Trust
The Helene Sebba Charitable Trust
The Samuel Sebba Charitable Trust
The Seedfield Trust
Leslie Sell Charitable Trust
Sellata Ltd
SEM Charitable Trust
The Ayrton Senna Foundation
The Seven Fifty Trust
The Severn Trent Water Charitable Trust Fund
SFIA Educational Trust Limited
The Cyril Shack Trust
The Shanti Charitable Trust
ShareGift (The Orr Mackintosh Foundation)
The Linley Shaw Foundation
The Sheepdrove Trust
The Sheffield and District Hospital Services Charitable Fund
The Sheldon Trust
The P and D Shepherd Charitable Trust
The Sylvia and Colin Shepherd Charitable Trust
The Archie Sherman Cardiff Foundation
The Archie Sherman Charitable Trust
The R C Sherriff Trust
The Shetland Charitable Trust
SHINE (Support and Help in Education)
The Barnett and Sylvia Shine No 2 Charitable Trust
The Bassil Shippam and Alsford Trust
The Shipwrights' Company Charitable Fund
The Shirley Foundation
Shlomo Memorial Fund Limited
The J A Shone Memorial Trust
The Charles Shorto Charitable Trust
The Barbara A Shuttleworth Memorial Trust
David and Jennifer Sieff Charitable Trust
The Julius Silman Charitable Trust
The Leslie Silver Charitable Trust
The Simpson Education and Conservation Trust
The Simpson Foundation

The Huntly and Margery Sinclair Charitable Trust
Sino-British Fellowship Trust
The Skelton Bounty
The Charles Skey Charitable Trust
Skipton Building Society Charitable Foundation
The John Slater Foundation
Rita and David Slowe Charitable Trust
The SMB Charitable Trust
The Mrs Smith and Mount Trust
The N Smith Charitable Settlement
The Amanda Smith Charitable Trust
The E H Smith Charitable Trust
The Smith Charitable Trust
The Leslie Smith Foundation
The Martin Smith Foundation
Stanley Smith General Charitable Trust
The Stanley Smith UK Horticultural Trust
Philip Smith's Charitable Trust
The Snowball Trust
Solev Co Ltd
Solihull Community Foundation
The Solo Charitable Settlement
Dr Richard Solomon's Charitable Trust
David Solomons Charitable Trust
Songdale Ltd
The E C Sosnow Charitable Trust
The Souter Charitable Trust
The South Square Trust
The Stephen R and Philippa H Southall Charitable Trust
The W F Southall Trust
The Southdown Trust
R H Southern Trust
The Southwold Trust
The Sovereign Health Care Charitable Trust
Spar Charitable Fund
Sparks Charity (Sport Aiding Medical Research For Kids)
Sparquote Limited
The Spear Charitable Trust
Spears-Stutz Charitable Trust
The Worshipful Company of Spectacle Makers' Charity
The Jessie Spencer Trust
The Ralph and Irma Sperring Charity
The Moss Spiro Will Charitable Foundation
W W Spooner Charitable Trust
Stanley Spooner Deceased Charitable Trust

The Spoore, Merry and Rixman
  Foundation
Rosalyn and Nicholas Springer
  Charitable Trust
Springfields Employees'
  Medical Research and
  Charity Trust Fund
Springrule Ltd
The Spurrell Charitable Trust
The Geoff and Fiona Squire
  Foundation
St Andrew Animal Fund
St Andrew's Conservation
  Trust
St Francis's Leprosy Guild
St Gabriel's Trust
St James' Trust Settlement
St James's Place Foundation
Sir Walter St John's
  Educational Charity
St Katharine and Shadwell
  Trust
St Mark's Overseas Aid Trust
  (SMOAT)
St Michael's and All Saints'
  Charities
The Late St Patrick White
  Charitable Trust
St Teilo's Trust
Miss Doreen Stanford Trust
The Stanley Foundation Ltd
The Stanton Ballard Charitable
  Trust
The Star Charitable Trust
The Starfish Trust
The Peter Stebbings Memorial
  Charity
The Steel Charitable Trust
The Cyril and Betty Stein
  Charitable Trust
The Steinberg Family
  Charitable Trust
The Hugh Stenhouse
  Foundation
The Sigmund Sternberg
  Charitable Foundation
Stervon Ltd
The Stevenage Community
  Trust
The June Stevens Foundation
Stevenson Family's Charitable
  Trust
The Steventon Allotments and
  Relief-in-Need Charity
The Leonard Laity Stoate
  Charitable Trust
The Edward Stocks-Massey
  Bequest Fund
The Stokenchurch Educational
  Charity
The Stoller Charitable Trust
The M J C Stone Charitable
  Trust
The Stone-Mallabar Charitable
  Foundation

The Samuel Storey Family
  Charitable Trust
Peter Stormonth Darling
  Charitable Trust
Peter Storrs Trust
The Strangward Trust
The Strasser Foundation
Stratford upon Avon Town
  Trust
Strathclyde Police Benevolent
  Fund
The A B Strom and R Strom
  Charitable Trust
The Sudborough Foundation
Sueberry Ltd
The Suffolk Historic Churches
  Trust
The Alan Sugar Foundation
The Summerfield Charitable
  Trust
The Bernard Sunley Charitable
  Foundation
The Surrey Historic Buildings
  Trust Ltd
The Sussex Historic Churches
  Trust
The Adrienne and Leslie
  Sussman Charitable Trust
The Sutasoma Trust
The Sutton Nursing
  Association
Swan Mountain Trust
The Swan Trust
Swansea and Brecon Diocesan
  Board of Finance Limited
The John Swire (1989)
  Charitable Trust
The Swire Charitable Trust
The Hugh and Ruby Sykes
  Charitable Trust
The Charles and Elsie Sykes
  Trust
The Sylvanus Charitable Trust
The Stella Symons Charitable
  Trust
The Tabeel Trust
The Tajtelbaum Charitable
  Trust
The Talbot Trusts
The Talbot Village Trust
Tallow Chandlers Benevolent
  Fund
Talteg Ltd
The Tangent Charitable Trust
The Lady Tangye Charitable
  Trust
The David Tannen Charitable
  Trust
The Tanner Trust
The Lili Tapper Charitable
  Foundation
The Mrs A Lacy Tate Trust
The Tay Charitable Trust
C B and H H Taylor 1984 Trust
Humphrey Richardson Taylor
  Charitable Trust

The Connie and Albert Taylor
  Charitable Trust
The Cyril Taylor Charitable
  Trust
A P Taylor Trust
Rosanna Taylor's 1987 Charity
  Trust
Tearfund
The Tedworth Charitable Trust
Tegham Limited
The Templeton Goodwill Trust
Tesco Charity Trust
Thackray Medical Research
  Trust
Thames Community
  Foundation
The Thames Wharf Charity
The Thistle Trust
The Loke Wan Tho Memorial
  Foundation
The Thomas Wall Trust
The Arthur and Margaret
  Thompson Charitable Trust
The Thompson Family
  Charitable Trust
The Len Thomson Charitable
  Trust
The Sue Thomson Foundation
The Thornton Foundation
The Thornton Trust
The Three Guineas Trust
The Three Oaks Trust
The Thriplow Charitable Trust
The Tinsley Foundation
The Tisbury Telegraph Trust
TJH Foundation
The Tolkien Trust
Tollemache (Buckminster)
  Charitable Trust
Tomchei Torah Charitable
  Trust
The Tompkins Foundation
The Tory Family Foundation
Tottenham Grammar School
  Foundation
The Tower Hill Trust
The Towry Law Charitable Trust
The Toy Trust
The Mayor of Trafford's Charity
  Fund
Annie Tranmer Charitable Trust
The Constance Travis
  Charitable Trust
The Treeside Trust
The True Colours Trust
Truedene Co. Ltd
The Truemark Trust
Truemart Limited
Trumros Limited
Trust for London
Trust Sixty Three
The Tubney Charitable Trust
Tudor Rose Ltd
The Tudor Trust
The Tufton Charitable Trust

The R D Turner Charitable
Trust
The Douglas Turner Trust
The Florence Turner Trust
Miss S M Tutton Charitable
Trust
The TUUT Charitable Trust
Trustees of Tzedakah
Ulster Garden Villages Ltd
Ultach Trust
Ulting Overseas Trust
The Ulverscroft Foundation
Ulverston Town Lands Charity
The Underwood Trust
The Union of Orthodox Hebrew
Congregation
The United Society for the
Propagation of the Gospel
United Trusts
The David Uri Memorial Trust
Uxbridge United Welfare Trust
Vale of Glamorgan – Welsh
Church Fund
The Valentine Charitable Trust
The Albert Van Den Bergh
Charitable Trust
The Van Neste Foundation
Mrs Maud Van Norden's
Charitable Foundation
The Vandervell Foundation
The Vardy Foundation
Veneziana Fund
The Verdon-Smith Family
Charitable Settlement
Roger Vere Foundation
Victoria Homes Trust
Viking Cares (For the Kids)
The Nigel Vinson Charitable
Trust
The William and Ellen Vinten
Trust
The Vintners' Company
Charitable Foundation
Vintners' Gifts Charity
Vision Charity
Vivdale Ltd
The Viznitz Foundation
Wade's Charity
The Scurrah Wainwright Charity
Wakeham Trust
The Community Foundation in
Wales
Wales Council for Voluntary
Action
Robert and Felicity Waley-
Cohen Charitable Trust
The Walker Trust
Wallington Missionary Mart
and Auctions
The F J Wallis Charitable
Settlement
War on Want
The Ward Blenkinsop Trust
The George Ward Charitable
Trust

The Barbara Ward Children's
Foundation
The John Warren Foundation
G R Waters Charitable Trust
2000
The Waterways Trust
Blyth Watson Charitable Trust
The Howard Watson Symington
Memorial Charity
John Watson's Trust
Weatherley Charitable Trust
The Weavers' Company
Benevolent Fund
The William Webster
Charitable Trust
The Weinberg Foundation
The Weinstein Foundation
The Weinstock Fund
The James Weir Foundation
The Barbara Welby Trust
The Weldon UK Charitable
Trust
Welsh Church Fund Dyfed
area (Carmarthenshire,
Ceredigion and
Pembrokeshire)
The Welton Foundation
Wessex Cancer Trust
The Wessex Youth Trust
The West Derby Wastelands
Charity
West London Synagogue
Charitable Fund
The West Yorkshire Police
Community Fund
Mrs S K West's Charitable
Trust
The Westminster Foundation
The Garfield Weston
Foundation
The Whitaker Charitable Trust
The Colonel W H Whitbread
Charitable Trust
The Simon Whitbread
Charitable Trust
White Rose Children's Aid
International Charity
The Whitecourt Charitable
Trust
A H and B C Whiteley
Charitable Trust
The Norman Whiteley Trust
The Whitley Animal Protection
Trust
The Whittlesey Charity
The Lionel Wigram Memorial
Trust
The Felicity Wilde Charitable
Trust
The Wilkinson Charitable
Foundation
The Kay Williams Charitable
Foundation
The Williams Family Charitable
Trust

The H D H Wills 1965
Charitable Trust
Dame Violet Wills Charitable
Trust
The Dame Violet Wills Will
Trust
The Wilmcote Charitrust
Sumner Wilson Charitable
Trust
David Wilson Foundation
The Wilson Foundation
J and J R Wilson Trust
The Community Foundation for
Wiltshire and Swindon
The Benjamin Winegarten
Charitable Trust
The Harold Hyam Wingate
Foundation
The Francis Winham
Foundation
Anona Winn Charitable Trust
Wirral Mayor's Charity
The Michael and Anna Wix
Charitable Trust
The Wixamtree Trust
The Woburn 1986 Charitable
Trust
The Maurice Wohl Charitable
Foundation
The Charles Wolfson
Charitable Trust
The Wolfson Family Charitable
Trust
The Wolfson Foundation
Women Caring Trust
Women's World Day of Prayer
The James Wood Bequest
Fund
Woodlands Green Ltd
Woodlands Trust
The Geoffrey Woods Charitable
Foundation
The Woodward Charitable
Trust
The A and R Woolf Charitable
Trust
The Woolnoth Society
Charitable Trust
Worcester Municipal Charities
The Worcestershire and
Dudley Historic Churches
Trust
The Fred and Della Worms
Charitable Trust
The Worwin UK Foundation
The Wragge and Co. Charitable
Trust
The Diana Edgson Wright
Charitable Trust
The Matthews Wrightson
Charity Trust
Miss E B Wrightson's
Charitable Settlement
Wychdale Ltd
Wychville Ltd
The Wyndham Charitable Trust

The Wyseliot Charitable Trust
The Xerox (UK) Trust
The Yardley Great Trust
The Dennis Alan Yardy
  Charitable Trust
The W Wing Yip and Brothers
  Foundation
The York Children's Trust
Yorkshire Agricultural Society
Yorkshire Building Society
  Charitable Foundation
The Yorkshire Dales
  Millennium Trust
The John Young Charitable
  Settlement
The William Allen Young
  Charitable Trust
The John K Young Endowment
  Fund
Youth Music
Elizabeth and Prince Zaiger
  Trust
Zephyr Charitable Trust
The Marjorie and Arnold Ziff
  Charitable Foundation
Stephen Zimmerman
  Charitable Trust
The Zochonis Charitable Trust
Zurich Community Trust (UK)
  Limited

....

■ Computer systems and equipment

The 1989 Willan Charitable
  Trust
The 29th May 1961 Charitable
  Trust
Aberbrothock Charitable Trust
The Aberdeen Endowments
  Trust
The Aberdeenshire Educational
  Trust Scheme
Achiezer Association Ltd
Achisomoch Aid Company
  Limited
The ACT Foundation
Action Medical Research
The Company of Actuaries'
  Charitable Trust Fund
The Sylvia Adams Charitable
  Trust
The Victor Adda Foundation
The Adint Charitable Trust
The Adnams Charity
AF Trust Company
Age Concern Scotland Grants
Aid to the Church in Need (UK)
The AIM Foundation
The Sylvia Aitken Charitable
  Trust
The Ajahma Charitable Trust
Alcohol Education and
  Research Council

Aldgate and All Hallows'
  Barking Exhibition
  Foundation
The Aldgate Freedom
  Foundation
Alexandra Rose Charities
The Alexis Trust
All Saints Educational Trust
Allchurches Trust Ltd
The H B Allen Charitable Trust
The Rita Allen Charitable Trust
The Alliance Family Foundation
Angus Allnatt Charitable
  Foundation
The Pat Allsop Charitable Trust
The Almond Trust
Almondsbury Charity
The Altajir Trust
Altamont Ltd
Alvor Charitable Trust
AM Charitable Trust
Ambika Paul Foundation
The Ammco Trust
Sir John and Lady Amory's
  Charitable Trust
Viscount Amory's Charitable
  Trust
The Ampelos Trust
The AMW Charitable Trust
The Anchor Foundation
The Andrew Anderson Trust
The Andre Christian Trust
Anguish's Educational
  Foundation
The Animal Defence Trust
The Eric Anker-Petersen
  Charity
The Annandale Charitable
  Trust
Ambrose and Ann Appelbe
  Trust
The Appletree Trust
The John Apthorp Charitable
  Trust
The Milly Apthorp Charitable
  Trust
The Arbib Foundation
The Archbishop of
  Canterbury's Charitable
  Trust
The John M Archer Charitable
  Trust
The Archer Trust
The Ardwick Trust
The Argus Appeal
Armenian General Benevolent
  Union London Trust
The Armenian Relief Society of
  Great Britain Trust
The Armourers' and Brasiers'
  Gauntlet Trust
The Army Benevolent Fund
Arsenal Charitable Trust
The Artemis Charitable Trust
The Arts and Entertainment
  Charitable Trust

Arts Council England
The Arts Council of Northern
  Ireland
The Arts Council of Wales
The Ove Arup Foundation
The AS Charitable Trust
Ashburnham Thanksgiving
  Trust
A J H Ashby Will Trust
The Ashden Trust
The Ashendene Trust
The Laura Ashley Foundation
The Norman C Ashton
  Foundation
The Ashworth Charitable Trust
The Ian Askew Charitable Trust
The Associated Country
  Women of the World
  (ACWW)
The Association of Colleges
  Charitable Trust
Astellas European Foundation
AstonMansfield Charitable
  Trust
The Astor Foundation
The Astor of Hever Trust
The Aurelius Charitable Trust
The Avenue Charitable Trust
The John Avins Trustees
The Avon and Somerset Police
  Community Trust
AW Charitable Trust
The Aylesford Family
  Charitable Trust
The BAA Communities Trust
Harry Bacon Foundation
The BACTA Charitable Trust
The Bagri Foundation
Veta Bailey Charitable Trust
The Austin Bailey Trust
The Baily Thomas Charitable
  Fund
The Baird Trust
The Baker Charitable Trust
The Balcombe Charitable Trust
The Balint Family Charitable
  Trusts
The Albert Casanova Ballard
  Deceased Trust
The Ballinger Charitable Trust
Balmain Charitable Trust
The Balmore Trust
The Balney Charitable Trust
The Baltic Charitable Fund
The Bamford Charitable
  Foundation
The Banbury Charities
William P Bancroft (No 2)
  Charitable Trust and
  Jenepher Gillett Trust
The Band Trust
The Barbers' Company General
  Charities
The Barbour Trust
Barchester Healthcare
  Foundation

David and Frederick Barclay
Foundation
The Baring Foundation
Peter Barker-Mill Memorial
Charity
Barleycorn Trust
The Barnabas Trust
Lord Barnby's Foundation
Barnes Workhouse Fund
The Barnsbury Charitable Trust
The Barnstaple Bridge Trust
The Barnwood House Trust
The Misses Barrie Charitable
Trust
Barrington Family Charitable
Trust
The Charity of William Barrow
Stephen J Barry Charitable
Trust
The Bartlett Taylor Charitable
Trust
The Paul Bassham Charitable
Trust
The Batchworth Trust
The Bay Tree Charitable Trust
D H and L H Baylin Charitable
Trust
The Louis Baylis (Maidenhead
Advertiser) Charitable Trust
BBC Children in Need
B-CH 1971 Charitable Trust
The Beacon Trust
Bear Mordechai Ltd
The Bearder Charity
The James Beattie Charitable
Trust
The Beaufort House Trust
Limited
Beauland Ltd
The Beaverbrook Foundation
The Beccles Town Lands
Charity
The Becker Family Charitable
Trust
The Becketts and Sargeants
Educational Foundation
The John Beckwith Charitable
Trust
The Peter Beckwith Charitable
Trust
The Bedford Charity (The
Harpur Trust)
The David and Ruth Behrend
Fund
The Beit Trust
The Bellahouston Bequest
Fund
Bellasis Trust
The Bellinger Donnay Trust
Belljoe Tzedoko Ltd
The Benfield Motors Charitable
Trust
The Benham Charitable
Settlement
The Hervey Benham Charitable
Trust

Maurice and Jacqueline
Bennett Charitable Trust
Michael and Leslie Bennett
Charitable Trust
The Gerald Bentall Charitable
Trust
Bergqvist Charitable Trust
The Berkshire Community
Foundation
The Bestway Foundation
The Betterware Foundation
Thomas Betton's Charity for
Pensions and Relief-in-Need
BHST
The Mason Bibby 1981 Trust
BibleLands
The Bideford Bridge Trust
The Big Lottery Fund
The Billmeir Charitable Trust
Percy Bilton Charity
The Bingham Trust
The Bintaub Charitable Trust
The Birmingham Community
Foundation
The Birmingham District
Nursing Charitable Trust
The Birmingham Hospital
Saturday Fund Medical
Charity and Welfare Trust
Birmingham International
Airport Community Trust
The Lord Mayor of
Birmingham's Charity
Birthday House Trust
The Bisgood Charitable Trust
(registered as Miss Jeanne
Bisgood's Charitable Trust)
The Michael Bishop
Foundation
The Bishop's Development
Fund
The Sydney Black Charitable
Trust
The Bertie Black Foundation
Isabel Blackman Foundation
The Herbert and Peter
Blagrave Charitable Trust
The Blair Foundation
Blakes Benevolent Trust
The Blanchminster Trust
The Sir Victor Blank Charitable
Settlement
Blatchington Court Trust
The Neville and Elaine Blond
Charitable Trust
The Bluston Charitable
Settlement
Enid Blyton Trust for Children
The Body Shop Foundation
The Boltons Trust
The Bonamy Charitable Trust
The John and Celia Bonham
Christie Charitable Trust
The Charlotte Bonham-Carter
Charitable Trust

Bonhomie United Charity
Society
The Booth Charities
The Boots Charitable Trust
The Bordon and Liphook
Charity
Salo Bordon Charitable Trust
The Oliver Borthwick Memorial
Trust
The Bothwell Charitable Trust
H E and E L Botteley
Charitable Trust
The Harry Bottom Charitable
Trust
P G and N J Boulton Trust
The A H and E Boulton Trust
Sir Clive Bourne Family Trust
The Anthony Bourne
Foundation
The Bower Trust
The Bowerman Charitable
Trust
John and Susan Bowers Fund
The Bowland Charitable Trust
The William Brake Charitable
Trust
The Tony Bramall Charitable
Trust
The Brewers' Company
General Charitable Trust
The Harold and Alice Bridges
Charity
Briggs Animal Welfare Trust
The Brighton District Nursing
Association Trust
Bristol Archdeaconry Charity
John Bristow and Thomas
Mason Trust
Britannia Foundation
The British Council for
Prevention of Blindness
The British Dietetic
Association General and
Education Trust Fund
The British Gas (Scottish Gas)
Energy Trust
British Heart Foundation
British Humane Association
British Institute at Ankara
British Ornithologists' Union
British Record Industry Trust
The Britto Foundation
The J and M Britton Charitable
Trust
The Charles and Edna
Broadhurst Charitable Trust
The Bromley Trust
The Roger Brooke Charitable
Trust
The David Brooke Charity
The Charles Brotherton Trust
Joseph Brough Charitable
Trust
The Swinfen Broun Charitable
Trust

Mrs E E Brown Charitable
   Settlement
Bill Brown's Charitable
   Settlement
R S Brownless Charitable
   Trust
T B H Brunner's Charitable
   Settlement
The Jack Brunton Charitable
   Trust
Brushmill Ltd
The Bryant Trust
Buckingham Trust
The Buckinghamshire
   Foundation
The Buckinghamshire Masonic
   Centenary Fund
Buckland Charitable Trust
The Rosemary Bugden
   Charitable Trust
The Bulldog Trust Limited
The E F Bulmer Benevolent
   Fund
Burdens Charitable Foundation
The Burdett Trust for Nursing
The Clara E Burgess Charity
The Burry Charitable Trust
The Audrey and Stanley Burton
   1960 Charitable Trust
The Arnold Burton 1998
   Charitable Trust
The Burton Breweries
   Charitable Trust
The Geoffrey Burton Charitable
   Trust
Consolidated Charity of Burton
   upon Trent
Butchers' Company General
   Charities
The Bill Butlin Charity Trust
C and F Charitable Trust
C J Cadbury Charitable Trust
Edward Cadbury Charitable
   Trust
Henry T and Lucy B Cadbury
   Charitable Trust
P H G Cadbury Charitable
   Trust
The Christopher Cadbury
   Charitable Trust
The G W Cadbury Charitable
   Trust
The Richard Cadbury
   Charitable Trust
The William A Cadbury
   Charitable Trust
The Edward and Dorothy
   Cadbury Trust
The George Cadbury Trust
The Barrow Cadbury Trust and
   the Barrow Cadbury Fund
The Cadogan Charity
CAF (Charities Aid Foundation)
CAFOD
The Callander Charitable Trust
Calleva Foundation

The Calpe Trust
Calypso Browning Trust
The Campden Charities
The Canning Trust
H and L Cantor Trust
Capital Community Foundation
Cardy Beaver Foundation
The Carew Pole Charitable
   Trust
The D W T Cargill Fund
Caring for Kids (Radio Tay)
Carlee Ltd
The Carlton House Charitable
   Trust
The Worshipful Company of
   Carmen Benevolent Trust
The Carnegie Dunfermline
   Trust
The Carnegie Trust for the
   Universities of Scotland
The Carpenter Charitable Trust
The Carpenters' Company
   Charitable Trust
The Carrington Charitable
   Trust
The Carron Charitable
   Settlement
The Leslie Mary Carter
   Charitable Trust
The Carvill Trust
The Casey Trust
Sir John Cass's Foundation
The Elizabeth Casson Trust
The Castang Foundation
The Catalyst Charitable Trust
The Catholic Charitable Trust
Catholic Foreign Missions
The Catholic Trust for England
   and Wales
The Joseph and Annie Cattle
   Trust
The Thomas Sivewright Catto
   Charitable Settlement
The Wilfrid and Constance
   Cave Foundation
The Cayo Foundation
Elizabeth Cayzer Charitable
   Trust
The B G S Cayzer Charitable
   Trust
The Cazenove Charitable Trust
Celtic Charity Fund
The Cemlyn-Jones Trust
The Amelia Chadwick Trust
The Pamela Champion
   Foundation
The Chapman Charitable Trust
John William Chapman's
   Charitable Trust
The Charities Advisory Trust
Charitworth Limited
The Charter 600 Charity
The Worshipful Company of
   Chartered Accountants
   General Charitable Trust
The Chasah Trust

The Chelsea Building Society
   Charitable Foundation
The Chelsea Square 1994
   Trust
The Cheruby Trust
The Cheshire Provincial Fund
   of Benevolence
The Chetwode Foundation
The Malcolm Chick Charity
Child Growth Foundation
Children's Liver Disease
   Foundation
Childs Charitable Trust
The Childwick Trust
The Chippenham Borough
   Lands Charity
The Chipping Sodbury Town
   Lands Charity
CHK Charities Limited
The Chownes Foundation
The Chrimes Family Charitable
   Trust
The Christabella Charitable
   Trust
Christadelphian Samaritan
   Fund
Christian Aid
Christian Response to Eastern
   Europe
The Church and Community
   Fund
The Church Burgesses
   Educational Foundation
Church Burgesses Trust
Church Lands and John
   Johnson's Estate Charities
Church of Ireland Priorities
   Fund
The Church Urban Fund
City and County of Swansea
   Welsh Church Act Fund
The City Bridge Trust
The City Educational Trust
   Fund
The City Parochial Foundation
CLA Charitable Trust
Stephen Clark 1957
   Charitable Trust
J A Clark Charitable Trust
The Hilda and Alice Clark
   Charitable Trust
The Roger and Sarah Bancroft
   Clark Charitable Trust
The Clarke Charitable
   Settlement
The Cleary Foundation
The Cleopatra Trust
Lord Clinton's Charitable Trust
The Clore Duffield Foundation
Miss V L Clore's 1967
   Charitable Trust
Closehelm Ltd
The Clothworkers' Foundation
Richard Cloudesley's Charity
The Clover Trust

The Robert Clutterbuck
Charitable Trust
Clydpride Ltd
The Coalfields Regeneration
Trust
The John Coates Charitable
Trust
Coats Foundation Trust
The Cobtree Charity Trust Ltd
The Denise Cohen Charitable
Trust
The Vivienne and Samuel
Cohen Charitable Trust
The R and S Cohen Fondation
The John S Cohen Foundation
The Colchester Catalyst
Charity
John Coldman Charitable Trust
The Cole Charitable Trust
The Colefax Charitable Trust
The John and Freda Coleman
Charitable Trust
The George Henry Collins
Charity
The E Alec Colman Charitable
Fund Ltd
The Sir Jeremiah Colman Gift
Trust
Col-Reno Ltd
The Colt Foundation
The Coltstaple Trust
Colwinston Charitable Trust
Colyer-Fergusson Charitable
Trust
Comic Relief
The Comino Foundation
Community Foundation for
Calderdale
The Community Foundation for
Greater Manchester
The Community Foundation for
Northern Ireland
The Company of Tobacco Pipe
Makers' and Tobacco
Blenders' Benevolent Fund
The Compton Charitable Trust
The Congleton Inclosure Trust
The Conservation Foundation
The Consolidated Charities for
the Infirm Merchant
Taylors' Company
The Construction Industry
Trust for Youth
Gordon Cook Foundation
The Ernest Cook Trust
The Cooks Charity
The Catherine Cookson
Charitable Trust
Harold and Daphne Cooper
Charitable Trust
Mabel Cooper Charity
The Alice Ellen Cooper Dean
Charitable Foundation
The Co-operative Foundation
The Marjorie Coote Animal
Charity Trust

The Marjorie Coote Old
People's Charity
The Helen Jean Cope Trust
The J Reginald Corah
Foundation Fund
The Gershon Coren Charitable
Foundation
The Corinthian Trust
Edwin Cornforth 1983 Charity
Trust
The Duke of Cornwall's
Benevolent Fund
The Cornwell Charitable Trust
The Sidney and Elizabeth
Corob Charitable Trust
The Corona Charitable Trust
The Costa Family Charitable
Trust
The Cotton Industry War
Memorial Trust
The Augustine Courtauld Trust
Coutts Charitable Trust
The General Charities of the
City of Coventry
Coventry Building Society
Charitable Foundation
The John Cowan Foundation
Cowley Charitable Foundation
The Sir William Coxen Trust
Fund
The Lord Cozens-Hardy Trust
The Craignish Trust
The Craps Charitable Trust
Michael Crawford Children's
Charity
The Cray Trust
The Crescent Trust
Criffel Charitable Trust
Cripplegate Foundation
The Violet and Milo Cripps
Charitable Trust
The Cromarty Trust
The Harry Crook Foundation
The Cross Trust
The Cross Trust
The Croydon Relief in Need
Charities
The Mayor of Croydon's
Charity Fund
Cruden Foundation Ltd
The Ronald Cruickshanks'
Foundation
Cuby Charitable Trust
The Culra Charitable Trust
The Cumber Family Charitable
Trust
Cumberland Building Society
Charitable Foundation
Cumbria Community
Foundation
The D J H Currie Memorial
Trust
The Dennis Curry Charitable
Trust
The Raymond Curtis Charitable
Trust

The Manny Cussins
Foundation
The Cwmbran Trust
Itzchok Meyer Cymerman Trust
Ltd
The D'Oyly Carte Charitable
Trust
The Roald Dahl Foundation
The Daily Prayer Union
Charitable Trust Ltd
The Daisy Trust
The Daiwa Anglo-Japanese
Foundation
Oizer Dalim Trust
The Dr and Mrs A Darlington
Charitable Trust
Baron Davenport's Charity
The Davidson (Nairn)
Charitable Trust
Davidson Charitable Trust
The Alderman Joe Davidson
Memorial Trust
Michael Davies Charitable
Settlement
The Gwendoline and Margaret
Davies Charity
The Wilfrid Bruce Davis
Charitable Trust
Davis-Rubens Charitable Trust
The Dawe Charitable Trust
The De Clermont Charitable
Company Ltd
Peter De Haan Charitable
Trust
The Leopold De Rothschild
Charitable Trust
The Deakin Charitable Trust
William Dean Countryside and
Educational Trust
The Debmar Benevolent Trust
The Delfont Foundation
The Dellal Foundation
The Delves Charitable Trust
The Demigryphon Trust
The Denman Charitable Trust
The Denton Charitable Trust
The Denton Wilde Sapte
Charitable Trust
The Earl of Derby's Charitable
Trust
Derbyshire Community
Foundation
The J N Derbyshire Trust
Devon Community Foundation
The Devon Educational Trust
The Duke of Devonshire's
Charitable Trust
The Sandy Dewhirst Charitable
Trust
DG Charitable Settlement
The Laduma Dhamecha
Charitable Trust
Diabetes UK
Alan and Sheila Diamond
Charitable Trust

The Diana, Princess of Wales
Memorial Fund
The Dibden Allotments Charity
The Dickon Trust
The Digbeth Trust
The Dinwoodie Settlement
Dischma Charitable Trust
The DLA Piper Charitable Trust
The DLM Charitable Trust
Louise Dobson Charitable
Trust
The Derek and Eileen Dodgson
Foundation
The Dollond Charitable Trust
Domepride Ltd
The Dorcas Trust
The Dorema Charitable Trust
The Dorus Trust
Double 'O' Charity Ltd
The Doughty Charity Trust
The R M Douglas Charitable
Trust
The Drapers' Charitable Fund
Dromintee Trust
The Dugdale Charitable Trust
The Duis Charitable Trust
The Dulverton Trust
The P B Dumbell Charitable
Trust
The Dumbreck Charity
Dunard Fund
Ronald Duncan Literary
Foundation
The Dunhill Medical Trust
The Houghton Dunn Charitable
Trust
The Dunn Family Charitable
Trust
The W E Dunn Trust
Dushinsky Trust Ltd
Mildred Duveen Charitable
Trust
The Dwek Family Charitable
Trust
The Dyers' Company
Charitable Trust
EAGA Partnership Charitable
Trust
The Eagle Charity Trust
Audrey Earle Charitable Trust
The Earley Charity
Earls Colne and Halstead
Educational Charity
The Earmark Trust
East Kent Provincial Charities
East London Community
Foundation
Eastern Counties Educational
Trust Limited
The Sir John Eastwood
Foundation
The Ebenezer Trust
The EBM Charitable Trust
Eden Arts Trust
EDF Energy Trust (EDFET)

The Gilbert and Eileen Edgar
Foundation
Gilbert Edgar Trust
Edinburgh Children's Holiday
Fund
The Edinburgh Trust, No 2
Account
Edinburgh Voluntary
Organisations' Trust Funds
Educational Foundation of
Alderman John Norman
The W G Edwards Charitable
Foundation
The William Edwards
Educational Charity
The Elephant Trust
The George Elias Charitable
Trust
The Gerald Palmer Eling Trust
Company
The Elizabeth Frankland Moore
and Star Foundation
The Wilfred and Elsie Elkes
Charity Fund
The Maud Elkington Charitable
Trust
Ellador Ltd
The Ellerdale Trust
The John Ellerman Foundation
The Ellinson Foundation Ltd
The Edith Maud Ellis 1985
Charitable Trust
The Ellis Campbell Foundation
James Ellis Charitable Trust
The Elmgrant Trust
The Elmley Foundation
Elshore Ltd
The Vernon N Ely Charitable
Trust
The Embleton Trust
The Emerton-Christie Charity
EMI Music Sound Foundation
The Emmandjay Charitable
Trust
The Worshipful Company of
Engineers Charitable Trust
Fund
The Englefield Charitable Trust
The English Schools' Football
Association
The Enkalon Foundation
Entindale Ltd
The Epigoni Trust
Epilepsy Research UK
The Equitable Charitable Trust
The Equity Trust Fund
The Ericson Trust
The Erskine Cunningham Hill
Trust
Essex Community Foundation
The Essex Fairway Charitable
Trust
The Essex Heritage Trust
Essex Provincial Charity Fund
The Essex Youth Trust
Euro Charity Trust

The Evangelical Covenants
Trust
The Alan Evans Memorial Trust
Sir John Evelyn's Charity
The Eventhall Family
Charitable Trust
The Everard Foundation
The Eveson Charitable Trust
The Beryl Evetts and Robert
Luff Animal Welfare Trust
The Execution Charitable Trust
The Mayor of Exeter's Appeal
Fund
The Exilarch's Foundation
F C Charitable Trust
The F P Limited Charitable
Trust
The Faber Charitable Trust
Esmée Fairbairn Foundation
The Fairway Trust
Faisaltex Charitable Trust
The Family Foundations Trust
The Family Rich Charities Trust
Famos Foundation Trust
The Lord Faringdon Charitable
Trust
Samuel William Farmer's Trust
The Farmers' Company
Charitable Fund
The Thomas Farr Charitable
Trust
Walter Farthing (Trust) Limited
Farthing Trust
The Fassnidge Memorial Trust
Joseph Fattorini Charitable
Trust 'B' Account
The Fawcett Charitable Trust
Federation of Jewish Relief
Organisations
Feed the Minds
The John Feeney Charitable
Bequest
The George Fentham
Birmingham Charity
The A M Fenton Trust
Allan and Nesta Ferguson
Charitable Settlement
Elizabeth Ferguson Charitable
Trust Fund
The Fidelity UK Foundation
The Bluff Field Charitable Trust
The Doris Field Charitable
Trust
Fife Council/Common Good
Funds and Trusts
Dixie Rose Findlay Charitable
Trust
Gerald Finzi Charitable Trust
Firtree Trust
The Sir John Fisher Foundation
The Fishmongers' Company's
Charitable Trust
Marc Fitch Fund
The Fitton Trust
The Earl Fitzwilliam Charitable
Trust

Bud Flanagan Leukaemia Fund
The Rose Flatau Charitable
 Trust
The Ian Fleming Charitable
 Trust
The Joyce Fletcher Charitable
 Trust
The Roy Fletcher Charitable
 Trust
Florence's Charitable Trust
The Florian Charitable Trust
The Flow Foundation
The Gerald Fogel Charitable
 Trust
The Follett Trust
The Football Association
 National Sports Centre
 Trust
The Football Association Youth
 Trust
The Football Foundation
The Forbes Charitable
 Foundation
Forbesville Limited
The Forces Trust
Ford Britain Trust
The Oliver Ford Charitable
 Trust
Fordeve Ltd
The Forest Hill Charitable Trust
The Foresters' Charity
 Stewards UK Trust
Gwyneth Forrester Trust
The Forte Charitable Trust
Lord Forte Foundation
Foundation for Management
 Education
Four Acre Trust
The Four Winds Trust
The Fowler, Smith and Jones
 Charitable Trust
The Foyle Foundation
The Isaac and Freda Frankel
 Memorial Charitable Trust
Sydney E Franklin Deceased's
 New Second Charity
The Jill Franklin Trust
The Gordon Fraser Charitable
 Trust
The Hugh Fraser Foundation
The Joseph Strong Frazer Trust
The Louis and Valerie
 Freedman Charitable
 Settlement
The Thomas Freke and Lady
 Norton Charity
The Charles S French
 Charitable Trust
The Anne French Memorial
 Trust
The Freshfield Foundation
The Freshgate Trust
 Foundation
The Friarsgate Trust
The Friends Hall Farm Street
 Trust

Friends of Biala Ltd
Friends of Wiznitz Limited
Friends Provident Charitable
 Foundation
The Frognal Trust
T F C Frost Charitable Trust
The Patrick Frost Foundation
Maurice Fry Charitable Trust
Mejer and Gertrude Miriam
 Frydman Foundation
The Fuellers Charitable Trust
 Fund
The Fulmer Charitable Trust
Worshipful Company of
 Furniture Makers Charitable
 Fund
Gableholt Limited
The Galbraith Trust
The Gale Family Charitable
 Trust
The Angela Gallagher Memorial
 Fund
The Gamlen Charitable Trust
The Gamma Trust
The Gannochy Trust
The Ganzoni Charitable Trust
The Worshipful Company of
 Gardeners of London
The Samuel Gardner Memorial
 Trust
The Garnett Charitable Trust
Garrick Charitable Trust
Garvan Limited
The Gatsby Charitable
 Foundation
Gatwick Airport Community
 Trust
The Robert Gavron Charitable
 Trust
Jacqueline and Michael Gee
 Charitable Trust
J Paul Getty Jr Charitable Trust
The Gibbs Charitable Trust
Simon Gibson Charitable Trust
The G C Gibson Charitable
 Trust
The Harvey and Hilary Gilbert
 Charitable Trust
The Girdlers' Company
 Charitable Trust
The B and P Glasser
 Charitable Trust
The Glass-House Trust
Global Care
Global Charities (formally
 GCap Charities)
Gloucestershire Community
 Foundation
Worshipful Company of
 Glovers of London Charity
 Fund
GMC Trust
The GNC Trust
The Meir Golda Trust

The Sydney and Phyllis
 Goldberg Memorial
 Charitable Trust
The Golden Bottle Trust
Golden Charitable Trust
The Jack Goldhill Charitable
 Trust
The Goldsmiths' Arts Trust
 Fund
The Goldsmiths' Company
 Charity
The Golsoncott Foundation
The Good Neighbours Trust
Nicholas and Judith
 Goodison's Charitable
 Settlement
The Everard and Mina
 Goodman Charitable
 Foundation
Mike Gooley Trailfinders
 Charity
Leonard Gordon Charitable
 Trust
The Gosling Foundation
 Limited
The Gough Charitable Trust
The Gould Charitable Trust
The Grace Charitable Trust
A B Grace Trust
The Graff Foundation
The Grahame Charitable
 Foundation Limited
Grampian Police Diced Cap
 Charitable Fund
The Granada Foundation
Grand Charitable Trust of the
 Order of Women
 Freemasons
The Grand Order of Water
 Rats' Charities Fund
The Grange Farm Centre Trust
Grantham Yorke Trust
The J G Graves Charitable
 Trust
The Gray Trust
The Great Stone Bridge Trust
 of Edenbridge
The Great Torrington Town
 Lands Charity
The Constance Green
 Foundation
The Barry Green Memorial
 Fund
The Philip Green Memorial
 Trust
Mrs H R Greene Charitable
 Settlement
Greenham Common
 Community Trust Limited
Naomi and Jeffrey Greenwood
 Charitable Trust
Greggs Foundation
Grimmitt Trust
The Grocers' Charity
The M and R Gross Charities
 Limited

The Grove Charitable Trust
The GRP Charitable Trust
The David and Marie Grumitt Foundation
The Bishop of Guildford's Foundation
The Guildry Incorporation of Perth
The Walter Guinness Charitable Trust
The Gunter Charitable Trust
The Gur Trust
Gurunanak
Dr Guthrie's Association
The H and M Charitable Trust
H C D Memorial Fund
The H P Charitable Trust
The Hackney Parochial Charities
The Hadfield Trust
The Hadley Trust
The Hadrian Trust
The Alfred Haines Charitable Trust
The Hale Trust
E F and M G Hall Charitable Trust
The Edith Winifred Hall Charitable Trust
Robert Hall Charity
The Hamamelis Trust
Hamilton Wallace Trust
Paul Hamlyn Foundation
Sue Hammerson's Charitable Trust
The Hammonds Charitable Trust
The Hampshire and Islands Historic Churches Trust
Hampton Fuel Allotment Charity
The W A Handley Charitable Trust
Beatrice Hankey Foundation Ltd
The Hanley Trust
The Kathleen Hannay Memorial Charity
The Doughty Hanson Charitable Foundation
Lord Hanson Foundation
The Haramead Trust
Miss K M Harbinson's Charitable Trust
Harbo Charities Limited
The Harborne Parish Lands Charity
The Harbour Charitable Trust
The Harbour Foundation
The Harding Trust
William Harding's Charity
The Hare of Steep Charitable Trust
The Harebell Centenary Fund
The Kenneth Hargreaves Charitable Trust

The Harris Charitable Trust
The Harris Charity
The Harrison and Potter Trust
The John Harrison Charitable Trust
The Peter Harrison Foundation
The Spencer Hart Charitable Trust
The Hartley Charitable Trust
The N and P Hartley Memorial Trust
William Geoffrey Harvey's Discretionary Settlement
The Edward Harvist Trust Fund
Haskel Family Foundation
The Hathaway Trust
The M A Hawe Settlement
The Hawthorne Charitable Trust
The Dorothy Hay-Bolton Charitable Trust
The Haydan Charitable Trust
The Haymills Charitable Trust
The Headley Trust
Headley-Pitt Charitable Trust
Heagerty Charitable Trust
The Heald Charitable Trust
Healthsure Group Ltd
May Hearnshaw's Charity
The Heart of England Community Foundation
The Heathcoat Trust
Heathside Charitable Trust
The Charlotte Heber-Percy Charitable Trust
Percy Hedley 1990 Charitable Trust
The Hedley Denton Charitable Trust
The Hedley Foundation
The H J Heinz Company Limited Charitable Trust
The Hellenic Foundation
The Michael and Morven Heller Charitable Foundation
The Simon Heller Charitable Settlement
Help the Aged
Help the Homeless
Help the Hospices
The Hemby Trust
The Christina Mary Hendrie Trust for Scottish and Canadian Charities
The Henley Educational Charity
Philip Henman Trust
Esther Hennell Charitable Trust
The G D Herbert Charitable Trust
The Joanna Herbert-Stepney Charitable Settlement
The Anne Herd Memorial Trust
The Herefordshire Historic Churches Trust

The Heritage of London Trust Ltd
The Hertfordshire Community Foundation
The Hesed Trust
The Hesslewood Children's Trust (Hull Seamen's and General Orphanage)
The Bernhard Heuberger Charitable Trust
Hexham and Newcastle Diocesan Trust (1947)
The P and C Hickinbotham Charitable Trust
The Higgs Charitable Trust
Alan Edward Higgs Charity
The High Sheriff's Police Trust for the County of West Midlands
Highcroft Charitable Trust
The Hilden Charitable Fund
The Joseph and Mary Hiley Trust
The Holly Hill Charitable Trust
The Charles Littlewood Hill Trust
The Hillingdon Partnership Trust
R G Hills Charitable Trust
Hinchley Charitable Trust
Lady Hind Trust
Stuart Hine Trust
The Hinrichsen Foundation
The Hitchin Educational Foundation
The Eleemosynary Charity of William Hobbayne
Hobson Charity Limited
Hockerill Educational Foundation
Matthew Hodder Charitable Trust
The Sir Julian Hodge Charitable Trust
The Jane Hodge Foundation
The J G Hogg Charitable Trust
The Holden Charitable Trust
John Holford's Charity
The Hollick Family Charitable Trust
The Dorothy Holmes Charitable Trust
P H Holt Foundation
The Edward Holt Trust
The Holywood Trust
The Homelands Charitable Trust
The Homestead Charitable Trust
Mary Homfray Charitable Trust
Sir Harold Hood's Charitable Trust
The Hope Trust
HopMarket Charity
The Cuthbert Horn Trust

The Antony Hornby Charitable Trust
The Horne Foundation
The Horne Trust
The Worshipful Company of Horners' Charitable Trusts
The Hornsey Parochial Charities
The Hospital of God at Greatham
The Hospital Saturday Fund
Houblon-Norman/George Fund
The House of Industry Estate
The Reta Lila Howard Foundation
The Daniel Howard Trust
The Clifford Howarth Charity Trust
The Huddersfield Medical Trust Fund
The Hudson Foundation
The Huggard Charitable Trust
The Geoffrey C Hughes Charitable Trust
The Hull and East Riding Charitable Trust
Hulme Trust Estates (Educational)
Human Relief Foundation
The Humanitarian Trust
The Michael and Shirley Hunt Charitable Trust
The Albert Hunt Trust
The Hunter Foundation
Miss Agnes H Hunter's Trust
The Huntingdon Foundation
Huntingdon Freemen's Charity
John Huntingdon's Charity
Hurdale Charity Limited
The Nani Huyu Charitable Trust
The P Y N and B Hyams Trust
The Hyde Charitable Trust – Youth Plus
The Idlewild Trust
The Iliffe Family Charitable Trust
The Indigo Trust
The Ingram Trust
The Inland Waterways Association
The Inlight Trust
The Inman Charity
The Inner London Magistrates Court Poor Box Charity and Feeder Charity
The Worshipful Company of Innholders General Charity Fund
The Ireland Fund of Great Britain
The Irish Youth Foundation (UK) Ltd
The Ironmongers' Foundation
Irshad Trust
Irwin Trust
The ISA Charity

The Isaacs Charitable Trust
The J Isaacs Charitable Trust
The Island Health Trust
The Isle of Anglesey Charitable Trust
Isle of Dogs Community Foundation
The ITF Seafarers Trust
J A R Charitable Trust
The J J Charitable Trust
The J R S S T Charitable Trust
Elizabeth Jackson Charitable Trust
Jacobs Charitable Trust
The Ruth and Lionel Jacobson Trust (Second Fund) No 2
Jaffe Family Relief Fund
John James Bristol Foundation
The Susan and Stephen James Charitable Settlement
The James Trust
The Jarman Charitable Trust
The John Jarrold Trust
JCA Charitable Foundation
The Jeffrey Charitable Trust
Rees Jeffreys Road Fund
The Jenour Foundation
The Jephcott Charitable Trust
The Jerusalem Trust
Jerwood Charitable Foundation
Jesus Hospital Charity
Jewish Child's Day
The Jewish Youth Fund
The JMK Charitable Trust
The Joanies Trust
The Harold Joels Charitable Trust
The Jonathan Joels Charitable Trust
The Nicholas Joels Charitable Trust
The Norman Joels Charitable Trust
The Joffe Charitable Trust
The Lillie Johnson Charitable Trust
The Johnson Group Cleaners Charity
The Johnnie Johnson Trust
The Johnson Wax Ltd Charitable Trust
The Joicey Trust
The Jones 1986 Charitable Trust
The Marjorie and Geoffrey Jones Charitable Trust
The Jordan Charitable Foundation
The J E Joseph Charitable Fund
The Lady Eileen Joseph Foundation
JTH Charitable Trust
The Judith Trust

The Anton Jurgens Charitable Trust
The Bernard Kahn Charitable Trust
The Stanley Kalms Foundation
The Karenza Foundation
The Boris Karloff Charitable Foundation
The Ian Karten Charitable Trust
The Kasner Charitable Trust
The Kass Charitable Trust
The Kathleen Trust
The Michael and Ilse Katz Foundation
The Katzauer Charitable Settlement
The C S Kaufman Charitable Trust
The Geoffrey John Kaye Charitable Foundation
The Emmanuel Kaye Foundation
Kelsick's Educational Foundation
The KempWelch Charitable Trust
The Kay Kendall Leukaemia Fund
William Kendall's Charity (Wax Chandlers' Company)
The Kennedy Charitable Foundation
The Kennel Club Charitable Trust
The Nancy Kenyon Charitable Trust
Keren Association
Kermaville Ltd
E and E Kernkraut Charities Limited
The Peter Kershaw Trust
The Kessler Foundation
Keswick Hall Charity
The Ursula Keyes Trust
The Robert Kiln Charitable Trust
The King Henry VIII Endowed Trust Warwick
The King/Cullimore Charitable Trust
The Kingsbury Charity
The Mary Kinross Charitable Trust
Kinsurdy Charitable Trust
Kirkley Poor's Lands Estate
The Richard Kirkman Charitable Trust
Kirschel Foundation
Robert Kitchin (Saddlers' Company)
Ernest Kleinwort Charitable Trust
The Marina Kleinwort Charitable Trust
The Sir James Knott Trust

The Kobler Trust
The Kohn Foundation
The Kreditor Charitable Trust
The Kreitman Foundation
The Neil Kreitman Foundation
The Heinz, Anna and Carol Kroch Foundation
The Kyte Charitable Trust
Lacims-Maclis Charitable Trust
The Late Sir Pierce Lacy Charity Trust
John Laing Charitable Trust
Maurice and Hilda Laing Charitable Trust
The Laing Family Foundations
The Christopher Laing Foundation
The Kirby Laing Foundation
The Martin Laing Foundation
The Beatrice Laing Trust
The Lambert Charitable Trust
Lancashire Environmental Fund
Duchy of Lancaster Benevolent Fund
The Lancaster Foundation
LandAid Charitable Trust
The Langdale Trust
The Langley Charitable Trust
The Langtree Trust
The LankellyChase Foundation
The Lanvern Foundation
The R J Larg Family Charitable Trust
Largsmount Ltd
The Lark Trust
Laslett's (Hinton) Charity
Lauchentilly Charitable Foundation 1988
Laufer Charitable Trust
The Lauffer Family Charitable Foundation
Mrs F B Laurence Charitable Trust
The Kathleen Laurence Trust
The Edgar E Lawley Foundation
The Herd Lawson and Muriel Lawson Charitable Trust
The Lawson Beckman Charitable Trust
The Raymond and Blanche Lawson Charitable Trust
The Carole and Geoffrey Lawson Foundation
The Mason Le Page Charitable Trust
The Leach Fourteenth Trust
The David Lean Foundation
The Leathersellers' Company Charitable Fund
The Leche Trust
The Arnold Lee Charitable Trust
The William Leech Charity
The Lord Mayor of Leeds Appeal Fund

Leeds Building Society Charitable Foundation
Leicester Charity Link
The Kennedy Leigh Charitable Trust
Morris Leigh Foundation
The Leigh Trust
Mrs Vera Leigh's Charity
The P Leigh-Bramwell Trust 'E'
The Lennox and Wyfold Foundation
The Erica Leonard Trust
The Leonard Trust
The Mark Leonard Trust
Lesley Lesley and Mutter Trust
Leukaemia Research Fund
The Leverhulme Trade Charities Trust
Lord Leverhulme's Charitable Trust
The Joseph Levy Charitable Foundation
Lewis Family Charitable Trust
The John Spedan Lewis Foundation
The Sir Edward Lewis Foundation
John Lewis Partnership General Community Fund
Lichfield Conduit Lands
Lifeline 4 Kids
The Thomas Lilley Memorial Trust
Limoges Charitable Trust
The Linbury Trust
The Lind Trust
Lindale Educational Foundation
The Linden Charitable Trust
The Enid Linder Foundation
The Linmardon Trust
The Ruth and Stuart Lipton Charitable Trust
The Lister Charitable Trust
Frank Litchfield Charitable Trust
The Andrew and Mary Elizabeth Little Charitable Trust
The Second Joseph Aaron Littman Foundation
The George John and Sheilah Livanos Charitable Trust
Liverpool Charity and Voluntary Services
Liverpool Sailors' Home Trust
Jack Livingstone Charitable Trust
The Elaine and Angus Lloyd Charitable Trust
The Charles Lloyd Foundation
The Lloyd Fund
Lloyd's Charities Trust
The Lloyd-Everett Trust
Lloyds TSB Foundation for England and Wales

Lloyds TSB Foundation for Northern Ireland
Lloyds TSB Foundation for the Channel Islands
Llysdinam Charitable Trust
Localtrent Ltd
The Locker Foundation
The Loftus Charitable Trust
The Lolev Charitable Trust
London Catalyst
The London Law Trust
The London Marathon Charitable Trust
The William and Katherine Longman Trust
The Lord's Taverners
The Loseley and Guildway Charitable Trust
The Lotus Foundation
The C L Loyd Charitable Trust
The Marie Helen Luen Charitable Trust
Robert Luff Foundation Ltd
Henry Lumley Charitable Trust
Lady Lumley's Educational Foundation
Paul Lunn-Rockliffe Charitable Trust
C F Lunoe Trust Fund
The Ruth and Jack Lunzer Charitable Trust
Lord and Lady Lurgan Trust
The Lyndhurst Trust
The Lynn Foundation
The Lynwood Trust
John Lyon's Charity
The Lyons Charitable Trust
The Sir Jack Lyons Charitable Trust
Malcolm Lyons Foundation
The Lyras Family Charitable Trust
Sylvanus Lyson's Charity
The M and C Trust
The M D and S Charitable Trust
The M K Charitable Trust
The Madeline Mabey Trust
The E M MacAndrew Trust
The R S Macdonald Charitable Trust
Macdonald-Buchanan Charitable Trust
The Macfarlane Walker Trust
The Mackay and Brewer Charitable Trust
The Mackintosh Foundation
The MacRobert Trust
Ian Mactaggart Trust
The Magdalen and Lasher Charity
Magdalen Hospital Trust
The Magen Charitable Trust
Mageni Trust
Mahavir Trust

Man Group plc Charitable
Trust
Manchester Airport Community
Trust Fund
The Manchester Guardian
Society Charitable Trust
Manchester Kids
Lord Mayor of Manchester's
Charity Appeal Trust
Mandeville Trust
The Manifold Charitable Trust
W M Mann Foundation
The Leslie and Lilian Manning
Trust
Maranatha Christian Trust
Marbeh Torah Trust
The Marchday Charitable Fund
Marchig Animal Welfare Trust
The Stella and Alexander
Margulies Charitable Trust
Mariapolis Limited
Market Harborough and The
Bowdens Charity
Michael Marks Charitable
Trust
The Ann and David Marks
Foundation
The Hilda and Samuel Marks
Foundation
J P Marland Charitable Trust
Marr-Munning Trust
The Michael Marsh Charitable
Trust
The Marsh Christian Trust
The Charlotte Marshall
Charitable Trust
The Jim Marshall Charitable
Trust
The D G Marshall of
Cambridge Trust
Marshall's Charity
Marshgate Charitable
Settlement
Sir George Martin Trust
John Martin's Charity
The Mason Porter Charitable
Trust
The Nancie Massey Charitable
Trust
The Mathew Trust
Matliwala Family Charitable
Trust
The Matt 6.3 Charitable Trust
The Violet Mauray Charitable
Trust
The Maxell Educational Trust
The Maxwell Family Foundation
Evelyn May Trust
Mayfair Charities Ltd
The Mayfield Valley Arts Trust
Mazars Charitable Trust
The Robert McAlpine
Foundation
The McDougall Trust
The A M McGreevy No 5
Charitable Settlement

The McKenna Charitable Trust
Martin McLaren Memorial
Trust
The Helen Isabella McMorran
Charitable Foundation
D D McPhail Charitable
Settlement
The James Frederick and Ethel
Anne Measures Charity
Medical Research Council
The Medlock Charitable Trust
The Anthony and Elizabeth
Mellows Charitable
Settlement
Melodor Ltd
Melow Charitable Trust
Meningitis Trust
Menuchar Ltd
Brian Mercer Charitable Trust
The Mercers' Charitable
Foundation
The Merchant Taylors'
Company Charities Fund
The Merchant Venturers'
Charity
The Merchants' House of
Glasgow
Mercury Phoenix Trust
The Mersey Docks and
Harbour Company
Charitable Fund
Community Foundation for
Merseyside
The Zachary Merton and
George Woofindin
Convalescent Trust
The Tony Metherell Charitable
Trust
The Methodist Relief and
Development Fund
The Metropolitan Drinking
Fountain and Cattle Trough
Association
Gerald Micklem Charitable
Trust
Midhurst Pensions Trust
The Migraine Trust
Miles Trust for the Putney and
Roehampton Community
Millennium Stadium Charitable
Trust
The Hugh and Mary Miller
Bequest Trust
The Miller Foundation
The Millfield Trust
The Millhouses Charitable
Trust
The Millichope Foundation
The Mills Charity
The Millward Charitable Trust
The Clare Milne Trust
Milton Keynes Community
Foundation
The Edgar Milward Charity

The Keith and Joan
Mindelsohn Charitable
Trust
The Peter Minet Trust
Minge's Gift and the Pooled
Trusts
The Minos Trust
The Mirfield Educational
Charity
The Laurence Misener
Charitable Trust
The Mishcon Family Charitable
Trust
The Misselbrook Trust
The Mitchell Charitable Trust
The Esmé Mitchell Trust
Keren Mitzvah Trust
The Mizpah Trust
The Mobbs Memorial Trust Ltd
The Modiano Charitable Trust
The Moette Charitable Trust
The Mole Charitable Trust
The D C Moncrieff Charitable
Trust
Monmouthshire County Council
Welsh Church Act Fund
The Montague Thompson
Coon Charitable Trust
The Colin Montgomerie
Charitable Foundation
The Monument Trust
Moody Charitable Trust
George A Moore Foundation
The Nigel Moores Family
Charitable Trust
John Moores Foundation
The Peter Moores Foundation
The Morel Charitable Trust
The Morgan Charitable
Foundation
The Mr and Mrs J T Morgan
Foundation
The J P Morgan Foundations
Diana and Allan Morgenthau
Charitable Trust
The Oliver Morland Charitable
Trust
S C and M E Morland's
Charitable Trust
The Morris Charitable Trust
The Willie and Mabel Morris
Charitable Trust
The Peter Morrison Charitable
Foundation
The Stanley Morrison
Charitable Trust
Moshal Charitable Trust
Vyoel Moshe Charitable Trust
The Moss Charitable Trust
The Robert and Margaret
Moss Charitable Trust
Moss Family Charitable Trust
The Mount Everest Foundation
Mountbatten Festival of Music
The Mountbatten Memorial
Trust

The Edwina Mountbatten Trust
The Mugdock Children's Trust
The F H Muirhead Charitable
   Trust
The Mulberry Trust
The Edith Murphy Foundation
Murphy-Neumann Charity
   Company Limited
The Mushroom Fund
The Music Sales Charitable
   Trust
Muslim Hands
The Mutual Trust Group
MYA Charitable Trust
The Kitty and Daniel Nabarro
   Charitable Trust
The Nadezhda Charitable Trust
The Willie Nagel Charitable
   Trust
The Naggar Charitable Trust
The Eleni Nakou Foundation
The Janet Nash Charitable
   Settlement
Nathan Charitable Trust
Asthma UK
The National Churches Trust
The National Manuscripts
   Conservation Trust
Nazareth Trust Fund
The Nchima Trust
Needham Market and Barking
   Welfare Charities
The Worshipful Company of
   Needlemakers' Charitable
   Fund
The Neighbourly Charitable
   Trust
The James Neill Trust Fund
Nemoral Ltd
Nesswall Ltd
Nestle Rowntree Employees
   Community Fund
Network for Social Change
The New Appeals Organisation
   for the City and County of
   Nottingham
New Court Charitable Trust
Newby Trust Limited
The Newcomen Collett
   Foundation
The Richard Newitt Fund
Mr and Mrs F E F Newman
   Charitable Trust
The Frances and Augustus
   Newman Foundation
Newpier Charity Ltd
Alderman Newton's
   Educational Foundation
The Chevras Ezras Nitzrochim
   Trust
The Noel Buxton Trust
The Noon Foundation
The Norda Trust
Norie Charitable Trust
Normalyn Charitable Trust

The Norman Family Charitable
   Trust
The Duncan Norman Trust
   Fund
The Normanby Charitable Trust
The North British Hotel Trust
The North West Cancer
   Research Fund
The Northampton Municipal
   Church Charities
The Northampton Queen's
   Institute Relief in Sickness
   Fund
The Earl of Northampton's
   Charity
The Northcott Devon
   Foundation
The Northcott Devon Medical
   Foundation
The Northmoor Trust
The Northumberland Village
   Homes Trust
The Northumbria Historic
   Churches Trust
The Northwood Charitable
   Trust
The Norton Foundation
The Norwich Church of England
   Young Men's Society
The Norwich Historic Churches
   Trust Ltd
The Norwich Town Close
   Estate Charity
The Norwood and Newton
   Settlement
The Noswad Charity
The Notgrove Trust
The Nottingham General
   Dispensary
The Nottingham Gordon
   Memorial Trust for Boys
   and Girls
Nottinghamshire Community
   Foundation
The Nottinghamshire Historic
   Churches Trust
The Nottinghamshire Miners'
   Welfare Trust Fund
Novi Most International
The Father O'Mahoney
   Memorial Trust
The Sir Peter O'Sullevan
   Charitable Trust
The Oak Trust
The Oakdale Trust
The Oakley Charitable Trust
The Oakmoor Charitable Trust
The Odin Charitable Trust
Ogilvie Charities Deed No.2
   (including the Charity of
   Mary Catherine Ford Smith)
The Ogle Christian Trust
Oglesby Charitable Trust
The Oikonomia Trust
The Oizer Charitable Trust

The Old Broad Street Charity
   Trust
The Old Enfield Charitable
   Trust
Old Possum's Practical Trust
The John Oldacre Foundation
The Oldham Foundation
Onaway Trust
Open Gate
The Ormsby Charitable Trust
Orrin Charitable Trust
The Ouseley Trust
The Owen Family Trust
Oxfam (GB)
The Oxfordshire Community
   Foundation
The P F Charitable Trust
Padwa Charitable Foundation
The Pallant Charitable Trust
The Palmer Foundation
Eleanor Palmer Trust
The Panacea Society
Panahpur Charitable Trust
Panton Trust
The James Pantyfedwen
   Foundation
The Paragon Trust
The Park House Charitable
   Trust
The Frank Parkinson
   Agricultural Trust
The Samuel and Freda
   Parkinson Charitable Trust
The Parthenon Trust
Arthur James Paterson
   Charitable Trust
The Constance Paterson
   Charitable Trust
Miss M E Swinton Paterson's
   Charitable Trust
The Patrick Charitable Trust
The Jack Patston Charitable
   Trust
Paycare Charity Trust
The Payne Charitable Trust
The Harry Payne Trust
The Susanna Peake Charitable
   Trust
The Pedmore Sporting Club
   Trust Fund
The Dowager Countess
   Eleanor Peel Trust
Peltz Trust
The Pennycress Trust
The Performing Right Society
   Foundation
B E Perl Charitable Trust
The Persson Charitable Trust
The Persula Foundation
The Pestalozzi Overseas
   Children's Trust
The Jack Petchey Foundation
The Petplan Charitable Trust
The Philips and Rubens
   Charitable Trust
The Phillips Charitable Trust

The Phillips Family Charitable
Trust
Philological Foundation
The David Pickford Charitable
Foundation
The Bernard Piggott Trust
The Claude and Margaret Pike
Charity
The Pilgrim Trust
The Cecil Pilkington Charitable
Trust
The Pilkington Charities Fund
The Austin and Hope
Pilkington Trust
The Sir Harry Pilkington Trust
The Col W W Pilkington Will
Trusts The General Charity
Fund
Miss A M Pilkington's
Charitable Trust
Mrs Pilkington's Charitable
Trust
The Plaisterers' Company
Charitable Trust
The Platinum Trust
G S Plaut Charitable Trust
Limited
The Poling Charitable Trust
The George and Esme Pollitzer
Charitable Settlement
The J S F Pollitzer Charitable
Settlement
The Ponton House Trust
The Mayor of Poole's Appeal
Fund
Edith and Ferdinand Porjes
Charitable Trust
The John Porter Charitable
Trust
The Porter Foundation
The Portishead Nautical Trust
The Portrack Charitable Trust
The J E Posnansky Charitable
Trust
The David and Elaine Potter
Foundation
The Powell Foundation
Prairie Trust
The W L Pratt Charitable Trust
Premierquote Ltd
Premishlaner Charitable Trust
The William Price Charitable
Trust
The Lucy Price Relief-in-Need
Charity
Sir John Priestman Charity
Trust
The Primrose Trust
The Prince's Charities
Foundation
Princess Anne's Charities
The Priory Foundation
Prison Service Charity Fund
The Privy Purse Charitable
Trust
The Proven Family Trust

The Provincial Grand Charity of
the Province of Derbyshire
PSA Peugeot Citroen Charity
Trust
The Puebla Charitable Trust
The Richard and Christine
Purchas Charitable Trust
The Puri Foundation
Mr and Mrs J A Pye's
Charitable Settlement
Quartet Community Foundation
Queen Mary's Roehampton
Trust
The Queen's Silver Jubilee
Trust
Quercus Trust
The R D Crusaders Foundation
R J M Charitable Trust
R S Charitable Trust
The R V W Trust
The Monica Rabagliati
Charitable Trust
Rachel Charitable Trust
The Mr and Mrs Philip
Rackham Charitable Trust
Richard Radcliffe Charitable
Trust
The Radcliffe Trust
The Ragdoll Foundation
The Rainford Trust
The Peggy Ramsay Foundation
The Joseph and Lena Randall
Charitable Trust
The Rank Foundation
Ranworth Trust
The Fanny Rapaport Charitable
Settlement
The Ratcliff Foundation
The Ratcliff Pension Charity
The Ratcliffe Charitable Trust
The Eleanor Rathbone
Charitable Trust
The Sigrid Rausing Trust
The Ravensdale Trust
The Rayden Charitable Trust
The Roger Raymond Charitable
Trust
The Rayne Foundation
The Rayne Trust
The John Rayner Charitable
Trust
The Albert Reckitt Charitable
Trust
The Sir James Reckitt Charity
The Red Arrows Trust
Red Hill Charitable Trust
The Red Rose Charitable Trust
The C A Redfern Charitable
Foundation
The Reed Foundation
Richard Reeve's Foundation
The Max Reinhardt Charitable
Trust
Relief Fund for Romania
Limited
REMEDI

The Rest Harrow Trust
Reuben Brothers Foundation
The Joan K Reynell Charitable
Trust
The Nathaniel Reyner Trust
Fund
The Rhododendron Trust
The Rhondda Cynon Taff
Welsh Church Acts Fund
Daisie Rich Trust
The Sir Cliff Richard Charitable
Trust
C B Richard Ellis Charitable
Trust
The Clive Richards Charity
The Richmond Parish Lands
Charity
The Muriel Edith Rickman
Trust
Ridgesave Limited
The Ripple Effect Foundation
The Sir John Ritblat Family
Foundation
The River Trust
Riverside Charitable Trust
Limited
The Daniel Rivlin Charitable
Trust
Thomas Roberts Trust
The Alex Roberts-Miller
Foundation
The Robertson Trust
Edwin George Robinson
Charitable Trust
Robyn Charitable Trust
The Rochester Bridge Trust
The Rock Foundation
The Rock Solid Trust
The Rofeh Trust
Richard Rogers Charitable
Settlement
Rokach Family Charitable Trust
The Helen Roll Charitable
Trust
The Sir James Roll Charitable
Trust
The Roman Research Trust
Romeera Foundation
The C A Rookes Charitable
Trust
The Rosca Trust
The Cecil Rosen Foundation
The Rothermere Foundation
The Rotherwick Foundation
The Rothley Trust
The Rothschild Foundation
The Roughley Charitable Trust
Mrs Gladys Row Fogo
Charitable Trust
Rowanville Ltd
The Christopher Rowbotham
Charitable Trust
The Rowing Foundation
The Rowlands Trust
The Joseph Rowntree
Charitable Trust

Royal Artillery Charitable Fund
Royal British Legion
Royal Docks Trust (London)
Royal Masonic Trust for Girls
and Boys
The Royal Scots Benevolent
Society
The Alfred and Frances
Rubens Charitable Trust
The Rubin Foundation
William Arthur Rudd Memorial
Trust
The Rufford Maurice Laing
Foundation
The Russell Trust
Ryklow Charitable Trust 1992
The J S and E C Rymer
Charitable Trust
S O Charitable Trust
The Michael Sacher Charitable
Trust
The Michael Harry Sacher
Trust
Dr Mortimer and Theresa
Sackler Foundation
The Raymond and Beverley
Sackler Foundation
The Ruzin Sadagora Trust
The Saddlers' Company
Charitable Fund
The Saga Charitable Trust
The Jean Sainsbury Animal
Welfare Trust
The Alan and Babette
Sainsbury Charitable Fund
Saint Sarkis Charity Trust
The Saintbury Trust
The Saints and Sinners Trust
The Salamander Charitable
Trust
The Salt Foundation
The Salt Trust
The Salters' Charities
The Andrew Salvesen
Charitable Trust
The Sammermar Trust
Basil Samuel Charitable Trust
Coral Samuel Charitable Trust
The Hon. M J Samuel
Charitable Trust
The Peter Samuel Charitable
Trust
The Camilla Samuel Fund
The Samworth Foundation
The Sandra Charitable Trust
Santander UK Foundation
Limited
Jimmy Savile Charitable Trust
The Scarfe Charitable Trust
The Schapira Charitable Trust
The Annie Schiff Charitable
Trust
The Schmidt-Bodner Charitable
Trust
The R H Scholes Charitable
Trust

The Schreib Trust
The Schreiber Charitable Trust
Schroder Charity Trust
The Scott Bader
Commonwealth Ltd
The Francis C Scott Charitable
Trust
The Frieda Scott Charitable
Trust
Sir Samuel Scott of Yews
Trust
The Sir James and Lady Scott
Trust
The Scott Trust Foundation
The Storrow Scott Will Trust
The Scottish Arts Council
Scottish Churches' Community
Trust
Scottish Coal Industry Special
Welfare Fund
The Scottish Community
Foundation
The Scottish International
Education Trust
The Scouloudi Foundation
Seafarers UK (King George's
Fund for Sailors)
Seamen's Hospital Society
The Searchlight Electric
Charitable Trust
The Searle Charitable Trust
The Helene Sebba Charitable
Trust
The Samuel Sebba Charitable
Trust
The Seedfield Trust
Leslie Sell Charitable Trust
Sellata Ltd
SEM Charitable Trust
The Ayrton Senna Foundation
The Seven Fifty Trust
The Severn Trent Water
Charitable Trust Fund
SFIA Educational Trust Limited
The Cyril Shack Trust
The Shanti Charitable Trust
ShareGift (The Orr Mackintosh
Foundation)
The Linley Shaw Foundation
The Sheepdrove Trust
The Sheffield and District
Hospital Services
Charitable Fund
The Sheldon Trust
The P and D Shepherd
Charitable Trust
The Sylvia and Colin Shepherd
Charitable Trust
The Archie Sherman Cardiff
Foundation
The Archie Sherman Charitable
Trust
The R C Sherriff Trust
The Shetland Charitable Trust
SHINE (Support and Help in
Education)

The Barnett and Sylvia Shine
No 2 Charitable Trust
The Bassil Shippam and
Alsford Trust
The Shipwrights' Company
Charitable Fund
The Shirley Foundation
Shlomo Memorial Fund Limited
The J A Shone Memorial Trust
The Charles Shorto Charitable
Trust
The Barbara A Shuttleworth
Memorial Trust
The Mary Elizabeth Siebel
Charity
David and Jennifer Sieff
Charitable Trust
The Julius Silman Charitable
Trust
The Leslie Silver Charitable
Trust
The Simpson Education and
Conservation Trust
The Simpson Foundation
The Huntly and Margery
Sinclair Charitable Trust
Sino-British Fellowship Trust
The Skelton Bounty
The Charles Skey Charitable
Trust
Skipton Building Society
Charitable Foundation
The John Slater Foundation
Rita and David Slowe
Charitable Trust
The SMB Charitable Trust
The Mrs Smith and Mount
Trust
The N Smith Charitable
Settlement
The Amanda Smith Charitable
Trust
The E H Smith Charitable Trust
The Smith Charitable Trust
The Henry Smith Charity
The Leslie Smith Foundation
The Martin Smith Foundation
Stanley Smith General
Charitable Trust
The Stanley Smith UK
Horticultural Trust
Philip Smith's Charitable Trust
The Snowball Trust
The Sobell Foundation
Solev Co Ltd
Solihull Community Foundation
The Solo Charitable
Settlement
Dr Richard Solomon's
Charitable Trust
David Solomons Charitable
Trust
Songdale Ltd
The E C Sosnow Charitable
Trust
The Souter Charitable Trust

The South Square Trust
The Stephen R and Philippa H
  Southall Charitable Trust
The W F Southall Trust
The Southdown Trust
R H Southern Trust
The Southover Manor General
  Education Trust
The Southwold Trust
The Sovereign Health Care
  Charitable Trust
Spar Charitable Fund
Sparks Charity (Sport Aiding
  Medical Research For Kids)
Sparquote Limited
The Spear Charitable Trust
Spears-Stutz Charitable Trust
The Worshipful Company of
  Spectacle Makers' Charity
The Jessie Spencer Trust
The Ralph and Irma Sperring
  Charity
The Moss Spiro Will Charitable
  Foundation
W W Spooner Charitable Trust
Stanley Spooner Deceased
  Charitable Trust
The Spoore, Merry and Rixman
  Foundation
The Spring Harvest Charitable
  Trust
Rosalyn and Nicholas Springer
  Charitable Trust
Springfields Employees'
  Medical Research and
  Charity Trust Fund
Springrule Ltd
The Spurrell Charitable Trust
The Geoff and Fiona Squire
  Foundation
St Andrew Animal Fund
St Andrew's Conservation
  Trust
St Francis's Leprosy Guild
St Gabriel's Trust
St James' Trust Settlement
St James's Place Foundation
Sir Walter St John's
  Educational Charity
St Katharine and Shadwell
  Trust
St Mark's Overseas Aid Trust
  (SMOAT)
St Michael's and All Saints'
  Charities
The Late St Patrick White
  Charitable Trust
St Teilo's Trust
Miss Doreen Stanford Trust
The Stanley Foundation Ltd
The Stanton Ballard Charitable
  Trust
The Staples Trust
The Star Charitable Trust
The Starfish Trust

The Peter Stebbings Memorial
  Charity
The Steel Charitable Trust
The Cyril and Betty Stein
  Charitable Trust
The Steinberg Family
  Charitable Trust
The Hugh Stenhouse
  Foundation
The Sigmund Sternberg
  Charitable Foundation
Stervon Ltd
The Stevenage Community
  Trust
The June Stevens Foundation
Stevenson Family's Charitable
  Trust
The Steventon Allotments and
  Relief-in-Need Charity
The Stewards' Company
  Limited
The Leonard Laity Stoate
  Charitable Trust
The Stobart Newlands
  Charitable Trust
The Edward Stocks-Massey
  Bequest Fund
The Stokenchurch Educational
  Charity
The Stoller Charitable Trust
The M J C Stone Charitable
  Trust
The Stone-Mallabar Charitable
  Foundation
The Samuel Storey Family
  Charitable Trust
Peter Stormonth Darling
  Charitable Trust
Peter Storrs Trust
The Strangward Trust
The Strasser Foundation
Stratford upon Avon Town
  Trust
Strathclyde Police Benevolent
  Fund
The W O Street Charitable
  Foundation
The A B Strom and R Strom
  Charitable Trust
The Sudborough Foundation
Sueberry Ltd
The Suffolk Historic Churches
  Trust
The Alan Sugar Foundation
The Summerfield Charitable
  Trust
The Bernard Sunley Charitable
  Foundation
The Surrey Historic Buildings
  Trust Ltd
The Sussex Historic Churches
  Trust
The Adrienne and Leslie
  Sussman Charitable Trust
The Sutasoma Trust

Sutton Coldfield Municipal
  Charities
The Sutton Nursing
  Association
Swan Mountain Trust
The Swan Trust
Swansea and Brecon Diocesan
  Board of Finance Limited
The John Swire (1989)
  Charitable Trust
The Swire Charitable Trust
The Hugh and Ruby Sykes
  Charitable Trust
The Charles and Elsie Sykes
  Trust
The Sylvanus Charitable Trust
The Stella Symons Charitable
  Trust
The Tabeel Trust
The Tajtelbaum Charitable
  Trust
The Talbot Trusts
The Talbot Village Trust
Tallow Chandlers Benevolent
  Fund
Talteg Ltd
The Tangent Charitable Trust
The Lady Tangye Charitable
  Trust
The David Tannen Charitable
  Trust
The Tanner Trust
The Lili Tapper Charitable
  Foundation
The Mrs A Lacy Tate Trust
The Tay Charitable Trust
C B and H H Taylor 1984 Trust
Humphrey Richardson Taylor
  Charitable Trust
The Connie and Albert Taylor
  Charitable Trust
The Cyril Taylor Charitable
  Trust
A P Taylor Trust
Rosanna Taylor's 1987 Charity
  Trust
Tearfund
The Tedworth Charitable Trust
Tees Valley Community
  Foundation
Tegham Limited
The Templeton Goodwill Trust
Tesco Charity Trust
Thackray Medical Research
  Trust
Thames Community
  Foundation
The Thames Wharf Charity
The Thistle Trust
The Loke Wan Tho Memorial
  Foundation
The Thomas Wall Trust
The Arthur and Margaret
  Thompson Charitable Trust
The Thompson Family
  Charitable Trust

The Len Thomson Charitable
Trust
The Sue Thomson Foundation
The Sir Jules Thorn Charitable
Trust
The Thornton Foundation
The Thornton Trust
The Three Guineas Trust
The Three Oaks Trust
The Thriplow Charitable Trust
The Tinsley Foundation
The Tisbury Telegraph Trust
TJH Foundation
The Tolkien Trust
Tollemache (Buckminster)
Charitable Trust
Tomchei Torah Charitable
Trust
The Tompkins Foundation
The Tory Family Foundation
Tottenham Grammar School
Foundation
The Tower Hill Trust
The Towry Law Charitable Trust
The Toy Trust
The Mayor of Trafford's Charity
Fund
Annie Tranmer Charitable Trust
The Constance Travis
Charitable Trust
The Treeside Trust
The Triangle Trust (1949) Fund
The True Colours Trust
Truedene Co. Ltd
The Truemark Trust
Truemart Limited
Trumros Limited
Trust for London
Trust Sixty Three
The Trusthouse Charitable
Foundation
The Tubney Charitable Trust
Tudor Rose Ltd
The Tudor Trust
The Tufton Charitable Trust
The R D Turner Charitable
Trust
The Douglas Turner Trust
The Florence Turner Trust
Miss S M Tutton Charitable
Trust
The TUUT Charitable Trust
Community Foundation Serving
Tyne and Wear and
Northumberland
Trustees of Tzedakah
Ulster Garden Villages Ltd
Ultach Trust
Ulting Overseas Trust
The Ulverscroft Foundation
Ulverston Town Lands Charity
The Underwood Trust
The Union of Orthodox Hebrew
Congregation
The United Society for the
Propagation of the Gospel

United Trusts
The David Uri Memorial Trust
Uxbridge United Welfare Trust
Vale of Glamorgan – Welsh
Church Fund
The Valentine Charitable Trust
The Albert Van Den Bergh
Charitable Trust
John and Lucille van Geest
Foundation
The Van Neste Foundation
Mrs Maud Van Norden's
Charitable Foundation
The Vandervell Foundation
The Vardy Foundation
The Variety Club Children's
Charity
Veneziana Fund
The Verdon-Smith Family
Charitable Settlement
Roger Vere Foundation
Victoria Homes Trust
Viking Cares (For the Kids)
The Nigel Vinson Charitable
Trust
The William and Ellen Vinten
Trust
The Vintners' Company
Charitable Foundation
Vintners' Gifts Charity
Vision Charity
Vivdale Ltd
The Viznitz Foundation
Wade's Charity
The Scurrah Wainwright Charity
Wakeham Trust
The Community Foundation in
Wales
Wales Council for Voluntary
Action
Robert and Felicity Waley-
Cohen Charitable Trust
The Walker Trust
Wallington Missionary Mart
and Auctions
The F J Wallis Charitable
Settlement
Walton on Thames Charity
War on Want
Sir Siegmund Warburg's
Voluntary Settlement
The Ward Blenkinsop Trust
The George Ward Charitable
Trust
The Barbara Ward Children's
Foundation
The John Warren Foundation
G R Waters Charitable Trust
2000
The Waterways Trust
The Wates Foundation
Blyth Watson Charitable Trust
The Howard Watson Symington
Memorial Charity
John Watson's Trust
Weatherley Charitable Trust

The Weavers' Company
Benevolent Fund
The William Webster
Charitable Trust
The Weinberg Foundation
The Weinstein Foundation
The Weinstock Fund
The James Weir Foundation
The Barbara Welby Trust
The Weldon UK Charitable
Trust
The Wellcome Trust
Welsh Church Fund Dyfed
area (Carmarthenshire,
Ceredigion and
Pembrokeshire)
The Welton Foundation
Wessex Cancer Trust
The Wessex Youth Trust
The West Derby Wastelands
Charity
West London Synagogue
Charitable Fund
The West Yorkshire Police
Community Fund
Mrs S K West's Charitable
Trust
The Westminster Foundation
The Garfield Weston
Foundation
The Whitaker Charitable Trust
The Colonel W H Whitbread
Charitable Trust
The Simon Whitbread
Charitable Trust
White Rose Children's Aid
International Charity
The Whitecourt Charitable
Trust
A H and B C Whiteley
Charitable Trust
The Norman Whiteley Trust
The Whitley Animal Protection
Trust
The Whittlesey Charity
The Lionel Wigram Memorial
Trust
The Felicity Wilde Charitable
Trust
The Wilkinson Charitable
Foundation
The Will Charitable Trust
The Kay Williams Charitable
Foundation
The Williams Family Charitable
Trust
The H D H Wills 1965
Charitable Trust
Dame Violet Wills Charitable
Trust
The Dame Violet Wills Will
Trust
The Wilmcote Charitrust
Sumner Wilson Charitable
Trust
David Wilson Foundation

The Wilson Foundation
J and J R Wilson Trust
The Community Foundation for Wiltshire and Swindon
The Benjamin Winegarten Charitable Trust
The Harold Hyam Wingate Foundation
The Francis Winham Foundation
Anona Winn Charitable Trust
Wirral Mayor's Charity
The Michael and Anna Wix Charitable Trust
The Wixamtree Trust
The Woburn 1986 Charitable Trust
The Maurice Wohl Charitable Foundation
The Charles Wolfson Charitable Trust
The Wolfson Family Charitable Trust
The Wolfson Foundation
Women Caring Trust
The James Wood Bequest Fund
Woodlands Green Ltd
Woodlands Trust
The Geoffrey Woods Charitable Foundation
The Woodward Charitable Trust
The A and R Woolf Charitable Trust
The Woolnoth Society Charitable Trust
Worcester Municipal Charities
The Worcestershire and Dudley Historic Churches Trust
The Fred and Della Worms Charitable Trust
The Worwin UK Foundation
The Wragge and Co. Charitable Trust
The Diana Edgson Wright Charitable Trust
The Matthews Wrightson Charity Trust
Miss E B Wrightson's Charitable Settlement
Wychdale Ltd
Wychville Ltd
The Wyndham Charitable Trust
The Wyseliot Charitable Trust
The Xerox (UK) Trust
The Yardley Great Trust
The Dennis Alan Yardy Charitable Trust
The W Wing Yip and Brothers Foundation
The York Children's Trust
Yorkshire Agricultural Society
Yorkshire Building Society Charitable Foundation

The South Yorkshire Community Foundation
The Yorkshire Dales Millennium Trust
The John Young Charitable Settlement
The William Allen Young Charitable Trust
The John K Young Endowment Fund
Youth Music
Elizabeth and Prince Zaiger Trust
Zephyr Charitable Trust
The Marjorie and Arnold Ziff Charitable Foundation
Stephen Zimmerman Charitable Trust
The Zochonis Charitable Trust
Zurich Community Trust (UK) Limited

....

■ Equipment

The 1989 Willan Charitable Trust
The 29th May 1961 Charitable Trust
Aberbrothock Charitable Trust
The Aberdeen Endowments Trust
The Aberdeenshire Educational Trust Scheme
Access Sport
Achiezer Association Ltd
Achisomoch Aid Company Limited
The ACT Foundation
Action Medical Research
The Company of Actuaries' Charitable Trust Fund
The Sylvia Adams Charitable Trust
The Victor Adda Foundation
The Adint Charitable Trust
The Adnams Charity
AF Trust Company
Age Concern Scotland Grants
Aid to the Church in Need (UK)
The AIM Foundation
The Sylvia Aitken Charitable Trust
Alcohol Education and Research Council
Aldgate and All Hallows' Barking Exhibition Foundation
The Aldgate Freedom Foundation
Alexandra Rose Charities
The Alexis Trust
Allchurches Trust Ltd
The H B Allen Charitable Trust
The Rita Allen Charitable Trust
The Alliance Family Foundation

Angus Allnatt Charitable Foundation
The Pat Allsop Charitable Trust
The Almond Trust
Almondsbury Charity
The Altajir Trust
Altamont Ltd
Alvor Charitable Trust
AM Charitable Trust
Ambika Paul Foundation
The Ammco Trust
Sir John and Lady Amory's Charitable Trust
Viscount Amory's Charitable Trust
The Ampelos Trust
The AMW Charitable Trust
The Anchor Foundation
The Andrew Anderson Trust
The André Christian Trust
Anguish's Educational Foundation
The Animal Defence Trust
The Eric Anker-Petersen Charity
The Annandale Charitable Trust
Ambrose and Ann Appelbe Trust
The Appletree Trust
The John Apthorp Charitable Trust
The Milly Apthorp Charitable Trust
The Arbib Foundation
The Archbishop of Canterbury's Charitable Trust
The John M Archer Charitable Trust
The Archer Trust
The Ardwick Trust
The Argus Appeal
Armenian General Benevolent Union London Trust
The Armenian Relief Society of Great Britain Trust
The Armourers' and Brasiers' Gauntlet Trust
The Army Benevolent Fund
Arsenal Charitable Trust
The Artemis Charitable Trust
The Arts and Entertainment Charitable Trust
Arts Council England
The Arts Council of Northern Ireland
The Arts Council of Wales
The Ove Arup Foundation
The AS Charitable Trust
Ashburnham Thanksgiving Trust
A J H Ashby Will Trust
The Ashden Trust
The Ashendene Trust
The Laura Ashley Foundation

The Norman C Ashton
Foundation
The Ashworth Charitable Trust
The Ian Askew Charitable Trust
The Associated Country
Women of the World
(ACWW)
The Association of Colleges
Charitable Trust
Astellas European Foundation
AstonMansfield Charitable
Trust
The Astor Foundation
The Astor of Hever Trust
The Aurelius Charitable Trust
The Avenue Charitable Trust
The John Avins Trustees
The Avon and Somerset Police
Community Trust
AW Charitable Trust
The Aylesford Family
Charitable Trust
The BAA Communities Trust
Harry Bacon Foundation
The BACTA Charitable Trust
The Bagri Foundation
Veta Bailey Charitable Trust
The Austin Bailey Trust
The Baily Thomas Charitable
Fund
The Baird Trust
The Baker Charitable Trust
The Balcombe Charitable Trust
The Balint Family Charitable
Trusts
The Albert Casanova Ballard
Deceased Trust
The Ballinger Charitable Trust
Balmain Charitable Trust
The Balmore Trust
The Balney Charitable Trust
The Baltic Charitable Fund
The Bamford Charitable
Foundation
The Banbury Charities
William P Bancroft (No 2)
Charitable Trust and
Jenepher Gillett Trust
The Band Trust
The Barbers' Company General
Charities
The Barbour Trust
Barchester Healthcare
Foundation
David and Frederick Barclay
Foundation
The Baring Foundation
Peter Barker-Mill Memorial
Charity
Barleycorn Trust
Lord Barnby's Foundation
Barnes Workhouse Fund
The Barnsbury Charitable Trust
The Barnstaple Bridge Trust
The Barnwood House Trust

The Misses Barrie Charitable
Trust
Barrington Family Charitable
Trust
The Charity of William Barrow
Stephen J Barry Charitable
Trust
The Bartlett Taylor Charitable
Trust
The Paul Bassham Charitable
Trust
The Batchworth Trust
The Bay Tree Charitable Trust
D H and L H Baylin Charitable
Trust
The Louis Baylis (Maidenhead
Advertiser) Charitable Trust
BBC Children in Need
B-CH 1971 Charitable Trust
The Beacon Trust
Bear Mordechai Ltd
The Bearder Charity
The James Beattie Charitable
Trust
The Beaufort House Trust
Limited
Beauland Ltd
The Beaverbrook Foundation
The Beccles Town Lands
Charity
The Becker Family Charitable
Trust
The Becketts and Sargeants
Educational Foundation
The John Beckwith Charitable
Trust
The Peter Beckwith Charitable
Trust
The Bedford Charity (The
Harpur Trust)
The David and Ruth Behrend
Fund
The Beit Trust
The Bellahouston Bequest
Fund
Bellasis Trust
The Bellinger Donnay Trust
Belljoe Tzedoko Ltd
The Benfield Motors Charitable
Trust
The Benham Charitable
Settlement
The Hervey Benham Charitable
Trust
Maurice and Jacqueline
Bennett Charitable Trust
Michael and Leslie Bennett
Charitable Trust
The Gerald Bentall Charitable
Trust
Bergqvist Charitable Trust
The Berkshire Community
Foundation
The Bestway Foundation
The Betterware Foundation

Thomas Betton's Charity for
Pensions and Relief-in-Need
BHST
The Mason Bibby 1981 Trust
BibleLands
The Bideford Bridge Trust
The Big Lottery Fund
The Billmeir Charitable Trust
Percy Bilton Charity
The Bingham Trust
The Bintaub Charitable Trust
The Birmingham Community
Foundation
The Birmingham District
Nursing Charitable Trust
The Birmingham Hospital
Saturday Fund Medical
Charity and Welfare Trust
Birmingham International
Airport Community Trust
The Lord Mayor of
Birmingham's Charity
Birthday House Trust
The Bisgood Charitable Trust
(registered as Miss Jeanne
Bisgood's Charitable Trust)
The Michael Bishop
Foundation
The Bishop's Development
Fund
The Sydney Black Charitable
Trust
The Bertie Black Foundation
Isabel Blackman Foundation
The Herbert and Peter
Blagrave Charitable Trust
The Blair Foundation
Blakes Benevolent Trust
The Blanchminster Trust
The Sir Victor Blank Charitable
Settlement
Blatchington Court Trust
The Neville and Elaine Blond
Charitable Trust
The Bluston Charitable
Settlement
Enid Blyton Trust for Children
The Body Shop Foundation
The Boltons Trust
The Bonamy Charitable Trust
The John and Celia Bonham
Christie Charitable Trust
The Charlotte Bonham-Carter
Charitable Trust
Bonhomie United Charity
Society
The Booth Charities
The Boots Charitable Trust
The Bordon and Liphook
Charity
Salo Bordon Charitable Trust
The Oliver Borthwick Memorial
Trust
The Bothwell Charitable Trust
H E and E L Botteley
Charitable Trust

The Harry Bottom Charitable Trust

P G and N J Boulton Trust

The A H and E Boulton Trust

Sir Clive Bourne Family Trust

The Anthony Bourne Foundation

The Bower Trust

The Bowerman Charitable Trust

John and Susan Bowers Fund

The Bowland Charitable Trust

The William Brake Charitable Trust

The Tony Bramall Charitable Trust

The Brewers' Company General Charitable Trust

The Harold and Alice Bridges Charity

Briggs Animal Welfare Trust

The Brighton District Nursing Association Trust

Bristol Archdeaconry Charity

John Bristow and Thomas Mason Trust

Britannia Foundation

The British Council for Prevention of Blindness

The British Dietetic Association General and Education Trust Fund

The British Gas (Scottish Gas) Energy Trust

British Heart Foundation

British Humane Association

British Institute at Ankara

British Ornithologists' Union

British Record Industry Trust

The Britto Foundation

The J and M Britton Charitable Trust

The Charles and Edna Broadhurst Charitable Trust

The Bromley Trust

The Roger Brooke Charitable Trust

The David Brooke Charity

The Charles Brotherton Trust

Joseph Brough Charitable Trust

The Swinfen Broun Charitable Trust

Mrs E E Brown Charitable Settlement

Bill Brown's Charitable Settlement

R S Brownless Charitable Trust

T B H Brunner's Charitable Settlement

The Jack Brunton Charitable Trust

Brushmill Ltd

The Bryant Trust

Buckingham Trust

The Buckinghamshire Foundation

The Buckinghamshire Masonic Centenary Fund

Buckland Charitable Trust

The Rosemary Bugden Charitable Trust

The Bulldog Trust Limited

The E F Bulmer Benevolent Fund

The BUPA Foundation

Burdens Charitable Foundation

The Burdett Trust for Nursing

The Clara E Burgess Charity

The Burry Charitable Trust

The Audrey and Stanley Burton 1960 Charitable Trust

The Arnold Burton 1998 Charitable Trust

The Burton Breweries Charitable Trust

The Geoffrey Burton Charitable Trust

Consolidated Charity of Burton upon Trent

Butchers' Company General Charities

The Bill Butlin Charity Trust

C and F Charitable Trust

C J Cadbury Charitable Trust

Edward Cadbury Charitable Trust

Henry T and Lucy B Cadbury Charitable Trust

P H G Cadbury Charitable Trust

The Christopher Cadbury Charitable Trust

The G W Cadbury Charitable Trust

The Richard Cadbury Charitable Trust

The William A Cadbury Charitable Trust

The Edward and Dorothy Cadbury Trust

The George Cadbury Trust

The Barrow Cadbury Trust and the Barrow Cadbury Fund

The Cadogan Charity

CAFOD

The Callander Charitable Trust

Calleva Foundation

The Calpe Trust

Calypso Browning Trust

The Campden Charities

The Canning Trust

H and L Cantor Trust

Capital Community Foundation

Cardy Beaver Foundation

The Carew Pole Charitable Trust

The D W T Cargill Fund

Caring for Kids (Radio Tay)

Carlee Ltd

The Carlton House Charitable Trust

The Worshipful Company of Carmen Benevolent Trust

The Carnegie Dunfermline Trust

The Carnegie Trust for the Universities of Scotland

The Carpenter Charitable Trust

The Carpenters' Company Charitable Trust

The Carrington Charitable Trust

The Carron Charitable Settlement

The Leslie Mary Carter Charitable Trust

The Carvill Trust

The Casey Trust

Sir John Cass's Foundation

The Elizabeth Casson Trust

The Castang Foundation

The Catalyst Charitable Trust

The Catholic Charitable Trust

Catholic Foreign Missions

The Catholic Trust for England and Wales

The Joseph and Annie Cattle Trust

The Thomas Sivewright Catto Charitable Settlement

The Wilfrid and Constance Cave Foundation

The Cayo Foundation

Elizabeth Cayzer Charitable Trust

The B G S Cayzer Charitable Trust

The Cazenove Charitable Trust

Celtic Charity Fund

The Cemlyn-Jones Trust

The Amelia Chadwick Trust

The Pamela Champion Foundation

Champneys Charitable Foundation

The Chapman Charitable Trust

John William Chapman's Charitable Trust

The Charities Advisory Trust

Charitworth Limited

The Charter 600 Charity

The Worshipful Company of Chartered Accountants General Charitable Trust

The Chasah Trust

The Chelsea Building Society Charitable Foundation

The Chelsea Square 1994 Trust

The Cheruby Trust

The Cheshire Provincial Fund of Benevolence

The Chetwode Foundation

The Malcolm Chick Charity

Child Growth Foundation

Children's Liver Disease
Foundation
Childs Charitable Trust
The Childwick Trust
The Chippenham Borough
Lands Charity
The Chipping Sodbury Town
Lands Charity
CHK Charities Limited
The Chownes Foundation
The Chrimes Family Charitable
Trust
The Christabella Charitable
Trust
Christadelphian Samaritan
Fund
Christian Aid
Christian Response to Eastern
Europe
The Church and Community
Fund
The Church Burgesses
Educational Foundation
Church Burgesses Trust
Church Lands and John
Johnson's Estate Charities
Church of Ireland Priorities
Fund
The Church Urban Fund
City and County of Swansea
Welsh Church Act Fund
The City Bridge Trust
The City Educational Trust
Fund
CLA Charitable Trust
Stephen Clark 1957
Charitable Trust
J A Clark Charitable Trust
The Hilda and Alice Clark
Charitable Trust
The Roger and Sarah Bancroft
Clark Charitable Trust
The Clarke Charitable
Settlement
The Cleary Foundation
The Cleopatra Trust
Lord Clinton's Charitable Trust
The Clore Duffield Foundation
Miss V L Clore's 1967
Charitable Trust
Closehelm Ltd
The Clothworkers' Foundation
Richard Cloudesley's Charity
The Clover Trust
The Robert Clutterbuck
Charitable Trust
Clydpride Ltd
The Coalfields Regeneration
Trust
The John Coates Charitable
Trust
Coats Foundation Trust
The Cobtree Charity Trust Ltd
The Denise Cohen Charitable
Trust

The Vivienne and Samuel
Cohen Charitable Trust
The R and S Cohen Fondation
The John S Cohen Foundation
The Colchester Catalyst
Charity
John Coldman Charitable Trust
The Cole Charitable Trust
The Colefax Charitable Trust
The John and Freda Coleman
Charitable Trust
The George Henry Collins
Charity
The E Alec Colman Charitable
Fund Ltd
The Sir Jeremiah Colman Gift
Trust
Col-Reno Ltd
The Colt Foundation
The Coltstaple Trust
Colwinston Charitable Trust
Colyer-Fergusson Charitable
Trust
The Comino Foundation
Community Foundation for
Calderdale
The Community Foundation for
Greater Manchester
The Community Foundation for
Northern Ireland
The Company of Tobacco Pipe
Makers' and Tobacco
Blenders' Benevolent Fund
The Compton Charitable Trust
The Congleton Inclosure Trust
The Conservation Foundation
The Consolidated Charities for
the Infirm Merchant
Taylors' Company
The Construction Industry
Trust for Youth
Gordon Cook Foundation
The Ernest Cook Trust
The Cooks Charity
The Catherine Cookson
Charitable Trust
Harold and Daphne Cooper
Charitable Trust
Mabel Cooper Charity
The Alice Ellen Cooper Dean
Charitable Foundation
The Co-operative Foundation
The Marjorie Coote Animal
Charity Trust
The Marjorie Coote Old
People's Charity
The Helen Jean Cope Trust
The J Reginald Corah
Foundation Fund
The Gershon Coren Charitable
Foundation
The Corinthian Trust
Edwin Cornforth 1983 Charity
Trust
The Duke of Cornwall's
Benevolent Fund

The Cornwell Charitable Trust
The Sidney and Elizabeth
Corob Charitable Trust
The Corona Charitable Trust
The Costa Family Charitable
Trust
The Cotton Industry War
Memorial Trust
The Cotton Trust
County Durham Foundation
Coutts Charitable Trust
The General Charities of the
City of Coventry
Coventry Building Society
Charitable Foundation
The John Cowan Foundation
Cowley Charitable Foundation
The Sir William Coxen Trust
Fund
The Lord Cozens-Hardy Trust
The Craignish Trust
The Craps Charitable Trust
Michael Crawford Children's
Charity
The Cray Trust
The Crescent Trust
Criffel Charitable Trust
Cripplegate Foundation
The Violet and Milo Cripps
Charitable Trust
The Cromarty Trust
The Harry Crook Foundation
The Cross Trust
The Cross Trust
The Croydon Relief in Need
Charities
The Mayor of Croydon's
Charity Fund
Cruden Foundation Ltd
The Ronald Cruickshanks'
Foundation
Cuby Charitable Trust
The Culra Charitable Trust
The Cumber Family Charitable
Trust
Cumberland Building Society
Charitable Foundation
Cumbria Community
Foundation
The D J H Currie Memorial
Trust
The Dennis Curry Charitable
Trust
The Raymond Curtis Charitable
Trust
The Manny Cussins
Foundation
The Cwmbran Trust
Itzchok Meyer Cymerman Trust
Ltd
The D'Oyly Carte Charitable
Trust
The Roald Dahl Foundation
The Daily Prayer Union
Charitable Trust Ltd
The Daisy Trust

The Daiwa Anglo-Japanese Foundation

Oizer Dalim Trust

The Dr and Mrs A Darlington Charitable Trust

Baron Davenport's Charity

The Davidson (Nairn) Charitable Trust

Davidson Charitable Trust

The Alderman Joe Davidson Memorial Trust

Michael Davies Charitable Settlement

The Gwendoline and Margaret Davies Charity

The Wilfrid Bruce Davis Charitable Trust

Davis-Rubens Charitable Trust

The Dawe Charitable Trust

The De Clermont Charitable Company Ltd

Peter De Haan Charitable Trust

The Leopold De Rothschild Charitable Trust

The Deakin Charitable Trust

William Dean Countryside and Educational Trust

The Debmar Benevolent Trust

The Delfont Foundation

The Dellal Foundation

The Delves Charitable Trust

The Demigryphon Trust

The Denman Charitable Trust

The Denton Charitable Trust

The Denton Wilde Sapte Charitable Trust

The Earl of Derby's Charitable Trust

The Derbyshire Churches and Chapels Preservation Trust

Derbyshire Community Foundation

The J N Derbyshire Trust

Devon Community Foundation

The Devon Educational Trust

The Devon Historic Churches Trust

The Duke of Devonshire's Charitable Trust

The Sandy Dewhirst Charitable Trust

DG Charitable Settlement

The Laduma Dhamecha Charitable Trust

Diabetes UK

Alan and Sheila Diamond Charitable Trust

The Diana, Princess of Wales Memorial Fund

The Dibden Allotments Charity

The Dickon Trust

The Digbeth Trust

The Dinwoodie Settlement

Disability Aid Fund (The Roger and Jean Jefcoate Trust)

Dischma Charitable Trust

The DLA Piper Charitable Trust

The DLM Charitable Trust

Louise Dobson Charitable Trust

The Derek and Eileen Dodgson Foundation

The Dollond Charitable Trust

Domepride Ltd

The Dorcas Trust

The Dorema Charitable Trust

The Dorset Historic Churches Trust

The Dorus Trust

Double 'O' Charity Ltd

The Doughty Charity Trust

The R M Douglas Charitable Trust

The Drapers' Charitable Fund

Dromintee Trust

The Dugdale Charitable Trust

The Duis Charitable Trust

The Dulverton Trust

The P B Dumbell Charitable Trust

The Dumbreck Charity

Dunard Fund

Ronald Duncan Literary Foundation

The Dunhill Medical Trust

The Houghton Dunn Charitable Trust

The Dunn Family Charitable Trust

The W E Dunn Trust

Dushinsky Trust Ltd

Mildred Duveen Charitable Trust

The Dwek Family Charitable Trust

The Dyers' Company Charitable Trust

EAGA Partnership Charitable Trust

The Eagle Charity Trust

Audrey Earle Charitable Trust

The Earley Charity

Earls Colne and Halstead Educational Charity

The Earmark Trust

East Kent Provincial Charities

East London Community Foundation

Eastern Counties Educational Trust Limited

The Sir John Eastwood Foundation

The Ebenezer Trust

The EBM Charitable Trust

Eden Arts Trust

EDF Energy Trust (EDFET)

The Gilbert and Eileen Edgar Foundation

Gilbert Edgar Trust

Edinburgh Children's Holiday Fund

The Edinburgh Trust, No 2 Account

Edinburgh Voluntary Organisations' Trust Funds

Educational Foundation of Alderman John Norman

The W G Edwards Charitable Foundation

The William Edwards Educational Charity

The Elephant Trust

The George Elias Charitable Trust

The Gerald Palmer Eling Trust Company

The Elizabeth Frankland Moore and Star Foundation

The Wilfred and Elsie Elkes Charity Fund

The Maud Elkington Charitable Trust

Ellador Ltd

The Ellerdale Trust

The John Ellerman Foundation

The Ellinson Foundation Ltd

The Edith Maud Ellis 1985 Charitable Trust

The Ellis Campbell Foundation

James Ellis Charitable Trust

The Elmgrant Trust

The Elmley Foundation

Elshore Ltd

The Vernon N Ely Charitable Trust

The Embleton Trust

The Emerton-Christie Charity

EMI Music Sound Foundation

The Emmandjay Charitable Trust

The Worshipful Company of Engineers Charitable Trust Fund

The Englefield Charitable Trust

The English Schools' Football Association

The Enkalon Foundation

Entindale Ltd

The Epigoni Trust

Epilepsy Research UK

The Equitable Charitable Trust

The Equity Trust Fund

The Ericson Trust

The Erskine Cunningham Hill Trust

Essex Community Foundation

The Essex Fairway Charitable Trust

The Essex Heritage Trust

Essex Provincial Charity Fund

The Essex Youth Trust

Euro Charity Trust

The Evangelical Covenants Trust

The Alan Evans Memorial Trust

Sir John Evelyn's Charity

The Eventhall Family Charitable Trust
The Everard Foundation
The Eveson Charitable Trust
The Beryl Evetts and Robert Luff Animal Welfare Trust
The Execution Charitable Trust
The Mayor of Exeter's Appeal Fund
The Exilarch's Foundation
F C Charitable Trust
The F P Limited Charitable Trust
The Faber Charitable Trust
Esmée Fairbairn Foundation
The Fairway Trust
Faisaltex Charitable Trust
The Family Foundations Trust
The Family Rich Charities Trust
Famos Foundation Trust
The Lord Faringdon Charitable Trust
Samuel William Farmer's Trust
The Farmers' Company Charitable Fund
The Thomas Farr Charitable Trust
Walter Farthing (Trust) Limited
Farthing Trust
The Fassnidge Memorial Trust
Joseph Fattorini Charitable Trust 'B' Account
The Fawcett Charitable Trust
Federation of Jewish Relief Organisations
Feed the Minds
The John Feeney Charitable Bequest
The George Fentham Birmingham Charity
The A M Fenton Trust
Allan and Nesta Ferguson Charitable Settlement
Elizabeth Ferguson Charitable Trust Fund
The Fidelity UK Foundation
The Bluff Field Charitable Trust
The Doris Field Charitable Trust
Fife Council/Common Good Funds and Trusts
Dixie Rose Findlay Charitable Trust
Gerald Finzi Charitable Trust
Firtree Trust
The Sir John Fisher Foundation
The Fishmongers' Company's Charitable Trust
Marc Fitch Fund
The Fitton Trust
The Earl Fitzwilliam Charitable Trust
Bud Flanagan Leukaemia Fund
The Rose Flatau Charitable Trust

The Ian Fleming Charitable Trust
The Joyce Fletcher Charitable Trust
The Roy Fletcher Charitable Trust
Florence's Charitable Trust
The Florian Charitable Trust
The Flow Foundation
The Gerald Fogel Charitable Trust
The Follett Trust
The Football Association National Sports Centre Trust
The Football Association Youth Trust
The Football Foundation
The Forbes Charitable Foundation
Forbesville Limited
The Forces Trust
Ford Britain Trust
The Oliver Ford Charitable Trust
Fordeve Ltd
The Forest Hill Charitable Trust
The Foresters' Charity Stewards UK Trust
Gwyneth Forrester Trust
The Forte Charitable Trust
Lord Forte Foundation
Foundation for Management Education
Four Acre Trust
The Four Winds Trust
The Fowler, Smith and Jones Charitable Trust
The Foyle Foundation
The Isaac and Freda Frankel Memorial Charitable Trust
Sydney E Franklin Deceased's New Second Charity
The Jill Franklin Trust
The Gordon Fraser Charitable Trust
The Hugh Fraser Foundation
The Joseph Strong Frazer Trust
The Louis and Valerie Freedman Charitable Settlement
The Thomas Freke and Lady Norton Charity
The Charles S French Charitable Trust
The Anne French Memorial Trust
The Freshfield Foundation
The Freshgate Trust Foundation
The Friarsgate Trust
The Friends Hall Farm Street Trust
Friends of Biala Ltd
Friends of Wiznitz Limited

Friends Provident Charitable Foundation
The Frognal Trust
T F C Frost Charitable Trust
The Patrick Frost Foundation
Maurice Fry Charitable Trust
Mejer and Gertrude Miriam Frydman Foundation
The Fuellers Charitable Trust Fund
The Fulmer Charitable Trust
Worshipful Company of Furniture Makers Charitable Fund
Gableholt Limited
The Galbraith Trust
The Gale Family Charitable Trust
The Gamlen Charitable Trust
The Gamma Trust
The Gannochy Trust
The Ganzoni Charitable Trust
The Worshipful Company of Gardeners of London
The Samuel Gardner Memorial Trust
The Garnett Charitable Trust
Garrick Charitable Trust
Garvan Limited
The Gatsby Charitable Foundation
Gatwick Airport Community Trust
The Robert Gavron Charitable Trust
Jacqueline and Michael Gee Charitable Trust
J Paul Getty Jr Charitable Trust
The Gibbs Charitable Trust
Simon Gibson Charitable Trust
The G C Gibson Charitable Trust
The Harvey and Hilary Gilbert Charitable Trust
The Girdlers' Company Charitable Trust
The B and P Glasser Charitable Trust
The Glass-House Trust
Global Care
Global Charities (formally GCap Charities)
Gloucestershire Community Foundation
Worshipful Company of Glovers of London Charity Fund
GMC Trust
The GNC Trust
The Meir Golda Trust
The Sydney and Phyllis Goldberg Memorial Charitable Trust
The Golden Bottle Trust
Golden Charitable Trust

The Jack Goldhill Charitable
Trust
The Goldsmiths' Arts Trust
Fund
The Goldsmiths' Company
Charity
The Golsoncott Foundation
The Good Neighbours Trust
Nicholas and Judith
Goodison's Charitable
Settlement
The Everard and Mina
Goodman Charitable
Foundation
Mike Gooley Trailfinders
Charity
Leonard Gordon Charitable
Trust
The Gosling Foundation
Limited
The Gough Charitable Trust
The Gould Charitable Trust
The Grace Charitable Trust
A B Grace Trust
The Graff Foundation
The Grahame Charitable
Foundation Limited
Grampian Police Diced Cap
Charitable Fund
The Granada Foundation
Grand Charitable Trust of the
Order of Women
Freemasons
The Grand Order of Water
Rats' Charities Fund
The Grange Farm Centre Trust
Grantham Yorke Trust
The J G Graves Charitable
Trust
The Gray Trust
The Great Stone Bridge Trust
of Edenbridge
The Great Torrington Town
Lands Charity
The Constance Green
Foundation
The Barry Green Memorial
Fund
The Philip Green Memorial
Trust
Mrs H R Greene Charitable
Settlement
Greenham Common
Community Trust Limited
Naomi and Jeffrey Greenwood
Charitable Trust
Greggs Foundation
Grimmitt Trust
The Grocers' Charity
The M and R Gross Charities
Limited
The Grove Charitable Trust
The GRP Charitable Trust
The David and Marie Grumitt
Foundation

The Bishop of Guildford's
Foundation
The Guildry Incorporation of
Perth
The Walter Guinness
Charitable Trust
The Gunter Charitable Trust
The Gur Trust
Gurunanak
Dr Guthrie's Association
The H and M Charitable Trust
H C D Memorial Fund
The H P Charitable Trust
The Hackney Parochial
Charities
The Hadfield Trust
The Hadley Trust
The Hadrian Trust
The Alfred Haines Charitable
Trust
The Hale Trust
E F and M G Hall Charitable
Trust
The Edith Winifred Hall
Charitable Trust
Robert Hall Charity
The Hamamelis Trust
Hamilton Wallace Trust
Sue Hammerson's Charitable
Trust
The Hammonds Charitable
Trust
The Hampshire and Islands
Historic Churches Trust
Hampton Fuel Allotment
Charity
The W A Handley Charitable
Trust
Beatrice Hankey Foundation
Ltd
The Hanley Trust
The Kathleen Hannay
Memorial Charity
The Doughty Hanson
Charitable Foundation
Lord Hanson Foundation
The Haramead Trust
Miss K M Harbinson's
Charitable Trust
Harbo Charities Limited
The Harborne Parish Lands
Charity
The Harbour Charitable Trust
The Harbour Foundation
The Harding Trust
William Harding's Charity
The Hare of Steep Charitable
Trust
The Harebell Centenary Fund
The Kenneth Hargreaves
Charitable Trust
The Harris Charitable Trust
The Harris Charity
The Harrison and Potter Trust
The John Harrison Charitable
Trust

The Peter Harrison Foundation
The Spencer Hart Charitable
Trust
The Hartley Charitable Trust
The N and P Hartley Memorial
Trust
William Geoffrey Harvey's
Discretionary Settlement
The Edward Harvist Trust Fund
Haskel Family Foundation
The Hathaway Trust
The M A Hawe Settlement
The Hawthorne Charitable
Trust
The Dorothy Hay-Bolton
Charitable Trust
The Haydan Charitable Trust
The Haymills Charitable Trust
The Headley Trust
Headley-Pitt Charitable Trust
Heagerty Charitable Trust
The Heald Charitable Trust
Healthsure Group Ltd
May Hearnshaw's Charity
The Heart of England
Community Foundation
The Heathcoat Trust
Heathside Charitable Trust
The Charlotte Heber-Percy
Charitable Trust
Percy Hedley 1990 Charitable
Trust
The Hedley Denton Charitable
Trust
The Hedley Foundation
The H J Heinz Company
Limited Charitable Trust
The Hellenic Foundation
The Michael and Morven Heller
Charitable Foundation
The Simon Heller Charitable
Settlement
Help the Aged
Help the Homeless
Help the Hospices
The Hemby Trust
The Christina Mary Hendrie
Trust for Scottish and
Canadian Charities
The Henley Educational Charity
Philip Henman Trust
Esther Hennell Charitable
Trust
The G D Herbert Charitable
Trust
The Joanna Herbert-Stepney
Charitable Settlement
The Anne Herd Memorial Trust
The Herefordshire Historic
Churches Trust
The Heritage of London Trust
Ltd
The Hertfordshire Community
Foundation
The Hesed Trust

The Hesslewood Children's Trust (Hull Seamen's and General Orphanage)

The Bernhard Heuberger Charitable Trust

Hexham and Newcastle Diocesan Trust (1947)

The P and C Hickinbotham Charitable Trust

The Higgs Charitable Trust

Alan Edward Higgs Charity

The High Sheriff's Police Trust for the County of West Midlands

Highcroft Charitable Trust

The Hilden Charitable Fund

The Joseph and Mary Hiley Trust

The Holly Hill Charitable Trust

The Charles Littlewood Hill Trust

The Hillingdon Partnership Trust

R G Hills Charitable Trust

Hinchley Charitable Trust

Lady Hind Trust

Stuart Hine Trust

The Hinrichsen Foundation

The Hitchin Educational Foundation

The Eleemosynary Charity of William Hobbayne

Hobson Charity Limited

Hockerill Educational Foundation

Matthew Hodder Charitable Trust

The Sir Julian Hodge Charitable Trust

The Jane Hodge Foundation

The J G Hogg Charitable Trust

The Holden Charitable Trust

John Holford's Charity

The Hollick Family Charitable Trust

The Dorothy Holmes Charitable Trust

P H Holt Foundation

The Edward Holt Trust

The Holywood Trust

The Homelands Charitable Trust

The Homestead Charitable Trust

Mary Homfray Charitable Trust

Sir Harold Hood's Charitable Trust

The Hope Trust

HopMarket Charity

The Cuthbert Horn Trust

The Antony Hornby Charitable Trust

The Horne Foundation

The Horne Trust

The Worshipful Company of Horners' Charitable Trusts

The Hornsey Parochial Charities

The Hospital of God at Greatham

The Hospital Saturday Fund

Houblon-Norman/George Fund

The House of Industry Estate

The Reta Lila Howard Foundation

The Daniel Howard Trust

The Clifford Howarth Charity Trust

The Huddersfield Medical Trust Fund

The Hudson Foundation

The Huggard Charitable Trust

The Geoffrey C Hughes Charitable Trust

The Hull and East Riding Charitable Trust

Hulme Trust Estates (Educational)

Human Relief Foundation

The Humanitarian Trust

The Michael and Shirley Hunt Charitable Trust

The Albert Hunt Trust

The Hunter Foundation

Miss Agnes H Hunter's Trust

The Huntingdon Foundation

Huntingdon Freemen's Charity

John Huntingdon's Charity

Hurdale Charity Limited

The Nani Huyu Charitable Trust

The P Y N and B Hyams Trust

The Hyde Charitable Trust – Youth Plus

The Idlewild Trust

The Iliffe Family Charitable Trust

The Indigo Trust

The Ingram Trust

The Inland Waterways Association

The Inlight Trust

The Inman Charity

The Inner London Magistrates Court Poor Box Charity and Feeder Charity

The Worshipful Company of Innholders General Charity Fund

The Ireland Fund of Great Britain

The Irish Youth Foundation (UK) Ltd

The Ironmongers' Foundation

Irshad Trust

Irwin Trust

The ISA Charity

The Isaacs Charitable Trust

The J Isaacs Charitable Trust

The Island Health Trust

The Isle of Anglesey Charitable Trust

Isle of Dogs Community Foundation

The ITF Seafarers Trust

J A R Charitable Trust

The J J Charitable Trust

The J R S S T Charitable Trust

Elizabeth Jackson Charitable Trust

Jacobs Charitable Trust

The Ruth and Lionel Jacobson Trust (Second Fund) No 2

Jaffe Family Relief Fund

John James Bristol Foundation

The Susan and Stephen James Charitable Settlement

The James Trust

The Jarman Charitable Trust

The John Jarrold Trust

JCA Charitable Foundation

The Jeffrey Charitable Trust

Rees Jeffreys Road Fund

The Jenour Foundation

The Jephcott Charitable Trust

The Jerusalem Trust

Jesus Hospital Charity

The Jewish Youth Fund

The JMK Charitable Trust

The Joanies Trust

The Harold Joels Charitable Trust

The Jonathan Joels Charitable Trust

The Nicholas Joels Charitable Trust

The Norman Joels Charitable Trust

The Joffe Charitable Trust

The Lillie Johnson Charitable Trust

The Johnson Group Cleaners Charity

The Johnnie Johnson Trust

The Johnson Wax Ltd Charitable Trust

The Joicey Trust

The Jones 1986 Charitable Trust

The Marjorie and Geoffrey Jones Charitable Trust

The Jordan Charitable Foundation

The J E Joseph Charitable Fund

The Lady Eileen Joseph Foundation

JTH Charitable Trust

The Judith Trust

The Anton Jurgens Charitable Trust

The Bernard Kahn Charitable Trust

The Stanley Kalms Foundation

The Karenza Foundation

The Boris Karloff Charitable Foundation

The Ian Karten Charitable Trust

The Kasner Charitable Trust

The Kass Charitable Trust

The Kathleen Trust

The Michael and Ilse Katz Foundation

The Katzauer Charitable Settlement

The C S Kaufman Charitable Trust

The Geoffrey John Kaye Charitable Foundation

The Emmanuel Kaye Foundation

Kelsick's Educational Foundation

The KempWelch Charitable Trust

The Kay Kendall Leukaemia Fund

William Kendall's Charity (Wax Chandlers' Company)

The Kennedy Charitable Foundation

The Kennel Club Charitable Trust

The Nancy Kenyon Charitable Trust

Keren Association

Kermaville Ltd

E and E Kernkraut Charities Limited

The Peter Kershaw Trust

The Kessler Foundation

Keswick Hall Charity

The Ursula Keyes Trust

The Robert Kiln Charitable Trust

The King Henry VIII Endowed Trust Warwick

The King/Cullimore Charitable Trust

The Kingsbury Charity

The Mary Kinross Charitable Trust

Kinsurdy Charitable Trust

Kirkley Poor's Lands Estate

The Richard Kirkman Charitable Trust

Kirschel Foundation

Robert Kitchin (Saddlers' Company)

Ernest Kleinwort Charitable Trust

The Marina Kleinwort Charitable Trust

The Sir James Knott Trust

The Kobler Trust

The Kohn Foundation

The Kreditor Charitable Trust

The Kreitman Foundation

The Neil Kreitman Foundation

The Heinz, Anna and Carol Kroch Foundation

The Kyte Charitable Trust

Lacims-Maclis Charitable Trust

The Late Sir Pierce Lacy Charity Trust

John Laing Charitable Trust

Maurice and Hilda Laing Charitable Trust

The Laing Family Foundations

The Christopher Laing Foundation

The Kirby Laing Foundation

The Martin Laing Foundation

The Beatrice Laing Trust

The Lambert Charitable Trust

Lancashire Environmental Fund

Duchy of Lancaster Benevolent Fund

The Lancaster Foundation

LandAid Charitable Trust

The Langdale Trust

The Langley Charitable Trust

The Langtree Trust

The LankellyChase Foundation

The Lanvern Foundation

The R J Larg Family Charitable Trust

Largsmount Ltd

The Lark Trust

Laslett's (Hinton) Charity

Lauchentilly Charitable Foundation 1988

Laufer Charitable Trust

The Lauffer Family Charitable Foundation

Mrs F B Laurence Charitable Trust

The Kathleen Laurence Trust

The Edgar E Lawley Foundation

The Herd Lawson and Muriel Lawson Charitable Trust

The Lawson Beckman Charitable Trust

The Raymond and Blanche Lawson Charitable Trust

The Carole and Geoffrey Lawson Foundation

The Mason Le Page Charitable Trust

The Leach Fourteenth Trust

The David Lean Foundation

The Leathersellers' Company Charitable Fund

The Leche Trust

The Arnold Lee Charitable Trust

The William Leech Charity

The Lord Mayor of Leeds Appeal Fund

Leeds Building Society Charitable Foundation

Leicester Charity Link

The Kennedy Leigh Charitable Trust

Morris Leigh Foundation

The Leigh Trust

Mrs Vera Leigh's Charity

The P Leigh-Bramwell Trust 'E'

The Lennox and Wyfold Foundation

The Erica Leonard Trust

The Leonard Trust

The Mark Leonard Trust

Lesley Lesley and Mutter Trust

Leukaemia Research Fund

The Leverhulme Trade Charities Trust

Lord Leverhulme's Charitable Trust

The Joseph Levy Charitable Foundation

Lewis Family Charitable Trust

The John Spedan Lewis Foundation

The Sir Edward Lewis Foundation

John Lewis Partnership General Community Fund

Lichfield Conduit Lands

Lifeline 4 Kids

The Thomas Lilley Memorial Trust

Limoges Charitable Trust

The Linbury Trust

The Lind Trust

Lindale Educational Foundation

The Linden Charitable Trust

The Enid Linder Foundation

The Linmardon Trust

The Ruth and Stuart Lipton Charitable Trust

The Lister Charitable Trust

Frank Litchfield Charitable Trust

The Andrew and Mary Elizabeth Little Charitable Trust

The Second Joseph Aaron Littman Foundation

The George John and Sheilah Livanos Charitable Trust

Liverpool Charity and Voluntary Services

Liverpool Sailors' Home Trust

Jack Livingstone Charitable Trust

The Elaine and Angus Lloyd Charitable Trust

The Charles Lloyd Foundation

The Lloyd Fund

Lloyd's Charities Trust

The Lloyd-Everett Trust

Lloyds TSB Foundation for England and Wales

Lloyds TSB Foundation for Northern Ireland

Lloyds TSB Foundation for the Channel Islands

Llysdinam Charitable Trust

Localtrent Ltd

The Locker Foundation

The Loftus Charitable Trust

The Lolev Charitable Trust
London Catalyst
The London Law Trust
The London Marathon
Charitable Trust
The William and Katherine
Longman Trust
The Lord's Taverners
The Loseley and Guildway
Charitable Trust
The Lotus Foundation
The C L Loyd Charitable Trust
The Marie Helen Luen
Charitable Trust
Robert Luff Foundation Ltd
Henry Lumley Charitable Trust
Lady Lumley's Educational
Foundation
Paul Lunn-Rockliffe Charitable
Trust
C F Lunoe Trust Fund
The Ruth and Jack Lunzer
Charitable Trust
Lord and Lady Lurgan Trust
The Lyndhurst Trust
The Lynn Foundation
The Lynwood Trust
John Lyon's Charity
The Lyons Charitable Trust
The Sir Jack Lyons Charitable
Trust
Malcolm Lyons Foundation
The Lyras Family Charitable
Trust
Sylvanus Lyson's Charity
The M and C Trust
The M D and S Charitable
Trust
The M K Charitable Trust
The Madeline Mabey Trust
The E M MacAndrew Trust
The R S Macdonald Charitable
Trust
Macdonald-Buchanan
Charitable Trust
The Macfarlane Walker Trust
The Mackay and Brewer
Charitable Trust
The Mackintosh Foundation
The MacRobert Trust
Ian Mactaggart Trust
The Magdalen and Lasher
Charity
Magdalen Hospital Trust
The Magen Charitable Trust
Mageni Trust
Mahavir Trust
Man Group plc Charitable
Trust
The Manchester Guardian
Society Charitable Trust
Manchester Kids
Lord Mayor of Manchester's
Charity Appeal Trust
Mandeville Trust
The Manifold Charitable Trust

W M Mann Foundation
The Leslie and Lilian Manning
Trust
Maranatha Christian Trust
Marbeh Torah Trust
The Marchday Charitable Fund
Marchig Animal Welfare Trust
The Stella and Alexander
Margulies Charitable Trust
Mariapolis Limited
Market Harborough and The
Bowdens Charity
Michael Marks Charitable
Trust
The Ann and David Marks
Foundation
The Hilda and Samuel Marks
Foundation
J P Marland Charitable Trust
Marr-Munning Trust
The Michael Marsh Charitable
Trust
The Marsh Christian Trust
The Charlotte Marshall
Charitable Trust
The Jim Marshall Charitable
Trust
The D G Marshall of
Cambridge Trust
Marshall's Charity
Marshgate Charitable
Settlement
Sir George Martin Trust
John Martin's Charity
The Mason Porter Charitable
Trust
The Nancie Massey Charitable
Trust
The Mathew Trust
Matliwala Family Charitable
Trust
The Matt 6.3 Charitable Trust
The Violet Mauray Charitable
Trust
The Maxell Educational Trust
The Maxwell Family Foundation
Evelyn May Trust
Mayfair Charities Ltd
The Mayfield Valley Arts Trust
Mazars Charitable Trust
The Robert McAlpine
Foundation
The McDougall Trust
The A M McGreevy No 5
Charitable Settlement
The McKenna Charitable Trust
Martin McLaren Memorial
Trust
The Helen Isabella McMorran
Charitable Foundation
D D McPhail Charitable
Settlement
The James Frederick and Ethel
Anne Measures Charity
Medical Research Council
The Medlock Charitable Trust

The Anthony and Elizabeth
Mellows Charitable
Settlement
Melodor Ltd
Melow Charitable Trust
Meningitis Trust
Menuchar Ltd
Brian Mercer Charitable Trust
The Mercers' Charitable
Foundation
The Merchant Taylors'
Company Charities Fund
The Merchant Venturers'
Charity
The Merchants' House of
Glasgow
Mercury Phoenix Trust
The Mersey Docks and
Harbour Company
Charitable Fund
Community Foundation for
Merseyside
The Zachary Merton and
George Woofindin
Convalescent Trust
The Tony Metherell Charitable
Trust
The Methodist Relief and
Development Fund
The Metropolitan Drinking
Fountain and Cattle Trough
Association
Gerald Micklem Charitable
Trust
Midhurst Pensions Trust
The Migraine Trust
Miles Trust for the Putney and
Roehampton Community
Millennium Stadium Charitable
Trust
The Hugh and Mary Miller
Bequest Trust
The Miller Foundation
The Millfield Trust
The Millhouses Charitable
Trust
The Millichope Foundation
The Mills Charity
The Millward Charitable Trust
The Clare Milne Trust
Milton Keynes Community
Foundation
The Edgar Milward Charity
The Keith and Joan
Mindelsohn Charitable
Trust
The Peter Minet Trust
Minge's Gift and the Pooled
Trusts
The Minos Trust
The Mirfield Educational
Charity
The Laurence Misener
Charitable Trust
The Mishcon Family Charitable
Trust

The Misselbrook Trust
The Mitchell Charitable Trust
The Esme Mitchell Trust
Keren Mitzvah Trust
The Mizpah Trust
The Mobbs Memorial Trust Ltd
The Modiano Charitable Trust
The Moette Charitable Trust
The Mole Charitable Trust
The D C Moncrieff Charitable
   Trust
Monmouthshire County Council
   Welsh Church Act Fund
The Montague Thompson
   Coon Charitable Trust
The Colin Montgomerie
   Charitable Foundation
The Monument Trust
Moody Charitable Trust
George A Moore Foundation
The Nigel Moores Family
   Charitable Trust
John Moores Foundation
The Peter Moores Foundation
The Morel Charitable Trust
The Morgan Charitable
   Foundation
The Mr and Mrs J T Morgan
   Foundation
The J P Morgan Foundations
Diana and Allan Morgenthau
   Charitable Trust
The Oliver Morland Charitable
   Trust
S C and M E Morland's
   Charitable Trust
The Morris Charitable Trust
The Willie and Mabel Morris
   Charitable Trust
The Peter Morrison Charitable
   Foundation
The Stanley Morrison
   Charitable Trust
Moshal Charitable Trust
Vyoel Moshe Charitable Trust
The Moss Charitable Trust
The Robert and Margaret
   Moss Charitable Trust
Moss Family Charitable Trust
The Mount Everest Foundation
Mountbatten Festival of Music
The Mountbatten Memorial
   Trust
The Edwina Mountbatten Trust
The Mugdock Children's Trust
The F H Muirhead Charitable
   Trust
The Mulberry Trust
The Edith Murphy Foundation
Murphy-Neumann Charity
   Company Limited
The Mushroom Fund
The Music Sales Charitable
   Trust
Muslim Hands
The Mutual Trust Group

MYA Charitable Trust
The Kitty and Daniel Nabarro
   Charitable Trust
The Nadezhda Charitable Trust
The Willie Nagel Charitable
   Trust
The Naggar Charitable Trust
The Eleni Nakou Foundation
The Janet Nash Charitable
   Settlement
Nathan Charitable Trust
Asthma UK
The National Manuscripts
   Conservation Trust
Nazareth Trust Fund
The Nchima Trust
Needham Market and Barking
   Welfare Charities
The Worshipful Company of
   Needlemakers' Charitable
   Fund
The Neighbourly Charitable
   Trust
The James Neill Trust Fund
Nemoral Ltd
Nesswall Ltd
Nestle Rowntree Employees
   Community Fund
Network for Social Change
The New Appeals Organisation
   for the City and County of
   Nottingham
New Court Charitable Trust
Newby Trust Limited
The Newcomen Collett
   Foundation
The Richard Newitt Fund
Mr and Mrs F E F Newman
   Charitable Trust
The Frances and Augustus
   Newman Foundation
Newpier Charity Ltd
Alderman Newton's
   Educational Foundation
The Chevras Ezras Nitzrochim
   Trust
The Noel Buxton Trust
The Noon Foundation
The Norda Trust
Norie Charitable Trust
Normalyn Charitable Trust
The Norman Family Charitable
   Trust
The Duncan Norman Trust
   Fund
The Normanby Charitable Trust
The North British Hotel Trust
The North West Cancer
   Research Fund
The Northampton Municipal
   Church Charities
The Northampton Queen's
   Institute Relief in Sickness
   Fund
The Earl of Northampton's
   Charity

The Northcott Devon
   Foundation
The Northcott Devon Medical
   Foundation
The Northmoor Trust
The Northumberland Village
   Homes Trust
The Northumbria Historic
   Churches Trust
The Northwood Charitable
   Trust
The Norton Foundation
The Norwich Church of England
   Young Men's Society
The Norwich Historic Churches
   Trust Ltd
The Norwich Town Close
   Estate Charity
The Norwood and Newton
   Settlement
The Noswad Charity
The Notgrove Trust
The Nottingham General
   Dispensary
The Nottingham Gordon
   Memorial Trust for Boys
   and Girls
Nottinghamshire Community
   Foundation
The Nottinghamshire Historic
   Churches Trust
The Nottinghamshire Miners'
   Welfare Trust Fund
Novi Most International
The Father O'Mahoney
   Memorial Trust
The Sir Peter O'Sullevan
   Charitable Trust
The Oak Trust
The Oakdale Trust
The Oakley Charitable Trust
The Oakmoor Charitable Trust
The Odin Charitable Trust
Ogilvie Charities Deed No.2
   (including the Charity of
   Mary Catherine Ford Smith)
The Ogle Christian Trust
Oglesby Charitable Trust
The Oikonomia Trust
The Oizer Charitable Trust
The Old Broad Street Charity
   Trust
The Old Enfield Charitable
   Trust
Old Possum's Practical Trust
The John Oldacre Foundation
The Oldham Foundation
Onaway Trust
Open Gate
The Ormsby Charitable Trust
Orrin Charitable Trust
The Owen Family Trust
Oxfam (GB)
The Oxfordshire Community
   Foundation
The P F Charitable Trust

Padwa Charitable Foundation
The Pallant Charitable Trust
The Palmer Foundation
Eleanor Palmer Trust
The Panacea Society
Panahpur Charitable Trust
Panton Trust
The James Pantyfedwen
Foundation
The Paragon Trust
The Park House Charitable
Trust
The Frank Parkinson
Agricultural Trust
The Samuel and Freda
Parkinson Charitable Trust
The Parthenon Trust
Arthur James Paterson
Charitable Trust
The Constance Paterson
Charitable Trust
Miss M E Swinton Paterson's
Charitable Trust
The Patrick Charitable Trust
The Jack Patston Charitable
Trust
Paycare Charity Trust
The Payne Charitable Trust
The Harry Payne Trust
The Susanna Peake Charitable
Trust
The Pedmore Sporting Club
Trust Fund
The Dowager Countess
Eleanor Peel Trust
Peltz Trust
The Pennycress Trust
The Performing Right Society
Foundation
B E Perl Charitable Trust
The Persson Charitable Trust
The Persula Foundation
The Pestalozzi Overseas
Children's Trust
The Jack Petchey Foundation
The Petplan Charitable Trust
The Philips and Rubens
Charitable Trust
The Phillips Charitable Trust
The Phillips Family Charitable
Trust
Philological Foundation
The David Pickford Charitable
Foundation
The Bernard Piggott Trust
The Claude and Margaret Pike
Charity
The Pilgrim Trust
The Cecil Pilkington Charitable
Trust
The Pilkington Charities Fund
The Austin and Hope
Pilkington Trust
The Sir Harry Pilkington Trust

The Col W W Pilkington Will
Trusts The General Charity
Fund
Miss A M Pilkington's
Charitable Trust
Mrs Pilkington's Charitable
Trust
The Plaisterers' Company
Charitable Trust
The Platinum Trust
G S Plaut Charitable Trust
Limited
The Poling Charitable Trust
The George and Esme Pollitzer
Charitable Settlement
The J S F Pollitzer Charitable
Settlement
The Ponton House Trust
The Mayor of Poole's Appeal
Fund
Edith and Ferdinand Porjes
Charitable Trust
The John Porter Charitable
Trust
The Porter Foundation
The Portishead Nautical Trust
The Portrack Charitable Trust
The J E Posnansky Charitable
Trust
The David and Elaine Potter
Foundation
The Powell Foundation
Prairie Trust
The W L Pratt Charitable Trust
Premierquote Ltd
Premishlaner Charitable Trust
The William Price Charitable
Trust
The Lucy Price Relief-in-Need
Charity
Sir John Priestman Charity
Trust
The Primrose Trust
The Prince's Charities
Foundation
Princess Anne's Charities
The Priory Foundation
Prison Service Charity Fund
The Privy Purse Charitable
Trust
The Proven Family Trust
The Provincial Grand Charity of
the Province of Derbyshire
PSA Peugeot Citroen Charity
Trust
The Puebla Charitable Trust
The Richard and Christine
Purchas Charitable Trust
The Puri Foundation
Mr and Mrs J A Pye's
Charitable Settlement
Quartet Community Foundation
Queen Mary's Roehampton
Trust
The Queen's Silver Jubilee
Trust

Quercus Trust
The R D Crusaders Foundation
R J M Charitable Trust
R S Charitable Trust
The R V W Trust
The Monica Rabagliati
Charitable Trust
Rachel Charitable Trust
The Mr and Mrs Philip
Rackham Charitable Trust
Richard Radcliffe Charitable
Trust
The Radcliffe Trust
The Ragdoll Foundation
The Rainford Trust
The Peggy Ramsay Foundation
The Joseph and Lena Randall
Charitable Trust
The Rank Foundation
Ranworth Trust
The Fanny Rapaport Charitable
Settlement
The Ratcliff Foundation
The Ratcliff Pension Charity
The Ratcliffe Charitable Trust
The Eleanor Rathbone
Charitable Trust
The Sigrid Rausing Trust
The Ravensdale Trust
The Rayden Charitable Trust
The Roger Raymond Charitable
Trust
The Rayne Foundation
The Rayne Trust
The John Rayner Charitable
Trust
The Albert Reckitt Charitable
Trust
The Sir James Reckitt Charity
The Red Arrows Trust
Red Hill Charitable Trust
The Red Rose Charitable Trust
The C A Redfern Charitable
Foundation
The Reed Foundation
Richard Reeve's Foundation
The Max Reinhardt Charitable
Trust
Relief Fund for Romania
Limited
REMEDI
The Rest Harrow Trust
Reuben Brothers Foundation
The Joan K Reynell Charitable
Trust
The Nathaniel Reyner Trust
Fund
The Rhododendron Trust
The Rhondda Cynon Taff
Welsh Church Acts Fund
Daisie Rich Trust
The Sir Cliff Richard Charitable
Trust
C B Richard Ellis Charitable
Trust
The Clive Richards Charity

The Richmond Parish Lands
    Charity
The Muriel Edith Rickman
    Trust
Ridgesave Limited
The Ripple Effect Foundation
The Sir John Ritblat Family
    Foundation
The River Trust
Riverside Charitable Trust
    Limited
The Daniel Rivlin Charitable
    Trust
Thomas Roberts Trust
The Alex Roberts-Miller
    Foundation
The Robertson Trust
Edwin George Robinson
    Charitable Trust
Robyn Charitable Trust
The Rochester Bridge Trust
The Rock Foundation
The Rock Solid Trust
The Rofeh Trust
Richard Rogers Charitable
    Settlement
Rokach Family Charitable Trust
The Helen Roll Charitable
    Trust
The Sir James Roll Charitable
    Trust
The Roman Research Trust
Romeera Foundation
The C A Rookes Charitable
    Trust
The Rosca Trust
The Cecil Rosen Foundation
The Rothermere Foundation
The Rotherwick Foundation
The Rothley Trust
The Rothschild Foundation
The Roughley Charitable Trust
Mrs Gladys Row Fogo
    Charitable Trust
Rowanville Ltd
The Christopher Rowbotham
    Charitable Trust
The Rowing Foundation
The Rowlands Trust
The Joseph Rowntree
    Charitable Trust
Royal Artillery Charitable Fund
Royal British Legion
Royal Docks Trust (London)
Royal Masonic Trust for Girls
    and Boys
The Royal Scots Benevolent
    Society
The Alfred and Frances
    Rubens Charitable Trust
The Rubin Foundation
William Arthur Rudd Memorial
    Trust
The Rufford Maurice Laing
    Foundation
The Russell Trust

Ryklow Charitable Trust 1992
The J S and E C Rymer
    Charitable Trust
S O Charitable Trust
The Michael Sacher Charitable
    Trust
The Michael Harry Sacher
    Trust
Dr Mortimer and Theresa
    Sackler Foundation
The Raymond and Beverley
    Sackler Foundation
The Ruzin Sadagora Trust
The Saddlers' Company
    Charitable Fund
The Saga Charitable Trust
The Jean Sainsbury Animal
    Welfare Trust
The Alan and Babette
    Sainsbury Charitable Fund
Saint Sarkis Charity Trust
The Saintbury Trust
The Saints and Sinners Trust
The Salamander Charitable
    Trust
The Salt Foundation
The Salt Trust
The Salters' Charities
The Andrew Salvesen
    Charitable Trust
The Sammermar Trust
Basil Samuel Charitable Trust
Coral Samuel Charitable Trust
The Hon. M J Samuel
    Charitable Trust
The Peter Samuel Charitable
    Trust
The Camilla Samuel Fund
The Samworth Foundation
The Sandra Charitable Trust
Santander UK Foundation
    Limited
Jimmy Savile Charitable Trust
The Scarfe Charitable Trust
The Schapira Charitable Trust
The Annie Schiff Charitable
    Trust
The Schmidt-Bodner Charitable
    Trust
The R H Scholes Charitable
    Trust
The Schreib Trust
The Schreiber Charitable Trust
Schroder Charity Trust
The Scott Bader
    Commonwealth Ltd
The Francis C Scott Charitable
    Trust
The Frieda Scott Charitable
    Trust
The Sir James and Lady Scott
    Trust
The Scott Trust Foundation
The Storrow Scott Will Trust
The Scottish Arts Council

Scottish Churches' Community
    Trust
Scottish Coal Industry Special
    Welfare Fund
The Scottish Community
    Foundation
The Scottish International
    Education Trust
The Scouloudi Foundation
Seafarers UK (King George's
    Fund for Sailors)
Seamen's Hospital Society
The Searchlight Electric
    Charitable Trust
The Searle Charitable Trust
The Helene Sebba Charitable
    Trust
The Samuel Sebba Charitable
    Trust
The Seedfield Trust
Leslie Sell Charitable Trust
Sellata Ltd
SEM Charitable Trust
The Ayrton Senna Foundation
The Seven Fifty Trust
The Severn Trent Water
    Charitable Trust Fund
SFIA Educational Trust Limited
The Cyril Shack Trust
The Shanti Charitable Trust
ShareGift (The Orr Mackintosh
    Foundation)
The Linley Shaw Foundation
The Sheepdrove Trust
The Sheffield and District
    Hospital Services
    Charitable Fund
The Sheldon Trust
The P and D Shepherd
    Charitable Trust
The Sylvia and Colin Shepherd
    Charitable Trust
The Archie Sherman Cardiff
    Foundation
The Archie Sherman Charitable
    Trust
The R C Sherriff Trust
The Shetland Charitable Trust
SHINE (Support and Help in
    Education)
The Barnett and Sylvia Shine
    No 2 Charitable Trust
The Bassil Shippam and
    Alsford Trust
The Shipwrights' Company
    Charitable Fund
The Shirley Foundation
Shlomo Memorial Fund Limited
The J A Shone Memorial Trust
The Charles Shorto Charitable
    Trust
The Barbara A Shuttleworth
    Memorial Trust
The Mary Elizabeth Siebel
    Charity

David and Jennifer Sieff
Charitable Trust
The Julius Silman Charitable
Trust
The Leslie Silver Charitable
Trust
The Simpson Education and
Conservation Trust
The Simpson Foundation
The Huntly and Margery
Sinclair Charitable Trust
Sino-British Fellowship Trust
The Skelton Bounty
The Charles Skey Charitable
Trust
Skipton Building Society
Charitable Foundation
The John Slater Foundation
Rita and David Slowe
Charitable Trust
The SMB Charitable Trust
The Mrs Smith and Mount
Trust
The N Smith Charitable
Settlement
The Amanda Smith Charitable
Trust
The E H Smith Charitable Trust
The Smith Charitable Trust
The Henry Smith Charity
The Leslie Smith Foundation
The Martin Smith Foundation
Stanley Smith General
Charitable Trust
The Stanley Smith UK
Horticultural Trust
Philip Smith's Charitable Trust
The Snowball Trust
The Sobell Foundation
Solev Co Ltd
Solihull Community Foundation
The Solo Charitable
Settlement
Dr Richard Solomon's
Charitable Trust
David Solomons Charitable
Trust
Songdale Ltd
The E C Sosnow Charitable
Trust
The Souter Charitable Trust
The South Square Trust
The Stephen R and Philippa H
Southall Charitable Trust
The W F Southall Trust
The Southdown Trust
R H Southern Trust
The Southover Manor General
Education Trust
The Southwold Trust
The Sovereign Health Care
Charitable Trust
Spar Charitable Fund
Sparks Charity (Sport Aiding
Medical Research For Kids)
Sparquote Limited

The Spear Charitable Trust
Spears-Stutz Charitable Trust
The Worshipful Company of
Spectacle Makers' Charity
The Jessie Spencer Trust
The Ralph and Irma Sperring
Charity
The Moss Spiro Will Charitable
Foundation
W W Spooner Charitable Trust
Stanley Spooner Deceased
Charitable Trust
The Spoore, Merry and Rixman
Foundation
The Spring Harvest Charitable
Trust
Rosalyn and Nicholas Springer
Charitable Trust
Springfields Employees'
Medical Research and
Charity Trust Fund
Springrule Ltd
The Spurrell Charitable Trust
The Geoff and Fiona Squire
Foundation
St Andrew Animal Fund
St Andrew's Conservation
Trust
St Francis's Leprosy Guild
St Gabriel's Trust
St James' Trust Settlement
St James's Place Foundation
Sir Walter St John's
Educational Charity
St Katharine and Shadwell
Trust
St Mark's Overseas Aid Trust
(SMOAT)
St Michael's and All Saints'
Charities
The Late St Patrick White
Charitable Trust
St Teilo's Trust
Miss Doreen Stanford Trust
The Stanley Foundation Ltd
The Stanton Ballard Charitable
Trust
The Staples Trust
The Star Charitable Trust
The Starfish Trust
The Peter Stebbings Memorial
Charity
The Steel Charitable Trust
The Cyril and Betty Stein
Charitable Trust
The Steinberg Family
Charitable Trust
The Hugh Stenhouse
Foundation
The Sigmund Sternberg
Charitable Foundation
Stervon Ltd
The Stevenage Community
Trust
The June Stevens Foundation

Stevenson Family's Charitable
Trust
The Steventon Allotments and
Relief-in-Need Charity
The Stewards' Company
Limited
The Leonard Laity Stoate
Charitable Trust
The Stobart Newlands
Charitable Trust
The Edward Stocks-Massey
Bequest Fund
The Stokenchurch Educational
Charity
The Stoller Charitable Trust
The M J C Stone Charitable
Trust
The Stone-Mallabar Charitable
Foundation
The Samuel Storey Family
Charitable Trust
Peter Stormonth Darling
Charitable Trust
Peter Storrs Trust
The Strangward Trust
The Strasser Foundation
Stratford upon Avon Town
Trust
Strathclyde Police Benevolent
Fund
The W O Street Charitable
Foundation
The A B Strom and R Strom
Charitable Trust
The Sudborough Foundation
Sueberry Ltd
The Suffolk Historic Churches
Trust
The Alan Sugar Foundation
The Summerfield Charitable
Trust
The Bernard Sunley Charitable
Foundation
The Surrey Historic Buildings
Trust Ltd
The Sussex Historic Churches
Trust
The Adrienne and Leslie
Sussman Charitable Trust
The Sutasoma Trust
Sutton Coldfield Municipal
Charities
The Sutton Nursing
Association
Swan Mountain Trust
The Swan Trust
Swansea and Brecon Diocesan
Board of Finance Limited
The John Swire (1989)
Charitable Trust
The Swire Charitable Trust
The Hugh and Ruby Sykes
Charitable Trust
The Charles and Elsie Sykes
Trust
The Sylvanus Charitable Trust

The Stella Symons Charitable
Trust
The Tabeel Trust
The Tajtelbaum Charitable
Trust
The Talbot Trusts
The Talbot Village Trust
Tallow Chandlers Benevolent
Fund
Talteg Ltd
The Tangent Charitable Trust
The Lady Tangye Charitable
Trust
The David Tannen Charitable
Trust
The Tanner Trust
The Lili Tapper Charitable
Foundation
The Mrs A Lacy Tate Trust
The Tay Charitable Trust
C B and H H Taylor 1984 Trust
Humphrey Richardson Taylor
Charitable Trust
The Connie and Albert Taylor
Charitable Trust
The Cyril Taylor Charitable
Trust
A P Taylor Trust
Rosanna Taylor's 1987 Charity
Trust
Tearfund
The Tedworth Charitable Trust
Tees Valley Community
Foundation
Tegham Limited
The Templeton Goodwill Trust
Tesco Charity Trust
Thackray Medical Research
Trust
Thames Community
Foundation
The Thames Wharf Charity
The Thistle Trust
The Loke Wan Tho Memorial
Foundation
The Thomas Wall Trust
The Arthur and Margaret
Thompson Charitable Trust
The Thompson Family
Charitable Trust
The Len Thomson Charitable
Trust
The Sue Thomson Foundation
The Sir Jules Thorn Charitable
Trust
The Thornton Foundation
The Thornton Trust
The Three Guineas Trust
The Three Oaks Trust
The Thriplow Charitable Trust
The Tinsley Foundation
The Tisbury Telegraph Trust
TJH Foundation
The Tolkien Trust
Tollemache (Buckminster)
Charitable Trust

Tomchei Torah Charitable
Trust
The Tompkins Foundation
The Tory Family Foundation
Tottenham Grammar School
Foundation
The Tower Hill Trust
The Towry Law Charitable Trust
The Toy Trust
The Mayor of Trafford's Charity
Fund
Annie Tranmer Charitable Trust
The Constance Travis
Charitable Trust
The Treeside Trust
The Triangle Trust (1949) Fund
The True Colours Trust
Truedene Co. Ltd
The Truemark Trust
Truemart Limited
Trumros Limited
Trust for London
Trust Sixty Three
The Trusthouse Charitable
Foundation
The Tubney Charitable Trust
Tudor Rose Ltd
The Tudor Trust
The Tufton Charitable Trust
The R D Turner Charitable
Trust
The Douglas Turner Trust
The Florence Turner Trust
Miss S M Tutton Charitable
Trust
The TUUT Charitable Trust
Community Foundation Serving
Tyne and Wear and
Northumberland
Trustees of Tzedakah
Ulster Garden Villages Ltd
Ultach Trust
Ulting Overseas Trust
The Ulverscroft Foundation
Ulverston Town Lands Charity
The Underwood Trust
The Union of Orthodox Hebrew
Congregation
The United Society for the
Propagation of the Gospel
United Trusts
The David Uri Memorial Trust
Uxbridge United Welfare Trust
Vale of Glamorgan – Welsh
Church Fund
The Valentine Charitable Trust
The Albert Van Den Bergh
Charitable Trust
John and Lucille van Geest
Foundation
The Van Neste Foundation
Mrs Maud Van Norden's
Charitable Foundation
The Vandervell Foundation
The Vardy Foundation

The Variety Club Children's
Charity
Veneziana Fund
The Verdon-Smith Family
Charitable Settlement
Roger Vere Foundation
Victoria Homes Trust
Viking Cares (For the Kids)
The Nigel Vinson Charitable
Trust
The William and Ellen Vinten
Trust
The Vintners' Company
Charitable Foundation
Vintners' Gifts Charity
Vision Charity
Vivdale Ltd
The Viznitz Foundation
Wade's Charity
The Scurrah Wainwright Charity
Wakeham Trust
The Community Foundation in
Wales
Wales Council for Voluntary
Action
Robert and Felicity Waley-
Cohen Charitable Trust
The Walker Trust
Wallington Missionary Mart
and Auctions
The F J Wallis Charitable
Settlement
Walton on Thames Charity
War on Want
Sir Siegmund Warburg's
Voluntary Settlement
The Ward Blenkinsop Trust
The George Ward Charitable
Trust
The Barbara Ward Children's
Foundation
The John Warren Foundation
G R Waters Charitable Trust
2000
The Waterways Trust
The Wates Foundation
Blyth Watson Charitable Trust
The Howard Watson Symington
Memorial Charity
John Watson's Trust
Weatherley Charitable Trust
The Weavers' Company
Benevolent Fund
The William Webster
Charitable Trust
The Weinberg Foundation
The Weinstein Foundation
The Weinstock Fund
The James Weir Foundation
The Barbara Welby Trust
The Weldon UK Charitable
Trust
The Wellcome Trust
Welsh Church Fund Dyfed
area (Carmarthenshire,

Ceredigion and
Pembrokeshire)
The Welton Foundation
Wessex Cancer Trust
The Wessex Youth Trust
The West Derby Wastelands
Charity
West London Synagogue
Charitable Fund
The West Yorkshire Police
Community Fund
Mrs S K West's Charitable
Trust
The Westminster Foundation
The Garfield Weston
Foundation
The Whitaker Charitable Trust
The Colonel W H Whitbread
Charitable Trust
The Simon Whitbread
Charitable Trust
White Rose Children's Aid
International Charity
The Whitecourt Charitable
Trust
A H and B C Whiteley
Charitable Trust
The Norman Whiteley Trust
The Whitley Animal Protection
Trust
The Whittlesey Charity
The Lionel Wigram Memorial
Trust
The Felicity Wilde Charitable
Trust
The Wilkinson Charitable
Foundation
The Will Charitable Trust
The Kay Williams Charitable
Foundation
The Williams Family Charitable
Trust
The H D H Wills 1965
Charitable Trust
Dame Violet Wills Charitable
Trust
The Dame Violet Wills Will
Trust
The Wilmcote Charitrust
Sumner Wilson Charitable
Trust
David Wilson Foundation
The Wilson Foundation
J and J R Wilson Trust
The Community Foundation for
Wiltshire and Swindon
The Benjamin Winegarten
Charitable Trust
The Harold Hyam Wingate
Foundation
The Francis Winham
Foundation
Anona Winn Charitable Trust
Wirral Mayor's Charity
WISCM

The Michael and Anna Wix
Charitable Trust
The Wixamtree Trust
The Woburn 1986 Charitable
Trust
The Maurice Wohl Charitable
Foundation
The Charles Wolfson
Charitable Trust
The Wolfson Family Charitable
Trust
The Wolfson Foundation
Women Caring Trust
The James Wood Bequest
Fund
Woodlands Green Ltd
Woodlands Trust
The Geoffrey Woods Charitable
Foundation
The Woodward Charitable
Trust
The A and R Woolf Charitable
Trust
The Woolnoth Society
Charitable Trust
Worcester Municipal Charities
The Worcestershire and
Dudley Historic Churches
Trust
The Fred and Della Worms
Charitable Trust
The Worwin UK Foundation
The Wragge and Co. Charitable
Trust
The Diana Edgson Wright
Charitable Trust
The Matthews Wrightson
Charity Trust
Miss E B Wrightson's
Charitable Settlement
Wychdale Ltd
Wychville Ltd
The Wyndham Charitable Trust
The Wyseliot Charitable Trust
The Xerox (UK) Trust
The Yardley Great Trust
The Dennis Alan Yardy
Charitable Trust
The W Wing Yip and Brothers
Foundation
The York Children's Trust
Yorkshire Agricultural Society
Yorkshire Building Society
Charitable Foundation
The South Yorkshire
Community Foundation
The Yorkshire Dales
Millennium Trust
The John Young Charitable
Settlement
The William Allen Young
Charitable Trust
The John K Young Endowment
Fund
Elizabeth and Prince Zaiger
Trust

Zephyr Charitable Trust
The Marjorie and Arnold Ziff
Charitable Foundation
Stephen Zimmerman
Charitable Trust
The Zochonis Charitable Trust
Zurich Community Trust (UK)
Limited

························

■ Vehicles

The 1989 Willan Charitable
Trust
The 29th May 1961 Charitable
Trust
Aberbrothock Charitable Trust
The Aberdeen Endowments
Trust
The Aberdeenshire Educational
Trust Scheme
Achiezer Association Ltd
Achisomoch Aid Company
Limited
The ACT Foundation
Action Medical Research
The Company of Actuaries'
Charitable Trust Fund
The Sylvia Adams Charitable
Trust
The Victor Adda Foundation
The Adint Charitable Trust
The Adnams Charity
Aid to the Church in Need (UK)
The AIM Foundation
The Sylvia Aitken Charitable
Trust
The Ajahma Charitable Trust
Alcohol Education and
Research Council
Aldgate and All Hallows'
Barking Exhibition
Foundation
The Aldgate Freedom
Foundation
Alexandra Rose Charities
The Alexis Trust
All Saints Educational Trust
Allchurches Trust Ltd
The H B Allen Charitable Trust
The Rita Allen Charitable Trust
The Alliance Family Foundation
Angus Allnatt Charitable
Foundation
The Pat Allsop Charitable Trust
The Almond Trust
Almondsbury Charity
The Altajir Trust
Altamont Ltd
Alvor Charitable Trust
AM Charitable Trust
Ambika Paul Foundation
The Ammco Trust
Sir John and Lady Amory's
Charitable Trust
Viscount Amory's Charitable
Trust

The Ampelos Trust
The AMW Charitable Trust
The Anchor Foundation
The Andrew Anderson Trust
The Andre Christian Trust
Anguish's Educational
　Foundation
The Animal Defence Trust
The Eric Anker-Petersen
　Charity
The Annandale Charitable
　Trust
Ambrose and Ann Appelbe
　Trust
The Appletree Trust
The John Apthorp Charitable
　Trust
The Milly Apthorp Charitable
　Trust
The Arbib Foundation
The Archbishop of
　Canterbury's Charitable
　Trust
The John M Archer Charitable
　Trust
The Archer Trust
The Ardwick Trust
The Argus Appeal
Armenian General Benevolent
　Union London Trust
The Armenian Relief Society of
　Great Britain Trust
The Armourers' and Brasiers'
　Gauntlet Trust
The Army Benevolent Fund
Arsenal Charitable Trust
The Artemis Charitable Trust
The Arts and Entertainment
　Charitable Trust
Arts Council England
The Arts Council of Northern
　Ireland
The Arts Council of Wales
The Ove Arup Foundation
The AS Charitable Trust
Ashburnham Thanksgiving
　Trust
A J H Ashby Will Trust
The Ashden Trust
The Ashendene Trust
The Laura Ashley Foundation
The Norman C Ashton
　Foundation
The Ashworth Charitable Trust
The Ian Askew Charitable Trust
The Associated Country
　Women of the World
　(ACWW)
The Association of Colleges
　Charitable Trust
Astellas European Foundation
AstonMansfield Charitable
　Trust
The Astor Foundation
The Astor of Hever Trust
The Aurelius Charitable Trust

The Avenue Charitable Trust
The John Avins Trustees
The Avon and Somerset Police
　Community Trust
AW Charitable Trust
The Aylesford Family
　Charitable Trust
The BAA Communities Trust
Harry Bacon Foundation
The BACTA Charitable Trust
The Bagri Foundation
Veta Bailey Charitable Trust
The Austin Bailey Trust
The Baily Thomas Charitable
　Fund
The Baird Trust
The Baker Charitable Trust
The Balcombe Charitable Trust
The Balint Family Charitable
　Trusts
The Albert Casanova Ballard
　Deceased Trust
The Ballinger Charitable Trust
Balmain Charitable Trust
The Balmore Trust
The Balney Charitable Trust
The Baltic Charitable Fund
The Bamford Charitable
　Foundation
The Banbury Charities
William P Bancroft (No 2)
　Charitable Trust and
　Jenepher Gillett Trust
The Band Trust
The Barbers' Company General
　Charities
The Barbour Trust
Barchester Healthcare
　Foundation
David and Frederick Barclay
　Foundation
The Baring Foundation
Peter Barker-Mill Memorial
　Charity
Barleycorn Trust
The Barnabas Trust
Lord Barnby's Foundation
Barnes Workhouse Fund
The Barnsbury Charitable Trust
The Barnstaple Bridge Trust
The Barnwood House Trust
The Misses Barrie Charitable
　Trust
Barrington Family Charitable
　Trust
The Charity of William Barrow
Stephen J Barry Charitable
　Trust
The Bartlett Taylor Charitable
　Trust
The Paul Bassham Charitable
　Trust
The Batchworth Trust
The Bay Tree Charitable Trust
D H and L H Baylin Charitable
　Trust

The Louis Baylis (Maidenhead
　Advertiser) Charitable Trust
BBC Children in Need
B-CH 1971 Charitable Trust
The Beacon Trust
Bear Mordechai Ltd
The Bearder Charity
The James Beattie Charitable
　Trust
The Beaufort House Trust
　Limited
Beauland Ltd
The Beaverbrook Foundation
The Beccles Town Lands
　Charity
The Becker Family Charitable
　Trust
The Becketts and Sargeants
　Educational Foundation
The John Beckwith Charitable
　Trust
The Peter Beckwith Charitable
　Trust
The Bedford Charity (The
　Harpur Trust)
The David and Ruth Behrend
　Fund
The Beit Trust
The Bellahouston Bequest
　Fund
Bellasis Trust
The Bellinger Donnay Trust
Belljoe Tzedoko Ltd
The Benfield Motors Charitable
　Trust
The Benham Charitable
　Settlement
The Hervey Benham Charitable
　Trust
Maurice and Jacqueline
　Bennett Charitable Trust
Michael and Leslie Bennett
　Charitable Trust
The Gerald Bentall Charitable
　Trust
Bergqvist Charitable Trust
The Berkshire Community
　Foundation
The Bestway Foundation
The Betterware Foundation
Thomas Betton's Charity for
　Pensions and Relief-in-Need
BHST
The Mason Bibby 1981 Trust
BibleLands
The Bideford Bridge Trust
The Big Lottery Fund
The Billmeir Charitable Trust
Percy Bilton Charity
The Bingham Trust
The Bintaub Charitable Trust
The Birmingham Community
　Foundation
The Birmingham District
　Nursing Charitable Trust

Birmingham International
Airport Community Trust

The Lord Mayor of
Birmingham's Charity

Birthday House Trust

The Bisgood Charitable Trust
(registered as Miss Jeanne
Bisgood's Charitable Trust)

The Michael Bishop
Foundation

The Bishop's Development
Fund

The Sydney Black Charitable
Trust

The Bertie Black Foundation

Isabel Blackman Foundation

The Herbert and Peter
Blagrave Charitable Trust

The Blair Foundation

Blakes Benevolent Trust

The Blanchminster Trust

The Sir Victor Blank Charitable
Settlement

Blatchington Court Trust

The Neville and Elaine Blond
Charitable Trust

The Bluston Charitable
Settlement

Enid Blyton Trust for Children

The Body Shop Foundation

The Boltons Trust

The Bonamy Charitable Trust

The John and Celia Bonham
Christie Charitable Trust

The Charlotte Bonham-Carter
Charitable Trust

Bonhomie United Charity
Society

The Booth Charities

The Boots Charitable Trust

The Bordon and Liphook
Charity

Salo Bordon Charitable Trust

The Oliver Borthwick Memorial
Trust

The Bothwell Charitable Trust

H E and E L Botteley
Charitable Trust

The Harry Bottom Charitable
Trust

P G and N J Boulton Trust

The A H and E Boulton Trust

Sir Clive Bourne Family Trust

The Anthony Bourne
Foundation

The Bower Trust

The Bowerman Charitable
Trust

John and Susan Bowers Fund

The Bowland Charitable Trust

The William Brake Charitable
Trust

The Tony Bramall Charitable
Trust

The Brewers' Company
General Charitable Trust

The Harold and Alice Bridges
Charity

Briggs Animal Welfare Trust

The Brighton District Nursing
Association Trust

Bristol Archdeaconry Charity

John Bristow and Thomas
Mason Trust

Britannia Foundation

The British Council for
Prevention of Blindness

The British Dietetic
Association General and
Education Trust Fund

The British Gas (Scottish Gas)
Energy Trust

British Heart Foundation

British Humane Association

British Institute at Ankara

British Ornithologists' Union

British Record Industry Trust

The Britto Foundation

The J and M Britton Charitable
Trust

The Charles and Edna
Broadhurst Charitable Trust

The Bromley Trust

The Roger Brooke Charitable
Trust

The David Brooke Charity

The Charles Brotherton Trust

Joseph Brough Charitable
Trust

The Swinfen Broun Charitable
Trust

Mrs E E Brown Charitable
Settlement

Bill Brown's Charitable
Settlement

R S Brownless Charitable
Trust

T B H Brunner's Charitable
Settlement

The Jack Brunton Charitable
Trust

Brushmill Ltd

The Bryant Trust

Buckingham Trust

The Buckinghamshire
Foundation

The Buckinghamshire Masonic
Centenary Fund

Buckland Charitable Trust

The Rosemary Bugden
Charitable Trust

The Bulldog Trust Limited

The E F Bulmer Benevolent
Fund

Burdens Charitable Foundation

The Burdett Trust for Nursing

The Clara E Burgess Charity

The Burry Charitable Trust

The Audrey and Stanley Burton
1960 Charitable Trust

The Arnold Burton 1998
Charitable Trust

The Burton Breweries
Charitable Trust

The Geoffrey Burton Charitable
Trust

Consolidated Charity of Burton
upon Trent

Butchers' Company General
Charities

The Bill Butlin Charity Trust

C and F Charitable Trust

C J Cadbury Charitable Trust

Edward Cadbury Charitable
Trust

Henry T and Lucy B Cadbury
Charitable Trust

P H G Cadbury Charitable
Trust

The Christopher Cadbury
Charitable Trust

The G W Cadbury Charitable
Trust

The Richard Cadbury
Charitable Trust

The William A Cadbury
Charitable Trust

The Edward and Dorothy
Cadbury Trust

The George Cadbury Trust

The Barrow Cadbury Trust and
the Barrow Cadbury Fund

The Cadogan Charity

CAFOD

The Callander Charitable Trust

Calleva Foundation

The Calpe Trust

Calypso Browning Trust

The Campden Charities

The Canning Trust

H and L Cantor Trust

Capital Community Foundation

Cardy Beaver Foundation

The Carew Pole Charitable
Trust

The D W T Cargill Fund

Caring for Kids (Radio Tay)

Carlee Ltd

The Carlton House Charitable
Trust

The Worshipful Company of
Carmen Benevolent Trust

The Carnegie Dunfermline
Trust

The Carnegie Trust for the
Universities of Scotland

The Carpenter Charitable Trust

The Carpenters' Company
Charitable Trust

The Carrington Charitable
Trust

The Carron Charitable
Settlement

The Leslie Mary Carter
Charitable Trust

The Carvill Trust

The Casey Trust

The Elizabeth Casson Trust

The Castang Foundation
The Catalyst Charitable Trust
The Catholic Charitable Trust
Catholic Foreign Missions
The Catholic Trust for England
and Wales
The Joseph and Annie Cattle
Trust
The Thomas Sivewright Catto
Charitable Settlement
The Wilfrid and Constance
Cave Foundation
The Cayo Foundation
Elizabeth Cayzer Charitable
Trust
The B G S Cayzer Charitable
Trust
The Cazenove Charitable Trust
Celtic Charity Fund
The Cemlyn-Jones Trust
The Amelia Chadwick Trust
The Pamela Champion
Foundation
The Chapman Charitable Trust
John William Chapman's
Charitable Trust
The Charities Advisory Trust
Charitworth Limited
The Charter 600 Charity
The Worshipful Company of
Chartered Accountants
General Charitable Trust
The Chasah Trust
The Chelsea Square 1994
Trust
The Cheruby Trust
The Cheshire Provincial Fund
of Benevolence
The Chetwode Foundation
The Malcolm Chick Charity
Child Growth Foundation
Children's Liver Disease
Foundation
Childs Charitable Trust
The Childwick Trust
The Chippenham Borough
Lands Charity
The Chipping Sodbury Town
Lands Charity
CHK Charities Limited
The Chownes Foundation
The Chrimes Family Charitable
Trust
The Christabella Charitable
Trust
Christadelphian Samaritan
Fund
Christian Aid
Christian Response to Eastern
Europe
The Church and Community
Fund
The Church Burgesses
Educational Foundation
Church Burgesses Trust

Church Lands and John
Johnson's Estate Charities
Church of Ireland Priorities
Fund
The Church Urban Fund
City and County of Swansea
Welsh Church Act Fund
The City Educational Trust
Fund
The City Parochial Foundation
CLA Charitable Trust
Stephen Clark 1957
Charitable Trust
J A Clark Charitable Trust
The Hilda and Alice Clark
Charitable Trust
The Roger and Sarah Bancroft
Clark Charitable Trust
The Clarke Charitable
Settlement
The Cleary Foundation
The Cleopatra Trust
Lord Clinton's Charitable Trust
The Clore Duffield Foundation
Miss V L Clore's 1967
Charitable Trust
Closehelm Ltd
The Clothworkers' Foundation
Richard Cloudesley's Charity
The Clover Trust
The Robert Clutterbuck
Charitable Trust
Clydpride Ltd
The Coalfields Regeneration
Trust
The John Coates Charitable
Trust
Coats Foundation Trust
The Cobtree Charity Trust Ltd
The Denise Cohen Charitable
Trust
The Vivienne and Samuel
Cohen Charitable Trust
The R and S Cohen Fondation
The John S Cohen Foundation
The Colchester Catalyst
Charity
John Coldman Charitable Trust
The Cole Charitable Trust
The Colefax Charitable Trust
The John and Freda Coleman
Charitable Trust
The George Henry Collins
Charity
The E Alec Colman Charitable
Fund Ltd
The Sir Jeremiah Colman Gift
Trust
Col-Reno Ltd
The Colt Foundation
The Coltstaple Trust
Colwinston Charitable Trust
The Comino Foundation
Community Foundation for
Calderdale

The Community Foundation for
Greater Manchester
The Company of Tobacco Pipe
Makers' and Tobacco
Blenders' Benevolent Fund
The Compton Charitable Trust
The Congleton Inclosure Trust
The Conservation Foundation
The Consolidated Charities for
the Infirm Merchant
Taylors' Company
The Construction Industry
Trust for Youth
Gordon Cook Foundation
The Ernest Cook Trust
The Cooks Charity
The Catherine Cookson
Charitable Trust
Harold and Daphne Cooper
Charitable Trust
Mabel Cooper Charity
The Alice Ellen Cooper Dean
Charitable Foundation
The Co-operative Foundation
The Marjorie Coote Animal
Charity Trust
The Marjorie Coote Old
People's Charity
The Helen Jean Cope Trust
The J Reginald Corah
Foundation Fund
The Gershon Coren Charitable
Foundation
The Corinthian Trust
Edwin Cornforth 1983 Charity
Trust
The Duke of Cornwall's
Benevolent Fund
The Cornwell Charitable Trust
The Sidney and Elizabeth
Corob Charitable Trust
The Corona Charitable Trust
The Costa Family Charitable
Trust
The Cotton Industry War
Memorial Trust
The Cotton Trust
The Augustine Courtauld Trust
Coutts Charitable Trust
The General Charities of the
City of Coventry
Coventry Building Society
Charitable Foundation
The John Cowan Foundation
Cowley Charitable Foundation
The Sir William Coxen Trust
Fund
The Lord Cozens-Hardy Trust
The Craignish Trust
The Craps Charitable Trust
Michael Crawford Children's
Charity
The Cray Trust
The Crescent Trust
Criffel Charitable Trust
Cripplegate Foundation

The Violet and Milo Cripps
  Charitable Trust
The Cromarty Trust
The Harry Crook Foundation
The Cross Trust
The Cross Trust
The Croydon Relief in Need
  Charities
The Mayor of Croydon's
  Charity Fund
Cruden Foundation Ltd
The Ronald Cruickshanks'
  Foundation
Cuby Charitable Trust
The Culra Charitable Trust
The Cumber Family Charitable
  Trust
Cumberland Building Society
  Charitable Foundation
Cumbria Community
  Foundation
The D J H Currie Memorial
  Trust
The Dennis Curry Charitable
  Trust
The Raymond Curtis Charitable
  Trust
The Manny Cussins
  Foundation
The Cwmbran Trust
Itzchok Meyer Cymerman Trust
  Ltd
The D'Oyly Carte Charitable
  Trust
The Roald Dahl Foundation
The Daily Prayer Union
  Charitable Trust Ltd
The Daisy Trust
The Daiwa Anglo-Japanese
  Foundation
Oizer Dalim Trust
The Dr and Mrs A Darlington
  Charitable Trust
Baron Davenport's Charity
The Davidson (Nairn)
  Charitable Trust
Davidson Charitable Trust
The Alderman Joe Davidson
  Memorial Trust
Michael Davies Charitable
  Settlement
The Gwendoline and Margaret
  Davies Charity
The Wilfrid Bruce Davis
  Charitable Trust
Davis-Rubens Charitable Trust
The Dawe Charitable Trust
The De Clermont Charitable
  Company Ltd
Peter De Haan Charitable
  Trust
The Leopold De Rothschild
  Charitable Trust
The Deakin Charitable Trust
William Dean Countryside and
  Educational Trust

The Debmar Benevolent Trust
The Delfont Foundation
The Dellal Foundation
The Delves Charitable Trust
The Demigryphon Trust
The Denman Charitable Trust
The Denton Charitable Trust
The Denton Wilde Sapte
  Charitable Trust
The Earl of Derby's Charitable
  Trust
Derbyshire Community
  Foundation
The J N Derbyshire Trust
Devon Community Foundation
The Devon Educational Trust
The Duke of Devonshire's
  Charitable Trust
The Sandy Dewhirst Charitable
  Trust
DG Charitable Settlement
The Laduma Dhamecha
  Charitable Trust
Alan and Sheila Diamond
  Charitable Trust
The Diana, Princess of Wales
  Memorial Fund
The Dibden Allotments Charity
The Dickon Trust
The Digbeth Trust
The Dinwoodie Settlement
Dischma Charitable Trust
The DLA Piper Charitable Trust
The DLM Charitable Trust
Louise Dobson Charitable
  Trust
The Derek and Eileen Dodgson
  Foundation
The Dollond Charitable Trust
Domepride Ltd
The Dorcas Trust
The Dorema Charitable Trust
The Dorus Trust
Double 'O' Charity Ltd
The Doughty Charity Trust
The R M Douglas Charitable
  Trust
The Drapers' Charitable Fund
Dromintee Trust
The Dugdale Charitable Trust
The Duis Charitable Trust
The Dulverton Trust
The P B Dumbell Charitable
  Trust
The Dumbreck Charity
Dunard Fund
Ronald Duncan Literary
  Foundation
The Houghton Dunn Charitable
  Trust
The Dunn Family Charitable
  Trust
The W E Dunn Trust
Dushinsky Trust Ltd
Mildred Duveen Charitable
  Trust

The Dwek Family Charitable
  Trust
The Dyers' Company
  Charitable Trust
EAGA Partnership Charitable
  Trust
The Eagle Charity Trust
Audrey Earle Charitable Trust
The Earley Charity
Earls Colne and Halstead
  Educational Charity
The Earmark Trust
East Kent Provincial Charities
East London Community
  Foundation
Eastern Counties Educational
  Trust Limited
The Sir John Eastwood
  Foundation
The Ebenezer Trust
The EBM Charitable Trust
Eden Arts Trust
EDF Energy Trust (EDFET)
The Gilbert and Eileen Edgar
  Foundation
Gilbert Edgar Trust
Edinburgh Children's Holiday
  Fund
The Edinburgh Trust, No 2
  Account
Edinburgh Voluntary
  Organisations' Trust Funds
Educational Foundation of
  Alderman John Norman
The W G Edwards Charitable
  Foundation
The William Edwards
  Educational Charity
The Elephant Trust
The George Elias Charitable
  Trust
The Gerald Palmer Eling Trust
  Company
The Elizabeth Frankland Moore
  and Star Foundation
The Wilfred and Elsie Elkes
  Charity Fund
The Maud Elkington Charitable
  Trust
Ellador Ltd
The Ellerdale Trust
The Ellinson Foundation Ltd
The Edith Maud Ellis 1985
  Charitable Trust
The Ellis Campbell Foundation
James Ellis Charitable Trust
The Elmgrant Trust
The Elmley Foundation
Elshore Ltd
The Vernon N Ely Charitable
  Trust
The Embleton Trust
The Emerton-Christie Charity
The Emmandjay Charitable
  Trust

The Worshipful Company of Engineers Charitable Trust Fund

The Englefield Charitable Trust

The English Schools' Football Association

The Enkalon Foundation

Entindale Ltd

The Epigoni Trust

Epilepsy Research UK

The Equitable Charitable Trust

The Equity Trust Fund

The Ericson Trust

The Erskine Cunningham Hill Trust

Essex Community Foundation

The Essex Fairway Charitable Trust

The Essex Heritage Trust

Essex Provincial Charity Fund

The Essex Youth Trust

Euro Charity Trust

The Evangelical Covenants Trust

The Alan Evans Memorial Trust

Sir John Evelyn's Charity

The Eventhall Family Charitable Trust

The Everard Foundation

The Eveson Charitable Trust

The Beryl Evetts and Robert Luff Animal Welfare Trust

The Execution Charitable Trust

The Mayor of Exeter's Appeal Fund

The Exilarch's Foundation

F C Charitable Trust

The F P Limited Charitable Trust

The Faber Charitable Trust

Esmée Fairbairn Foundation

The Fairway Trust

Faisaltex Charitable Trust

The Family Foundations Trust

The Family Rich Charities Trust

Famos Foundation Trust

The Lord Faringdon Charitable Trust

Samuel William Farmer's Trust

The Farmers' Company Charitable Fund

The Thomas Farr Charitable Trust

Walter Farthing (Trust) Limited

Farthing Trust

The Fassnidge Memorial Trust

Joseph Fattorini Charitable Trust 'B' Account

The Fawcett Charitable Trust

Federation of Jewish Relief Organisations

Feed the Minds

The John Feeney Charitable Bequest

The George Fentham Birmingham Charity

The A M Fenton Trust

Allan and Nesta Ferguson Charitable Settlement

Elizabeth Ferguson Charitable Trust Fund

The Fidelity UK Foundation

The Bluff Field Charitable Trust

The Doris Field Charitable Trust

Fife Council/Common Good Funds and Trusts

Dixie Rose Findlay Charitable Trust

Gerald Finzi Charitable Trust

Firtree Trust

The Sir John Fisher Foundation

The Fishmongers' Company's Charitable Trust

Marc Fitch Fund

The Fitton Trust

The Earl Fitzwilliam Charitable Trust

Bud Flanagan Leukaemia Fund

The Rose Flatau Charitable Trust

The Ian Fleming Charitable Trust

The Joyce Fletcher Charitable Trust

The Roy Fletcher Charitable Trust

Florence's Charitable Trust

The Florian Charitable Trust

The Flow Foundation

The Gerald Fogel Charitable Trust

The Follett Trust

The Football Association National Sports Centre Trust

The Football Association Youth Trust

The Football Foundation

The Forbes Charitable Foundation

Forbesville Limited

The Forces Trust

Ford Britain Trust

The Oliver Ford Charitable Trust

Fordeve Ltd

The Forest Hill Charitable Trust

The Foresters' Charity Stewards UK Trust

Gwyneth Forrester Trust

The Forte Charitable Trust

Lord Forte Foundation

Foundation for Management Education

Four Acre Trust

The Four Winds Trust

The Fowler, Smith and Jones Charitable Trust

The Foyle Foundation

The Isaac and Freda Frankel Memorial Charitable Trust

Sydney E Franklin Deceased's New Second Charity

The Jill Franklin Trust

The Gordon Fraser Charitable Trust

The Hugh Fraser Foundation

The Joseph Strong Frazer Trust

The Louis and Valerie Freedman Charitable Settlement

The Thomas Freke and Lady Norton Charity

The Charles S French Charitable Trust

The Anne French Memorial Trust

The Freshfield Foundation

The Freshgate Trust Foundation

The Friarsgate Trust

The Friends Hall Farm Street Trust

Friends of Biala Ltd

Friends of Wiznitz Limited

Friends Provident Charitable Foundation

The Frognal Trust

T F C Frost Charitable Trust

The Patrick Frost Foundation

Maurice Fry Charitable Trust

Mejer and Gertrude Miriam Frydman Foundation

The Fuellers Charitable Trust Fund

The Fulmer Charitable Trust

Worshipful Company of Furniture Makers Charitable Fund

Gableholt Limited

The Galbraith Trust

The Gale Family Charitable Trust

The Angela Gallagher Memorial Fund

The Gamlen Charitable Trust

The Gamma Trust

The Gannochy Trust

The Ganzoni Charitable Trust

The Worshipful Company of Gardeners of London

The Samuel Gardner Memorial Trust

The Garnett Charitable Trust

Garrick Charitable Trust

Garvan Limited

The Gatsby Charitable Foundation

Gatwick Airport Community Trust

The Robert Gavron Charitable Trust

Jacqueline and Michael Gee Charitable Trust

J Paul Getty Jr Charitable Trust

The Gibbs Charitable Trust

Simon Gibson Charitable Trust

The G C Gibson Charitable
  Trust
The Harvey and Hilary Gilbert
  Charitable Trust
The Girdlers' Company
  Charitable Trust
The B and P Glasser
  Charitable Trust
The Glass-House Trust
Global Care
Gloucestershire Community
  Foundation
Worshipful Company of
  Glovers of London Charity
  Fund
GMC Trust
The GNC Trust
The Meir Golda Trust
The Sydney and Phyllis
  Goldberg Memorial
  Charitable Trust
The Golden Bottle Trust
Golden Charitable Trust
The Jack Goldhill Charitable
  Trust
The Goldsmiths' Arts Trust
  Fund
The Goldsmiths' Company
  Charity
The Golsoncott Foundation
The Good Neighbours Trust
Nicholas and Judith
  Goodison's Charitable
  Settlement
The Everard and Mina
  Goodman Charitable
  Foundation
Mike Gooley Trailfinders
  Charity
Leonard Gordon Charitable
  Trust
The Gosling Foundation
  Limited
The Gough Charitable Trust
The Gould Charitable Trust
The Grace Charitable Trust
A B Grace Trust
The Graff Foundation
The Grahame Charitable
  Foundation Limited
Grampian Police Diced Cap
  Charitable Fund
The Granada Foundation
Grand Charitable Trust of the
  Order of Women
  Freemasons
The Grand Order of Water
  Rats' Charities Fund
The Grange Farm Centre Trust
Grantham Yorke Trust
The J G Graves Charitable
  Trust
The Gray Trust
The Great Stone Bridge Trust
  of Edenbridge

The Great Torrington Town
  Lands Charity
The Constance Green
  Foundation
The Barry Green Memorial
  Fund
The Philip Green Memorial
  Trust
Mrs H R Greene Charitable
  Settlement
Greenham Common
  Community Trust Limited
Naomi and Jeffrey Greenwood
  Charitable Trust
Greggs Foundation
Grimmitt Trust
The Grocers' Charity
The M and R Gross Charities
  Limited
The Grove Charitable Trust
The GRP Charitable Trust
The David and Marie Grumitt
  Foundation
The Bishop of Guildford's
  Foundation
The Guildry Incorporation of
  Perth
The Walter Guinness
  Charitable Trust
The Gunter Charitable Trust
The Gur Trust
Gurunanak
Dr Guthrie's Association
The H and M Charitable Trust
H C D Memorial Fund
The H P Charitable Trust
The Hackney Parochial
  Charities
The Hadfield Trust
The Hadley Trust
The Hadrian Trust
The Alfred Haines Charitable
  Trust
The Hale Trust
E F and M G Hall Charitable
  Trust
The Edith Winifred Hall
  Charitable Trust
Robert Hall Charity
The Hamamelis Trust
Hamilton Wallace Trust
Paul Hamlyn Foundation
Sue Hammerson's Charitable
  Trust
The Hammonds Charitable
  Trust
The Hampshire and Islands
  Historic Churches Trust
Hampton Fuel Allotment
  Charity
The W A Handley Charitable
  Trust
Beatrice Hankey Foundation
  Ltd
The Hanley Trust

The Kathleen Hannay
  Memorial Charity
The Doughty Hanson
  Charitable Foundation
Lord Hanson Foundation
The Haramead Trust
Miss K M Harbinson's
  Charitable Trust
Harbo Charities Limited
The Harborne Parish Lands
  Charity
The Harbour Charitable Trust
The Harbour Foundation
The Harding Trust
William Harding's Charity
The Hare of Steep Charitable
  Trust
The Harebell Centenary Fund
The Kenneth Hargreaves
  Charitable Trust
The Harris Charitable Trust
The Harris Charity
The Harrison and Potter Trust
The John Harrison Charitable
  Trust
The Spencer Hart Charitable
  Trust
The Hartley Charitable Trust
The N and P Hartley Memorial
  Trust
William Geoffrey Harvey's
  Discretionary Settlement
The Edward Harvist Trust Fund
Haskel Family Foundation
The Hathaway Trust
The M A Hawe Settlement
The Hawthorne Charitable
  Trust
The Dorothy Hay-Bolton
  Charitable Trust
The Haydan Charitable Trust
The Haymills Charitable Trust
The Headley Trust
Headley-Pitt Charitable Trust
Heagerty Charitable Trust
The Heald Charitable Trust
Healthsure Group Ltd
May Hearnshaw's Charity
The Heart of England
  Community Foundation
The Heathcoat Trust
Heathside Charitable Trust
The Charlotte Heber-Percy
  Charitable Trust
Percy Hedley 1990 Charitable
  Trust
The Hedley Denton Charitable
  Trust
The Hedley Foundation
The H J Heinz Company
  Limited Charitable Trust
The Hellenic Foundation
The Michael and Morven Heller
  Charitable Foundation
The Simon Heller Charitable
  Settlement

Help the Aged
Help the Homeless
Help the Hospices
The Hemby Trust
The Christina Mary Hendrie
Trust for Scottish and
Canadian Charities
The Henley Educational Charity
Philip Henman Trust
Esther Hennell Charitable
Trust
The G D Herbert Charitable
Trust
The Joanna Herbert-Stepney
Charitable Settlement
The Anne Herd Memorial Trust
The Herefordshire Historic
Churches Trust
The Heritage of London Trust
Ltd
The Hertfordshire Community
Foundation
The Hesed Trust
The Hesslewood Children's
Trust (Hull Seamen's and
General Orphanage)
The Bernhard Heuberger
Charitable Trust
Hexham and Newcastle
Diocesan Trust (1947)
The P and C Hickinbotham
Charitable Trust
The Higgs Charitable Trust
Alan Edward Higgs Charity
The High Sheriff's Police Trust
for the County of West
Midlands
Highcroft Charitable Trust
The Hilden Charitable Fund
The Joseph and Mary Hiley
Trust
The Holly Hill Charitable Trust
The Charles Littlewood Hill
Trust
The Hillingdon Partnership
Trust
R G Hills Charitable Trust
Hinchley Charitable Trust
Lady Hind Trust
Stuart Hine Trust
The Hinrichsen Foundation
The Hitchin Educational
Foundation
The Eleemosynary Charity of
William Hobbayne
Hobson Charity Limited
Hockerill Educational
Foundation
Matthew Hodder Charitable
Trust
The Sir Julian Hodge
Charitable Trust
The Jane Hodge Foundation
The J G Hogg Charitable Trust
The Holden Charitable Trust
John Holford's Charity

The Hollick Family Charitable
Trust
The Dorothy Holmes Charitable
Trust
P H Holt Foundation
The Edward Holt Trust
The Holywood Trust
The Homelands Charitable
Trust
The Homestead Charitable
Trust
Mary Homfray Charitable Trust
Sir Harold Hood's Charitable
Trust
The Hope Trust
HopMarket Charity
The Cuthbert Horn Trust
The Antony Hornby Charitable
Trust
The Horne Foundation
The Horne Trust
The Worshipful Company of
Horners' Charitable Trusts
The Hornsey Parochial
Charities
The Hospital of God at
Greatham
The Hospital Saturday Fund
Houblon-Norman/George Fund
The House of Industry Estate
The Reta Lila Howard
Foundation
The Daniel Howard Trust
The Clifford Howarth Charity
Trust
The Huddersfield Medical Trust
Fund
The Hudson Foundation
The Huggard Charitable Trust
The Geoffrey C Hughes
Charitable Trust
The Hull and East Riding
Charitable Trust
Hulme Trust Estates
(Educational)
Human Relief Foundation
The Humanitarian Trust
The Michael and Shirley Hunt
Charitable Trust
The Albert Hunt Trust
The Hunter Foundation
Miss Agnes H Hunter's Trust
The Huntingdon Foundation
Huntingdon Freemen's Charity
John Huntingdon's Charity
Hurdale Charity Limited
The Nani Huyu Charitable Trust
The P Y N and B Hyams Trust
The Hyde Charitable Trust –
Youth Plus
The Idlewild Trust
The Iliffe Family Charitable
Trust
The Indigo Trust
The Ingram Trust

The Inland Waterways
Association
The Inlight Trust
The Inman Charity
The Inner London Magistrates
Court Poor Box Charity and
Feeder Charity
The Worshipful Company of
Innholders General Charity
Fund
The Ireland Fund of Great
Britain
The Irish Youth Foundation
(UK) Ltd
The Ironmongers' Foundation
Irshad Trust
The Charles Irving Charitable
Trust
Irwin Trust
The ISA Charity
The Isaacs Charitable Trust
The J Isaacs Charitable Trust
The Island Health Trust
The Isle of Anglesey Charitable
Trust
Isle of Dogs Community
Foundation
The ITF Seafarers Trust
J A R Charitable Trust
The J J Charitable Trust
The J R S S T Charitable Trust
Elizabeth Jackson Charitable
Trust
Jacobs Charitable Trust
The Ruth and Lionel Jacobson
Trust (Second Fund) No 2
Jaffe Family Relief Fund
John James Bristol Foundation
The Susan and Stephen
James Charitable
Settlement
The James Trust
The Jarman Charitable Trust
The John Jarrold Trust
JCA Charitable Foundation
The Jeffrey Charitable Trust
Rees Jeffreys Road Fund
The Jenour Foundation
The Jephcott Charitable Trust
The Jerusalem Trust
Jerwood Charitable Foundation
Jesus Hospital Charity
Jewish Child's Day
The Jewish Youth Fund
The JMK Charitable Trust
The Joanies Trust
The Harold Joels Charitable
Trust
The Jonathan Joels Charitable
Trust
The Nicholas Joels Charitable
Trust
The Norman Joels Charitable
Trust
The Joffe Charitable Trust

The Lillie Johnson Charitable Trust

The Johnson Group Cleaners Charity

The Johnnie Johnson Trust

The Johnson Wax Ltd Charitable Trust

The Joicey Trust

The Jones 1986 Charitable Trust

The Marjorie and Geoffrey Jones Charitable Trust

The Jordan Charitable Foundation

The J E Joseph Charitable Fund

The Lady Eileen Joseph Foundation

JTH Charitable Trust

The Judith Trust

The Anton Jurgens Charitable Trust

The Bernard Kahn Charitable Trust

The Stanley Kalms Foundation

The Karenza Foundation

The Boris Karloff Charitable Foundation

The Ian Karten Charitable Trust

The Kasner Charitable Trust

The Kass Charitable Trust

The Kathleen Trust

The Michael and Ilse Katz Foundation

The Katzauer Charitable Settlement

The C S Kaufman Charitable Trust

The Geoffrey John Kaye Charitable Foundation

The Emmanuel Kaye Foundation

Kelsick's Educational Foundation

The KempWelch Charitable Trust

The Kay Kendall Leukaemia Fund

William Kendall's Charity (Wax Chandlers' Company)

The Kennedy Charitable Foundation

The Kennel Club Charitable Trust

The Nancy Kenyon Charitable Trust

Keren Association

Kermaville Ltd

E and E Kernkraut Charities Limited

The Peter Kershaw Trust

The Kessler Foundation

Keswick Hall Charity

The Ursula Keyes Trust

The Robert Kiln Charitable Trust

The King Henry VIII Endowed Trust Warwick

The King/Cullimore Charitable Trust

The Kingsbury Charity

The Mary Kinross Charitable Trust

Kinsurdy Charitable Trust

Kirkley Poor's Lands Estate

The Richard Kirkman Charitable Trust

Kirschel Foundation

Robert Kitchin (Saddlers' Company)

Ernest Kleinwort Charitable Trust

The Marina Kleinwort Charitable Trust

The Sir James Knott Trust

The Kobler Trust

The Kohn Foundation

The Kreditor Charitable Trust

The Kreitman Foundation

The Neil Kreitman Foundation

The Heinz, Anna and Carol Kroch Foundation

The Kyte Charitable Trust

Lacims-Maclis Charitable Trust

The Late Sir Pierce Lacy Charity Trust

John Laing Charitable Trust

Maurice and Hilda Laing Charitable Trust

The Laing Family Foundations

The Christopher Laing Foundation

The Kirby Laing Foundation

The Martin Laing Foundation

The Beatrice Laing Trust

The Lambert Charitable Trust

Lancashire Environmental Fund

Duchy of Lancaster Benevolent Fund

The Lancaster Foundation

LandAid Charitable Trust

The Langdale Trust

The Langley Charitable Trust

The Langtree Trust

The LankellyChase Foundation

The Lanvern Foundation

The R J Larg Family Charitable Trust

Largsmount Ltd

The Lark Trust

Laslett's (Hinton) Charity

Lauchentilly Charitable Foundation 1988

Laufer Charitable Trust

The Lauffer Family Charitable Foundation

Mrs F B Laurence Charitable Trust

The Kathleen Laurence Trust

The Edgar E Lawley Foundation

The Herd Lawson and Muriel Lawson Charitable Trust

The Lawson Beckman Charitable Trust

The Raymond and Blanche Lawson Charitable Trust

The Carole and Geoffrey Lawson Foundation

The Mason Le Page Charitable Trust

The Leach Fourteenth Trust

The David Lean Foundation

The Leathersellers' Company Charitable Fund

The Leche Trust

The Arnold Lee Charitable Trust

The William Leech Charity

The Lord Mayor of Leeds Appeal Fund

Leeds Building Society Charitable Foundation

Leicester Charity Link

The Kennedy Leigh Charitable Trust

Morris Leigh Foundation

The Leigh Trust

Mrs Vera Leigh's Charity

The P Leigh-Bramwell Trust 'E'

The Lennox and Wyfold Foundation

The Erica Leonard Trust

The Leonard Trust

The Mark Leonard Trust

Lesley Lesley and Mutter Trust

The Leverhulme Trade Charities Trust

Lord Leverhulme's Charitable Trust

The Joseph Levy Charitable Foundation

Lewis Family Charitable Trust

The John Spedan Lewis Foundation

The Sir Edward Lewis Foundation

John Lewis Partnership General Community Fund

Lichfield Conduit Lands

Lifeline 4 Kids

The Thomas Lilley Memorial Trust

Limoges Charitable Trust

The Linbury Trust

The Lind Trust

Lindale Educational Foundation

The Linden Charitable Trust

The Enid Linder Foundation

The Linmardon Trust

The Ruth and Stuart Lipton Charitable Trust

The Lister Charitable Trust

Frank Litchfield Charitable Trust

The Andrew and Mary Elizabeth Little Charitable Trust
The Second Joseph Aaron Littman Foundation
The George John and Sheilah Livanos Charitable Trust
Liverpool Charity and Voluntary Services
Liverpool Sailors' Home Trust
Jack Livingstone Charitable Trust
The Elaine and Angus Lloyd Charitable Trust
The Charles Lloyd Foundation
The Lloyd Fund
Lloyd's Charities Trust
The Lloyd-Everett Trust
Lloyds TSB Foundation for England and Wales
Lloyds TSB Foundation for Northern Ireland
Lloyds TSB Foundation for the Channel Islands
Llysdinam Charitable Trust
Localtrent Ltd
The Locker Foundation
The Loftus Charitable Trust
The Lolev Charitable Trust
London Catalyst
The London Law Trust
The London Marathon Charitable Trust
The William and Katherine Longman Trust
The Lord's Taverners
The Loseley and Guildway Charitable Trust
The Lotus Foundation
The C L Loyd Charitable Trust
The Marie Helen Luen Charitable Trust
Robert Luff Foundation Ltd
Henry Lumley Charitable Trust
Lady Lumley's Educational Foundation
Paul Lunn-Rockliffe Charitable Trust
C F Lunoe Trust Fund
The Ruth and Jack Lunzer Charitable Trust
Lord and Lady Lurgan Trust
The Lyndhurst Trust
The Lynn Foundation
The Lynwood Trust
John Lyon's Charity
The Lyons Charitable Trust
The Sir Jack Lyons Charitable Trust
Malcolm Lyons Foundation
The Lyras Family Charitable Trust
Sylvanus Lyson's Charity
The M and C Trust
The M D and S Charitable Trust

The M K Charitable Trust
The Madeline Mabey Trust
The E M MacAndrew Trust
The R S Macdonald Charitable Trust
Macdonald-Buchanan Charitable Trust
The Macfarlane Walker Trust
The Mackay and Brewer Charitable Trust
The Mackintosh Foundation
The MacRobert Trust
Ian Mactaggart Trust
The Magdalen and Lasher Charity
Magdalen Hospital Trust
The Magen Charitable Trust
Mageni Trust
Mahavir Trust
Man Group plc Charitable Trust
The Manchester Guardian Society Charitable Trust
Manchester Kids
Lord Mayor of Manchester's Charity Appeal Trust
Mandeville Trust
The Manifold Charitable Trust
W M Mann Foundation
The Leslie and Lilian Manning Trust
Maranatha Christian Trust
Marbeh Torah Trust
The Marchday Charitable Fund
Marchig Animal Welfare Trust
The Stella and Alexander Margulies Charitable Trust
Mariapolis Limited
Market Harborough and The Bowdens Charity
Michael Marks Charitable Trust
The Ann and David Marks Foundation
The Hilda and Samuel Marks Foundation
J P Marland Charitable Trust
Marr-Munning Trust
The Michael Marsh Charitable Trust
The Marsh Christian Trust
The Charlotte Marshall Charitable Trust
The Jim Marshall Charitable Trust
The D G Marshall of Cambridge Trust
Marshall's Charity
Marshgate Charitable Settlement
Sir George Martin Trust
John Martin's Charity
The Mason Porter Charitable Trust
The Nancie Massey Charitable Trust

The Mathew Trust
Matliwala Family Charitable Trust
The Matt 6.3 Charitable Trust
The Violet Mauray Charitable Trust
The Maxell Educational Trust
The Maxwell Family Foundation
Evelyn May Trust
Mayfair Charities Ltd
The Mayfield Valley Arts Trust
Mazars Charitable Trust
The Robert McAlpine Foundation
The McDougall Trust
The A M McGreevy No 5 Charitable Settlement
The McKenna Charitable Trust
Martin McLaren Memorial Trust
The Helen Isabella McMorran Charitable Foundation
D D McPhail Charitable Settlement
The James Frederick and Ethel Anne Measures Charity
Medical Research Council
The Medlock Charitable Trust
The Anthony and Elizabeth Mellows Charitable Settlement
Melodor Ltd
Melow Charitable Trust
Meningitis Trust
Menuchar Ltd
Brian Mercer Charitable Trust
The Mercers' Charitable Foundation
The Merchant Taylors' Company Charities Fund
The Merchant Venturers' Charity
The Merchants' House of Glasgow
Mercury Phoenix Trust
The Mersey Docks and Harbour Company Charitable Fund
Community Foundation for Merseyside
The Zachary Merton and George Woofindin Convalescent Trust
The Tony Metherell Charitable Trust
The Methodist Relief and Development Fund
The Metropolitan Drinking Fountain and Cattle Trough Association
Gerald Micklem Charitable Trust
Midhurst Pensions Trust
The Migraine Trust
Miles Trust for the Putney and Roehampton Community

The Hugh and Mary Miller
  Bequest Trust
The Miller Foundation
The Millfield Trust
The Millhouses Charitable
  Trust
The Millichope Foundation
The Mills Charity
The Millward Charitable Trust
The Clare Milne Trust
Milton Keynes Community
  Foundation
The Edgar Milward Charity
The Keith and Joan
  Mindelsohn Charitable
  Trust
The Peter Minet Trust
Minge's Gift and the Pooled
  Trusts
The Minos Trust
The Mirfield Educational
  Charity
The Laurence Misener
  Charitable Trust
The Mishcon Family Charitable
  Trust
The Misselbrook Trust
The Mitchell Charitable Trust
The Esme Mitchell Trust
Keren Mitzvah Trust
The Mizpah Trust
The Mobbs Memorial Trust Ltd
The Modiano Charitable Trust
The Moette Charitable Trust
The Mole Charitable Trust
The D C Moncrieff Charitable
  Trust
Monmouthshire County Council
  Welsh Church Act Fund
The Montague Thompson
  Coon Charitable Trust
The Colin Montgomerie
  Charitable Foundation
The Monument Trust
Moody Charitable Trust
George A Moore Foundation
The Nigel Moores Family
  Charitable Trust
The Peter Moores Foundation
The Morel Charitable Trust
The Morgan Charitable
  Foundation
The Mr and Mrs J T Morgan
  Foundation
The J P Morgan Foundations
Diana and Allan Morgenthau
  Charitable Trust
The Oliver Morland Charitable
  Trust
S C and M E Morland's
  Charitable Trust
The Morris Charitable Trust
The Willie and Mabel Morris
  Charitable Trust
The Peter Morrison Charitable
  Foundation

The Stanley Morrison
  Charitable Trust
Moshal Charitable Trust
Vyoel Moshe Charitable Trust
The Moss Charitable Trust
The Robert and Margaret
  Moss Charitable Trust
Moss Family Charitable Trust
The Mount Everest Foundation
Mountbatten Festival of Music
The Mountbatten Memorial
  Trust
The Edwina Mountbatten Trust
The Mugdock Children's Trust
The F H Muirhead Charitable
  Trust
The Mulberry Trust
The Edith Murphy Foundation
Murphy-Neumann Charity
  Company Limited
The Mushroom Fund
The Music Sales Charitable
  Trust
Muslim Hands
The Mutual Trust Group
MYA Charitable Trust
The Kitty and Daniel Nabarro
  Charitable Trust
The Nadezhda Charitable Trust
The Willie Nagel Charitable
  Trust
The Naggar Charitable Trust
The Eleni Nakou Foundation
The Janet Nash Charitable
  Settlement
Nathan Charitable Trust
Asthma UK
The National Churches Trust
The National Manuscripts
  Conservation Trust
Nazareth Trust Fund
The Nchima Trust
Needham Market and Barking
  Welfare Charities
The Worshipful Company of
  Needlemakers' Charitable
  Fund
The Neighbourly Charitable
  Trust
The James Neill Trust Fund
Nemoral Ltd
Nesswall Ltd
Nestle Rowntree Employees
  Community Fund
Network for Social Change
The New Appeals Organisation
  for the City and County of
  Nottingham
New Court Charitable Trust
Newby Trust Limited
The Newcomen Collett
  Foundation
The Richard Newitt Fund
Mr and Mrs F E F Newman
  Charitable Trust
Newpier Charity Ltd

Alderman Newton's
  Educational Foundation
The Chevras Ezras Nitzrochim
  Trust
The Noel Buxton Trust
The Noon Foundation
The Norda Trust
Norie Charitable Trust
Normalyn Charitable Trust
The Norman Family Charitable
  Trust
The Duncan Norman Trust
  Fund
The Normanby Charitable Trust
The North British Hotel Trust
The North West Cancer
  Research Fund
The Northampton Municipal
  Church Charities
The Northampton Queen's
  Institute Relief in Sickness
  Fund
The Earl of Northampton's
  Charity
The Northcott Devon
  Foundation
The Northcott Devon Medical
  Foundation
The Northmoor Trust
The Northumberland Village
  Homes Trust
The Northumbria Historic
  Churches Trust
The Northwood Charitable
  Trust
The Norton Foundation
The Norwich Church of England
  Young Men's Society
The Norwich Historic Churches
  Trust Ltd
The Norwich Town Close
  Estate Charity
The Norwood and Newton
  Settlement
The Noswad Charity
The Notgrove Trust
The Nottingham General
  Dispensary
The Nottingham Gordon
  Memorial Trust for Boys
  and Girls
Nottinghamshire Community
  Foundation
The Nottinghamshire Historic
  Churches Trust
The Nottinghamshire Miners'
  Welfare Trust Fund
Novi Most International
The Father O'Mahoney
  Memorial Trust
The Sir Peter O'Sullevan
  Charitable Trust
The Oak Trust
The Oakdale Trust
The Oakley Charitable Trust
The Oakmoor Charitable Trust

The Odin Charitable Trust
Ogilvie Charities Deed No.2 (including the Charity of Mary Catherine Ford Smith)
The Ogle Christian Trust
Oglesby Charitable Trust
The Oikonomia Trust
The Oizer Charitable Trust
The Old Broad Street Charity Trust
The Old Enfield Charitable Trust
Old Possum's Practical Trust
The John Oldacre Foundation
The Oldham Foundation
Onaway Trust
Open Gate
The Ormsby Charitable Trust
Orrin Charitable Trust
The Ouseley Trust
The Owen Family Trust
Oxfam (GB)
The Oxfordshire Community Foundation
The P F Charitable Trust
Padwa Charitable Foundation
The Pallant Charitable Trust
The Palmer Foundation
Eleanor Palmer Trust
The Panacea Society
Panahpur Charitable Trust
Panton Trust
The James Pantyfedwen Foundation
The Paragon Trust
The Park House Charitable Trust
The Frank Parkinson Agricultural Trust
The Samuel and Freda Parkinson Charitable Trust
The Parthenon Trust
Arthur James Paterson Charitable Trust
The Constance Paterson Charitable Trust
Miss M E Swinton Paterson's Charitable Trust
The Patrick Charitable Trust
The Jack Patston Charitable Trust
The Payne Charitable Trust
The Harry Payne Trust
The Susanna Peake Charitable Trust
The Pedmore Sporting Club Trust Fund
The Dowager Countess Eleanor Peel Trust
Peltz Trust
The Pennycress Trust
The Performing Right Society Foundation
B E Perl Charitable Trust
The Persson Charitable Trust
The Persula Foundation

The Pestalozzi Overseas Children's Trust
The Jack Petchey Foundation
The Petplan Charitable Trust
The Philips and Rubens Charitable Trust
The Phillips Charitable Trust
The Phillips Family Charitable Trust
Philological Foundation
The David Pickford Charitable Foundation
The Bernard Piggott Trust
The Claude and Margaret Pike Charity
The Pilgrim Trust
The Cecil Pilkington Charitable Trust
The Pilkington Charities Fund
The Austin and Hope Pilkington Trust
The Sir Harry Pilkington Trust
The Col W W Pilkington Will Trusts The General Charity Fund
Miss A M Pilkington's Charitable Trust
Mrs Pilkington's Charitable Trust
The Plaisterers' Company Charitable Trust
The Platinum Trust
G S Plaut Charitable Trust Limited
The Poling Charitable Trust
The George and Esme Pollitzer Charitable Settlement
The J S F Pollitzer Charitable Settlement
The Ponton House Trust
The Mayor of Poole's Appeal Fund
Edith and Ferdinand Porjes Charitable Trust
The John Porter Charitable Trust
The Porter Foundation
The Portishead Nautical Trust
The Portrack Charitable Trust
The J E Posnansky Charitable Trust
The Powell Foundation
Prairie Trust
The W L Pratt Charitable Trust
Premierquote Ltd
Premishlaner Charitable Trust
The William Price Charitable Trust
The Lucy Price Relief-in-Need Charity
Sir John Priestman Charity Trust
The Primrose Trust
The Prince's Charities Foundation
Princess Anne's Charities

The Priory Foundation
Prison Service Charity Fund
The Privy Purse Charitable Trust
The Proven Family Trust
The Provincial Grand Charity of the Province of Derbyshire
PSA Peugeot Citroen Charity Trust
The Puebla Charitable Trust
The Richard and Christine Purchas Charitable Trust
The Puri Foundation
Mr and Mrs J A Pye's Charitable Settlement
Queen Mary's Roehampton Trust
The Queen's Silver Jubilee Trust
Quercus Trust
The R D Crusaders Foundation
R J M Charitable Trust
R S Charitable Trust
The R V W Trust
The Monica Rabagliati Charitable Trust
Rachel Charitable Trust
The Mr and Mrs Philip Rackham Charitable Trust
Richard Radcliffe Charitable Trust
The Radcliffe Trust
The Rainford Trust
The Peggy Ramsay Foundation
The Joseph and Lena Randall Charitable Trust
The Rank Foundation
Ranworth Trust
The Fanny Rapaport Charitable Settlement
The Ratcliff Foundation
The Ratcliff Pension Charity
The Ratcliffe Charitable Trust
The Eleanor Rathbone Charitable Trust
The Sigrid Rausing Trust
The Ravensdale Trust
The Rayden Charitable Trust
The Roger Raymond Charitable Trust
The Rayne Foundation
The Rayne Trust
The John Rayner Charitable Trust
The Albert Reckitt Charitable Trust
The Sir James Reckitt Charity
The Red Arrows Trust
Red Hill Charitable Trust
The Red Rose Charitable Trust
The C A Redfern Charitable Foundation
The Reed Foundation
Richard Reeve's Foundation
The Max Reinhardt Charitable Trust

Relief Fund for Romania
Limited
REMEDI
The Rest Harrow Trust
Reuben Brothers Foundation
The Joan K Reynell Charitable
Trust
The Nathaniel Reyner Trust
Fund
The Rhododendron Trust
The Rhondda Cynon Taff
Welsh Church Acts Fund
Daisie Rich Trust
The Sir Cliff Richard Charitable
Trust
C B Richard Ellis Charitable
Trust
The Clive Richards Charity
The Richmond Parish Lands
Charity
The Muriel Edith Rickman
Trust
Ridgesave Limited
The Ripple Effect Foundation
The Sir John Ritblat Family
Foundation
The River Trust
Riverside Charitable Trust
Limited
The Daniel Rivlin Charitable
Trust
Thomas Roberts Trust
The Alex Roberts-Miller
Foundation
The Robertson Trust
Edwin George Robinson
Charitable Trust
Robyn Charitable Trust
The Rochester Bridge Trust
The Rock Foundation
The Rock Solid Trust
The Rofeh Trust
Richard Rogers Charitable
Settlement
Rokach Family Charitable Trust
The Helen Roll Charitable
Trust
The Sir James Roll Charitable
Trust
The Roman Research Trust
Romeera Foundation
The C A Rookes Charitable
Trust
The Rosca Trust
The Cecil Rosen Foundation
The Rothermere Foundation
The Rotherwick Foundation
The Rothley Trust
The Rothschild Foundation
The Roughley Charitable Trust
Mrs Gladys Row Fogo
Charitable Trust
Rowanville Ltd
The Christopher Rowbotham
Charitable Trust
The Rowing Foundation

The Rowlands Trust
Royal Artillery Charitable Fund
Royal British Legion
Royal Docks Trust (London)
Royal Masonic Trust for Girls
and Boys
The Royal Scots Benevolent
Society
The Alfred and Frances
Rubens Charitable Trust
The Rubin Foundation
William Arthur Rudd Memorial
Trust
The Rufford Maurice Laing
Foundation
The Russell Trust
Ryklow Charitable Trust 1992
The J S and E C Rymer
Charitable Trust
S O Charitable Trust
The Michael Sacher Charitable
Trust
The Michael Harry Sacher
Trust
Dr Mortimer and Theresa
Sackler Foundation
The Ruzin Sadagora Trust
The Saddlers' Company
Charitable Fund
The Saga Charitable Trust
The Jean Sainsbury Animal
Welfare Trust
The Alan and Babette
Sainsbury Charitable Fund
Saint Sarkis Charity Trust
The Saintbury Trust
The Saints and Sinners Trust
The Salamander Charitable
Trust
The Salt Foundation
The Salt Trust
The Salters' Charities
The Andrew Salvesen
Charitable Trust
The Sammermar Trust
Basil Samuel Charitable Trust
Coral Samuel Charitable Trust
The Hon. M J Samuel
Charitable Trust
The Peter Samuel Charitable
Trust
The Camilla Samuel Fund
The Samworth Foundation
The Sandra Charitable Trust
Santander UK Foundation
Limited
Jimmy Savile Charitable Trust
The Scarfe Charitable Trust
The Schapira Charitable Trust
The Annie Schiff Charitable
Trust
The Schmidt-Bodner Charitable
Trust
The R H Scholes Charitable
Trust
The Schreib Trust

The Schreiber Charitable Trust
Schroder Charity Trust
The Scott Bader
Commonwealth Ltd
The Francis C Scott Charitable
Trust
The Frieda Scott Charitable
Trust
The Sir James and Lady Scott
Trust
The Scott Trust Foundation
The Scottish Arts Council
Scottish Churches' Community
Trust
Scottish Coal Industry Special
Welfare Fund
The Scottish Community
Foundation
The Scottish International
Education Trust
The Scouloudi Foundation
Seafarers UK (King George's
Fund for Sailors)
Seamen's Hospital Society
The Searchlight Electric
Charitable Trust
The Searle Charitable Trust
The Helene Sebba Charitable
Trust
The Samuel Sebba Charitable
Trust
The Seedfield Trust
Leslie Sell Charitable Trust
Sellata Ltd
SEM Charitable Trust
The Ayrton Senna Foundation
The Seven Fifty Trust
The Severn Trent Water
Charitable Trust Fund
SFIA Educational Trust Limited
The Cyril Shack Trust
The Shanti Charitable Trust
ShareGift (The Orr Mackintosh
Foundation)
The Linley Shaw Foundation
The Sheepdrove Trust
The Sheffield and District
Hospital Services
Charitable Fund
The Sheldon Trust
The P and D Shepherd
Charitable Trust
The Sylvia and Colin Shepherd
Charitable Trust
The Archie Sherman Cardiff
Foundation
The Archie Sherman Charitable
Trust
The R C Sherriff Trust
The Shetland Charitable Trust
SHINE (Support and Help in
Education)
The Barnett and Sylvia Shine
No 2 Charitable Trust
The Bassil Shippam and
Alsford Trust

The Shipwrights' Company
   Charitable Fund
The Shirley Foundation
Shlomo Memorial Fund Limited
The J A Shone Memorial Trust
The Charles Shorto Charitable
   Trust
The Barbara A Shuttleworth
   Memorial Trust
David and Jennifer Sieff
   Charitable Trust
The Julius Silman Charitable
   Trust
The Leslie Silver Charitable
   Trust
The Simpson Education and
   Conservation Trust
The Simpson Foundation
The Huntly and Margery
   Sinclair Charitable Trust
Sino-British Fellowship Trust
The Skelton Bounty
The Charles Skey Charitable
   Trust
Skipton Building Society
   Charitable Foundation
The John Slater Foundation
Rita and David Slowe
   Charitable Trust
The SMB Charitable Trust
The Mrs Smith and Mount
   Trust
The N Smith Charitable
   Settlement
The Amanda Smith Charitable
   Trust
The E H Smith Charitable Trust
The Smith Charitable Trust
The Henry Smith Charity
The Leslie Smith Foundation
The Martin Smith Foundation
Stanley Smith General
   Charitable Trust
The Stanley Smith UK
   Horticultural Trust
Philip Smith's Charitable Trust
The Snowball Trust
The Sobell Foundation
Solev Co Ltd
Solihull Community Foundation
The Solo Charitable
   Settlement
Dr Richard Solomon's
   Charitable Trust
David Solomons Charitable
   Trust
Songdale Ltd
The E C Sosnow Charitable
   Trust
The Souter Charitable Trust
The South Square Trust
The Stephen R and Philippa H
   Southall Charitable Trust
The W F Southall Trust
The Southdown Trust
R H Southern Trust

The Southover Manor General
   Education Trust
The Southwold Trust
The Sovereign Health Care
   Charitable Trust
Spar Charitable Fund
Sparks Charity (Sport Aiding
   Medical Research For Kids)
Sparquote Limited
The Spear Charitable Trust
Spears-Stutz Charitable Trust
The Worshipful Company of
   Spectacle Makers' Charity
The Jessie Spencer Trust
The Ralph and Irma Sperring
   Charity
The Moss Spiro Will Charitable
   Foundation
W W Spooner Charitable Trust
Stanley Spooner Deceased
   Charitable Trust
The Spoore, Merry and Rixman
   Foundation
The Spring Harvest Charitable
   Trust
Rosalyn and Nicholas Springer
   Charitable Trust
Springfields Employees'
   Medical Research and
   Charity Trust Fund
Springrule Ltd
The Spurrell Charitable Trust
The Geoff and Fiona Squire
   Foundation
St Andrew Animal Fund
St Andrew's Conservation
   Trust
St Francis's Leprosy Guild
St Gabriel's Trust
St James' Trust Settlement
St James's Place Foundation
Sir Walter St John's
   Educational Charity
St Mark's Overseas Aid Trust
   (SMOAT)
St Michael's and All Saints'
   Charities
The Late St Patrick White
   Charitable Trust
St Teilo's Trust
Miss Doreen Stanford Trust
The Stanley Foundation Ltd
The Stanton Ballard Charitable
   Trust
The Staples Trust
The Star Charitable Trust
The Starfish Trust
The Peter Stebbings Memorial
   Charity
The Steel Charitable Trust
The Cyril and Betty Stein
   Charitable Trust
The Steinberg Family
   Charitable Trust
The Hugh Stenhouse
   Foundation

The Sigmund Sternberg
   Charitable Foundation
Stervon Ltd
The Stevenage Community
   Trust
The June Stevens Foundation
Stevenson Family's Charitable
   Trust
The Steventon Allotments and
   Relief-in-Need Charity
The Stewards' Company
   Limited
The Leonard Laity Stoate
   Charitable Trust
The Stobart Newlands
   Charitable Trust
The Edward Stocks-Massey
   Bequest Fund
The Stokenchurch Educational
   Charity
The Stoller Charitable Trust
The M J C Stone Charitable
   Trust
The Stone-Mallabar Charitable
   Foundation
The Samuel Storey Family
   Charitable Trust
Peter Stormonth Darling
   Charitable Trust
Peter Storrs Trust
The Strangward Trust
The Strasser Foundation
Stratford upon Avon Town
   Trust
Strathclyde Police Benevolent
   Fund
The W O Street Charitable
   Foundation
The A B Strom and R Strom
   Charitable Trust
The Sudborough Foundation
Sueberry Ltd
The Suffolk Historic Churches
   Trust
The Alan Sugar Foundation
The Summerfield Charitable
   Trust
The Bernard Sunley Charitable
   Foundation
The Surrey Historic Buildings
   Trust Ltd
The Sussex Historic Churches
   Trust
The Adrienne and Leslie
   Sussman Charitable Trust
The Sutasoma Trust
Sutton Coldfield Municipal
   Charities
The Sutton Nursing
   Association
Swan Mountain Trust
The Swan Trust
Swansea and Brecon Diocesan
   Board of Finance Limited
The John Swire (1989)
   Charitable Trust

The Swire Charitable Trust
The Hugh and Ruby Sykes
Charitable Trust
The Charles and Elsie Sykes
Trust
The Sylvanus Charitable Trust
The Stella Symons Charitable
Trust
The Tabeel Trust
The Tajtelbaum Charitable
Trust
The Talbot Trusts
The Talbot Village Trust
Tallow Chandlers Benevolent
Fund
Talteg Ltd
The Tangent Charitable Trust
The Lady Tangye Charitable
Trust
The David Tannen Charitable
Trust
The Tanner Trust
The Lili Tapper Charitable
Foundation
The Mrs A Lacy Tate Trust
The Tay Charitable Trust
C B and H H Taylor 1984 Trust
Humphrey Richardson Taylor
Charitable Trust
The Connie and Albert Taylor
Charitable Trust
The Cyril Taylor Charitable
Trust
A P Taylor Trust
Rosanna Taylor's 1987 Charity
Trust
Tearfund
The Tedworth Charitable Trust
Tees Valley Community
Foundation
Tegham Limited
The Templeton Goodwill Trust
Tesco Charity Trust
Thackray Medical Research
Trust
Thames Community
Foundation
The Thistle Trust
The Loke Wan Tho Memorial
Foundation
The Thomas Wall Trust
The Arthur and Margaret
Thompson Charitable Trust
The Thompson Family
Charitable Trust
The Len Thomson Charitable
Trust
The Sue Thomson Foundation
The Sir Jules Thorn Charitable
Trust
The Thornton Foundation
The Thornton Trust
The Three Guineas Trust
The Three Oaks Trust
The Thriplow Charitable Trust
The Tinsley Foundation

The Tisbury Telegraph Trust
TJH Foundation
The Tolkien Trust
Tollemache (Buckminster)
Charitable Trust
Tomchei Torah Charitable
Trust
The Tompkins Foundation
The Tory Family Foundation
Tottenham Grammar School
Foundation
The Tower Hill Trust
The Towry Law Charitable Trust
The Toy Trust
The Mayor of Trafford's Charity
Fund
Annie Tranmer Charitable Trust
The Constance Travis
Charitable Trust
The Treeside Trust
The Triangle Trust (1949) Fund
The True Colours Trust
Truedene Co. Ltd
The Truemark Trust
Truemart Limited
Trumros Limited
Trust for London
Trust Sixty Three
The Trusthouse Charitable
Foundation
The Tubney Charitable Trust
Tudor Rose Ltd
The Tudor Trust
The Tufton Charitable Trust
The R D Turner Charitable
Trust
The Douglas Turner Trust
The Florence Turner Trust
Miss S M Tutton Charitable
Trust
The TUUT Charitable Trust
Community Foundation Serving
Tyne and Wear and
Northumberland
Trustees of Tzedakah
Ulster Garden Villages Ltd
Ultach Trust
Ulting Overseas Trust
The Ulverscroft Foundation
Ulverston Town Lands Charity
The Union of Orthodox Hebrew
Congregation
The United Society for the
Propagation of the Gospel
United Trusts
The David Uri Memorial Trust
Uxbridge United Welfare Trust
Vale of Glamorgan – Welsh
Church Fund
The Valentine Charitable Trust
The Albert Van Den Bergh
Charitable Trust
John and Lucille van Geest
Foundation
The Van Neste Foundation

Mrs Maud Van Norden's
Charitable Foundation
The Vandervell Foundation
The Vardy Foundation
The Variety Club Children's
Charity
Veneziana Fund
The Verdon-Smith Family
Charitable Settlement
Roger Vere Foundation
Victoria Homes Trust
Viking Cares (For the Kids)
The Nigel Vinson Charitable
Trust
The William and Ellen Vinten
Trust
The Vintners' Company
Charitable Foundation
Vintners' Gifts Charity
Vision Charity
Vivdale Ltd
The Viznitz Foundation
Wade's Charity
The Scurrah Wainwright Charity
The Community Foundation in
Wales
Wales Council for Voluntary
Action
Robert and Felicity Waley-
Cohen Charitable Trust
The Walker Trust
Wallington Missionary Mart
and Auctions
The F J Wallis Charitable
Settlement
Walton on Thames Charity
War on Want
Sir Siegmund Warburg's
Voluntary Settlement
The Ward Blenkinsop Trust
The George Ward Charitable
Trust
The Barbara Ward Children's
Foundation
G R Waters Charitable Trust
2000
The Waterways Trust
The Wates Foundation
Blyth Watson Charitable Trust
The Howard Watson Symington
Memorial Charity
John Watson's Trust
Weatherley Charitable Trust
The Weavers' Company
Benevolent Fund
The William Webster
Charitable Trust
The Weinberg Foundation
The Weinstein Foundation
The Weinstock Fund
The James Weir Foundation
The Barbara Welby Trust
The Weldon UK Charitable
Trust
Welsh Church Fund Dyfed
area (Carmarthenshire,

Ceredigion and
Pembrokeshire)
The Welton Foundation
Wessex Cancer Trust
The Wessex Youth Trust
The West Derby Wastelands
Charity
West London Synagogue
Charitable Fund
The West Yorkshire Police
Community Fund
Mrs S K West's Charitable
Trust
The Westminster Foundation
The Garfield Weston
Foundation
The Whitaker Charitable Trust
The Colonel W H Whitbread
Charitable Trust
The Simon Whitbread
Charitable Trust
White Rose Children's Aid
International Charity
The Whitecourt Charitable
Trust
A H and B C Whiteley
Charitable Trust
The Norman Whiteley Trust
The Whitley Animal Protection
Trust
The Whittlesey Charity
The Lionel Wigram Memorial
Trust
The Felicity Wilde Charitable
Trust
The Will Charitable Trust
The Kay Williams Charitable
Foundation
The Williams Family Charitable
Trust
The H D H Wills 1965
Charitable Trust
Dame Violet Wills Charitable
Trust
The Dame Violet Wills Will
Trust
The Wilmcote Charitrust
Sumner Wilson Charitable
Trust
David Wilson Foundation
The Wilson Foundation
J and J R Wilson Trust
The Community Foundation for
Wiltshire and Swindon
The Benjamin Winegarten
Charitable Trust
The Harold Hyam Wingate
Foundation
The Francis Winham
Foundation
Anona Winn Charitable Trust
Wirral Mayor's Charity
WISCM
The Michael and Anna Wix
Charitable Trust
The Wixamtree Trust

The Woburn 1986 Charitable
Trust
The Maurice Wohl Charitable
Foundation
The Charles Wolfson
Charitable Trust
The Wolfson Family Charitable
Trust
The Wolfson Foundation
Women Caring Trust
The James Wood Bequest
Fund
Woodlands Green Ltd
Woodlands Trust
The Geoffrey Woods Charitable
Foundation
The Woodward Charitable
Trust
The A and R Woolf Charitable
Trust
The Woolnoth Society
Charitable Trust
Worcester Municipal Charities
The Worcestershire and
Dudley Historic Churches
Trust
The Fred and Della Worms
Charitable Trust
The Worwin UK Foundation
The Wragge and Co. Charitable
Trust
The Diana Edgson Wright
Charitable Trust
The Matthews Wrightson
Charity Trust
Miss E B Wrightson's
Charitable Settlement
Wychdale Ltd
Wychville Ltd
The Wyndham Charitable Trust
The Wyseliot Charitable Trust
The Xerox (UK) Trust
The Yardley Great Trust
The Dennis Alan Yardy
Charitable Trust
The W Wing Yip and Brothers
Foundation
The York Children's Trust
Yorkshire Agricultural Society
Yorkshire Building Society
Charitable Foundation
The South Yorkshire
Community Foundation
The Yorkshire Dales
Millennium Trust
The John Young Charitable
Settlement
The William Allen Young
Charitable Trust
The John K Young Endowment
Fund
Youth Music
Elizabeth and Prince Zaiger
Trust
Zephyr Charitable Trust

The Marjorie and Arnold Ziff
Charitable Foundation
Stephen Zimmerman
Charitable Trust
The Zochonis Charitable Trust
Zurich Community Trust (UK)
Limited

Core support

■ Development funding

The 1989 Willan Charitable
Trust
The 29th May 1961 Charitable
Trust
The A B Charitable Trust
Aberbrothock Charitable Trust
The Aberdeen Endowments
Trust
The Aberdeenshire Educational
Trust Scheme
Brian Abrams Charitable Trust
Eric Abrams Charitable Trust
The Acacia Charitable Trust
Achiezer Association Ltd
Achisomoch Aid Company
Limited
The ACT Foundation
Action Medical Research
The Company of Actuaries'
Charitable Trust Fund
The Sylvia Adams Charitable
Trust
The Adamson Trust
The Victor Adda Foundation
Adenfirst Ltd
The Adint Charitable Trust
The Adnams Charity
AF Trust Company
Age Concern Scotland Grants
Aid to the Church in Need (UK)
The AIM Foundation
The Green and Lilian F M
Ainsworth and Family
Benevolent Fund
The Sylvia Aitken Charitable
Trust
The Ajahma Charitable Trust
The Alabaster Trust
Alba Charitable Trust
The Alborada Trust
D G Albright Charitable Trust
The Alchemy Foundation
Alcohol Education and
Research Council
Aldgate and All Hallows'
Barking Exhibition
Foundation
The Aldgate Freedom
Foundation
Alexandra Rose Charities
The Alexis Trust
All Saints Educational Trust

Allchurches Trust Ltd
The H B Allen Charitable Trust
The Rita Allen Charitable Trust
The Alliance Family Foundation
Angus Allnatt Charitable
Foundation
The Pat Allsop Charitable Trust
The Almond Trust
Almondsbury Charity
The Altajir Trust
Altamont Ltd
Alvor Charitable Trust
AM Charitable Trust
Ambika Paul Foundation
The Ammco Trust
Sir John and Lady Amory's
Charitable Trust
Viscount Amory's Charitable
Trust
The Ampelos Trust
The AMW Charitable Trust
The Anchor Foundation
The Andrew Anderson Trust
Andor Charitable Trust
The Andre Christian Trust
Anglo American Group
Foundation
Anguish's Educational
Foundation
The Animal Defence Trust
The Eric Anker-Petersen
Charity
The Annandale Charitable
Trust
The Anson Charitable Trust
The Apax Foundation
Ambrose and Ann Appelbe
Trust
The Appletree Trust
The John Apthorp Charitable
Trust
The Milly Apthorp Charitable
Trust
The Arbib Foundation
The Archbishop of
Canterbury's Charitable
Trust
Archbishop of Wales' Fund for
Children
The John M Archer Charitable
Trust
The Archer Trust
The Architectural Heritage
Fund
The Ardwick Trust
The Argentarius Foundation
The Argus Appeal
Armenian General Benevolent
Union London Trust
The Armenian Relief Society of
Great Britain Trust
The Armourers' and Brasiers'
Gauntlet Trust
The Army Benevolent Fund
The Arnold Foundation
Arsenal Charitable Trust

The Artemis Charitable Trust
The Arts and Entertainment
Charitable Trust
Arts Council England
The Arts Council of Northern
Ireland
The Arts Council of Wales
The Ove Arup Foundation
The AS Charitable Trust
Ashburnham Thanksgiving
Trust
A J H Ashby Will Trust
The Ashden Trust
The Ashendene Trust
The Laura Ashley Foundation
The Norman C Ashton
Foundation
The Ian Askew Charitable Trust
The Associated Country
Women of the World
(ACWW)
The Association of Colleges
Charitable Trust
Astellas European Foundation
AstonMansfield Charitable
Trust
The Astor Foundation
The Astor of Hever Trust
The Aurelius Charitable Trust
The Lord Austin Trust
The Avenue Charitable Trust
The John Avins Trustees
The Avon and Somerset Police
Community Trust
AW Charitable Trust
The Aylesford Family
Charitable Trust
The BAA Communities Trust
Harry Bacon Foundation
The BACTA Charitable Trust
The Bagri Foundation
Veta Bailey Charitable Trust
The Austin Bailey Trust
The Baily Thomas Charitable
Fund
The Baird Trust
The Baker Charitable Trust
The Roy and Pixie Baker
Charitable Trust
The Balcombe Charitable Trust
The Balint Family Charitable
Trusts
The Albert Casanova Ballard
Deceased Trust
The Ballinger Charitable Trust
Balmain Charitable Trust
The Balmore Trust
The Balney Charitable Trust
The Baltic Charitable Fund
The Bamford Charitable
Foundation
The Banbury Charities
William P Bancroft (No 2)
Charitable Trust and
Jenepher Gillett Trust
The Band Trust

The Barbers' Company General
Charities
The Barbour Trust
The Barcapel Foundation
Barchester Healthcare
Foundation
David and Frederick Barclay
Foundation
The Baring Foundation
Peter Barker-Mill Memorial
Charity
Barleycorn Trust
The Barnabas Trust
Lord Barnby's Foundation
Barnes Workhouse Fund
The Barnsbury Charitable Trust
The Barnstaple Bridge Trust
The Barnwood House Trust
The Misses Barrie Charitable
Trust
Barrington Family Charitable
Trust
The Charity of William Barrow
Stephen J Barry Charitable
Trust
The Bartlett Taylor Charitable
Trust
The Paul Bassham Charitable
Trust
The Batchworth Trust
Bay Charitable Trust
The Bay Tree Charitable Trust
D H and L H Baylin Charitable
Trust
The Louis Baylis (Maidenhead
Advertiser) Charitable Trust
BBC Children in Need
B-CH 1971 Charitable Trust
The Beacon Trust
Bear Mordechai Ltd
The Bearder Charity
The James Beattie Charitable
Trust
The Beaufort House Trust
Limited
Beauland Ltd
The Beaverbrook Foundation
The Beccles Town Lands
Charity
The Becker Family Charitable
Trust
The Becketts and Sargeants
Educational Foundation
The John Beckwith Charitable
Trust
The Peter Beckwith Charitable
Trust
The Bedford Charity (The
Harpur Trust)
The Bedfordshire and Luton
Community Foundation
The David and Ruth Behrend
Fund
The Beit Trust
The Bellahouston Bequest
Fund

Bellasis Trust
The Bellhouse Foundation
The Bellinger Donnay Trust
Belljoe Tzedoko Ltd
The Benfield Motors Charitable
 Trust
The Benham Charitable
 Settlement
Maurice and Jacqueline
 Bennett Charitable Trust
Michael and Leslie Bennett
 Charitable Trust
The Ruth Berkowitz Charitable
 Trust
The Berkshire Community
 Foundation
The Bestway Foundation
The Betterware Foundation
Thomas Betton's Charity for
 Pensions and Relief-in-Need
BHST
The Mason Bibby 1981 Trust
BibleLands
The Bideford Bridge Trust
The Big Lottery Fund
The Billmeir Charitable Trust
The Bingham Trust
The Bintaub Charitable Trust
The Birmingham Community
 Foundation
The Birmingham District
 Nursing Charitable Trust
The Birmingham Hospital
 Saturday Fund Medical
 Charity and Welfare Trust
Birmingham International
 Airport Community Trust
The Lord Mayor of
 Birmingham's Charity
Birthday House Trust
The Bisgood Charitable Trust
 (registered as Miss Jeanne
 Bisgood's Charitable Trust)
The Michael Bishop
 Foundation
The Bishop's Development
 Fund
The Sydney Black Charitable
 Trust
The Bertie Black Foundation
Sir Alec Black's Charity
Isabel Blackman Foundation
The BlackRock (UK) Charitable
 Trust
The Herbert and Peter
 Blagrave Charitable Trust
The Blair Foundation
Blakes Benevolent Trust
The Blanchminster Trust
The Sir Victor Blank Charitable
 Settlement
Blatchington Court Trust
The Neville and Elaine Blond
 Charitable Trust
The Blueberry Charitable Trust

The Bluston Charitable
 Settlement
Enid Blyton Trust for Children
The Nicholas Boas Charitable
 Trust
The Body Shop Foundation
The Boltons Trust
The Bonamy Charitable Trust
The John and Celia Bonham
 Christie Charitable Trust
The Charlotte Bonham-Carter
 Charitable Trust
Bonhomie United Charity
 Society
BOOST Charitable Trust
The Booth Charities
The Boots Charitable Trust
The Bordon and Liphook
 Charity
Salo Bordon Charitable Trust
The Oliver Borthwick Memorial
 Trust
The Boshier-Hinton Foundation
The Bothwell Charitable Trust
H E and E L Botteley
 Charitable Trust
The Harry Bottom Charitable
 Trust
P G and N J Boulton Trust
The A H and E Boulton Trust
Sir Clive Bourne Family Trust
The Anthony Bourne
 Foundation
Bourneheights Limited
Community Foundation for
 Bournemouth, Dorset and
 Poole
The Bower Trust
The Bowerman Charitable
 Trust
John and Susan Bowers Fund
The Bowland Charitable Trust
The William Brake Charitable
 Trust
The Tony Bramall Charitable
 Trust
The Bransford Trust
The Brewers' Company
 General Charitable Trust
The Harold and Alice Bridges
 Charity
Briggs Animal Welfare Trust
The Brighton District Nursing
 Association Trust
Bristol Archdeaconry Charity
The Bristol Charities
John Bristow and Thomas
 Mason Trust
Britannia Foundation
The British Council for
 Prevention of Blindness
The British Dietetic
 Association General and
 Education Trust Fund
The British Gas (Scottish Gas)
 Energy Trust

British Heart Foundation
British Humane Association
British Institute at Ankara
British Ornithologists' Union
British Record Industry Trust
The Britto Foundation
The J and M Britton Charitable
 Trust
The Charles and Edna
 Broadhurst Charitable Trust
The Bromley Trust
The Roger Brooke Charitable
 Trust
The David Brooke Charity
The Rory and Elizabeth Brooks
 Foundation
The Charles Brotherton Trust
Joseph Brough Charitable
 Trust
The Swinfen Broun Charitable
 Trust
Mrs E E Brown Charitable
 Settlement
Bill Brown's Charitable
 Settlement
R S Brownless Charitable
 Trust
Brownsword Charitable
 Foundation
T B H Brunner's Charitable
 Settlement
Brushmill Ltd
The Bryant Trust
Buckingham Trust
The Buckinghamshire
 Foundation
The Buckinghamshire Masonic
 Centenary Fund
Buckland Charitable Trust
The Rosemary Bugden
 Charitable Trust
The Bulldog Trust Limited
The E F Bulmer Benevolent
 Fund
The Burden Trust
Burdens Charitable Foundation
The Burdett Trust for Nursing
The Clara E Burgess Charity
The Burry Charitable Trust
The Audrey and Stanley Burton
 1960 Charitable Trust
The Arnold Burton 1998
 Charitable Trust
The Burton Breweries
 Charitable Trust
The Geoffrey Burton Charitable
 Trust
Consolidated Charity of Burton
 upon Trent
Butchers' Company General
 Charities
The Bill Butlin Charity Trust
Ann Byrne Charitable Trust
C and F Charitable Trust
C J Cadbury Charitable Trust

Edward Cadbury Charitable Trust

Henry T and Lucy B Cadbury Charitable Trust

P H G Cadbury Charitable Trust

The Christopher Cadbury Charitable Trust

The G W Cadbury Charitable Trust

The Richard Cadbury Charitable Trust

The William A Cadbury Charitable Trust

The Cadbury Foundation

The Edward and Dorothy Cadbury Trust

The George Cadbury Trust

The Barrow Cadbury Trust and the Barrow Cadbury Fund

The Cadogan Charity

CAF (Charities Aid Foundation)

CAFOD

The Callander Charitable Trust

Calleva Foundation

The Calpe Trust

Calypso Browning Trust

The Cambridgeshire Community Foundation

The Camelia Trust

The Campden Charities

The Canning Trust

M R Cannon 1998 Charitable Trust

H and L Cantor Trust

Capital Community Foundation

Cardy Beaver Foundation

The Carew Pole Charitable Trust

The D W T Cargill Fund

Caring for Kids (Radio Tay)

Carlee Ltd

The Carlton House Charitable Trust

The Worshipful Company of Carmen Benevolent Trust

The Carnegie Dunfermline Trust

The Carnegie Trust for the Universities of Scotland

The Carpenter Charitable Trust

The Carpenters' Company Charitable Trust

The Carrington Charitable Trust

The Carron Charitable Settlement

The Leslie Mary Carter Charitable Trust

The Carvill Trust

The Casey Trust

Cash for Kids Radio Clyde

Sir John Cass's Foundation

The Elizabeth Casson Trust

The Castang Foundation

The Catalyst Charitable Trust

The Catholic Charitable Trust

Catholic Foreign Missions

The Catholic Trust for England and Wales

The Cattanach Charitable Trust

The Joseph and Annie Cattle Trust

The Thomas Sivewright Catto Charitable Settlement

The Wilfrid and Constance Cave Foundation

The Cayo Foundation

Elizabeth Cayzer Charitable Trust

The B G S Cayzer Charitable Trust

The Cazenove Charitable Trust

Celtic Charity Fund

The Cemlyn-Jones Trust

CfBT Education Trust

The CH (1980) Charitable Trust

R E Chadwick Charitable Trust

The Amelia Chadwick Trust

The Pamela Champion Foundation

The Chapman Charitable Trust

John William Chapman's Charitable Trust

The Charities Advisory Trust

Charitworth Limited

The Charter 600 Charity

The Worshipful Company of Chartered Accountants General Charitable Trust

The Chasah Trust

Chasdei Tovim Me'oros

The Chelsea Building Society Charitable Foundation

The Chelsea Square 1994 Trust

The Cheruby Trust

The Cheshire Provincial Fund of Benevolence

The Chetwode Foundation

The Malcolm Chick Charity

Child Growth Foundation

Children's Liver Disease Foundation

Childs Charitable Trust

The Childwick Trust

The Chippenham Borough Lands Charity

The Chipping Sodbury Town Lands Charity

CHK Charities Limited

The Chownes Foundation

The Chrimes Family Charitable Trust

The Christabella Charitable Trust

Christadelphian Samaritan Fund

Christian Aid

Christian Response to Eastern Europe

The Church and Community Fund

The Church Burgesses Educational Foundation

Church Burgesses Trust

Church Lands and John Johnson's Estate Charities

Church of Ireland Priorities Fund

The Church Urban Fund

City and County of Swansea Welsh Church Act Fund

The City Bridge Trust

The City Educational Trust Fund

The City Parochial Foundation

CLA Charitable Trust

Stephen Clark 1957 Charitable Trust

J A Clark Charitable Trust

The Hilda and Alice Clark Charitable Trust

The Roger and Sarah Bancroft Clark Charitable Trust

The Clarke Charitable Settlement

The Cleary Foundation

The Cleopatra Trust

Lord Clinton's Charitable Trust

The Clore Duffield Foundation

Miss V L Clore's 1967 Charitable Trust

Closehelm Ltd

The Clothworkers' Foundation

Richard Cloudesley's Charity

The Clover Trust

The Robert Clutterbuck Charitable Trust

Clydpride Ltd

The Coalfields Regeneration Trust

The John Coates Charitable Trust

Coats Foundation Trust

The Cobalt Trust

The Cobtree Charity Trust Ltd

The Denise Cohen Charitable Trust

The Vivienne and Samuel Cohen Charitable Trust

The R and S Cohen Fondation

The John S Cohen Foundation

The Colchester Catalyst Charity

John Coldman Charitable Trust

The Cole Charitable Trust

The Colefax Charitable Trust

The John and Freda Coleman Charitable Trust

The Bernard Coleman Charitable Trust

The George Henry Collins Charity

The E Alec Colman Charitable Fund Ltd

The Sir Jeremiah Colman Gift
Trust
Col-Reno Ltd
The Colt Foundation
The Coltstaple Trust
Colwinston Charitable Trust
Colyer-Fergusson Charitable
Trust
Comic Relief
The Comino Foundation
Community Foundation for
Calderdale
The Community Foundation for
Greater Manchester
The Community Foundation for
Northern Ireland
The Company of Tobacco Pipe
Makers' and Tobacco
Blenders' Benevolent Fund
The Compton Charitable Trust
The Congleton Inclosure Trust
The Conscience Trust
The Conservation Foundation
The Consolidated Charities for
the Infirm Merchant
Taylors' Company
The Construction Industry
Trust for Youth
The Cook and Wolstenholme
Charitable Trust
Gordon Cook Foundation
The Ernest Cook Trust
The Cooks Charity
The Catherine Cookson
Charitable Trust
The Cookson Charitable Trust
Harold and Daphne Cooper
Charitable Trust
Mabel Cooper Charity
The Alice Ellen Cooper Dean
Charitable Foundation
The Co-operative Foundation
The Marjorie Coote Animal
Charity Trust
The Marjorie Coote Old
People's Charity
The Helen Jean Cope Trust
The J Reginald Corah
Foundation Fund
The Gershon Coren Charitable
Foundation
The Corinthian Trust
Edwin Cornforth 1983 Charity
Trust
The Evan Cornish Foundation
The Duke of Cornwall's
Benevolent Fund
The Cornwell Charitable Trust
The Sidney and Elizabeth
Corob Charitable Trust
The Corona Charitable Trust
The Costa Family Charitable
Trust
The Cotton Industry War
Memorial Trust
The Cotton Trust

County Durham Foundation
The Augustine Courtauld Trust
Coutts Charitable Trust
The General Charities of the
City of Coventry
Coventry Building Society
Charitable Foundation
The John Cowan Foundation
Cowley Charitable Foundation
The Sir William Coxen Trust
Fund
The Lord Cozens-Hardy Trust
The Craignish Trust
The Craps Charitable Trust
Michael Crawford Children's
Charity
The Cray Trust
The Crescent Trust
Criffel Charitable Trust
Cripplegate Foundation
The Violet and Milo Cripps
Charitable Trust
The Cromarty Trust
The Harry Crook Foundation
The Cross Trust
The Cross Trust
The Croydon Relief in Need
Charities
The Mayor of Croydon's
Charity Fund
The Peter Cruddas Foundation
Cruden Foundation Ltd
The Ronald Cruickshanks'
Foundation
Cuby Charitable Trust
The Culra Charitable Trust
The Cumber Family Charitable
Trust
Cumberland Building Society
Charitable Foundation
Cumbria Community
Foundation
The D J H Currie Memorial
Trust
The Dennis Curry Charitable
Trust
The Raymond Curtis Charitable
Trust
The Manny Cussins
Foundation
The Cutler Trust (the
Worshipful Company of
Makers of Playing Cards)
The Cwmbran Trust
Itzchok Meyer Cymerman Trust
Ltd
The D'Oyly Carte Charitable
Trust
The Roald Dahl Foundation
The Daily Prayer Union
Charitable Trust Ltd
The Daisy Trust
The Daiwa Anglo-Japanese
Foundation
Oizer Dalim Trust

The Dr and Mrs A Darlington
Charitable Trust
Baron Davenport's Charity
The Davidson (Nairn)
Charitable Trust
Davidson Charitable Trust
The Alderman Joe Davidson
Memorial Trust
Michael Davies Charitable
Settlement
The Gwendoline and Margaret
Davies Charity
The Wilfrid Bruce Davis
Charitable Trust
Davis-Rubens Charitable Trust
The Dawe Charitable Trust
The De Clermont Charitable
Company Ltd
Peter De Haan Charitable
Trust
The De Laszlo Foundation
The Leopold De Rothschild
Charitable Trust
The Deakin Charitable Trust
William Dean Countryside and
Educational Trust
The Debmar Benevolent Trust
The Delfont Foundation
The Dellal Foundation
The Delves Charitable Trust
The Demigryphon Trust
The Denman Charitable Trust
The Denton Charitable Trust
The Denton Wilde Sapte
Charitable Trust
The Earl of Derby's Charitable
Trust
Derbyshire Community
Foundation
The J N Derbyshire Trust
Devon Community Foundation
The Devon Educational Trust
The Duke of Devonshire's
Charitable Trust
The Sandy Dewhirst Charitable
Trust
DG Charitable Settlement
The Laduma Dhamecha
Charitable Trust
Diabetes UK
Alan and Sheila Diamond
Charitable Trust
The Diana, Princess of Wales
Memorial Fund
The Dibden Allotments Charity
The Dickon Trust
The Digbeth Trust
The Dinwoodie Settlement
Dischma Charitable Trust
The DLA Piper Charitable Trust
The DLM Charitable Trust
Louise Dobson Charitable
Trust
The Derek and Eileen Dodgson
Foundation
The Dollond Charitable Trust

Domepride Ltd
The Dorcas Trust
The Dorema Charitable Trust
The Dorus Trust
Double 'O' Charity Ltd
The Doughty Charity Trust
The R M Douglas Charitable
Trust
The Drapers' Charitable Fund
Dromintee Trust
The Dugdale Charitable Trust
The Duis Charitable Trust
The Dulverton Trust
The P B Dumbell Charitable
Trust
The Dumbreck Charity
Dunard Fund
Ronald Duncan Literary
Foundation
The Dunhill Medical Trust
The Houghton Dunn Charitable
Trust
The Dunn Family Charitable
Trust
The W E Dunn Trust
Dushinsky Trust Ltd
Mildred Duveen Charitable
Trust
The Dwek Family Charitable
Trust
The Dyers' Company
Charitable Trust
EAGA Partnership Charitable
Trust
The Eagle Charity Trust
Audrey Earle Charitable Trust
The Earley Charity
Earls Colne and Halstead
Educational Charity
The Earmark Trust
East Kent Provincial Charities
East London Community
Foundation
Eastern Counties Educational
Trust Limited
The Sir John Eastwood
Foundation
The Ebenezer Trust
The EBM Charitable Trust
Eden Arts Trust
EDF Energy Trust (EDFET)
The Gilbert and Eileen Edgar
Foundation
Gilbert Edgar Trust
Edinburgh Children's Holiday
Fund
The Edinburgh Trust, No 2
Account
Edinburgh Voluntary
Organisations' Trust Funds
Educational Foundation of
Alderman John Norman
The W G Edwards Charitable
Foundation
The William Edwards
Educational Charity

The Elephant Trust
The George Elias Charitable
Trust
The Gerald Palmer Eling Trust
Company
The Elizabeth Frankland Moore
and Star Foundation
The Wilfred and Elsie Elkes
Charity Fund
The Maud Elkington Charitable
Trust
Ellador Ltd
The Ellerdale Trust
The John Ellerman Foundation
The Ellinson Foundation Ltd
The Edith Maud Ellis 1985
Charitable Trust
The Ellis Campbell Foundation
James Ellis Charitable Trust
The Elmgrant Trust
The Elmley Foundation
Elshore Ltd
The Vernon N Ely Charitable
Trust
The Embleton Trust
The Emerton-Christie Charity
The Emilienne Charitable Trust
The Emmandjay Charitable
Trust
The Worshipful Company of
Engineers Charitable Trust
Fund
The Englefield Charitable Trust
The English Schools' Football
Association
The Enkalon Foundation
Entindale Ltd
The Epigoni Trust
Epilepsy Research UK
The Equitable Charitable Trust
The Equity Trust Fund
The Ericson Trust
The Erskine Cunningham Hill
Trust
Essex Community Foundation
The Essex Fairway Charitable
Trust
The Essex Heritage Trust
Essex Provincial Charity Fund
The Essex Youth Trust
Euro Charity Trust
The Evangelical Covenants
Trust
The Alan Evans Memorial Trust
Sir John Evelyn's Charity
The Eventhall Family
Charitable Trust
The Everard Foundation
The Eveson Charitable Trust
The Beryl Evetts and Robert
Luff Animal Welfare Trust
The Execution Charitable Trust
The Mayor of Exeter's Appeal
Fund
The Exilarch's Foundation

The Matthew Eyton Animal
Welfare Trust
F C Charitable Trust
The F P Limited Charitable
Trust
The Faber Charitable Trust
Esmée Fairbairn Foundation
The Fairstead Trust
The Fairway Trust
Faisaltex Charitable Trust
The Family Foundations Trust
The Family Rich Charities Trust
Famos Foundation Trust
The Lord Faringdon Charitable
Trust
Samuel William Farmer's Trust
The Farmers' Company
Charitable Fund
The Thomas Farr Charitable
Trust
Walter Farthing (Trust) Limited
Farthing Trust
The Fassnidge Memorial Trust
Joseph Fattorini Charitable
Trust 'B' Account
The Fawcett Charitable Trust
Federation of Jewish Relief
Organisations
Feed the Minds
The John Feeney Charitable
Bequest
The George Fentham
Birmingham Charity
The A M Fenton Trust
Allan and Nesta Ferguson
Charitable Settlement
Elizabeth Ferguson Charitable
Trust Fund
The Fidelity UK Foundation
The Bluff Field Charitable Trust
The Doris Field Charitable
Trust
Fife Council/Common Good
Funds and Trusts
The Fifty Fund
Dixie Rose Findlay Charitable
Trust
Finnart House School Trust
Gerald Finzi Charitable Trust
Firtree Trust
The Sir John Fisher Foundation
The Fishmongers' Company's
Charitable Trust
Marc Fitch Fund
The Fitton Trust
The Earl Fitzwilliam Charitable
Trust
Bud Flanagan Leukaemia Fund
The Rose Flatau Charitable
Trust
The Ian Fleming Charitable
Trust
The Joyce Fletcher Charitable
Trust
The Roy Fletcher Charitable
Trust

Florence's Charitable Trust
The Florian Charitable Trust
The Flow Foundation
The Gerald Fogel Charitable
  Trust
The Follett Trust
The Football Association
  National Sports Centre
  Trust
The Football Association Youth
  Trust
The Football Foundation
The Forbes Charitable
  Foundation
Forbesville Limited
The Forces Trust
Ford Britain Trust
The Oliver Ford Charitable
  Trust
Fordeve Ltd
The Forest Hill Charitable Trust
The Foresters' Charity
  Stewards UK Trust
Gwyneth Forrester Trust
The Forte Charitable Trust
Lord Forte Foundation
Foundation for Management
  Education
Four Acre Trust
The Four Winds Trust
The Fowler, Smith and Jones
  Charitable Trust
The Foyle Foundation
The Isaac and Freda Frankel
  Memorial Charitable Trust
Sydney E Franklin Deceased's
  New Second Charity
The Jill Franklin Trust
The Gordon Fraser Charitable
  Trust
The Hugh Fraser Foundation
The Joseph Strong Frazer Trust
The Louis and Valerie
  Freedman Charitable
  Settlement
The Freemasons' Grand
  Charity
The Thomas Freke and Lady
  Norton Charity
The Charles S French
  Charitable Trust
The Anne French Memorial
  Trust
The Freshfield Foundation
The Freshgate Trust
  Foundation
The Friarsgate Trust
The Friends Hall Farm Street
  Trust
Friends of Biala Ltd
Friends of Wiznitz Limited
Friends Provident Charitable
  Foundation
The Frognal Trust
T F C Frost Charitable Trust
The Patrick Frost Foundation

Maurice Fry Charitable Trust
Mejer and Gertrude Miriam
  Frydman Foundation
The Fuellers Charitable Trust
  Fund
The Fulmer Charitable Trust
Worshipful Company of
  Furniture Makers Charitable
  Fund
Gableholt Limited
The Galbraith Trust
The Gale Family Charitable
  Trust
The Angela Gallagher Memorial
  Fund
The Gamlen Charitable Trust
The Gamma Trust
The Gannochy Trust
The Ganzoni Charitable Trust
The Worshipful Company of
  Gardeners of London
The Samuel Gardner Memorial
  Trust
The Garnett Charitable Trust
Garrick Charitable Trust
Garvan Limited
The Gatsby Charitable
  Foundation
Gatwick Airport Community
  Trust
The Robert Gavron Charitable
  Trust
Jacqueline and Michael Gee
  Charitable Trust
The General Nursing Council
  for England and Wales
  Trust
J Paul Getty Jr Charitable Trust
The Gibbs Charitable Trust
Simon Gibson Charitable Trust
The G C Gibson Charitable
  Trust
The Harvey and Hilary Gilbert
  Charitable Trust
The Girdlers' Company
  Charitable Trust
The B and P Glasser
  Charitable Trust
The Glass-House Trust
The Glastonbury Trust Limited
Global Care
Global Charities (formally
  GCap Charities)
Gloucestershire Community
  Foundation
Worshipful Company of
  Glovers of London Charity
  Fund
GMC Trust
The GNC Trust
The Mrs Godfrey-Payton Trust
The Meir Golda Trust
The Sydney and Phyllis
  Goldberg Memorial
  Charitable Trust
The Golden Bottle Trust

Golden Charitable Trust
The Jack Goldhill Charitable
  Trust
The Goldsmiths' Arts Trust
  Fund
The Goldsmiths' Company
  Charity
The Golsoncott Foundation
The Good Neighbours Trust
Nicholas and Judith
  Goodison's Charitable
  Settlement
The Everard and Mina
  Goodman Charitable
  Foundation
Mike Gooley Trailfinders
  Charity
Leonard Gordon Charitable
  Trust
The Gosling Foundation
  Limited
The Gough Charitable Trust
The Gould Charitable Trust
The Grace Charitable Trust
A B Grace Trust
The Graff Foundation
The Grahame Charitable
  Foundation Limited
Grampian Police Diced Cap
  Charitable Fund
The Granada Foundation
Grand Charitable Trust of the
  Order of Women
  Freemasons
The Grand Order of Water
  Rats' Charities Fund
The Grange Farm Centre Trust
Grantham Yorke Trust
The Gray Trust
The Great Britain Sasakawa
  Foundation
The Great Stone Bridge Trust
  of Edenbridge
The Great Torrington Town
  Lands Charity
The Constance Green
  Foundation
The Barry Green Memorial
  Fund
The Philip Green Memorial
  Trust
Mrs H R Greene Charitable
  Settlement
Greenham Common
  Community Trust Limited
Naomi and Jeffrey Greenwood
  Charitable Trust
Greggs Foundation
The Greys Charitable Trust
Grimmitt Trust
The Grocers' Charity
The M and R Gross Charities
  Limited
The Grove Charitable Trust
The GRP Charitable Trust

The David and Marie Grumitt Foundation

The Bishop of Guildford's Foundation

The Guildry Incorporation of Perth

The Walter Guinness Charitable Trust

The Gulbenkian Foundation

The Gunter Charitable Trust

The Gur Trust

Gurunanak

Dr Guthrie's Association

The H and M Charitable Trust

H C D Memorial Fund

The H P Charitable Trust

The Hackney Parochial Charities

The Hadfield Trust

The Hadley Trust

The Hadrian Trust

The Alfred Haines Charitable Trust

The Hale Trust

E F and M G Hall Charitable Trust

The Edith Winifred Hall Charitable Trust

Robert Hall Charity

The Hamamelis Trust

Hamilton Wallace Trust

Paul Hamlyn Foundation

Sue Hammerson's Charitable Trust

The Hammonds Charitable Trust

The Hampshire and Islands Historic Churches Trust

Hampton Fuel Allotment Charity

The W A Handley Charitable Trust

Beatrice Hankey Foundation Ltd

The Hanley Trust

The Kathleen Hannay Memorial Charity

The Doughty Hanson Charitable Foundation

Lord Hanson Foundation

The Haramead Trust

Miss K M Harbinson's Charitable Trust

Harbo Charities Limited

The Harborne Parish Lands Charity

The Harbour Charitable Trust

The Harbour Foundation

The Harding Trust

William Harding's Charity

The Hare of Steep Charitable Trust

The Harebell Centenary Fund

The Kenneth Hargreaves Charitable Trust

The Harris Charitable Trust

The Harris Charity

The Harris Family Charitable Trust

The Harrison and Potter Trust

The John Harrison Charitable Trust

The Peter Harrison Foundation

The Spencer Hart Charitable Trust

The Hartley Charitable Trust

The N and P Hartley Memorial Trust

William Geoffrey Harvey's Discretionary Settlement

Haskel Family Foundation

The Hathaway Trust

The Maurice Hatter Foundation

The M A Hawe Settlement

The Hawthorne Charitable Trust

The Dorothy Hay-Bolton Charitable Trust

The Haydan Charitable Trust

The Haymills Charitable Trust

The Headley Trust

Headley-Pitt Charitable Trust

Heagerty Charitable Trust

The Heald Charitable Trust

Healthsure Group Ltd

May Hearnshaw's Charity

The Heart of England Community Foundation

The Heathcoat Trust

Heathside Charitable Trust

The Charlotte Heber-Percy Charitable Trust

Percy Hedley 1990 Charitable Trust

The Hedley Denton Charitable Trust

The Hedley Foundation

The H J Heinz Company Limited Charitable Trust

The Hellenic Foundation

The Michael and Morven Heller Charitable Foundation

The Simon Heller Charitable Settlement

Help the Aged

Help the Homeless

Help the Hospices

The Hemby Trust

The Christina Mary Hendrie Trust for Scottish and Canadian Charities

The Henley Educational Charity

Philip Henman Trust

Esther Hennell Charitable Trust

The G D Herbert Charitable Trust

The Joanna Herbert-Stepney Charitable Settlement

The Anne Herd Memorial Trust

The Herefordshire Historic Churches Trust

The Heritage of London Trust Ltd

The Hertfordshire Community Foundation

The Hesed Trust

The Hesslewood Children's Trust (Hull Seamen's and General Orphanage)

The Bernhard Heuberger Charitable Trust

Hexham and Newcastle Diocesan Trust (1947)

The Higgs Charitable Trust

Alan Edward Higgs Charity

The High Sheriff's Police Trust for the County of West Midlands

Highcroft Charitable Trust

The Hilden Charitable Fund

The Joseph and Mary Hiley Trust

The Holly Hill Charitable Trust

The Derek Hill Foundation

The Charles Littlewood Hill Trust

The Hillingdon Partnership Trust

R G Hills Charitable Trust

Hinchley Charitable Trust

Lady Hind Trust

Hinduja Foundation

Stuart Hine Trust

The Hinrichsen Foundation

The Hitchin Educational Foundation

The Eleemosynary Charity of William Hobbayne

Hobson Charity Limited

Hockerill Educational Foundation

Matthew Hodder Charitable Trust

The Sir Julian Hodge Charitable Trust

The Jane Hodge Foundation

The J G Hogg Charitable Trust

The Holbeck Charitable Trust

The Holden Charitable Trust

John Holford's Charity

The Hollick Family Charitable Trust

The Holliday Foundation

The Dorothy Holmes Charitable Trust

The Holst Foundation

P H Holt Foundation

The Edward Holt Trust

The Holywood Trust

The Homelands Charitable Trust

The Homestead Charitable Trust

Mary Homfray Charitable Trust

Sir Harold Hood's Charitable Trust

The Hope Trust

HopMarket Charity
The Cuthbert Horn Trust
The Antony Hornby Charitable
 Trust
The Horne Foundation
The Horne Trust
The Worshipful Company of
 Horners' Charitable Trusts
The Hornsey Parochial
 Charities
The Hospital of God at
 Greatham
The Hospital Saturday Fund
Houblon-Norman/George Fund
The House of Industry Estate
The Reta Lila Howard
 Foundation
The Daniel Howard Trust
The Clifford Howarth Charity
 Trust
The Huddersfield Medical Trust
 Fund
The Hudson Foundation
The Huggard Charitable Trust
The Geoffrey C Hughes
 Charitable Trust
The Hull and East Riding
 Charitable Trust
Hulme Trust Estates
 (Educational)
Human Relief Foundation
The Humanitarian Trust
The Michael and Shirley Hunt
 Charitable Trust
The Albert Hunt Trust
The Hunter Foundation
Miss Agnes H Hunter's Trust
The Huntingdon Foundation
Huntingdon Freemen's Charity
John Huntingdon's Charity
Hurdale Charity Limited
The Hutton Foundation
The Nani Huyu Charitable Trust
The P Y N and B Hyams Trust
The Hyde Charitable Trust –
 Youth Plus
The Idlewild Trust
The Iliffe Family Charitable
 Trust
Impetus Trust
The Indigo Trust
The Ingram Trust
The Inland Waterways
 Association
The Inlight Trust
The Inman Charity
The Inner London Magistrates
 Court Poor Box Charity and
 Feeder Charity
The Worshipful Company of
 Innholders General Charity
 Fund
The Innocent Foundation
The Ireland Fund of Great
 Britain

The Irish Youth Foundation
 (UK) Ltd
The Ironmongers' Foundation
Irshad Trust
The Charles Irving Charitable
 Trust
Irwin Trust
The ISA Charity
The Isaacs Charitable Trust
The J Isaacs Charitable Trust
The Isle of Anglesey Charitable
 Trust
Isle of Dogs Community
 Foundation
The ITF Seafarers Trust
J A R Charitable Trust
The J J Charitable Trust
The J R S S T Charitable Trust
Elizabeth Jackson Charitable
 Trust
Jacobs Charitable Trust
The Ruth and Lionel Jacobson
 Trust (Second Fund) No 2
Jaffe Family Relief Fund
John James Bristol Foundation
The Susan and Stephen
 James Charitable
 Settlement
The James Trust
The Jarman Charitable Trust
The John Jarrold Trust
Jay Education Trust
JCA Charitable Foundation
The Jeffrey Charitable Trust
Rees Jeffreys Road Fund
The Jenour Foundation
The Jephcott Charitable Trust
The Jerusalem Trust
Jerwood Charitable Foundation
Jesus Hospital Charity
Jewish Child's Day
The Jewish Youth Fund
The JMK Charitable Trust
The Joanies Trust
The Harold Joels Charitable
 Trust
The Jonathan Joels Charitable
 Trust
The Nicholas Joels Charitable
 Trust
The Norman Joels Charitable
 Trust
The Joffe Charitable Trust
The Elton John Aids
 Foundation
The Michael John Trust
The Lillie Johnson Charitable
 Trust
The Johnson Group Cleaners
 Charity
The Johnnie Johnson Trust
The Johnson Wax Ltd
 Charitable Trust
The Joicey Trust
The Jones 1986 Charitable
 Trust

The Marjorie and Geoffrey
 Jones Charitable Trust
The Jordan Charitable
 Foundation
The J E Joseph Charitable
 Fund
The Lady Eileen Joseph
 Foundation
JTH Charitable Trust
The Judith Trust
The Cyril and Eve Jumbo
 Charitable Trust
The Anton Jurgens Charitable
 Trust
The Bernard Kahn Charitable
 Trust
The Stanley Kalms Foundation
The Karenza Foundation
The Boris Karloff Charitable
 Foundation
The Ian Karten Charitable
 Trust
The Kasner Charitable Trust
The Kass Charitable Trust
The Kathleen Trust
The Michael and Ilse Katz
 Foundation
The Katzauer Charitable
 Settlement
The C S Kaufman Charitable
 Trust
The Geoffrey John Kaye
 Charitable Foundation
The Emmanuel Kaye
 Foundation
Kelsick's Educational
 Foundation
The KempWelch Charitable
 Trust
The Kay Kendall Leukaemia
 Fund
William Kendall's Charity (Wax
 Chandlers' Company)
The Kennel Club Charitable
 Trust
Kent Community Foundation
The Nancy Kenyon Charitable
 Trust
Keren Association
Kermaville Ltd
E and E Kernkraut Charities
 Limited
The Peter Kershaw Trust
The Kessler Foundation
Keswick Hall Charity
The Ursula Keyes Trust
The Kiawah Charitable Trust
The Robert Kiln Charitable
 Trust
The King Henry VIII Endowed
 Trust Warwick
The King/Cullimore Charitable
 Trust
The King's Fund
The Kingsbury Charity

The Mary Kinross Charitable Trust

Kinsurdy Charitable Trust

Kirkley Poor's Lands Estate

The Richard Kirkman Charitable Trust

Kirschel Foundation

Robert Kitchin (Saddlers' Company)

Ernest Kleinwort Charitable Trust

The Marina Kleinwort Charitable Trust

The Kobler Trust

The Kohn Foundation

Kollel and Co. Limited

The Kreditor Charitable Trust

The Kreitman Foundation

The Neil Kreitman Foundation

The Heinz, Anna and Carol Kroch Foundation

The Kyte Charitable Trust

Lacims-Maclis Charitable Trust

The Late Sir Pierce Lacy Charity Trust

The K P Ladd Charitable Trust

John Laing Charitable Trust

Maurice and Hilda Laing Charitable Trust

The Laing Family Foundations

The Christopher Laing Foundation

The Kirby Laing Foundation

The Martin Laing Foundation

The Beatrice Laing Trust

The Lambert Charitable Trust

Community Foundation for Lancashire

Lancashire Environmental Fund

Duchy of Lancaster Benevolent Fund

The Lancaster Foundation

LandAid Charitable Trust

The Allen Lane Foundation

The Langdale Trust

The Langley Charitable Trust

The Langtree Trust

The LankellyChase Foundation

The Lanvern Foundation

The R J Larg Family Charitable Trust

Largsmount Ltd

The Lark Trust

Laslett's (Hinton) Charity

Lauchentilly Charitable Foundation 1988

Laufer Charitable Trust

The Lauffer Family Charitable Foundation

Mrs F B Laurence Charitable Trust

The Kathleen Laurence Trust

The Law Society Charity

The Edgar E Lawley Foundation

The Herd Lawson and Muriel Lawson Charitable Trust

The Lawson Beckman Charitable Trust

The Raymond and Blanche Lawson Charitable Trust

The Carole and Geoffrey Lawson Foundation

The Mason Le Page Charitable Trust

The Leach Fourteenth Trust

The David Lean Foundation

The Leathersellers' Company Charitable Fund

The Leche Trust

The Arnold Lee Charitable Trust

The William Leech Charity

The Lord Mayor of Leeds Appeal Fund

Leeds Building Society Charitable Foundation

The Leeds Community Foundation

Leicester Charity Link

The Kennedy Leigh Charitable Trust

Morris Leigh Foundation

The Leigh Trust

Mrs Vera Leigh's Charity

The P Leigh-Bramwell Trust 'E'

The Lennox and Wyfold Foundation

The Erica Leonard Trust

The Leonard Trust

The Mark Leonard Trust

Lesley Lesley and Mutter Trust

Leukaemia Research Fund

The Leverhulme Trade Charities Trust

Lord Leverhulme's Charitable Trust

The Joseph Levy Charitable Foundation

Lewis Family Charitable Trust

The John Spedan Lewis Foundation

The Sir Edward Lewis Foundation

John Lewis Partnership General Community Fund

Lichfield Conduit Lands

Lifeline 4 Kids

The Thomas Lilley Memorial Trust

Limoges Charitable Trust

The Linbury Trust

The Lincolnshire Old Churches Trust

The Lind Trust

Lindale Educational Foundation

The Linden Charitable Trust

The Enid Linder Foundation

The Linmardon Trust

The Ruth and Stuart Lipton Charitable Trust

The Lister Charitable Trust

Frank Litchfield Charitable Trust

The Andrew and Mary Elizabeth Little Charitable Trust

The Second Joseph Aaron Littman Foundation

The George John and Sheilah Livanos Charitable Trust

Liverpool Charity and Voluntary Services

Liverpool Sailors' Home Trust

Jack Livingstone Charitable Trust

The Elaine and Angus Lloyd Charitable Trust

The Charles Lloyd Foundation

The Lloyd Fund

Lloyd's Charities Trust

The Lloyd-Everett Trust

Lloyds TSB Foundation for England and Wales

Lloyds TSB Foundation for Northern Ireland

Lloyds TSB Foundation for the Channel Islands

Llysdinam Charitable Trust

Localtrent Ltd

The Locker Foundation

The Loftus Charitable Trust

The Lolev Charitable Trust

London Catalyst

The London Law Trust

The London Marathon Charitable Trust

London Masonic Charitable Trust

The William and Katherine Longman Trust

The Loseley and Guildway Charitable Trust

The Lotus Foundation

The Lowy Mitchell Foundation

The C L Loyd Charitable Trust

LSA Charitable Trust

The Marie Helen Luen Charitable Trust

Robert Luff Foundation Ltd

Henry Lumley Charitable Trust

Lady Lumley's Educational Foundation

Paul Lunn-Rockliffe Charitable Trust

C F Lunoe Trust Fund

The Ruth and Jack Lunzer Charitable Trust

Lord and Lady Lurgan Trust

The Lyndhurst Trust

The Lynn Foundation

The Lynwood Trust

John Lyon's Charity

The Lyons Charitable Trust

The Sir Jack Lyons Charitable
Trust
The Lyras Family Charitable
Trust
Sylvanus Lyson's Charity
The M and C Trust
The M D and S Charitable
Trust
The M K Charitable Trust
The Madeline Mabey Trust
The E M MacAndrew Trust
The R S Macdonald Charitable
Trust
Macdonald-Buchanan
Charitable Trust
The Macfarlane Walker Trust
The Mackay and Brewer
Charitable Trust
The Mackintosh Foundation
The MacRobert Trust
Ian Mactaggart Trust
The Magdalen and Lasher
Charity
Magdalen Hospital Trust
The Magen Charitable Trust
Mageni Trust
The Brian Maguire Charitable
Trust
Mahavir Trust
The Makin Charitable Trust
Man Group plc Charitable
Trust
Manchester Airport Community
Trust Fund
The Manchester Guardian
Society Charitable Trust
Manchester Kids
Lord Mayor of Manchester's
Charity Appeal Trust
Mandeville Trust
The Manifold Charitable Trust
W M Mann Foundation
The Leslie and Lilian Manning
Trust
Maranatha Christian Trust
Marbeh Torah Trust
The Marchday Charitable Fund
Marchig Animal Welfare Trust
The Stella and Alexander
Margulies Charitable Trust
Mariapolis Limited
Market Harborough and The
Bowdens Charity
Michael Marks Charitable
Trust
The Ann and David Marks
Foundation
The Hilda and Samuel Marks
Foundation
J P Marland Charitable Trust
Marr-Munning Trust
The Michael Marsh Charitable
Trust
The Marsh Christian Trust
The Charlotte Marshall
Charitable Trust

The Jim Marshall Charitable
Trust
The D G Marshall of
Cambridge Trust
Marshall's Charity
Marshgate Charitable
Settlement
Sir George Martin Trust
John Martin's Charity
The Mason Porter Charitable
Trust
The Nancie Massey Charitable
Trust
The Mathew Trust
Matliwala Family Charitable
Trust
The Matt 6.3 Charitable Trust
The Violet Mauray Charitable
Trust
The Maxell Educational Trust
The Maxwell Family Foundation
Evelyn May Trust
Mayfair Charities Ltd
The Mayfield Valley Arts Trust
Mazars Charitable Trust
The McDougall Trust
The A M McGreevy No 5
Charitable Settlement
The McKenna Charitable Trust
Martin McLaren Memorial
Trust
The Helen Isabella McMorran
Charitable Foundation
D D McPhail Charitable
Settlement
The James Frederick and Ethel
Anne Measures Charity
Medical Research Council
The Medlock Charitable Trust
The Anthony and Elizabeth
Mellows Charitable
Settlement
Melodor Ltd
Melow Charitable Trust
Meningitis Trust
Menuchar Ltd
Brian Mercer Charitable Trust
The Mercers' Charitable
Foundation
The Merchant Taylors'
Company Charities Fund
The Merchant Venturers'
Charity
The Merchants' House of
Glasgow
Mercury Phoenix Trust
The Mersey Docks and
Harbour Company
Charitable Fund
Community Foundation for
Merseyside
The Zachary Merton and
George Woofindin
Convalescent Trust
The Tony Metherell Charitable
Trust

The Methodist Relief and
Development Fund
The Metropolitan Drinking
Fountain and Cattle Trough
Association
T and J Meyer Family
Foundation Limited
Gerald Micklem Charitable
Trust
Midhurst Pensions Trust
The Migraine Trust
Miles Trust for the Putney and
Roehampton Community
Millennium Stadium Charitable
Trust
The Hugh and Mary Miller
Bequest Trust
The Miller Foundation
The Millfield Trust
The Millhouses Charitable
Trust
The Millichope Foundation
The Mills Charity
The Millward Charitable Trust
The Clare Milne Trust
Milton Keynes Community
Foundation
The Edgar Milward Charity
The Peter Minet Trust
Minge's Gift and the Pooled
Trusts
The Minos Trust
Minton Charitable Trust
The Mirfield Educational
Charity
The Mirianog Trust
The Laurence Misener
Charitable Trust
The Mishcon Family Charitable
Trust
The Misselbrook Trust
The Mitchell Charitable Trust
The Esme Mitchell Trust
Keren Mitzvah Trust
The Mizpah Trust
The Mobbs Memorial Trust Ltd
The Modiano Charitable Trust
The Moette Charitable Trust
The Mole Charitable Trust
The D C Moncrieff Charitable
Trust
Monmouthshire County Council
Welsh Church Act Fund
The Montague Thompson
Coon Charitable Trust
The Colin Montgomerie
Charitable Foundation
The Monument Trust
Moody Charitable Trust
George A Moore Foundation
The Henry Moore Foundation
The Nigel Moores Family
Charitable Trust
John Moores Foundation
The Peter Moores Foundation
The Morel Charitable Trust

The Morgan Charitable Foundation

The Mr and Mrs J T Morgan Foundation

The J P Morgan Foundations

Diana and Allan Morgenthau Charitable Trust

The Oliver Morland Charitable Trust

S C and M E Morland's Charitable Trust

The Morris Charitable Trust

The Willie and Mabel Morris Charitable Trust

The Peter Morrison Charitable Foundation

G M Morrison Charitable Trust

The Stanley Morrison Charitable Trust

Moshal Charitable Trust

Vyoel Moshe Charitable Trust

The Moshulu Charitable Trust

Brian and Jill Moss Charitable Trust

The Moss Charitable Trust

The Robert and Margaret Moss Charitable Trust

Moss Family Charitable Trust

The Mount Everest Foundation

Mountbatten Festival of Music

The Mountbatten Memorial Trust

The Edwina Mountbatten Trust

The Mugdock Children's Trust

The F H Muirhead Charitable Trust

The Mulberry Trust

The Edith Murphy Foundation

Murphy-Neumann Charity Company Limited

The Mushroom Fund

The Music Sales Charitable Trust

Muslim Hands

The Mutual Trust Group

MYA Charitable Trust

The Kitty and Daniel Nabarro Charitable Trust

The Nadezhda Charitable Trust

The Willie Nagel Charitable Trust

The Naggar Charitable Trust

The Eleni Nakou Foundation

The Janet Nash Charitable Settlement

Nathan Charitable Trust

Asthma UK

The National Churches Trust

The National Manuscripts Conservation Trust

Nazareth Trust Fund

The Nchima Trust

Needham Market and Barking Welfare Charities

The Worshipful Company of Needlemakers' Charitable Fund

The Neighbourly Charitable Trust

The James Neill Trust Fund

Nemoral Ltd

Nesswall Ltd

Nestle Rowntree Employees Community Fund

Network for Social Change

The New Appeals Organisation for the City and County of Nottingham

New Court Charitable Trust

Newby Trust Limited

The Newcomen Collett Foundation

The Richard Newitt Fund

Mr and Mrs F E F Newman Charitable Trust

The Frances and Augustus Newman Foundation

Newpier Charity Ltd

Alderman Newton's Educational Foundation

The Chevras Ezras Nitzrochim Trust

Alice Noakes Memorial Charitable Trust

The Noel Buxton Trust

The Noon Foundation

The Norda Trust

Norie Charitable Trust

Normalyn Charitable Trust

The Norman Family Charitable Trust

The Duncan Norman Trust Fund

The Normanby Charitable Trust

The North British Hotel Trust

The North West Cancer Research Fund

The Northampton Municipal Church Charities

The Northampton Queen's Institute Relief in Sickness Fund

The Earl of Northampton's Charity

The Northcott Devon Foundation

The Northcott Devon Medical Foundation

The Northern Rock Foundation

The Northmoor Trust

The Northumberland Village Homes Trust

The Northumbria Historic Churches Trust

The Northwood Charitable Trust

The Norton Foundation

The Norwich Church of England Young Men's Society

The Norwich Historic Churches Trust Ltd

The Norwich Town Close Estate Charity

The Norwood and Newton Settlement

The Noswad Charity

The Notgrove Trust

The Nottingham General Dispensary

The Nottingham Gordon Memorial Trust for Boys and Girls

Nottinghamshire Community Foundation

The Nottinghamshire Historic Churches Trust

The Nottinghamshire Miners' Welfare Trust Fund

Novi Most International

The Father O'Mahoney Memorial Trust

The Sir Peter O'Sullevan Charitable Trust

The Oak Trust

The Oakdale Trust

The Oakley Charitable Trust

The Oakmoor Charitable Trust

The Odin Charitable Trust

Ogilvie Charities Deed No.2 (including the Charity of Mary Catherine Ford Smith)

The Ogle Christian Trust

Oglesby Charitable Trust

The Oikonomia Trust

The Oizer Charitable Trust

The Old Broad Street Charity Trust

The Old Enfield Charitable Trust

Old Possum's Practical Trust

The John Oldacre Foundation

The Oldham Foundation

The Olga Charitable Trust

Onaway Trust

Open Gate

The Ormsby Charitable Trust

Orrin Charitable Trust

The Ouseley Trust

The Owen Family Trust

Oxfam (GB)

The Oxfordshire Community Foundation

The P F Charitable Trust

Padwa Charitable Foundation

The Pallant Charitable Trust

The Palmer Foundation

Eleanor Palmer Trust

The Panacea Society

Panahpur Charitable Trust

Panton Trust

The Paphitis Charitable Trust

The Paragon Trust

The Park Charitable Trust

The Park House Charitable Trust

The Frank Parkinson Agricultural Trust

The Samuel and Freda Parkinson Charitable Trust

The Parthenon Trust

Arthur James Paterson Charitable Trust

The Constance Paterson Charitable Trust

Miss M E Swinton Paterson's Charitable Trust

The Patrick Charitable Trust

The Jack Patston Charitable Trust

Paycare Charity Trust

The Payne Charitable Trust

The Harry Payne Trust

The Peacock Charitable Trust

The Susanna Peake Charitable Trust

The Pears Foundation

The Pedmore Sporting Club Trust Fund

The Dowager Countess Eleanor Peel Trust

Pegasus (Stanley) Trust

Peltz Trust

The Pennycress Trust

The Performing Right Society Foundation

B E Perl Charitable Trust

The Persson Charitable Trust

The Persula Foundation

The Pestalozzi Overseas Children's Trust

The Jack Petchey Foundation

The Petplan Charitable Trust

The Philips and Rubens Charitable Trust

The Phillips Charitable Trust

The Phillips Family Charitable Trust

Philological Foundation

The David Pickford Charitable Foundation

The Bernard Piggott Trust

The Claude and Margaret Pike Charity

The Pilgrim Trust

The Cecil Pilkington Charitable Trust

The Pilkington Charities Fund

The Austin and Hope Pilkington Trust

The Sir Harry Pilkington Trust

The Col W W Pilkington Will Trusts The General Charity Fund

Miss A M Pilkington's Charitable Trust

Mrs Pilkington's Charitable Trust

The Plaisterers' Company Charitable Trust

The Platinum Trust

G S Plaut Charitable Trust Limited

Polden-Puckham Charitable Foundation

The Polehanger Trust

The Poling Charitable Trust

The George and Esme Pollitzer Charitable Settlement

The J S F Pollitzer Charitable Settlement

The Ponton House Trust

The Mayor of Poole's Appeal Fund

Edith and Ferdinand Porjes Charitable Trust

The John Porter Charitable Trust

The Porter Foundation

Porticus UK

The Portrack Charitable Trust

The J E Posnansky Charitable Trust

The Mary Potter Convent Hospital Trust

The David and Elaine Potter Foundation

The Powell Foundation

Prairie Trust

The W L Pratt Charitable Trust

Premierquote Ltd

Premishlaner Charitable Trust

The Lucy Price Relief-in-Need Charity

Sir John Priestman Charity Trust

The Primrose Trust

The Prince's Charities Foundation

Princess Anne's Charities

The Priory Foundation

Prison Service Charity Fund

The Privy Purse Charitable Trust

The Proven Family Trust

The Provincial Grand Charity of the Province of Derbyshire

PSA Peugeot Citroen Charity Trust

The Puebla Charitable Trust

The Richard and Christine Purchas Charitable Trust

The Puri Foundation

Mr and Mrs J A Pye's Charitable Settlement

Quartet Community Foundation

The Queen Anne's Gate Foundation

Queen Mary's Roehampton Trust

The Queen's Silver Jubilee Trust

Quercus Trust

The R D Crusaders Foundation

R J M Charitable Trust

R S Charitable Trust

The R V W Trust

The Monica Rabagliati Charitable Trust

Rachel Charitable Trust

The Mr and Mrs Philip Rackham Charitable Trust

Richard Radcliffe Charitable Trust

The Radcliffe Trust

The Bishop Radford Trust

The Ragdoll Foundation

The Rainford Trust

The Peggy Ramsay Foundation

The Joseph and Lena Randall Charitable Trust

The Rank Foundation

The Joseph Rank Trust

Ranworth Trust

The Fanny Rapaport Charitable Settlement

The Ratcliff Foundation

The Ratcliff Pension Charity

The Ratcliffe Charitable Trust

The E L Rathbone Charitable Trust

The Eleanor Rathbone Charitable Trust

The Sigrid Rausing Trust

The Ravensdale Trust

The Rayden Charitable Trust

The Roger Raymond Charitable Trust

The Rayne Foundation

The Rayne Trust

The John Rayner Charitable Trust

The Albert Reckitt Charitable Trust

The Sir James Reckitt Charity

The Eva Reckitt Trust Fund

The Red Arrows Trust

The Red Rose Charitable Trust

The C A Redfern Charitable Foundation

Redfern Charitable Trust

The Reed Foundation

Richard Reeve's Foundation

The Max Reinhardt Charitable Trust

Relief Fund for Romania Limited

REMEDI

The Rest Harrow Trust

Reuben Brothers Foundation

The Joan K Reynell Charitable Trust

The Nathaniel Reyner Trust Fund

The Rhododendron Trust

Daisie Rich Trust

The Sir Cliff Richard Charitable Trust

C B Richard Ellis Charitable Trust

The Clive Richards Charity

The Richmond Parish Lands Charity

Ridgesave Limited
The Ripple Effect Foundation
The Sir John Ritblat Family
    Foundation
The River Trust
Riverside Charitable Trust
    Limited
The Daniel Rivlin Charitable
    Trust
Thomas Roberts Trust
The Alex Roberts-Miller
    Foundation
The Robertson Trust
Edwin George Robinson
    Charitable Trust
Robyn Charitable Trust
The Rochester Bridge Trust
The Rock Foundation
The Rock Solid Trust
The Rofeh Trust
Richard Rogers Charitable
    Settlement
Rokach Family Charitable Trust
The Helen Roll Charitable
    Trust
The Sir James Roll Charitable
    Trust
The Roman Research Trust
Romeera Foundation
The C A Rookes Charitable
    Trust
The Rosca Trust
The Cecil Rosen Foundation
Rosetrees Trust
The Rothermere Foundation
The Rotherwick Foundation
The Rothschild Foundation
The Roughley Charitable Trust
Mrs Gladys Row Fogo
    Charitable Trust
The Rowan Charitable Trust
Rowanville Ltd
The Christopher Rowbotham
    Charitable Trust
The Rowing Foundation
The Rowlands Trust
The Joseph Rowntree
    Charitable Trust
The Joseph Rowntree
    Foundation
Joseph Rowntree Reform Trust
    Limited
Royal Artillery Charitable Fund
Royal British Legion
Royal Docks Trust (London)
Royal Masonic Trust for Girls
    and Boys
The Royal Scots Benevolent
    Society
The Alfred and Frances
    Rubens Charitable Trust
The Rubin Foundation
William Arthur Rudd Memorial
    Trust
The Rufford Maurice Laing
    Foundation

The Russell Trust
Ryklow Charitable Trust 1992
The J S and E C Rymer
    Charitable Trust
S F Foundation
S O Charitable Trust
The Michael Sacher Charitable
    Trust
The Michael Harry Sacher
    Trust
Dr Mortimer and Theresa
    Sackler Foundation
The Ruzin Sadagora Trust
The Saddlers' Company
    Charitable Fund
The Saga Charitable Trust
The Jean Sainsbury Animal
    Welfare Trust
The Alan and Babette
    Sainsbury Charitable Fund
Saint Sarkis Charity Trust
The Saintbury Trust
The Saints and Sinners Trust
The Salamander Charitable
    Trust
The Salt Foundation
The Salt Trust
The Salters' Charities
The Andrew Salvesen
    Charitable Trust
The Sammermar Trust
Basil Samuel Charitable Trust
Coral Samuel Charitable Trust
The Hon. M J Samuel
    Charitable Trust
The Peter Samuel Charitable
    Trust
The Camilla Samuel Fund
The Samworth Foundation
The Sandra Charitable Trust
Santander UK Foundation
    Limited
Jimmy Savile Charitable Trust
The Scarfe Charitable Trust
The Schapira Charitable Trust
The Annie Schiff Charitable
    Trust
The Schmidt-Bodner Charitable
    Trust
The R H Scholes Charitable
    Trust
The Schreib Trust
The Schreiber Charitable Trust
Schroder Charity Trust
Scott (Eredine) Charitable
    Trust
The Scott Bader
    Commonwealth Ltd
The Francis C Scott Charitable
    Trust
The Frieda Scott Charitable
    Trust
Sir Samuel Scott of Yews
    Trust
The Sir James and Lady Scott
    Trust

The Scott Trust Foundation
The Storrow Scott Will Trust
The Scottish Arts Council
Scottish Churches' Community
    Trust
Scottish Coal Industry Special
    Welfare Fund
The Scottish Community
    Foundation
The Scottish International
    Education Trust
The Scouloudi Foundation
Seafarers UK (King George's
    Fund for Sailors)
Seamen's Hospital Society
The Searchlight Electric
    Charitable Trust
The Searle Charitable Trust
The Helene Sebba Charitable
    Trust
The Samuel Sebba Charitable
    Trust
The Seedfield Trust
Sellata Ltd
SEM Charitable Trust
The Ayrton Senna Foundation
The Seven Fifty Trust
The Severn Trent Water
    Charitable Trust Fund
SFIA Educational Trust Limited
The Cyril Shack Trust
Peter Shalson Family
    Charitable Trust
The Jean Shanks Foundation
The Shanti Charitable Trust
ShareGift (The Orr Mackintosh
    Foundation)
The Linley Shaw Foundation
The Sheepdrove Trust
The Sheffield and District
    Hospital Services
    Charitable Fund
The Sheldon Trust
The P and D Shepherd
    Charitable Trust
The Sylvia and Colin Shepherd
    Charitable Trust
The Archie Sherman Cardiff
    Foundation
The Archie Sherman Charitable
    Trust
The R C Sherriff Trust
The Shetland Charitable Trust
SHINE (Support and Help in
    Education)
The Barnett and Sylvia Shine
    No 2 Charitable Trust
The Bassil Shippam and
    Alsford Trust
The Shipwrights' Company
    Charitable Fund
The Shirley Foundation
Shlomo Memorial Fund Limited
The J A Shone Memorial Trust
The Charles Shorto Charitable
    Trust

The Barbara A Shuttleworth
　Memorial Trust
The Mary Elizabeth Siebel
　Charity
David and Jennifer Sieff
　Charitable Trust
The Julius Silman Charitable
　Trust
The Leslie Silver Charitable
　Trust
The Simpson Education and
　Conservation Trust
The Simpson Foundation
The Huntly and Margery
　Sinclair Charitable Trust
Sino-British Fellowship Trust
The Skelton Bounty
The Charles Skey Charitable
　Trust
Skipton Building Society
　Charitable Foundation
The John Slater Foundation
Rita and David Slowe
　Charitable Trust
Ruth Smart Foundation
The SMB Charitable Trust
The Mrs Smith and Mount
　Trust
The N Smith Charitable
　Settlement
The Amanda Smith Charitable
　Trust
The E H Smith Charitable Trust
The Smith Charitable Trust
The Henry Smith Charity
The Leslie Smith Foundation
The Martin Smith Foundation
Stanley Smith General
　Charitable Trust
The Stanley Smith UK
　Horticultural Trust
Philip Smith's Charitable Trust
The R C Snelling Charitable
　Trust
The Snowball Trust
The Sobell Foundation
Solev Co Ltd
Solihull Community Foundation
The Solo Charitable
　Settlement
Dr Richard Solomon's
　Charitable Trust
Songdale Ltd
The E C Sosnow Charitable
　Trust
The Souter Charitable Trust
The South Square Trust
The Stephen R and Philippa H
　Southall Charitable Trust
The W F Southall Trust
The Southdown Trust
R H Southern Trust
The Southover Manor General
　Education Trust
The Southwold Trust

The Sovereign Health Care
　Charitable Trust
Spar Charitable Fund
Sparks Charity (Sport Aiding
　Medical Research For Kids)
Sparquote Limited
The Spear Charitable Trust
Spears-Stutz Charitable Trust
The Jessie Spencer Trust
The Ralph and Irma Sperring
　Charity
The Moss Spiro Will Charitable
　Foundation
W W Spooner Charitable Trust
Stanley Spooner Deceased
　Charitable Trust
The Spoore, Merry and Rixman
　Foundation
The Spring Harvest Charitable
　Trust
Rosalyn and Nicholas Springer
　Charitable Trust
Springfields Employees'
　Medical Research and
　Charity Trust Fund
Springrule Ltd
The Spurrell Charitable Trust
The Geoff and Fiona Squire
　Foundation
St Andrew Animal Fund
St Andrew's Conservation
　Trust
St Francis's Leprosy Guild
St Gabriel's Trust
St Hilda's Trust
St James' Trust Settlement
St James's Place Foundation
Sir Walter St John's
　Educational Charity
St Katharine and Shadwell
　Trust
St Mark's Overseas Aid Trust
　(SMOAT)
St Michael's and All Saints'
　Charities
The Late St Patrick White
　Charitable Trust
St Teilo's Trust
The Stafford Trust
Miss Doreen Stanford Trust
The Stanley Foundation Ltd
The Stanton Ballard Charitable
　Trust
The Staples Trust
The Star Charitable Trust
The Starfish Trust
The Peter Stebbings Memorial
　Charity
The Steel Charitable Trust
The Cyril and Betty Stein
　Charitable Trust
The Steinberg Family
　Charitable Trust
The Hugh Stenhouse
　Foundation
C E K Stern Charitable Trust

The Sigmund Sternberg
　Charitable Foundation
Stervon Ltd
The Stevenage Community
　Trust
The June Stevens Foundation
Stevenson Family's Charitable
　Trust
The Steventon Allotments and
　Relief-in-Need Charity
The Stewards' Charitable Trust
The Stewards' Company
　Limited
The Sir Halley Stewart Trust
The Stobart Newlands
　Charitable Trust
The Edward Stocks-Massey
　Bequest Fund
The Stokenchurch Educational
　Charity
The Stoller Charitable Trust
The M J C Stone Charitable
　Trust
The Stone-Mallabar Charitable
　Foundation
The Samuel Storey Family
　Charitable Trust
Peter Stormonth Darling
　Charitable Trust
Peter Storrs Trust
The Strangward Trust
The Strasser Foundation
Stratford upon Avon Town
　Trust
Strathclyde Police Benevolent
　Fund
The W O Street Charitable
　Foundation
The A B Strom and R Strom
　Charitable Trust
The Sudborough Foundation
Sueberry Ltd
The Suffolk Foundation
The Suffolk Historic Churches
　Trust
The Alan Sugar Foundation
The Summerfield Charitable
　Trust
The Bernard Sunley Charitable
　Foundation
The Surrey Historic Buildings
　Trust Ltd
The Sussex Historic Churches
　Trust
The Adrienne and Leslie
　Sussman Charitable Trust
The Sutasoma Trust
Sutton Coldfield Municipal
　Charities
The Sutton Nursing
　Association
The Sutton Trust
Swan Mountain Trust
The Swan Trust
Swansea and Brecon Diocesan
　Board of Finance Limited

The John Swire (1989) Charitable Trust
The Swire Charitable Trust
The Hugh and Ruby Sykes Charitable Trust
The Charles and Elsie Sykes Trust
The Sylvanus Charitable Trust
The Stella Symons Charitable Trust
The Tabeel Trust
The Tajtelbaum Charitable Trust
The Talbot Trusts
The Talbot Village Trust
Tallow Chandlers Benevolent Fund
Talteg Ltd
The Tangent Charitable Trust
The Lady Tangye Charitable Trust
The David Tannen Charitable Trust
The Tanner Trust
The Lili Tapper Charitable Foundation
The Mrs A Lacy Tate Trust
The Tay Charitable Trust
C B and H H Taylor 1984 Trust
Humphrey Richardson Taylor Charitable Trust
The A R Taylor Charitable Trust
The Connie and Albert Taylor Charitable Trust
The Cyril Taylor Charitable Trust
A P Taylor Trust
Rosanna Taylor's 1987 Charity Trust
Tearfund
The Tedworth Charitable Trust
Tees Valley Community Foundation
Tegham Limited
The Templeton Goodwill Trust
Tesco Charity Trust
Thackray Medical Research Trust
Thames Community Foundation
The Thames Wharf Charity
The Thistle Trust
The Loke Wan Tho Memorial Foundation
The David Thomas Charitable Trust
The Thomas Wall Trust
The Arthur and Margaret Thompson Charitable Trust
The Maurice and Vivien Thompson Charitable Trust
The Thompson Family Charitable Trust
The Len Thomson Charitable Trust
The Sue Thomson Foundation

The Sir Jules Thorn Charitable Trust
The Thornton Foundation
The Thornton Trust
The Three Guineas Trust
The Three Oaks Trust
The Thriplow Charitable Trust
Mrs R P Tindall's Charitable Trust
The Tinsley Foundation
The Tisbury Telegraph Trust
TJH Foundation
The Tolkien Trust
Tollemache (Buckminster) Charitable Trust
Tomchei Torah Charitable Trust
The Tompkins Foundation
The Torah Temimah Trust
Toras Chesed (London) Trust
The Tory Family Foundation
Tottenham Grammar School Foundation
The Tower Hill Trust
The Towry Law Charitable Trust
The Toy Trust
The Mayor of Trafford's Charity Fund
Annie Tranmer Charitable Trust
Anthony Travis Charitable Trust
The Constance Travis Charitable Trust
The Treeside Trust
The Tresillian Trust
The Triangle Trust (1949) Fund
The True Colours Trust
Truedene Co. Ltd
The Truemark Trust
Truemart Limited
Trumros Limited
Trust for London
Trust Sixty Three
The Trusthouse Charitable Foundation
The Tubney Charitable Trust
Tudor Rose Ltd
The Tudor Trust
The Tufton Charitable Trust
The R D Turner Charitable Trust
The Douglas Turner Trust
The Florence Turner Trust
Miss S M Tutton Charitable Trust
The TUUT Charitable Trust
Community Foundation Serving Tyne and Wear and Northumberland
Trustees of Tzedakah
UKI Charitable Foundation
Ulster Garden Villages Ltd
Ultach Trust
Ulting Overseas Trust
The Ulverscroft Foundation
Ulverston Town Lands Charity
The Underwood Trust

The Union of Orthodox Hebrew Congregation
The Unite Foundation (The Amicus Foundation)
The United Society for the Propagation of the Gospel
United Trusts
The David Uri Memorial Trust
Uxbridge United Welfare Trust
'v'
Vale of Glamorgan – Welsh Church Fund
The Valentine Charitable Trust
The Albert Van Den Bergh Charitable Trust
John and Lucille van Geest Foundation
The Van Neste Foundation
Mrs Maud Van Norden's Charitable Foundation
The Vandervell Foundation
The Vardy Foundation
The Variety Club Children's Charity
Veneziana Fund
The Verdon-Smith Family Charitable Settlement
Roger Vere Foundation
Victoria Homes Trust
Viking Cares (For the Kids)
The Nigel Vinson Charitable Trust
The William and Ellen Vinten Trust
The Vintners' Company Charitable Foundation
Vintners' Gifts Charity
Vision Charity
Vivdale Ltd
The Viznitz Foundation
Wade's Charity
The Scurrah Wainwright Charity
The Wakefield and Tetley Trust
Wakeham Trust
The Community Foundation in Wales
Wales Council for Voluntary Action
Robert and Felicity Waley-Cohen Charitable Trust
The Walker Trust
Wallace and Gromit's Children's Foundation
Wallington Missionary Mart and Auctions
The F J Wallis Charitable Settlement
War on Want
Sir Siegmund Warburg's Voluntary Settlement
The Ward Blenkinsop Trust
The George Ward Charitable Trust
The Barbara Ward Children's Foundation
The John Warren Foundation

G R Waters Charitable Trust
2000
The Waterways Trust
The Wates Foundation
Blyth Watson Charitable Trust
The Howard Watson Symington
Memorial Charity
John Watson's Trust
Weatherley Charitable Trust
The Weavers' Company
Benevolent Fund
The David Webster Charitable
Trust
The William Webster
Charitable Trust
The Weinberg Foundation
The Weinstein Foundation
The Weinstock Fund
The Barbara Welby Trust
The Weldon UK Charitable
Trust
The Wellcome Trust
Welsh Church Fund Dyfed
area (Carmarthenshire,
Ceredigion and
Pembrokeshire)
The Welton Foundation
The Wessex Youth Trust
The West Derby Wastelands
Charity
West London Synagogue
Charitable Fund
The West Yorkshire Police
Community Fund
Mrs S K West's Charitable
Trust
The Westcroft Trust
The Westminster Foundation
The Garfield Weston
Foundation
The Barbara Whatmore
Charitable Trust
The Whitaker Charitable Trust
The Colonel W H Whitbread
Charitable Trust
The Simon Whitbread
Charitable Trust
The Melanie White Foundation
Limited
White Rose Children's Aid
International Charity
The Whitecourt Charitable
Trust
A H and B C Whiteley
Charitable Trust
The Norman Whiteley Trust
The Whitley Animal Protection
Trust
The Whittlesey Charity
The Lionel Wigram Memorial
Trust
The Richard Wilcox Welfare
Charity
The Felicity Wilde Charitable
Trust

The Wilkinson Charitable
Foundation
The Will Charitable Trust
The Kay Williams Charitable
Foundation
The Williams Charitable Trust
The Williams Family Charitable
Trust
Williams Serendipity Trust
The H D H Wills 1965
Charitable Trust
Dame Violet Wills Charitable
Trust
The Dame Violet Wills Will
Trust
The Wilmcote Charitrust
Sumner Wilson Charitable
Trust
David Wilson Foundation
The Wilson Foundation
J and J R Wilson Trust
The Community Foundation for
Wiltshire and Swindon
The Benjamin Winegarten
Charitable Trust
The Harold Hyam Wingate
Foundation
The Francis Winham
Foundation
Anona Winn Charitable Trust
Wirral Mayor's Charity
The Witzenfeld Foundation
The Michael and Anna Wix
Charitable Trust
The Wixamtree Trust
The Woburn 1986 Charitable
Trust
The Maurice Wohl Charitable
Foundation
The Charles Wolfson
Charitable Trust
Women Caring Trust
The James Wood Bequest
Fund
The Wood Family Trust
The Woodcock Charitable Trust
Woodlands Foundation Limited
Woodlands Green Ltd
Woodlands Trust
The Woodroffe Benton
Foundation
The Geoffrey Woods Charitable
Foundation
The Woodward Charitable
Trust
The A and R Woolf Charitable
Trust
The Woolnoth Society
Charitable Trust
Worcester Municipal Charities
The Worcestershire and
Dudley Historic Churches
Trust
The Fred and Della Worms
Charitable Trust
The Worwin UK Foundation

The Wragge and Co. Charitable
Trust
The Diana Edgson Wright
Charitable Trust
The Matthews Wrightson
Charity Trust
Miss E B Wrightson's
Charitable Settlement
Wychdale Ltd
Wychville Ltd
The Wyndham Charitable Trust
The Wyseliot Charitable Trust
The Xerox (UK) Trust
Yankov Charitable Trust
The Yapp Charitable Trust
The Yardley Great Trust
The Dennis Alan Yardy
Charitable Trust
The W Wing Yip and Brothers
Foundation
York and North Yorkshire
Community Foundation
The York Children's Trust
Yorkshire Agricultural Society
Yorkshire Building Society
Charitable Foundation
The South Yorkshire
Community Foundation
The Yorkshire Dales
Millennium Trust
The John Young Charitable
Settlement
The William Allen Young
Charitable Trust
The John K Young Endowment
Fund
The Young Foundation
Youth Music
Elizabeth and Prince Zaiger
Trust
Zephyr Charitable Trust
The Marjorie and Arnold Ziff
Charitable Foundation
Stephen Zimmerman
Charitable Trust
The Zochonis Charitable Trust
Zurich Community Trust (UK)
Limited

■ Strategic funding

The 1989 Willan Charitable
Trust
The 29th May 1961 Charitable
Trust
The A B Charitable Trust
Aberbrothock Charitable Trust
The Aberdeen Endowments
Trust
The Aberdeenshire Educational
Trust Scheme
Brian Abrams Charitable Trust
Eric Abrams Charitable Trust
The Acacia Charitable Trust
Achiezer Association Ltd

Achisomoch Aid Company
  Limited
The ACT Foundation
Action Medical Research
The Company of Actuaries'
  Charitable Trust Fund
The Sylvia Adams Charitable
  Trust
The Adamson Trust
The Victor Adda Foundation
Adenfirst Ltd
The Adint Charitable Trust
The Adnams Charity
AF Trust Company
Age Concern Scotland Grants
Aid to the Church in Need (UK)
The AIM Foundation
The Green and Lilian F M
  Ainsworth and Family
  Benevolent Fund
The Sylvia Aitken Charitable
  Trust
The Ajahma Charitable Trust
The Alabaster Trust
Alba Charitable Trust
The Alborada Trust
D G Albright Charitable Trust
The Alchemy Foundation
Alcohol Education and
  Research Council
Aldgate and All Hallows'
  Barking Exhibition
  Foundation
The Aldgate Freedom
  Foundation
Alexandra Rose Charities
The Alexis Trust
All Saints Educational Trust
Allchurches Trust Ltd
The H B Allen Charitable Trust
The Rita Allen Charitable Trust
The Alliance Family Foundation
Angus Allnatt Charitable
  Foundation
The Pat Allsop Charitable Trust
The Almond Trust
Almondsbury Charity
The Altajir Trust
Altamont Ltd
Alvor Charitable Trust
AM Charitable Trust
Ambika Paul Foundation
The Ammco Trust
Sir John and Lady Amory's
  Charitable Trust
Viscount Amory's Charitable
  Trust
The Ampelos Trust
The AMW Charitable Trust
The Anchor Foundation
The Andrew Anderson Trust
Andor Charitable Trust
The André Christian Trust
Anglo American Group
  Foundation

Anguish's Educational
  Foundation
The Animal Defence Trust
The Eric Anker-Petersen
  Charity
The Annandale Charitable
  Trust
The Anson Charitable Trust
The Apax Foundation
Ambrose and Ann Appelbe
  Trust
The Appletree Trust
The John Apthorp Charitable
  Trust
The Milly Apthorp Charitable
  Trust
The Arbib Foundation
The Archbishop of
  Canterbury's Charitable
  Trust
Archbishop of Wales' Fund for
  Children
The John M Archer Charitable
  Trust
The Archer Trust
The Ardwick Trust
The Argentarius Foundation
The Argus Appeal
Armenian General Benevolent
  Union London Trust
The Armenian Relief Society of
  Great Britain Trust
The Armourers' and Brasiers'
  Gauntlet Trust
The Army Benevolent Fund
The Arnold Foundation
Arsenal Charitable Trust
The Artemis Charitable Trust
The Arts and Entertainment
  Charitable Trust
Arts Council England
The Arts Council of Northern
  Ireland
The Arts Council of Wales
The Ove Arup Foundation
The AS Charitable Trust
Ashburnham Thanksgiving
  Trust
A J H Ashby Will Trust
The Ashden Trust
The Ashendene Trust
The Laura Ashley Foundation
The Ian Askew Charitable Trust
The Associated Country
  Women of the World
  (ACWW)
The Association of Colleges
  Charitable Trust
Astellas European Foundation
AstonMansfield Charitable
  Trust
The Astor Foundation
The Astor of Hever Trust
The Aurelius Charitable Trust
The Avenue Charitable Trust
The John Avins Trustees

The Avon and Somerset Police
  Community Trust
AW Charitable Trust
The Aylesford Family
  Charitable Trust
The BAA Communities Trust
Harry Bacon Foundation
The BACTA Charitable Trust
The Bagri Foundation
Veta Bailey Charitable Trust
The Austin Bailey Trust
The Baily Thomas Charitable
  Fund
The Baird Trust
The Baker Charitable Trust
The Roy and Pixie Baker
  Charitable Trust
The Balcombe Charitable Trust
The Balint Family Charitable
  Trusts
The Albert Casanova Ballard
  Deceased Trust
The Ballinger Charitable Trust
Balmain Charitable Trust
The Balmore Trust
The Balney Charitable Trust
The Baltic Charitable Fund
The Bamford Charitable
  Foundation
The Banbury Charities
William P Bancroft (No 2)
  Charitable Trust and
  Jenepher Gillett Trust
The Band Trust
The Barbers' Company General
  Charities
The Barbour Trust
The Barcapel Foundation
Barchester Healthcare
  Foundation
David and Frederick Barclay
  Foundation
The Baring Foundation
Peter Barker-Mill Memorial
  Charity
Barleycorn Trust
The Barnabas Trust
Lord Barnby's Foundation
Barnes Workhouse Fund
The Barnsbury Charitable Trust
The Barnstaple Bridge Trust
The Barnwood House Trust
The Misses Barrie Charitable
  Trust
Barrington Family Charitable
  Trust
The Charity of William Barrow
Stephen J Barry Charitable
  Trust
The Bartlett Taylor Charitable
  Trust
The Paul Bassham Charitable
  Trust
The Batchworth Trust
Bay Charitable Trust
The Bay Tree Charitable Trust

D H and L H Baylin Charitable
Trust

The Louis Baylis (Maidenhead
Advertiser) Charitable Trust

BBC Children in Need

B-CH 1971 Charitable Trust

The Beacon Trust

Bear Mordechai Ltd

The Bearder Charity

The James Beattie Charitable
Trust

The Beaufort House Trust
Limited

Beauland Ltd

The Beaverbrook Foundation

The Beccles Town Lands
Charity

The Becker Family Charitable
Trust

The Becketts and Sargeants
Educational Foundation

The John Beckwith Charitable
Trust

The Peter Beckwith Charitable
Trust

The Bedford Charity (The
Harpur Trust)

The Bedfordshire and Luton
Community Foundation

The David and Ruth Behrend
Fund

The Beit Trust

The Bellahouston Bequest
Fund

Bellasis Trust

The Bellhouse Foundation

The Bellinger Donnay Trust

Belljoe Tzedoko Ltd

The Benfield Motors Charitable
Trust

The Benham Charitable
Settlement

Maurice and Jacqueline
Bennett Charitable Trust

Michael and Leslie Bennett
Charitable Trust

The Gerald Bentall Charitable
Trust

Bergqvist Charitable Trust

The Ruth Berkowitz Charitable
Trust

The Berkshire Community
Foundation

The Bestway Foundation

The Betterware Foundation

Thomas Betton's Charity for
Pensions and Relief-in-Need

BHST

The Mason Bibby 1981 Trust

BibleLands

The Bideford Bridge Trust

The Big Lottery Fund

The Billmeir Charitable Trust

The Bingham Trust

The Bintaub Charitable Trust

The Birmingham Community
Foundation

The Birmingham District
Nursing Charitable Trust

The Birmingham Hospital
Saturday Fund Medical
Charity and Welfare Trust

Birmingham International
Airport Community Trust

The Lord Mayor of
Birmingham's Charity

Birthday House Trust

The Bisgood Charitable Trust
(registered as Miss Jeanne
Bisgood's Charitable Trust)

The Michael Bishop
Foundation

The Bishop's Development
Fund

The Sydney Black Charitable
Trust

The Bertie Black Foundation

Sir Alec Black's Charity

Isabel Blackman Foundation

The BlackRock (UK) Charitable
Trust

The Herbert and Peter
Blagrave Charitable Trust

The Blair Foundation

Blakes Benevolent Trust

The Blanchminster Trust

The Sir Victor Blank Charitable
Settlement

Blatchington Court Trust

The Neville and Elaine Blond
Charitable Trust

The Blueberry Charitable Trust

The Bluston Charitable
Settlement

Enid Blyton Trust for Children

The Nicholas Boas Charitable
Trust

The Body Shop Foundation

The Boltons Trust

The Bonamy Charitable Trust

The John and Celia Bonham
Christie Charitable Trust

The Charlotte Bonham-Carter
Charitable Trust

Bonhomie United Charity
Society

BOOST Charitable Trust

The Booth Charities

The Boots Charitable Trust

The Bordon and Liphook
Charity

Salo Bordon Charitable Trust

The Oliver Borthwick Memorial
Trust

The Boshier-Hinton Foundation

The Bothwell Charitable Trust

H E and E L Botteley
Charitable Trust

The Harry Bottom Charitable
Trust

P G and N J Boulton Trust

The A H and E Boulton Trust

Sir Clive Bourne Family Trust

The Anthony Bourne
Foundation

Bourneheights Limited

Community Foundation for
Bournemouth, Dorset and
Poole

The Bower Trust

The Bowerman Charitable
Trust

John and Susan Bowers Fund

The Bowland Charitable Trust

The William Brake Charitable
Trust

The Tony Bramall Charitable
Trust

The Bransford Trust

The Brewers' Company
General Charitable Trust

The Harold and Alice Bridges
Charity

Briggs Animal Welfare Trust

The Brighton District Nursing
Association Trust

Bristol Archdeaconry Charity

The Bristol Charities

John Bristow and Thomas
Mason Trust

Britannia Foundation

The British Council for
Prevention of Blindness

The British Dietetic
Association General and
Education Trust Fund

The British Gas (Scottish Gas)
Energy Trust

British Heart Foundation

British Humane Association

British Institute at Ankara

British Ornithologists' Union

British Record Industry Trust

The Britto Foundation

The J and M Britton Charitable
Trust

The Charles and Edna
Broadhurst Charitable Trust

The Bromley Trust

The Roger Brooke Charitable
Trust

The David Brooke Charity

The Rory and Elizabeth Brooks
Foundation

Joseph Brough Charitable
Trust

The Swinfen Broun Charitable
Trust

Mrs E E Brown Charitable
Settlement

Bill Brown's Charitable
Settlement

R S Brownless Charitable
Trust

Brownsword Charitable
Foundation

T B H Brunner's Charitable
Settlement
Brushmill Ltd
The Bryant Trust
Buckingham Trust
The Buckinghamshire
Foundation
The Buckinghamshire Masonic
Centenary Fund
Buckland Charitable Trust
The Rosemary Bugden
Charitable Trust
The Bulldog Trust Limited
The E F Bulmer Benevolent
Fund
The Burden Trust
Burdens Charitable Foundation
The Burdett Trust for Nursing
The Clara E Burgess Charity
The Burry Charitable Trust
The Audrey and Stanley Burton
1960 Charitable Trust
The Arnold Burton 1998
Charitable Trust
The Burton Breweries
Charitable Trust
The Geoffrey Burton Charitable
Trust
Consolidated Charity of Burton
upon Trent
Butchers' Company General
Charities
The Bill Butlin Charity Trust
Ann Byrne Charitable Trust
C and F Charitable Trust
C J Cadbury Charitable Trust
Edward Cadbury Charitable
Trust
Henry T and Lucy B Cadbury
Charitable Trust
P H G Cadbury Charitable
Trust
The Christopher Cadbury
Charitable Trust
The G W Cadbury Charitable
Trust
The Richard Cadbury
Charitable Trust
The William A Cadbury
Charitable Trust
The Cadbury Foundation
The Edward and Dorothy
Cadbury Trust
The George Cadbury Trust
The Barrow Cadbury Trust and
the Barrow Cadbury Fund
The Cadogan Charity
CAFOD
The Callander Charitable Trust
Calleva Foundation
The Calpe Trust
Calypso Browning Trust
The Cambridgeshire
Community Foundation
The Camelia Trust
The Campden Charities

The Canning Trust
M R Cannon 1998 Charitable
Trust
H and L Cantor Trust
Capital Community Foundation
Cardy Beaver Foundation
The Carew Pole Charitable
Trust
The D W T Cargill Fund
Caring for Kids (Radio Tay)
Carlee Ltd
The Carlton House Charitable
Trust
The Worshipful Company of
Carmen Benevolent Trust
The Carnegie Dunfermline
Trust
The Carnegie Trust for the
Universities of Scotland
The Carpenter Charitable Trust
The Carpenters' Company
Charitable Trust
The Carrington Charitable
Trust
The Carron Charitable
Settlement
The Leslie Mary Carter
Charitable Trust
The Carvill Trust
The Casey Trust
Cash for Kids Radio Clyde
Sir John Cass's Foundation
The Elizabeth Casson Trust
The Castang Foundation
The Catalyst Charitable Trust
The Catholic Charitable Trust
Catholic Foreign Missions
The Catholic Trust for England
and Wales
The Cattanach Charitable Trust
The Joseph and Annie Cattle
Trust
The Thomas Sivewright Catto
Charitable Settlement
The Wilfrid and Constance
Cave Foundation
The Cayo Foundation
Elizabeth Cayzer Charitable
Trust
The B G S Cayzer Charitable
Trust
The Cazenove Charitable Trust
Celtic Charity Fund
The Cemlyn-Jones Trust
CfBT Education Trust
The CH (1980) Charitable
Trust
R E Chadwick Charitable Trust
The Amelia Chadwick Trust
The Pamela Champion
Foundation
The Chapman Charitable Trust
John William Chapman's
Charitable Trust
The Charities Advisory Trust
Charitworth Limited

The Charter 600 Charity
The Worshipful Company of
Chartered Accountants
General Charitable Trust
The Chasah Trust
Chasdei Tovim Me'oros
The Chelsea Building Society
Charitable Foundation
The Chelsea Square 1994
Trust
The Cheruby Trust
The Cheshire Provincial Fund
of Benevolence
The Chetwode Foundation
The Malcolm Chick Charity
Child Growth Foundation
Children's Liver Disease
Foundation
Childs Charitable Trust
The Childwick Trust
The Chippenham Borough
Lands Charity
The Chipping Sodbury Town
Lands Charity
CHK Charities Limited
The Chownes Foundation
The Chrimes Family Charitable
Trust
The Christabella Charitable
Trust
Christadelphian Samaritan
Fund
Christian Aid
Christian Response to Eastern
Europe
The Church and Community
Fund
The Church Burgesses
Educational Foundation
Church Burgesses Trust
Church Lands and John
Johnson's Estate Charities
Church of Ireland Priorities
Fund
The Church Urban Fund
City and County of Swansea
Welsh Church Act Fund
The City Bridge Trust
The City Educational Trust
Fund
The City Parochial Foundation
CLA Charitable Trust
Stephen Clark 1957
Charitable Trust
J A Clark Charitable Trust
The Hilda and Alice Clark
Charitable Trust
The Roger and Sarah Bancroft
Clark Charitable Trust
The Clarke Charitable
Settlement
The Cleary Foundation
The Cleopatra Trust
Lord Clinton's Charitable Trust
The Clore Duffield Foundation

Miss V L Clore's 1967 Charitable Trust

Closehelm Ltd

The Clothworkers' Foundation

Richard Cloudesley's Charity

The Clover Trust

The Robert Clutterbuck Charitable Trust

Clydpride Ltd

The Coalfields Regeneration Trust

The John Coates Charitable Trust

Coats Foundation Trust

The Cobalt Trust

The Cobtree Charity Trust Ltd

The Denise Cohen Charitable Trust

The Vivienne and Samuel Cohen Charitable Trust

The R and S Cohen Fondation

The John S Cohen Foundation

The Colchester Catalyst Charity

John Coldman Charitable Trust

The Cole Charitable Trust

The Colefax Charitable Trust

The John and Freda Coleman Charitable Trust

The Bernard Coleman Charitable Trust

The George Henry Collins Charity

The E Alec Colman Charitable Fund Ltd

The Sir Jeremiah Colman Gift Trust

Col-Reno Ltd

The Colt Foundation

The Coltstaple Trust

Colwinston Charitable Trust

Colyer-Fergusson Charitable Trust

Comic Relief

The Comino Foundation

Community Foundation for Calderdale

The Community Foundation for Greater Manchester

The Community Foundation for Northern Ireland

The Company of Tobacco Pipe Makers' and Tobacco Blenders' Benevolent Fund

The Compton Charitable Trust

The Congleton Inclosure Trust

The Conscience Trust

The Conservation Foundation

The Consolidated Charities for the Infirm Merchant Taylors' Company

The Construction Industry Trust for Youth

The Cook and Wolstenholme Charitable Trust

Gordon Cook Foundation

The Ernest Cook Trust

The Cooks Charity

The Catherine Cookson Charitable Trust

The Cookson Charitable Trust

Harold and Daphne Cooper Charitable Trust

Mabel Cooper Charity

The Alice Ellen Cooper Dean Charitable Foundation

The Co-operative Foundation

The Marjorie Coote Animal Charity Trust

The Marjorie Coote Old People's Charity

The Helen Jean Cope Trust

The J Reginald Corah Foundation Fund

The Gershon Coren Charitable Foundation

The Corinthian Trust

Edwin Cornforth 1983 Charity Trust

The Evan Cornish Foundation

The Cornwell Charitable Trust

The Sidney and Elizabeth Corob Charitable Trust

The Corona Charitable Trust

The Costa Family Charitable Trust

The Cotton Industry War Memorial Trust

The Cotton Trust

County Durham Foundation

The Augustine Courtauld Trust

Coutts Charitable Trust

The General Charities of the City of Coventry

Coventry Building Society Charitable Foundation

The John Cowan Foundation

Cowley Charitable Foundation

The Sir William Coxen Trust Fund

The Lord Cozens-Hardy Trust

The Craignish Trust

The Craps Charitable Trust

Michael Crawford Children's Charity

The Cray Trust

The Crescent Trust

Criffel Charitable Trust

Cripplegate Foundation

The Violet and Milo Cripps Charitable Trust

The Cromarty Trust

The Harry Crook Foundation

The Cross Trust

The Cross Trust

The Croydon Relief in Need Charities

The Mayor of Croydon's Charity Fund

Cruden Foundation Ltd

The Ronald Cruickshanks' Foundation

Cuby Charitable Trust

The Culra Charitable Trust

The Cumber Family Charitable Trust

Cumberland Building Society Charitable Foundation

Cumbria Community Foundation

The D J H Currie Memorial Trust

The Dennis Curry Charitable Trust

The Raymond Curtis Charitable Trust

The Manny Cussins Foundation

The Cutler Trust (the Worshipful Company of Makers of Playing Cards)

The Cwmbran Trust

Itzchok Meyer Cymerman Trust Ltd

The D'Oyly Carte Charitable Trust

The Roald Dahl Foundation

The Daily Prayer Union Charitable Trust Ltd

The Daisy Trust

The Daiwa Anglo-Japanese Foundation

Oizer Dalim Trust

The Dr and Mrs A Darlington Charitable Trust

Baron Davenport's Charity

The Davidson (Nairn) Charitable Trust

Davidson Charitable Trust

The Alderman Joe Davidson Memorial Trust

Michael Davies Charitable Settlement

The Gwendoline and Margaret Davies Charity

The Wilfrid Bruce Davis Charitable Trust

Davis-Rubens Charitable Trust

The Dawe Charitable Trust

The De Clermont Charitable Company Ltd

Peter De Haan Charitable Trust

The De Laszlo Foundation

The Leopold De Rothschild Charitable Trust

The Deakin Charitable Trust

William Dean Countryside and Educational Trust

The Debmar Benevolent Trust

The Delfont Foundation

The Dellal Foundation

The Delves Charitable Trust

The Demigryphon Trust

The Denman Charitable Trust

The Denton Charitable Trust

The Denton Wilde Sapte Charitable Trust

The Earl of Derby's Charitable Trust

Derbyshire Community Foundation

The J N Derbyshire Trust

Devon Community Foundation

The Devon Educational Trust

The Duke of Devonshire's Charitable Trust

The Sandy Dewhirst Charitable Trust

DG Charitable Settlement

The Laduma Dhamecha Charitable Trust

Alan and Sheila Diamond Charitable Trust

The Diana, Princess of Wales Memorial Fund

The Dibden Allotments Charity

The Dickon Trust

The Digbeth Trust

The Dinwoodie Settlement

Dischma Charitable Trust

The DLA Piper Charitable Trust

Louise Dobson Charitable Trust

The Derek and Eileen Dodgson Foundation

The Dollond Charitable Trust

Domepride Ltd

The Dorcas Trust

The Dorema Charitable Trust

Double 'O' Charity Ltd

The Doughty Charity Trust

The R M Douglas Charitable Trust

The Drapers' Charitable Fund

Dromintee Trust

The Dugdale Charitable Trust

The Duis Charitable Trust

The Dulverton Trust

The P B Dumbell Charitable Trust

The Dumbreck Charity

Dunard Fund

Ronald Duncan Literary Foundation

The Dunhill Medical Trust

The Houghton Dunn Charitable Trust

The Dunn Family Charitable Trust

The W E Dunn Trust

Dushinsky Trust Ltd

Mildred Duveen Charitable Trust

The Dwek Family Charitable Trust

The Dyers' Company Charitable Trust

EAGA Partnership Charitable Trust

The Eagle Charity Trust

Audrey Earle Charitable Trust

The Earley Charity

Earls Colne and Halstead Educational Charity

The Earmark Trust

East Kent Provincial Charities

East London Community Foundation

Eastern Counties Educational Trust Limited

The Sir John Eastwood Foundation

The Ebenezer Trust

The EBM Charitable Trust

Eden Arts Trust

EDF Energy Trust (EDFET)

The Gilbert and Eileen Edgar Foundation

Gilbert Edgar Trust

Edinburgh Children's Holiday Fund

The Edinburgh Trust, No 2 Account

Edinburgh Voluntary Organisations' Trust Funds

Educational Foundation of Alderman John Norman

The W G Edwards Charitable Foundation

The William Edwards Educational Charity

The Elephant Trust

The George Elias Charitable Trust

The Gerald Palmer Eling Trust Company

The Elizabeth Frankland Moore and Star Foundation

The Wilfred and Elsie Elkes Charity Fund

The Maud Elkington Charitable Trust

Ellador Ltd

The Ellerdale Trust

The John Ellerman Foundation

The Ellinson Foundation Ltd

The Edith Maud Ellis 1985 Charitable Trust

The Ellis Campbell Foundation

James Ellis Charitable Trust

The Elmgrant Trust

The Elmley Foundation

Elshore Ltd

The Vernon N Ely Charitable Trust

The Embleton Trust

The Emerton-Christie Charity

The Emilienne Charitable Trust

The Emmandjay Charitable Trust

The Worshipful Company of Engineers Charitable Trust Fund

The Englefield Charitable Trust

The English Schools' Football Association

The Enkalon Foundation

Entindale Ltd

The Epigoni Trust

Epilepsy Research UK

The Equitable Charitable Trust

The Equity Trust Fund

The Ericson Trust

The Erskine Cunningham Hill Trust

Essex Community Foundation

The Essex Fairway Charitable Trust

The Essex Heritage Trust

Essex Provincial Charity Fund

The Essex Youth Trust

Euro Charity Trust

The Evangelical Covenants Trust

The Alan Evans Memorial Trust

Sir John Evelyn's Charity

The Eventhall Family Charitable Trust

The Everard Foundation

The Eveson Charitable Trust

The Beryl Evetts and Robert Luff Animal Welfare Trust

The Execution Charitable Trust

The Mayor of Exeter's Appeal Fund

The Exilarch's Foundation

The Matthew Eyton Animal Welfare Trust

F C Charitable Trust

The F P Limited Charitable Trust

The Faber Charitable Trust

Esmée Fairbairn Foundation

The Fairstead Trust

The Fairway Trust

Faisaltex Charitable Trust

The Family Foundations Trust

The Family Rich Charities Trust

Famos Foundation Trust

The Lord Faringdon Charitable Trust

Samuel William Farmer's Trust

The Farmers' Company Charitable Fund

The Thomas Farr Charitable Trust

Walter Farthing (Trust) Limited

Farthing Trust

The Fassnidge Memorial Trust

Joseph Fattorini Charitable Trust 'B' Account

The Fawcett Charitable Trust

Federation of Jewish Relief Organisations

Feed the Minds

The John Feeney Charitable Bequest

The George Fentham Birmingham Charity

The A M Fenton Trust

Allan and Nesta Ferguson Charitable Settlement

Elizabeth Ferguson Charitable Trust Fund

The Fidelity UK Foundation
The Bluff Field Charitable Trust
The Doris Field Charitable
Trust
Fife Council/Common Good
Funds and Trusts
Dixie Rose Findlay Charitable
Trust
Gerald Finzi Charitable Trust
Firtree Trust
The Sir John Fisher Foundation
The Fishmongers' Company's
Charitable Trust
Marc Fitch Fund
The Fitton Trust
The Earl Fitzwilliam Charitable
Trust
Bud Flanagan Leukaemia Fund
The Rose Flatau Charitable
Trust
The Ian Fleming Charitable
Trust
The Joyce Fletcher Charitable
Trust
The Roy Fletcher Charitable
Trust
Florence's Charitable Trust
The Flow Foundation
The Gerald Fogel Charitable
Trust
The Follett Trust
The Football Association
National Sports Centre
Trust
The Football Association Youth
Trust
The Football Foundation
The Forbes Charitable
Foundation
Forbesville Limited
The Forces Trust
Ford Britain Trust
The Oliver Ford Charitable
Trust
Fordeve Ltd
The Forest Hill Charitable Trust
The Foresters' Charity
Stewards UK Trust
Gwyneth Forrester Trust
The Forte Charitable Trust
Lord Forte Foundation
Foundation for Management
Education
Four Acre Trust
The Four Winds Trust
The Fowler, Smith and Jones
Charitable Trust
The Foyle Foundation
The Isaac and Freda Frankel
Memorial Charitable Trust
Sydney E Franklin Deceased's
New Second Charity
The Jill Franklin Trust
The Gordon Fraser Charitable
Trust
The Hugh Fraser Foundation

The Joseph Strong Frazer Trust
The Louis and Valerie
Freedman Charitable
Settlement
The Freemasons' Grand
Charity
The Thomas Freke and Lady
Norton Charity
The Charles S French
Charitable Trust
The Anne French Memorial
Trust
The Freshfield Foundation
The Freshgate Trust
Foundation
The Friarsgate Trust
The Friends Hall Farm Street
Trust
Friends of Biala Ltd
Friends of Wiznitz Limited
Friends Provident Charitable
Foundation
The Frognal Trust
T F C Frost Charitable Trust
The Patrick Frost Foundation
Maurice Fry Charitable Trust
Mejer and Gertrude Miriam
Frydman Foundation
The Fuellers Charitable Trust
Fund
The Fulmer Charitable Trust
Worshipful Company of
Furniture Makers Charitable
Fund
Gableholt Limited
The Galbraith Trust
The Gale Family Charitable
Trust
The Angela Gallagher Memorial
Fund
The Gamlen Charitable Trust
The Gamma Trust
The Gannochy Trust
The Ganzoni Charitable Trust
The Worshipful Company of
Gardeners of London
The Samuel Gardner Memorial
Trust
The Garnett Charitable Trust
Garrick Charitable Trust
Garvan Limited
The Gatsby Charitable
Foundation
Gatwick Airport Community
Trust
The Robert Gavron Charitable
Trust
Jacqueline and Michael Gee
Charitable Trust
The General Nursing Council
for England and Wales
Trust
J Paul Getty Jr Charitable Trust
The Gibbs Charitable Trust
Simon Gibson Charitable Trust

The G C Gibson Charitable
Trust
The Harvey and Hilary Gilbert
Charitable Trust
The Girdlers' Company
Charitable Trust
The B and P Glasser
Charitable Trust
The Glass-House Trust
The Glastonbury Trust Limited
Global Care
Global Charities (formally
GCap Charities)
Gloucestershire Community
Foundation
Worshipful Company of
Glovers of London Charity
Fund
GMC Trust
The GNC Trust
The Mrs Godfrey-Payton Trust
The Meir Golda Trust
The Sydney and Phyllis
Goldberg Memorial
Charitable Trust
The Golden Bottle Trust
Golden Charitable Trust
The Jack Goldhill Charitable
Trust
The Goldsmiths' Arts Trust
Fund
The Goldsmiths' Company
Charity
The Golsoncott Foundation
The Good Neighbours Trust
Nicholas and Judith
Goodison's Charitable
Settlement
The Everard and Mina
Goodman Charitable
Foundation
Mike Gooley Trailfinders
Charity
Leonard Gordon Charitable
Trust
The Gosling Foundation
Limited
The Gough Charitable Trust
The Gould Charitable Trust
The Grace Charitable Trust
A B Grace Trust
The Graff Foundation
The Grahame Charitable
Foundation Limited
Grampian Police Diced Cap
Charitable Fund
The Granada Foundation
Grand Charitable Trust of the
Order of Women
Freemasons
The Grand Order of Water
Rats' Charities Fund
The Grange Farm Centre Trust
Grantham Yorke Trust
The J G Graves Charitable
Trust

The Gray Trust
The Great Britain Sasakawa
Foundation
The Great Stone Bridge Trust
of Edenbridge
The Great Torrington Town
Lands Charity
The Constance Green
Foundation
The Barry Green Memorial
Fund
The Philip Green Memorial
Trust
Mrs H R Greene Charitable
Settlement
Greenham Common
Community Trust Limited
Naomi and Jeffrey Greenwood
Charitable Trust
Greggs Foundation
The Greys Charitable Trust
Grimmitt Trust
The Grocers' Charity
The M and R Gross Charities
Limited
The Grove Charitable Trust
The GRP Charitable Trust
The David and Marie Grumitt
Foundation
The Bishop of Guildford's
Foundation
The Guildry Incorporation of
Perth
The Walter Guinness
Charitable Trust
The Gulbenkian Foundation
The Gunter Charitable Trust
The Gur Trust
Gurunanak
Dr Guthrie's Association
The H and M Charitable Trust
H C D Memorial Fund
The H P Charitable Trust
The Hackney Parochial
Charities
The Hadfield Trust
The Hadley Trust
The Hadrian Trust
The Alfred Haines Charitable
Trust
The Hale Trust
E F and M G Hall Charitable
Trust
The Edith Winifred Hall
Charitable Trust
Robert Hall Charity
The Hamamelis Trust
Hamilton Wallace Trust
Paul Hamlyn Foundation
Sue Hammerson's Charitable
Trust
The Hammonds Charitable
Trust
The Hampshire and Islands
Historic Churches Trust

Hampton Fuel Allotment
Charity
The W A Handley Charitable
Trust
Beatrice Hankey Foundation
Ltd
The Hanley Trust
The Kathleen Hannay
Memorial Charity
The Doughty Hanson
Charitable Foundation
Lord Hanson Foundation
The Haramead Trust
Miss K M Harbinson's
Charitable Trust
Harbo Charities Limited
The Harborne Parish Lands
Charity
The Harbour Charitable Trust
The Harbour Foundation
The Harding Trust
William Harding's Charity
The Hare of Steep Charitable
Trust
The Harebell Centenary Fund
The Kenneth Hargreaves
Charitable Trust
The Harris Charitable Trust
The Harris Charity
The Harris Family Charitable
Trust
The Harrison and Potter Trust
The John Harrison Charitable
Trust
The Peter Harrison Foundation
The Spencer Hart Charitable
Trust
The Hartley Charitable Trust
The N and P Hartley Memorial
Trust
William Geoffrey Harvey's
Discretionary Settlement
Haskel Family Foundation
The Hathaway Trust
The Maurice Hatter Foundation
The M A Hawe Settlement
The Hawthorne Charitable
Trust
The Dorothy Hay-Bolton
Charitable Trust
The Haydan Charitable Trust
The Haymills Charitable Trust
The Headley Trust
Headley-Pitt Charitable Trust
Heagerty Charitable Trust
The Heald Charitable Trust
Healthsure Group Ltd
May Hearnshaw's Charity
The Heart of England
Community Foundation
The Heathcoat Trust
Heathside Charitable Trust
The Charlotte Heber-Percy
Charitable Trust
Percy Hedley 1990 Charitable
Trust

The Hedley Denton Charitable
Trust
The Hedley Foundation
The H J Heinz Company
Limited Charitable Trust
The Hellenic Foundation
The Michael and Morven Heller
Charitable Foundation
The Simon Heller Charitable
Settlement
Help the Aged
Help the Homeless
Help the Hospices
The Hemby Trust
The Christina Mary Hendrie
Trust for Scottish and
Canadian Charities
The Henley Educational Charity
Philip Henman Trust
Esther Hennell Charitable
Trust
The G D Herbert Charitable
Trust
The Joanna Herbert-Stepney
Charitable Settlement
The Anne Herd Memorial Trust
The Herefordshire Historic
Churches Trust
The Heritage of London Trust
Ltd
The Hertfordshire Community
Foundation
The Hesed Trust
The Hesslewood Children's
Trust (Hull Seamen's and
General Orphanage)
The Bernhard Heuberger
Charitable Trust
Hexham and Newcastle
Diocesan Trust (1947)
The Higgs Charitable Trust
Alan Edward Higgs Charity
The High Sheriff's Police Trust
for the County of West
Midlands
Highcroft Charitable Trust
The Hilden Charitable Fund
The Joseph and Mary Hiley
Trust
The Holly Hill Charitable Trust
The Derek Hill Foundation
The Charles Littlewood Hill
Trust
The Hillingdon Partnership
Trust
R G Hills Charitable Trust
Hinchley Charitable Trust
Lady Hind Trust
Hinduja Foundation
Stuart Hine Trust
The Hinrichsen Foundation
The Hitchin Educational
Foundation
The Eleemosynary Charity of
William Hobbayne
Hobson Charity Limited

Hockerill Educational
Foundation
Matthew Hodder Charitable
Trust
The Sir Julian Hodge
Charitable Trust
The Jane Hodge Foundation
The J G Hogg Charitable Trust
The Holbeck Charitable Trust
The Holden Charitable Trust
John Holford's Charity
The Hollick Family Charitable
Trust
The Holliday Foundation
The Dorothy Holmes Charitable
Trust
The Holst Foundation
P H Holt Foundation
The Edward Holt Trust
The Holywood Trust
The Homelands Charitable
Trust
The Homestead Charitable
Trust
Mary Homfray Charitable Trust
Sir Harold Hood's Charitable
Trust
The Hope Trust
HopMarket Charity
The Cuthbert Horn Trust
The Antony Hornby Charitable
Trust
The Horne Foundation
The Horne Trust
The Worshipful Company of
Horners' Charitable Trusts
The Hornsey Parochial
Charities
The Hospital of God at
Greatham
The Hospital Saturday Fund
Houblon-Norman/George Fund
The House of Industry Estate
The Reta Lila Howard
Foundation
The Daniel Howard Trust
The Clifford Howarth Charity
Trust
The Huddersfield Medical Trust
Fund
The Hudson Foundation
The Huggard Charitable Trust
The Geoffrey C Hughes
Charitable Trust
The Hull and East Riding
Charitable Trust
Hulme Trust Estates
(Educational)
Human Relief Foundation
The Humanitarian Trust
The Michael and Shirley Hunt
Charitable Trust
The Albert Hunt Trust
The Hunter Foundation
Miss Agnes H Hunter's Trust
The Huntingdon Foundation

Huntingdon Freemen's Charity
John Huntingdon's Charity
Hurdale Charity Limited
The Hutton Foundation
The Nani Huyu Charitable Trust
The P Y N and B Hyams Trust
The Hyde Charitable Trust –
Youth Plus
The Idlewild Trust
The Iliffe Family Charitable
Trust
Impetus Trust
The Indigo Trust
The Ingram Trust
The Inland Waterways
Association
The Inlight Trust
The Inman Charity
The Inner London Magistrates
Court Poor Box Charity and
Feeder Charity
The Worshipful Company of
Innholders General Charity
Fund
The Innocent Foundation
The Ireland Fund of Great
Britain
The Irish Youth Foundation
(UK) Ltd
The Ironmongers' Foundation
Irshad Trust
The Charles Irving Charitable
Trust
Irwin Trust
The ISA Charity
The Isaacs Charitable Trust
The J Isaacs Charitable Trust
The Isle of Anglesey Charitable
Trust
Isle of Dogs Community
Foundation
The ITF Seafarers Trust
J A R Charitable Trust
The J J Charitable Trust
The J R S S T Charitable Trust
Elizabeth Jackson Charitable
Trust
Jacobs Charitable Trust
The Ruth and Lionel Jacobson
Trust (Second Fund) No 2
Jaffe Family Relief Fund
John James Bristol Foundation
The Susan and Stephen
James Charitable
Settlement
The James Trust
The Jarman Charitable Trust
The John Jarrold Trust
Jay Education Trust
JCA Charitable Foundation
The Jeffrey Charitable Trust
Rees Jeffreys Road Fund
The Jenour Foundation
The Jephcott Charitable Trust
The Jerusalem Trust
Jerwood Charitable Foundation

Jesus Hospital Charity
Jewish Child's Day
The Jewish Youth Fund
The JMK Charitable Trust
The Joanies Trust
The Harold Joels Charitable
Trust
The Jonathan Joels Charitable
Trust
The Nicholas Joels Charitable
Trust
The Norman Joels Charitable
Trust
The Joffe Charitable Trust
The Elton John Aids
Foundation
The Michael John Trust
The Lillie Johnson Charitable
Trust
The Johnson Group Cleaners
Charity
The Johnnie Johnson Trust
The Johnson Wax Ltd
Charitable Trust
The Joicey Trust
The Jones 1986 Charitable
Trust
The Marjorie and Geoffrey
Jones Charitable Trust
The Jordan Charitable
Foundation
The J E Joseph Charitable
Fund
The Lady Eileen Joseph
Foundation
JTH Charitable Trust
The Judith Trust
The Cyril and Eve Jumbo
Charitable Trust
The Anton Jurgens Charitable
Trust
The Bernard Kahn Charitable
Trust
The Stanley Kalms Foundation
The Karenza Foundation
The Boris Karloff Charitable
Foundation
The Ian Karten Charitable
Trust
The Kasner Charitable Trust
The Kass Charitable Trust
The Kathleen Trust
The Michael and Ilse Katz
Foundation
The Katzauer Charitable
Settlement
The C S Kaufman Charitable
Trust
The Geoffrey John Kaye
Charitable Foundation
The Emmanuel Kaye
Foundation
Kelsick's Educational
Foundation
The KempWelch Charitable
Trust

The Kay Kendall Leukaemia
Fund
William Kendall's Charity (Wax
Chandlers' Company)
The Kennedy Charitable
Foundation
The Kennel Club Charitable
Trust
Kent Community Foundation
The Nancy Kenyon Charitable
Trust
Keren Association
Kermaville Ltd
E and E Kernkraut Charities
Limited
The Peter Kershaw Trust
The Kessler Foundation
Keswick Hall Charity
The Ursula Keyes Trust
The Kiawah Charitable Trust
The Robert Kiln Charitable
Trust
The King Henry VIII Endowed
Trust Warwick
The King/Cullimore Charitable
Trust
The King's Fund
The Kingsbury Charity
The Mary Kinross Charitable
Trust
Kinsurdy Charitable Trust
Kirkley Poor's Lands Estate
The Richard Kirkman
Charitable Trust
Kirschel Foundation
Robert Kitchin (Saddlers'
Company)
Ernest Kleinwort Charitable
Trust
The Marina Kleinwort
Charitable Trust
The Sir James Knott Trust
The Kobler Trust
The Kohn Foundation
Kollel and Co. Limited
The Kreditor Charitable Trust
The Kreitman Foundation
The Neil Kreitman Foundation
The Heinz, Anna and Carol
Kroch Foundation
The Kyte Charitable Trust
Lacims-Maclis Charitable Trust
The Late Sir Pierce Lacy
Charity Trust
The K P Ladd Charitable Trust
John Laing Charitable Trust
Maurice and Hilda Laing
Charitable Trust
The Laing Family Foundations
The Christopher Laing
Foundation
The Kirby Laing Foundation
The Martin Laing Foundation
The Beatrice Laing Trust
The Lambert Charitable Trust

Community Foundation for
Lancashire
Lancashire Environmental
Fund
Duchy of Lancaster Benevolent
Fund
The Lancaster Foundation
LandAid Charitable Trust
The Allen Lane Foundation
The Langdale Trust
The Langley Charitable Trust
The Langtree Trust
The LankellyChase Foundation
The Lanvern Foundation
The R J Larg Family Charitable
Trust
Largsmount Ltd
The Lark Trust
Laslett's (Hinton) Charity
Lauchentilly Charitable
Foundation 1988
Laufer Charitable Trust
The Lauffer Family Charitable
Foundation
Mrs F B Laurence Charitable
Trust
The Kathleen Laurence Trust
The Law Society Charity
The Edgar E Lawley Foundation
The Herd Lawson and Muriel
Lawson Charitable Trust
The Lawson Beckman
Charitable Trust
The Raymond and Blanche
Lawson Charitable Trust
The Carole and Geoffrey
Lawson Foundation
The Mason Le Page Charitable
Trust
The Leach Fourteenth Trust
The David Lean Foundation
The Leathersellers' Company
Charitable Fund
The Leche Trust
The Arnold Lee Charitable
Trust
The William Leech Charity
The Lord Mayor of Leeds
Appeal Fund
Leeds Building Society
Charitable Foundation
The Leeds Community
Foundation
Leicester Charity Link
The Kennedy Leigh Charitable
Trust
Morris Leigh Foundation
The Leigh Trust
Mrs Vera Leigh's Charity
The P Leigh-Bramwell Trust 'E'
The Lennox and Wyfold
Foundation
The Erica Leonard Trust
The Leonard Trust
The Mark Leonard Trust
Lesley Lesley and Mutter Trust

Leukaemia Research Fund
The Leverhulme Trade
Charities Trust
Lord Leverhulme's Charitable
Trust
The Joseph Levy Charitable
Foundation
Lewis Family Charitable Trust
The John Spedan Lewis
Foundation
The Sir Edward Lewis
Foundation
John Lewis Partnership
General Community Fund
Lichfield Conduit Lands
Lifeline 4 Kids
The Thomas Lilley Memorial
Trust
Limoges Charitable Trust
The Linbury Trust
The Lincolnshire Old Churches
Trust
The Lind Trust
Lindale Educational
Foundation
The Linden Charitable Trust
The Enid Linder Foundation
The Linmardon Trust
The Ruth and Stuart Lipton
Charitable Trust
The Lister Charitable Trust
Frank Litchfield Charitable
Trust
The Andrew and Mary
Elizabeth Little Charitable
Trust
The Second Joseph Aaron
Littman Foundation
The George John and Sheilah
Livanos Charitable Trust
Liverpool Charity and Voluntary
Services
Liverpool Sailors' Home Trust
Jack Livingstone Charitable
Trust
The Elaine and Angus Lloyd
Charitable Trust
The Charles Lloyd Foundation
The Lloyd Fund
Lloyd's Charities Trust
The Lloyd-Everett Trust
Lloyds TSB Foundation for
England and Wales
Lloyds TSB Foundation for
Northern Ireland
Lloyds TSB Foundation for the
Channel Islands
Llysdinam Charitable Trust
Localtrent Ltd
The Locker Foundation
The Loftus Charitable Trust
The Lolev Charitable Trust
London Catalyst
The London Law Trust
The London Marathon
Charitable Trust

London Masonic Charitable Trust

The William and Katherine Longman Trust

The Loseley and Guildway Charitable Trust

The Lotus Foundation

The Lowy Mitchell Foundation

The C L Loyd Charitable Trust

LSA Charitable Trust

The Marie Helen Luen Charitable Trust

Robert Luff Foundation Ltd

Henry Lumley Charitable Trust

Lady Lumley's Educational Foundation

Paul Lunn-Rockliffe Charitable Trust

C F Lunoe Trust Fund

The Ruth and Jack Lunzer Charitable Trust

Lord and Lady Lurgan Trust

The Lyndhurst Trust

The Lynn Foundation

The Lynwood Trust

John Lyon's Charity

The Lyons Charitable Trust

The Sir Jack Lyons Charitable Trust

Malcolm Lyons Foundation

The Lyras Family Charitable Trust

Sylvanus Lyson's Charity

The M and C Trust

The M D and S Charitable Trust

The M K Charitable Trust

The Madeline Mabey Trust

The E M MacAndrew Trust

The R S Macdonald Charitable Trust

Macdonald-Buchanan Charitable Trust

The Macfarlane Walker Trust

The Mackay and Brewer Charitable Trust

The Mackintosh Foundation

The MacRobert Trust

Ian Mactaggart Trust

The Magdalen and Lasher Charity

Magdalen Hospital Trust

The Magen Charitable Trust

Mageni Trust

The Brian Maguire Charitable Trust

Mahavir Trust

The Makin Charitable Trust

Man Group plc Charitable Trust

Manchester Airport Community Trust Fund

The Manchester Guardian Society Charitable Trust

Manchester Kids

Lord Mayor of Manchester's Charity Appeal Trust

Mandeville Trust

The Manifold Charitable Trust

W M Mann Foundation

The Leslie and Lilian Manning Trust

Maranatha Christian Trust

Marbeh Torah Trust

The Marchday Charitable Fund

Marchig Animal Welfare Trust

Mariapolis Limited

Market Harborough and The Bowdens Charity

Michael Marks Charitable Trust

The Ann and David Marks Foundation

The Hilda and Samuel Marks Foundation

J P Marland Charitable Trust

Marr-Munning Trust

The Michael Marsh Charitable Trust

The Marsh Christian Trust

The Charlotte Marshall Charitable Trust

The Jim Marshall Charitable Trust

The D G Marshall of Cambridge Trust

Marshall's Charity

Marshgate Charitable Settlement

Sir George Martin Trust

John Martin's Charity

The Mason Porter Charitable Trust

The Nancie Massey Charitable Trust

The Mathew Trust

Matliwala Family Charitable Trust

The Matt 6.3 Charitable Trust

The Violet Mauray Charitable Trust

The Maxell Educational Trust

The Maxwell Family Foundation

Evelyn May Trust

Mayfair Charities Ltd

The Mayfield Valley Arts Trust

Mazars Charitable Trust

The Robert McAlpine Foundation

The McDougall Trust

The A M McGreevy No 5 Charitable Settlement

The McKenna Charitable Trust

Martin McLaren Memorial Trust

The Helen Isabella McMorran Charitable Foundation

D D McPhail Charitable Settlement

The James Frederick and Ethel Anne Measures Charity

Medical Research Council

The Medlock Charitable Trust

The Anthony and Elizabeth Mellows Charitable Settlement

Melodor Ltd

Melow Charitable Trust

Meningitis Trust

Menuchar Ltd

Brian Mercer Charitable Trust

The Mercers' Charitable Foundation

The Merchant Taylors' Company Charities Fund

The Merchant Venturers' Charity

The Merchants' House of Glasgow

Mercury Phoenix Trust

The Mersey Docks and Harbour Company Charitable Fund

Community Foundation for Merseyside

The Zachary Merton and George Woofindin Convalescent Trust

The Tony Metherell Charitable Trust

The Methodist Relief and Development Fund

The Metropolitan Drinking Fountain and Cattle Trough Association

T and J Meyer Family Foundation Limited

Gerald Micklem Charitable Trust

Midhurst Pensions Trust

The Migraine Trust

Miles Trust for the Putney and Roehampton Community

Millennium Stadium Charitable Trust

The Hugh and Mary Miller Bequest Trust

The Miller Foundation

The Millfield Trust

The Millhouses Charitable Trust

The Millichope Foundation

The Mills Charity

The Millward Charitable Trust

The Clare Milne Trust

Milton Keynes Community Foundation

The Edgar Milward Charity

The Peter Minet Trust

Minge's Gift and the Pooled Trusts

The Minos Trust

Minton Charitable Trust

The Mirfield Educational Charity

The Mirianog Trust

The Laurence Misener
   Charitable Trust
The Mishcon Family Charitable
   Trust
The Misselbrook Trust
The Mitchell Charitable Trust
The Esme Mitchell Trust
Keren Mitzvah Trust
The Mizpah Trust
The Mobbs Memorial Trust Ltd
The Modiano Charitable Trust
The Moette Charitable Trust
The Mole Charitable Trust
The D C Moncrieff Charitable
   Trust
Monmouthshire County Council
   Welsh Church Act Fund
The Montague Thompson
   Coon Charitable Trust
The Colin Montgomerie
   Charitable Foundation
The Monument Trust
Moody Charitable Trust
George A Moore Foundation
The Nigel Moores Family
   Charitable Trust
John Moores Foundation
The Peter Moores Foundation
The Morel Charitable Trust
The Morgan Charitable
   Foundation
The Mr and Mrs J T Morgan
   Foundation
The J P Morgan Foundations
Diana and Allan Morgenthau
   Charitable Trust
The Oliver Morland Charitable
   Trust
S C and M E Morland's
   Charitable Trust
The Morris Charitable Trust
The Willie and Mabel Morris
   Charitable Trust
The Peter Morrison Charitable
   Foundation
G M Morrison Charitable Trust
The Stanley Morrison
   Charitable Trust
Moshal Charitable Trust
Vyoel Moshe Charitable Trust
The Moshulu Charitable Trust
Brian and Jill Moss Charitable
   Trust
The Moss Charitable Trust
The Robert and Margaret
   Moss Charitable Trust
Moss Family Charitable Trust
The Mount Everest Foundation
Mountbatten Festival of Music
The Mountbatten Memorial
   Trust
The Edwina Mountbatten Trust
The Mugdock Children's Trust
The F H Muirhead Charitable
   Trust
The Mulberry Trust

The Edith Murphy Foundation
Murphy-Neumann Charity
   Company Limited
The Mushroom Fund
The Music Sales Charitable
   Trust
Muslim Hands
The Mutual Trust Group
MYA Charitable Trust
The Kitty and Daniel Nabarro
   Charitable Trust
The Nadezhda Charitable Trust
The Willie Nagel Charitable
   Trust
The Naggar Charitable Trust
The Eleni Nakou Foundation
The Janet Nash Charitable
   Settlement
Nathan Charitable Trust
Asthma UK
The National Churches Trust
The National Manuscripts
   Conservation Trust
Nazareth Trust Fund
The Nchima Trust
Needham Market and Barking
   Welfare Charities
The Worshipful Company of
   Needlemakers' Charitable
   Fund
The Neighbourly Charitable
   Trust
The James Neill Trust Fund
Nemoral Ltd
Nesswall Ltd
Nestle Rowntree Employees
   Community Fund
Network for Social Change
The New Appeals Organisation
   for the City and County of
   Nottingham
New Court Charitable Trust
Newby Trust Limited
The Newcomen Collett
   Foundation
The Richard Newitt Fund
Mr and Mrs F E F Newman
   Charitable Trust
Newpier Charity Ltd
Alderman Newton's
   Educational Foundation
The Chevras Ezras Nitzrochim
   Trust
Alice Noakes Memorial
   Charitable Trust
The Noel Buxton Trust
The Noon Foundation
The Norda Trust
Norie Charitable Trust
Normalyn Charitable Trust
The Norman Family Charitable
   Trust
The Duncan Norman Trust
   Fund
The Normanby Charitable Trust
The North British Hotel Trust

The North West Cancer
   Research Fund
The Northampton Municipal
   Church Charities
The Northampton Queen's
   Institute Relief in Sickness
   Fund
The Earl of Northampton's
   Charity
The Northcott Devon
   Foundation
The Northcott Devon Medical
   Foundation
The Northern Rock Foundation
The Northmoor Trust
The Northumberland Village
   Homes Trust
The Northumbria Historic
   Churches Trust
The Northwood Charitable
   Trust
The Norton Foundation
The Norwich Church of England
   Young Men's Society
The Norwich Historic Churches
   Trust Ltd
The Norwich Town Close
   Estate Charity
The Norwood and Newton
   Settlement
The Noswad Charity
The Notgrove Trust
The Nottingham General
   Dispensary
The Nottingham Gordon
   Memorial Trust for Boys
   and Girls
Nottinghamshire Community
   Foundation
The Nottinghamshire Historic
   Churches Trust
The Nottinghamshire Miners'
   Welfare Trust Fund
Novi Most International
The Father O'Mahoney
   Memorial Trust
The Sir Peter O'Sullevan
   Charitable Trust
The Oak Trust
The Oakdale Trust
The Oakley Charitable Trust
The Oakmoor Charitable Trust
The Odin Charitable Trust
Ogilvie Charities Deed No.2
   (including the Charity of
   Mary Catherine Ford Smith)
The Ogle Christian Trust
Oglesby Charitable Trust
The Oikonomia Trust
The Oizer Charitable Trust
The Old Broad Street Charity
   Trust
The Old Enfield Charitable
   Trust
Old Possum's Practical Trust
The John Oldacre Foundation

The Oldham Foundation
The Olga Charitable Trust
Onaway Trust
Open Gate
The Ormsby Charitable Trust
Orrin Charitable Trust
The Ouseley Trust
The Owen Family Trust
Oxfam (GB)
The Oxfordshire Community
    Foundation
The P F Charitable Trust
Padwa Charitable Foundation
The Pallant Charitable Trust
The Palmer Foundation
Eleanor Palmer Trust
The Panacea Society
Panahpur Charitable Trust
Panton Trust
The Paphitis Charitable Trust
The Paragon Trust
The Park Charitable Trust
The Park House Charitable
    Trust
The Frank Parkinson
    Agricultural Trust
The Samuel and Freda
    Parkinson Charitable Trust
The Parthenon Trust
Arthur James Paterson
    Charitable Trust
The Constance Paterson
    Charitable Trust
Miss M E Swinton Paterson's
    Charitable Trust
The Patrick Charitable Trust
The Jack Patston Charitable
    Trust
Paycare Charity Trust
The Payne Charitable Trust
The Harry Payne Trust
The Susanna Peake Charitable
    Trust
The Pears Foundation
The Pedmore Sporting Club
    Trust Fund
The Dowager Countess
    Eleanor Peel Trust
Pegasus (Stanley) Trust
Peltz Trust
The Pennycress Trust
The Performing Right Society
    Foundation
B E Perl Charitable Trust
The Persson Charitable Trust
The Persula Foundation
The Pestalozzi Overseas
    Children's Trust
The Jack Petchey Foundation
The Petplan Charitable Trust
The Philips and Rubens
    Charitable Trust
The Phillips Charitable Trust
The Phillips Family Charitable
    Trust
Philological Foundation

The David Pickford Charitable
    Foundation
The Bernard Piggott Trust
The Claude and Margaret Pike
    Charity
The Pilgrim Trust
The Cecil Pilkington Charitable
    Trust
The Pilkington Charities Fund
The Austin and Hope
    Pilkington Trust
The Sir Harry Pilkington Trust
The Col W W Pilkington Will
    Trusts The General Charity
    Fund
Miss A M Pilkington's
    Charitable Trust
Mrs Pilkington's Charitable
    Trust
The Plaisterers' Company
    Charitable Trust
The Platinum Trust
G S Plaut Charitable Trust
    Limited
Polden-Puckham Charitable
    Foundation
The Polehanger Trust
The Poling Charitable Trust
The George and Esme Pollitzer
    Charitable Settlement
The J S F Pollitzer Charitable
    Settlement
The Ponton House Trust
The Mayor of Poole's Appeal
    Fund
Edith and Ferdinand Porjes
    Charitable Trust
The John Porter Charitable
    Trust
The Porter Foundation
Porticus UK
The Portrack Charitable Trust
The J E Posnansky Charitable
    Trust
The Mary Potter Convent
    Hospital Trust
The David and Elaine Potter
    Foundation
The Powell Foundation
Prairie Trust
The W L Pratt Charitable Trust
Premierquote Ltd
Premishlaner Charitable Trust
The Lucy Price Relief-in-Need
    Charity
Sir John Priestman Charity
    Trust
The Primrose Trust
The Prince's Charities
    Foundation
Princess Anne's Charities
The Priory Foundation
Prison Service Charity Fund
The Privy Purse Charitable
    Trust
The Proven Family Trust

PSA Peugeot Citroen Charity
    Trust
The Puebla Charitable Trust
The Richard and Christine
    Purchas Charitable Trust
The Puri Foundation
Mr and Mrs J A Pye's
    Charitable Settlement
Quartet Community Foundation
The Queen Anne's Gate
    Foundation
Queen Mary's Roehampton
    Trust
The Queen's Silver Jubilee
    Trust
Quercus Trust
The R D Crusaders Foundation
R J M Charitable Trust
R S Charitable Trust
The R V W Trust
The Monica Rabagliati
    Charitable Trust
Rachel Charitable Trust
The Mr and Mrs Philip
    Rackham Charitable Trust
Richard Radcliffe Charitable
    Trust
The Radcliffe Trust
The Bishop Radford Trust
The Ragdoll Foundation
The Rainford Trust
The Peggy Ramsay Foundation
The Joseph and Lena Randall
    Charitable Trust
The Rank Foundation
The Joseph Rank Trust
Ranworth Trust
The Fanny Rapaport Charitable
    Settlement
The Ratcliff Foundation
The Ratcliff Pension Charity
The Ratcliffe Charitable Trust
The Eleanor Rathbone
    Charitable Trust
The Sigrid Rausing Trust
The Ravensdale Trust
The Rayden Charitable Trust
The Roger Raymond Charitable
    Trust
The Rayne Foundation
The Rayne Trust
The John Rayner Charitable
    Trust
The Albert Reckitt Charitable
    Trust
The Sir James Reckitt Charity
The Eva Reckitt Trust Fund
The Red Arrows Trust
The Red Rose Charitable Trust
The C A Redfern Charitable
    Foundation
Redfern Charitable Trust
The Reed Foundation
Richard Reeve's Foundation
The Max Reinhardt Charitable
    Trust

Relief Fund for Romania
Limited
REMEDI
The Rest Harrow Trust
Reuben Brothers Foundation
The Joan K Reynell Charitable
Trust
The Nathaniel Reyner Trust
Fund
The Rhododendron Trust
Daisie Rich Trust
The Sir Cliff Richard Charitable
Trust
C B Richard Ellis Charitable
Trust
The Clive Richards Charity
The Richmond Parish Lands
Charity
The Muriel Edith Rickman
Trust
Ridgesave Limited
The Ripple Effect Foundation
The Sir John Ritblat Family
Foundation
The River Trust
Riverside Charitable Trust
Limited
The Daniel Rivlin Charitable
Trust
Thomas Roberts Trust
The Alex Roberts-Miller
Foundation
The Robertson Trust
Edwin George Robinson
Charitable Trust
Robyn Charitable Trust
The Rochester Bridge Trust
The Rock Foundation
The Rock Solid Trust
The Rofeh Trust
Richard Rogers Charitable
Settlement
Rokach Family Charitable Trust
The Helen Roll Charitable
Trust
The Sir James Roll Charitable
Trust
The Roman Research Trust
Romeera Foundation
The C A Rookes Charitable
Trust
The Rosca Trust
The Cecil Rosen Foundation
Rosetrees Trust
The Rothermere Foundation
The Rotherwick Foundation
The Rothschild Foundation
The Roughley Charitable Trust
Mrs Gladys Row Fogo
Charitable Trust
The Rowan Charitable Trust
Rowanville Ltd
The Christopher Rowbotham
Charitable Trust
The Rowing Foundation
The Rowlands Trust

The Joseph Rowntree
Charitable Trust
Joseph Rowntree Reform Trust
Limited
Royal Artillery Charitable Fund
Royal British Legion
Royal Docks Trust (London)
Royal Masonic Trust for Girls
and Boys
The Royal Scots Benevolent
Society
The Alfred and Frances
Rubens Charitable Trust
The Rubin Foundation
William Arthur Rudd Memorial
Trust
The Rufford Maurice Laing
Foundation
The Russell Trust
Ryklow Charitable Trust 1992
The J S and E C Rymer
Charitable Trust
S F Foundation
S O Charitable Trust
The Michael Sacher Charitable
Trust
The Michael Harry Sacher
Trust
Dr Mortimer and Theresa
Sackler Foundation
The Ruzin Sadagora Trust
The Saddlers' Company
Charitable Fund
The Saga Charitable Trust
The Jean Sainsbury Animal
Welfare Trust
The Alan and Babette
Sainsbury Charitable Fund
Saint Sarkis Charity Trust
The Saintbury Trust
The Saints and Sinners Trust
The Salamander Charitable
Trust
The Salt Foundation
The Salt Trust
The Salters' Charities
The Andrew Salvesen
Charitable Trust
The Sammermar Trust
Basil Samuel Charitable Trust
Coral Samuel Charitable Trust
The Hon. M J Samuel
Charitable Trust
The Peter Samuel Charitable
Trust
The Camilla Samuel Fund
The Samworth Foundation
The Sandra Charitable Trust
Santander UK Foundation
Limited
Jimmy Savile Charitable Trust
The Scarfe Charitable Trust
The Schapira Charitable Trust
The Annie Schiff Charitable
Trust

The Schmidt-Bodner Charitable
Trust
The R H Scholes Charitable
Trust
The Schreib Trust
The Schreiber Charitable Trust
Schroder Charity Trust
Scott (Eredine) Charitable
Trust
The Scott Bader
Commonwealth Ltd
The Francis C Scott Charitable
Trust
The Frieda Scott Charitable
Trust
The Sir James and Lady Scott
Trust
The Scott Trust Foundation
The Storrow Scott Will Trust
The Scottish Arts Council
Scottish Churches' Community
Trust
Scottish Coal Industry Special
Welfare Fund
The Scottish Community
Foundation
The Scottish International
Education Trust
The Scouloudi Foundation
Seafarers UK (King George's
Fund for Sailors)
Seamen's Hospital Society
The Searchlight Electric
Charitable Trust
The Searle Charitable Trust
The Helene Sebba Charitable
Trust
The Samuel Sebba Charitable
Trust
The Seedfield Trust
Sellata Ltd
SEM Charitable Trust
The Ayrton Senna Foundation
The Seven Fifty Trust
The Severn Trent Water
Charitable Trust Fund
SFIA Educational Trust Limited
The Cyril Shack Trust
Peter Shalson Family
Charitable Trust
The Jean Shanks Foundation
The Shanti Charitable Trust
ShareGift (The Orr Mackintosh
Foundation)
The Linley Shaw Foundation
The Sheepdrove Trust
The Sheffield and District
Hospital Services
Charitable Fund
The Sheldon Trust
The P and D Shepherd
Charitable Trust
The Sylvia and Colin Shepherd
Charitable Trust
The Archie Sherman Cardiff
Foundation

The Archie Sherman Charitable Trust

The R C Sherriff Trust

The Shetland Charitable Trust

SHINE (Support and Help in Education)

The Barnett and Sylvia Shine No 2 Charitable Trust

The Bassil Shippam and Alsford Trust

The Shipwrights' Company Charitable Fund

The Shirley Foundation

Shlomo Memorial Fund Limited

The J A Shone Memorial Trust

The Charles Shorto Charitable Trust

The Barbara A Shuttleworth Memorial Trust

The Mary Elizabeth Siebel Charity

David and Jennifer Sieff Charitable Trust

The Julius Silman Charitable Trust

The Leslie Silver Charitable Trust

The Simpson Education and Conservation Trust

The Simpson Foundation

The Huntly and Margery Sinclair Charitable Trust

Sino-British Fellowship Trust

The Skelton Bounty

The Charles Skey Charitable Trust

Skipton Building Society Charitable Foundation

The John Slater Foundation

Rita and David Slowe Charitable Trust

Ruth Smart Foundation

The SMB Charitable Trust

The Mrs Smith and Mount Trust

The N Smith Charitable Settlement

The Amanda Smith Charitable Trust

The E H Smith Charitable Trust

The Smith Charitable Trust

The Henry Smith Charity

The Leslie Smith Foundation

The Martin Smith Foundation

Stanley Smith General Charitable Trust

The Stanley Smith UK Horticultural Trust

Philip Smith's Charitable Trust

The R C Snelling Charitable Trust

The Snowball Trust

The Sobell Foundation

Solev Co Ltd

Solihull Community Foundation

The Solo Charitable Settlement

Dr Richard Solomon's Charitable Trust

Songdale Ltd

The E C Sosnow Charitable Trust

The Souter Charitable Trust

The South Square Trust

The Stephen R and Philippa H Southall Charitable Trust

The W F Southall Trust

The Southdown Trust

R H Southern Trust

The Southover Manor General Education Trust

The Southwold Trust

The Sovereign Health Care Charitable Trust

Spar Charitable Fund

Sparks Charity (Sport Aiding Medical Research For Kids)

Sparquote Limited

The Spear Charitable Trust

Spears-Stutz Charitable Trust

The Worshipful Company of Spectacle Makers' Charity

The Jessie Spencer Trust

The Ralph and Irma Sperring Charity

The Moss Spiro Will Charitable Foundation

W W Spooner Charitable Trust

Stanley Spooner Deceased Charitable Trust

The Spoore, Merry and Rixman Foundation

The Spring Harvest Charitable Trust

Rosalyn and Nicholas Springer Charitable Trust

Springfields Employees' Medical Research and Charity Trust Fund

Springrule Ltd

The Spurrell Charitable Trust

The Geoff and Fiona Squire Foundation

St Andrew Animal Fund

St Andrew's Conservation Trust

St Francis's Leprosy Guild

St Gabriel's Trust

St Hilda's Trust

St James' Trust Settlement

St James's Place Foundation

Sir Walter St John's Educational Charity

St Katharine and Shadwell Trust

St Mark's Overseas Aid Trust (SMOAT)

St Michael's and All Saints' Charities

The Late St Patrick White Charitable Trust

St Teilo's Trust

The Stafford Trust

Miss Doreen Stanford Trust

The Stanley Foundation Ltd

The Stanton Ballard Charitable Trust

The Staples Trust

The Star Charitable Trust

The Starfish Trust

The Peter Stebbings Memorial Charity

The Steel Charitable Trust

The Cyril and Betty Stein Charitable Trust

The Steinberg Family Charitable Trust

The Hugh Stenhouse Foundation

C E K Stern Charitable Trust

The Sigmund Sternberg Charitable Foundation

Stervon Ltd

The Stevenage Community Trust

The June Stevens Foundation

Stevenson Family's Charitable Trust

The Steventon Allotments and Relief-in-Need Charity

The Stewards' Charitable Trust

The Stewards' Company Limited

The Sir Halley Stewart Trust

The Stobart Newlands Charitable Trust

The Edward Stocks-Massey Bequest Fund

The Stokenchurch Educational Charity

The Stoller Charitable Trust

The M J C Stone Charitable Trust

The Stone-Mallabar Charitable Foundation

The Samuel Storey Family Charitable Trust

Peter Stormonth Darling Charitable Trust

Peter Storrs Trust

The Strangward Trust

The Strasser Foundation

Stratford upon Avon Town Trust

Strathclyde Police Benevolent Fund

The W O Street Charitable Foundation

The A B Strom and R Strom Charitable Trust

The Sudborough Foundation

Sueberry Ltd

The Suffolk Historic Churches Trust

The Alan Sugar Foundation

The Summerfield Charitable Trust

The Bernard Sunley Charitable
Foundation
The Surrey Historic Buildings
Trust Ltd
The Sussex Historic Churches
Trust
The Adrienne and Leslie
Sussman Charitable Trust
The Sutasoma Trust
Sutton Coldfield Municipal
Charities
The Sutton Nursing
Association
Swan Mountain Trust
The Swan Trust
Swansea and Brecon Diocesan
Board of Finance Limited
The John Swire (1989)
Charitable Trust
The Swire Charitable Trust
The Hugh and Ruby Sykes
Charitable Trust
The Charles and Elsie Sykes
Trust
The Sylvanus Charitable Trust
The Stella Symons Charitable
Trust
The Tabeel Trust
The Tajtelbaum Charitable
Trust
The Talbot Trusts
The Talbot Village Trust
Tallow Chandlers Benevolent
Fund
Talteg Ltd
The Tangent Charitable Trust
The Lady Tangye Charitable
Trust
The David Tannen Charitable
Trust
The Tanner Trust
The Lili Tapper Charitable
Foundation
The Mrs A Lacy Tate Trust
The Tay Charitable Trust
C B and H H Taylor 1984 Trust
Humphrey Richardson Taylor
Charitable Trust
The Connie and Albert Taylor
Charitable Trust
The Cyril Taylor Charitable
Trust
A P Taylor Trust
Rosanna Taylor's 1987 Charity
Trust
Tearfund
The Tedworth Charitable Trust
Tees Valley Community
Foundation
Tegham Limited
The Templeton Goodwill Trust
Tesco Charity Trust
Thackray Medical Research
Trust
Thames Community
Foundation

The Thames Wharf Charity
The Thistle Trust
The Loke Wan Tho Memorial
Foundation
The David Thomas Charitable
Trust
The Thomas Wall Trust
The Arthur and Margaret
Thompson Charitable Trust
The Maurice and Vivien
Thompson Charitable Trust
The Thompson Family
Charitable Trust
The Len Thomson Charitable
Trust
The Sue Thomson Foundation
The Sir Jules Thorn Charitable
Trust
The Thornton Foundation
The Thornton Trust
The Three Guineas Trust
The Three Oaks Trust
The Thriplow Charitable Trust
Mrs R P Tindall's Charitable
Trust
The Tinsley Foundation
The Tisbury Telegraph Trust
TJH Foundation
The Tolkien Trust
Tollemache (Buckminster)
Charitable Trust
Tomchei Torah Charitable
Trust
The Tompkins Foundation
The Torah Temimah Trust
Toras Chesed (London) Trust
The Tory Family Foundation
Tottenham Grammar School
Foundation
The Tower Hill Trust
The Towry Law Charitable Trust
The Toy Trust
The Mayor of Trafford's Charity
Fund
Annie Tranmer Charitable Trust
Anthony Travis Charitable Trust
The Constance Travis
Charitable Trust
The Treeside Trust
The Tresillian Trust
The Triangle Trust (1949) Fund
The True Colours Trust
Truedene Co. Ltd
The Truemark Trust
Truemart Limited
Trumros Limited
Trust for London
Trust Sixty Three
The Trusthouse Charitable
Foundation
The Tubney Charitable Trust
Tudor Rose Ltd
The Tudor Trust
The Tufton Charitable Trust
The R D Turner Charitable
Trust

The Douglas Turner Trust
The Florence Turner Trust
Miss S M Tutton Charitable
Trust
The TUUT Charitable Trust
Community Foundation Serving
Tyne and Wear and
Northumberland
Trustees of Tzedakah
UKI Charitable Foundation
Ulster Garden Villages Ltd
Ultach Trust
Ulting Overseas Trust
The Ulverscroft Foundation
Ulverston Town Lands Charity
The Underwood Trust
The Union of Orthodox Hebrew
Congregation
The Unite Foundation (The
Amicus Foundation)
The United Society for the
Propagation of the Gospel
United Trusts
The David Uri Memorial Trust
Uxbridge United Welfare Trust
'v'
Vale of Glamorgan – Welsh
Church Fund
The Valentine Charitable Trust
The Albert Van Den Bergh
Charitable Trust
John and Lucille van Geest
Foundation
The Van Neste Foundation
Mrs Maud Van Norden's
Charitable Foundation
The Vandervell Foundation
The Vardy Foundation
The Variety Club Children's
Charity
Veneziana Fund
The Verdon-Smith Family
Charitable Settlement
Roger Vere Foundation
Victoria Homes Trust
Viking Cares (For the Kids)
The Nigel Vinson Charitable
Trust
The William and Ellen Vinten
Trust
The Vintners' Company
Charitable Foundation
Vintners' Gifts Charity
Vision Charity
Vivdale Ltd
The Viznitz Foundation
Wade's Charity
The Scurrah Wainwright Charity
Wakeham Trust
The Community Foundation in
Wales
Wales Council for Voluntary
Action
Robert and Felicity Waley-
Cohen Charitable Trust
The Walker Trust

Wallace and Gromit's Children's Foundation

Wallington Missionary Mart and Auctions

The F J Wallis Charitable Settlement

War on Want

Sir Siegmund Warburg's Voluntary Settlement

The Ward Blenkinsop Trust

The George Ward Charitable Trust

The Barbara Ward Children's Foundation

G R Waters Charitable Trust 2000

The Waterways Trust

The Wates Foundation

Blyth Watson Charitable Trust

The Howard Watson Symington Memorial Charity

John Watson's Trust

Weatherley Charitable Trust

The Weavers' Company Benevolent Fund

The David Webster Charitable Trust

The William Webster Charitable Trust

The Weinberg Foundation

The Weinstein Foundation

The Weinstock Fund

The James Weir Foundation

The Barbara Welby Trust

The Weldon UK Charitable Trust

The Wellcome Trust

Welsh Church Fund Dyfed area (Carmarthenshire, Ceredigion and Pembrokeshire)

The Welton Foundation

The Wessex Youth Trust

The West Derby Wastelands Charity

West London Synagogue Charitable Fund

The West Yorkshire Police Community Fund

Mrs S K West's Charitable Trust

The Westcroft Trust

The Westminster Foundation

The Garfield Weston Foundation

The Barbara Whatmore Charitable Trust

The Whitaker Charitable Trust

The Colonel W H Whitbread Charitable Trust

The Simon Whitbread Charitable Trust

The Melanie White Foundation Limited

White Rose Children's Aid International Charity

The Whitecourt Charitable Trust

A H and B C Whiteley Charitable Trust

The Norman Whiteley Trust

The Whitley Animal Protection Trust

The Whittlesey Charity

The Lionel Wigram Memorial Trust

The Richard Wilcox Welfare Charity

The Felicity Wilde Charitable Trust

The Wilkinson Charitable Foundation

The Will Charitable Trust

The Kay Williams Charitable Foundation

The Williams Charitable Trust

The Williams Family Charitable Trust

Williams Serendipity Trust

The H D H Wills 1965 Charitable Trust

Dame Violet Wills Charitable Trust

The Dame Violet Wills Will Trust

The Wilmcote Charitrust

Sumner Wilson Charitable Trust

David Wilson Foundation

The Wilson Foundation

J and J R Wilson Trust

The Community Foundation for Wiltshire and Swindon

The Benjamin Winegarten Charitable Trust

The Harold Hyam Wingate Foundation

The Francis Winham Foundation

Anona Winn Charitable Trust

Wirral Mayor's Charity

The Witzenfeld Foundation

The Michael and Anna Wix Charitable Trust

The Wixamtree Trust

The Woburn 1986 Charitable Trust

The Maurice Wohl Charitable Foundation

The Charles Wolfson Charitable Trust

Women Caring Trust

The James Wood Bequest Fund

The Wood Family Trust

The Woodcock Charitable Trust

Woodlands Foundation Limited

Woodlands Green Ltd

Woodlands Trust

The Woodroffe Benton Foundation

The Geoffrey Woods Charitable Foundation

The Woodward Charitable Trust

The A and R Woolf Charitable Trust

The Woolnoth Society Charitable Trust

Worcester Municipal Charities

The Worcestershire and Dudley Historic Churches Trust

The Fred and Della Worms Charitable Trust

The Worwin UK Foundation

The Wragge and Co. Charitable Trust

The Diana Edgson Wright Charitable Trust

The Matthews Wrightson Charity Trust

Miss E B Wrightson's Charitable Settlement

Wychdale Ltd

Wychville Ltd

The Wyndham Charitable Trust

The Wyseliot Charitable Trust

The Xerox (UK) Trust

Yankov Charitable Trust

The Yapp Charitable Trust

The Yardley Great Trust

The Dennis Alan Yardy Charitable Trust

The W Wing Yip and Brothers Foundation

York and North Yorkshire Community Foundation

The York Children's Trust

Yorkshire Agricultural Society

Yorkshire Building Society Charitable Foundation

The South Yorkshire Community Foundation

The Yorkshire Dales Millennium Trust

The John Young Charitable Settlement

The William Allen Young Charitable Trust

The John K Young Endowment Fund

Youth Music

Elizabeth and Prince Zaiger Trust

Zephyr Charitable Trust

The Marjorie and Arnold Ziff Charitable Foundation

Stephen Zimmerman Charitable Trust

The Zochonis Charitable Trust

Zurich Community Trust (UK) Limited

Project support

■ Full project funding

The 1989 Willan Charitable Trust

The 29th May 1961 Charitable Trust

Aberbrothock Charitable Trust

The Aberdeen Endowments Trust

The Aberdeenshire Educational Trust Scheme

Achiezer Association Ltd

Achisomoch Aid Company Limited

The ACT Foundation

Action Medical Research

The Sylvia Adams Charitable Trust

The Victor Adda Foundation

The Adint Charitable Trust

The Adnams Charity

AF Trust Company

Age Concern Scotland Grants

Aid to the Church in Need (UK)

The AIM Foundation

The Sylvia Aitken Charitable Trust

The Ajahma Charitable Trust

Alcohol Education and Research Council

Aldgate and All Hallows' Barking Exhibition Foundation

The Aldgate Freedom Foundation

Alexandra Rose Charities

The Alexis Trust

All Saints Educational Trust

Allchurches Trust Ltd

The H B Allen Charitable Trust

The Rita Allen Charitable Trust

The Alliance Family Foundation

Angus Allnatt Charitable Foundation

The Pat Allsop Charitable Trust

The Almond Trust

Almondsbury Charity

The Altajir Trust

Altamont Ltd

Alvor Charitable Trust

AM Charitable Trust

Ambika Paul Foundation

The Ammco Trust

Sir John and Lady Amory's Charitable Trust

Viscount Amory's Charitable Trust

The Ampelos Trust

The AMW Charitable Trust

The Anchor Foundation

The Andre Christian Trust

Anguish's Educational Foundation

The Animal Defence Trust

The Eric Anker-Petersen Charity

The Annandale Charitable Trust

Ambrose and Ann Appelbe Trust

The Appletree Trust

The John Apthorp Charitable Trust

The Milly Apthorp Charitable Trust

The Arbib Foundation

The Archbishop of Canterbury's Charitable Trust

The John M Archer Charitable Trust

The Archer Trust

The Architectural Heritage Fund

The Ardwick Trust

The Argus Appeal

Armenian General Benevolent Union London Trust

The Armenian Relief Society of Great Britain Trust

The Armourers' and Brasiers' Gauntlet Trust

The Army Benevolent Fund

Arsenal Charitable Trust

The Artemis Charitable Trust

Arthritis Research Campaign

The Arts and Entertainment Charitable Trust

Arts Council England

The Arts Council of Northern Ireland

The Arts Council of Wales

The Ove Arup Foundation

The AS Charitable Trust

Ashburnham Thanksgiving Trust

A J H Ashby Will Trust

The Ashden Trust

The Ashendene Trust

The Laura Ashley Foundation

The Norman C Ashton Foundation

The Ashworth Charitable Trust

The Ian Askew Charitable Trust

The Associated Country Women of the World (ACWW)

The Association of Colleges Charitable Trust

Astellas European Foundation

AstonMansfield Charitable Trust

The Astor Foundation

The Astor of Hever Trust

The Aurelius Charitable Trust

The Lord Austin Trust

The Avenue Charitable Trust

The John Avins Trustees

AW Charitable Trust

The Aylesford Family Charitable Trust

The BAA Communities Trust

Harry Bacon Foundation

The BACTA Charitable Trust

The Bagri Foundation

Veta Bailey Charitable Trust

The Austin Bailey Trust

The Baily Thomas Charitable Fund

The Baird Trust

The Baker Charitable Trust

The Balcombe Charitable Trust

The Balint Family Charitable Trusts

The Albert Casanova Ballard Deceased Trust

The Ballinger Charitable Trust

Balmain Charitable Trust

The Balmore Trust

The Balney Charitable Trust

The Baltic Charitable Fund

The Bamford Charitable Foundation

The Banbury Charities

William P Bancroft (No 2) Charitable Trust and Jenepher Gillett Trust

The Band Trust

The Barbers' Company General Charities

The Barbour Trust

Barchester Healthcare Foundation

David and Frederick Barclay Foundation

The Baring Foundation

Peter Barker-Mill Memorial Charity

Barleycorn Trust

The Barnabas Trust

Lord Barnby's Foundation

Barnes Workhouse Fund

The Barnsbury Charitable Trust

The Barnstaple Bridge Trust

The Barnwood House Trust

The Misses Barrie Charitable Trust

Barrington Family Charitable Trust

The Charity of William Barrow

Stephen J Barry Charitable Trust

The Bartlett Taylor Charitable Trust

The Paul Bassham Charitable Trust

The Batchworth Trust

The Bay Tree Charitable Trust

D H and L H Baylin Charitable Trust

The Louis Baylis (Maidenhead Advertiser) Charitable Trust

BBC Children in Need

B-CH 1971 Charitable Trust

The Beacon Trust

Bear Mordechai Ltd
The Bearder Charity
The James Beattie Charitable Trust
The Beaufort House Trust Limited
Beauland Ltd
The Beaverbrook Foundation
The Beccles Town Lands Charity
The Becker Family Charitable Trust
The Becketts and Sargeants Educational Foundation
The John Beckwith Charitable Trust
The Peter Beckwith Charitable Trust
The Bedford Charity (The Harpur Trust)
The David and Ruth Behrend Fund
The Beit Trust
The Bellahouston Bequest Fund
Bellasis Trust
The Bellinger Donnay Trust
Belljoe Tzedoko Ltd
The Benfield Motors Charitable Trust
The Benham Charitable Settlement
Maurice and Jacqueline Bennett Charitable Trust
Michael and Leslie Bennett Charitable Trust
The Berkshire Community Foundation
The Bestway Foundation
The Betterware Foundation
Thomas Betton's Charity for Pensions and Relief-in-Need
BHST
The Mason Bibby 1981 Trust
BibleLands
The Bideford Bridge Trust
The Big Lottery Fund
The Billmeir Charitable Trust
The Bingham Trust
The Bintaub Charitable Trust
The Birmingham Community Foundation
The Birmingham District Nursing Charitable Trust
The Birmingham Hospital Saturday Fund Medical Charity and Welfare Trust
Birmingham International Airport Community Trust
The Lord Mayor of Birmingham's Charity
Birthday House Trust
The Bisgood Charitable Trust (registered as Miss Jeanne Bisgood's Charitable Trust)

The Michael Bishop Foundation
The Bishop's Development Fund
The Sydney Black Charitable Trust
The Bertie Black Foundation
Isabel Blackman Foundation
The Herbert and Peter Blagrave Charitable Trust
The Blair Foundation
Blakes Benevolent Trust
The Blanchminster Trust
The Sir Victor Blank Charitable Settlement
Blatchington Court Trust
The Neville and Elaine Blond Charitable Trust
The Bluston Charitable Settlement
Enid Blyton Trust for Children
The Body Shop Foundation
The Boltons Trust
The Bonamy Charitable Trust
The John and Celia Bonham Christie Charitable Trust
The Charlotte Bonham-Carter Charitable Trust
Bonhomie United Charity Society
The Booth Charities
The Boots Charitable Trust
The Bordon and Liphook Charity
Salo Bordon Charitable Trust
The Oliver Borthwick Memorial Trust
The Bothwell Charitable Trust
H E and E L Botteley Charitable Trust
The Harry Bottom Charitable Trust
P G and N J Boulton Trust
The A H and E Boulton Trust
Sir Clive Bourne Family Trust
The Anthony Bourne Foundation
The Bower Trust
The Bowerman Charitable Trust
John and Susan Bowers Fund
The Bowland Charitable Trust
The William Brake Charitable Trust
The Tony Bramall Charitable Trust
The Brewers' Company General Charitable Trust
The Harold and Alice Bridges Charity
Briggs Animal Welfare Trust
The Brighton District Nursing Association Trust
Bristol Archdeaconry Charity
John Bristow and Thomas Mason Trust

Britannia Foundation
The British Council for Prevention of Blindness
The British Dietetic Association General and Education Trust Fund
The British Gas (Scottish Gas) Energy Trust
British Heart Foundation
British Humane Association
British Institute at Ankara
British Ornithologists' Union
The Britten-Pears Foundation
The Britto Foundation
The J and M Britton Charitable Trust
The Charles and Edna Broadhurst Charitable Trust
The Bromley Trust
The Roger Brooke Charitable Trust
The David Brooke Charity
The Charles Brotherton Trust
Joseph Brough Charitable Trust
The Swinfen Broun Charitable Trust
Mrs E E Brown Charitable Settlement
Bill Brown's Charitable Settlement
R S Brownless Charitable Trust
T B H Brunner's Charitable Settlement
Brushmill Ltd
The Bryant Trust
Buckingham Trust
The Buckinghamshire Foundation
The Buckinghamshire Masonic Centenary Fund
Buckland Charitable Trust
The Rosemary Bugden Charitable Trust
The Bulldog Trust Limited
The E F Bulmer Benevolent Fund
The BUPA Foundation
Burdens Charitable Foundation
The Burdett Trust for Nursing
The Clara E Burgess Charity
The Burry Charitable Trust
The Audrey and Stanley Burton 1960 Charitable Trust
The Arnold Burton 1998 Charitable Trust
The Burton Breweries Charitable Trust
The Geoffrey Burton Charitable Trust
Consolidated Charity of Burton upon Trent
Butchers' Company General Charities
The Bill Butlin Charity Trust

C and F Charitable Trust
C J Cadbury Charitable Trust
Edward Cadbury Charitable Trust
Henry T and Lucy B Cadbury Charitable Trust
P H G Cadbury Charitable Trust
The Christopher Cadbury Charitable Trust
The G W Cadbury Charitable Trust
The Richard Cadbury Charitable Trust
The William A Cadbury Charitable Trust
The Edward and Dorothy Cadbury Trust
The Barrow Cadbury Trust and the Barrow Cadbury Fund
The Cadogan Charity
CAF (Charities Aid Foundation)
CAFOD
The Callander Charitable Trust
Calleva Foundation
The Calpe Trust
Calypso Browning Trust
The Campden Charities
The Canning Trust
H and L Cantor Trust
Capital Community Foundation
Cardy Beaver Foundation
The Carew Pole Charitable Trust
The D W T Cargill Fund
Caring for Kids (Radio Tay)
Carlee Ltd
The Carlton House Charitable Trust
The Worshipful Company of Carmen Benevolent Trust
The Carnegie Dunfermline Trust
The Carnegie Trust for the Universities of Scotland
The Carpenter Charitable Trust
The Carpenters' Company Charitable Trust
The Carrington Charitable Trust
The Carron Charitable Settlement
The Leslie Mary Carter Charitable Trust
The Carvill Trust
The Casey Trust
Cash for Kids Radio Clyde
Sir John Cass's Foundation
The Elizabeth Casson Trust
The Castang Foundation
The Catalyst Charitable Trust
The Catholic Charitable Trust
Catholic Foreign Missions
The Catholic Trust for England and Wales
The Cattanach Charitable Trust

The Joseph and Annie Cattle Trust
The Thomas Sivewright Catto Charitable Settlement
The Wilfrid and Constance Cave Foundation
The Cayo Foundation
Elizabeth Cayzer Charitable Trust
The B G S Cayzer Charitable Trust
The Cazenove Charitable Trust
Celtic Charity Fund
The Cemlyn-Jones Trust
CfBT Education Trust
The Amelia Chadwick Trust
The Pamela Champion Foundation
The Chapman Charitable Trust
John William Chapman's Charitable Trust
The Charities Advisory Trust
Charitworth Limited
The Charter 600 Charity
The Worshipful Company of Chartered Accountants General Charitable Trust
The Chasah Trust
The Chelsea Building Society Charitable Foundation
The Chelsea Square 1994 Trust
The Cheruby Trust
The Cheshire Provincial Fund of Benevolence
The Chetwode Foundation
The Malcolm Chick Charity
Child Growth Foundation
Children's Liver Disease Foundation
Childs Charitable Trust
The Childwick Trust
The Chippenham Borough Lands Charity
The Chipping Sodbury Town Lands Charity
CHK Charities Limited
The Chownes Foundation
The Chrimes Family Charitable Trust
The Christabella Charitable Trust
Christadelphian Samaritan Fund
Christian Aid
Christian Response to Eastern Europe
The Church and Community Fund
The Church Burgesses Educational Foundation
Church Burgesses Trust
Church Lands and John Johnson's Estate Charities
Church of Ireland Priorities Fund

The Church Urban Fund
City and County of Swansea Welsh Church Act Fund
The City Bridge Trust
The City Educational Trust Fund
The City Parochial Foundation
CLA Charitable Trust
Stephen Clark 1957 Charitable Trust
J A Clark Charitable Trust
The Hilda and Alice Clark Charitable Trust
The Roger and Sarah Bancroft Clark Charitable Trust
The Clarke Charitable Settlement
The Cleary Foundation
The Cleopatra Trust
Lord Clinton's Charitable Trust
The Clore Duffield Foundation
Miss V L Clore's 1967 Charitable Trust
Closehelm Ltd
Richard Cloudesley's Charity
The Clover Trust
The Robert Clutterbuck Charitable Trust
Clydpride Ltd
The Coalfields Regeneration Trust
The John Coates Charitable Trust
Coats Foundation Trust
The Cobtree Charity Trust Ltd
The Denise Cohen Charitable Trust
The Vivienne and Samuel Cohen Charitable Trust
The R and S Cohen Fondation
The John S Cohen Foundation
The Colchester Catalyst Charity
John Coldman Charitable Trust
The Cole Charitable Trust
The Colefax Charitable Trust
The John and Freda Coleman Charitable Trust
The George Henry Collins Charity
The E Alec Colman Charitable Fund Ltd
The Sir Jeremiah Colman Gift Trust
Col-Reno Ltd
The Coltstaple Trust
Colwinston Charitable Trust
Colyer-Fergusson Charitable Trust
Comic Relief
The Comino Foundation
Community Foundation for Calderdale
The Community Foundation for Greater Manchester

The Community Foundation for Northern Ireland

The Company of Tobacco Pipe Makers' and Tobacco Blenders' Benevolent Fund

The Compton Charitable Trust

The Congleton Inclosure Trust

The Conservation Foundation

The Consolidated Charities for the Infirm Merchant Taylors' Company

The Construction Industry Trust for Youth

Gordon Cook Foundation

The Ernest Cook Trust

The Cooks Charity

The Catherine Cookson Charitable Trust

Harold and Daphne Cooper Charitable Trust

Mabel Cooper Charity

The Alice Ellen Cooper Dean Charitable Foundation

The Co-operative Foundation

The Marjorie Coote Animal Charity Trust

The Marjorie Coote Old People's Charity

The Helen Jean Cope Trust

The J Reginald Corah Foundation Fund

The Gershon Coren Charitable Foundation

The Corinthian Trust

Edwin Cornforth 1983 Charity Trust

The Cornwell Charitable Trust

The Sidney and Elizabeth Corob Charitable Trust

The Corona Charitable Trust

The Costa Family Charitable Trust

The Cotton Industry War Memorial Trust

The Cotton Trust

County Durham Foundation

The Augustine Courtauld Trust

Coutts Charitable Trust

The General Charities of the City of Coventry

Coventry Building Society Charitable Foundation

The John Cowan Foundation

Cowley Charitable Foundation

The Sir William Coxen Trust Fund

The Lord Cozens-Hardy Trust

The Craignish Trust

The Craps Charitable Trust

Michael Crawford Children's Charity

The Cray Trust

The Crescent Trust

Criffel Charitable Trust

Cripplegate Foundation

The Violet and Milo Cripps Charitable Trust

The Cromarty Trust

The Harry Crook Foundation

The Cross Trust

The Cross Trust

The Croydon Relief in Need Charities

The Mayor of Croydon's Charity Fund

Cruden Foundation Ltd

The Ronald Cruickshanks' Foundation

Cuby Charitable Trust

The Culra Charitable Trust

Cumberland Building Society Charitable Foundation

Cumbria Community Foundation

The Cunningham Trust

The D J H Currie Memorial Trust

The Dennis Curry Charitable Trust

The Raymond Curtis Charitable Trust

The Manny Cussins Foundation

The Cwmbran Trust

Itzchok Meyer Cymerman Trust Ltd

The D'Oyly Carte Charitable Trust

The Roald Dahl Foundation

The Daily Prayer Union Charitable Trust Ltd

The Daisy Trust

The Daiwa Anglo-Japanese Foundation

Oizer Dalim Trust

The Dr and Mrs A Darlington Charitable Trust

Baron Davenport's Charity

The Davidson (Nairn) Charitable Trust

Davidson Charitable Trust

The Alderman Joe Davidson Memorial Trust

Michael Davies Charitable Settlement

The Gwendoline and Margaret Davies Charity

The Wilfrid Bruce Davis Charitable Trust

Davis-Rubens Charitable Trust

The Dawe Charitable Trust

The De Clermont Charitable Company Ltd

Peter De Haan Charitable Trust

The Leopold De Rothschild Charitable Trust

The Deakin Charitable Trust

William Dean Countryside and Educational Trust

The Debmar Benevolent Trust

The Delfont Foundation

The Dellal Foundation

The Delves Charitable Trust

The Demigryphon Trust

The Denman Charitable Trust

The Denton Charitable Trust

The Denton Wilde Sapte Charitable Trust

The Earl of Derby's Charitable Trust

Derbyshire Community Foundation

The J N Derbyshire Trust

Devon Community Foundation

The Devon Educational Trust

The Duke of Devonshire's Charitable Trust

The Sandy Dewhirst Charitable Trust

DG Charitable Settlement

The Laduma Dhamecha Charitable Trust

Diabetes UK

Alan and Sheila Diamond Charitable Trust

The Diana, Princess of Wales Memorial Fund

The Dibden Allotments Charity

The Dickon Trust

The Digbeth Trust

The Dinwoodie Settlement

Dischma Charitable Trust

The DLA Piper Charitable Trust

The DLM Charitable Trust

Louise Dobson Charitable Trust

The Derek and Eileen Dodgson Foundation

The Dollond Charitable Trust

Domepride Ltd

The Dorcas Trust

The Dorema Charitable Trust

The Dorus Trust

Double 'O' Charity Ltd

The Doughty Charity Trust

The R M Douglas Charitable Trust

The Drapers' Charitable Fund

Dromintee Trust

The Dugdale Charitable Trust

The Dulverton Trust

The P B Dumbell Charitable Trust

The Dumbreck Charity

Dunard Fund

Ronald Duncan Literary Foundation

The Houghton Dunn Charitable Trust

The Dunn Family Charitable Trust

The W E Dunn Trust

Dushinsky Trust Ltd

Mildred Duveen Charitable Trust

The Dwek Family Charitable Trust

The Dyers' Company Charitable Trust

EAGA Partnership Charitable Trust

The Eagle Charity Trust

Audrey Earle Charitable Trust

The Earley Charity

Earls Colne and Halstead Educational Charity

The Earmark Trust

East Kent Provincial Charities

East London Community Foundation

Eastern Counties Educational Trust Limited

The Sir John Eastwood Foundation

The Ebenezer Trust

The EBM Charitable Trust

Eden Arts Trust

EDF Energy Trust (EDFET)

The Gilbert and Eileen Edgar Foundation

Gilbert Edgar Trust

Edinburgh Children's Holiday Fund

The Edinburgh Trust, No 2 Account

Edinburgh Voluntary Organisations' Trust Funds

Educational Foundation of Alderman John Norman

The W G Edwards Charitable Foundation

The William Edwards Educational Charity

The Elephant Trust

The George Elias Charitable Trust

The Gerald Palmer Eling Trust Company

The Elizabeth Frankland Moore and Star Foundation

The Wilfred and Elsie Elkes Charity Fund

The Maud Elkington Charitable Trust

Ellador Ltd

The Ellerdale Trust

The John Ellerman Foundation

The Ellinson Foundation Ltd

The Edith Maud Ellis 1985 Charitable Trust

James Ellis Charitable Trust

The Elmgrant Trust

The Elmley Foundation

Elshore Ltd

The Vernon N Ely Charitable Trust

The Embleton Trust

The Emerton-Christie Charity

The Emmandjay Charitable Trust

The Worshipful Company of Engineers Charitable Trust Fund

The Englefield Charitable Trust

The English Schools' Football Association

The Enkalon Foundation

Entindale Ltd

The Epigoni Trust

Epilepsy Research UK

The Equitable Charitable Trust

The Equity Trust Fund

The Ericson Trust

The Erskine Cunningham Hill Trust

Essex Community Foundation

The Essex Fairway Charitable Trust

The Essex Heritage Trust

Essex Provincial Charity Fund

The Essex Youth Trust

Euro Charity Trust

The Evangelical Covenants Trust

The Alan Evans Memorial Trust

Sir John Evelyn's Charity

The Eventhall Family Charitable Trust

The Everard Foundation

The Eveson Charitable Trust

The Beryl Evetts and Robert Luff Animal Welfare Trust

The Execution Charitable Trust

The Mayor of Exeter's Appeal Fund

The Exilarch's Foundation

F C Charitable Trust

The F P Limited Charitable Trust

The Faber Charitable Trust

Esmée Fairbairn Foundation

The Fairway Trust

Faisaltex Charitable Trust

The Family Foundations Trust

The Family Rich Charities Trust

Famos Foundation Trust

The Lord Faringdon Charitable Trust

Samuel William Farmer's Trust

The Farmers' Company Charitable Fund

The Thomas Farr Charitable Trust

Walter Farthing (Trust) Limited

Farthing Trust

The Fassnidge Memorial Trust

Joseph Fattorini Charitable Trust 'B' Account

The Fawcett Charitable Trust

Federation of Jewish Relief Organisations

Feed the Minds

The John Feeney Charitable Bequest

The George Fentham Birmingham Charity

The A M Fenton Trust

Allan and Nesta Ferguson Charitable Settlement

Elizabeth Ferguson Charitable Trust Fund

The Bluff Field Charitable Trust

The Doris Field Charitable Trust

The Fifty Fund

Dixie Rose Findlay Charitable Trust

Gerald Finzi Charitable Trust

Firtree Trust

The Sir John Fisher Foundation

The Fishmongers' Company's Charitable Trust

Marc Fitch Fund

The Fitton Trust

The Earl Fitzwilliam Charitable Trust

Bud Flanagan Leukaemia Fund

The Rose Flatau Charitable Trust

The Ian Fleming Charitable Trust

The Joyce Fletcher Charitable Trust

The Roy Fletcher Charitable Trust

Florence's Charitable Trust

The Flow Foundation

The Gerald Fogel Charitable Trust

The Follett Trust

The Football Association National Sports Centre Trust

The Football Association Youth Trust

The Football Foundation

The Forbes Charitable Foundation

Forbesville Limited

The Forces Trust

Ford Britain Trust

The Oliver Ford Charitable Trust

Fordeve Ltd

The Forest Hill Charitable Trust

Gwyneth Forrester Trust

The Forte Charitable Trust

Lord Forte Foundation

Foundation for Management Education

Four Acre Trust

The Four Winds Trust

The Fowler, Smith and Jones Charitable Trust

The Foyle Foundation

The Isaac and Freda Frankel Memorial Charitable Trust

Sydney E Franklin Deceased's New Second Charity

The Jill Franklin Trust

The Gordon Fraser Charitable Trust

The Hugh Fraser Foundation
The Joseph Strong Frazer Trust
The Louis and Valerie
   Freedman Charitable
   Settlement
The Freemasons' Grand
   Charity
The Thomas Freke and Lady
   Norton Charity
The Charles S French
   Charitable Trust
The Anne French Memorial
   Trust
The Freshfield Foundation
The Freshgate Trust
   Foundation
The Friarsgate Trust
The Friends Hall Farm Street
   Trust
Friends of Biala Ltd
Friends of Wiznitz Limited
Friends Provident Charitable
   Foundation
The Frognal Trust
T F C Frost Charitable Trust
Maurice Fry Charitable Trust
Mejer and Gertrude Miriam
   Frydman Foundation
The Fuellers Charitable Trust
   Fund
The Fulmer Charitable Trust
Worshipful Company of
   Furniture Makers Charitable
   Fund
Gableholt Limited
The Galbraith Trust
The Gale Family Charitable
   Trust
The Angela Gallagher Memorial
   Fund
The Gamlen Charitable Trust
The Gamma Trust
The Gannochy Trust
The Ganzoni Charitable Trust
The Worshipful Company of
   Gardeners of London
The Samuel Gardner Memorial
   Trust
The Garnett Charitable Trust
Garrick Charitable Trust
Garvan Limited
The Gatsby Charitable
   Foundation
The Robert Gavron Charitable
   Trust
Jacqueline and Michael Gee
   Charitable Trust
The General Nursing Council
   for England and Wales
   Trust
J Paul Getty Jr Charitable Trust
The Gibbs Charitable Trust
Simon Gibson Charitable Trust
The G C Gibson Charitable
   Trust

The Harvey and Hilary Gilbert
   Charitable Trust
The Girdlers' Company
   Charitable Trust
The B and P Glasser
   Charitable Trust
The Glass-House Trust
Global Care
Global Charities (formally
   GCap Charities)
Gloucestershire Community
   Foundation
Worshipful Company of
   Glovers of London Charity
   Fund
GMC Trust
The GNC Trust
The Meir Golda Trust
The Sydney and Phyllis
   Goldberg Memorial
   Charitable Trust
The Golden Bottle Trust
Golden Charitable Trust
The Jack Goldhill Charitable
   Trust
The Goldsmiths' Arts Trust
   Fund
The Goldsmiths' Company
   Charity
The Golsoncott Foundation
The Good Neighbours Trust
Nicholas and Judith
   Goodison's Charitable
   Settlement
The Everard and Mina
   Goodman Charitable
   Foundation
Mike Gooley Trailfinders
   Charity
Leonard Gordon Charitable
   Trust
The Gosling Foundation
   Limited
The Gough Charitable Trust
The Gould Charitable Trust
The Grace Charitable Trust
A B Grace Trust
The Graff Foundation
The Grahame Charitable
   Foundation Limited
Grampian Police Diced Cap
   Charitable Fund
The Granada Foundation
Grand Charitable Trust of the
   Order of Women
   Freemasons
The Grand Order of Water
   Rats' Charities Fund
The Grange Farm Centre Trust
Grantham Yorke Trust
The Gray Trust
The Great Stone Bridge Trust
   of Edenbridge
The Great Torrington Town
   Lands Charity

The Constance Green
   Foundation
The Barry Green Memorial
   Fund
The Philip Green Memorial
   Trust
Mrs H R Greene Charitable
   Settlement
Greenham Common
   Community Trust Limited
Naomi and Jeffrey Greenwood
   Charitable Trust
Greggs Foundation
Grimmitt Trust
The Grocers' Charity
The M and R Gross Charities
   Limited
The Grove Charitable Trust
The GRP Charitable Trust
The David and Marie Grumitt
   Foundation
The Bishop of Guildford's
   Foundation
The Guildry Incorporation of
   Perth
The Walter Guinness
   Charitable Trust
The Gulbenkian Foundation
The Gunter Charitable Trust
The Gur Trust
Gurunanak
Dr Guthrie's Association
The H and M Charitable Trust
H C D Memorial Fund
The H P Charitable Trust
The Hackney Parochial
   Charities
The Hadfield Trust
The Hadley Trust
The Hadrian Trust
The Alfred Haines Charitable
   Trust
The Hale Trust
E F and M G Hall Charitable
   Trust
The Edith Winifred Hall
   Charitable Trust
Robert Hall Charity
The Hamamelis Trust
Hamilton Wallace Trust
Paul Hamlyn Foundation
Sue Hammerson's Charitable
   Trust
The Hammonds Charitable
   Trust
The Hampshire and Islands
   Historic Churches Trust
Hampton Fuel Allotment
   Charity
The W A Handley Charitable
   Trust
Beatrice Hankey Foundation
   Ltd
The Hanley Trust
The Kathleen Hannay
   Memorial Charity

The Doughty Hanson
   Charitable Foundation
Lord Hanson Foundation
The Haramead Trust
Miss K M Harbinson's
   Charitable Trust
Harbo Charities Limited
The Harborne Parish Lands
   Charity
The Harbour Charitable Trust
The Harbour Foundation
The Harding Trust
William Harding's Charity
The Hare of Steep Charitable
   Trust
The Harebell Centenary Fund
The Kenneth Hargreaves
   Charitable Trust
The Harris Charitable Trust
The Harris Charity
The Harrison and Potter Trust
The John Harrison Charitable
   Trust
The Peter Harrison Foundation
The Spencer Hart Charitable
   Trust
The Hartley Charitable Trust
The N and P Hartley Memorial
   Trust
William Geoffrey Harvey's
   Discretionary Settlement
Haskel Family Foundation
The Hathaway Trust
The Maurice Hatter Foundation
The M A Hawe Settlement
The Hawthorne Charitable
   Trust
The Dorothy Hay-Bolton
   Charitable Trust
The Haydan Charitable Trust
The Haymills Charitable Trust
The Headley Trust
Headley-Pitt Charitable Trust
Heagerty Charitable Trust
The Heald Charitable Trust
Healthsure Group Ltd
May Hearnshaw's Charity
The Heart of England
   Community Foundation
The Heathcoat Trust
Heathside Charitable Trust
The Charlotte Heber-Percy
   Charitable Trust
Percy Hedley 1990 Charitable
   Trust
The Hedley Denton Charitable
   Trust
The Hedley Foundation
The H J Heinz Company
   Limited Charitable Trust
The Hellenic Foundation
The Michael and Morven Heller
   Charitable Foundation
The Simon Heller Charitable
   Settlement
Help the Aged

Help the Homeless
Help the Hospices
The Hemby Trust
The Christina Mary Hendrie
   Trust for Scottish and
   Canadian Charities
The Henley Educational Charity
Philip Henman Trust
Esther Hennell Charitable
   Trust
The G D Herbert Charitable
   Trust
The Joanna Herbert-Stepney
   Charitable Settlement
The Anne Herd Memorial Trust
The Herefordshire Historic
   Churches Trust
The Heritage of London Trust
   Ltd
The Hertfordshire Community
   Foundation
The Hesed Trust
The Hesslewood Children's
   Trust (Hull Seamen's and
   General Orphanage)
The Bernhard Heuberger
   Charitable Trust
Hexham and Newcastle
   Diocesan Trust (1947)
The Higgs Charitable Trust
Alan Edward Higgs Charity
The High Sheriff's Police Trust
   for the County of West
   Midlands
Highcroft Charitable Trust
The Hilden Charitable Fund
The Joseph and Mary Hiley
   Trust
The Holly Hill Charitable Trust
The Charles Littlewood Hill
   Trust
The Hillingdon Partnership
   Trust
R G Hills Charitable Trust
Hinchley Charitable Trust
Lady Hind Trust
Stuart Hine Trust
The Hinrichsen Foundation
The Hitchin Educational
   Foundation
The Eleemosynary Charity of
   William Hobbayne
Hobson Charity Limited
Hockerill Educational
   Foundation
Matthew Hodder Charitable
   Trust
The Sir Julian Hodge
   Charitable Trust
The Jane Hodge Foundation
The J G Hogg Charitable Trust
The Holden Charitable Trust
John Holford's Charity
The Hollick Family Charitable
   Trust

The Dorothy Holmes Charitable
   Trust
The Holst Foundation
P H Holt Foundation
The Edward Holt Trust
The Holywood Trust
The Homelands Charitable
   Trust
The Homestead Charitable
   Trust
Mary Homfray Charitable Trust
Sir Harold Hood's Charitable
   Trust
The Hope Trust
HopMarket Charity
The Cuthbert Horn Trust
The Antony Hornby Charitable
   Trust
The Horne Foundation
The Horne Trust
The Worshipful Company of
   Horners' Charitable Trusts
The Hornsey Parochial
   Charities
The Hospital of God at
   Greatham
The Hospital Saturday Fund
Houblon-Norman/George Fund
The House of Industry Estate
The Reta Lila Howard
   Foundation
The Daniel Howard Trust
The Huddersfield Medical Trust
   Fund
The Hudson Foundation
The Huggard Charitable Trust
The Geoffrey C Hughes
   Charitable Trust
The Hull and East Riding
   Charitable Trust
Hulme Trust Estates
   (Educational)
Human Relief Foundation
The Humanitarian Trust
The Michael and Shirley Hunt
   Charitable Trust
The Hunter Foundation
Miss Agnes H Hunter's Trust
The Huntingdon Foundation
Huntingdon Freemen's Charity
John Huntingdon's Charity
Hurdale Charity Limited
The Huxham Charitable Trust
The Nani Huyu Charitable Trust
The P Y N and B Hyams Trust
The Hyde Charitable Trust –
   Youth Plus
The Idlewild Trust
The Iliffe Family Charitable
   Trust
The Indigo Trust
The Ingram Trust
The Inland Waterways
   Association
The Inlight Trust
The Inman Charity

The Inner London Magistrates
Court Poor Box Charity and
Feeder Charity
The Worshipful Company of
Innholders General Charity
Fund
The International Bankers
Charitable Trust (The
Worshipful Compnay of
Interntional Bankers)
The Ireland Fund of Great
Britain
The Irish Youth Foundation
(UK) Ltd
The Ironmongers' Foundation
Irshad Trust
The Charles Irving Charitable
Trust
Irwin Trust
The ISA Charity
The Isaacs Charitable Trust
The J Isaacs Charitable Trust
The Island Health Trust
Isle of Dogs Community
Foundation
The ITF Seafarers Trust
J A R Charitable Trust
The J J Charitable Trust
The J R S S T Charitable Trust
Elizabeth Jackson Charitable
Trust
Jacobs Charitable Trust
The Ruth and Lionel Jacobson
Trust (Second Fund) No 2
Jaffe Family Relief Fund
The Susan and Stephen
James Charitable
Settlement
The James Trust
The Jarman Charitable Trust
The John Jarrold Trust
JCA Charitable Foundation
The Jeffrey Charitable Trust
Rees Jeffreys Road Fund
The Jenour Foundation
The Jephcott Charitable Trust
The Jerusalem Trust
Jerwood Charitable Foundation
Jesus Hospital Charity
Jewish Child's Day
The Jewish Youth Fund
The JMK Charitable Trust
The Joanies Trust
The Harold Joels Charitable
Trust
The Jonathan Joels Charitable
Trust
The Nicholas Joels Charitable
Trust
The Norman Joels Charitable
Trust
The Joffe Charitable Trust
The Elton John Aids
Foundation
The Lillie Johnson Charitable
Trust

The Johnson Group Cleaners
Charity
The Johnnie Johnson Trust
The Johnson Wax Ltd
Charitable Trust
The Joicey Trust
The Jones 1986 Charitable
Trust
The Marjorie and Geoffrey
Jones Charitable Trust
The Jordan Charitable
Foundation
The J E Joseph Charitable
Fund
The Lady Eileen Joseph
Foundation
JTH Charitable Trust
The Judith Trust
The Anton Jurgens Charitable
Trust
The Bernard Kahn Charitable
Trust
The Stanley Kalms Foundation
The Karenza Foundation
The Boris Karloff Charitable
Foundation
The Ian Karten Charitable
Trust
The Kasner Charitable Trust
The Kass Charitable Trust
The Kathleen Trust
The Michael and Ilse Katz
Foundation
The Katzauer Charitable
Settlement
The C S Kaufman Charitable
Trust
The Geoffrey John Kaye
Charitable Foundation
The Emmanuel Kaye
Foundation
Kelsick's Educational
Foundation
The KempWelch Charitable
Trust
The Kay Kendall Leukaemia
Fund
William Kendall's Charity (Wax
Chandlers' Company)
The Kennedy Charitable
Foundation
The Kennel Club Charitable
Trust
The Nancy Kenyon Charitable
Trust
Keren Association
Kermaville Ltd
E and E Kernkraut Charities
Limited
The Peter Kershaw Trust
The Kessler Foundation
Keswick Hall Charity
The Ursula Keyes Trust
The Robert Kiln Charitable
Trust

The King Henry VIII Endowed
Trust Warwick
The King/Cullimore Charitable
Trust
The King's Fund
The Kingsbury Charity
The Mary Kinross Charitable
Trust
Kinsurdy Charitable Trust
Kirkley Poor's Lands Estate
The Richard Kirkman
Charitable Trust
Kirschel Foundation
Robert Kitchin (Saddlers'
Company)
Ernest Kleinwort Charitable
Trust
The Marina Kleinwort
Charitable Trust
The Kobler Trust
The Kohn Foundation
The Kreditor Charitable Trust
The Kreitman Foundation
The Neil Kreitman Foundation
The Kyte Charitable Trust
Lacims-Maclis Charitable Trust
The Late Sir Pierce Lacy
Charity Trust
John Laing Charitable Trust
Maurice and Hilda Laing
Charitable Trust
The Laing Family Foundations
The Christopher Laing
Foundation
The Kirby Laing Foundation
The Martin Laing Foundation
The Beatrice Laing Trust
The Lambert Charitable Trust
Duchy of Lancaster Benevolent
Fund
The Lancaster Foundation
LandAid Charitable Trust
The Allen Lane Foundation
The Langdale Trust
The Langley Charitable Trust
The Langtree Trust
The LankellyChase Foundation
The Lanvern Foundation
The R J Larg Family Charitable
Trust
Largsmount Ltd
The Lark Trust
Laslett's (Hinton) Charity
Lauchentilly Charitable
Foundation 1988
Laufer Charitable Trust
The Lauffer Family Charitable
Foundation
Mrs F B Laurence Charitable
Trust
The Kathleen Laurence Trust
The Law Society Charity
The Edgar E Lawley Foundation
The Herd Lawson and Muriel
Lawson Charitable Trust

The Lawson Beckman
  Charitable Trust
The Raymond and Blanche
  Lawson Charitable Trust
The Carole and Geoffrey
  Lawson Foundation
The Mason Le Page Charitable
  Trust
The Leach Fourteenth Trust
The David Lean Foundation
The Leathersellers' Company
  Charitable Fund
The Leche Trust
The Arnold Lee Charitable
  Trust
The William Leech Charity
The Lord Mayor of Leeds
  Appeal Fund
Leeds Building Society
  Charitable Foundation
Leicester Charity Link
The Kennedy Leigh Charitable
  Trust
Morris Leigh Foundation
The Leigh Trust
Mrs Vera Leigh's Charity
The P Leigh-Bramwell Trust 'E'
The Lennox and Wyfold
  Foundation
The Erica Leonard Trust
The Leonard Trust
The Mark Leonard Trust
Lesley Lesley and Mutter Trust
Leukaemia Research Fund
The Leverhulme Trade
  Charities Trust
Lord Leverhulme's Charitable
  Trust
The Joseph Levy Charitable
  Foundation
Lewis Family Charitable Trust
The John Spedan Lewis
  Foundation
The Sir Edward Lewis
  Foundation
John Lewis Partnership
  General Community Fund
Lichfield Conduit Lands
Lifeline 4 Kids
The Thomas Lilley Memorial
  Trust
Limoges Charitable Trust
The Linbury Trust
The Lind Trust
Lindale Educational
  Foundation
The Linden Charitable Trust
The Enid Linder Foundation
The Linmardon Trust
The Ruth and Stuart Lipton
  Charitable Trust
The Lister Charitable Trust
Frank Litchfield Charitable
  Trust

The Andrew and Mary
  Elizabeth Little Charitable
  Trust
The Second Joseph Aaron
  Littman Foundation
The George John and Sheilah
  Livanos Charitable Trust
Liverpool Charity and Voluntary
  Services
Liverpool Sailors' Home Trust
Jack Livingstone Charitable
  Trust
The Elaine and Angus Lloyd
  Charitable Trust
The Charles Lloyd Foundation
The Lloyd Fund
Lloyd's Charities Trust
The Lloyd-Everett Trust
Lloyds TSB Foundation for
  England and Wales
Lloyds TSB Foundation for
  Northern Ireland
Lloyds TSB Foundation for the
  Channel Islands
Llysdinam Charitable Trust
Localtrent Ltd
The Locker Foundation
The Loftus Charitable Trust
The Lolev Charitable Trust
London Catalyst
The London Law Trust
The London Marathon
  Charitable Trust
The William and Katherine
  Longman Trust
The Loseley and Guildway
  Charitable Trust
The Lotus Foundation
The Lowy Mitchell Foundation
The C L Loyd Charitable Trust
LSA Charitable Trust
The Marie Helen Luen
  Charitable Trust
Robert Luff Foundation Ltd
Henry Lumley Charitable Trust
Lady Lumley's Educational
  Foundation
Paul Lunn-Rockliffe Charitable
  Trust
C F Lunoe Trust Fund
The Ruth and Jack Lunzer
  Charitable Trust
Lord and Lady Lurgan Trust
The Lyndhurst Trust
The Lynn Foundation
The Lynwood Trust
John Lyon's Charity
The Lyons Charitable Trust
The Sir Jack Lyons Charitable
  Trust
Malcolm Lyons Foundation
The Lyras Family Charitable
  Trust
Sylvanus Lyson's Charity
The M and C Trust

The M D and S Charitable
  Trust
The M K Charitable Trust
The Madeline Mabey Trust
The E M MacAndrew Trust
Macdonald-Buchanan
  Charitable Trust
The Macfarlane Walker Trust
The Mackay and Brewer
  Charitable Trust
The Mackintosh Foundation
The MacRobert Trust
Ian Mactaggart Trust
James Madison Trust
The Magdalen and Lasher
  Charity
The Magen Charitable Trust
Mageni Trust
Mahavir Trust
Man Group plc Charitable
  Trust
Manchester Airport Community
  Trust Fund
The Manchester Guardian
  Society Charitable Trust
Manchester Kids
Lord Mayor of Manchester's
  Charity Appeal Trust
Mandeville Trust
The Manifold Charitable Trust
W M Mann Foundation
The Leslie and Lilian Manning
  Trust
Maranatha Christian Trust
Marbeh Torah Trust
The Marchday Charitable Fund
Marchig Animal Welfare Trust
The Stella and Alexander
  Margulies Charitable Trust
Mariapolis Limited
Market Harborough and The
  Bowdens Charity
Michael Marks Charitable
  Trust
The Ann and David Marks
  Foundation
The Hilda and Samuel Marks
  Foundation
J P Marland Charitable Trust
Marr-Munning Trust
The Michael Marsh Charitable
  Trust
The Marsh Christian Trust
The Charlotte Marshall
  Charitable Trust
The Jim Marshall Charitable
  Trust
The D G Marshall of
  Cambridge Trust
Marshall's Charity
Marshgate Charitable
  Settlement
Sir George Martin Trust
John Martin's Charity
The Mason Porter Charitable
  Trust

The Nancie Massey Charitable Trust
The Mathew Trust
Matliwala Family Charitable Trust
The Matt 6.3 Charitable Trust
The Violet Mauray Charitable Trust
The Maxell Educational Trust
The Maxwell Family Foundation
Evelyn May Trust
Mayfair Charities Ltd
The Mayfield Valley Arts Trust
Mazars Charitable Trust
The McDougall Trust
The A M McGreevy No 5 Charitable Settlement
The McKenna Charitable Trust
Martin McLaren Memorial Trust
The Helen Isabella McMorran Charitable Foundation
D D McPhail Charitable Settlement
The James Frederick and Ethel Anne Measures Charity
Medical Research Council
The Medlock Charitable Trust
The Anthony and Elizabeth Mellows Charitable Settlement
Melodor Ltd
Melow Charitable Trust
Meningitis Trust
Menuchar Ltd
Brian Mercer Charitable Trust
The Mercers' Charitable Foundation
The Merchant Taylors' Company Charities Fund
The Merchant Venturers' Charity
The Merchants' House of Glasgow
Mercury Phoenix Trust
The Mersey Docks and Harbour Company Charitable Fund
Community Foundation for Merseyside
The Zachary Merton and George Woofindin Convalescent Trust
The Tony Metherell Charitable Trust
The Methodist Relief and Development Fund
The Metropolitan Drinking Fountain and Cattle Trough Association
Gerald Micklem Charitable Trust
The Masonic Province of Middlesex Charitable Trust
Midhurst Pensions Trust
The Migraine Trust

Miles Trust for the Putney and Roehampton Community
Millennium Stadium Charitable Trust
The Hugh and Mary Miller Bequest Trust
The Miller Foundation
The Millfield House Foundation
The Millfield Trust
The Millhouses Charitable Trust
The Millichope Foundation
The Mills Charity
The Millward Charitable Trust
The Clare Milne Trust
Milton Keynes Community Foundation
The Edgar Milward Charity
The Peter Minet Trust
Minge's Gift and the Pooled Trusts
The Minos Trust
The Mirfield Educational Charity
The Laurence Misener Charitable Trust
The Mishcon Family Charitable Trust
The Misselbrook Trust
The Esmé Mitchell Trust
Keren Mitzvah Trust
The Mizpah Trust
The Mobbs Memorial Trust Ltd
The Modiano Charitable Trust
The Moette Charitable Trust
The Mole Charitable Trust
The D C Moncrieff Charitable Trust
Monmouthshire County Council Welsh Church Act Fund
The Montague Thompson Coon Charitable Trust
The Colin Montgomerie Charitable Foundation
The Monument Trust
Moody Charitable Trust
George A Moore Foundation
The Nigel Moores Family Charitable Trust
John Moores Foundation
The Peter Moores Foundation
The Morel Charitable Trust
The Morgan Charitable Foundation
The Mr and Mrs J T Morgan Foundation
The J P Morgan Foundations
Diana and Allan Morgenthau Charitable Trust
The Oliver Morland Charitable Trust
S C and M E Morland's Charitable Trust
The Morris Charitable Trust
The Willie and Mabel Morris Charitable Trust

The Peter Morrison Charitable Foundation
The Stanley Morrison Charitable Trust
Moshal Charitable Trust
Vyoel Moshe Charitable Trust
The Moss Charitable Trust
The Robert and Margaret Moss Charitable Trust
Moss Family Charitable Trust
The Mount Everest Foundation
Mountbatten Festival of Music
The Mountbatten Memorial Trust
The Edwina Mountbatten Trust
The Mugdock Children's Trust
The F H Muirhead Charitable Trust
The Mulberry Trust
The Edith Murphy Foundation
Murphy-Neumann Charity Company Limited
The Mushroom Fund
The Music Sales Charitable Trust
Muslim Hands
The Mutual Trust Group
MYA Charitable Trust
The Kitty and Daniel Nabarro Charitable Trust
The Nadezhda Charitable Trust
The Willie Nagel Charitable Trust
The Naggar Charitable Trust
The Eleni Nakou Foundation
The Janet Nash Charitable Settlement
Nathan Charitable Trust
Asthma UK
The National Churches Trust
The National Manuscripts Conservation Trust
Nazareth Trust Fund
The Nchima Trust
Needham Market and Barking Welfare Charities
The Worshipful Company of Needlemakers' Charitable Fund
The Neighbourly Charitable Trust
The James Neill Trust Fund
Nemoral Ltd
Nesswall Ltd
Nestle Rowntree Employees Community Fund
Network for Social Change
The New Appeals Organisation for the City and County of Nottingham
New Court Charitable Trust
Newby Trust Limited
The Newcomen Collett Foundation
The Richard Newitt Fund

Mr and Mrs F E F Newman
  Charitable Trust
The Frances and Augustus
  Newman Foundation
Newpier Charity Ltd
Alderman Newton's
  Educational Foundation
The Chevras Ezras Nitzrochim
  Trust
The Noel Buxton Trust
The Noon Foundation
The Norda Trust
Norie Charitable Trust
Normalyn Charitable Trust
The Norman Family Charitable
  Trust
The Duncan Norman Trust
  Fund
The Normanby Charitable Trust
The North British Hotel Trust
The North West Cancer
  Research Fund
The Northampton Municipal
  Church Charities
The Northampton Queen's
  Institute Relief in Sickness
  Fund
The Earl of Northampton's
  Charity
The Northcott Devon
  Foundation
The Northcott Devon Medical
  Foundation
The Northern Rock Foundation
The Northmoor Trust
The Northumberland Village
  Homes Trust
The Northumbria Historic
  Churches Trust
The Northwood Charitable
  Trust
The Norton Foundation
The Norwich Church of England
  Young Men's Society
The Norwich Historic Churches
  Trust Ltd
The Norwich Town Close
  Estate Charity
The Noswad Charity
The Notgrove Trust
The Nottingham General
  Dispensary
The Nottingham Gordon
  Memorial Trust for Boys
  and Girls
Nottinghamshire Community
  Foundation
The Nottinghamshire Historic
  Churches Trust
The Nottinghamshire Miners'
  Welfare Trust Fund
Novi Most International
The Nuffield Foundation
The Father O'Mahoney
  Memorial Trust

The Sir Peter O'Sullevan
  Charitable Trust
The Oak Trust
The Oakdale Trust
The Oakley Charitable Trust
The Oakmoor Charitable Trust
The Odin Charitable Trust
Ogilvie Charities Deed No.2
  (including the Charity of
  Mary Catherine Ford Smith)
The Ogle Christian Trust
Oglesby Charitable Trust
The Oizer Charitable Trust
The Old Broad Street Charity
  Trust
The Old Enfield Charitable
  Trust
Old Possum's Practical Trust
The John Oldacre Foundation
The Oldham Foundation
The Olga Charitable Trust
Onaway Trust
Open Gate
The Ormsby Charitable Trust
Orrin Charitable Trust
The Ouseley Trust
The Owen Family Trust
Oxfam (GB)
City of Oxford Charity
The Oxfordshire Community
  Foundation
The P F Charitable Trust
Padwa Charitable Foundation
The Pallant Charitable Trust
The Palmer Foundation
Eleanor Palmer Trust
The Panacea Society
Panahpur Charitable Trust
Panton Trust
The Paragon Trust
The Park House Charitable
  Trust
The Frank Parkinson
  Agricultural Trust
The Samuel and Freda
  Parkinson Charitable Trust
The Parthenon Trust
Arthur James Paterson
  Charitable Trust
The Constance Paterson
  Charitable Trust
Miss M E Swinton Paterson's
  Charitable Trust
The Patrick Charitable Trust
The Jack Patston Charitable
  Trust
Paycare Charity Trust
The Payne Charitable Trust
The Harry Payne Trust
The Susanna Peake Charitable
  Trust
Pearson's Holiday Fund
The Pedmore Sporting Club
  Trust Fund
The Dowager Countess
  Eleanor Peel Trust

Peltz Trust
The Pennycress Trust
The Performing Right Society
  Foundation
B E Perl Charitable Trust
The Persson Charitable Trust
The Persula Foundation
The Pestalozzi Overseas
  Children's Trust
The Jack Petchey Foundation
The Petplan Charitable Trust
The Philips and Rubens
  Charitable Trust
The Phillips Charitable Trust
The Phillips Family Charitable
  Trust
Philological Foundation
The David Pickford Charitable
  Foundation
The Claude and Margaret Pike
  Charity
The Pilgrim Trust
The Cecil Pilkington Charitable
  Trust
The Pilkington Charities Fund
The Austin and Hope
  Pilkington Trust
The Sir Harry Pilkington Trust
The Col W W Pilkington Will
  Trusts The General Charity
  Fund
Miss A M Pilkington's
  Charitable Trust
Mrs Pilkington's Charitable
  Trust
The Plaisterers' Company
  Charitable Trust
The Platinum Trust
G S Plaut Charitable Trust
  Limited
The Poling Charitable Trust
The George and Esme Pollitzer
  Charitable Settlement
The J S F Pollitzer Charitable
  Settlement
The Ponton House Trust
The Mayor of Poole's Appeal
  Fund
Edith and Ferdinand Porjes
  Charitable Trust
The John Porter Charitable
  Trust
The Porter Foundation
The Portrack Charitable Trust
The J E Posnansky Charitable
  Trust
The Mary Potter Convent
  Hospital Trust
The David and Elaine Potter
  Foundation
The Powell Foundation
Prairie Trust
The W L Pratt Charitable Trust
Premierquote Ltd
Premishlaner Charitable Trust

The Lucy Price Relief-in-Need
Charity
Sir John Priestman Charity
Trust
The Primrose Trust
The Prince's Charities
Foundation
Princess Anne's Charities
The Priory Foundation
Prison Service Charity Fund
The Privy Purse Charitable
Trust
The Proven Family Trust
The Provincial Grand Charity of
the Province of Derbyshire
PSA Peugeot Citroen Charity
Trust
The Puebla Charitable Trust
The Richard and Christine
Purchas Charitable Trust
The Puri Foundation
Mr and Mrs J A Pye's
Charitable Settlement
Quartet Community Foundation
Queen Mary's Roehampton
Trust
The Queen's Silver Jubilee
Trust
Quercus Trust
The R D Crusaders Foundation
R J M Charitable Trust
R S Charitable Trust
The R V W Trust
The Monica Rabagliati
Charitable Trust
Rachel Charitable Trust
The Mr and Mrs Philip
Rackham Charitable Trust
Richard Radcliffe Charitable
Trust
The Radcliffe Trust
The Ragdoll Foundation
The Rainford Trust
The Peggy Ramsay Foundation
The Joseph and Lena Randall
Charitable Trust
The Rank Foundation
Ranworth Trust
The Fanny Rapaport Charitable
Settlement
The Ratcliff Foundation
The Ratcliff Pension Charity
The Ratcliffe Charitable Trust
The Eleanor Rathbone
Charitable Trust
The Sigrid Rausing Trust
The Ravensdale Trust
The Rayden Charitable Trust
The Roger Raymond Charitable
Trust
The Rayne Foundation
The Rayne Trust
The John Rayner Charitable
Trust
The Albert Reckitt Charitable
Trust

The Sir James Reckitt Charity
The Red Arrows Trust
Red Hill Charitable Trust
The Red Rose Charitable Trust
The C A Redfern Charitable
Foundation
The Reed Foundation
Richard Reeve's Foundation
The Max Reinhardt Charitable
Trust
Relief Fund for Romania
Limited
REMEDI
The Rest Harrow Trust
Reuben Brothers Foundation
The Joan K Reynell Charitable
Trust
The Nathaniel Reyner Trust
Fund
The Rhododendron Trust
Daisie Rich Trust
The Sir Cliff Richard Charitable
Trust
C B Richard Ellis Charitable
Trust
The Clive Richards Charity
The Violet M Richards Charity
The Richmond Parish Lands
Charity
The Muriel Edith Rickman
Trust
Ridgesave Limited
The Ripple Effect Foundation
The Sir John Ritblat Family
Foundation
The River Trust
Riverside Charitable Trust
Limited
The Daniel Rivlin Charitable
Trust
Thomas Roberts Trust
The Alex Roberts-Miller
Foundation
The Robertson Trust
Edwin George Robinson
Charitable Trust
Robyn Charitable Trust
The Rochester Bridge Trust
The Rock Foundation
The Rock Solid Trust
The Rofeh Trust
Richard Rogers Charitable
Settlement
Rokach Family Charitable Trust
The Helen Roll Charitable
Trust
The Sir James Roll Charitable
Trust
The Roman Research Trust
Romeera Foundation
The C A Rookes Charitable
Trust
Mrs L D Rope Third Charitable
Settlement
The Rosca Trust
The Rose Foundation

The Cecil Rosen Foundation
Rosetrees Trust
The Rothermere Foundation
The Rotherwick Foundation
The Rothschild Foundation
The Roughley Charitable Trust
Mrs Gladys Row Fogo
Charitable Trust
The Rowan Charitable Trust
Rowanville Ltd
The Christopher Rowbotham
Charitable Trust
The Rowing Foundation
The Rowlands Trust
The Joseph Rowntree
Charitable Trust
The Joseph Rowntree
Foundation
Joseph Rowntree Reform Trust
Limited
Royal Artillery Charitable Fund
Royal British Legion
Royal Docks Trust (London)
Royal Masonic Trust for Girls
and Boys
The Royal Scots Benevolent
Society
The Alfred and Frances
Rubens Charitable Trust
The Rubin Foundation
William Arthur Rudd Memorial
Trust
The Rufford Maurice Laing
Foundation
The Russell Trust
Ryklow Charitable Trust 1992
The J S and E C Rymer
Charitable Trust
S O Charitable Trust
The Michael Sacher Charitable
Trust
The Michael Harry Sacher
Trust
Dr Mortimer and Theresa
Sackler Foundation
The Raymond and Beverley
Sackler Foundation
The Ruzin Sadagora Trust
The Saddlers' Company
Charitable Fund
Erach and Roshan Sadri
Foundation
The Saga Charitable Trust
The Jean Sainsbury Animal
Welfare Trust
The Alan and Babette
Sainsbury Charitable Fund
Saint Sarkis Charity Trust
The Saintbury Trust
The Saints and Sinners Trust
The Salamander Charitable
Trust
The Salt Foundation
The Salt Trust
The Salters' Charities

The Andrew Salvesen
   Charitable Trust
The Sammermar Trust
Basil Samuel Charitable Trust
Coral Samuel Charitable Trust
The Hon. M J Samuel
   Charitable Trust
The Peter Samuel Charitable
   Trust
The Camilla Samuel Fund
The Samworth Foundation
The Sandra Charitable Trust
Santander UK Foundation
   Limited
Jimmy Savile Charitable Trust
The Scarfe Charitable Trust
The Schapira Charitable Trust
The Annie Schiff Charitable
   Trust
The Schmidt-Bodner Charitable
   Trust
The R H Scholes Charitable
   Trust
The Schreib Trust
The Schreiber Charitable Trust
Schroder Charity Trust
The Scott Bader
   Commonwealth Ltd
The Francis C Scott Charitable
   Trust
The Frieda Scott Charitable
   Trust
Sir Samuel Scott of Yews
   Trust
The Sir James and Lady Scott
   Trust
The Scott Trust Foundation
The Storrow Scott Will Trust
The Scottish Arts Council
Scottish Churches' Community
   Trust
Scottish Coal Industry Special
   Welfare Fund
The Scottish Community
   Foundation
The Scottish International
   Education Trust
The Scouloudi Foundation
Seafarers UK (King George's
   Fund for Sailors)
Seamen's Hospital Society
The Searchlight Electric
   Charitable Trust
The Searle Charitable Trust
The Helene Sebba Charitable
   Trust
The Samuel Sebba Charitable
   Trust
The Seedfield Trust
Sellata Ltd
SEM Charitable Trust
The Ayrton Senna Foundation
The Seven Fifty Trust
The Severn Trent Water
   Charitable Trust Fund
SFIA Educational Trust Limited

The Cyril Shack Trust
The Jean Shanks Foundation
The Shanti Charitable Trust
ShareGift (The Orr Mackintosh
   Foundation)
The Linley Shaw Foundation
The Sheepdrove Trust
The Sheffield and District
   Hospital Services
   Charitable Fund
The Sheldon Trust
The P and D Shepherd
   Charitable Trust
The Sylvia and Colin Shepherd
   Charitable Trust
The Archie Sherman Cardiff
   Foundation
The Archie Sherman Charitable
   Trust
The R C Sherriff Trust
The Shetland Charitable Trust
SHINE (Support and Help in
   Education)
The Barnett and Sylvia Shine
   No 2 Charitable Trust
The Bassil Shippam and
   Alsford Trust
The Shipwrights' Company
   Charitable Fund
The Shirley Foundation
Shlomo Memorial Fund Limited
The J A Shone Memorial Trust
The Charles Shorto Charitable
   Trust
The Barbara A Shuttleworth
   Memorial Trust
The Mary Elizabeth Siebel
   Charity
David and Jennifer Sieff
   Charitable Trust
The Julius Silman Charitable
   Trust
The Leslie Silver Charitable
   Trust
The Simpson Education and
   Conservation Trust
The Simpson Foundation
The Huntly and Margery
   Sinclair Charitable Trust
Sino-British Fellowship Trust
The Skelton Bounty
The Charles Skey Charitable
   Trust
Skipton Building Society
   Charitable Foundation
The John Slater Foundation
Rita and David Slowe
   Charitable Trust
The SMB Charitable Trust
The Mrs Smith and Mount
   Trust
The N Smith Charitable
   Settlement
The Amanda Smith Charitable
   Trust
The E H Smith Charitable Trust

The Smith Charitable Trust
The Henry Smith Charity
The Leslie Smith Foundation
The Martin Smith Foundation
Stanley Smith General
   Charitable Trust
The Stanley Smith UK
   Horticultural Trust
Philip Smith's Charitable Trust
The Snowball Trust
The Sobell Foundation
Solev Co Ltd
Solihull Community Foundation
The Solo Charitable
   Settlement
Dr Richard Solomon's
   Charitable Trust
David Solomons Charitable
   Trust
Songdale Ltd
The E C Sosnow Charitable
   Trust
The Souter Charitable Trust
The South Square Trust .
The Stephen R and Philippa H
   Southall Charitable Trust
The W F Southall Trust
The Southdown Trust
R H Southern Trust
The Southover Manor General
   Education Trust
The Southwold Trust
The Sovereign Health Care
   Charitable Trust
Spar Charitable Fund
Sparks Charity (Sport Aiding
   Medical Research For Kids)
Sparquote Limited
The Spear Charitable Trust
Spears-Stutz Charitable Trust
The Jessie Spencer Trust
The Ralph and Irma Sperring
   Charity
The Moss Spiro Will Charitable
   Foundation
W W Spooner Charitable Trust
Stanley Spooner Deceased
   Charitable Trust
The Spoore, Merry and Rixman
   Foundation
The Spring Harvest Charitable
   Trust
Rosalyn and Nicholas Springer
   Charitable Trust
Springfields Employees'
   Medical Research and
   Charity Trust Fund
Springrule Ltd
The Spurrell Charitable Trust
The Geoff and Fiona Squire
   Foundation
St Andrew Animal Fund
St Andrew's Conservation
   Trust
St Christopher's College
   Educational Trust

St Francis's Leprosy Guild
St Gabriel's Trust
St James' Trust Settlement
St James's Place Foundation
Sir Walter St John's
 Educational Charity
St Katharine and Shadwell
 Trust
St Mark's Overseas Aid Trust
 (SMOAT)
St Michael's and All Saints'
 Charities
The Late St Patrick White
 Charitable Trust
St Teilo's Trust
Miss Doreen Stanford Trust
The Stanley Foundation Ltd
The Stanton Ballard Charitable
 Trust
The Staples Trust
The Star Charitable Trust
The Starfish Trust
The Peter Stebbings Memorial
 Charity
The Steel Charitable Trust
The Cyril and Betty Stein
 Charitable Trust
The Steinberg Family
 Charitable Trust
The Hugh Stenhouse
 Foundation
The Sigmund Sternberg
 Charitable Foundation
Stervon Ltd
The Stevenage Community
 Trust
The June Stevens Foundation
Stevenson Family's Charitable
 Trust
The Steventon Allotments and
 Relief-in-Need Charity
The Stewards' Charitable Trust
The Stewards' Company
 Limited
The Sir Halley Stewart Trust
The Stobart Newlands
 Charitable Trust
The Edward Stocks-Massey
 Bequest Fund
The Stokenchurch Educational
 Charity
The Stoller Charitable Trust
The M J C Stone Charitable
 Trust
The Stone-Mallabar Charitable
 Foundation
The Samuel Storey Family
 Charitable Trust
Peter Stormonth Darling
 Charitable Trust
Peter Storrs Trust
The Strangward Trust
The Strasser Foundation
Stratford upon Avon Town
 Trust

Strathclyde Police Benevolent
 Fund
The W O Street Charitable
 Foundation
The A B Strom and R Strom
 Charitable Trust
The Sudborough Foundation
Sueberry Ltd
The Suffolk Foundation
The Suffolk Historic Churches
 Trust
The Alan Sugar Foundation
The Summerfield Charitable
 Trust
The Bernard Sunley Charitable
 Foundation
The Surrey Historic Buildings
 Trust Ltd
The Sussex Historic Churches
 Trust
The Adrienne and Leslie
 Sussman Charitable Trust
The Sutasoma Trust
Sutton Coldfield Municipal
 Charities
The Sutton Nursing
 Association
Swan Mountain Trust
The Swan Trust
Swansea and Brecon Diocesan
 Board of Finance Limited
The John Swire (1989)
 Charitable Trust
The Swire Charitable Trust
The Hugh and Ruby Sykes
 Charitable Trust
The Charles and Elsie Sykes
 Trust
The Sylvanus Charitable Trust
The Stella Symons Charitable
 Trust
The Tabeel Trust
The Tajtelbaum Charitable
 Trust
The Talbot Trusts
The Talbot Village Trust
Tallow Chandlers Benevolent
 Fund
Talteg Ltd
The Tangent Charitable Trust
The Lady Tangye Charitable
 Trust
The David Tannen Charitable
 Trust
The Tanner Trust
The Lili Tapper Charitable
 Foundation
The Mrs A Lacy Tate Trust
The Tay Charitable Trust
C B and H H Taylor 1984 Trust
Humphrey Richardson Taylor
 Charitable Trust
The Connie and Albert Taylor
 Charitable Trust
The Cyril Taylor Charitable
 Trust

A P Taylor Trust
Rosanna Taylor's 1987 Charity
 Trust
Tearfund
The Tedworth Charitable Trust
Tees Valley Community
 Foundation
Tegham Limited
The Templeton Goodwill Trust
Tesco Charity Trust
Thackray Medical Research
 Trust
Thames Community
 Foundation
The Thames Wharf Charity
The Thistle Trust
The Loke Wan Tho Memorial
 Foundation
The Thomas Wall Trust
The Arthur and Margaret
 Thompson Charitable Trust
The Thompson Family
 Charitable Trust
The Len Thomson Charitable
 Trust
The Sue Thomson Foundation
The Sir Jules Thorn Charitable
 Trust
The Thornton Foundation
The Thornton Trust
The Three Guineas Trust
The Three Oaks Trust
The Thriplow Charitable Trust
The Tinsley Foundation
The Tisbury Telegraph Trust
TJH Foundation
The Tolkien Trust
Tollemache (Buckminster)
 Charitable Trust
Tomchei Torah Charitable
 Trust
The Tompkins Foundation
The Tory Family Foundation
Tottenham Grammar School
 Foundation
The Tower Hill Trust
The Towry Law Charitable Trust
The Toy Trust
The Mayor of Trafford's Charity
 Fund
Annie Tranmer Charitable Trust
The Constance Travis
 Charitable Trust
The Treeside Trust
The Triangle Trust (1949) Fund
The True Colours Trust
Truedene Co. Ltd
The Truemark Trust
Truemart Limited
Trumros Limited
Trust for London
Trust Sixty Three
The Trusthouse Charitable
 Foundation
The Tubney Charitable Trust
Tudor Rose Ltd

The Tudor Trust
The Tufton Charitable Trust
The R D Turner Charitable
Trust
The Douglas Turner Trust
The Florence Turner Trust
Miss S M Tutton Charitable
Trust
The TUUT Charitable Trust
Community Foundation Serving
Tyne and Wear and
Northumberland
Trustees of Tzedakah
Ulster Garden Villages Ltd
Ultach Trust
Ulting Overseas Trust
The Ulverscroft Foundation
Ulverston Town Lands Charity
The Underwood Trust
The Union of Orthodox Hebrew
Congregation
The United Society for the
Propagation of the Gospel
United Trusts
The David Uri Memorial Trust
Uxbridge United Welfare Trust
Vale of Glamorgan – Welsh
Church Fund
The Valentine Charitable Trust
The Albert Van Den Bergh
Charitable Trust
John and Lucille van Geest
Foundation
The Van Neste Foundation
Mrs Maud Van Norden's
Charitable Foundation
The Vandervell Foundation
The Vardy Foundation
The Variety Club Children's
Charity
Veneziana Fund
The Verdon-Smith Family
Charitable Settlement
Roger Vere Foundation
Victoria Homes Trust
Viking Cares (For the Kids)
The Nigel Vinson Charitable
Trust
The William and Ellen Vinten
Trust
The Vintners' Company
Charitable Foundation
Vintners' Gifts Charity
Vision Charity
Vivdale Ltd
The Viznitz Foundation
Wade's Charity
The Scurrah Wainwright Charity
Wakeham Trust
The Community Foundation in
Wales
Wales Council for Voluntary
Action
Robert and Felicity Waley-
Cohen Charitable Trust
The Walker Trust

Wallington Missionary Mart
and Auctions
The F J Wallis Charitable
Settlement
War on Want
The Ward Blenkinsop Trust
The George Ward Charitable
Trust
The Barbara Ward Children's
Foundation
The John Warren Foundation
G R Waters Charitable Trust
2000
The Waterways Trust
The Wates Foundation
Blyth Watson Charitable Trust
The Howard Watson Symington
Memorial Charity
John Watson's Trust
Weatherley Charitable Trust
The Weavers' Company
Benevolent Fund
The William Webster
Charitable Trust
The Weinberg Foundation
The Weinstein Foundation
The Weinstock Fund
The Barbara Welby Trust
The Weldon UK Charitable
Trust
The Wellcome Trust
Welsh Church Fund Dyfed
area (Carmarthenshire,
Ceredigion and
Pembrokeshire)
The Welton Foundation
Wessex Cancer Trust
The Wessex Youth Trust
The West Derby Wastelands
Charity
West London Synagogue
Charitable Fund
The West Yorkshire Police
Community Fund
Mrs S K West's Charitable
Trust
The Westminster Foundation
The Garfield Weston
Foundation
The Whitaker Charitable Trust
The Colonel W H Whitbread
Charitable Trust
The Simon Whitbread
Charitable Trust
White Rose Children's Aid
International Charity
The Whitecourt Charitable
Trust
A H and B C Whiteley
Charitable Trust
The Norman Whiteley Trust
The Whitley Animal Protection
Trust
The Whittlesey Charity
The Lionel Wigram Memorial
Trust

The Felicity Wilde Charitable
Trust
The Will Charitable Trust
The Kay Williams Charitable
Foundation
The Williams Family Charitable
Trust
The H D H Wills 1965
Charitable Trust
Dame Violet Wills Charitable
Trust
The Dame Violet Wills Will
Trust
The Wilmcote Charitrust
Sumner Wilson Charitable
Trust
David Wilson Foundation
The Wilson Foundation
J and J R Wilson Trust
The Community Foundation for
Wiltshire and Swindon
The Benjamin Winegarten
Charitable Trust
The Francis Winham
Foundation
Anona Winn Charitable Trust
Wirral Mayor's Charity
The Michael and Anna Wix
Charitable Trust
The Wixamtree Trust
The Woburn 1986 Charitable
Trust
The Maurice Wohl Charitable
Foundation
The Charles Wolfson
Charitable Trust
Women Caring Trust
Women's World Day of Prayer
The James Wood Bequest
Fund
Woodlands Green Ltd
Woodlands Trust
The Geoffrey Woods Charitable
Foundation
The Woodward Charitable
Trust
The A and R Woolf Charitable
Trust
The Woolnoth Society
Charitable Trust
Worcester Municipal Charities
The Worcestershire and
Dudley Historic Churches
Trust
The Fred and Della Worms
Charitable Trust
The Worwin UK Foundation
The Wragge and Co. Charitable
Trust
The Diana Edgson Wright
Charitable Trust
The Matthews Wrightson
Charity Trust
Miss E B Wrightson's
Charitable Settlement
Wychdale Ltd

Wychville Ltd
The Wyndham Charitable Trust
The Wyseliot Charitable Trust
The Xerox (UK) Trust
The Yapp Charitable Trust
The Yardley Great Trust
The Dennis Alan Yardy
Charitable Trust
The W Wing Yip and Brothers
Foundation
The York Children's Trust
Yorkshire Agricultural Society
Yorkshire Building Society
Charitable Foundation
The South Yorkshire
Community Foundation
The Yorkshire Dales
Millennium Trust
The John Young Charitable
Settlement
The William Allen Young
Charitable Trust
The John K Young Endowment
Fund
Elizabeth and Prince Zaiger
Trust
Zephyr Charitable Trust
The Marjorie and Arnold Ziff
Charitable Foundation
Stephen Zimmerman
Charitable Trust
The Zochonis Charitable Trust
Zurich Community Trust (UK)
Limited

....

■ Project funding (excluding overheads)

The 1989 Willan Charitable
Trust
The 29th May 1961 Charitable
Trust
Aberbrothock Charitable Trust
The Aberdeen Endowments
Trust
The Aberdeenshire Educational
Trust Scheme
Achiezer Association Ltd
Achisomoch Aid Company
Limited
The ACT Foundation
Action Medical Research
The Company of Actuaries'
Charitable Trust Fund
The Sylvia Adams Charitable
Trust
The Victor Adda Foundation
The Adint Charitable Trust
The Adnams Charity
AF Trust Company
Age Concern Scotland Grants
Aid to the Church in Need (UK)
The AIM Foundation
The Sylvia Aitken Charitable
Trust

The Ajahma Charitable Trust
Alcohol Education and
Research Council
Aldgate and All Hallows'
Barking Exhibition
Foundation
The Aldgate Freedom
Foundation
Alexandra Rose Charities
The Alexis Trust
All Saints Educational Trust
Allchurches Trust Ltd
The H B Allen Charitable Trust
The Rita Allen Charitable Trust
The Alliance Family Foundation
Angus Allnatt Charitable
Foundation
The Pat Allsop Charitable Trust
The Almond Trust
Almondsbury Charity
The Altajir Trust
Altamont Ltd
Alvor Charitable Trust
AM Charitable Trust
Ambika Paul Foundation
The Ammco Trust
Sir John and Lady Amory's
Charitable Trust
Viscount Amory's Charitable
Trust
The Ampelos Trust
The AMW Charitable Trust
The Anchor Foundation
The Andrew Anderson Trust
The Andre Christian Trust
Anguish's Educational
Foundation
The Animal Defence Trust
The Eric Anker-Petersen
Charity
The Annandale Charitable
Trust
Ambrose and Ann Appelbe
Trust
The Appletree Trust
The John Apthorp Charitable
Trust
The Milly Apthorp Charitable
Trust
The Arbib Foundation
The Archbishop of
Canterbury's Charitable
Trust
The John M Archer Charitable
Trust
The Archer Trust
The Ardwick Trust
The Argus Appeal
Armenian General Benevolent
Union London Trust
The Armenian Relief Society of
Great Britain Trust
The Armourers' and Brasiers'
Gauntlet Trust
The Army Benevolent Fund
Arsenal Charitable Trust

The Artemis Charitable Trust
The Arts and Entertainment
Charitable Trust
Arts Council England
The Arts Council of Northern
Ireland
The Arts Council of Wales
The Ove Arup Foundation
The AS Charitable Trust
Ashburnham Thanksgiving
Trust
A J H Ashby Will Trust
The Ashden Trust
The Ashendene Trust
The Laura Ashley Foundation
The Ian Askew Charitable Trust
The Associated Country
Women of the World
(ACWW)
The Association of Colleges
Charitable Trust
Astellas European Foundation
AstonMansfield Charitable
Trust
The Astor Foundation
The Astor of Hever Trust
The Aurelius Charitable Trust
The Lord Austin Trust
The Avenue Charitable Trust
The John Avins Trustees
AW Charitable Trust
The Aylesford Family
Charitable Trust
The BAA Communities Trust
Harry Bacon Foundation
The BACTA Charitable Trust
The Bagri Foundation
Veta Bailey Charitable Trust
The Austin Bailey Trust
The Baily Thomas Charitable
Fund
The Baird Trust
The Baker Charitable Trust
The Balcombe Charitable Trust
The Balint Family Charitable
Trusts
The Albert Casanova Ballard
Deceased Trust
The Ballinger Charitable Trust
Balmain Charitable Trust
The Balmore Trust
The Balney Charitable Trust
The Baltic Charitable Fund
The Bamford Charitable
Foundation
The Banbury Charities
William P Bancroft (No 2)
Charitable Trust and
Jenepher Gillett Trust
The Band Trust
The Barbers' Company General
Charities
The Barbour Trust
Barchester Healthcare
Foundation

David and Frederick Barclay
　　Foundation
The Baring Foundation
Peter Barker-Mill Memorial
　　Charity
Barleycorn Trust
The Barnabas Trust
Lord Barnby's Foundation
Barnes Workhouse Fund
The Barnsbury Charitable Trust
The Barnstaple Bridge Trust
The Barnwood House Trust
The Misses Barrie Charitable
　　Trust
Barrington Family Charitable
　　Trust
The Charity of William Barrow
Stephen J Barry Charitable
　　Trust
The Bartlett Taylor Charitable
　　Trust
The Paul Bassham Charitable
　　Trust
The Batchworth Trust
The Bay Tree Charitable Trust
D H and L H Baylin Charitable
　　Trust
The Louis Baylis (Maidenhead
　　Advertiser) Charitable Trust
BBC Children in Need
B-CH 1971 Charitable Trust
The Beacon Trust
Bear Mordechai Ltd
The Bearder Charity
The James Beattie Charitable
　　Trust
The Beaufort House Trust
　　Limited
Beauland Ltd
The Beaverbrook Foundation
The Beccles Town Lands
　　Charity
The Becker Family Charitable
　　Trust
The Becketts and Sargeants
　　Educational Foundation
The John Beckwith Charitable
　　Trust
The Peter Beckwith Charitable
　　Trust
The Bedford Charity (The
　　Harpur Trust)
The David and Ruth Behrend
　　Fund
The Beit Trust
The Bellahouston Bequest
　　Fund
Bellasis Trust
The Bellinger Donnay Trust
Belljoe Tzedoko Ltd
The Benfield Motors Charitable
　　Trust
The Benham Charitable
　　Settlement
Maurice and Jacqueline
　　Bennett Charitable Trust

Michael and Leslie Bennett
　　Charitable Trust
The Berkshire Community
　　Foundation
The Bestway Foundation
The Betterware Foundation
Thomas Betton's Charity for
　　Pensions and Relief-in-Need
BHST
The Mason Bibby 1981 Trust
BibleLands
The Bideford Bridge Trust
The Big Lottery Fund
The Billmeir Charitable Trust
The Bingham Trust
The Bintaub Charitable Trust
The Birmingham Community
　　Foundation
The Birmingham District
　　Nursing Charitable Trust
The Birmingham Hospital
　　Saturday Fund Medical
　　Charity and Welfare Trust
Birmingham International
　　Airport Community Trust
The Lord Mayor of
　　Birmingham's Charity
Birthday House Trust
The Bisgood Charitable Trust
　　(registered as Miss Jeanne
　　Bisgood's Charitable Trust)
The Michael Bishop
　　Foundation
The Bishop's Development
　　Fund
The Sydney Black Charitable
　　Trust
The Bertie Black Foundation
Isabel Blackman Foundation
The Herbert and Peter
　　Blagrave Charitable Trust
The Blair Foundation
Blakes Benevolent Trust
The Blanchminster Trust
The Sir Victor Blank Charitable
　　Settlement
Blatchington Court Trust
The Neville and Elaine Blond
　　Charitable Trust
The Bluston Charitable
　　Settlement
Enid Blyton Trust for Children
The Nicholas Boas Charitable
　　Trust
The Body Shop Foundation
The Boltons Trust
The Bonamy Charitable Trust
The John and Celia Bonham
　　Christie Charitable Trust
The Charlotte Bonham-Carter
　　Charitable Trust
Bonhomie United Charity
　　Society
The Booth Charities
The Boots Charitable Trust

The Bordon and Liphook
　　Charity
Salo Bordon Charitable Trust
The Oliver Borthwick Memorial
　　Trust
The Bothwell Charitable Trust
H E and E L Botteley
　　Charitable Trust
The Harry Bottom Charitable
　　Trust
P G and N J Boulton Trust
The A H and E Boulton Trust
Sir Clive Bourne Family Trust
The Anthony Bourne
　　Foundation
The Bower Trust
The Bowerman Charitable
　　Trust
John and Susan Bowers Fund
The Bowland Charitable Trust
The William Brake Charitable
　　Trust
The Tony Bramall Charitable
　　Trust
The Brewers' Company
　　General Charitable Trust
The Harold and Alice Bridges
　　Charity
Briggs Animal Welfare Trust
The Brighton District Nursing
　　Association Trust
Bristol Archdeaconry Charity
John Bristow and Thomas
　　Mason Trust
Britannia Foundation
The British Council for
　　Prevention of Blindness
The British Dietetic
　　Association General and
　　Education Trust Fund
The British Gas (Scottish Gas)
　　Energy Trust
British Heart Foundation
British Humane Association
British Institute at Ankara
British Ornithologists' Union
British Record Industry Trust
The Britten-Pears Foundation
The Britto Foundation
The J and M Britton Charitable
　　Trust
The Charles and Edna
　　Broadhurst Charitable Trust
The Bromley Trust
The Roger Brooke Charitable
　　Trust
The David Brooke Charity
The Charles Brotherton Trust
Joseph Brough Charitable
　　Trust
The Swinfen Broun Charitable
　　Trust
Mrs E E Brown Charitable
　　Settlement
Bill Brown's Charitable
　　Settlement

R S Brownless Charitable Trust

T B H Brunner's Charitable Settlement

Brushmill Ltd

The Bryant Trust

Buckingham Trust

The Buckinghamshire Foundation

The Buckinghamshire Masonic Centenary Fund

Buckland Charitable Trust

The Rosemary Bugden Charitable Trust

The Bulldog Trust Limited

The E F Bulmer Benevolent Fund

Burdens Charitable Foundation

The Burdett Trust for Nursing

The Clara E Burgess Charity

The Burry Charitable Trust

The Arnold Burton 1998 Charitable Trust

The Burton Breweries Charitable Trust

The Geoffrey Burton Charitable Trust

Consolidated Charity of Burton upon Trent

Butchers' Company General Charities

The Bill Butlin Charity Trust

C and F Charitable Trust

C J Cadbury Charitable Trust

Edward Cadbury Charitable Trust

Henry T and Lucy B Cadbury Charitable Trust

P H G Cadbury Charitable Trust

The Christopher Cadbury Charitable Trust

The G W Cadbury Charitable Trust

The Richard Cadbury Charitable Trust

The William A Cadbury Charitable Trust

The Edward and Dorothy Cadbury Trust

The George Cadbury Trust

The Barrow Cadbury Trust and the Barrow Cadbury Fund

The Cadogan Charity

CAF (Charities Aid Foundation)

CAFOD

The Callander Charitable Trust

Calleva Foundation

The Calpe Trust

Calypso Browning Trust

The Campden Charities

The Canning Trust

H and L Cantor Trust

Capital Community Foundation

Cardy Beaver Foundation

The Carew Pole Charitable Trust

The D W T Cargill Fund

Caring for Kids (Radio Tay)

Carlee Ltd

The Carlton House Charitable Trust

The Worshipful Company of Carmen Benevolent Trust

The Carnegie Dunfermline Trust

The Carnegie Trust for the Universities of Scotland

The Carpenter Charitable Trust

The Carpenters' Company Charitable Trust

The Carrington Charitable Trust

The Carron Charitable Settlement

The Leslie Mary Carter Charitable Trust

The Carvill Trust

The Casey Trust

Cash for Kids Radio Clyde

Sir John Cass's Foundation

The Elizabeth Casson Trust

The Castang Foundation

The Catalyst Charitable Trust

The Catholic Charitable Trust

Catholic Foreign Missions

The Catholic Trust for England and Wales

The Cattanach Charitable Trust

The Joseph and Annie Cattle Trust

The Thomas Sivewright Catto Charitable Settlement

The Wilfrid and Constance Cave Foundation

The Cayo Foundation

Elizabeth Cayzer Charitable Trust

The B G S Cayzer Charitable Trust

The Cazenove Charitable Trust

Celtic Charity Fund

The Cemlyn-Jones Trust

CfBT Education Trust

The Amelia Chadwick Trust

The Pamela Champion Foundation

The Chapman Charitable Trust

John William Chapman's Charitable Trust

The Charities Advisory Trust

Charitworth Limited

The Charter 600 Charity

The Worshipful Company of Chartered Accountants General Charitable Trust

The Chasah Trust

The Chelsea Building Society Charitable Foundation

The Chelsea Square 1994 Trust

The Cheruby Trust

The Cheshire Provincial Fund of Benevolence

The Chetwode Foundation

The Malcolm Chick Charity

Child Growth Foundation

Children's Liver Disease Foundation

Childs Charitable Trust

The Childwick Trust

The Chippenham Borough Lands Charity

The Chipping Sodbury Town Lands Charity

CHK Charities Limited

The Chownes Foundation

The Chrimes Family Charitable Trust

The Christabella Charitable Trust

Christadelphian Samaritan Fund

Christian Aid

Christian Response to Eastern Europe

The Church and Community Fund

The Church Burgesses Educational Foundation

Church Burgesses Trust

Church Lands and John Johnson's Estate Charities

Church of Ireland Priorities Fund

The Church Urban Fund

City and County of Swansea Welsh Church Act Fund

The City Bridge Trust

The City Educational Trust Fund

The City Parochial Foundation

CLA Charitable Trust

Stephen Clark 1957 Charitable Trust

J A Clark Charitable Trust

The Hilda and Alice Clark Charitable Trust

The Roger and Sarah Bancroft Clark Charitable Trust

The Clarke Charitable Settlement

The Cleary Foundation

The Cleopatra Trust

Lord Clinton's Charitable Trust

The Clore Duffield Foundation

Miss V L Clore's 1967 Charitable Trust

Closehelm Ltd

Richard Cloudesley's Charity

The Clover Trust

The Robert Clutterbuck Charitable Trust

Clydpride Ltd

The Coalfields Regeneration Trust

The John Coates Charitable
Trust
Coats Foundation Trust
The Cobtree Charity Trust Ltd
The Denise Cohen Charitable
Trust
The Vivienne and Samuel
Cohen Charitable Trust
The R and S Cohen Fondation
The John S Cohen Foundation
The Colchester Catalyst
Charity
John Coldman Charitable Trust
The Cole Charitable Trust
The Colefax Charitable Trust
The John and Freda Coleman
Charitable Trust
The George Henry Collins
Charity
The E Alec Colman Charitable
Fund Ltd
The Sir Jeremiah Colman Gift
Trust
Col-Reno Ltd
The Colt Foundation
The Coltstaple Trust
Colwinston Charitable Trust
Colyer-Fergusson Charitable
Trust
Comic Relief
The Comino Foundation
Community Foundation for
Calderdale
The Community Foundation for
Greater Manchester
The Community Foundation for
Northern Ireland
The Company of Tobacco Pipe
Makers' and Tobacco
Blenders' Benevolent Fund
The Compton Charitable Trust
The Congleton Inclosure Trust
The Conservation Foundation
The Consolidated Charities for
the Infirm Merchant
Taylors' Company
The Construction Industry
Trust for Youth
Gordon Cook Foundation
The Ernest Cook Trust
The Cooks Charity
The Catherine Cookson
Charitable Trust
Harold and Daphne Cooper
Charitable Trust
Mabel Cooper Charity
The Alice Ellen Cooper Dean
Charitable Foundation
The Co-operative Foundation
The Marjorie Coote Animal
Charity Trust
The Marjorie Coote Old
People's Charity
The Helen Jean Cope Trust
The J Reginald Corah
Foundation Fund

The Gershon Coren Charitable
Foundation
The Corinthian Trust
Edwin Cornforth 1983 Charity
Trust
The Cornwell Charitable Trust
The Sidney and Elizabeth
Corob Charitable Trust
The Corona Charitable Trust
The Costa Family Charitable
Trust
The Cotton Industry War
Memorial Trust
The Cotton Trust
County Durham Foundation
The Augustine Courtauld Trust
Coutts Charitable Trust
The General Charities of the
City of Coventry
Coventry Building Society
Charitable Foundation
The John Cowan Foundation
Cowley Charitable Foundation
The Sir William Coxen Trust
Fund
The Lord Cozens-Hardy Trust
The Craignish Trust
The Craps Charitable Trust
Michael Crawford Children's
Charity
The Cray Trust
The Crescent Trust
Criffel Charitable Trust
Cripplegate Foundation
The Violet and Milo Cripps
Charitable Trust
The Cromarty Trust
The Harry Crook Foundation
The Cross Trust
The Cross Trust
The Croydon Relief in Need
Charities
The Mayor of Croydon's
Charity Fund
Cruden Foundation Ltd
The Ronald Cruickshanks'
Foundation
Cuby Charitable Trust
The Culra Charitable Trust
Cumberland Building Society
Charitable Foundation
Cumbria Community
Foundation
The Cunningham Trust
The D J H Currie Memorial
Trust
The Dennis Curry Charitable
Trust
The Raymond Curtis Charitable
Trust
The Manny Cussins
Foundation
The Cwmbran Trust
Itzchok Meyer Cymerman Trust
Ltd

The D'Oyly Carte Charitable
Trust
The Roald Dahl Foundation
The Daily Prayer Union
Charitable Trust Ltd
The Daisy Trust
The Daiwa Anglo-Japanese
Foundation
Oizer Dalim Trust
The Dr and Mrs A Darlington
Charitable Trust
Baron Davenport's Charity
The Davidson (Nairn)
Charitable Trust
Davidson Charitable Trust
The Alderman Joe Davidson
Memorial Trust
Michael Davies Charitable
Settlement
The Gwendoline and Margaret
Davies Charity
The Wilfrid Bruce Davis
Charitable Trust
Davis-Rubens Charitable Trust
The Dawe Charitable Trust
The De Clermont Charitable
Company Ltd
Peter De Haan Charitable
Trust
The Leopold De Rothschild
Charitable Trust
The Deakin Charitable Trust
William Dean Countryside and
Educational Trust
The Debmar Benevolent Trust
The Delfont Foundation
The Dellal Foundation
The Delves Charitable Trust
The Demigryphon Trust
The Denman Charitable Trust
The Denton Charitable Trust
The Denton Wilde Sapte
Charitable Trust
The Earl of Derby's Charitable
Trust
Derbyshire Community
Foundation
The J N Derbyshire Trust
Devon Community Foundation
The Devon Educational Trust
The Duke of Devonshire's
Charitable Trust
The Sandy Dewhirst Charitable
Trust
DG Charitable Settlement
The Laduma Dhamecha
Charitable Trust
Diabetes UK
Alan and Sheila Diamond
Charitable Trust
The Diana, Princess of Wales
Memorial Fund
The Dibden Allotments Charity
The Dickon Trust
The Digbeth Trust
The Dinwoodie Settlement

Dischma Charitable Trust
The DLA Piper Charitable Trust
The DLM Charitable Trust
Louise Dobson Charitable
   Trust
The Derek and Eileen Dodgson
   Foundation
The Dollond Charitable Trust
Domepride Ltd
The Dorcas Trust
The Dorema Charitable Trust
The Dorus Trust
Double 'O' Charity Ltd
The Doughty Charity Trust
The R M Douglas Charitable
   Trust
The Drapers' Charitable Fund
Dromintee Trust
The Dugdale Charitable Trust
The Duis Charitable Trust
The Dulverton Trust
The P B Dumbell Charitable
   Trust
The Dumbreck Charity
Dunard Fund
Ronald Duncan Literary
   Foundation
The Dunhill Medical Trust
The Houghton Dunn Charitable
   Trust
The Dunn Family Charitable
   Trust
The W E Dunn Trust
Dushinsky Trust Ltd
Mildred Duveen Charitable
   Trust
The Dwek Family Charitable
   Trust
The Dyers' Company
   Charitable Trust
EAGA Partnership Charitable
   Trust
The Eagle Charity Trust
Audrey Earle Charitable Trust
The Earley Charity
Earls Colne and Halstead
   Educational Charity
The Earmark Trust
East Kent Provincial Charities
East London Community
   Foundation
Eastern Counties Educational
   Trust Limited
The Sir John Eastwood
   Foundation
The Ebenezer Trust
The EBM Charitable Trust
Eden Arts Trust
EDF Energy Trust (EDFET)
The Gilbert and Eileen Edgar
   Foundation
Gilbert Edgar Trust
Edinburgh Children's Holiday
   Fund
The Edinburgh Trust, No 2
   Account

Edinburgh Voluntary
   Organisations' Trust Funds
Educational Foundation of
   Alderman John Norman
The W G Edwards Charitable
   Foundation
The William Edwards
   Educational Charity
The Elephant Trust
The George Elias Charitable
   Trust
The Gerald Palmer Eling Trust
   Company
The Elizabeth Frankland Moore
   and Star Foundation
The Wilfred and Elsie Elkes
   Charity Fund
The Maud Elkington Charitable
   Trust
Ellador Ltd
The Ellerdale Trust
The John Ellerman Foundation
The Ellinson Foundation Ltd
The Edith Maud Ellis 1985
   Charitable Trust
James Ellis Charitable Trust
The Elmgrant Trust
The Elmley Foundation
Elshore Ltd
The Vernon N Ely Charitable
   Trust
The Embleton Trust
The Emerton-Christie Charity
The Emmandjay Charitable
   Trust
The Worshipful Company of
   Engineers Charitable Trust
   Fund
The Englefield Charitable Trust
The English Schools' Football
   Association
The Enkalon Foundation
Entindale Ltd
The Epigoni Trust
Epilepsy Research UK
The Equitable Charitable Trust
The Equity Trust Fund
The Ericson Trust
The Erskine Cunningham Hill
   Trust
Essex Community Foundation
The Essex Fairway Charitable
   Trust
The Essex Heritage Trust
Essex Provincial Charity Fund
The Essex Youth Trust
Euro Charity Trust
The Evangelical Covenants
   Trust
The Alan Evans Memorial Trust
Sir John Evelyn's Charity
The Eventhall Family
   Charitable Trust
The Everard Foundation
The Eveson Charitable Trust

The Beryl Evetts and Robert
   Luff Animal Welfare Trust
The Execution Charitable Trust
The Mayor of Exeter's Appeal
   Fund
The Exilarch's Foundation
F C Charitable Trust
The F P Limited Charitable
   Trust
The Faber Charitable Trust
Esmée Fairbairn Foundation
The Fairway Trust
Faisaltex Charitable Trust
The Family Foundations Trust
The Family Rich Charities Trust
Famos Foundation Trust
The Lord Faringdon Charitable
   Trust
Samuel William Farmer's Trust
The Farmers' Company
   Charitable Fund
The Thomas Farr Charitable
   Trust
Walter Farthing (Trust) Limited
Farthing Trust
The Fassnidge Memorial Trust
Joseph Fattorini Charitable
   Trust 'B' Account
The Fawcett Charitable Trust
Federation of Jewish Relief
   Organisations
Feed the Minds
The John Feeney Charitable
   Bequest
The George Fentham
   Birmingham Charity
The A M Fenton Trust
Allan and Nesta Ferguson
   Charitable Settlement
Elizabeth Ferguson Charitable
   Trust Fund
The Fidelity UK Foundation
The Bluff Field Charitable Trust
The Doris Field Charitable
   Trust
The Fifty Fund
Dixie Rose Findlay Charitable
   Trust
Gerald Finzi Charitable Trust
Firtree Trust
The Sir John Fisher Foundation
The Fishmongers' Company's
   Charitable Trust
Marc Fitch Fund
The Fitton Trust
The Earl Fitzwilliam Charitable
   Trust
Bud Flanagan Leukaemia Fund
The Rose Flatau Charitable
   Trust
The Ian Fleming Charitable
   Trust
The Joyce Fletcher Charitable
   Trust
The Roy Fletcher Charitable
   Trust

Florence's Charitable Trust
The Flow Foundation
The Gerald Fogel Charitable
    Trust
The Follett Trust
The Football Association
    National Sports Centre
    Trust
The Football Association Youth
    Trust
The Football Foundation
The Forbes Charitable
    Foundation
Forbesville Limited
The Forces Trust
Ford Britain Trust
The Oliver Ford Charitable
    Trust
Fordeve Ltd
The Forest Hill Charitable Trust
Gwyneth Forrester Trust
The Forte Charitable Trust
Lord Forte Foundation
Foundation for Management
    Education
Four Acre Trust
The Four Winds Trust
The Fowler, Smith and Jones
    Charitable Trust
The Foyle Foundation
The Isaac and Freda Frankel
    Memorial Charitable Trust
Sydney E Franklin Deceased's
    New Second Charity
The Jill Franklin Trust
The Gordon Fraser Charitable
    Trust
The Hugh Fraser Foundation
The Joseph Strong Frazer Trust
The Louis and Valerie
    Freedman Charitable
    Settlement
The Freemasons' Grand
    Charity
The Thomas Freke and Lady
    Norton Charity
The Charles S French
    Charitable Trust
The Anne French Memorial
    Trust
The Freshfield Foundation
The Freshgate Trust
    Foundation
The Friarsgate Trust
The Friends Hall Farm Street
    Trust
Friends of Biala Ltd
Friends of Wiznitz Limited
Friends Provident Charitable
    Foundation
The Frognal Trust
T F C Frost Charitable Trust
Maurice Fry Charitable Trust
Mejer and Gertrude Miriam
    Frydman Foundation

The Fuellers Charitable Trust
    Fund
The Fulmer Charitable Trust
Worshipful Company of
    Furniture Makers Charitable
    Fund
Gableholt Limited
The Galbraith Trust
The Gale Family Charitable
    Trust
The Angela Gallagher Memorial
    Fund
The Gamlen Charitable Trust
The Gamma Trust
The Gannochy Trust
The Ganzoni Charitable Trust
The Worshipful Company of
    Gardeners of London
The Samuel Gardner Memorial
    Trust
The Garnett Charitable Trust
Garrick Charitable Trust
Garvan Limited
The Gatsby Charitable
    Foundation
Gatwick Airport Community
    Trust
The Robert Gavron Charitable
    Trust
Jacqueline and Michael Gee
    Charitable Trust
The General Nursing Council
    for England and Wales
    Trust
J Paul Getty Jr Charitable Trust
The Gibbs Charitable Trust
Simon Gibson Charitable Trust
The G C Gibson Charitable
    Trust
The Harvey and Hilary Gilbert
    Charitable Trust
The Girdlers' Company
    Charitable Trust
The B and P Glasser
    Charitable Trust
The Glass-House Trust
Global Care
Global Charities (formally
    GCap Charities)
Gloucestershire Community
    Foundation
Worshipful Company of
    Glovers of London Charity
    Fund
GMC Trust
The GNC Trust
The Mrs Godfrey-Payton Trust
The Meir Golda Trust
The Sydney and Phyllis
    Goldberg Memorial
    Charitable Trust
The Golden Bottle Trust
Golden Charitable Trust
The Jack Goldhill Charitable
    Trust

The Goldsmiths' Arts Trust
    Fund
The Goldsmiths' Company
    Charity
The Golsoncott Foundation
The Good Neighbours Trust
Nicholas and Judith
    Goodison's Charitable
    Settlement
The Everard and Mina
    Goodman Charitable
    Foundation
Mike Gooley Trailfinders
    Charity
Leonard Gordon Charitable
    Trust
The Gosling Foundation
    Limited
The Gough Charitable Trust
The Gould Charitable Trust
The Grace Charitable Trust
A B Grace Trust
The Graff Foundation
The Grahame Charitable
    Foundation Limited
Grampian Police Diced Cap
    Charitable Fund
The Granada Foundation
Grand Charitable Trust of the
    Order of Women
    Freemasons
The Grand Order of Water
    Rats' Charities Fund
The Grange Farm Centre Trust
Grantham Yorke Trust
The Gray Trust
The Great Britain Sasakawa
    Foundation
The Great Stone Bridge Trust
    of Edenbridge
The Great Torrington Town
    Lands Charity
The Constance Green
    Foundation
The Barry Green Memorial
    Fund
The Philip Green Memorial
    Trust
Mrs H R Greene Charitable
    Settlement
Greenham Common
    Community Trust Limited
Naomi and Jeffrey Greenwood
    Charitable Trust
Greggs Foundation
Grimmitt Trust
The Grocers' Charity
The M and R Gross Charities
    Limited
The Grove Charitable Trust
The GRP Charitable Trust
The David and Marie Grumitt
    Foundation
The Bishop of Guildford's
    Foundation

The Guildry Incorporation of
Perth
The Walter Guinness
Charitable Trust
The Gulbenkian Foundation
The Gunter Charitable Trust
The Gur Trust
Gurunanak
Dr Guthrie's Association
The H and M Charitable Trust
H C D Memorial Fund
The H P Charitable Trust
The Hackney Parochial
Charities
The Hadfield Trust
The Hadley Trust
The Hadrian Trust
The Alfred Haines Charitable
Trust
The Hale Trust
E F and M G Hall Charitable
Trust
The Edith Winifred Hall
Charitable Trust
Robert Hall Charity
The Hamamelis Trust
Hamilton Wallace Trust
Paul Hamlyn Foundation
Sue Hammerson's Charitable
Trust
The Hammonds Charitable
Trust
The Hampshire and Islands
Historic Churches Trust
Hampton Fuel Allotment
Charity
The W A Handley Charitable
Trust
Beatrice Hankey Foundation
Ltd
The Hanley Trust
The Kathleen Hannay
Memorial Charity
The Doughty Hanson
Charitable Foundation
Lord Hanson Foundation
The Haramead Trust
Miss K M Harbinson's
Charitable Trust
Harbo Charities Limited
The Harborne Parish Lands
Charity
The Harbour Charitable Trust
The Harbour Foundation
The Harding Trust
William Harding's Charity
The Hare of Steep Charitable
Trust
The Harebell Centenary Fund
The Kenneth Hargreaves
Charitable Trust
The Harris Charitable Trust
The Harris Charity
The Harrison and Potter Trust
The John Harrison Charitable
Trust

The Peter Harrison Foundation
The Spencer Hart Charitable
Trust
The Hartley Charitable Trust
The N and P Hartley Memorial
Trust
William Geoffrey Harvey's
Discretionary Settlement
Haskel Family Foundation
The Hathaway Trust
The Maurice Hatter Foundation
The M A Hawe Settlement
The Hawthorne Charitable
Trust
The Dorothy Hay-Bolton
Charitable Trust
The Haydan Charitable Trust
The Haymills Charitable Trust
The Charles Hayward
Foundation
The Headley Trust
Headley-Pitt Charitable Trust
Heagerty Charitable Trust
The Heald Charitable Trust
Healthsure Group Ltd
May Hearnshaw's Charity
The Heart of England
Community Foundation
The Heathcoat Trust
Heathside Charitable Trust
The Charlotte Heber-Percy
Charitable Trust
Percy Hedley 1990 Charitable
Trust
The Hedley Denton Charitable
Trust
The Hedley Foundation
The H J Heinz Company
Limited Charitable Trust
The Hellenic Foundation
The Michael and Morven Heller
Charitable Foundation
The Simon Heller Charitable
Settlement
Help the Aged
Help the Homeless
Help the Hospices
The Hemby Trust
The Christina Mary Hendrie
Trust for Scottish and
Canadian Charities
The Henley Educational Charity
Philip Henman Trust
Esther Hennell Charitable
Trust
The G D Herbert Charitable
Trust
The Joanna Herbert-Stepney
Charitable Settlement
The Anne Herd Memorial Trust
The Herefordshire Historic
Churches Trust
The Heritage of London Trust
Ltd
The Hertfordshire Community
Foundation

The Hesed Trust
The Hesslewood Children's
Trust (Hull Seamen's and
General Orphanage)
The Bernhard Heuberger
Charitable Trust
Hexham and Newcastle
Diocesan Trust (1947)
The Higgs Charitable Trust
Alan Edward Higgs Charity
The High Sheriff's Police Trust
for the County of West
Midlands
Highcroft Charitable Trust
The Hilden Charitable Fund
The Joseph and Mary Hiley
Trust
The Holly Hill Charitable Trust
The Charles Littlewood Hill
Trust
The Hillingdon Partnership
Trust
R G Hills Charitable Trust
Hinchley Charitable Trust
Lady Hind Trust
Stuart Hine Trust
The Hinrichsen Foundation
The Hitchin Educational
Foundation
The Eleemosynary Charity of
William Hobbayne
Hobson Charity Limited
Hockerill Educational
Foundation
Matthew Hodder Charitable
Trust
The Sir Julian Hodge
Charitable Trust
The Jane Hodge Foundation
The J G Hogg Charitable Trust
The Holden Charitable Trust
John Holford's Charity
The Hollick Family Charitable
Trust
The Dorothy Holmes Charitable
Trust
The Holst Foundation
P H Holt Foundation
The Edward Holt Trust
The Holywood Trust
The Homelands Charitable
Trust
The Homestead Charitable
Trust
Mary Homfray Charitable Trust
Sir Harold Hood's Charitable
Trust
The Hope Trust
HopMarket Charity
The Cuthbert Horn Trust
The Antony Hornby Charitable
Trust
The Horne Foundation
The Horne Trust
The Worshipful Company of
Horners' Charitable Trusts

The Hornsey Parochial
  Charities
The Hospital of God at
  Greatham
The Hospital Saturday Fund
Houblon-Norman/George Fund
The House of Industry Estate
The Reta Lila Howard
  Foundation
The Daniel Howard Trust
The Clifford Howarth Charity
  Trust
The Huddersfield Medical Trust
  Fund
The Hudson Foundation
The Huggard Charitable Trust
The Geoffrey C Hughes
  Charitable Trust
The Hull and East Riding
  Charitable Trust
Hulme Trust Estates
  (Educational)
Human Relief Foundation
The Humanitarian Trust
The Michael and Shirley Hunt
  Charitable Trust
The Albert Hunt Trust
The Hunter Foundation
Miss Agnes H Hunter's Trust
The Huntingdon Foundation
Huntingdon Freemen's Charity
John Huntingdon's Charity
Hurdale Charity Limited
The Nani Huyu Charitable Trust
The P Y N and B Hyams Trust
The Hyde Charitable Trust –
  Youth Plus
The Idlewild Trust
The Iliffe Family Charitable
  Trust
The Indigo Trust
The Ingram Trust
The Inland Waterways
  Association
The Inlight Trust
The Inman Charity
The Inner London Magistrates
  Court Poor Box Charity and
  Feeder Charity
The Worshipful Company of
  Innholders General Charity
  Fund
The International Bankers
  Charitable Trust (The
  Worshipful Compnay of
  Interntional Bankers)
The Ireland Fund of Great
  Britain
The Irish Youth Foundation
  (UK) Ltd
The Ironmongers' Foundation
Irshad Trust
The Charles Irving Charitable
  Trust
Irwin Trust
The ISA Charity

The Isaacs Charitable Trust
The J Isaacs Charitable Trust
The Isle of Anglesey Charitable
  Trust
Isle of Dogs Community
  Foundation
The ITF Seafarers Trust
J A R Charitable Trust
The J J Charitable Trust
The J R S S T Charitable Trust
Elizabeth Jackson Charitable
  Trust
Jacobs Charitable Trust
The Ruth and Lionel Jacobson
  Trust (Second Fund) No 2
Jaffe Family Relief Fund
The Susan and Stephen
  James Charitable
  Settlement
The James Trust
The Jarman Charitable Trust
The John Jarrold Trust
JCA Charitable Foundation
The Jeffrey Charitable Trust
Rees Jeffreys Road Fund
The Jenour Foundation
The Jephcott Charitable Trust
The Jerusalem Trust
Jerwood Charitable Foundation
Jesus Hospital Charity
Jewish Child's Day
The Jewish Youth Fund
The JMK Charitable Trust
The Joanies Trust
The Harold Joels Charitable
  Trust
The Jonathan Joels Charitable
  Trust
The Nicholas Joels Charitable
  Trust
The Norman Joels Charitable
  Trust
The Joffe Charitable Trust
The Elton John Aids
  Foundation
The Lillie Johnson Charitable
  Trust
The Johnson Group Cleaners
  Charity
The Johnnie Johnson Trust
The Johnson Wax Ltd
  Charitable Trust
The Joicey Trust
The Jones 1986 Charitable
  Trust
The Marjorie and Geoffrey
  Jones Charitable Trust
The Jordan Charitable
  Foundation
The J E Joseph Charitable
  Fund
The Lady Eileen Joseph
  Foundation
JTH Charitable Trust
The Judith Trust

The Anton Jurgens Charitable
  Trust
The Bernard Kahn Charitable
  Trust
The Stanley Kalms Foundation
The Karenza Foundation
The Boris Karloff Charitable
  Foundation
The Ian Karten Charitable
  Trust
The Kasner Charitable Trust
The Kass Charitable Trust
The Kathleen Trust
The Michael and Ilse Katz
  Foundation
The Katzauer Charitable
  Settlement
The C S Kaufman Charitable
  Trust
The Geoffrey John Kaye
  Charitable Foundation
The Emmanuel Kaye
  Foundation
Kelsick's Educational
  Foundation
The KempWelch Charitable
  Trust
The Kay Kendall Leukaemia
  Fund
William Kendall's Charity (Wax
  Chandlers' Company)
The Kennedy Charitable
  Foundation
The Nancy Kenyon Charitable
  Trust
Keren Association
Kermaville Ltd
E and E Kernkraut Charities
  Limited
The Peter Kershaw Trust
The Kessler Foundation
Keswick Hall Charity
The Ursula Keyes Trust
The Robert Kiln Charitable
  Trust
The King Henry VIII Endowed
  Trust Warwick
The King/Cullimore Charitable
  Trust
The King's Fund
The Kingsbury Charity
The Mary Kinross Charitable
  Trust
Kinsurdy Charitable Trust
Kirkley Poor's Lands Estate
The Richard Kirkman
  Charitable Trust
Kirschel Foundation
Robert Kitchin (Saddlers'
  Company)
Ernest Kleinwort Charitable
  Trust
The Marina Kleinwort
  Charitable Trust
The Kobler Trust
The Kohn Foundation

The Kreditor Charitable Trust
The Kreitman Foundation
The Neil Kreitman Foundation
The Heinz, Anna and Carol Kroch Foundation
The Kyte Charitable Trust
Lacims-Maclis Charitable Trust
The Late Sir Pierce Lacy Charity Trust
John Laing Charitable Trust
Maurice and Hilda Laing Charitable Trust
The Laing Family Foundations
The Christopher Laing Foundation
The Kirby Laing Foundation
The Martin Laing Foundation
The Beatrice Laing Trust
The Lambert Charitable Trust
Lancashire Environmental Fund
Duchy of Lancaster Benevolent Fund
The Lancaster Foundation
LandAid Charitable Trust
The Allen Lane Foundation
The Langdale Trust
The Langley Charitable Trust
The Langtree Trust
The LankellyChase Foundation
The Lanvern Foundation
The R J Larg Family Charitable Trust
Largsmount Ltd
The Lark Trust
Laslett's (Hinton) Charity
Lauchentilly Charitable Foundation 1988
Laufer Charitable Trust
The Lauffer Family Charitable Foundation
Mrs F B Laurence Charitable Trust
The Kathleen Laurence Trust
The Law Society Charity
The Edgar E Lawley Foundation
The Herd Lawson and Muriel Lawson Charitable Trust
The Lawson Beckman Charitable Trust
The Raymond and Blanche Lawson Charitable Trust
The Carole and Geoffrey Lawson Foundation
The Mason Le Page Charitable Trust
The Leach Fourteenth Trust
The David Lean Foundation
The Leathersellers' Company Charitable Fund
The Leche Trust
The Arnold Lee Charitable Trust
The William Leech Charity
The Lord Mayor of Leeds Appeal Fund

Leeds Building Society Charitable Foundation
Leicester Charity Link
The Kennedy Leigh Charitable Trust
Morris Leigh Foundation
The Leigh Trust
Mrs Vera Leigh's Charity
The P Leigh-Bramwell Trust 'E'
The Lennox and Wyfold Foundation
The Erica Leonard Trust
The Leonard Trust
The Mark Leonard Trust
Lesley Lesley and Mutter Trust
Leukaemia Research Fund
The Leverhulme Trade Charities Trust
The Leverhulme Trust
Lord Leverhulme's Charitable Trust
The Joseph Levy Charitable Foundation
Lewis Family Charitable Trust
The John Spedan Lewis Foundation
The Sir Edward Lewis Foundation
John Lewis Partnership General Community Fund
Lichfield Conduit Lands
Lifeline 4 Kids
The Thomas Lilley Memorial Trust
Limoges Charitable Trust
The Linbury Trust
The Lind Trust
Lindale Educational Foundation
The Linden Charitable Trust
The Enid Linder Foundation
The Linmardon Trust
The Ruth and Stuart Lipton Charitable Trust
The Lister Charitable Trust
Frank Litchfield Charitable Trust
The Andrew and Mary Elizabeth Little Charitable Trust
The Second Joseph Aaron Littman Foundation
The George John and Sheilah Livanos Charitable Trust
Liverpool Sailors' Home Trust
Jack Livingstone Charitable Trust
The Elaine and Angus Lloyd Charitable Trust
The Charles Lloyd Foundation
The Lloyd Fund
Lloyd's Charities Trust
The Lloyd-Everett Trust
Lloyds TSB Foundation for England and Wales

Lloyds TSB Foundation for Northern Ireland
Lloyds TSB Foundation for the Channel Islands
Llysdinam Charitable Trust
Localtrent Ltd
The Locker Foundation
The Loftus Charitable Trust
The Lolev Charitable Trust
London Catalyst
The London Law Trust
The London Marathon Charitable Trust
The William and Katherine Longman Trust
The Loseley and Guildway Charitable Trust
The Lotus Foundation
The C L Loyd Charitable Trust
LSA Charitable Trust
The Marie Helen Luen Charitable Trust
Robert Luff Foundation Ltd
Henry Lumley Charitable Trust
Lady Lumley's Educational Foundation
Paul Lunn-Rockliffe Charitable Trust
C F Lunoe Trust Fund
The Ruth and Jack Lunzer Charitable Trust
Lord and Lady Lurgan Trust
The Lyndhurst Trust
The Lynn Foundation
The Lynwood Trust
John Lyon's Charity
The Lyons Charitable Trust
The Sir Jack Lyons Charitable Trust
Malcolm Lyons Foundation
The Lyras Family Charitable Trust
Sylvanus Lyson's Charity
The M and C Trust
The M D and S Charitable Trust
The M K Charitable Trust
The Madeline Mabey Trust
The E M MacAndrew Trust
Macdonald-Buchanan Charitable Trust
The Macfarlane Walker Trust
The Mackay and Brewer Charitable Trust
The Mackintosh Foundation
The MacRobert Trust
Ian Mactaggart Trust
James Madison Trust
The Magdalen and Lasher Charity
The Magen Charitable Trust
Mageni Trust
Mahavir Trust
Man Group plc Charitable Trust

Manchester Airport Community
Trust Fund
The Manchester Guardian
Society Charitable Trust
Manchester Kids
Lord Mayor of Manchester's
Charity Appeal Trust
Mandeville Trust
The Manifold Charitable Trust
W M Mann Foundation
The Leslie and Lilian Manning
Trust
Maranatha Christian Trust
Marbeh Torah Trust
The Marchday Charitable Fund
Marchig Animal Welfare Trust
The Stella and Alexander
Margulies Charitable Trust
Mariapolis Limited
Market Harborough and The
Bowdens Charity
Michael Marks Charitable
Trust
The Ann and David Marks
Foundation
The Hilda and Samuel Marks
Foundation
J P Marland Charitable Trust
Marr-Munning Trust
The Michael Marsh Charitable
Trust
The Marsh Christian Trust
The Charlotte Marshall
Charitable Trust
The Jim Marshall Charitable
Trust
The D G Marshall of
Cambridge Trust
Marshall's Charity
Marshgate Charitable
Settlement
Sir George Martin Trust
John Martin's Charity
The Mason Porter Charitable
Trust
The Nancie Massey Charitable
Trust
The Mathew Trust
Matliwala Family Charitable
Trust
The Matt 6.3 Charitable Trust
The Violet Mauray Charitable
Trust
The Maxell Educational Trust
The Maxwell Family Foundation
Evelyn May Trust
Mayfair Charities Ltd
The Mayfield Valley Arts Trust
Mazars Charitable Trust
The McDougall Trust
The A M McGreevy No 5
Charitable Settlement
The McKenna Charitable Trust
Martin McLaren Memorial
Trust

The Helen Isabella McMorran
Charitable Foundation
D D McPhail Charitable
Settlement
The James Frederick and Ethel
Anne Measures Charity
Medical Research Council
The Medlock Charitable Trust
The Anthony and Elizabeth
Mellows Charitable
Settlement
Melodor Ltd
Melow Charitable Trust
Meningitis Trust
Menuchar Ltd
Brian Mercer Charitable Trust
The Mercers' Charitable
Foundation
The Merchant Taylors'
Company Charities Fund
The Merchant Venturers'
Charity
The Merchants' House of
Glasgow
Mercury Phoenix Trust
The Mersey Docks and
Harbour Company
Charitable Fund
Community Foundation for
Merseyside
The Zachary Merton and
George Woofindin
Convalescent Trust
The Tony Metherell Charitable
Trust
The Methodist Relief and
Development Fund
The Metropolitan Drinking
Fountain and Cattle Trough
Association
Gerald Micklem Charitable
Trust
Midhurst Pensions Trust
The Migraine Trust
Miles Trust for the Putney and
Roehampton Community
Millennium Stadium Charitable
Trust
The Hugh and Mary Miller
Bequest Trust
The Miller Foundation
The Millfield Trust
The Millhouses Charitable
Trust
The Millichope Foundation
The Mills Charity
The Millward Charitable Trust
The Clare Milne Trust
Milton Keynes Community
Foundation
The Edgar Milward Charity
The Peter Minet Trust
Minge's Gift and the Pooled
Trusts
The Minos Trust

The Mirfield Educational
Charity
The Laurence Misener
Charitable Trust
The Mishcon Family Charitable
Trust
The Misselbrook Trust
The Esmé Mitchell Trust
Keren Mitzvah Trust
The Mizpah Trust
The Mobbs Memorial Trust Ltd
The Modiano Charitable Trust
The Moette Charitable Trust
The Mole Charitable Trust
The D C Moncrieff Charitable
Trust
Monmouthshire County Council
Welsh Church Act Fund
The Montague Thompson
Coon Charitable Trust
The Colin Montgomerie
Charitable Foundation
The Monument Trust
Moody Charitable Trust
George A Moore Foundation
The Henry Moore Foundation
The Nigel Moores Family
Charitable Trust
John Moores Foundation
The Peter Moores Foundation
The Morel Charitable Trust
The Morgan Charitable
Foundation
The Mr and Mrs J T Morgan
Foundation
The J P Morgan Foundations
Diana and Allan Morgenthau
Charitable Trust
The Oliver Morland Charitable
Trust
S C and M E Morland's
Charitable Trust
The Morris Charitable Trust
The Willie and Mabel Morris
Charitable Trust
The Peter Morrison Charitable
Foundation
The Stanley Morrison
Charitable Trust
Moshal Charitable Trust
Vyoel Moshe Charitable Trust
The Moss Charitable Trust
The Robert and Margaret
Moss Charitable Trust
Moss Family Charitable Trust
The Mount Everest Foundation
Mountbatten Festival of Music
The Mountbatten Memorial
Trust
The Edwina Mountbatten Trust
The Mugdock Children's Trust
The F H Muirhead Charitable
Trust
The Mulberry Trust
The Edith Murphy Foundation

Murphy-Neumann Charity
Company Limited
The Mushroom Fund
The Music Sales Charitable
Trust
Muslim Hands
The Mutual Trust Group
MYA Charitable Trust
The Kitty and Daniel Nabarro
Charitable Trust
The Nadezhda Charitable Trust
The Willie Nagel Charitable
Trust
The Naggar Charitable Trust
The Eleni Nakou Foundation
The Janet Nash Charitable
Settlement
Nathan Charitable Trust
Asthma UK
The National Churches Trust
The National Manuscripts
Conservation Trust
Nazareth Trust Fund
The Nchima Trust
Needham Market and Barking
Welfare Charities
The Worshipful Company of
Needlemakers' Charitable
Fund
The Neighbourly Charitable
Trust
The James Neill Trust Fund
Nemoral Ltd
Nesswall Ltd
Nestle Rowntree Employees
Community Fund
Network for Social Change
The New Appeals Organisation
for the City and County of
Nottingham
New Court Charitable Trust
Newby Trust Limited
The Newcomen Collett
Foundation
The Richard Newitt Fund
Mr and Mrs F E F Newman
Charitable Trust
The Frances and Augustus
Newman Foundation
Newpier Charity Ltd
Alderman Newton's
Educational Foundation
The Chevras Ezras Nitzrochim
Trust
The Noel Buxton Trust
The Noon Foundation
The Norda Trust
Norie Charitable Trust
Normalyn Charitable Trust
The Norman Family Charitable
Trust
The Duncan Norman Trust
Fund
The Normanby Charitable Trust
The North British Hotel Trust

The North West Cancer
Research Fund
The Northampton Municipal
Church Charities
The Northampton Queen's
Institute Relief in Sickness
Fund
The Earl of Northampton's
Charity
The Northcott Devon
Foundation
The Northcott Devon Medical
Foundation
The Northern Rock Foundation
The Northmoor Trust
The Northumberland Village
Homes Trust
The Northumbria Historic
Churches Trust
The Northwood Charitable
Trust
The Norton Foundation
The Norwich Church of England
Young Men's Society
The Norwich Historic Churches
Trust Ltd
The Norwich Town Close
Estate Charity
The Norwood and Newton
Settlement
The Noswad Charity
The Notgrove Trust
The Nottingham General
Dispensary
The Nottingham Gordon
Memorial Trust for Boys
and Girls
Nottinghamshire Community
Foundation
The Nottinghamshire Historic
Churches Trust
The Nottinghamshire Miners'
Welfare Trust Fund
Novi Most International
The Father O'Mahoney
Memorial Trust
The Sir Peter O'Sullevan
Charitable Trust
The Oak Trust
The Oakdale Trust
The Oakley Charitable Trust
The Oakmoor Charitable Trust
The Odin Charitable Trust
Ogilvie Charities Deed No.2
(including the Charity of
Mary Catherine Ford Smith)
The Ogle Christian Trust
Oglesby Charitable Trust
The Oizer Charitable Trust
The Old Broad Street Charity
Trust
The Old Enfield Charitable
Trust
Old Possum's Practical Trust
The John Oldacre Foundation
The Oldham Foundation

The Olga Charitable Trust
Onaway Trust
Open Gate
The Ormsby Charitable Trust
Orrin Charitable Trust
The Ouseley Trust
The Owen Family Trust
Oxfam (GB)
The Oxfordshire Community
Foundation
The P F Charitable Trust
Padwa Charitable Foundation
The Pallant Charitable Trust
The Palmer Foundation
Eleanor Palmer Trust
The Panacea Society
Panahpur Charitable Trust
Panton Trust
The Paragon Trust
The Park House Charitable
Trust
The Frank Parkinson
Agricultural Trust
The Samuel and Freda
Parkinson Charitable Trust
The Parthenon Trust
Arthur James Paterson
Charitable Trust
The Constance Paterson
Charitable Trust
Miss M E Swinton Paterson's
Charitable Trust
The Patrick Charitable Trust
The Jack Patston Charitable
Trust
Paycare Charity Trust
The Payne Charitable Trust
The Harry Payne Trust
The Susanna Peake Charitable
Trust
Pearson's Holiday Fund
The Pedmore Sporting Club
Trust Fund
The Dowager Countess
Eleanor Peel Trust
Peltz Trust
The Pennycress Trust
The Performing Right Society
Foundation
B E Perl Charitable Trust
The Persson Charitable Trust
The Persula Foundation
The Pestalozzi Overseas
Children's Trust
The Jack Petchey Foundation
The Petplan Charitable Trust
The Philips and Rubens
Charitable Trust
The Phillips Charitable Trust
The Phillips Family Charitable
Trust
Philological Foundation
The David Pickford Charitable
Foundation
The Claude and Margaret Pike
Charity

The Pilgrim Trust
The Cecil Pilkington Charitable
Trust
The Pilkington Charities Fund
The Austin and Hope
Pilkington Trust
The Sir Harry Pilkington Trust
The Col W W Pilkington Will
Trusts The General Charity
Fund
Miss A M Pilkington's
Charitable Trust
Mrs Pilkington's Charitable
Trust
The Plaisterers' Company
Charitable Trust
The Platinum Trust
G S Plaut Charitable Trust
Limited
Polden-Puckham Charitable
Foundation
The Poling Charitable Trust
The George and Esme Pollitzer
Charitable Settlement
The J S F Pollitzer Charitable
Settlement
The Ponton House Trust
The Mayor of Poole's Appeal
Fund
Edith and Ferdinand Porjes
Charitable Trust
The John Porter Charitable
Trust
The Porter Foundation
The Portrack Charitable Trust
The J E Posnansky Charitable
Trust
The Mary Potter Convent
Hospital Trust
The David and Elaine Potter
Foundation
The Powell Foundation
Prairie Trust
The W L Pratt Charitable Trust
Premierquote Ltd
Premishlaner Charitable Trust
The Lucy Price Relief-in-Need
Charity
Sir John Priestman Charity
Trust
The Primrose Trust
The Prince's Charities
Foundation
Princess Anne's Charities
The Priory Foundation
Prison Service Charity Fund
The Privy Purse Charitable
Trust
The Proven Family Trust
The Provincial Grand Charity of
the Province of Derbyshire
PSA Peugeot Citroen Charity
Trust
The Puebla Charitable Trust
The Richard and Christine
Purchas Charitable Trust

The Puri Foundation
Mr and Mrs J A Pye's
Charitable Settlement
Quartet Community Foundation
Queen Mary's Roehampton
Trust
The Queen's Silver Jubilee
Trust
Quercus Trust
The R D Crusaders Foundation
R J M Charitable Trust
R S Charitable Trust
The R V W Trust
The Monica Rabagliati
Charitable Trust
Rachel Charitable Trust
The Mr and Mrs Philip
Rackham Charitable Trust
Richard Radcliffe Charitable
Trust
The Radcliffe Trust
The Ragdoll Foundation
The Rainford Trust
The Peggy Ramsay Foundation
The Joseph and Lena Randall
Charitable Trust
The Rank Foundation
Ranworth Trust
The Fanny Rapaport Charitable
Settlement
The Ratcliff Foundation
The Ratcliff Pension Charity
The Ratcliffe Charitable Trust
The Eleanor Rathbone
Charitable Trust
The Sigrid Rausing Trust
The Ravensdale Trust
The Rayden Charitable Trust
The Roger Raymond Charitable
Trust
The Rayne Foundation
The Rayne Trust
The John Rayner Charitable
Trust
The Albert Reckitt Charitable
Trust
The Sir James Reckitt Charity
The Red Arrows Trust
The Red Rose Charitable Trust
The C A Redfern Charitable
Foundation
The Reed Foundation
Richard Reeve's Foundation
The Max Reinhardt Charitable
Trust
Relief Fund for Romania
Limited
REMEDI
The Rest Harrow Trust
Reuben Brothers Foundation
The Joan K Reynell Charitable
Trust
The Nathaniel Reyner Trust
Fund
The Rhododendron Trust
Daisie Rich Trust

The Sir Cliff Richard Charitable
Trust
C B Richard Ellis Charitable
Trust
The Clive Richards Charity
The Violet M Richards Charity
The Richmond Parish Lands
Charity
The Muriel Edith Rickman
Trust
Ridgesave Limited
The Ripple Effect Foundation
The Sir John Ritblat Family
Foundation
The River Trust
Riverside Charitable Trust
Limited
The Daniel Rivlin Charitable
Trust
Thomas Roberts Trust
The Alex Roberts-Miller
Foundation
The Robertson Trust
Edwin George Robinson
Charitable Trust
Robyn Charitable Trust
The Rochester Bridge Trust
The Rock Foundation
The Rock Solid Trust
The Rofeh Trust
Richard Rogers Charitable
Settlement
Rokach Family Charitable Trust
The Helen Roll Charitable
Trust
The Sir James Roll Charitable
Trust
The Roman Research Trust
Romeera Foundation
The C A Rookes Charitable
Trust
The Rosca Trust
The Rose Foundation
The Cecil Rosen Foundation
Rosetrees Trust
The Rothermere Foundation
The Rotherwick Foundation
The Rothschild Foundation
The Roughley Charitable Trust
Mrs Gladys Row Fogo
Charitable Trust
The Rowan Charitable Trust
Rowanville Ltd
The Christopher Rowbotham
Charitable Trust
The Rowing Foundation
The Rowlands Trust
The Joseph Rowntree
Charitable Trust
The Joseph Rowntree
Foundation
Joseph Rowntree Reform Trust
Limited
Royal Artillery Charitable Fund
Royal British Legion
Royal Docks Trust (London)

Royal Masonic Trust for Girls
and Boys
The Royal Scots Benevolent
Society
The Alfred and Frances
Rubens Charitable Trust
The Rubin Foundation
William Arthur Rudd Memorial
Trust
The Rufford Maurice Laing
Foundation
The Rufford Small Grants
Foundation
The Russell Trust
Ryklow Charitable Trust 1992
The J S and E C Rymer
Charitable Trust
S O Charitable Trust
The Michael Sacher Charitable
Trust
The Michael Harry Sacher
Trust
Dr Mortimer and Theresa
Sackler Foundation
The Ruzin Sadagora Trust
The Saddlers' Company
Charitable Fund
The Saga Charitable Trust
The Jean Sainsbury Animal
Welfare Trust
The Alan and Babette
Sainsbury Charitable Fund
Saint Sarkis Charity Trust
The Saintbury Trust
The Saints and Sinners Trust
The Salamander Charitable
Trust
The Salt Foundation
The Salt Trust
The Salters' Charities
The Andrew Salvesen
Charitable Trust
The Sammermar Trust
Basil Samuel Charitable Trust
Coral Samuel Charitable Trust
The Hon. M J Samuel
Charitable Trust
The Peter Samuel Charitable
Trust
The Camilla Samuel Fund
The Samworth Foundation
The Sandra Charitable Trust
Santander UK Foundation
Limited
Jimmy Savile Charitable Trust
The Scarfe Charitable Trust
The Schapira Charitable Trust
The Annie Schiff Charitable
Trust
The Schmidt-Bodner Charitable
Trust
The R H Scholes Charitable
Trust
The Schreib Trust
The Schreiber Charitable Trust
Schroder Charity Trust

The Scott Bader
Commonwealth Ltd
The Francis C Scott Charitable
Trust
The Frieda Scott Charitable
Trust
Sir Samuel Scott of Yews
Trust
The Sir James and Lady Scott
Trust
The Scott Trust Foundation
The Storrow Scott Will Trust
The Scottish Arts Council
Scottish Churches' Community
Trust
Scottish Coal Industry Special
Welfare Fund
The Scottish Community
Foundation
The Scottish International
Education Trust
The Scouloudi Foundation
Seafarers UK (King George's
Fund for Sailors)
Seamen's Hospital Society
The Searchlight Electric
Charitable Trust
The Searle Charitable Trust
The Helene Sebba Charitable
Trust
The Samuel Sebba Charitable
Trust
The Seedfield Trust
Leslie Sell Charitable Trust
Sellata Ltd
SEM Charitable Trust
The Ayrton Senna Foundation
The Seven Fifty Trust
The Severn Trent Water
Charitable Trust Fund
SFIA Educational Trust Limited
The Cyril Shack Trust
The Jean Shanks Foundation
The Shanti Charitable Trust
ShareGift (The Orr Mackintosh
Foundation)
The Linley Shaw Foundation
The Sheepdrove Trust
The Sheffield and District
Hospital Services
Charitable Fund
The Sheldon Trust
The P and D Shepherd
Charitable Trust
The Sylvia and Colin Shepherd
Charitable Trust
The Archie Sherman Cardiff
Foundation
The Archie Sherman Charitable
Trust
The R C Sherriff Trust
The Shetland Charitable Trust
SHINE (Support and Help in
Education)
The Barnett and Sylvia Shine
No 2 Charitable Trust

The Bassil Shippam and
Alsford Trust
The Shipwrights' Company
Charitable Fund
The Shirley Foundation
Shlomo Memorial Fund Limited
The J A Shone Memorial Trust
The Charles Shorto Charitable
Trust
The Barbara A Shuttleworth
Memorial Trust
The Mary Elizabeth Siebel
Charity
David and Jennifer Sieff
Charitable Trust
The Julius Silman Charitable
Trust
The Leslie Silver Charitable
Trust
The Simpson Education and
Conservation Trust
The Simpson Foundation
The Huntly and Margery
Sinclair Charitable Trust
Sino-British Fellowship Trust
The Skelton Bounty
The Charles Skey Charitable
Trust
Skipton Building Society
Charitable Foundation
The John Slater Foundation
Rita and David Slowe
Charitable Trust
The SMB Charitable Trust
The Mrs Smith and Mount
Trust
The N Smith Charitable
Settlement
The Amanda Smith Charitable
Trust
The E H Smith Charitable Trust
The Smith Charitable Trust
The Henry Smith Charity
The Leslie Smith Foundation
The Martin Smith Foundation
Stanley Smith General
Charitable Trust
The Stanley Smith UK
Horticultural Trust
Philip Smith's Charitable Trust
The Snowball Trust
The Sobell Foundation
Solev Co Ltd
Solihull Community Foundation
The Solo Charitable
Settlement
Dr Richard Solomon's
Charitable Trust
Songdale Ltd
The E C Sosnow Charitable
Trust
The Souter Charitable Trust
The South Square Trust
The Stephen R and Philippa H
Southall Charitable Trust
The W F Southall Trust

The Southdown Trust

R H Southern Trust

The Southover Manor General Education Trust

The Southwold Trust

The Sovereign Health Care Charitable Trust

Spar Charitable Fund

Sparks Charity (Sport Aiding Medical Research For Kids)

Sparquote Limited

The Spear Charitable Trust

Spears-Stutz Charitable Trust

The Worshipful Company of Spectacle Makers' Charity

The Jessie Spencer Trust

The Ralph and Irma Sperring Charity

The Moss Spiro Will Charitable Foundation

W W Spooner Charitable Trust

Stanley Spooner Deceased Charitable Trust

The Spoore, Merry and Rixman Foundation

The Spring Harvest Charitable Trust

Rosalyn and Nicholas Springer Charitable Trust

Springfields Employees' Medical Research and Charity Trust Fund

Springrule Ltd

The Spurrell Charitable Trust

The Geoff and Fiona Squire Foundation

St Andrew Animal Fund

St Andrew's Conservation Trust

St Francis's Leprosy Guild

St Gabriel's Trust

St Hilda's Trust

St James' Trust Settlement

St James's Place Foundation

Sir Walter St John's Educational Charity

St Katharine and Shadwell Trust

St Mark's Overseas Aid Trust (SMOAT)

St Michael's and All Saints' Charities

The Late St Patrick White Charitable Trust

St Teilo's Trust

Miss Doreen Stanford Trust

The Stanley Foundation Ltd

The Stanton Ballard Charitable Trust

The Staples Trust

The Star Charitable Trust

The Starfish Trust

The Peter Stebbings Memorial Charity

The Steel Charitable Trust

The Cyril and Betty Stein Charitable Trust

The Steinberg Family Charitable Trust

The Hugh Stenhouse Foundation

The Sigmund Sternberg Charitable Foundation

Stervon Ltd

The Stevenage Community Trust

The June Stevens Foundation

Stevenson Family's Charitable Trust

The Steventon Allotments and Relief-in-Need Charity

The Stewards' Charitable Trust

The Stewards' Company Limited

The Sir Halley Stewart Trust

The Leonard Laity Stoate Charitable Trust

The Stobart Newlands Charitable Trust

The Edward Stocks-Massey Bequest Fund

The Stokenchurch Educational Charity

The Stoller Charitable Trust

The M J C Stone Charitable Trust

The Stone-Mallabar Charitable Foundation

The Samuel Storey Family Charitable Trust

Peter Stormonth Darling Charitable Trust

Peter Storrs Trust

The Strangward Trust

The Strasser Foundation

Stratford upon Avon Town Trust

Strathclyde Police Benevolent Fund

The W O Street Charitable Foundation

The A B Strom and R Strom Charitable Trust

The Sudborough Foundation

Sueberry Ltd

The Suffolk Historic Churches Trust

The Alan Sugar Foundation

The Summerfield Charitable Trust

The Bernard Sunley Charitable Foundation

The Surrey Historic Buildings Trust Ltd

The Sussex Historic Churches Trust

The Adrienne and Leslie Sussman Charitable Trust

The Sutasoma Trust

Sutton Coldfield Municipal Charities

The Sutton Nursing Association

The Sutton Trust

Swan Mountain Trust

The Swan Trust

Swansea and Brecon Diocesan Board of Finance Limited

The John Swire (1989) Charitable Trust

The Swire Charitable Trust

The Hugh and Ruby Sykes Charitable Trust

The Charles and Elsie Sykes Trust

The Sylvanus Charitable Trust

The Stella Symons Charitable Trust

The Tabeel Trust

The Tajtelbaum Charitable Trust

The Talbot Trusts

The Talbot Village Trust

Tallow Chandlers Benevolent Fund

Talteg Ltd

The Tangent Charitable Trust

The Lady Tangye Charitable Trust

The David Tannen Charitable Trust

The Tanner Trust

The Lili Tapper Charitable Foundation

The Mrs A Lacy Tate Trust

The Tay Charitable Trust

C B and H H Taylor 1984 Trust

Humphrey Richardson Taylor Charitable Trust

The Connie and Albert Taylor Charitable Trust

The Cyril Taylor Charitable Trust

A P Taylor Trust

Rosanna Taylor's 1987 Charity Trust

Tearfund

The Tedworth Charitable Trust

Tees Valley Community Foundation

Tegham Limited

The Templeton Goodwill Trust

Tesco Charity Trust

Thackray Medical Research Trust

Thames Community Foundation

The Thames Wharf Charity

The Thistle Trust

The Loke Wan Tho Memorial Foundation

The Thomas Wall Trust

The Arthur and Margaret Thompson Charitable Trust

The Thompson Family Charitable Trust

The Len Thomson Charitable Trust

The Sue Thomson Foundation

The Sir Jules Thorn Charitable Trust

The Thornton Foundation

The Thornton Trust

The Three Guineas Trust

The Three Oaks Trust

The Thriplow Charitable Trust

The Tinsley Foundation

The Tisbury Telegraph Trust

TJH Foundation

The Tolkien Trust

Tollemache (Buckminster) Charitable Trust

Tomchei Torah Charitable Trust

The Tompkins Foundation

The Tory Family Foundation

Tottenham Grammar School Foundation

The Tower Hill Trust

The Towry Law Charitable Trust

The Toy Trust

The Mayor of Trafford's Charity Fund

Annie Tranmer Charitable Trust

The Constance Travis Charitable Trust

The Treeside Trust

The Triangle Trust (1949) Fund

The True Colours Trust

Truedene Co. Ltd

The Truemark Trust

Truemart Limited

Trumros Limited

Trust for London

Trust Sixty Three

The Trusthouse Charitable Foundation

The Tubney Charitable Trust

Tudor Rose Ltd

The Tudor Trust

The Tufton Charitable Trust

The R D Turner Charitable Trust

The Douglas Turner Trust

The Florence Turner Trust

Miss S M Tutton Charitable Trust

The TUUT Charitable Trust

Community Foundation Serving Tyne and Wear and Northumberland

Trustees of Tzedakah

Ulster Garden Villages Ltd

Ultach Trust

Ulting Overseas Trust

The Ulverscroft Foundation

Ulverston Town Lands Charity

The Underwood Trust

The Union of Orthodox Hebrew Congregation

The United Society for the Propagation of the Gospel

United Trusts

The David Uri Memorial Trust

Uxbridge United Welfare Trust

Vale of Glamorgan – Welsh Church Fund

The Valentine Charitable Trust

The Albert Van Den Bergh Charitable Trust

John and Lucille van Geest Foundation

The Van Neste Foundation

Mrs Maud Van Norden's Charitable Foundation

The Vandervell Foundation

The Vardy Foundation

The Variety Club Children's Charity

Veneziana Fund

The Verdon-Smith Family Charitable Settlement

Roger Vere Foundation

Victoria Homes Trust

Viking Cares (For the Kids)

The Nigel Vinson Charitable Trust

The William and Ellen Vinten Trust

The Vintners' Company Charitable Foundation

Vintners' Gifts Charity

Vision Charity

Vivdale Ltd

The Viznitz Foundation

Wade's Charity

The Scurrah Wainwright Charity

Wakeham Trust

The Community Foundation in Wales

Wales Council for Voluntary Action

Robert and Felicity Waley-Cohen Charitable Trust

The Walker Trust

Wallington Missionary Mart and Auctions

The F J Wallis Charitable Settlement

War on Want

Sir Siegmund Warburg's Voluntary Settlement

The Ward Blenkinsop Trust

The George Ward Charitable Trust

The Barbara Ward Children's Foundation

The John Warren Foundation

G R Waters Charitable Trust 2000

The Waterways Trust

The Wates Foundation

Blyth Watson Charitable Trust

The Howard Watson Symington Memorial Charity

John Watson's Trust

Weatherley Charitable Trust

The Weavers' Company Benevolent Fund

The William Webster Charitable Trust

The Weinberg Foundation

The Weinstein Foundation

The Weinstock Fund

The Barbara Welby Trust

The Weldon UK Charitable Trust

The Wellcome Trust

Welsh Church Fund Dyfed area (Carmarthenshire, Ceredigion and Pembrokeshire)

The Welton Foundation

The Wessex Youth Trust

The West Derby Wastelands Charity

West London Synagogue Charitable Fund

The West Yorkshire Police Community Fund

Mrs S K West's Charitable Trust

The Westminster Foundation

The Garfield Weston Foundation

The Whitaker Charitable Trust

The Colonel W H Whitbread Charitable Trust

The Simon Whitbread Charitable Trust

White Rose Children's Aid International Charity

The Whitecourt Charitable Trust

A H and B C Whiteley Charitable Trust

The Norman Whiteley Trust

The Whitley Animal Protection Trust

The Whittlesey Charity

The Lionel Wigram Memorial Trust

The Felicity Wilde Charitable Trust

The Will Charitable Trust

The Kay Williams Charitable Foundation

The Williams Family Charitable Trust

The H D H Wills 1965 Charitable Trust

Dame Violet Wills Charitable Trust

The Dame Violet Wills Will Trust

The Wilmcote Charitrust

Sumner Wilson Charitable Trust

David Wilson Foundation

The Wilson Foundation

J and J R Wilson Trust

The Community Foundation for Wiltshire and Swindon

The Benjamin Winegarten
    Charitable Trust
The Harold Hyam Wingate
    Foundation
The Francis Winham
    Foundation
Anona Winn Charitable Trust
Wirral Mayor's Charity
The Michael and Anna Wix
    Charitable Trust
The Wixamtree Trust
The Woburn 1986 Charitable
    Trust
The Maurice Wohl Charitable
    Foundation
The Charles Wolfson
    Charitable Trust
Women Caring Trust
The James Wood Bequest
    Fund
Woodlands Green Ltd
Woodlands Trust
The Geoffrey Woods Charitable
    Foundation
The Woodward Charitable
    Trust
The A and R Woolf Charitable
    Trust
The Woolnoth Society
    Charitable Trust
Worcester Municipal Charities
The Worcestershire and
    Dudley Historic Churches
    Trust
The Fred and Della Worms
    Charitable Trust
The Worwin UK Foundation
The Wragge and Co. Charitable
    Trust
The Diana Edgson Wright
    Charitable Trust
The Matthews Wrightson
    Charity Trust
Miss E B Wrightson's
    Charitable Settlement
Wychdale Ltd
Wychville Ltd
The Wyndham Charitable Trust
The Wyseliot Charitable Trust
The Xerox (UK) Trust
The Yapp Charitable Trust
The Yardley Great Trust
The Dennis Alan Yardy
    Charitable Trust
The W Wing Yip and Brothers
    Foundation
The York Children's Trust
Yorkshire Agricultural Society
Yorkshire Building Society
    Charitable Foundation
The South Yorkshire
    Community Foundation
The Yorkshire Dales
    Millennium Trust
The John Young Charitable
    Settlement

The William Allen Young
    Charitable Trust
The John K Young Endowment
    Fund
Youth Music
Elizabeth and Prince Zaiger
    Trust
Zephyr Charitable Trust
The Marjorie and Arnold Ziff
    Charitable Foundation
Stephen Zimmerman
    Charitable Trust
The Zochonis Charitable Trust
Zurich Community Trust (UK)
    Limited

....

■ Seed funding

The 1989 Willan Charitable
    Trust
The 29th May 1961 Charitable
    Trust
Aberbrothock Charitable Trust
The Aberdeen Endowments
    Trust
The Aberdeenshire Educational
    Trust Scheme
Achiezer Association Ltd
Achisomoch Aid Company
    Limited
The ACT Foundation
Action Medical Research
The Sylvia Adams Charitable
    Trust
The Victor Adda Foundation
The Adint Charitable Trust
The Adnams Charity
Age Concern Scotland Grants
Aid to the Church in Need (UK)
The AIM Foundation
The Sylvia Aitken Charitable
    Trust
The Ajahma Charitable Trust
Alcohol Education and
    Research Council
Aldgate and All Hallows'
    Barking Exhibition
    Foundation
The Aldgate Freedom
    Foundation
Alexandra Rose Charities
The Alexis Trust
All Saints Educational Trust
Allchurches Trust Ltd
The H B Allen Charitable Trust
The Rita Allen Charitable Trust
The Alliance Family Foundation
Angus Allnatt Charitable
    Foundation
The Pat Allsop Charitable Trust
The Almond Trust
Almondsbury Charity
The Altajir Trust
Altamont Ltd
Alvor Charitable Trust
AM Charitable Trust

Ambika Paul Foundation
The Ammco Trust
Sir John and Lady Amory's
    Charitable Trust
Viscount Amory's Charitable
    Trust
The Ampelos Trust
The AMW Charitable Trust
The Anchor Foundation
The Andre Christian Trust
Anguish's Educational
    Foundation
The Animal Defence Trust
The Eric Anker-Petersen
    Charity
The Annandale Charitable
    Trust
Ambrose and Ann Appelbe
    Trust
The Appletree Trust
The John Apthorp Charitable
    Trust
The Milly Apthorp Charitable
    Trust
The Arbib Foundation
The Archbishop of
    Canterbury's Charitable
    Trust
The John M Archer Charitable
    Trust
The Archer Trust
The Ardwick Trust
The Argus Appeal
Armenian General Benevolent
    Union London Trust
The Armenian Relief Society of
    Great Britain Trust
The Armourers' and Brasiers'
    Gauntlet Trust
The Army Benevolent Fund
Arsenal Charitable Trust
The Artemis Charitable Trust
The Arts and Entertainment
    Charitable Trust
Arts Council England
The Arts Council of Northern
    Ireland
The Arts Council of Wales
The Ove Arup Foundation
The AS Charitable Trust
Ashburnham Thanksgiving
    Trust
A J H Ashby Will Trust
The Ashden Trust
The Ashendene Trust
The Laura Ashley Foundation
The Norman C Ashton
    Foundation
The Ashworth Charitable Trust
The Ian Askew Charitable Trust
The Associated Country
    Women of the World
    (ACWW)
The Association of Colleges
    Charitable Trust
Astellas European Foundation

AstonMansfield Charitable Trust
The Astor Foundation
The Astor of Hever Trust
The Aurelius Charitable Trust
The Avenue Charitable Trust
The John Avins Trustees
AW Charitable Trust
The Aylesford Family Charitable Trust
The BAA Communities Trust
Harry Bacon Foundation
The BACTA Charitable Trust
The Bagri Foundation
Veta Bailey Charitable Trust
The Austin Bailey Trust
The Baily Thomas Charitable Fund
The Baird Trust
The Baker Charitable Trust
The Balcombe Charitable Trust
The Balint Family Charitable Trusts
The Albert Casanova Ballard Deceased Trust
The Ballinger Charitable Trust
Balmain Charitable Trust
The Balmore Trust
The Balney Charitable Trust
The Baltic Charitable Fund
The Bamford Charitable Foundation
The Banbury Charities
William P Bancroft (No 2) Charitable Trust and Jenepher Gillett Trust
The Band Trust
The Barbers' Company General Charities
The Barbour Trust
Barchester Healthcare Foundation
David and Frederick Barclay Foundation
The Baring Foundation
Peter Barker-Mill Memorial Charity
Barleycorn Trust
The Barnabas Trust
Lord Barnby's Foundation
Barnes Workhouse Fund
The Barnsbury Charitable Trust
The Barnstaple Bridge Trust
The Barnwood House Trust
The Misses Barrie Charitable Trust
Barrington Family Charitable Trust
The Charity of William Barrow
Stephen J Barry Charitable Trust
The Bartlett Taylor Charitable Trust
The Paul Bassham Charitable Trust
The Batchworth Trust

The Bay Tree Charitable Trust
D H and L H Baylin Charitable Trust
The Louis Baylis (Maidenhead Advertiser) Charitable Trust
BBC Children in Need
B-CH 1971 Charitable Trust
The Beacon Trust
Bear Mordechai Ltd
The Bearder Charity
The James Beattie Charitable Trust
The Beaufort House Trust Limited
Beauland Ltd
The Beaverbrook Foundation
The Beccles Town Lands Charity
The Becker Family Charitable Trust
The Becketts and Sargeants Educational Foundation
The John Beckwith Charitable Trust
The Peter Beckwith Charitable Trust
The Bedford Charity (The Harpur Trust)
The David and Ruth Behrend Fund
The Beit Trust
The Bellahouston Bequest Fund
Bellasis Trust
The Bellinger Donnay Trust
Belljoe Tzedoko Ltd
The Benfield Motors Charitable Trust
The Benham Charitable Settlement
Maurice and Jacqueline Bennett Charitable Trust
Michael and Leslie Bennett Charitable Trust
The Berkshire Community Foundation
The Bestway Foundation
The Betterware Foundation
Thomas Betton's Charity for Pensions and Relief-in-Need
BHST
The Mason Bibby 1981 Trust
BibleLands
The Bideford Bridge Trust
The Big Lottery Fund
The Billmeir Charitable Trust
The Bingham Trust
The Bintaub Charitable Trust
The Birmingham Community Foundation
The Birmingham District Nursing Charitable Trust
The Birmingham Hospital Saturday Fund Medical Charity and Welfare Trust

Birmingham International Airport Community Trust
The Lord Mayor of Birmingham's Charity
Birthday House Trust
The Bisgood Charitable Trust (registered as Miss Jeanne Bisgood's Charitable Trust)
The Michael Bishop Foundation
The Bishop's Development Fund
The Sydney Black Charitable Trust
The Bertie Black Foundation
Isabel Blackman Foundation
The Herbert and Peter Blagrave Charitable Trust
The Blair Foundation
Blakes Benevolent Trust
The Blanchminster Trust
The Sir Victor Blank Charitable Settlement
Blatchington Court Trust
The Neville and Elaine Blond Charitable Trust
The Bluston Charitable Settlement
Enid Blyton Trust for Children
The Nicholas Boas Charitable Trust
The Body Shop Foundation
The Boltons Trust
The Bonamy Charitable Trust
The John and Celia Bonham Christie Charitable Trust
The Charlotte Bonham-Carter Charitable Trust
Bonhomie United Charity Society
The Booth Charities
The Boots Charitable Trust
The Bordon and Liphook Charity
Salo Bordon Charitable Trust
The Oliver Borthwick Memorial Trust
The Bothwell Charitable Trust
H E and E L Botteley Charitable Trust
The Harry Bottom Charitable Trust
P G and N J Boulton Trust
The A H and E Boulton Trust
Sir Clive Bourne Family Trust
The Anthony Bourne Foundation
The Bower Trust
The Bowerman Charitable Trust
John and Susan Bowers Fund
The Bowland Charitable Trust
The William Brake Charitable Trust
The Tony Bramall Charitable Trust

The Brewers' Company
General Charitable Trust
The Harold and Alice Bridges
Charity
Briggs Animal Welfare Trust
The Brighton District Nursing
Association Trust
Bristol Archdeaconry Charity
John Bristow and Thomas
Mason Trust
Britannia Foundation
The British Council for
Prevention of Blindness
The British Dietetic
Association General and
Education Trust Fund
The British Gas (Scottish Gas)
Energy Trust
British Heart Foundation
British Humane Association
British Institute at Ankara
British Ornithologists' Union
British Record Industry Trust
The Britto Foundation
The J and M Britton Charitable
Trust
The Charles and Edna
Broadhurst Charitable Trust
The Bromley Trust
The Roger Brooke Charitable
Trust
The David Brooke Charity
The Charles Brotherton Trust
Joseph Brough Charitable
Trust
The Swinfen Broun Charitable
Trust
Mrs E E Brown Charitable
Settlement
Bill Brown's Charitable
Settlement
R S Brownless Charitable
Trust
T B H Brunner's Charitable
Settlement
Brushmill Ltd
The Bryant Trust
Buckingham Trust
The Buckinghamshire
Foundation
The Buckinghamshire Masonic
Centenary Fund
Buckland Charitable Trust
The Rosemary Bugden
Charitable Trust
The Bulldog Trust Limited
The E F Bulmer Benevolent
Fund
Burdens Charitable Foundation
The Burdett Trust for Nursing
The Clara E Burgess Charity
The Burry Charitable Trust
The Audrey and Stanley Burton
1960 Charitable Trust
The Arnold Burton 1998
Charitable Trust

The Burton Breweries
Charitable Trust
The Geoffrey Burton Charitable
Trust
Consolidated Charity of Burton
upon Trent
Butchers' Company General
Charities
The Bill Butlin Charity Trust
C and F Charitable Trust
C J Cadbury Charitable Trust
Edward Cadbury Charitable
Trust
Henry T and Lucy B Cadbury
Charitable Trust
P H G Cadbury Charitable
Trust
The Christopher Cadbury
Charitable Trust
The G W Cadbury Charitable
Trust
The Richard Cadbury
Charitable Trust
The William A Cadbury
Charitable Trust
The Edward and Dorothy
Cadbury Trust
The George Cadbury Trust
The Barrow Cadbury Trust and
the Barrow Cadbury Fund
The Cadogan Charity
CAF (Charities Aid Foundation)
CAFOD
The Callander Charitable Trust
Calleva Foundation
The Calpe Trust
Calypso Browning Trust
The Campden Charities
The Canning Trust
H and L Cantor Trust
Capital Community Foundation
Cardy Beaver Foundation
The Carew Pole Charitable
Trust
The D W T Cargill Fund
Caring for Kids (Radio Tay)
Carlee Ltd
The Carlton House Charitable
Trust
The Worshipful Company of
Carmen Benevolent Trust
The Carnegie Dunfermline
Trust
The Carnegie Trust for the
Universities of Scotland
The Carpenter Charitable Trust
The Carpenters' Company
Charitable Trust
The Carrington Charitable
Trust
The Carron Charitable
Settlement
The Leslie Mary Carter
Charitable Trust
The Carvill Trust
The Casey Trust

Cash for Kids Radio Clyde
Sir John Cass's Foundation
The Elizabeth Casson Trust
The Castang Foundation
The Catalyst Charitable Trust
The Catholic Charitable Trust
Catholic Foreign Missions
The Catholic Trust for England
and Wales
The Cattanach Charitable Trust
The Joseph and Annie Cattle
Trust
The Thomas Sivewright Catto
Charitable Settlement
The Wilfrid and Constance
Cave Foundation
The Cayo Foundation
Elizabeth Cayzer Charitable
Trust
The B G S Cayzer Charitable
Trust
The Cazenove Charitable Trust
Celtic Charity Fund
The Cemlyn-Jones Trust
CfBT Education Trust
The Amelia Chadwick Trust
The Pamela Champion
Foundation
The Chapman Charitable Trust
John William Chapman's
Charitable Trust
The Charities Advisory Trust
Charitworth Limited
The Charter 600 Charity
The Worshipful Company of
Chartered Accountants
General Charitable Trust
The Chasah Trust
The Chelsea Building Society
Charitable Foundation
The Chelsea Square 1994
Trust
The Cheruby Trust
The Cheshire Provincial Fund
of Benevolence
The Chetwode Foundation
The Malcolm Chick Charity
Child Growth Foundation
Children's Liver Disease
Foundation
Childs Charitable Trust
The Childwick Trust
The Chippenham Borough
Lands Charity
The Chipping Sodbury Town
Lands Charity
CHK Charities Limited
The Chownes Foundation
The Chrimes Family Charitable
Trust
The Christabella Charitable
Trust
Christadelphian Samaritan
Fund
Christian Aid

Christian Response to Eastern
  Europe
The Church and Community
  Fund
The Church Burgesses
  Educational Foundation
Church Burgesses Trust
Church Lands and John
  Johnson's Estate Charities
Church of Ireland Priorities
  Fund
The Church Urban Fund
City and County of Swansea
  Welsh Church Act Fund
The City Bridge Trust
The City Educational Trust
  Fund
The City Parochial Foundation
CLA Charitable Trust
Stephen Clark 1957
  Charitable Trust
J A Clark Charitable Trust
The Hilda and Alice Clark
  Charitable Trust
The Roger and Sarah Bancroft
  Clark Charitable Trust
The Clarke Charitable
  Settlement
The Cleary Foundation
The Cleopatra Trust
Lord Clinton's Charitable Trust
The Clore Duffield Foundation
Miss V L Clore's 1967
  Charitable Trust
Closehelm Ltd
Richard Cloudesley's Charity
The Clover Trust
The Robert Clutterbuck
  Charitable Trust
Clydpride Ltd
The Coalfields Regeneration
  Trust
The John Coates Charitable
  Trust
Coats Foundation Trust
The Cobtree Charity Trust Ltd
The Denise Cohen Charitable
  Trust
The Vivienne and Samuel
  Cohen Charitable Trust
The R and S Cohen Fondation
The John S Cohen Foundation
The Colchester Catalyst
  Charity
John Coldman Charitable Trust
The Cole Charitable Trust
The Colefax Charitable Trust
The John and Freda Coleman
  Charitable Trust
The George Henry Collins
  Charity
The E Alec Colman Charitable
  Fund Ltd
The Sir Jeremiah Colman Gift
  Trust
Col-Reno Ltd

The Colt Foundation
The Coltstaple Trust
Colwinston Charitable Trust
Colyer-Fergusson Charitable
  Trust
Comic Relief
The Comino Foundation
Community Foundation for
  Calderdale
The Community Foundation for
  Greater Manchester
The Community Foundation for
  Northern Ireland
The Company of Tobacco Pipe
  Makers' and Tobacco
  Blenders' Benevolent Fund
The Compton Charitable Trust
The Congleton Inclosure Trust
The Conservation Foundation
The Consolidated Charities for
  the Infirm Merchant
  Taylors' Company
The Construction Industry
  Trust for Youth
Gordon Cook Foundation
The Ernest Cook Trust
The Cooks Charity
The Catherine Cookson
  Charitable Trust
Harold and Daphne Cooper
  Charitable Trust
Mabel Cooper Charity
The Alice Ellen Cooper Dean
  Charitable Foundation
The Co-operative Foundation
The Marjorie Coote Animal
  Charity Fund
The Marjorie Coote Old
  People's Charity
The Helen Jean Cope Trust
The J Reginald Corah
  Foundation Fund
The Gershon Coren Charitable
  Foundation
The Corinthian Trust
Edwin Cornforth 1983 Charity
  Trust
The Cornwell Charitable Trust
The Sidney and Elizabeth
  Corob Charitable Trust
The Corona Charitable Trust
The Costa Family Charitable
  Trust
The Cotton Industry War
  Memorial Trust
County Durham Foundation
The Augustine Courtauld Trust
Coutts Charitable Trust
The General Charities of the
  City of Coventry
Coventry Building Society
  Charitable Foundation
The John Cowan Foundation
Cowley Charitable Foundation
The Sir William Coxen Trust
  Fund

The Lord Cozens-Hardy Trust
The Craignish Trust
The Craps Charitable Trust
Michael Crawford Children's
  Charity
The Cray Trust
The Crescent Trust
Criffel Charitable Trust
Cripplegate Foundation
The Violet and Milo Cripps
  Charitable Trust
The Cromarty Trust
The Harry Crook Foundation
The Cross Trust
The Cross Trust
The Croydon Relief in Need
  Charities
The Mayor of Croydon's
  Charity Fund
Cruden Foundation Ltd
The Ronald Cruickshanks'
  Foundation
Cuby Charitable Trust
The Culra Charitable Trust
Cumberland Building Society
  Charitable Foundation
Cumbria Community
  Foundation
The Cunningham Trust
The D J H Currie Memorial
  Trust
The Dennis Curry Charitable
  Trust
The Raymond Curtis Charitable
  Trust
The Manny Cussins
  Foundation
The Cwmbran Trust
Itzchok Meyer Cymerman Trust
  Ltd
The D'Oyly Carte Charitable
  Trust
The Roald Dahl Foundation
The Daily Prayer Union
  Charitable Trust Ltd
The Daisy Trust
The Daiwa Anglo-Japanese
  Foundation
Oizer Dalim Trust
The Dr and Mrs A Darlington
  Charitable Trust
Baron Davenport's Charity
The Davidson (Nairn)
  Charitable Trust
Davidson Charitable Trust
The Alderman Joe Davidson
  Memorial Trust
Michael Davies Charitable
  Settlement
The Gwendoline and Margaret
  Davies Charity
The Wilfrid Bruce Davis
  Charitable Trust
Davis-Rubens Charitable Trust
The Dawe Charitable Trust

The De Clermont Charitable
Company Ltd
Peter De Haan Charitable
Trust
The Leopold De Rothschild
Charitable Trust
The Deakin Charitable Trust
William Dean Countryside and
Educational Trust
The Debmar Benevolent Trust
The Delfont Foundation
The Dellal Foundation
The Delves Charitable Trust
The Demigryphon Trust
The Denman Charitable Trust
The Denton Charitable Trust
The Denton Wilde Sapte
Charitable Trust
The Earl of Derby's Charitable
Trust
Derbyshire Community
Foundation
The J N Derbyshire Trust
Devon Community Foundation
The Devon Educational Trust
The Duke of Devonshire's
Charitable Trust
The Sandy Dewhirst Charitable
Trust
DG Charitable Settlement
The Laduma Dhamecha
Charitable Trust
Diabetes UK
Alan and Sheila Diamond
Charitable Trust
The Diana, Princess of Wales
Memorial Fund
The Dibden Allotments Charity
The Dickon Trust
The Digbeth Trust
Dischma Charitable Trust
The Djanogly Foundation
The DLA Piper Charitable Trust
The DLM Charitable Trust
Louise Dobson Charitable
Trust
The Derek and Eileen Dodgson
Foundation
The Dollond Charitable Trust
Domepride Ltd
The Dorcas Trust
The Dorema Charitable Trust
The Dorus Trust
Double 'O' Charity Ltd
The Doughty Charity Trust
The R M Douglas Charitable
Trust
The Drapers' Charitable Fund
Dromintee Trust
The Dugdale Charitable Trust
The Duis Charitable Trust
The Dulverton Trust
The P B Dumbell Charitable
Trust
The Dumbreck Charity
Dunard Fund

Ronald Duncan Literary
Foundation
The Dunhill Medical Trust
The Houghton Dunn Charitable
Trust
The Dunn Family Charitable
Trust
The W E Dunn Trust
Dushinsky Trust Ltd
Mildred Duveen Charitable
Trust
The Dwek Family Charitable
Trust
The Dyers' Company
Charitable Trust
EAGA Partnership Charitable
Trust
The Eagle Charity Trust
Audrey Earle Charitable Trust
The Earley Charity
Earls Colne and Halstead
Educational Charity
The Earmark Trust
East Kent Provincial Charities
East London Community
Foundation
Eastern Counties Educational
Trust Limited
The Sir John Eastwood
Foundation
The Ebenezer Trust
The EBM Charitable Trust
Eden Arts Trust
EDF Energy Trust (EDFET)
The Gilbert and Eileen Edgar
Foundation
Gilbert Edgar Trust
Edinburgh Children's Holiday
Fund
The Edinburgh Trust, No 2
Account
Edinburgh Voluntary
Organisations' Trust Funds
Educational Foundation of
Alderman John Norman
The W G Edwards Charitable
Foundation
The William Edwards
Educational Charity
The Elephant Trust
The George Elias Charitable
Trust
The Gerald Palmer Eling Trust
Company
The Elizabeth Frankland Moore
and Star Foundation
The Wilfred and Elsie Elkes
Charity Fund
The Maud Elkington Charitable
Trust
Ellador Ltd
The Ellerdale Trust
The John Ellerman Foundation
The Ellinson Foundation Ltd
The Edith Maud Ellis 1985
Charitable Trust

James Ellis Charitable Trust
The Elmgrant Trust
The Elmley Foundation
Elshore Ltd
The Vernon N Ely Charitable
Trust
The Embleton Trust
The Emerton-Christie Charity
The Emmandjay Charitable
Trust
The Worshipful Company of
Engineers Charitable Trust
Fund
The Englefield Charitable Trust
The English Schools' Football
Association
The Enkalon Foundation
Entindale Ltd
The Epigoni Trust
Epilepsy Research UK
The Equitable Charitable Trust
The Equity Trust Fund
The Ericson Trust
The Erskine Cunningham Hill
Trust
Essex Community Foundation
The Essex Fairway Charitable
Trust
The Essex Heritage Trust
Essex Provincial Charity Fund
The Essex Youth Trust
Euro Charity Trust
The Evangelical Covenants
Trust
The Alan Evans Memorial Trust
Sir John Evelyn's Charity
The Eventhall Family
Charitable Trust
The Everard Foundation
The Eveson Charitable Trust
The Beryl Evetts and Robert
Luff Animal Welfare Trust
The Execution Charitable Trust
The Mayor of Exeter's Appeal
Fund
The Exilarch's Foundation
F C Charitable Trust
The F P Limited Charitable
Trust
The Faber Charitable Trust
Esmée Fairbairn Foundation
The Fairway Trust
Faisaltex Charitable Trust
The Family Foundations Trust
The Family Rich Charities Trust
Famos Foundation Trust
The Lord Faringdon Charitable
Trust
Samuel William Farmer's Trust
The Farmers' Company
Charitable Fund
The Thomas Farr Charitable
Trust
Walter Farthing (Trust) Limited
Farthing Trust
The Fassnidge Memorial Trust

Joseph Fattorini Charitable
Trust 'B' Account
The Fawcett Charitable Trust
Federation of Jewish Relief
Organisations
Feed the Minds
The John Feeney Charitable
Bequest
The George Fentham
Birmingham Charity
The A M Fenton Trust
Allan and Nesta Ferguson
Charitable Settlement
Elizabeth Ferguson Charitable
Trust Fund
The Bluff Field Charitable Trust
The Doris Field Charitable
Trust
The Fifty Fund
Dixie Rose Findlay Charitable
Trust
Gerald Finzi Charitable Trust
Firtree Trust
The Sir John Fisher Foundation
The Fishmongers' Company's
Charitable Trust
Marc Fitch Fund
The Fitton Trust
The Earl Fitzwilliam Charitable
Trust
Bud Flanagan Leukaemia Fund
The Rose Flatau Charitable
Trust
The Ian Fleming Charitable
Trust
The Joyce Fletcher Charitable
Trust
The Roy Fletcher Charitable
Trust
Florence's Charitable Trust
The Flow Foundation
The Gerald Fogel Charitable
Trust
The Follett Trust
The Football Association
National Sports Centre
Trust
The Football Association Youth
Trust
The Football Foundation
The Forbes Charitable
Foundation
Forbesville Limited
The Forces Trust
Ford Britain Trust
The Oliver Ford Charitable
Trust
Fordeve Ltd
The Forest Hill Charitable Trust
The Foresters' Charity
Stewards UK Trust
Gwyneth Forrester Trust
The Forte Charitable Trust
Lord Forte Foundation
Foundation for Management
Education

Four Acre Trust
The Four Winds Trust
The Fowler, Smith and Jones
Charitable Trust
The Foyle Foundation
The Isaac and Freda Frankel
Memorial Charitable Trust
Sydney E Franklin Deceased's
New Second Charity
The Jill Franklin Trust
The Gordon Fraser Charitable
Trust
The Hugh Fraser Foundation
The Joseph Strong Frazer Trust
The Louis and Valerie
Freedman Charitable
Settlement
The Freemasons' Grand
Charity
The Thomas Freke and Lady
Norton Charity
The Charles S French
Charitable Trust
The Anne French Memorial
Trust
The Freshfield Foundation
The Freshgate Trust
Foundation
The Friarsgate Trust
The Friends Hall Farm Street
Trust
Friends of Biala Ltd
Friends of Wiznitz Limited
Friends Provident Charitable
Foundation
The Frognal Trust
T F C Frost Charitable Trust
Maurice Fry Charitable Trust
Mejer and Gertrude Miriam
Frydman Foundation
The Fuellers Charitable Trust
Fund
The Fulmer Charitable Trust
Worshipful Company of
Furniture Makers Charitable
Fund
Gableholt Limited
The Galbraith Trust
The Gale Family Charitable
Trust
The Angela Gallagher Memorial
Fund
The Gamlen Charitable Trust
The Gamma Trust
The Gannochy Trust
The Ganzoni Charitable Trust
The Worshipful Company of
Gardeners of London
The Samuel Gardner Memorial
Trust
The Garnett Charitable Trust
Garrick Charitable Trust
Garvan Limited
The Gatsby Charitable
Foundation

Gatwick Airport Community
Trust
The Robert Gavron Charitable
Trust
Jacqueline and Michael Gee
Charitable Trust
The General Nursing Council
for England and Wales
Trust
J Paul Getty Jr Charitable Trust
The Gibbs Charitable Trust
Simon Gibson Charitable Trust
The G C Gibson Charitable
Trust
The Harvey and Hilary Gilbert
Charitable Trust
The Girdlers' Company
Charitable Trust
The B and P Glasser
Charitable Trust
The Glass-House Trust
Global Care
Global Charities (formally
GCap Charities)
Gloucestershire Community
Foundation
Worshipful Company of
Glovers of London Charity
Fund
GMC Trust
The GNC Trust
The Mrs Godfrey-Payton Trust
The Meir Golda Trust
The Sydney and Phyllis
Goldberg Memorial
Charitable Trust
The Golden Bottle Trust
Golden Charitable Trust
The Jack Goldhill Charitable
Trust
The Goldsmiths' Arts Trust
Fund
The Goldsmiths' Company
Charity
The Good Neighbours Trust
Nicholas and Judith
Goodison's Charitable
Settlement
The Everard and Mina
Goodman Charitable
Foundation
Mike Gooley Trailfinders
Charity
Leonard Gordon Charitable
Trust
The Gosling Foundation
Limited
The Gough Charitable Trust
The Gould Charitable Trust
The Grace Charitable Trust
A B Grace Trust
The Graff Foundation
The Grahame Charitable
Foundation Limited
Grampian Police Diced Cap
Charitable Fund

The Granada Foundation
Grand Charitable Trust of the Order of Women Freemasons
The Grand Order of Water Rats' Charities Fund
The Grange Farm Centre Trust
Grantham Yorke Trust
The Gray Trust
The Great Stone Bridge Trust of Edenbridge
The Great Torrington Town Lands Charity
The Constance Green Foundation
The Barry Green Memorial Fund
The Philip Green Memorial Trust
Mrs H R Greene Charitable Settlement
Greenham Common Community Trust Limited
Naomi and Jeffrey Greenwood Charitable Trust
Greggs Foundation
Grimmitt Trust
The Grocers' Charity
The M and R Gross Charities Limited
The Grove Charitable Trust
The GRP Charitable Trust
The David and Marie Grumitt Foundation
The Bishop of Guildford's Foundation
The Guildry Incorporation of Perth
The Walter Guinness Charitable Trust
The Gulbenkian Foundation
The Gunter Charitable Trust
The Gur Trust
Gurunanak
Dr Guthrie's Association
The H and M Charitable Trust
H C D Memorial Fund
The H P Charitable Trust
The Hackney Parochial Charities
The Hadfield Trust
The Hadley Trust
The Hadrian Trust
The Alfred Haines Charitable Trust
The Hale Trust
E F and M G Hall Charitable Trust
The Edith Winifred Hall Charitable Trust
Robert Hall Charity
The Hamamelis Trust
Hamilton Wallace Trust
Paul Hamlyn Foundation
Sue Hammerson's Charitable Trust

The Hammonds Charitable Trust
The Hampshire and Islands Historic Churches Trust
Hampton Fuel Allotment Charity
The W A Handley Charitable Trust
Beatrice Hankey Foundation Ltd
The Hanley Trust
The Kathleen Hannay Memorial Charity
The Doughty Hanson Charitable Foundation
Lord Hanson Foundation
The Haramead Trust
Miss K M Harbinson's Charitable Trust
Harbo Charities Limited
The Harborne Parish Lands Charity
The Harbour Charitable Trust
The Harbour Foundation
The Harding Trust
William Harding's Charity
The Hare of Steep Charitable Trust
The Harebell Centenary Fund
The Kenneth Hargreaves Charitable Trust
The Harris Charitable Trust
The Harris Charity
The Harrison and Potter Trust
The John Harrison Charitable Trust
The Peter Harrison Foundation
The Spencer Hart Charitable Trust
The Hartley Charitable Trust
The N and P Hartley Memorial Trust
William Geoffrey Harvey's Discretionary Settlement
Haskel Family Foundation
The Hathaway Trust
The Maurice Hatter Foundation
The M A Hawe Settlement
The Hawthorne Charitable Trust
The Dorothy Hay-Bolton Charitable Trust
The Haydan Charitable Trust
The Haymills Charitable Trust
The Headley Trust
Headley-Pitt Charitable Trust
Heagerty Charitable Trust
The Heald Charitable Trust
Healthsure Group Ltd
May Hearnshaw's Charity
The Heart of England Community Foundation
The Heathcoat Trust
Heathside Charitable Trust
The Charlotte Heber-Percy Charitable Trust

Percy Hedley 1990 Charitable Trust
The Hedley Denton Charitable Trust
The Hedley Foundation
The H J Heinz Company Limited Charitable Trust
The Hellenic Foundation
The Michael and Morven Heller Charitable Foundation
The Simon Heller Charitable Settlement
Help the Aged
Help the Homeless
Help the Hospices
The Hemby Trust
The Christina Mary Hendrie Trust for Scottish and Canadian Charities
The Henley Educational Charity
Philip Henman Trust
Esther Hennell Charitable Trust
The G D Herbert Charitable Trust
The Joanna Herbert-Stepney Charitable Settlement
The Anne Herd Memorial Trust
The Herefordshire Historic Churches Trust
The Heritage of London Trust Ltd
The Hertfordshire Community Foundation
The Hesed Trust
The Hesslewood Children's Trust (Hull Seamen's and General Orphanage)
The Bernhard Heuberger Charitable Trust
Hexham and Newcastle Diocesan Trust (1947)
The Higgs Charitable Trust
Alan Edward Higgs Charity
The High Sheriff's Police Trust for the County of West Midlands
Highcroft Charitable Trust
The Hilden Charitable Fund
The Joseph and Mary Hiley Trust
The Holly Hill Charitable Trust
The Charles Littlewood Hill Trust
The Hillingdon Partnership Trust
R G Hills Charitable Trust
Hinchley Charitable Trust
Lady Hind Trust
Stuart Hine Trust
The Hinrichsen Foundation
The Hitchin Educational Foundation
The Eleemosynary Charity of William Hobbayne
Hobson Charity Limited

Hockerill Educational Foundation
Matthew Hodder Charitable Trust
The Sir Julian Hodge Charitable Trust
The Jane Hodge Foundation
The J G Hogg Charitable Trust
The Holden Charitable Trust
John Holford's Charity
The Hollick Family Charitable Trust
The Dorothy Holmes Charitable Trust
The Holst Foundation
P H Holt Foundation
The Edward Holt Trust
The Holywood Trust
The Homelands Charitable Trust
The Homestead Charitable Trust
Mary Homfray Charitable Trust
Sir Harold Hood's Charitable Trust
The Hope Trust
HopMarket Charity
The Cuthbert Horn Trust
The Antony Hornby Charitable Trust
The Horne Foundation
The Horne Trust
The Worshipful Company of Horners' Charitable Trusts
The Hornsey Parochial Charities
The Hospital of God at Greatham
The Hospital Saturday Fund
Houblon-Norman/George Fund
The House of Industry Estate
The Reta Lila Howard Foundation
The Daniel Howard Trust
The Clifford Howarth Charity Trust
The Huddersfield Medical Trust Fund
The Hudson Foundation
The Huggard Charitable Trust
The Geoffrey C Hughes Charitable Trust
The Hull and East Riding Charitable Trust
Hulme Trust Estates (Educational)
Human Relief Foundation
The Humanitarian Trust
The Michael and Shirley Hunt Charitable Trust
The Hunter Foundation
Miss Agnes H Hunter's Trust
The Huntingdon Foundation
Huntingdon Freemen's Charity
John Huntingdon's Charity
Hurdale Charity Limited

The Nani Huyu Charitable Trust
The P Y N and B Hyams Trust
The Hyde Charitable Trust – Youth Plus
The Idlewild Trust
The Iliffe Family Charitable Trust
The Indigo Trust
The Ingram Trust
The Inland Waterways Association
The Inlight Trust
The Inman Charity
The Inner London Magistrates Court Poor Box Charity and Feeder Charity
The Worshipful Company of Innholders General Charity Fund
The Ireland Fund of Great Britain
The Irish Youth Foundation (UK) Ltd
The Ironmongers' Foundation
Irshad Trust
The Charles Irving Charitable Trust
Irwin Trust
The ISA Charity
The Isaacs Charitable Trust
The J Isaacs Charitable Trust
The Island Health Trust
The Isle of Anglesey Charitable Trust
Isle of Dogs Community Foundation
The ITF Seafarers Trust
J A R Charitable Trust
The J J Charitable Trust
The J R S S T Charitable Trust
Elizabeth Jackson Charitable Trust
Jacobs Charitable Trust
The Ruth and Lionel Jacobson Trust (Second Fund) No 2
Jaffe Family Relief Fund
The Susan and Stephen James Charitable Settlement
The James Trust
The Jarman Charitable Trust
The John Jarrold Trust
JCA Charitable Foundation
The Jeffrey Charitable Trust
Rees Jeffreys Road Fund
The Jenour Foundation
The Jephcott Charitable Trust
The Jerusalem Trust
Jerwood Charitable Foundation
Jesus Hospital Charity
Jewish Child's Day
The Jewish Youth Fund
The JMK Charitable Trust
The Joanies Trust
The Harold Joels Charitable Trust

The Jonathan Joels Charitable Trust
The Nicholas Joels Charitable Trust
The Norman Joels Charitable Trust
The Joffe Charitable Trust
The Elton John Aids Foundation
The Lillie Johnson Charitable Trust
The Johnson Group Cleaners Charity
The Johnnie Johnson Trust
The Johnson Wax Ltd Charitable Trust
The Joicey Trust
The Jones 1986 Charitable Trust
The Marjorie and Geoffrey Jones Charitable Trust
The Jordan Charitable Foundation
The J E Joseph Charitable Fund
The Lady Eileen Joseph Foundation
JTH Charitable Trust
The Judith Trust
The Anton Jurgens Charitable Trust
The Bernard Kahn Charitable Trust
The Stanley Kalms Foundation
The Karenza Foundation
The Boris Karloff Charitable Foundation
The Ian Karten Charitable Trust
The Kasner Charitable Trust
The Kass Charitable Trust
The Kathleen Trust
The Michael and Ilse Katz Foundation
The Katzauer Charitable Settlement
The C S Kaufman Charitable Trust
The Geoffrey John Kaye Charitable Foundation
The Emmanuel Kaye Foundation
Kelsick's Educational Foundation
The KempWelch Charitable Trust
The Kay Kendall Leukaemia Fund
William Kendall's Charity (Wax Chandlers' Company)
The Kennedy Charitable Foundation
The Nancy Kenyon Charitable Trust
Keren Association
Kermaville Ltd

E and E Kernkraut Charities
Limited
The Peter Kershaw Trust
The Kessler Foundation
Keswick Hall Charity
The Ursula Keyes Trust
The Robert Kiln Charitable
Trust
The King Henry VIII Endowed
Trust Warwick
The King/Cullimore Charitable
Trust
The King's Fund
The Kingsbury Charity
The Mary Kinross Charitable
Trust
Kinsurdy Charitable Trust
Kirkley Poor's Lands Estate
The Richard Kirkman
Charitable Trust
Kirschel Foundation
Robert Kitchin (Saddlers'
Company)
Ernest Kleinwort Charitable
Trust
The Marina Kleinwort
Charitable Trust
The Kobler Trust
The Kohn Foundation
The Kreditor Charitable Trust
The Kreitman Foundation
The Neil Kreitman Foundation
The Kyte Charitable Trust
Lacims-Maclis Charitable Trust
The Late Sir Pierce Lacy
Charity Trust
John Laing Charitable Trust
Maurice and Hilda Laing
Charitable Trust
The Laing Family Foundations
The Christopher Laing
Foundation
The Kirby Laing Foundation
The Martin Laing Foundation
The Beatrice Laing Trust
The Lambert Charitable Trust
Lancashire Environmental
Fund
Duchy of Lancaster Benevolent
Fund
The Lancaster Foundation
LandAid Charitable Trust
The Allen Lane Foundation
The Langdale Trust
The Langley Charitable Trust
The Langtree Trust
The LankellyChase Foundation
The Lanvern Foundation
The R J Larg Family Charitable
Trust
Largsmount Ltd
The Lark Trust
Laslett's (Hinton) Charity
Lauchentilly Charitable
Foundation 1988
Laufer Charitable Trust

The Lauffer Family Charitable
Foundation
Mrs F B Laurence Charitable
Trust
The Kathleen Laurence Trust
The Law Society Charity
The Edgar E Lawley Foundation
The Herd Lawson and Muriel
Lawson Charitable Trust
The Lawson Beckman
Charitable Trust
The Raymond and Blanche
Lawson Charitable Trust
The Carole and Geoffrey
Lawson Foundation
The Mason Le Page Charitable
Trust
The Leach Fourteenth Trust
The David Lean Foundation
The Leathersellers' Company
Charitable Fund
The Leche Trust
The Arnold Lee Charitable
Trust
The William Leech Charity
The Lord Mayor of Leeds
Appeal Fund
Leeds Building Society
Charitable Foundation
Leicester Charity Link
The Kennedy Leigh Charitable
Trust
Morris Leigh Foundation
The Leigh Trust
Mrs Vera Leigh's Charity
The P Leigh-Bramwell Trust 'E'
The Lennox and Wyfold
Foundation
The Erica Leonard Trust
The Leonard Trust
The Mark Leonard Trust
Lesley Lesley and Mutter Trust
The Leverhulme Trade
Charities Trust
Lord Leverhulme's Charitable
Trust
The Joseph Levy Charitable
Foundation
Lewis Family Charitable Trust
The John Spedan Lewis
Foundation
The Sir Edward Lewis
Foundation
John Lewis Partnership
General Community Fund
Lichfield Conduit Lands
Lifeline 4 Kids
The Thomas Lilley Memorial
Trust
Limoges Charitable Trust
The Linbury Trust
The Lincolnshire Old Churches
Trust
The Lind Trust
Lindale Educational
Foundation

The Linden Charitable Trust
The Enid Linder Foundation
The Linmardon Trust
The Ruth and Stuart Lipton
Charitable Trust
The Lister Charitable Trust
Frank Litchfield Charitable
Trust
The Andrew and Mary
Elizabeth Little Charitable
Trust
The Second Joseph Aaron
Littman Foundation
The George John and Sheilah
Livanos Charitable Trust
Liverpool Charity and Voluntary
Services
Liverpool Sailors' Home Trust
Jack Livingstone Charitable
Trust
The Elaine and Angus Lloyd
Charitable Trust
The Charles Lloyd Foundation
The Lloyd Fund
Lloyd's Charities Trust
The Lloyd-Everett Trust
Lloyds TSB Foundation for
England and Wales
Lloyds TSB Foundation for
Northern Ireland
Lloyds TSB Foundation for the
Channel Islands
Llysdinam Charitable Trust
Localtrent Ltd
The Locker Foundation
The Loftus Charitable Trust
The Lolev Charitable Trust
London Catalyst
The London Law Trust
The William and Katherine
Longman Trust
The Loseley and Guildway
Charitable Trust
The Lotus Foundation
The C L Loyd Charitable Trust
LSA Charitable Trust
The Marie Helen Luen
Charitable Trust
Robert Luff Foundation Ltd
Henry Lumley Charitable Trust
Lady Lumley's Educational
Foundation
Paul Lunn-Rockliffe Charitable
Trust
C F Lunoe Trust Fund
The Ruth and Jack Lunzer
Charitable Trust
Lord and Lady Lurgan Trust
The Lyndhurst Trust
The Lynn Foundation
The Lynwood Trust
John Lyon's Charity
The Lyons Charitable Trust
The Sir Jack Lyons Charitable
Trust
Malcolm Lyons Foundation

The Lyras Family Charitable Trust
Sylvanus Lyson's Charity
The M and C Trust
The M D and S Charitable Trust
The M K Charitable Trust
The Madeline Mabey Trust
The E M MacAndrew Trust
The R S Macdonald Charitable Trust
Macdonald-Buchanan Charitable Trust
The Macfarlane Walker Trust
The Mackay and Brewer Charitable Trust
The Mackintosh Foundation
The MacRobert Trust
Ian Mactaggart Trust
The Magdalen and Lasher Charity
The Magen Charitable Trust
Mageni Trust
Mahavir Trust
Man Group plc Charitable Trust
Manchester Airport Community Trust Fund
The Manchester Guardian Society Charitable Trust
Manchester Kids
Lord Mayor of Manchester's Charity Appeal Trust
Mandeville Trust
The Manifold Charitable Trust
W M Mann Foundation
The Leslie and Lilian Manning Trust
Maranatha Christian Trust
Marbeh Torah Trust
The Marchday Charitable Fund
Marchig Animal Welfare Trust
The Stella and Alexander Margulies Charitable Trust
Mariapolis Limited
Market Harborough and The Bowdens Charity
Michael Marks Charitable Trust
The Ann and David Marks Foundation
The Hilda and Samuel Marks Foundation
J P Marland Charitable Trust
Marr-Munning Trust
The Michael Marsh Charitable Trust
The Marsh Christian Trust
The Charlotte Marshall Charitable Trust
The Jim Marshall Charitable Trust
The D G Marshall of Cambridge Trust
Marshall's Charity

Marshgate Charitable Settlement
Sir George Martin Trust
John Martin's Charity
The Mason Porter Charitable Trust
The Nancie Massey Charitable Trust
The Mathew Trust
Matliwala Family Charitable Trust
The Matt 6.3 Charitable Trust
The Violet Mauray Charitable Trust
The Maxell Educational Trust
The Maxwell Family Foundation
Evelyn May Trust
Mayfair Charities Ltd
The Mayfield Valley Arts Trust
Mazars Charitable Trust
The McDougall Trust
The A M McGreevy No 5 Charitable Settlement
The McKenna Charitable Trust
Martin McLaren Memorial Trust
The Helen Isabella McMorran Charitable Foundation
D D McPhail Charitable Settlement
The James Frederick and Ethel Anne Measures Charity
Medical Research Council
The Medlock Charitable Trust
The Anthony and Elizabeth Mellows Charitable Settlement
Melodor Ltd
Melow Charitable Trust
Meningitis Trust
Menuchar Ltd
Brian Mercer Charitable Trust
The Mercers' Charitable Foundation
The Merchant Taylors' Company Charities Fund
The Merchant Venturers' Charity
The Merchants' House of Glasgow
Mercury Phoenix Trust
The Mersey Docks and Harbour Company Charitable Fund
Community Foundation for Merseyside
The Zachary Merton and George Woofindin Convalescent Trust
The Tony Metherell Charitable Trust
The Methodist Relief and Development Fund
The Metropolitan Drinking Fountain and Cattle Trough Association

Gerald Micklem Charitable Trust
Midhurst Pensions Trust
The Migraine Trust
Miles Trust for the Putney and Roehampton Community
Millennium Stadium Charitable Trust
The Hugh and Mary Miller Bequest Trust
The Miller Foundation
The Millfield Trust
The Millhouses Charitable Trust
The Millichope Foundation
The Mills Charity
The Millward Charitable Trust
The Clare Milne Trust
Milton Keynes Community Foundation
The Edgar Milward Charity
The Peter Minet Trust
Minge's Gift and the Pooled Trusts
The Minos Trust
The Mirfield Educational Charity
The Laurence Misener Charitable Trust
The Mishcon Family Charitable Trust
The Misselbrook Trust
The Esmé Mitchell Trust
Keren Mitzvah Trust
The Mizpah Trust
The Mobbs Memorial Trust Ltd
The Modiano Charitable Trust
The Moette Charitable Trust
The Mole Charitable Trust
The D C Moncrieff Charitable Trust
Monmouthshire County Council Welsh Church Act Fund
The Montague Thompson Coon Charitable Trust
The Colin Montgomerie Charitable Foundation
The Monument Trust
Moody Charitable Trust
George A Moore Foundation
The Nigel Moores Family Charitable Trust
John Moores Foundation
The Peter Moores Foundation
The Morel Charitable Trust
The Morgan Charitable Foundation
The Mr and Mrs J T Morgan Foundation
The J P Morgan Foundations
Diana and Allan Morgenthau Charitable Trust
The Oliver Morland Charitable Trust
S C and M E Morland's Charitable Trust

The Morris Charitable Trust

The Willie and Mabel Morris
Charitable Trust

The Peter Morrison Charitable
Foundation

G M Morrison Charitable Trust

The Stanley Morrison
Charitable Trust

Moshal Charitable Trust

Vyoel Moshe Charitable Trust

The Moss Charitable Trust

The Robert and Margaret
Moss Charitable Trust

Moss Family Charitable Trust

The Mount Everest Foundation

Mountbatten Festival of Music

The Mountbatten Memorial
Trust

The Edwina Mountbatten Trust

The Mugdock Children's Trust

The F H Muirhead Charitable
Trust

The Mulberry Trust

The Edith Murphy Foundation

Murphy-Neumann Charity
Company Limited

The Mushroom Fund

The Music Sales Charitable
Trust

Muslim Hands

The Mutual Trust Group

MYA Charitable Trust

The Kitty and Daniel Nabarro
Charitable Trust

The Nadezhda Charitable Trust

The Willie Nagel Charitable
Trust

The Naggar Charitable Trust

The Eleni Nakou Foundation

The Janet Nash Charitable
Settlement

Nathan Charitable Trust

Asthma UK

The National Churches Trust

The National Manuscripts
Conservation Trust

Nazareth Trust Fund

The Nchima Trust

Needham Market and Barking
Welfare Charities

The Worshipful Company of
Needlemakers' Charitable
Fund

The Neighbourly Charitable
Trust

The James Neill Trust Fund

Nemoral Ltd

Nesswall Ltd

Nestle Rowntree Employees
Community Fund

Network for Social Change

The New Appeals Organisation
for the City and County of
Nottingham

New Court Charitable Trust

Newby Trust Limited

The Newcomen Collett
Foundation

The Richard Newitt Fund

Mr and Mrs F E F Newman
Charitable Trust

The Frances and Augustus
Newman Foundation

Newpier Charity Ltd

Alderman Newton's
Educational Foundation

The Chevras Ezras Nitzrochim
Trust

The Noel Buxton Trust

The Noon Foundation

The Norda Trust

Norie Charitable Trust

Normalyn Charitable Trust

The Norman Family Charitable
Trust

The Duncan Norman Trust
Fund

The Normanby Charitable Trust

The North British Hotel Trust

The North West Cancer
Research Fund

The Northampton Municipal
Church Charities

The Northampton Queen's
Institute Relief in Sickness
Fund

The Earl of Northampton's
Charity

The Northcott Devon
Foundation

The Northcott Devon Medical
Foundation

The Northern Rock Foundation

The Northmoor Trust

The Northumberland Village
Homes Trust

The Northumbria Historic
Churches Trust

The Northwood Charitable
Trust

The Norton Foundation

The Norwich Church of England
Young Men's Society

The Norwich Historic Churches
Trust Ltd

The Norwich Town Close
Estate Charity

The Norwood and Newton
Settlement

The Noswad Charity

The Notgrove Trust

The Nottingham General
Dispensary

The Nottingham Gordon
Memorial Trust for Boys
and Girls

Nottinghamshire Community
Foundation

The Nottinghamshire Historic
Churches Trust

The Nottinghamshire Miners'
Welfare Trust Fund

Novi Most International

The Father O'Mahoney
Memorial Trust

The Sir Peter O'Sullevan
Charitable Trust

The Oak Trust

The Oakdale Trust

The Oakley Charitable Trust

The Oakmoor Charitable Trust

The Odin Charitable Trust

Ogilvie Charities Deed No.2
(including the Charity of
Mary Catherine Ford Smith)

The Ogle Christian Trust

Oglesby Charitable Trust

The Oikonomia Trust

The Oizer Charitable Trust

The Old Broad Street Charity
Trust

The Old Enfield Charitable
Trust

Old Possum's Practical Trust

The John Oldacre Foundation

The Oldham Foundation

The Olga Charitable Trust

Onaway Trust

Open Gate

The Ormsby Charitable Trust

Orrin Charitable Trust

The Ouseley Trust

The Owen Family Trust

Oxfam (GB)

The Oxfordshire Community
Foundation

The P F Charitable Trust

Padwa Charitable Foundation

The Pallant Charitable Trust

The Palmer Foundation

Eleanor Palmer Trust

The Panacea Society

Panahpur Charitable Trust

Panton Trust

The Paragon Trust

The Park House Charitable
Trust

The Frank Parkinson
Agricultural Trust

The Samuel and Freda
Parkinson Charitable Trust

The Parthenon Trust

Arthur James Paterson
Charitable Trust

The Constance Paterson
Charitable Trust

Miss M E Swinton Paterson's
Charitable Trust

The Patrick Charitable Trust

The Jack Patston Charitable
Trust

Paycare Charity Trust

The Payne Charitable Trust

The Harry Payne Trust

The Susanna Peake Charitable
Trust

Pearson's Holiday Fund

The Pedmore Sporting Club Trust Fund

The Dowager Countess Eleanor Peel Trust

Peltz Trust

The Pennycress Trust

The Performing Right Society Foundation

B E Perl Charitable Trust

The Persson Charitable Trust

The Persula Foundation

The Pestalozzi Overseas Children's Trust

The Jack Petchey Foundation

The Petplan Charitable Trust

The Philips and Rubens Charitable Trust

The Phillips Charitable Trust

The Phillips Family Charitable Trust

Philological Foundation

The David Pickford Charitable Foundation

The Bernard Piggott Trust

The Claude and Margaret Pike Charity

The Pilgrim Trust

The Cecil Pilkington Charitable Trust

The Pilkington Charities Fund

The Austin and Hope Pilkington Trust

The Sir Harry Pilkington Trust

The Col W W Pilkington Will Trusts The General Charity Fund

Miss A M Pilkington's Charitable Trust

Mrs Pilkington's Charitable Trust

The Plaisterers' Company Charitable Trust

The Platinum Trust

G S Plaut Charitable Trust Limited

Polden-Puckham Charitable Foundation

The Poling Charitable Trust

The George and Esme Pollitzer Charitable Settlement

The J S F Pollitzer Charitable Settlement

The Ponton House Trust

The Mayor of Poole's Appeal Fund

Edith and Ferdinand Porjes Charitable Trust

The John Porter Charitable Trust

The Porter Foundation

The Portrack Charitable Trust

The J E Posnansky Charitable Trust

The Mary Potter Convent Hospital Trust

The David and Elaine Potter Foundation

The Powell Foundation

Prairie Trust

The W L Pratt Charitable Trust

Premierquote Ltd

Premishlaner Charitable Trust

The Lucy Price Relief-in-Need Charity

Sir John Priestman Charity Trust

The Primrose Trust

The Prince's Charities Foundation

Princess Anne's Charities

The Priory Foundation

Prison Service Charity Fund

The Privy Purse Charitable Trust

The Proven Family Trust

The Provincial Grand Charity of the Province of Derbyshire

PSA Peugeot Citroen Charity Trust

The Puebla Charitable Trust

The Richard and Christine Purchas Charitable Trust

The Puri Foundation

Mr and Mrs J A Pye's Charitable Settlement

Quartet Community Foundation

Queen Mary's Roehampton Trust

The Queen's Silver Jubilee Trust

Quercus Trust

The R D Crusaders Foundation

R J M Charitable Trust

R S Charitable Trust

The R V W Trust

The Monica Rabagliati Charitable Trust

Rachel Charitable Trust

The Mr and Mrs Philip Rackham Charitable Trust

Richard Radcliffe Charitable Trust

The Radcliffe Trust

The Ragdoll Foundation

The Rainford Trust

The Peggy Ramsay Foundation

The Joseph and Lena Randall Charitable Trust

The Rank Foundation

Ranworth Trust

The Fanny Rapaport Charitable Settlement

The Ratcliff Foundation

The Ratcliff Pension Charity

The Ratcliffe Charitable Trust

The Eleanor Rathbone Charitable Trust

The Sigrid Rausing Trust

The Ravensdale Trust

The Rayden Charitable Trust

The Roger Raymond Charitable Trust

The Rayne Foundation

The Rayne Trust

The John Rayner Charitable Trust

The Albert Reckitt Charitable Trust

The Sir James Reckitt Charity

The Red Arrows Trust

The Red Rose Charitable Trust

The C A Redfern Charitable Foundation

The Reed Foundation

Richard Reeve's Foundation

The Max Reinhardt Charitable Trust

Relief Fund for Romania Limited

REMEDI

The Rest Harrow Trust

Reuben Brothers Foundation

The Joan K Reynell Charitable Trust

The Nathaniel Reyner Trust Fund

The Rhododendron Trust

Daisie Rich Trust

The Sir Cliff Richard Charitable Trust

C B Richard Ellis Charitable Trust

The Clive Richards Charity

The Violet M Richards Charity

The Richmond Parish Lands Charity

Ridgesave Limited

The Ripple Effect Foundation

The Sir John Ritblat Family Foundation

The River Trust

Riverside Charitable Trust Limited

The Daniel Rivlin Charitable Trust

Thomas Roberts Trust

The Alex Roberts-Miller Foundation

The Robertson Trust

Edwin George Robinson Charitable Trust

Robyn Charitable Trust

The Rochester Bridge Trust

The Rock Foundation

The Rock Solid Trust

The Rofeh Trust

Richard Rogers Charitable Settlement

Rokach Family Charitable Trust

The Helen Roll Charitable Trust

The Sir James Roll Charitable Trust

The Roman Research Trust

Romeera Foundation

The C A Rookes Charitable Trust
The Rosca Trust
The Cecil Rosen Foundation
Rosetrees Trust
The Rothermere Foundation
The Rotherwick Foundation
The Rothschild Foundation
The Roughley Charitable Trust
Mrs Gladys Row Fogo Charitable Trust
The Rowan Charitable Trust
Rowanville Ltd
The Christopher Rowbotham Charitable Trust
The Rowing Foundation
The Rowlands Trust
The Joseph Rowntree Charitable Trust
The Joseph Rowntree Foundation
Joseph Rowntree Reform Trust Limited
Royal Artillery Charitable Fund
Royal British Legion
Royal Docks Trust (London)
Royal Masonic Trust for Girls and Boys
The Royal Scots Benevolent Society
The Alfred and Frances Rubens Charitable Trust
The Rubin Foundation
William Arthur Rudd Memorial Trust
The Rufford Maurice Laing Foundation
The Russell Trust
Ryklow Charitable Trust 1992
The J S and E C Rymer Charitable Trust
S O Charitable Trust
The Michael Sacher Charitable Trust
The Michael Harry Sacher Trust
Dr Mortimer and Theresa Sackler Foundation
The Ruzin Sadagora Trust
The Saddlers' Company Charitable Fund
The Saga Charitable Trust
The Jean Sainsbury Animal Welfare Trust
The Alan and Babette Sainsbury Charitable Fund
Saint Sarkis Charity Trust
The Saintbury Trust
The Saints and Sinners Trust
The Salamander Charitable Trust
The Salt Foundation
The Salt Trust
The Salters' Charities
The Andrew Salvesen Charitable Trust

The Sammermar Trust
Basil Samuel Charitable Trust
Coral Samuel Charitable Trust
The Hon. M J Samuel Charitable Trust
The Peter Samuel Charitable Trust
The Camilla Samuel Fund
The Samworth Foundation
The Sandra Charitable Trust
Santander UK Foundation Limited
Jimmy Savile Charitable Trust
The Scarfe Charitable Trust
The Schapira Charitable Trust
The Annie Schiff Charitable Trust
The Schmidt-Bodner Charitable Trust
The R H Scholes Charitable Trust
The Schreib Trust
The Schreiber Charitable Trust
Schroder Charity Trust
The Scott Bader Commonwealth Ltd
The Francis C Scott Charitable Trust
The Frieda Scott Charitable Trust
Sir Samuel Scott of Yews Trust
The Sir James and Lady Scott Trust
The Scott Trust Foundation
The Storrow Scott Will Trust
The Scottish Arts Council
Scottish Churches' Community Trust
Scottish Coal Industry Special Welfare Fund
The Scottish Community Foundation
The Scottish International Education Trust
The Scouloudi Foundation
Seafarers UK (King George's Fund for Sailors)
Seamen's Hospital Society
The Searchlight Electric Charitable Trust
The Searle Charitable Trust
The Helene Sebba Charitable Trust
The Samuel Sebba Charitable Trust
The Seedfield Trust
Sellata Ltd
SEM Charitable Trust
The Ayrton Senna Foundation
The Seven Fifty Trust
SFIA Educational Trust Limited
The Cyril Shack Trust
The Jean Shanks Foundation
The Shanti Charitable Trust

ShareGift (The Orr Mackintosh Foundation)
The Linley Shaw Foundation
The Sheepdrove Trust
The Sheffield and District Hospital Services Charitable Fund
The Sheldon Trust
The P and D Shepherd Charitable Trust
The Sylvia and Colin Shepherd Charitable Trust
The Archie Sherman Cardiff Foundation
The Archie Sherman Charitable Trust
The R C Sherriff Trust
The Shetland Charitable Trust
SHINE (Support and Help in Education)
The Barnett and Sylvia Shine No 2 Charitable Trust
The Bassil Shippam and Alsford Trust
The Shipwrights' Company Charitable Fund
The Shirley Foundation
Shlomo Memorial Fund Limited
The J A Shone Memorial Trust
The Charles Shorto Charitable Trust
The Barbara A Shuttleworth Memorial Trust
The Mary Elizabeth Siebel Charity
David and Jennifer Sieff Charitable Trust
The Julius Silman Charitable Trust
The Leslie Silver Charitable Trust
The Simpson Education and Conservation Trust
The Simpson Foundation
The Huntly and Margery Sinclair Charitable Trust
Sino-British Fellowship Trust
The Skelton Bounty
The Charles Skey Charitable Trust
Skipton Building Society Charitable Foundation
The John Slater Foundation
Rita and David Slowe Charitable Trust
The SMB Charitable Trust
The Mrs Smith and Mount Trust
The N Smith Charitable Settlement
The Amanda Smith Charitable Trust
The E H Smith Charitable Trust
The Smith Charitable Trust
The Henry Smith Charity
The Leslie Smith Foundation

The Martin Smith Foundation
Stanley Smith General
  Charitable Trust
The Stanley Smith UK
  Horticultural Trust
Philip Smith's Charitable Trust
The Snowball Trust
The Sobell Foundation
Solev Co Ltd
Solihull Community Foundation
The Solo Charitable
  Settlement
Dr Richard Solomon's
  Charitable Trust
Songdale Ltd
The E C Sosnow Charitable
  Trust
The Souter Charitable Trust
The South Square Trust
The Stephen R and Philippa H
  Southall Charitable Trust
The W F Southall Trust
The Southdown Trust
R H Southern Trust
The Southover Manor General
  Education Trust
The Southwold Trust
The Sovereign Health Care
  Charitable Trust
Spar Charitable Fund
Sparks Charity (Sport Aiding
  Medical Research For Kids)
Sparquote Limited
The Spear Charitable Trust
Spears-Stutz Charitable Trust
The Jessie Spencer Trust
The Ralph and Irma Sperring
  Charity
The Moss Spiro Will Charitable
  Foundation
W W Spooner Charitable Trust
Stanley Spooner Deceased
  Charitable Trust
The Spoore, Merry and Rixman
  Foundation
The Spring Harvest Charitable
  Trust
Rosalyn and Nicholas Springer
  Charitable Trust
Springfields Employees'
  Medical Research and
  Charity Trust Fund
Springrule Ltd
The Spurrell Charitable Trust
The Geoff and Fiona Squire
  Foundation
St Andrew Animal Fund
St Andrew's Conservation
  Trust
St Francis's Leprosy Guild
St Gabriel's Trust
St Hilda's Trust
St James' Trust Settlement
St James's Place Foundation
Sir Walter St John's
  Educational Charity

St Katharine and Shadwell
  Trust
St Mark's Overseas Aid Trust
  (SMOAT)
St Michael's and All Saints'
  Charities
The Late St Patrick White
  Charitable Trust
St Teilo's Trust
Miss Doreen Stanford Trust
The Stanley Foundation Ltd
The Stanton Ballard Charitable
  Trust
The Staples Trust
The Star Charitable Trust
The Starfish Trust
The Peter Stebbings Memorial
  Charity
The Steel Charitable Trust
The Cyril and Betty Stein
  Charitable Trust
The Steinberg Family
  Charitable Trust
The Hugh Stenhouse
  Foundation
The Sigmund Sternberg
  Charitable Foundation
Stervon Ltd
The Stevenage Community
  Trust
The June Stevens Foundation
Stevenson Family's Charitable
  Trust
The Steventon Allotments and
  Relief-in-Need Charity
The Stewards' Charitable Trust
The Stewards' Company
  Limited
The Sir Halley Stewart Trust
The Stobart Newlands
  Charitable Trust
The Edward Stocks-Massey
  Bequest Fund
The Stokenchurch Educational
  Charity
The Stoller Charitable Trust
The M J C Stone Charitable
  Trust
The Stone-Mallabar Charitable
  Foundation
The Samuel Storey Family
  Charitable Trust
Peter Stormonth Darling
  Charitable Trust
Peter Storrs Trust
The Strangward Trust
The Strasser Foundation
Stratford upon Avon Town
  Trust
Strathclyde Police Benevolent
  Fund
The W O Street Charitable
  Foundation
The A B Strom and R Strom
  Charitable Trust
The Sudborough Foundation

Sueberry Ltd
The Suffolk Historic Churches
  Trust
The Alan Sugar Foundation
The Summerfield Charitable
  Trust
The Bernard Sunley Charitable
  Foundation
The Surrey Historic Buildings
  Trust Ltd
The Sussex Historic Churches
  Trust
The Adrienne and Leslie
  Sussman Charitable Trust
The Sutasoma Trust
Sutton Coldfield Municipal
  Charities
The Sutton Nursing
  Association
Swan Mountain Trust
The Swan Trust
Swansea and Brecon Diocesan
  Board of Finance Limited
The John Swire (1989)
  Charitable Trust
The Swire Charitable Trust
The Hugh and Ruby Sykes
  Charitable Trust
The Charles and Elsie Sykes
  Trust
The Sylvanus Charitable Trust
The Stella Symons Charitable
  Trust
The Tabeel Trust
The Tajtelbaum Charitable
  Trust
The Talbot Trusts
The Talbot Village Trust
Tallow Chandlers Benevolent
  Fund
Talteg Ltd
The Tangent Charitable Trust
The Lady Tangye Charitable
  Trust
The David Tannen Charitable
  Trust
The Tanner Trust
The Lili Tapper Charitable
  Foundation
The Mrs A Lacy Tate Trust
The Tay Charitable Trust
C B and H H Taylor 1984 Trust
Humphrey Richardson Taylor
  Charitable Trust
The Connie and Albert Taylor
  Charitable Trust
The Cyril Taylor Charitable
  Trust
A P Taylor Trust
Rosanna Taylor's 1987 Charity
  Trust
Tearfund
The Tedworth Charitable Trust
Tees Valley Community
  Foundation
Tegham Limited

The Templeton Goodwill Trust
Tesco Charity Trust
Thackray Medical Research Trust
Thames Community Foundation
The Thames Wharf Charity
The Thistle Trust
The Loke Wan Tho Memorial Foundation
The Thomas Wall Trust
The Arthur and Margaret Thompson Charitable Trust
The Thompson Family Charitable Trust
The Len Thomson Charitable Trust
The Sue Thomson Foundation
The Sir Jules Thorn Charitable Trust
The Thornton Foundation
The Thornton Trust
The Three Guineas Trust
The Three Oaks Trust
The Thriplow Charitable Trust
The Tinsley Foundation
The Tisbury Telegraph Trust
TJH Foundation
The Tolkien Trust
Tollemache (Buckminster) Charitable Trust
Tomchei Torah Charitable Trust
The Tompkins Foundation
The Tory Family Foundation
Tottenham Grammar School Foundation
The Tower Hill Trust
The Towry Law Charitable Trust
The Toy Trust
The Mayor of Trafford's Charity Fund
Annie Tranmer Charitable Trust
The Constance Travis Charitable Trust
The Treeside Trust
The Triangle Trust (1949) Fund
The True Colours Trust
Truedene Co. Ltd
The Truemark Trust
Truemart Limited
Trumros Limited
Trust for London
Trust Sixty Three
The Trusthouse Charitable Foundation
The Tubney Charitable Trust
Tudor Rose Ltd
The Tudor Trust
The Tufton Charitable Trust
The R D Turner Charitable Trust
The Douglas Turner Trust
The Florence Turner Trust
Miss S M Tutton Charitable Trust

The TUUT Charitable Trust
Community Foundation Serving Tyne and Wear and Northumberland
Trustees of Tzedakah
Ulster Garden Villages Ltd
Ultach Trust
Ulting Overseas Trust
The Ulverscroft Foundation
Ulverston Town Lands Charity
The Underwood Trust
The Union of Orthodox Hebrew Congregation
The United Society for the Propagation of the Gospel
United Trusts
The David Uri Memorial Trust
Uxbridge United Welfare Trust
Vale of Glamorgan – Welsh Church Fund
The Valentine Charitable Trust
The Albert Van Den Bergh Charitable Trust
John and Lucille van Geest Foundation
The Van Neste Foundation
Mrs Maud Van Norden's Charitable Foundation
The Vandervell Foundation
The Vardy Foundation
The Variety Club Children's Charity
Veneziana Fund
The Verdon-Smith Family Charitable Settlement
Roger Vere Foundation
Victoria Homes Trust
Viking Cares (For the Kids)
The Nigel Vinson Charitable Trust
The William and Ellen Vinten Trust
The Vintners' Company Charitable Foundation
Vintners' Gifts Charity
Vision Charity
Vivdale Ltd
The Viznitz Foundation
Wade's Charity
The Scurrah Wainwright Charity
Wakeham Trust
The Community Foundation in Wales
Wales Council for Voluntary Action
Robert and Felicity Waley-Cohen Charitable Trust
The Walker Trust
Wallington Missionary Mart and Auctions
The F J Wallis Charitable Settlement
War on Want
Sir Siegmund Warburg's Voluntary Settlement
The Ward Blenkinsop Trust

The George Ward Charitable Trust
The Barbara Ward Children's Foundation
G R Waters Charitable Trust 2000
The Waterways Trust
The Wates Foundation
Blyth Watson Charitable Trust
The Howard Watson Symington Memorial Charity
John Watson's Trust
Weatherley Charitable Trust
The Weavers' Company Benevolent Fund
The William Webster Charitable Trust
The Weinberg Foundation
The Weinstein Foundation
The Weinstock Fund
The Barbara Welby Trust
The Weldon UK Charitable Trust
The Wellcome Trust
Welsh Church Fund Dyfed area (Carmarthenshire, Ceredigion and Pembrokeshire)
The Welton Foundation
The Wessex Youth Trust
The West Derby Wastelands Charity
West London Synagogue Charitable Fund
The West Yorkshire Police Community Fund
Mrs S K West's Charitable Trust
The Westminster Foundation
The Garfield Weston Foundation
The Whitaker Charitable Trust
The Colonel W H Whitbread Charitable Trust
The Simon Whitbread Charitable Trust
White Rose Children's Aid International Charity
The Whitecourt Charitable Trust
A H and B C Whiteley Charitable Trust
The Norman Whiteley Trust
The Whitley Animal Protection Trust
The Whittlesey Charity
The Lionel Wigram Memorial Trust
The Felicity Wilde Charitable Trust
The Will Charitable Trust
The Kay Williams Charitable Foundation
The Williams Family Charitable Trust

The H D H Wills 1965
Charitable Trust
Dame Violet Wills Charitable
Trust
The Dame Violet Wills Will
Trust
The Wilmcote Charitrust
Sumner Wilson Charitable
Trust
David Wilson Foundation
The Wilson Foundation
J and J R Wilson Trust
The Community Foundation for
Wiltshire and Swindon
The Benjamin Winegarten
Charitable Trust
The Harold Hyam Wingate
Foundation
The Francis Winham
Foundation
Anona Winn Charitable Trust
Wirral Mayor's Charity
The Michael and Anna Wix
Charitable Trust
The Wixamtree Trust
The Woburn 1986 Charitable
Trust
The Maurice Wohl Charitable
Foundation
The Charles Wolfson
Charitable Trust
Women Caring Trust
The James Wood Bequest
Fund
Woodlands Green Ltd
Woodlands Trust
The Woodroffe Benton
Foundation
The Geoffrey Woods Charitable
Foundation
The Woodward Charitable
Trust
The A and R Woolf Charitable
Trust
The Woolnoth Society
Charitable Trust
Worcester Municipal Charities
The Worcestershire and
Dudley Historic Churches
Trust
The Fred and Della Worms
Charitable Trust
The Worwin UK Foundation
The Wragge and Co. Charitable
Trust
The Diana Edgson Wright
Charitable Trust
The Matthews Wrightson
Charity Trust
Miss E B Wrightson's
Charitable Settlement
Wychdale Ltd
Wychville Ltd
The Wyndham Charitable Trust
The Wyseliot Charitable Trust
The Xerox (UK) Trust

The Yapp Charitable Trust
The Yardley Great Trust
The Dennis Alan Yardy
Charitable Trust
The W Wing Yip and Brothers
Foundation
The York Children's Trust
Yorkshire Agricultural Society
Yorkshire Building Society
Charitable Foundation
The South Yorkshire
Community Foundation
The Yorkshire Dales
Millennium Trust
The John Young Charitable
Settlement
The William Allen Young
Charitable Trust
The John K Young Endowment
Fund
Youth Music
Elizabeth and Prince Zaiger
Trust
Zephyr Charitable Trust
The Marjorie and Arnold Ziff
Charitable Foundation
Stephen Zimmerman
Charitable Trust
The Zochonis Charitable Trust
Zurich Community Trust (UK)
Limited

Campaigning

The A B Charitable Trust
The Adint Charitable Trust
The Ajahma Charitable Trust
The Alchemy Foundation
The Animal Defence Trust
The Arts Council of Wales
The Ove Arup Foundation
The Association of Colleges
Charitable Trust
AstonMansfield Charitable
Trust
The Bartholomew Christian
Trust
The Beaverbrook Foundation
The Bedford Charity (The
Harpur Trust)
The Bedfordshire and Luton
Community Foundation
The Bingham Trust
The Bisgood Charitable Trust
(registered as Miss Jeanne
Bisgood's Charitable Trust)
The Bodfach Trust
The Body Shop Foundation
The Anthony Bourne
Foundation
The Charles and Edna
Broadhurst Charitable Trust
The Bromley Trust
CAFOD
The Carlton House Charitable
Trust

Christian Aid
The City Bridge Trust
The City Parochial Foundation
The Clover Trust
The Cobalt Trust
The Sir Jeremiah Colman Gift
Trust
Cornwall Community
Foundation
The Cotton Trust
Coventry Building Society
Charitable Foundation
Criffel Charitable Trust
Cripplegate Foundation
The Cumber Family Charitable
Trust
Cumbria Community
Foundation
The Diana, Princess of Wales
Memorial Fund
EAGA Partnership Charitable
Trust
The W G Edwards Charitable
Foundation
The John Ellerman Foundation
The Englefield Charitable Trust
Essex Community Foundation
The Matthew Eyton Animal
Welfare Trust
Esmée Fairbairn Foundation
Finnart House School Trust
Firtree Trust
The Fishmongers' Company's
Charitable Trust
The J and C Fleming Trust
Ford Britain Trust
Foundation for Management
Education
The Jill Franklin Trust
The Hugh Fraser Foundation
Friends Provident Charitable
Foundation
Fung Shan Foundation
The General Nursing Council
for England and Wales
Trust
J Paul Getty Jr Charitable Trust
The Gibbs Charitable Trust
The Goldmark Trust
The Gould Charitable Trust
The Grocers' Charity
H C D Memorial Fund
The Hadley Trust
The Hadrian Trust
Hampshire and Isle of Wight
Community Foundation
The Kathleen Hannay
Memorial Charity
Miss K M Harbinson's
Charitable Trust
The Harebell Centenary Fund
Haskel Family Foundation
Healthsure Group Ltd
The Hertfordshire Community
Foundation
The Hospital Saturday Fund

The Inchrye Trust
The ITF Seafarers Trust
The J R S S T Charitable Trust
The Joffe Charitable Trust
JTH Charitable Trust
The Judith Trust
Jusaca Charitable Trust
The Robert Kiln Charitable
    Trust
The KPMG Foundation
The Allen Lane Foundation
The LankellyChase Foundation
The Edgar E Lawley Foundation
The Leeds Community
    Foundation
The Lennox and Wyfold
    Foundation
The Joseph Levy Charitable
    Foundation
The Lloyd Fund
Lloyd's Charities Trust
London Catalyst
The Lowy Mitchell Foundation
Man Group plc Charitable
    Trust
W M Mann Foundation
J P Marland Charitable Trust
The Mercers' Charitable
    Foundation
Community Foundation for
    Merseyside
The Millfield House Foundation
The Millfield Trust
The Mitchell Charitable Trust
Mitsubishi Corporation Fund
    for Europe and Africa
S C and M E Morland's
    Charitable Trust
The Moss Charitable Trust
Moss Family Charitable Trust
Moto in the Community Trust
The National Churches Trust
Newby Trust Limited
The Noel Buxton Trust
Norfolk Community Foundation
The Northcott Devon
    Foundation
The Northern Rock Foundation
The Notgrove Trust
Open Gate
The David Pickford Charitable
    Foundation
G S Plaut Charitable Trust
    Limited
Polden-Puckham Charitable
    Foundation
The David and Elaine Potter
    Foundation
Prairie Trust
The Simone Prendergast
    Charitable Settlement
Private Equity Foundation
The Queen's Silver Jubilee
    Trust
The Sigrid Rausing Trust

The John Rayner Charitable
    Trust
Richard Reeve's Foundation
The Rest Harrow Trust
Rosa – the UK fund for women
    and girls
The Roughley Charitable Trust
The Rowan Charitable Trust
The Joseph Rowntree
    Charitable Trust
The Joseph Rowntree
    Foundation
The Rufford Maurice Laing
    Foundation
The Scottish Community
    Foundation
The Samuel Sebba Charitable
    Trust
Sherburn House Charity
Slaughter and May Charitable
    Trust
R H Southern Trust
The St Mary's Charity
Surrey Community Foundation
The Tay Charitable Trust
The Taylor Family Foundation
Tearfund
Thames Community
    Foundation
The David Thomas Charitable
    Trust
The Len Thomson Charitable
    Trust
Trust for London
The Douglas Turner Trust
The Vardy Foundation
The Waterloo Foundation
The Wates Foundation
Webb Memorial Trust
The Westcroft Trust
The Community Foundation for
    Wiltshire and Swindon
The Michael and Anna Wix
    Charitable Trust
The Woodroffe Benton
    Foundation
The Matthews Wrightson
    Charity Trust
The Wyndham Charitable Trust
The Yapp Charitable Trust
Zurich Community Trust (UK)
    Limited

George A Moore Foundation
The Edward Stocks-Massey
    Bequest Fund
Ulster Garden Villages Ltd

Loan finance

The Architectural Heritage
    Fund
The Burton Breweries
    Charitable Trust
The Coalfields Regeneration
    Trust
The Execution Charitable Trust
The February Foundation
Impetus Trust
The Lincolnshire Old Churches
    Trust

Duration of grant

Trusts listed here have
expressly stated on a
questionniare used as part
of the research for this
book that they give grants
for the specified time
period. Other trusts in this
book which did not respond
to the questionnaire may
also give grants as stated
below.

....

■ One-off grant

The A B Charitable Trust
The Adamson Trust
The Adint Charitable Trust
The Adnams Charity
The Alchemy Foundation
All Saints Educational Trust
The H B Allen Charitable Trust
The Rita Allen Charitable Trust
Angus Allnatt Charitable
     Foundation
The Amalur Foundation Limited
Sir John and Lady Amory's
     Charitable Trust
The Andrew Anderson Trust
The Animal Defence Trust
The Archbishop of
     Canterbury's Charitable
     Trust
The Archer Trust
The Architectural Heritage
     Fund
The Armourers' and Brasiers'
     Gauntlet Trust
The Army Benevolent Fund
The Arnold Foundation
Arthritis Research Campaign
The Arts Council of Wales
The Ove Arup Foundation
The Laura Ashley Foundation
The Norman C Ashton
     Foundation
The Ashworth Charitable Trust
The Associated Country
     Women of the World
     (ACWW)
The Association of Colleges
     Charitable Trust
AstonMansfield Charitable
     Trust
The Astor Foundation
The Aurelius Charitable Trust
The Lord Austin Trust
The John Avins Trustees
The Baird Trust
The Balint Family Charitable
     Trusts
The Balmore Trust
Barchester Healthcare
     Foundation
The Beaverbrook Foundation

The Bedfordshire and Luton
     Community Foundation
The Bellhouse Foundation
The Hervey Benham Charitable
     Trust
The Gerald Bentall Charitable
     Trust
The Berkshire Community
     Foundation
The Betterware Foundation
BibleLands
Percy Bilton Charity
The Bingham Trust
The Lord Mayor of
     Birmingham's Charity
Sir Alec Black's Charity
Enid Blyton Trust for Children
The Nicholas Boas Charitable
     Trust
The Booth Charities
The Bordon and Liphook
     Charity
The Harry Bottom Charitable
     Trust
The Anthony Bourne
     Foundation
Bristol Archdeaconry Charity
John Bristow and Thomas
     Mason Trust
The British Gas (Scottish Gas)
     Energy Trust
British Humane Association
The J and M Britton Charitable
     Trust
The Bromley Trust
The Charles Brotherton Trust
The Bryant Trust
The E F Bulmer Benevolent
     Fund
The Burden Trust
The Richard Cadbury
     Charitable Trust
Capital Community Foundation
The Carlton House Charitable
     Trust
The Carnegie Dunfermline
     Trust
The Carrington Charitable
     Trust
The Leslie Mary Carter
     Charitable Trust
The Catholic Trust for England
     and Wales
The Wilfrid and Constance
     Cave Foundation
The Cemlyn-Jones Trust
Champneys Charitable
     Foundation
The Chapman Charitable Trust
The Chelsea Building Society
     Charitable Foundation
The Chrimes Family Charitable
     Trust
Christian Aid
The Church and Community
     Fund

The Church Burgesses
     Educational Foundation
City and County of Swansea
     Welsh Church Act Fund
The City Bridge Trust
CLA Charitable Trust
The Cobtree Charity Trust Ltd
The George Henry Collins
     Charity
The Congleton Inclosure Trust
The Congregational and
     General Charitable Trust
The Consolidated Charities for
     the Infirm Merchant
     Taylors' Company
Gordon Cook Foundation
Cornwall Community
     Foundation
The Duke of Cornwall's
     Benevolent Fund
The Cotton Trust
Coventry Building Society
     Charitable Foundation
The John Cowan Foundation
The Lord Cozens-Hardy Trust
The Cray Trust
Criffel Charitable Trust
Cripplegate Foundation
The Peter Cruddas Foundation
Cruden Foundation Ltd
Cumbria Community
     Foundation
The Cutler Trust (the
     Worshipful Company of
     Makers of Playing Cards)
The Roald Dahl Foundation
The De Laszlo Foundation
The Delius Trust
The Derbyshire Churches and
     Chapels Preservation Trust
The J N Derbyshire Trust
Devon Community Foundation
The Devon Educational Trust
The Diana, Princess of Wales
     Memorial Fund
The Dinwoodie Settlement
Disability Aid Fund (The Roger
     and Jean Jefcoate Trust)
Dischma Charitable Trust
The DLA Piper Charitable Trust
The DLM Charitable Trust
The Derek and Eileen Dodgson
     Foundation
The Dorset Historic Churches
     Trust
Double 'O' Charity Ltd
The Dugdale Charitable Trust
The Duis Charitable Trust
The Dulverton Trust
The Dumbreck Charity
The Dunhill Medical Trust
The W E Dunn Trust
The Dwek Family Charitable
     Trust
EAGA Partnership Charitable
     Trust

....

The Earley Charity
The Earmark Trust
Eastern Counties Educational
  Trust Limited
The Ebenezer Trust
EDF Energy Trust (EDFET)
Edinburgh Children's Holiday
  Fund
The Edinburgh Trust, No 2
  Account
The W G Edwards Charitable
  Foundation
The Elephant Trust
The John Ellerman Foundation
The Edith Maud Ellis 1985
  Charitable Trust
The Ellis Campbell Foundation
James Ellis Charitable Trust
The Elmley Foundation
The Embleton Trust
EMI Music Sound Foundation
The Worshipful Company of
  Engineers Charitable Trust
  Fund
The Equitable Charitable Trust
The Essex Fairway Charitable
  Trust
The Essex Heritage Trust
The Everard Foundation
The Matthew Eyton Animal
  Welfare Trust
Esmée Fairbairn Foundation
The February Foundation
Federation of Jewish Relief
  Organisations
Fife Council/Common Good
  Funds and Trusts
The Fifty Fund
Finnart House School Trust
Gerald Finzi Charitable Trust
The Ian Fleming Charitable
  Trust
The Joyce Fletcher Charitable
  Trust
The Florian Charitable Trust
The Forbes Charitable
  Foundation
Ford Britain Trust
The Oliver Ford Charitable
  Trust
The Forte Charitable Trust
Lord Forte Foundation
The Fowler, Smith and Jones
  Charitable Trust
The Foyle Foundation
The Hugh Fraser Foundation
The Joseph Strong Frazer Trust
The Freemasons' Grand
  Charity
The Patrick Frost Foundation
The Fulmer Charitable Trust
The Angela Gallagher Memorial
  Fund
The Gamma Trust
The Gannochy Trust

Gatwick Airport Community
  Trust
The General Nursing Council
  for England and Wales
  Trust
The Gibbs Charitable Trust
Simon Gibson Charitable Trust
Gloucestershire Community
  Foundation
The Gloucestershire Historic
  Churches Trust
The Mrs Godfrey-Payton Trust
The Golden Bottle Trust
The Goldmark Trust
The Goldsmiths' Company
  Charity
The Good Neighbours Trust
Nicholas and Judith
  Goodison's Charitable
  Settlement
The Everard and Mina
  Goodman Charitable
  Foundation
The Grahame Charitable
  Foundation Limited
Grantham Yorke Trust
The J G Graves Charitable
  Trust
Grimmitt Trust
The Grocers' Charity
The Hadfield Trust
The Hadrian Trust
Hampshire and Isle of Wight
  Community Foundation
The Kathleen Hannay
  Memorial Charity
The Harborne Parish Lands
  Charity
The Harebell Centenary Fund
The Harris Charitable Trust
The Harris Charity
The N and P Hartley Memorial
  Trust
The Edward Harvist Trust Fund
Haskel Family Foundation
Hasluck Charitable Trust
The Charlotte Heber-Percy
  Charitable Trust
Help the Homeless
The Hemby Trust
The Tim Henman Charitable
  Foundation
The Herefordshire Historic
  Churches Trust
The Heritage of London Trust
  Ltd
The Hertfordshire Community
  Foundation
The Hesslewood Children's
  Trust (Hull Seamen's and
  General Orphanage)
The P and C Hickinbotham
  Charitable Trust
The Charles Littlewood Hill
  Trust
Lady Hind Trust

Stuart Hine Trust
The Hinrichsen Foundation
The Eleemosynary Charity of
  William Hobbayne
Matthew Hodder Charitable
  Trust
The Sir Julian Hodge
  Charitable Trust
The Holbeck Charitable Trust
The Dorothy Holmes Charitable
  Trust
Sir Harold Hood's Charitable
  Trust
The Cuthbert Horn Trust
The Hospital of God at
  Greatham
The Hospital Saturday Fund
The Humanitarian Trust
The Michael and Shirley Hunt
  Charitable Trust
The Albert Hunt Trust
Miss Agnes H Hunter's Trust
The Worshipful Company of
  Innholders General Charity
  Fund
The Island Health Trust
The Isle of Anglesey Charitable
  Trust
The J R S S T Charitable Trust
John James Bristol Foundation
The Jephcott Charitable Trust
Jewish Child's Day
The Jewish Youth Fund
The Joicey Trust
The Marjorie and Geoffrey
  Jones Charitable Trust
JTH Charitable Trust
Jusaca Charitable Trust
The Kass Charitable Trust
The Kathleen Trust
William Kendall's Charity (Wax
  Chandlers' Company)
The Kennel Club Charitable
  Trust
The Kessler Foundation
The Robert Kiln Charitable
  Trust
The Mary Kinross Charitable
  Trust
Robert Kitchin (Saddlers'
  Company)
The Sir James Knott Trust
The KPMG Foundation
Lancashire Environmental
  Fund
The Lancaster Foundation
The Langtree Trust
The LankellyChase Foundation
The Lark Trust
The Kathleen Laurence Trust
The Edgar E Lawley Foundation
The Leathersellers' Company
  Charitable Fund
The Leche Trust
The William Leech Charity

Leeds Building Society
  Charitable Foundation
The Leeds Community
  Foundation
Leicestershire Historic
  Churches Trust
The Lennox and Wyfold
  Foundation
Lord Leverhulme's Charitable
  Trust
The John Spedan Lewis
  Foundation
Lindale Educational
  Foundation
Liverpool Charity and Voluntary
  Services
The Lloyd Fund
Lloyd's Charities Trust
London Catalyst
The London Marathon
  Charitable Trust
The Lowy Mitchell Foundation
The Lynn Foundation
John Lyon's Charity
Malcolm Lyons Foundation
The E M MacAndrew Trust
Macdonald-Buchanan
  Charitable Trust
The Macfarlane Walker Trust
The Mackintosh Foundation
The MacRobert Trust
Man Group plc Charitable
  Trust
The Manchester Guardian
  Society Charitable Trust
The Ann and David Marks
  Foundation
The Hilda and Samuel Marks
  Foundation
J P Marland Charitable Trust
Marr-Munning Trust
The Jim Marshall Charitable
  Trust
Sir George Martin Trust
John Martin's Charity
The Nancie Massey Charitable
  Trust
The Mathew Trust
Evelyn May Trust
The Robert McAlpine
  Foundation
The Medlock Charitable Trust
The Zachary Merton and
  George Woofindin
  Convalescent Trust
The Tony Metherell Charitable
  Trust
The Metropolitan Drinking
  Fountain and Cattle Trough
  Association
Gerald Micklem Charitable
  Trust
The Masonic Province of
  Middlesex Charitable Trust
The Millfield Trust

The Keith and Joan
  Mindelsohn Charitable
  Trust
The Mizpah Trust
The Modiano Charitable Trust
John Moores Foundation
The Morel Charitable Trust
The Morris Charitable Trust
The Moss Charitable Trust
Moss Family Charitable Trust
The Mothercare Charitable
  Foundation
Moto in the Community Trust
Murphy-Neumann Charity
  Company Limited
Muslim Hands
The National Art Collections
  Fund
Needham Market and Barking
  Welfare Charities
The New Appeals Organisation
  for the City and County of
  Nottingham
New Court Charitable Trust
Newby Trust Limited
The Frances and Augustus
  Newman Foundation
The Noon Foundation
The Norda Trust
The North British Hotel Trust
The Northampton Municipal
  Church Charities
The Earl of Northampton's
  Charity
The Northcott Devon
  Foundation
The Northmoor Trust
The Northumbria Historic
  Churches Trust
The Norwich Church of England
  Young Men's Society
The Norwood and Newton
  Settlement
The Notgrove Trust
Novi Most International
The Nuffield Foundation
The Oakley Charitable Trust
The Oikonomia Trust
The Old Enfield Charitable
  Trust
The Olga Charitable Trust
Open Gate
The Ouseley Trust
The Doris Pacey Charitable
  Foundation
The James Pantyfedwen
  Foundation
The Park House Charitable
  Trust
The Payne Charitable Trust
The Harry Payne Trust
The Susanna Peake Charitable
  Trust
Pearson's Holiday Fund
The Dowager Countess
  Eleanor Peel Trust

The Pennycress Trust
The Phillips Family Charitable
  Trust
The David Pickford Charitable
  Foundation
The Bernard Piggott Trust
The Sir Harry Pilkington Trust
The Polehanger Trust
The Ponton House Trust
The Portishead Nautical Trust
The Mary Potter Convent
  Hospital Trust
Prairie Trust
The William Price Charitable
  Trust
The Prince's Charities
  Foundation
Princess Anne's Charities
The Provincial Grand Charity of
  the Province of Derbyshire
Queen Mary's Roehampton
  Trust
The Queen's Silver Jubilee
  Trust
The R V W Trust
The Radcliffe Trust
The Bishop Radford Trust
The Peggy Ramsay Foundation
The E L Rathbone Charitable
  Trust
The Eleanor Rathbone
  Charitable Trust
The John Rayner Charitable
  Trust
Red Hill Charitable Trust
Richard Reeve's Foundation
The Rest Harrow Trust
The Rhondda Cynon Taff
  Welsh Church Acts Fund
The Sir Cliff Richard Charitable
  Trust
The Violet M Richards Charity
The Muriel Edith Rickman
  Trust
The Robertson Trust
The Rochester Bridge Trust
The Helen Roll Charitable
  Trust
The Roman Research Trust
The Rosca Trust
Rosetrees Trust
The Rotherwick Foundation
The Rothley Trust
The Rowan Charitable Trust
The Christopher Rowbotham
  Charitable Trust
The Rowing Foundation
The Joseph Rowntree
  Charitable Trust
The Joseph Rowntree
  Foundation
The Alfred and Frances
  Rubens Charitable Trust
Erach and Roshan Sadri
  Foundation

The Jean Sainsbury Animal
    Welfare Trust
The Peter Samuel Charitable
    Trust
Sir Samuel Scott of Yews
    Trust
The Sir James and Lady Scott
    Trust
The Scottish Arts Council
The Scottish Community
    Foundation
The Scottish International
    Education Trust
Seafarers UK (King George's
    Fund for Sailors)
The Searchlight Electric
    Charitable Trust
The Seedfield Trust
sfgroup Charitable Fund for
    Disabled People
The Shanti Charitable Trust
The Sylvia and Colin Shepherd
    Charitable Trust
The Shipwrights' Company
    Charitable Fund
The Barbara A Shuttleworth
    Memorial Trust
The Julius Silman Charitable
    Trust
Sino-British Fellowship Trust
The Skelton Bounty
The Charles Skey Charitable
    Trust
Skipton Building Society
    Charitable Foundation
The E H Smith Charitable Trust
The Martin Smith Foundation
Philip Smith's Charitable Trust
The Sobell Foundation
David Solomons Charitable
    Trust
The Southdown Trust
The Jessie Spencer Trust
Split Infinitive Trust
Springfields Employees'
    Medical Research and
    Charity Trust Fund
The Spurrell Charitable Trust
St Andrew's Conservation
    Trust
St Gabriel's Trust
The Starfish Trust
The Stevenage Community
    Trust
The June Stevens Foundation
The Sir Halley Stewart Trust
The Leonard Laity Stoate
    Charitable Trust
The Edward Stocks-Massey
    Bequest Fund
Peter Storrs Trust
Stratford upon Avon Town
    Trust
The Sudborough Foundation
The Suffolk Foundation

The Summerfield Charitable
    Trust
The Bernard Sunley Charitable
    Foundation
Surrey Community Foundation
The Surrey Historic Buildings
    Trust Ltd
The Sussex Historic Churches
    Trust
Swansea and Brecon Diocesan
    Board of Finance Limited
The Stella Symons Charitable
    Trust
The Talbot Village Trust
The A R Taylor Charitable Trust
A P Taylor Trust
Tearfund
Tesco Charity Trust
Thames Community
    Foundation
The David Thomas Charitable
    Trust
The Len Thomson Charitable
    Trust
The Sir Jules Thorn Charitable
    Trust
The Thriplow Charitable Trust
The Tompkins Foundation
Toni and Guy Charitable
    Foundation Limited
The Treeside Trust
The Trusthouse Charitable
    Foundation
The R D Turner Charitable
    Trust
The Douglas Turner Trust
John and Lucille van Geest
    Foundation
The Vardy Foundation
The Nigel Vinson Charitable
    Trust
The Wakefield and Tetley Trust
Wakeham Trust
The Walker Trust
Wallace and Gromit's
    Children's Foundation
Wallington Missionary Mart
    and Auctions
Walton on Thames Charity
Sir Siegmund Warburg's
    Voluntary Settlement
The Barbara Ward Children's
    Foundation
The Waterloo Foundation
The Wates Foundation
John Watson's Trust
Webb Memorial Trust
The James Weir Foundation
Wessex Cancer Trust
Mrs S K West's Charitable
    Trust
The Westcroft Trust
The Westminster Foundation
White Rose Children's Aid
    International Charity

The Whitley Animal Protection
    Trust
The Lionel Wigram Memorial
    Trust
The Harold Hyam Wingate
    Foundation
The Francis Winham
    Foundation
The Michael and Anna Wix
    Charitable Trust
The Wolfson Family Charitable
    Trust
The Wolfson Foundation
Women's World Day of Prayer
The Woodroffe Benton
    Foundation
The Geoffrey Woods Charitable
    Foundation
The Matthews Wrightson
    Charity Trust
The Wyndham Charitable Trust
The Wyseliot Charitable Trust
The John K Young Endowment
    Fund
The Marjorie and Arnold Ziff
    Charitable Foundation
Zurich Community Trust (UK)
    Limited

....
■ **Two years**

The Adint Charitable Trust
The Ajahma Charitable Trust
Aldgate and All Hallows'
    Barking Exhibition
    Foundation
All Saints Educational Trust
The H B Allen Charitable Trust
Arthritis Research Campaign
The Ove Arup Foundation
The Laura Ashley Foundation
The Associated Country
    Women of the World
    (ACWW)
The Astor Foundation
The John Avins Trustees
The Bedfordshire and Luton
    Community Foundation
The Berkshire Community
    Foundation
BibleLands
The Body Shop Foundation
The Booth Charities
The Anthony Bourne
    Foundation
The British Gas (Scottish Gas)
    Energy Trust
British Humane Association
The Charles and Edna
    Broadhurst Charitable Trust
The Swinfen Broun Charitable
    Trust
Capital Community Foundation
The Carlton House Charitable
    Trust

The Wilfrid and Constance
  Cave Foundation
Christian Aid
The Church and Community
  Fund
The Church Burgesses
  Educational Foundation
The City Bridge Trust
The Cobtree Charity Trust Ltd
The John and Freda Coleman
  Charitable Trust
The Consolidated Charities for
  the Infirm Merchant
  Taylors' Company
Gordon Cook Foundation
The Lord Cozens-Hardy Trust
Cripplegate Foundation
The Peter Cruddas Foundation
Cumbria Community
  Foundation
The Cunningham Trust
The Cutler Trust (the
  Worshipful Company of
  Makers of Playing Cards)
The Roald Dahl Foundation
The De Laszlo Foundation
Devon Community Foundation
The Diana, Princess of Wales
  Memorial Fund
The DLM Charitable Trust
The Dulverton Trust
Dunard Fund
The Dunhill Medical Trust
EAGA Partnership Charitable
  Trust
EDF Energy Trust (EDFET)
The John Ellerman Foundation
The Edith Maud Ellis 1985
  Charitable Trust
The Elmley Foundation
The Equitable Charitable Trust
Essex Community Foundation
Esmée Fairbairn Foundation
Foundation for Management
  Education
The Fowler, Smith and Jones
  Charitable Trust
The Foyle Foundation
The Hugh Fraser Foundation
The Freemasons' Grand
  Charity
The Friends of Kent Churches
The General Nursing Council
  for England and Wales
  Trust
Gloucestershire Community
  Foundation
The Golden Bottle Trust
The Goldmark Trust
Grimmitt Trust
Hampshire and Isle of Wight
  Community Foundation
The Hospital of God at
  Greatham
The Hull and East Riding
  Charitable Trust

Miss Agnes H Hunter's Trust
The Worshipful Company of
  Innholders General Charity
  Fund
The Island Health Trust
The J R S S T Charitable Trust
John James Bristol Foundation
The Jephcott Charitable Trust
Jewish Child's Day
The Joicey Trust
The Kennel Club Charitable
  Trust
The KPMG Foundation
Lancashire Environmental
  Fund
The Allen Lane Foundation
The LankellyChase Foundation
The Leathersellers' Company
  Charitable Fund
John Lyon's Charity
The Mackintosh Foundation
The MacRobert Trust
Man Group plc Charitable
  Trust
W M Mann Foundation
Marr-Munning Trust
The Nancie Massey Charitable
  Trust
The Medlock Charitable Trust
The Merchant Taylors'
  Company Charities Fund
The Millfield Trust
The Edgar Milward Charity
John Moores Foundation
Murphy-Neumann Charity
  Company Limited
The Frances and Augustus
  Newman Foundation
The Noon Foundation
The North British Hotel Trust
The Earl of Northampton's
  Charity
The Northern Rock Foundation
Novi Most International
The Nuffield Foundation
Open Gate
The Ouseley Trust
The Doris Pacey Charitable
  Foundation
The Dowager Countess
  Eleanor Peel Trust
The Mary Potter Convent
  Hospital Trust
Prairie Trust
The Radcliffe Trust
The Eleanor Rathbone
  Charitable Trust
Red Hill Charitable Trust
The Violet M Richards Charity
The Robertson Trust
Rosetrees Trust
The Rotherwick Foundation
The Rowan Charitable Trust
The Christopher Rowbotham
  Charitable Trust

The Joseph Rowntree
  Charitable Trust
The Peter Samuel Charitable
  Trust
The Scottish Arts Council
The Scottish Community
  Foundation
Seafarers UK (King George's
  Fund for Sailors)
The Samuel Sebba Charitable
  Trust
The Seedfield Trust
The Shipwrights' Company
  Charitable Fund
Sino-British Fellowship Trust
The Charles Skey Charitable
  Trust
The Martin Smith Foundation
The Sobell Foundation
St Gabriel's Trust
The Sir Halley Stewart Trust
The Edward Stocks-Massey
  Bequest Fund
Stratford upon Avon Town
  Trust
Surrey Community Foundation
Tearfund
Thackray Medical Research
  Trust
John and Lucille van Geest
  Foundation
The Vardy Foundation
The Wakefield and Tetley Trust
The Barbara Ward Children's
  Foundation
The Waterloo Foundation
The Wates Foundation
John Watson's Trust
Webb Memorial Trust
Wessex Cancer Trust
The Wessex Youth Trust
The Whitecourt Charitable
  Trust
The Whitley Animal Protection
  Trust
The Harold Hyam Wingate
  Foundation
The Geoffrey Woods Charitable
  Foundation
Yorkshire Building Society
  Charitable Foundation
The Yorkshire Historic
  Churches Trust
The Marjorie and Arnold Ziff
  Charitable Foundation
Zurich Community Trust (UK)
  Limited

....
■ **Three years**

The A B Charitable Trust
The Adint Charitable Trust
The AIM Foundation
The Ajahma Charitable Trust

Aldgate and All Hallows'
   Barking Exhibition
   Foundation
All Saints Educational Trust
The H B Allen Charitable Trust
Arthritis Research Campaign
The Ove Arup Foundation
The Laura Ashley Foundation
The Astor Foundation
The John Avins Trustees
The Barnwood House Trust
The Misses Barrie Charitable
   Trust
The Bedfordshire and Luton
   Community Foundation
The Beit Trust
BibleLands
The Bisgood Charitable Trust
   (registered as Miss Jeanne
   Bisgood's Charitable Trust)
The Booth Charities
The Anthony Bourne
   Foundation
The British Gas (Scottish Gas)
   Energy Trust
The Bromley Trust
The Bulldog Trust Limited
The Burden Trust
The Geoffrey Burton Charitable
   Trust
Capital Community Foundation
The Carlton House Charitable
   Trust
The Casey Trust
Sir John Cass's Foundation
The Wilfrid and Constance
   Cave Foundation
Children's Liver Disease
   Foundation
Christian Aid
The Church and Community
   Fund
The Church Burgesses
   Educational Foundation
The City Bridge Trust
The City Parochial Foundation
The Clover Trust
The Francis Coales Charitable
   Foundation
The Cobalt Trust
The Cobtree Charity Trust Ltd
The Sir Jeremiah Colman Gift
   Trust
The Consolidated Charities for
   the Infirm Merchant
   Taylors' Company
Gordon Cook Foundation
The Lord Cozens-Hardy Trust
Cripplegate Foundation
The Peter Cruddas Foundation
The Cumber Family Charitable
   Trust
Cumbria Community
   Foundation

The Cutler Trust (the
   Worshipful Company of
   Makers of Playing Cards)
The Roald Dahl Foundation
The De Laszlo Foundation
The Denman Charitable Trust
The Diana, Princess of Wales
   Memorial Fund
The Dulverton Trust
The Dunhill Medical Trust
EAGA Partnership Charitable
   Trust
EDF Energy Trust (EDFET)
The Gilbert and Eileen Edgar
   Foundation
The John Ellerman Foundation
The Edith Maud Ellis 1985
   Charitable Trust
The Elmley Foundation
The Englefield Charitable Trust
The Equitable Charitable Trust
Essex Community Foundation
The Everard Foundation
Esmee Fairbairn Foundation
Marc Fitch Fund
The Football Foundation
Lord Forte Foundation
The Fowler, Smith and Jones
   Charitable Trust
The Foyle Foundation
The Jill Franklin Trust
The Hugh Fraser Foundation
The Freemasons' Grand
   Charity
The Gannochy Trust
Garrick Charitable Trust
The General Nursing Council
   for England and Wales
   Trust
J Paul Getty Jr Charitable Trust
Simon Gibson Charitable Trust
The Golden Bottle Trust
The Goldmark Trust
The Goldsmiths' Company
   Charity
The Gould Charitable Trust
Greggs Foundation
Grimmitt Trust
H C D Memorial Fund
The Hadrian Trust
The N and P Hartley Memorial
   Trust
The Dorothy Hay-Bolton
   Charitable Trust
Healthsure Group Ltd
The Holbeck Charitable Trust
The Edward Holt Trust
The Hospital of God at
   Greatham
The Hull and East Riding
   Charitable Trust
The Worshipful Company of
   Innholders General Charity
   Fund
The Charles Irving Charitable
   Trust

The Island Health Trust
The ITF Seafarers Trust
John James Bristol Foundation
The Jephcott Charitable Trust
Jewish Child's Day
The Joffe Charitable Trust
The Joicey Trust
The Judith Trust
The Kennel Club Charitable
   Trust
The Peter Kershaw Trust
Keswick Hall Charity
The Robert Kiln Charitable
   Trust
The Mary Kinross Charitable
   Trust
The KPMG Foundation
The David Laing Foundation
The Allen Lane Foundation
The LankellyChase Foundation
The Leathersellers' Company
   Charitable Fund
The William Leech Charity
The Lowy Mitchell Foundation
John Lyon's Charity
The R S Macdonald Charitable
   Trust
The Mackintosh Foundation
The MacRobert Trust
Man Group plc Charitable
   Trust
Marr-Munning Trust
The Nancie Massey Charitable
   Trust
The Anthony and Elizabeth
   Mellows Charitable
   Settlement
The Merchant Taylors'
   Company Charities Fund
The Millfield House Foundation
The Millfield Trust
Milton Keynes Community
   Foundation
The Mitchell Charitable Trust
John Moores Foundation
The Frances and Augustus
   Newman Foundation
The Noon Foundation
The North British Hotel Trust
The Earl of Northampton's
   Charity
The Northern Rock Foundation
Novi Most International
The Nuffield Foundation
Open Gate
The Doris Pacey Charitable
   Foundation
The Patrick Charitable Trust
The Dowager Countess
   Eleanor Peel Trust
Philological Foundation
Polden-Puckham Charitable
   Foundation
The Mary Potter Convent
   Hospital Trust
Private Equity Foundation

The Radcliffe Trust
The Eleanor Rathbone Charitable Trust
The Sigrid Rausing Trust
The Violet M Richards Charity
The Robertson Trust
Rosetrees Trust
The Rotherwick Foundation
The Rowan Charitable Trust
The Christopher Rowbotham Charitable Trust
The Joseph Rowntree Charitable Trust
Saint Luke's College Foundation
The Peter Samuel Charitable Trust
The Francis C Scott Charitable Trust
The Scottish Community Foundation
Seafarers UK (King George's Fund for Sailors)
The Seedfield Trust
The Shanti Charitable Trust
The Shipwrights' Company Charitable Fund
Sino-British Fellowship Trust
The Charles Skey Charitable Trust
The Martin Smith Foundation
The Sobell Foundation
Stanley Spooner Deceased Charitable Trust
St Christopher's College Educational Trust
St Gabriel's Trust
The Sir Halley Stewart Trust
The Edward Stocks-Massey Bequest Fund
Stratford upon Avon Town Trust
The Bernard Sunley Charitable Foundation
Surrey Community Foundation
Tearfund
Trust for London
John and Lucille van Geest Foundation
The Wakefield and Tetley Trust
The Barbara Ward Children's Foundation
The Waterloo Foundation
The Wates Foundation
The Weavers' Company Benevolent Fund
Wessex Cancer Trust
The Westminster Foundation
The Whitecourt Charitable Trust
The Whitley Animal Protection Trust
The Community Foundation for Wiltshire and Swindon
The Harold Hyam Wingate Foundation

The Yapp Charitable Trust
The Marjorie and Arnold Ziff Charitable Foundation
Zurich Community Trust (UK) Limited

....

■ Longer than three years

The A B Charitable Trust
The Adint Charitable Trust
Aldgate and All Hallows' Barking Exhibition Foundation
All Saints Educational Trust
Arthritis Research Campaign
The John Avins Trustees
The Balmore Trust
The Harry Bottom Charitable Trust
The Anthony Bourne Foundation
The Jack Brunton Charitable Trust
CAFOD
The Cambridgeshire Historic Churches Trust
The Campden Charities
The Wilfrid and Constance Cave Foundation
The Church Burgesses Educational Foundation
Church Burgesses Trust
The City Bridge Trust
Gordon Cook Foundation
The Corona Charitable Trust
The Cotton Trust
The Lord Cozens-Hardy Trust
Criffel Charitable Trust
Cripplegate Foundation
The Cutler Trust (the Worshipful Company of Makers of Playing Cards)
The De Laszlo Foundation
The Diana, Princess of Wales Memorial Fund
EAGA Partnership Charitable Trust
The Ebenezer Trust
The John Ellerman Foundation
The Edith Maud Ellis 1985 Charitable Trust
The Elmley Foundation
Esmée Fairbairn Foundation
Finnart House School Trust
Fisherbeck Charitable Trust
The Oliver Ford Charitable Trust
The Forest Hill Charitable Trust
The Foyle Foundation
The Hugh Fraser Foundation
The Freemasons' Grand Charity
The Thomas Freke and Lady Norton Charity

Friends Provident Charitable Foundation
The Gamlen Charitable Trust
The David and Marie Grumitt Foundation
The Hadley Trust
Miss K M Harbinson's Charitable Trust
The Hartley Charitable Trust
The Rosalind Hicks Charitable Trust
The Huggard Charitable Trust
William Kendall's Charity (Wax Chandlers' Company)
The Mary Kinross Charitable Trust
The Lancaster Foundation
The Leach Fourteenth Trust
The Leathersellers' Company Charitable Fund
The Joseph Levy Charitable Foundation
LSA Charitable Trust
The Macfarlane Walker Trust
Man Group plc Charitable Trust
Marr-Munning Trust
The Robert McAlpine Foundation
The Migraine Trust
The Millfield Trust
The Millichope Foundation
S C and M E Morland's Charitable Trust
G M Morrison Charitable Trust
Murphy-Neumann Charity Company Limited
Nazareth Trust Fund
The North British Hotel Trust
The Northern Rock Foundation
Novi Most International
The Nuffield Foundation
The Doris Pacey Charitable Foundation
The Patrick Charitable Trust
The Dowager Countess Eleanor Peel Trust
G S Plaut Charitable Trust Limited
The David and Elaine Potter Foundation
The Muriel Edith Rickman Trust
The Robertson Trust
Rosetrees Trust
The Peter Samuel Charitable Trust
The Scouloudi Foundation
The Bassil Shippam and Alsford Trust
The Shirley Foundation
Sino-British Fellowship Trust
The Martin Smith Foundation
The Sobell Foundation
R H Southern Trust
St Hilda's Trust

St Katharine and Shadwell
    Trust
The Edward Stocks-Massey
    Bequest Fund
Surrey Community Foundation
The Gay and Keith Talbot Trust
The Tay Charitable Trust
The Connie and Albert Taylor
    Charitable Trust
The Sir Jules Thorn Charitable
    Trust
Mrs R P Tindall's Charitable
    Trust
John and Lucille van Geest
    Foundation
The Waterloo Foundation
The Westcroft Trust
The Whitley Animal Protection
    Trust
The Lionel Wigram Memorial
    Trust
The Marjorie and Arnold Ziff
    Charitable Foundation
Zurich Community Trust (UK)
    Limited

The alphabetical register of grant-making trusts

This section lists the individual entries for the grant-making trusts.

■ The 1989 Willan Charitable Trust

WHERE FUNDING CAN BE GIVEN Worldwide, but in practice mainly the north east of England.

WHO CAN BENEFIT Registered charities for the benefit of children; disabled people; carers; volunteers; refugees; and offenders.

WHAT IS FUNDED Grants are given to: advance the education of children and help children in need; benefit people with physical or mental disabilities and alleviate hardship and distress either generally or individually; and further medical research.

WHAT IS NOT FUNDED Grants are not given directly to individuals. Grants for gap year students may be considered if the individual will be working for a charity (in this case the grant would be paid to the charity).

RANGE OF GRANTS £500–£10,000.

SAMPLE GRANTS SAFC Foundation and Cancer Connexions (£10,000 each); Amble Multi Agency Crime Prevention Initiative (£6,000); Durham City Centre Youth Project, The Children's Society and the Calvert Trust (£5,000 each); Chester le Street Youth Centre (£4,000); Different Strokes North East, Northern Roots and People and Drugs (£3,000 each); Leukaemia Research and Coast Video Club (£2,000 each); Northumberland Mountain Rescue and the Association of British Poles (£1,000 each); and Healthwise and Newcastle Gang Show (£500).

FINANCES *Year* 2007–08 *Income* £602,935 *Grants* £467,337 *Assets* £10,205,474

TRUSTEES Francis A Chapman; Alex Ohlsson; Willan Trustee Ltd.

HOW TO APPLY In writing to the correspondent at the Community Foundation Serving Tyne and Wear. Applications are processed, collated and shortlisted by the Community Foundation on a quarterly basis. The shortlist is then circulated to each of the trustees for consideration and approval.

WHO TO APPLY TO Karen Griffiths, Fund Manager, Community Foundation Serving Tyne & Wear, 9th Floor, Cale Cross, 156 Pilgrim Street, Newcastle upon Tyne NE1 6SU *Tel* 0191 222 0945 *Fax* 0191 230 0689 *email* kg@ communityfoundation.org.uk

CC NO 802749   **ESTABLISHED** 1989

■ The 29th May 1961 Charitable Trust

WHERE FUNDING CAN BE GIVEN UK, with a special interest in the Warwickshire/Birmingham/Coventry area.

WHO CAN BENEFIT Charitable organisations in the UK. People who are socially disadvantaged may be favoured.

WHAT IS FUNDED General charitable purposes across a broad spectrum, including: art, leisure and young people; health; social welfare; education and training; homelessness and housing; offenders; and conservation and protection.

WHAT IS NOT FUNDED Grants only to registered charities. No grants to individuals.

TYPE OF GRANT One-off, recurring and some spread over two to three years. Grants are given for capital and revenue purposes.

RANGE OF GRANTS £500–£220,000, but the great majority are less than £10,000.

SAMPLE GRANTS University of Warwick (£220,000), towards the running costs of the arts centre; NSPCC (£110,000 in total), mainly towards the 'Stop Organised Abuse' campaign; Shelter (£85,000), towards a programme for ex-offenders; Sadler's Wells Trust (£70,000 in total), towards subsidised tickets and a schools access programme; Crisis (£50,000), towards core costs; Warwickshire Association of Youth Clubs (£28,000), towards running costs; Trent Vineyard (£20,000), towards a building extension; Family Holiday Association (£15,000), towards holidays for families in need; Counselling in Prison (£7,500), towards counselling services; and Feed the Children (£5,000), towards the costs of providing breakfasts to deprived schoolchildren in Birmingham.

FINANCES *Year* 2007–08 *Income* £4,023,914 *Grants* £3,673,000 *Assets* £107,525,157

TRUSTEES Vanni Emanuele Treves; Andrew C Jones; Anthony J Mead; Paul Varney.

HOW TO APPLY To the secretary in writing, enclosing in triplicate the most recent annual report and accounts. Trustees normally meet in February, May, August and November. Due to the large number of applications received, they cannot be acknowledged.

WHO TO APPLY TO The Secretary, 1st Floor, 123 Buckingham Palace Road, London SW1W 9DZ *Tel* 020 7312 3100 *email* enquiries@ 29may1961charity.org.uk

CC NO 200198   **ESTABLISHED** 1961

■ 4 Charity Foundation

WHERE FUNDING CAN BE GIVEN UK and Israel.

WHO CAN BENEFIT Jewish charities and causes.

WHAT IS FUNDED Religious activities and education.

SAMPLE GRANTS Previous grants include those to: the American Jewish Joint Distribution Committee (£78,000); the Millennium Trust (£66,000); Keren Yehoshua V'Yisroel (£43,000); Project Seed (£35,000); World Jewish Relief (£29,000); Menorah Grammar School (£27,000); British Friends of Jaffa Institute (£23,000); Friends of Mir (£19,000); Heichal Hatorah Foundation (£15,000); Chai Life Line Cancer Care (£12,000); Jewish Care (£11,000); and British Friends of Ezer Mizion (£10,000).

FINANCES *Year* 2007–08 *Income* £6,852,460 *Grants* £679,000 *Assets* £10,302,565

TRUSTEES Jacob Schimmel; Marc Schimmel; D Rabson; Mrs A Schimmel.

HOW TO APPLY This trust does not respond to unsolicited applications.

WHO TO APPLY TO Jacob Schimmel, Trustee, 54–56 Euston Street, London NW1 2ES *Tel* 020 7387 0155

CC NO 1077143   **ESTABLISHED** 1999

■ The A B Charitable Trust

WHERE FUNDING CAN BE GIVEN Mainly UK.

WHO CAN BENEFIT UK registered charities.

WHAT IS FUNDED Charities working where human dignity is imperilled and where there are opportunities for human dignity to be affirmed. 'Applications are particularly welcomed from charities working to support: refugees and victims of torture; prisoners; older people; people with mental health problems. 'In relation to the above, the following cross-cutting themes are of interest to the trustees: women; homelessness; therapeutic art.'

WHAT IS NOT FUNDED Individuals are not eligible for support.

TYPE OF GRANT The trust has a small-grants programme (up to £5,000) which responds to appeals on a one-off basis. It seeks to identify charities working on its priorities for larger grants, which could be awarded on a regular basis subject to annual reports and an agreed exit strategy. It is happy to provide funding for core costs.

SAMPLE GRANTS Asylum Support Appeals Project, Redress and Women's Therapy Centre (£7,500 each); Asian Women's Organisation, C P Support, Citizenship Foundation, Contact the Elderly, Furniture Now, Harrogate Homeless, Praxis, Soundabout, Sudbury Neighbourhood Centre and Women's Link (£5,000 each); Soundabout and Tools for Self Reliance (£3,000 each); and Burnbake Trust and Headway (£2,500 each).

FINANCES *Year* 2007–08 *Income* £548,820 *Grants* £268,000 *Assets* £557,936

TRUSTEES Y J M Bonavero; Mrs A G M L Bonavero; Miss C Bonavero; O Bonavero; P Bonavero; P Day; A Harley; Mrs A Swan Parente.

HOW TO APPLY Applications can be completed online at the trust's website. 'As well as administrative and financial details, the online application form will ask you for a two-page summary of your work, including: background; aims and objectives; activities; achievements over the last year. 'After filling in the online application form you will be sent a reference number. Please send the Director the following documents in hard copy quoting the reference number: a signed copy of your latest certified accounts/ statements, published within six months of the end of the previous financial year; publicity materials that illustrate the work of your charity, such as annual reviews or leaflets. 'Send in your application six weeks ahead of the trustees' meeting at which you would like it to be considered. The trustees meet four times a year, in January, April, July and October. To get the exact dates, please contact us.'

WHO TO APPLY TO Mrs S Harrity, Director, Monmouth House, 87–93 Westbourne Grove, London W2 4UL *Tel* 020 7313 8070 *Fax* 020 7313 9607 *email* mail@abcharitabletrust.org.uk *Website* www.abcharitabletrust.org.uk

CC NO 1000147   **ESTABLISHED** 1990

■ Aberbrothock Charitable Trust

WHERE FUNDING CAN BE GIVEN East of Scotland, north of the Firth of Tay.

WHO CAN BENEFIT Organisations benefiting the community with charitable status.

WHAT IS FUNDED Children/young people; disability; environment/conservation; hospitals/hospices; and medical research are all considered.

WHAT IS NOT FUNDED The geographical restriction is strictly adhered to. Applications from outside the area, and/or from individuals, will not be considered.

TYPE OF GRANT One-off, including project, research, capital and core costs.

RANGE OF GRANTS £1,000–£5,000.

SAMPLE GRANTS Previous beneficiaries have included Red Cross, Colon Cancer Care, Princess Royal Trust, International League of Horses, Kids Out and Dundee Heritage Trust.

FINANCES *Year* 2008–09 *Income* £106,429

TRUSTEES G McNicol; J G Mathieson; Mrs A T L Grant; J D B Smart.

HOW TO APPLY In writing to the correspondent. Trustees meet to consider grants in March, July and December.

WHO TO APPLY TO The Trustees, Thorntons Law LLP, Brothockbank House, Arbroath, Angus DD11 1NE

SC NO SC003110   **ESTABLISHED** 1971

■ The Aberdeen Endowments Trust

WHERE FUNDING CAN BE GIVEN The former City and Royal Burgh of Aberdeen (i.e. pre-1975).

WHO CAN BENEFIT Persons of organisations which belong to the former City and Royal Burgh of Aberdeen.

WHAT IS FUNDED Education and the arts. The main purpose of the trust is to give financial assistance to individuals for educational purposes.

WHAT IS NOT FUNDED No grants to people or organisations from outside the former City and Royal Burgh of Aberdeen.

RANGE OF GRANTS Around £200 each.

FINANCES *Year* 2008 *Income* £957,401

TRUSTEES Three persons elected by Aberdeen City Council; one by the Senatus Academicus of the University of Aberdeen; two by the governors of Robert Gordon's College, Aberdeen; two by the Church of Scotland Presbytery of Aberdeen; one by the churches of Aberdeen other than the Church of Scotland; one by the Society of Advocates in Aberdeen; one by the Convener Court of the Seven Incorporated Trades of Aberdeen; one by the trade unions having branches in Aberdeen; one by the Aberdeen Local Association of the Educational Institute of Scotland; plus not less than two and not more than four co-optees.

OTHER INFORMATION The trust awards a number of free places to Robert Gordon's Secondary College, also school bursaries, post-graduate scholarships, travel scholarships, grants for special equipment, sports facilities, promoting education in the arts and adult education

HOW TO APPLY Application forms are available from the correspondent. The Benefactions Committee of the trust, which makes financial awards, normally meets nine or ten times a year.

WHO TO APPLY TO W Russell, Clerk, 19 Albert Street, Aberdeen AB9 1QF *Tel* 01224 640194

SC NO SC010507   **ESTABLISHED** 1909

Think carefully about every application. Is it justified?

315

■ The Aberdeenshire Educational Trust Scheme

WHERE FUNDING CAN BE GIVEN The former county of Aberdeen.

WHO CAN BENEFIT Individuals in education, schools and further education centres, as well as to clubs and other organisations.

WHAT IS FUNDED Providing and maintaining playing fields and other sports facilities including equipment; schools and further education centres to assist in providing special equipment; clubs, societies and organisations which include amongst their activities work of an educational nature; schools and organisations to assist education in art, music and drama; individuals and bodies to undertake educational experiments and research which will be for the benefit of people belonging to Aberdeen County. Help may also be given towards 'regional and national enterprises of an educational nature'.

FINANCES *Year* 2007–08 *Income* £104,958

HOW TO APPLY On a form available from the correspondent. Full guidelines are also available upon request.

WHO TO APPLY TO The Administrator, Finance Section, Aberdeenshire Council, St Leonard's, Sandyhill Road, Banff, Aberdeenshire AB45 1BH

SC NO SC028382

■ Brian Abrams Charitable Trust

WHERE FUNDING CAN BE GIVEN UK.

WHO CAN BENEFIT Jewish organisations.

WHAT IS FUNDED Jewish causes.

WHAT IS NOT FUNDED No grants to individuals.

SAMPLE GRANTS Previous beneficiaries have included Centre for Torah Education Trust, Friends of Ohr Akiva Institution, Halacha Lemoshe Trust, Hale Adult Hebrew Education Trust, the Heathlands Village, Manchester Jewish Federation, Rabbi Nachman of Breslov Charitable Foundation, Rainsough Charitable Trust, UK Friends of Magen David Adom and United Jewish Israel Appeal.

FINANCES *Year* 2007–08 *Income* £50,765 *Grants* £37,530 *Assets* £808,839

TRUSTEES Betty Abrams; Brian Abrams; Eric Abrams; Gail Gabbie.

HOW TO APPLY The trust has previously stated that its funds are fully committed and applications are not invited.

WHO TO APPLY TO Robert Taylor, Alexander Layton, 130–132 Nantwich Road, Crewe CW2 6AZ

CC NO 275941   **ESTABLISHED** 1978

■ Eric Abrams Charitable Trust

WHERE FUNDING CAN BE GIVEN UK.

WHO CAN BENEFIT Jewish organisations.

WHAT IS FUNDED Jewish causes.

WHAT IS NOT FUNDED No grants to individuals.

SAMPLE GRANTS Previous beneficiaries have included Friends of Ohr Akiva Institution, Centre for Torah Education Trust, Halacha Lemoshe Trust, Hale Adult Hebrew Education Trust, the Heathlands Village, Manchester Jewish Federation, Rabbi Nachman of Breslov Charitable Foundation, UK Friends of Magen David Adom and United Jewish Israel Appeal.

FINANCES *Year* 2007–08 *Income* £37,565 *Grants* £37,565 *Assets* £916,095

TRUSTEES Brian Abrams; Eric Abrams; Marcia Anne Jacobs; Susan Melanie Abrams.

HOW TO APPLY 'The trustees do not invite appeals, as the trust is fully committed until further notice.'

WHO TO APPLY TO The Trustees, 130–132 Nantwich Road, Crewe CW2 6AZ

CC NO 275939   **ESTABLISHED** 1968

■ The Acacia Charitable Trust

WHERE FUNDING CAN BE GIVEN UK and Israel.

WHO CAN BENEFIT Registered charities.

WHAT IS FUNDED Educational and medical charities in the UK. Jewish charities, both in the UK and the State of Israel.

WHAT IS NOT FUNDED No grants to individuals.

TYPE OF GRANT Core and project costs will be considered.

RANGE OF GRANTS Up to £30,000, although most for under £5,000.

SAMPLE GRANTS The Jewish Museum (£30,000); World Jewish Relief (£10,500); British Organisation for Rehabilitation Through Training and Community Security Trust (£5,000 each); Jewish Historical Society of England (£3,000); the Hampstead Theatre (£2,500); Spanish and Portuguese Jews' Congregation (£2,200); Institute for Jewish Policy Research and Jewish Care (£2,000 each); and Magen David Adom (£1,000).

FINANCES *Year* 2007–08 *Income* £84,001 *Grants* £77,868 *Assets* £1,821,629

TRUSTEES K D Rubens; Mrs A G Rubens; S A Rubens.

HOW TO APPLY In writing to the correspondent.

WHO TO APPLY TO The Secretary, 5 Clarke's Mews, London W1G 6QN *Tel* 020 7486 1884 *email* acacia@dircon.co.uk

CC NO 274275   **ESTABLISHED** 1977

■ Access Sport

WHERE FUNDING CAN BE GIVEN UK.

WHO CAN BENEFIT Grass roots sports clubs working with children, particularly in disadvantaged areas.

WHAT IS FUNDED The development of 'quality sporting programmes which promote fitness and fun'.

TYPE OF GRANT Grants may cover the cost of: club promotion; participant recruitment and subsidies; coach development and education; sports equipment.

FINANCES *Year* 2007–08 *Income* £265,455 *Grants* £44,589 *Assets* £53,335

TRUSTEES J Cracknell; C Beauchamp; J Glover; N Pinkham; J Roper; Q Boyes; F Hardie; C Harley-Martin.

OTHER INFORMATION 'Founded in 2004 Access Sport is a dynamic charity whose mission is to give more children, particularly in disadvantaged areas, access to a wide range of quality local sport. We empower the inspirational community volunteers who set up and run local sports clubs with cash, expert advice and networking.'

HOW TO APPLY To nominate a club for selection, or to discuss the possibility further, please contact Access Sport by phone or email.

WHO TO APPLY TO The Secretary, Lamb House, Church Street, London W4 2PD *Tel* 020 8811 4555 *email* club@accesssport.co.uk *Website* www.accesssport.co.uk

CC NO 1104687   **ESTABLISHED** 2004

■ Achiezer Association Ltd

WHERE FUNDING CAN BE GIVEN Worldwide.

WHO CAN BENEFIT Charitable organisations. In practice mainly Jewish causes.

WHAT IS FUNDED The relief of older people and people in need; advancement of education; advancement of religion; and general charitable purposes.

WHAT IS NOT FUNDED No grants to individuals.

TYPE OF GRANT One-off and recurring.

SAMPLE GRANTS The accounts for the year do not list the individual beneficiaries of the grants made. In the past, the trust has mainly supported Jewish charities with a few small grants being given to medical and welfare charities.

FINANCES *Year* 2007–08 *Income* £738,786 *Grants* £601,595 *Assets* £1,832,806

TRUSTEES David Chontow; Sydney S Chontow; Michael M Chontow.

PUBLICATIONS According to the trust, a list of grant beneficiaries is 'detailed in a separate publication which is available from the Registered Office'. A copy has been requested but is yet to be received.

HOW TO APPLY In writing to the correspondent.

WHO TO APPLY TO David Chontow, Trustee, 130–134 Granville Road, London NW2 2LD *Tel* 020 8209 3880 *email* genoffice@dasim.co.uk

CC NO 255031   **ESTABLISHED** 1965

■ Achisomoch Aid Company Limited

WHERE FUNDING CAN BE GIVEN UK and worldwide.

WHO CAN BENEFIT Jewish religious charities.

WHAT IS FUNDED The advancement of religion in accordance with the Jewish faith.

SAMPLE GRANTS Previous beneficiaries have included: the Ah Trust, Beis Malka Trust, Chevras Maoz Ladol, Comet Charities Ltd, Davis Elias Charitable Trust, Havenpoint Ltd, Heritage Retreats, Jewish Educational Trust, Lolev Charitable Trust, Menorah Primary School, Michlala Jerusalem College, SOFT, Tomchei Cholim Trust and Yad Eliezer – Israel.

FINANCES *Year* 2007–08 *Income* £7,039,950 *Grants* £5,989,725 *Assets* £2,793,607

TRUSTEES Isaac M Katz; D C Chontow; J Emanuel.

HOW TO APPLY In writing to the correspondent.

WHO TO APPLY TO Isaac Mark Katz, Secretary, 35 Templars Avenue, London NW11 0NU *Tel* 020 8731 8988 *email* admin@achisomoch.org *Website* www.achisomoch.org

CC NO 278387   **ESTABLISHED** 1979

■ The ACT Foundation

WHERE FUNDING CAN BE GIVEN UK and overseas.

WHO CAN BENEFIT Health, welfare and housing.

WHAT IS FUNDED Grants generally fall into the following areas: building – funding modifications to homes, schools, hospices etc.; equipment – provision of specialised wheelchairs, other mobility aids and equipment including medical equipment to assist independent living; financial assistance – towards the cost of short-term respite breaks at a registered respite centre. Projects that intend to be a platform for continuing services will be expected to demonstrate sustainability. ACT would be concerned to be a sole funder of projects that require ongoing support.

WHAT IS NOT FUNDED The foundation will not make grants: to replace statutory funding; to pay for work that has already commenced or equipment already purchased or on order; towards the operating costs of other charities except in connection with setting up new services; to charities that have not been registered for at least three years; for projects which promote a particular religion or faith; to community centres and youth clubs except where those served are in special need of help (e.g. older people or persons with special needs); to Local Authorities; to umbrella or grant-making organisations except where they undertake special assessments not readily available from the foundation's own resources; to universities and colleges, and grant-maintained, private or local education authority schools or their parent-teacher associations, except if those schools are for students with special needs; for costs associated with political or publicity campaigns.

SAMPLE GRANTS Hollybank Trust (£50,000); Dame Hannah Rogers Trust (£30,000); Elizabeth Fitzroy Support (£25,000); Treloar Trust (£14,000); Corbet Tey School, Federation of London Youth Clubs, Kent Kids Miles of Smiles and Royal Hospital for Neuro Disability (£10,000 each); Cedar Foundation, Hampshire Autistic Society and Royal Blind Society; and Community Link Up (£2,500).

FINANCES *Year* 2007–08 *Income* £16,362,979 *Grants* £861,000 *Assets* £58,723,661

TRUSTEES Paul Nield; John J O'Sullivan; Michael Street; David Hyde; Robert F White; Denis Taylor.

OTHER INFORMATION Grant total includes: £445,000 to 386 individuals; £415,000 to 74 organisations.

HOW TO APPLY 'Application by registered charities and overseas charitable organisations has to be by way of letter on the organisation's headed paper and should: give a brief description of your organisation including any statutory or voluntary registration; provide a summary of the work you plan to undertake with the grant, together with a cost breakdown, plans and/or specification if available and a summary of the key milestones for the work; provide information on why you need to do this work and what would happen if you were unable to do it; give details of any other UK-based support received or pledged for your project; specify what you expect the results of the work to be and the number of beneficiaries helped; tell us how you plan to evaluate whether the work achieved its goals; tell us if the work will require capital and/or ongoing operational funding and if so how you plan to meet these costs. In addition you need to attach the following financial information to the letter: a cashflow projection of income and expenditure budget for the work; details of any income already raised for the work and income outstanding and where you plan to raise it from; your latest annual report and accounts. You can apply for a grant at any time. Trustees meet four times a year, but you do not need to time your application to coincide with these meetings. Procedures exist to give approvals between meeting dates, where necessary. We do not publish the dates of Trustees' meetings. We will send you an acknowledgement letter within one week of receiving your application. If your proposal is either in an unacceptable form, or ineligible, or a low priority, we will tell you in this letter. We will assess all acceptable applications and we may contact you for further information and/or make a personal visit. In the case of charitable bodies we may also ask for a presentation. We aim to make decisions on grants of up to £50,000 within one month of receiving your application. Decisions on grants over £50,000 can take up to three months. If the application is for an emergency you may request a faster timescale and we will do our best to assist.'

WHO TO APPLY TO Maralyn Gill, Grants Coordinator, The Gate House, 2 Park Street, Windsor, Berkshire SL4 1LU *Tel* 01753 753900 *Fax* 01753 753901 *email* info@ theactfoundation.co.uk *Website* www. theactfoundation.co.uk

CC NO 1068617   **ESTABLISHED** 1998

....
■ Action Medical Research

WHERE FUNDING CAN BE GIVEN UK.

WHO CAN BENEFIT University departments, hospitals and research institutes for specific research projects.

WHAT IS FUNDED Child health, including problems affecting pregnancy, childbirth, babies, children and young people. 'We support a broad spectrum of research with the objective of: preventing disease and disability; and alleviating physical disability. Please note that our emphasis is on clinical research or research at the interface between clinical and basic science. We pride ourselves that our research is both innovative and of a high standard as judged by rigorous peer review. Within the above criteria, we also support research and development of equipment and techniques to improve diagnosis, therapy and assistive technology (including orthoses, prostheses and aids to daily living) and we encourage applications in the field of medical engineering.'

WHAT IS NOT FUNDED The charity does not provide: grants towards service provision or audit studies; grants purely for higher education, e.g. BSc/MSc/PhD course fees and subsistence costs; grants for medical or dental electives; grants specifically for PhD studentships (although researchers may independently register for a higher degree); grants for work undertaken outside the UK; any indirect costs such as administrative or other overheads imposed by the university or other institution; costs associated with advertising and recruitment; 'top up' funding for work supported by other funding bodies; costs to attend conferences and meetings (current Action Medical Research grantholders may apply separately); grants to MRC Units, other than RTF awards where the training/facilities cannot be offered elsewhere; grants to other charities; grants for research into complementary/ alternative medicine.

TYPE OF GRANT Research comprising: project grants and Research Training Fellowship scheme.

RANGE OF GRANTS The average award is about £80,000. It is unusual to fund projects over £150,000 in their entirety.

FINANCES *Year* 2008 *Income* £6,600,000 *Grants* £3,500,000 *Assets* £5,400,000

TRUSTEES Ms Valerie Hammond; Mrs Karen Jankel; Charles Jackson; Diana Marsland; Prof. Andrew George; Richard Price; Ann Paul; Sir John Wickerson; David Gibbs; Mark Gardiner; Colin Hunsley.

PUBLICATIONS Newsletter; medical conditions leaflets.

HOW TO APPLY '**Outline proposal:** all applicants should complete a two page outline proposal form [available from the charity's website] summarising the research and giving an estimation of costs, and email it to the Research Department. The details on the outline form should include the potential clinical application of the work, how it fits the remit of the charity and a description of the work proposed. The purpose of the outline proposal is to establish that your proposed work clearly falls within the charity's remit and priorities. If your work is considered peripheral to our aims, or clearly falls within the remit of another funding organisation, and in cases where demand on our funds is high, we may be unable to pursue an application from you. **Full application:** if the outline proposal is acceptable, you will be invited to complete a full application form online and you will be advised of the timetable. Applications are assessed by peer review, first by independent external referees and then by our scientific advisory panel. The decision to approve a grant is made by the council on the recommendations of the panel. Closing dates for proposals and applications are available on the charity's website.'

WHO TO APPLY TO The Research Department, Vincent House, North Parade, Horsham, West Sussex RH12 2DP *Tel* 01403 210406 *Fax* 01403 210541 *email* research@action.org.uk *Website* www.action.org.uk

CC NO 208701   **ESTABLISHED** 1952

....
■ The Company of Actuaries' Charitable Trust Fund

WHERE FUNDING CAN BE GIVEN UK and overseas, with a preference for the City of London.

WHO CAN BENEFIT Charitable organisations and individuals involved in, or training for, a career in actuary.

WHAT IS FUNDED Support for older or disabled people; charities helping children and young people; those involved in treating medical conditions or funding medical research; other worthy charities, such as those working with people who are in need.

WHAT IS NOT FUNDED No grants for the propagation of religious or political beliefs, the maintenance of historic buildings or for conservation. The trustees do not usually support an organisation which has received a grant in the previous 24 months.

RANGE OF GRANTS £500–£2,000, with larger amounts given where liverymen have a significant connection.

SAMPLE GRANTS North London Hospice (£4,500); Children's Liver Foundation (£4,000); St Catherine's Hospice (£3,000); Edmonton Sea Cadets (£2,000); Chiltern MS (£1,500); Cerebral Palsy Sport (£1,400); and British Stammering Association, Care for Carers, Changing Faces, Disabled Holiday Information, National Deaf Children's Society, Space, Trafford Multiple Sclerosis Therapy Centre and Volunteer Link Scheme (£1,000).

FINANCES *Year* 2007–08 *Income* £120,518 *Grants* £94,137 *Assets* £270,182

TRUSTEES J A Jolliffe; Nick Dumbreck; Jeff Medlock; F J Morrison; Michael Turner.

HOW TO APPLY On a form which can be downloaded from the fund's website. Further information about the Trust can be obtained from the correspondent.

WHO TO APPLY TO Lyndon Jones, Honorary Almoner, 55 Station Road, Beaconsfield, Bucks HP9 1QL *email* charity@companyofactuaries.co.uk *Website* www.actuariescompany.co.uk

CC NO 280702   **ESTABLISHED** 1980

■ The Sylvia Adams Charitable Trust

WHERE FUNDING CAN BE GIVEN UK with a preference for Hertfordshire and its immediate area; national projects that have a national benefit; the developing world.

WHO CAN BENEFIT All grants are made through UK registered charities. About 50% of the trust's grant total is given to UK causes, with the remaining 50% going to causes in the developing world.

WHAT IS FUNDED Projects benefiting people with disabilities, people living in poverty, children and young people. It is particularly interested in helping people to become self-supporting and self-help projects. UK focus is on enabling people to participate fully in society. Worldwide, the focus is on primary healthcare and health education, access to education, appropriate technology and community enterprise schemes. Geographical areas of interest are: the developing world; national projects that have a national benefit and local projects in Hertfordshire and its immediate area.

WHAT IS NOT FUNDED The trust does not give grants to: individuals; projects in the Middle East or Eastern Europe or the countries of the ex-Soviet Union; work that solely benefits older people; or organisations helping animals, medical research or environmental causes.

TYPE OF GRANT One off, recurring and three to five year partnerships.

RANGE OF GRANTS £5,000–£25,000.

SAMPLE GRANTS UK charities: NCVO, Shelter and ERIC (£25,000 each); Treehouse (£20,000); TB Alert (£15,000); Get Connected and Youth Sports Trust (£10,000 each); Spinal Injuries Association (£7,600); Ehlers Danolos Support Group and Friends of St Lukes – Redbourne (£1,000 each); and Youth Create (£500). Charities operating overseas: Esther Benjamin Trust (£65,000); Camfed (£25,000); Farm Africa (£20,000); Solar Aid (£15,000); and Pattaya (£10,000). The trust is also currently in partnership with: Basic Needs; NCVO; Sense International; VSO and Shelter. Two 'trustee grants' of £10,000 each were also made during the year to the Children's Trust and Trade Aid.

FINANCES *Year* 2007–08 *Income* £474,071 *Grants* £495,956 *Assets* £12,242,475

TRUSTEES R J Golland; M Heasman; T Lawler.

OTHER INFORMATION The stated grant total includes £265,000 given to overseas organisations.

HOW TO APPLY *Please note: at the time of writing, the trust stated that it would not be considering any more funding enquiries or applications until 1st March 2010 due to an unforeseen change to the staff team.*
Full guidelines for applicants are available from the trust and through its website; applications can also be made online (when the application window has reopened).

WHO TO APPLY TO Kate Baldwin, Director, Sylvia Adams House, 24 The Common, Hatfield, Hertfordshire AL10 0NB *Tel* 01707 259259 *Fax* 01707 259268 *email* info@sylvia-adams. org.uk *Website* www.sylvia-adams.org.uk

CC NO 1050678   **ESTABLISHED** 1995

■ The Adamson Trust

WHERE FUNDING CAN BE GIVEN UK, but preference will be given to requests on behalf of Scottish children.

WHO CAN BENEFIT Physically or mentally disabled children aged 16 or under, both groups and individuals.

WHAT IS FUNDED Assistance with holidays for children with a physical or mental disability. Grants may be given to the parent(s) of children or as block grants; for example, to the special needs unit of a school.

TYPE OF GRANT Usually one-off.

SAMPLE GRANTS Previous beneficiaries have included Barnardo's Dundee Family Support Team, Children's Hospice Association Scotland, Lady Hoare Trust for Physically Disabled Children, Hopscotch Holidays, Over the Wall Gang Group, Peak Holidays, React, Scotland Yard Adventure Centre, Sense Scotland, Special Needs Adventure Play Ground and Scottish Spina Bifida Association.

FINANCES *Year* 2007–08 *Income* £75,061

TRUSTEES R C Farrell; J W H Allen; Dr H Kirkwood; Dr M MacDonald Simpson; Mrs A Cowan.

HOW TO APPLY On a form available from the correspondent. A copy of the latest audited accounts should be included together with details of the organisation, the number of children who would benefit and the proposed holiday. Applications are considered in February, May, August and November.

WHO TO APPLY TO Edward Elworthy, Secretary, PO Box 26334, Crieff PH7 9AB *email* edward@ elworthy.net

SC NO SC016517   **ESTABLISHED** 1946

■ The Victor Adda Foundation

WHERE FUNDING CAN BE GIVEN UK, but in practice Greenwich.

WHO CAN BENEFIT Charitable organisations.

WHAT IS FUNDED This trust mainly supports the Fan Museum in Greenwich.

SAMPLE GRANTS Fan Museum Trust (£42,000).

FINANCES *Year* 2007–08 *Income* £39,805 *Grants* £42,000 *Assets* £1,300,459

TRUSTEES Helene Alexander; Roy Gluckstein; Ann Mosseri.

HOW TO APPLY In writing to the correspondent. Only successful applications are notified of a decision.

WHO TO APPLY TO The Trustees, c/o Kleinwort Benson Trustees, PO Box 57005, 30 Gresham Street, London EC2V 7PG

CC NO 291456   **ESTABLISHED** 1984

■ Adenfirst Ltd

WHERE FUNDING CAN BE GIVEN Worldwide.

WHO CAN BENEFIT Jewish organisations only.

WHAT IS FUNDED Jewish causes related to education, medical care, relief of poverty and the advancement of religion.

RANGE OF GRANTS Up to £20,000.

SAMPLE GRANTS Chevras Mo'os Ladol and Beis Aaron Trust (£20,000 each); Beis Rochel D'Satmar, Beis Yaakov Institutions, Friends of Harim Establishments, Telz Talmudical Academy Trust, Torah Vechesed Ezra L'Do, Gevuros Ari Torah Academy Trust and Yeshivat Kollel Breslov (£10,000 each); and Yeshivah Lev Simcha (£5,000).

FINANCES *Year* 2007 *Income* £191,969 *Grants* £123,320

TRUSTEES Mrs H F Bondi; I M Cymerman; Mrs R Cymerman.
HOW TO APPLY In writing to the correspondent.
WHO TO APPLY TO I M Cymerman, Governor, 479 Holloway Road, London N7 6LE
CC NO 291647   **ESTABLISHED** 1984

··

■ The Adint Charitable Trust

WHERE FUNDING CAN BE GIVEN Worldwide, in practice UK.
WHO CAN BENEFIT Registered charities.
WHAT IS FUNDED Health and social welfare.
WHAT IS NOT FUNDED Individuals are not supported.
TYPE OF GRANT One-off grants and recurrent grants for more than three years are considered, for capital costs (including buildings) and core costs.
RANGE OF GRANTS £50–£15,000. Grants are usually for £10,000 and £5,000.
FINANCES *Year* 2007–08 *Income* £383,363 *Grants* £305,000 *Assets* £6,337,006
TRUSTEES Anthony J Edwards; Mrs Margaret Edwards; Douglas R Oram; Brian Pate.
HOW TO APPLY To the correspondent, in writing only. There is no particular form in which applications are required; each applicant should make its own case in the way it considers best. The trust notes that it cannot enter into correspondence and unsuccessful applicants will not be notified.
WHO TO APPLY TO Douglas R Oram, Trustee, Suite 42, 571 Finchley Road, London NW3 7BN
CC NO 265290   **ESTABLISHED** 1973

··

■ The Adnams Charity

WHERE FUNDING CAN BE GIVEN Within a 25-mile radius of St Edmund's Church, Southwold.
WHO CAN BENEFIT Small local projects.
WHAT IS FUNDED General charitable purposes. The charity gives support to a wide variety of organisations including those involved with social welfare, education, recreation, the arts and historic buildings.
WHAT IS NOT FUNDED No grants are made to individuals, nor does it provide sponsorship of any kind. The charity does not normally make grants to religious organisations or private clubs unless these can demonstrate that the purpose of the grant is for something of clear public benefit, accessible to all. The charity does not provide raffle prizes.
TYPE OF GRANT The trustees prefer applications for specific items. Grants are generally of a one-off nature. The trustees are reluctant to give grants to cover ongoing running costs, although in very exceptional circumstances they may do so.
RANGE OF GRANTS £50–£5,000.
SAMPLE GRANTS NORCAS (£2,700); Waveney Crossroads Ltd (£2,300); Breakout (£2,200); Ipswich and East Suffolk Headway, More Fun and the Suffolk Foundation (£2,000 each); the Country Trust and TUTTI (£1,600 each); Cut Dance (£1,100); Bredfield Youth Club, Great Yarmouth Community Trust for Ageless Opportunities, Ilketshall St Andrew's Church and the Poetry Trust (£1,000 each); the Warden's Trust (£940); Wrentham Village Hall (£750); Lowestoft Shopmobility (£730); Greenfingers (£650); the May Centre (£500); and Waveney Sinfonia (£300).
FINANCES *Year* 2007–08 *Income* £91,828 *Grants* £67,623
TRUSTEES Jonathan Adnams, Chair; Rob Chase; Guy Heald; Emma Hibbert; Melvyn Horn; Sadie Lofthouse; Simon Loftus; Andy Wood.

HOW TO APPLY In writing to the correspondent. Applicants are asked to provide information on: the aims and objectives of the organisation requiring a grant; what the grant is for; who will benefit and how; how much the item(s) will cost; other fundraising activities being undertaken and amount raised so far; to whom cheques should be made payable in the event of a grant being made. Where possible the most recent set of audited accounts should be enclosed with the application. If applying from a registered charity, a copy of the organisation's reserves policy should be included. Trustees meet quarterly (usually January, April, July and October).
WHO TO APPLY TO Rebecca Abrahall, The Charity Administrator, Sole Bay Brewery, Southwold, Suffolk IP18 6JW *Tel* 01502 727200 *Fax* 01502 727267 *email* charity@adnams.co.uk
CC NO 1000203   **ESTABLISHED** 1990

··

■ AF Trust Company

WHERE FUNDING CAN BE GIVEN England.
WHO CAN BENEFIT Higher education institutions.
WHAT IS FUNDED Charitable purposes connected with the provision of higher education.
WHAT IS NOT FUNDED No grants to individuals.
SAMPLE GRANTS University of Nottingham (£21,000); Imperial College (£17,000); University of Reading (£14,000); University of Southampton (£13,000); University of Canterbury Christ Church (£8,000); University of Surrey (£6,500); Royal Holloway (£3,500); University of Kent (£3,500); and University of Exeter Foundation (£2,000).
FINANCES *Year* 2007–08 *Income* £4,491,630 *Grants* £99,600 *Assets* £228,316
TRUSTEES Martin Wynne-Jones; David Charles Savage; Jeremy Lindley; Andrew Murphy; David Leah; Jean Strudley.
OTHER INFORMATION The income figure of £4,491,630 also relates to funds used to lease buildings from educational establishments and then enter into lease-back arrangements rather than indicating the size of funds available.
HOW TO APPLY In writing to the correspondent. However, unsolicited applications are only accepted from higher education institutions within England.
WHO TO APPLY TO P D Welch, Secretary, 34 Chapel Street, Thatcham, Berkshire RG18 4QL
CC NO 1060319   **ESTABLISHED** 1996

··

■ Age Concern Scotland Grants

WHERE FUNDING CAN BE GIVEN Scotland.
WHO CAN BENEFIT Age Concern member groups.
WHAT IS FUNDED Projects for older people.
WHAT IS NOT FUNDED No grants to statutory authorities, commercial organisations and individuals. No grants are awarded for minibuses, holidays/outings, dinners/parties, running costs, major building costs and general appeals.
FINANCES *Year* 2008 *Grants* £25,000
TRUSTEES Members of Age Concern Scotland's Assembly.
HOW TO APPLY An application form and further details are available from the correspondent. Applications are considered every two months, except for the special assistance grants to Age Concern member organisations which are given in February.

WHO TO APPLY TO The Membership Resource Officer, Causewayside House, 160 Causewayside, Edinburgh EH9 1PR *Tel* 0845 833 0200 *Website* www.ageconcernsscotland.org.uk
SC NO SC010100

■ Aid to the Church in Need (UK)

WHERE FUNDING CAN BE GIVEN Eastern Europe, Africa, Russia, Asia and South America.
WHO CAN BENEFIT Persecuted and suffering Christians, especially Roman Catholics, Russian Orthodox and refugees.
WHAT IS FUNDED Religion and pastoral projects.
TYPE OF GRANT Buildings, capital, core costs, endowment, one-off, project, running costs, salaries and start-up costs.
FINANCES *Year* 2008 *Income* £6,614,746 *Grants* £4,232,173 *Assets* £1,877,526
TRUSTEES Peter Sefton-Williams, Chair; Joanna Bogle; Fr Ronald Creighton-Jobe; Philipp Habsburg-Lothringen; Graham Hutton; Piers Paul Read; Lisa Sanchez-Corea Simpson; Julian Chadwick.
OTHER INFORMATION Please note: the focus of this charity is the church overseas and that individuals without the backing as required may not apply for funding.
HOW TO APPLY All applications by individuals must have the backing of a Catholic Bishop or religious superior.
WHO TO APPLY TO Neville Kyrke-Smith, National Director, 12–14 Benhill Avenue, Sutton SM1 4DA *Tel* 020 8642 8668 *email* acn@acnuk.org *Website* www.acnuk.org
CC NO 1097984   **ESTABLISHED** 1947

■ The AIM Foundation

WHERE FUNDING CAN BE GIVEN Worldwide, in practice UK.
WHO CAN BENEFIT Charitable organisations.
WHAT IS FUNDED Healthcare, community development, young people, environmental matters and other charitable activities particularly related to influencing long-term social change.
WHAT IS NOT FUNDED No grants to individuals.
RANGE OF GRANTS Up to £50,000.
SAMPLE GRANTS New Economics Foundation (£65,000); Essex Community Foundation and Devon Community Foundation (£50,000 each); Antidote (£30,000); Friends of the Earth (£15,000); Soil Association and Penny Brohn Cancer Care (£10,000 each); Clare College Cambridge (£5,000).
FINANCES *Year* 2007–08 *Income* £1,111,042 *Grants* £577,275 *Assets* £9,644,419
TRUSTEES Ian Roy Marks; Mrs Angela D Marks; Nicolas Marks; Joanna Pritchard-Barrett; Caroline Marks; Phillipa Bailey.
HOW TO APPLY It cannot be stressed enough that this foundation 'is proactive in its approach' and does not wish to receive applications. Unsolicited requests for assistance will not be responded to under any circumstance.
WHO TO APPLY TO Miss Louisa Tippett, Whittle and Co, 15 High Street, West Mersea, Colchester, Essex CO5 8QA *Tel* 01206 385049 *email* louisa@whittles.co.uk
CC NO 263294   **ESTABLISHED** 1971

■ The Green and Lilian F M Ainsworth and Family Benevolent Fund

WHERE FUNDING CAN BE GIVEN UK, with some preference for Northwest England.
WHO CAN BENEFIT Charities benefiting young people, older people and people with disabilities.
WHAT IS FUNDED The trustees have a comprehensive list of national charities from which they select each year, requesting the money is spent in the North West. Smaller grants are given to local charities.
WHAT IS NOT FUNDED No grants to individuals or non-registered charities.
TYPE OF GRANT Prefers specific projects.
RANGE OF GRANTS Up to £1,000.
SAMPLE GRANTS Dogs for the Disabled (£1,000); the John Holt Cancer Foundation (£800); Edale Mountain Rescue (£750); Butterflies Children's Charity, Chopsticks, Community of the Holy Fire, Everyman Support Group, Groundwork Solent, Independent Age, the Joshua Foundation, the Macular Disease Society and Off the Fence (£500 each);.
FINANCES *Year* 2007–08 *Income* £26,344 *Grants* £19,000
TRUSTEES The Royal Bank of Scotland plc.
HOW TO APPLY In writing to the trustees, there is no application form.
WHO TO APPLY TO The Trust Section Manager, RBS Trust Services, Eden, Lakeside, Chester Business Park, Wrexham Road, Chester CH4 9QT
CC NO 267577   **ESTABLISHED** 1974

■ The Sylvia Aitken Charitable Trust

WHERE FUNDING CAN BE GIVEN UK, with a preference for Scotland.
WHO CAN BENEFIT Registered medical research and welfare charities, and any small local groups – particularly in Scotland.
WHAT IS FUNDED General charitable purposes, with a preference for medical and welfare organisations.
WHAT IS NOT FUNDED No grants to individuals: the trust can only support UK registered charities.
SAMPLE GRANTS Previous beneficiaries have included Association for International Cancer Research, Barn Owl Trust, British Lung Foundation, British Stammering Association, the Roy Castle Lung Cancer Foundation, Disabled Living Foundation, Epilepsy Research Trust, Friends of the Lake District, Motor Neurone Disease Association, Network for Surviving Stalking, Royal Scots Dragoon Guards Museum Trust, Sense Scotland, Scottish Child Psychotherapy Trust, Tall Ships Youth Trust, Tenovus Scotland, Wood Green Animal Shelters and Young Minds.
FINANCES *Year* 2007–08 *Income* £283,970
TRUSTEES Mrs S M Aitken; Mrs M Harkis; J Ferguson.
HOW TO APPLY In writing to the correspondent. Applicants should outline the charity's objectives and current projects for which funding may be required. The trustees meet at least twice a year, usually in March/April and September/October.
WHO TO APPLY TO The Administrator, Fergusons Chartered Accountants, 24 Woodside, Houston, Renfrewshire PA6 7DD
SC NO SC010556   **ESTABLISHED** 1985

■ The Ajahma Charitable Trust

WHERE FUNDING CAN BE GIVEN UK and overseas.
WHO CAN BENEFIT Registered charities.
WHAT IS FUNDED Development, health, disability, poverty, women's issues, family planning, human rights and social need.
WHAT IS NOT FUNDED Large organisations with a turnover above £4 million will not normally be considered, nor will applications with any sort of religious bias or those which support animal rights/welfare, arts, medical research, buildings, equipment, local groups or overseas projects where the charity income is less than £500,000 a year. Applications for grants or sponsorship for individuals will not be supported.
TYPE OF GRANT Core and running costs, projects and salaries. Funding is available for up to three years.
SAMPLE GRANTS CAMFED, Global Witness, Merlin and WOMANKIND Worldwide (£50,000 each); Headway groups (£42,000 in 11 grants); Fawcett Society (£7,000); and Project HOPE UK and Refugee Council (£5,000 each).
FINANCES *Year* 2007–08 *Income* £127,347 *Grants* £282,750 *Assets* £2,968,521
TRUSTEES Jennifer Sheridan; Elizabeth Simpson; James Sinclair Taylor.
HOW TO APPLY The trust have reviewed their grant-making criteria and will now pro-actively seek and select organisations to which they wish to award grants. They will no longer consider unsolicited applications.
WHO TO APPLY TO Suzanne Hunt, Administrator, 275 Dover House Road, London SW15 5BP
CC NO 273823 **ESTABLISHED** 1977

■ The Alabaster Trust

WHERE FUNDING CAN BE GIVEN UK and overseas.
WHO CAN BENEFIT Organisations benefiting evangelical Christian organisations.
WHAT IS FUNDED General charitable purposes, particularly the advancement of the Christian faith.
WHAT IS NOT FUNDED No grants to individuals.
FINANCES *Year* 2007–08 *Income* £37,187 *Grants* £57,377
TRUSTEES G A Kendrick; Mrs J Kendrick; Mrs A Sheldrake.
HOW TO APPLY In writing to the correspondent. The trustees meet to consider grants quarterly, in March, June, September and December.
WHO TO APPLY TO J R Caladine, 1 The Avenue, Eastbourne, East Sussex BN21 3YA *Tel* 01323 644579 *email* john@caladine.co.uk
CC NO 1050568 **ESTABLISHED** 1995

■ Alba Charitable Trust

WHERE FUNDING CAN BE GIVEN UK and overseas.
WHO CAN BENEFIT Educational institutions.
WHAT IS FUNDED Predominantly Jewish organisations.
SAMPLE GRANTS Lolev Charitable Trust (£33,000); Chasdey Kohn (£11,000); Inspirations (£6,000); Edu Poor and Friends of Yeshiva Was Sholem Shotz (£5,000 each); Hadras Kodesh Trust (£3,000); HAYC (£2,900); IJDS (£2,200); Ner Yisroel (£1,500); and Gateshead Beis Hatalmud Scholarship Fund (£1,000).
FINANCES *Year* 2006–07 *Income* £84,540 *Grants* £71,443 *Assets* £260,830
TRUSTEES L Glatt, Chair; Mrs R Glatt; Mrs D Kestel.
HOW TO APPLY In writing to the correspondent.

WHO TO APPLY TO Leslie Glatt, Trustee, 3 Goodyers Gardens, London NW4 2HD *Tel* 020 7434 3494
CC NO 276391 **ESTABLISHED** 1978

■ The Alborada Trust

WHERE FUNDING CAN BE GIVEN Worldwide.
WHO CAN BENEFIT Charitable organisations.
WHAT IS FUNDED Veterinary causes in the United Kingdom and Ireland with activities primarily devoted to the welfare of animals and/or in their associated research. Projects throughout the world associated with the relief of poverty, human suffering, sickness or ill health.
SAMPLE GRANTS Animal Health Trust (£100,000); Médecins Sans Frontières (£70,000); Royal Veterinary College Animal Care Trust (£50,000); the Brooke Hospital (£30,000); Greenwich Hospital Foundation and Wildlife Vets International (£22,000); British Racing School, International League for Protection of Horses and Racing Welfare (£20,000 each); and Blue Cross and Injured Jockeys Fund (£10,000 each).
FINANCES *Year* 2007–08 *Income* £5,219,690 *Grants* £374,373 *Assets* £10,331,336
TRUSTEES Miss K E Rausing; D J Way; R Lerner; Capt. J Nicholson.
HOW TO APPLY Funds are fully committed. The trust does not accept unsolicited applications.
WHO TO APPLY TO The Trustees, Fladgate Fielder, 25 North Row, London W1K 6DJ
CC NO 1091660 **ESTABLISHED** 2001

■ D G Albright Charitable Trust

WHERE FUNDING CAN BE GIVEN UK, with a preference for Gloucestershire.
WHO CAN BENEFIT Registered charities.
WHAT IS FUNDED General charitable purposes.
WHAT IS NOT FUNDED Grants are not usually made to individuals.
TYPE OF GRANT One-off and recurrent.
RANGE OF GRANTS £500–£6,000.
SAMPLE GRANTS St Mary's School – Bromesberrow (£6,000); Maggie's Centres (£5,000); Bromesberrow Parochial Church Council (£2,500); and British Empire and Commonwealth Museum, the Countryside Foundation for Education, the Family Haven – Gloucester, Game Conservancy Trust, Gloucester Family Support, Gloucestershire Macmillan Cancer Service, SSAFA Gloucester Branch and St. Luke's Hospital for the Clergy (£2,000 each).
FINANCES *Year* 2007–08 *Income* £39,770 *Grants* £44,050 *Assets* £1,108,370
TRUSTEES Hon. Dr G Greenall; R G Wood.
HOW TO APPLY In writing to the correspondent.
WHO TO APPLY TO Richard G Wood, Trustee, Old Church School, Hollow Street, Great Somerford, Chippenham, Wiltshire SN15 5JD
CC NO 277367 **ESTABLISHED** 1978

■ The Alchemy Foundation

WHERE FUNDING CAN BE GIVEN UK and overseas.
WHO CAN BENEFIT Community projects, voluntary organisations and registered charities.
WHAT IS FUNDED 'The charity's objects are particularly focused on The Orpheus Centre, water projects in the developing world, disability (particularly mobility, access, helplines and communications), social welfare (inner city

community projects, disaffected youth, family mediation, homelessness), personal reform, penal reform (work with prisoners, especially young prisoners, and their families), medical research and aid (especially in areas of blindness and disfigurement), individual enterprise (by helping Raleigh International and similar organisations to give opportunities to young people according to need) and respite for carers.'

TYPE OF GRANT Capital; revenue; one-off; salaries.

FINANCES *Year* 2007–08 *Income* £305,064 *Grants* £298,844 *Assets* £2,573,500

TRUSTEES Alex Armitage; Tony Elias; Andrew Murison; Esther Rantzen; Annabel Stilgoe; Holly Stilgoe; Jack E Z Stilgoe; Dr Jemima Stilgoe; Joseph Stilgoe; Richard Stilgoe; Rufus Stilgoe.

HOW TO APPLY In writing to the correspondent.

WHO TO APPLY TO Annabel Stilgoe, Trustee, Trevereux Manor, Limpsfield Chart, Oxted, Surrey RH8 0TL

CC NO 292500   **ESTABLISHED** 1985

....

■ Alcohol Education and Research Council

WHERE FUNDING CAN BE GIVEN UK.

WHO CAN BENEFIT Universities and academic research institutions, educational organisations and students.

WHAT IS FUNDED Educational and research projects concerning alcohol misuse. The council's main aims are to: (i) Generate and disseminate research based evidence to inform and influence policy and practice. (ii) Develop the capacity of people and organisations to address alcohol issues.

TYPE OF GRANT Four types of grant are awarded: research grants; development grants; small grants; studentship grants.

FINANCES *Year* 2007–08 *Income* £741,582 *Grants* £421,404 *Assets* £11,727,103

TRUSTEES Prof. Robin Davidson, Chair; Rhoda Emlyn-Jones; Ian Ford; Dr Pui-Ling Li; Prof. Virginia Berridge; Joyce Craig; Prof. Christopher Day; Prof. David Foxcroft; Prof. Ian Gilmore; Prof. Gerard Hastings; Prof. Richard Hobbs; Prof. Eileen Kaner; Mrs Lesley King Lewis; Drew Munro.

HOW TO APPLY Application forms and full guidelines can be found on the council's website.

WHO TO APPLY TO Andrea Tilouche, Committees and Grants Manager, Queen Anne Business Centre, 28 Broadway, London SW1H 9JX *Website* www. aerc.org.uk

CC NO 284748   **ESTABLISHED** 1981

....

■ Aldgate and All Hallows' Barking Exhibition Foundation

WHERE FUNDING CAN BE GIVEN City of London and the London borough of Tower Hamlets.

WHO CAN BENEFIT Children or young people under the age of 25.

WHAT IS FUNDED The foundation is particularly keen to encourage and support: (i) projects initiated by schools that enhance the National Curriculum; (ii) projects aimed at improving literacy and numeracy; (iii) projects aimed at promoting the study of science, mathematics and the arts. Priority will be given to projects that are not yet part of a school's or organisation's regular activities; to developments that are strategic, such as practical initiatives seeking to address the root

causes of problems, and those that have the potential to influence policy and practice more widely. The foundation may also from time to time initiate new projects that do not fall into the priority areas for grant making to enable governors to explore ground-breaking or emergent fields of educational practice.

WHAT IS NOT FUNDED Please note that the foundation does not give grants for: equipment or teachers' salaries that are the responsibility of education authorities; youth groups or community projects; supplementary schools or mother tongue teaching; the purchase, repair or furnishing of buildings; conferences or seminars; university or medical research; trips abroad; stage, film, publication or video production costs; performances, exhibitions or festivals; retrospective requests (i.e. any activity that has already taken place); requests to substitute for the withdrawal or reduction of statutory funding; general fund-raising campaigns or appeals.

FINANCES *Year* 2008 *Income* £79,252 *Grants* £273,600 *Assets* £5,133,579

TRUSTEES J Hall; H W Whitbread; G Forbes; W J Hamilton-Hinds; R Hazlewood; Cllr S Islam; P James; Mrs D Jones; Mrs S Knowles; Mrs M Kellett; D Mash; D J Ross; K Everett; Revd B. Olivier; Revd Laura Burgess.

OTHER INFORMATION The 2008 grant total included £27,500 given in grants to individuals.

HOW TO APPLY Initial enquiries should be sent to the foundation. These must include the following information: (i) Information about your school or organisation; including an outline of its current activities, its legal status, aims, brief history, details of staffing levels, management structure and composition of the management committee. (ii) An outline description of, and timetable for, the project for which funding is being sought, including information about who will be involved in and/or benefit from the project. (iii) Details of the aims and outcomes for the project, including information about how you will monitor and evaluate the project. (iv) A detailed budget for the project. (v) Information about any other sources of income and partnership funding for the project.

WHO TO APPLY TO Richard Foley, Clerk to the Governors, 31 Jewry Street, London EC3N 2EY *Tel* 020 7488 2518 *Fax* 020 7488 2519 *email* aldgateandallhallows@sirjohncass.org *Website* www.aldgateallhallows.org.uk

CC NO 312500   **ESTABLISHED** 1893

....

■ The Aldgate Freedom Foundation

WHERE FUNDING CAN BE GIVEN Freedom part of the parish of St Botolph-without-Aldgate.

WHO CAN BENEFIT Organisations benefiting older people and people who are homeless or otherwise in need.

WHAT IS FUNDED Hospitals and voluntary organisations.

FINANCES *Year* 2007 *Income* £38,320 *Grants* £20,300 *Assets* £1,499,717

TRUSTEES Revd B J Lee, Chair; W H Dove; Ms M Everingham; R Stephenson; Ms M Peirce; S Borton; P Bignell.

HOW TO APPLY In writing to the correspondent.

WHO TO APPLY TO M Pierce, Clerk to the Trustees, St Botolph's Church, St Botolph-without-Aldgate, Aldgate, London EC3N 1AB

CC NO 207046   **ESTABLISHED** 1962

■ Alexandra Rose Charities

WHERE FUNDING CAN BE GIVEN England and Wales.

WHO CAN BENEFIT UK registered charities that are involved in caring for people.

WHAT IS FUNDED Grants to registered charities only, who take part in the Alexandra Rose Day collections.

TYPE OF GRANT For Flag Days, this charity makes the arrangements and supplies equipment whilst the partner charity provides the flag sellers. Alexandra Rose Day makes an immediate grant to the partner equivalent to 90% of its gross collection. For raffles, Alexandra Rose Day organises the prizes and prints the tickets, which the partner charity sells and receives 80% of all gross sales. The charity organises its own fundraising events including the Rose Ball and donates any surplus through its Special Appeal Fund, an annual programme of grants designed to bring immediate, practical benefits to people-caring charities and voluntary groups.

SAMPLE GRANTS Manor Farm Boys' Club (£4,200); League of Friends of Rutland Hospitals (£3,100); Sequal Trust (£3,000); Supporters of the Disabled at Yateley (£1,900); Personal Support Unit (£1,800); RAFA Surrey Region (£1,700); Winchmore Hill Community Care (£1,300); Estuary League of Friends and Woodside Bereavement Service (£1,200 each); Headwayhouse Manchester and SSAFA Forces – Waveney (£1,100 each); and Ledbury Evergreen Club (£1,000).

FINANCES *Year* 2008 *Income* £262,000 *Grants* £130,000 *Assets* £648,000

TRUSTEES Rt Hon. Lord Wakeham; Andrew Mitchell; March Hancock; Lady Grade; Rt Hon. the Lord Mayor of London (ex-officio); Ms Angela Anderson; Mrs Caroline Clark; March Hancock; Stephen King; Lady Falconer of Thoroton; Mrs Kathryn Langridge; Roger Lomax; Mike Morris; Sir Ian Rankin; Raymond Salisbury-Jones; Lord St John of Bletso; Dominic Tayler; Mrs Sophia Tayler.

HOW TO APPLY Only charities participating in Flag Days or raffles are eligible to apply.

WHO TO APPLY TO The National Director, 5 Mead Lane, Farmhan, Surrey GU9 7DY *Tel* 01252 726171 *email* enquiries@alexandrarose.org.uk *Website* www.alexandrarosecharities.org.uk

CC NO 211535   **ESTABLISHED** 1912

■ The Alexis Trust

WHERE FUNDING CAN BE GIVEN UK and overseas.

WHO CAN BENEFIT Individuals and organisations.

WHAT IS FUNDED Support for a variety of causes, principally Christian.

WHAT IS NOT FUNDED No grants for building appeals, or to individuals for education.

TYPE OF GRANT One-off, project and some recurring costs will be considered.

SAMPLE GRANTS £2,000 to County Workers Essex; £1,200 to UCCF; £1,000 each to Barnabas Fund, Epping Forest Youth for Christ and Scripture Gift Mission.

FINANCES *Year* 2007–08 *Income* £39,827 *Grants* £37,600 *Assets* £449,586

TRUSTEES Prof. D W Vere; C P Harwood; Mrs E M Harwood; Mrs V Vere.

HOW TO APPLY In writing to the correspondent, although the trust states that most of the funds are regularly committed.

WHO TO APPLY TO Prof. D W Vere, Trustee, 14 Broadfield Way, Buckhurst Hill, Essex IG9 5AG

CC NO 262861   **ESTABLISHED** 1971

■ The Alice Trust

WHERE FUNDING CAN BE GIVEN UK, in practice, Buckinghamshire.

WHO CAN BENEFIT The trust's giving is focused on its principal beneficiary, Waddesdon Manor, but very occasionally grants are made to other organisations.

WHAT IS FUNDED The preservation, protection, maintenance and improvement of Waddesdon Manor, its lands and its contents, for the benefit of the public generally, together with the advancement of education in matters of historic, artistic, architectural or aesthetic interest.

SAMPLE GRANTS £2.4 million to National Trust for Waddesdon Manor running costs, repair and refurbishment and £300,000 to the Prince's Charities Foundation.

FINANCES *Year* 2007–08 *Income* £13,017,338 *Grants* £2,720,000 *Assets* £89,036,831

TRUSTEES Lord Rothschild; Lady Rothschild; Sir Edward Cazalet; Hon. Beth Rothschild; Lord Cholmondeley; SJP Trustee Company Limited.

HOW TO APPLY Applications can be made for the advancement of education in matters of historic, artistic, architectural or aesthetic interest, but in view of the commitment of the trust to its principal beneficiary, Waddesdon Manor, it is unlikely that many applications will be successful. The trust states that the trustees meet twice a year to consider grant applications and that grants are occasionally made to other charitable organisations. However, in reality very few grants are made. We would suggest that an informal enquiry is made to the trust before undertaking the preparation of any grant application. The trust acknowledges postal enquiries.

WHO TO APPLY TO Fiona Sinclair, The Dairy, Queen Street, Waddesdon, Aylesbury, Buckinghamshire HP18 0JW *Tel* 01296 653235

CC NO 290859   **ESTABLISHED** 1984

■ All Saints Educational Trust

WHERE FUNDING CAN BE GIVEN UK and Commonwealth.

WHO CAN BENEFIT Ultimately, persons who are or intend to become engaged as teachers or in other capacities connected with education, in particular home economics and religious subjects, and those who teach or intend to teach in multicultural areas.

WHAT IS FUNDED Primarily, the training of Christian teachers. Its main purposes is to: help increase the number of new teachers with Qualified Teacher Status; improve the skills and qualifications of experienced teachers; encourage research that can assist teachers in their work; support specifically the teaching of religious studies and home economics and related areas – such as the promotion of public health and nutrition, both at home and in the Commonwealth.

WHAT IS NOT FUNDED Please note that the trust will not support: general or core funds of any organisation; public appeals; school buildings, equipment or supplies (except library resources); the establishment of new departments in universities and colleges; general bursary funds of other organisations.

TYPE OF GRANT One-off, project or annual grants for a limited duration. Funding may be given for more than three years. Preference will be given to 'pump-priming' projects.

SAMPLE GRANTS Sheffield Hallam University (£36,000); National Society (£25,000); British

Nutrition Foundation (£20,000); and London Institute for Contemporary Christianity (£6,000).

FINANCES *Year* 2007–08 *Income* £617,225 *Grants* £619,474 *Assets* £9,445,952

TRUSTEES Revd Dr K G Riglin, Chair; D J Trillo; Mrs A E Cumbers; Dr R L Gwynne; Revd Canon P Hartley; Mrs B E Harvey; J K Hoskin; Dr A R Leeds; Ms D McCrea; Ms J R Moriarty; Dr C C A Pearce; Mrs F M Smith; Ms S J Valentine; Ven. S J Welch; C J Wright.

OTHER INFORMATION in 2007–08 grants to organisations (Corporate Awards) totalled £156,000, with £423,000 going to individuals in scholarships and bursaries and £40,000 given for the All Saxton Fellowship.

HOW TO APPLY For applications from organisations (not individuals): applicants are invited to discuss their ideas informally with the clerk before requesting an application form. In some cases, a 'link trustee' is appointed to assist the organisation in preparing the application and who will act in a liaison role with the trust. Completed applications are put before the awards committee in April/May, with final decisions made in June. Application forms are available on the trust's website, either in interactive or printable form. In 2009 the trust stated: 'In the present financial climate, the trust is not, as far as possible, awarding multi-year grants. Existing grants with a duration of more that one year will be honoured.'

WHO TO APPLY TO The Clerk, St Katharine Cree Church, 86 Leadenhall Street, London EC3A 3DH *Tel* 020 7283 4485 *Fax* 020 7621 9758 *email* aset@aset.org.uk *Website* www. aset.org.uk

CC NO 312934   **ESTABLISHED** 1978

■ Allchurches Trust Ltd

WHERE FUNDING CAN BE GIVEN UK.

WHO CAN BENEFIT Churches and charitable institutions benefiting Christians.

WHAT IS FUNDED Promotion of the Christian religion and contributions to the funds of other charitable institutions.

WHAT IS NOT FUNDED The trust is unable to support: charities with political associations; national charities; individuals; appeals for running costs and salaries. Applications cannot be considered from the same recipient twice in one year or in two consecutive years.

TYPE OF GRANT Primarily one-off.

RANGE OF GRANTS Usually £100–£5,000.

SAMPLE GRANTS Rural Life & Faith Project (£25,000); AllChurches Bureau, Wellington, New Zealand (£20,000); Christ Church Cathedral, Dublin (£8,100); Shallowford House, Stone, Staffordshire (£8,000); Cottingley Cornerstone Centre, West Yorkshire (£5,000); and The Children's Society, London (£3,000).

FINANCES *Year* 2008 *Income* £7,985,000 *Grants* £6,267,000 *Assets* £301,766,000

TRUSTEES Michael Chamberlain; Rt Revd Nigel Stock; Fraser Hart; Bill Yates; Nick J E Sealy; The Ven. Annette Cooper; William Samuel.

HOW TO APPLY On an application form available from the trust's website.

WHO TO APPLY TO Mrs Rachael J Hall, Company Secretary, Beaufort House, Brunswick Road, Gloucester GL1 1JZ *Tel* 01452 528533 *email* atl@eigmail.com *Website* www. allchurches.co.uk

CC NO 263960   **ESTABLISHED** 1972

■ The H B Allen Charitable Trust

WHERE FUNDING CAN BE GIVEN Worldwide.

WHO CAN BENEFIT Registered charities in the UK.

WHAT IS FUNDED General charitable purposes including, children and young people, general community, medical research, disability, environment and overseas aid.

WHAT IS NOT FUNDED No grants to individuals, organisations which are not UK-registered charities or gap-year students (even if payable to a registered charity).

TYPE OF GRANT One-off and recurrent up to three years, revenue and capital including core costs.

RANGE OF GRANTS Mainly £5,000–£25,000.

SAMPLE GRANTS Royal Hall (Harrogate) Restoration Trust (£150,000); Skeletal Cancer Action Trust (£50,000); Wildlife Conservation Research Unit at Oxford University's Department of Zoology (£40,000); Hebridean Trust (£25,000); Practical Action (£20,000); Children's Hospice South West and AgeCare (£10,000 each); Fight for Sight, Mencap and Bat Conservation Trust (£5,000 each); and Tree Aid (£2,000).

FINANCES *Year* 2007 *Income* £1,292,046 *Grants* £994,000 *Assets* £31,352,696

TRUSTEES Helen Ratcliffe; Peter Shone.

HOW TO APPLY In writing to the correspondent: including a copy of the organisation's latest annual report and accounts. Applications should be submitted by post, not email, although enquiries prior to any application can be made by email. Please note the following comments from the trust. 'Applicants should note that, at their main annual meeting (usually in January or February), the trustees consider applications received up to 31 December each year but do not carry them forward. Having regard for the time of year when this meeting takes place, it makes sense for applications to be made as late as possible in the calendar year so that the information they contain is most up to date when the trustees meet. It would be preferable, from all points of view, if applications were made only in the last quarter of the calendar year. Although, preferably not in December. The trustees receive a very substantial number of appeals each year. It is not their practice to acknowledge appeals, and they prefer not to enter into correspondence with applicants other than those to whom grants are being made or from whom further information is required. Only successful applicants are notified of the outcome of their application.'

WHO TO APPLY TO Peter Shone, Teigncombe Barn, Chagford, Newton Abbot, Devon TQ13 8ET *Tel* 01647 433235 *email* mail@hballenct.org.uk *Website* www.hballenct.org.uk

CC NO 802306   **ESTABLISHED** 1985

■ The Rita Allen Charitable Trust

WHERE FUNDING CAN BE GIVEN UK.

WHO CAN BENEFIT Charitable organisations.

WHAT IS FUNDED General charitable purposes, especially welfare.

WHAT IS NOT FUNDED No grants to individuals.

RANGE OF GRANTS Up to £3,000.

SAMPLE GRANTS Alzheimer's Disease Society, Arthritis Research Campaign, BRACE, British Red Cross, National Council for YMCAs, NCH Action for Children, Royal National Institute for the Blind, Royal Star and Garter Home, Salvation Army and Tettenhall Horse Sanctuary (£3,000 each).

FINANCES *Year* 2007 *Income* £44,301 *Grants* £39,000 *Assets* £780,305

TRUSTEES P B Shone; Miss H L Ratcliffe.

HOW TO APPLY In writing to the correspondent, although the trust supports the same organisations each year. Unsolicited applications are 'not recommended'.

WHO TO APPLY TO Peter B Shone, Trustee, Teigncombe Barn, Chagford, Devon TQ13 8ET *Tel* 01647 433 235 *Fax* 01647 433 053 *email* peter.shone@btinternet.com

CC NO 1014947   ESTABLISHED 1992

■ The Alliance Family Foundation

WHERE FUNDING CAN BE GIVEN Unrestricted, but mainly UK, with some preference for the Manchester area.

WHO CAN BENEFIT Organisations, particularly Jewish causes, benefiting young people and people disadvantaged by poverty.

WHAT IS FUNDED The relief of poverty and advancement of religion, education and medical knowledge.

RANGE OF GRANTS Up to £674,000.

SAMPLE GRANTS Tel Aviv University Centre of Iranian Studies (£674,000); Imperial College Trust (£100,000); Maimonides Academy Baltimore (£51,000); LR Jiao Research Fund Hammersmith Hospital (£50,000); Centre for Study of Muslim-Jewish Relations (£30,000); and Kabbalah Centre Charitable Foundation, Dor Vador Institution and Centre Forum (£25,000 each). Only grants representing 2.5% or more of the total expended for the year were listed in the accounts.

FINANCES *Year* 2007–08 *Income* £514,044 *Grants* £1,258,315 *Assets* £14,324,335

TRUSTEES Lord David Alliance; Hon. Graham Alliance; Hon. Sara Esterkin; Hon. Joshua Alliance.

OTHER INFORMATION £91,000 of the grant total went to individuals.

HOW TO APPLY The trust has previously stated that unsolicited applications will not be responded to.

WHO TO APPLY TO Miss J M Ridgway, Secretary, 12th Floor, Bank House, Charlotte Street, Manchester M1 4ET *Tel* 0161 236 8193 *Fax* 0161 236 4814 *email* jridgway@bluebolt. com

CC NO 258721   ESTABLISHED 1968

■ Angus Allnatt Charitable Foundation

WHERE FUNDING CAN BE GIVEN UK.

WHO CAN BENEFIT Young people.

WHAT IS FUNDED This trust makes grants to organisations which offer opportunities for young musicians aged 13 to 25 or which provide water-based activities for those up to the age of 20.

WHAT IS NOT FUNDED No grants to individuals, and none to organisations which use music primarily for therapeutic or social purposes.

TYPE OF GRANT One-off for specific needs or start-up costs. Funding is available for up to one year.

RANGE OF GRANTS £250–£1,000 with a maximum of £2,000.

FINANCES *Year* 2007–08 *Income* £23,546

TRUSTEES David Briggs; Rodney Dartnall; Marian Durban; Calton Younger; Andrew Hutchison; Leigh Roll.

HOW TO APPLY In writing to the correspondent. Trustees meet three times a year to consider applications. The trust has no staff and no telephone. Appeals falling outside the guidelines will not be considered.

WHO TO APPLY TO Marian Durban, Trustee, 1 The Court, High Street, Harwell, Oxfordshire OX11 0EY

CC NO 1019793   ESTABLISHED 1993

■ The Pat Allsop Charitable Trust

WHERE FUNDING CAN BE GIVEN UK.

WHO CAN BENEFIT UK organisations benefiting: children; people in property management; people disadvantaged by poverty; people living in urban areas; refugees; and the victims of famine.

WHAT IS FUNDED Medicine and health; welfare; and education. Particularly concerned with: almshouses; housing associations; hospices; medical studies and research; schools and colleges; special needs education; and emergency care for refugees and people affected by famine. The founder of the trust was a partner in Allsop and Co. Chartered Surveyors, Auctioneers and Property Managers, therefore the trust favours supporting those educational projects and charities which have connections with surveying and property management professions.

WHAT IS NOT FUNDED No grants to individuals.

TYPE OF GRANT One-off, project, research and recurring costs.

RANGE OF GRANTS £100–£5,000. The trustees have a policy of making a small number of major donations (over £2,500) and a larger number of smaller donations.

SAMPLE GRANTS Duke of Edinburgh's Award, Jewish Care – Minerva Business Lunch (£5,000 each); the Story of Christmas (£3,800); Cambridge International Land Institute, Geoff Marsh Scholarship Fund and Reading Real Estate Foundation (£2,500 each); Crisis, the Honeypot Charity and the Willow Foundation (£1,000 each); Maggie's Cancer Caring Centre and Scottish Community Charity (£500 each); Race for Life (£250); and Variety Club Children's Charity (£100).

FINANCES *Year* 2006–07 *Income* £62,082 *Grants* £32,156

TRUSTEES J P G Randel; P W E Kerr; W J K Taylor; N W M MacKilligin.

HOW TO APPLY The trust does not accept unsolicited applications.

WHO TO APPLY TO J P G Randel, Trustee, c/o Brown Cooper Monier-Williams, 71 Lincoln's Inn Fields, London WC2A 3JF

CC NO 1030950   ESTABLISHED 1973

■ The Almond Trust

WHERE FUNDING CAN BE GIVEN UK and worldwide.

WHO CAN BENEFIT Mostly individuals or organisations of which the trustees have personal knowledge, particularly those benefiting Christians and evangelists.

WHAT IS FUNDED Support of evangelical Christian projects, Christian evangelism, and advancement of Scripture.

TYPE OF GRANT Largely recurrent.

RANGE OF GRANTS Up to £16,000. The average grant in 2007–08 was £4,974.

SAMPLE GRANTS Lawyers' Christian Fellowship (£16,000 in two grants); London Institute for Contemporary Christianity (£10,000); Agape, Claypath Trust, Barnabas Fund, Daylight Christian Prison Trust, Friends International, Jesus Lane Trust, Latin Link, Overseas

Missionary Fellowship, Prison Fellowship, St Mary's Warbleton, UCCF and Wycliffe Bible Translators (£5,000 each); and Baptist Missionary Society (£1,250).

FINANCES *Year* 2007–08 *Income* £60,874 *Grants* £109,000 *Assets* £210,740

TRUSTEES Sir Jeremy Cooke; Jonathan Cooke; Lady Cooke.

OTHER INFORMATION In 2007–08 a grant of £2,000 went to an individual.

HOW TO APPLY In writing to the correspondent, but please note that the trust states it rarely responds to uninvited applications.

WHO TO APPLY TO Sir Jeremy Cooke, Trustee, 19 West Square, London SE11 4SN

CC NO 328583   **ESTABLISHED** 1990

....

■ Almondsbury Charity

WHERE FUNDING CAN BE GIVEN The parish of Almondsbury as it existed in 1892, i.e. Almondsbury, Patchway, Easter Compton and parts of Pilning and Bradley Stoke North.

WHO CAN BENEFIT Church of England; residents and organisations in the beneficial area.

WHAT IS FUNDED Grants are made to maintain and repair churches, to further the religious and charitable work of the Church of England and to support educational requirements and sick and needy residents and organisations within the old parish of Almondsbury.

RANGE OF GRANTS Up to £6,700. Grants generally around £1,000.

SAMPLE GRANTS Holy Trinity Church (£6,700); Patchway Community Centre (£2,800); St Peter's Church (£1,600); Patchway Community College and Wheatfield Primary School (£1,500 each); Bowsland Green Primary School (£895); and Holy Family Catholic Primary School (£500). A further ten organisations received grants ranging between including: Coniston Community Association (£3,000); Four Towns Play Association (£1,000); Patchway Festival (£750); and Patchway Library (£270).

FINANCES *Year* 2008 *Income* £71,235 *Grants* £38,622 *Assets* £1,691,142

TRUSTEES A B Gaydon; I Humphries; K J Beard; L Gray; J A Bamforth; Mrs D Wilson; Revd D Byrne; Revd B Topalian; M C D Kirby; Mrs S M Futon; Mrs J Jones.

OTHER INFORMATION Includes £5,489 to 328 individuals

HOW TO APPLY On a form available from the correspondent.

WHO TO APPLY TO A B Gaydon, Secretary, Highbank, 7A The Scop, Almondsbury, Bristol BS32 4DU *Tel* 01454 613424 *email* highbankabg@tiscali.co.uk

CC NO 202263   **ESTABLISHED** 1963

....

■ The Altajir Trust

WHERE FUNDING CAN BE GIVEN UK and Arab or Islamic states.

WHO CAN BENEFIT Individuals and organisations.

WHAT IS FUNDED The advancement of science, education and research beneficial to the community in Britain or any Arab or Islamic state. Support is given to students at universities in the UK, USA and Bahrain, and conferences and exhibitions are sponsored which promote understanding and the study of Islamic culture and arts throughout the world.

SAMPLE GRANTS The Prince's School of Traditional Arts (£93,000); University of York – Lectureship (£44,000); the British Museum (£29,000);

University of York – Scholarships (£17,000); the Women's Council (£14,000); St Ethelburga's Centre for Reconciliation and Peace (£12,000); Medical Aid for Palestinians (£10,000); Council for British Research in the Levant (£8,300); and Chatham House and University of Birmingham – Interfaith Conference (£1,000 each).

FINANCES *Year* 2008 *Income* £614,643 *Grants* £229,412 *Assets* £284,019

TRUSTEES Prof. Alan Jones, Chair; Peter Tripp; Prof. Roger Williams; Prof. Charles Tripp; Dr Noel Brehony.

OTHER INFORMATION The trust also gave a further £134,765 in student fees and £86,200 in student maintenance.

HOW TO APPLY On a form available from the trust's website.

WHO TO APPLY TO The Trustees, 11 Elvaston Place, London SW7 5QG *Tel* 020 7581 3522 *Fax* 020 7584 1977 *email* awitrust@tiscali.co.uk *Website* www.altajirtrust.org.uk

CC NO 284116   **ESTABLISHED** 1982

....

■ Altamont Ltd

WHERE FUNDING CAN BE GIVEN Worldwide.

WHO CAN BENEFIT Organisations benefiting Jewish people.

WHAT IS FUNDED Jewish charitable purposes.

FINANCES *Year* 2007–08 *Income* £72,815 *Grants* £850,000

TRUSTEES D Last; H Last; Mrs H Kon; Mrs S Adler; Mrs G Wiesenfeld.

HOW TO APPLY In writing to the correspondent.

WHO TO APPLY TO David Last, Trustee, 18 Green Walk, London NW4 2AJ

CC NO 273971   **ESTABLISHED** 1977

....

■ Alvor Charitable Trust

WHERE FUNDING CAN BE GIVEN UK, with a preference for Sussex, Norfolk and north east Scotland.

WHO CAN BENEFIT Charitable organisations.

WHAT IS FUNDED Christian social change and general charitable purposes on a local basis.

WHAT IS NOT FUNDED The trust does not look to support animal charities or medical charities outside of the geographic areas mentioned above.

TYPE OF GRANT The trust tends to support smaller projects where the grant will meet a specific need.

RANGE OF GRANTS £500 upwards. The trust typically makes a few larger donations each year and a number of smaller grants.

SAMPLE GRANTS Kenward Trust (£50,000 in two grants); Salt Sussex Trading Ltd (£40,000 in four grants); Anne Marie School, Ghana (£35,000); Urban Saints (£33,000); Hymns Ancient and Modern (£30,000 in two grants); Romance Academy (£25,000) World In Need (£20,000); Trussell Trust (£15,000); Release International (£10,000); Brighton Fareshare (£5,000 each); Chestnut Tree House (£2,000); and Impact Initiatives (£500).

FINANCES *Year* 2007–08 *Income* £686,604 *Grants* £773,250 *Assets* £1,554,382

TRUSTEES C Wills; Mrs S Wills; M Atherton; Mrs F Atherton; I Wilkins; Mrs J Wilkins.

HOW TO APPLY In writing to the correspondent.

WHO TO APPLY TO I Wilkins, Chair, Monks Wood, Tompsets Bank, Forest Row, East Sussex RH18 5LW

CC NO 1093890   **ESTABLISHED** 2002

Think carefully about every application. Is it justified?

327

■ AM Charitable Trust

WHERE FUNDING CAN BE GIVEN UK and overseas.
WHO CAN BENEFIT Registered charities; Jewish organisations.
WHAT IS FUNDED General charitable purposes, including medical, welfare, arts and conservation causes.
WHAT IS NOT FUNDED No grants to individuals.
TYPE OF GRANT Certain charities are supported for more than one year, although no commitment is usually given to the recipients.
RANGE OF GRANTS £50–£15,000. Mainly smaller amounts under £500 each to non-Jewish organisations.
SAMPLE GRANTS World Jewish Relief and Youth Aliyah – Child Rescue (£15,000 each); Weizmann Institute Foundation (£12,000); British Friends of the Hebrew University of Jerusalem, Jerusalem Foundation and Magen David Adom UK (£10,000 each); British Friends of Israel Free Loan Association (£4,000); Cancer Research UK (£2,500); British Heart Foundation and Norwood (£2,000 each); Blond McIndoe Research Foundation (£1,500); and NSPCC (£500).
FINANCES *Year* 2007–08 *Income* £92,334 *Grants* £92,500 *Assets* £1,843,750
TRUSTEES Kleinwort Benson Trustees Ltd.
HOW TO APPLY 'Donations are decided periodically by the Trustee having regard to the wishes of the Settlors, and unsolicited appeals are considered as well as causes which have already been supported. Only successful applicants are notified of the trustee's decision.'
WHO TO APPLY TO The Administrator, Kleinwort Benson Trustees Ltd, 30 Gresham Street, London EC2V 7PG
CC NO 256283   **ESTABLISHED** 1968

■ The Amalur Foundation Limited

WHERE FUNDING CAN BE GIVEN Worldwide.
WHO CAN BENEFIT Charitable organisations.
WHAT IS FUNDED General charitable purposes.
SAMPLE GRANTS Absolute Return for Kids (£110,000); St Patrick's Catholic Church (£50,000); Prostate Research Campaign UK (£10,000); Brain Tumour Research Campaign (£5,500); Breakthrough Breast Cancer (£3,000); and the Extra Care Charitable Trust (£2,000).
FINANCES *Year* 2007–08 *Income* £79,102 *Grants* £180,500 *Assets* £1,505,514
TRUSTEES Rodolfo Zurcher; David Way; Michael Giedroyc; Helen Mellor.
HOW TO APPLY In writing to the correspondent.
WHO TO APPLY TO Kate Pink, Administrator, 22 Cheyne Walk, London NW4 3QJ
CC NO 1090476   **ESTABLISHED** 2002

■ Amarillo Limited

WHERE FUNDING CAN BE GIVEN UK with a preference for north west London.
WHO CAN BENEFIT Jewish charities.
WHAT IS FUNDED The advancement of education and religious practice in accordance with the teachings of the Orthodox Jewish faith.
SAMPLE GRANTS Previous beneficiaries include: Kasha Chassidim Bubo; MYER; BOON Trust; Beth Haberdasher Elion Golders Green Ltd; Friends of Shekel Haloes Ltd; Friends of Mir and Pasha Ltd; Cosmo Bells Ltd; United Talmudical Academy; British Friends of Modes Chernobyl; Mayfair Charities Ltd; Friends of To-dos Vroom Yitzchak; Achisomoch Aid Company; the Gartner

Charitable Trust; and Higher Talmudical Education Ltd.
FINANCES *Year* 2007–08 *Income* £2,229,347 *Grants* £2,048,327 *Assets* £3,735,380
TRUSTEES Charles Lerner; Frances R Lerner; Salmon Noël; Israel Grossness.
HOW TO APPLY Appeal letters are received from, and personal visits made by representatives of Jewish charitable, religious and educational institutions. These requests are then considered by the trustees and grants are made in accordance with the trustees decisions.
WHO TO APPLY TO Charles Lerner, Trustee, 1 Golders' Manor Drive, London NW11 9HU *Tel* 020 8455 6785
CC NO 1078968   **ESTABLISHED** 2000

■ The Ammco Trust

WHERE FUNDING CAN BE GIVEN Oxfordshire and adjoining counties.
WHO CAN BENEFIT Small local charities and charitable projects based in the area of benefit.
WHAT IS FUNDED Disability, health, medical, special needs education, ex-services, sport and arts/ heritage.
WHAT IS NOT FUNDED No grants to individuals, students or for research.
TYPE OF GRANT One-off.
RANGE OF GRANTS Usually up to £2,000, except in exceptional circumstances.
SAMPLE GRANTS Previous beneficiaries have included BEWSA, Contact a Family Oxford, DebRA Berkshire, Dorothy House Hospice Care Wiltshire, Live Music Now!, Oxford Children's Hospital Campaign, Pathway Workshop Oxford, Riding for the Disabled Association Abingdon Group and Wellbeing of Women.
FINANCES *Year* 2007–08 *Income* £86,800 *Grants* £82,144 *Assets* £1,462,790
TRUSTEES Mrs E M R Lewis; Mrs R S E Vickers; N P Cobbold.
HOW TO APPLY In writing to the correspondent; there are no application forms. Applications are considered at any time. An sae is appreciated.
WHO TO APPLY TO Mrs E M R Lewis, Trustee, Glebe Farm, Hinton Waldrist, Faringdon, Oxfordshire SN7 8RX
CC NO 327962   **ESTABLISHED** 1988

■ Sir John and Lady Amory's Charitable Trust

WHERE FUNDING CAN BE GIVEN Devon, and elsewhere in the UK.
WHO CAN BENEFIT Local organisations, plus a few UK charities.
WHAT IS FUNDED General charitable purposes, including education, health and welfare.
TYPE OF GRANT One-off grants for core or running costs.
RANGE OF GRANTS Up to £16,500. Generally for smaller amounts.
SAMPLE GRANTS Knightshayes Garden Trust (£16,500); Relief for the Elderly and Infirm (£1,400); Tiverton Market Centre (£2,000); and Churches Housing Action Team, Dorchester Abbey Appeal, Queen Alexandra Hospital Home and Shelterbox (£1,000).
FINANCES *Year* 2007–08 *Income* £440,344 *Grants* £73,462 *Assets* £2,079,873
TRUSTEES Sir Ian Heathcoat Amory; Lady Heathcoat Amory; William Heathcoat Amory.
OTHER INFORMATION The sale and purchase of investments during 2007–08 showed a

significant increase in income (£363,404) and expenditure (£248,061).

HOW TO APPLY In writing to the correspondent.
WHO TO APPLY TO Lady Heathcoat Amory, Trustee, The Island, Lowman Green, Tiverton, Devon EX16 4LA *Tel* 01884 254899
CC NO 203970   **ESTABLISHED** 1961

....

■ Viscount Amory's Charitable Trust

WHERE FUNDING CAN BE GIVEN UK, primarily in Devon.
WHO CAN BENEFIT Particular favour is given to young adults and older people. Charities benefiting people from different family situations, clergy, ex-service and service people, people with disabilities, people disadvantaged by poverty, homeless people and people living in rural areas are also considered.
WHAT IS FUNDED The income is employed mostly in the field of youth service and older people particularly to help a number of charitable objects with which the trust has been associated for a number of years, mostly within the county of Devon, including education and training for children and young people. Conservation and heritage causes are also considered.
WHAT IS NOT FUNDED No grants to individuals from outside south west England.
TYPE OF GRANT Usually one-off including capital (including building) costs. Grants for up to three years will be considered.
RANGE OF GRANTS £1,000–£86,000; typically for £5,000 or less.
SAMPLE GRANTS London Sailing Project (£86,000); Blundells Foundation (£20,000); Tiverton Market Centre (£12,000); Devon Community Foundation and Exeter Cathedral Third Millennium Campaign (£10,000 each); National Trust (£8,000); Langley House Trust (£2,000); Project Gem (£1,500); and Army Benevolent Fund, Exeter and District Mencap Society, Truro School and University of Liverpool (£1,000 each).
FINANCES *Year* 2007–08 *Income* £509,653 *Grants* £360,110 *Assets* £12,394,269
TRUSTEES Sir Ian Heathcoat Amory; Mrs Catherine Cavender.
HOW TO APPLY In writing to the correspondent, giving general background information, total costs involved, amount raised so far and details of applications to other organisations.
WHO TO APPLY TO The Trust Secretary, The Island, Lowman Green, Tiverton, Devon EX16 4LA *Tel* 01884 254899
CC NO 204958   **ESTABLISHED** 1962

....

■ The Ampelos Trust

WHERE FUNDING CAN BE GIVEN UK.
WHO CAN BENEFIT Registered charities.
WHAT IS FUNDED General charitable purposes.
TYPE OF GRANT Usually one-off.
SAMPLE GRANTS Kids for Kids (£25,000); Handel House Trust (£20,000); Chester Zoo (£15,000); Medical Foundation for the Care of Victims of Torture, Shelter and Stroke Association (£10,000 each); Princess Royal Trust for Carers (£3,000); and the Seeing Ear (£1,000);.
FINANCES *Year* 2007–08 *Income* £253,982 *Grants* £95,000 *Assets* £391,478
TRUSTEES G W N Stewart; Baroness Rendell of Babergh; A M Witt.
HOW TO APPLY In writing to the correspondent.

WHO TO APPLY TO G W N Stewart, Secretary, 9 Trinity Street, Colchester, Essex CO1 1JN
CC NO 1048778   **ESTABLISHED** 1995

....

■ The AMW Charitable Trust

WHERE FUNDING CAN BE GIVEN Scotland only, with a priority for the West of Scotland.
WHO CAN BENEFIT Charitable organisations.
WHAT IS FUNDED A broad range of activity is supported including those connected with religion, education, culture, poverty, sickness, disability, social welfare and young adults.
WHAT IS NOT FUNDED No grants for individuals, or to organisations outside Scotland.
SAMPLE GRANTS Previous beneficiaries have included the Dixon Community, Girl Guiding School, Kelvingrove Refurb Appeal, Lifeboats of the Cycle Appeal, Friends of Glasgow Humane Society, Maryhill Parish Church, Aberlour Child Care Trust, Dystonia Society, Glasgow School of Arts, Momentum, Hansel Foundation and Muscular Dystrophy Campaign.
FINANCES *Year* 2008–09 *Income* £171,917
TRUSTEES Joy Travers; Campbell Denholm; Prof. R B Jack.
HOW TO APPLY In writing to the correspondent. Appeals are not acknowledged and the trust only advises successful applicants.
WHO TO APPLY TO The Trustees, c/o KPMG, 191 West George Street, Glasgow G2 2LJ
SC NO SC006959   **ESTABLISHED** 1974

....

■ The Anchor Foundation

WHERE FUNDING CAN BE GIVEN UK.
WHO CAN BENEFIT Christian charities.
WHAT IS FUNDED Social inclusion, particularly through ministries of healing and the arts.
WHAT IS NOT FUNDED No grants to individuals.
TYPE OF GRANT Applications for capital and revenue funding are considered. Only in very exceptional circumstances will grants be given for building work. It is not the normal practice of the charity to support the same project for more than three years (projects which have had three years funding may apply again two years from the payment of the last grant).
RANGE OF GRANTS Up to £10,000. Mostly for £5,000 or less.
SAMPLE GRANTS Acorn Healing Trust and Good News Family Care (£10,000 each); St John's Church – Edinburgh (£7,500); Exousia (£7,000); London Jesus Centre (£6,100); Bournemouth Spirals Partnerships (£5,600); Sycamore Project (£5,500); and Dundas Foundation, Oasis Uganda, Liverpool YFC, Saltburn Christian Projects, SAT 7 Trust, Hospices of Hope (£5,000 each).
FINANCES *Year* 2007–08 *Income* £239,708 *Grants* £260,318 *Assets* £5,526,969
TRUSTEES Prudence Thimbleby; Michael Mitton; Revd Anker-Petersen.
HOW TO APPLY Application forms and information for applicants is available in pdf format on the foundation's website. Applications are considered at twice yearly trustees meetings in April and November and need to be received by 31 January and 31 July each year. The foundation regrets that applications cannot be acknowledged. Successful applicants will be notified as soon as possible after trustees' meetings. Unsuccessful applicants may reapply after 12 months.
WHO TO APPLY TO The Secretary, PO Box 21107, Alloa FK12 5WA *email* secretary@

theanchorfoundation.org.uk *Website* www.
theanchorfoundation.org.uk
cc no 1082485   established 2000

■ The Andrew Anderson Trust

where funding can be given UK and overseas.

who can benefit Organisations benefiting: Christians and evangelists; at risk groups; carers; people with disabilities; people disadvantaged by poverty; socially isolated people; and victims of abuse, crime and domestic violence.

what is funded Grants to evangelical organisations and churches, small grants to health, disability and social welfare causes.

what is not funded Individuals should not apply for travel or education.

sample grants Previous beneficiaries have included Aycliffe Evangelical Church, Christian Medical Fellowship, Concern Worldwide, Fellowship of Independent Evangelical Churches, Good Shepherd Mission, Kenward Trust, Rehoboth Christian Centre – Blackpool, Scientific Exploration Society, St Helen's Church – Bishopsgate, Trinity Baptist Church – Gloucester, Whitefield Christian Trust, Weald Trust and Worldshare.

finances *Year* 2007–08 *Income* £278,386 *Grants* £269,190 *Assets* £9,845,823

trustees Revd A R Anderson, Chair; Miss A A Anderson; Miss M S Anderson; Mrs M L Anderson.

how to apply The trust has previously stated that 'we prefer to honour existing commitments and initiate new ones through our own contacts rather than respond to applications'.

who to apply to Miss M S Anderson, Trustee, 84 Uphill Road, Mill Hill, London NW7 4QE
cc no 212170   established 1954

■ Andor Charitable Trust

where funding can be given UK and overseas.

who can benefit Charitable organisations.

what is funded Jewish, arts, health and general charitable purposes.

sample grants Prostate Cancer Charitable Trust (£10,000); British Library – Turning the Pages, the Chicken Shed Theatre Trust and Multiple Sclerosis Trust (£7,500 each); National Autistic Society (£6,000); Battersea Arts Centre, Cove Park, Hampstead Theatre Limited, Pavilion Opera Educational Trust, the Slade School of Fine Art, the Wiener Library Institute of Contemporary History and the Willow Trust (£5,000 each); English National Ballet and National Youth Orchestra of Great Britain (£4,000 each); North London Piano School (£3,000); Young Music Makers (£1,500); and Cato Trust (£1,000).

finances *Year* 2007–08 *Income* £151,382 *Grants* £98,015 *Assets* £3,414,502

trustees W D Tothenberg; N C Lederer; Dr D Dean; J Szego.

how to apply In writing to the correspondent.

who to apply to The Trustees, c/o Blick Rothenberg, 12 York Gate, Regent's Park, London NW1 4QS
cc no 1083572   established 2000

■ The André Christian Trust

where funding can be given UK.

who can benefit Christian organisations.

what is funded Charities specified in the trust deed; advancement of the Christian religion.

sample grants Care for the Family and Exeter Community Family Trust (£8,000 each); Open Air Campaigners – West Country, St Francis – Selsdon and SIFT (£5,000 each); Strangers' Rest Mission (£3,000); and Overseas Missionary Fellowship (£2,000).

finances *Year* 2008 *Income* £48,771 *Grants* £46,000 *Assets* £1,050,387

trustees Andrew K Mowll; Stephen Daykin.

how to apply In writing to the correspondent. However, the trust states: 'Applications are discouraged since grants are principally made to those organisations which are listed in the trust deed.' Funds are therefore fully committed and unsolicited requests cannot be supported.

who to apply to Andrew K Mowll, Trustee, 2 Clevedon Close, Exeter EX4 6HQ
cc no 248466   established 1950

■ The Henry Angest Foundation

where funding can be given UK and overseas.

who can benefit Charitable organisations.

what is funded General charitable purposes.

sample grants Perth College Development Trust (£80,000); World Pheasant Association (£6,000); Bowel and Cancer Research, British Olympic Association, the R D Crusaders Foundation and East Midlands Zoological Society (£5,000 each); Cancer Research UK (£2,000); the Salvation Army (£1,000); and Botanic Foundation, PACT, Scottish Ballet and Wycombe Abbey School Foundation (£500).

finances *Year* 2008 *Income* £85,691 *Grants* £112,550 *Assets* £34,798

trustees H Angest; D Angest.

how to apply In writing to the correspondent.

who to apply to The Trustees, Arbuthnot House, 20 Ropemaker Street, London EC2Y 9AR
cc no 1114761   established 2006

■ Anglo American Group Foundation

where funding can be given Worldwide.

who can benefit Charitable organisations.

what is funded Education, international development, health/HIV, environment and London-based community development.

sample grants CARE International (£65,000); Plan International (£50,000); Connection at St Martins (£42,000); Children of the Andes (£35,000); Engineers Without Boarders (£29,000); MicroLoan Foundation (£22,000; Aidspan (£15,000); National AIDS Trust (£13,000); Alone in London and Fairbridge (£10,000 each); Cecily's Fund and Zimbabwe Farmers Trust (£5,000 each); and Ecton Mine Trust (£2,500).

finances *Year* 2007 *Income* £1,055,301 *Grants* £835,818

trustees E S C Bickham; C B Corrin; N Jordan; N K Von Schirnding.

other information Established by Anglo American plc who make donations to the foundation from its annual pre-tax profits. Financial information detailed here covers the 15 month period to the end of 2007.

how to apply 'Meetings are held throughout the year when the trustees consider applications for funding from bona fide charities whose objectives match those of the foundation. A working party, made up of two members of Anglo American plc staff, consider the applications and puts forward proposals to the trustees.'

WHO TO APPLY TO Miss C L Marshall, Secretary, 20 Carlton House Terrace, London SW1Y 5AN *Website* www.angloamerican.co.uk

CC NO 1111719   **ESTABLISHED** 2005

....

■ Anguish's Educational Foundation

WHERE FUNDING CAN BE GIVEN Norwich and the parishes of Costessey, Hellesdon, Catton, Sprowston, Thorpe St Andrews and Corpusty.

WHO CAN BENEFIT Residents of the area of benefit under the age of 25.

WHAT IS FUNDED School clothing, school trips, books/equipment, sports and musical training, grants for fees/maintenance at university/ tertiary education.

SAMPLE GRANTS The Academy Trust (£12,000); the Tall Ships Youth Trust (£10,000); UEA School of Chemical Science and Technology (£8,800); Norwich Playhouse (£6,000); Norwich International Youth Project (£5,000); Larkman Primary School (£3,300); Realth Heath Action (£2,500); Cherwood Trust (£1,600); and Arden Grove Infant Nursery and Pre-school (£1,100).

FINANCES *Year* 2007–08 *Income* £777,447 *Grants* £526,961 *Assets* £17,856,426

TRUSTEES Brenda Arthur; Sally Barham; Philip Blanchflower; Roy Blower; Iain Brooksby; Brenda Ferris; David Fullman; Joyce Hopwood; Jean Kentfield; Geoffrey Loades; Pamela Scutter; Jeanne Southgate; Marian Wexler.

OTHER INFORMATION The 2007–08 grant total was mostly made up £477,000 distributed to individuals.

HOW TO APPLY In writing to the correspondent. Applications from other charities are considered at two meetings in a year. Applications from individuals are considered at seven meetings throughout the year. Individuals are usually invited to the office for an informal interview.

WHO TO APPLY TO David Walker, Clerk to the Trustees, 1 Woolgate Court, St Benedict's Street, Norwich NR2 4AP *Tel* 01603 621023 *email* david.walker@norwichcharitabletrusts.org. uk

CC NO 311288   **ESTABLISHED** 1605

....

■ The Animal Defence Trust

WHERE FUNDING CAN BE GIVEN UK.

WHO CAN BENEFIT UK organisations benefiting animals.

WHAT IS FUNDED Capital projects for animal welfare/ protection.

WHAT IS NOT FUNDED No grants to individuals.

TYPE OF GRANT Usually one-off payments.

SAMPLE GRANTS Les Amis des Chats (£4,000); Ferne Animal Sanctuary, Safe Haven for Donkeys in Holy Land and Tree of Life for Animals (£3,000 each); Animals Asia, Blue Cross, Canterbury Horse Rescue, the Cat and Rabbit Centre, Great Dane Adoption Society, Greek Cat Welfare Society, Celia Hammond Animal Trust, Mayhew Animal Home, Saltburn Animal Rescue Association and Yorkshire Swan Rescue Hospital (£2,000 each); and Haworth Animal Rescue, Lagos Animal Protection and Worldwide Veterinary Service (£1,000 each).

FINANCES *Year* 2007–08 *Income* £63,159 *Grants* £81,000 *Assets* £1,232,024

TRUSTEES Marion Saunders; Carole Bowles; Richard J Vines; Jenny Wheadon.

HOW TO APPLY On a form which can be downloaded from the trust's website. Application must be returned by post to: PO Box 44, Plymouth, PL7 5YW.

WHO TO APPLY TO Roy Stokes, Grants Application Secretary, Horsey Lightly Fynn, Devon House, 12–15 Dartmouth Street, Queen Anne's Gate, London SW1H 9BL *Website* www. animaldefencetrust.org

CC NO 263095   **ESTABLISHED** 1971

....

■ The Eric Anker-Petersen Charity

WHERE FUNDING CAN BE GIVEN UK.

WHO CAN BENEFIT Charitable causes in the fields of screen and stage.

WHAT IS FUNDED Grants are made towards the conservation of classic films.

WHAT IS NOT FUNDED No grants to individuals or for non-charitable purposes.

SAMPLE GRANTS Previous grants were made to Theatrical Ladies Guild, and Imperial War Museum for the following films: *The British Atomic Trials at Maralinga*, *Everybody's Business*, *The Women's Portion* and for the book: *This Film is Dangerous.*.

FINANCES *Year* 2007–08 *Income* £19,832 *Grants* £35,000

TRUSTEES George Lindsay Duncan; Shan Warnock-Smith; David Eric Long.

HOW TO APPLY In writing to the correspondent. The trust has previously wished to emphasise that it is always looking for projects to support which meet its criteria, outlined above.

WHO TO APPLY TO D E Long, Trustee, 8–10 New Fetter Lane, London EC4A 1RS *Tel* 020 2703 5096

CC NO 1061428   **ESTABLISHED** 1997

....

■ The Annandale Charitable Trust

WHERE FUNDING CAN BE GIVEN UK.

WHO CAN BENEFIT Major charities.

WHAT IS FUNDED General charitable organisations.

SAMPLE GRANTS Blue Cross, British Heart Foundation, Cystic Fibrosis Trust, Headway, Kidney Research UK, Make a Wish Foundation, National Stroke Association, NSPCC, RBIB, RNLI and Victim Support (£3,000 each).

FINANCES *Year* 2007–08 *Income* £296,713 *Grants* £45,000 *Assets* £10,324,915

TRUSTEES Mrs C J Duggan; HSBC Trust Company (UK) Ltd.

HOW TO APPLY In writing to the correspondent. The trust stated that it has an ongoing programme of funding for specific charities and all its funds are fully committed.

WHO TO APPLY TO The Trust Manager, HSBC Trust Services, Norwich House, Nelson Gate, Commercial Road, Southampton SO15 1GX

CC NO 1049193   **ESTABLISHED** 1995

....

■ The Anson Charitable Trust

WHERE FUNDING CAN BE GIVEN UK.

WHO CAN BENEFIT Charitable organisations and individuals.

WHAT IS FUNDED General charitable purposes, there is a preference for work with children and older people. Health and medical research causes are also widely supported.

Think carefully about every application. Is it justified?

331

RANGE OF GRANTS £250–£10,000.

SAMPLE GRANTS St John Ambulance (£10,000); Royal Opera House (£7,800); Oundle Society (£7,300); Army Benevolent Fund, British Red Cross and the Pace Centre (£6,000 each); Children in Need (£5,000); Independent Age (£3,000); Child Bereavement, Sense, Starlight Children's Foundation and UNICEF (£1,000 each); Family Holiday Association (£500); and Alzheimer's Society (£250).

FINANCES *Year* 2007–08 *Income* £100,000 *Grants* £115,271 *Assets* £86,010

TRUSTEES G Anson; K Anson; P Nichols.

HOW TO APPLY In writing to the correspondent.

WHO TO APPLY TO George Anson, Trustee, Lilies, High Street, Weedon, Buckinghamshire HP22 4NS

CC NO 1111010 **ESTABLISHED** 2005

■ The Apax Foundation

WHERE FUNDING CAN BE GIVEN UK.

WHO CAN BENEFIT Charitable organisations.

WHAT IS FUNDED Relief in need and education.

SAMPLE GRANTS Cambridge University (£300,000); The Prince's Trust (£150,000); Private Equity Foundation (£125,000); International Bridges to Justice and Judge Business School (£52,000 each); St James's Church – Piccadilly (£20,000); and Bridges Community Ventures, Bromley By Bow Centre and Millennium Promise (£13,000 each).

FINANCES *Year* 2007–08 *Income* £4,759,775 *Grants* £925,871 *Assets* £5,783,156

TRUSTEES Sir Ronald Cohen, Chair; Peter Englander; Martin Halusa; Khawar Mann; David Marks; John Megrue; Michael Phillips; Richard Wilson.

OTHER INFORMATION 'The Apax Foundation is the formal channel for Apax Partners' charitable giving and receives a percentage of the firm's profits and carried interest.'

HOW TO APPLY 'Organisations which the trustees identify as potentially suitable recipients of grants are invited to submit funding proposals, which are reviewed by the trustees.' The trustees meet quarterly to review donations and grants.

WHO TO APPLY TO David Marks, Trustee, 33 Jermyn Street, London SW1Y 6DN

CC NO 1112845 **ESTABLISHED** 2006

■ Ambrose and Ann Appelbe Trust

WHERE FUNDING CAN BE GIVEN UK.

WHO CAN BENEFIT Organisations benefiting students and research workers and individuals.

WHAT IS FUNDED Education and training, especially postgraduate education (bursaries and fees), literacy, professional or specialist training; general charitable purposes.

WHAT IS NOT FUNDED Buildings are not funded. No funding to for sponsorship with Operation Raleigh, the Project Trust or similar establishments, for medical electives, for school children or for theatrical training.

RANGE OF GRANTS Up to £3,000.

SAMPLE GRANTS Anatomical Donors Association (£7,000); the Firbank Charitable Trust (£5,500); Orchestra of the Age of Enlightenment (£3,000); Godshill Trust (£2,800); Soil Association (£2,500); WPF (£1,500); National Youth Orchestra, Peterhouse Development Fund, St Gabriel's School Foundation, Tommy's and Zanzibar Aid Project (£1,000 each); Camphill St Albans, the Project Trust and RNLI (£500 each); Southbank Sinfonia (£500 each); and Wednesday's Child (£250).

FINANCES *Year* 2007–08 *Income* £45,900 *Grants* £37,014 *Assets* £791,751

TRUSTEES Valentine Thomas; Felix Appelbe; Lucy Hobby; Alexander Appelbe.

HOW TO APPLY In writing to the correspondent, enclosing an sae. Individuals should apply through their college/university.

WHO TO APPLY TO Felix Appelbe, Trustee, Ambrose Appelbe Solicitors, Lincoln's Inn, 7 New Square, London WC2A 3RA

CC NO 208658 **ESTABLISHED** 1944

■ The Appletree Trust

WHERE FUNDING CAN BE GIVEN UK and overseas, with a preference for Scotland and the north east Fife district.

WHO CAN BENEFIT Charitable organisations.

WHAT IS FUNDED Disability, sickness and poverty causes.

WHAT IS NOT FUNDED No grants to individuals.

TYPE OF GRANT Capital, buildings, project, research. Grants can be for up to two years.

SAMPLE GRANTS Beneficiaries included 1st St Andrews Boys Brigade, Alzheimer Scotland, Arthritis Care In Scotland, the Broomhouse Centre, Children's Hospice Association, Discovery Camps Trust, Home Start East Fife, Marie Curie Cancer Care, PDSA, Prince and Princess of Wales Hospice, RNID, the Salvation Army, Scottish Motor Neurone Disease Association and Scottish Spina Bifida Association.

FINANCES *Year* 2008–09 *Income* £41,653

TRUSTEES The Royal Bank of Scotland plc; Revd W McKane; Revd Dr J D Martin; Revd L R Brown.

HOW TO APPLY In writing to the correspondent. Trustees meet to consider grants in April.

WHO TO APPLY TO The Royal Bank of Scotland plc, Administrator, The Royal Bank of Scotland plc, Trust and Estate Services, Eden Lakeside, Chester Business Park, Wrexham Road, Chester, CH4 9QT

SC NO SC004851 **ESTABLISHED** 1982

■ The John Apthorp Charitable Trust

WHERE FUNDING CAN BE GIVEN UK, with a preference for Radlett.

WHO CAN BENEFIT Charitable organisations.

WHAT IS FUNDED General charitable purposes.

RANGE OF GRANTS Typically up to £5,000.

SAMPLE GRANTS the Radlett Centre (£21,000); Radlett Lodge School – National Autistic Society (£11,000); All Saints Church, NACOA, London Academy, Radlett Music Club and Tay Ghillies Association (£10,000 each); RAFT (£6,000); Radlett Choral Society (£5,800); Radlett Art Society (£5,200); the Rotary Club of Radlett (£1,000); and Bronsdale Kids Club (£500).

FINANCES *Year* 2008 *Income* £117,100 *Grants* £100,508 *Assets* £100,014

TRUSTEES John Dorrington Apthorp; Dr D Arnold.

HOW TO APPLY Unsolicited appeals are not welcome and will not be answered. The trustees carry out their own research into prospective grant areas.

WHO TO APPLY TO Mrs L D Fenton, Myers Clark, Iveco House, Station Road, Watford WD17 1DL

CC NO 289713 **ESTABLISHED** 1983

■ The Milly Apthorp Charitable Trust

WHERE FUNDING CAN BE GIVEN North west London, mainly the London borough of Barnet.

WHO CAN BENEFIT Individuals and voluntary and charitable organisations.

WHAT IS FUNDED Grants are made to a wide variety of organisations and individuals, providing holidays for disabled people and their carers, sports facilities, subsidised instrumental lessons, and job training and character-building activities for young people. Students receiving grants for educational purposes are required to pay back a proportion of these after completing their courses.

WHAT IS NOT FUNDED No unsolicited appeals to the 'General Fund'.

TYPE OF GRANT Buildings, capital, feasibility studies, start-up costs for up to three years. One-off grants and educational loans.

FINANCES *Year* 2007–08 *Income* £1,173,595 *Grants* £479,913 *Assets* £10,810,404

TRUSTEES John D Apthorp; Lawrence S Fenton.

OTHER INFORMATION Applicants to the three Barnet-based funds must be residents of, studying in, or working in the London borough of Barnet.

HOW TO APPLY Applications to the 'Designated Funds' are open to organisations and individuals in the area of the London borough of Barnet can apply for the three funds administered by the borough. Organisations must be a registered charity or other non-profit-making body which provides a service for residents of the borough and its environs and will normally be based in the Barnet area. Application forms for grants from the designated funds are available from the London Borough of Barnet Libraries, other official buildings and directly from the Grants Unit, London Borough of Barnet, North London Business Park, Oakleigh Road South, London N11 1NP (Tel: 020 8359 2092).

WHO TO APPLY TO Lawrence S Fenton, London Borough of Barnet, North London Business Park, Oakleigh Road South, London N11 1NP *Tel* 020 8359 2000 *Fax* 020 8359 2480 *email* first. contact@barnet.gov.uk

CC NO 284415   **ESTABLISHED** 1982

■ The Arbib Foundation

WHERE FUNDING CAN BE GIVEN Unrestricted.

WHO CAN BENEFIT Registered charities and local organisations with charitable purposes.

WHAT IS FUNDED In particular to establish and maintain a River and Rowing Museum in the Thames Valley for the education of the general public in the history, geography and ecology of the Thames Valley and the River Thames, with some donations for general purposes.

WHAT IS NOT FUNDED Unsolicited applications are unlikely to be successful unless there is a geographical connection to the foundation.

TYPE OF GRANT Recurrent and single donations.

RANGE OF GRANTS £100–£600,000.

SAMPLE GRANTS River and Rowing Museum Foundation (£600,000); Institute of Cancer Research (£100,000); RNIB and Barbados Community Foundation (£50,000 each); Ramsbury Recreational Centre (£20,000); Watermill Theatre Trust (£15,000); Water Vole Project (£10,000); Restore Burns and Wounds Research (£5,000); Mitchemp Trust (£1,000); and Breasthaven Carers (£200).

FINANCES *Year* 2007–08 *Income* £989,450 *Grants* £892,142 *Assets* £188,539

TRUSTEES Sir Martyn Arbib; Lady Arbib; J S Kirkwood: Mrs A Nicoll.

HOW TO APPLY Please note: the trust has previously stated that unsolicited applications are not being considered as funds are fully committed for the 'foreseeable future'.

WHO TO APPLY TO Carol O'Neill, The Old Rectory, 17 Thameside, Henley-on-Thames, Oxfordshire RG9 1BH *Tel* 01491 848890

CC NO 296358   **ESTABLISHED** 1987

■ Arcadia (formerly the Lisbet Rausing Charitable Fund)

WHERE FUNDING CAN BE GIVEN Worldwide.

WHO CAN BENEFIT Registered charities and eligible institutions.

WHAT IS FUNDED The fund currently makes grants to organisations in the fields of environmental conservation and cultural knowledge, with large grants being made to high profile projects and institutions.

TYPE OF GRANT Capital and project costs.

RANGE OF GRANTS From tens of thousands to multi-millions.

SAMPLE GRANTS $5 million (approx £3.5 million) each to the university libraries of Harvard, Yale, and UCLA; $5 million (approx £3.5 million) to The Wende Museum; $1.5 million (approx £1.1 million) to Birdlife International; $1.2 million (approx £857,000) to Royal Botanical Gardens – Kew Seed Bank.

FINANCES *Year* 2009

TRUSTEES Charities Aid Foundation; Dr Lisbet Rausing and Peter Baldwin (Donor Board).

PUBLICATIONS Various reports are available from the fund's website.

HOW TO APPLY Unsolicited applications will not be considered. 'Grants are made only to charitable institutions. The donor board concentrates on a few themes. These are identified on the basis of its members' own scholarly and practical interests and experience, and informed expert advice. The donor board is solely responsible for the choice of programmes or fields to be supported, and *we do not consider uninvited applications.*'

WHO TO APPLY TO David Sisam, Director of Administration, Fourth Floor, 192 Sloane Street, London SW1X 9QX *email* david.sisam@nyland. org.uk *Website* www.arcadiafund.org.uk

          ESTABLISHED 2001

■ The Archbishop of Canterbury's Charitable Trust

WHERE FUNDING CAN BE GIVEN Worldwide.

WHO CAN BENEFIT Individuals and organisations benefiting the clergy and their dependants and other followers of the Church of England. Named charitable funds have been recipients in the past.

WHAT IS FUNDED The trust deed states that trustees should hold particular interest towards: people training for the ministry and church work; ministers, teachers and the church workers who are in need, and their dependants; the extension of education in, and knowledge of, the faith and practice of the Church of England; the development of work of any church, union of churches, denominations or sects which will further the Christian religion generally.

SAMPLE GRANTS The Lambeth Conference (£60,000); Common World Seminar (£10,000); Anglican Centre in Rome (£6,500); Windle Trust

(£7,500); Diocese in Europe (£5,000); St Andrew's Ecumenical Trust (£2,000); and Action Around Bethlehem, Burning Bush Barn Project, the Cathedral Archer Project, Crisis, National Churches Trust, St John's College Durham and Terrence Higgins Trust (£1,000 each).

FINANCES *Year* 2008 *Income* £202,017 *Grants* £354,612 *Assets* £2,217,282

TRUSTEES Archbishop of Canterbury; Miss Sheila Cameron; Christopher Smith; Timothy Livesey.

HOW TO APPLY 'The trust receives a number of enquiries for grants which are dealt with initially by the Bursar at Lambeth Palace. If the enquiry meets the grant criteria then the request is put to the trustees who will then consider and approve those grant requests which meet the objectives of the trust.'

WHO TO APPLY TO Peter Beesley, Secretary, 1 The Sanctuary, Westminster, London SW1P 3JT *Tel* 020 7222 5381

CC NO 287967   **ESTABLISHED** 1983

- -

■ Archbishop of Wales' Fund for Children

WHERE FUNDING CAN BE GIVEN Wales.

WHO CAN BENEFIT Children in need and their families and local communities.

WHAT IS FUNDED The work of organisations in this order of priority: (1) those in the Dioceses of the Church in Wales; (2) those associated with other Christian bodies which are members of Cytun – Churches Together in Wales; (3) other organisations working with children in Wales.

SAMPLE GRANTS Beneficiaries included: the Bridge Mentoring Plus Scheme; Cardiff People First; Family Awareness Drug and Support; MENFA; Pontllanfraith, Brecon, Aberdare and Merthyr Tydfil Contact Centres; and Valley Kids.

FINANCES *Year* 2008 *Income* £64,855 *Grants* £51,584

TRUSTEES Revd J Michael Williams, Chair; Cheryl Beach; Ruth Forrester; Caroline Owen; James Tovey.

HOW TO APPLY Application forms are available from the correspondent.

WHO TO APPLY TO The Secretary, Church in Wales, 37–39 Cathedral Road, Cardiff CF11 9XF *email* awfc@churchinwales.org.uk

CC NO 1102236   **ESTABLISHED** 2004

- -

■ The John M Archer Charitable Trust

WHERE FUNDING CAN BE GIVEN UK and overseas.

WHO CAN BENEFIT Registered charities.

WHAT IS FUNDED General charitable purposes, including: the prevention or relief of individuals in need; welfare of people who are sick or distressed; alleviation of need; advancement of education; advancement of religious or missionary work; advancement of scientific research and discovery; and preservation of Scottish heritage and the advancement of associated cultural activities.

SAMPLE GRANTS Previous beneficiaries have included Cambodian Hospital Siem Reap for Children, the Canonmills Baptist Church, Castlebrae School Tutoring Programme, Erskine Stewarts Melville College – Arts Centre, Mercy Corps Scotland, the Bobby Moore Fund, Red Cross – Aberdeen Guest House and Royal Liverpool University Hospital – Macular Degeneration Research.

FINANCES *Year* 2008–09 *Income* £98,759

TRUSTEES Gilbert B Archer; Mrs A Morgan; Mrs W Grant; Mrs C Fraser; Mrs I C Smith.

HOW TO APPLY In writing to the correspondent.

WHO TO APPLY TO Mrs W Grant, Secretary, 12 Broughton Place, Edinburgh EH1 3RX

SC NO SC010583   **ESTABLISHED** 1969

- -

■ The Archer Trust

WHERE FUNDING CAN BE GIVEN Worldwide.

WHO CAN BENEFIT Voluntary organisations, especially those which make good use of volunteers or are located in areas of high unemployment or disadvantage. Preference is given to smaller organisations. Support is given to projects both in the UK and overseas, but for overseas projects only via UK charities.

WHAT IS FUNDED Provision of aid and support to a defined group of needy or deserving people, such as people with mental disabilities or people who are otherwise disadvantaged; Christian causes.

WHAT IS NOT FUNDED No grants are made to individuals (including for gap years), conservation or heritage projects, environmental causes, disability access or animal charities.

RANGE OF GRANTS Usually £250–£3,000.

SAMPLE GRANTS Lilias Graham Trust (£4,000); Christians Against Poverty, International Refugee Trust, Sycamore Project and Unity of Children (£3,000 each); Angels International, Slough Homeless Our Concern and the Respite Association (£2,000 each); Christian Care Centre, Kisiizi Hospital and Willowfield Parish Community Association (£1,500 each); Anchor House, Stockbridge Village Community Association, the Pavement, Turning Point and Women's Counselling Centre (£1,000 each); and Aid for Romanian Orphanages, Books Abroad and Freshwaters Contact Centre (£500 each).

FINANCES *Year* 2007–08 *Income* £81,945 *Grants* £55,570 *Assets* £1,383,622

TRUSTEES Mrs C M Archer; M F Baker; J N Archer; F D R MacDougall.

HOW TO APPLY In writing to the correspondent. Unsuccessful applicants will not receive a response, even if an sae is enclosed. Applications are considered twice a year, usually in March and September.

WHO TO APPLY TO The Secretary, Bourne House, Wadesmill, Ware, Hertfordshire SG12 0TT *Website* www.archertrust.org.uk

CC NO 1033534   **ESTABLISHED** 1994

- -

■ The Architectural Heritage Fund

WHERE FUNDING CAN BE GIVEN UK (excluding the Channel Islands and the Isle of Man).

WHO CAN BENEFIT Any UK charity.

WHAT IS FUNDED Support is given in the form of grants, loans, advice and information for the preservation and sustainable re-use of historic buildings.

WHAT IS NOT FUNDED Applications from private individuals and non-charitable organisations. Applications for projects not involving a change of ownership or of use, or for a building not on a statutory list or in a conservation area.

TYPE OF GRANT Loans; feasibility study grants; project administration grants; project organiser grants; refundable project development grants.

RANGE OF GRANTS Grants up to £15,000; loans up to £500,000 (more in exceptional circumstances).

SAMPLE GRANTS Projects supported included those initiated by: Highland Buildings Preservation Trust; Glasgow Building Preservation Trust; Heritage of London Operations Limited; Heritage Trust for the North West; Manchester Historic Buildings Trust; The Vivat Trust; West Midlands Historic Buildings Trust; Cadwgan Building Preservation Trust; and The Strawberry Hill Trust.

FINANCES *Year* 2007–08 *Income* £1,228,330 *Grants* £717,776 *Assets* £13,465,704

TRUSTEES Colin Amery; Nicholas Baring; Malcolm Crowder; Roy Dantzic; Fionnuala Jay-O'Boyle; George McNeill; John Pavitt; Merlin Waterson; Thomas Lloyd; Liz Davidson; John Townsend; Michael Hoare.

OTHER INFORMATION In addition to the amount given in grants, £299,000 was given in loans.

HOW TO APPLY Detailed notes for applicants for loans and feasibility studies are supplied with the application forms, all of which are available from the fund's website. The trustees meet in March, June, September and December; applications must be received six weeks before meetings.

WHO TO APPLY TO Barbara Wright, Loans and Grants Manager, Alhambra House, 27–31 Charing Cross Road, London WC2H 0AU *Tel* 020 7925 0199 *Fax* 020 7930 0295 *email* ahf@ahfund. org.uk *Website* www.ahfund.org.uk

CC NO 266780   ESTABLISHED 1973

■ The Ardwick Trust

WHERE FUNDING CAN BE GIVEN UK, Israel and the developing world.

WHO CAN BENEFIT Institutions and registered charities (mainly UK charities) benefiting people of all ages, students and Jews.

WHAT IS FUNDED To support Jewish welfare, along with a wide range of non-Jewish causes to include social welfare, health, education (especially special schools), older people, conservation and the environment, child welfare, disability and medical research. In general most of the largest grants go to Jewish organisations, with most of the smaller grants to non-Jewish organisations.

WHAT IS NOT FUNDED No grants to individuals.

TYPE OF GRANT One-off or recurrent grants up to two years. Capital, including buildings, research and start-up costs.

RANGE OF GRANTS Mostly for £500, £200 or £100 each.

SAMPLE GRANTS British Friends of the Hebrew University – Jerusalem, British Technion Society, Jewish Care, UJIA, Weizmann UK and World Jewish Relief (£1,000 each); Cheltenham Ladies' College – bursaries fund, Community Security Trust, Council of Christians and Jews, Headway, Magen David Adorn UK and Shaare Zedek UK (£500 each); Book Aid International, Food Lifeline, Help the Aged and WellChild (£200 each); and Allergy UK, Mind and Shelter (£100 each).

FINANCES *Year* 2007–08 *Income* £189,883 *Grants* £39,500 *Assets* £1,092,509

TRUSTEES Mrs J B Bloch; Dominic Flynn; Miss Judith Portrait.

HOW TO APPLY In writing to the correspondent.

WHO TO APPLY TO Janet Bloch, Trustee, c/o Knox Cropper, 24 Petworth Road, Haslemere, Surrey GU27 2HR

CC NO 266981   ESTABLISHED 1975

■ The Argentarius Foundation

WHERE FUNDING CAN BE GIVEN UK.

WHO CAN BENEFIT Charitable organisations.

WHAT IS FUNDED General charitable purposes.

FINANCES *Year* 2007–08 *Income* £49,683 *Grants* £111,189 *Assets* £823,151

TRUSTEES E Marbach; J Jackson; A Josse.

HOW TO APPLY In writing to the correspondent.

WHO TO APPLY TO Philip Goodman, Goodman & Co, 14 Basing Hill, London NW11 8TH

CC NO 1079980   ESTABLISHED 2000

■ The Argus Appeal

WHERE FUNDING CAN BE GIVEN Sussex.

WHO CAN BENEFIT Local organisations.

WHAT IS FUNDED General charitable purposes.

SAMPLE GRANTS Brighton and Hove Music and Performing Arts – Soundmakers Project (£9,300); the Dame Vera Lynn Trust (£6,000); and Crime Reduction Initiatives and Sussex Oakleaf Housing Association (£5,000 each).

FINANCES *Year* 2007 *Income* £252,976 *Grants* £206,137 *Assets* £111,162

TRUSTEES Martyn Willis, Chair; Karen Macmillan; Elsa Gillio; David Goldin; Roger French; Julien Boast; Michael Beard; Sue Addis.

OTHER INFORMATION The grant total in 2007 included £96,000 distributed to individuals.

HOW TO APPLY In writing to the correspondent.

WHO TO APPLY TO Rachel Griffiths, Trustee, Argus House, Crowhurst Road, Hollingbury, Brighton BN1 8AR

CC NO 1013647   ESTABLISHED 1990

■ Armenian General Benevolent Union London Trust

WHERE FUNDING CAN BE GIVEN UK and overseas.

WHO CAN BENEFIT Armenian individuals and organisations.

WHAT IS FUNDED 'The purpose of the trust is to advance education among Armenians, particularly those in the UK, and to promote the study of Armenian history, literature, language, culture and religion.'

WHAT IS NOT FUNDED No support for projects of a commercial nature or for education for individual students.

SAMPLE GRANTS The Rural Development Project (£21,000); RP Musical Management (£3,000); and Spring Remembrance Concert (£2,500).

FINANCES *Year* 2008 *Income* £164,985 *Grants* £85,644 *Assets* £3,063,523

TRUSTEES Dr Berge Azadian; Berge Setrakian; Hampar Chakardjian; Aris Atamian; Mrs Annie Kouyoumdjian; Mrs Noushig Yakoubian Setrakian; Assadour Guzelian; Mrs Anahid Manoukian; Mrs Arline Medazoumian; Haig Messerlian; Ms Armine Afrikian.

OTHER INFORMATION The grant total in 2008 included £44,000 given in 18 student loans and grants.

HOW TO APPLY In writing to the correspondent. Applications are considered all year around.

WHO TO APPLY TO The Chair, 51c Parkside, Wimbledon Common, London SW19 5NE

CC NO 282070   ESTABLISHED 1981

Think carefully about every application. Is it justified?

335

■ The Armenian Relief Society of Great Britain Trust

WHERE FUNDING CAN BE GIVEN Worldwide.
WHO CAN BENEFIT Individuals and organisations.
WHAT IS FUNDED Welfare of Armenians.
SAMPLE GRANTS Armenian Relief Society Inc USA (£30,000); Armenian Scouting Association and Hamazkayin (£1,800 each); Navasardian Charity Trust (£1,500); K Tahta Armenian Community School (£300); Armenian National Committee (£250); and Armenian Medical Association (£100).
FINANCES *Year* 2007–08 *Income* £46,219 *Grants* £36,529 *Assets* £74,758
TRUSTEES Matilda Megerdichian; Arshalouys Babayan; Sonig Jogaghayan; Rubina Boghosian; Silva Beshirian; Mariette Nazloomian; Heghine Bedrossian.
HOW TO APPLY In writing to the correspondent.
WHO TO APPLY TO Matilda Megerdichian, Trustee, 180 Great West Road, Hounslow TW5 9AR
CC NO 327389   **ESTABLISHED** 1987

■ The John Armitage Charitable Trust

WHERE FUNDING CAN BE GIVEN England and Wales.
WHO CAN BENEFIT Institutions and registered charities.
WHAT IS FUNDED Medical, relief-in-need, education, religion.
SAMPLE GRANTS Seeing is Believing (£1.25 million).
FINANCES *Year* 2007–08 *Income* £21,000,000 *Grants* £4,600,000 *Assets* £33,000,000
TRUSTEES J C Armitage; Ms H Avery; W Francklin.
OTHER INFORMATION 'During the year, the trustees particularly wanted to help further medical research and care and a donation of £1.25 million was made to the charity Seeing is Believing. 11 other donations were made in this area with a total of £1.9 million being donated. The trustees are keen to support existing medical research and care projects.'
HOW TO APPLY Applications received by the trust are 'reviewed by the trustees and grants awarded at their discretion'.
WHO TO APPLY TO The Trustees, c/o Sampson West and Christo, 34 Ely Place, London EC1N 6TD
CC NO 1079688   **ESTABLISHED** 2000

■ The Armourers' and Brasiers' Gauntlet Trust

WHERE FUNDING CAN BE GIVEN UK, with some preference for London.
WHO CAN BENEFIT Charitable organisations.
WHAT IS FUNDED The objectives of the trust are: support for education and research in materials science and technology and for basic science in schools; encouragement of the understanding and preservation of historic armour; encouragement of the armourers' trade in the armed services; encouragement of professional excellence in the training of young officers in the Royal Armoured Corps. It also considers appeals in the following overall categories: (i) community, social care and armed forces; (ii) children, young people and general education; medical and health; (iii) art, arms and armour; and (iv) Christian mission.
WHAT IS NOT FUNDED In general grants are not made to: organisations or groups which are not registered charities; individuals (including sponsorship); organisations or groups whose main object is to fund or support other charitable bodies; organisations or groups which are in direct relief of any reduction of financial support from public funds; charities with a turnover of over £1 million; charities which spend over 10% of their income on fundraising activities; political or commercial appeals; charities whose accounts disclose substantial financial reserves. Nor towards general maintenance, repair or restoration of buildings, including ecclesiastical buildings, unless there is a long standing connection with the Armourers' and Brasiers' Company or unless of outstanding importance to the national heritage.
TYPE OF GRANT 'Regular annual grants are not a policy of the trust at present, but charities can still apply for grants on an annual basis.'
RANGE OF GRANTS 'The trust funds are relatively modest; therefore applications for large sums should be avoided.'
FINANCES *Year* 2006–07 *Income* £367,000 *Grants* £217,000 *Assets* £6,600,000
TRUSTEES S G B Martin, Chair; J S Haw; D E H Chapman; Prof. C J Humphreys; Ven. C J H Wagstaff; Rr Adm. J P W Middleton.
HOW TO APPLY In writing to the correspondent, with a copy of the latest annual report and audited accounts. Applications are considered quarterly.
WHO TO APPLY TO The Secretary, Armourers' Hall, 81 Coleman Street, London EC2R 5BJ *Tel* 020 7374 4000 *Fax* 020 7606 7481 *email* info@armourersandbrasiers.co.uk *Website* www.armourersandbrasiers.co.uk
CC NO 279204   **ESTABLISHED** 1979

■ The Army Benevolent Fund

WHERE FUNDING CAN BE GIVEN Worldwide.
WHO CAN BENEFIT National headquarters of charities and charitable funds of Corps and Regimental Associations benefiting service and former service people, and their dependants.
WHAT IS FUNDED Support and benefit of people serving, or who have served, in the British Army, or their families/dependants. The work of the charity/service concerned must be of direct benefit to a number of soldiers, former soldiers or their dependants. Not only should this number be considerable but it must also comprise an appreciable portion of the numbers of people who benefit from the work or service of the charity.
TYPE OF GRANT One-off grants.
SAMPLE GRANTS Previous beneficiaries included: Army Families Federation, Royal Commonwealth Ex-Services League, Officers' Association, Portland Training College, Royal Star and Garter Home, Thistle Foundation, Queen Alexandra Hospital Home, Wilton Memorial Trust and the Royal Hospital – Chelsea.
FINANCES *Year* 2008–09 *Income* £9,654,477 *Grants* £4,743,663 *Assets* £31,454,851
TRUSTEES Gen. the Lord Walker; Guy Davies; Peter Sheppard; S M Andrews; P J Carr; S Clark; A W Freemantle; Mrs A M Gallico; A R Gregroy; M B Hockney; A I G Kennedy; Sir Michael Parker; D J M Roberts.
OTHER INFORMATION £2,494,316 went to regiments and corps for the benefit of individuals in 2008–09.
HOW TO APPLY Individual cases should be referred initially to the appropriate Corps or Regimental Association. Charities should apply in writing and enclose the latest annual report and accounts.
WHO TO APPLY TO Paul Cummings, Director of Grants and Welfare, Mountbarrow House, 6–20

Elizabeth Street, London SW1W 9RB *Tel* 08458 737 133 *Fax* 08452 414 821
email pcummings@armybenfund.org
Website www.armybenfund.org
cc no 211645   established 1944

··

■ **The Arnold Foundation**

where funding can be given UK.
who can benefit Charitable organisations.
what is funded General charitable purposes.
sample grants Previous beneficiaries have included Anglo-Brazilian Society, Architecture Foundation, Chelsea Festival, Design Museu, Marie Curie Cancer Care, Motivation, NSPCC, Oundle School Foundation, the Roundhouse Trust Ltd, Sussex House School and the Savitri Waney Charitable Trust.
finances *Year* 2007–08 *Income* £9,235
trustees Luqman Arnold; Chumsri Arnold; John Guy Rhodes.
other information In 2006/07 the foundation had an income of £443,774.
how to apply In writing to the correspondent.
who to apply to The Trustees, c/o Macfarlanes, 10 Norwich Street, London EC4A 1BD
cc no 1109746   established 2005

··

■ **Arsenal Charitable Trust**

where funding can be given Mainly Greater London.
who can benefit Organisations and individuals.
what is funded Youth projects and the provision of recreational facilities for the use of people living in the Greater London boroughs; any charitable purpose for the inhabitants of Islington and Hackney.
range of grants Up to £29,000.
sample grants Willow Foundation (£20,000); Arsenal FC – Double Clubs Project (£19,000); Arsenal FC – Arsenal in Israel Project (£17,000); London Playing Fields (£5,000); Whittington Hospital (£4,500); Kentish Town FC and London Youth Games (£1,500 each); S&C Association and Teenage Cancer Trust (£1,100 each); and British Aid for Deprived Children and Grove House (£1,000 each).
finances *Year* 2007–08 *Income* £218,539
Grants £91,644 *Assets* £518,666
trustees K J Friar; D Miles; A Sefton.
other information The grants total in 2007–08 includes grants made to five individuals totalling £2,898.
how to apply In writing to the correspondent.
who to apply to The Trustees, Highbury House, 75 Drayton Park, London N5 1BU *Tel* 020 7704 4000
cc no 1008024   established 1992

··

■ **The Artemis Charitable Trust**

where funding can be given UK.
who can benefit Registered charities benefiting parents, counsellors and psychotherapists.
what is funded Counselling, psychotherapy, parenting, and human relationship training.
what is not funded The trust cannot entertain applications either from individuals or from organisations which are not registered charities.
type of grant Recurring.
sample grants University of Leeds (£34,000); Durham University (£13,000); Primhe (£12,000); Chichester Harbour Trust (£5,000); and Core System Trust (£270).

finances *Year* 2007 *Income* £64,416
Grants £59,241 *Assets* £1,429,474
trustees R W Evans; D S Bergin; W A Evans; D J Evans; M W Evans.
how to apply 'Applicants should [. . .] be aware that most of the trust's funds are committed to a number of major ongoing projects and that spare funds available to meet new applications are very limited.'
who to apply to Richard Evans, Trustee, Brook House, Quay Meadow, Bosham, West Sussex PO18 8LY
cc no 291328   established 1985

··

■ **Arthritis Research Campaign**

where funding can be given Mainly UK.
who can benefit Mostly universities.
what is funded Research into the cause and cure of arthritis and related musculoskeletal diseases.
what is not funded Applications for welfare and social matters will not be considered.
type of grant One-off, project, recurring, running costs, and salaries. Programme support is for five years; project grants are usually for three years.
finances *Year* 2007–08 *Income* £33,956,000
Grants £25,976,000 *Assets* £47,590,000
trustees Charles Maisey, Chair; Lord Lewis of Newham; Prof. Patrick Sissons; Sue Arnott; Jonathan Baker; Graham Brown; Prof. Andrew Carr; Prof. Kevin Davies; Dr Ian Griffiths; Peter Henderson; Tom McGrath; Richard Raworth; Prof. Mike Pringle; Chris Cowpe.
how to apply Application forms and guidelines are available from the Arthritis Research Campaign website.
who to apply to Michael Patrick, Copeman House, St Mary's Court, St Mary's Gate, Chesterfield, Derbyshire S41 7TD *Website* www.arc-research. org.uk
cc no 207711   established 1936

··

■ **The Arts and Entertainment Charitable Trust**

where funding can be given UK.
who can benefit Charitable organisations.
what is funded Welfare, medical, disability, including those causes relating to children.
sample grants Previous beneficiaries have included Cancer Treatment and Research, the Children's Leukaemia Ward, Childline, the Metropolitan Police Peel Ski Club, the Phoenix Garden Charity, the Royal Grammar School and SOS Children Tsunami Disaster.
finances *Year* 2007–08 *Income* £27,985
Grants £42,699 *Assets* £65
trustees D A Graham; P D C Collins; C N Parsons; Sir W Blackburn; P Madoc; Hon S Nicholls; D R King; I Stokes.
other information The trust distributes funds raised by The Heritage Foundation.
how to apply In writing to the correspondent. Trustees meet every three months.
who to apply to David A Graham, Administrator, Greenacres, 3 Birchwood Chase, Great Kings Hill, Buckinghamshire HP15 6EH *Tel* 01494 714388 *email* ian.stokes@ theheritagefoundation.co.uk *Website* www. theheritagefoundation.co.uk
cc no 1031027   established 1994

■ Arts Council England

WHERE FUNDING CAN BE GIVEN England.
WHO CAN BENEFIT Organisations and individuals.
WHAT IS FUNDED Developing, sustaining and promoting the arts. The majority of funding is provided to organisations that are regularly funded by the Arts Council.
FINANCES *Year* 2008–09 *Grants* £392,218,000
TRUSTEES Members of the Arts Council of England: Alice Rawsthorn; Alistair Spalding; Anil Ruia; Diran Adebayo; Dorothy Wilson; Dr Tom Shakespeare; Ekow Eshun; Francois Matarasso; Janet Barnes; Keith Khan; Lady Sue Woodford Hollick; Prof. Jon Cook; Rosemary Squire; Sir Chris Clarke; Sir Nicholas Kenyon.
HOW TO APPLY Please see the Arts Council website for full information on how and when to apply to Arts Council England for a grant.
WHO TO APPLY TO Enquiries Team, 14 Great Peter Street, London SW1P 3NQ *Tel* 0845 300 6200 *Website* www.artscouncil.org.uk
CC NO 1036733   **ESTABLISHED** 1994

■ Arts Council of Northern Ireland

WHERE FUNDING CAN BE GIVEN UK and Ireland (but projects must benefit people of Northern Ireland).
WHO CAN BENEFIT Artists and arts organisations.
WHAT IS FUNDED 'The Arts Council is the lead development agency for the arts in Northern Ireland. We are the main support for artists and arts organisations, offering a broad range of funding opportunities through our Exchequer and National Lottery funds.'
FINANCES *Year* 2008–09 *Grants* £17,700,000
TRUSTEES Council Members: Ms Rosemary Kelly, Chair; Damien Coyle; Eithne Benson; Kate Bond; William Montgomery; Raymond Fullerton; David Irvine; Anthony Kennedy; Prof Ian Montgomery; Sharon O'Connor; Joseph Rice; Prof. Paul Seawright; Janine Walker; Peter Spratt; Brian Sore.
HOW TO APPLY Guidelines and full details of how to apply can be found at the Arts Council of Northern Ireland website.
WHO TO APPLY TO The Arts Development Department, MacNeice House, 77 Malone Road, Belfast BT9 6AQ *Tel* 028 9038 5200 *Fax* 028 9066 1715 *email* info@artscouncil-ni.org *Website* www.artscouncil-ni.org
          ESTABLISHED 1995

■ The Arts Council of Wales

WHERE FUNDING CAN BE GIVEN Wales.
WHO CAN BENEFIT Arts organisations and individuals.
WHAT IS FUNDED Arts activities in Wales.
WHAT IS NOT FUNDED Individual schemes may stipulate restrictions on the origin of beneficiary organisations or individuals. Applications for funding for projects that have already started will not be considered.
FINANCES *Year* 2007–08 *Grants* £12,000,000
TRUSTEES Prof. Dai Smith, Chair; Rhiannon Wyn Hughes; Norah Campbell; Simon Dancey; Emma Evans; Maggie Hampton; Margaret Jervis; John Metcalf; Robin Morrison; Christopher O'Neil; Dr Ian J Rees; Clive Sefia; Ruth Till; David Vokes; Debbie Wilcox; Kate Woodward.
HOW TO APPLY Applicants are asked to contact the relevant local office for details of individual grants schemes.

WHO TO APPLY TO The Arts Funding Unit, Bute Place, Cardiff CF10 5AL *Tel* 0845 8734 900 *Fax* 029 2044 1400 *Minicom* 029 2045 1023 *email* info@artswales.org.uk *Website* www.artswales.org.uk
CC NO 1034245   **ESTABLISHED** 1994

■ The Ove Arup Foundation

WHERE FUNDING CAN BE GIVEN Unrestricted.
WHO CAN BENEFIT Organisations benefiting research workers and designers.
WHAT IS FUNDED Education and research in matters related to the built environment, particularly if related to multi-disciplinary design, through educational institutions and charities.
WHAT IS NOT FUNDED No grants to individuals, including students.
TYPE OF GRANT Research and project, including start-up and feasibility costs. They can be one-off or recurrent.
RANGE OF GRANTS Up to £50,000.
SAMPLE GRANTS University of Cape Town Trust (£50,000); John Doyle Construction Ltd – 'Constructionarium' (£15,000); the Industrial Trust (£14,000); Human Resources Theatre (£10,000); Midlands Architecture and Designed Environment (£7,000); Association of Teachers of Mathematics (£5,000); and Anglo-Danish Society (£1,500).
FINANCES *Year* 2007–08 *Income* £107,414 *Grants* £102,000 *Assets* £2,682,848
TRUSTEES M Shears; D Michael; R F Emmerson; R B Haryott; T M Hill; C Cole; R Hough; T O'Brien; R Yau.
HOW TO APPLY In writing to the correspondent, with brief supporting financial information. Trustees meet quarterly to consider applications (March, June, September and December).
WHO TO APPLY TO The Secretary, c/o 13 Fitzroy Street, London W1T 4BQ *Website* www.theovearupfoundation.com
CC NO 328138   **ESTABLISHED** 1989

■ The AS Charitable Trust

WHERE FUNDING CAN BE GIVEN UK and developing countries.
WHO CAN BENEFIT Preference for charities in which the trust has special interest, knowledge of or association with. Christian organisations will benefit. Support may go to victims of famine, man-made or natural disasters, and war.
WHAT IS FUNDED The trust is sympathetic to projects which combine the advancement of the Christian religion with Christian lay leadership, third world development, peacemaking and reconciliation, or other areas of social concern.
WHAT IS NOT FUNDED Grants to individuals or large charities are very rare. Such applications are discouraged.
SAMPLE GRANTS Christian International Peace Service (£40,000 in nine grants); The De Laszlo Foundation (£10,000); GRACE (£9,000 in nine grants); Congo Church Association (£5,000); and Christian Healing Centre – the Well, Leamington Spa, Lambeth Partnership, the Message Trust and Toynbee Hall (£1,000 each).
FINANCES *Year* 2007–08 *Income* £210,027 *Grants* £70,432 *Assets* £8,449,006
TRUSTEES Roy Calvocoressi; Mrs Caroline Eady; George Calvocoressi; Simon Sampson.
HOW TO APPLY In writing to the correspondent.
WHO TO APPLY TO The Administrator, Bix Bottom Farm, Henley-on-Thames, Oxfordshire RG9 6BH
CC NO 242190   **ESTABLISHED** 1965

■ Ashburnham Thanksgiving Trust

WHERE FUNDING CAN BE GIVEN UK and worldwide.

WHO CAN BENEFIT Individuals and organisations benefiting Christians and evangelists.

WHAT IS FUNDED Only Christian work already known to the trustees is supported, particularly evangelical overseas missionary work.

WHAT IS NOT FUNDED No grants for buildings.

RANGE OF GRANTS Up to £4,800.

SAMPLE GRANTS New Destiny Trust (£4,800); Genesis Arts Trust (£3,900); St Stephen's Society – Hong Kong (£3,400); Open Doors (£3,000); Wycliffe Bible Translators (£2,500); Interserve (£2,000); Overseas Missionary Fellowship (£1,800); Latin American Missions (£1,200); Lambeth Partnership (£1,000); Advantage Africa (£700); Titus Trust (£600); Seed Savers Trust and Trinity Fellowship (£500 each); Operation Mobilisation (£250); and Latin Link (£100).

FINANCES *Year* 2007–08 *Income* £180,876 *Grants* £97,626 *Assets* £5,489,797

TRUSTEES Mrs M Bickersteth; E R Bickersteth; R D Bickersteth; Mrs R F Dowdy.

OTHER INFORMATION In 2007–08 the sum of £8,276 was distributed to nine individuals.

HOW TO APPLY The trust has stated that its funds are fully committed to current beneficiaries. Unfortunately, it receives far more applications than it is able to deal with.

WHO TO APPLY TO The Trustees, Agmerhurst House, Ashburnham, Battle, East Sussex TN33 9NB

CC NO 249109   **ESTABLISHED** 1965

■ A J H Ashby Will Trust

WHERE FUNDING CAN BE GIVEN UK, especially Lea Valley area of Hertfordshire.

WHO CAN BENEFIT Charitable organisations and schools.

WHAT IS FUNDED Wildlife, particularly birds; heritage; education projects; and children.

WHAT IS NOT FUNDED No grants to individuals or students.

TYPE OF GRANT One-off and recurrent.

SAMPLE GRANTS RSPB (£25,000 in four grants); Downhills Primary School and St Joseph's R C Primary School (£5,000 each); the Hertford Museum Charity (£4,400); Cromwell Park Primary School and Greenhouse Schools Project Limited (£3,000 each); and Whizz Kidz (£500).

FINANCES *Year* 2007–08 *Income* £242,885 *Grants* £52,900 *Assets* £70,371

TRUSTEES HSBC Trust Company (UK) Ltd.

HOW TO APPLY In writing to the correspondent.

WHO TO APPLY TO The Trust Manager, HSBC Trust Company (UK) Ltd, Trust Services, Norwich House, Nelson Gate, Commercial Road, Southampton SO15 1GX

CC NO 803291   **ESTABLISHED** 1990

■ The Ashden Trust

WHERE FUNDING CAN BE GIVEN UK and overseas.

WHO CAN BENEFIT Registered charities.

WHAT IS FUNDED The environment UK – in the areas of transport policy, sustainable agriculture, energy efficiency and renewable energy technology; Environment overseas – community-based renewable energy projects that aim to help people to help themselves in an environmentally sustainable way; People at Risk – support for organisations that help homeless people to access emergency shelter and support, to secure permanent accommodation and to regain economic independence; Sustainable Regeneration – aimed at schemes that help people to develop skills, improve self-esteem and increase employment prospects in areas of urban deprivation, including projects concerning drug misuse and offending through training and education programmes; Environment and Community Arts – grass-roots arts activities and in particular those groups for which relatively modest grants can have a considerable impact, with an interest in environmental drama; General charitable purposes. The trustees prefer to support innovative schemes that can be successfully replicated or become self-sustaining.

WHAT IS NOT FUNDED The trustees generally do not make grants in response to unsolicited applications. However, see Applications.

TYPE OF GRANT Primarily project.

SAMPLE GRANTS £200,000 allocated for the Ashden Awards for Sustainable Energy. University of Cambridge (£50,000); Dartington Hall Trust (£33,000); Project 58 (£25,000); Alliance of Religions and Conservation (£20,000); Food Up Front (£18,000); Cardboard Citizens (£15,000); Farms for City Children (£10,000); Yorke Trust (£7,800); Thames Reach (£3,000).

FINANCES *Year* 2007–08 *Income* £1,709,335 *Grants* £798,664 *Assets* £26,393,729

TRUSTEES Mrs S Butler-Sloss; R Butler-Sloss; Miss Judith Portrait.

OTHER INFORMATION The trust is one of the Sainsbury Family Charitable Trusts which share a common administration. An application to one is taken as an application to all.

HOW TO APPLY 'The Ashden Trust is one of the Sainsbury Family Charitable Trusts. Before applying to one of the trusts, please read these guidelines: The trust does not normally fund individuals for projects, educational fees or to join expeditions. If you apply for a grant in one of these categories, we are afraid the trustees are unable to help. If you are a registered charity or institution with charitable status applying for a grant we must warn you that only an extremely small number of unsolicited applications are successful. Do not apply to more than one of the Sainsbury Family Charitable Trusts. Each application will be considered by each trust which may have an interest in this field. All of the Sainsbury Family Charitable Trusts have pro-active grant-making policies and have chosen to concentrate their support in a limited number of activities. If you have read through the Ashden Trust's website and feel your project fits into the trust's priorities we would be very interested to hear from you by post. The trustees generally do not make grants in response to unsolicited applications. If you would like to apply to the trust you should send a brief description of the proposed project, by post only, to the director. The proposed project needs to cover: why the project is needed; how, where, when the project will be delivered; who will benefit and in what way; income and expenditure budget; details of funding – secured, applied for; description of the organisation. Please do not send any more than two to four sides of A4 when applying to the trust, at this point additional material is unnecessary.'

WHO TO APPLY TO Alan Bookbinder, Director, Allington House, 1st Floor, 150 Victoria Street, London SW1E 5AE *Tel* 020 7410 0330 *Fax* 020 7410 0332 *email* ashdentrust@sfct.org.uk *Website* www.ashdentrust.org.uk

CC NO 802623   **ESTABLISHED** 1989

■ The Ashendene Trust

WHERE FUNDING CAN BE GIVEN Unrestricted, in practice mainly London, Oxfordshire and Berkshire.

WHO CAN BENEFIT Registered charities.

WHAT IS FUNDED Small organisations including those assisting ex-offenders, people who are socially deprived, horticulture, the arts and churches. This is a small trust that gives to organisations where the grant will really make an impact.

WHAT IS NOT FUNDED No support for large organisations, education or health. No scholarships or individual grants.

TYPE OF GRANT Capital, core costs and project. Funding available for up to three years.

SAMPLE GRANTS Chiswick House Garden Trust and Royal Horticultural Society (£6,250 each); Eton College and Watermill Theatre (£5,000 each); St Luke's Hospital (£2,500); Abingdon Bridge, Butler Trust and UBS (£2,000 each); Terrence Higgins Trust (£1,000); Ashmolean Museum, London Parks and Gardens Trust, Wantage Parish Church and ZANE – Zimbabwe (£250 each); Garsington Opera (£150); and Victorian Society and Wantage Choral Society (£100 each).

FINANCES *Year* 2007–08 *Income* £45,778 *Grants* £56,796 *Assets* £1,092,128

TRUSTEES Sir Simon Hornby; Sir Edward Cazalet; A D Loehnis; Nicholas Hornby.

HOW TO APPLY In writing to the correspondent. Replies are only made to those who enclose an sae.

WHO TO APPLY TO Sir Simon Hornby, The Ham, Wantage, Oxfordshire OX12 9JA *Tel* 01235 770222

CC NO 270749   **ESTABLISHED** 1975

■ The Laura Ashley Foundation

WHERE FUNDING CAN BE GIVEN Mostly Wales, other areas considered.

WHO CAN BENEFIT Charitable organisations.

WHAT IS FUNDED The foundation has a strong commitment to art and design and also to Wales, particularly Powys, where the Ashley business was first established. 'The Laura Ashley Foundation is constantly reviewing funding policies. For this reason, we tend to be re-active grant givers, rather than pro-active. Very few unsolicited applications receive funding. To avoid disappointment, we suggest checking before applying.'

WHAT IS NOT FUNDED The foundation does not fund individuals or business ventures.

FINANCES *Year* 2007–08 *Income* £314,250 *Grants* £464,485 *Assets* £10,445,522

TRUSTEES Jane Ashley, Chair; Prof. Susan Golombok; Martyn C Gowar; Emma Shuckburgh; Helena Appio; David Goldstone.

HOW TO APPLY Potential applicants are encouraged to check the foundation's website before submitting an application.

WHO TO APPLY TO The Secretary, The Laura Ashley Foundation, Rhydoldog House, Cwmdauddwr, Rhayader, Powys LD6 5HB *Website* www.lauraashleyfoundation.org.uk

CC NO 288099   **ESTABLISHED** 1985

■ The Norman C Ashton Foundation

WHERE FUNDING CAN BE GIVEN Preference for the Leeds area.

WHO CAN BENEFIT Charitable organisations.

WHAT IS FUNDED Educational, healthcare and homelessness.

TYPE OF GRANT One-off.

SAMPLE GRANTS Genesis (£3,000); Action for Sick Children, Child Care Action Group, New Hope and Rothwell Baptist Church (£2,000 each); and Tall Ships Youth Trust (£1,000).

FINANCES *Year* 2007–08 *Income* £31,167 *Grants* £16,909 *Assets* £738,597

TRUSTEES Mrs Susan Sharp, Chair; Mrs Catherine Ashton; Mrs Georgina Stevens.

HOW TO APPLY The foundation does not accept unsolicited applications.

WHO TO APPLY TO Mrs Susan Sharp, Ivy House Barn, School Lane, Walton, Wetherby, West Yorkshire LS23 7DW *Tel* 01937 849608

CC NO 260036   **ESTABLISHED** 1969

■ The Ashworth Charitable Trust

WHERE FUNDING CAN BE GIVEN UK and worldwide, with some preference for certain specific needs in Honiton, Ottery St Mary, Sidmouth and Wonford Green surgery, Exeter.

WHO CAN BENEFIT Individuals (living in the areas covered by the medical practices in Ottery St Mary, Honiton and Sidmouth only) and organisations.

WHAT IS FUNDED General charitable purposes. Particular emphasis is given to support for the Ironbridge Gorge Museum Trust and to humanitarian projects.

WHAT IS NOT FUNDED No grants for research-based charities; animal charities; 'heritage charities' such as National Trust or other organisations whose aim is the preservation of a building, museum, library and so on (with the exception of the Ironbridge Gorge Museum).; 'faith-based' charities, unless the project is for primarily humanitarian purposes and is neither exclusive to those of that particular faith or evangelical in its purpose. Grants to individuals are strictly limited to the geographical area and purpose specified in the general section.

RANGE OF GRANTS £500–£11,000.

SAMPLE GRANTS UNICEF UK (£11,000); Hospiscare and Ironbridge Gorge Museum Trust (£10,000 each); Find Your Feet (£5,000); Zero Centre (Merseyside) and Children's Overseas Relief Fund (£4,000 each); The John Fawcett Foundation and Cerebral Palsy Africa (£3,000 each); Hope Direct and The Woodford Foundation (£2,500 each); New Bridge (£2,000); Hope's Place (£1,500); Dream Holidays (£1,000); and Back to Work (£500).

FINANCES *Year* 2007–08 *Income* £146,213 *Grants* £126,528 *Assets* £3,921,859

TRUSTEES C F Bennett, Chair; Mrs S E Webberley; Mrs K A Gray; G D R Cockram.

HOW TO APPLY In writing to the correspondent.

WHO TO APPLY TO Mrs G Towner, Foot Anstey, Senate Court, Southernhay Gardens, Exeter EX1 1NT *Tel* 01392 411221 *Fax* 01392 685220 *email* ashworthtrust@btinternet.com

CC NO 1045492   **ESTABLISHED** 1995

■ The Ian Askew Charitable Trust

WHERE FUNDING CAN BE GIVEN UK, with a preference for Sussex, and overseas.

WHO CAN BENEFIT Mainly headquarters organisations.

WHAT IS FUNDED General charitable purposes; education; health research; particularly mental health; preservation of ancient buildings; maintenance and conservation of woodlands.

RANGE OF GRANTS Most grants for £500 or less.

SAMPLE GRANTS Sussex Heritage Trust (£2,500); Friends of Home Physiotherapy Service AND Meningitis UK (£1,500 each); and Friends of Nakura, Kambia Hospital Appeal, Kids Kidney Research, the Landmark Trust, Laughton Community Primary School, the Salvation Army, Save the Children Fund, St Barnabas Hospice, St John Ambulance and Wells for India (£1,000 each).

FINANCES *Year* 2007–08 *Income* £388,201 *Grants* £91,748 *Assets* £8,775,284

TRUSTEES J R Hecks, Chair; R A R Askew; J B Rank; R P G Lewis.

OTHER INFORMATION The trust also maintains the woodlands at Plashett Estate, East Sussex, the main part of which is designated as a site of special and scientific interest. The woodlands are used principally for educational purposes.

HOW TO APPLY In writing to the correspondent. Applications are considered every other month.

WHO TO APPLY TO The Trustees, c/o Baker Tilly, 18 Mount Ephraim Road, Tunbridge Wells, Kent TN1 1ED

CC NO 264515   **ESTABLISHED** 1972

■ The Associated Country Women of the World (ACWW)

WHERE FUNDING CAN BE GIVEN Overseas.

WHO CAN BENEFIT Small local projects and established organisations benefiting children, young adults and rural communities in particular. Projects must have a female emphasis.

WHAT IS FUNDED Education, environmental resources and projects in connection with: literacy, agriculture and income generating schemes.

WHAT IS NOT FUNDED No grants to individuals or students unless they are a member of an ACWW society.

TYPE OF GRANT One-off.

SAMPLE GRANTS Beneficiaries of grants approved in 2008 include: project for livestock and poultry raising in China (£12,000); training in income generation skills to 40 women with disabilities in South Lorea (£8,100); programme for sustainable economic development of 180 Dalit women in India (£8,000); completion of literacy and skills development centre in the Gambia (£6,000); and project for income generation through training in textile production in Cameroon (£3,000);.

FINANCES *Year* 2007–08 *Income* £482,749 *Grants* £210,000 *Assets* £2,019,977

TRUSTEES Margaret Cadzow; Dato Ursula Goh; May Kidd; Anphia Grobler.

PUBLICATIONS *Working with Women Worldwide.* (Please visit the trusts website for a full list of publications.)

HOW TO APPLY In writing to the correspondent.

WHO TO APPLY TO The General Secretary, Mary Sumner House, 24 Tufton Street, London SW1P 3RB *Tel* 020 7799 3875 *Fax* 020 7340 9950 *email* info@acww.org.uk *Website* www.acww.org.uk

CC NO 290367   **ESTABLISHED** 1933

■ The Association of Colleges Charitable Trust

WHERE FUNDING CAN BE GIVEN UK.

WHO CAN BENEFIT Further education establishments.

WHAT IS FUNDED Further education. The charitable trust is responsible for administering two programmes. The largest of these is the Beacon Awards, which provide monetary grants to award-winning initiatives within further education colleges. The other scheme is the AoC Gold Awards for Further Education Alumni, which reward former members of further education colleges who have since excelled in their chosen field or profession.

WHAT IS NOT FUNDED Grants are not made to individuals.

FINANCES *Year* 2007–08 *Income* £65,867 *Grants* £222,046 *Assets* £140,096

TRUSTEES Alice Thiagaraj; Peter Brophy; M Doel; R Eve; David Forrester; John Bingham.

OTHER INFORMATION The charitable trust is responsible for administering two programmes. The largest of these is the Beacon Awards, which provide monetary grants to award-winning initiatives within further education colleges. The other scheme is the AoC Gold Awards for Further Education Alumni, which reward former members of further education colleges who have since excelled in their chosen field or profession.

HOW TO APPLY See the trust's website for further information.

WHO TO APPLY TO The Trust Manager, 2–6 Stedham Place, London WC1A 1HU *Website* www.aoc.co.uk

CC NO 1040631   **ESTABLISHED** 1994

■ The Association of Friends of Essex Churches

WHERE FUNDING CAN BE GIVEN Essex and the boroughs of Waltham Forest, Redbridge, Newham, Barking and Dagenham and Havering.

WHO CAN BENEFIT Any Christian church.

WHAT IS FUNDED Churches, irrespective of denomination, where the repairs necessary are beyond parish resources.

WHAT IS NOT FUNDED Grants are not given for new work or annual maintenance, for example gutter clearance, or redecoration. No grants towards heating systems.

TYPE OF GRANT One-off (but may apply again in subsequent years) and buildings.

RANGE OF GRANTS £200–£20,000.

FINANCES *Year* 2008 *Income* £145,163 *Grants* £194,450 *Assets* £319,383

TRUSTEES Mrs J Abel Smith, Chair; Mrs C Cottrell; K Gardner; I G Dudley; D Lodge; Dr J Bettley; D Woracker; Mrs F Nelmes; R Meloy; Mrs M Blaxall.

HOW TO APPLY On a form available from the correspondent. The Grants Committee meets quarterly.

WHO TO APPLY TO John Bloomfield, Grants Hon. Secretary, 39 Lake Rise, Romford RM1 4DZ *Tel* 01708 745273 *email* john.bloomfield@btinternet.com *Website* www.foect.org.uk

CC NO 236033   **ESTABLISHED** 1952

■ Astellas European Foundation

WHERE FUNDING CAN BE GIVEN Worldwide.

WHO CAN BENEFIT Scientific research institutes, universities, research workers and medical professionals.

WHAT IS FUNDED The objects of the foundation are: committing long-term support to basic medical and related scientific programmes through organisations such as the Societe Internationale D'Urologie; supporting selected short, medium and long-term projects, aimed at integrating basic science and clinical research through interdisciplinary projects; providing facilities, promoting or sponsoring the exchange of ideas and views through lectures and discussions of an educational or cultural nature; promoting, assisting or otherwise supporting charitable institutions aimed at serving good causes.

FINANCES *Year* 2007–08 *Income* £333,000 *Grants* £38,000

TRUSTEES Dr Toichi Takenaka; Yasho Ishii; Ken Jones; Masafumi Nogimori; Masao Yoshida; Dr John Bolodeoku; Yoshirou Miyokawa.

OTHER INFORMATION All figures in the annual report were shown in US Dollars. In 2007–08 donations to charities totalled US$62,000.

HOW TO APPLY In writing to the correspondent.

WHO TO APPLY TO The Trustees, Lovett House, Causeway Corporate Centre, Staines, Middlesex TW18 3AZ

CC NO 1036344   **ESTABLISHED** 1993

■ Aston–Mansfield Charitable Trust

WHERE FUNDING CAN BE GIVEN The borough of Newham.

WHO CAN BENEFIT Organisations.

WHAT IS FUNDED 'The objects of the charity are to develop the community wealth of East London and promote a diverse and inclusive society in which all are free to participate.'

WHAT IS NOT FUNDED Revenue funding for salaries and maintenance is unlikely to be given. No national appeals and no grants to individuals.

TYPE OF GRANT Capital (including buildings), feasibility studies, one-off, project and research. Funding of one year or less will be considered.

FINANCES *Year* 2007–08 *Income* £536,753 *Grants* £1,025,148 *Assets* £1,399,101

TRUSTEES Christopher C Keen, Chair; Alan J Shelley; Catherine M Brett; Rt Revd John Gladwin; Dharam B Lall; Andrew F West.

HOW TO APPLY In writing to the correspondent. No guidelines; no forms.

WHO TO APPLY TO Geoffrey Wheeler, Company Secretary, Durning Hall, Earlham Grove, Forest Gate, London E7 9AB *Tel* 020 8536 3812 *email* geoffrey.wheeler@aston-mansfield.org.uk *Website* www.aston-mansfield.org.uk

CC NO 208155   **ESTABLISHED** 1930

■ The Astor Foundation

WHERE FUNDING CAN BE GIVEN UK.

WHO CAN BENEFIT Medical research organisations. Children and youth groups, people who are disabled, the countryside, the arts, sport, carers groups and animal welfare.

WHAT IS FUNDED Medical research in its widest sense, favouring research on a broad front rather than in specialised fields. In addition to its medical connection, historically the foundation has also supported initiatives for children and youth groups, people who are disabled, the countryside, the arts, sport, carers groups and animal welfare.

WHAT IS NOT FUNDED No grants to individuals or towards salaries. Grants are given to registered charities only.

TYPE OF GRANT Preference for assistance with the launching and initial stages of new projects and filling in gaps/shortfalls.

RANGE OF GRANTS £500–£45,000; generally £250–£1,500.

SAMPLE GRANTS Special Boat Service (£7,000); League of Friends – University College London Hospitals (£5,000); Combat Stress (£4,000); Samaritans (£3,000); Alzheimer's Disease Society (£2,500); British Forces Foundation, RoSPA and Tank Museum (£2,000 each); Winton's Wish (£1,500); and Aldeburgh Music and Two Moors Festival (£1,000 each).

FINANCES *Year* 2007–08 *Income* £140,487 *Grants* £107,000 *Assets* £3,507,533

TRUSTEES J R Astor, Chair; Sir William Slack; Lord Astor of Hever; Dr H Swanton; R H Astor; C Money-Coutts.

HOW TO APPLY There are no deadline dates or application forms. Applications should be in writing to the correspondent and must include accounts and an annual report if available. The trustees meet twice yearly, usually in October and April. If the appeal arrives too late for one meeting it will automatically be carried over for consideration at the following meeting. An acknowledgement will be sent on receipt of an appeal. No further communication will be entered into unless the trustees raise any queries regarding the appeal, or unless the appeal is subsequently successful.

WHO TO APPLY TO Lisa Rothwell-Orr, Secretary, PO Box 3096, Marlborough, Wiltshire SN8 3WP *email* astor.foundation@virgin.net

CC NO 225708   **ESTABLISHED** 1963

■ The Astor of Hever Trust

WHERE FUNDING CAN BE GIVEN UK and worldwide, with a preference for Kent and the Grampian region of Scotland.

WHO CAN BENEFIT Both headquarters and local branches of charities, mainly established organisations with particular emphasis on Kent.

WHAT IS FUNDED Charitable bodies in the fields of the arts, medicine, religion, education, conservation, young people and sport.

WHAT IS NOT FUNDED No grants to individuals.

RANGE OF GRANTS £20–£1,000.

SAMPLE GRANTS Royal British Legion (£2,100 in four grants); National Autistic Society (£1,800 in three grants); Bryanston School, Game Conservancy Trust, Launde Abbey Trust and Leicester Samaritans, Logie Coldstone Trust, Mercy Ships, Luke Rees-Pulley Charitable Trust and Take Heart (£1,000 each); Compaid Trust (£500); NSPCC (£300); Whizz Kidz (£250); Bone Cancer Research UK (£100); Kent Autistic Trust (£50).

FINANCES *Year* 2007–08 *Income* £39,133 *Grants* £32,020 *Assets* £1,069,995

TRUSTEES John Jacob, Third Baron Astor of Hever; Hon. Philip D P Astor; Hon Camilla Astor.

HOW TO APPLY In writing to the correspondent. Trustees meet twice each year. Unsuccessful applications are not acknowledged.

WHO TO APPLY TO The Trustees, Frenchstreet House, Westerham, Kent TN16 1PW *Tel* 01959 565070

CC NO 264134   **ESTABLISHED** 1955

■ The Aurelius Charitable Trust

WHERE FUNDING CAN BE GIVEN UK.

WHO CAN BENEFIT Registered charities, historic societies, museums/galleries and academic bodies.

WHAT IS FUNDED Conservation/preservation of culture inherited from the past; the dissemination of knowledge, particularly in the humanities field; research or publications.

WHAT IS NOT FUNDED No grants to individuals.

TYPE OF GRANT Seed-corn or completion funding not otherwise available, usually one-off.

RANGE OF GRANTS Generally £500–£3,000.

SAMPLE GRANTS The British Academy (£7,500); British School at Athens (£6,000); the Wallace Collection (£5,000); London International Film School (£4,000); University of Roehampton (£5,000); English National Opera (£3,400); National Museums Liverpool (£2,900); Courtauld Institute of Art (£2,800); Glasgow School of Art (£2,750); Royal Academy of Arts (£2,000); the Seeing Ear (£1,000); the Worcestershire Historical Society (£600); and the Dugdale Society (£200).

FINANCES *Year* 2007–08 *Income* £95,912 *Grants* £81,050 *Assets* £2,086,580

TRUSTEES W J Wallis; P E Haynes.

HOW TO APPLY In writing to the correspondent. Donations are generally made on the recommendation of the trust's board of advisors. Unsolicited applications will only be responded to if an sae is included. Trustees meet twice a year.

WHO TO APPLY TO P E Haynes, Trustee, Briarsmead, Old Road, Buckland, Betchworth, Surrey RH3 7DU *Tel* 01737 842186 *email* philip.haynes@tiscali.co.uk

CC NO 271333   **ESTABLISHED** 1975

■ The Lord Austin Trust

WHERE FUNDING CAN BE GIVEN Birmingham and its immediate area.

WHO CAN BENEFIT Charitable institutions or projects in England, restricted to: local charities based in Birmingham and West Midlands; and national organisations (but not their provincial branches).

WHAT IS FUNDED Emphasis on the welfare of children, the care of older people, medical institutions and research.

WHAT IS NOT FUNDED No support for appeals from, or on behalf of, individual applicants.

TYPE OF GRANT One-off.

RANGE OF GRANTS Usually £500–£3,000.

SAMPLE GRANTS St Giles Hospice (£7,500); Birmingham Children's Hospital (£5,000); St Joseph's Old People's Home – Little Sisters of the Poor and Avoncroft Museum of Buildings (£3,000 each); Accord, Birmingham Boys and Girls Union and Birmingham Federation of Clubs for Young People (£2,500 each); Birmingham Settlement, Blond McIndoee Research Foundation, DePaul Trust, Epilepsy Action, Family Holiday Association, Primrose Hospice, St Jasmes Playgroup, Whizz Kids and 870 House (£1,000 each).

FINANCES *Year* 2007–08 *Income* £126,320 *Grants* £129,750 *Assets* £3,375,117

TRUSTEES J M G Fea; R S Kettel; A N Andrews

HOW TO APPLY In writing to the correspondent, including a set of recent accounts. Trustees meet twice a year in or around May and November to consider grants. The trustees stress that new awards are now severely limited.

WHO TO APPLY TO Ms Chrissy Norgrove, c/o Martineau Johnson, 1 Colmore Square, Birmingham B4 6AA *Tel* 0870 763 2000 *email* christine.norgrove@martineau-uk.com

CC NO 208394   **ESTABLISHED** 1937

■ The Avenue Charitable Trust

WHERE FUNDING CAN BE GIVEN Worldwide.

WHO CAN BENEFIT Registered charities and individuals.

WHAT IS FUNDED General charitable purposes.

TYPE OF GRANT One-off and recurrent.

RANGE OF GRANTS Generally £25–£50,000, although occasionally larger grants are given.

SAMPLE GRANTS Delta Trust (£150,000); Prison Video Trust and Tavistock and Portman Charitable Fund (£25,000 each); Living Landscape Project and Prisoners Abroad (£10,000 each); Adam von Trott Memorial Appeal (£5,000); Amnesty International (£2,000); Toynbee Hall (£1,000); and Polish Institute Sikowski Museum (£25).

FINANCES *Year* 2007–08 *Income* £378,079 *Grants* £256,839 *Assets* £595,712

TRUSTEES R D L Astor; Hon. Mrs B A Astor; G W B Todd.

OTHER INFORMATION The grant total in 2007–08 includes £13,000 given to an individual.

HOW TO APPLY The trust has previously stated that all available income is now committed to existing beneficiaries.

WHO TO APPLY TO Susan Simmons, c/o Messrs Sayers Butterworth, 18 Bentinck Street, London W1M 5RL *Tel* 020 7935 8504

CC NO 264804   **ESTABLISHED** 1972

■ The John Avins Trustees

WHERE FUNDING CAN BE GIVEN Birmingham and district.

WHO CAN BENEFIT Medical charities. Support may be given to medical professionals and research workers.

WHAT IS FUNDED Medical charities in Birmingham and neighbourhood, and the following charities mentioned in the will of John Avins: Birmingham Blue Coat School; Birmingham Royal Institution for the Blind; and Middlemore Homes, Birmingham.

WHAT IS NOT FUNDED No grants to individuals, non-medical charities or for purposes outside the beneficial area.

TYPE OF GRANT One-off.

RANGE OF GRANTS Up to £7,500.

SAMPLE GRANTS Sir John Middlemore Charitable Trust (£7,500); Birmingham Focus on Blindness (£5,000); Home from Hospital Care, Multiple Births Foundation and Independence at Home (£3,000 each); Spinal Research, St Martin's Centre for Health and Healing and Vitalise (£2,000 each); and Dream Holidays and Birmingham Bluecoat School (£1,000 each).

FINANCES *Year* 2007–08 *Income* £73,554 *Grants* £54,275 *Assets* £1,300,375

TRUSTEES Hon Alderman I McArdle, Chair; C F Smith; C J Timbrell; V C Sharma; Prof D Cox.

OTHER INFORMATION In 2007–08 a further £2,000 was given in scholarships.

HOW TO APPLY On a form available from the correspondent. Trustees meet in April and November.

WHO TO APPLY TO J M G Fea, Joint Secretary, 1 Colmore Square, Birmingham B4 6AA *Tel* 0870 763 2000

CC NO 217301   **ESTABLISHED** 1931

Think carefully about every application. Is it justified?

343

■ The Avon and Somerset Police Community Trust

WHERE FUNDING CAN BE GIVEN The Avon and Somerset Constabulary area.

WHO CAN BENEFIT Organisations.

WHAT IS FUNDED The trustees favour projects that: promote safety and quality of life in the Avon and Somerset Constabulary area; through the prevention of crime and disorder, protect young people, people who are vulnerable and older people from criminal acts; advance education, including that related to alcohol, drugs, solvent misuse, community relations and responsible citizenship.

WHAT IS NOT FUNDED The trust does not support: individuals, including students; expeditions; bursaries or scholarships; replacement of statutory funding; building works; projects that fall outside the constabulary's geographical area.

SAMPLE GRANTS TRFK Community Gates to match-fund cost of supplying and installing security gates (£5,000); 2 Bridges Drug and Alcohol Trust to assist in the resettlement of drug and alcohol misusers and Goblin Coomb Environment Centre towards activities for young people (£3,000 each); Cheddar Grove – Hartcliffe towards multi-use games area for young people (£2,500); Clevedon Youth Forum towards event and activities for young people (£1,500); Prital Alleygate Scheme – Bristol to match-fund cost of supplying and installing gates security gates (£1,200); Barton Hill Young Women's Group towards materials and equipment, Bath Youth for Christ Graffiti Project towards paints and materials for graffiti project, Portishead Activity Week towards events and activities for children and South Gloucestershire PE Association towards mentor support (£1,000 each); North Somerset Schools Road Safety Week towards purchase of role-play playground road safety equipment (£750); Sparkford Playing Field Association for equipment for young people (£600); and TGI Friday Kidz Klub – Horfield towards cost of equipment for weekly youth club (£500).

FINANCES *Year* 2007–08 *Income* £578,000 *Grants* £280,000

TRUSTEES Dr Moira Hamlin; Colin Port; Mary Prior; Henry Elwes; Lady Gass; Ian Hoddell; Roger James; Brian Tanner; Paul Upham.

OTHER INFORMATION The grant total includes funds used to run the trust's own projects and initiatives.

HOW TO APPLY For further information about the trust or advice on obtaining or completing the trust's application form please contact the Trust Manager. The trustees meet quarterly to consider the business of the trust and approve grants in accordance with the trust's aims and objectives. Grants in support of major projects are routinely reviewed and awarded by the trustees at the commencement of each financial year at their April meeting. All other grants are considered on their merit, having met the criteria for a grant as set out in the trust's aims and objectives.

WHO TO APPLY TO Paul Lillington, Trust Manager, PO Box 37, Valley Road, Portishead, Bristol BS20 8QJ *Tel* 01275 816240 *Fax* 01275 816129 *email* paul.lillington@avonandsomerset.police.uik *Website* www.avonandsomerset.police.uk

CC NO 1076770   **ESTABLISHED** 1999

■ AW Charitable Trust

WHERE FUNDING CAN BE GIVEN Unrestricted.

WHO CAN BENEFIT Jewish educational and religious organisations; registered charities.

WHAT IS FUNDED General charitable purposes.

SAMPLE GRANTS TET (£725,000); Asser Bishvil Foundation (£287,000); Chevras Oneg Shabbos-Yomtov (£227,000); Friends of Mir (£225,000); CML (£98,000); Toimchei Shabbos Manchester (£37,000); British Friends of Kupat Hair (£25,000); Purim Fund (£10,000); Beenstock Home (£5,000); and Zoreya Tzedokos (£1,800).

FINANCES *Year* 2007–08 *Income* £10,593,657 *Grants* £4,133,650 *Assets* £54,435,736

TRUSTEES Rabbi Aubrey Weis; Mrs R Weis; Rabbi Z Cohen.

HOW TO APPLY In writing to the correspondent. The trust considers 'all justified applications for support of educational establishments, places of worship and other charitable actives.'

WHO TO APPLY TO Rabbi Aubrey Weis, 66 Waterpark Road, Manchester M7 4JL *Tel* 0161 740 0116

CC NO 283322   **ESTABLISHED** 1961

■ Awards for All (see also the Big Lottery Fund)

WHERE FUNDING CAN BE GIVEN UK.

WHO CAN BENEFIT Community groups/clubs/societies; registered charity or exempt or excepted charities registered with the Inland Revenue in England; parish or town councils; schools; health bodies; companies limited by guarantee.

WHAT IS NOT FUNDED Generally, organisations with an income more than £20,000 a year (though there are exceptions to this, particularly for projects coming through schools and similar bodies). Also: costs related to existing projects, activities or resources currently provided by your group, for example, ongoing staff costs and utility bills, regular rent payments, maintenance (including maintenance equipment) and annual events; items which only benefit an individual, for example, scholarships or bursaries; activities promoting religious beliefs; activities that are part of statutory obligations or replace statutory funding, including curricular activity in schools; endowments; loan payments; second hand road vehicles; projects with high ongoing maintenance costs – unless your group can show that you have the funds/skills to maintain them once your Awards for All grant runs out.

TYPE OF GRANT Here are some of the things that a grant could be spent on: publicity materials; venue hire; computers; research costs; transport costs; volunteers' expenses; updating equipment for health and safety reasons; refurbishment; training; sessional staff; fees to hire equipment; educational toys and games.

RANGE OF GRANTS £300–£10,000.

FINANCES *Year* 2009–10 *Grants* £61,400,000

OTHER INFORMATION Detailed guidance notes are provided by Awards for All.

HOW TO APPLY All information is in the application pack. The application form is simple, but the applicant organisation must be organised to the extent of having a constitution, a bank account and a set of accounts (unless a new organisation). If you have a general enquiry or want an application form to be sent to you, please contact Awards for All on one of the following: Tel: 0845 600 20 40; Textphone: 0845 755 66 56; Email: general.enquiries@awardsforall.org.uk. The application form and guidance notes may also be downloaded from the Awards for All website. For projects where the beneficiaries are based in the Eastern, North East, North West, South East or Yorkshire and the Humber regions: Awards for All, 2 St James' Gate, Newcastle Upon Tyne, NE1 4BE; Tel: 0191 376 1600; Fax: 0191 376 1661; Textphone: 0191 376 1776.For projects where the beneficiaries are based in the East Midlands, West Midlands, London or South West regions: Big Lottery Fund, Apex House, 3 Embassy Drive, Calthorpe Road, Edgbaston, Birmingham, B15 1TR; Tel: 0121 345 7700; Fax: 0121 345 8888; Minicom: 0121 345 7666.For information about Awards for All Wales: Tel: 0845 410 2030; Fax: 01686 622458; Textphone: 0845 602 1659; Email: enquiries.wales@biglotteryfund.org.uk.Awards for All – Scotland, 4th Floor, Atlantic Quay, 1 Robertson Street, Glasgow, G2 8JB; Tel: 0141 242 1400; Fax: 0141 242 1401; Textphone: 0141 242 1500; Email: scotland@awardsforall.org.uk.Awards for All – Northern Ireland, 1 Cromac Quay, Cromac Wood, Ormeau Road, Belfast, BT7 2JD; Tel: 028 9055 1455; Fax: 028 9055 1444; Textphone: 028 9055 1431; Email: enquiries.ni@awardsforall.org.uk.

WHO TO APPLY TO (See 'How to apply' section) *Tel* 0845 600 2040 *Website* www.awardsforall.org.uk

···

■ The Aylesford Family Charitable Trust

WHERE FUNDING CAN BE GIVEN West Midlands and Warwickshire.

WHO CAN BENEFIT Registered charities.

WHAT IS FUNDED General charitable purposes.

WHAT IS NOT FUNDED Grants are not normally given to individuals.

RANGE OF GRANTS £50–£10,000.

SAMPLE GRANTS The Prince's Trust (£5,000); ARC Addington Fund (£2,000); Save the Elephant (£1,500); Army Benevolent Fund, Farm Africa and Seafarers UK (£1,000 each); Albrighton Trust, Highland Hospice and Water Aid (£500); SSAFA and Waterbog Welfare Trust (£250 each); and Rainbow Trust (£200).

FINANCES *Year* 2007–08 *Income* £64,393 *Grants* £34,000 *Assets* £1,820,757

TRUSTEES Lord Guernsey; Lady Guernsey.

HOW TO APPLY In writing to the correspondent at any time.

WHO TO APPLY TO The Trustees, Packington Hall, Meriden, Warwickshire CV7 7HF

CC NO 328299   **ESTABLISHED** 1989

■ The B-CH Charitable Trust

WHERE FUNDING CAN BE GIVEN UK, with preference for Cornwall and Devon.

WHO CAN BENEFIT Registered charities only, benefiting children and sick people. Support may be given to medical professionals and research workers.

WHAT IS FUNDED Children's and medical charities.

WHAT IS NOT FUNDED No grants to individuals.

RANGE OF GRANTS £500 or £1,000.

SAMPLE GRANTS The British Red Cross Disaster Fund, Cornwall Disabled Association, Macmillan Nursing Fund (£1,000 each); and Action for medical Research, Bikeability South Coast, the Blue Cross, Children in Crisis, Compaid Trust, Dogs for the Disabled, Extracare Charitable Trust, Hospicecare, Motability, North Devon Hospice, Starlight Children's Trust and West of England School (£500 each).

FINANCES *Year* 2007–08 *Income* £74,316 *Grants* £22,500 *Assets* £713,099

TRUSTEES Miss J Holman; E N Reed.

HOW TO APPLY In writing to the correspondent. The trustees meet twice a year to consider applications.

WHO TO APPLY TO Edward N Reed, c/o Macfarlanes, 10 Norwich Street, London EC4A 1BD

CC NO 263241   **ESTABLISHED** 1971

■ The BAA Communities Trust

WHERE FUNDING CAN BE GIVEN Local communities around the following BAA run airports: Heathrow, Gatwick, Stansted, Southampton, Edinburgh, Glasgow and Aberdeen. Limited help is available for projects in the area immediately surrounding BAA's HQ in Victoria, London.

WHO CAN BENEFIT Charitable organisations.

WHAT IS FUNDED 'The trust was established to help communities, primarily those around BAA Limited airports, meet the challenges of the 21st Century, focusing on education, environment and economic regeneration/ employment. Following a strategic review in July 2005, the trust has grown its area of activities to include support for community initiatives brought forward by staff and local community opportunities, in particular for young people, created through global or national programmes.'

WHAT IS NOT FUNDED Anything which falls outside the criteria will not be considered. In particular, applications which benefit individuals only, whether or not they meet the other criteria, will fail. No support for religious or political projects. Grants will not be made to nationally based organisations unless the direct benefit will be felt locally and the other criteria are satisfied.

RANGE OF GRANTS £500–£60,000.

SAMPLE GRANTS VSO (£158,000); Young Engineers (£52,000); Groundwork Thames Valley (£30,000); National Trust Scotland Community Partnership Project (£25,000); Whitecrook Park Project Glasgow (£15,000); Hockerill School – Bishop Stortford, Little Hallingbury Primary School, St Nicholas Church Charlwood, Surrey and Sussex Youth Games and Sussex Community Council (£10,000 each); Unity Enterprises (£7,500); 999 Dunmow Squadron

Air Training Corp (£5,000); Bitterne Park School Enterprise Days and Sele School – Hertford Minibus Fund (£3,000 each); the Box – Youth Project Essex and the Mayor of Southampton Charities (£2,000 each); Young Enterprise Airport Masterclass (£1,800); Chelmer and Blackwater Navigation (£1,500); Breast Cancer Care and Guide Dogs for the Blind (£1,400); and Fire Service National Benevolent Fund and Forget Me Not Club (£1,000 each).

FINANCES *Year* 2007 *Income* £772,797 *Grants* £566,430 *Assets* £1,095,077

TRUSTEES Helen Murley, Chair; Brendan Gold; Tom Kelly; Alastair McDermid; David McMillan.

HOW TO APPLY In writing to the correspondent.

WHO TO APPLY TO Caroline Nicholls, Director, The Compass Centre, Nelson Road, Hounslow, Middlesex TW6 2GW *email* caroline_nicholls@baa.com *Website* www.baa.com

CC NO 1058617   **ESTABLISHED** 1996

■ Harry Bacon Foundation

WHERE FUNDING CAN BE GIVEN UK.

WHO CAN BENEFIT Registered charities.

WHAT IS FUNDED Particularly medical charities and animal welfare.

SAMPLE GRANTS Beneficiaries were Arthritis Research Campaign, British Heart Foundation, Cancer Research UK, the Donkey Sanctuary, International League for the Protection of Horses, Parkinson's Disease Society, PDSA and RNLI.

FINANCES *Year* 2007–08 *Income* £73,246 *Grants* £36,000

TRUSTEES NatWest Bank plc.

HOW TO APPLY In writing to the correspondent.

WHO TO APPLY TO The Trust Manager, National Westminster Bank PLC, Trust and Estate Services, 5th Floor, Trinity Quay 2, Avon Street, Bristol BS2 0PT

CC NO 1056500   **ESTABLISHED** 1996

■ The BACTA Charitable Trust

WHERE FUNDING CAN BE GIVEN UK.

WHO CAN BENEFIT UK registered charities.

WHAT IS FUNDED Generally to support causes recommended to it by members of the British Amusement Catering Trade Association (BACTA).

WHAT IS NOT FUNDED No grants for overseas charities or religious purposes.

TYPE OF GRANT Long-term support (usually two to three years) to a specific project or charity and one-off donations.

RANGE OF GRANTS £1,000 upwards.

SAMPLE GRANTS Responsibility in Gambling Trust (£300,000); Association of Children's Hospices (£19,000); Sunfield School (£2,000); and BIBIC (£1,300).

FINANCES *Year* 2007–08 *Income* £347,548 *Grants* £321,824 *Assets* £56,953

TRUSTEES J Thomas, Chair; R Higgins; N Harding; M Horwood; S I Meaden; D Orton; J Stergides; M Gemson.

HOW TO APPLY In writing to the correspondent via a BACTA member.

WHO TO APPLY TO The Clerk to the Trustees, Alders House, 133 Aldersgate Street, London EC1A 4JA *Website* www.bacta.org.uk

CC NO 328668   **ESTABLISHED** 1991

■ The Bagri Foundation

WHERE FUNDING CAN BE GIVEN Worldwide.
WHO CAN BENEFIT Institutions and individuals.
WHAT IS FUNDED General charitable purposes.
FINANCES *Year* 2007–08 *Income* £118,266
  Grants £169,949 *Assets* £2,175,909
TRUSTEES Lord Bagri; Hon. A Bagri; Lady Bagri.
HOW TO APPLY In writing to the correspondent.
WHO TO APPLY TO The Hon. A Bagri, Secretary, 80
  Cannon Street, London EC4N 6EJ *Tel* 020 7280
  0089
CC NO 1000219   **ESTABLISHED** 1990

■ Veta Bailey Charitable Trust

WHERE FUNDING CAN BE GIVEN Developing countries
  (generally those with GNP less than US$1,000 a
  head), or UK for work in developing countries.
WHO CAN BENEFIT Organisations (UK or overseas
  based) training medical personnel in developing
  countries.
WHAT IS FUNDED Training of doctors and other
  medical personnel and the development of good
  healthcare practices in third world and
  developing countries.
WHAT IS NOT FUNDED No grants to individuals.
TYPE OF GRANT One-off grants.
RANGE OF GRANTS Up to £10,000.
SAMPLE GRANTS Orbis (£6,000); International Centre
  for Eye Health (£5,000); Sightsavers (£4,000);
  and Gurkha Welfare Trust (£2,800).
FINANCES *Year* 2007–08 *Income* £31,419
  Grants £43,072 *Assets* £148,766
TRUSTEES Brian Worth; John Humphreys; Sue Yates;
  Dr Madura Gupta; David Trim.
HOW TO APPLY In writing to the correspondent by
  June, for consideration at a trustees' meeting in
  August.
WHO TO APPLY TO Brian Worth, Trustee, The Cottage,
  Tiltups End, Horsley, Stroud, Gloucestershire
  GL6 0QE *Tel* 01453 833399
CC NO 1007411   **ESTABLISHED** 1981

■ The Austin Bailey Trust

WHERE FUNDING CAN BE GIVEN Swansea and
  worldwide.
WHO CAN BENEFIT Churches, overseas aids
  organisations and local organisations.
WHAT IS FUNDED The foundation was set up to give
  approximately 25% of its income towards the
  advancement of religion by supporting the
  activities of local churches, 25% to relief
  agencies in poorer nations and 50% to local
  charities or branches of national charities to
  help people who are disabled, infirm or aged.
SAMPLE GRANTS Y-Care India – HIV/AIDS programme
  (£9,300); the Family Centre – Bonymaen
  (£2,500); Blaen Wern Farm Trust and Macmillan
  Cancer Support (£750 each); Shelter Cymru
  (£700); Mandeville – Jamaica (£600); CAFOD –
  Zimbabwe and Oxfam – Darfur and Chad
  emergency appeal (£500 each); Reynoldston
  Village Hall (£400); and BikeAbility and Brecon
  and District Disabled Club (£250 each).
FINANCES *Year* 2007–08 *Income* £43,054
  Grants £41,933 *Assets* £489,163
TRUSTEES Clive Vernon Austin Bailey, Chair; Mrs
  Sandra Morton; Archdeacon Robert Williams;
  Revd Ann Lewis; Penelope Ryan.
HOW TO APPLY In writing to the correspondent.
  Applications are considered in May, September
  and December.

WHO TO APPLY TO Clive Vernon Austin Bailey, Chair,
  64 Bosworth Road, New Barnet, Hertfordshire
  EN5 5LP *Tel* 020 8449 4327
CC NO 514912   **ESTABLISHED** 1984

■ The Baily Thomas Charitable Fund

WHERE FUNDING CAN BE GIVEN UK.
WHO CAN BENEFIT Community groups, support groups
  and organisations benefiting people affected by
  learning disability.
WHAT IS FUNDED The trustees restrict their remit to
  learning disability. This can include residential
  facilities; respite; sheltered accommodation;
  crafts and music; support to volunteers; special
  schools and special needs education; care in
  the community; day centres; holidays and
  outings; playschemes; and research.
WHAT IS NOT FUNDED Grants are not normally
  awarded to individuals. The following areas are
  unlikely to receive funding: hospices; minibuses
  except those for residential and/or day care
  services for the learning disabled; advocacy
  projects; arts and theatre projects; physical
  disabilities unless accompanied by significant
  learning disabilities.
TYPE OF GRANT Capital and revenue. Loans may be
  made in certain circumstances. Grants are
  usually one-off.
RANGE OF GRANTS £250 to £130,000.
SAMPLE GRANTS King's College – London
  (£131,000); Autism Cymru and the Calvert Trust
  (£100,000 each); University of Oxford
  (£94,000); CASE Training Services (£80,000);
  RTR Foundation (£70,000); West Sussex
  Learning Links (£60,000); and the Children's
  Trust (£50,000).
FINANCES *Year* 2007–08 *Income* £4,932,831
  Grants £4,100,000 *Assets* £71,030,263
TRUSTEES Charles J T Nangle; Prof. W I Fraser; Prof.
  Anne Farmer; Toby N J nangle; Suzanne Jane
  Marriott.
HOW TO APPLY 'Meetings of the Trustees are usually
  held in June and early December each year and
  applications should therefore be submitted no
  later than 1 May or 1 October for consideration
  at the next relevant meeting. Late applications
  will not be considered. If your application is
  considered under the Small Grants procedure
  then this will be reviewed by the Trustees ahead
  of the usual meetings in June and December.
  Following the meeting all applicants are
  contacted formally to advise on the status of
  their application. Please feel free to submit your
  application whenever you are ready, rather than
  waiting for the deadline. Applications can be
  made online via the trust's website.
  General applications: funding is normally
  considered for capital and revenue costs and for
  both specific projects and for general running/
  core costs. Grants are awarded for amounts from
  £250 and depend on a number of factors
  including the purpose, the total funding
  requirement and the potential sources of other
  funds including, in some cases, matching
  funding. Normally one-off grants are awarded but
  exceptionally a new project may be funded over
  two or three years, subject to satisfactory reports
  of progress. Grants should normally be taken up
  within one year of the issue of the grant offer
  letter which will include conditions relating to the
  release of the grant. The following areas of work
  normally fall within the Fund's policy: capital
  building/renovation/refurbishment works for
  residential, nursing and respite care, and

Think carefully about every application. Is it justified?

347

schools; employment schemes including woodwork, crafts, printing and horticulture; play schemes and play therapy schemes; day and social activities centres including building costs and running costs; support for families, including respite schemes; independent living schemes; support in the community schemes; swimming and hydro-therapy pools and snoezelen rooms. **Research applications:** we consider under learning disability the conditions generally referred to as severe learning difficulties, together with autism. In this area, we consider projects concerning children or adults. Learning disability, thus defined, is our priority for funding. We do not give grants for research into or care of those with mental illness or dyslexia. We generally direct our limited funds towards the initiation of research so that it can progress to the point at which there is sufficient data to support an application to one of the major funding bodies. Applications will only be considered from established research workers and will be subject to normal professional peer review procedures. Applications, limited to five pages with the type no smaller than Times New Roman 12, should be in the form of a scientific summary with a research plan to include a brief background and a short account of the design of the study and number of subjects, the methods of assessment and analysis, timetable, main outcomes and some indication of other opportunities arising from the support of such research. A detailed budget of costs should be submitted together with a justification for the support requested. Details should be included of any other applications for funding which have been made to other funders and their outcomes, if known. We do not expect to contribute towards university overheads. A one page Curriculum Vitae will be required for each of the personnel actually carrying out the study and for their supervisor together with a note of the total number of their peer reviewed publications and details of the ten most significant publications. Evidence may be submitted of the approval of the Ethics Committee of the applicant to the study and approval of the University for the application to the Fund. An 80 word lay summary should also be submitted with the scientific summary. Any papers submitted in excess of those stipulated above will not be passed to the Research Committee for consideration. Before submitting a full application, researchers may submit a one-page summary of the proposed study so that the Trustees may indicate whether they are prepared to consider a full application.
WHO TO APPLY TO Ann Cooper, Secretary to the Trustees, c/o TMF Management (UK) Ltd, 400 Capability Green, Luton LU1 3AE *Tel* 01582 439225 *Fax* 01582 439206 *email* info@ bailythomas.org.uk *Website* www.bailythomas. org.uk'
CC NO 262334   **ESTABLISHED** 1970

....

■ The Baird Trust

WHERE FUNDING CAN BE GIVEN Scotland.
WHO CAN BENEFIT Generally, the Church of Scotland.
WHAT IS FUNDED The trust is chiefly concerned with supporting the repair and refurbishment of the churches and halls belonging to the Church of Scotland. It also endows parishes and gives help to the Church of Scotland in its work.
TYPE OF GRANT One-off for capital and revenue.
SAMPLE GRANTS Previous beneficiaries have included Airth Parish Church, Bellshill West Parish Church, Canisbay Church of Scotland, Church of Scotland Board Ministry, Coltness Memorial

Church – Newmains, Kinross Parish Church, Kinnaird Church – Dundee, Lodging House Mission, London Road Church – Edinburgh, Newmachar Parish Church, St Andrew's Erskine Parish Church, St Michael's Parish Church – Edinburgh, Scottish Churches House and South Parish Church – East Kilbride.
FINANCES *Year* 2008 *Income* £352,019
TRUSTEES Marianne Baird; Hon. Mrs Mary Coltman; Maj. J. Henry Callander; Maj. J M K Erskine; Revd Dr Johnston R McKay; Alan Borthwick; Dr Alison Elliot; Luke M Borwick; Walter Barbour.
HOW TO APPLY On a form which can be downloaded from the trust's website.
WHO TO APPLY TO The Secretary, 182 Bath Street, Glasgow G2 4HG *Tel* 0141 332 0476 *email* info@bairdtrust.org.uk *Website* www. bairdtrust.org.uk
SC NO SC016549   **ESTABLISHED** 1873

....

■ The Baker Charitable Trust

WHERE FUNDING CAN BE GIVEN UK and overseas.
WHO CAN BENEFIT Mainly headquarters organisations.
WHAT IS FUNDED Priority is given to charities concerned with the welfare of Jewish, older and disabled people; neurological research; and people with diabetes and epilepsy. Preference is given to charities in which the trust has special interest, knowledge or association.
WHAT IS NOT FUNDED No grants to individuals or non-registered charities.
TYPE OF GRANT Core costs.
RANGE OF GRANTS £250–£10,000; typical grant £500–£3,000.
SAMPLE GRANTS Previous beneficiaries have included British Council Shaare Zedek Medical Centre, Chai Cancer Care, Community Security Trust, Disabled Living Foundation, Friends of Magen David Adom in Great Britain, Hillel Foundation, Institute of Jewish Policy Research, Jewish Women's Aid, Marie Curie Cancer Care, National Society for Epilepsy, Norwood Ltd, United Jewish Israel Appeal, St John's Hospice, United Synagogue, Winged Fellowship and World Jewish Relief.
FINANCES *Year* 2007–08 *Income* £76,536 *Grants* £56,900 *Assets* £1,214,488
TRUSTEES Dr Harvey Baker; Dr Adrienne Baker.
HOW TO APPLY In writing to the correspondent. The trustees meet to consider applications in January, April, July and October.
WHO TO APPLY TO Dr Harvey Baker, Trustee, 16 Sheldon Avenue, Highgate, London N6 4JT
CC NO 273629   **ESTABLISHED** 1977

....

■ The Roy and Pixie Baker Charitable Trust

WHERE FUNDING CAN BE GIVEN North East of England.
WHO CAN BENEFIT Charitable organisations.
WHAT IS FUNDED Medical research, education, heritage, relief-in-need.
TYPE OF GRANT One-off and recurrent.
RANGE OF GRANTS £3,000–£5,000.
SAMPLE GRANTS Beamish Museum, Dementia Care Partnership, Key Enterprises, Marie Curie Cancer Care and Nunnykirk Centre for Dyslexia (£5,000 each); St Clare's Hospice (£4,000); and the North of England Cadet Forces Trust (£3,000).
FINANCES *Year* 2007–08 *Income* £1,279,136 *Grants* £32,000 *Assets* £2,828,169

TRUSTEES A A E Glenton; G W Straker; L A Caisley; D T Irvin; W J Dryden.

HOW TO APPLY In writing to the correspondent, providing full back up information. Trustees' meetings are held half yearly. The trustees require a receipt from the donee in respect of each grant.

WHO TO APPLY TO The Trustees, Ryecroft Glenton, 32 Portland Terrace, Newcastle upon Tyne NE2 1QP *Tel* 0191 281 1292 *email* bakercharitabletrust@ryecroft-glenton.co.uk

CC NO 1101988   **ESTABLISHED** 1995

■ The C Alma Baker Trust

WHERE FUNDING CAN BE GIVEN UK and overseas, particularly New Zealand.

WHO CAN BENEFIT Individuals or scientific research institutions benefiting young adults, farmers, academics, research workers and students.

WHAT IS FUNDED Agriculture and education with an agricultural connection, particularly in New Zealand and UK. (a) Agricultural research particularly New Zealand. (b) Massey University, New Zealand – Wye College, UK, Undergraduate Scheme. (c) UK YFC Scheme for young farmers to experience New Zealand farming on the trust's property in New Zealand. (d) Annual Travel Fellowship New Zealand–UK, UK–New Zealand. (e) Maori Language Education Scholarship, Wailato University, New Zealand. (f) Postgraduate study grants for agriculture-related subjects in New Zealand.

WHAT IS NOT FUNDED No general education grants.

TYPE OF GRANT Range of grants, though normally one-off annual grants.

FINANCES *Year* 2007–08 *Income* £115,671 *Grants* £98,119 *Assets* £5,603,929

TRUSTEES C R Boyes, Chair; R Moore; S F B Taylor.

PUBLICATIONS Limestone Downs Annual Report in New Zealand.

OTHER INFORMATION The trust's main asset is Limestone Downs, a sheep and beef property in the North Island, New Zealand utilised for new ideas and development in agriculture to be explored and debated in a working farm environment.

HOW TO APPLY In writing to the correspondent.

WHO TO APPLY TO The Clerk to the Trustees, 20 Hartford Road, Huntingdon, Cambridgeshire PE29 3QH

CC NO 1113864   **ESTABLISHED** 1981

■ The Balcombe Charitable Trust

WHERE FUNDING CAN BE GIVEN UK and overseas.

WHO CAN BENEFIT Registered charities benefiting children and young adults, students, at risk groups, disabled people, people disadvantaged by poverty, socially isolated people, and people who are sick.

WHAT IS FUNDED Education; the environment; health and welfare.

WHAT IS NOT FUNDED No grants to individuals or non-registered charities.

TYPE OF GRANT One-off and recurrent grants.

RANGE OF GRANTS £1,000–£82,500.

SAMPLE GRANTS Durrell Wildlife Conservation Trust (£82,500); Oxfam (£31,500); NSPCC (£25,000); Royal National Theatre (£15,500); Leuka 2000 (£13,000); Cancer Care Appeal (£10,000); Family Planning Association (£8,000); Wildlife Vets International and Bath Preservation Trust (£5,000 each); and

Blackheath Conservatoire of Music and the Arts Ltd (£3,000).

FINANCES *Year* 2007–08 *Income* £742,932 *Grants* £356,245 *Assets* £26,185,061

TRUSTEES R A Kreitman; Patricia M Kreitman.

HOW TO APPLY In writing to the correspondent.

WHO TO APPLY TO Jonathan W Prevezer, c/o Citroen Wells, Devonshire House, 1 Devonshire Street, London W1W 5DR *Tel* 020 7304 2000 *email* jonathan.prevezer@citroenwells.co.uk

CC NO 267172   **ESTABLISHED** 1975

■ The Balint Family Charitable Trusts

WHERE FUNDING CAN BE GIVEN UK and overseas, especially Israel.

WHO CAN BENEFIT Charitable organisations.

WHAT IS FUNDED Jewish charitable purposes.

FINANCES *Year* 2007–08 *Income* £136,000 *Grants* £267,000

TRUSTEES Andrew Balint Charitable Trust: Agnes Balint; Dr Gabriel Balint-Kurti; Roy David Balint-Kurti. George Balint Charitable Trust: Dr Andrew Balint; George Balint; George Rothschild; Marion Farkas-Balint. Paul Balint Charitable Trust: Dr Andrew Balint; Dr Gabriel Balint-Kurti; Paul Balint; Marc Balint.

OTHER INFORMATION This entry comprises of combined information on Andrew Balint Charitable Trust, George Balint Charitable Trust and Paul Balint Charitable Trust. The trusts' grant-making capacity has diminished significantly in recent years, down from £1.7 million in 1999/2000. The correspondent confirmed that grant expenditure totalled around £100,000 in 2008/09 and 2009/10.

HOW TO APPLY In writing to the correspondent.

WHO TO APPLY TO David Kramer, c/o Carter Backer Winter, Enterprise House, 21 Buckle Street, London E1 8NN *Tel* 020 7309 3800 *Fax* 020 7309 3801 *email* david.kramer@cbw.co.uk

■ The Albert Casanova Ballard Deceased Trust

WHERE FUNDING CAN BE GIVEN Within a seven-mile radius of Plymouth.

WHO CAN BENEFIT Local charities, local branches of national organisations and individuals.

WHAT IS FUNDED General charitable purposes, health, welfare and young people. Grants are made to schoolchildren towards uniforms and other costs.

WHAT IS NOT FUNDED The trust cannot fund anyone or any charity organisation outside of Plymouth (a seven-mile radius from the city centre is the trust's limit).

RANGE OF GRANTS Charities: £150–£2,500. Individuals: £100–£200.

SAMPLE GRANTS Young Devon and YMCA (£2,500 each); Ford Youth and Community Centre (£2,000); MacMillan Cancer Support and NSPCC (£1,300 each); Budge Youth and PHAB Club, Horizons and St Luke's Hospice (£1,000 each); Plymouth Guild of Social Service (£500); RELATE, RNID and Southway Information Centre (£400 each); Scouts 3rd Plympton (£300); Chaddlewood Farm Community Association (£250); and Bee Keeping Club (£150).

FINANCES *Year* 2007–08 *Income* £58,989 *Grants* £55,550 *Assets* £1,198,088

TRUSTEES Kenneth Banfield, Chair; Audrey Houston; Margaret Pengelly; Joy Rendle; Nigel Norris; Frances Norris; Paul Aldersley.

OTHER INFORMATION The 2007–08 grant total included the sum of £20,500 donated to 150 individuals.

HOW TO APPLY In writing to the correspondent. Applications from local charities are considered in November and notices appear in the Evening Herald and The Plymouth Extra around that time. There are no application forms available. Grants for individuals are made once a year in June. Grants will NOT be entertained outside these periods.

WHO TO APPLY TO The Trustees, Sandpiper, Linkadells, Plympton, Plymouth PL7 4EF

CC NO 201759   **ESTABLISHED** 1962

■ The Ballinger Charitable Trust

WHERE FUNDING CAN BE GIVEN North east England, Tyne and Wear.

WHO CAN BENEFIT Registered charities only.

WHAT IS FUNDED 'The focus of the Ballinger Charitable Trust is currently to support projects in the North East of England, principally by providing funds that: support the health, development and well being of young people; support older people; improve the quality of life for people and communities; promote cultural/arts projects based in the North East of England.'

WHAT IS NOT FUNDED No grants to individuals.

SAMPLE GRANTS Previous beneficiaries have included: Bath Institute of Medical Engineering Limited, Durham Association of Clubs for Young People, the Lady Hoare Trust and St Mary's Cathedral.

FINANCES Year 2007–08 Grants £300,000

TRUSTEES Diana Ballinger; John Flynn; Andrew Ballinger; Nicola Crowther.

HOW TO APPLY An online application form can be completed in the first instance at the trust's website. The trust may then make contact at a later date for additional documentation. Alternatively, the application form can be downloaded with the completed application retuned by post. For amounts up to £5,000, the trust is happy to receive a written request in the form of a letter. There is no annual deadline. The larger the fund applied for, the greater the amount of detail will be required in the application form. A decision may take up to six months depending on the size of fund applied for.

WHO TO APPLY TO M S A Ballinger, Trustee, Bolam Hall East, Morpeth NE61 3UA *Tel* 0191 488 0520 *email* info@ballingercharitabletrust.org.uk *Website* www.ballingercharitabletrust.org.uk

CC NO 1121739   **ESTABLISHED** 1994

■ Balmain Charitable Trust

WHERE FUNDING CAN BE GIVEN UK.

WHO CAN BENEFIT Charitable organisations.

WHAT IS FUNDED General charitable purposes.

SAMPLE GRANTS British Red Cross and Oxfam (£8,000 each); the Light Dragoons Charitable Trust (£6,000); the Suzy Lamplugh Trust and Royal Opera House Foundation (£5,000 each); Crisis and Zimbabwe Benefit Foundation (£3,000 each); Alzheimer's Society and the Wildfowl and Wetlands Trust (£2,000 each); and Age Concern, Foxglove Covert and the Zambezi Society (£1,000 each).

FINANCES Year 2007–08 Income £105,020 Grants £95,000 Assets £2,435,902

TRUSTEES P G Eaton; A Tappin; S Balmain; I D S Balmain; Mrs L Balmain; C A G Wells.

HOW TO APPLY In writing to the correspondent.

WHO TO APPLY TO S Balmain, Trustee, c/o Rutter and Alhusen, 2 Longmead, Shaftesbury, Dorset SP7 8PL

CC NO 1079972   **ESTABLISHED** 1998

■ The Balmore Trust

WHERE FUNDING CAN BE GIVEN Developing countries and UK, with a preference for Strathclyde.

WHO CAN BENEFIT Organisations.

WHAT IS FUNDED Two-thirds of grants are given to overseas projects and the remainder to local projects in the UK, working in the areas of education, health, alleviation of poverty and community development. Grant giving in the UK is concentrated mainly in the Glasgow area and favours families, teenagers, and women's aid groups. Overseas, the trust has close connections with community development programmes in India (Kolkata, Rajasthan and Kerala), Burma and Africa (Kenya, South Africa, Swaziland, Lesotho and Namibia).

WHAT IS NOT FUNDED No grants to individuals.

RANGE OF GRANTS £50–£7,000.

SAMPLE GRANTS Previous beneficiaries have included Church House – Bridgeton, Daynes Education Fund – South Africa, East Dunbartonshire Women's Aid, Family Action in Rogerfield and Easterhouse, Friends of CINI – India, Glasgow Children's Holiday Scheme, Humura Child Care Family – Uganda, Inverclyde Youth for Christ Reality at Work, Mission Aviation Fellowship, the Village Storytelling Centre – Pollok and Wells for India – Rajasthan.

FINANCES Year 2008–09 Income £81,070 Grants £70,000

TRUSTEES J Riches; G Burns; J Eldridge; B Holman; Ms R Jarvis; Ms R Riches.

PUBLICATIONS Newsletter.

OTHER INFORMATION The Balmore Trust distributes the profits of the Coach House charity craft shop as well as other donations. The trust's policy in grantmaking is increasingly to build on partnerships already established.

HOW TO APPLY The trust is run entirely voluntarily and the trust states that it is unlikely that money will be available for new applicants, unless they have a personal link with the trust or its shop, the Coach House charity craft shop.

WHO TO APPLY TO The Secretary, Viewfield, Balmore, Torrance, Glasgow G64 4AE *Tel* 01360 620742 *email* mail@balmoretrust.org.uk *Website* www.balmoretrust.org.uk

SC NO SC008930   **ESTABLISHED** 1980

■ The Balney Charitable Trust

WHERE FUNDING CAN BE GIVEN UK, with a preference for north Buckinghamshire and north Bedfordshire.

WHO CAN BENEFIT Individuals and registered charities.

WHAT IS FUNDED the furtherance of any religious and charitable purposes in connection with the parishes of Chicheley, North Crawley and the SCAN Group i.e. Sherington, Astwood, Hardmead and churches with a Chester family connection; the provision of housing for persons in necessitous circumstances; agriculture, forestry and armed service charities; care of older people and people who are sick and disabled.

WHAT IS NOT FUNDED Local community organisations and individuals outside north Buckinghamshire and north Bedfordshire.

TYPE OF GRANT Start-up costs, capital grants (including contributions to building projects, e.g. local churches) and research. Funding for up to three years will be considered.

RANGE OF GRANTS £25–£5,000.

SAMPLE GRANTS St Lawrence Church – Chicheley (£7,500); National Trust – Montecute House (£7,000 in two grants); Queen Alexandra Hospital Home (£5,000); CHIT, Combat Stress, Motor Neurone Disease Association and St Luke's Hospital for the Clergy (£2,000 each); Emmaus Village – Carlton, Help for Heroes, MS Therapy Centre and Tree Aid – Ghana Village Tree Enterprise (£1,000 each); and Fun 4 Young People (£500).

FINANCES *Year* 2007–08 *Income* £73,673 *Grants* £63,368 *Assets* £792,166

TRUSTEES Maj. J G B Chester; R Ruck-Keene.

OTHER INFORMATION In 2007–98 the sum of £1,100 was donated to 'necessitous cases'.

HOW TO APPLY In writing to the correspondent. Applications are acknowledged if an sae is enclosed, otherwise if the charity has not received a reply within six weeks the application has not been successful.

WHO TO APPLY TO G C W Beazley, Clerk, The Chicheley Estate, Bartlemas Office, Paveham, Bedford MK43 7PF *Tel* 01234 823663

CC NO 288575   **ESTABLISHED** 1983

■ The Baltic Charitable Fund

WHERE FUNDING CAN BE GIVEN UK, with a preference for the City of London.

WHO CAN BENEFIT Registered charities benefiting residents of the City of London, seafarers, fishermen, and ex-service and service people.

WHAT IS FUNDED Registered charities only which must be connected with the City of London or shipping or the military forces.

WHAT IS NOT FUNDED No support for advertising or charity dinners, and so on.

TYPE OF GRANT One-off.

RANGE OF GRANTS £300–£36,000.

SAMPLE GRANTS City of London School for Girls (£36,000); Lord Mayor's Appeal (£7,500); Marine Society and Sea Cadets, Sailors Society and UCL Development Fund (£5,000 each); the Mission to Seafarers (£3,600); Trinity Sailing Trust (£3,000); Falkland Islands Chapel (£2,000); Jubilee Sailing Trust (£2,500); Medway Seamans Trust (£1,000); Royal British Legion Poppy Appeal (£500); and Merchant Navy Medal Award (£300).

FINANCES *Year* 2007–08 *Income* £69,656 *Grants* £89,794 *Assets* £1,586,439

TRUSTEES The directors of the Baltic Exchange Limted.

HOW TO APPLY Unsolicited applications are not considered.

WHO TO APPLY TO The Company Secretary, The Baltic Exchange, 38 St Mary Axe, London EC3A 8BH

CC NO 279194   **ESTABLISHED** 1979

■ The Bamford Charitable Foundation

WHERE FUNDING CAN BE GIVEN Within a 40-mile radius of Rocester.

WHO CAN BENEFIT Mainly local organisations.

WHAT IS FUNDED General charitable purposes.

TYPE OF GRANT One-off.

SAMPLE GRANTS Denstone Foundation (£60,000); the Price of Progress Ltd (£10,000); Friends of St Mary's Church (£7,000); CLIC Sargent, Denstone Parish Council, English National Ballet School and University of Cambridge (£5,000 each); NSPCC (£3,000); and Canine Partners (£1,000).

FINANCES *Year* 2007–08 *Income* £58,758 *Grants* £113,250 *Assets* £1,493,382

TRUSTEES Sir A P Bamford; Lady C Bamford.

HOW TO APPLY In writing to the correspondent. 'Successful applicants are required to demonstrate to the trustees that the receipt of the grant is wholly necessary to enable them to fulfil their own objectives.'

WHO TO APPLY TO S E R Owens, Administrator, J C Bamford Excavators Ltd, Lakeside Works, Rocester, Uttoxeter, Staffordshire ST14 5JP

CC NO 279848   **ESTABLISHED** 1979

■ The Banbury Charities

WHERE FUNDING CAN BE GIVEN Banbury or its immediate environs.

WHO CAN BENEFIT Individuals and groups.

WHAT IS FUNDED General charitable purposes.

WHAT IS NOT FUNDED No grants for debts or ongoing expenses.

TYPE OF GRANT One-off grants.

RANGE OF GRANTS Up to £30,000.

SAMPLE GRANTS Cheshire Homes (£30,000); Banbury Welfare Trust (£27,000); Banbury School and St Peters and St Paul Church Kings Sutton (£10,000 each); Banbury CAB, Bluecoat Foundation and WRVS (£5,000 each); Samaritans (£4,500); Banbury and District Scout Council and St Mary's Church Warkworth (£4,000 each); Cropredy PCC (£3,000); Easington Sports, Kings Sutton Baptist Church and PHAB (£2,500 each); and Ryder Cheshire Volunteers (£1,000).

FINANCES *Year* 2007 *Income* £329,632 *Grants* £229,861 *Assets* £5,172,341

TRUSTEES F Blackwell, Chair; C A Brodey; N F Halford; J P Friswell; Mrs J W May; Mrs J M Colegrave; K P Mallon; M A Humphris; R P Walford; Mrs R A Higham; Miss A M Heritage.

OTHER INFORMATION The Banbury Charities are The Bridge Estate, Lady Arran's Charity, Banbury Arts and Educational Charity, Banbury Sick Poor Fund, Banbury Almshouse Charity, and the Banbury Welfare Trust. The grant total in 2007 included £88,965 given to 213 individuals

HOW TO APPLY In writing to the correspondent.

WHO TO APPLY TO Anthony Scott Andrews, Clerk to the Trustees, 36 West Bar, Banbury, Oxfordshire OX16 9RU *Tel* 01295 251234

CC NO 201418   **ESTABLISHED** 1961

Think carefully about every application. Is it justified?

351

■ William P Bancroft (No 2) Charitable Trust and Jenepher Gillett Trust

WHERE FUNDING CAN BE GIVEN UK and overseas.

WHO CAN BENEFIT Mainly charities benefiting Quakers.

WHAT IS FUNDED Mainly Quaker charities or projects.

WHAT IS NOT FUNDED No appeals unconnected with Quakers. No support for individual or student grant applications.

TYPE OF GRANT Buildings, core costs, endowment, one-off and start-up costs. Funding of up to three years will be considered.

SAMPLE GRANTS Previous beneficiaries have included Alternates to Violence, Bootham School, Cape Town – Quaker Peace Centre, Chaigley Educational Centre, FWCC, Mount School York Foundation, Oxford Homeless Medial Fund, Quaker Voluntary Action, QUIET – Ramallah Friends School, Sibford School – bursaries and Woodbrooke College.

FINANCES *Year* 2008 *Income* £39,274 *Grants* £38,000 *Assets* £749,890

TRUSTEES Dr Roger Gillett; Tony Yelloly; Dr Godfrey Gillett; Martin B Gillett; Dr D S Gillett; Mrs Jenepher Moseley.

HOW TO APPLY In writing to the correspondent. Trustees meet in May, applications must be received no later than April.

WHO TO APPLY TO Dr Roger Gillett, Trustee, Fernroyd, St Margaret's Road, Altrincham, Cheshire WA14 2AW

CC NO 288968   **ESTABLISHED** 1984

■ The Band Trust

WHERE FUNDING CAN BE GIVEN Worldwide in practice UK.

WHO CAN BENEFIT Registered UK charities.

WHAT IS FUNDED People with disabilities, children and young people, scholarships, hospices and hospitals, education, older people and people who are disadvantaged.

TYPE OF GRANT 'One-off' and recurring.

RANGE OF GRANTS Up to £50,000.

SAMPLE GRANTS Chelsea Pensioners' Appeal (£50,000); Fine Cell Work (£30,000); Raynauld's & Scleroderma Association (£25,000); U Can Do I.T. (£20,000); Friends of the Courtauld Institute (£16,000); Starehe UK Association (£10,000); Andover Young Carers (£5,000); and Bag Books (£1,000).

FINANCES *Year* 2007–08 *Income* £798,913 *Grants* £664,920 *Assets* £21,555,224

TRUSTEES The Hon. Lavinia Wallop; The Hon. Nicholas Wallop; Richard J S Mason; Bruce G Streather.

HOW TO APPLY The trust's accounts state that 'the trustees do not wish to receive unsolicited applications for grants'. The trustees identify potential recipients themselves, although their method of doing this is not known. One would assume that they need to be made aware of organisations that fit in with their objectives. The trustees' meetings are held three times a year.

WHO TO APPLY TO Richard J S Mason, Trustee, Moore Stephens, St Paul's House, 8–12 Warwick Lane, London EC4M 7BP *Tel* 020 7334 9191 *email* richard.mason@ moorestephens.com

CC NO 279802   **ESTABLISHED** 1976

■ The Barbers' Company General Charities

WHERE FUNDING CAN BE GIVEN UK.

WHO CAN BENEFIT Organisations and individuals.

WHAT IS FUNDED General charitable purposes, including medicine' education and nursing.

SAMPLE GRANTS Royal College of Surgeons (£40,000); Phyllis Tuckwell Hospice (£22,000); the corporation of London School for Girls and Reed's School (£5,000 each); the Guildhall School Trust (£2,500); the Lord Mayor's Appeal 2007 and Mercy Ships (£2,000 each); and City of London Freeman's School, Mansion House – Scholarship Scheme and St Giles Chipplegate (£1,000 each).

FINANCES *Year* 2006–07 *Income* £152,326 *Grants* £112,359 *Assets* £1,264,126

TRUSTEES The Barbers Company.

OTHER INFORMATION The trust no longer has direct contact with the hairdressing fraternity. However, a small amount is given each year to satisfy its historical links.

HOW TO APPLY The charities do not welcome unsolicited applications.

WHO TO APPLY TO The Clerk, Barber-Surgeons' Hall, Monkwell Square, Wood Street, London EC2Y 5BL

CC NO 265579   **ESTABLISHED** 1973

■ The Barbour Trust

WHERE FUNDING CAN BE GIVEN Mainly Tyne and Wear, Northumberland and South Tyneside.

WHO CAN BENEFIT The trust likes to support local activities, and also supports local branches of national charities.

WHAT IS FUNDED Relief of patients suffering from any form of illness or disease, promotion of research into causes of such illnesses; furtherance of education; preservation of buildings and countryside of environmental, historical or architectural interest; relief of people in need. Charities working in the fields of infrastructure development, religious umbrella bodies and animal welfare will also be considered.

WHAT IS NOT FUNDED No support for: requests from outside the geographical area; requests from educational establishments; individual applications, unless backed by a particular charitable organisation; capital grants for building projects.

TYPE OF GRANT Capital, core costs, one-off, project, research, running costs, recurring costs, salaries, and start-up costs. Funding for up to one year will be considered.

RANGE OF GRANTS Small grants £50–£500. Main grants £500 upwards.

SAMPLE GRANTS Northumbria Youth Action Limited (£30,000); Alzheimer's Trust (£13,000); Action Medical Research (£10,000); Derwentside Domestic Abuse Centre, Genesis Appeal and Shelter (£5,000 each); Fairbridge Tyne and Wear (£3,000); Wellbeing of Women (£2,000); Listening Books and Rainbow Trust (£1,500 each); and Butterwick Hospice Care, Save the Children, Someone Cares, Textile Benevolent Association and Whizz-Kids (£1,000 each).

FINANCES *Year* 2007–08 *Income* £2,368,154 *Grants* £425,142 *Assets* £8,371,424

TRUSTEES Dame Margaret Barbour, Chair; Henry Jacob Tavroges; Helen Barbour.

HOW TO APPLY On an application form available from PO Box 21, Guisborough, Cleveland, TS14 8YH. The applications should include full back-up information, a statement of accounts and the official charity number of the applicant. A main grants meeting is held every three to four months to consider grants of £500 plus. Applications are processed and researched by the administrator and secretary and further information may be requested. A small grants meeting is held monthly to consider grants up to £500. The trust always receives more applications than it can support. Even if a project fits its policy priority areas, it may not be possible to make a grant.

WHO TO APPLY TO The Secretary, J Barbour & Sons Ltd, Simonside, Tyne and Wear NE34 9PD *Tel* 0191 455 4444 *Website* www.barbour.com **CC NO** 328081   **ESTABLISHED** 1988

■ The Barcapel Foundation

WHERE FUNDING CAN BE GIVEN Scotland and other parts of the UK.

WHO CAN BENEFIT Charitable organisations.

WHAT IS FUNDED The three priority areas of interest for funding are health, heritage and young people. (1) Health: 'The foundation supports all aspects of health, a wide ranging remit acknowledging that "health is a state of complete physical, mental and social well-being and not merely the absence of disease or infirmity".' (2) Heritage: 'The original financiers of the foundation had a keen interest in our heritage, specifying that one of the foundations aims was *the preservation and beautification of historic properties.* The foundation continues to support the built environment and will support our literary and artistic heritage as well as architectural.' (3) Youth: 'The *development of people* is one of the principal objectives of the Foundation. Whilst charitable giving can be used to alleviate problems it can also be used to empower people and this is particularly true of the young.'

WHAT IS NOT FUNDED No support for: individual applications for travel or similar; organisations or individuals engaged in promoting religious or political beliefs; applications for funding costs of feasibility studies or similar. Support is unlikely to be given for local charities whose work takes place outside the British Isles.

SAMPLE GRANTS The Princess Royal Trust for Carers and the Story Museum (£15,000 each); the Tunnell Trust (£12,000); and Scottish Civic Trust and the Scottish Lime Centre (£10,000).

FINANCES *Year* 2008 *Income* £2,104,542 *Grants* £736,110

TRUSTEES Robert Wilson, Chair; James Wilson; Andrew Wilson; Jed Wilson; Clement Wilson; Niall Scott.

HOW TO APPLY A preliminary application form can be downloaded from the foundation's website. Please ensure that interests, aims and objectives are compatible with those of the foundation. Applications are not accepted by email.

WHO TO APPLY TO Moira Givens, The Mews, Skelmorlie Castle, Skelmorlie, Ayrshire PA17 5EY *Tel* 01475 521616 *email* admin@barcapelfoundation.org *Website* www.barcapelfoundation.org
SC NO SC009211   **ESTABLISHED** 1964

■ Barchester Healthcare Foundation

WHERE FUNDING CAN BE GIVEN England, Scotland and Wales.

WHO CAN BENEFIT Individuals and organisations.

WHAT IS FUNDED Older people and other adults (18 plus) with a physical or mental disability whose health and/or social care needs cannot be met by the statutory public sector or by the individual. 'Our mission is to make a difference to the lives of older people and other adults with a physical or mental disability, supporting practical solutions that lead to increased personal independence, self-sufficiency and dignity.'

WHAT IS NOT FUNDED Funds will not normally be given to: provide services for which the health and social care authorities have a statutory responsibility; services normally offered in a care home operated by Barchester Healthcare or by any other company; indirect services such as help lines, newsletters, leaflets or research; core/running costs or salaries or give financial support to general projects; major building projects; provide continuing year on year support for a project following an initial grant. Any further applications in respect of the same beneficiary will be considered after a period of three years from the initial grant.

The trustees reserve the right to put a cap on grants to a single charity (including all its branches) in any one year.

FINANCES *Year* 2008 *Income* £324,000 *Grants* £306,000

TRUSTEES Prof Malcolm Johnson; Elizabeth Mills; Christopher P Vellenoweth; Christine Hodgson; Michael D Parsons; Janice Robinson; Nick Oulton.

OTHER INFORMATION The Barchester Healthcare Foundation was established by Barchester Healthcare to reinvest into the communities it serves. The 2008 grant total includes £34,000 given to small charities/community groups – the remaining funds went to individuals.

HOW TO APPLY Application can be made via the foundation's website. A decision usually takes approximately ten weeks from the date of application. All applications supported by Barchester Healthcare staff will be given priority.

WHO TO APPLY TO The Administrator, Suite 201, The Chambers, Chelsea Harbour, London SW10 0XF *Tel* 0800 328 3328 *email* info@bhcfoundation.org.uk *Website* www.bhcfoundation.org.uk
CC NO 1083272   **ESTABLISHED** 2000

■ David and Frederick Barclay Foundation

WHERE FUNDING CAN BE GIVEN Not defined, in practice, the UK.

WHO CAN BENEFIT Registered charities or organisations undertaking charitable activities.

WHAT IS FUNDED Medical research; young people; older people; advancement of religion; people with disabilities; the sick; and the disadvantaged.

TYPE OF GRANT Projects and one-off grants.

RANGE OF GRANTS £5,000–£1 million.

SAMPLE GRANTS Great Ormond Street Hospital and Alder Hey Imagine Appeal (£1 million each); CFS Research Foundation (£150,000); the Passage (£50,000); Wellbeing for Women (£20,000); Make a Wish Foundation (£18,000); Dorset Orthopaedic Limited (£17,000); Abbeyfield (Reading) Society and St. Brides Appeal

(£10,000 each); and Foundation for Conductive Education, Farleigh Hospice and British Institution for Brain Injured Children (£5,000 each).

FINANCES *Year* 2008 *Income* £2,102,729 *Grants* £2,309,701 *Assets* £4,213

TRUSTEES Sir David Barclay; Sir Frederick Barclay; Lord Alistair McAlpine of West Green; Aidan Barclay; Howard Barclay.

OTHER INFORMATION Four individuals received grants totalling £12,000

HOW TO APPLY Applications should be in writing, clearly outlining the details of the proposed project, (if for medical research, so far as possible in lay terms). The total cost and duration should be stated, also the amount, if any, which has already been raised. Following an initial screening, applications are selected according to their merits, suitability and funds available. Visits are usually made to projects where substantial funds are involved. The foundation welcomes reports as to progress and requires these on completion of a project.

WHO TO APPLY TO Michael Seal, 3rd Floor, 20 St James's Street, London SW1A 1ES *Tel* 020 7915 0915 *email* mseal@ellerman.co.uk

CC NO 803696   **ESTABLISHED** 1990

....

■ The Baring Foundation

WHERE FUNDING CAN BE GIVEN England and Wales, with a special interest in London, Merseyside, Cornwall and Devon; also UK charities working with NGO partners in developing countries.

WHO CAN BENEFIT Varies from programme to programme; please refer to the foundation's guidelines.

WHAT IS FUNDED Strengthening the voluntary sector, arts and international development.

WHAT IS NOT FUNDED See guidelines for specific programmes. More generally: appeals or charities set up to support statutory organisations; animal welfare charities; grant maintained, private, or local education authority schools or their parent-teacher associations; individuals.

SAMPLE GRANTS Law Centres Federation (£200,000); Coventry Law Centre (£191,000); Avon and Bristol Law Centre (£175,000); Minority Rights Group International (£167,000); Camfed International (£155,000); Akina Mama Wa Afrika (£152,000); Peace Direct (£115,000); Charnwood Arts (£75,000); Craftspace (£68,000); North East Theatre Trust – Live Theatre (£50,000); Bridge and Tunnel Voices and Artsdepot (£45,000 each); Send a Cow UK (£39,400); and Grapevine Coventry and Warwickshire (£35,600).

FINANCES *Year* 2008 *Income* £1,666,360 *Grants* £2,889,992 *Assets* £51,300,140

TRUSTEES Amanda Jordan, Chair; Mark Baring; Geoffrey Barnett; Prof. Ann Buchanan; Prof. Nicholas Deakin; Katherine Garrett-Cox; Janet Morrison; Jim Peers; Ranjit Sondhi; Dr Danny Sriskandarajah; Christopher Steane; Prof. Myles Wickstead.

PUBLICATIONS Various reports connected with its work are available from the foundation's website.

OTHER INFORMATION New guidelines and deadlines were yet to be announced at the time of writing (November 2009) – check the foundation's website for current information.

HOW TO APPLY On application forms available via the foundation's website. Potential applicants should check the foundation's website for current guidelines and application deadlines.

WHO TO APPLY TO David Cutler, Director, 60 London Wall, London EC2M 5TQ *Tel* 020 7767 1348 *Fax* 020 7767 7121 *email* baring.foundation@uk.ing.com *Website* www.baringfoundation.org.uk

CC NO 258583   **ESTABLISHED** 1969

....

■ Peter Barker-Mill Memorial Charity

WHERE FUNDING CAN BE GIVEN UK, with a preference for Hampshire, including Southampton.

WHO CAN BENEFIT Charitable organisations.

WHAT IS FUNDED General charitable purposes, arts and culture, community facilities and conservation.

WHAT IS NOT FUNDED No grants to individuals.

RANGE OF GRANTS Usually £250–£20,000.

SAMPLE GRANTS Colbury Scouts (£86,000); Colbury Parochial Church Council (£12,000); Nursling and Rownhams Village Hall (£10,000); the Pinder Centre (£8,000); the Rugby Portobello Trust (£6,000); Southampton Society for the Blind and Special Schools and Academy Trust (£5,000 each); Sussex House School (£4,000); Huntington's Disease Association (£3,000); Groundswell (£2,000); Volunteer Reading Help (£1,000 each); and Planet Kids (£500).

FINANCES *Year* 2007–08 *Income* £70,852 *Grants* £232,374 *Assets* £2,497,479

TRUSTEES C Gwyn-Evans; T Jobling; R M Moyse.

HOW TO APPLY In writing to the correspondent.

WHO TO APPLY TO Christopher Gwyn-Evans, Administrator, c/o Longdown Management Ltd, The Estate Office, Longdown, Marchwood, Southampton SO40 4UH

CC NO 1045479   **ESTABLISHED** 1995

....

■ Barleycorn Trust

WHERE FUNDING CAN BE GIVEN Worldwide.

WHO CAN BENEFIT Christian.

WHAT IS FUNDED The advancement of the Christian faith, furtherance of religious or secular education, the encouragement of missionary activity, relief-in-need and welfare.

SAMPLE GRANTS Pathway Project (£70,000); Demand Design (£17,000); Off the Fence (£9,000); Bishop Hannington Church and Dorothy Kerin Trust (£5,000 each); Ethiopia School of Nursing (£3,800); Moldova Ministries (£3,000); Adriatic Christian Trust and Hope HIV (£2,000 each); Keychange (£1,000); Chalfont Heights Scouts (£500).

FINANCES *Year* 2007 *Income* £44,127 *Grants* £187,995 *Assets* £1,187,451

TRUSTEES Mrs H M Hazelwood; M R C Citro?n; Mrs S A Beckwith.

HOW TO APPLY In writing to the correspondent.

WHO TO APPLY TO The Trustees, 32 Arundel Road, Sutton, Surrey SM2 6EU

CC NO 296386   **ESTABLISHED** 1987

....

■ The Barnabas Trust

WHERE FUNDING CAN BE GIVEN UK and overseas. Overseas projects are supported only if they are personally known by the trustees.

WHO CAN BENEFIT Organisations and individuals benefiting Christians and evangelists.

WHAT IS FUNDED Christian evangelical projects – overtly evangelical, not social, unless for a particular evangelical input. The trust will consider funding Christian theological education and outreach; missionaries and evangelicals; and Anglican and Free Church bodies.

WHAT IS NOT FUNDED 'The trust is no longer able to help with building, refurbishment or equipment for any church, since to be of any value grants need to be large.' Ongoing revenue costs such as salaries are not supported.

TYPE OF GRANT One-off for one year or less, for project funding.

RANGE OF GRANTS Mainly up to £5,000 each.

SAMPLE GRANTS SGM Lifewords (£60,000); Naval, Military and Air Force Bible Society (£10,000 in two grants); Green Hill Outreach (£8,000); Princess Alice Hospice (£7,000); Counties Evangelical Trust Echoes of Service, Redcliffe College and WEC International (£5,000 each); Haggai Institute (£4,500); London School of Theology and Release International (£3,000 each); Abernathy Trust, Latin Link and Open Air Mission (£2,500 each); the Barnabas Fund (£1,500); and Trustees for Timothy House (£1,000); Stirling Baptist Church (£750); and Hope City Church (£500).

FINANCES *Year* 2008–09 *Income* £135,060 *Grants* £273,430 *Assets* £2,616,400

TRUSTEES Norman Brown; Kenneth C Griffiths; David S Helden.

OTHER INFORMATION In 2008–09 grants were made to individuals for: educational purposes (£16,000 in 18 grants); Christian mission overseas (£2,000 in two grants); and Christian mission UK (£1,500 in two grants).

HOW TO APPLY In writing to the correspondent, giving as much detail as possible, and enclosing a copy of the latest audited accounts, if applicable. The trust states: 'Much of the available funds generated by this trust are allocated to existing donees. The trustees are willing to consider new applications, providing they refer to a project which is overtly evangelical in nature.' If in doubt about whether to submit an application, please telephone the secretary to the trust for guidance. The trustees meet four times a year, or more often as required, and applications will be put before the next available meeting. Please note it is likely that the trust will cease to exist by 2012. Very little money is available for unsolicited applications.

WHO TO APPLY TO Mrs Doris Edwards, Secretary, c/o 63 Wolsey Drive, Walton-on-Thames, Surrey KT12 3BB

CC NO 284511   **ESTABLISHED** 1983

■ Lord Barnby's Foundation

WHERE FUNDING CAN BE GIVEN UK.

WHO CAN BENEFIT Registered charities.

WHAT IS FUNDED The preservation of the environment; heritage; the countryside and ancient buildings, particularly the 'great Anglican cathedrals'; ex-service and service people; Polish people; welfare of horses and those who look after them; youth and other local organisations in Ashtead – Surrey, Blyth – Nottinghamshire and Bradford – Yorkshire; people who are disabled; refugees; technical education for the woollen industry.

WHAT IS NOT FUNDED No grants to individuals.

TYPE OF GRANT One-off, capital (including buildings), core costs, project, research. Funding is up to two years.

RANGE OF GRANTS Grants range from £500–£50,000; but are generally for £1,000–£2,000.

SAMPLE GRANTS European Squirrel Initiative (£50,000); Barnby Memorial Hall (£18,000); Help for Heroes (£12,000); Farms for City

Children and St Luke's Hospital for the Clergy (£10,000 each); the Queen Alexandra Hospital Home (£7,000); Polish Veterans Association (£5,000); CLIC Sargent – Billy's Appeal, Listening Books, the Outward Bound Trust, Second Chance, Tall Ships Youth Trust and Wotton Under Edge Community Sports (£2,000 each); Dorothy House Hospice and the ISIS Project (£1,000 each); and Care International UK and the York Joint Scout Trust (£500 each).

FINANCES *Year* 2007–08 *Income* £239,449 *Grants* £249,081 *Assets* £4,701,518

TRUSTEES Hon. George Lopes; the Countess Peel; Sir Michael Farquhar; E J A Smith-Maxwell.

HOW TO APPLY Applications will only be considered if received in writing accompanied by a set of the latest accounts. Applicants do not need to send an sae. Appeals are considered three times a year, in February, June and November.

WHO TO APPLY TO Mrs J A Lethbridge, Secretary, PO Box 71, Plymstock, Plymouth PL8 2YP

CC NO 251016   **ESTABLISHED** 1966

■ Barnes Workhouse Fund

WHERE FUNDING CAN BE GIVEN Ancient parish of Barnes only (SW13 postal district in London).

WHO CAN BENEFIT Charitable organisations and individuals.

WHAT IS FUNDED The fund makes grants to organisations who can demonstrate that their activities will benefit some of the inhabitants of its area of benefit.

TYPE OF GRANT Capital (including buildings), core costs, feasibility studies, one-off, project, research, running costs, recurring costs, salaries and start-up costs.

SAMPLE GRANTS Richmond Citizens Advice Bureaux (£32,000); Castelnau Centre Project (£25,000); Shenehom Housing Association (£18,000); Richmond Crossroads Care (£11,000); FISH (£7,500); Age Concern (£5,000); Richmond Carers Centre (£3,500); Richmond Aid (£3,300); Ethnic Minorities Advocacy Group and Relate (£2,500 each); Richmond Mencap (£2,200); Mediation in Divorce (£1,500); Barnes MusicSociety, Integrated Neurological Services and Thames Artists (£1,000 each); Cruse Bereavement Care (£500); Victim Support (£400); and Synergy Theatre Project (£300).

FINANCES *Year* 2008 *Income* £507,051 *Grants* £166,666 *Assets* £6,893,205

TRUSTEES C Reilly; Mrs J Mallinson; Mrs W V Kyrle-Pope; P B Conrath; R D Jefferies; Cllr C C Percival; Ms B Westmorland; J Brocklebank; Mrs K Pengelley.

HOW TO APPLY In writing to the Clerk to the Trustees. Application forms and guidelines are available from the clerk or downloaded from the website. Applications must state clearly the extent to which any project will benefit residents of Barnes (postal district SW13) and include details of other sources of funding. Trustees meet to consider grants every two months in January, March, May, July, September and November each year. For consideration at a meeting, applications must be received by the 13th of the preceding month.

WHO TO APPLY TO The Clerk to the Trustees, PO Box 665, Richmond, London TW10 6YL *Tel* 020 8241 3994 *email* barnesworkhousefund@tiscali.co.uk *Website* www.barnesworkhousefund.org.uk

CC NO 200103   **ESTABLISHED** 1970

Think carefully about every application. Is it justified?

355

■ The Barnsbury Charitable Trust

WHERE FUNDING CAN BE GIVEN UK, but no local charities outside Oxfordshire.

WHO CAN BENEFIT Charitable organisations.

WHAT IS FUNDED General charitable purposes.

WHAT IS NOT FUNDED No grants to individuals.

RANGE OF GRANTS £15–£10,000.

SAMPLE GRANTS Oxfordshire Chamber Music Festival (£10,000); the Oxfordshire Victoria County History Trust (£5,000); St Giles PCC (£3,000); Charlbury Community Centre and Oxfordshire Family Medication (£2,500 each); Blackfriars Priory, Hagbourne School, Merton College Charitable Trust, Oxford Christian Institute for Counselling, Oxford District Mencap, PCC of St Mary – Chalgrove and Trinity College – Oxford (£1,000 each); Oxfordshire Nature Conservation Forum (£500); Chipping Norton Town Charities, Oxford Oratory Trust and Royal British Legion Poppy Appeal (£100 each); the Royal Society of St George (£25); and Priory of England and the Islands (£15).

FINANCES *Year* 2007–08 *Income* £74,199 *Grants* £71,283 *Assets* £2,783,726

TRUSTEES H L J Brunner; M R Brunner; T E Yates.

HOW TO APPLY In writing to the correspondent.

WHO TO APPLY TO H L J Brunner, Trustee, 26 Norham Road, Oxford OX2 6SF

CC NO 241383   **ESTABLISHED** 1964

■ The Barnstaple Bridge Trust

WHERE FUNDING CAN BE GIVEN Barnstaple and immediate neighbourhood.

WHO CAN BENEFIT Local organisations.

WHAT IS FUNDED General, grants are made to a wide range of causes, including welfare, older people and young people, health and medical, schools and sport.

WHAT IS NOT FUNDED No grants to individuals, other than on referral through a caring agency.

TYPE OF GRANT Capital including buildings, core costs, one-off, project, research, running costs, recurring costs and start-up costs will be considered. Funding may be given for up to one year.

RANGE OF GRANTS Up to £20,000.

SAMPLE GRANTS Bishops Tawton Almshouses (£20,000); ND Hospice Care (£10,000); Barnstaple Skate Board Track, Children's Hospice and St Peter's – Fremington (£5,000 each); Barnstaple-in-Bloom, Barnstaple Poverty Action Group, Freedom Social Projects, Pilton House and Vivien Moon Foundation (£3,000 each); Bishops Tawton PCC (£2,500); Holy Trinity Church Barnstaple (£2,000); Cruse Bereavement Care (£1,750); Relate (£1,500); and Abbey Gateway Club, Christians Against Poverty, Friendship House, Home Start and Pilton (£1,000 each).

FINANCES *Year* 2008 *Income* £396,208 *Grants* £120,000 *Assets* £4,547,814

TRUSTEES J W Moore, Chair; F E Edwards; R P Isaac, J W Waldron; D C Burgess; R W Forward; A J Bradbury; S Harvey; J Lynch; Cllr J Bartlett; F Edwards; Cllr S Upcott; Cllr G Lofthouse; Mrs D Piercy; I Scott; Mrs S Hayward; The Mayor of Barnstable.

HOW TO APPLY In writing to the correspondent. The trustees meet quarterly on the first Tuesday of March, June, September and December.

WHO TO APPLY TO C J Bartlett, Clerk, 7 Bridge Chambers, The Strand, Barnstaple, Devon EX31 1HB *Tel* 01271 343995

CC NO 201288   **ESTABLISHED** 1961

■ The Barnwood House Trust

WHERE FUNDING CAN BE GIVEN Gloucestershire.

WHO CAN BENEFIT Gloucestershire-based charitable and voluntary organisations whose services seek to improve the quality of life of local people with long-term disabilities.

WHAT IS FUNDED The relief of sickness, poverty and distress affecting people with mental or nervous disorders or with serious physical infirmity or disability.

WHAT IS NOT FUNDED Grants are not normally made in the following circumstances: to organisations outside Gloucestershire; for building or adapting private, public sector or social housing; to start-up or subsidise services purchased or contracted out by the public sector; where the applicant organisation has significant unrestricted reserves; where the applicant organisation operates an exclusive policy, e.g. by charging excessive fees; for core funding to the public sector; to non-disability organisations seeking to make community buildings more accessible, unless there is exceptional need; for a management charge applied to a project; for any work that is not aimed specifically at disabled people.

TYPE OF GRANT Capital and full project funding. Funding may be given for up to three years.

RANGE OF GRANTS Usually £500–£20,000, occasionally larger grants are made.

SAMPLE GRANTS St Vincents Centre (£236,000); Forest Pulse (£37,000); Cotswolds Care Hospice (£20,000); Inglos (£18,000); NCH, People and Places in Gloucestershire and the Lions Club of Cheltenham (£10,000 each).

FINANCES *Year* 2008 *Income* £3,189,059 *Grants* £679,924 *Assets* £57,558,666

TRUSTEES John Colquhoun; James Davidson; Anne Cadbury; Richard Ashenden; Simon Fisher; Caroline Penley; David A Acland; Clare de Haan; Sara Shipway; Roger Ker; Annabella Scott; Jonathan Carr.

OTHER INFORMATION A total of £283,386 was given to individuals.

HOW TO APPLY The trust advises potential applicants to ring before making an application to confirm the eligibility of their proposal. Grant application forms can be downloaded from the website or requested by telephone or post. Applications are assessed on a quarterly basis, meaning applicants should not have to wait more than three months for a decision. Applications for less than £750 will be 'fast tracked' and should be processed within 15 days. Please note: holiday and playscheme grants are also fast-tracked and have a dedicated application form. If successful, applicants have the option of drawing down their grant immediately on production of required invoices, or can ask the trust to hold it open for up to 12 months. Organisations that have received a grant from the trust can also apply for a repeat grant of up to £750. For further information about grants for individuals, contact the trust, or see *A Guide to Grants for Individuals in Need*, published by the Directory of Social Change.

WHO TO APPLY TO Gail Rodway, Grants Manager, The Manor House, 162 Barnwood Road, Gloucester GL4 7JX *Tel* 01452 611292 *Fax* 01452 372594 *email* gail.rodway@barnwoodtrust.org *Website* www.barnwoodhousetrust.org

CC NO 218401   **ESTABLISHED** 1972

■ The Misses Barrie Charitable Trust

WHERE FUNDING CAN BE GIVEN UK.
WHO CAN BENEFIT Registered charities.
WHAT IS FUNDED General charitable purposes.
WHAT IS NOT FUNDED No grants to individuals.
TYPE OF GRANT Mainly one-off.
RANGE OF GRANTS Mostly £1,000–£3,000.
SAMPLE GRANTS Scottish Chamber Orchestra and University of Oxford (£10,000 each); and ARC Addington Fund, East Neuk Festival and Queen Victoria School Centenary Appeal (£5,000); National Association of Youth Orchestras (£4,000); Brighton and Hove Parents and Children Group, St Peter and St James Charitable Trust and Youth Link – Dundee (£3,000 each); British Wireless for the Blind (£2,000); and Cornerstone Community Care (£1,000 each).
FINANCES *Year* 2007–08 *Income* £245,796 *Grants* £263,300 *Assets* £5,679,494
TRUSTEES R G Carter; R S Ogg; Mrs R Fraser.
HOW TO APPLY In writing to the correspondent accompanied, where appropriate, by up to date accounts or financial information. Trustees meet three times a year, in April, August and December. 'The trustees regret that due to the large number of unsolicited applications for grants received each week they are not able to notify those which are unsuccessful.'
WHO TO APPLY TO Raymond Carter, Trustee, Messrs Raymond Carter and Co, 1b Haling Road, South Croydon CR2 6HS *Tel* 020 8686 1686
CC NO 279459   **ESTABLISHED** 1979

■ Barrington Family Charitable Trust

WHERE FUNDING CAN BE GIVEN UK.
WHO CAN BENEFIT Registered charities.
WHAT IS FUNDED Mainly arts and culture.
FINANCES *Year* 2007–08 *Income* £32,846 *Grants* £34,600 *Assets* £101,306
TRUSTEES Jessica Barrington; Jill Barrington; Michael Barrington; Saul Barrington; Amanda Thompson.
HOW TO APPLY In writing to the correspondent.
WHO TO APPLY TO Michael Barrington, Trustee, Fourth Floor, 87 Wimpole Street, London W1G 9RL *Tel* 020 7486 0266
CC NO 1078702

■ The Charity of William Barrow

WHERE FUNDING CAN BE GIVEN The ancient parish of Borden.
WHO CAN BENEFIT Individuals and schools.
WHAT IS FUNDED The charity distributes its income equally between the Barrows Eleemosynary Charity and Barrows Educational Foundation. The latter supports local schools, one of which is supported each year in accordance with the trust deed. No other organisations were supported.
WHAT IS NOT FUNDED No grants outside the parish of Borden.
FINANCES *Year* 2008 *Income* £175,449 *Grants* £48,700 *Assets* £5,300,176
TRUSTEES P J Mair, Chair; W G Best; J Burton; Mrs E P Cole; E G Doubleday; D A Jarrett; J J Jefferiss; D Jordan; Fr Lewis; Mrs A P Ramage; S C Batt.

HOW TO APPLY In writing to the correspondent for consideration at quarterly meetings of the trustees.
WHO TO APPLY TO The Clerk, c/o George Webb Finn, 43 Park Road, Sittingbourne, Kent ME10 1DX
CC NO 307574   **ESTABLISHED** 1965

■ Stephen J Barry Charitable Trust

WHERE FUNDING CAN BE GIVEN UK.
WHO CAN BENEFIT Charitable organisations.
WHAT IS FUNDED General charitable purposes.
RANGE OF GRANTS Up to £7,000.
SAMPLE GRANTS I Rescue (£7,000); Alzheimer's Research Trust (£5,000); National Gallery (£2,000); Hampstead Synagogue (31,500); and Royal Academy of Arts (£1,250); Jewish Care, Macmillan Cancer Support and Tate Foundation (£1,000 each); Ear Foundation, National Youth Orchestra and Tropical Health Foundation Trust (£500 each); Docklands Settlement and NSPCC (3300 each); Blind Art (£200); and Action Aid (£100).
FINANCES *Year* 2007–08 *Income* £37,188 *Grants* £31,000 *Assets* £991,183
TRUSTEES Nicholas Barry; Oliver Barry; Stephen Barry; Linda Barry.
HOW TO APPLY In writing to the correspondent.
WHO TO APPLY TO Stephen Barry, Trustee, 19 Newman Street, London W1T 1PF *Tel* 020 7580 6696 *email* sjb@limecourt.com
CC NO 265056   **ESTABLISHED** 1973

■ The Bartlett Taylor Charitable Trust

WHERE FUNDING CAN BE GIVEN Preference for Oxfordshire.
WHO CAN BENEFIT Registered charities.
WHAT IS FUNDED General charitable purposes, with grants given in the following categories: (a) international charities; (b) UK national charities – medical; UK national charities – educational; (c) local organisations – community projects; local organisations – medical; local organisations – other; (d) individuals – educational; individuals – relief.
RANGE OF GRANTS £100–£1,000.
FINANCES *Year* 2007–08 *Income* £67,592 *Grants* £48,135 *Assets* £1,658,872
TRUSTEES Richard Bartlett; Gareth Alty; Katherine Bradley; Brenda Cook; James W Dingle; Rosemary Warner; Mrs S Boyd.
HOW TO APPLY In writing to the correspondent. Trustees meet bi-monthly.
WHO TO APPLY TO Katherine Robertson, 24 Church Green, Witney, Oxfordshire OX8 6AT *Tel* 01993 703941 *email* krobertson@johnwelchandstammers.co.uk
CC NO 285249   **ESTABLISHED** 1982

■ The Worshipful Company of Basketmakers' Charitable Trust

WHERE FUNDING CAN BE GIVEN UK with a preference for inner London.
WHO CAN BENEFIT Support small charities who have innovative solutions to problems.
WHAT IS FUNDED Grants go to a 'variety of causes, for example support hospices in London where the service is free, addiction rehabilitation centres where the person who persists with the treatment is carried through to a job and a home, charities training the disabled for

employment and similar small charities where our size of contribution can make a real impact'.

SAMPLE GRANTS Grants were made in the following areas: £13,500 to social care; £9,000 to education, £8,000 to disability, £7,000 to hospices, £5,000 to illness, £3,000 each to St Margaret Pattens and to blind causes.

FINANCES *Year* 2007–08 *Income* £67,716 *Grants* £51,795 *Assets* £1,059,396

TRUSTEES Peter Costain; John Robinson; Geoffrey Rowley; Melvin Bruce; Carole Hawes.

OTHER INFORMATION The charity supports training in the craft, the Lord Mayor's Appeal and St Margaret Pattens on an ongoing basis. In 2004–05 the sum of £2,000 went to individuals.

HOW TO APPLY In writing to the correspondent. 'After considering the pattern of grants made over a ten year period, trustees selected a number of charities, grouped them by subject, and created rotas under each subject for grants of specific sums: e.g. every second meeting (or third or fourth). The rotas are now in operation and those charities keep in touch by sending their annual reports rather than masses of appeal papers. Trustees will visit these charities from time to time to ensure that our grants are being well used.'

WHO TO APPLY TO John Robinson, Trustee, Tythe Cottage, Duke Street, Hintlesham, Ipswich IP8 3QP

CC NO 286901   **ESTABLISHED** 1982

■ The Paul Bassham Charitable Trust

WHERE FUNDING CAN BE GIVEN UK, mainly Norfolk.
WHO CAN BENEFIT UK registered charities.
WHAT IS FUNDED General charitable purposes. Preference given to Norfolk charitable causes; if funds permit, other charities with national coverage will be considered.
WHAT IS NOT FUNDED Grants are not made directly to individuals, nor to unregistered organisations.
RANGE OF GRANTS £1,000–£20,000.
SAMPLE GRANTS East Anglia Children's Hospice Quidenham and Norwich Theatre Royal Trust (£20,000 each); Leonard Cheshire Disability (£11,000); Norfolk Wildlife Trust (£7,500); Assist Trust, the Hawk and Owl Trust, Norfolk and Norwich Families' House and the Plantation Garden Preservation Trust (£5,000 each); City of Norwich School Association (£3,000 each); Norwich Door to Door (£2,000); and London Road Methodist Church and Whizz-Kidz (£1,000 each).
FINANCES *Year* 2007–08 *Income* £403,030 *Grants* £246,100 *Assets* £10,514,377
TRUSTEES C J Lingwood; R Lovett.
HOW TO APPLY Only in writing to the correspondent – no formal application forms issued. Telephone enquiries are not invited because of administrative costs. The trustees meet quarterly to consider general applications.
WHO TO APPLY TO R Lovett, Trustee, c/o Howes Percival, The Guildyard, 51 Colegate, Norwich NR3 1DD
CC NO 266842   **ESTABLISHED** 1973

■ The Batchworth Trust

WHERE FUNDING CAN BE GIVEN Worldwide.
WHO CAN BENEFIT Major UK and international charities.
WHAT IS FUNDED General charitable purposes, medical, humanitarian aid, social welfare. 'The trustees have a policy of mainly distributing to nationally recognised charities but consider other charities where it felt a grant would be of significant benefit when matched with other funds to launch a new enterprise or initiative.'
WHAT IS NOT FUNDED No applications from individuals can be considered.
RANGE OF GRANTS £1,000–£25,000.
SAMPLE GRANTS University of Bristol Research Post (£50,000); Cure Parkinsons (£30,000); Alzheimer's Society, Back Care, Brick by Brick, British Legion, Centre Point, Merlin and Oxford Radcliffe Hospital (£10,000 each); Age Concern (£8,000); the Salvation Army (£7,000); the Waterside Trust (£5,000); and the Colston Society (£2,000).
FINANCES *Year* 2007–08 *Income* £357,309 *Grants* £341,000 *Assets* £8,833,386
TRUSTEES Lockwell Trustees Ltd.
HOW TO APPLY In writing to the correspondent. An sae should be included if a reply is required.
WHO TO APPLY TO M R Neve, Administrative Executive, CLB Gatwick LLP, Imperial Buildings, 68 Victoria Road, Horley, Surrey RH6 7PZ *Tel* 01293 776411 *email* mrn@clbgatwick.co.uk
CC NO 245061   **ESTABLISHED** 1965

■ Bay Charitable Trust

WHERE FUNDING CAN BE GIVEN UK and overseas.
WHO CAN BENEFIT Jewish organisations.
WHAT IS FUNDED 'The objectives of the charity are to give charity for the relief of poverty and the advancement of traditions of the Orthodox Jewish Religion and the study of Torah.'
FINANCES *Year* 2008 *Income* £881,412 *Grants* £762,930 *Assets* £366,335
TRUSTEES I M Kreditor; M Lisser.
HOW TO APPLY In writing to the correspondent.
WHO TO APPLY TO I M Kreditor, Trustee, Hermolis House, Abbeydale Road, Wembley, Middlesex HA0 1AY
CC NO 1060537   **ESTABLISHED** 1997

■ The Bay Tree Charitable Trust

WHERE FUNDING CAN BE GIVEN UK and overseas.
WHO CAN BENEFIT Charitable organisations.
WHAT IS FUNDED Development work.
WHAT IS NOT FUNDED No grants to individuals.
RANGE OF GRANTS Up to £30,000.
SAMPLE GRANTS Queen Alexander Hospital Home (£30,000); Médecins Sans Frontières – UK (£28,000); Disasters Emergency Committee Bangladesh Cyclone Appeal, NSPCC and UNICEF UK – South Asia Floods Children's Appeal (£20,000 each); Friends of the Earth and Help Tibet (£15,000 each); Friends of Home from Home – UK and Save the Children (£10,000 each); and IFAW Charitable Trust and the Nelson Trust (£5,000 each).
FINANCES *Year* 2007 *Income* £157,090 *Grants* £188,000 *Assets* £3,262,532
TRUSTEES I M P Benton; Miss E L Benton; P H Benton.
HOW TO APPLY 'All appeals should be by letter containing the following: aims and objectives of the charity; nature of appeal; total target if for a specific project; contributions received against

target; registered charity number; any other relevant factors. Letters should be accompanied by a set of the charitable organisation's latest report and full accounts.'

WHO TO APPLY TO The Trustees, PO Box 53983, London SW15 1VT

CC NO 1044091   **ESTABLISHED** 1994

....

■ D H and L H Baylin Charitable Trust

WHERE FUNDING CAN BE GIVEN UK.
WHO CAN BENEFIT Charitable organisations.
WHAT IS FUNDED General charitable purposes.
FINANCES *Year* 2007–08 *Income* £57,251
    Grants £57,175
TRUSTEES D M Baylin; Mrs L H Baylin.
HOW TO APPLY In writing to the correspondent.
WHO TO APPLY TO Dennis Baylin, Trustee, 28 Manchester Street, London W1U 7LF
CC NO 298708   **ESTABLISHED** 1988

....

■ The Louis Baylis (Maidenhead Advertiser) Charitable Trust

WHERE FUNDING CAN BE GIVEN Berkshire, Buckinghamshire and Oxfordshire with a preference for Maidenhead.
WHO CAN BENEFIT General charitable purposes.
WHAT IS FUNDED The trust states that it was 'established to safeguard the newspaper, The Maidenhead Advertiser, from all outside influence and provide for the newspaper's continuance as part of the civic and social life of the community it serves'. Grants can be given towards any charitable purpose, and from the grants list it appears that all the organisations supported were within the area covered by the newspaper.
WHAT IS NOT FUNDED No grants to individuals.
RANGE OF GRANTS £500–£65,000.
SAMPLE GRANTS Benficiary organisations included: Charvil Girls' Choir, Maidenhead Drama Festival, Maidenhead Festival of Music, Dance and Speech, Norden Farm Centre adn Windsor & Maidenhead Symphony Orchestra.
FINANCES *Year* 2007–08 *Income* £4,795,464
    Grants £505,989 *Assets* £12,449,754
TRUSTEES Tony Stoughton-Harris; P J Sands; Peter Murcott.
HOW TO APPLY In writing to the correspondent. The trustees meet twice a year.
WHO TO APPLY TO Peter Murcott, Trustee, Hale and Co, 14 Crauford Rise, Maidenhead, Berkshire SL6 7LX
CC NO 210533   **ESTABLISHED** 1962

....

■ BBC Children in Need

WHERE FUNDING CAN BE GIVEN UK.
WHO CAN BENEFIT Non-profit-making groups and organisations benefiting children in the UK aged 18 and under.
WHAT IS FUNDED Practical and lasting support for children disadvantaged by poverty, disability, illness, abuse and neglect.
WHAT IS NOT FUNDED The appeal does not consider applications from private individuals or the friends or families of individual children. In addition, grants will not be given for trips and projects abroad; medical treatment or medical research; unspecified expenditure; deficit funding or repayment of loans; projects which take place before applications can be processed

(this takes up to five months from the closing dates); projects which are unable to start within 12 months; distribution to another/other organisation(s); general appeals and endowment funds; the relief of statutory responsibilities.
TYPE OF GRANT Capital, revenue and recurring for up to three years.
RANGE OF GRANTS No fixed upper or lower limit; in practice very few grants over £25,000 a year.
SAMPLE GRANTS Larger grants: Renfield Centre Children's Fund – Scotland (£346,000); Women's Aid Federation England – Bristol (£154,000); Seaham Youth Initiative – County Durham (£144,000); and Mencap Greenwich – London (£133,000). Smaller grants: Berwickshire Group Riding for the Disabled (£777); Dumfries High School Home Link Service (£570); St Paul's Child Contact Centre Bracknell (£495); and Seesaw Playgroup Ballymoney – Northern Ireland (£350).
FINANCES *Year* 2007–08 *Income* £42,266,000
    Grants £37,919,000 *Assets* £23,176,000
TRUSTEES Stevie Spring, Chair; Tim Davie; Neena Mahal; Beverley Tew; Sir Terry Wogan; Yogesh Chauhan; Alan Broughton; Susan Elizabeth; Peter McBride; Nicholas Eldred.
HOW TO APPLY Straightforward and excellent application forms and guidelines are available from the website or from national BBC Children in Need offices. There are four application deadlines each year – 15 January, 15 April, 15 July and 15 October. Occasional programmes have other deadlines – check the charity's website for up-to-date information. Organisations may submit only one application to either of these dates. Applicants should allow up to five months after each closing date for notification of a decision. Application forms can also be completed online – visit the website for more information (www.bbc.co.uk/pudsey).
WHO TO APPLY TO David Ramsden, Chief Executive, PO Box 1000, London W12 7WJ *Tel* 020 8576 7788 *Fax* 020 8576 8887 *email* pudsey@bbc.co.uk *Website* bbc.co.uk/pudsey
CC NO 802052   **ESTABLISHED** 1989

....

■ The Beacon Trust

WHERE FUNDING CAN BE GIVEN Mainly UK, but also some overseas (usually in the British Commonwealth) and Spain and Portugal.
WHO CAN BENEFIT Organisations benefiting evangelical Protestants, including Baptists, Anglican and Methodists. Funding is usually given to headquarters organisations.
WHAT IS FUNDED The emphasis of the trust's support is on Christian work overseas, particularly amongst students, although the trust does not support individuals.
WHAT IS NOT FUNDED Applications from individuals are not considered.
TYPE OF GRANT One-off grants for development funding. Longer-term grants may be considered.
SAMPLE GRANTS L'Abri Fellowship (£10,000); Arocha – Portugal (£4,000); Zambia Chicken Farm Project (£3,000); Cascadas (£2,000); Heythrop College (£1,700); and STREAT Trust (£1,500).
FINANCES *Year* 2007–08 *Income* £350,217
    Grants £38,240 *Assets* £1,484,152
TRUSTEES Miss J Benson; Miss J M Spink; M Spink.
HOW TO APPLY The trust does not respond to unsolicited applications.
WHO TO APPLY TO Grahame Scofield, Unit 3, Newhouse Farm, Old Crawley Road, Horsham, West Sussex RH12 4RU
CC NO 230087   **ESTABLISHED** 1963

....

Think carefully about every application. Is it justified?

359

■ Bear Mordechai Ltd

WHERE FUNDING CAN BE GIVEN Worldwide.

WHO CAN BENEFIT Individuals, small local projects and national organisations benefiting Jewish people.

WHAT IS FUNDED Jewish charities.

TYPE OF GRANT Recurring costs and core costs will be considered.

SAMPLE GRANTS Previous beneficiaries shave included Agudat Yad Yemin Jerusalem, Almat, Chevras Mo'oz Ladol, Craven Walk Charities Trust, Havenpoint, Keren Tzedaka Vachesed, Lolev, UTA and Yetev Lev Yerusholaim.

FINANCES *Year* 2007–08 *Income* £68,135 *Grants* £148,510 *Assets* £1,029,039

TRUSTEES Y Benedikt; E Benedikt.

HOW TO APPLY In writing to the correspondent.

WHO TO APPLY TO The Secretary, 40 Fountayne Road, London N16 7DT

CC NO 286806   **ESTABLISHED** 1982

■ The Bearder Charity

WHERE FUNDING CAN BE GIVEN Calderdale.

WHO CAN BENEFIT Registered charities and individuals.

WHAT IS FUNDED General charitable purposes, particularly the arts, infrastructure support and development, education and training and community facilities and services.

SAMPLE GRANTS Poetry Workshops (£8,800); Overgate Hospice Choir (£5,000); Calderdale College and Calderdale Robot Challenge (£4,000 each); Roses Charitable Trust (£3,000); MacMillan Cancer (£2,500); Halifax Junior Cricket League and St Bartholomew's Church (£2,000 each); Hebden Bridge Arts Mill (£1,700); Square Leg Productions (£1,500); Live Music Now! (£1,200); Central Methodist Church, NOEL Singers, Scope and Southgate Methodist Church (£1,000).

FINANCES *Year* 2007–08 *Income* £130,191 *Grants* £126,448 *Assets* £3,337,470

TRUSTEES R D Smithies, Chair; P W Townend; T Simpson; D Sharpe; L Smith; B Mowforth.

OTHER INFORMATION The grant total in 2007–08 included £59,000 given to 68 individuals.

HOW TO APPLY In writing to the correspondent, detailing requirements and costings. Trustee board meetings are held six times a year.

WHO TO APPLY TO R D Smithies, Trustee, 5 King St, Brighouse, West Yorkshire HD6 1NX *email* bearders@btinternet.com *Website* www.bearder-charity.org.uk

CC NO 1010529   **ESTABLISHED** 1992

■ The James Beattie Charitable Trust

WHERE FUNDING CAN BE GIVEN Wolverhampton area.

WHO CAN BENEFIT Local projects and organisations benefiting the people of Wolverhampton.

WHAT IS FUNDED General charitable purposes including accommodation and housing; community development, support to voluntary and community organisations; and social care professional bodies. Also health; conservation and the environment; education; community facilities and services; dance groups and orchestras; volunteer bureaux; Christian education and churches; schools; and youth projects such as scouts and air training corps may be considered.

WHAT IS NOT FUNDED No grants to individuals, organisations outside the West Midlands, or

exclusive organisations (e.g. all-white or all-Asian groups).

TYPE OF GRANT Grants awarded for capital including buildings, core costs, project research, running costs, salaries and start-up costs. Grants may be one-off or recurring and funding for a single project may be available for less than one year to more than three.

SAMPLE GRANTS Previous beneficiaries have included Barnardos, James Beattie House, Cottage Homes, Marie Curie Cancer Care, St Chad's – Pattingham, St Martin's School, Whizz Kidz, Wolverhampton Grammar School and YMCA.

FINANCES *Year* 2007–08 *Income* £58,925 *Grants* £128,686 *Assets* £2,733,919

TRUSTEES Mrs Jane Victoria Redshaw; Michael Walter Redshaw; Kenneth Charles Dolman; Mrs Susannah Jane Norbury.

HOW TO APPLY In writing to the correspondent, including accounts.

WHO TO APPLY TO The Trustees, PO Box 12, Bridgnorth, Shropshire WV15 5LQ *Tel* 01746 716207

CC NO 265654   **ESTABLISHED** 1961

■ The Beaufort House Trust Limited

WHERE FUNDING CAN BE GIVEN UK.

WHO CAN BENEFIT Organisations benefiting Christians, children and young adults.

WHAT IS FUNDED To support schools, colleges, universities or other charitable bodies engaged in the advancement, promotion and furtherance of education, religion or any other charitable purposes.

WHAT IS NOT FUNDED No grants are made to organisations with political associations, UK wide charities or individuals.

TYPE OF GRANT Some recurring, majority one-off.

FINANCES *Year* 2007 *Income* £236,288 *Grants* £38,300 *Assets* £97,381

TRUSTEES M R Cornwall-Jones, Chair; W H Yates; N J E Sealy; H F Hart; M A Chamberlain; W N Stock; Ven A J Cooper.

OTHER INFORMATION Each year the trust receives donations from Ecclesiastical Insurance Office plc and school fee annuities from Ecclesiastical Life Limited. Ecclesiastical Life Limited and Ecclesiastical Insurance Office plc are subsidiaries of Allchurches Trust Limited. Beaufort House Trust Limited and Allchurches Trust Limited are companies that are controlled by a common board of trustees.

HOW TO APPLY On an application form. The following details will be required: the objectives of the charity; the appeal target; how the funds are to be utilised; funds raised to date; and previous support received from the trust.

WHO TO APPLY TO Mrs R J Hall, Secretary, Beaufort House, Brunswick Road, Gloucester GL1 1JZ

CC NO 286606   **ESTABLISHED** 1983

■ Beauland Ltd

WHERE FUNDING CAN BE GIVEN Worldwide, possibly with a preference for the Manchester area.

WHO CAN BENEFIT To benefit Jewish people and people who are sick.

WHAT IS FUNDED Healthcare charities and exclusively Jewish projects are supported.

SAMPLE GRANTS Previous beneficiaries have included Asos Chesed, Cosmon Belz, Famos Charity Trust, Radford Education Trust, Sunderland Yeshiva and Yetev Lev.

FINANCES *Year* 2007–08 *Income* £449,185 *Grants* £199,980 *Assets* £7,196,442

TRUSTEES F Neumann; H Neumann; M Friedlander; H Rosemann; J Bleier; R Delange; M Neumann; P Neumann; E Neumann; E Henry.

HOW TO APPLY In writing to the correspondent.

WHO TO APPLY TO M Neumann, Trustee, 309 Bury New Road, Salford M7 2YN

CC NO 511374   **ESTABLISHED** 1981

....

■ The Beaverbrook Foundation

WHERE FUNDING CAN BE GIVEN UK and Canada.

WHO CAN BENEFIT Registered charities, mainly headquarters organisations or national charities.

WHAT IS FUNDED 'The object of this foundation include: (i) the erection or improvement of the fabric of any church building; (ii) the purchase of books, papers, manuscripts or works of art; (iii) care of the aged or infirm in the UK. One of the areas that the foundation has concentrated on over the past twenty years has been supporting small charitable projects. We recognise that it is often more difficult to raise a few thousand to refurbish a church hall than it is to raise millions for a major public building. In the past twenty years, the foundation has donated to more than 400 charities.'

WHAT IS NOT FUNDED Only registered charities are supported.

TYPE OF GRANT One-off capital grants.

SAMPLE GRANTS Previous beneficiaries have included AIDS Ark, Alzheimer's Society, Book Aid International, Bob Champion Trust, Down's Syndrome Organisation, London Lighthouse, NSPCC, Royal Academy of Dramatic Art, the Samaritans, St Teresa's Home for the Elderly, Surrey County Scouts Council, Victim Support, West of England School and College and Whizz Kids.

FINANCES *Year* 2006–07 *Income* £155,248 *Grants* £13,700 *Assets* £12,801,000

TRUSTEES Lord Beaverbrook, Chair; Lady Beaverbrook; Lady Aitken; T M Aitken; Hon. Laura Levi; J E A Kidd; Hon. M F Aitken.

OTHER INFORMATION The major project of the last decade has been the renovation of Beaverbrook's country house and gardens at Cherkley Court, near Leatherhead, Surrey.

HOW TO APPLY There is an online application form at the foundation's website.

WHO TO APPLY TO The Secretary, Cherkley Court, Reigate Road, Leatherhead, Surrey KT22 8QX *Tel* 01372 380986 *email* jane@ beaverbrookfoundation.org *Website* www. beaverbrookfoundation.org

CC NO 310003   **ESTABLISHED** 1954

....

■ The Beccles Town Lands Charity

WHERE FUNDING CAN BE GIVEN Beccles only.

WHO CAN BENEFIT Organisations and individuals in Beccles.

WHAT IS FUNDED General charitable purposes.

WHAT IS NOT FUNDED Applications from outside of, or not to the benefit of, Beccles and its inhabitants will not be considered.

FINANCES *Year* 2007–08 *Income* £247,139 *Grants* £62,690

TRUSTEES James Hartley; Dennis Hipperson; Montagu Pitkin; Kenneth Leggett; Gillian Campbell; Gordon Hickman; Jennifer Langeskov; Richard Garrood; Keith Gregory; Jane Seppings.

HOW TO APPLY In writing to the correspondent.

WHO TO APPLY TO R W Peck, Secretary, 6 Cherry Hill Close, Worlingham, Beccles NR34 7EG

CC NO 210714   **ESTABLISHED** 1963

....

■ The Becker Family Charitable Trust

WHERE FUNDING CAN BE GIVEN UK and overseas.

WHO CAN BENEFIT Registered charities.

WHAT IS FUNDED General charitable purposes, particularly Orthodox Jewish organisations.

SAMPLE GRANTS Previous beneficiaries have included Keren Shabbas, Lolev CT, Menora Grammar School, Torah Temima and WST.

FINANCES *Year* 2007–08 *Income* £192,043 *Grants* £144,254 *Assets* £232,390

TRUSTEES A Becker; L Becker; Ms R Becker; Ms D Fried; C Guttentag.

HOW TO APPLY In writing to the correspondent. However, please note that the trust has previously stated that its funds were fully committed.

WHO TO APPLY TO L Becker, Trustee, 5 North End Road, London NW11 7RJ

CC NO 1047968   **ESTABLISHED** 1995

....

■ The Becketts and Sargeants Educational Foundation

WHERE FUNDING CAN BE GIVEN The borough of Northampton.

WHO CAN BENEFIT Church schools, and individuals under 25 years of age and in need of financial assistance, and either a resident in the borough or attending schools or full-time courses of education at any further education establishment in the borough, or a former pupil of All Saints' Middle School for at least two years.

WHAT IS FUNDED Education.

WHAT IS NOT FUNDED No grants are given for part-time courses.

RANGE OF GRANTS Up to £11,300.

FINANCES *Year* 2008 *Income* £227,121 *Grants* £108,349 *Assets* £3,279,469

TRUSTEES Philip Richard Saunderson; Digby Michael Auden; Richard Pestell; Eileen Beeby; Linda Ann Mayne; Ven. Christine Allsopp; David Smith; Hilary Spenceley; Margaret Pickard; Andrew Cowling; Christopher Davidge; Revd Simon Henry; Archdeacon Of Northampton.

OTHER INFORMATION The 2008 grant total includes £54,000 given to individuals.

HOW TO APPLY On a form available from the correspondent. Applications are considered four times a year, usually in February/March, May, September and December.

WHO TO APPLY TO Mrs Gill R Evans, Grants Sub-committee Clerk, Hewitsons, 7 Spencer Parade, Northampton NN1 5AB *Tel* 01604 233233 *email* gillevans@hewitsons.com

CC NO 309766   **ESTABLISHED** 1986

....

■ The Victoria and David Beckham Children's Charity

WHERE FUNDING CAN BE GIVEN UK and overseas.

WHO CAN BENEFIT Organisations and individuals.

WHAT IS FUNDED Work benefiting children and general charitable purposes.

SAMPLE GRANTS Previous beneficiaries include UNICEF, Action for Kids, Motability, Demand, Theraplay, Wheelchair Centre, St Joseph's in the Park Parent Fellowship, Gerald Symonds Healthcare Limited and Helping Hand Company.

FINANCES *Year* 2007–08 *Income* £111,606 *Grants* £330,802 *Assets* £48,311

TRUSTEES Victoria Beckham; David Beckham; Jacqueline Adams.

OTHER INFORMATION The charity's basic accounts provide no information on its achievements during the year or who its beneficiaries were.

HOW TO APPLY In writing to the correspondent; however, a letter requesting information from the charity received a standard reply stating that the charity has 'limited funds', and that our request was 'outside the objectives and criteria set and therefore we are unable to help you'. This indicates that correspondence to the charity are not read.

WHO TO APPLY TO Charles Bradbrook, Administrator, Deloitte LLP, 2 New Street Square, London EC4A 3BZ *Tel* 020 7007 6023 *email* cbradbrook@deloitte.co.uk

CC NO 1091838 **ESTABLISHED** 2002

The John Beckwith Charitable Trust

WHERE FUNDING CAN BE GIVEN UK and overseas.

WHO CAN BENEFIT Registered charities.

WHAT IS FUNDED General charitable purposes with a preference for: sports programmes for young people; education; children's charities; medical research; the arts; and charities involved with overseas aid.

TYPE OF GRANT Capital, one-off and recurring.

SAMPLE GRANTS Top Foundation (£100,000); Harrow Development Trust (£92,000); Unicorn theatre (£45,000); RNIB (£30,000); Caudwell Charitable Trust and Sense International (£10,000 each); Royal Opera House Trust (£8,100); Children's Hospice South West, Fairbridge, Tall Ships Youth Trust and Whizz Kids (£5,000 each); Wycombe Abbey School (£2,000); and KIDS (£1,000).

FINANCES *Year* 2007–08 *Income* £439,876 *Grants* £392,824 *Assets* £2,526,767

TRUSTEES J L Beckwith; H M Beckwith; C M Meech.

HOW TO APPLY In writing to the correspondent.

WHO TO APPLY TO Ms Sally Holder, Administrator, 124 Sloane Street, London SW1X 9BW

CC NO 800276 **ESTABLISHED** 1987

The Peter Beckwith Charitable Trust

WHERE FUNDING CAN BE GIVEN UK.

WHO CAN BENEFIT Institutions and registered charities benefiting at risk groups, people disadvantaged by poverty and socially isolated people.

WHAT IS FUNDED A broad range of medical and welfare charities. General charitable purposes.

SAMPLE GRANTS Great Ormond Street Hospital (£26,000); WCTT (£15,000); Polka Theatre (£4,200); Teenage Cancer Trust (£4,000); the Lucas Johnston Appeal (£2,000); Shelter (£1,100); and WWF – UK (£1,000).

FINANCES *Year* 2007–08 *Income* £96,154 *Grants* £78,592 *Assets* £23,282

TRUSTEES P M Beckwith; Mrs P G Beckwith; Mrs C T Van Dam; Miss T J Beckwith.

HOW TO APPLY In writing to the correspondent.

WHO TO APPLY TO The Trustees, Hill Place House, 55a High Street, Wimbledon Village, London SW19 5BA *Tel* 020 8944 1288

CC NO 802113 **ESTABLISHED** 1989

The Bedford Charity (The Harpur Trust)

WHERE FUNDING CAN BE GIVEN Borough of Bedford and surrounding area.

WHO CAN BENEFIT Community groups, schools, individuals (under education object), and organisations. Particularly children and young adults, people with additional support needs, older people, and people disadvantaged by poverty.

WHAT IS FUNDED The promotion of education; the relief of people who are sick or in need, hardship or distress; homelessness; child and adolescent mental health; the provision in the interest of social welfare of facilities for recreation and other leisure-time occupations.

WHAT IS NOT FUNDED Grants are not made in support of commercial ventures; for any project that relates primarily to the promotion of any religion; in support of projects that do not benefit the residents of the borough of Bedford; to cover costs already incurred, although exceptions are considered and this should be discussed with the trust prior to an application being submitted; for services which are the responsibility of the local authority, for example, a school applying for a grant to cover the cost of employing a teacher is unlikely to be successful. However, the trust could consider an application from a school for a creative arts project that involved paying a voluntary organisation to deliver lunch time or after school workshops.

TYPE OF GRANT Capital, revenue, salaries, running costs. The very great majority of grant giving is targeted at organisations.

SAMPLE GRANTS Bedfordshire Alliance of Nursery and Lower Schools (£102,400), for the Mind Mapping Research Project; King's Arms Project (£75,000), towards ongoing support; Autism Bedfordshire (£63,700), for a full time development officer; Cecil Higgins Art Gallery and Bedford Museum (£32,000), for a audience development project; Bedford Prep School and Pilgrims School (£20,000), for the Bedford Maths Academy; Ormiston Children and Families Trust (£15,000), for Children of Offenders – Parenting Programme; HMP Bedford (£14,000), for a feasibility study on the Resettlement Support Project; Bedfordshire Primary Care Trust (£10,000), for the Early Intervention Project; Bedford Chamber Music Festival (£8,000), towards the 2008 festival; Bedford Sea Cadet Corps (£5,500), to replace heating and hot water boilers; Addaction Bedford (£5,000), for the Health, Employment and Lifestyle Programme; Queen's Park Lower School (£2,500), to enhance the playground; Bedford Cricket Club (£2,000), for new nets; and Tavistock Community Centre (£1,000), for flame retardant curtains.

FINANCES *Year* 2007–08 *Income* £51,035,000 *Grants* £830,600 *Assets* £111,398,000

TRUSTEES David Palfreyman; Prof. William Stephens; David W Doran; David A Berry; Mrs Jean Abbott; Mrs Sue Clark; Ian McEwen; Mrs Judith Bray; Simon Brown; David K Brownridge; Frank D G Cattley; Dr Ann H Cook; Rae Levene; Mrs Rosemary Wallace; Tony Wildman; Mrs Sally Peck; John K S Mingay; Cllr Colleen Atkins; Jean McCardle; Tina Beddoes; Phillip Wallace; Prof. Stephen Mayson; Murray Stewart; Justin Phillimore.

OTHER INFORMATION Grants to organisations: £754,000. Grants to individuals: £76,600.

HOW TO APPLY 'Please contact us to discuss your request well before you intend to submit an application. We have a two stage application process which is outlined below. We are happy to provide assistance at any stage during the application process.

Preliminary Proposals (first stage): We ask you to send us an outline of the project on a Preliminary Proposal form for initial consideration before you submit a formal application. We will share your Preliminary Proposal with trustees at one of their meetings. We will then write to you with their comments and if appropriate invite you to make a formal, second stage application. We will advise you of the next appropriate committee date. **The formal application process (second stage):** We will acknowledge receipt of your application form within a week of receiving it. Please contact us if you have not heard from us within two working weeks of submission. Our staff will first look through your application. If it is ineligible under our current grant programmes we will tell you at this stage. We will ask you some additional questions, based on the areas of your application that we believe our trustees will focus on when they consider your request. Depending on the size of grant you are requesting, and the type of project you are proposing, your application will be considered in the following ways: the chairman and deputy chairman of the grants committee can make a decision on full applications of up to £5,000. A decision on an application of this size normally takes two to three months from the preliminary proposal submission date; the full grants committee can consider applications for grants of up to £50,000 for a single project in any one year and up to £150,000 for a project over a three year period. The committee meets approximately every three months. If the committee requires further information from you to support your application, they may defer making a decision until the next meeting. You can therefore expect to hear a decision on this size of request three to six months after submission of your preliminary proposal. Please allow more time if you are submitting a request that will be processed during the summer months as there are no committee meeting in July and August. Grants awarded by the committee above £50,000 will need to be endorsed by the full trustee body of the Bedford Charity, which meets three times a year. These meetings usually take place in March, July and December. Awards of this size are rare, and the decision making process will almost certainly be longer than for more modest requests. Please make sure you submit your application well before you need a final decision on your request. Please contact us or see our website for latest submission deadlines.'

WHO TO APPLY TO Lucy Bardner, Grants Manager, Princeton Court, Pilgrim Centre, Brickhill Drive, Bedford MK41 7PZ *Tel* 01234 369500 *Fax* 01234 369505 *email* grants@harpur-trust. org.uk *Website* www.bedfordcharity.org.uk

CC NO 204817   **ESTABLISHED** 1566

....
■ **The Bedfordshire and Hertfordshire Historic Churches Trust**

WHERE FUNDING CAN BE GIVEN Bedfordshire, Hertfordshire and that part of Barnet within the Diocese of St Albans.

WHO CAN BENEFIT Those entrusted with the upkeep of places of active Christian worship.

WHAT IS FUNDED Work to ensure that places of active Christian worship are maintained in a structurally sound and weatherproof condition.

WHAT IS NOT FUNDED No grants to individuals.

TYPE OF GRANT One-off and buildings. Funding may be given for one year or less.

RANGE OF GRANTS £1,000–£5,000.

FINANCES *Year* 2007–08 *Income* £353,321 *Grants* £111,500 *Assets* £183,722

TRUSTEES C P Green, Chair; R C H Genochio; A A I Jenkins; P F D Lepper; P A Lomax; S A Russell; T Warburton; R W Wilson.

OTHER INFORMATION Annual income comes from member subscription and from the annual 'Bike 'n Hike' event. The trust also acts as a distributive agent for church grants made by the Wixamtree Trust and Waste Recycling Environmental Ltd.

HOW TO APPLY Initial enquiries should be made to the Grants Secretary. Applications can only be made by members of the trust.

WHO TO APPLY TO Archie Russell, Grants Secretary, Wychbrook, 31 Ivel Gardens, Biggleswade, Bedfordshire SG18 0AN *Tel* 01767 312966 *email* wychbrook@yahoo.co.uk *Website* www. bedshertshct.org.uk

CC NO 1005697   **ESTABLISHED** 1991

....
■ **The Bedfordshire and Luton Community Foundation**

WHERE FUNDING CAN BE GIVEN The county of Bedfordshire and the borough of Luton.

WHO CAN BENEFIT 'The grant schemes aim to assist community voluntary organisations and groups in Bedfordshire and Luton in new or exciting projects that can help make a positive difference in the local community.'

WHAT IS FUNDED 'The foundation is dedicated to improving the quality of community life of those in Bedfordshire and Luton and in particular those in special need by reason of disability, age, financial or other disadvantage.

WHAT IS NOT FUNDED No grants are made: to profit-making organisations; for the furtherance of any one religion; to fund political activities; to private business (other than social enterprises); to projects that would otherwise be funded from statutory sources.

FINANCES *Year* 2007–08 *Income* £350,691 *Grants* £324,979 *Assets* £155,796

TRUSTEES Malcolm Newman, Chair; Mark West; Richard Combes; Veta Hudson Rae; Janet Ridge; Peter Chilton; Judy Oliver; Clifton Ibbett; Dr Wendi Momen; Geoff Lambert; John Worboys; Andy Rayment; Keith Rawlings.

HOW TO APPLY Further information and application forms are available from the foundation. Please consult the foundation's website for details of up-to-date schemes.

WHO TO APPLY TO Mark West, Chief Executive, The Smithy, The Village, Old Warden, Bedfordshire SG18 9HQ *email* mark.west@blcf.org.uk *Website* www.blcf.org.uk

CC NO 1086516   **ESTABLISHED** 2001

....
■ **The David and Ruth Behrend Fund**

WHERE FUNDING CAN BE GIVEN UK, with a preference for Merseyside.

WHO CAN BENEFIT Registered charities.

WHAT IS FUNDED General charitable purposes. The trust only gives funding to charities known to the settlors.

WHAT IS NOT FUNDED Anyone not known to the settlors.

TYPE OF GRANT Up to £6,000.

Think carefully about every application. Is it justified?

363

SAMPLE GRANTS Merseyside Development Foundation, PSS (£6,000 each); Christian Aid and St John's Hospice in Wirral (£2,500 each); Dingle Multi Agency Centre Ltd, Liverpool Somali Youth Association, Northwest Disability Arts Forum and Smart Charitable Trust (£2,000 each); Home Farm Trust and the Missionary Training Service (£1,500 each); and Merseyside Holiday Foundation, Oxfam and Shelter (£1,000 each).

FINANCES *Year* 2007–08 *Income* £85,760 *Grants* £79,340 *Assets* £1,421,104

TRUSTEES Liverpool Charity and Voluntary Services.

HOW TO APPLY **This trust states that it does not respond to unsolicited applications.** 'The charity only makes grants to charities already known to the settlors as this is a personal charitable trust.'

WHO TO APPLY TO The Secretary, 151 Dale Street, Liverpool L2 2AH

CC NO 261567   ESTABLISHED 1969

■ The Beit Trust

WHERE FUNDING CAN BE GIVEN Zimbabwe, Zambia and Malawi.

WHO CAN BENEFIT Individuals and charities benefiting young adults, students, teachers and academics, at-risk groups, people disadvantaged by poverty, and homeless and socially isolated people.

WHAT IS FUNDED Post-primary education; health and welfare. Most grants are for buildings and infrastructure, with occasional grants made for environmental projects.

WHAT IS NOT FUNDED Grants are only given to charities in the areas above and the trust is reluctant to give grants to other grant-making charities. The trust has previously stated that it does not provide support for gap year students, undergraduates, individual schoolchildren or vehicles.

TYPE OF GRANT Recurring, one-off, capital, bursaries, postgraduate fellowships.

RANGE OF GRANTS Not normally in excess of £30,000.

FINANCES *Year* 2008 *Income* £2,819,366 *Grants* £1,947,435 *Assets* £57,513,111

TRUSTEES R A C Byatt; A I Ramsey; C J Driver; Dame Maeve Fort; R P Lander.

HOW TO APPLY Contact the trust by telephone or in writing for an application form. Grants are approved by trustees at their six-monthly meetings.

WHO TO APPLY TO Major General A I Ramsey, Secretary, Beit House, Grove Road, Woking, Surrey GU21 5JB *Tel* 01483 772575 *Fax* 01483 725833 *email* enquiries@beittrust. org *Website* www.beittrust.org.uk

CC NO 232478   ESTABLISHED 1906

■ The Bellahouston Bequest Fund

WHERE FUNDING CAN BE GIVEN Glasgow and district, but not more than five miles beyond the Glasgow city boundary.

WHO CAN BENEFIT Churches and registered charities in Glasgow or within five miles especially those benefiting Protestant evangelical denominations and clergy of such churches, as well as people disadvantaged by poverty.

WHAT IS FUNDED The trust supports a wide variety of causes. Its main priority is to help build, expand and repair Protestant evangelical churches or places of religious worship, as well as supporting the clergy of these churches. It

further states that it is set up to give grants to charities for the relief of poverty or disease and to organisations concerned with promotion of the Protestant religion, education, and conservation of places of historical and artistic significance. It will consider social welfare causes generally and also animal welfare and sport and recreation.

WHAT IS NOT FUNDED No grants to organisations or churches whose work does not fall within the geographical remit of the fund. Overseas projects and political appeals are not supported.

SAMPLE GRANTS Previous beneficiaries have included 119th Glasgow Boys Brigade, Airborne Initiative, Ballieston Community Care, Bellahouston Academy, Calvay Social Action Group, Citizens' Theatre, Church of Scotland, Colquhoun Trust, Crosshill Evangelical Church, Dalmarnock After School Care, Erskine Hospital, Girlguiding Scotland, Glasgow School of Art, Glasgow Old People's Welfare Association, Glasgow YMCA, Govanhill Youth Project, House for an Art Lover, Kelvingrove Refurbishment Appeal, Maryhill Parish Church, William McCunn's Trust, Northwest Women's Centre, Pearce Institute, Prince and Princess of Wales Hospice, Shawlands United Reformed Church, St Paul's Parish Council, Strathclyde Youth Club Association, University of Strathclyde and Williamwood Parish Church.

FINANCES *Year* 2005–06 *Income* £176,906

TRUSTEES Bonar G Hardie; David H Galbraith; J Forbes MacPherson; Eric H Webster; Peter C Paisley; Peter L Fairley.

HOW TO APPLY On a form available from the trust for church applications only. Other charitable organisations can apply in writing to the correspondent. The trustees meet to consider grants in March, July, October and December.

WHO TO APPLY TO The Administrator, Mitchells Roberton Solicitors, George House, 36 North Hanover Street, Glasgow G1 2AD

SC NO SC011781   ESTABLISHED 1888

■ Bellasis Trust

WHERE FUNDING CAN BE GIVEN UK.

WHO CAN BENEFIT Local charities.

WHAT IS FUNDED General charitable purposes.

SAMPLE GRANTS Royal Horticultural Society, St Anne's School – Banstead, St Mary's School – Ascot and St Michael's PCC (£5,000 each); the David Lynne Charitable Trust (£3,500); Book Power (£3,000); the Laser Trust Fund and St John Ambulance (£2,000 each); Macmillan Cancer Support (£1,500); and the National Maritime Museum and St Catherine's Hospice (£1,000 each).

FINANCES *Year* 2007–08 *Income* £49,143 *Grants* £42,163 *Assets* £921,048

TRUSTEES P C R Wates; Mrs A B Wates; Mrs A L M Elliott; J R F Lulham.

HOW TO APPLY 'The trustees research and consider applicants for grants.'

WHO TO APPLY TO P C R Wates, Trustee, 4th Floor, 65 Kingsway, London WC2B 6TD

CC NO 1085972   ESTABLISHED 2000

■ The Bellhouse Foundation

WHERE FUNDING CAN BE GIVEN UK.

WHO CAN BENEFIT Organisations working in the fields of engineering and pharmacology.

WHAT IS FUNDED The advancement of education through the promotion of medical research in the field of engineering and pharmacology.

364

Does the trust you have chosen match your needs? Haphazard applications waste postage and time

SAMPLE GRANTS Oxford University Development Trust (£400,000); Magdalen College Development Trust (£150,000); Medical Foundation (£10,000); and the Woodland Trust (£1,000).

FINANCES *Year* 2007–08 *Income* £251,355 *Grants* £561,000 *Assets* £382,969

TRUSTEES Prof. Brian Bellhouse; Elisabeth Bellhouse; Clare Maurice.

OTHER INFORMATION 'The trustees are funding a junior research fellow at Magdalen College. The funding is to the value of £150,000, split into three annual instalments, the first of which was payable by 1 January 2008.'

HOW TO APPLY In writing to the correspondent.

WHO TO APPLY TO The Trustees, The Lodge, North Street, Islip, Oxfordshire OX5 2QS

CC NO 1076698   **ESTABLISHED** 1999

....

■ The Bellinger Donnay Trust

WHERE FUNDING CAN BE GIVEN Unrestricted, in practice, London, Wiltshire and the south east of England.

WHO CAN BENEFIT Small, independent charities.

WHAT IS FUNDED General charitable causes, in particular, those concerned with young people, older people, people with disabilities and the relief of poverty and deprivation.

WHAT IS NOT FUNDED No grants towards: animal organisations; travel overseas for individuals; medical research; or building projects.

RANGE OF GRANTS Usually up to £1,000; occasionally up to £5,000 or higher.

SAMPLE GRANTS the Arsenal Charitable Trust (£15,000); Bag Books, the Broderers Charity Trust, European Union Youth Orchestra and Operation New World (£5,000 each); Encompass (£3,500); the Buckinghamshire Foundation (£2,000); Cystic Fibrosis Dream Holidays (£1,500); Royal Academy Trust (£1,100); Prospect Hospice (£1,000); Friends of the Elderly (£500); Action Aid (£100); Swiss Cultural Fund in Britain (£50); and Christian Aid (£10).

FINANCES *Year* 2007–08 *Income* £92,941 *Grants* £73,516 *Assets* £2,027,692

TRUSTEES Lady C M L Bellinger; Mrs L E Spackman; I A Bellinger.

HOW TO APPLY In writing to the correspondent, on no more than two sides of A4 plus the latest audited accounts. Applicants should provide: brief details of the charitable aims of the organisation and of how those aims are being achieved; the organisation's current financial position (income, expenditure, balances and reserves); funding already received/ anticipated from other sources; the proportion of income which is spent on administration, including staff salaries, and raising funds; the amount requested and the purpose for which the grant is to be used. If your application is urgent and requires immediate consideration, please say so when applying. Applications should be submitted by 31 January at the latest. Telephone calls are not accepted, although e-mail queries are welcomed. Applications will not be acknowledged. Applicants from Wiltshire, or for projects in the county, should apply to: Mrs L E Spackman, Callas Hill Farm, High Street, Wanborough, Wiltshire SN4 0AE. All other applications should please be made in writing to: I A Bellinger, Byways, Coombe Hill Road, Kingston upon Thames, Surrey KT2 7DY.

WHO TO APPLY TO I A Bellinger, Byways, Coombe Hill Road, Kingston upon Thames, Surrey KT2 7DY

email bdct@ianbellinger.co.uk *Website* www.bellingerdonnay.ik.com

CC NO 289462   **ESTABLISHED** 1984

....

■ Belljoe Tzedoko Ltd

WHERE FUNDING CAN BE GIVEN UK.

WHO CAN BENEFIT Registered charities and institutions.

WHAT IS FUNDED Advancement of religion in accordance with the orthodox Jewish faith and the relief of poverty.

SAMPLE GRANTS Previous beneficiaries have included Adath Yisroel Synagogue, the B and G Charitable Trust, Beer Miriam, CWC, Kupat Hair, Marbe Torah, Shomre Hachomos, Yeshivo Horomo and Yesodey Hatora.

FINANCES *Year* 2007 *Income* £36,923 *Grants* £36,565 *Assets* £86,958

TRUSTEES H J Lobenstein; Mrs B Lobenstein; D Lobenstein; M Lobenstein; Mrs S Falk; Mrs N Stern.

HOW TO APPLY In writing to the correspondent.

WHO TO APPLY TO H J Lobenstein, Trustee, 27 Fairholt Road, London N16 5EW

CC NO 282726   **ESTABLISHED** 1981

....

■ The Benfield Motors Charitable Trust

WHERE FUNDING CAN BE GIVEN Worldwide with preferences for north east England, Leeds and Edinburgh.

WHO CAN BENEFIT Neighbourhood-based community projects and national schemes.

WHAT IS FUNDED Grants are given to mainly health and welfare charities.

WHAT IS NOT FUNDED Expeditions, scholarships and animal charities are not funded.

TYPE OF GRANT One-off.

RANGE OF GRANTS £25–£25,000; typical grant £1,000.

SAMPLE GRANTS Community Foundation – Sage Endowment (£20,000); Cry in the Dark (£15,000); Traidcraft Exchange (£8,100); PICA (£5,000); Calvert Kielder Trust (£4,000); Tynedale Citizens Advice (£2,500); Hill Top Special School (£1,500); Bubble Foundation UK, the Cedarwood Trust, Depaul Trust and Fairbridge Tyne and Wear (£1,000 each); Henshaws Society for Blind People (£800); Kidsafe UK and Salvation Army (£500); and Bible Society and Ethiopiaid (£100 each).

FINANCES *Year* 2007–08 *Income* £93,000 *Grants* £93,323 *Assets* £23,054

TRUSTEES John Squires, Chair; Malcolm Squires; Stephen Squires.

HOW TO APPLY In writing to the correspondent. The trustees' meet twice a year, this is usually in May and November with applications needing to be received by the beginning of April or October respectively.

WHO TO APPLY TO Mrs Lynn Squires, Hon. Secretary, c/o Benfield Motor Group, Asama Court, Newcastle Business Park, Newcastle upon Tyne NE4 7YD *Tel* 0191 226 1700 *email* charitabletrust@benfieldmotorgroup.com

CC NO 328149   **ESTABLISHED** 1989

■ The Benham Charitable Settlement

WHERE FUNDING CAN BE GIVEN UK, with very strong emphasis on Northamptonshire.

WHO CAN BENEFIT Registered charities.

WHAT IS FUNDED The trust's policy is to make a large number of relatively small grants to groups working in many charitable fields, including charities involved in medical research, disability, older people, children and young people, disadvantaged people, overseas aid, missions to seamen, the welfare of ex-servicemen, wildlife, the environment, and the arts. The trust also supports the Church of England, and the work of Christian mission throughout the world. Special emphasis is placed upon those churches and charitable organisations within the county of Northamptonshire [especially as far as new applicants are concerned].

WHAT IS NOT FUNDED No grants to individuals.

TYPE OF GRANT One-off and recurring grants will be considered.

SAMPLE GRANTS Northamptonshire Association of Youth Clubs (£35,000 in two grants); All Saints Church – Peckham (£10,000); Progressive Supranuclear Palsy Association (£6,000); Holy Trinity Church – Muheza Hospital, Tanzania (£5,000); the Besom Foundation and Coworth Flexlands School (£5,000 each); Arthritis Care, British heart Foundation, Camphill Village Trust, Cathedral Camps, the Children's Trust, and Victim Support – Northamptonshire (£600 each); Cued Speech Association, Tall Ships Youth Trust, the Willow Trust (£500 each); and Peterborough Cathedral Trust and Whizz Kidz (£400 each).

FINANCES *Year* 2007–08 *Income* £182,835 *Grants* £148,950 *Assets* £4,615,580

TRUSTEES Mrs M M Tittle; Lady Hutton; E N Langley; D A H Tittle; Revd. J A Nickols.

HOW TO APPLY In recent years the trust has not been considering new applications.

WHO TO APPLY TO The Secretary, Hurstbourne, Portnall Drive, Virginia Water, Surrey GU25 4NR

CC NO 239371   **ESTABLISHED** 1964

■ The Hervey Benham Charitable Trust

WHERE FUNDING CAN BE GIVEN Colchester and North East Essex.

WHO CAN BENEFIT Individuals or self-help organisations from Colchester and North East Essex.

WHAT IS FUNDED Artistic (particularly musical) activities which benefit the people of Colchester and district and which would benefit from pump-priming by the trust and/or a contribution which enables self-help to function more effectively; individuals with potential artistic (especially musical) talent who are held back by physical, environmental or financial disability; preservation of Colchester and district's heritage with particular emphasis on industrial heritage and the maritime traditions of the Essex/Suffolk coast; local history and conservation affecting the heritage and environment of the area.

WHAT IS NOT FUNDED Capital including buildings, feasibility studies, interest-free loans, one-off, and pump-priming costs. Funding is available for up to three years. Tuition fees are normally paid direct to educational institutions.

TYPE OF GRANT Capital including buildings, feasibility studies, interest-free loans, one-off, and pump-

priming costs. Funding is available for up to three years. Tuition fees are normally paid direct to educational institutions.

RANGE OF GRANTS Up to £50,000.

SAMPLE GRANTS Mersea Museum Trust (£15,000); Rowledge Heritage Trust (£1,500); Brightlingsea Music Festival, Coastnet and Colchester Gateway Clubs (£1,000 each); and 9th Colchester Sea Scouts (£600);.

FINANCES *Year* 2008–09 *Income* £37,766 *Grants* £29,420 *Assets* £1,037,293

TRUSTEES M Ellis, Chair; A B Phillips; M R Carr; K E Mirams.

PUBLICATIONS Brochure.

OTHER INFORMATION The 2008–09 grant total included £4,000 distributed to individuals

HOW TO APPLY In writing to the correspondent by the normal quarterly dates.

WHO TO APPLY TO J Woodman, Clerk to the Trustees, 3 Cadman House, off Peartree Road, Colchester, Essex CO3 0NW *Tel* 01206 561086 *email* jwoodman@aspects.net

CC NO 277578   **ESTABLISHED** 1978

■ Maurice and Jacqueline Bennett Charitable Trust

WHERE FUNDING CAN BE GIVEN UK and overseas.

WHO CAN BENEFIT Charitable organisations; Jewish charities.

WHAT IS FUNDED General charitable purposes; support of Jewish charitable organisations.

SAMPLE GRANTS 'Distributions' were: Iron Fell Consult (£22,500); Camphill St Albans (£3,100); World Jewish Relief (£2,000); and CST Trust (£1,000).

FINANCES *Year* 2007–08 *Income* £25,883 *Grants* £30,835 *Assets* £13,496

TRUSTEES Maurice Bennett; M Jacqueline Bennett.

HOW TO APPLY In writing to the correspondent.

WHO TO APPLY TO Maurice Bennett, 9 Ingram Avenue, London NW11 6TG

CC NO 1047566   **ESTABLISHED** 1995

■ Michael and Leslie Bennett Charitable Trust

WHERE FUNDING CAN BE GIVEN UK.

WHO CAN BENEFIT Jewish organisations.

WHAT IS FUNDED The trust supports a range of causes, but the largest donations were to Jewish organisations.

SAMPLE GRANTS Chai Cancer Care (£20,000); Jewish Care (£11,000); World Jewish Relief (£10,000); Magen David Adorn (£2,600); and Tel Aviv Foundation (£1,000).

FINANCES *Year* 2007–08 *Income* £45,562 *Grants* £66,066 *Assets* £394,696

TRUSTEES Michael Bennett; Lesley V Bennett.

HOW TO APPLY In writing to the correspondent.

WHO TO APPLY TO Michael Bennett, Trustee, Bedegars Lea, Kenwood Close, London NW3 7JL

CC NO 1047611   **ESTABLISHED** 1995

■ The Gerald Bentall Charitable Trust

WHERE FUNDING CAN BE GIVEN Mainly southern England including London.

WHO CAN BENEFIT Older people, people with disabilities and young people.

WHAT IS FUNDED hospitals, churches, youth organisations, education.

RANGE OF GRANTS £100–£10,000.

SAMPLE GRANTS Old Bentallians Association (£500); Back to Africa and Phyllis Tuckwell Hospice (£300 each); NSPCC (£250); Action Medical Research and Police Dependants Trust (£175 each); Age Concern England and Children with Leukaemia (£150 each); and Mount Alvernia Hospital and Disability Challengers (£125 each).

FINANCES *Year* 2008–09 *Income* £32,061 *Grants* £16,856

TRUSTEES A J D Anstee; Mrs C L Thorp; Mrs E C Purcell; Mrs C E Jackson.

HOW TO APPLY In writing to the correspondent.

WHO TO APPLY TO Mrs Z Peters, 24 Stoudes Close, Worcester Park, Surrey KT4 7RB *Tel* 020 8330 4586

CC NO 271993   **ESTABLISHED** 1976

■ Bergqvist Charitable Trust

WHERE FUNDING CAN BE GIVEN Buckinghamshire and neighbouring counties.

WHO CAN BENEFIT Registered charities and community organisations.

WHAT IS FUNDED Education; medical health; environment; and disaster and famine relief.

WHAT IS NOT FUNDED Grants are not made to individuals, non-registered charities or for animal causes.

TYPE OF GRANT One-off and recurrent grants.

SAMPLE GRANTS Previous beneficiaries have included Generation Trust for medical research, Abracadabra – Royal Surrey Hospital Paediatric Unit, Stoke Mandeville Hospital for MRI scanner appeal, British Epilepsy Association for general purposes, Cancer Care and Haematology at Stoke Mandeville Hospital, PACE school for children with cerebral palsy, British Heart Foundation for research, Church Urban Fund for diocese expenses and Sight Savers International for eyesight research.

FINANCES *Year* 2007 *Income* £74,673 *Grants* £66,655 *Assets* £1,620,184

TRUSTEES Mrs P A Bergqvist, Chair; Philip Bergqvist; Sophia Bergqvist.

HOW TO APPLY In writing to the correspondent.

WHO TO APPLY TO Mrs P A Bergqvist, Trustee, Moat Farm, Water Lane, Ford, Aylesbury, Buckinghamshire HP17 8XD *Tel* 01296 748560

CC NO 1015707   **ESTABLISHED** 1992

■ The Ruth Berkowitz Charitable Trust

WHERE FUNDING CAN BE GIVEN UK and overseas.

WHO CAN BENEFIT Charitable organisations.

WHAT IS FUNDED Young people; medical research; education; Jewish causes, including education and community.

RANGE OF GRANTS £2,500–£50,000.

SAMPLE GRANTS Wiener Library Institute of Contemporary History (£50,000); National Jewish Chaplaincy Board (£43,000); Community Security Trust (£35,000); Friends of Magen David Adorn and World Jewish Relief (£30,000 each); Bnai Brith Hillel Foundation (£28,000); London School of Jewish Studies (£25,000); Cancer Research UK (£15,000); University College London (£7,500); ZSV Trust (£5,000); and Laniado Hospital UK (£2,500).

FINANCES *Year* 2007–08 *Income* £493,436 *Grants* £507,500 *Assets* £4,365,909

TRUSTEES Philip Beckman; Brian Beckman.

HOW TO APPLY In writing to the correspondent.

WHO TO APPLY TO The Trustees, 39 Farm Avenue, London NW2 2BJ

CC NO 1111673

■ The Berkshire Community Foundation

WHERE FUNDING CAN BE GIVEN Berkshire, i.e. the unitary authorities of Bracknell, Reading, Slough, Windsor and Maidenhead, West Berkshire and Wokingham.

WHO CAN BENEFIT Voluntary organisations or groups established for charitable purposes and individual children. Grants are directed to: older people; children and young people; people with a long-term illness or disability and their carers; people with mental health needs; minority ethnic communities; those suffering from addiction.

WHAT IS FUNDED Grants are made through various funds to support groups addressing need in the county. Up-to-date details can be found at the foundation's website.

FINANCES *Year* 2007–08 *Grants* £550,000

TRUSTEES Chris Barrett; Cllr May Dodds; Kelly Hales; John Horsey; Ramesh Kukar; Richard Nevill; Sue Ormiston; Hugh Priestley; Richard Rand; Gordon Storey; Dick Taylor; Susie Tremlett; Emma van Zeller; Revd Allen Walker; Christine Weston.

OTHER INFORMATION 'Donations from individuals, companies and charitable trusts are pooled in the foundation's Community Capital Fund from which the foundation draws income to make its grants.'

HOW TO APPLY Full details of how to apply to the various funding streams can be found at the foundation's website.

WHO TO APPLY TO The Grants Team, Arlington Business Park, Theale, Reading, Berkshire RG7 4SA *Tel* 0118 930 3021 *Fax* 0118 930 4933 *email* grants@berkshirecommunityfoundation.org.uk *Website* www.berkshirecommunityfoundation.org.uk

CC NO 294220   **ESTABLISHED** 1985

■ The Bestway Foundation

WHERE FUNDING CAN BE GIVEN UK and overseas.

WHO CAN BENEFIT Individuals, UK registered charities, non-registered charities and overseas charities.

WHAT IS FUNDED Advancement of education by grants to schoolchildren and students who are of Indian, Pakistani, Bangladeshi or Sri Lankan origin; relief of sickness, and preservation and protection of health in the UK and overseas, especially in India, Pakistan, Bangladesh and Sri Lanka.

WHAT IS NOT FUNDED No grants for trips/travel abroad.

SAMPLE GRANTS Bestway Foundation Pakistan (£200,000); Northern University (£50,000); Leonard Cheshire Disability (£10,000); Concern for Mental Health (£2,000); and Fleetwood Tigers (£500).

FINANCES *Year* 2007–08 *Income* £979,714 *Grants* £500,102 *Assets* £4,414,131

TRUSTEES A K Bhatti; A K Chaudhary; M Y Sheikh; Z M Chaudrey; A K Chaudhary; M A Pervez.

OTHER INFORMATION All trustees of this foundation are directors and shareholders of Bestway (Holdings) Limited, the parent company of Bestway Cash and Carry Limited.

Think carefully about every application. Is it justified?

367

HOW TO APPLY In writing to the correspondent, enclosing an sae. Applications are considered in March/April. Telephone calls are not welcome.

WHO TO APPLY TO M Y Sheikh, Trustee, Bestway Cash and Carry Ltd, Abbey Road, Park Royal, London NW10 7BW

CC NO 297178   **ESTABLISHED** 1987

■ The Betterware Foundation

WHERE FUNDING CAN BE GIVEN UK.

WHO CAN BENEFIT Charitable organisations.

WHAT IS FUNDED Mainly children's charities.

TYPE OF GRANT One-off towards revenue costs.

FINANCES *Year* 2006–07 *Income* £21,542 *Grants* £27,473 *Assets* £11,345

TRUSTEES Andrew Cohen; Wendy Cohen.

OTHER INFORMATION This foundation receives most of its income directly from the Betterware plc.

HOW TO APPLY Grants are mostly given to children's charities which are of personal interest to the trustees. 'We are a very small trust and do not consider unsolicited applications.'

WHO TO APPLY TO Iain Williamson, Wood Hall Lane, Shenley, Hertfordshire WD7 9AA

CC NO 1093834   **ESTABLISHED** 2002

■ Thomas Betton's Charity for Pensions and Relief-in-Need

WHERE FUNDING CAN BE GIVEN UK.

WHO CAN BENEFIT Registered charities only.

WHAT IS FUNDED This charity makes grants for educational activities for children and young people up to the age of 25 from disadvantaged backgrounds. It also gives to specific charitable organisations with which the trustee has an ongoing relationship (a block grant is made to Housing the Homeless which allocates grants to individuals).

WHAT IS NOT FUNDED Applications for grants to individuals are accepted only from registered social workers or other agencies, not directly from individuals.

RANGE OF GRANTS £1,000–£5,000.

SAMPLE GRANTS Housing the Homeless Central Fund (£22,000); the Art Room and North East Community Forests (£5,000 each); Ivorian Advice and Support Group (£4,700); Living Paintings Trust (£2,500); John Boste Youth Centre (£2,100); Rainy Day Trust and Sheriffs' and Recorder's Fund (£2,000 each); and Hope's Place (£1,200).

FINANCES *Year* 2007–08 *Income* £62,567 *Grants* £56,768 *Assets* £948,230

TRUSTEES The Worshipful Company of Ironmongers.

HOW TO APPLY In writing to the correspondent.

WHO TO APPLY TO The Charities Administrator, Ironmongers' Hall, Barbican, London EC2Y 8AA *Tel* 020 7776 2311 *Website* www.ironhall.co.uk

CC NO 280143   **ESTABLISHED** 1973

■ BHST

WHERE FUNDING CAN BE GIVEN UK and Israel.

WHO CAN BENEFIT Jewish organisations.

WHAT IS FUNDED Jewish charitable purposes.

RANGE OF GRANTS Usually £300–£7,400.

SAMPLE GRANTS Adath Yisroel Burial Society (£64,000); Easy Chasnea (£7,000); Shulum Berger Association (£3,000); United Talmudical Association (£2,500); and Beis Rochel (£1,600).

FINANCES *Year* 2007–08 *Income* £399,720 *Grants* £166,518 *Assets* £1,469,032

TRUSTEES Solomon Laufer; Pinchas Ostreicher; Joshua Sternlicht.

OTHER INFORMATION A total of £72,000 was given in student grants.

HOW TO APPLY In writing to the correspondent.

WHO TO APPLY TO Solomon Laufer, Secretary, Cohen Arnold and Co., New Burlington House, 1075 Finchley Road, London NW11 0PU *Tel* 020 8731 0777 *Fax* 020 8731 0778

CC NO 1004327   **ESTABLISHED** 1991

■ The Mason Bibby 1981 Trust

WHERE FUNDING CAN BE GIVEN Merseyside and other areas where the company has or had a presence.

WHO CAN BENEFIT Priority to older people and employees and ex-employees of J Bibby and Sons Plc (since renamed Barloworld PLC).

WHAT IS FUNDED Main area of interest is older people but applications are considered from other groups, particularly from areas in which the company has a presence.

WHAT IS NOT FUNDED Apart from employees and ex-employees of J Bibby and Sons Plc, applications are considered from registered charities only.

RANGE OF GRANTS £250–£3,500.

SAMPLE GRANTS Home Farm Trust (£6,000); Liverpool Personal Service Society (£4,400); Age Concern – Liverpool (£3,700); Liverpool Council of Social Services (£2,200); Cancer Relief – MacMillan Fund (£1,800); Katharine House Hospice – Adderbury, St. John's Hospice – Wirral, the Shakespeare Hospice and Hoylake Cottage Hospital (£1,500 each); and Wirral Holistic Centre (£1,000).

FINANCES *Year* 2007–08 *Income* £105,215 *Grants* £89,502 *Assets* £2,326,313

TRUSTEES J B Bibby, Chair; J P Wood; Mrs D M Fairclough; S W Bowman; J McPheat; A S Gresty; P A Blocksidge; Mrs L F Stead.

OTHER INFORMATION In 2007–08 donations to employees and ex-employees totalled £9,702.

HOW TO APPLY In writing to the correspondent. Trustees meet half yearly. Applications are only acknowledged if a grant is agreed.

WHO TO APPLY TO Mrs D M Fairclough, Trustee, c/o Rathbone Brothers and Co. Ltd, Port of Liverpool Building, Pier head, Liverpool L3 1NW

CC NO 283231   **ESTABLISHED** 1981

■ BibleLands

WHERE FUNDING CAN BE GIVEN Lands of the Bible, especially Lebanon, the Holy Land and Egypt.

WHO CAN BENEFIT Local organisations working in the beneficial area that benefit people of all ages, faiths and nationalities in the region especially those who are marginalised or vulnerable. Support is given to areas including education, special needs, vocational training, care and support of refugees, medical, social care.

WHAT IS FUNDED BibleLands exists to support and encourage local Christians in the lands of the Bible, who are dedicated to fulfilling the compassionate ministry of Christ.

WHAT IS NOT FUNDED Individuals and UK bodies are not eligible. Grants are confined to Christian-led work, but beneficiaries are helped regardless of faith or nationality.

TYPE OF GRANT Capital including buildings, recurring, core costs, one-off, running costs and start-up costs. Funding is for up to or more than three years. Child sponsorship schemes and ongoing grants to specific projects are also in place.

RANGE OF GRANTS £1,000–£350,000.

FINANCES *Year* 2008 *Income* £2,371,771 *Grants* £1,739,114 *Assets* £3,740,695

TRUSTEES Dr H Boulter, President; Rev D Burton, Chair; Hugh Bradley; Victoria Smith; Douglas Callander; Revd Michael Cleves; Dr Ros Davies; Judy Hackney; Revd Brian Jolly; Revd Nichola Jones; Joanna Robertson; Dr Cyril Young.

PUBLICATIONS *The Star in the East*, quarterly magazine.

HOW TO APPLY Apply in writing for an application form, giving brief outline of the support being sought.

WHO TO APPLY TO Jeremy Moodey, PO Box 50, High Wycombe, Buckinghamshire HP15 7QU *Tel* 01494 897950 *Fax* 01494 897951 *email* info@biblelands.org.uk *Website* www.biblelands.org.uk

CC NO 1076329   **ESTABLISHED** 1854

■ The Bideford Bridge Trust

WHERE FUNDING CAN BE GIVEN Bideford, Devon and its neighbourhood.

WHO CAN BENEFIT Charities and individuals.

WHAT IS FUNDED Grants are dictated by the scheme of the trust, which maintains that the following grants should be made: (i) to encourage education; (ii) to encourage poor people to become more self-sufficient by assisting them in business start-up schemes (iii); to individual applications for charitable assistance (such as on the grounds of poverty or ill health); (iv) to clubs, organisations and charities (v); to assist people with disabilities living in the Parish of Bideford.

WHAT IS NOT FUNDED Computer purchases for individuals. Political donations.

TYPE OF GRANT Core and recurring costs.

RANGE OF GRANTS Generally £500–£50,000.

SAMPLE GRANTS Torridge Training Service – Business Start-Ups (£27,000); Bideford Rugby Football Club (£26,000); East-the-Water Community Primary School (£16,000); Bideford Blues and Appledore Junior Football Club (£10,000); Torridge and Bude Citizens Advice Bureau and Torridge Volunteer Centre (£5,000 each); Bideford Folk Festival 2,500 and Macmillan Cancer Relief – Bideford (£2,500); Appledore Book Festival and North Devon Down Syndrome Association (£1,500 each); and Sure Start Bideford Children's Centre (£300).

FINANCES *Year* 2008 *Income* £797,222 *Grants* £436,734 *Assets* £12,138,512

TRUSTEES P Christie; W G Isaac; Mrs E Junkison; E Hubber; J Baker; O Chope; A Harper; S Inch; T J Johns; A T Powell; B J Lacey; D J Dark.

HOW TO APPLY Grants are not made for computers for individuals. Political donations are not made.

WHO TO APPLY TO P R Sims, Steward, 24 Bridgeland Street, Bideford, Devon EX39 2QB

CC NO 204536   **ESTABLISHED** 1973

■ The Big Lottery Fund (see also Awards for All)

WHERE FUNDING CAN BE GIVEN UK.

WHO CAN BENEFIT Charities, statutory bodies.

WHAT IS FUNDED BIG runs many different programmes, some UK-wide and others specific to England, Northern Ireland, Scotland and Wales. New programmes are introduced from time to time, and others close. Potential applicants are advised to check the fund's website for up-to-date information on current and upcoming programmes.

FINANCES *Year* 2009 *Income* £668,671,000 *Grants* £558,000,000 *Assets* £575,000,000

TRUSTEES Prof. Sir Clive Booth, Chair; Roland Doven; Breidge Gadd; John Gartside; Rajay Naik; Anna Southall; Huw Vaughan Thomas; Diana Whitworth; Sanjay Dighe; Alison Magee; Judith Donovan; Albert Tucker.

OTHER INFORMATION There are a number of regional offices. Call 08454 102030 for details.

HOW TO APPLY All application forms and guidance are available via the website or by calling 08454 102030.

WHO TO APPLY TO (See below) *Tel* 08454 102030 *email* enquiries@biglotteryfund.org.uk *Website* www.biglotteryfund.org.uk

ESTABLISHED 2004

■ The Billmeir Charitable Trust

WHERE FUNDING CAN BE GIVEN UK, with a preference for the Surrey area, specifically Elstead, Tilford, Farnham and Frensham.

WHO CAN BENEFIT Charitable organisations.

WHAT IS FUNDED General charitable purposes. About a quarter of the grants are for health and medical causes.

RANGE OF GRANTS £2,000–£10,000.

SAMPLE GRANTS Reed's School – Cobham and the Watts Gallery (£10,000 each); Arundel Castle Cricket Foundation, the Meath Home and the New Ashgate Gallery (£7,000 each); Army Benevolent Fund, Disability Challengers – Farnham and Youth Sport Trust (£5,000 each); Fairbridge and Surrey Community Foundation (£3,000 each); and Frensham Church (£2,000).

FINANCES *Year* 2007–08 *Income* £160,987 *Grants* £161,000 *Assets* £4,445,429

TRUSTEES B C Whitaker; M R Macfadyen; S Marriott; J Whitaker.

HOW TO APPLY The trust states that it does not request applications and that its funds are fully committed.

WHO TO APPLY TO Keith Lawrence, Moore Stephens, St Paul's House, Warwick Lane, London EC4M 7BP *Tel* 020 7334 9191

CC NO 208561   **ESTABLISHED** 1956

■ Percy Bilton Charity

WHERE FUNDING CAN BE GIVEN UK.

WHO CAN BENEFIT Registered charities in the UK.

WHAT IS FUNDED Projects working with disadvantaged and underprivileged young people (under 25), people with disabilities (physical or learning disabilities or mental health problems) and/or older people (aged over 60).

WHAT IS NOT FUNDED The charity will not consider the following (the list is not exhaustive): running expenses for the organisation or individual projects; salaries, training costs or office equipment/furniture; consumables (e.g. stationery, craft materials); publication costs (e.g. printing/distributing promotional information leaflets); projects for general community use even if facilities for the disabled are included; projects that have been completed; items that have already been purchased; provision of disabled facilities in schemes mainly for the able-bodied; general funding/circular appeals; playschemes/summer schemes; holidays or expeditions for individuals or groups; trips, activities or events; community centres or village halls for wider community use;

community sports/play area facilities; pre-schools or playgroups (other than predominantly for disabled children); refurbishment or repair of places of worship/church halls; research projects; mainstream pre-schools, schools, colleges and universities (other than special schools); welfare funds for individuals; hospital/ medical equipment; works to premises not used primarily by the eligible groups.

TYPE OF GRANT One-off.

RANGE OF GRANTS Grants to individuals: up to £200; small grants to organisations: up to £500 towards furnishing and equipment for small projects; main funding single grants for capital expenditure: in excess of £2,000.

SAMPLE GRANTS Children's Hospice South West – North Somerset (£17,000), for the purchase of a wheelchair accessible multi-people vehicle to transport families to and from the hospice and on day trips; Friends of Longridge – Marlow (£6,000), for the purchase of the freehold of Longridge Boating Centre in order to secure the site which is used for water sports training and activities for youth groups; 4SIGHT – West Sussex (£5,000), for the installation and equipping of a training kitchen as part of the refurbishment of the Bradbury Resource Centre for people with a visual impairment; Voluntary Action Rutland (£4,000), for the construction of an extension to the Rutland Volunteer Centre to provide a resource centre facility for older/ disabled people; Avon Tyrrell UK – Hampshire (£3,000), towards the construction of a six-berth log cabin to provide upgraded accommodation at their outdoor residential centre for young people of all backgrounds and abilities; Phoenix Group Homes – Essex (£2,700), for the installation of a new fitted kitchen at the residential and day project at 6 Oxford Road for adults with alcohol misuse and mental health problems; Furzedown Project – London (£2,000), for the purchase of a wheelchair accessible minibus for the day centre which provides activities for older people, many of whom are housebound or disabled; and Norman Laud Association – West Midlands (£1,800), for the purchase of a plasma flat screen television for the lounge at the respite care home for children with disabilities.

FINANCES *Year* 2007–08 *Income* £723,542 *Grants* £447,449 *Assets* £17,653,353

TRUSTEES Miles A Bilton, Chair; James R Lee; Stefan J Paciorek; Kim Lansdown.

OTHER INFORMATION Assistance is also given on a one-off basis to individuals and families who fall within the following categories: older people on a low income and people with physical or learning disabilities or mental health problems. All applications for individuals to be sent in by the relevant social worker on local or health authority headed notepaper. A total of £153,000 was awarded to individuals during 2007/08.

HOW TO APPLY If in doubt regarding the suitability of an appeal, contact the charity either in writing, giving a brief outline, or by telephone. If you have already received a grant, please allow at least one year from the date of payment before re-applying.
'*Large grants (£2,000 and over)* – Please apply on your organisation's headed notepaper giving or attaching the following information. 1–6 must be provided in all cases and 7 as applicable to your appeal: 1. A brief history of your charity, its objectives and work. 2. Description of the project and what you intend to achieve. 3. A copy of your most recent annual report and audited accounts. 4. Details of funds already raised and other

sources that you have approached. 5. Proposals to monitor and evaluate the project. 6. Any other relevant information that will help to explain your application. 7. The following additional information that applies to your appeal.
Building/Refurbishment appeals – Please include: a statement of all costs involved. Please itemise major items and professional fees; confirmation that the project has ongoing revenue funding; confirmation that all planning and other consents and building regulations approvals have been obtained; details of ownership of the premises and if leased, the length of the unexpired term; timetable of construction/ refurbishment and anticipated date of completion.
Equipment appeals – An itemised list of all equipment with estimate of costs. Please obtain at least two competitive estimates except where this is not practicable e.g. specialised equipment
Contribution towards purchase of minibuses – Please note that minibuses can only be considered if used to transport older and disabled people with mobility problems. Please give details of provision made for insurance, tax and maintenance etc. We require confirmation that your organisation can meet future running costs.
Small grants (up to £500) – Please apply on your organisation's headed notepaper with the following information: brief details about your organisation and its work; a copy of your most recent annual accounts; outline of the project and its principal aims; breakdown of the cost of item/ s required; if your organisation is not a registered charity, please supply a reference from a registered charity with whom you work or from the Voluntary Service Council.'

WHO TO APPLY TO Wendy Fuller, Charity Administrator, Bilton House, 7 Culmington Road, Ealing, London W13 9NB *Tel* 020 8579 2829 *Fax* 020 8579 3650 *Website* www. percybiltoncharity.org.uk

CC NO 1094720   **ESTABLISHED** 1962

■ The Bingham Trust

WHERE FUNDING CAN BE GIVEN Buxton and district.

WHO CAN BENEFIT Organisations and individuals.

WHAT IS FUNDED Community needs.

WHAT IS NOT FUNDED Generally, limited to the town of Buxton and district.

TYPE OF GRANT One-off, capital including buildings, project, running costs, salaries and start-up costs. Funding is for up to three years.

RANGE OF GRANTS £50–£10,000.

SAMPLE GRANTS The Sequal Trust (£4,100); Buxton Community School and Milnthorpe Homes (£4,000 each); Peak District Music Centres (£3,400); Arthritis Research Campaign and Buxton Mountain Rescue (£3,000 each); Buxton for Youth, Samaritans and Tideswell Methodist Church (£2,500 each); Derbyshire Carers Association – Blythe House (£2,000); Justice UK Ltd (£1,100); and Adullam Homes, Glossopdale Furniture Project and National Missing Persons Helpline (£1,000 each).

FINANCES *Year* 2007–08 *Income* £107,924 *Grants* £102,218 *Assets* £2,287,146

TRUSTEES Dr R G B Willis, Chair; R A Horne; Mrs J H Lawton; Revd P J Meek; Mrs A M Hurst.

HOW TO APPLY In writing to the correspondent on no more than two pages of A4, stating the total cost of the project and sources of other funding. Applications should arrive before the end of February, June, September and December each year.

WHO TO APPLY TO R Horne, Trustee, Blinder House, Flagg, Buxton, Derbyshire SK17 9QG
email binghamtrust@aol.com
CC NO 287636   **ESTABLISHED** 1977

....

■ The Bintaub Charitable Trust

WHERE FUNDING CAN BE GIVEN Greater London, worldwide.

WHO CAN BENEFIT Jewish, health, education, children.

WHAT IS FUNDED Mainly London organisations, towards 'the advancement of education in and the religion of the orthodox Jewish faith'. Grants are also given for other charitable causes, mainly towards medical and children's work.

SAMPLE GRANTS Yeshiva Tiferes Yaacov (£12,000); Kupat Ha'ir (£7,700); EMF (£7,300); Gateshead Jewish Boys School (£6,500); Eitz Chaim Schools (£6,000); Va'ad Harabbanim L'inyanei Tzedaka (£5,700); Menorah Foundation School (£3,900); Jewish Day School (£3,000); LJGH. (£2,900); Well of Torah (£2,000); and Jewish Rescue and Relief (£1,500).

FINANCES *Year* 2007–08 *Income* £78,252 *Grants* £83,696

TRUSTEES James Frohwein; Tania Frohwein; Daniel Frohwein; Rabbi E Stefansky.

HOW TO APPLY The trust has previously stated that new applications are not being accepted.

WHO TO APPLY TO Joshua Wahon, 125 Wolmer Gardens, Edgware HA8 8QF
CC NO 1003915   **ESTABLISHED** 1991

....

■ The Birmingham Community Foundation

WHERE FUNDING CAN BE GIVEN Greater Birmingham.

WHO CAN BENEFIT Small community-based groups and organisations involved in activities that regenerate and rebuild communities.

WHAT IS FUNDED Small grants are generally given to community based groups involved in activities that regenerate and build communities, however priority is given to those projects which: encourage community responsibility; develop community capacity; are unable to access other forms of funding; and do not duplicate other work being done within the area.

WHAT IS NOT FUNDED No funding is available for projects operating outside the Greater Birmingham area; general appeals or large national charities (except for local branches working specifically for local people); individuals, for whatever purpose; organisations and individuals in the promotion of political or religious ideology.

RANGE OF GRANTS £3,000 on average.

SAMPLE GRANTS Great Bridge Community Forum (£39,000); Netherton Cricket Club (£15,000); Families for Peace (£7,000); Talking with Hands (£5,000); Aston Link (£2,500); City of Birmingham Special Olympics (£1,700); Deep Impact Theatre Company (£1,000); Friends of Hawkesley (£600); and Warwickshire Air Ambulance (£300).

FINANCES *Year* 2007–08 *Income* £4,914,454 *Grants* £3,742,807 *Assets* £1,213,829

TRUSTEES David Bucknall, Chair; Ian Warwick-Moore McArdle; John Andrews; Cllr Mahmood Hussain; John Kimberley; Kay Cadman; Dorian Chan; Angela Henry.

HOW TO APPLY Applicants should complete the appropriate form, depending on whether they are applying for a specific fund or making a general application. Forms are available from the foundation or can be downloaded from its website (follow the links to the relevant fund page). Grants are allocated on a rolling programme and there are no deadlines for the receipt of applications. The foundation aims to make a decision within 12 weeks.

WHO TO APPLY TO Karen Argyle, Grants Officer, Nechells Baths, Nechells Park Road, Nechells, Birmingham B7 5PD *Tel* 0121 214 2080 *Fax* 0121 322 5579 *email* team@bhamfoundation.co.uk *Website* www.bhamfoundation.co.uk
CC NO 1048162   **ESTABLISHED** 1995

....

■ The Birmingham District Nursing Charitable Trust

WHERE FUNDING CAN BE GIVEN Within a 20-mile radius of the Council House in Birmingham.

WHO CAN BENEFIT Local organisations benefiting medical professionals. Grants may be made to local branches of national organisations.

WHAT IS FUNDED Medical or nursing organisations; convalescent homes; convalescent homes or rest homes for nurses or other medical or nursing institution; amenities for patients or nursing staff of Birmingham Domiciliary Nursing Service; amenities for patients or nursing staff of any state hospital.

WHAT IS NOT FUNDED No grants are given to individuals.

TYPE OF GRANT One-off and recurrent.

RANGE OF GRANTS £1,000–£6,000.

SAMPLE GRANTS Age Concern (£6,000); Vitalise (£5,500); Birmingham Focus on Blindness (£4,000); Acorns and Interact Reading Services (£3,500 each); Birmingham and Three Counties Trust for Nurses, Bryony House and Motor Neurone Disease Association (£3,000 each); Birmingham Centre for Arts Therapies and Mary Stevens Hospice (£2,500 each); Contact a Family (£2,000); and Extracare Charitable Trust (£1,000).

FINANCES *Year* 2007–08 *Income* £68,577 *Grants* £60,000 *Assets* £1,539,863

TRUSTEES H W Tuckey; Prof. W A Littler; Prof. J R Mann; Mrs T Cull; Mrs A Willis; Mrs J Wright; Prof C M Clifford; Dr P Mayer.

HOW TO APPLY In writing to the correspondent with a copy of the latest accounts. Applications should be sent in August/September. Trustees meet to consider grants in the first week of November.

WHO TO APPLY TO Anthony Jones, c/o Shakespeare Putsman, Somerset House, Temple Street, Birmingham B2 5DJ
CC NO 215652   **ESTABLISHED** 1960

....

■ The Birmingham Hospital Saturday Fund Medical Charity and Welfare Trust

WHERE FUNDING CAN BE GIVEN UK, but mostly centred around the West Midlands and Birmingham area.

WHO CAN BENEFIT Hospitals and other medical and welfare organisations and charities.

WHAT IS FUNDED To improve the quality of life for those disadvantaged in society; provide comforts and amenities for patients in hospital and medical charities, assist medical research, education and science, and support charitable organisations concerned with people who are sick. The trust will consider funding: health; speech therapy; scholarships; building services;

information technology and computers; publishing and printing; and health professional bodies.

WHAT IS NOT FUNDED The trust will not generally fund: direct appeals from individuals or students; administration expenditure including salaries; bank loans/deficits/mortgages; items or services which should normally be publicly funded; large general appeals; vehicle operating costs; or motor vehicles for infrequent use and where subsidised vehicle share schemes are available to charitable organisations.

TYPE OF GRANT One-off grants, capital, project and research, all funded for up to one year.

RANGE OF GRANTS Usually up to £2,000.

SAMPLE GRANTS Friends of Victoria School – Northfield (£3,800); NHS West Midlands (£3,400); Birmingham Centre for Arts Therapies and Starlight Children's Foundation (£2,500 each); Vascular Department, Selly Oak Hospital (£2,000); Dream Holidays, Isle of Wight (£1,900); the Mary Stevens Hospice, Stourbridge, West Midlands (£1,600); Institute of Ageing and Health, Birmingham (£1,500); Contact the Elderly, Birmingham (£1,200); Christian Lewis Trust – Cardiff (£1,100); Action Medical Research – Horsham, Children's Heart Foundation and REACT Surrey (£1,000); Katherine House – Stafford (£900); St Martin's Centre for Health and Healing (£750); Deep Impact Theatre Company and Birmingham Heart Care – Walsall (£500 each); and Acorns Children's Hospice – Birmingham (£315).

FINANCES *Year* 2007 *Income* £26,900 *Grants* £40,900 *Assets* £500,200

TRUSTEES Dr R P Kanas; S G Hall; E S Hickman; M Malone; D J Read; J Salmons.

HOW TO APPLY On a form available from the correspondent. The form requires basic information and should be submitted with financial details. Evidence should be provided that the project has been adequately considered through the provision of quotes or supporting documents, although the trust dislikes applications which provide too much general information or have long-winded descriptions of projects. Applicants should take great care to read the guidance notes on the application form. The trustees' meet four times a year and deadlines are given when application forms are sent out.

WHO TO APPLY TO The Secretary, Gamgee House, 2 Darnley Road, Birmingham B16 8TE *Tel* 0121 454 3601 *email* charitabletrust@bhsf.co.uk

CC NO 502428   **ESTABLISHED** 1972

····················

■ Birmingham International Airport Community Trust

WHERE FUNDING CAN BE GIVEN The areas affected by the airport's operation (East Birmingham, Solihull and parts of north Warwickshire).

WHO CAN BENEFIT Established local charities.

WHAT IS FUNDED Areas of work the trust supports are: environment improvement and heritage conservation; bringing the community closer together through facilities for sport, recreation and other leisure-time activities; improving awareness of environmental issues or environmental education and training activities; encouraging and protecting wildlife. It describes the types of projects it wishes to support as including community centres, community groups, sports, playgroups, schools, youth clubs, scouts, gardens/parks, environment, music and churches. Work should benefit a substantial

section of the community rather than less inclusive groups, although work with older people or people with special needs is positively encouraged.

WHAT IS NOT FUNDED The following are not eligible for grants: individuals; projects which have already been carried out or paid for; organisations which have statutory responsibilities e.g. hospitals, surgeries, clinics, schools etc. unless the project is clearly not a statutory responsibility. Grants are not normally recurrent, or given towards the purchase of land or buildings.

TYPE OF GRANT Grants may be for capital or revenue projects, although the trust will not commit to recurrent or running costs, such as salaries.

RANGE OF GRANTS Generally up to £3,000.

SAMPLE GRANTS Previous beneficiaries have included: 298th Birmingham Brownies/Rangers Pack, Age Concern – Castle Bromwich, Blakenhale Infant School, Chelmsley Town Football Club, Coleshill Bell Ringers, Coleshill Town Football Club, George Fentham Endowed School, Hatchford Brook Youth and Community Centre and Land Lane Baptist Free Church.

FINANCES *Year* 2007–08 *Income* £52,778 *Grants* £53,028 *Assets* £19,443

TRUSTEES The trust acts independently of the airport management, with nine representatives of the following bodies making up the trustees: The Airport Consultative Committee (3), Birmingham City Council (2), Birmingham International Airport (2) and Solihull Council (2).

HOW TO APPLY On a form available from the correspondent. Full guidelines can be downloaded from the trust's website.

WHO TO APPLY TO The Administrator, Birmingham International Airport Ltd, Birmingham B26 3QJ *Tel* 0121 767 7448 *email* commtrust@bhx.co. uk *Website* www.bhx.co.uk

CC NO 1071176   **ESTABLISHED** 1998

····················

■ The Lord Mayor of Birmingham's Charity

WHERE FUNDING CAN BE GIVEN Birmingham.

WHO CAN BENEFIT Charities determined by the Lord Mayor at the commencement of term of office.

WHAT IS FUNDED Beneficiaries are determined by the Lord Mayor prior to taking up office. Three or four charities/voluntary organisations are usually selected at the beginning of the year. No other donations are made.

WHAT IS NOT FUNDED Charities working outside the area of Birmingham.

TYPE OF GRANT One-off.

FINANCES *Year* 2007–08 *Income* £110,382 *Grants* £62,304 *Assets* £230,696

TRUSTEES Lord Mayor of Birmingham; Deputy Lord Mayor of Birmingham; Sue Anderson; J Whorwood; J Alden; Z Hopkins.

HOW TO APPLY In writing to the correspondent. Although the beneficiaries are often predetermined, applications can be sent in January/February for the new Lord Mayor to consider.

WHO TO APPLY TO Mrs C Dukes, Civic Affairs Manager, Lord Mayor's Parlour, Council House, Birmingham B1 1BB *Tel* 0121 303 2040 *email* lord.mayor@birmingham.gov.uk *Website* www.birmingham.gov.uk

CC NO 1036968   **ESTABLISHED** 1994

■ Birthday House Trust

WHERE FUNDING CAN BE GIVEN England and Wales.

WHO CAN BENEFIT Charitable organisations and individuals.

WHAT IS FUNDED General charitable purposes.

WHAT IS NOT FUNDED No applications will be considered from individuals or non-charitable organisations.

SAMPLE GRANTS Drukpa Trust (£25,000); Soil Association Limited (£17,000); Merton Park Scouts and Sussex Community Foundation (£5,000 each); Mary Rose Appeal (£2,500); Royal Hospital Chelsea Appeal (£1,000); Fire Services National Benevolent Fund (£500); Bob Champion Cancer Trust, Mind in Brighton and Hove and National Memorial Aboretum (£250 each); Breakthrough Breast Cancer (£100); and the Murray Downland Trust (£50).

FINANCES *Year* 2007–08 *Income* £251,705 *Grants* £64,617 *Assets* £5,042,116

TRUSTEES The Dickinson Trust Limited and Rathbone Trust Company Limited.

OTHER INFORMATION The main work of this trust is engaged with the running of a residential home for older people in Midhurst, West Sussex. In 2007–08 a further £72,180 was distributed to 14 pensioners.

HOW TO APPLY In writing to the correspondent, including a sae. No application forms are issued and there is no deadline. Only successful applicants are acknowledged.

WHO TO APPLY TO Laura Gosling, Dickinson Trust Ltd, Pollen House, 10–12 Cork Street, London W1S 3LW

CC NO 248028   **ESTABLISHED** 1966

■ The Bisgood Charitable Trust (registered as Miss Jeanne Bisgood's Charitable Trust)

WHERE FUNDING CAN BE GIVEN UK, overseas and locally in Bournemouth and Dorset, especially Poole.

WHO CAN BENEFIT Registered charities.

WHAT IS FUNDED General charitable purposes. Main grants have been and will be concentrated on the following categories: (a) operating under Roman Catholic auspices; (b) operating in Poole, Bournemouth and the county of Dorset; (c) national (not local) charities concerned with older people.

WHAT IS NOT FUNDED Grants are not given to local charities which do not fit categories (a) or (b) above. Individuals and non-registered charities are not supported.

TYPE OF GRANT One-off, capital and recurring.

RANGE OF GRANTS £25–£2,500.

SAMPLE GRANTS Previous beneficiaries have included Apex Trust, ITDG, Horder Centre for Arthritis, Impact, St Barnabas' Society, St Francis Leprosy Guild, Sight Savers International and YMCA.

FINANCES *Year* 2007–08 *Income* £215,764 *Grants* £210,250 *Assets* £5,587,020

TRUSTEES Miss J M Bisgood, Chair; Miss P Schulte; P J K Bisgood.

OTHER INFORMATION The trust operates a sub-fund – the Bertram Fund from which grants are usually made anonymously.

HOW TO APPLY In writing to the correspondent, quoting the UK registration number and registered title of the charity. A copy of the most recent accounts should also be enclosed. Applications should NOT be made directly to the Bertram Fund. Applications for capital projects

'should provide brief details of the main purposes, the total target and the current state of the appeal'. The trustees regret that they are unable to acknowledge appeals. The trustees normally meet in late February/early March and September.

WHO TO APPLY TO Miss J M Bisgood, Trustee, 12 Waters Edge, Brudenell Road, Poole BH13 7NN

CC NO 208714   **ESTABLISHED** 1963

■ The Michael Bishop Foundation

WHERE FUNDING CAN BE GIVEN Worldwide with a preference for Birmingham and the Midlands.

WHO CAN BENEFIT Registered charities.

WHAT IS FUNDED Arts, health, child welfare, education and religion.

RANGE OF GRANTS Up to £82,000.

SAMPLE GRANTS The Royal Flying Doctor Service of Australia (£82,000); the D'Oyly Carte Opera Trust Ltd (£70,000); Alcohol and Drugs Abstinence Service (£30,000); Live Music Now! (£20,000); the Terrence Higgins Trust and Policy Exchange (£15,000 each); Expat UK (£5,000); Nightingales Children's Project (£3,000); Wellbeing (£2,500); the Morris Venables Charitable Trust (£2,000); Cancer Research (£1,250); and Birmingham Early Music Festival (£1,000).

FINANCES *Year* 2007–08 *Income* £105,661 *Grants* £265,078 *Assets* £2,573,909

TRUSTEES Sir Michael Bishop, Chair; Grahame N Elliott; John T Wolfe; John S Coulson.

HOW TO APPLY In writing to the correspondent.

WHO TO APPLY TO The Trustees, Donington Hall, Castle Donington, Derby DE74 2SB

CC NO 297627   **ESTABLISHED** 1987

■ The Bishop's Development Fund

WHERE FUNDING CAN BE GIVEN The diocese of Wakefield.

WHO CAN BENEFIT Church of England organisations.

WHAT IS FUNDED The objects of the trust are 'to promote any charitable purposes within the areas of the diocese of Wakefield which are in need of spiritual and material assistance by reason of social or economic changes with a view to reinforcing the work of the Church of England among the people of those areas' and 'to promote and assist the charitable work of the Church Urban Fund'.

WHAT IS NOT FUNDED Any application which does not meet the criteria outlined here.

RANGE OF GRANTS £200–£5,000.

FINANCES *Year* 2007–08 *Income* £32,302 *Grants* £22,999 *Assets* £758,454

TRUSTEES The Right Revd Anthony Robinson, Chair; The Right Revd Stephen Platten; The Ven. Robert Freeman; Mrs Mary Judkins; David Buckingham; Alison Dean; Christine Haigh; Carol Burniston; Kenn Winter; The Ven. Peter Townley.

HOW TO APPLY In writing to the correspondent. Only applications formally approved by the parochial church councils of Church of England churches in the diocese of Wakefield will be considered. The trustees meet four times a year.

WHO TO APPLY TO The Trustees, Church House, 1 South Parade, Wakefield, West Yorkshire WF1 1LP

CC NO 700588   **ESTABLISHED** 1988

■ The Sydney Black Charitable Trust

WHERE FUNDING CAN BE GIVEN UK.

WHO CAN BENEFIT Charitable organisations.

WHAT IS FUNDED Youth organisations, religious, medical and other institutions, such as those helping people who are disadvantaged.

TYPE OF GRANT One-off grants for core support, equipment and vehicles.

RANGE OF GRANTS A substantial grant was made to Endeavour (£20,000); others totalled £88,000 and were of between £125–£250 each. About 700 institutions benefited.

FINANCES *Year* 2007–08 *Income* £162,671 *Grants* £108,334 *Assets* £3,105,547

TRUSTEES Mrs J D Crabtree; Mrs H J Dickenson; S J Crabtree; P M Crabtree.

OTHER INFORMATION In 2001 The Edna Black Charitable Trust and The Cyril Black Charitable Trust were incorporated into this trust.

HOW TO APPLY Applications, made in writing to the correspondent, will be considered by the appropriate trust.

WHO TO APPLY TO The Secretary, 30 Welford Place, London SW19 5AJ

CC NO 219855   **ESTABLISHED** 1949

■ The Bertie Black Foundation

WHERE FUNDING CAN BE GIVEN UK, Israel.

WHO CAN BENEFIT Registered charities.

WHAT IS FUNDED The relief and assistance of people who are in need, the advancement of education and religion, and other charitable purposes.

SAMPLE GRANTS I Rescue (£50,000); Magen David Adom (£47,000 in three grants); Alyn Hospital (£49,000 in two grants); Emunah (£38,000); Laniardo Hospital and Shaare Zedek (£25,000 each); Friends of Israel Sports Centre for Disabled (£20,000); Child Resettlement Trust (£10,000 in four grants); Norwood (£7,600 in four grants); and Hope (£5,200 in four grants).

FINANCES *Year* 2007–08 *Income* £143,083 *Grants* £328,959 *Assets* £2,795,016

TRUSTEES I B Black; D Black; H S Black; Mrs I R Seddon.

HOW TO APPLY The trust states it 'supports causes known to the trustees' and that they 'do not respond to unsolicited requests'.

WHO TO APPLY TO Harry Black, Trustee, Abbots House, 198 Lower High Street, Watford WDI7 2FG

CC NO 245207   **ESTABLISHED** 1965

■ Sir Alec Black's Charity

WHERE FUNDING CAN BE GIVEN UK, with a preference for Grimsby.

WHO CAN BENEFIT Ex-employees of Sir Alec Black, charitable institutions benefiting the sick and infirm including hospices, and poor fishermen and dockworkers of Grimsby.

WHAT IS FUNDED Primarily to benefit former employees of Sir Alec Black and to provide bed linen and pillows to hospitals. Secondarily to benefit sick poor fishermen and dockworkers of Grimsby.

FINANCES *Year* 2007–08 *Income* £100,896 *Grants* £81,930 *Assets* £1,499,485

TRUSTEES J N Harrison; P A Mounfield; Dr D F Wilson; S Wilson.

OTHER INFORMATION In 2007–08 grants to former employees of the settlor totalled £15,000. A further £66,000 went in grants to 41 organisations, with £300 given to fishermen and dockworkers.

HOW TO APPLY In writing to the correspondent. Trustees meet in May and November; applications need to be received in March or September.

WHO TO APPLY TO Stewart Wilson, Trustee, Wilson Sharpe and Co., 27 Osborne Street, Grimsby, North East Lincolnshire DN31 1NU *email* sabc@wilsonsharpe.co.uk

CC NO 220295   **ESTABLISHED** 1942

■ Isabel Blackman Foundation

WHERE FUNDING CAN BE GIVEN UK, but the majority of grants are confined to organisations in the Hastings area.

WHO CAN BENEFIT Organisations benefiting children, young adults, older people, retired people, people with disabilities, Christians and people with sight loss or blindness.

WHAT IS FUNDED Older, blind or disabled people; hospitals; churches; voluntary charitable bodies; youth organisations; education.

WHAT IS NOT FUNDED Please note only applications from Hastings and district are considered.

RANGE OF GRANTS £150–£20,000.

SAMPLE GRANTS Hastings Fish CIC (£30,000); William Parker Sports College (£20,000); The Parchment Trust (£10,000); MacMillan Cancer Support and St Michaels Hospice (£5,000 each); Hastings and Bexhill Mencap Society (£4,500); The Stables Trust (£3,000); Myasthenia Gravis Association and Great Ormond Street Hospital (£2,500 each); Combat Stress, Royal National Institute for the Blind and Elimination of Leukaemia Fund (£2,000 each); Fight for Sight (£1,500); Vitalise (£1,000); and Alzheimers Society (£750).

FINANCES *Year* 2007–08 *Income* £268,973 *Grants* £230,589 *Assets* £5,150,769

TRUSTEES D J Jukes; Mrs P H Connolly; Mrs M Haley; J F Lamplugh; Mrs W M Mabbett; K Ashmore.

HOW TO APPLY In writing to the correspondent. The trustees meet bi-monthly to consider applications.

WHO TO APPLY TO D J Jukes, Secretary, 13 Laton Road, Hastings, East Sussex TN34 2ES

CC NO 313577   **ESTABLISHED** 1966

■ The BlackRock (UK) Charitable Trust

WHERE FUNDING CAN BE GIVEN UK.

WHO CAN BENEFIT Charitable organisations.

WHAT IS FUNDED General charitable purposes.

SAMPLE GRANTS Chernobyl Children's Trust (£50,000); Kids in Need of Education and SOS Children's Villages (£5,000 each); Ability Sports, CHASE Hospice Care for Children and St Giles Trust (£2,500 each); Macmillan Cancer Support and Treloar Trust (£1,500 each); and Just for Kids Law and London Oriana Choir (£1,000 each).

FINANCES *Year* 2007 *Income* £185,121 *Grants* £85,401 *Assets* £206,412

TRUSTEES BlackRock Executor and Trustee Co. Limited.

OTHER INFORMATION The trust was set up by BlackRock, an investment management company,

HOW TO APPLY 'The trustees invite staff, clients and business associates of BlackRock Investment Management (UK) Limited to submit applications for grants to a registered charity of their choice.' Other appeals would usually be declined.

WHO TO APPLY TO The Trustees, BlackRock, 33 King William Street, London EC4R 9AS

CC NO 1065447   **ESTABLISHED** 1999

....

■ The Herbert and Peter Blagrave Charitable Trust

WHERE FUNDING CAN BE GIVEN Hampshire, Wiltshire and Berkshire.

WHO CAN BENEFIT Registered charities only working in the geographical areas stated.

WHAT IS FUNDED 'Typical applications include organisations that cater for: projects that work with people aged over 65 years; projects that work with children up to 16 years, or young people aged 16 to 25 years who have physical disabilities and/or learning difficulties; projects that work with injured sports people; projects that cater for people with a chronic or terminal illness who fall within our age ranges (children young people under 25 and older people); projects that provide respite for the carers of those that fall within our criteria.'

WHAT IS NOT FUNDED Applications are only considered from registered charities. Individuals, including students, are not eligible for grants. Normally, grants are not made in response to general appeals from large national organisations. No grants may be made where funds from statutory sources can be obtained. 'In the interests of good grant-making practice it is trust policy to place a time limit on further applications from the same organisations. Further applications are only considered after a three-year interval.'

TYPE OF GRANT Usually one-off but can be recurrent.

RANGE OF GRANTS Up to £10,000. Small Grants programmes have been set up with Community Foundations in Berkshire and Wiltshire. They administer a programme of direct grants under £3,000 on behalf of the trust.

SAMPLE GRANTS Berkshire Community Foundation (£25,000); Community Foundation for Wiltshire & Swindon (£12,000); CP Centre/Enable Ability, Research Institute for the Care of the Elderly (£10,000 each); Countryside Foundation for Education, Music in Hospitals and Counsel & Care (£5,000 each); Disability Challengers (£2,000); and Andover District Scout Council (£500).

FINANCES *Year* 2007–08 *Income* £458,580 *Grants* £221,211 *Assets* £17,282,535

TRUSTEES Julian R Whately; Timothy W A Jackson-Stops; Sir Paul A Neave.

OTHER INFORMATION Small Grants programmes have been set up with Community Foundations in Berkshire and Wiltshire. They administer a programme of direct grants under £3,000 on behalf of the trust.

HOW TO APPLY The trustees meet three times a year in March, July and November. Applications should be made using the trust's application form, which can be requested from the trust's offices. Application forms should be received at least eight weeks before the next trustees' meeting. A copy of the latest signed accounts, annual report, annual income and expenditure budget and a detailed income and expenditure budget for the specific project should be enclosed. Once your application has arrived you will be contacted by the director who may arrange to visit your project or carry out an extensive telephone interview to assess your

grant request in more detail. Assessment is based mainly on evidence of need, what the grant will deliver and what other resources are available. Successful applicants will be asked to give a report about how a grant has been used within 12 months of receiving it.

WHO TO APPLY TO The Trustees, c/o Rathbone Trust Company Limited, 159 New Bond Street, London W1S 2UD *Tel* 020 7399 0000 *email* blagravetrust@rathbones.com

CC NO 277074   **ESTABLISHED** 1978

....

■ The Blair Foundation

WHERE FUNDING CAN BE GIVEN UK, particularly southern England and Scotland; overseas.

WHO CAN BENEFIT Organisations, particularly disability and wildlife groups.

WHAT IS FUNDED General, especially conservation and protection of the environment; improving disabled access to wildlife areas; and medical charities.

WHAT IS NOT FUNDED Charities that have objectives the trustees consider harmful to the environment are not supported.

SAMPLE GRANTS Ayrshire Wildlife Services (£20,000); Queen Elizabeth Foundation for the Disabled (£12,000); Scottish National Trust (£7,000); Home Farm Trust (£5,000); Sense (£4,000); Music in Hospital (£1,500); and RSPB (£1,000).

FINANCES *Year* 2007–08 *Income* £98,042 *Grants* £75,483 *Assets* £1,505,938

TRUSTEES Robert Thornton; Jennifer Thornton; Graham Healy; Alan Thornton; Philippa Thornton.

HOW TO APPLY In writing to the correspondent, for consideration at trustees' meetings held at least once a year. A receipt for donations is requested from all donees.

WHO TO APPLY TO The Trustees, Smith and Williamson, 1 Bishops Wharf, Walnut Tree Close, Guildford, Surrey GU1 4RA *Tel* 01483 407100

CC NO 801755   **ESTABLISHED** 1989

....

■ Blakes Benevolent Trust

WHERE FUNDING CAN BE GIVEN UK.

WHO CAN BENEFIT Charities and individuals connected with the J Blake and Co. Ltd Group of companies.

WHAT IS FUNDED General charitable purposes.

SAMPLE GRANTS Motor Trade Benevolent Fund (£25,000); Crisis, Front Line, Liverpool City Mission and Salvation Army (£6,000 each); and Nugent Care Society, the Universal Beneficent Society and Wirral Churches (£3,000 each).

FINANCES *Year* 2007–08 *Income* £102,188 *Grants* £71,450 *Assets* £2,505,468

TRUSTEES N K Silk; B Ball; P M Davies.

OTHER INFORMATION In 2007–08 the sum of £14,450 went to 25 individuals.

HOW TO APPLY This trust has previously stated that it only gives to 'private beneficiaries'.

WHO TO APPLY TO The Trustees, 2 Yew Tree Road, Huyton-with-Roby, Liverpool L36 5UQ

CC NO 225268   **ESTABLISHED** 1958

....

■ The Blanchminster Trust

WHERE FUNDING CAN BE GIVEN The parishes of Bude, Stratton and Poughill (i.e. the former urban district of Bude-Stratton on 31 March 1974).

WHO CAN BENEFIT Organisations or individuals residing in the area of benefit and showing proof

Think carefully about every application. Is it justified?

375

of financial need. Organisations benefiting children; young adults; older people; academics; students; actors and entertainment professionals; and musicians may be considered.

WHAT IS FUNDED Charities working in the fields of education, social welfare and community aid.

WHAT IS NOT FUNDED Applications from Bude-Stratton only will be considered, or in respect of educational applications from people who have at least one parent so residing.

TYPE OF GRANT Cash or equipment. Cash may be grant or loan, equipment normally 'permanent loan'. Capital including buildings, core costs, feasibility studies, interest free loans, one-off, project, running costs and start-up costs. Funding will be considered for one year or less.

SAMPLE GRANTS Budehaven Community School (£126,000); Bude Town Band (£80,000); Bude Nippers (£8,000); Bude Children's Centre (£6,100); Bude Area Resource Base (£3,400); Helebridge House (£1,900); Bullied Way Residents Association (£700); Bude Infant School and North Cornwall Tinnitus (£500 each); and Bude Tennis Club (£360).

FINANCES *Year* 2008 *Income* £459,882 *Grants* £468,093 *Assets* £10,159,413

TRUSTEES Miss M H Clowes; C B Cornish; J E Gardiner; W J Keat; Mrs V A Newman; C D Nichols; G C Rogers; B C Rowlands; Mrs J M Shepherd; L M J Tozer; O A May; I J Whitfield.

HOW TO APPLY In writing to the correspondent. Applicants may be called for an informal interview by the relevant committee. Following this a recommendation is made to the full board of trustees who make the final decision. Applications are considered at monthly meetings. All applications are acknowledged.

WHO TO APPLY TO The Clerk to the Trustees, Blanchminster Building, 38 Lansdown Road, Bude, Cornwall EX23 8EE *Tel* 01288 352851 *email* office@blanchminster.plus.com

CC NO 202118   **ESTABLISHED** 1421

■ The Sir Victor Blank Charitable Settlement

WHERE FUNDING CAN BE GIVEN Worldwide.

WHO CAN BENEFIT Jewish organisations and other registered charities.

WHAT IS FUNDED Jewish causes and general charitable purposes.

SAMPLE GRANTS United Jewish Israel Appeal (£52,000); Jewish Care and Oxford Centre for Hebrew and Jewish Studies (£25,000 each); One Voice Europe (£20,000); Oxford Philomusica (£15,000); Norwood Ravenswood (£11,000); the Lord Taverners (£5,000); Jewish Deaf Association (£3,000); St John of Jerusalem Eye Hospital (£2,500); Delamere Forest School (£2,000); and World Jewish Relief (£1,000 each).

FINANCES *Year* 2007–08 *Income* £150,396 *Grants* £208,970 *Assets* £1,617,238

TRUSTEES Sir M V Blank; Lady S H Blank; R Gulliver.

HOW TO APPLY In writing to the correspondent.

WHO TO APPLY TO R Gulliver, Trustee, c/o Wilkins Kennedy, Bridge House, London Bridge, London SE1 9QR

CC NO 1084187   **ESTABLISHED** 2000

■ Blatchington Court Trust

WHERE FUNDING CAN BE GIVEN UK, preference for Sussex.

WHO CAN BENEFIT Charities and other bodies in the field of education for the under 30 age group who are visually impaired.

WHAT IS FUNDED To provide funding for the education of children and young people under 30 years of age with visual impairment.

FINANCES *Year* 2007–08 *Income* £581,181 *Grants* £186,725 *Assets* £10,937,795

TRUSTEES Richard Martin, Chair; Alison Acason; Daniel Ellman-Brown; Georgina James; Roger Jones; Stephen Pavey; Robert Perkins; Jonathan Wilson; Anna Hunter.

OTHER INFORMATION The grant total in 2007–08 included £119,616 payable in 335 grants to individuals.

HOW TO APPLY In writing to the correspondent from whom individual or charity grant application forms can be obtained. Applications can be considered at any time. An application on behalf of a registered charity should include audited accounts and up-to-date information on the charity and its commitments.

WHO TO APPLY TO The Executive Manager, Ridgeland House, 165 Dyke Road, Hove, East Sussex BN3 1TL *Tel* 01273 727222 *Website* www.blatchington-court.co.uk

CC NO 306350   **ESTABLISHED** 1966

■ The Neville and Elaine Blond Charitable Trust

WHERE FUNDING CAN BE GIVEN Worldwide.

WHO CAN BENEFIT Particularly Jewish charities.

WHAT IS FUNDED Jewish causes and general charitable purposes.

WHAT IS NOT FUNDED Only registered charities are supported.

RANGE OF GRANTS Up to £50,000.

SAMPLE GRANTS Beth Shalom Holocaust Memorial Centre (£50,000); United Jewish Israel Appeal (£30,000); British WIZO (£10,000); Community Security Trust (£8,000); Holocaust Educational Trust (£5,000); Halle Orchestra (£4,000); Weizmann Institute Foundation (£2,000); British ORT (£1,000); and Kids Company (£500).

FINANCES *Year* 2007–08 *Income* £65,393 *Grants* £113,500 *Assets* £1,334,374

TRUSTEES Dame Simone Prendergast; P Blond; Mrs A E Susman; S N Susman; Mrs J Skidmore.

HOW TO APPLY In writing to the correspondent. Applications should arrive by 31 January for consideration in late spring.

WHO TO APPLY TO The Trustees, c/o H W Fisher and Co, Chartered Accountants, Acre House, 11–15 William Road, London NW1 3ER *Tel* 020 7388 7000

CC NO 206319   **ESTABLISHED** 1953

■ The Blueberry Charitable Trust

WHERE FUNDING CAN BE GIVEN UK.

WHO CAN BENEFIT Jewish community and voluntary organisations.

WHAT IS FUNDED Relief-in-need among people who are Jewish; advancement of the Jewish religion.

SAMPLE GRANTS United Jewish Israel Appeal (£13,000); Hale and District Hebrew Congregation (£8,700); Manchester Jewish Federation (£5,500); Outward Bound Trust (£4,500); Yeshwas Lubavitch (£3,750); King David School (£3,200); Lubavitch South Manchester (£3,000); North Cheshire Jewish

376

Does the trust you have chosen match your needs? Haphazard applications waste postage and time

Primary School (£1,400); and Community Security Trust (£1,250).

FINANCES *Year* 2007–08 *Income* £418,242 *Grants* £53,047 *Assets* £793,834

TRUSTEES J H Lyons; I Aspinall; K Pinnell.

HOW TO APPLY In writing to the correspondent.

WHO TO APPLY TO I Aspinall, Trustee, Number 14, The Embankment, Vale Road, Heaton Mersey, Stockport, Cheshire SK4 3GN

CC NO 1080950 **ESTABLISHED** 2000

■ The Bluston Charitable Settlement

WHERE FUNDING CAN BE GIVEN Mostly UK.

WHO CAN BENEFIT Registered charities, particularly Jewish organisations.

WHAT IS FUNDED General charitable purposes, particularly education, welfare and medical.

WHAT IS NOT FUNDED No grants to individuals.

RANGE OF GRANTS £5,000 to £200,000.

SAMPLE GRANTS Jewish Care (£200,000); Gateshead Talmudical College and Jewish Museum (£100,000 each); Ohel Torah Beth David (£60,000); Dalaid (£50,000); London Academy of Jewish Studies (£40,000); Meir Medical Centre (£38,000); Chai Cancer Care and Prisoners Abroad (£25,000); Common Denominator (£12,000); Hammerson Home Charitable Trust (£10,000); Friends of the Sick (£6,300); and Camp Simcha (£5,000).

FINANCES *Year* 2007–08 *Income* £1,021,412 *Grants* £1,393,023 *Assets* £9,989,083

TRUSTEES Daniel Dover; Martin Paisner.

HOW TO APPLY In writing to the correspondent. The trustees meet annually in the spring.

WHO TO APPLY TO Martin Paisner, 20 Seymour Mews, London W1H 6BQ *Tel* 020 7486 7760

CC NO 256691 **ESTABLISHED** 1968

■ Enid Blyton Trust for Children

WHERE FUNDING CAN BE GIVEN UK and overseas.

WHO CAN BENEFIT Children up to the age of 16 years where there is a need not supplied from the non-charitable sector; including children who are in care, sick or disabled.

WHAT IS FUNDED Special schools; some primary schools; literacy; playschemes; arts activities; holidays; and some medical support. Particularly small projects or ongoing requirements of small charities.

WHAT IS NOT FUNDED No grants for further education, private education or for the benefit of anyone over the age of 16 years. No grants to individuals.

TYPE OF GRANT One-off and some recurring. Capital and full project funding.

RANGE OF GRANTS Up to £2,500.

SAMPLE GRANTS Previous beneficiaries include: Jessie May Trust, Sickle Cell and Young Stroke Survivors, Farley Bank Estate Action, James Hopkins Trust, Deafway, PDSA, West Suffolk Blind Child and Parent Support, Photovoice, Heartline and Edinburgh Young Carers.

FINANCES *Year* 2007–08 *Income* £39,212 *Grants* £24,200 *Assets* £646,416

TRUSTEES Sophie Smallwood, Chair; Fiona Rowett; Robert Wood; Imogen Smallwood.

HOW TO APPLY In writing to the correspondent, including annual accounts or at least good financial details. Trustees meet three times a year, usually in March, July and November.

WHO TO APPLY TO Sophie Smallwood, Chair, 3 Hgh Path, Easebourne, Midhurst, West Sussex GU29 9BD *Tel* 01730 810942

CC NO 284999 **ESTABLISHED** 1982

■ The Nicholas Boas Charitable Trust

WHERE FUNDING CAN BE GIVEN Worldwide.

WHO CAN BENEFIT Educational institutions, charities and other organisations connected with the arts.

WHAT IS FUNDED Education, performing and visual arts.

TYPE OF GRANT One-off.

SAMPLE GRANTS Beneficiaries have included British Youth Opera ENO, IMS Prussia Cove and London String Quartet Foundation.

FINANCES *Year* 2007–08 *Income* £42,574 *Grants* £30,482

TRUSTEES Robert Boas; Christopher Boas; Katherine Boas; Karen Boas.

OTHER INFORMATION Grants include travel scholarships for students of architecture

HOW TO APPLY In writing to the correspondent.

WHO TO APPLY TO Robert Boas, Trustee, 22 Mansfield Street, London W1G 9NR *Tel* 020 7436 0344 *email* boas22m@btinternet.com

CC NO 1073359 **ESTABLISHED** 1998

■ The Body Shop Foundation

WHERE FUNDING CAN BE GIVEN UK and overseas.

WHO CAN BENEFIT Organisations at the forefront of social and environmental change; groups with little hope of conventional funding; projects working to increase public awareness.

WHAT IS FUNDED Grants are given to innovative, grassroots organisations working in the field of human and civil rights, and environmental and animal protection.

WHAT IS NOT FUNDED As the majority of applications come from projects nominated by staff, the foundation does not ask for public applications or nominations. Nor does it: sponsor individuals; fund sporting activities or the arts; sponsor or support fundraising events, receptions or conferences.

TYPE OF GRANT One-off and recurring grants.

RANGE OF GRANTS £5,000–£70,000.

SAMPLE GRANTS Global Action Plan (£40,000 over two years); Born Bree Foundation (£30,000 over two years); Africa Now (£20,000); Children with AIDS Charity (£15,000); Malaysian Nature Society (£12,000); Enable Me, the Green Project, Rags2Riches and Tree Aid (£10,000 each); Lifesaver Wild Horse Rescue (£8,500); Wild at Heart Wildlife Refuge (£6,000); and Displacement Solutions, STEP Cambodia and Sudan Women in Develeoment and Peace (£5,000 each).

FINANCES *Year* 2008–09 *Income* £1,451,233 *Grants* £784,765 *Assets* £541,482

TRUSTEES Lady Jay Of Ewelme; Janice R Buckingham; Julian Simpson; Lisa Mary Gaynor; Candida De Lourdes Pinto Goes De Souza; Paul David Sanderson; Paul McGreevy.

OTHER INFORMATION 'The Body Shop Foundation is The Body Shop International Plc's charitable trust which supports innovative projects across the world working for social and environmental change.'

HOW TO APPLY The Body Shop Foundation does not accept unsolicited applications. The trustees research projects which meet their funding criteria and only then invite organisations to make an application.

WHO TO APPLY TO The Grants Manager, Watersmead, Littlehampton, West Sussex BN17 6LS *Tel* 01903 844039 *email* bodyshopfoundation@thebodyshop.com *Website* thebodyshopfoundation.org **CC NO** 802757 **ESTABLISHED** 1990

■ The Boltons Trust

WHERE FUNDING CAN BE GIVEN Unrestricted.
WHO CAN BENEFIT Charitable organisations.
WHAT IS FUNDED Relief of suffering; Jewish causes; cultural and religious teaching; international rights of the individual; other charitable purposes.
TYPE OF GRANT Generally single grants for core costs, project, recurring costs and running costs. Funding is available for one year or less.
SAMPLE GRANTS Global Health Foundation (£15,000).
FINANCES *Year* 2007–08 *Income* £44,421 *Grants* £15,000 *Assets* £1,212,037
TRUSTEES Mrs C Albuquerque; R M Baldock; S D Albuquerque.
HOW TO APPLY In writing to the correspondent. The trustees meet on a regular basis to consider applications.
WHO TO APPLY TO The Trustees, 12 York Gare, Regent's Park, London NW1 4QS
CC NO 257951 **ESTABLISHED** 1967

■ The Bonamy Charitable Trust

WHERE FUNDING CAN BE GIVEN UK and overseas, with a preference for Liverpool.
WHO CAN BENEFIT Charitable organisations.
WHAT IS FUNDED Jewish causes and general charitable purposes.
FINANCES *Year* 2007 *Income* £195,964 *Grants* £70,979 *Assets* £357,795
TRUSTEES M Moryoussef; J Moryoussef; R Moryoussef.
HOW TO APPLY In writing to the correspondent.
WHO TO APPLY TO M Moryoussef, Trustees, Flat 2, Forest Hills, South Downs Road, Bowdon, Cheshire WA14 3HD
CC NO 326424 **ESTABLISHED** 1983

■ The Charlotte Bonham-Carter Charitable Trust

WHERE FUNDING CAN BE GIVEN UK, with some emphasis on Hampshire.
WHO CAN BENEFIT Registered charities.
WHAT IS FUNDED General charitable purposes which were of particular concern to Lady Charlotte Bonham-Carter during her lifetime or are within the county of Hampshire. 'The trustees continue to support a core number of charities to whom they have made grants in the past as well as reviewing all applications received and making grants to new charities within their grant-giving criteria.'
WHAT IS NOT FUNDED No grants to individuals or non-registered charities.
RANGE OF GRANTS £500–£10,000.
SAMPLE GRANTS National Trust (£10,000); Hampshire Archives Trust (£5,000); Ashmolean Museum (£4,000); Clifton College, Handel House Museum, Holbourne Museum of Art, Pitt Rivers Museum, Rambert Dance Company and Wordsworth Trust (£2,000 each); and British

Library, Charleston Trust, Deafway, Jubilee Sailing Trust, Listening Books, Oakhaven Hospice Trust, Royal Academy, Seeing Ear and St Paul's Cathedral Foundation (£1,000 each).
FINANCES *Year* 2007–08 *Income* £167,403 *Grants* £89,004 *Assets* £3,946,968
TRUSTEES Sir Matthew Farrer; Norman Bonham-Carter; Georgina Nayler; David Bonham-Carter; Eliza Bonham-Carter.
HOW TO APPLY In writing to the correspondent. There are no application forms. The application should include details of the funds required, funds raised so far and the timescale involved. The trust states that unsolicited general applications are unlikely to be successful and only increase the cost of administration. Trustees meet in January and July; applications need to be received by May or November.
WHO TO APPLY TO Sir Matthew Farrer, Trustee, 66 Lincoln's Inn Fields, London WC2A 3LH
CC NO 292839 **ESTABLISHED** 1985

■ The John and Celia Bonham Christie Charitable Trust

WHERE FUNDING CAN BE GIVEN UK, with some preference for the former county of Avon.
WHO CAN BENEFIT Local and national organisations.
WHAT IS FUNDED Medical charities and organisations, though smaller grants are made to a wide range of other organisations.
WHAT IS NOT FUNDED No grants to individuals.
TYPE OF GRANT Recurrent, over three to five years.
RANGE OF GRANTS £200–£2,000.
SAMPLE GRANTS Previous beneficiaries have included BIBIC, Butterwick Hospice, Cancer Research Campaign, Derby TOC, Digestive Disorder Foundation, Dorothy House, Elizabeth Finn Trust, Foundation for the Study of Infant Cot Deaths, Frome Festival, Home Start South Wiltshire, Inspire Foundation, Kings Medical Trust, Royal Society for the Blind Winsley, Sea Cadet Association, St John Ambulance and Ten of Us.
FINANCES *Year* 2007–08 *Income* £50,057 *Grants* £27,514 *Assets* £1,309,765
TRUSTEES Richard Bonham Christie; Robert Bonham Christie; Rosemary Ker.
HOW TO APPLY In writing to the correspondent. The trustees regret that the income is fully allocated for the foreseeable future. Only a small number of new applications are supported each year.
WHO TO APPLY TO The Trustees, PO Box 9081, Taynton, Gloucester GL19 3WX
CC NO 326296 **ESTABLISHED** 1983

■ Bonhomie United Charity Society

WHERE FUNDING CAN BE GIVEN Southampton and district.
WHO CAN BENEFIT Local organisations.
WHAT IS FUNDED Disability causes.
WHAT IS NOT FUNDED Individual applications are not eligible, except those made by voluntary organisations and social services on the individual's behalf.
TYPE OF GRANT One-off for buildings and capital.
SAMPLE GRANTS Previous beneficiaries include Wessex Heart – Cardiac Trust, Salvation Army – Southampton, Southampton Mayor's Appeal, Thorner's Homes Southampton, British Red Cross, Southampton Care Association, Hampshire and Isle of Wight Outward Bound Association and Hampshire Autistic Society.

FINANCES *Year* 2007–08 *Income* £175,362 *Grants* £39,299 *Assets* £1,475,505

TRUSTEES B J Davies; Mrs S Davies; J Davies; R Davies.

HOW TO APPLY The trust states that funds are fully committed, but will consider all applications from within the Southampton and district area only.

WHO TO APPLY TO B J Davies, Trustee, 48 Lingwood Close, Southampton SO16 7GJ

CC NO 247816   **ESTABLISHED** 1966

....

■ BOOST Charitable Trust

WHERE FUNDING CAN BE GIVEN UK.

WHO CAN BENEFIT Individuals and groups involved in sport.

WHAT IS FUNDED Activities designed to 'champion the disabled and disadvantaged and to inspire them to overcome their challenges through the power of sport'.

RANGE OF GRANTS Grants are categorised into small awards (£500 or less) and large awards (over £500). The majority (by value) of the awards made are large awards where the charity is involved in longer term initiatives.

SAMPLE GRANTS Loughborough Development Trust (£80,000); Great Britain Wheelchair Rugby Association (£42,000); AHOY (£18,000); Paddlers for Life (£13,000); CP Sport – Boccia (£11,000); Windsor and Maidenhead District Sports Association for the Disabled (£7,000); Charnwood Tennis, Disability Snowsport UK and Wheelpower (£5,000 each); Kelly College (£4,000); and Shepshed Alley Group (£3,000).

FINANCES *Year* 2007–08 *Income* £288,795 *Grants* £233,896 *Assets* £1,077,675

TRUSTEES Robert Houston, Chair; Gillian Houston; Alurie Dutton; Howard Rogg.

OTHER INFORMATION The trust aims to **B**uild **O**n **O**verlooked **S**porting **T**alent. All of its activities, are designed to 'champion the disabled and disadvantaged and to inspire them to overcome their challenges through the power of sport'.

HOW TO APPLY For further information, contact the administrator. The trustees meet quarterly to consider what grants they will make and to review the existing awards. Nominations for grants are elicited by formal and informal means.

WHO TO APPLY TO Lucy Till, Administrator, 2nd Floor, 25 Copthall Avenue, London EC2R 7BP *Tel* 020 7767 5559 *Fax* 020 7767 5600 *email* lucy.till@boostct.org *Website* www.boostct.org

CC NO 1111961   **ESTABLISHED** 2005

....

■ The Booth Charities

WHERE FUNDING CAN BE GIVEN Salford.

WHO CAN BENEFIT Inhabitants of the City of Salford, especially those over 60 years of age.

WHAT IS FUNDED Relief of older people and people in need, including payments of pensions and provision of almshouses; relief of distress and sickness; provision and support of facilities for recreation and other leisure-time occupation; provision and support of educational facilities; any other charitable purpose.

TYPE OF GRANT One-off and recurring.

SAMPLE GRANTS The Booth Centre (£90,000); Salford Children's Holiday Camp (£30,000); Salford Methodist Centre (£18,600); Waterside Resource Centre (£15,500); St John's Bridge Project (£10,000); Barnardo's and the Heritage Learning Centre and Museum (£5,000 each); Listening Books (£3,000); Age Concern

(£2,000); and the People's Dispensary for Sick Animals (£1,000).

FINANCES *Year* 2007–08 *Income* £1,088,000 *Grants* £760,000 *Assets* £27,269,000

TRUSTEES William T Whittle, Chair; Richard J Christmas; Angela D Ginger; Edward W Hunt; Michael J Prior; Edward S Tudor-Evans; David J Tully; Roger J Weston; Richard P Kershaw; Philip E Webb; John C Willis.

OTHER INFORMATION £4,600 was awarded to individuals.

HOW TO APPLY In writing to the correspondent.

WHO TO APPLY TO Mrs L J Needham, Chief Executive, The William Jones Building, 1 Eccles Old Road, Salford, Manchester M6 7DE *Tel* 0161 736 2989 *Fax* 0161 737 4775 *email* boothcharities@waitrose.com

CC NO 221800   **ESTABLISHED** 1963

....

■ The Boots Charitable Trust

WHERE FUNDING CAN BE GIVEN Nottinghamshire and Nottingham.

WHO CAN BENEFIT Registered charities benefiting people who live in Nottinghamshire. Also small voluntary organisations whose income and expenditure are both less than £5,000 per year, who are not yet therefore required to register with the Charity Commission.

WHAT IS FUNDED (1) Health: community healthcare such as community healthcare services, home care, after care, relief of people who are disabled or have a medical condition and continuing care; and health education and prevention by promoting knowledge and awareness of specific diseases and medical conditions. (2) Lifelong learning: Helping people of any age to achieve their educational potential, supporting supplementary schools, literacy and numeracy projects, community education, vocational/restart education for the unemployed and alternative education for excluded school pupils. (3) Community development: Helping groups to organise and respond to problems and needs in their communities or networks. This could include groups such as Councils for Voluntary Services and self-help groups. (4) Social care including: personal social services – organisations assisting individuals or families to overcome social deprivation, such as people who are homeless or disabled and their carers, lone parent and childcare groups and other family support groups; social preventive schemes – activities preventing crime, dropping out and general delinquency and providing other social care outreach work, social health and safety awareness schemes and so on; and community social activity – activities to promote social engagement for vulnerable people, mitigating against isolation and loneliness. 'We are especially interested in projects with the capacity to deliver significant impact and which reach the greatest number of people.'

WHAT IS NOT FUNDED The trust does not provide funding for: projects benefiting people outside Nottinghamshire; individuals; organisations which are not registered charities and which have income or expenditure of more than £5,000 per year; charities seeking funds to redistribute to other charities; projects for which there is a legal statutory obligation or which replace statutory funding.

SAMPLE GRANTS Nottinghamshire Hospice (£15,000); Think Children (£11,000); Wheelbase Motor Project (£10,000); Home Start Nottingham (£9,000); School Home

Support Services (£8,000); the Furniture Project (£7,500); Ollerton Youth Project (£6,000); and Beeston Volunteer Centre, Life Education Centres Nottinghamshire, Newark Mind (£5,000 each).

FINANCES *Year* 2007–08 *Income* £253,853 *Grants* £226,115 *Assets* £17,658

TRUSTEES Kay Alison Croot; John Cohen; Ken Piggott; Sandra Rose; Oonagh Turnbull; Evelyn Dickey; Katherine Jayne Mayled.

HOW TO APPLY On a form available, with guidelines, from the website or by post. Completed forms should be sent to the correspondent with the latest annual report and accounts. The trustees meet every two months, although applications under £2,000 are dealt with by more quickly.

WHO TO APPLY TO Rachel McGuire, The Appeals Officer, Boots plc, D90 Building West G14, Nottingham NG90 1BS *Tel* 0115 949 2185 *email* rachel.mcguire@boots.co.uk *Website* www.boots-csr.com

CC NO 1045927   **ESTABLISHED** 1971

■ The Bordon and Liphook Charity

WHERE FUNDING CAN BE GIVEN Bordon, Liphook and surrounding areas, Hampshire.

WHO CAN BENEFIT Organisations and Individuals.

WHAT IS FUNDED General charitable purposes.

WHAT IS NOT FUNDED Non-priority loans.

TYPE OF GRANT Cash or loan.

SAMPLE GRANTS Previous beneficiaries have included Bordon Harlequins, Community Mental Health Team, Friends of Meadow School, Furniture Helpline, Highview Surgery, NSPCC and Red Cross Luncheon Club.

FINANCES *Year* 2008 *Income* £57,849 *Grants* £67,113 *Assets* £37,364

TRUSTEES C J Tartum; D N Hay; Revd S W Melhuish; R Reina; G Alexander; V Webb; Mrs J A Vernon-Smith.

HOW TO APPLY In writing to the correspondent.

WHO TO APPLY TO C J Tantum, Trustee, Room 32, The Forest Centre, Bordon, Hampshire GU35 OTN *Tel* 01420 477787 *email* info@bordonandliphookcharity.co.uk *Website* www.bordonandliphookcharity.co.uk

CC NO 1032428   **ESTABLISHED** 1994

■ Salo Bordon Charitable Trust

WHERE FUNDING CAN BE GIVEN UK and worldwide.

WHO CAN BENEFIT Organisations, primarily Jewish.

WHAT IS FUNDED Religious education and social welfare.

SAMPLE GRANTS Previous beneficiaries have included Agudas Israel Housing Association Ltd, Baer Hatorah, Beth Jacob Grammar School, Brisk Yeshivas, Golders Green Beth Hamedrash Congregation Jaffa Institute, Jewish Learning Exchange, London Academy of Jewish Studies, Society of Friends of Torah and WST Charity.

FINANCES *Year* 2007–08 *Income* £335,202 *Grants* £333,934 *Assets* £7,527,103

TRUSTEES S Bordon; Mrs L Bordon; M Bordon.

HOW TO APPLY In writing to the correspondent.

WHO TO APPLY TO S Bordon, Trustee, 78 Corringham Road, London NW11 7EB

CC NO 266439   **ESTABLISHED** 1973

■ The Oliver Borthwick Memorial Trust

WHERE FUNDING CAN BE GIVEN UK.

WHO CAN BENEFIT Registered charities benefiting homeless people and people disadvantaged by poverty. In particular the trustees welcome applications from small but viable charities in disadvantaged inner-city areas.

WHAT IS FUNDED Currently the main areas of interest are to provide shelter and help for homeless people.

WHAT IS NOT FUNDED No grants to individuals, including people working temporarily overseas for a charity where the request is for living expenses, together with applications relating to health, disability and those from non-registered charitable organisations.

TYPE OF GRANT Mainly one-off.

RANGE OF GRANTS Up to £5,000.

SAMPLE GRANTS St Matthew Housing (£5,000); Manna Society, Mission in Hounslow Trust, Northampton Kitchen, Only Connect UK, Porch, Shrewsbury Homes for All, St George Dragon Trust and Streets Alive Theatre Company Ltd (£3,000 each); Scottish Churches Housing Action (£2,000); Derbyshire Housing Aid Ltd (£1,500); and Almshouse Association (£1,000).

FINANCES *Year* 2007–08 *Income* £48,704 *Grants* £49,000 *Assets* £903,770

TRUSTEES M H R Brethedon; R A Graham; J Macdonald; J R Marriott; Mrs V Wrigley; Ms J S Mace; D Scott.

HOW TO APPLY Letters should be set out on a maximum of two sides of A4, giving full details of the project with costs, who the project will serve and the anticipated outcome of the project. Meetings take place once a year in May. Applications should be received no later than April.

WHO TO APPLY TO The Trustees, c/o Donor Grants Department, Charities Aid Foundation, Kings Hill, West Malling, Kent ME19 4TA

CC NO 256206   **ESTABLISHED** 1968

■ The Boshier-Hinton Foundation

WHERE FUNDING CAN BE GIVEN UK and overseas.

WHO CAN BENEFIT Charitable organisations.

WHAT IS FUNDED Work with children and adults with special educational or other needs.

SAMPLE GRANTS ACCURO (£11,000); Ability Sports, British Paralympic Association and Demand (£5,000 each); CHASE Children's Hospice (£3,000); Blind in Business (£2,500); Caring for Life and Royal London Society for the Blind (£2,000 each); Youth Create (£1,500); and Music Alive and Starlight Children's Foundation (£1,000 each).

FINANCES *Year* 2007–08 *Income* £71,833 *Grants* £128,944 *Assets* £724,474

TRUSTEES Thea Boshier, Chair; Peter Boshier; Peter Carr; Janet Beale.

HOW TO APPLY In writing to the correspondent.

WHO TO APPLY TO Peter Boshier, Trustee, Yeomans, Aythorpe Roding, Great Dunmow, Essex CM6 1PD

CC NO 1108886   **ESTABLISHED** 2005

■ The Bothwell Charitable Trust

WHERE FUNDING CAN BE GIVEN England, particularly the South East.

WHO CAN BENEFIT Registered charities benefiting carers, people with disabilities and people disadvantaged by poverty.

WHAT IS FUNDED Health, disability and research.

WHAT IS NOT FUNDED No grants for animal charities, overseas causes, individuals, or charities not registered with the Charity Commission.

TYPE OF GRANT Core costs, running costs and research grants, for one year or less.

RANGE OF GRANTS £1,000 or £2,500.

SAMPLE GRANTS Arthritis Research Campaign,British Home andHospital for Incurables, ECHO International Health Services Ltd, Friends of the Elderly, Leukaemia Research Fund, Parkinson's Disease Society, St Christopher's Hospice and Vitalise (£2,500 each); and Alzheimer's Society, British Trust for Conservation Volunteers, Children's Country Holiday Fund, Headway, National Autistic Society and Royal National Institute for Deaf People (£1,000 each).

FINANCES *Year* 2007–08 *Income* £39,780 *Grants* £46,000

TRUSTEES Paul L James; Crispian M P Howard.

HOW TO APPLY In writing to the correspondent. Distributions are usually made in February or March each year.

WHO TO APPLY TO 14 Kirkly Close, Sanderstead, Surrey CR2 0ET *Tel* 020 8657 3369

CC NO 299056   **ESTABLISHED** 1987

■ H E and E L Botteley Charitable Trust

WHERE FUNDING CAN BE GIVEN England and Wales, with some preference for Birmingham area.

WHO CAN BENEFIT Children, young people, older people, people with disabilities.

WHAT IS FUNDED General, overseas aid, Christian welfare.

SAMPLE GRANTS REACH for Rwanda and Rema UK (£7,000 each); Sutton Coldfield Baptist Church (£2,000); Agape (£1,000); Toy Box Charity (£500); and Birmingham University Guild of Students (£250).

FINANCES *Year* 2007–08 *Income* £28,727 *Grants* £27,400 *Assets* £657,555

TRUSTEES Ms S L Botteley; Mrs R Barney.

HOW TO APPLY In writing to the correspondent. The trustees normally meet biannually to consider applications for funding.

WHO TO APPLY TO Ms S L Botteley, Trustee, c/o 10 Oaklands Road, Sutton Coldfield B74 2TB *Tel* 0121 308 0220

CC NO 1036927

■ The Harry Bottom Charitable Trust

WHERE FUNDING CAN BE GIVEN UK, with a preference for Yorkshire and Derbyshire.

WHO CAN BENEFIT Registered charities.

WHAT IS FUNDED The trust states that support is divided roughly equally between religion, education and medical causes. Within these categories grants are given to: religion – small local appeals and cathedral appeals; education – universities and schools; and medical – equipment for hospitals and charities concerned with disability.

WHAT IS NOT FUNDED No grants to individuals.

RANGE OF GRANTS £250–£25,000.

SAMPLE GRANTS Yorkshire Baptist Trust (£25,000); University of Sheffield School of Medicine (£5,500); Cherry Tree Children's Home, Sheffield Association for Cerebral Palsy and St Luke's Hospice (£3,250 each); Sheffield Mencap (£2,800); and Heeley City Farm (£2,000).

FINANCES *Year* 2007–08 *Income* £559,669 *Grants* £77,595 *Assets* £5,010,159

TRUSTEES Revd J M Kilner; Prof. T H Lilley; Prof. I G Rennie; Prof. A Rawlinson.

HOW TO APPLY In writing to the correspondent at any time.

WHO TO APPLY TO J S Hinsley, c/o Westons, Chartered Accountants, Queen's Buildings, 55 Queen Street, Sheffield S1 2DX

CC NO 204675   **ESTABLISHED** 1960

■ P G and N J Boulton Trust

WHERE FUNDING CAN BE GIVEN Worldwide.

WHO CAN BENEFIT Organisations with whom the trustees have existing commitments/special interest.

WHAT IS FUNDED Christian missionary work; disaster and poverty relief; medical research and healthcare; disability relief and care of older people.

WHAT IS NOT FUNDED No grants are made directly to individuals. No grants towards environment and conservation, culture and heritage, sport and leisure, animal welfare or church building repairs.

SAMPLE GRANTS Children Alone (£11,000); New Life Centre (£10,000); Intercessors for Britain (£8,000); Longcroft Christian Trust (£6,000); Just Care and Shalom Christian Fellowship (£4,000 each); Barnabas Fund, Charles Thompson's Mission and Vision for China (£1,500 each); and Anglo-Peruvian Child Care Mission, New Tribes Mission and SAO Cambodia (£1,000 each).

FINANCES *Year* 2007–08 *Income* £129,521 *Grants* £65,500 *Assets* £4,145,902

TRUSTEES Miss N J Boulton, Chair; Miss L M Butchart; A L Perry; Mrs S Perry.

HOW TO APPLY The trust only makes donations to organisations with which it has existing commitments. Any new requests for funding will almost certainly be unsuccessful.

WHO TO APPLY TO Andrew L Perry, Trustee, PO Box 72, Wirral, Merseyside CH46 6AA *Website* www. boultontrust.org.uk

CC NO 272525   **ESTABLISHED** 1976

■ The A H and E Boulton Trust

WHERE FUNDING CAN BE GIVEN Worldwide.

WHO CAN BENEFIT Particularly Christian charities.

WHAT IS FUNDED The trust mainly supports the erection and maintenance of buildings to be used for preaching the Christian gospel, and teaching its doctrines. The trustees can also support other Christian institutions, especially missions in the UK and developing world.

TYPE OF GRANT Mostly recurrent.

SAMPLE GRANTS Liverpool City Mission (£42,000); Holy Trinity Church (£22,000); the Slavic Gospel Association (£20,000); Bethesda Church and Pioneer People Wirral (£15,000 each); Operation Mobilisation (£12,000); Leprosy Mission (£6,000); Peel Beach Mission (£5,000); Salvation Army (£4,000); and Charles Thompson Mission (£3,000).

FINANCES *Year* 2007–08 *Income* £130,864 *Grants* £153,781 *Assets* £2,857,446

TRUSTEES Mrs J R Gopsill; F P Gopsill.

HOW TO APPLY In writing to the correspondent. The trust tends to support a set list of charities and applications are very unlikely to be successful.

WHO TO APPLY TO The Trustees, c/o Moore Stephens, 110–114 Duke Street, Liverpool L1 5AG
CC NO 225328   **ESTABLISHED** 1935

■ Sir Clive Bourne Family Trust

WHERE FUNDING CAN BE GIVEN UK.
WHO CAN BENEFIT Individuals and institutions benefiting Jewish people.
WHAT IS FUNDED The trustees favour Jewish causes. A number of health and medical charities (particularly relating to cancer) have also benefited.
SAMPLE GRANTS Prostate Cancer Research Foundation (£17,000); Sydney Gold Trust (£12,000); Mossbourne Community Academy (£10,000); World Jewish Relief, WIZO UK and United Synagogue (£3,000 each); Drugsline (£2,500); the Langdon Foundation (£2,000); British WIZO (£1,000); Jewish Blind and Disabled (£500); Cancer Research (£300); UK Friends of AWIS (£250); Jewish Child's Day (£200); Walk the Walk (£150); and UJIA (£100).
FINANCES *Year* 2008–09 *Income* £119,208 *Grants* £66,167 *Assets* £4,399,667
TRUSTEES Lady Bourne; Mrs Katie Cohen; Mrs Lucy Furman; Mrs Claire Lefton; Mrs Merryl Flitterman.
HOW TO APPLY In writing to the correspondent.
WHO TO APPLY TO Janet Bater, 134–136 High Street, Epping, Essex CM16 4AG
CC NO 290620   **ESTABLISHED** 1984

■ The Anthony Bourne Foundation

WHERE FUNDING CAN BE GIVEN Unrestricted, in particular, Warwickshire.
WHO CAN BENEFIT Primarily organisations benefiting children and young people.
WHAT IS FUNDED 'Through supporting a wide range of charitable organisations, the trustees have resolved to give support to charities which seek to promote the wellbeing of young people and to foster their active positive engagement in their local communities.'
WHAT IS NOT FUNDED No grants to individuals.
TYPE OF GRANT One-off grants for capital (including buildings), core costs and start-up costs. Funding of up to three years will be considered.
RANGE OF GRANTS £350–£3,000.
SAMPLE GRANTS Kids 'n' Action, Lancaster and District YMCA – YZUP Young Offender Project, Life Church, Maximum Life Youth Project and Tiverton Market Drop-In-Centre (£3,000 each); Living Hope Charity, St Margaret's Hospice Somerset and Straight Talking (£1,000); and Warwickshire Association of Youth Clubs – Dream Catcher Appeal (£350).
FINANCES *Year* 2007–08 *Income* £25,363 *Grants* £18,350 *Assets* £618,511
TRUSTEES Mrs V A Bourne; Mariota Kinross; Celia Louise Jeune; Chuka Umunna.
HOW TO APPLY In writing to the correspondent, including a full set of accounts and an annual report, for consideration in May and November.
WHO TO APPLY TO Mariota Kinross, Trustee, Payne Hicks Beach Solicitors, 10 New Square, Lincoln's Inn, London WC2A 3QG *Tel* 020 7465 4300
CC NO 1015759   **ESTABLISHED** 1992

■ Bourneheights Limited

WHERE FUNDING CAN BE GIVEN UK.
WHO CAN BENEFIT Orthodox Jews.
WHAT IS FUNDED Orthodox Jewish organisations.
SAMPLE GRANTS Moreshet Hatorah (£378,000); Mercaz Torah Vahesed Ltd (£152,000); BFOT (£126,000); Belz Synagogue (£104,000); Telz Academy Trust (£95,000); Gevurath Ari Academy (£75,000); UTA (£34,000); Toreth Emeth (£30,000); Olam Chesed Yiboneh (£20,000); Before Trust (£12,000); Heaven Point (£10,000); Yeshivas Avas Torah (£5,000); and Lubavitch Mechina (£3,000).
FINANCES *Year* 2006–07 *Income* £2,942,522 *Grants* £1,542,961 *Assets* £5,146,736
TRUSTEES Chaskel Rand; Esther Rand; Erno Berger; Yechiel Chersky; Schloime Rand.
HOW TO APPLY In writing to the correspondent.
WHO TO APPLY TO Schloime Rand, Trustee, Flat 10, Palm Court, Queen Elizabeth's Walk, London N16 5XA
CC NO 298359   **ESTABLISHED** 1984

■ Community Foundation for Bournemouth, Dorset and Poole

WHERE FUNDING CAN BE GIVEN The county of Dorset, including the unitary authorities of Bournemouth and Poole.
WHO CAN BENEFIT Local organisations.
WHAT IS FUNDED Community initiatives. Available funding changes on ongoing basis, please see the foundation's website for up-to-date information.
FINANCES *Year* 2007–08 *Income* £837,128 *Grants* £798,323 *Assets* £690,664
TRUSTEES Colin Brady; Gwyn Bates; Christopher Beale; Richard Dimbleby; Michael Green; Gordon Page; Jane Raimes; Ashley Rowlands; Helen Starkie; Mark Woodhouse; Gary Bentham.
HOW TO APPLY Contact the foundation for details of up-to-date programmes. An online contact form is available on the site.
WHO TO APPLY TO The Grants Manager, Abchurch Chambers, 24 St Peter's Road, Bournemouth BH1 2LN *Tel* 01202 292255 *email* grants@cfbdp.org *Website* www.cfbdp.org
CC NO 1122113

■ The Bower Trust

WHERE FUNDING CAN BE GIVEN Wales and developing countries.
WHO CAN BENEFIT Generally, registered charities.
WHAT IS FUNDED Charities connected activities in the 'third world' and Wales.
WHAT IS NOT FUNDED No personal sponsorships. Generally the trustees are not interested in regional requests from charities.
SAMPLE GRANTS Children in Crisis (£4,000); Llanilltyd Fawr in Flower (£3,000); and Gwent Wildlife Trust, Prostate Cancer, Tanzad, Work Aid and World Wildlife Fund (£1,000 each).
FINANCES *Year* 2007–08 *Income* £44,952 *Grants* £28,150 *Assets* £786,370
TRUSTEES Mrs C V E Benfield; G Benfield; F C Slater.
HOW TO APPLY In writing to the correspondent. Trustees meet quarterly to consider grants.
WHO TO APPLY TO Graham Benfield, Trust Administrator, Old Rosedew House, Colhugh Street, Llantwit Major CF61 1RF
CC NO 283025   **ESTABLISHED** 1981

■ The Bowerman Charitable Trust

WHERE FUNDING CAN BE GIVEN UK, with a preference for West Sussex.

WHO CAN BENEFIT Registered charities.

WHAT IS FUNDED Church activities, the arts, medical charities, youth work and other charitable activities.

TYPE OF GRANT One-off.

RANGE OF GRANTS Usually up to £20,000.

SAMPLE GRANTS St Margaret's Church – Angmering (£400,000); Royal College of Music (£18,000); Macmillan Cancer Care (£13,000); British Youth Opera (£11,000); and St Helen's Bishopsgate (£10,000).

FINANCES *Year* 2007–08 *Income* £188,579 *Grants* £508,522 *Assets* £11,890,454

TRUSTEES D W Bowerman; Mrs C M Bowerman; Mrs J M Taylor; Miss K E Bowerman; Mrs A M Downham; J M Capper; M Follis.

HOW TO APPLY In writing to the correspondent. The trustees have previously stated that they are bombarded with applications and unsolicited applications will not be considered.

WHO TO APPLY TO D W Bowerman, Trustee, Champs Hill, Coldwatham, Pulborough, West Sussex RH20 1LY

CC NO 289446   **ESTABLISHED** 1984

■ John and Susan Bowers Fund

WHERE FUNDING CAN BE GIVEN UK and overseas.

WHO CAN BENEFIT Registered charities.

WHAT IS FUNDED Social justice, health and welfare, arts, environment, religion, emergency appeals and development.

RANGE OF GRANTS Up to £1,000.

SAMPLE GRANTS Impact Foundation (£700); Oxford Night Shelter, Appropriate Technology Asia and Excellent Development (£600 each); Pesticide Action Network, Responding to Conflict and Olive Tree Educational Trust (£500 each); Harvest Help and Computeraid (£400 each); Anti-Slavery International and Music Alive (£300 each); Prisoners Advice Service and Railway Land Wildlife Trust (£200 each); and Shelterbox (£100).

FINANCES *Year* 2007–08 *Income* £97,649 *Grants* £19,790 *Assets* £17,202

TRUSTEES Chris Bowers; John Bowers; Sue Bowers; Louise Gorst; Jenny Johns, Stephen Johns; Jennifer Armistead.

HOW TO APPLY In writing to the correspondent. The charity tends to make recurrent grants – 'our reluctance to drop charities we have supported in the past and spread ourselves more thinly, invariably means that only a very small number of new applications receive a positive response.'

WHO TO APPLY TO Sue Bowers, 5 Greenacres Drive, Ringmer, Lewes, East Sussex BN8 5LZ *Tel* 01273 813722 *email* cbowers@gn.apc.org

CC NO 266616

■ The Bowland Charitable Trust

WHERE FUNDING CAN BE GIVEN North west England.

WHO CAN BENEFIT Individuals, institutions, and registered charities benefiting, in general, children and young adults.

WHAT IS FUNDED 'The majority of the support provided is to outdoor and character building activities by young people based in the north west of England and educational, religious and cultural activities and institutions.'

SAMPLE GRANTS National Maths Case Studies Project (£1.3 million); University of Wolverhampton Reveal Project (£225,000); Lord David Puttnam (£125,000); Ron Clark Academy (£100,000); Young Foundation (£80,000); Centre for Crime and Justice Studies (£25,000); Emmaus Preston and Lancashire County Council Education Conference (£20,000 each); St Albans Cathedral Music Trust (£15,000); Nazareth Unitarian Chapel (£14,000); and Grindleton Recreation Ground Charity (£5,000).

FINANCES *Year* 2007 *Income* £8,788,833 *Grants* £1,974,125 *Assets* £13,706,016

TRUSTEES H A Cann; R A Cann; C Fahy; H D Turner.

HOW TO APPLY 'The charity invites applications for funding of projects from individuals, charities and other charitable organisations. The applications are made directly to the trustees, who meet regularly to assess the applications.'

WHO TO APPLY TO Mrs Carol Fahy, Trustee, Activhouse, Philips Road, Blackburn, Lancashire BB1 5TH

CC NO 292027   **ESTABLISHED** 1985

■ The William Brake Charitable Trust

WHERE FUNDING CAN BE GIVEN UK, with a preference for Kent.

WHO CAN BENEFIT Registered charities.

WHAT IS FUNDED General charitable purposes.

TYPE OF GRANT £1,000–£50,000.

RANGE OF GRANTS £1,000–£50,000.

SAMPLE GRANTS the Whitely Fund for Nature (£50,000); the Royal Masonic Benevolent Institution (£25,000); NSPCC (£14,000); the Duke of Edinburgh's Award (£11,000); and the Ecology Trust and Royal Academy of Arts (£10,000 each); Wooden Spoon Society (£7,000); the Aurora Tsunami Orphanage (£5,000); the Friends of St Peters Hospital Chertsey (£3,000); Canterbury Cathedral Development (£2,500); RNLI (£2,000); and Wellbeing of Women (£1,000).

FINANCES *Year* 2007–08 *Income* £78,341 *Grants* £282,000 *Assets* £9,251,287

TRUSTEES Philip R Wilson; Deborah J Isaac; Penelope A Lang; Michael Trigg.

HOW TO APPLY In writing to the correspondent.

WHO TO APPLY TO The Trustees, c/o Gill Turner and Tucker, Colman House, King Street, Maidstone, Kent ME14 1JE

CC NO 1023244   **ESTABLISHED** 1984

■ The Tony Bramall Charitable Trust

WHERE FUNDING CAN BE GIVEN UK, with some preference for Yorkshire.

WHO CAN BENEFIT Local charities within Yorkshire and national medical institutions.

WHAT IS FUNDED Medical research, ill health and social welfare.

RANGE OF GRANTS Usually £1,000–£5,000.

SAMPLE GRANTS Cancer Research UK (£200,000); Tamzin's Quest (£5,600); Henshaws Society for Blind People and Motor and Allied Trades Benevolent Fund (£5,000 each); Harrogate White Rose Theatre Trust Limited, Pondside Neighbours Group and Within Reach – Sheffield (£1,000 each); the Happy Wanderers Ambulance Association (£750); York and North Yorkshire Community Foundation (£500); Martin House Hospice (£300); and the Peter Hollis Memorial Fund (£250).

Think carefully about every application. Is it justified?

383

FINANCES *Year* 2007–08 *Income* £217,182 *Grants* £221,691 *Assets* £3,751,698
TRUSTEES D C A Bramall; Mrs K S Bramall Odgen; Mrs M J Foody; G M Tate; Miss A Bramall.
HOW TO APPLY In writing to the correspondent.
WHO TO APPLY TO The Trustees, 12 Cardale Court, Beckwith Head Road, Harrogate, North Yorkshire HG3 1RY *Tel* 01423 535300 *email* johnholroyd64@hotmail.com
CC NO 1001522　　ESTABLISHED 1990

....

■ The Bransford Trust

WHERE FUNDING CAN BE GIVEN Preference for the West Midlands.
WHO CAN BENEFIT Registered charities.
WHAT IS FUNDED General charitable purposes.
SAMPLE GRANTS The Leys School (£200,000); St Richard Hospice (£50,000); Acorns Children's Trust (£15,000); Prince's Trust and Worcester Festival and Worcester Porcelain Museum (£10,000 each); Noah's Ark Trust (£6,000); Dyslexia Association, Worcester Young Carers and Young Enterprise West Midlands (£5,000 each); and Elgar Birthplace Development Fund (£2,000).
FINANCES *Year* 2007–08 *Income* £426,591 *Grants* £351,050 *Assets* £147,425
TRUSTEES C A Kinnear; Mrs B Kinnear; L E S Freeman; A J C Kinnear; A J Neil.
HOW TO APPLY In writing to the correspondent.
WHO TO APPLY TO The Trustees, PO Box 600, Worcester WR1 2XG
CC NO 1106554　　ESTABLISHED 2004

....

■ The Breast Cancer Research Trust

WHERE FUNDING CAN BE GIVEN UK.
WHO CAN BENEFIT Recognised cancer centres or research institutions.
WHAT IS FUNDED Clinical and translational research into the prevention, early diagnosis and treatment of breast cancer.
WHAT IS NOT FUNDED No grants to students.
TYPE OF GRANT Limited grants available up to a term of three years. Grants reviewed annually.
FINANCES *Year* 2007–08 *Income* £173,766 *Grants* £367,669 *Assets* £582,540
TRUSTEES Dame Vera Lynn; Prof. Charles Coombes; Jean-Claude Gazet; Virginia Lewis-Jones; Bob Potter; Prof. Trevor J Powles; R M Rainsbury; Hon Mrs Justice Rafferty; Dr Margaret Spittle.
HOW TO APPLY Application forms available only from the trust's website.
WHO TO APPLY TO The Honorary Administrator, 48 Wayneflete Tower Avenue, Esher, Surrey KT10 8QG *Tel* 01372 463235 *email* bcrtoffice@aol.com *Website* www.breastcancerresearchtrust.org.uk
CC NO 272214　　ESTABLISHED 1961

....

■ The Brewers' Company General Charitable Trust

WHERE FUNDING CAN BE GIVEN UK.
WHO CAN BENEFIT Generally, existing beneficiaries.
WHAT IS FUNDED General charitable purposes. In practice, however, funding is restricted to existing beneficiaries with no scope to support unsolicited applications.
WHAT IS NOT FUNDED No grants to individuals.
RANGE OF GRANTS Up to £100 except for existing beneficiaries.

SAMPLE GRANTS Previously: Aldenham School for Breweries scholarships; City University; City and Guilds of London Institute; St Paul's Cathedral.
FINANCES *Year* 2008 *Income* £21,058 *Grants* £20,000
TRUSTEES The Brewers' Company.
HOW TO APPLY In writing to the correspondent. But please note the above comments regarding unsolicited applicants.
WHO TO APPLY TO The Clerk to the Brewers' Company, Brewers' Hall, Aldermanbury Square, London EC2V 7HR *Tel* 020 7600 1801
CC NO 1059811　　ESTABLISHED 1996

....

■ The Harold and Alice Bridges Charity

WHERE FUNDING CAN BE GIVEN South Cumbria and North Lancashire (as far south as Preston).
WHO CAN BENEFIT Particular favour is given to children, young adults, older people and village activities.
WHAT IS FUNDED General charitable purposes, particularly young people, older people and supporting village activities.
WHAT IS NOT FUNDED No grants to individuals.
TYPE OF GRANT The trustees prefer mainly capital projects which have an element of self help.
RANGE OF GRANTS Usually £500–£5,000.
SAMPLE GRANTS Bowland Pennine Mountain Rescue, Bryning with Warton Parish Council, St John the Baptist Church – Broughton, St John the Baptist Church – Tunstall and Storth Village Hall (£5,000 each); Early Mines Research Group Museum Trust (£4,000); Promenade Concert Orchestra (£3,000); Fylde Rugby Club (£2,500); Ingleton Scout Group (£2,000); WRVS (£1,700); Steveley Village Enterprises (£1,500); and Lake District Summer Music (£1,000).
FINANCES *Year* 2007–08 *Income* £112,874 *Grants* £89,750 *Assets* £2,573,718
TRUSTEES Richard N Hardy.
HOW TO APPLY In writing to the correspondent, followed by completion of a standard application form. The trustees meet three times a year to discuss and approve grant applications and review finances. Cheques are sent out to those successful applicants within days of each meeting.
WHO TO APPLY TO Richard N Hardy, Trustee, Senior Calveley and Hardy Solicitors, 8 Hastings Place, Lytham FY8 5NA *Tel* 01253 733333 *email* rnh@seniorslaw.co.uk
CC NO 236654　　ESTABLISHED 1963

....

■ Briggs Animal Welfare Trust

WHERE FUNDING CAN BE GIVEN UK and overseas.
WHO CAN BENEFIT Charities concerned with animal welfare, particularly animals in distress caused by man including wildlife.
WHAT IS FUNDED Although the original objects of the trust were general, but with particular support for animal welfare, the trust's policy is to support only animal welfare causes.
TYPE OF GRANT Ongoing grants.
RANGE OF GRANTS £1,000–£2,000.
SAMPLE GRANTS There are five named beneficiaries in the trust deed: RSPCA, Reystede Animal Sanctuary Ringmer, Brooke Hospital for Animals Cairo, Care of British Columbia House and the Society for the Protection of Animals in North Africa.
FINANCES *Year* 2007–08 *Income* £36,664 *Grants* £100,080 *Assets* £778,680

TRUSTEES Miss L M Hartnett; A P M Schouten.
HOW TO APPLY In writing to the correspondent.
WHO TO APPLY TO The Trustees, Little Champions Farm, Maplehurst Road, West Grinstead, West Sussex RH13 6RN
CC NO 276459   **ESTABLISHED** 1978

■ The Brighton District Nursing Association Trust

WHERE FUNDING CAN BE GIVEN Brighton and Hove.
WHO CAN BENEFIT Individuals, organisations benefiting sick people and carers.
WHAT IS FUNDED Health, the relief of sickness and respite care.
TYPE OF GRANT One-off and funding for one year or less may be considered.
SAMPLE GRANTS Somerset Day Centre (£15,000 in 12 grants); St Johns Ambulance and Threshold (£10,000 each); MacMillan Cancer Support and Theodor Children's Trust (£5,000 each); Mind in Brighton and Hove (£4,800); the Children's Clinic (£4,000); Oasis Brighton Project (£3,700); Pathway to Health (£2,800); and Royal Blind Society (£2,000).
FINANCES *Year* 2007 *Income* £66,222 *Grants* £70,313 *Assets* £2,248,571
TRUSTEES P J Field, Chair; A D Paige; A D Druce; J Krolick; A Pannett; D Royce; J Watts.
HOW TO APPLY In writing to the correspondent. Trustees meet on a quarterly basis to consider applications.
WHO TO APPLY TO Anthony Druce, Secretary, c/o Fitzhugh Gates, 3 Pavilion Parade, Brighton BN2 1RY *Tel* 01273 686811 *email* anthonyd@ fitzhugh.co.uk
CC NO 213851   **ESTABLISHED** 1963

■ Bristol Archdeaconry Charity

WHERE FUNDING CAN BE GIVEN Archdeaconry of Bristol.
WHO CAN BENEFIT Charities and individuals for advancement of the Church of England.
WHAT IS FUNDED Religious and other charitable purposes of the Church of England in the area of benefit. Grants should generally be associated with church-based ministry and community projects in UPA parishes and made wherever possible by way of start-up funding'.
TYPE OF GRANT Recurrent.
SAMPLE GRANTS Bristol Diocesan Board of Finance (£60,000); AllHallows (£20,000); AGORA (£3,100); St Stephens – Southmead (£2,000); and Community of Sisters of the Church (£1,500).
FINANCES *Year* 2008 *Income* £163,658 *Grants* £86,626 *Assets* £2,911,446
TRUSTEES J Tidmarsh; R C Metcalfe; Miss S J Mumford; P E Woolf; H D M Wares; S J Baughen; Mrs L E Farrall; Canon T J Higgins; T R Thom; A R E Brown; Ven T E McClure.
HOW TO APPLY In writing to the correspondent.
WHO TO APPLY TO Mrs E J Wright, Clerk, All Saints' Church, 1 All Saints Court, Bristol BS1 1JN *Tel* 0117 929 2709 *Fax* 0117 929 2709
CC NO 1058853   **ESTABLISHED** 1996

■ The Bristol Charities

WHERE FUNDING CAN BE GIVEN Within a ten-mile radius of Bristol city centre.
WHO CAN BENEFIT Individuals and organisations.
WHAT IS FUNDED Education; relief of sickness; and relief of need.
FINANCES *Year* 2007–08 *Grants* £40,000
TRUSTEES Barry England, Chair; Dudley Lewis; James Ackland; Dr Robert Acheson; Keith Bonham; Kamala Das; Helen E Evans; Clive Halton; Susan Hampton; Andrew Hillman; Jeffery Howard-Brown; Nick Hutchen; Alfred Morris; Christine Porter; Vanessa Stevenson; Stephen Thomas; David Watts.
OTHER INFORMATION The 2007–08 grant total represents donations made to organisations. Additional funds were distributed to individuals.
HOW TO APPLY On an application form available from the correspondent.
WHO TO APPLY TO David Jones, Chief Executive, 17 St Augustine's Parade, Bristol BS1 4UL *Tel* 0117 930 0301 *Fax* 0117 925 3824 *email* info@bristolcharities.org.uk *Website* www. bristolcharities.org.uk
CC NO 1109141   **ESTABLISHED** 1960

■ John Bristow and Thomas Mason Trust

WHERE FUNDING CAN BE GIVEN Parish of Charlwood (as the boundaries stood in 1926).
WHO CAN BENEFIT Children, people with disabilities and people in need.
WHAT IS FUNDED Churches, community amenities, disability, and education.
WHAT IS NOT FUNDED Any application that will not benefit the residents of the Parish of Charlwood (as the boundaries stood in 1926) will not be considered.
RANGE OF GRANTS Usually up to £3,000.
SAMPLE GRANTS St Nicholas PCC (£40,000); Charlwood Parish Hall (£15,000); Lowfield Heath Church (£4,000); St Catherine's Hospice (£3,300); Charlwood Parish Venture Week (£3,000); Charlwood Pre-School (£1,700); 1st Horley Guides (£1,200); Charlwood Mothers Union (£200); and the Charlwood Woman's Institute (£100).
FINANCES *Year* 2008 *Income* £98,699 *Grants* £78,038 *Assets* £2,220,360
TRUSTEES Tim Spinney, Chair; Revd Bill Campen; Martin Cooper; Colin Gates; Feargal Hogan; Martin James; Gavin Purser; Jean Smith; Pat Wilson.
HOW TO APPLY Applications should be made on a form available from the correspondent upon written request, and should include an estimate of the total cost of the project, with three quotations where applicable.
WHO TO APPLY TO Miss M Singleton, Secretary, 20 Meadway, Horley, Surrey RH6 9AW *Tel* 01293 785556 *email* trust.secretary@jbtmt.org.uk *Website* www.jbtmt.org.uk
CC NO 1075971   **ESTABLISHED** 1999

■ Britannia Foundation

WHERE FUNDING CAN BE GIVEN 'Within 25 miles of Leek, where the society is based, in the counties of Staffordshire, Cheshire and Derbyshire. This area covers the city of Stoke on Trent, and the towns of Stafford, Stone, Uttoxeter, Ashbourne, Buxton, Macclesfield, Congleton and Crewe and the rural communities between them.'

WHO CAN BENEFIT Organisations benefiting homeless people, people in need of training, especially in financial matters and community safety.

WHAT IS FUNDED Initiatives and projects that will make a difference to local communities. Priorities are: homelessness, including helping people to stay in their homes; educational achievement and aspirations; community safety, including crime prevention schemes; and encouraging prudent money management, by improving financial literacy and money advice services. Infrastructure development is also considered.

WHAT IS NOT FUNDED The following areas are not eligible for support: activities which are mainly the responsibility of the state (unless it is for added support services); hospitals, medical centres, medical treatment or research (except for projects which are clearly extra to statutory responsibilities); grant-making organisations; political or pressure groups; animal welfare organisations; profit-making organisations; individuals or individual fundraising efforts, including expeditions or overseas travel; general fundraising events, activities or appeals; fabric appeals for places of worship; promotion of religion; sponsorship of marketing appeals (including advertising in charity brochures or souvenir programmes); overseas charities.

TYPE OF GRANT Funding for core costs normally restricted to one-off grants. Capital including buildings, feasibility studies, one-off, project, research all considered. Recurring costs, running costs, salaries and start-up costs are exceptional.

RANGE OF GRANTS Usually up to £25,000.

SAMPLE GRANTS St Cuthbert's Catholic College (£24,000); The Outward Bound Trust (£21,000); Bolton Lads and Girls Club (£16,000); Tower Hamlets Summer University (£14,000); Young Enterprise North West, Pitsmoor Citizens Advice Bureau and Prince's Trust (£10,000 each); Manchester Camerata (£6,500); Royal Society for the Blind and Yemeni Community Association of Sandwell (£5,000 each); and New Life Church Valley Debt Advice (£2,500).

FINANCES *Year* 2008 *Income* £519,156 *Grants* £248,194 *Assets* £382,061

TRUSTEES S Chattaway; G Leftwich; N B Richardson; Lord Lawrence Sawyer of Darlington; N Stephenson; D J N Gray; P H Wilkes.

PUBLICATIONS Grants and donations policy leaflet.

HOW TO APPLY On a form available from the correspondent. Before making an application a copy of the grants and donations policy should be obtained from the foundation to check eligibility. Initial telephone calls are welcomed. Applications for more than £25,000 will only be considered in exceptional cases. Trustees meet three times a year to approve donations. It may take up to four months before a decision is reached.

WHO TO APPLY TO Christine Massey, Secretary, Britannia House, Leek, Staffordshire ST13 5RG *Tel* 01538 391805 *Fax* 01538 399261 *email* christine.massey@britannia.co.uk
CC NO 1069081   **ESTABLISHED** 1998

■ **The British Council for Prevention of Blindness**

WHERE FUNDING CAN BE GIVEN Worldwide.

WHO CAN BENEFIT Organisations benefiting people with sight loss, and medical professionals, research workers and scientists in the field.

WHAT IS FUNDED Funding research, including fellowships, which has the potential to make breakthroughs in understanding and treating currently incurable eye diseases; and operational research to determine the best methods of preventing blindness.

WHAT IS NOT FUNDED BCPB do not deal with the individual welfare of blind people in the UK.

RANGE OF GRANTS Usually for a maximum of £40,000.

FINANCES *Year* 2007–08 *Income* £408,814 *Grants* £228,588 *Assets* £705,898

TRUSTEES A R Elkington; C Walker; S M Brooker; Prof. A Dick; Dr C Harper; R Jackson; R Porter; R Titley; Lady J Wilson.

HOW TO APPLY Applications can be made throughout the year.

WHO TO APPLY TO The Trustees, 4 Bloomsbury Square, London WC1A 2RP *Tel* 020 7404 7114 *email* info@bcpb.org *Website* www.bcpb.org
CC NO 270941   **ESTABLISHED** 1976

■ **The British Dietetic Association General and Education Trust Fund**

WHERE FUNDING CAN BE GIVEN UK.

WHO CAN BENEFIT Individuals and to recognised associations or groups of people engaged in dietetic research and associated activities.

WHAT IS FUNDED Education, research and other purposes related to the science of dietetics.

WHAT IS NOT FUNDED Direct support of dietetic students in training or postgraduate qualifications for individuals, i.e. the trust will not pay postgraduate fees/expenses, or elective/MSc study for doctors.

TYPE OF GRANT Project, one-off, research, recurring costs, salaries, start-up costs, interest-free loans and running costs. Funding can be given for up to three years.

FINANCES *Year* 2007–08 *Income* £54,847 *Grants* £19,910 *Assets* £1,534,700

TRUSTEES Mrs P L Douglas, Chair; Dame Barbara Clayton; P Brindley; Miss E Elliot; W T Seddon; Miss U Martin.

HOW TO APPLY Application forms can be downloaded from the trust's website.

WHO TO APPLY TO The Secretary to the Trustees, 5th Floor, Charles House, 148–149 Great Charles Street, Queensway, Birmingham B3 3HT *Tel* 0121 200 8080 *email* info@bda.uk.com *Website* www.bda.uk.com
CC NO 282553   **ESTABLISHED** 1981

■ **The British Gas (Scottish Gas) Energy Trust**

WHERE FUNDING CAN BE GIVEN England, Scotland and Wales.

WHO CAN BENEFIT Voluntary sector organisations and current domestic customers of British Gas or Scottish Gas.

WHAT IS FUNDED Relief-in-need; the provision of money and debt prevention advice and education, often with a particular fuel poverty emphasis.

WHAT IS NOT FUNDED No grants for: fines for criminal offences; educational or training needs; debts to central government departments; medical equipment, aids and adaptations; holidays; business debts; catalogues; credit cards; personal loans; deposits for secure accommodation; or overpayment of benefits.

TYPE OF GRANT One-off grants for individuals; one-off and recurrent capital and revenue grants for organisations.

FINANCES *Year* 2008 *Income* £3,672,595 *Grants* £419,728 *Assets* £344,971

TRUSTEES Michael Lake, Chair; Barbara Ruffell; Jennifer Saunders; Harry Cathcart; Helen Mcleod

OTHER INFORMATION The 2008 grant total represents grant to organisations. A further £2,848,882 was distributed to individuals in respect of energy debt.

HOW TO APPLY Grants for organisations: funding rounds are publicised on the trust's website and in its newsletter. Grants for individuals: applications should be made by post using a form available from the trust's website.

WHO TO APPLY TO The Trustees, Freepost RRZJ-XBSY-GYRG, British Gas Energy Trust, PO Box 42, Peterborough PE3 8XH *Tel* 01733 421020 *email* bget@charisgrants.com *Website* www.britishgasenergytrust.org.uk

CC NO 1106218   **ESTABLISHED** 2004

···

■ British Heart Foundation

WHERE FUNDING CAN BE GIVEN UK.

WHO CAN BENEFIT Organisations that benefit people of all ages; academics; medical professionals; students; and people with heart disease.

WHAT IS FUNDED Medical research into all aspects of heart disease.

WHAT IS NOT FUNDED Applications are accepted only from appropriately qualified individuals.

TYPE OF GRANT Project, programme and fellowship grants.

RANGE OF GRANTS No limit.

FINANCES *Year* 2008–09 *Income* £198,366,000 *Grants* £120,757,000

TRUSTEES The Council.

HOW TO APPLY Application forms and guidelines are available on request.

WHO TO APPLY TO The Research Funds Manager, 14 Fitzhardinge Street, London W1H 6DH *Tel* 020 7935 0185 *email* research@bhf.org.uk *Website* www.bhf.org.uk

CC NO 225971   **ESTABLISHED** 1961

···

■ British Humane Association

WHERE FUNDING CAN BE GIVEN UK.

WHO CAN BENEFIT (a) Charities directly involved in humanitarian activities; (b) charities distributing grants to individuals; (c) charities providing relief of poverty or sickness, or benefit to the community.

WHAT IS FUNDED Welfare causes.

TYPE OF GRANT One-off, capital and recurring grants will be considered.

SAMPLE GRANTS Artists' General Benevolent Institution Guild of Freemenof the City of London (£34,000); St John of Jerusalem Eye Hospital (£7,000); Argyll and Bute Care and Repair, Challenging Behaviour, Children with Cancer and Leukaemia, City Gate Community, Extend and St Luke's Hospital for the Clergy (£5,000 each); and Church Lads' and Girls' Brigade and Neighbourhood Southall (£2,500 each).

FINANCES *Year* 2008 *Income* £125,695 *Grants* £78,500 *Assets* £2,976,204

TRUSTEES H Gould, Chair; B Campbell-Johnson; C Campbell-Johnston; Sir Anthony Grant; J M Huntington; P Gee; D J Eldridge; D A Cantly; A H Chignell.

HOW TO APPLY The trust only supports one new cause each year and applications are unlikely to be successful.

WHO TO APPLY TO The Trustees, Priory House, 25 St John's Lane, Clerkenwell, London EC1M 4PP

CC NO 207120   **ESTABLISHED** 1922

···

■ British Institute at Ankara

WHERE FUNDING CAN BE GIVEN UK, Turkey and the Black Sea region.

WHO CAN BENEFIT British and UK-resident students and academics of archaeology and associated fields.

WHAT IS FUNDED Research focused on Turkey and the Black Sea littoral in all academic disciplines within the arts, humanities and social sciences.

FINANCES *Year* 2007–08 *Income* £515,645 *Grants* £102,506 *Assets* £394,469

TRUSTEES Council of Management.

PUBLICATIONS *Anatolian Studies and Anatolian Archaeology.* Both annual publications.

OTHER INFORMATION The trust provides a number of grant programmes to individual researchers (grants totalled £62,000 in 2007–08) as well as conducting its own research and housing a large research library in Ankara.

HOW TO APPLY Initial inquiries regarding potential applications are welcomed. Full details can be found on the institute's website.

WHO TO APPLY TO The Administrator, 10 Carlton House Terrace, London SW1Y 5AH *Tel* 020 7969 5204 *email* biaa@britac.ac.uk *Website* www.biaa.ac.uk

CC NO 313940   **ESTABLISHED** 1948

···

■ British Ornithologists' Union

WHERE FUNDING CAN BE GIVEN Worldwide, with a preference for eastern Europe and northern Asia.

WHO CAN BENEFIT 'The BOU tries to support as wide a range of research projects as is possible, including applications from both amateurs and professionals.'

WHAT IS FUNDED Financial support for research and expeditions. It administers the David Lack and Landsborough Thomson Trusts, funded by bequests and donations, from which research grants are awarded annually to sponsor scientific and conservation projects. The BOU tries to support as wide a range of research projects as is possible, including applications from both amateurs and professionals. Applications may be on any aspect of ornithology but the BOU will look especially favourably on areas where there are particular difficulties in funding research from national or local sources.

WHAT IS NOT FUNDED UK-based applicants seeking funding for overseas projects should note that the funds being sought should only be used towards defined project requirements outside the UK.

RANGE OF GRANTS Usually up to £1,000.

FINANCES *Year* 2008 *Income* £175,784 *Grants* £4,995 *Assets* £535,798

TRUSTEES Dr W Peach; Dr P Shaw; P J Oliver; S Bearhop; T Birkhead; R Bradbury; A Dawson; P Donald; R J Fuller; K Hamer; I R Hartley; G Martin; R Y McGowan; G R Potts; H Sitters; S Wandless.

PUBLICATIONS The BOU's international journal *Ibis* is published quarterly.

HOW TO APPLY Further information and application forms can be obtained from the BOU website. Applications are only accepted via e-mail to the following address: grants@bou.org.uk. The deadline for applications is 31 December.

WHO TO APPLY TO The British Ornithologists' Union, PO Box 417, Peterborough, E7 3FX, UK
Tel 01733 844 820 *email* bou@bou.org.uk
Website www.bou.org.uk

CC NO 249877   ESTABLISHED 1966

■ British Record Industry Trust

WHERE FUNDING CAN BE GIVEN Worldwide, in practice UK.

WHO CAN BENEFIT Registered charities benefiting young people involved in the arts, particularly music.

WHAT IS FUNDED The mission of the British Record Industry Trust (BRIT) is to encourage young people in the exploration and pursuit of educational, cultural or therapeutic benefits emanating from music. The trust has an ongoing commitment to the BRIT School for Performing Arts and Technology and Nordoff-Robbins Music Therapy but will also give to other appropriate good causes.

WHAT IS NOT FUNDED No scholarships or grants to individuals. No capital funding projects are considered. Only registered charities in the UK are supported.

TYPE OF GRANT One-off and recurring grants.

RANGE OF GRANTS £1,000–£325,000.

SAMPLE GRANTS BRIT School for the Performing Arts & Technology (£325,000); Nordoff-Robbins Music Therapy (£275,000); Music 4 Good and EMI Music Sound Foundation (£50,000 each); Drugscope (£20,000); Young Persons Concert Foundation (£11,000); National Youth Music Theatre (£10,000); Teaching Awards Trust, Julies Bicycle and Release (£5,000 each); and Radio 2 Annual Guitar Prize and LIPA – Make It, Break It (£1,000 each).

FINANCES *Year* 2007 *Income* £1,945,388 *Grants* £757,700 *Assets* £6,510,846

TRUSTEES Paul Burger; Andrew Cleary; John Craig; Rob Dickins; David Kassner; Jonathan Morrish; Tony Wadsworth; Derek Green; Geoff Taylor; David Bryant; Korda Marshall; Ged Doherty.

HOW TO APPLY The trust considers all applications that meet its criteria within the mission statement: 'to encourage young people in the exploration and pursuit of educational, cultural or therapeutic benefits emanating from music'. The trust has a long standing relationship with a number of organisations that receive funding each year and consequently is limited to the amount of resources it can offer. Applicants should visit the trust's website and complete the on-line application form or contact the correspondent for further information. Please note: the trust states that applications where the organisation or project is known to the UK music industry have an advantage. There is space to include an industry contact on the application form.

WHO TO APPLY TO Louise Smith, Riverside Building, County Hall, Westminster Bridge Road, London SE1 7JA *email* louise.smith@bpi.co.uk *Website* www.brittrust.co.uk

CC NO 1000413   ESTABLISHED 1989

■ The Britten-Pears Foundation

WHERE FUNDING CAN BE GIVEN UK, with a preference for East Anglia and Suffolk in particular.

WHO CAN BENEFIT Registered charities organisations or individuals whose aims and objectives are of charitable intent. UK-based commissioning bodies such as festivals, concert halls or professional performers, ranging from solo instrumentalist to symphony orchestra and/or chorus.

WHAT IS FUNDED The commissioning of new music. The Grants Panel will look more favourably on applications that can demonstrate that the work will receive more than one performance and will be looking to support composers who have demonstrated a real gift for their craft or a recognised potential and for a partnership of composer and performer/s that impresses them as a significant project.

WHAT IS NOT FUNDED The Britten-Pears Foundation does not invite applications for grants of a capital nature (including those for instrumental purchase or restoration), for tuition fees, performance costs, recordings, educational or non-musical projects. The foundation does not consider applications for support for performances or recordings of the works of Benjamin Britten, of whose estate it is the beneficiary. Subsidy for works by Britten which, in the Estate's view, need further promotion can be sought from the Britten Estate Limited.

TYPE OF GRANT One-off, some recurring and project. Funding may be given for one year or less, or more than three years. Partnership funding will be considered, though it will wish to be a major contributor in all cases. Matching funding will not be a condition of grant.

RANGE OF GRANTS Up to a maximum of £10,000 per award.

FINANCES *Year* 2008–09 *Grants* £50,000

TRUSTEES Sir Robert Carnwath, Chair; Chris Banks; Michael Berkeley; Peter Carter; Lady Sally Irvine; Ghislaine Kenyon; Dr Colin Matthews; Sir Stephen Oliver; Phil Ramsbottom; Janis Susskind; Tessa Wild; Sybella Zisman.

OTHER INFORMATION The foundation's annual income largely derives from the royalties from the performance worldwide of the works of Benjamin Britten and is channelled to the foundation through its trading subsidiary, the Britten Estate Ltd, by Gift Aid. The grantmaking of this foundation hopes to reflect the wishes of Benjamin Britten and Peter Pears who, in their lifetimes, did much to support the work of fellow composers.

HOW TO APPLY In the first instance details of the work to be commissioned should be submitted, with details of the composer and of the performer/s involved. Full details of how to apply, along with deadlines for applications can be found on the foundation's website.

WHO TO APPLY TO Amanda Arnold, The Red House, Golf Lane, Aldeburgh, Suffolk IP15 5PZ *Tel* 01728 451700 *email* c.shepherd@ brittenpears.org *Website* www.brittenpears.org

CC NO 295595   ESTABLISHED 1986

■ The Britto Foundation

WHERE FUNDING CAN BE GIVEN UK.

WHO CAN BENEFIT Children and organisations benefiting the people of Israel.

WHAT IS FUNDED The largest grants were to Israeli organisations (The trustees emphasised that these causes were 'Israeli' rather than 'Jewish')

with arts, sporting and children's organisations also supported.

SAMPLE GRANTS British Friends of the Art Museums of Israel (£6,100); Royal Academy of Arts (£1,500); UJS Hillel (£1,000); Friends of Hazon Yesshaya, Laniado UK and UK Friends of AWIS (£250 each); and Magen David Adom UK and ZF Shalom Foundation (£100 each).

FINANCES *Year* 2007–08 *Income* £29,986 *Grants* £26,178 *Assets* £553,971

TRUSTEES J C Y P Gommes; C L Corman; H K Lewis; T Gommes.

HOW TO APPLY The trustees stated: 'Applications are not sought at this time – trustees choose causes.'

WHO TO APPLY TO The Trustees, Flat 2, 21 Eaton Place, London SW1X 8PT

CC NO 1010897   **ESTABLISHED** 1992

■ The J and M Britton Charitable Trust

WHERE FUNDING CAN BE GIVEN Mainly Bristol and the former county of Avon.

WHO CAN BENEFIT General, education.

WHAT IS FUNDED Local charities such as hospital appeals and other charities that the trustees are involved in.

WHAT IS NOT FUNDED No grants to individuals or to non-registered charities.

RANGE OF GRANTS Up to £10,000.

SAMPLE GRANTS Bristol Old Vic Refurbishment Appeal and Taunton School (£10,000 each); Avon Wildlife Trust, Children's Hospice South West, and Church Housing Trust (£2,000 each); Colstons Girls School (£1,400); and Clifton College and Leonard Cheshire Disability (£1,000 each).

FINANCES *Year* 2007–08 *Income* £93,064 *Grants* £71,850 *Assets* £2,813,475

TRUSTEES R E J Bernays; R O Bernays; Lady Merrison; Mrs A Bernays.

HOW TO APPLY In writing to the correspondent enclosing an sae. Charities can apply at any time, but the trust makes distributions twice a year, usually in May and November.

WHO TO APPLY TO R E J Bernays, Trustee, Kilcot House, Kilcot, Wotton-Under-Edge, Gloucestershire GL12 7RL *Tel* 01454 238571

CC NO 1081979   **ESTABLISHED** 1996

■ The Charles and Edna Broadhurst Charitable Trust

WHERE FUNDING CAN BE GIVEN Southport area.

WHO CAN BENEFIT Academics; research workers; Christians; at risk groups; people disadvantaged by poverty; socially isolated people; people with arthritis/rheumatism or cancer.

WHAT IS FUNDED Grants are mainly given to social welfare organisations, and medical academic research, arts and Christian causes.

WHAT IS NOT FUNDED No grants to individuals.

RANGE OF GRANTS £250–£3,000.

SAMPLE GRANTS Cancer Research UK (£4,000); Southport Music Festival (£2,000); Listening Books and UK Sports Association (£1,000 each); and Royal British Legion (£250).

FINANCES *Year* 2007–08 *Income* £30,069 *Grants* £34,100 *Assets* £709,446

TRUSTEES Mrs J Carver, Chair; Mrs G Edmondson; Mrs K A Griffith; D A T Wood.

HOW TO APPLY In writing to the correspondent. Applications are considered twice a year, usually in July and November.

WHO TO APPLY TO D H Hobley, Administrator, 11 Silverthorne Drive, Southport PR9 9PF

CC NO 702543   **ESTABLISHED** 1988

■ The Bromley Trust

WHERE FUNDING CAN BE GIVEN Worldwide.

WHO CAN BENEFIT UK registered charities only.

WHAT IS FUNDED The trust supports charities concerned with human rights, prison reform and conservation and sustainability. This well organised and focused trust also offers other organisations with similar interests and objectives the chance to participate in a network of like-minded groups.

WHAT IS NOT FUNDED Grants are only given to UK registered charities. The following are not supported: individuals; expeditions; scholarships, although in certain cases the trust supports research that falls within its aims (but always through a registered charity); statutory authorities, or charities whose main source of funding is via statutory agencies; overseas development, healthcare or education per se. The trust only supports these areas in conjunction with the violation of human rights and where discrimination has accounted for deprivation; local conservation projects or charities that work with single species.

TYPE OF GRANT Mainly recurrent; one-off grants are occasionally made, but these are infrequent. It is the trust's policy to give larger amounts to fewer charities rather than to spread income over a large number of small grants. Buildings, capital, project, research, running costs, salaries and start-up costs will be considered. The trust's mainstream charities normally receive their grants in two half-yearly payments for a period of not less than three years, barring unforeseen circumstances.

RANGE OF GRANTS Up to £25,000.

SAMPLE GRANTS Ashden Awards (£25,000); Global Dialogue and Prison Reform Trust (£20,000 each); Writers and Scholars Educational Trust (£18,000); Anti-Slavery International and Survival International (£15,000 each); Birdlife International (£13,000); Action for Prisoner's Families and Prison Video Trust (£10,000 each); and London Detainee Support Group (£5,000).

FINANCES *Year* 2007–08 *Income* £771,582 *Grants* £853,700 *Assets* £17,234,592

TRUSTEES Anne Lady Prance, Chair; Peter Edwards; Anthony Roberts; Bryan Blamey; Jean Ritchie.

HOW TO APPLY New applications are directed, where possible, to the website where the trust's criteria, guidelines and application process are posted. An initial questionnaire can be accessed from the website for charities that fit the trust's remit, and should be completed and returned via email to applicant@thebromleytrust.org.uk. All charities are visited before a grant is made. A grant is made for one year and in most cases renewed automatically for two further years. Although most grants are unrestricted, the trust monitors each charity annually and requires certain conditions to be fulfilled before further funding is made available. A grant is always made subject to the availability of funds. The trustees meet twice a year in April and October and applications should be received the previous month. *Urgent appeals may be dealt with at any time.*

Please note: the trust asks that organisations which have previously submitted an application (whether successful or unsuccessful) do not submit a further application. Applicant details are held on the trust's database and if any assistance can be provided in the future they will make contact.

WHO TO APPLY TO Teresa Elwes, Grants Executive, Studio 7, 2 Pinchin Street, Whitechapel, London E1 1SA *Tel* 020 7481 4899 *email* info@thebromleytrust.org.uk *Website* www.thebromleytrust.org.uk

CC NO 801875 **ESTABLISHED** 1989

■ The Roger Brooke Charitable Trust

WHERE FUNDING CAN BE GIVEN UK, with a preference for Hampshire.

WHO CAN BENEFIT Registered charities.

WHAT IS FUNDED General charitable purposes, especially medical research, support for carers and social action.

WHAT IS NOT FUNDED In general, individuals are not supported.

SAMPLE GRANTS The Southampton University Development Fund (£100,000).

FINANCES *Year* 2007–08 *Income* £481,029 *Grants* £194,220 *Assets* £1,311,792

TRUSTEES J P Arnold; C R E Brooke; Mrs N B Brooke; Ms J R Rousso; S H R Brooke.

HOW TO APPLY In writing to the correspondent. Applications will only be acknowledged if successful.

WHO TO APPLY TO J P Arnold, Trustee, Withers, 16 Old Bailey, London EC4M 7EG *Tel* 020 7597 6123

CC NO 1071250 **ESTABLISHED** 1998

■ The David Brooke Charity

WHERE FUNDING CAN BE GIVEN UK.

WHO CAN BENEFIT Voluntary and community-based groups, especially those concerned with disadvantaged young people.

WHAT IS FUNDED Preference is given to organisations which provide opportunities for self-help programmes and outdoor activity training. Medical charities are also supported.

TYPE OF GRANT Long-term support.

RANGE OF GRANTS Up to £4,500.

SAMPLE GRANTS Great Ormond Street Hospital (£4,500); the Children's Society, Finchale Training College, the Fortune Riding Centre, RNID and YMCA (£3,500 each); Alzheimer's Society, Lord Wandsworth College, Stanbridge Earls School Trust and Yorkshire Dales Millennium Trust (£3,000 each); Wyfold Riding for the Disabled (£2,500); NSPCC (£2,000); Berkshire Girl Guides (£1,000); and Hospice in the Weald (£500).

FINANCES *Year* 2007–08 *Income* £141,023 *Grants* £91,250 *Assets* £1,918,072

TRUSTEES D J Rusman; P M Hutt; N A Brooke.

HOW TO APPLY The correspondent stated that the trust's annual income is not for general distribution as it is committed to a limited number of charities on a long-term basis.

WHO TO APPLY TO D J Rusman, Trustee, Cook Sutton, Tay Court, Blounts Court Road, Sonning Common, Oxfordshire RG4 9RS

CC NO 283658 **ESTABLISHED** 1961

■ The Rory and Elizabeth Brooks Foundation

WHERE FUNDING CAN BE GIVEN Worldwide.

WHO CAN BENEFIT Charitable organisations.

WHAT IS FUNDED The main objects of the charity are to promote and advance education, medical research, healthcare, community care and arts and culture.

FINANCES *Year* 2008–09 *Income* £375,000 *Grants* £365,000 *Assets* £2,042

TRUSTEES Elizabeth Brooks; Roderick Brooks; David Way.

OTHER INFORMATION Rory Brooks was a co-founder of the private equity investment group MML Capital. No details of awards made were given in the foundation's accounts; however there are a number of references to its activities on the internet. In 2008 the foundation announced a £1.4 million award over three years to The University of Manchester's Brooks World Poverty Institute.

HOW TO APPLY In writing to the correspondent.

WHO TO APPLY TO The Trustees, 25 North Row, London W1K 6DJ

CC NO 1111587 **ESTABLISHED** 2005

■ The Charles Brotherton Trust

WHERE FUNDING CAN BE GIVEN The cities of Birmingham, Leeds, Liverpool, Wakefield, York and Bebington in the borough of Wirral.

WHO CAN BENEFIT Charitable organisations.

WHAT IS FUNDED 'The charity is principally directed to encourage young people to improve their own lives by taking advantage of educational opportunities and organised recreational activities. The charity is also empowered to help improve the standard of living of older people and disabled people and relieve the suffering caused by illness.'

WHAT IS NOT FUNDED Grants to registered charities and recognised bodies only. No grants to individuals.

RANGE OF GRANTS Mostly £200 or less.

SAMPLE GRANTS University of Leeds – Brotherton Library (£6,300); Brotherton Park – Dibbinsdale Nature Centre (£1,000); Yorkshire Association of Boys' Clubs (£275); Leeds Parish Church Choral Appeal (£250); Birmingham City Mission, Countryside Foundation for England, Groundwork Leeds, League of Welldoers, Relate – York, Stonehouse Gang, Whizz Kidz – York, York Joint Scout Trust and Yorkshire Youth Orchestra (£200 each); Samaritans of Liverpool and Merseyside (£175); Birmingham Rathbone Society, Independent Age, Tall Ships Youth Trust, Victim Support Wakefield District and Wakefield Gateway Club (£150 each); Astrigg Foundation, Family Tree, Merseyside Project and York Women's Aid (£125 each); and Acorns Children's Hospice, Ripon and Leeds Diocesan Council for Social Aid (£100 each).

FINANCES *Year* 2007–08 *Income* £79,222 *Grants* £67,500 *Assets* £1,837,425

TRUSTEES C Brotherton-Ratcliffe; D R Brotherton; J Riches.

OTHER INFORMATION Grants were broken down geographically as follows: £27,000 to the city of Leeds; £13,500 to the city of Birmingham; £6,750 each to the borough of Bebington, the city of Liverpool, the city of Wakefield and the city of York.

HOW TO APPLY In writing to the correspondent. The application should clearly show the organisation's activities, geographical area of operations, and for what the funds are required.

Applications should be accompanied by the organisation's most recent set of accounts. There is no formal application form and applications are not acknowledged. Grants are considered by the trustees at the start of the trust's accounting year in April, and a single payment made to successful applicants in October. (Scholarships are available to students on scientific courses at the universities of Leeds, Liverpool, Birmingham and York, but applications for these must be made to the university in question, not to the above correspondent.)

WHO TO APPLY TO The Secretary, PO Box 374, Harrogate HG1 4YW *Website* www. charlesbrothertontrust.com

CC NO 227067   **ESTABLISHED** 1940

....

■ Joseph Brough Charitable Trust

WHERE FUNDING CAN BE GIVEN The historic counties of Northumberland and Tyne and Wear and some areas of Durham.

WHO CAN BENEFIT Small community groups with a special interest in Methodist courses.

WHAT IS FUNDED Social and community work.

WHAT IS NOT FUNDED Major appeals are not supported unless they are very close to their target.

RANGE OF GRANTS Up to £10,000.

SAMPLE GRANTS Greggs Charitable Trust (£10,000); County Durham Foundation and Fruit Salad Media Group (£5,000 each); County Durham Foundation (£3,000); Westerhope Methodist Church and Castle Morpeth Citizens Advice Bureau (£2,500 each); Roker Methodist Church and Aspire – Byker Hill Partnership (£1,500 each); Allenheads Regeneration Company (£1,300); and Roker Methodist Church, Benwell Christian Shop Project and Newcastle Muungano Community Association (£1,000 each).

FINANCES *Year* 2007–08 *Income* £37,275 *Grants* £34,260 *Assets* £1,165,359

TRUSTEES Community Foundation (serving Tyne and Wear and Northumberland).

HOW TO APPLY Applicants from Tyne and Wear and Northumberland should obtain the Community Foundation's guidelines by contacting the correspondent Karen Griffiths and make a written application to the foundation rather than to this trust (see separate entry for further information). Applicants from County Durham should write to: County Durham Foundation, Jordan House, Finchal Road, Durham DH1 5HL (Tel: 0191 383 0055; e-mail: cdf@freenet.co.uk).

WHO TO APPLY TO Karen Griffiths, 9th Floor, Cale Cross, 156 Pilgrim Street, Newcastle upon Tyne NE1 6SU *Tel* 0191 222 0945 *Fax* 0191 230 0689 *email* general@communityfoundation.org. uk *Website* www.communityfoundation.org.uk

CC NO 227332   **ESTABLISHED** 1940

....

■ The Swinfen Broun Charitable Trust

WHERE FUNDING CAN BE GIVEN City of Lichfield.

WHO CAN BENEFIT City of Lichfield, residents/ organisations.

WHAT IS FUNDED Support for public buildings and facilities, and general charitable purposes.

WHAT IS NOT FUNDED No grants for the benefit of ecclesiastical or relief of poverty charities.

RANGE OF GRANTS £300–£4,000.

SAMPLE GRANTS St Mary's Centre (£4,000); 6th Lichfield Scout Group, LDAA – Fuse Festival 2009 and LDC – Proms in the Park (£2,000 each); Erasmus Darwin Foundation (£1,800); Lichfield Festival Ltd (£1,250); Lichfield Singers (£500); and Lichfield Cricket Club and Lichfield RUFC (£300 each).

FINANCES *Year* 2008–09 *Income* £31,138 *Grants* £15,654 *Assets* £484,521

TRUSTEES J N Wilks, Chair; Mrs D English; A D Thompson; B D Diggle; Cllr T V Finn; Mrs J M Eagland; Mrs J A Allsopp; Cllr Norma Bacon; C Lamb; C J Spruce; D Smedley; B W Derrick.

OTHER INFORMATION Grants to seven individuals totalled £1,775.

HOW TO APPLY Application form available from the correspondent.

WHO TO APPLY TO A G Birch, Clerk, 42 Lincoln Close, Lichfield, Staffordshire WS13 7SW *Tel* 01543 304 948 *email* alan.birch@ntlworld.com

CC NO 503515   **ESTABLISHED** 1973

....

■ Mrs E E Brown Charitable Settlement

WHERE FUNDING CAN BE GIVEN UK and Israel.

WHO CAN BENEFIT Registered charities.

WHAT IS FUNDED General charitable purposes.

WHAT IS NOT FUNDED No grants to individuals or to medical research.

TYPE OF GRANT Recurring and one-off.

RANGE OF GRANTS Up to £2,000.

SAMPLE GRANTS Grants exceeding £1,000 included those made to: Age Concern, Jewish Museum, Save the Children, Youth at Risk, and Anna Scher Theatre.

FINANCES *Year* 2007–08 *Income* £33,700 *Grants* £26,650 *Assets* £778,714

TRUSTEES M D Brown; Lord Brown of Eaton-under-Heywood.

HOW TO APPLY In writing to the correspondent. However, the trust states that it is not currently considering appeals for assistance, preferring to concentrate on organisations already supported.

WHO TO APPLY TO J Rowan, Barber Harrison and Platt, Accountants, 2 Rutland Park, Sheffield S10 2PD *Tel* 0114 266 7171 *Fax* 0114 266 9846 *email* info@bhp.co.uk

CC NO 261397   **ESTABLISHED** 1970

....

■ Bill Brown's Charitable Settlement

WHERE FUNDING CAN BE GIVEN UK.

WHO CAN BENEFIT Registered charities.

WHAT IS FUNDED Health and welfare charities, including those for older people.

WHAT IS NOT FUNDED No grants to individuals.

TYPE OF GRANT Mainly recurrent.

RANGE OF GRANTS £1,000–£10,000.

SAMPLE GRANTS Charities Aid Foundation Trust (£50,000 in two grants); Christ's Hospital Horsham (£32,000); Macmillan Cancer Relief and Salvation Army (£10,000 each); Alzheimer's Society, Cancer Research UK, DebRA, Leonard Cheshire Foundation, Linden Lodge Charitable Trust, Princess Alice Hospice, St Christopher's Hospice and Treloar Trust (£5,000 each); the Scout Association (£4,000); and Barnardos and NCH Action for Children (£2,500 each).

FINANCES *Year* 2007–08 *Income* £483,176 *Grants* £158,500 *Assets* £11,056,214

TRUSTEES G S Brown; A J Barnett.

OTHER INFORMATION In 2007–08 future commitments were made to Churchill College

Think carefully about every application. Is it justified?

391

and Moorfields Eye Hospital Development Fund totalling £493,000.

HOW TO APPLY In writing containing the following: aims and objectives of the charity; nature of appeal; total target if for a specific project; contributions received against target; registered charity number; any other relevant factors. Appeals should be accompanied by a set of the organisation's latest report and full accounts.

WHO TO APPLY TO The Trustees, BM BOX 4567, London WC1N 3XX

CC NO 801756   **ESTABLISHED** 1989

■ R S Brownless Charitable Trust

WHERE FUNDING CAN BE GIVEN Mainly UK and occasionally overseas.

WHO CAN BENEFIT Organisations working with children, young adults and people with disabilities.

WHAT IS FUNDED Accommodation and housing, education, job creation and voluntary work.

WHAT IS NOT FUNDED Grants are rarely given to individuals for educational projects or to education or conservation causes or overseas aid.

TYPE OF GRANT Usually one-off; sometimes annual.

RANGE OF GRANTS Up to £2,000 (occasionally more); usually £100–£500.

SAMPLE GRANTS Previous beneficiaries have included Alzheimer's Society, Camp Mohawk, Casa Allianza UK, Crisis, Foundation for Study of Infant Deaths, Prader-Willi Foundation, St Andrew's Hall, UNICEF, Wargrave PCC and Witham on the Hill PCC.

FINANCES *Year* 2007–08 *Income* £58,018 *Grants* £58,421 *Assets* £1,197,587

TRUSTEES Mrs F A Plummer; Mrs P M Nicolai.

HOW TO APPLY In writing to the correspondent. The trustees meet twice a year, but in special circumstances will meet at other times. The trust is unable to acknowledge all requests.

WHO TO APPLY TO Mrs P M A Nicolai, Trustee, Hennerton Holt, Wargrave, Reading RG10 8PD *Tel* 0118 940 4029

CC NO 1000320   **ESTABLISHED** 1990

■ Brownsword Charitable Foundation

WHERE FUNDING CAN BE GIVEN The City of Bath, principally but not exclusively.

WHO CAN BENEFIT Charitable organisations.

WHAT IS FUNDED General charitable purposes.

SAMPLE GRANTS Previous beneficiaries have included Bath Film Festival, Bath Film Festival, Bath Postal Museum, Cancer Vaccine Institute, Children's Hospice South West, CRUSE, Dorothy House Hospice, Fight for Sight, Friends of Bristol Children's Hospital, Grateful Society, Iford Arts, Lady Mayoress Charity – Canterbury, the Mary Rose Trust, National Youth Orchestra, Quartet Community Foundation, Research Into the Care of the Elderly and RNIB.

FINANCES *Year* 2008 *Income* £98,232

TRUSTEES A D Brownsword; C J Brownsword; G E Goodall; R F Calleja.

HOW TO APPLY In writing to the correspondent.

WHO TO APPLY TO Nicholas Burrows, 4 Queen Square, Bath BA1 2HA

CC NO 1012615   **ESTABLISHED** 1992

■ The T B H Brunner Charitable Settlement

WHERE FUNDING CAN BE GIVEN UK with some preference for Oxfordshire.

WHO CAN BENEFIT Registered charities and individuals.

WHAT IS FUNDED Church of England preservation projects and other charities dealing with historical preservation, both local to Oxfordshire and nationally; the arts; music; and general charitable purposes.

SAMPLE GRANTS The Institute of Economic Affairs (£5,000 in two grants); Rotherfield Greys PCC (£2,500); Live Music Now (£2,000); the National Centre for Early Music, the Royal Theatrical Fund and St Mary – Chalgrove (£1,000 each); the National Trust (£900); Rotherfield Greys PCC (£700); the London Library and the Oxfordshire Historic Churches Trust (£500 each); Sue Ryder Care (£250); and Venice in Peril Fund (£100).

FINANCES *Year* 2007–08 *Income* £43,100 *Grants* £37,150 *Assets* £1,793,834

TRUSTEES Timothy Brunner; Helen Brunner; Dr Imogen Brunner.

HOW TO APPLY In writing to the correspondent.

WHO TO APPLY TO T B H Brunner, Trustee, Flat 4, 2 Inverness Gardens, London W8 4RN *Tel* 020 7727 6277

CC NO 260604   **ESTABLISHED** 1969

■ The Jack Brunton Charitable Trust

WHERE FUNDING CAN BE GIVEN Old North Riding area of Yorkshire.

WHO CAN BENEFIT Registered charities for the benefit of the population of the rural villages and towns within the beneficial area.

WHAT IS FUNDED General charitable purposes.

WHAT IS NOT FUNDED 'Grants to individuals or out of area applicants are only made in very rare and exceptional circumstances.'

TYPE OF GRANT One-off.

RANGE OF GRANTS Usually up to £5,000.

SAMPLE GRANTS York Minster (£80,000); Fylingdales Memorial Playground and James Cook Hospital – Middlesbrough (£5,000 each); Listening Books for North Yorkshire, Whitby Disablement Action Group, KARA Family Project – South Bank and Goathland Parish Hall (£2,000 each); Chopsticks – Northallerton (£1,200); and Cleveland Concert Band, Kirbymoorside Friends Meeting House, Dermatrust and Scarborough Blind & Partially Sighted Society (£1,000 each).

FINANCES *Year* 2007–08 *Income* £138,579 *Grants* £131,900 *Assets* £4,237,421

TRUSTEES Mrs A J Brunton; J G Brunton; E Marquis; D W Noble; P Reed; J A Lumb; Dr C Hurst.

HOW TO APPLY In writing to the correspondent including full details of costings if relevant.

WHO TO APPLY TO D A Swallow, Administrator, Commercial House, 10 Bridge Road, Stokesley, North Yorkshire TS9 5AA *Tel* 01642 711407

CC NO 518407   **ESTABLISHED** 1986

■ Brushmill Ltd

WHERE FUNDING CAN BE GIVEN Worldwide.

WHO CAN BENEFIT Organisations benefiting Jewish people.

WHAT IS FUNDED Jewish charitable purposes, education and social welfare.

SAMPLE GRANTS Previous beneficiaries have included Bais Rochel, Friends of Yeshivas Shaar Hashomaim and Holmleigh Trust.

FINANCES *Year* 2007–08 *Income* £386,371 *Grants* £324,042 *Assets* £39,080

TRUSTEES C Getter, Chair; J Weinberger; Mrs E Weinberger.

OTHER INFORMATION A list of beneficiaries was not available.

HOW TO APPLY In writing to the correspondent.

WHO TO APPLY TO C Getter, Trustee, 76 Fairholt Road, London N16 5HN

CC NO 285420　　　　**ESTABLISHED** 1982

■ The Bryant Trust

WHERE FUNDING CAN BE GIVEN The following post codes: B1–B48, B51–B59, B62–B76, B81–B94, AS1–WS5, WS9, WS10.

WHO CAN BENEFIT Registered charities only.

WHAT IS FUNDED The trustees welcome grant applications from registered charities working in any of the following areas: community and neighbourhood projects; community projects based on places of worship; disability and special needs; education; environmental and heritage projects; health and wellbeing; the arts; young people; vulnerable groups including: the homeless, addicts, refugees, asylum seekers, victims of crime, ex-prisoners, older people and the bereaved.

WHAT IS NOT FUNDED No grants to non-registered charities, animal welfare or individuals. UK-wide charities, even when based in Birmingham, will not be supported unless there are separate local accounts.

TYPE OF GRANT Capital projects are preferred to core funding. Buildings, project, research, salaries, start-up costs will be considered. Funding is available for up to three years.

RANGE OF GRANTS 70–80% of the trust fund is applied making 'Special Grants' to a small number of registered charities of which one or more of the trustees or the Settlors have a special knowledge. The remainder is spent in 'Small Grants' (usually £1,000 or less) to a wide range of local registered charities whose sphere of activity is within a very few miles of Birmingham city centre.

SAMPLE GRANTS Birmingham Law Society (£47,000); Midlands Arts Centre (£45,000); Birmingham Settlement (£43,000); RAPt (£42,000); Shakespeare Link (£10,000); Relate and Sampad (£5,000 each); and Adoption Support and MCA Sutton Coldfield (£3,000 each); Anglican Churches in Kingstanding, Headway, Dorothy Parkes Centre and Weoley Castle Community Church (£2,000 each); 20th Walsall Scout Group and Edward's Trust (£1,500 each); Birmingham Conservatoire (£1,300); Bangladesh Community Trust and St Matthews Centre – Walsall (£1,000 each); and Yemeni Elderly (£500).

FINANCES *Year* 2007–08 *Income* £305,792 *Grants* £300,000 *Assets* £5,634,045

TRUSTEES John Smith; Victoria Houghton; Anne Thomas; Diana Newton; Martin Smith; Timothy Cole; Charles Jordan; Ranjit Sondhi.

HOW TO APPLY On a form available from the trust's website. All applicants are reminded to send in a completed application form and the latest accounts with any application. Requests are considered twice a year, in May or June and November or December. All applications are acknowledged, and applicants are notified of the outcome, normally within six weeks of the meeting.

WHO TO APPLY TO Mr W M Galliard, Secretary, PO Box 1624, Shirley, Solihull, West Midlands B90 9QZ *email* admin@bryanttrust.org.uk *Website* www.bryanttrust.org.uk

CC NO 501450　　　　**ESTABLISHED** 1972

■ Buckingham Trust

WHERE FUNDING CAN BE GIVEN UK and worldwide.

WHO CAN BENEFIT Organisations and individuals.

WHAT IS FUNDED Advancement of religion (including missionary activities); relief of people disadvantaged by poverty and older people or those who are ill.

FINANCES *Year* 2007–08 *Income* £205,899 *Grants* £164,338 *Assets* £1,009,338

TRUSTEES R W D Foot; Mrs C T Clay.

OTHER INFORMATION Preference is given to charities of which the trustees have personal interest, knowledge, or association. The trust acts mainly as an agency charity acting on behalf of other donors.

HOW TO APPLY Unsolicited applicants are not considered.

WHO TO APPLY TO The Trustees, Foot Davson, 17 Church Road, Tunbridge Wells, Kent TN1 1LG *Tel* 01892 774774 *Fax* 01892 774775

CC NO 237350　　　　**ESTABLISHED** 1962

■ The Buckinghamshire Foundation

WHERE FUNDING CAN BE GIVEN Buckinghamshire.

WHO CAN BENEFIT Voluntary and community groups.

WHAT IS FUNDED Community development. Please visit the foundation's website for details of up-to-date schemes.

FINANCES *Year* 2007–08 *Income* £509,435 *Grants* £379,111 *Assets* £671,845

TRUSTEES Anita English; Peter Keen; Guy Birkby; Graham Peart; Bill McDonald; Tim Constable; Mike Clare; Denis Burrell; Alexander Shephard; David Sumpter; Roy Collis; Cherry Aston.

OTHER INFORMATION 'We provide a one-stop shop for all charitable giving needs and are the vital link between donors and local needs; connecting people with causes and enabling our clients and donors to achieve far more than they could ever by themselves.'

HOW TO APPLY An 'expression of interest' form can be completed at the foundation's website.

WHO TO APPLY TO The Grants Committee, 119A Bicester Road, Aylesbury, Buckinghamshire HP19 9BA *Tel* 01296 330134 *Fax* 01296 330158 *email* info@buckscf.org.uk *Website* www.thebucksfoundation.org.uk

CC NO 1073861　　　　**ESTABLISHED** 1998

■ The Buckinghamshire Historic Churches Trust

WHERE FUNDING CAN BE GIVEN The county or archdeaconry of Buckingham.

WHO CAN BENEFIT Parochial church councils or trustees of Christian churches and chapels, including Baptist, Anglican, Methodist and Catholic.

WHAT IS FUNDED The preservation, repair, maintenance and upkeep of the fabric of churches or chapels in Buckinghamshire. Grants are made to churches and chapels embarking upon restoration.

WHAT IS NOT FUNDED Grants cannot be given for repairs to bells, bell frames, bell chambers, window glass, organs, furnishings and work on heating, lighting, decoration or churchyard maintenance. Churches and chapels not in use for public worship are not supported.

TYPE OF GRANT One-off.

FINANCES *Year* 2007–08 *Income* £79,758 *Grants* £38,450 *Assets* £754,540

TRUSTEES Sir Henry Aubrey-Fletcher; Mrs C Abel-Smith; Mrs C Aston; Hon Rupert Carington; Revd Canon C H J Cavell-Northam; Mrs A Cutcliffe; Mjr M Davis; R W Evans; Hon Mrs J A Farncombe; Mrs G Miscampbell; Mrs J Moss; T Oliver; C F Robinson; Mrs M Villiers; Rt Rev Alan Wilson.

HOW TO APPLY An application form is available from the correspondent.

WHO TO APPLY TO Mrs P Keens, Hon. Secretary, 9 St Paul's Court, Stony Stratford, Milton Keynes MK11 1LJ *Tel* 01908 571232 *email* penny. keens@talktalk.net *Website* www. bucks-historic-churches.org

CC NO 206471   **ESTABLISHED** 1957

■ The Buckinghamshire Masonic Centenary Fund

WHERE FUNDING CAN BE GIVEN Buckinghamshire.

WHO CAN BENEFIT Registered charities and individuals.

WHAT IS FUNDED The fund will normally only give consideration to: non-Masonic charitable causes within Buckinghamshire; specific projects or facilities, rather than general appeals or requests to fund routine activities; Buckinghamshire charities that deal solely with cases in Buckinghamshire, and Buckinghamshire charities that also have connections in adjacent areas; individual cases within Buckinghamshire, or outside Buckinghamshire if there is a strong Buckinghamshire connection, only if referred through, or supported by, community welfare or health agencies because of the implications for State and other welfare benefit provisions.

WHAT IS NOT FUNDED No grants to individuals for expeditions or for youth work overseas, no sponsorship of events or individuals. No grants to heritage, wildlife or conservation projects. No grants towards routine expenditure and activities, including staff costs.

TYPE OF GRANT The focus is normally on specific projects or facilities, complete in themselves, rather than general appeals or requests to fund activities.

RANGE OF GRANTS £500–£5,500.

SAMPLE GRANTS Milton Keynes YMCE (£5,500); the Ark Charity and PACE (£5,000 each); Friends of Broughton Infants School (£2,000); Waddesdon Cricket Club (£1,300); Age Concern – Buckinghamshire (£1,100); Hospice of St Francis (£1,000); and Beaconsfield Mayor's Charity Appeal, British Red Cross – Buckingham and League of Friends Buckingham Hospital and Marlow Town Mayor's Charity Appeal (£500 each).

FINANCES *Year* 2007–08 *Income* £50,041 *Grants* £48,495 *Assets* £751,375

TRUSTEES R Reed; P N I Harborne; H N Hall; C T Drake.

HOW TO APPLY In writing to the correspondent, setting out aims and objectives on one page of A4 with a copy of the latest audited annual report and accounts if available. Details should be supplied of the specific facilities or projects for which funding is sought. The trustees meet three or four times a year to consider

applications. The trust states that some grants are made after the organisation has been visited by a committee member.

WHO TO APPLY TO A R Watkins, Hon. Secretary, 51 Townside, Haddenham, Aylesbury, Buckinghamshire HP17 8AW *Website* www. buckspgl.org

CC NO 1007193   **ESTABLISHED** 1991

■ Buckland Charitable Trust

WHERE FUNDING CAN BE GIVEN UK and overseas.

WHO CAN BENEFIT Charitable organisations.

WHAT IS FUNDED General, international development, welfare and health research.

SAMPLE GRANTS Alzheimer's Disease Society (£2,500); Bishop Simeon Trust, Islamic Universal Association, Macmillan Cancer Relief, Médecins Sans Frontières, North Lakeland Hospice at Home and UNICEF (£2,000 each); Clinic of UK Africa Floods Children's Appeal, Eden Valley Hospice and The Smile Train (£1,500 each); the Bubble Foundation UK (£1,000); Barnardos (£750); Mind (£500); and IPCI (£250); and Children's Heart Unit Fund (£50).

FINANCES *Year* 2007–08 *Income* £162,833 *Grants* £42,710 *Assets* £1,306,047

TRUSTEES Eleanor Afsari; Ali Afsari; Anna Bannister.

HOW TO APPLY In writing to the correspondent.

WHO TO APPLY TO The Trustees, Smith and WIlliamson Limited, 1 Bishops Wharf, Walnut Tree Close, Guildford, Surrey GU1 4RA

CC NO 273679   **ESTABLISHED** 1977

■ The Buffini Chao Foundation

WHERE FUNDING CAN BE GIVEN UK.

WHO CAN BENEFIT Charitable organisations.

WHAT IS FUNDED General charitable purposes, especially organisations working in the field of education and with children.

SAMPLE GRANTS St John's College – student bursaries (£75,000); EYLA – education co-ordinator (£40,000); UCL Development fund – NMR brain scanner upgrade (£20,000); London Children's Ballet – Outreach programme (£5,000); and London Children's Ballet – dancer sponsorship (£1,000).

FINANCES *Year* 2006–07 *Income* £521,110 *Grants* £140,500 *Assets* £1,481,633

TRUSTEES Ms D Buffini; D M Buffini; Mrs M G Hindmarsh.

OTHER INFORMATION In 2006–07 the foundation had an income of £521,000 including a £390,000 gift from D M Buffini, one of the trustees.

HOW TO APPLY In writing to the correspondent.

WHO TO APPLY TO Mrs D Buffini, Trustee, 12 Mount Ephraim Road, Tunbridge Wells, Kent TN1 1EG

CC NO 1111022   **ESTABLISHED** 2005

■ The Rosemary Bugden Charitable Trust

WHERE FUNDING CAN BE GIVEN UK, with a preference for the former county of Avon (in practice Bath and North East Somerset, Bristol, North Somerset and South Gloucestershire).

WHO CAN BENEFIT Arts, education, general charitable causes.

WHAT IS FUNDED Local schools for the purchase musical instruments.

SAMPLE GRANTS £25,000 to 113 state schools; £10,000 to the Royal College of Music.

FINANCES *Year* 2007–08 *Income* £33,146 *Grants* £35,180 *Assets* £638,176

TRUSTEES John Wetherherd Sharpe; Mrs Elizabeth Anne Frimston.

OTHER INFORMATION A grant of £520 was made to an individual.

HOW TO APPLY In writing to the correspondent. However, the trust states that its funds are fully committed for the foreseeable future. No applications will be considered.

WHO TO APPLY TO J Sharpe, Trustee, c/o Osborne Clarke, 2 Temple Back East, Temple Quay, Bristol BS1 6EG *Tel* 0117 917 3022

CC NO 327626   **ESTABLISHED** 1987

....

■ The Bulldog Trust Limited

WHERE FUNDING CAN BE GIVEN Worldwide, with a preference for the south of England.

WHO CAN BENEFIT Charitable organisations.

WHAT IS FUNDED General charitable purposes.

WHAT IS NOT FUNDED No grants are given to individuals or to unsolicited applications.

SAMPLE GRANTS Previous beneficiaries have included Hampshire and Isle of Wight Foundation, National Playing Fields Association, David Robbie Charitable Trust, Portsmouth Cathedral Development Trust, The Prince's Trust, Royal National Theatre and University of Winchester.

FINANCES *Year* 2007–08 *Grants* £200,000

TRUSTEES Patrick Burgess; Martin Riley; Brian Smouha; Mary Fagan; Charles Hoare.

HOW TO APPLY The trust regrets that unsolicited applications cannot be accepted.

WHO TO APPLY TO The Trustees, 2 Temple Place, London WC2R 3BD *Website* www.bulldogtrust.org

CC NO 1123081   **ESTABLISHED** 1983

....

■ The E F Bulmer Benevolent Fund

WHERE FUNDING CAN BE GIVEN Herefordshire.

WHO CAN BENEFIT Organisations, employees of H P Bulmer Holdings plc or its subsidiaries and individuals.

WHAT IS FUNDED Organisations benefiting people who are sick or disadvantaged by poverty. Employees of H P Bulmer Holdings plc and individuals who are in need.

WHAT IS NOT FUNDED Large UK charities and those from outside Herefordshire are unlikely to be supported.

TYPE OF GRANT One-off for capital (including buildings), core costs, feasibility studies, project, research, running costs, salaries and start-up costs. Funding may be given for up to three years.

RANGE OF GRANTS £100–£30,000.

SAMPLE GRANTS Macmillan Renton Appeal (£100,000); Lifebuoy Charitable Trust (£6,000); Herefordshire Rural Support Network (£5,000); Age Concern Bromyard (£4,700); Bromyard Community Transport (£3,800); and Combat Stress, Action Centres UK, British Red Cross, Teme Valley Youth Project and Small Woods Association (£3,000 each).

FINANCES *Year* 2007–08 *Income* £348,046 *Grants* £370,417 *Assets* £11,230,164

TRUSTEES Nigel Bulmer; Anna Knight; Edward Bulmer; John Caiger; Jocelyn Harvey Wood.

OTHER INFORMATION The grant total included £78,000 to pensioners of H P Bulmer Holdings plc or its subsidiaries.

HOW TO APPLY In writing to the correspondent, although a voluntary application form is available and will be sent if requested.

Applications should be accompanied by a copy of the latest report and accounts. The administrator is very happy to discuss applications by e-mail or telephone prior to the application being submitted. The trustees usually meet four times a year. Smaller groups who may have difficulty in receiving support from large national trusts are normally given priority.

WHO TO APPLY TO James Greenfield, Administrator, Fred Bulmer Centre, Wall Street, Hereford, Herefordshire HR4 9HP *Tel* 01432 271293 *Fax* 01432 271293 *email* kinnersleykids@aol.com *Website* www.efbulmer.co.uk/pages/index.php

CC NO 214831   **ESTABLISHED** 1938

....

■ The BUPA Foundation

WHERE FUNDING CAN BE GIVEN UK.

WHO CAN BENEFIT Medical research institutions.

WHAT IS FUNDED The foundation currently invites applications for medical research grants in the following areas: Surgical research and development; epidemiology and preventive medicine; communication and health information between health professionals and/or patients; mental health of older people; health at work. Each year the foundation runs a specialist themed grants programme to promote focused research in a specific area of medical care. Each year a call for submissions on a specified topic in one of its focus areas is made. In addition, the BUPA Foundation awards recognise and reward researchers' previous work as well as 'seeding' follow-on studies if appropriate, or piloting work in a new direction prompted by the successful project. These are presented in November each year, at the BUPA Foundation awards dinner.

WHAT IS NOT FUNDED No grants are made for applications for general appeals, applications from students for sponsorship through college or applications from other charitable organisations.

FINANCES *Year* 2007 *Income* £7,516,080 *Grants* £2,297,809 *Assets* £7,621,559

TRUSTEES Dame Deirdre J Hine, Chair; Dr J Evans; C Hasluck; Prof P A Poole-Wilson; Prof J M Popay; Dr A J Vallance-Owen; Dr V J Warren; Prof G K Wilcock; Prof A R Kendrick; Prof P J Kumar; E M Todd; P Jones.

HOW TO APPLY Applications can be made online at the foundation's website. There are two meetings each year to consider medical research grant applications, in February and November. Please note that proposals for the February meeting must be submitted by 31 October of the preceding year and proposals for the November meeting must be submitted by 31 July each year.

WHO TO APPLY TO The Administrator, BUPA House, 15–19 Bloomsbury Way, London WC1A 2BA *Website* www.bupafoundation.co.uk

CC NO 277598   **ESTABLISHED** 1979

....

■ The Burden Trust

WHERE FUNDING CAN BE GIVEN UK and overseas.

WHO CAN BENEFIT Charitable organisations and institutions; hospitals; retirement homes; schools and training institutions.

WHAT IS FUNDED Medical research, the priority is to support research in neurosciences; education and training; the care of older people, children, people who are sick and people in need. There

Think carefully about every application. Is it justified?

....

395

is an overall adherence to the tenets and principles of the Church of England.

WHAT IS NOT FUNDED No grants to individuals.

TYPE OF GRANT Recurring and one-off. Grants are not automatic and must be applied for annually.

SAMPLE GRANTS Burden Neurological Institute (£80,000); Trinity College – Bristol (£23,000); Langham Research Scholarships (£13,000); Easton Families Project and Oxford Centre for Mission Studies (£12,000 each); Union Biblical Seminary – Pune (£10,000); Association for Theological Education by Extension – Bangalore (£8,500); Urban Saints (£5,000); St Paul's Divinity College – Kenya (£2,000); Redcliffe College (£1,500); and St Luke's Hospital for the Clergy (£1,000).

FINANCES *Year* 2007–08 *Income* £166,589 *Grants* £175,040 *Assets* £3,707,581

TRUSTEES A C Miles, Chair; R E J Bernays; Dr M G Barker; Prof. G M Stirrat; Bishop of Southwell and Nottingham; Prof. A Halestrap.

HOW TO APPLY In writing to the correspondent. Financial information is required in support of the project for which help is requested. No application is responded to without an sae. Applications are considered at the annual trustees meeting.

WHO TO APPLY TO Patrick O'Conor, Secretary, 51 Downs Park West, Westbury Park, Bristol BS6 7QL *Tel* 0117 962 8611 *email* p.oconor@netgates.co.uk

CC NO 235859   **ESTABLISHED** 1913

■ Burdens Charitable Foundation

WHERE FUNDING CAN BE GIVEN UK, but mostly overseas, with special interest in Sub-Saharan Africa.

WHO CAN BENEFIT Registered charities only.

WHAT IS FUNDED 'There are no formal restrictions on the charitable activities that can be supported, but the trustees' main activities currently embrace the prevention and relief of acute poverty, substantially through the medium of education and healthcare and most especially in countries such as those of sub-Saharan Africa.'

WHAT IS NOT FUNDED Causes which rarely or never benefit include animal welfare (except in less developed countries), the arts and museums, political activities, most medical research, preservation etc. of historic buildings and monuments, individual educational grants and sport, except sport for people with disabilities. No grants are made to individuals.

TYPE OF GRANT Generally one-off grants, exceptionally more than one-year. Capital, project, research, running and recurring costs, salaries and start-up costs will also be considered. No loans are made.

SAMPLE GRANTS Across (£10,000); Build-It (£5,000); Newtown Evangelical Church (£2,500); the Reid Foundation (£2,000); Safe Anchor Trust (£750); National Children's Homes and South Street Evangelical Church (£500 each); Tearfund (£350); Caring for Life (£250); and St Andrew's Evangelical Mission (£100).

FINANCES *Year* 2007–08 *Income* £321,967 *Grants* £71,548 *Assets* £12,998,137

TRUSTEES A J Burden; G Burden; Mrs H Perkins; Mrs S Schofield; Dr A D Burden.

HOW TO APPLY In writing to the correspondent, accompanied by recent, audited accounts and statutory reports, coupled with at least an outline business plan where relevant. Trustees usually meet in March, June, September and December.

WHO TO APPLY TO A J Burden, Trustee, St George's House, 215–219 Chester Road, Manchester M15 4JE

CC NO 273535   **ESTABLISHED** 1977

■ The Burdett Trust for Nursing

WHERE FUNDING CAN BE GIVEN Mostly UK.

WHO CAN BENEFIT Nurses and other healthcare professionals involved in innovative projects.

WHAT IS FUNDED In 2008 the trustees carried out a comprehensive review of the grant-making policies and procedures. As a result of the review, the trustees decided that they would introduce four new grant funding programmes for 2009: Building Nursing Research Capacity – to support clinical nursing research and research addressing policy, leadership development and delivery of nursing care; Building Nurse Leadership Capacity – supporting nurses in their professional development to create a cadre of excellent nursing and allied health professionals who will become leaders of the future and foster excellence and capacity-building in advancing the nursing profession; Supporting Local Nurse-led Initiatives – to support nurse-led initiatives that make a difference at local level and are focussed explicitly on improving care for patients and users of services; and proactive grants.
It was agreed that the trust would invite charitable organisations to operate as its 'funding partners' to manage the first three of these programmes. After a rigorous selection process the trustees appointed the following four organisations to become their initial funding partners: Help the Hospices; Florence Nightingale Foundation; Foundation of Nursing Studies; Queen's Nursing Institute.

WHAT IS NOT FUNDED Please contact the relevant funding partner for information on the programme criteria.

TYPE OF GRANT Usually one-off, although up to three years will be considered.

SAMPLE GRANTS University of Sterling – Cancer Care Research Centre (£250,000); Florence Nightingale Foundation (£150,000); Sue Ryder Care (£129,000); Junius S Morgan Benevolent Fund (£100,000); University of Nottingham (£97,000); University of Glasgow (£57,000); Air Balloon Surgery – Research Unit (£22,000); and World Orthopaedic Concern UK (£15,000).

FINANCES *Year* 2008 *Income* £1,532,173 *Grants* £1,891,110 *Assets* £56,611,589

TRUSTEES Alan Gibbs, Chair; Sue Norman; Prof Eileen Sills; Victor West; Ray Greenwood; Andrew Smith; Dr Soek Khim Horton; Lady Henrietta St George; Joanna Webber; Jack Gibbs; William Gordon.

OTHER INFORMATION A further £148,153 was given in grants to individuals.

HOW TO APPLY The successful funding partners are listed here – please visit their websites for information about how to apply to these joint programmes: Help the Hospices – www.helpthehospices.org.uk; Florence Nightingale Foundation – www.florence-nightingale-foundation.org.uk; Foundation of Nursing Studies – www.fons.org; Queen's Nursing Institute – www.qni.org.uk.

WHO TO APPLY TO Shirley Baines, Administrator, SG Hambros Trust Company, 41 Tower Hill, London EC3N 4SG *Tel* 020 7597 3000 *Fax* 020 7702 9263 *email* administrator@burdettnursingtrust.org.uk *Website* www.burdettnursingtrust.org.uk

CC NO 1089849   **ESTABLISHED** 2001

■ The Clara E Burgess Charity

WHERE FUNDING CAN BE GIVEN UK and worldwide.

WHO CAN BENEFIT Registered charities benefiting children.

WHAT IS FUNDED Provision of facilities and assistance to enhance the education, health and physical well-being of children, particularly (but not exclusively) those under the age of ten who have lost one or both parents.

WHAT IS NOT FUNDED No grants to non-registered charities.

TYPE OF GRANT One-off and recurrent grants (up to three years) for capital costs, core costs, salaries, projects, research, and start-up costs.

RANGE OF GRANTS Mostly up to £15,000.

SAMPLE GRANTS Save the Children (£100,000); St Kentigern Hospice (£52,000); Woodlands Hospice (£37,500); Winnies Castle of Love (£28,000); Rainbow Centre for Children and PSS (£20,000 each); Positive Action on Cancer (£17,500); Sefton Children's Trust (£15,000); Treetops Hospice (£10,000); Macmillan Cancer Support (£9,000); Chernobyl Children in Need (£6,000); Sand Rose Project (£5,000); and Home Start (£1,000).

FINANCES *Year* 2007–08 *Income* £348,982 *Grants* £429,054 *Assets* £8,388,337

TRUSTEES The Royal Bank of Scotland

HOW TO APPLY In writing to the correspondent.

WHO TO APPLY TO The Trust Section Manager, RBS Trust Services, Eden, Lakeside, Chester Business Park, Wrexham Road, Chester CH4 9QT

CC NO 1072546   **ESTABLISHED** 1998

■ The Burry Charitable Trust

WHERE FUNDING CAN BE GIVEN UK, with a preference for Highcliffe and the surrounding and further areas.

WHO CAN BENEFIT Charities, voluntary groups and other not for profit organisations.

WHAT IS FUNDED Medicine and health.

WHAT IS NOT FUNDED No grants to individuals or students.

SAMPLE GRANTS Oakhaven Hospital Trust (£10,000); Not Forgotten Association and Wessex Cardiac Trust (£5,000 each); Ability Net and John Grooms Association (£2,500 each); Julia's House Hospice and Wessex Autistic Society (£2,000 each); Life Education Centres (£1,500); Cellular Pathology Charitable Fund (£1,100); British Red Cross and WRVS (£1,000 each); Myeloma UK (£500); Sway Welfare Aid Group (£250); and First Opportunities (£250).

FINANCES *Year* 2007–08 *Income* £627,943 *Grants* £48,600

TRUSTEES R J Burry; Mrs J A Knight; A J Osman: N J Lapage.

HOW TO APPLY **This trust states that it does not respond to unsolicited applications.**

WHO TO APPLY TO R J Burry, Trustee, 261 Lymington Road, Highcliffe, Christchurch, Dorset BH23 5EE

CC NO 281045   **ESTABLISHED** 1961

■ The Audrey and Stanley Burton 1960 Charitable Trust

WHERE FUNDING CAN BE GIVEN Worldwide. In practice, mainly UK with a preference for Yorkshire.

WHO CAN BENEFIT Charitable organisations.

WHAT IS FUNDED Charities supporting education and the arts; Jewish people/Israel; social welfare; health; and overseas and developing countries.

WHAT IS NOT FUNDED No grants to individuals.

TYPE OF GRANT Preferably one-off donations and project grants, occasionally for more than three years.

RANGE OF GRANTS Up to around £20,000.

SAMPLE GRANTS OXFAM (£35,000 in total); Henshaws College and the Medical Foundation for the Care of Victims of Torture (£10,000 each); MND Association (£3,000); Cookridge Cancer Centre (£2,500); and Changing Faces and Spinal Injuries Association (£1,000 each).

FINANCES *Year* 2007–08 *Income* £1,675,833 *Grants* £1,851,296 *Assets* £1,228,493

TRUSTEES Amanda Burton; Raymond Burton; Jeremy Burton.

OTHER INFORMATION An exceptional grant from restricted funds of more than £1.5 million was also made to the University of Leeds for the refurbishment of the Art Gallery.

HOW TO APPLY In writing to the correspondent. Unsuccessful applicants may not always receive a reply.

WHO TO APPLY TO Keith Pailing, Trustee Management Limited, Trustee Management Ltd, 19 Cookridge Street, Leeds LS2 3AG *Tel* 0113 243 6466 *email* trustee.mgmt@btconnect.com

CC NO 1028430   **ESTABLISHED** 1960

■ The Arnold Burton 1998 Charitable Trust

WHERE FUNDING CAN BE GIVEN Worldwide.

WHO CAN BENEFIT Jewish charities.

WHAT IS FUNDED Medical research, education, social welfare and heritage.

WHAT IS NOT FUNDED No grants to individuals.

SAMPLE GRANTS UJIA (£100,000); Breakthrough Breast Cancer, Fight for Sight and Royal College of Surgeons (£5,000 each); the Children's Society (£2,500); London Metropolitan University (£1,200); Historic Royal Palaces, Beth Shalom, the Jewish Museum and UNICEF (£1,000 each); Olive Tree Educational Trust (£500); Smile Train (£250); Project Trust (£100); and Galapogas Conservation Trust (£50).

FINANCES *Year* 2007–08 *Income* £179,762 *Grants* £286,331 *Assets* £5,203,050

TRUSTEES A J Burton; J J Burton; N A Burton; M T Burton.

HOW TO APPLY In writing to the trust managers. Unsuccessful appeals will not necessarily be acknowledged.

WHO TO APPLY TO The Trust Managers, c/o Trustee Management Ltd, 19 Cookridge Street, Leeds LS2 3AG

CC NO 1074633   **ESTABLISHED** 1998

■ The Burton Breweries Charitable Trust

WHERE FUNDING CAN BE GIVEN Burton, East Staffordshire and South Derbyshire district (including a small area of North West Leicestershire).

WHO CAN BENEFIT Young people (11–25 years), education and training for individuals of any age who assist young people and youth/community organisations.

WHAT IS FUNDED Young people and youth organisations. Funding is given in areas such as equipment facilities and services, and extra-curricular education and training.

WHAT IS NOT FUNDED Beneficiaries must be aged between 11 and 25 – other age groups are excluded. Organisations and individuals living, or in full-time education, outside the beneficial area are not supported. No support for education where there is provision by the state.

TYPE OF GRANT Capital including buildings, core costs, one-off, project, recurring costs, running costs and start-up costs. Funding is available for up to two years.

RANGE OF GRANTS Up to £5,000.

SAMPLE GRANTS Hilton Scouts and Guides (£2,500); Midway Football Club and St Johns Ambulance (£1,500 each); Church Broughton Tennis Club (£1,200); Burton Venture Trust (£1,100); Burton College Dance Company, Burton Cricket Club, Derbyshire Housing Aid, Over The Wall, Yoxall Cricket Club and Tutbury Cricket Club (£1,000 each).

FINANCES *Year* 2007–08 *Income* £42,169 *Grants* £32,886 *Assets* £835,019

TRUSTEES Janet Dean, Chair; Keith M H Donald; John Polglass; Richard Westwood; Nigel Turpin; Neil Preston; Adrian Wedgwood.

HOW TO APPLY In writing to the correspondent. The trustees meet in February, June and October. A copy of the trust's guidelines is available on request or on its website.

WHO TO APPLY TO Brian E Keates, Secretary to the Trustees, Gretton House, Waterside Court, Third Avenue, Centrum 100, Burton on Trent DE14 2WQ *Tel* 01283 740600 *Fax* 01283 511899 *email* info@burtonbctrust.co.uk *Website* www.burtonbctrust.co.uk

CC NO 1068847   **ESTABLISHED** 1998

■ The Geoffrey Burton Charitable Trust

WHERE FUNDING CAN BE GIVEN UK, especially Suffolk and the Needham Market area.

WHO CAN BENEFIT Charitable organisations.

WHAT IS FUNDED General charitable purposes; welfare and environment/conservation projects.

WHAT IS NOT FUNDED No grants to individuals.

TYPE OF GRANT Buildings and core costs. Funding for one year or less will be considered.

RANGE OF GRANTS Up to £3,000.

SAMPLE GRANTS Needham Market Community Centre (£7,500); Needham Market Bowls Club (£2,500); RSPB (£2,000); Mid Suffolk Citizens Advice Bureau (£1,500); Waveney Stardust (£1,000); University of Manchester – Blond McIndoe Research (£930); BREAK (£800); Listening Books (£750) Diss, Thetford and District CAB (£500); Jubilee Sailing Trust (£300); and West Suffolk Voluntary Association for the Blind (£250).

FINANCES *Year* 2007–08 *Income* £36,838 *Grants* £33,330 *Assets* £596,591

TRUSTEES Ted Nash; Eric Maule.

HOW TO APPLY In writing to the correspondent.

WHO TO APPLY TO Eric Maule, Trustee, Salix House, Falkenham, Ipswich IP10 0QY *Tel* 01394 448339 *email* ericmaule@hotmail.com

CC NO 290854   **ESTABLISHED** 1984

■ Consolidated Charity of Burton upon Trent

WHERE FUNDING CAN BE GIVEN The former county borough of Burton upon Trent and the parishes of Branston, Stretton and Outwoods.

WHO CAN BENEFIT Individuals, and organisations that benefit people in need, who live in the beneficial area.

WHAT IS FUNDED General charitable purposes.

RANGE OF GRANTS Up to £10,000.

SAMPLE GRANTS Burton Transformation Trust, SARAC, St Giles Hospice and Shobnall Parish Council (£10,000 each); All Saints with Christ Church (£9,000); Burton Uxbridge Table Tennis Club, Claverhouse Allotment Association and Horninglow and Eton Parish Council (£5,000 each); Touch of Life Dance Crew (£3,000); Burton Chinese Community Association and Paget High School (£2,000); Burton Playday Committee (£1,500); Burton and District Arts Council and Grange Community School (£1,000); Staffordshire Youth Service (£700); and the Sailors Families Society (£320).

FINANCES *Year* 2008 *Income* £486,614 *Grants* £95,704 *Assets* £9,417,252

TRUSTEES Mrs V Burton, Chair; G M Hamilton; Cllr Mrs P L Ackroyd; Mrs M A Heather; Cllr Mr P J Beresford; Alderman Mrs P P Hill; Alderman P R Davies; Alderman Mrs M L Nash; Alderman T M Dawn; Mrs A M Parker; Mrs G M Foster; J M Peach; Revd A Gale; D E Salter; Cllr D F Fletcher; Cllr F D Startin; Cllr T G Hathaway; Cllr Mrs E J Staples; Cllr C F Insley.

OTHER INFORMATION In 2008 the sum of £81,000 was also distributed to individuals.

HOW TO APPLY On a form available from the correspondent. Applications for grants from organisations are considered by the main committee which meets three times a year.

WHO TO APPLY TO T J Bramall, Clerk to the Trustees, Talbot and Co, 148 High Street, Burton upon Trent, Staffordshire DE14 1JY *Tel* 01283 564716 *email* consolidatedcharity@ talbotandco.freeserve.co.uk

CC NO 239072   **ESTABLISHED** 1981

■ Butchers' Company General Charities

WHERE FUNDING CAN BE GIVEN City of London or its adjacent boroughs.

WHO CAN BENEFIT Organisations benefiting people in need.

WHAT IS FUNDED The charities aim to: provide relief to persons who are in conditions of need, hardship, or distress; further its broad remit of charitable giving through grants to appropriate groups and organisations.

WHAT IS NOT FUNDED The committee does not fund groups which it considers have large financial reserves. No grants to individuals.

RANGE OF GRANTS Generally £70–£2,500.

SAMPLE GRANTS Bart's and Royal London Children's Trust and the Treloar Trust (£7,500 each); Lord Mayor's Appeal (£2,500); BDCI and London Youth Trust (£1,000 each); St Luke's Hospital for the Clergy (£500); Activenture, Countryside Foundation, Fairbridge, Stuart Low Trust and Toynbee Hall (£300 each); Friends and Neighbours, Hackney Youth Orchestra, Royal British Legion, Spitalfields City Farm, Tower Hamlets Opportunity Group, Westbourne Park Family Centre and Whizz Kidz (£250 each); and the Bridge School (£100).

FINANCES *Year* 2007–08 *Income* £112,696 *Grants* £34,970 *Assets* £1,029,000

TRUSTEES The members of the court of the Worshipful Company of Butchers.

HOW TO APPLY In writing to the correspondent. The committee meets monthly.

WHO TO APPLY TO The Chairman of the Charities Committee, Butchers Hall, 87 Bartholomew Close, London EC1A 7EB *Tel* 020 7600 4106 *email* clerk@butchershall.com *Website* www. butchershall.com

CC NO 257928   **ESTABLISHED** 1969

■ The Derek Butler Trust

WHERE FUNDING CAN BE GIVEN Worldwide, in practice UK.

WHO CAN BENEFIT Institutions and charitable organisations.

WHAT IS FUNDED Medical, arts (particularly music), general charitable purposes.

RANGE OF GRANTS Usually up to £10,000.

SAMPLE GRANTS Core (formerly Digestive Disorders Foundation) (£108,000); Trinity College of Music Bursaries (£72,000 in total); Crusaid (£65,000); The Food Chain UK (£30,000); St Christopher's Hospice (£21,000); Holidays for Carers and Bampton Classical Opera (£10,000 each); Animal Health Trust (£5,500); GMFT Charity (£3,000); and Pimlico Opera (£2,000).

FINANCES *Year* 2007–08 *Income* £461,673 *Grants* £537,226 *Assets* £11,724,104

TRUSTEES Bernard W Dawson; Donald F Freeman; Revd Michael Fuller; Miss Hilary A E Guest.

HOW TO APPLY In writing to the correspondent. 'The trustees continue to seek new charities to which they can make suitable donations.'

WHO TO APPLY TO Miss Hilary A E Guest, Trustee, Underwood Solicitors, 40 Welbeck Street, London W1G 8LN *Tel* 020 7526 6000 *email* hguest@underwoodco.com

CC NO 1081995   **ESTABLISHED** 2000

■ The Bill Butlin Charity Trust

WHERE FUNDING CAN BE GIVEN UK.

WHO CAN BENEFIT Registered charities.

WHAT IS FUNDED Normally to assist disabled children, and older and needy people through recognised institutions.

RANGE OF GRANTS Up to £15,000.

SAMPLE GRANTS Canadian Veterans Association of the UK (£15,000); Cancer Research UK and Home Farm Trust (£5,000 each); Arundel Castle Cricket Foundation (£3,800); Grand Order of Water Rats, St Richard's Hospital – Chichester and Spinal Research (£3,000 each); National Centre for Young People with Epilepsy and Saints and Sinners Club of London (£2,500); and Royal Marsden Hospital and VSO (£1,000 each).

FINANCES *Year* 2007–08 *Income* £86,356 *Grants* £68,590 *Assets* £2,045,909

TRUSTEES Robert F Butlin; Lady Sheila Butlin; Peter A Hetherington; Trevor Watts; Frederick T Devine; Sonia I Meaden; Terence H North.

HOW TO APPLY In writing to the correspondent, unsuccessful applications do not receive a response. Trustees usually meet twice a year.

WHO TO APPLY TO The Secretary, Eighth Floor, 6 New Street Square, London EC4A 3AQ *Tel* 020 7842 2000 *email* bbct@rawlinson-hunter.com

CC NO 228233   **ESTABLISHED** 1963

■ Ann Byrne Charitable Trust

WHERE FUNDING CAN BE GIVEN Norfolk.

WHO CAN BENEFIT Charitable organisations.

WHAT IS FUNDED The main objects of the charity are to provide relief for people who are disabled (physically and mentally), people in need and people who are homeless.

RANGE OF GRANTS £500–£7,500.

SAMPLE GRANTS Hebron House (£7,500); Salvation Army (£5,000); BREAK (£3,300); Vitalise (£3,200); Children's Trust (£3,000); Brainwave, Hamlet Centre Trust and West Norwich Partnership (£2,000 each); AIDIS Trust, Bowthorpe Community Trust, Dreams and Visions, Leprosy Mission, Magdalene Group, Matthew Project, Norwich and District Carers Forum, Shaftesbury Society, Stepping Stones and Tree House (£1,000 each); and Mildmay (£500).

FINANCES *Year* 2007–08 *Income* £117,111 *Grants* £58,470 *Assets* £1,525,725

TRUSTEES P R Norton, Chair; Revd S F Nunney; Mrs J A Richardson.

HOW TO APPLY In writing to the correspondent.

WHO TO APPLY TO P R Norton, Chair, 13 The Close, Norwich NR1 4DS

CC NO 1048360   **ESTABLISHED** 1995

Think carefully about every application. Is it justified?

399

C and F Charitable Trust

WHERE FUNDING CAN BE GIVEN UK and overseas.
WHO CAN BENEFIT Orthodox Jewish charities.
WHAT IS FUNDED Relief of poverty amongst the Jewish Community; the furtherance of the Jewish education and religion.
WHAT IS NOT FUNDED Registered charities only.
SAMPLE GRANTS Previous beneficiaries have included Community Council of Gateshead, Ezras Nitrochim, Gur Trust, Kollel Shaarei Shlomo, SOFT and Yetev Lev Jerusalem Trust.
FINANCES *Year* 2007–08 *Income* £155,877 *Grants* £205,180 *Assets* £1,267,030
TRUSTEES C S Kaufman; F H Kaufman; S Kaufman.
HOW TO APPLY In writing to the correspondent.
WHO TO APPLY TO The Trustees, c/o New Burlington House, 1075 Finchley House Road, London NW11 0PU
CC NO 274529   **ESTABLISHED** 1977

C J Cadbury Charitable Trust

WHERE FUNDING CAN BE GIVEN UK.
WHO CAN BENEFIT Registered charities.
WHAT IS FUNDED General, preference for environmental/conservation projects.
TYPE OF GRANT One-off.
SAMPLE GRANTS Island Conservation Society UK (£13,000 in two grants); Kingfisher's Bridge Wetland Creation Trust (£5,500 in three grants); Bedfordshire, Cambridge and Northamptonshire Wildlife Trust (£2,000); and Plantlife international (£1,000).
FINANCES *Year* 2007–08 *Income* £45,641 *Grants* £23,100 *Assets* £730,339
TRUSTEES Hugh Carslake; Joy Cadbury; Thomas Cadbury; Lucy Cadbury.
HOW TO APPLY In writing to the correspondent. The trust does not generally support unsolicited applications.
WHO TO APPLY TO The Clerk, Martineau, No. 1 Colmore Square, Birmingham B4 6AA
CC NO 270609   **ESTABLISHED** 1969

Edward Cadbury Charitable Trust

WHERE FUNDING CAN BE GIVEN Worldwide, in practice mainly UK.
WHO CAN BENEFIT Registered charities only.
WHAT IS FUNDED General – including conservation and the environment, Christianity, young people, welfare and education. Also ecumenical movements, inter-faith relations, integration, people who are oppressed or disadvantaged, the arts and research.
WHAT IS NOT FUNDED No student grants or support for individuals.
TYPE OF GRANT One-off and recurring.
RANGE OF GRANTS £250–£1 million. Generally £500–£5,000.
SAMPLE GRANTS Ironbridge Gorge Museum Trust (£250,000); Centre for Studies in Security & Diplomacy, University of Birmingham (£88,000); Responding to Conflict (£50,000); South Birmingham Young Homeless Project (£45,000); Northfield Eco Centre – Birmingham (£38,000); Beacon Centre for the Blind – Wolverhampton

(£25,000); St John of Jerusalem Eye Hospital (£10,000); Farming and Countryside Education (£5,000); Community Service Volunteers (£2,000); and Deafblind UK (£1,000).
FINANCES *Year* 2007–08 *Income* £895,605 *Grants* £789,071 *Assets* £27,871,352
TRUSTEES Dr Charles E Gillett, Chair; William Southall; Charles R Gillett; Andrew Littleboy; Nigel Cadbury; Hugh Marriott.
HOW TO APPLY In writing to the correspondent at any time and allowing three months for a response. Appeals should clearly and concisely give relevant information concerning the project and its benefits, an outline budget and how the project is to be funded initially and in the future. Up-to-date accounts and the organisation's latest annual report are also required. Applications that do not come within the trust's policy may not be considered or acknowledged.
WHO TO APPLY TO Sue Anderson, Trust Manager, Rokesley, University of Birmingham Selly Oak, Bristol Road, Selly Oak, Birmingham B29 6QF *Tel* 0121 472 1838 *Fax* 0121 472 7013 *email* ecadburytrust@fsmail.net
CC NO 227384   **ESTABLISHED** 1945

Henry T and Lucy B Cadbury Charitable Trust

WHERE FUNDING CAN BE GIVEN Mainly UK, but also the developing world.
WHO CAN BENEFIT Registered charities only.
WHAT IS FUNDED Quaker causes and institutions, health, homelessness and support groups.
WHAT IS NOT FUNDED No grants to non-registered charities.
TYPE OF GRANT One-off.
RANGE OF GRANTS £500–£3,500.
SAMPLE GRANTS Quaker United Nations Office (£5,000); Battle Against Tranquillisers, British Pugwash Trust, the People's Kitchen and Slower Speeds Trust (£2,000 each); Action for ME, Money for Madagascar and Tools for Self Reliance (£1,500 each); and Calcutta Rescue Fund, Quaker Opportunity Playgroup and Youth Education Service Midnapore (£1,000 each).
FINANCES *Year* 2008 *Income* £26,727 *Grants* £26,000 *Assets* £592,386
TRUSTEES Candia Carolan; C Ruth Charity; Suzannah Gibson; M Bevis Gillett; Tristram Hambly; Elizabeth Rawlins; Tamsin Yates.
HOW TO APPLY The trust's income is committed each year and so unsolicited applications are not normally accepted. The trustees meet in March to consider applications.
WHO TO APPLY TO The Secretary, c/o B C M, Box 2024, London WC1N 3XX
CC NO 280314   **ESTABLISHED** 1924

P H G Cadbury Charitable Trust

WHERE FUNDING CAN BE GIVEN UK and overseas.
WHO CAN BENEFIT Registered charities.
WHAT IS FUNDED General charitable purposes, particularly the arts; conservation and cancer-related charities also considered.
RANGE OF GRANTS Up to £2,500.
SAMPLE GRANTS The Art Fund, Helen and Douglas House, Natural History Museum and Sadlers Wells (£2,500 each); Dulwich Picture Gallery (£2,000); Magic Bus, Sir John Soames Museum and Trinity Hospice (£1,500 each); Garsington Opera (£1,250); and St Martins in the Fields and Watermill Theatre Trust (£1,000 each).

FINANCES *Year* 2007–08 *Income* £43,692
Grants £31,260 *Assets* £625,357

TRUSTEES Derek Larder; Peter Cadbury; Sally
Cadbury.

HOW TO APPLY The trust does not usually respond to
unsolicited applications.

WHO TO APPLY TO Derek Larder, Trustee, KS
Carmichael, PO Box 4UD, London W1A 4UD
Tel 020 7258 1577 *email* dlarder@
kscarmichael.com

CC NO 327174   **ESTABLISHED** 1986

■ The Christopher Cadbury Charitable Trust

WHERE FUNDING CAN BE GIVEN UK, with a strong
preference for the Midlands.

WHO CAN BENEFIT Registered charities.

WHAT IS FUNDED To support approved charities by
annual contribution. The trustees have drawn up
a schedule of commitments covering charities
which they have chosen to support.

WHAT IS NOT FUNDED No support for individuals.

SAMPLE GRANTS Fircroft College and Island
Conservation Society UK – Aride and (£11,000
each); Playthings Past Museum Trust (£7,500);
P H G Cadbury Charitable Trust (£7,000); Devon
Wildlife Trust (£6,000); Norfolk Wildlife Trust
(£5,000); Bower Trust (£4,000); Guide
Association – Beaconfield Campsites (£2,000);
Survival International (£1,000); and Avoncroft
Arts Society and Selly Oak Nursery School
(£500 each).

FINANCES *Year* 2007–08 *Income* £86,041
Grants £72,950 *Assets* £1,921,971

TRUSTEES R V J Cadbury; Dr C James Cadbury; Mrs
V B Reekie; Dr T N D Peet; P H G Cadbury; Mrs
C V E Benfield.

HOW TO APPLY Unsolicited applications are unlikely
to be successful.

WHO TO APPLY TO The Trust Administrator, PKF (UK)
LLP, New Guild House, 45 Great Charles Street,
Queensway, Birmingham B3 2LX *Tel* 0121 212
2222

CC NO 231859   **ESTABLISHED** 1922

■ The G W Cadbury Charitable Trust

WHERE FUNDING CAN BE GIVEN Worldwide.

WHO CAN BENEFIT Organisations benefiting at-risk
groups, people disadvantaged by poverty, and
socially isolated people.

WHAT IS FUNDED General charitable purposes with a
bias towards population control and
conservation.

WHAT IS NOT FUNDED No grants to individuals or non-
registered charities, or for scholarships.

SAMPLE GRANTS Pacific NorthWest Ballet (£46,000);
Cancer Counselling Trust (£20,000); School of
American Ballet (£13,000); Joseph Rowntree
Charitable Trust and World Development
Movement Trust (£10,000 each); Asylum
Seekers in Islington Relief Trust, Fawcett
Society, Haverford College and Help the Rural
Children (£5,000 each); Amnesty International,
Sustrans and Islington Boat Club (£2,000
each); Bridge the Gap (£1,500); and
WOMANKIND UK (£1,000).

FINANCES *Year* 2007–08 *Income* £271,456
Grants £247,963 *Assets* £6,306,486

TRUSTEES Miss J C Boal; Mrs L E Boal; P C Boal;
Miss J L Woodroffe; Mrs C A Woodroffe;
N B Woodroffe.

HOW TO APPLY In writing to the correspondent.
However, it should be noted that trustees'
current commitments are such that no
unsolicited applications can be considered at
present.

WHO TO APPLY TO The Trust Administrator, PKF (UK)
LLP, New Guild House, 45 Great Charles Street,
Queensway, Birmingham B3 2LX *Tel* 0121 212
2222

CC NO 231861   **ESTABLISHED** 1922

■ The Richard Cadbury Charitable Trust

WHERE FUNDING CAN BE GIVEN UK, but mainly
Birmingham, Coventry and Worcester.

WHO CAN BENEFIT Organisations with charitable
status.

WHAT IS FUNDED Community centres and village
halls; libraries and museums; counselling; crime
prevention; playschemes; gay and lesbian
rights; racial equality, discrimination and
relations; social advocacy; health care; hospices
and rehabilitation centres; cancer and prenatal
research; health promotion; and health-related
volunteer schemes. Grants also for
accommodation and housing; infrastructure
support and development; conservation and
environment; and religion.

WHAT IS NOT FUNDED No grants for running costs or
core funding.

TYPE OF GRANT One-off. Project costs.

RANGE OF GRANTS £250–£1,000.

SAMPLE GRANTS Barnardos, Centrepoint, Marie Curie
Cancer Centre and RNLI (£1,000 each);
Birmingham Settlement, Dodford Children's
Holiday Farm and NSPCC (£750 each); LEPRA
and VSO (£500 each); ESO (£400); Worcester
Live and Youth at Risk – Nottingham (£300
each); and Sandwell Asian Development
Association and St David's Church – Selly Oak
(£250 each).

FINANCES *Year* 2007–08 *Income* £26,156
Grants £44,400 *Assets* £596,587

TRUSTEES R B Cadbury; Chair; Mrs M M Eardley;
D G Slora; Miss J A Slora.

HOW TO APPLY In writing to the correspondent giving
reasons why a grant is needed and including a
copy of the latest accounts if possible.
Meetings are held in February, June and
October. Unsolicited applications are not
accepted.

WHO TO APPLY TO Mrs M M Eardley, Trustee, 26
Randall Road, Kenilworth, Warwickshire CV8 1JY

CC NO 224348   **ESTABLISHED** 1948

■ The William A Cadbury Charitable Trust

WHERE FUNDING CAN BE GIVEN West Midlands,
especially Birmingham and to a lesser extent,
UK, Ireland and overseas.

WHO CAN BENEFIT Organisations serving Birmingham
and the West Midlands; organisations whose
work has a national significance; organisations
outside the West Midlands where the trust has
well-established links; organisations in Northern
Ireland, and UK-based charities working
overseas. All organisations must be registered
charities.

WHAT IS FUNDED Birmingham and the West
Midlands: social welfare, community and self-
help groups working with people who are
disadvantaged, counselling and mediation
agencies; medical and healthcare projects

including medical research; education and training, schools and universities, adult literacy schemes, training for employment; Religious Society of Friends; places of religious worship and associated social projects; conservation of the environment including the preservation of listed buildings and monuments; the performing and visual arts, museums and art galleries; penal affairs, work with offenders and ex-offenders, penal reform and police projects. UK: Religious Society of Friends; penal reform. Ireland: cross-community initiatives promoting peace and reconciliation. International: social welfare, healthcare and environmental projects; sustainable development.

WHAT IS NOT FUNDED The trust does not fund individuals (whether for research, expeditions or educational purposes); projects concerned with travel, adventure, sports or recreation; organisations which do not have UK charity registration (except those legally exempt); overseas charities not registered in the UK. The trust receives many more applications than can be supported. 'Even if your project meets our requirements we may not be able to help, particularly if you are located outside the West Midlands.'

TYPE OF GRANT Specific grant applications are favoured. Grants are generally one-off or for projects of one year or less. The trust will consider building grants, capital, core and running costs, recurring and start-up costs, research, endowment, feasibility studies and salaries. Grants are not usually awarded on an annual basis, except to a small number of charities for revenue costs.

RANGE OF GRANTS Mostly £100 to £5,000. Larger grants are seldom awarded.

SAMPLE GRANTS Concern Universal (£120,000 – two grants); Birmingham Citizens Advice Bureau (£48,000); Quaker Peace and Social Witness (£25,000); Church Housing Trust (£15,000); Friends of Victoria (£12,000); Worcester Acute Hospitals NHS Trust, Litchfield Cathedral, Albatross Arts Project and Avoncroft Museum of Historic Buildings (£10,000 each); Warstock and Billesley Detached Youth Work Project (£6,000); Birmingham Tribunal Unit and Cerebral Palsy Africa (£5,000 each); and Four Square and Shropshire Wildlife Trust (£2,000 each).

FINANCES *Year* 2007–08 *Income* £786,947 *Grants* £684,800 *Assets* £21,190,201

TRUSTEES James Taylor; Rupert Cadbury; Katherine van Hagen Cadbury; Margaret Salmon; Sarah Stafford; Adrian Thomas; John Penny; Sophy Blandy; Janine Cobain.

PUBLICATIONS Policy statement and guidelines for applicants.

OTHER INFORMATION Telephone calls should only be made in the mornings.

HOW TO APPLY Applications to the correspondent in writing including the following information: charity registration number; a description of the charity's aims and achievements; a copy of the latest set of accounts; an outline and budget for the project for which funding is sought; details of funds raised and the current shortfall. Applications can also be submitted on the trust's online application form. Please also forward a copy of the organisation's latest set of accounts. Applications are considered on a continuing basis throughout the year. Small grants (amounts not exceeding £1,000) are assessed each month. Major grants are awarded at the trustees' meetings held twice annually, normally in May and November. Applicants whose appeals are to be considered

at one of the meetings will be notified in advance.

WHO TO APPLY TO Carolyn Bettis, Trust Administrator, Rokesley, University of Birmingham Selly Oak, Bristol Road, Selly Oak, Birmingham B29 6QF *Tel* 0121 472 1464 (am only) *email* info@wa-cadbury.org.uk *Website* www.wa-cadbury.org.uk

CC NO 213629   **ESTABLISHED** 1923

■ The Cadbury Foundation

WHERE FUNDING CAN BE GIVEN UK, particularly in areas where the company has operations.

WHO CAN BENEFIT Registered charities.

WHAT IS FUNDED The foundation's main focus is on 'education and enterprise projects in areas of social deprivation. The national focus is on 'Enterprise in Schools': promoting awareness of the world of work; the relationship between school and future success; attitudes and skills for work and for lifelong learning; and links between schools and the local economy'. Health, welfare and environmental projects are also funded.

FINANCES *Year* 2007 *Income* £859,891 *Grants* £834,500

TRUSTEES Neil Makinmr; Richard Michael Doyle; Alex Cole; Emma West; Mike Barrington; Lawrence Macdougall.

HOW TO APPLY In writing to the correspondent.

WHO TO APPLY TO The Administrator, Cadbury Holdings Ltd, Cadbury House, Sanderson Road, Uxbridge UB8 1DH

CC NO 1050482   **ESTABLISHED** 1994

■ The Edward and Dorothy Cadbury Trust

WHERE FUNDING CAN BE GIVEN Preference for the West Midlands area.

WHO CAN BENEFIT Registered charities and community projects.

WHAT IS FUNDED The trust continues to support, where appropriate, the interests of the founders and the particular charitable interests of the trustees. Grants are grouped under six main headings: arts and culture; community projects and integration; compassionate support; education and training; conservation and environment; and research.

WHAT IS NOT FUNDED No grants to individuals.

TYPE OF GRANT Ongoing funding commitments rarely considered.

RANGE OF GRANTS Usually £500–£2,500, with occasional larger grants made.

SAMPLE GRANTS Sunfield Children's Home (£15,000); Acorns Hospice – Worcester (£7,500); Age Concern, Bromsgrove and District (£5,000); South Birmingham Young Homeless Project (£3,000); Willow Trust (£2,000); Wildlife Trust for Birmingham and the Black Country (£1,500); Birmingham Royal Ballet, RNIB and Warwick Hospital Cancer Ward Appeal (£1,000 each); and Fight for Sight, Relate – Walsall, Voices Foundation, Winston's Wish and WRVS (£500 each).

FINANCES *Year* 2007–08 *Income* £140,935 *Grants* £104,200 *Assets* £4,562,308

TRUSTEES Mrs P A Gillett, Chair; Dr C M Elliott; Mrs P S Ward; Mrs S E Anfilogoff; Mrs J E Gillett; Mrs J A Cadbury.

HOW TO APPLY In writing to the correspondent, giving clear, relevant information concerning the project's aims and its benefits, an outline budget and how the project is to be funded initially and in the future. Up-to-date accounts and annual reports, where available, should be included. Applications can be submitted at any time but three months should be allowed for a response. Applications that do not come within the policy as stated above may not be considered or acknowledged.

WHO TO APPLY TO Miss S Anderson, Trust Manager, Rokesley, University of Birmingham Selly Oak, Bristol Road, Selly Oak, Birmingham B29 6QF *Tel* 0121 472 1838
CC NO 1107327   **ESTABLISHED** 1928

■ The George Cadbury Trust

WHERE FUNDING CAN BE GIVEN Preference for the West Midlands, Hampshire and Gloucestershire.
WHO CAN BENEFIT UK-based charities.
WHAT IS FUNDED General charitable purposes.
WHAT IS NOT FUNDED No support for individuals for projects, courses of study, expeditions or sporting tours. No support for overseas appeals.
RANGE OF GRANTS Mostly for £1,000 or less.
SAMPLE GRANTS National Star Centre Appeal (£30,000); National Youth Ballet (£25,000); Dean and Chapter of Gloucester Cathedral (£20,000); Gloucestershire Community Foundation (£10,000); Sarnia Charitable Trust (£8,000); Alnwick Garden Trust (£5,500); RNLI (£5,300); North Hampshire Medical Fund (£5,000); Action on Addiction (£3,000); DeafBlind UK (£2,500); RNIB (£2,000); and Princes Trust and Royal London Society for the Blind (£1,000 each).
FINANCES *Year* 2007–08 *Income* £377,602 *Grants* £392,874 *Assets* £9,697,643
TRUSTEES Mrs Anne L K Cadbury; Robin N Cadbury; Sir Adrian Cadbury; Roger V J Cadbury; Mrs A Janie Cadbury.
HOW TO APPLY In writing to the correspondent to be considered quarterly. Please note that very few new applications are supported due to ongoing and alternative commitments.
WHO TO APPLY TO The Trust Administrator, PKF (UK) LLP, New Guild House, 45 Great Charles Street, Queensway, Birmingham B3 2LX *Tel* 0121 212 2222
CC NO 1040999   **ESTABLISHED** 1924

■ The Barrow Cadbury Trust and the Barrow Cadbury Fund

WHERE FUNDING CAN BE GIVEN Unrestricted, with a preference for Birmingham and the Black Country (Wolverhampton, Dudley, West Bromwich, Smethwick, Sandwell).
WHO CAN BENEFIT Charities and voluntary organisations which benefit causes within the trust's programmes. Organisations working on grassroots, user-led projects are preferred. Groups do not have to be a registered charity but should have a formal structure and governing documents.
WHAT IS FUNDED The trust promotes social justice through grant-making, research, influencing public policy and supporting local communities. There are three main programme areas: criminal justice, migration and poverty and inclusion.
WHAT IS NOT FUNDED The trust does not fund: activities that central or local government is responsible for; animal welfare; arts and cultural projects; capital costs for building, refurbishment and outfitting; endowment funds; fundraising events or activities; general appeals;

general health; debt counselling; individuals; housing; learning disability; medical research or equipment; mental health; older people; physical disability; promoting religion or belief systems; schools; sponsorship or marketing appeals. The following areas of work are also unlikely to receive funding: 'counselling – unless it forms part of a wider project within one of our programme areas; colleges and universities – only under the research funding of the trust; drug and alcohol users – this remains as a possible area of funding under our criminal justice programme only as part of a broader project; environmental projects – this would only be considered under the poverty and inclusion programme as part of a broader project; homelessness and destitution – only for those leaving the criminal justice system or in relation to our migration programme; IT training – only if it forms part of a wider project; sporting activities – only if it forms part of a wider project'.
TYPE OF GRANT Project funding, recurring costs, running costs and start-up costs. Funding is usually given for one to three years.
RANGE OF GRANTS Up to £50,000 but mostly £25,000–£30,000.
SAMPLE GRANTS Detailed examples of previously funded projects are available on the trust's website.
FINANCES *Year* 2007–08 *Income* £3,111,000 *Grants* £2,380,000 *Assets* £69,307,000
TRUSTEES Ruth Cadbury, Chair; Anna C Southall; Anna Hickinbotham; Erica R Cadbury; Nicola Cadbury; Tim Compton; Tamsin Rupprechter; Gordon Mitchell; Harry Searle.
PUBLICATIONS A number of publications and reports are published on the trust's website.
HOW TO APPLY In writing to the correspondent. The trust does not have an application form but asks that organisations submit an outline proposal which covers the following key points; the organisation and what it does – this should include a brief background of the organisation, its aims, activities and contact details. If you have been funded previously for the same project you should describe the successes to date; the programme area and grant programme being applied for – projects cannot cover more than one programme area but under the poverty and inclusion programme, proposals may cover more than one grant criteria (bridging communities, poverty, inequality); where the project will take place – applicants should provide as much detail as possible about the specific area in which the project will take place; a description of the specific project for which funding is sought – explain what is intended and how it will be done; who will benefit from the project – identify the individuals or organisations that will benefit from the project; the size of grant needed – how much money you are requesting, for what and over what period?; what success will look like – applicants should explain what they hope will change as a result of this project and how they will know that it has been successful; proposals should be no more than two to three sides of A4 and no further information need be submitted at this stage. The grants team will assess the application and contact you. The trust aims to make initial contact within one month of receiving a proposal. If it decides to proceed further, it will work with the applicant to develop the proposal. If you would like to speak to a member of the grants team prior to submitting your proposal please contact Asma Aroui on 020 7632 9068 or email a.aroui@barrowcadbury.org.uk.

WHO TO APPLY TO Jackie Collins, Grants and Outreach Manager, Kean House, 6 Kean Street, London WC2B 4AS *Tel* 020 7632 9060 *Fax* 020 7632 9061 *email* general@barrowcadbury.org.uk *Website* www.barrowcadbury.org.uk

CC NO 1115476   **ESTABLISHED** 1920

■ The Cadogan Charity

WHERE FUNDING CAN BE GIVEN Worldwide. In practice UK with a preference for charities operating or based in London or Scotland.

WHO CAN BENEFIT Registered charities.

WHAT IS FUNDED General, in particular social welfare, medical research, services charities, animal welfare, education and conservation and the environment.

WHAT IS NOT FUNDED No grants to individuals.

TYPE OF GRANT Support is usually given over one to two years, although some one-off grants may be made.

RANGE OF GRANTS Up to £250,000.

SAMPLE GRANTS Natural History Museum, Royal Veterinary College and St Paul's Cathedral Foundation (£250,000 each); In-Pensioners' Mobility Fund and Christchurch Chelsea (£100,000 each); Help for Heroes (£35,000); London Playing Fields Foundation (£20,000); Wildlife Conservation Trust (£10,000); Guild of Air Pilots and Navigators (£8,000); World Wildlife Fund (£5,000); Tommy's – the Baby Charity (£2,000); Chelsea Old Church (£1,500); and Addaction (£1,000).

FINANCES *Year* 2007–08 *Income* £1,359,747 *Grants* £1,380,500 *Assets* £31,884,296

TRUSTEES Earl Cadogan; Countess Cadogan; Viscount Chelsea; Lady Anna Thomson.

HOW TO APPLY In writing to the correspondent.

WHO TO APPLY TO P M Loutit, Secretary, 18 Cadogan Gardens, London SW3 2RP *Tel* 020 7730 4567 *Fax* 0207 881 2300

CC NO 247773   **ESTABLISHED** 1966

■ CAF (Charities Aid Foundation)

WHERE FUNDING CAN BE GIVEN Worldwide.

WHO CAN BENEFIT Any registered (or Inland Revenue approved) charity.

WHAT IS FUNDED Generally, the development of small and medium-sized charitable organisations.

WHAT IS NOT FUNDED Grants will not usually be given for: capital items, buildings, vehicles, maintenance costs; start-up costs of a new charitable organisation; funding that should properly be the responsibility of statutory agencies; schools, universities or NHS trusts; or work already completed. Note: full eligibility criteria will be available on the foundation's website when the new grants programme is launched.

TYPE OF GRANT One-off grants. Loans and investment support is available through the Venturesome initiative.

RANGE OF GRANTS Around £500–£100,000.

SAMPLE GRANTS Previous beneficiaries include: London Business School, City Centre for Charity Effectiveness Trust – CASS Business School, Nottingham Law Centre, Kairos in Soho, UK Youth Parliament, People in Action, Northern Ireland Childminding Association, Scottish Adult Learning Partnership and African and Caribbean Voices Association.

FINANCES *Year* 2008–09 *Income* £327,987,000 *Assets* £623,624,000

TRUSTEES David Weymouth; Kim Lavely; Lord Cairns; Adele Blakeborough; Sir Graham Melmoth; David Locke; Dominic Casserley; Connie Jackson; Philip Hardaker; Peter Wolton; John Lorimer; Iain Mackinnon; Jenny Watson.

OTHER INFORMATION At the time of writing, the foundation's main grant programme was closed and under review. A new programme is due to be launched soon. The foundation offers the following overview of the future programme in its 2008–09 accounts: 'For our 2009–10 programme we will focus on supporting initiatives that aim to make positive changes in the way people give to charity and the way that charities work with donors. We will engage and seek the views of key stakeholders to determine the focus. A proportion of each grant will support research, analysis and dissemination and we will seek to use approaches and learning to underpin the further development of our broader activities. The programme will be funded by our donor clients. Awards that meet our funding priorities will be made by CAF employees with responsibilities delegated by the Board of Trustees with the support of a newly formed Advisory Committee.' For the latest information please go to the website or contact the foundation directly. Previously around £1.5 million has been available through this programme.

HOW TO APPLY All applications must be submitted on an application form. There are several ways to view the guidelines and request an application form: visit the website; in writing to the correspondent; email enquiries@cafonline.org; or telephone 01732 520 000. Please note: at the time of writing, the foundation's main grant programme was closed and under review. The Venturesome programme remains open.

WHO TO APPLY TO Grants Team, 25 Kings Hill Avenue, Kings Hill, West Malling, Kent ME19 4TA *Tel* 01732 520000 *Fax* 01732 520001 *email* enquiries@cafonline.org *Website* www.cafonline.org/ (follow the link 'for charities')

CC NO 268369   **ESTABLISHED** 1974

■ CAFOD

WHERE FUNDING CAN BE GIVEN Predominantly overseas, with some funding to partners in the UK.

WHO CAN BENEFIT Poorer communities overseas and victims of famine, disasters or war.

WHAT IS FUNDED Long-term development work with some of the world's poorest communities. In almost all cases work overseas is planned and run by local people. Programmes include education and skills training, human rights promotion, healthcare, HIV/AIDS, safe water, agriculture and small businesses. Immediate help for people affected by emergencies such as wars and natural disasters is also funded, as is the analysis of the causes of underdevelopment and campaigns on behalf of the world's poor. All programmes seek to promote gender equality. In England and Wales CAFOD's Development Education Fund makes small grants to local or national groups with young people and adults for projects developing education and action on local/global poverty and injustice issues.

WHAT IS NOT FUNDED CAFOD generally does not award grants on application, but funds work through long term partnerships with predominantly Southern based civil society organisations. CAFOD does not make grants to individuals or to organisations whose aims are primarily political.

TYPE OF GRANT Partnership, programme and project.

FINANCES *Year* 2007–08 *Income* £47,914,000 *Grants* £27,034,000 *Assets* £26,968,000

TRUSTEES Right Revd. John Rawsthorne; Right Revd. Kieran Conry; Dr Mary Hallaway OBE; Nicholas Warren.

HOW TO APPLY UK applicants are advised to contact the Education Fund Coordinator for further details. Guidelines for Development Education Fund grants can be found on the CAFOD website.

WHO TO APPLY TO James Steel, Director of Finance and Services Division, Romero Close, Stockwell Road, London SW9 9TY *Tel* 020 7733 7900 *Fax* 020 7274 9630 *email* hqcafod@cafod.org. uk *Website* www.cafod.org.uk

CC NO 285776   **ESTABLISHED** 1962

■ The Callander Charitable Trust

WHERE FUNDING CAN BE GIVEN Falkirk, other parts of central Scotland and Galloway.

WHO CAN BENEFIT Charitable organisations.

WHAT IS FUNDED General charitable purposes.

WHAT IS NOT FUNDED No grants to individuals and non-registered charities.

FINANCES *Year* 2007–08 *Income* £93,939

HOW TO APPLY In writing to the correspondent.

WHO TO APPLY TO The Secretary, Morisons, 105 West George Street, Glasgow G2 1QA

SC NO SC016609

■ Calleva Foundation

WHERE FUNDING CAN BE GIVEN UK and worldwide.

WHO CAN BENEFIT Charitable organisations.

WHAT IS FUNDED Grants were categorised as follows: social services; children's holidays; overseas/ international relief; education; arts and culture; medical research; and animal welfare.

FINANCES *Year* 2008 *Income* £194,033 *Grants* £156,930 *Assets* £43,417

TRUSTEES S C Butt; C Butt.

HOW TO APPLY In writing to the correspondent.

WHO TO APPLY TO The Trustees, PO Box 22554, London W8 5GN

CC NO 1078808   **ESTABLISHED** 1999

■ The Calpe Trust

WHERE FUNDING CAN BE GIVEN Worldwide.

WHO CAN BENEFIT Registered charities benefiting people in need including refugees, homeless people, people who are socially disadvantaged, victims of war, victims of disasters and so on.

WHAT IS FUNDED Grants towards human rights, health and welfare, emergencies and so on.

WHAT IS NOT FUNDED No grants towards animal welfare or to individuals.

SAMPLE GRANTS Ecumenical Project (£5,100); Salt of the Earth (£5,000); New Israel Fund (£4,000); OXFAM (£1,000); and CAFOD, International Refugee Trust, LEPRA, Survival International Charitable Trust, SSAFA, TRAX and UNICEF (£500 each).

FINANCES *Year* 2007–08 *Income* £32,465 *Grants* £27,920 *Assets* £1,044,201

TRUSTEES R H L R Norton, Chair; B E M Norton; E R H Perks.

HOW TO APPLY In writing to the correspondent. Applicants must contact the trust before making an application.

WHO TO APPLY TO R Norton, Trustee, The Hideaway, Sandy Lane, Hatford Down, Faringdon, Oxfordshire SN7 8JH *Tel* 01367 870665 *email* reggienorton@talktalk.net

CC NO 1004193   **ESTABLISHED** 1990

■ Calypso Browning Trust

WHERE FUNDING CAN BE GIVEN UK.

WHO CAN BENEFIT Organisations benefiting homeless people and animals.

WHAT IS FUNDED Regular grants made to some chosen charities but very occasionally to new charities in line with the trust's objects.

WHAT IS NOT FUNDED No grants to individuals.

SAMPLE GRANTS Kensington Housing Trust and Notting Hill Housing Trust (£6,500 each); Housing Associations Charitable Trust (£3,800); Brighton Housing Trust and SHELTER (£3,300 each); SPEAR (£1,600); People's Dispensary for Sick Animals and RSPCA (£1,000); and Dogs Trust (£500).

FINANCES *Year* 2007–08 *Income* £36,186 *Grants* £29,000 *Assets* £732,863

TRUSTEES A B S Weir; Ms A Kapp.

HOW TO APPLY In writing to the correspondent. Please note that most of the donations/grants are ongoing, as specified in the trust's deed.

WHO TO APPLY TO Michael Byrne, Vizards Tweedie, Barnards Inn, 86 Fetter Lane, London EC4A 1AD

CC NO 281986   **ESTABLISHED** 1979

■ The Cambridgeshire Community Foundation

WHERE FUNDING CAN BE GIVEN Cambridgeshire.

WHO CAN BENEFIT Voluntary and charitable groups.

WHAT IS FUNDED Community projects seeking to tackle a need or disadvantage. The foundation administers a number of funds. For up-to-date details, please see its website.

RANGE OF GRANTS The majority of the grants awarded are for small amounts of between £500–£5,000.

FINANCES *Year* 2007–08 *Income* £877,888 *Grants* £693,709 *Assets* £172,078

TRUSTEES Peter Gutteridge, Chair;Allyson Broadhurst; Anthony Clay; John Bridge; Nigel Atkinson; Bill Dastur; Jerry Turner; Richard Barnwell; Valerie Holt; Anne Ridgeon.

OTHER INFORMATION 'We award grants from the funds that local individuals, companies, and local and national government set up with us. The funds have different criteria (including the amounts they give out) and on receiving your application we will match your request to the most appropriate fund (unfortunately we will not be able to find a match for all requests received).'

HOW TO APPLY Guidelines and applications form can be downloaded from the foundation's website.

WHO TO APPLY TO Jane Darlington, Chief Executive, The Quorum, Barnwell Road, Cambridge CB5 8RE *Tel* 01223 410535 *email* info@cambscf.org.uk *Website* www.cambscf.org.uk

CC NO 1103314   **ESTABLISHED** 2003

■ The Cambridgeshire Historic Churches Trust

WHERE FUNDING CAN BE GIVEN Cambridgeshire.

WHO CAN BENEFIT Bodies responsible for the upkeep, repair and maintenance of a church, chapel or other building used for public worship.

WHAT IS FUNDED The preservation, repair, maintenance, improvement, upkeep and reconstruction of churches in the county of Cambridge and the monuments, fittings, fixtures, stained glass, furniture, ornaments and chattels in such churches and the churchyards belonging to any such churches.

WHAT IS NOT FUNDED Grants are not usually available for additional building work, re-ordering, re-decoration or minor programmes of maintenance.

TYPE OF GRANT The grants scheme is funded from an annual payment made by Waste Recycling Environmental and is resourced entirely from Landfill Tax credits assigned by Waste Recycling plc.

RANGE OF GRANTS From £1,000–£7,000 primarily for urgent repairs to fabric or renewal of essential services in churches and chapels.

FINANCES *Year* 2007–08 *Income* £168,873 *Grants* £67,602 *Assets* £711,699

TRUSTEES Richard Halsey; Pamela, Lady Wedgwood; Ven. David Fleming; Ven. Richard Sledge; Everard Poole; Julian Limentani; Dr John Maddison; Revd. Canon Christopher Barber; Nick Cleaver.

PUBLICATIONS Newsletter.

HOW TO APPLY For further information on how to apply, please see the trust's website.

WHO TO APPLY TO David Collingswood, Grants Officer, 21 The Pasture, Somersham, Huntingdon PE28 3YX *Tel* 01487 741171 *email* grants@cambshistoricchurchestrust.co.uk *Website* www.cambshistoricchurchestrust.co.uk

CC NO 287486   **ESTABLISHED** 1983

■ The Camelia trust

WHERE FUNDING CAN BE GIVEN Liverpool City and Manchester City.

WHO CAN BENEFIT Charitable organisations.

WHAT IS FUNDED General charitable purposes.

WHAT IS NOT FUNDED Royal School (£4,800); Lifeboat Hoylake (£4,000); NYO (£3,500); Brainwave, Deafblind UK and I Can (£3,000 each); Harvest Trust, Mobility and Salvation Army (£2,000 each); Action 4 Kids and Sense (£1500 each); Thrive (£1,100); Headway, St Ann's Hospice and Tall Ships (£1,000); Terrance Higgins (£500); and PSDA (£250).

SAMPLE GRANTS Royal School (£4,800); Lifeboat Hoylake (£4,000); NYO (£3,500); Brainwave, Deafblind UK and I Can (£3,000 each); Harvest Trust, Mobility and Salvation Army (£2,000 each); Action 4 Kids and Sense (£1500 each); Thrive (£1,100); Headway, St Ann's Hospice and Tall Ships (£1,000); Terrance Higgins (£500); and PSDA (£250).

FINANCES *Year* 2007–08 *Income* £54,135 *Grants* £52,050 *Assets* £927,671

TRUSTEES Jennifer Sykes, Dr Prudence Gillett; David Sykes; Michael Taxman.

HOW TO APPLY In writing to the correspondent.

WHO TO APPLY TO Jennifer Sykes, Trustee, Hillside, 9 Wainwright Road, Altrincham, Cheshire WA1 4 4BW

CC NO 1081074   **ESTABLISHED** 2000

■ The Campden Charities

WHERE FUNDING CAN BE GIVEN The former parish of Kensington, London; a north-south corridor, roughly from north of the Fulham Road to the north of Ladbroke Grove (a map can be viewed on the website).

WHO CAN BENEFIT Individuals (particularly the under-25s) and non-statutory not for profit organisations which refer and support individuals.

WHAT IS FUNDED Supporting outcomes for disadvantaged people, particularly young people and adults who have experienced a long period of unemployment.

WHAT IS NOT FUNDED UK charities or charities outside Kensington, unless they are of significant benefit to Kensington residents; schemes or activities which are generally regarded as the responsibility of the statutory authorities; UK fundraising appeals; environmental projects unless connected with education or social need; medical research or equipment; animal welfare; advancement of religion or religious groups, unless they offer non-religious services to the community; commercial and business activities; endowment appeals; projects of a political nature; retrospective capital grants.

TYPE OF GRANT One-off and recurrent funding for buildings, capital, core costs, feasibility studies and full project costs. Pensions to older people, grants in cash or in kind to relieve need, bursaries and all kinds of grants to Kensington-based organisations.

RANGE OF GRANTS £1,000–£119,000.

SAMPLE GRANTS NOVA (£119,000); Westway Community Transport (£91,000); My Generation (£66,000); Earls Court YMCA (£60,000); Nucleus Legal Advice Centre (£42,000); Staying Put (£18,000); Servite Houses (£6,000); Sixty Plus (£4,000); London Cyrenians (£3,000); Streetlytes (£2,000); and Ethiopia Woman's Group (£1,000).

FINANCES *Year* 2008–09 *Income* £2,837,301 *Grants* £2,057,720 *Assets* £70,552,448

TRUSTEES Revd Gillean Craig, Chair; David Banks; Elisabeth Brockmann; Chris Calman; Dr Kit Davis; Steve Hoier; Susan Lockhart; Tim Martin; Terry Myers; Ben Pilling; Victoria Stark; Richard Walker-Arnott.

OTHER INFORMATION The grant total includes £1.5 million in grants to individuals.

HOW TO APPLY 'The Charities is trying to target its resources where they can be of the most direct benefit to financially disadvantaged individuals. The Charities therefore do not receive unsolicited applications for funding from organisations. However the Charities' officers are eager to meet with colleagues from other not-for-profit organisations to explore ways in which we can work together to help individuals to end dependency on benefits or improve a low wage. If you have contact with individuals whom you would like to refer [. . .] telephone 020 7313 3797.'

WHO TO APPLY TO Chris Stannard, Clerk to the Trustees, 27a Pembridge Villas, London W11 3EP *Tel* 020 7243 0551 *Fax* 020 7229 4920 *Website* www.cctrustee.org.uk

CC NO 1003641   **ESTABLISHED** 1629

■ The Frederick and Phyllis Cann Trust

WHERE FUNDING CAN BE GIVEN Northamptonshire.

WHO CAN BENEFIT The Trust Deed names seven charities, but trustees are prepared to consider other charities that fall within the charitable objects of the trust.

WHAT IS FUNDED The main objects of the trust are animal welfare, welfare of children and safety at sea.

RANGE OF GRANTS Up to £10,000.

SAMPLE GRANTS Northampton Association of Youth Clubs (£10,000); Salvation Army (£6,400); Brainwave (£5,000); Northampton Sailability (£3,500); Extra Care Charitable Trust and Dreams Come Truth (£2,000 each); Happy Days (£1,000); and MacMillan Cancer Support (£650).

FINANCES *Year* 2008–09 *Income* £84,733 *Grants* £67,200 *Assets* £1,534,265

TRUSTEES Michael Percival; David Sharp; Keith Panter; Philip Saunderson; Christopher Tommer.

HOW TO APPLY In writing to the correspondent.

WHO TO APPLY TO David Sharp, Trustee, Moore Stephens, Oakley House, Headway Business Park, 3 Saxon Way West, Corby NN18 9EZ *Tel* 01536 461900

CC NO 1087863   **ESTABLISHED** 1998

■ The Canning Trust

WHERE FUNDING CAN BE GIVEN UK and the developing world.

WHO CAN BENEFIT Small concerns.

WHAT IS FUNDED Only donations proposed internally by staff members.

SAMPLE GRANTS Village Water (£10,000); Tushar Project – Herbertpur Christian Hospital (£4,000); Dogodogo Centre, Softpower and TESFA (£3,000 each); Alive and Kicking (£2,100); Kafue Fisheries (£2,000); St Mary's National School (£1,600); and Loldia (£1,000).

FINANCES *Year* 2007–08 *Income* £25,720 *Grants* £33,700 *Assets* £216,631

TRUSTEES A J MacDonald; Mrs R R Pooley; Mrs R Griffiths.

HOW TO APPLY Unsolicited applications are not considered. The trust states that it generally only makes grants to charities which staff; ex-staff and friends are directly involved with.

WHO TO APPLY TO The Trustees, 593–599 Fulham Road, London SW6 5UA

CC NO 292675   **ESTABLISHED** 1985

■ M R Cannon 1998 Charitable Trust

WHERE FUNDING CAN BE GIVEN Preference for North Devon, Dorset, Bristol, North Yorkshire and County Durham.

WHO CAN BENEFIT Charities and community groups.

WHAT IS FUNDED 'The objectives of the charity are general charitable purposes to the benefit of the general public. The trustees have no specific grant making criteria but are interested in supporting medical/health charities and conservation and countryside related initiatives, as well as small local projects in North Devon, Dorset, Bristol, North Yorkshire and County Durham. The trustees also support young people who wish to carry out vocational training or studies.'

SAMPLE GRANTS Wings South West (£5,000); Portsmouth Cathedral and Second Chance

(£2,000); Forget Me Not (£1,500); Countryside Foundation for Education (£1,000); North Devon Hospice (£1,000 in two grants); Appledore Arts and Peters Church – Bratton Fleming (£250); Devon and Somerset Air Ambulance (£200); Alwington PCC, Canine Partners, Children's Hospice South West and Dorset Wildlife Trust (£100 each); and RSPCA (£50).

FINANCES *Year* 2007–08 *Income* £1,000,000 *Grants* £14,000 *Assets* £1,500,000

TRUSTEES M R Cannon; Mrs S A T Cannon; C J Mitchell.

HOW TO APPLY In writing to the correspondent.

WHO TO APPLY TO The Trustees, 53 Stoke Lane, Westbury On Trym, Bristol BS9 3DW

CC NO 1072769

■ H and L Cantor Trust

WHERE FUNDING CAN BE GIVEN UK, with some preference for Sheffield.

WHO CAN BENEFIT Registered charities, with particular consideration to be given to Jewish charities.

WHAT IS FUNDED Jewish causes and general charitable purposes.

SAMPLE GRANTS Delamere Forest School Ltd (£31,000 in two grants); Sheffield Jewish Congregation & Centre (980 in seven grants); Sheffield Jewish Welfare Organisation (£150 in two grants); I Rescue, Jewish Childs Day, Sense and Share Zadek UK (£100 each); Brain Research Trust (£50); PDSA Sheffield (£25); and World Cancer Research (£10).

FINANCES *Year* 2007–08 *Income* £27,472 *Grants* £32,943 *Assets* £937,871

TRUSTEES L Cantor; N Jeffrey.

HOW TO APPLY Unsolicited applications are not invited.

WHO TO APPLY TO Mrs Lilly Cantor, Trustee, 3 Ivy Park Court, 35 Ivy Park Road, Sheffield S10 3LA

CC NO 220300   **ESTABLISHED** 1959

■ Capital Community Foundation

WHERE FUNDING CAN BE GIVEN The London boroughs including the City of London.

WHO CAN BENEFIT Community organisations benefiting unemployed people, volunteers, people disadvantaged by poverty, refugees and people living in urban areas.

WHAT IS FUNDED Community based projects enhancing the quality of life of people in the community and addressing discrimination and disadvantage. Each scheme run by the foundation has its own local grant criteria and awards panel.

WHAT IS NOT FUNDED Generally, no grants for individuals, political groups or activities which promote religion.

TYPE OF GRANT Normally one-off for core costs, feasibility studies, project, running costs, salaries and start up costs. Funding is available for up to two years on some programmes. Most are up to one year.

RANGE OF GRANTS Small grant programmes up to £5,000. Large grants up to £35,000.

SAMPLE GRANTS Beneficiaries included: Southbank Centre (£50,000); Lewisham Muslim Women's Group (£35,000); Second Wave (£30,000); Chickenshed (£25,000); Ebony Horse Club (£6,600); Westminster Society (£5,000); Stone Crabs (£3,600); Friends of Kennington Park (£3,000); Deafroots Association (£2,000); and Renton Close Community Centre (£1,900).

Think carefully about every application. Is it justified?

407

FINANCES *Year* 2007–08 *Income* £3,508,369 *Grants* £2,726,888 *Assets* £1,476,709

TRUSTEES Carole Souter, Chair; Gordon Williamson; Ade Sawyerr; Clive Cutbill; Michael Brophy; Kathy Seligman; Nicholas Hammond; Richard Battesby.

OTHER INFORMATION The foundation is primarily the local distributor of funds from a number of government programmes under a variety of different schemes.

HOW TO APPLY In order to apply for a grant from the foundation your organisation must have: a management committee of at least three people who are not related and are not paid wages by your group; a governing document (e.g. constitution or Memorandum & Articles of Association); a bank account with at least two unrelated signatories for transactions (Pass Book accounts or those which permit only cash withdrawals are not accepted); a child protection policy and procedures if you will be working with children.

As the foundation offers funds on behalf of different donors, you may apply to each and every programme for which your group is eligible. However, the criteria do vary for each grant programme, so be sure to read the guidance carefully. If you are unsure about your eligibility, please call the grants team on Tel: 020 7582 5117 before making an application. Application forms and guidance notes specific to each programme are available from the foundation and/or the website. Each programme has its own set of closing dates. All applications must reach Capital Community Foundation by 5pm on that date.

WHO TO APPLY TO Victoria Warne, Head of Grants, 357 Kennington Lane, London SE11 5QY *Tel* 020 7582 5117 *Fax* 020 7582 4020 *email* enquiries@capitalcf.org.uk *Website* www. capitalcf.org.uk

CC NO 1091263   ESTABLISHED 2002

....

■ Cardy Beaver Foundation

WHERE FUNDING CAN BE GIVEN UK with preference for the Reading and Berkshire areas.

WHO CAN BENEFIT National and local charities.

WHAT IS FUNDED General charitable purposes.

SAMPLE GRANTS WAMPSAD (£9,000); Action Medical Research, Alzheimer's Disease Society, Berkshire Multiple Sclerosis Centre, the Children's Transplant Foundation, Duchess of Kent House Trust, Newbury and District Cancer Care Trust, Pets as Therapy, Prostate Cancer Research Campaign UK, RNLI, Thames Valley Air Ambulance, the Charlie Waller Memorial Trust and the Watermill Theatre Appeal (£4,500 each); and St Matthew's Church – Midgham (£2,500).

FINANCES *Year* 2007–08 *Income* £186,580 *Grants* £117,500 *Assets* £2,370,277

TRUSTEES G R Coia, Chair; M G Cardy; S I Rice.

HOW TO APPLY In writing to the correspondent.

WHO TO APPLY TO G R Coia, Clifton House, 17 Reading Road, Pangbourne, Berkshire RG8 7LU *Tel* 0118 984 4713

CC NO 265763   ESTABLISHED 1973

....

■ The Carew Pole Charitable Trust

WHERE FUNDING CAN BE GIVEN UK, in practice, mainly Cornwall.

WHO CAN BENEFIT Donations normally made only to registered charities, but applications will be considered from individuals for non-full-time education purposes.

WHAT IS FUNDED General charitable purposes principally in Cornwall. In the case of support to churches and village halls, donations are in practice only made to those in the immediate vicinity to Antony House, Torpoint or to those with connections to the Carew Pole Family.

WHAT IS NOT FUNDED The trustees do not support applications from individuals for full-time education.

RANGE OF GRANTS £100–£31,000.

SAMPLE GRANTS National Trust (£12,500); Combat Stress (£2,000); Antony Church and Home Start West Cornwall (£1,000); Maryfield Church and Sheviock Church (£600 each); National Youth Theatre (£300); Falmouth and Exeter Students Union (£250); RNLI – Rame Division (£250); and St John's Church (£100).

FINANCES *Year* 2007–08 *Income* £62,426 *Grants* £18,900 *Assets* £1,657,298

TRUSTEES T J Carew Pole; J Kitson; J Williams.

OTHER INFORMATION This charitable trust was founded by Sir John Gawen Carew Pole, whose family has both lived in and been connected with Cornwall for many years.

HOW TO APPLY In writing to the correspondent. The trustees consider and approve major donations in November each year, while other smaller appeals are considered, and donations made, throughout the year.

WHO TO APPLY TO Paul Cressy, The Estate Office, Antony, Torpoint, Cornwall PL11 3AB

CC NO 255375   ESTABLISHED 1968

....

■ The D W T Cargill Fund

WHERE FUNDING CAN BE GIVEN UK, with a preference for the west of Scotland.

WHO CAN BENEFIT Registered charities.

WHAT IS FUNDED General charitable purposes, particularly religious causes, medical charities and help for older people.

WHAT IS NOT FUNDED No grants are made to individuals.

TYPE OF GRANT One-off and recurrent.

SAMPLE GRANTS Previous beneficiaries have included City of Glasgow Society of Social Service, Colquhoun Bequest Fund for Incurables, Crathie Opportunity Holidays, Glasgow and West of Scotland Society for the Blind, Glasgow City Mission, Greenock Medical Aid Society, North Glasgow Community Forum, Scottish Maritime Museum – Irvine, Scottish Episcopal Church, Scottish Motor Neurone Disease Association, Lead Scotland and Three Towns Blind Bowling/ Social Club.

FINANCES *Year* 2007–08 *Income* £302,966

TRUSTEES A C Fyfe; W G Peacock; N A Fyfe; Mirren Elizabeth Graham.

HOW TO APPLY In writing to the correspondent, supported by up-to-date accounts. Trustees meet quarterly.

WHO TO APPLY TO Norman A Fyfe, Trustee, Miller Beckett and Jackson Solicitors, 190 St Vincent Street, Glasgow G2 5SP

SC NO SC012703   ESTABLISHED 1939

....

408   *Does the trust you have chosen match your needs? Haphazard applications waste postage and time*

■ Caring for Kids (Radio Tay)

WHERE FUNDING CAN BE GIVEN Tayside and Fife.

WHO CAN BENEFIT Individuals and organisations benefiting children and young people, especially those from one parent families, and those who are at risk, disabled, disadvantaged by poverty, socially isolated or victims of abuse.

WHAT IS FUNDED Children's education, disability and recreation.

WHAT IS NOT FUNDED No grants for staff wages or rent.

SAMPLE GRANTS Previous beneficiaries have included Brechin Youth Project, Ninewells Hospital, Oasis Youth Project, Strathmore Comfort Fund, Special Needs at Play and Youth Care.

FINANCES *Year* 2008 *Income* £233,004

TRUSTEES Paul Smith, Chair; Arthur Ballingall; Boris Klapiscak; Lorraine Stevenson; Lady Fiona Fraser; Mrs M Young; Alison Wiseman; Norma Gamble.

HOW TO APPLY Application forms are available from the correspondent from early December. They must be returned by the end of January for consideration for the distribution in March. Applications from individuals must be recommended from a third party such as a social worker, doctor, head teacher, or charitable organisation and so on.

WHO TO APPLY TO The Charity Coordinator, Radio Tay Ltd, 6 North Isla Street, Dundee DD3 7JQ *Website* www.tayfm.co.uk

SC NO SC008440

■ Carlee Ltd

WHERE FUNDING CAN BE GIVEN Worldwide.

WHO CAN BENEFIT Talmudical scholars and Jewish people.

WHAT IS FUNDED The advancement of religion in accordance with the orthodox Jewish faith; the relief of poverty; general charitable purposes.

SAMPLE GRANTS Previous beneficiaries have included Antryvale Ltd, Asos Cheshed, Egerton Road Building Fund, Glasgow Kollel, HTVC, Rav Chesed Trust, Tevini, Union of Hebrew Congregations, YHS and YHTC.

FINANCES *Year* 2005–06 *Income* £149,121 *Grants* £155,730 *Assets* £746,307

TRUSTEES Hershel Grunhut; Mrs P Grunhut; Bernard Dor Stroh; Mrs B Stroh.

OTHER INFORMATION Accounts for the years ending 2006–07 and 2007–08 were overdue at the Charity Commission.

HOW TO APPLY In writing to the correspondent.

WHO TO APPLY TO The Secretary, 32 Pagent Road, London N16 5NQ

CC NO 282873   **ESTABLISHED** 1981

■ The Carlsson Family Foundation

WHERE FUNDING CAN BE GIVEN UK.

WHO CAN BENEFIT Charitable organisations.

WHAT IS FUNDED The promotion of the health and educational welfare of disadvantaged children and their families. 'Committed to this principle the foundation aims: to assist children in poverty with special reference to those in one parent families; to promote child and family welfare, including physical, emotional and mental well-being; to foster the intellectual and personal development of children to promote and encourage a strong sense of responsibility with an emphasis on co-operation and self-help among families; to relate in creative and innovative ways with other charities and social agencies in the wider field of child poverty; to raise consciousness by building educational and communication networks within financial, political and cultural spheres.'

SAMPLE GRANTS Georgetown University (£251,000); and St Mary's School – Ascot (£7,200).

FINANCES *Year* 2007–08 *Income* £78,473 *Grants* £258,444 *Assets* £1,549,089

TRUSTEES Roger Carlsson; Courtney Carlsson; Carina Carlsson; Carrie Hague; Matthew Hunt.

HOW TO APPLY In writing to the correspondent.

WHO TO APPLY TO The Trustees, 3rd Floor, Dauntsey House, 4B Frederick's Place, London EC2R 8AB *Tel* 020 7964 9821 *email* info@ thecarlssonfamilyfoundation.org.uk *Website* www.thecarlssonfamilyfoundation.co.uk

CC NO 1072954

■ The Carlton House Charitable Trust

WHERE FUNDING CAN BE GIVEN UK and overseas.

WHO CAN BENEFIT Charitable organisations and Jewish organisations.

WHAT IS FUNDED The advancement of education, research work and fellowships. Most funds are committed to various charitable institutions in the UK and abroad; a limited number of bursaries are given, mainly connected with the professional interests of the trustees.

TYPE OF GRANT One-off.

RANGE OF GRANTS £35–£9,000.

SAMPLE GRANTS National Trust (£5,500); Godalfm Latymer School (£3,500); Westminster Advocacy Service (£3,000); Western Marble Arch Synagogue (£1,900); Bnai Brith Hillel Foundation, Jewish Care, Royal Academy of Dramatic Art, St Edmunds Hall and University of Bristol (£1,000 each); Jewish Music Institute (£900); London Philharmonic Orchestra (£750); Holocaust Centre (£500); British Friends of the Hebrew University (£250).

FINANCES *Year* 2007–08 *Income* £360,736 *Grants* £41,288 *Assets* £1,066,460

TRUSTEES S Cohen; Mrs P G Cohen; Mrs F A Stein.

HOW TO APPLY In writing to the correspondent.

WHO TO APPLY TO Stewart S Cohen, Trustee, Craven House, 121 Kingsway, London WC2B 6PA

CC NO 296791   **ESTABLISHED** 1986

■ The Worshipful Company of Carmen Benevolent Trust

WHERE FUNDING CAN BE GIVEN City of London and UK.

WHO CAN BENEFIT People connected with transport.

WHAT IS FUNDED Objects of relieving necessitous past or present Liverymen or Freemen of the Company, its employees and servants, or those connected with transport in the UK. The trust is also allowed to made grants to any charitable fund in the City of London or elsewhere.

RANGE OF GRANTS £100–£6,000.

SAMPLE GRANTS Christ's Hospital (£25,000); Breast Cancer Research (£9,000); King Edwards Witley (£6,000); Everyman (£4,000); Treloar Trust (£2,000); Army Benevolent Fund, Sheriff & Recorders Fund and Emmaus (£1,000 each); and Childrens Fire & Burns, Trust Disability Aid Fund, Mudchute and Save The Children Fund (£500 each).

FINANCES *Year* 2008–09 *Income* £123,789 *Grants* £72,775 *Assets* £841,385

TRUSTEES J A T Saywell; M J Power; Brig. M H Turner; M W J Older; Mrs M Bonar; M Simpkin; R H Russett.

HOW TO APPLY In writing to the correspondent.

WHO TO APPLY TO Robin East, The Hon. Secretary, Painter's Hall Chambers, 8 Little Trinity Lane, London EC4V 2AN *Tel* 020 7489 8289 *email* bentrust@thecarmen.co.uk *Website* www.thecarmen.co.uk

CC NO 1050893   **ESTABLISHED** 1995

■ The Richard Carne Trust

WHERE FUNDING CAN BE GIVEN UK.

WHO CAN BENEFIT Young people.

WHAT IS FUNDED The performing arts.

SAMPLE GRANTS Royal College of Music (£50,000); Royal Academy of Dramatic Art (£30,000); London Academy of Music and Drama (£25,000); Royal Welsh College of Music and Drama (£20,000); Classical Opera Company and Trinity College of Music (£10,000 each); South Bank Sinfonia (£7,000); Rakhi Sing/Barbiroili Quartet (£4,000); and ENO Young Singers Programme (£2,500).

FINANCES *Year* 2006–07 *Income* £566,000 *Grants* £169,000

TRUSTEES Kleinwort Benson Trustees Ltd; Philip Edward Carne; Marjorie Christine Carne.

HOW TO APPLY 'The trustees' current policy is to consider all written appeals received, but only successful applications are notified of the trustees' decision. [...] The trustees review the selected charities, and consider new appeals received at their annual trustee meeting, normally held in June. Only successful applicants are notified of the trustees' decision.'

WHO TO APPLY TO Christopher Gilbert, Administrator, Kleinwort Benson Trustees Ltd, 30 Gresham Street, London EC2V 7PG *Tel* 020 3207 7356

CC NO 1115903   **ESTABLISHED** 2006

■ The Carnegie Dunfermline Trust

WHERE FUNDING CAN BE GIVEN Dunfermline and Rosyth.

WHO CAN BENEFIT Local communities, clubs and societies.

WHAT IS FUNDED 'Projects, activities and schemes with social, community, educational, cultural, sport and recreational purposes for the benefit of those within the defined geographic area of the operation of the trust. This can include community facilities and services, voluntary sector activities, clubs and societies and environmental and infrastructure development. Proposals that are innovative and far reaching together with those that particularly impact on young people are looked for with interest together with active partnerships.'

WHAT IS NOT FUNDED Individuals; closed groups (with the exception of those catering for specialist needs); political, military or sectarian bodies; activities outwith the geographic scope of the trust; medical organisations; routine running or salary costs; costs which are the responsibility of a government body.

TYPE OF GRANT Principally single grants and capital funding. Pump priming and start up funding is offered on a one-off basis.

RANGE OF GRANTS Typical grant between £300 and £10,000.

SAMPLE GRANTS Previous beneficiarie shave included Carnegie Festival, City First, Dunfermline Fencing Club, Friends of Pittencrieff Park, Fusion Dance Group, Head in the Clouds, Gig in the Glen and Peace in the Park – Dunfermline.

FINANCES *Year* 2008 *Income* £422,483

TRUSTEES The trust has a board of 20 trustees.

HOW TO APPLY On a form which can be downloaded from the trust's website. 'Trustees meet every two months and applications can be submitted at any time. Application forms are available and initial discussion with the Chief Executive or Administrator is encouraged. Where possible applications will be acknowledged and further information may be sought. Once all the necessary background is available the application will be considered by the appropriate assessing trustee in the first instance who will decide if a grant under delegated powers is applicable, if it should go to the board, or if it is not suitable to progress. When a grant is awarded the recipient will be notified in writing with any related terms and conditions which will include the take up of the grant within a twelve month period.'

WHO TO APPLY TO The Chief Executive, Andrew Carnegie House, Pittencieff Street, Dunfermline KY12 8AW *Tel* 01383 749789 *Fax* 01383 749799 *email* admin@carnegietrust.com *Website* www.andrewcarnegie.co.uk

SC NO SC015710   **ESTABLISHED** 1903

■ The Carnegie Trust for the Universities of Scotland

WHERE FUNDING CAN BE GIVEN Scotland.

WHO CAN BENEFIT Undergraduates of Scottish birth, Scottish parentage or Scottish schooling; graduates and members of staff of the Scottish universities.

WHAT IS FUNDED Universities in Scotland through the improvement of facilities and support of research. Graduates and members of staff of Scottish universities, and undergraduates of Scottish birth or extraction for fees for first degrees at Scottish universities.

TYPE OF GRANT Capital for projects of value to the Scottish universities, with wide discretion on what is allowable.

FINANCES *Year* 2008 *Income* £2,689,253 *Grants* £2,163,480 *Assets* £50,367,670

TRUSTEES 12 nominated trustees and 14 ex-offcio trustees.

OTHER INFORMATION All of the trust's schemes are described in detail on its website.

HOW TO APPLY Regulations and application forms can be obtained from the secretary and from the website. Preliminary telephone enquiries are welcome.

WHO TO APPLY TO The Secretary, Andrew Carnegie House, Pittencrieff Street, Dunfermline, Fife KY12 8AW *Tel* 01383 724990 *email* jgray@carnegie-trust.org *Website* www.carnegie-trust.org

SC NO SC015600   **ESTABLISHED** 1901

■ The Carpenter Charitable Trust

WHERE FUNDING CAN BE GIVEN UK and overseas.

WHO CAN BENEFIT Humanitarian and Christian outreach charities are preferred.

WHAT IS FUNDED General charitable objects with a Christian bias. 'The charity is established on wide grant giving terms. The trustees continue to pursue their 'preferred' list approach – a list of charities with which the trustees have developed a good relationship over the years.'

WHAT IS NOT FUNDED 'The trustees do not consider applications for church repairs (other than in respect of Kimpton Church) not applications from individuals nor any applications received from abroad unless clearly 'sponsored' by an established charity based in England and Wales.'

TYPE OF GRANT One-off (but some are in practice repeated).

RANGE OF GRANTS £250–£2,500.

SAMPLE GRANTS Mission Aviation Fellowship Europe (£7,500); ORBIS Charitable Trust (£6,000); Andrew Christian Trust, Barnabas Fund, Help in Suffering UK and Relationships Foundation (£5,000 each); DEC Bangladesh (£2,500); Brooke Hospital for Animals, Crisis UK, Merlin and Salvation Army (£1,000 each); Blue Cross, Fight for Sight, Mercy Ships, Prison Fellowship, RSPB, Send a Cow and Tibet Relief (£500 each); and Cats Protection League (£250).

FINANCES *Year* 2007–08 *Income* £269,815 *Grants* £69,075 *Assets* £1,125,386

TRUSTEES M S E Carpenter; Mrs G M L Carpenter.

HOW TO APPLY In writing to the correspondent including sufficient details to enable a decision to be made. However, as about half the donations made are repeat grants, the amount available for unsolicited applications remains small.

WHO TO APPLY TO M S E Carpenter, Trustee, The Old Vicarage, Hitchin Road, Kimpton, Hitchin, Hertfordshire SG4 8EF

CC NO 280692   **ESTABLISHED** 1980

■ The Carpenters' Company Charitable Trust

WHERE FUNDING CAN BE GIVEN UK.

WHO CAN BENEFIT Individuals and schools, colleges, universities and other charitable organisations promoting the craft of carpentry.

WHAT IS FUNDED Charitable causes benefiting from grants include organisations supporting older people, people with disabilities, the homeless, young people and children, education, medical and museums. Craft causes receive a high priority when awards are considered.

WHAT IS NOT FUNDED Grants are not normally made to individual churches or cathedrals, or to educational establishments having no association to the Carpenters' Company. No grants (except educational grants) are made to individual applicants. Funds are usually only available to charities registered with the charity commission or exempt from registration.

SAMPLE GRANTS The Building Crafts College (£357,000).

FINANCES *Year* 2007–08 *Income* £2,743,691 *Grants* £829,718 *Assets* £19,774,380

TRUSTEES Peter A Luton; Malcolm R Francis; Michael I Montague-Smith; Guy Morton-Smith.

OTHER INFORMATION The grant total in 2007–08 included £18,000 given in grants to individuals.

HOW TO APPLY In writing to the correspondent.

WHO TO APPLY TO The Clerk, Carpenters' Hall, 1 Throgmorton Avenue, London EC2N 2JJ *Tel* 020 7588 7001 *email* info@carpentersco.com *Website* www.carpentersco.com/charitable_ccct.php

CC NO 276996   **ESTABLISHED** 1978

■ The Carr-Gregory Trust

WHERE FUNDING CAN BE GIVEN UK.

WHO CAN BENEFIT Charitable organisations.

WHAT IS FUNDED Arts, social welfare, health and education.

SAMPLE GRANTS The Royal National Theatre and St Thomas's – Goring on Thames (£10,000 each);

Royal Shakespeare Company and St James Priory Project (£2,500 each); Alzheimer's Research Trust, Action on Disability and Development, the Cheltenham Ladies' College and Connect (£2,000 each); the Gate Theatre, the Holburne Museum, the Royal Marsden Cancer Campaign and Victoria and Albert Museum (£1,000 each); NSPCC (£800); and Alabare Christian Care Centres, Emmaus Bristol, Quartet Community Foundation, Prisoners' Education Trust and St Mungo's (£500 each).

FINANCES *Year* 2007–08 *Income* £47,339 *Grants* £47,275 *Assets* £409,974

TRUSTEES Russ Carr; Heather Wheelhouse; Linda Carr.

HOW TO APPLY In writing to the correspondent.

WHO TO APPLY TO Russ Carr, Trustee, 56 Pembroke Road, Clifton, Bristol BS8 3DT

CC NO 1085580

■ The Carrington Charitable Trust

WHERE FUNDING CAN BE GIVEN UK with a preference for Buckinghamshire.

WHO CAN BENEFIT Local branches of a wide range of charities, and local charities.

WHAT IS FUNDED General charitable purposes.

WHAT IS NOT FUNDED No grants to individuals.

RANGE OF GRANTS Up to £21,000, mostly for smaller amounts.

SAMPLE GRANTS Combat stress (£21,000); Grenadier Guards – Colonel's Fund (£10,000); Bedlow PCC (£6,000); Hope and Homes for Children (£5,000); Royal British legion (£2,000); Army Benevolent Fund (£1,500); Buckinghamshire Disability Information Network and the Buckinghamshire Foundation (£1,000 each); Whizz Kidz (£750); Gurkha Welfare Trust (£250); Guides Association (£25); and National Playing Fields Association (£15).

FINANCES *Year* 2007–08 *Income* £101,464 *Grants* £65,973 *Assets* £4,408,644

TRUSTEES Rt Hon. Lord Carrington; J A Cloke; Rt Hon. V Carrington.

HOW TO APPLY In writing to the correspondent.

WHO TO APPLY TO J A Cloke, Trustee, c/o Cloke and Co, Warnford Court, 29 Throgmorton Street, London EC2N 2AT

CC NO 265824   **ESTABLISHED** 1973

■ The Carron Charitable Trust

WHERE FUNDING CAN BE GIVEN UK and overseas.

WHO CAN BENEFIT Charitable organisations.

WHAT IS FUNDED 'The trust was created for charitable purposes in connection with wildlife, education, medicine, the countryside and the printing and publishing trade.' Ongoing support is given to the St Bride's Church – Fleet Street.

WHAT IS NOT FUNDED No grants to individuals.

TYPE OF GRANT Project, research, running costs and salaries.

SAMPLE GRANTS St Bride's Church Appeal (£20,000); INTBAU (£10,000); Academy of Aviation and Space Medicine (£3,000); and Curwen Print Study Centre (£1,500).

FINANCES *Year* 2007–08 *Income* £77,125 *Grants* £84,834 *Assets* £214,400

TRUSTEES P G Fowler; W M Allen; D L Morgan.

HOW TO APPLY The trust does not invite applications from the general public.

WHO TO APPLY TO The Trustees, c/o Rothman Panthall and Co., 10 Romsey Road, Eastleigh, Hampshire SO50 9AL

CC NO 289164   **ESTABLISHED** 1984

Think carefully about every application. Is it justified?

411

■ The Leslie Mary Carter Charitable Trust

WHERE FUNDING CAN BE GIVEN UK, with a preference for Norfolk, Suffolk and North Essex.

WHO CAN BENEFIT Registered charities.

WHAT IS FUNDED The preferred areas for grant giving are conservation/environment and welfare causes. Other applications will be considered but acknowledgements may not always be sent. Trustees prefer well thought-out applications for larger gifts, than many applications for smaller grants.

WHAT IS NOT FUNDED No grants to individuals.

TYPE OF GRANT Capital including buildings, core costs, one-off, project, research, running costs and recurring costs will be considered.

RANGE OF GRANTS Grants generally range from £500–£5,000, but larger grants are sometimes considered.

SAMPLE GRANTS East Coast Sail Trust and East Anglia Children's Hospices (£7,500 each); Barn Owl Trust, Field Studies Council – Flatford Mill Appeal, RNID – Language Service Professional and YMCA Norfolk (5,000 each); Long Melford Church Appeal, Plantlife, Shelter – East Anglia and SSAFA Forces Help (£3,000 each); Acorn Village – Oakroom Project (£2,000); Royal Anglian Regiment Museum Appeal and Wildlife Trust – Awash with Wildlife (£1,000 each).

FINANCES *Year* 2008 *Income* £122,581 *Grants* £101,000 *Assets* £2,578,960

TRUSTEES Miss L M Carter; S R M Wilson; Martyn Carr.

HOW TO APPLY In writing to the correspondent. Telephone calls are not welcome. There is no need to enclose an sae unless applicants wish to have materials returned. Applications made outside the preferred areas for grant giving will be considered, but acknowledgements may not always be sent.

WHO TO APPLY TO Sam Wilson, Trustee, c/o Birketts, 24–26 Museum Street, Ipswich IP1 1HZ

CC NO 284782   **ESTABLISHED** 1982

■ Carter's Educational Foundation

WHERE FUNDING CAN BE GIVEN The ancient parish of Wilford.

WHO CAN BENEFIT The trust supports the South Wilford Endowed Church of England School. It may also give grants to individuals under 25 living in the ancient parish and organisations for such people, with a broadly educational nature, operating within the beneficial area.

WHAT IS FUNDED Education.

FINANCES *Year* 2008 *Income* £269,694 *Grants* £40,125 *Assets* £6,019,627

TRUSTEES Mrs P Hammond; R W Stanley; P Wicks; Cllr T Spencer.

HOW TO APPLY Subject to the availability of funds, grants to voluntary charitable organisations in the ancient parish are normally considered at the same time as educational grants for individuals and awarded on the basis of the school year. Letters of application should therefore be with the clerk to the foundation before 31 May. Letters should identify the base for the organisation's work, outline the nature of the activities involved and the approximate number of young people participating from the ancient parish. If this is the first application from your organisation, please give full details and include a copy of your latest accounts. Applications must be made in writing.

WHO TO APPLY TO The Clerk to the Trustees, Pennine House, 8 Stanford Street, Nottingham NG1 7BQ *Website* www.wilford-carters-education.org.uk

CC NO 528161   **ESTABLISHED** 1888

■ The Carvill Trust

WHERE FUNDING CAN BE GIVEN UK.

WHO CAN BENEFIT Registered charities.

WHAT IS FUNDED General charitable purposes.

SAMPLE GRANTS Irish Youth Foundation (£14,000); and Academy Ocean Reef and War Child (£10,000 each).

FINANCES *Year* 2007–08 *Income* £120,978 *Grants* £36,739 *Assets* £427,540

TRUSTEES R K Carvill; R E Pooley; K D Tuson.

HOW TO APPLY In writing to the correspondent, although the trust states that it only supports beneficiaries known to or connected with the trustees. Unsolicited applications from individuals will not be supported.

WHO TO APPLY TO K D Tuson, Trustee, 5th Floor, Minories House, 2–5 Minories, London EC3N 1BJ *Tel* 020 7780 6900

CC NO 1036420   **ESTABLISHED** 1994

■ The Casey Trust

WHERE FUNDING CAN BE GIVEN UK and developing countries.

WHO CAN BENEFIT Charities benefiting children.

WHAT IS FUNDED Children and young people in the UK and developing countries by supporting new projects.

WHAT IS NOT FUNDED Grants are not given to 'individual applicants requesting funds to continue studies or travel'.

TYPE OF GRANT £750–£10,000. The average grant was for £1,943.

SAMPLE GRANTS Norwood (£10,000); Family Welfare Association and UNICEF Myanmar Cyclone Children's Appeal (£5,000 each); Rainbow Trust (£3,000); Hollybank Trust (£2,600); BLISS, EMMS International, Hope and Homes for Children and the Woodford Foundation (£2,500 each); Hope House (£2,000); Action for Kids, and Rose Road Association (£1,000 each); Health Unlimited (£900); and Deep Impact Theatre (£750).

FINANCES *Year* 2007–08 *Income* £140,600 *Grants* £79,660 *Assets* £2,809,814

TRUSTEES Kenneth Howard; Edwin Green; Hon. Judge Leonard Krikler.

HOW TO APPLY 'Not being a reactive trust, it is regretted that the trustees will be unable to respond to the majority of requests for assistance. In order to both reduce costs and administration the trustees will respond mainly to those charitable institutions known to them. There is no application form.'

WHO TO APPLY TO Kenneth Howard, Trustee, 27 Arkwright Road, London NW3 6BJ

CC NO 1055726   **ESTABLISHED** 1996

■ Cash for Kids – Radio Clyde

WHERE FUNDING CAN BE GIVEN Radio Clyde transmission area, i.e. Inverclyde, Argyll and Bute, Dumfries and Galloway, East Ayrshire, South Ayrshire, North Ayrshire, East Dumbartonshire, West Dumbartonshire, Renfrewshire, East Renfrewshire, Glasgow City Council, North Lanarkshire and South Lanarkshire.

412

Does the trust you have chosen match your needs? Haphazard applications waste postage and time

WHO CAN BENEFIT Children and young adults up to the age of 16 disadvantaged through: illness, distress, abuse or neglect; any kind of disability; behavioural or psychological difficulties; living in poverty or situations of deprivation. Organisations benefiting this group.

WHAT IS FUNDED Christmas presents, food, pantomime trips, clothing and other support is given to children via social work departments and through community and voluntary groups.

WHAT IS NOT FUNDED The trust does not fund: trips or projects abroad; medical treatment/research; unspecified expenditure; deficit funding or repayment of loans; retrospective funding (projects taking place before the grant award date); projects unable to start within six months of the grant award date; distribution to another/other organisation/s; general appeals or endowment funds; relief of statutory responsibility; the promotion of religion. No funding for capital expenditure except in very special circumstances that must be made clear at the time of applying. Organisations whose administration costs exceed 15% of total expenditure will not be supported.

FINANCES *Year* 2008–09 *Income* £1,192,618 *Grants* £1,192,618

TRUSTEES Paul Cooney; Ewan Hunter; Ian Grabiner; Sir Tom Hunter.

HOW TO APPLY Application forms and guidelines are available from the trust's website.

WHO TO APPLY TO Trust Administrator, Radio Clyde, 3 South Avenue, Clydebank Business Park, Glasgow G81 2RX *Tel* 0141 204 1025 *Fax* 0141 565 2370 *email* cashforkids@radioclyde.com *Website* www.clyde1.com/cashforkids

SC NO SCO03334   **ESTABLISHED** 1984

···
■ Sir John Cass's Foundation

WHERE FUNDING CAN BE GIVEN The inner London boroughs – Camden, Greenwich, Hackney, Hammersmith and Fulham, Islington, Kensington and Chelsea, Lambeth, Lewisham, Newham, Southwark, Tower Hamlets, Wandsworth, Westminster and the City of London.

WHO CAN BENEFIT Individuals; schools and organisations. The foundation will only consider proposals from schools and organisations that benefit: children or young people under the age of 25, who are permanent residents of named *inner* London boroughs (Camden, Greenwich, Hackney, Hammersmith and Fulham, Islington, Kensington and Chelsea, Lambeth, Lewisham, Newham, Southwark, Tower Hamlets, Wandsworth, Westminster and the City of London), and from disadvantaged backgrounds or areas of high deprivation.

WHAT IS FUNDED Education, especially of people in financial need. The foundation has four areas of focus for grant giving: widening participation in further and higher education; truancy, exclusion and behaviour management; prisoner education; new initiatives.

WHAT IS NOT FUNDED There are many activities and costs that the foundation will not fund. The following list gives an idea of the type the foundation cannot support: projects that do not meet a foundation priority; conferences, seminars and academic research; holiday projects, school journeys, trips abroad or exchange visits; supplementary schools or mother tongue teaching; independent schools; youth and community groups, or projects taking place in these settings; pre-school and nursery education; general fund-raising campaigns or appeals; costs for equipment or salaries that are the statutory responsibility of education authorities; costs to substitute for the withdrawal or reduction of statutory funding; costs for work or activities that have already taken place prior to the grant application; costs already covered by core funding or other grants; capital costs, that are exclusively for the purchase, repair or furnishing of buildings, purchase of vehicles, computers, sports equipment or improvements to school grounds.

TYPE OF GRANT Recurrent for individuals; project, recurrent or one-off support for groups, organisations and schools. Funding may be given for up to three years.

RANGE OF GRANTS Usually £5,000–£65,000.

SAMPLE GRANTS Beneficiaries of schools and organisations grants included: Spitalfields Festival – for musical projects in Tower Hamlets schools (£50,000); St Giles Trust – NVQ 3 training for prisoners (£35,000); Parliament Hill School – a project with disaffected white girls in Camden (£30,000); Bud Umbrella – complementary treatment for children with behavioural disorders (£14,000); National Literacy Trust – literacy programme with the Science Museum (£6,000); and Prisoner's Education Trust – for bursaries for ex-prisoners (£4,500).

FINANCES *Year* 2007–08 *Income* £2,163,167 *Grants* £1,714,603 *Assets* £49,795,867

TRUSTEES Michael Bear; Kevin Everett; Mark Boleat; HH Judge Brian Barker; Revd Christopher Burke; Barbara Lane; Graham Forbes; David Turner; Prof Manuel Alvarado; Mervyn Streatfeild; Helen Meixner; Dr Ray Ellis; Revd Nigel Kirkup; Sarah Dalgarno; David Hogben; Prof Michael Thorne.

OTHER INFORMATION A further £229,000 was distributed to individuals.

HOW TO APPLY The foundation operates a two stage application process – an initial enquiry and a full application stage. At stage 1, applicants are required to complete and submit the initial enquiry form which is available from the foundation's website and on request from the correspondent. The form asks for outline information about your proposed project; information about how the project meets the foundation's priorities; a summary of the project that includes the following information: the aims of the project including outputs and outcomes; how the project will be delivered; the duration of the project, including when and where it will take place; and a budget covering project costs. Enquiries will then be considered and applicants informed of the decision taken within three weeks. Successful stage 1 applicants will be invited to proceed to Stage 2 and submit a full application. A copy of the stage 2 guidelines will be sent to you at that time. This form should be completed and submitted with copies of the memorandum and articles of association (or constitution) of your organisation, together with the latest annual report and accounts. On receipt of your application foundation staff may meet with you as part of the assessment process. The grants committee meets in March, June and November each year. It normally takes between two and four months from receipt of a full application until a decision is made. All applicants will be sent formal notification of the outcome of their applications within two weeks of the committee decision. Those who are offered a grant will be sent a formal offer letter and copies of our standard terms and conditions of grant. Copies of the standard terms and conditions of grant are available on the foundation's website. Additional conditions are sometimes included depending on the nature of the grant. All applications are assessed on merit. If your application is refused you can apply again twelve months after the date you submitted your last application.

WHO TO APPLY TO Richard Foley, Grants Manager, 31 Jewry Street, London EC3N 2EY *Tel* 020 7480 5884 *Fax* 020 7488 2519 *email* contactus@ sirjohncass.org *Website* www.sirjohncass.org
CC NO 312425   **ESTABLISHED** 1748

■ The Elizabeth Casson Trust

WHERE FUNDING CAN BE GIVEN Worldwide.
WHO CAN BENEFIT Occupational therapy schools/ departments and individual occupational therapists.
WHAT IS FUNDED The training and development of occupational therapists. Ongoing support is given to Oxford Brookes University.
WHAT IS NOT FUNDED No support for anything other than occupational therapy education and training.
TYPE OF GRANT Research projects and courses/ travel bursaries that will benefit the profession as well as the individual.
FINANCES *Year* 2007–08 *Income* £236,112 *Grants* £97,920 *Assets* £5,691,748
TRUSTEES Mrs C Rutland, Chair; K D Grevling; Prof. D T Wade; Mrs J S Croft; Dr P L Agulnik; G A Paine; Mrs R Hallam.
OTHER INFORMATION The trust was founded in 1930 as Dorset House School of Occupational Therapy (a registered company). In 1948 the founder Dr Elizabeth Casson, registered this trust and an associated trust, the Casson Trust, under the same number at the Charity Commission. In 1992 Dorset House site was leased to Oxford Brookes University and in 1993 the company changed its name to the Elizabeth Casson Trust.
HOW TO APPLY On the trust's application form which can be obtained from the correspondent.
WHO TO APPLY TO Mrs C A G Gray, Secretary to the Trustees, Corner House, Cote, Oxfordshire OX18 2EG *Website* www.elizabethcassontrust. org.uk
CC NO 227166   **ESTABLISHED** 1930

■ The Castang Foundation

WHERE FUNDING CAN BE GIVEN UK.
WHO CAN BENEFIT Registered charities.
WHAT IS FUNDED Research into neurodevelopmental disorders in children.
SAMPLE GRANTS In 2008 it was funding four research projects: The Multicentre European Cerebral Palsy Study; The Autism and Epilepsy Study; The Human Placenta Study; Infantile Spasms.
FINANCES *Year* 2007–08 *Income* £128,022 *Grants* £97,636 *Assets* £2,463,514
TRUSTEES I A Burman; M B Glynn.
HOW TO APPLY In writing to the correspondent.
WHO TO APPLY TO Ian Burman, Correspondent, c/o Laytons, 'Carmelite', 50 Victoria Embankment, Blackfriars, London EC4Y OLS *email* contact@ castangfoundation.net *Website* www. castangfoundation.net
CC NO 1003867   **ESTABLISHED** 1991

■ The Catalyst Charitable Trust (formerly the Buckle Family Charitable Trust)

WHERE FUNDING CAN BE GIVEN Mainly Suffolk and Essex.
WHO CAN BENEFIT Charitable causes.
WHAT IS FUNDED This trust has an interest in supporting small charities in the Suffolk/Essex area.
SAMPLE GRANTS The Suffolk Foundation (£20,000); and the Oundle Schools Foundation and Whatfield Village Hall (£10,000 each).
FINANCES *Year* 2007–08 *Income* £154,000 *Grants* £48,000 *Assets* £114,000
TRUSTEES Gillian Buckle; James Buckle; Joanna Thomson; Charles Course.
OTHER INFORMATION In 2007–08 a further £6,000 went to individuals.
HOW TO APPLY In writing to the correspondent although beneficiaries are normally selected through personal contact.
WHO TO APPLY TO G W N Stewart, Trustee, 9 Trinity Street, Colchester, Essex CO1 1JN
CC NO 1001962   **ESTABLISHED** 1990

■ The Catholic Charitable Trust

WHERE FUNDING CAN BE GIVEN America and Europe.
WHO CAN BENEFIT Traditional Catholic organisations.
WHAT IS FUNDED The traditional teachings of the Roman Catholic faith. The trust's income is usually fully committed.
WHAT IS NOT FUNDED The trust does not normally support a charity unless it is known to the trustees. Grants are not made to individuals.
RANGE OF GRANTS £1,500–£15,000.
SAMPLE GRANTS Society of Saint Pius X – England (£15,000); Society of Latin Mass Society (£5,100); Fraternity of St Pius X Switzerland and Little Sisters of the Poor (£5,000 each); Worth Abbey (£4,000); Cardinal Newman Library Project (£2,500); California Friends of the Society of St Pius X, St Peter's Catholic Church, Society of the Grail (£2,000 each); and the Carmelite Monastery Carmel California (£1,500).
FINANCES *Year* 2007 *Income* £45,844 *Grants* £52,588 *Assets* £1,703,107
TRUSTEES J C Vernor Miles; W E Vernor Miles; D P Orr.
HOW TO APPLY Applications can only be accepted from registered charities and should be in writing to the correspondent. In order to save administration costs replies are not sent to unsuccessful applicants. For the most part funds are fully committed.
WHO TO APPLY TO J C Vernor Miles, Trustee, Vernor, Miles and Noble, 5 Raymond Buildings, Gray's Inn, London WC1R 5DD
CC NO 215553   **ESTABLISHED** 1935

■ Catholic Foreign Missions

WHERE FUNDING CAN BE GIVEN UK and overseas.
WHO CAN BENEFIT Catholic Foreign Missions.
WHAT IS FUNDED Grants are made in support of Catholic Foreign Missions in any part of the world.
FINANCES *Year* 2007–08 *Income* £864,939 *Grants* £1,548,508 *Assets* £17,349,106
TRUSTEES Desmond Bierne; Jean Marie Lesbats; Abel Maniez; Bernard Meade; Eric Saint-Sevin; Philip Walshe; Phillipe Lamblin; Kieran Magovern.

HOW TO APPLY No external applications are considered. The funds are fully committed.
WHO TO APPLY TO The Secretary, 70 St George's Square, London SW1V 3RD
CC NO 249252   **ESTABLISHED** 1941

■ The Catholic Trust for England and Wales

WHERE FUNDING CAN BE GIVEN England and Wales.
WHO CAN BENEFIT Roman Catholic organisations.
WHAT IS FUNDED The advancement of the Roman Catholic religion in England and Wales. Five categories of grants have been agreed by the trustees: (1) Small grants to charities that attract their major funding from other sources. (2) Grants to organisations, charities and projects that have a national role recognised by the Bishops' Conference and are therefore considered as being part of the national ecclesiastical structures. (3) Grants to organisations, charities and projects that either contribute to the life and work of the Catholic community in more than one diocese and require significant funding or require initial funding in order to develop the work of the Bishops' Conference. (4) Grants for purposes associated with social communications and media. (5) Grants to fulfil the purposes of the Lisbon Trust Fund.
WHAT IS NOT FUNDED No grants to individuals, local projects or projects not immediately advancing the Roman Catholic religion in England and Wales.
SAMPLE GRANTS CARITAS Social Action (£56,000); Linacre Centre (£50,000); Churches Legislation Advisory Service (£23,000); National Board of Catholic Women and National Confederation of Catholic Women (£12,000 each); Churches Media Council (£6,000); Lisbonia Society (£5,000); Churches Initiative Trust (£3,000); and Independent Catholic News (£1,000).
FINANCES *Year* 2008 *Income* £5,453,765 *Grants* £736,667 *Assets* £10,080,278
TRUSTEES Rt Revd Malcolm McMahon, Chair; Mgr Michael McKenna; Ben Andradi; Alison Cowdall; John Gibbs; Peter Lomas; Canon Nicholas Rothon; Robin Smith; Dr James Whiston.
HOW TO APPLY In writing to the correspondent.
WHO TO APPLY TO Revd Marcus Stock, 39 Eccleston Square, London SW1V 1BX *Tel* 020 7901 4810 *email* secretariat@cbcew.org.uk *Website* www.catholicchurch.org.uk
CC NO 1097482   **ESTABLISHED** 1968

■ The Cattanach Charitable Trust

WHERE FUNDING CAN BE GIVEN Scotland.
WHO CAN BENEFIT The trust will fund charities registered either in Scotland or in England for work done exclusively in Scotland. 'Organisations should be registered with the Office of the Scottish Charity Regulator, or, if registered with the Charity Commission, should be in the process of registering with OSCR.'
WHAT IS FUNDED 'The Cattanach Charitable Trustbelieves that helping young children and improving their well-being can bring about a healthier and happier community. The trust will therefore focus, for the five years from 2007, on organisations and projects which offer hope of a better life to children, especially those under ten years of age, and their families and communities. By targeting its grants in this way, the trust means to address the needs of young children living in difficult and deprived circumstances, and to help them make the most of their talents and opportunities.'
WHAT IS NOT FUNDED The trust will not fund individuals, hospices and palliative care, appliances for illness or disability, organisations concerned with specific diseases, or animal charities.
TYPE OF GRANT The trust prefers to make grants which contribute substantially to smaller-scale projects.
RANGE OF GRANTS Mostly £2,000–£10,000.
SAMPLE GRANTS The Lilias Graham Trust (£13,000); Barnardos (£10,000); PATCH (£9,500); Greater Pollock CAB (£6,000); Dr Bell's Family Centre, the Princess Royal Trust for Carers, Stepping Stones for Families and Women's Aid Orkney (£5,000 each); Ayreshire Household Recycling (£3,500); Home-Start Lorn (£3,000); Citylife Ministries (£2,500); and Community Family Support (£2,000).
FINANCES *Year* 2007–08 *Income* £277,091 *Grants* £283,824 *Assets* £5,562,254
TRUSTEES Colette Douglas Home; Lord MacLay; Frank Fletcher; Malcolm Borthwick; Anne Houston; Euan Davidson.
HOW TO APPLY On a form which can be completed online or downloaded from the trust's website. 'The trust does not normally accept hand-written applications – please phone if you do not have access to a computer.' Trustees meet quarterly (normally in March, June, September and December). The deadline for applications is normally about six weeks before the trustees' meeting and these dates are always on the website and are kept up to date.
WHO TO APPLY TO Alison Campbell, 15 Warriston Crescent, Edinburgh EH3 5LA *Tel* 0131 557 2052 *email* info@cattanach.org.uk *Website* www.cattanach.org.uk
SC NO SC020902   **ESTABLISHED** 1992

■ The Joseph and Annie Cattle Trust

WHERE FUNDING CAN BE GIVEN Worldwide, with a preference for Hull and East Yorkshire.
WHO CAN BENEFIT Organisations and individuals. 'The aged, disabled and underprivileged are assisted wherever possible as are children suffering from dyslexia. Financial assistance is provided as far as possible by supporting institutions specialising in these areas.'
WHAT IS FUNDED General charitable purposes.
WHAT IS NOT FUNDED Grants are very rarely given to individuals and are only supported through social services or relevant charitable or welfare organisations.
TYPE OF GRANT One-off, capital, recurring and interest-free loans are considered.
RANGE OF GRANTS Up to £15,000.
SAMPLE GRANTS Hull City Council Social Services (£80,000); Sobriety Project (£20,000); Dyslexia Action (£15,000); Holderness Road Methodist Church – the Bridge Community Project (£10,000); Archbishop Thurston Church of England School and Boulevard Baptist Church (£5,000 each); Hull and East Riding Institute for the Blind (£3,000); Yorkshire Eye Research (£2,000 each); and Hull Lighthouse Project and Prison Fellowship Hull and East Riding (£1,000 each).
FINANCES *Year* 2007–08 *Income* £432,118 *Grants* £351,363 *Assets* £8,163,403
TRUSTEES J A Collier; M T Gyte; P A Robins.

Think carefully about every application. Is it justified?

415

OTHER INFORMATION Grants to 63 individuals totalled £34,000.

HOW TO APPLY In writing to the correspondent. Meetings are usually held on the third Monday of each month.

WHO TO APPLY TO Roger Waudby, Administrator, 389–395 Anlaby Road, Hull HU3 6AB

CC NO 262011   **ESTABLISHED** 1970

··

■ The Thomas Sivewright Catto Charitable Settlement

WHERE FUNDING CAN BE GIVEN Unrestricted (for UK-based registered charities).

WHO CAN BENEFIT Registered charities only.

WHAT IS FUNDED General charitable purposes.

WHAT IS NOT FUNDED The trust does not support non-registered charities, expeditions, travel bursaries and so on, or unsolicited applications from churches of any denomination. Grants are unlikely to be considered in the areas of community care, playschemes and drug misuse, or for local branches of national organisations.

RANGE OF GRANTS Up to £14,000.

SAMPLE GRANTS Royal College of Music (£14,000) Royal Scottish Academy of Music and Drama (£12,000); Bowel Cancer Research and King VII's Hospital for Officers (£10,000 each); Haddo House Choral and Operatic Society and World YWCA (£5,000 each); Aviation for Paraplegics and Tetraplegics Trust (£2,000); NACRO (£1,500); Refugee Council, St Mungo's, Shelter and Charlie Waller Memorial Trust (£1,000 each); Crisis (£750); and Sportability (£500).

FINANCES *Year* 2007–08 *Income* £192,731 *Grants* £210,523 *Assets* £3,164,629

TRUSTEES Lord Catto; Olivia Marchant; Zoe Richmond-Watson.

HOW TO APPLY In writing to the correspondent, including an sae.

WHO TO APPLY TO The Secretary to the Trustees, PO Box 47408, London N21 1YW

CC NO 279549   **ESTABLISHED** 1979

··

■ The Wilfrid and Constance Cave Foundation

WHERE FUNDING CAN BE GIVEN UK, with preference for Berkshire, Cornwall, Devon, Dorset, Hampshire, Oxfordshire, Somerset, Warwickshire and Wiltshire.

WHO CAN BENEFIT Registered charities. Mainly local charities or charities which the trustees have personal knowledge of, interest in, or association with are considered.

WHAT IS FUNDED General charitable purposes including conservation, animal welfare, health and social welfare.

WHAT IS NOT FUNDED No grants to individuals.

TYPE OF GRANT Buildings, core costs, one-off, project, research, and running costs. Grants may be given for up to three years.

RANGE OF GRANTS £500–£60,000.

SAMPLE GRANTS Oxford Museum of Children's Literature (£60,000); East Berkshire Women's Aid (£12,000); Northcott Theatre (£10,000); Royal Agricultural Benevolent Institution (£5,000); North Devon Hospice, Prospect Hospice and the West Country River Trust (£3,000 each); Countryside Foundation for Education, Dyslexia Institute, Exmoor Woodland Trust, Thames Restoration Trust and War Memorials Trust (£2,000 each); and Regain (£1,000).

FINANCES *Year* 2007–08 *Income* £185,022 *Grants* £195,858 *Assets* £4,379,990

TRUSTEES Mrs T Jones; P Simpson; F H C Jones; Mrs J Archer; Mrs J Pickin; M Pickin; Mrs M Waterworth; Mrs N Thompson; R Walker; G Howells; W Howells; M Beckett.

HOW TO APPLY In writing to the correspondent a month before the trustees' meetings held twice each year, in May and October.

WHO TO APPLY TO The Secretary, New Lodge Farm, Drift Road, Winkfield, Windsor SL4 4QQ

CC NO 241900   **ESTABLISHED** 1965

··

■ The Cayo Foundation

WHERE FUNDING CAN BE GIVEN UK.

WHO CAN BENEFIT Charitable organisations.

WHAT IS FUNDED Medical research, the fight against crime, children and youth charities and general charitable purposes.

SAMPLE GRANTS Beneficiaries included: NSPCC (£125,000); the Disability Foundation, PACT, RNIB and Royal Opera House (£25,000 each); the Princes Foundation (£20,000); SURF (£15,000); Wessex Youth Trust (£10,000); Christian Blind Mission (£6,000); British WIZO (£5,000); Crimestoppers (£3,100); Wellbeing of Women (£3,000); Erskine (£2,000); and Homes in Zimbabwe (£1,000).

FINANCES *Year* 2007–08 *Income* £323,925 *Grants* £296,100 *Assets* £170,421

TRUSTEES Angela E McCarville; Stewart A Harris.

HOW TO APPLY In writing to the correspondent.

WHO TO APPLY TO Angela E McCarville, 7 Cowley Street, London SW1P 3NB

CC NO 1080607   **ESTABLISHED** 1999

··

■ Elizabeth Cayzer Charitable Trust

WHERE FUNDING CAN BE GIVEN UK.

WHO CAN BENEFIT Charitable organisations.

WHAT IS FUNDED Funds are used in promoting activities related to art, including education and conferences and exhibitions.

SAMPLE GRANTS Previous beneficiaries have included Elias Ashmole Trust, Dulwich Picture Gallery, the National Gallery and Sir John Soane's Museum.

FINANCES *Year* 2007–08 *Income* £224,791 *Grants* £62,900 *Assets* £2,043,668

TRUSTEES The Hon. Elizabeth Gilmour; Diana Lloyd; Dominic Gibbs.

OTHER INFORMATION This charity was established by The Honourable Elizabeth Gilmour, who has made significant donations to the charity since 1996. In formulating policy the trustees have taken into account the wishes of the Settlor, which are that the assets of the charity should be used in supporting and promoting activities relating to art.

HOW TO APPLY 'The trustees identify the projects and organisations they wish to support and so do not consider grants to people or organisations who apply speculatively. The trust also has a policy of not responding to any correspondence unless it relates to grants it has agreed to make or to the general management of the trust.'

WHO TO APPLY TO Helen D'Marco, The Cayzer Trust Company Limited, Cayzer House, 30 Buckingham Gate, London SW1E 6NN *Tel* 020 7802 8422

CC NO 1059265   **ESTABLISHED** 1996

■ The B G S Cayzer Charitable Trust

WHERE FUNDING CAN BE GIVEN UK.
WHO CAN BENEFIT Registered charities.
WHAT IS FUNDED General charitable purposes.
WHAT IS NOT FUNDED No grants to organisations outside the UK.
RANGE OF GRANTS Up to £25,000.
SAMPLE GRANTS Previous beneficiaries have included: Friends of the National Maritime Museum, Hike for Hope, Marie Curie Cancer Care, RAFT, St Paul's Cathedral Foundation, Scottish Countryside Alliance Education Trust and Worshipful Company of Shipwrights Charitable Fund.
FINANCES *Year* 2007–08 *Income* £90,141 *Grants* £80,350 *Assets* £2,418,145
TRUSTEES P R Davies; Mrs M Buckley; Mrs A M Hunter; Mrs R N Leslie.
HOW TO APPLY The trust tends to support only people/projects known to the Cayzer family or the trustees. Unsolicited appeals will not be supported.
WHO TO APPLY TO Jeanne Cook, c/o Cayzer House, 30 Buckingham Gate, London SW1E 6NN
CC NO 286063   **ESTABLISHED** 1982

■ The Cazenove Charitable Trust

WHERE FUNDING CAN BE GIVEN UK.
WHO CAN BENEFIT Charitable organisations. This Trust primarily supports the charitable activities sponsored by current and ex Cazenove employees.
WHAT IS FUNDED General charitable purposes.
SAMPLE GRANTS Adam Cole Foundation (£5,500); St Michael's Church, Battersea and Samaritans (£5,000 each); Refuge (£3,900); Beormund School – Southwark and St Mungo's (£3,400 each); Cancer Research UK (£2,700); Kids Company (£1,300); and Whizz Kidz, Oxfam Great Britain and Macmillan Cancer Relief (£1,000 each).
FINANCES *Year* 2007 *Income* £44,950 *Grants* £46,820 *Assets* £1,239,175
TRUSTEES C R M Bishop; J Earl; E M Harley.
HOW TO APPLY This trust does not respond to unsolicited applications.
WHO TO APPLY TO The Secretary, 20 Moorgate, London EC2R 6DA
CC NO 1086899   **ESTABLISHED** 1969

■ Celtic Charity Fund

WHERE FUNDING CAN BE GIVEN Worldwide but with a preference for Scotland and Ireland.
WHO CAN BENEFIT Charitable organisations.
WHAT IS FUNDED The fund has three main areas of support are as follows: children; drug-related projects; promoting religious and ethnic harmony. It also supports three subsidiary areas which are: homelessness; unemployment; alleviation of suffering caused by illness and famine and to aid innocent families within areas of war.
RANGE OF GRANTS £100–£3,000.
FINANCES *Year* 2008 *Grants* £100,000
TRUSTEES The Board of Trustees is selected by Celtic Football and Athletic Co Ltd.
OTHER INFORMATION There is approximately £100,000 available on an annual basis.
HOW TO APPLY An application form should be requested in writing.

WHO TO APPLY TO The Community Relations Manager, Celtic Football Club, Celtic Park, Glasgow G40 3RE *Website* www.celticfc.net
SC NO SC024648

■ The Cemlyn-Jones Trust

WHERE FUNDING CAN BE GIVEN North Wales and Anglesey.
WHO CAN BENEFIT Small local projects.
WHAT IS FUNDED Conservation and protection of general public amenities, historic or public interests in Wales; medical research; protection and welfare of animals and birds; study and promotion of music; activities and requirements of religious and educational bodies.
WHAT IS NOT FUNDED No grants to individuals or non-charitable organisations.
TYPE OF GRANT One-off.
RANGE OF GRANTS £100 upwards.
SAMPLE GRANTS Bangor University (£20,000); UCNW Development Trust – Fellowship Fund (£6,600); UCNW Development Trust (£5,500); Menai Bridge Community Heritage Trust (£5,000); St David's Hospice (£4,500); Ty Gobaith (£4,000); Beaumaris Festival (£2,000); Ocean Youth Trust (£1,800); and Rowen Scout Camp (£1,000).
FINANCES *Year* 2007–08 *Income* £410,580 *Grants* £50,400 *Assets* £1,161,016
TRUSTEES P G Brown; Mrs J E Lea; Mrs E G Jones.
HOW TO APPLY In writing to the correspondent.
WHO TO APPLY TO P G Brown, Trustee, 59 Madoc Street, Llandudno LL30 2TW *Tel* 01492 874391 *email* philip.brown@brewin.co.uk
CC NO 1039164   **ESTABLISHED** 1994

■ CfBT Education Trust

WHERE FUNDING CAN BE GIVEN Worldwide.
WHO CAN BENEFIT Organisations involved in education, particularly those concerned with the development and management of schools; managing and delivering effective learning and teaching; overcoming barriers to learning; and projects involving communication, language and multi-lingualism.
WHAT IS FUNDED Support from CfBT comes under the Evidence for Education programme where support is given through: commissioned research and development projects; research awards by competition/tender; and funding for projects in response to applications and invitation.
WHAT IS NOT FUNDED The trust will generally not consider funding for: business development; funding an extension or expansion of current service delivery; funding an extension of existing R&D projects which are funded by other sources; projects which are only innovative because they are being carried out at a local rather than a national level; buildings; equipment or capital costs; staff salaries (apart from researcher/consultant fees); day-to-day running costs; general appeals; grants to replace statutory funding; funding for individuals to undertake professional development, including those undertaking Masters degrees or Doctorates; expeditions; travel, adventure/holiday projects; 'gap year' projects; arts, religion, sports and recreation; conservation, heritage or environmental projects; animal rights or welfare; educational exchanges between institutions.
TYPE OF GRANT One-off and recurring grants.
RANGE OF GRANTS £1,000–£500,000.

SAMPLE GRANTS Education in Conflict, Emergencies, Reconstruction and Fragile States (£302,000); Public Private Partnerships in Basic Education: An International Review (£234,000); Student Integration in the United World College, Bosnia and Herzegovina (£55,000); Designing Educational Technologies for Social Justice (£52,000); How Effective are Bullying Prevention Programmes for Children with Special Educational Needs? (£31,000); English Language Teaching- Bridging Programmes for Further Education (£20,000); Programme scoping: Start-up phase for Gifted and Talented and Learning and Skills Programmes (£16,000); and Adult Skills and Higher Education: Separation or Union? (£12,000).

FINANCES *Year* 2007–08 *Income* £119,119,000 *Grants* £1,502,392 *Assets* £32,537,000

TRUSTEES Stephen Yeo; John Webb; John Harwood; Cameron Bowles; Sara Hodson; Graham Colls; Marion Headicar; Anita Higham; Stuart Laing; Sue Hunt.

PUBLICATIONS *Guide to Applicants.*

HOW TO APPLY Applicants should first submit an outline proposal to the research manager, Karen Whitby who will advise whether the proposal meets the agreed criteria and also how to proceed. The outline should be no more than three sides of A4 and include the following information: the issue or problem to be addressed; the reasons for addressing it; the expected outcome(s); what happens in the course of the project; the amount of funding required and how long it will be needed. Full applications are considered at the meetings of trustees in March, July, September and December. Further application information and upcoming deadline dates are available on the trust's website and in the 'Guide to Applicants' document.

WHO TO APPLY TO Karen Whitby, Research Manager, 60 Queens Road, Reading, Berkshire RG1 4BS *Tel* 0118 902 1000 *Fax* 0118 902 1434 *email* research@cfbt.com *Website* www.cfbt.com

CC NO 270901   ESTABLISHED 1965

■ The CH (1980) Charitable Trust

WHERE FUNDING CAN BE GIVEN UK and Israel.

WHO CAN BENEFIT Jewish organisations.

WHAT IS FUNDED Jewish causes.

SAMPLE GRANTS Oxford Centre for Hebrew and Jewish Studies (£21,000); Jewish Care (£20,000); British ORT (£17,000); United Jewish Israel Appeal (£15,000); British Technion Society (12,000); Anglo Israel Association (£6,700); Friends of Boys Town Jerusalem in Great Britain (£5,000); West London Synagogue Charitable Fund (£3,000); Maccabi GB (£2,000); B'nai B'rith Hillel Foundation (£1,000); and British Friends of the Israel Guide Dogs Centre for the Blind (£500).

FINANCES *Year* 2007–08 *Income* £138,684 *Grants* £106,200 *Assets* £1,816,366

TRUSTEES Kleinwort Benson Trustees Limited.

HOW TO APPLY In writing to the correspondent.

WHO TO APPLY TO The Administrator, 30 Gresham Street, London EC2V 7PG

CC NO 279481   ESTABLISHED 1980

■ R E Chadwick Charitable Trust

WHERE FUNDING CAN BE GIVEN UK.

WHO CAN BENEFIT Registered charities.

WHAT IS FUNDED General charitable purposes.

SAMPLE GRANTS Grammar School at Leeds (£2,000); British Red Cross (£1,500); Crisis, Leeds Festival Chorus, Myasthenia Gravis Association and RNIB (£1,000 each); UNICEF (£750); Arthritis Research, CAFOD, the Country Trust, Friends of St Winifred's, Gloucester Choral Society, Leeds Parish Church Choral Foundation Appeal and Yorkshire Dales Millennium Trust (£500 each); and Landmark Trust (£250).

FINANCES *Year* 2007–08 *Income* £33,145 *Grants* £27,250 *Assets* £882,589

TRUSTEES Peter Chadwick; Esme Knowles; Paul Knowles; Ann Chadwick.

HOW TO APPLY In writing to the correspondent.

WHO TO APPLY TO Peter Chadwick, Trustee, 19 Cookridge Street, Leeds, West Yorkshire LS2 3AG *Tel* 0113 244 6100 *email* peter.chadwick@wrigleys.co.uk

CC NO 1104805   ESTABLISHED 2004

■ The Amelia Chadwick Trust

WHERE FUNDING CAN BE GIVEN UK, especially Merseyside.

WHO CAN BENEFIT Neighbourhood-based community projects, some UK organisations.

WHAT IS FUNDED General charitable purposes including education, health, the arts, social welfare and the environment.

TYPE OF GRANT Recurring.

RANGE OF GRANTS £250–£31,000.

SAMPLE GRANTS Merseyside Development Foundation (£31,000); Liverpool PSS (£12,000); St Helen's Women's Aid (£7,200); Oxfordshire Dyslexia Association and Phoenix Futures (£5,000 each); Volunteer Reading Help (£3,000); Alzheimer's Disease Society, St. John's Hospice Wirral and the Sylvia Fund (£2,000 each); Council for the Protection of Rural England and Oxfam (£1,000 each); Wirral Women's Aid (£750); the Fortune Centre (£500); and Neston Nomads (£250).

FINANCES *Year* 2007–08 *Income* £133,422 *Grants* £100,165 *Assets* £3,696,656

TRUSTEES J R McGibbon; J C H Bibby.

HOW TO APPLY All donations are made through Liverpool Council for Social Services. Grants are only made to charities known to the trustees, and unsolicited applications are not considered.

WHO TO APPLY TO J R McGibbon, Trustee, Guy Williams Layton, Pacific Chambers, 11–13 Victoria Street, Liverpool L2 5QQ *Tel* 0151 236 7171

CC NO 213795   ESTABLISHED 1960

■ The Pamela Champion Foundation

WHERE FUNDING CAN BE GIVEN UK, with a preference for Kent.

WHO CAN BENEFIT Registered charities.

WHAT IS FUNDED General charitable purposes.

WHAT IS NOT FUNDED No grants to non-registered charities.

RANGE OF GRANTS Up to £2,500.

SAMPLE GRANTS St Mary's Eastling (£2,500); Canterbury Cathedral Fund, Citizens Advice Maidstone, Independence at Home and Leonard Cheshire (£2,000 each); Demelza House (£1,500); Army Benevolent Fund, CHASE, Crimestoppers Kent, RUKBA and St Mary's

Church Shackleford (£1,000 each); Vauxhall City Farm (£750 each); 7th Petts Wood Scout Group and Barnado's (£500 each); and the Ripple Down House Trust (£250).

FINANCES *Year* 2007 *Income* £35,032 *Grants* £28,500 *Assets* £833,449

TRUSTEES Miss M Stanlake; Mrs C Winser; Mrs E Bell; P M Williams.

HOW TO APPLY In writing to the correspondent.

WHO TO APPLY TO Elizabeth Bell, Trustee, Wiltons, Newnham Lane, Eastling, Faversham, Kent ME13 0AS *Tel* 01795 890233

CC NO 268819   **ESTABLISHED** 1974

■ Champneys Charitable Foundation

WHERE FUNDING CAN BE GIVEN UK.

WHO CAN BENEFIT Charitable organisations.

WHAT IS FUNDED Health, medical and disability causes.

SAMPLE GRANTS Scope (£80,000); Variety Club (£19,000); Teenage Cancer Trust (£7,500); Forest Way School (£5,100); and Hornsey Trust, Hearing Dogs and Papworth Trust (£5,000 each).

FINANCES *Year* 2007–08 *Income* £239,872 *Grants* £148,642 *Assets* £29,244

TRUSTEES Dorothy Purdew; Stephen Purdew; Michael Hawkins.

HOW TO APPLY In writing to the correspondent.

WHO TO APPLY TO Bev Strong, Charity Administrator, Henlow Grange, Henlow, Bedfordshire SG16 6DB *email* charity@champneys.co.uk *Website* www.champneys.com

CC NO 1114429   **ESTABLISHED** 2006

■ The Chapman Charitable Trust

WHERE FUNDING CAN BE GIVEN Eastern and south east England, including London, and Wales.

WHO CAN BENEFIT Any recognised charity, but mainly those charities in which the late settlor had, or the trustees have, a personal interest or concern.

WHAT IS FUNDED General charitable purposes. Main areas supported are social services, culture and recreation, education and research, health, environment and heritage.

WHAT IS NOT FUNDED No grants to or for the benefit of individuals, local branches of UK charities, animal welfare, sports tours or sponsored adventure holidays.

RANGE OF GRANTS £500–£10,000.

SAMPLE GRANTS Pesticide Action Network UK (£15,000 in two grants); Leonard Cheshire – Rustington, Methodist Homes for the Aged, NCH and Queen Alexandra Hospital Home (£12,000 in two grants each); Fragile X Society and TreeHouse Trust (£11,000 in two grants each); Aldeburgh Music (£6,000); Cambridge University Veterinary School (£5,000); Action for Kids, Home-Start UK and Meningitis Research Foundation (£2,000 each); and Vitalise (£1,500).

FINANCES *Year* 2007–08 *Income* £282,308 *Grants* £280,000 *Assets* £6,335,084

TRUSTEES Roger Chapman; Richard Chapman; Bruce Chapman; Guy Chapman; Bryony Chapman.

HOW TO APPLY In writing at any time. The trustees currently meet to consider grants twice a year at the end of September and in March. They receive a large number of applications and regret that they cannot acknowledge receipt of them. The absence of any communication for six

months would mean that an application must have been unsuccessful.

WHO TO APPLY TO Roger S Chapman, Trustee, Crouch Chapman, 62 Wilson Street, London EC2A 2BU *Tel* 020 7782 0007 *email* cct@crouchchapman. co.uk

CC NO 232791   **ESTABLISHED** 1963

■ John William Chapman's Charitable Trust

WHERE FUNDING CAN BE GIVEN The borough of Doncaster.

WHO CAN BENEFIT Individuals or other bodies assisting individuals in need.

WHAT IS FUNDED Relief-in-need.

WHAT IS NOT FUNDED The trust funds are to be used for the relief of hardship and distress but will not be given for payments in respect of council tax, income tax or where public funds are available for the relief of that hardship. Grants are not given for large, national appeals.

RANGE OF GRANTS £200–£15,000.

SAMPLE GRANTS Previous beneficiaries included: Age Concern; Barnardos; British Red Cross; British Legion; Doncaster and District Welfare for the Disabled; Doncaster Housing for Young People; National Schizophrenia Society; William Nuttall Cottage Homes; Winged Fellowship.

FINANCES *Year* 2007–08 *Income* £193,523 *Grants* £95,320 *Assets* £3,950,793

TRUSTEES Lady Neill; Miss V R Ferres; M J Hunter; M Gornall.

HOW TO APPLY In writing to the correspondent.

WHO TO APPLY TO Rosemarie Sharp, Charity Correspondent, Jordans Solicitors, 4 Priory Place, Doncaster DN1 1BP

CC NO 223002   **ESTABLISHED** 1942

■ The Charities Advisory Trust

WHERE FUNDING CAN BE GIVEN UK and overseas.

WHO CAN BENEFIT Any charitable purpose is considered, but generally the trust is proactive.

WHAT IS FUNDED General charitable purposes, particularly: income generation projects; homelessness; museums; cancer research and treatment; peace and reconciliation; and refugees.

WHAT IS NOT FUNDED 'Nearly all our grants are made because we have prior knowledge of the project or area of concern. In most cases the idea for the project comes from us; we work with suitable organisations to achieve our objectives. We rarely respond to unsolicited applications for projects of which we know nothing. In such cases where support is given, the amounts are usually £200 or less. We do not consider grants to individuals in need. Neither do we give to individuals going on gap year trips to the developing world. We are unlikely to give to large fund-raising charities. We do not give for missionary work.'

TYPE OF GRANT Buildings, capital, core costs, endowments, interest-free loans; one-off, project, research, running costs, recurring costs, salaries and start-up costs. Funding is available for up to and over three years.

RANGE OF GRANTS Typically £5,000 or less.

SAMPLE GRANTS Survivors Fund – Rwanda (£114,500); Mozaik Foundation – Bosnia and Herzegovina (£100,000); Africa Education Trust (£92,000); Rainforest Concern (£81,500); Sight Savers International (£62,000); Chira Fund (£54,000); ORBIS UK (£47,000); Sahabhagi

Vikash Abhiyan (£41,500); Ashwini (£34,000); Accord (£24,500); VETAID (£23,000); Kings College Hospital (£2,700).

FINANCES *Year* 2007–08 *Income* £2,886,324 *Grants* £656,000 *Assets* £2,607,653

TRUSTEES Dr Cornelia Navari; Dr Carolyne Dennis; Brij Bhasin; Ms Dawn Penso.

HOW TO APPLY 'We are willing to consider applications for any charitable purpose. To apply, simply send us details of your proposal (no more than two pages in length) in the form of a letter. You might try to include the following information: the aims and objectives of your organisation; the project for which you need money; who benefits from the project and how; breakdown of the costs and total estimated costs; how much money you need from us; other funding secured for the project; a summary of your latest annual accounts. If we refuse you it is not because your project is not worthwhile – it is because we do not have sufficient funds, or it is simply outside our current area of interest.'

WHO TO APPLY TO Dame Hilary Blume, Director, Radius Works, Back Lane, London NW3 1HL *Tel* 020 7794 9835 *Fax* 020 7431 3739 *email* people@charitiesadvisorytrust.org.uk *Website* www.charitiesadvisorytrust.org.uk

CC NO 1040487   **ESTABLISHED** 1994

■ Charitworth Limited

WHERE FUNDING CAN BE GIVEN Worldwide.

WHO CAN BENEFIT Charitable organisations.

WHAT IS FUNDED Religious, educational and charitable purposes. In practice, mainly Jewish causes.

TYPE OF GRANT One-off and recurring.

RANGE OF GRANTS Up to £185,000.

SAMPLE GRANTS Zichron Nahum (£185,000); British Friends of Tchernobil (£165,000); Cosmon Belz (£130,000); Chevras Maoz Ladal (£90,000); Dushinsky Trust (£39,000); Centre for Torah Education Trust (£25,000); Finchley Road Synagogue (£13,000); Friends of Viznitz (£10,000); Beer Yaakov (£8,500); and Beis Soroh Schneirer (£6,000). Sundry donations of under £6,000 totalled £42,000.

FINANCES *Year* 2007–08 *Income* £5,884,975 *Grants* £912,500 *Assets* £28,964,581

TRUSTEES David Halpern; Reilly Halpern; Sidney Halpern; Samuel J Halpern.

HOW TO APPLY In writing to the correspondent.

WHO TO APPLY TO David Halpern, Trustee, Cohen Arnold and Co., New Burlington House, 1075 Finchley Road, London NW11 0PU *Tel* 020 8731 0777 *Fax* 020 8731 0778

CC NO 286908   **ESTABLISHED** 1983

■ The Charter 600 Charity

WHERE FUNDING CAN BE GIVEN UK.

WHO CAN BENEFIT Registered charities. Community-based, grass-roots organisations.

WHAT IS FUNDED General charitable purposes, with particular emphasis on education, social and medical welfare support for young people and communities.

WHAT IS NOT FUNDED Applications for charitable grants will only be accepted when put forward by a member of the Mercers' Company.

RANGE OF GRANTS Up to £2,500.

SAMPLE GRANTS Scotts Project Trust (£2,400); World Pheasant Association (£2,000); 1st Headcorn Scout Group, Gwennili Trust, Project Peru and Walton-on-the-Hill Scout and Guide Association

(£1,500 each); Braintree and Bocking Community Association and Sinfield Nature Conservation Trust (£1,000 each); Crystal Palace Museum (£700); Look Good Feel Better and St Mary Magdalene PCC (£500 each); and Federation of London Youth Clubs (£250).

FINANCES *Year* 2007–08 *Income* £179,877 *Grants* £44,689 *Assets* £752,804

TRUSTEES The Mercers Company.

HOW TO APPLY The charity does not consider unsolicited applications.

WHO TO APPLY TO The Clerk, Mercers' Hall, Ironmongers Lane, London EC2V 8HE *Website* www.mercers.co.uk

CC NO 1051146   **ESTABLISHED** 1994

■ The Worshipful Company of Chartered Accountants General Charitable Trust (also known as CALC)

WHERE FUNDING CAN BE GIVEN UK.

WHO CAN BENEFIT Registered charities and voluntary organisations.

WHAT IS FUNDED At least one theme directly or indirectly of relevance to the work of the profession (chosen by the master on their appointment in October of each year). Other recommendations and proposals put to the trustees by members of the Livery.

SAMPLE GRANTS St Peter and St James Hospice – Sussex (£20,000); St Ann's Hospice – Manchester (£10,000); and Hospice At Home – Carlisle and North Lakeland and Hospice In The Weald – Tunbridge Wells Kent (£5,000 each).

FINANCES *Year* 2007–08 *Income* £130,421 *Grants* £108,880 *Assets* £1,034,272

TRUSTEES Ian Plaistowe, Rachel Adams, Colin Brown, John Cardnell, Michael Fowle, James Macnamara, David Allvey.

HOW TO APPLY Applications must be sponsored by a liveryman of the company.

WHO TO APPLY TO Peter Lusty, Clerk, Hampton City Services, Hampton House, High Street, East Grinstead, West Sussex RH19 3AW

CC NO 327681   **ESTABLISHED** 1988

■ The Chasah Trust

WHERE FUNDING CAN BE GIVEN Greater London and UK.

WHO CAN BENEFIT Evangelists and Christians.

WHAT IS FUNDED The encouragement of missionary activity as well as the advancement of the evangelical tenets of Christianity.

WHAT IS NOT FUNDED Buildings or general appeals are not funded.

RANGE OF GRANTS Up to £15,000.

FINANCES *Year* 2007–08 *Income* £54,680 *Grants* £48,682 *Assets* £31,425

TRUSTEES Karen Collier-Keywood; Richard Collier-Keywood.

OTHER INFORMATION The grant total in 2007–08 includes £22,425 donated to individuals.

HOW TO APPLY In writing to the correspondent.

WHO TO APPLY TO Richard D Collier-Keywood, Glydwish Hall, Fontridge Lane, Etchingham, East Sussex TN19 7DG

CC NO 294898   **ESTABLISHED** 1986

....
■ Chasdei Tovim Me'oros

WHERE FUNDING CAN BE GIVEN UK and Israel.

WHO CAN BENEFIT Jewish organisations and individuals.

WHAT IS FUNDED Jewish causes.

SAMPLE GRANTS Tovim Meoros – Israel (£17,000); ZBE Trust (£5,000); and Chevars Meoz Ladol (£4,300).

FINANCES *Year* 2006–07 *Income* £55,018 *Grants* £42,223 *Assets* £1,527

TRUSTEES F Spitz; M Salamon; Y Bleier.

HOW TO APPLY In writing to the correspondent.

WHO TO APPLY TO Yoel Bleier, Trustee, 10 Seymour Court, Cazenove Road, London N16 6AU

CC NO 1110623   **ESTABLISHED** 2005

....
■ The Chelsea Building Society Charitable Foundation

WHERE FUNDING CAN BE GIVEN Beneficiary organisations must be UK based and within a ten-mile radius of a Chelsea Building Society branch office.

WHO CAN BENEFIT Registered charities only. In particular, the trustees are keen to support community based charities.

WHAT IS FUNDED In particular, the trustees are keen to support community based charities where small donations can make a significant difference to local people's lives. Grants are given in the following categories: homelessness; housing; debt advice – encouraging prudent money management. e.g. money advice services which include giving advice and helping disadvantaged people take control of their money including budgeting skills; mental health and learning difficulties; all forms of disability; children and young people; older people. 'Please provide clear information on need, effectiveness, impact and the specific value our grant could have to a particular project.'

WHAT IS NOT FUNDED The trustees will not consider grants relating to the following: non registered charities; charities which have applied to the foundation within the previous 24 months; activities which are mainly/normally the statutory responsibility of central or local government or some other responsible body (except proposals for added support services); schools, universities and colleges (except for projects which will specifically benefit disabled students and are additional to statutory responsibilities); hospitals, medical centres, medical treatment research (except projects extra to statutory responsibilities); collecting funds for later distribution to other charities or to individuals; political or pressure groups; profit-distributing organisations; individuals or individual fund-raising efforts, including expeditions or overseas travel; general fund raising events, activities or appeals; general funding for salaries and core costs; fabric appeals for places of worship; the promotion of religion; animal welfare or wildlife; charities which have substantial reserves (in excess of 12 months expenditure) or in serious deficit; charities which have an annual income in excess of £500,000; the purchase of minibuses or other vehicles; the acquisition, renovation and refurbishment of buildings.

RANGE OF GRANTS £250–£5,000.

SAMPLE GRANTS Winston's Wish (£5,000); the Heart of Kent Hospice (£2,000); the Rose Road Association (£1,500); Carousel Project, Ealing No. 1 Club, House of St Barnabas-in-Soho, Moulsecoomb Neighbourhood Trust and

Waltham Forest Churches Night Shelter (£1,000 each); 870 House (£900); The Great Bridge Community Forum Project, Friends of Colnbrook Special School, Guildford and Waverley Cruse Bereavement Care, Off the Fence Trust and Spinal Injuries Association (£500 each); the St Paul's Centre (£450); and Christians Against Poverty (£250).

FINANCES *Year* 2007–08 *Income* £60,076 *Grants* £60,323

TRUSTEES Mrs D A R Anderson; D Stevens; D Porter; Mrs M Corke; Ms N Corner.

HOW TO APPLY Applications can only be considered if made in writing on the foundation's application form. The opening date for applications will be confirmed on its website. Please check its website for up-to-date information.

WHO TO APPLY TO The Secretary, Administrative Headquarters, Thirlestaine Hall, Thirlestaine Road, Cheltenham, Gloucestershire GL53 7AL *Tel* 01242 283605 *Fax* 01242 283551 *email* charitablefoundation@thechelsea.co.uk *Website* www.thechelsea-charity-foundation.co. uk

CC NO 1079292   **ESTABLISHED** 2000

....
■ The Chelsea Square 1994 Trust

WHERE FUNDING CAN BE GIVEN Southern England, and to a limited extent, overseas.

WHO CAN BENEFIT Charitable organisations.

WHAT IS FUNDED Chiefly projects related to animals and people who are older or underprivileged.

WHAT IS NOT FUNDED No grants to individuals.

TYPE OF GRANT One-off grants.

SAMPLE GRANTS Cystic Fibrosis Trust, Kids for Kids, Home Start Elmbridge, the Ripieno Choir, Sussex Choir and Treloar Trust (£2,000 each).

FINANCES *Year* 2007–08 *Income* £34,154 *Grants* £12,000 *Assets* £1,166,050

TRUSTEES J B Talbot; P J Talbot; J T Woods.

HOW TO APPLY In writing to the correspondent with report and accounts. Unsuccessful applicants will not receive a reply; send an sae if you wish documents to be returned.

WHO TO APPLY TO Paul Shiels, Moon Beaver Solicitors, 24–25 Bloomsbury Square, London WC1A 2PL

CC NO 1040479   **ESTABLISHED** 1994

....
■ The Cheruby Trust

WHERE FUNDING CAN BE GIVEN UK and worldwide.

WHO CAN BENEFIT Registered charities.

WHAT IS FUNDED Welfare, education and general charitable purposes.

RANGE OF GRANTS £200–£5,000.

SAMPLE GRANTS Actionaid, Amnesty International, Children in Crisis, Concern Worldwide UK – Darfur, Crisis UK, HOPE Charity, ICELP, Save the Children, Sightsavers and Wateraid (£5,000 each); Help the Aged (£3,500); Alzheimer's Society (£3,000); Childhope (2,500); Tibet Relief Fund (£2,000); British Deaf Association (£1,500); Norwood and Woodland Trust (£1,000 each); Arthur Rank Hospice Charity (£500); and Listening Books (£200).

FINANCES *Year* 2007–08 *Income* £71,760 *Grants* £105,000 *Assets* £43,048

TRUSTEES A L Corob; L E Corob; T A Corob; C J Cook; S A Wechsler.

HOW TO APPLY In writing to the correspondent.

WHO TO APPLY TO Mrs S Wechsler, Trustee, 62 Grosvenor Street, London W1K 3JF *Tel* 020 7499 4301

CC NO 327069   **ESTABLISHED** 1986

■ The Cheshire Provincial Fund of Benevolence

WHERE FUNDING CAN BE GIVEN Cheshire and parts of Greater Manchester and Merseyside.

WHO CAN BENEFIT Individuals and organisations benefiting Masons and their families.

WHAT IS FUNDED The relief of Masons and their dependants, Masonic charities and other charities, especially medical.

SAMPLE GRANTS Previous beneficiaries have included Children's Cancer Support Group, Mencap, Wirral Autistic Society, Bollington and Macclesfield Sea Cadets and Cathedral Road Kids Project.

FINANCES *Year* 2007–08 *Income* £460,090 *Grants* £82,400 *Assets* £3,112,210

TRUSTEES A Glazier; P E Carroll; S A Kinsey; R G Hewitt; J Ellershaw; D Hinde; G Viner.

OTHER INFORMATION In previous years the trust has given around £2,000 to non-Masonic organisations.

HOW TO APPLY In writing to the correspondent.

WHO TO APPLY TO Peter Carroll, Provincial Grand Secretary, Ashcroft House, 36 Clay Lane, Timperley, Altrincham, Greater Manchester WA15 7AB *Tel* 0161 980 6090 *email* enquiries@cheshiremasons.co.uk

CC NO 219177   **ESTABLISHED** 1963

■ Chest, Heart and Stroke Scotland

WHERE FUNDING CAN BE GIVEN Scotland.

WHO CAN BENEFIT Academics, research workers and medical professionals living and working in Scotland.

WHAT IS FUNDED Medical research into all aspects of the aetiology, diagnosis, prevention, treatment and social impact of chest, heart and stroke illness. Applications directly relating to improvements in patient care, quality of life and health promotion are particularly welcomed.

WHAT IS NOT FUNDED Research involving animals is not funded. Research grants are restricted to those living and working in Scotland.

TYPE OF GRANT Research fellowships, project grants, travel and equipment grants, career development awards, research secondments, and student electives. Funding may be given for up to three years.

RANGE OF GRANTS Research grants up to £90,000.

FINANCES *Year* 2008–09 *Income* £7,363,182 *Grants* £653,454 *Assets* £4,696,702

HOW TO APPLY Please contact the correspondent for further details of how to apply.

WHO TO APPLY TO David H Clark, Secretary, 65 North Castle Street, Edinburgh EH2 3LT *Tel* 0131 225 6963 *email* admin@chss.org.uk *Website* www.chss.org.uk

SC NO SC018761   **ESTABLISHED** 1990

■ The Chetwode Foundation

WHERE FUNDING CAN BE GIVEN UK, with a preference for Nottinghamshire, Leicestershire and Derby.

WHO CAN BENEFIT Registered charities only.

WHAT IS FUNDED General charitable purposes.

SAMPLE GRANTS The Music Space Trust (£20,000); St Ann's Advice Centre (£11,000); the Zone Youth Project (£9,800); Think Children (£6,300); Weston Spirit (£5,000); Tythby and Cropwell Butler PCC (£3,000); Derby Toc H Children's Camp (£2,500); Newark and

Nottinghamshire Agricultural Society (£2,400); and the National Trust for Scotland (£200).

FINANCES *Year* 2007–08 *Income* £87,417 *Grants* £59,861 *Assets* £1,432,527

TRUSTEES J G Ellis; R N J S Price; A C Price.

HOW TO APPLY 'The foundation's grant making policy is to support a limited number of causes known to the trustees, particularly those supported by the settlor. Unsolicited applications are not normally considered.'

WHO TO APPLY TO J G Ellis, Trustee, Samworth Brothers (Holdings) Ltd, Chetwode House, 1 Samworth Way, Leicester Road, Melton Mowbray, Leicestershire LE13 1GA *Tel* 01664 414500

CC NO 265950   **ESTABLISHED** 1973

■ The Malcolm Chick Charity

WHERE FUNDING CAN BE GIVEN UK.

WHO CAN BENEFIT Registered charities.

WHAT IS FUNDED General charitable purposes, but effectively small grants to organisations the trustees are familiar with in the following areas: youth character building – there is an emphasis on grants towards sailing training; armed service charities – grants are limited to those charities supporting ex-army personnel and to charities providing direct care for ex-army personnel, for example grants to homes and charities providing welfare services for such persons; medical research and care – grants are made towards research into causes and treatment of heart disease and for buying equipment suitable for the treatment and care of people recovering from coronary heart disease.

RANGE OF GRANTS Usually up to £5,000.

SAMPLE GRANTS AHOY Centre and St Dunstans (£9,000 each); Children's Heart Foundation (£4,000); Barts and the London Charity, the Daneforth Trust, Hove and the Adur Sea Cadet Unity and Tall Ships Youth Trust (£3,000 each); and Soft Power Education, Ocen Youth Trust South and Project Trust (£500 each).

FINANCES *Year* 2007–08 *Income* £30,222 *Grants* £38,000 *Assets* £765,966

TRUSTEES D J L Mobsby; R S Fowler; N D Waldman.

HOW TO APPLY In the first place, applicants should write to ask for a copy of the criteria and application forms. Telephone calls are not welcomed. The trustees meet to consider applications in November and completed forms must be returned by the middle of October. There is a separate application form and guidance notes for individual applicants.

WHO TO APPLY TO The Trust Administrator, White Horse Court, 25c North Street, Bishops Stortford, Hertfordshire CM23 2LD

CC NO 327732   **ESTABLISHED** 1988

■ Child Growth Foundation

WHERE FUNDING CAN BE GIVEN UK.

WHO CAN BENEFIT Institutions researching child/adult growth disorders, and people with such diseases.

WHAT IS FUNDED Research into the causes and cure of growth disorders in children within the area of benefit and to publish the results of such research.

TYPE OF GRANT Research.

FINANCES *Year* 2007–08 *Income* £356,345 *Grants* £176,585 *Assets* £692,392

TRUSTEES Tam Fry, Chair; Nick Child; Russell Chaplin; Simon Lane; Gillian McRobie; Rachel

Pidcock; Linda Washington; Mark Coyle; Sue Davies.

HOW TO APPLY In writing to the correspondent.

WHO TO APPLY TO T Fry, Hon. Chair, 2 Mayfield Avenue, Chiswick W4 1PY *Tel* 020 8995 0257 *email* info@childgrowthfoundation.org *Website* www.childgrowthfoundation.org

CC NO 274325   **ESTABLISHED** 1977

■ Children's Liver Disease Foundation

WHERE FUNDING CAN BE GIVEN UK.

WHO CAN BENEFIT Organisations benefiting children (up to the age of 18) with liver disease.

WHAT IS FUNDED 'A key aspect of Children's Liver Disease Foundation's work is funding medical (basic and clinical), nursing and social research connected with addressing the basic mechanisms, causes, prevention, diagnosis, cure and treatment of diseases of the liver and biliary system in children.'

WHAT IS NOT FUNDED The charity does not accept applications from organisations whose work is not associated with paediatric liver disease. No grants to individuals, whether medical professionals or patients. No grants for travel or personal education. No grants for general appeals.

TYPE OF GRANT Research and project. Occasionally medical equipment.

SAMPLE GRANTS Institute of Biomedical Research – Birmingham, Liver Research Laboratories – University Hospital Birmingham, Royal Free and University College – London, University College Hospital and Institute of Liver Studies – King's College Hospital and University of Nottingham.

FINANCES *Year* 2007–08 *Income* £919,894 *Grants* £229,557 *Assets* £634,390

TRUSTEES Tom Ross, Chair; Bob Benton; Nick Budd; Jayne Carroll; Kellie Charge; Mairi Everard; Michele Hunter; Ann Mowat; David Tildesley.

HOW TO APPLY Applicants are strongly advised to look at the relevant pages on the Children's Liver Disease Foundation website.

WHO TO APPLY TO Catherine Arkley, Chief Executive, 36 Great Charles Street, Queensway, Birmingham B3 3JY *Tel* 0121 212 3839 *Fax* 0121 212 4300 *email* info@childliverdisease.org *Website* www.childliverdisease.org

CC NO 1067331   **ESTABLISHED** 1998

■ The Children's Research Fund

WHERE FUNDING CAN BE GIVEN UK.

WHO CAN BENEFIT Institutes of child health and university child health departments.

WHAT IS FUNDED Promoting, encouraging and fostering research into all aspects of diseases in children, child health and prevention of illness in children. Support of research centres and research units by grants to academic institutions, hospitals and other bodies with similar aims and objects to the fund. Support after the first year is dependent on receipt of a satisfactory report.

WHAT IS NOT FUNDED No grants for capital projects.

TYPE OF GRANT Research.

SAMPLE GRANTS Great Ormond St Hospital (£75,000); Alder Hey Children's Hospital (£25,000); St James Hospital – Yorkshire Eye Research (£10,000); KIDSTEM International Conference (£5,000); and the Puffin Appeal and University of Cardiff (£1,000 each).

FINANCES *Year* 2008–09 *Income* £104,116 *Grants* £119,637 *Assets* £1,488,265

TRUSTEES Hugh Greenwood, Chair; Gerald Inkin; Hugo Greenwood; Rt Hon. Lord Morris of Manchester; Elizabeth Theobald; David Lloyd.

HOW TO APPLY Applicants from child health research units and university departments are invited to send in an initial outline of their proposal; if it is eligible they will then be sent an application form. Applications are considered in March and November.

WHO TO APPLY TO The Trustees, 668 India Buildings, Water Street, Liverpool L2 0RA *Tel* 0151 236 2844 *Website* www.childrensresearchfund.org.uk

CC NO 226128   **ESTABLISHED** 1962

■ The Childs Charitable Trust

WHERE FUNDING CAN BE GIVEN Worldwide.

WHO CAN BENEFIT Churches or Christian organisations.

WHAT IS FUNDED Christian activity at home and overseas, especially the furtherance of the Christian Gospel.

TYPE OF GRANT One-off and recurrent. Preference for large-scale project grants.

RANGE OF GRANTS Up to around £60,000.

SAMPLE GRANTS Previous beneficiaries include: Home Evangelism, ICC Mission Reserve, Latin Link, Mission Aviation Fellowship, Counties Evangelistic Work, Echoes of Service and Mustard Seed Relief, Scripture Union, Orphaids, LAMA Ministries, ELAM Ministries, Hour of Revival and University of Bristol.

FINANCES *Year* 2007–08 *Income* £552,333 *Grants* £352,305 *Assets* £8,934,267

TRUSTEES D N Martin; R H Williams; A B Griffiths; S Puttock.

OTHER INFORMATION No grants list was available from the latest accounts.

HOW TO APPLY In writing to the correspondent. The trust has previously stated that its funds are fully committed and further applications are not welcomed.

WHO TO APPLY TO Melanie Churchyard, 3 Cornfield Terrace, Eastbourne BN21 4NN *email* info@childstrust.org *Website* childstrust.org

CC NO 234618   **ESTABLISHED** 1962

■ The Childwick Trust

WHERE FUNDING CAN BE GIVEN UK and South Africa.

WHO CAN BENEFIT Registered charities only.

WHAT IS FUNDED In the UK, health, people with disabilities and older people, welfare and research in connection with the bloodstock industry and Jewish charities; in South Africa, education.

WHAT IS NOT FUNDED No funding for: general appeals; animal welfare charities; support students' individual education or gap year costs; drug or alcohol related causes or HIV/AIDS related charities; or organizations outside of the UK, apart from pre-school education in South Africa.

TYPE OF GRANT Mainly one-off, project and capital for research and medical equipment.

RANGE OF GRANTS Up to £150,000. Most grants under £10,000.

SAMPLE GRANTS UK: Racing Welfare – Suffolk (£200,000); British Racing School – Suffolk (£174,000); RAFT – Middlesex (£50,000); Leonard Cheshire Homes – Oxfordshire (£30,000); Jessie May Trust – Wiltshire (£20,000); Disability Trust – West Sussex

(£11,000); Chase Hospice – Surrey (£10,000); Brain Research Trust – London (£8,000); Regain – Oxfordshire (£7,000); and Jewish Child's Day – London (£5,000). South Africa: Ntataise Rural Pre-school Development Trust (£91,000); ASHA Training and Development Trust (£54,000); Sekhukhune Educare Project (£25,000); Thusanang Association (£14,000); NECTA (£6,600); and Jim Joel Music Scholarship – the Orchestra Company (£4,300).

FINANCES *Year* 2007–08 *Income* £2,188,300 *Grants* £2,803,961 *Assets* £68,861,091

TRUSTEES John Wood, Chair; Anthony Cane; Peter Glossop; Sarah Frost; Peter Anwyl-Harris.

HOW TO APPLY In writing to the correspondent. Please note: the trust welcomes initial enquiries by email or telephone, but asks that formal applications are sent by post. There is no official application form but the trust does provide the following guidelines for potential applicants: applications should be made to Karen Groom (Trust Administrator) on the charity's official headed paper and include the email address of the writer; letters should be no longer than two sides of A4 and describe 'fully, clearly and concisely' the project for which funding is being sought and who the beneficiaries will be; detailed costing or a project budget should be included and, if possible, a copy of the latest annual report; details of other sources of funding and any funding applications currently being made are also helpful to include. The trustees meet in May and December to consider applications. Applications are assessed before each meeting to check that they meet the trust's objectives. Applicants will be informed of the outcome within six weeks following the meeting. N.B. Applications for funding in South Africa should be made to Mrs G. Bland (Fund Director) at: jimjoel@iafrica.com.

WHO TO APPLY TO Karen Groom, Trust Secretary, 9 The Green, Childwick Bury, St Albans, Hertfordshire AL3 6JJ *Tel* 01727 844666 *email* karen@childwicktrust.org *Website* www.childwicktrust.org

CC NO 326853   **ESTABLISHED** 1985

■ The Chippenham Borough Lands Charity

WHERE FUNDING CAN BE GIVEN Chippenham parish.

WHO CAN BENEFIT Individuals or community/charitable organisations which benefit the people of the Parish of Chippenham. Individuals must be living within the Parish of Chippenham at the date of application, and for a minimum of two years immediately prior to applying.

WHAT IS FUNDED The charity's income can be used by, or for the benefit of, the inhabitants of the Parish of Chippenham for: (i) relief of the aged, sick, disabled or poor; (ii) provision of facilities for recreation or other leisure time occupation; (iii) the advancement of education; (iv) the promotion of any other charitable purpose.

WHAT IS NOT FUNDED No help can be given for the following: individual adult sportsmen/woman; direct subsidy to local authorities; religious organisations (except for projects involving substantial non-denominational use for community benefit); retrospective applications; first degrees.

RANGE OF GRANTS £100–£10,000.

SAMPLE GRANTS North Wiltshire CAB (£34,000); Chippenham Town Partnership (£25,000); SPLASH (£10,000); Dorothy House Hospice

(£9,200); St Nicholas School (£7,000); Hardenhuish School and Sheldon School (£6,000 each); Ivy Lane School and Young People's Support Service (£3,500 each); Queen's Crescent School (£2,000); Chippenham Light OperaGroup (£1,500); Chippenham Cantata (£1,100); and Chippenham Community Festival Association (£1,000).

FINANCES *Year* 2007–08 *Income* £399,424 *Grants* £216,994 *Assets* £12,161,457

TRUSTEES Chris Dawe, Chair; Peter Kemp; Mike Braun; Ian Bridges; Christine Crisp; Sylvia Doubell; Bill Douglas; Kit Harding; Margaret Harrison; Jack Konynenburg; Barbara Oatley; Mark Packard.

OTHER INFORMATION The 2007–08 grants total includes £32,000 went in 64 grants to individuals.

HOW TO APPLY On a form available from the correspondent, either via an agency or self referral.

WHO TO APPLY TO Catherine Flynn, Jubilee Building, 32 Market Place, Chippenham, Wiltshire SN15 3HP *Tel* 01249 658180 *Fax* 01249 446048 *email* admin@cblc.org.uk *Website* www.cblc.org.uk

CC NO 270062   **ESTABLISHED** 1990

■ The Chipping Sodbury Town Lands Charity

WHERE FUNDING CAN BE GIVEN The parishes of Chipping Sodbury and Old Sodbury.

WHO CAN BENEFIT Individuals and organisations.

WHAT IS FUNDED The trust gives grants for relief-in-need and educational purposes, and also other purposes within Sodbury, including the provision of leisure facilities.

TYPE OF GRANT Buildings, capital, one-off and recurring costs will be considered.

FINANCES *Year* 2008 *Income* £360,496 *Grants* £113,109 *Assets* £7,124,280

TRUSTEES P J Elsworth, Chair; W J Ainsley; C A R Hatfield; B Seymour; D Shipp; R Smith; P Rumney; P Tily; Mrs M Cook.

OTHER INFORMATION In 2008 the sum of £9,400 was given in winter grants and £8,200 in educational grants.

HOW TO APPLY In writing to the correspondent. The trustees meet on the third week of each month except August.

WHO TO APPLY TO Mrs Nicola Gideon, Clerk, Town Hall, 57–59 Broad Street, Chipping Sodbury, South Gloucestershire BS37 6AD *Tel* 01454 852223 *email* nicola.gideon@chippingsodburytownhall.co.uk

CC NO 236364   **ESTABLISHED** 1977

■ CHK Charities Limited

WHERE FUNDING CAN BE GIVEN Worldwide, in practice mainly UK with a preference for national and West Midlands charities.

WHO CAN BENEFIT Registered charities.

WHAT IS FUNDED Charities working in countryside matters, drug prevention, education, job creation, population control, culture, conservation, deafness, blindness, and the provision of treatment and care for people with disabilities.

WHAT IS NOT FUNDED The following will not normally be considered for funding: organisations not registered as charities or those that have been registered for less than a year; pre-school groups; out of school playschemes including pre-school and holiday schemes; projects which promote a particular religion; 'bottomless pits' and unfocussed causes; very small and narrowly specialised activities; community centres; appeals for places of worship; local authorities; umbrella or grant-making organisations; universities and colleges and grant maintained private or local education authority schools or their parent-teacher associations, except if these schools are for students with special needs; individuals or charities applying on behalf of individuals; general requests for donations; professional associations and training of professionals; projects which are abroad even though the charity is based in the UK; expeditions or overseas travel; 'campaigning organisations' or citizens advice projects providing legal advice; community transport projects; general counselling projects, except those in areas of considerable deprivation and with a clearly defined client group.

TYPE OF GRANT Start-up capital costs and ongoing expenses (three to five years).

RANGE OF GRANTS Mostly £2,000–£5,000.

SAMPLE GRANTS Life Education Centres UK and Home Start UK (£200,000 each); St Clement & St James' Community Development Project (£100,000); Home Farm Trust (£50,000); Prince's Youth Business Trust (£27,000); European Squirrel Initiative and Interact Worldwide – Formerly Population Concern (£10,000 each); Midlands Art Centre (£7,500); Cricket Foundation, Eyeless Trust and Oxford Citizens Advice Bureau (£5,000 each); Gordon Russell Trust (£4,000); Association for Post-Natal Illness and Porch Steppin' Stone Centre Project (£3,000 each); and Asthma Relief (£2,000).

FINANCES *Year* 2007–08 *Income* £2,491,800 *Grants* £2,255,950 *Assets* £71,174,065

TRUSTEES David Peake; Charlotte Percy; David Acland; Joanna Prest; Katharine Loyd; Lucy Morris; Rupert Prest; Serena Acland; Susanna Peake.

HOW TO APPLY The trust does not have an application form, but suggests that the following guidelines be used when making an application: applications should be no longer than four A4 sides; include a short summary of the organisation and its status, e.g., registered charity; confirm the organisation has a Child Protection Policy and carries out CRB checks, if appropriate; provide a summary of the project and why a grant is needed; explain how it will be monitored and evaluated; state any funds that have already been raised/applied for; explain where ongoing funding (if required) will be obtained when the grant has been used; state the amount needed if the request is for revenue funding for a specific item; and enclose a job description if the request is for a salary. Applications should also include the most recent audited accounts. Additional information on the application process can be found on the trust's website. Applications can be submitted at any time during the year. Trustees usually meet every two months. Both successful and unsuccessful applicants are expected to wait at least one year before reapplying.

WHO TO APPLY TO Nick R Kerr-Sheppard, Administrator, c/o Kleinwort Benson Trustees Limited, 30 Gresham Street, London EC2V 7PG *Tel* 020 3207 7338 *Fax* 020 3207 7665 *Website* www.chkcharities.co.uk

CC NO 1050900   **ESTABLISHED** 1995

■ The Chownes Foundation

WHERE FUNDING CAN BE GIVEN UK, priority is given to charities based in Sussex, particularly in mid Sussex.

WHO CAN BENEFIT Organisations and individuals.

WHAT IS FUNDED The advancement of religion, the advancement of education among the young, the amelioration of social problems, and the relief of poverty amongst older people and the former members of Sound Diffusion PLC who lost their pensions when the company went into receivership. Preference will be given to projects where a donation may have some meaningful impact on an identified need rather than simply being absorbed into a larger funding requirement.

TYPE OF GRANT One-off, recurrent, buildings, capital, core costs, research and running costs. Funding is available for up to and over three years.

SAMPLE GRANTS Worth Abbey (£7,000 in three grants); Amnesty International (£5,000 in two grants); St Anne's Convent (£4,000 in three grants); Fybromyalgia Support Group (£3,500); Burnside Amenity Fund (£3,000 in two grants); Burnside Social Club, Chestnut Tree House and Friends of the Samaritans (£2,000 in two grants each); 3H Fund, Association of Wheelchair Children and Streetmate (£2,000 each); Ace of Clubs, CamFed, FareShare Brighton and Hove, St Peter and St James Hospice and Trinity Hospice (£1,500 each); and Cancer Research UK, Mencap, NSPCC, St Paul's Church and Spinal Injuries Association (£1,000 in two grants each).

FINANCES *Year* 2007–08 *Income* £102,289 *Grants* £114,172 *Assets* £1,641,424

TRUSTEES Mrs U Hazeel; The Rt Revd S Ortiger; M Woolley.

OTHER INFORMATION the grant total in 2007–08 includes over £54,000 distributed to individuals.

HOW TO APPLY In writing to the correspondent.

WHO TO APPLY TO Sylvia Spencer, Secretary, The Courtyard, Beeding Court, Shoreham Road, Steyning, West Sussex BN44 3TN *Tel* 01903 816699

CC NO 327451   **ESTABLISHED** 1987

■ The Chrimes Family Charitable Trust

WHERE FUNDING CAN BE GIVEN Merseyside, Wirral and North Wales.

WHO CAN BENEFIT Registered charities.

WHAT IS FUNDED The relief of poverty and distress and in the provision of funds towards projects for community welfare and the improvement of health and education with a preference for the support of community welfare in Merseyside and North Wales.

WHAT IS NOT FUNDED No grants to individuals, arts, conservation or education and training.

FINANCES *Year* 2007–08 *Income* £34,554 *Grants* £22,130 *Assets* £724,700

TRUSTEES Anne Williams; Helen Prosser.

HOW TO APPLY In writing to the correspondent – there are no deadlines. The trust prefers not to receive contact via telephone.

WHO TO APPLY TO Anne Williams, Trustee, Northfield, Upper Raby Road, Meston, Wirral CH64 7TZ

CC NO 210199   **ESTABLISHED** 1955

■ The Christabella Charitable Trust

WHERE FUNDING CAN BE GIVEN General but mainly Essex and surrounding areas.

WHO CAN BENEFIT Registered charities, local organisations and individuals.

WHAT IS FUNDED Christian causes are much favoured and there are several local organisations regularly supported including St Francis Church in West Horndon and Viz-a-Viz's evangelical work. The trustees prefer 'seed corn' funding of projects involving volunteers. Normally only one or two additional projects of special interest to the trust are supported each year.

WHAT IS NOT FUNDED No support for UK-wide or international charities. Applications for grants towards general running costs or building refurbishment are very unlikely to be supported.

TYPE OF GRANT The trust prefer 'seed corn' funding of projects involving volunteers.

SAMPLE GRANTS Viz-à-Viz (£20,000); LDF Charitable Trust (£9,000); Samaritans (£6,500); St Francis Church (£6,400); and National Garden Scheme (£6,000).

FINANCES *Year* 2007–08 *Income* £172,335 *Grants* £72,020 *Assets* £4,392,020

TRUSTEES E B Munroe; Miss C Turner; R Hiburn; I Elliot.

OTHER INFORMATION This trust's primary objective is to maintain the charity's property at Barnards Farm in West Horndon as the house of the National Malus Collection, to allow the general public access on various published dates each year and for use by other charitable organisations.

HOW TO APPLY In writing to the correspondent, from whom an application form is available. Please note the trust's 2007–08 accounts stated that 'the lower investment returns experienced in recent years has meant that very little, if any, income has remained for other projects'.

WHO TO APPLY TO Christina Turner, Administrator, 97–99 High Street, Rayleigh, Essex SS6 7BY *Website* www.barnardsfarm.eu

CC NO 800610   **ESTABLISHED** 1988

■ Christadelphian Samaritan Fund

WHERE FUNDING CAN BE GIVEN UK and overseas.

WHO CAN BENEFIT Registered charities.

WHAT IS FUNDED Preference is given to human causes and aid to the developing world.

WHAT IS NOT FUNDED Individuals and non-registered charities are not eligible for support.

TYPE OF GRANT Single donations.

SAMPLE GRANTS Oxfam (£12,000); DEC – Darfur and Chad Crisis Appeal (£10,000); British Red Cross – UK Floods and Christian Aid – Asia Floods Appeal (£5,000 each); and Action Aid, British Red Cross and Save the Children Fund (£2,000 each).

FINANCES *Year* 2007 *Income* £67,462 *Grants* £93,700 *Assets* £121,331

TRUSTEES K H A Smith; D P Ensell; Mrs C M Howarth; W N Moss; J M Hellawell; J M Buckler.

HOW TO APPLY In writing to the correspondent.

WHO TO APPLY TO K H A Smith, Treasurer, Westhaven House, Arleston Way, Shirley, Solihull, West Midlands B90 4HL

CC NO 1004457   **ESTABLISHED** 1991

■ Christian Aid

WHERE FUNDING CAN BE GIVEN Mainly the developing world. Limited assistance for development education projects in the UK.

WHO CAN BENEFIT Councils of Churches; other ecumenical bodies, development and relief groups; UN agencies which benefit at risk groups; people disadvantaged by poverty; homeless people; refugees; immigrants; socially isolated people; victims of famine, man-made or natural disasters, and war.

WHAT IS FUNDED Organisations which work with the world's poorest people and communities. Funding is given to partner organisations only.

WHAT IS NOT FUNDED Individuals, political causes or organisations whose aims are primarily political are not eligible for grants.

TYPE OF GRANT Project.

FINANCES *Year* 2007–08 *Income* £86,500,000 *Grants* £39,900,000

TRUSTEES J Gladwin, Chair; Noel Davies; Felicity Blair; Christine Eames; Bob Fyffe; Ceri George; Carolyn Gray; Stephen Hale; Philip Hodkison; Kumar Jacob; Gillian Kingston; Katei Kirby; Michael Langrish; Kenneth Mackenzie; George McSorley; Roger Purce Brian Ridsdale; Charlotte Seymour-Smith; Graham Sparkes; Bridget Walker.

HOW TO APPLY Initial approaches by potential partner organisations should be made in writing.

WHO TO APPLY TO 35–41 Lower Marsh, London SE1 7RI *Tel* 020 7523 2222 *email* info@ christian-aid.org *Website* www.christianaid.org. uk

CC NO 258003   **ESTABLISHED** 1945

■ Christian Response to Eastern Europe

WHERE FUNDING CAN BE GIVEN Eastern Europe (in practice Romania and Moldova).

WHO CAN BENEFIT Christian organisations working in Eastern Europe.

WHAT IS FUNDED The objects of the charity are to provide relief to disadvantages and vulnerable people living in Eastern Europe. Help is given by supporting families, churches and medical organisations.

FINANCES *Year* 2008 *Income* £216,625 *Grants* £361,959 *Assets* £514,548

TRUSTEES David Northcote Passmore, Chair; Timothy Mason; Hugh Scudder.

OTHER INFORMATION The 2008 grant total includes 63 grants totalling £135,000 to 'responsible individuals for onward distribution to families and individuals for the relief of hardship and for special projects'.

HOW TO APPLY In writing to the correspondent.

WHO TO APPLY TO David Northcote-Passmore, Chair, Cherith, 130 Honiton Road, Exeter EX1 3EW *Website* www.cr2ee.org.uk

CC NO 1062623   **ESTABLISHED** 1997

■ The Church and Community Fund

WHERE FUNDING CAN BE GIVEN England and Wales.

WHO CAN BENEFIT Parish, deanery or diocesan projects.

WHAT IS FUNDED The main objects of the fund are: 'to enhance the Church's mission by promoting spiritual and numerical growth, enabling and supporting the worshipping Church and encouraging and promoting new ways of being Church, and engaging with issues of social justice and environmental stewardship; to sustain and advance the Church's work in education, life long learning and discipleship to encourage the maintenance and development of the inherited fabric of church buildings for worship and service to the community. Typical projects supported by the CCF might include employing a youth worker, renovating an old church hall for use as a community centre, providing hot meals for the homeless in a church room and much more. The CCF is a very flexible fund and there is plenty of scope for imagination. We can support both capital and revenue projects as well as some preliminary costs such as feasibility studies or professional fees. In brief, all projects should seek to strengthen the relationship between the church and the local community, should benefit the Church locally and as a whole, and should manifest a sense of vision in responding to need(s).'

WHAT IS NOT FUNDED No funding is given towards: projects that are essentially insular and inward looking; the routine maintenance of or extraordinary repairs to the fabric of buildings, including churches, church halls, parsonage houses; projects which are primarily about maintaining the nation's architectural heritage; projects which are primarily about liturgical reordering; restoration works to bells or organs; research projects or personal grants; the repayment of debts or overdrafts; projects which are not directly connected with the Church of England, ecumenical or other faith; partnerships in which the Church of England element is small and projects which are predominantly secular in nature; anything for which the Church Commissioners' funds or diocesan core funding are normally available, including stipend support; feasibility studies (the fund is able to offer limited support towards the preliminary costs of projects, for example professional fees, but where a grants is awarded at this stage, no further funding will be available for the main body of the work).

TYPE OF GRANT Grants and loans.

RANGE OF GRANTS Usually less than £5,000.

SAMPLE GRANTS St. Michael's, Sutton (£9,000), towards the running costs of a church-based community project, providing youth work, employment-related support and community activities; Doncaster Minster – Sheffield (£5,000), towards the salary of a Heritage Access Worker, who is responsible for improving the opportunities for the wider community to access the church and its grounds; St. David's, Tudhoe, Durham (£4,500), to help employ a Youth Leader, running a weekly youth club for children and young people across three parishes. Invitations have been sent to other churches, the local school, and housing estates in the area, with the result that a group of 14 has now grown to 29; St. Michael's, Handsworth – Birmingham (£3,000), to help in the creation of a community garden on the site of the derelict church hall; and GAP Community Project – Canterbury (£1,000), to help run a recreational group for young people and adults with special needs across Thanet. This includes craft, drama and music activities, as well as outings and camping trips.

FINANCES *Year* 2008 *Income* £759,260 *Grants* £956,043 *Assets* £15,062,779

TRUSTEES The Archbishop's Council.

HOW TO APPLY The committee meets four times a year to consider eligible applications. Full guidelines and application forms are available from the fund's website or from the secretary.

WHO TO APPLY TO Kevin Norris, Secretary, Church House, Great Smith Street, London SW1P 3AZ *Tel* 020 7898 1541 *email* kevin.norris@c-of-e.org.uk *Website* www.centralchurchfund.org.uk

CC NO 1074857

··

■ The Church Burgesses Educational Foundation

WHERE FUNDING CAN BE GIVEN Sheffield.

WHO CAN BENEFIT Individuals and schools benefiting children and young adults.

WHAT IS FUNDED Church schools, independent schools, junior schools, language schools, primary and secondary schools, special schools, tertiary and higher education, and youth organisations. Also funded are bursaries, fees, scholarships, and the purchase of books.

TYPE OF GRANT Core costs, one-off and running costs. Funding may be given for up to three years.

SAMPLE GRANTS Previous beneficiaries have included Dyslexia Institute, the Flower Estate Community Association, Pitstop, Sheffield County Guide Association, Sheffield YMCA, South Yorkshire and Hallam Clubs for Young People, Whirlow Hall Farm Trust and Wybourn Youth Trust.

FINANCES *Year* 2008 *Income* £358,303 *Grants* £248,642 *Assets* £501,470

TRUSTEES Prof. G D Sims; Revd S A P Hunter; J F W Peters; Dr D Bradshaw; Cllr Mrs M Barker; Mrs B R Hickman; Miss H Morris; D Stanley.

HOW TO APPLY In writing to the correspondent. Trustees meet four times a year.

WHO TO APPLY TO G J Smallman, Law Clerk, c/o Wrigleys, 3rd Floor, Fountain Precinct, Balm Green, Sheffield S1 2JA

CC NO 529357   **ESTABLISHED** 1963

··

■ Church Burgesses Trust

WHERE FUNDING CAN BE GIVEN Sheffield.

WHO CAN BENEFIT Voluntary organisations and registered charities.

WHAT IS FUNDED Ecclesiastical purposes, education, and other charitable purposes.

TYPE OF GRANT One-off and recurring.

FINANCES *Year* 2008 *Income* £2,626,232 *Grants* £1,500,000 *Assets* £34,942,852

TRUSTEES D F Booker; Revd S A P Hunter; Nicholas J A Hutton; Julie Banham; Peter W Lee; J F W Peters; Prof.G D Sims; Ian G Walker; Mike R Woffenden; D Stanley; B R Hickman; Mrs S Bain.

HOW TO APPLY In writing to the correspondent. The trustees meet in January, April, July and October and at other times during the year through its various committees. At these meetings decisions are made about the work of the trust, which are then implemented through its officers and advisors. The day to day administration of the trust, work in connection with its assets, liaison with outside bodies such as the Diocese of Sheffield, the administration of its grant programmes and the processing and handling of applications prior to their consideration by relevant committees is delegated to the Law Clerk and applications should be made to him/her. The trust invites applications from Anglican parishes, from individuals involved in Christian work of a wide variety of types and from charities both national and local, involved in general charitable work within the trust's geographical area of remit. The trust makes it a condition of most grants that follow up reports

Think carefully about every application. Is it justified?

427

are made to the Trust so that the impact of its grant making can be assessed.

WHO TO APPLY TO Godfrey J Smallman, Clerk, c/o Wrigleys Solicitors LLP, 3rd Floor, Fountain Precinct, Balm Green, Sheffield S1 2JA *Tel* 0114 267 5594 *Fax* 0114 267 5630 *email* godfrey.smallman@wrigleys.co.uk
CC NO 221284   **ESTABLISHED** 1554

■ Church Lands and John Johnson's Estate Charities

WHERE FUNDING CAN BE GIVEN The ancient parish of St Laurence and the borough of Reading.
WHO CAN BENEFIT Welfare organisations and individuals.
WHAT IS FUNDED Welfare purposes.
SAMPLE GRANTS St Laurence Ecclesiastical Charities (£73,000); and St Laurence Charities for the Poor (£67,000).
FINANCES *Year* 2008 *Income* £145,704 *Grants* £140,567 *Assets* £2,282,387
TRUSTEES Revd Canon Brian Shenton, Chair; Mrs P Thomas; Mrs R Williams; Revd C I Russell; I G Hammond; M G Burges; S. Hotston; Ms L C Joslin.
HOW TO APPLY In writing to the correspondent. The trustees meet twice a year.
WHO TO APPLY TO John Michael James, Treasurer, Vale and West, 26 Queen Victoria Street, Reading RG1 1TG
CC NO 272566   **ESTABLISHED** 1941

■ Church of Ireland Priorities Fund

WHERE FUNDING CAN BE GIVEN Ireland.
WHO CAN BENEFIT Charitable organisations.
WHAT IS FUNDED Church of Ireland projects. Areas currently supported by the fund are education, ministry, outreach initiatives, community, innovative ministry in a rural context, areas of need and retirement.
WHAT IS NOT FUNDED The committee make the following choices whilst considering applications: people not buildings; new projects rather than recurrent expenditure; mission and outreach rather than maintenance; projects and programmes rather than structure.
RANGE OF GRANTS €500–€25,000.
FINANCES *Year* 2008 *Grants* €561,777
PUBLICATIONS *Priorities News* – Published each year in May
OTHER INFORMATION All the financial information is in Euros.
HOW TO APPLY In writing to the correspondent, by 31 October each year. Applications are considered in February and approved in March.
WHO TO APPLY TO Mrs Sylvia Simpson, Organiser, Church of Ireland House, Church Avenue, Rathmines, Dublin 6 *Tel* (353) 497 8422 *email* priorities@ireland.anglican.org *Website* www.priorities.ireland.anglican.org
          ESTABLISHED 1980

■ The Church Urban Fund

WHERE FUNDING CAN BE GIVEN The most deprived areas of England.
WHO CAN BENEFIT Community-based projects that tackle issues of disadvantage, homelessness, poverty and marginalisation.
WHAT IS FUNDED The fund's key objectives are to confront disadvantage and inequality in deprived communities and promote their economic,

social and spiritual renewal. In particular the trust will support projects that: tackle major problems in their area, such as poverty, unemployment, disaffected young people, lack of community facilities, loneliness and isolation, or housing and homelessness; equip local communities to address local needs and issues and encourage people to take control of their lives; empower the faith community to take an active role in wider community development, particularly through interfaith and ecumenical developments; are innovative, will make a practical impact and can develop partnerships with other agencies.

WHAT IS NOT FUNDED Projects outside England; individuals; projects not directly tackling profound poverty or specific issues caused by poverty; direct support for other grant giving bodies; publications, research and campaigning activities; revenue and capital funding for national voluntary/community organisations and public and private sector organisations; replacement of statutory funding; projects without faith links; work that has already been funded by the trust for six years; activities open only to church members and evangelistic activity not part of a response to poverty; clergy stipends including church army posts; internal re-ordering of churches for worship, church maintenance and repairs; work that does not increase the capacity of the organisation e.g. DDA compliance unless as part of a wider scheme; organisations with an annual turnover of over £150,000 or with significant reserves; ongoing costs of credit unions; general appeals. The trust does not give 100% funding, make retrospective grants, nor does it help pay off deficits or loans.

TYPE OF GRANT Capital, project and revenue funding for up to three years.
RANGE OF GRANTS Usually £100–£30,000.
SAMPLE GRANTS Holy Trinity Church – Walton Breck (£33,000); Nightstop Teesside (£24,000); A Rocha UK (£20,000); Allens Croft Project (£18,000); Strood Community Project, the Rock – Carlisle (£15,000); South Brent Deanery (£5,000); and Northampton Hope Centre (£2,000).
FINANCES *Year* 2008 *Income* £2,747,000 *Grants* £1,920,667 *Assets* £2,754,000
TRUSTEES Bishop Peter Broadbent; Patrick Coldstream; Michael Eastwood; Ven Paul Hackwood; Andrew Hunter Johnston; Rev Dennis Poole; Derek Twine; Betty Thayer; Rev David Walker; Brian Carroll.
PUBLICATIONS The trust has produced a detailed and helpful grants policy and procedure manual and applicants are advised to read this before making an application. The manual is available from the trust's website.
HOW TO APPLY *Church Urban Fund grant – the main programme:* To help ensure that projects are rooted in their communities, the fund has developed a two-stage application process in which proposals are considered by the local diocese before being forwarded to the national office. The first step is to contact the CUF link officer in your diocese. A list of all link officers can be found on the trust's website or obtained by email to resources@cuf.org.uk. Applicants should clearly state the location of their project. As an integral element of the process all applicants must liaise and work closely with the link officer in the development of their ideas and bid. All applications must be submitted to the respective link officer in the first instance (any applications sent directly to the trust will be forwarded to the diocese for consideration and

validation). The officer will help you to determine whether your project meets the fund's criteria. They will also guide you through the process of securing a recommendation from the diocesan bishop, who prioritises all requests against the overall urban strategy for the diocese and forwards them to the fund. When the application reaches the trust's offices, a member of the grants unit will contact the project to arrange an assessment visit. The application and the recommendation of the grants officer who has visited the project are then carefully considered by the grants committee, whose award decisions are ratified by the trustees. The fund always receives more applications than it has resources to support. Therefore, even if a project fits the criteria, it may not be possible to make a grant. The trust's funding committee meets four times a year, in the first week of March, June, September and December. Deadlines for applications vary between dioceses as each has its own assessment process prior to submission to the trust. *Mustard seed grant:* The trust welcomes applications from churches and faith-based groups that 'want to turn their ideas into action.' There is a simple application form to fill in, available from the relevant link officer. Alternatively, a form of application tailored to the individual project can be used (e.g. DVD, letter). For the latter, please ensure that the questions asked in the form are answered in this alternative format. The trust will undertake the assessment of applications. It will want to talk to those setting up the project; this may be face to face or by telephone. The aim of these conversations is to assist in effectively describing the project and to help ensure that the issues involved have been thought through. It is expected that work supported under this programme will grow into more substantive and established activities.

WHO TO APPLY TO Lucy Palfreyman, Director of Finance and Resources, Church House, Great Smith Street, Westminster, London SW1P 3AZ *Tel* 020 7898 1647 *email* enquiries@cuf.org.uk *Website* www.cuf.org.uk
CC NO 297483   **ESTABLISHED** 1988

■ City and County of Swansea Welsh Church Act Fund

WHERE FUNDING CAN BE GIVEN City and County of Swansea.
WHO CAN BENEFIT Registered charities.
WHAT IS FUNDED General charitable purposes.
WHAT IS NOT FUNDED No grants to individuals. 'Applications will not be considered for grants, which would normally be dealt with out of the annual budgets of the council's service departments or by public agencies or that would commit the fund to regular payments for a particular purpose.'
TYPE OF GRANT Revenue projects, up to a maximum of £5,000. For capital costs, only churches are eligible, up to a maximum of £1,000.
RANGE OF GRANTS Up to £5,000.
SAMPLE GRANTS Fairbridge Swansea (£4,200); City of Swansea Pipe Band, Elysium Gallery and Longfields Association (£2,500 each); Friends of Parc Llewellyn, Linden Church Trust and Red Cafe (£2,000); Rural Swansea Local Action Group (£1,500); Tabernacle Morriston Choir (£1,200); and St Barnabus Church, St James' Church, St Joseph's Cathedral and Taliesin Arts Centre (£1,000 each).

FINANCES *Year* 2007–08 *Income* £45,966 *Grants* £37,903 *Assets* £888,942
TRUSTEES City and County of Swansea.
HOW TO APPLY On a form available from the correspondent. Trustees meet twice a year to consider grants. Applications should be sent by April or the end of September. Successful applicants cannot re-apply for three years.
WHO TO APPLY TO The Clerk, Financial Department, City and County of Swansea, County Hall, Oystermouth Road, Swansea SA1 3SN
CC NO 1071913   **ESTABLISHED** 1997

■ The City Bridge Trust (formerly Bridge House Trust)

WHERE FUNDING CAN BE GIVEN Greater London.
WHO CAN BENEFIT Third sector organisations, mainly registered charities.
WHAT IS FUNDED The trust has seven main grant programmes, each with specific aims and objectives. In all cases priority is given to projects which tackle the greatest deprivation or disadvantage. (1) Accessible London – To reduce disadvantage experienced by disabled people by removing those barriers that prevent full participation in society. Emphasis is given to artistic and sporting activities and improving the accessibility of transport and community buildings. (2) Bridging Communities – to strengthen links between communities by building on commonalities and encouraging groups to come together. (3) London's Environment – to improve the quality of London's environment and its sustainable development. (4) Improving Londoners' Mental Health – supports work which meets a wide range of mental health needs and ensures that services are reaching marginalised communities. (5) Older Londoners – to contribute to a London where people can enjoy active, independent and healthy lives in their old age. (6) Positive Transitions to Independent Living – to improve the range of services for people who are going through difficult transitions and challenges. (7) Strengthening the Third Sector – To strengthen the Voluntary and Community Sector so that it can deliver effective, efficient and sustainable services helping reduce disadvantage.
WHAT IS NOT FUNDED The trust cannot fund: political parties; political lobbying; non-charitable activities; and work which does not benefit the inhabitants of Greater London. The trust does not fund: individuals; grant-making bodies to make grants on its behalf; schools, PTAs, universities or other educational establishments (except where they are undertaking ancillary charitable activities specifically directed towards one of the agreed priority areas); medical or academic research; churches or other religious bodies where the monies will be used for religious purposes; hospitals; projects which have already taken place or building work which has already been completed; statutory bodies; profit-making organisations (except social enterprises); and charities established outside the UK. Grants will not usually be given to: work where there is statutory responsibility to provide funding; organisations seeking funding to replace cuts by statutory authorities, except where that funding was explicitly time-limited and for a discretionary (non-statutory) purpose; organisations seeking funding to top up on under-priced contracts; and work where there is

significant public funding available (including funding from sports governing bodies).

TYPE OF GRANT Grants for either running costs or capital costs. Grants for running costs can be from one to three years. Projects of an exceptional or strategic nature may then make an application for a further two years, a maximum total of five years in all.

RANGE OF GRANTS No minimum amount but applications over £25,000 need to be accompanied by a detailed proposal. Large grants to small organisations are unlikely to be made.

SAMPLE GRANTS Age Concern Sutton (£126,000 – three years); Advocacy Project – Camden & Westminster Citizen Advocacy (£120,000 – three years); Hillingdon Mind Enterprises (£105,000 – three years); Prisoners Abroad (£90,000 – three years); Interlink Foundation (£80,000 – two years); Ethiopian Community in Britain (£63,000 – three years); Bradians Trust and St Patricks Community Outreach (£50,000 each); Green Thing – Green Thing Trust for Green Thing Limited (£25,000); Association of Eritrean Jeberti in the UK (£19,000 – two years); Archway Project (£16,000); Theatre Peckham (£5,000); House of Illustration (£3,000); and Twickenham United Reformed Church (£850).

FINANCES *Year* 2007–08 *Income* £42,000,000 *Grants* £16,904,414 *Assets* £797,900,000

TRUSTEES The Corporation of the City of London. Membership of the grants committee: Joyce Nash, Chair; William Fraser; Kenneth Ayers; John Barker; John Bird; Raymond Catt; William Dove; Revd Dr Martin Dudley; Gordon Haines; Michael Henderson-Begg; Barbara Newman; Rt Hon the Lord Mayor Ian Luder; and Simon Walsh.

OTHER INFORMATION The prime objective of the trust is the provision and maintenance of the four bridges across the Thames into the City of London.

HOW TO APPLY Application forms are available from the trust or downloadable from its website, along with full and up-to-date guidelines. Please note: the trust will not consider applications sent by fax or conventional e-mail.

WHO TO APPLY TO Clare Thomas, Chief Grants Officer, PO Box 270, Guildhall, London EC2P 2EJ *Tel* 020 7332 3710 *Fax* 020 7332 3127 *Minicom* 020 7332 3151 *email* citybridgetrust@cityoflondon.gov.uk *Website* www.citybridgetrust.org. uk/CityBridgeTrust

CC NO 1035628   **ESTABLISHED** 1995

....

■ The City Educational Trust Fund

WHERE FUNDING CAN BE GIVEN Generally Greater London.

WHO CAN BENEFIT Institutions in London benefiting young adults, research workers, students and teachers.

WHAT IS FUNDED A variety of educational groups and institutions to promote study, teaching and training in areas such as science, technology, business management, commerce, biology, ecology and the cultural arts.

WHAT IS NOT FUNDED No grants to individuals.

TYPE OF GRANT One-off, ongoing and fixed period grants.

SAMPLE GRANTS City University (£100,000).

FINANCES *Year* 2007–08 *Income* £141,327 *Grants* £100,000 *Assets* £2,696,122

TRUSTEES The Corporation of London.

HOW TO APPLY In writing to the correspondent. Guidelines are available from the trust.

WHO TO APPLY TO The Town Clerk, Corporation of London, PO Box 270, Guildhall, London EC2P 2EJ

CC NO 290840   **ESTABLISHED** 1967

....

■ The City Parochial Foundation

WHERE FUNDING CAN BE GIVEN The Metropolitan Police District of London and the City of London.

WHO CAN BENEFIT Organisations providing advice, information and individual advocacy, especially those which are user-led or which encourage user involvement, participation and which lead to user empowerment. Organisations developing, promoting and providing education, training and employment schemes. Organisations which are attempting to develop initiatives which tackle violence and hate crimes against the target groups; applications will be considered for work with people who commit crimes and violence as well as work with the victims of it.

WHAT IS FUNDED Work that aims to bring about policy changes relating to discrimination, isolations and violence and improving people's quality of life; second tier and infrastructure organisations which meet the needs of the targeted groups; projects involving working together with others to meet the needs of their members.

WHAT IS NOT FUNDED No grants for endowment appeals; individual members of the public; major expenses for buying or building premises; medical research and equipment; organisations currently receiving funding from Trust for London; replacing public funds; trips abroad.

TYPE OF GRANT Core and management costs; work that aims to change policy.

RANGE OF GRANTS Usually £15,000–£70,000 often up to three years.

SAMPLE GRANTS London Citizens (£805,000 in total, including £685,000 for a Special Initiative); Black Training and Enterprise Group (£102,000); Foundation for Women's Health Research and Development (£90,000); Hammersmith and Fulham Community Law Centre (£76,500); Central London Law Centre (£67,000); Newham Community Renewal Programme (£54,000); Centre for Corporate Accountability (£50,000); Conflict and Change (£35,500); North Kensington Women's Textile Workshop (£30,000); Islington Refugee Forum (£20,000); and Development Adult Neuro-Diversity Association (£4,700).

FINANCES *Year* 2008 *Income* £9,131,010 *Grants* £11,524,629 *Assets* £171,147,045

TRUSTEES Nigel Pantling, Chair; Maggie Baxter; Tzeggai Yohannes Deres; Revd Dr Martin Dudley; The Archdeacon of London, The Ven. Peter Delaney; Archie Galloway; Roger Evans; Deborah Finkler; Cllr Lynne Hillan; Robert Hughes-Penney; Robert Laurence; Elahe Panahi; Ingrid Posen; Wilfred Weeks; Peter Williams.

HOW TO APPLY The foundation's funding guidelines for 2007–11 are available to download from its website. Alternatively contact the foundation's office for hard copies. It is strongly recommended that potential applicants read the guidelines before making an application. There is a two-stage application process: *Stage one* – an initial proposal to be submitted by post. There are three closing dates for proposals to be submitted by – you may submit your proposal at any time but it will only be assessed once the next closing date has passed. Closing dates are: 7 February for the June Grants Committee; 30 May for the October Grants Committee; 25 October for the March Grants Committee. *Stage two:* all organisations whose initial proposals are shortlisted will be visited by the foundation to assess their suitability for funding.

WHO TO APPLY TO Bharat Mehta, Chief Executive to the Trustees, 6 Middle Street, London EC1A 7PH *Tel* 020 7606 6145 *Fax* 020 7600 1866 *email* info@cityparochial.org.uk *Website* www.cityparochial.org.uk

CC NO 205629   **ESTABLISHED** 2004

■ CLA Charitable Trust

WHERE FUNDING CAN BE GIVEN England and Wales only.

WHO CAN BENEFIT Small local projects, innovative projects and newly established projects, where a grant can make a 'real contribution to the success of the project'.

WHAT IS FUNDED (i) To encourage education about the countryside for those who are disabled or disadvantaged, particularly youngsters from urban areas. (ii) To provide facilities for those with disabilities to have access to recreation in the countryside. (iii) To promote education in agriculture, horticulture and conservation for those who are disabled or disadvantaged.

WHAT IS NOT FUNDED No grants to individuals.

TYPE OF GRANT Specific projects or items rather than for ongoing running costs.

RANGE OF GRANTS Rarely more than £2,000.

SAMPLE GRANTS Harper Adams College (£3,000); Eden Rivers Trust (£2,500); Caring for Life (£2,100); Countryside Foundation, Hamelin Trust, Marrick Priory and NDFM (£2,000 each); Oxford Young Farmers and Royal School for the Deaf (£1,500 each); and Bridewell Organic Gardens (£1,100).

FINANCES *Year* 2007–08 *Income* £59,607 *Grants* £51,084 *Assets* £288,325

TRUSTEES A Duckworth-Chad; A H Duberly; G E Lee-Strong; G N Mainwaring.

OTHER INFORMATION The CLA Charitable Trust was founded by CLA members in 1980.

HOW TO APPLY In writing to the correspondent. Trustees meet four times a year.

WHO TO APPLY TO Peter Geldart, Caunton Grange, Caunton, Newark, Nottinghamshire NG23 6AB *Tel* 01636 636171 *Website* www.cla.org.uk

CC NO 280264   **ESTABLISHED** 1980

■ Stephen Clark 1957 Charitable Trust

WHERE FUNDING CAN BE GIVEN Some preference for Bath and Somerset.

WHO CAN BENEFIT Registered charities.

WHAT IS FUNDED The trust's priorities are 'to make donations to charities in respect of the preservation, embellishment, maintenance, improvement or development of any monuments, churches or other buildings'. The trust prefers local charities to national ones.

WHAT IS NOT FUNDED No grants to animal charities or to individuals.

SAMPLE GRANTS Bath Industrial Heritage Trust (£18,000); Friends of Holburne Museum (£10,000); Friends of Nunney Church (£5,000); and All Saints' – Maiden Bradley, St Mary's – Witney and Wells Cathedral Development Project (£3,000 each; Bridge Care (£2,000); Dorothy House Foundation (£1,200); Herschel Museum and Woodlands Trust (£1,000 each); Ulster

Youth Orchestra (£500); Action Ethiopia (£400); BikeAbility (£300); The Lundy fund (£200); Dying in Dignity (£100); and Crisis at Christmas (£50).

FINANCES *Year* 2008 *Income* £65,899 *Grants* £107,969 *Assets* £1,635,761

TRUSTEES Dr Marianna Clark; Mrs M P Lovell; Ms A Clark.

HOW TO APPLY In writing to the correspondent. Please note, replies are not usually made to unsuccessful applications.

WHO TO APPLY TO Dr Marianna Clark, Trustee, 16 Lansdown Place East, Bath BA1 5ET

CC NO 258690   **ESTABLISHED** 1969

■ J A Clark Charitable Trust

WHERE FUNDING CAN BE GIVEN UK, with a preference for South West England.

WHO CAN BENEFIT Charitable organisations.

WHAT IS FUNDED Health, education, peace, preservation of the earth and the arts.

SAMPLE GRANTS Eucalyptus Charitable Foundation (£64,000 in two grants); C&J Clark Property Fund (£35,000); Arts Education (£20,000); Conflicts Forum (£16,000); Pesticide Action, UK Theatre for a Change and UK Friends of Kwendo Kor (£15,000 each); Global Partnership (£14,000); Offscreen Education Programme (£12,000); Christian Aid and Open Bethlehem (£10,000 each); Adams Institute for Change, Camfed International and Watershed Arts Trust (£5,000 each); and Haiti Support Group (£1,200).

FINANCES *Year* 2006–07 *Income* £432,410 *Grants* £347,536 *Assets* £13,905,539

TRUSTEES Tom Clark, Chair; Lance Clark; William Pym; Aidan Pelly.

HOW TO APPLY This trust does not respond to unsolicited applications.

WHO TO APPLY TO Mrs P Grant, Secretary, PO Box 1704, Glastonbury, Somerset BA16 0YB

CC NO 1010520   **ESTABLISHED** 1992

■ The Hilda and Alice Clark Charitable Trust

WHERE FUNDING CAN BE GIVEN Street, Somerset.

WHO CAN BENEFIT There is a preference given to the Society of Friends (Quakers) and to children and young adults.

WHAT IS FUNDED General charitable purposes and Quaker causes.

WHAT IS NOT FUNDED Only registered charities are considered.

SAMPLE GRANTS Britain Yearly Meeting (£15,000 in two grants); Greenbank Swimming Pool and Hope Flowers School (£10,000); QPSW – Friends Bursaries (£6,000); Ulster Quaker Service Committee (£5,000); and Holy Trinity Church Bell Appeal, Medical Aid for Palestinians, Quaker Council for European Affairs, Sightsavers International and Thirsk Friends Meeting (£1,000 each).

FINANCES *Year* 2007 *Income* £61,638 *Grants* £52,700 *Assets* £1,716,279

TRUSTEES Richard Clark; Thomas Clark; Martin Lovell; Alice Clark; Susannah Clark.

HOW TO APPLY In writing to the correspondent by 30 September. Trustees meet in December each year.

WHO TO APPLY TO The Secretary, c/o KPMG, 100 Temple Street, Bristol BS1 1AG

CC NO 290916   **ESTABLISHED** 1953

■ The Roger and Sarah Bancroft Clark Charitable Trust

WHERE FUNDING CAN BE GIVEN UK and overseas, with preference for Somerset and Scotland.

WHO CAN BENEFIT Society of Friends, registered charities and individuals. Preference is given to local appeals.

WHAT IS FUNDED General charitable purposes with particular reference to: Religious Society of Friends and associated bodies; charities connected with Somerset; education (for individuals).

TYPE OF GRANT Recurrent grants.

RANGE OF GRANTS Mostly £50–£1,000.

SAMPLE GRANTS University of Edinburgh (£2,500).

FINANCES *Year* 2007 *Income* £48,514 *Grants* £2,500 *Assets* £1,200,709

TRUSTEES Mary P Lovell; Sarah C Gould; Roger S Goldby; Alice Clark; Robert B Robertson; Martin Lovell.

HOW TO APPLY In writing to the correspondent. There is no application form and telephone calls are not accepted. Trustees meet about three times a year. Applications will be acknowledged if an sae is enclosed or email address given.

WHO TO APPLY TO The Trustees, c/o KPMG LLP, 100 Temple Street, Bristol BS1 6AG

CC NO 211513 **ESTABLISHED** 1960

■ The Clarke Charitable Settlement

WHERE FUNDING CAN BE GIVEN Staffordshire and Derbyshire.

WHO CAN BENEFIT Funding may be considered for Christians, research workers and medical professionals.

WHAT IS FUNDED The advancement of Christian religion, medical research and hospices.

RANGE OF GRANTS Most grants are for under £1,000, although they can be for much more.

SAMPLE GRANTS Litchfield Cathedral (£1.1 million); Merseyside Holiday Service and St Giles Hospice (£10,000 each); Meir and Normcot Methodist Church (£5,000); Spinal Injures Association (£4,000); St Lawrence's Church (£2,500); Animal Health Trust (£2,000); CLIC Cancer and Leukaemia Research and Douglas Macmillan Hospice (£1,000 each); British Forces Foundation (£500); Burton-on-Trent Lions Club and NSPCC (£100 each); and Mind (£50).

FINANCES *Year* 2007–08 *Income* £1,322,248 *Grants* £1,175,834 *Assets* £1,418,788

TRUSTEES Lady Hilda Clarke; Sally Hayward; Mary MacGregor; Jane Gerard-Pearse.

HOW TO APPLY In writing to the correspondent, although the trust has previously stated that support is only given to charities known to the trustees or the Clarke family.

WHO TO APPLY TO Lady H J Clarke, Trustee, The Knoll, Main Street, Barton-under-Needwood, Burton-on-Trent, Staffordshire DE13 8AB *Tel* 01283 712294

CC NO 702980 **ESTABLISHED** 1990

■ The Cleary Foundation

WHERE FUNDING CAN BE GIVEN UK, with a preference for Kent.

WHO CAN BENEFIT Registered charities.

WHAT IS FUNDED Principally to apply the income of the foundation for various selected charities for the relief of pain and hardship, and conservation. These include: civil society

development; community development; social care professional bodies; churches; music; visual art; arts activities; dance and ballet; dance groups; theatrical companies and theatre groups; horticulture; special schools; community centres and village halls; and parks.

WHAT IS NOT FUNDED No grants to individuals who require aid with further education.

SAMPLE GRANTS Ripple Down House Trust (£15,000); Deal Summer Music Festival (£1,500); London Children's Flower Society (£650); British Red Cross (£350); St Martin-in-the-Fields Christmas Appeal (£300); and NSPCC Kent (£150).

FINANCES *Year* 2007–08 *Income* £29,882 *Grants* £19,250 *Assets* £1,053,979

TRUSTEES P M Gould, Chair; A T F Gould; W T Westwater.

HOW TO APPLY In writing to the correspondent, although the trust would welcome a preliminary telephone call to check whether they are in the position of being able to offer grants to new beneficiaries.

WHO TO APPLY TO The Secretary to the Trustees, South Sands Lodge, Beach Road, St Margaret's Bay, Kent CT15 6DZ

CC NO 242675 **ESTABLISHED** 1965

■ The Cleopatra Trust

WHERE FUNDING CAN BE GIVEN Mainly UK.

WHO CAN BENEFIT Registered charities with a national focus.

WHAT IS FUNDED The trust makes grants in the following areas: mental health; cancer welfare/education – not research; diabetes; physical disability – not research; homelessness; addiction; children who are disadvantaged.

WHAT IS NOT FUNDED No grants to individuals, expeditions, research, scholarships, charities with a local focus, local branches of UK-wide charities or towards running costs.

RANGE OF GRANTS £500–£16,000.

SAMPLE GRANTS Fairbridge (£11,000); All Star Youth Tennis Scholarship Trust and Finton House Educational Trust (£1,000 each); and Friends of Finton House Trust (£150).

FINANCES *Year* 2008 *Income* £158,694 *Grants* £13,280 *Assets* £2,985,591

TRUSTEES Dr C Peacock; Mrs B Bond; C H Peacock.

HOW TO APPLY This trust no longer accepts applications.

WHO TO APPLY TO C H Peacock, Trustee, c/o Charities Aid Foundation, King's Hill, West Malling, Kent ME19 4TA

CC NO 1004551 **ESTABLISHED** 1990

■ Lord Clinton's Charitable Trust

WHERE FUNDING CAN BE GIVEN North and East Devon.

WHO CAN BENEFIT Registered charities benefiting people of all ages, ex-service and service people, seafarers and fishermen, sportsmen and women, volunteers, parents and children, people with disabilities, victims of man-made or natural disasters, people with cancer, paediatric diseases, or sight loss, and people who are terminally ill.

WHAT IS FUNDED Young people and the encouragement of youth activities, people who have disabilities, support for older people, medical aid and research, maritime charities. Respite and sheltered accommodation; churches; information technology and computers; personnel and human resources; support to voluntary and community organisations and volunteers; professional bodies; community centres; village halls and clubs.

WHAT IS NOT FUNDED No support for animal charities. No grants made in response to general appeals from large UK organisations or to smaller bodies working in areas other than those set out above.

TYPE OF GRANT For projects, recurring costs and start-up costs. Funding is available for one year or less.

RANGE OF GRANTS Up to £10,000.

SAMPLE GRANTS University of Exeter Sponsorship x two grants (£4,600 each); Vicar's Christmas Fund (£1,400); Kingfisher Award Scheme (£1,200); North Devon Cancer Care (£1,000); Exmouth Lifeboat Station Appeal and Families for Children (£500 each); Brixington Pre-School and the Countryside Foundation (£200 each); and Charity Golf Day (£50).

FINANCES *Year* 2007–08 *Income* £31,480 *Grants* £23,654 *Assets* £648,338

TRUSTEES Hon. Charles Fane Trefusis; John C Varley.

HOW TO APPLY In writing to the correspondent. Applications not falling within the trust's objects and funding priorities will not be considered or acknowledged.

WHO TO APPLY TO John C Varley, Trustee, Rolle Estate Office, East Budleigh, Budleigh Salterton, Devon EX9 7BL *Tel* 01395 443881 *Fax* 01395 446126 *email* mail@clintondevon.co.uk *Website* www.clintondevon.co.uk

CC NO 268061   **ESTABLISHED** 1974

■ The Clore Duffield Foundation

WHERE FUNDING CAN BE GIVEN UK, the larger grants go to London-based institutions.

WHO CAN BENEFIT Institutions and registered charities, particular emphasis on supporting children, young people and society's more vulnerable individuals.

WHAT IS FUNDED Main grants programme, mainly in the fields of museums, galleries and heritage sites (particularly for learning spaces), the arts, education, health, social care and disability and Jewish charities with interests in any of these areas.

WHAT IS NOT FUNDED Potential applicants should note that their organisation must be a registered charity to be eligible. Unfortunately, the foundation does not fund projects retrospectively and will not support applications from the following: individuals; general appeals and circulars. It should also be noted that the following are funded only very rarely: projects outside the UK; staff posts; local branches of national charities; academic or project research; conference costs.

TYPE OF GRANT Capital.

SAMPLE GRANTS South Bank Foundation (£1 million); London Zoo (£200,000); Imperial War Museum (£150,000); National Museum of Wales (£100,000); Whitechapel Gallery (£60,000); Royal Society (£50,000); Foundling Museum (£25,000); Engage (£21,000); Scott Polar Research Institute (£10,000); National Youth Theatre (£9,000); Mid Argyll Pipe Band (£8,000); British Library (£5,000); Chicken Shed Theatre (£2,000); and the Jewish Funders' Network (£1,800).

FINANCES *Year* 2008 *Income* £3,642,267 *Grants* £4,323,475 *Assets* £76,782,664

TRUSTEES Dame Vivien Duffield, Chair; Caroline Deltra; David Harrel; Michael Trask; Sir Mark Weinberg.

HOW TO APPLY There is no application form for your initial approach to the foundation. If your project falls within the foundation's funding criteria, please send a letter of application. This letter should be no longer than two sides of A4 paper, and should include the following information: a brief overview of the work of your organisation; a concise account of the project you are seeking funding for; a clear statement of the sum you are seeking from the foundation and the total cost of the project. You should enclose a standard-sized (DL), stamped, self-addressed envelope – if this is not included, the foundation will not be able to respond to your application. No annual accounts or additional information should be included at this stage, and all applications should be on your organisation's headed paper with your contact details and charity number clearly displayed. There is no deadline for the Main Grants Programme and applications are accepted on a rolling basis. You should receive a response from the foundation within four weeks of contacting the foundation if you have included a self-addressed envelope. All letters of application will reviewed by the foundation's staff in the first instance, and then by the trustees. If the foundation decides to progress your application to the next stage (i.e. a meeting of the trustees), you will be contacted within six weeks and asked to submit a full proposal, for which guidance will be provided. Trustees meetings are typically held twice a year. Successful and unsuccessful applicants are usually contacted in writing within two weeks of the meeting. Please do not send applications by recorded delivery as the foundation is not able to guarantee that a member of staff will be on site to receive them. Email applications will not be accepted.

WHO TO APPLY TO Sally Bacon, Executive Director, Studio 3, Chelsea Manor Studios, Flood Street, London SW3 5SR *Tel* 020 7351 6061 *Fax* 020 7351 5308 *email* info@cloreduffield.org.uk *Website* www.cloreduffield.org.uk

CC NO 1084412   **ESTABLISHED** 2000

■ Miss V L Clore's 1967 Charitable Trust

WHERE FUNDING CAN BE GIVEN UK.

WHO CAN BENEFIT Registered charities.

WHAT IS FUNDED General charitable purposes, especially performing arts, education, social welfare, health and disability. Jewish causes are also supported.

WHAT IS NOT FUNDED No grants are given to individuals.

RANGE OF GRANTS Usually £200–£5,000.

SAMPLE GRANTS Chelsea Physic Gardens, Family Friends and Maccabi GB (£5,000 each); North London Hospice (£4,000); West London Synagogue (£2,500); Friends of Castle of Mey, NSPCC, the Pearl Foundation and UF Elias Ashmole Trust (£1,000 each); and Institute for Polish-Jewish Studies and JTMM Mission (£500 each).

FINANCES *Year* 2007–08 *Income* £44,261 *Grants* £31,853 *Assets* £1,278,501

TRUSTEES Dame V L Duffield; David Harrel; Caroline Deltra.

HOW TO APPLY In writing to the correspondent on one to two sides of A4, enclosing an sae.

WHO TO APPLY TO Sally Bacon, Unit 3, Chelsea Manor Studios, Flood Street, London SW3 5SR *Tel* 020 7351 6061 *email* info@cloreduffield.org.uk
CC NO 253660   ESTABLISHED 1967

....

■ Closehelm Ltd

WHERE FUNDING CAN BE GIVEN UK and Israel.
WHO CAN BENEFIT Individuals and institutions benefiting Jewish people and people disadvantaged by poverty.
WHAT IS FUNDED The advancement of religion in accordance with the Jewish faith; the relief of poverty; and general charitable purposes.
FINANCES *Year* 2007–08 *Income* £4,524,142 *Grants* £537,600 *Assets* £7,037,454
TRUSTEES A Van Praagh; Henrietta W Van Praagh; Hannah R Van Praagh.
OTHER INFORMATION A list of grants was not available.
HOW TO APPLY In writing to the correspondent.
WHO TO APPLY TO Henrietta W Van Praagh, Secretary, 30 Armitage Road, London NW11 8RD *Tel* 020 8201 8688
CC NO 291296   ESTABLISHED 1983

....

■ The Clothworkers' Foundation

WHERE FUNDING CAN BE GIVEN UK.
WHO CAN BENEFIT UK registered charities only.
WHAT IS FUNDED Social inclusion, visual impairment and textiles.
WHAT IS NOT FUNDED The foundation does not make grants to: 'non UK-registered charities; organisations with an annual turnover of over £10 million (charities working in textiles with an annual turnover of over £10 million, wishing to make an application, are requested to contact the foundation); non-capital costs i.e. running costs, salary costs; organisations that have received a grant from the foundation in the last five years; heritage projects (other than textiles); environment projects; arts and education projects are unlikely to be funded unless they are predominantly focused on disadvantaged young people, older people or people with disabilities; projects that do not fit in with one of our programme areas; individuals; general or marketing appeals; educational establishments; grant-makers; overseas work/projects; medical research or equipment; political, industrial, or commercial appeals; relief of state aid or reduction of support from public funds; events; appeals from any organisation where the money will be used for religious purposes, or projects which promote a particular religion'.
TYPE OF GRANT Capital; one-off; occasionally recurring for more than three years.
SAMPLE GRANTS Maths Inspiration (£202,000 over three years), for UK-wide interactive lectures to engage and inspire young people in maths education; Institute of Conservation (£180,000), for the chief executive's salary over three years; Royal Star and Garter Home for Disabled Sailors Soldiers and Airmen (£150,000), for en-suite shower rooms at the new nursing care home in Solihull; Halton YMCA (£75,000), for the redevelopment of facilities for homeless young people in Cheshire; Wirral Autistic Society (£50,000), towards the building costs of a respite unit for people with autism; Metropolitan Society for the Blind (£34,000), grants and pensions for needy visually-impaired individuals; Edward Mayes Trust (£25,000), towards the construction of four new properties

for older people in Manchester; Burma Star Association (£17,000), for grants for needy older UK veterans and their dependents; All Hallows Centre (£15,000), towards disabled and upgraded toilet facilities at a community centre for older people in Liverpool; and Cardinal Hume Centre (£11,000), for an IT server and hardware at a centre for homeless young people in London.
FINANCES *Year* 2008 *Income* £6,335,000 *Grants* £4,951,000 *Assets* £90,932,000
TRUSTEES John Stoddart-Scott, Chair; Carolyn Boulter; Neil Foster; Melville Haggard; Oliver Howard; Michael Howell; Michael Jarvis; Christopher Jonas; Richard Jonas; Michael Malyon; Christopher McLean May; Sir Jonathan Portal.
HOW TO APPLY There are separate application forms for the main and small grants programmes both available from the foundation's website and with full details of the application process and criteria for funding. Both require the following information: completed application form; full project budget; latest accounts for the organisation as submitted to the Charity Commission; copy of the correspondence confirming Northern Ireland charitable status if registered in NI. The foundation does not accept draft applications or applications by email; please post your finished application. Applications are accepted at any time, there are no deadlines. Decisions normally take six weeks for the small grants programme and six months for the main grants programme. Any applicants who have specific queries after reading the foundation's guidelines should contact the grants assistant on 020 7623 7041. The foundation does not however, provide advice on matters which are covered on its website. If your application is not successful, you must wait six months before re-applying.
WHO TO APPLY TO Sam Grimmett, Grants Assistant, Clothworkers' Hall, Dunster Court, Mincing Lane, London EC3R 7AH *Tel* 020 7623 7041 *Fax* 020 7397 0107 *email* foundation@clothworkers.co.uk *Website* www.clothworkers.co.uk
CC NO 274100   ESTABLISHED 1977

....

■ Richard Cloudesley's Charity

WHERE FUNDING CAN BE GIVEN Ancient parish of Islington, London.
WHO CAN BENEFIT Voluntary and charitable organisations. Individuals are assisted through the trust's welfare fund.
WHAT IS FUNDED Church of England churches, medical and welfare.
TYPE OF GRANT One-off grants are preferred; the vast majority of grants are free of restrictions. Grants for capital, core, recurring, running and start-up costs will be considered, as will grants for buildings, feasibility studies, project, research and salaries.
RANGE OF GRANTS £100–£40,000.
SAMPLE GRANTS St. Mary's Church, Ashley Road (£40,000); St. John's District Church (£31,000); St. David's Church, Lough Road (£24,000); CARIS (Islington) Churches Bereavement Service (£23,000); Islington Mind (£18,000); Choices Confidential Pregnancy Advice (£11,000); Union Chapel Homelessness Project (£10,000); Sunnyside Community Gardens Association (£6,000); Medical Foundation for Care of Victims of Torture (£5,000); Factory Community Mental Health

Drop in Group (£3,000); Equinox Care (£2,000); and Islington Pensioners Forum (£1,000).

FINANCES *Year* 2007–08 *Income* £999,306 *Grants* £705,171 *Assets* £24,762,484

TRUSTEES Kevin A Streater, Chair; Kathleen Frenchman; Roger Goodman; Revd Canon Graham Kings; Brian H March; Michael Simmonds; David R Stephens; Cllr Terry Stacy; Martin Black; Christopher Moss; Rupert Perry; Miranda Coates; Dorothy Newton; Courtney Bailey.

HOW TO APPLY Applicants should write to the correspondent requesting an application form. Applications should be in time for the trustees' meetings in April and November and should be accompanied by the organisation's accounts. The following information should be supplied: details of the work your organisation undertakes; how it falls within the geographical area of the trust; and details what the grant will fund. If you would like acknowledgement of receipt of your application please send an sae. Block grants are considered twice a year, around late April, and early November at a grants committee meeting. Recommendations are made by the grants committee at these meetings and are reviewed and authorised by the trustees two weeks later. The trust will give brief reasons with any application that is not successful.

WHO TO APPLY TO Keith Wallace, Clerk, Reed Smith LLP, 26th Floor, Broadgate Tower, 20 Primrose Street, London EC2A 2RS *Tel* 020 3116 3624 *email* kwallace@reedsmith.com

CC NO 205959   **ESTABLISHED** 1517

....

■ The Clover Trust

WHERE FUNDING CAN BE GIVEN UK, and occasionally overseas, with a slight preference for West Dorset.

WHO CAN BENEFIT Registered charities.

WHAT IS FUNDED Health, disability, young people, older people and Catholic activities.

WHAT IS NOT FUNDED The arts, monuments and non-registered charities are not supported. No grants are given towards building work.

TYPE OF GRANT General running costs. Unsolicited applications which impress the trustees are given one-off grants. However, most grants are given to a 'core list' of beneficiaries.

RANGE OF GRANTS £1,000–£27,000.

SAMPLE GRANTS Friends of Children in Romania (£25,000); Action Medical Research, Cotswold Care, CAFOD and Cardinal Hume Centre (£10,000 each); Childhood First and JOLT (£7,500 each); BIBIC, Demand, Dorset Association for the Disabled, Kidsactive and Sue Ryder Foundation (£5,000 each); Disability Snowsport UK (£3,000); Essex Association of Boys' Clubs (£2,000); and English Catholic History Association (£500).

FINANCES *Year* 2007 *Income* £240,905 *Grants* £196,600 *Assets* £4,689,608

TRUSTEES N C Haydon; S Woodhouse.

HOW TO APPLY In writing to the correspondent. Replies are not given to unsuccessful applications.

WHO TO APPLY TO G F D Wright, DTE Business Advisory Services Limited, Park House, 26 North End Road, London NW11 7PT

CC NO 213578   **ESTABLISHED** 1961

....

■ The Robert Clutterbuck Charitable Trust

WHERE FUNDING CAN BE GIVEN UK, with preference for Cheshire and Hertfordshire.

WHO CAN BENEFIT Registered charities.

WHAT IS FUNDED Personnel within the armed forces and ex-servicemen and women; sport and recreational facilities for young people benefiting Cheshire and Hertfordshire; the welfare, protection and preservation of domestic animal life benefiting Cheshire and Hertfordshire; natural history and wildlife; other charities associated with the counties of Cheshire and Hertfordshire; charities which have particular appeal to the founder, Major Robert Clutterbuck.

WHAT IS NOT FUNDED No grants to individuals.

TYPE OF GRANT Specific items and projects rather than running costs.

RANGE OF GRANTS £500–£5,000. No grants are made below £500.

SAMPLE GRANTS Music in Hospitals (£2,000); Nottinghamshire Wildlife Trust (£1,725); Queen Alexandra Hospital Home (£1,500); 11th Letchworth Scout Group, Filey Sea Cadets, Groundwork Cheshire, Hearing Dogs for Deaf People, South Manchester Gymnastics, Whizz Kids and Youth with a Mission (£1,000 each); Buglife and Rochdale Special Needs Cycling (£750 each); and Aspire Trust, Marine Conservation Society and Southern Uplands Partnership (£500 each).

FINANCES *Year* 2007–08 *Income* £42,282 *Grants* £44,181 *Assets* £1,229,625

TRUSTEES Maj. R G Clutterbuck; I A Pearson; R J Pincham.

HOW TO APPLY In writing to the correspondent. There are no application forms. Applications are acknowledged and considered by the trustees twice a year. The trustees will not normally consider appeals from charities within two years of a previous grant being approved.

WHO TO APPLY TO G A Wolfe, Secretary, 28 Brookfields, Calver, Hope Valley, Derbyshire S32 3XB *Tel* 01433 631308 *email* secretary@clutterbucktrust.org.uk *Website* www.clutterbucktrust.org.uk

CC NO 1010559   **ESTABLISHED** 1992

....

■ Clydpride Ltd

WHERE FUNDING CAN BE GIVEN Unrestricted.

WHO CAN BENEFIT Individuals and institutions benefiting Jewish people and people disadvantaged by poverty.

WHAT IS FUNDED Advancement of the orthodox Jewish faith; relief of poverty; general charitable purposes. The main focus is to support the 'renaissance of religious study and to alleviate the plight of poor scholars'.

SAMPLE GRANTS Previous beneficiaries include: Achiezer; Achisomoch Aid Company; Beis Chinuch Lebonos; Beis Soroh Scheneirer Seminary; Bnei Braq Hospital; Comet Charities Limited; EM Shasha Foundation; Friends of Mir; Gevurath Ari Torah Academy Trust; Mosdos Tchernobil; Notzar Chesed; Seed; Society of Friends of Torah; and Telz Talmudical Academy Trust.

FINANCES *Year* 2008 *Income* £3,475,422 *Grants* £2,634,512 *Assets* £9,376,314

TRUSTEES L Faust; M H Linton; A Faust.

OTHER INFORMATION A list of grant beneficiaries was not included in the trust's accounts.

HOW TO APPLY The trust states that unsolicited applications are not considered.

WHO TO APPLY TO L Faust, Secretary, 144 Bridge Lane, London NW11 9JS *Tel* 020 8731 7744 *Fax* 020 8731 8373
CC NO 295393   ESTABLISHED 1982

....

■ The Co-operative Foundation

WHERE FUNDING CAN BE GIVEN The trading area of the Co-operative Group – United Region which has interests in the North West, south Cumbria, Yorkshire, north Midlands, Northern Ireland and North Wales.

WHO CAN BENEFIT Local groups and organisations. 'It is particularly interested in locally led and run groups which can demonstrate evidence of co-operative values and principles: self-help, equality, democracy, concern for the community.'

WHAT IS FUNDED 'Supporting community groups to find co-operative solutions to community challenges.' In support of its community-led approach the foundation has one focussed grant-making programme, the *Community Support Programme*. This programme was developed to help groups who want to 'make a difference' in their own communities, through grass roots community activity. The community can be geographically-based, such as a village, town or housing estate, or could be a community of people brought together to address a specific issue. Examples of work the foundation may fund under the programme include: activities that encourage people to work with others who have similar needs or face similar challenges, including the development of community groups; work that aims to resolve or reduce conflict, such as community mediation or the reduction of harassment; the setting up or development of community safety schemes; provision and improvement of community facilities that allow premises and equipment to be shared between organisations; work to assist people, who would not otherwise have the opportunity, to gain access to IT equipment, training or support; development of out-reach work to offer services to the most vulnerable in society; improvement of access to information, advice and advocacy services that enable people to make informed choices about their lives or lifestyle; work which supports that undertaken by volunteers; work with communities with significant needs such as minority groups, people with disabilities and their carers, or those with special needs, mental health problems and learning disabilities.

WHAT IS NOT FUNDED No funding for: applications from outside the Co-operative Group – United Region area, including overseas applications; organisations whose activities are not recognised as charitable or philanthropic; charities that have large unrestricted reserves; national charities (unless there is a specific local project, which has been initiated by the local community benefiting from the grant); applications for salaries; replacement of statutory funding; applications from local authorities; applications from health authorities; activities that are the responsibility of local or central government; organisations that promote political parties; applications for projects which are deemed to promote a particular religious group or activity; applications to help animals; the Scout movement, including Guides, Cubs, Brownies, Beavers and Rainbows; groundwork; YMCA and YWCA; schools, including PTAs; residential homes which are the responsibility of the local authority; retrospective grants; groups not demonstrating self help; applications benefiting individuals; grants for outstanding debts or down payments for loans; groups that have received a grant from the foundation in the last twelve months; groups which are applying for more than one year's worth of funding; applications where the questions on the form have been amended or altered.

TYPE OF GRANT One-year projects – for either part or total funding, capital costs and revenue costs (but not salaries).

RANGE OF GRANTS £500–£30,000.

SAMPLE GRANTS Peacemaker and Gipton Together Youth Project (£30,000); Rotherham Play and Learn Bus (£27,000); Leeds Community Mediation Service (£22,000); Get Sorted Academy of Music (£21,000); Choose Life (£14,000); Hulme Community Garden Centre (£13,000); Open Door Furniture Recycling Limited and Sahir House (£10,000 each); Milun's Women's Centre (£7,000); Lai Yin Association (£6,000); The Prospects Foundation (£4,000); and Parent Network (£2,000).

FINANCES *Year* 2007–08 *Income* £3,176,799 *Grants* £1,020,152 *Assets* £10,517,669

TRUSTEES A Brett; P Grange; F Makinson; S Sherrington; S Howarth; P Lockley; Stephen Youd-Thomas; J Wakefield; Joyce Baruch; Mike Greenacre.

HOW TO APPLY Full guidelines, application details and application forms can be downloaded from the foundation's website. The trustees meet four times a year to approve grants, deadline dates can be found on the Co-operative website.

WHO TO APPLY TO The Charity Manager, New Century House, 6th Floor, Corporation Street, Manchester M60 4ES *Tel* 0161 246 3044 *email* foundation@coop.co.uk *Website* www.co-operative.co.uk/en/foundation
CC NO 1080834   ESTABLISHED 2000

....

■ The Francis Coales Charitable Foundation

WHERE FUNDING CAN BE GIVEN UK, with a preference for Bedfordshire, Buckinghamshire, Hertfordshire and Northamptonshire.

WHO CAN BENEFIT Old buildings open to the public, usually churches. Organisations involved in archaeological research and related causes.

WHAT IS FUNDED The repair/restoration of buildings built before 1875; also monuments, tombs, hatchments, memorial brasses, and so on. Grants are also made towards the cost of archaeological research and related causes, the purchase of documents or items for record offices and museums, and the publication of architectural and archaeological books or papers. Assistance for structural repairs is normally given to churches and their contents in Buckinghamshire, Bedfordshire, Northamptonshire and Hertfordshire where most of the business of Francis Coales and Son was carried out with farmers. However, no territorial restriction is placed upon church monuments, and so on.

WHAT IS NOT FUNDED In respect of buildings, assistance is only given towards fabric repairs, but not to 'domestic' items such as heating, lighting, wiring, installation of facilities etc.

TYPE OF GRANT Largely one-off (or recurrent if for an ongoing application).

FINANCES *Year* 2008 *Income* £758,674 *Grants* £91,095 *Assets* £2,269,191

TRUSTEES H M Stuchfield, Chair; A G Harding; Revd B H Wilcox; I G Barnett.

HOW TO APPLY On a form which can be downloaded from the foundation's website. Trustees normally meet three times a year to consider grants. 'In respect of a building or contents, include a copy of the relevant portion only of the architect's (or conservator's) specification showing the actual work proposed. Photographs illustrating this are a necessity, and only in exceptional circumstances will an application be considered without supporting photographs here. It is of help if six copies of any supporting documentation are submitted in order that each trustee may have a copy in advance of the meeting.'

WHO TO APPLY TO Trevor Parker, Administrator, The Bays, Hillcote, Bleadon Hill, Weston-super-Mare, Somerset BS24 9JS *Tel* 01934 814009 *email* enquiries@franciscoales.co.uk *Website* franciscoales.co.uk

CC NO 270718   **ESTABLISHED** 1975

■ The Coalfields Regeneration Trust

WHERE FUNDING CAN BE GIVEN Coalfield and former coalfield communities in England (North West and North East, Yorkshire, West Midlands and East Midlands, Kent), Scotland (West and East) and Wales.

WHO CAN BENEFIT Community and voluntary organisations who are working to tackle problems at grass-roots level within coalfield communities.

WHAT IS FUNDED Welfare of coalfield communities.

WHAT IS NOT FUNDED The following are not eligible to apply: individuals; private businesses; organisations that are in a poor financial position or whose financial management systems are not in good order. The trust's opinion on this will be based on an organisation's financial position and management systems, an analysis of their accounts and other management information, as well as contact with referees and interviews with the organisation itself; voluntary and community organisations and groups who hold 'free reserves' that total more than 12 months' operating costs and who are not contributing enough funds to the project. The trust will assess how much money the organisation has available in free reserves using information from their accounts. (Free reserves are the amounts of money an organisation hold that are not restricted by any other funder for any other purpose). The following are not eligible to apply for the Bridging the Gap programme: individuals; statutory organisations; national organisations; private businesses.

TYPE OF GRANT Usually one-off grants.

SAMPLE GRANTS Previous beneficiaries include: Manchester Enterprises; Higher Folds Community Centre; Mexborough Community Partnership Limited; Derbyshire County Council; Nottinghamshire Community Foundation; Huthwaite Parochial Church Council; Skill Force Development; and Blantyre Miners' Welfare Charitable Society.

FINANCES *Year* 2007–08 *Income* £12,590,000 *Grants* £11,498,000 *Assets* £902,000

TRUSTEES Peter McNestry, Chair; Ken Greenfield; Jim Crewdson; Prof. Anthony Crook; Dawn Davies; John Edwards; Peter Fanning; Vernon Jones; Peter Rowley; Joe Thomas; Wayne Thomas; Fran Walker; Sylvia Wileman; Nicholas Wilson; Shaun Wright.

OTHER INFORMATION The trust provides advice, support and financial assistance to community and voluntary organisations who are working to tackle problems at grass-roots level within coalfield communities. It is closely connected with the areas it serves, operating through a network of staff based at offices located within coalfield regions themselves.

HOW TO APPLY The trust has produced a very detailed information booklet covering all aspects of its grant making including eligibility, the application process, funding themes, exclusions, match funding, duplicate bids, terms and conditions, etc., and applicants are advised to read through this before contacting the trust or making application. For the main grants programme the trust states that all applications will be acknowledged within ten working days and a detailed check of the application and supporting documentation will be made. If the application is considered ineligible applicants will receive an explanatory letter. If the application is considered eligible, you will be sent forms of protocol to complete and if they meet requirements your application will be passed to an assessor who will make an appointment for a telephone or site interview. This assessment will be passed to the panel/ trustees for consideration and you will be informed in writing of their decision. For the Bridging the Gap programme, all applications will be acknowledged within five working days of receipt. Your application and supporting documentation will be checked for completeness and at this stage eligibility will also be considered. If your application is not successful at this stage, you will receive an explanatory letter. If the application is eligible, it will be assessed based on the information sent; if more information is required, you will be notified. The panel meets every six weeks and if successful, you will receive a grant offer letter, if unsuccessful, you will receive an explanatory letter. There are four funding themes, identified to support projects across the coalfields. However, there are national plans and regional differences, which look at each funding theme in more detail. The trust advises that the local regeneration manager will be pleased to discuss these themes with you in relation to your project idea. They recommend that if you are planning to make an application, you should contact your regeneration manager at the project-idea stage.

WHO TO APPLY TO Janet Bibby, Chief Executive, Silkstone House, Pioneer Close, Manvers Way, Wath Upon Dearne, Rotherham S63 7JZ *Tel* 01709 760272 *Fax* 01709 765599 *email* info@coalfields-regen.org.uk *Website* www.coalfields-regen.org.uk

CC NO 1074930   **ESTABLISHED** 1999

■ The John Coates Charitable Trust

WHERE FUNDING CAN BE GIVEN UK, mainly southern England.

WHO CAN BENEFIT Institutions either national or of personal or local interest to one or more of the trustees.

WHAT IS FUNDED Preference is given to education, arts and culture, children, environment and health.

WHAT IS NOT FUNDED Grants are given to individuals only in exceptional circumstances.

TYPE OF GRANT Capital and recurring.

RANGE OF GRANTS £500–£10,000.

SAMPLE GRANTS the Landmark Trust (£8,000); Arthritis Care, the Cancer Resource Centre, Meningitis Research Foundation and the Solent Protection Society (£5,000 each); Pimlico Opera and Tall Ships Youth Trust (£3,000 each); Whizz Kids (£2,500); InterAct Reading Service and Two Moors Festival Limited (£2,000 each); Best Beginnings, Dreams Come True and Winchester and District Young Carers Project (£1,000 each); and Bury C of E First School (£500).

FINANCES *Year* 2007–08 *Income* £380,705 *Grants* £363,000 *Assets* £10,559,981

TRUSTEES Mrs G F McGregor; Mrs C A Kesley; Mrs R J Lawes; Mrs P L Youngman; Mrs C P Cartledge.

HOW TO APPLY In writing to the correspondent. Small local charities are visited by the trust.

WHO TO APPLY TO Mrs R J Lawes, Trustee, PO Box 529, Cambridge CB1 0BT

CC NO 262057   **ESTABLISHED** 1969

■ Coats Foundation Trust

WHERE FUNDING CAN BE GIVEN UK.

WHO CAN BENEFIT Students on textile and thread-related training courses and research, as well as organisations benefiting such people.

WHAT IS FUNDED Preference is given, but not specifically restricted, to applicants from textile-related training courses.

TYPE OF GRANT One-off grants for capital and revenue costs.

RANGE OF GRANTS £170–£10,000.

FINANCES *Year* 2007–08 *Income* £84,101 *Grants* £140,323 *Assets* £1,828,373

TRUSTEES The Coats Trustee Company Limited.

OTHER INFORMATION The 2007–08 grant total included £66,323 paid to individuals.

HOW TO APPLY Please write, enclosing a cv and an sae, giving details of circumstances and the nature and amount of funding required. There is no formal application form. Only applicants enclosing an sae will receive a reply. Applications are considered four times a year.

WHO TO APPLY TO The Secretary, Coats plc, Pacific House, 70 Wellington Street, Glasgow G2 6UB

CC NO 268735   **ESTABLISHED** 1974

■ The Cobalt Trust

WHERE FUNDING CAN BE GIVEN UK and overseas.

WHO CAN BENEFIT Registered charities known to the trustees,.

WHAT IS FUNDED General charitable purposes.

TYPE OF GRANT Capital and revenue grants over three years.

SAMPLE GRANTS Impetus Trust (£200,000); Eating Disorders Association (£20,000); EVPA, Rosetrees Trust, Streats Limited and Tree Aid (£10,000 each); Banana Link, Bath Abbey, Care, Climate Group and Money for Madagascar (£1,000 each); Iford Arts (£350); and Avon Wildlife Trust and National Trust (£100 each).

FINANCES *Year* 2007–08 *Income* £90,000 *Grants* £267,000 *Assets* £1,500,000

TRUSTEES Stephen Dawson; Brigitte Dawson; Jan Dawson.

HOW TO APPLY The trustees do not respond to unsolicited applications.

WHO TO APPLY TO Stephen Dawson, Trustee, 17 New Row, London WC2N 4LA

CC NO 1096342   **ESTABLISHED** 2002

■ The Cobtree Charity Trust Ltd

WHERE FUNDING CAN BE GIVEN Maidstone and district.

WHO CAN BENEFIT Registered charities.

WHAT IS FUNDED The maintenance and development of Cobtree Manor Estate, and other general charitable purposes by other charities in the Maidstone and district area.

WHAT IS NOT FUNDED No support for individuals, non-registered charities and charities outside Maidstone and district.

TYPE OF GRANT Largely recurrent.

SAMPLE GRANTS Museum of Kent Rural Life – Cobtree (£10,000); Leeds and Broomfield Cricket Club (£5,000); Kent Association for the Blind, Kent Wildlife Trust and Samaritans (£3,200 each); Footprints Respite Care Home (£2,750); Cobtree Manor Park Golf Club (£2,000); Vitalise (£1,600); Maidstone Volunteer Bureau (£1,400); Blackthorn Trust (£1,300); Macmillan Cancer Relief (£1,200); Bearsted Woodland Trust, Maidstone Citizens Advice Bureau and Relate in Kent (£1,000 each); and Symbol Trust (£750).

FINANCES *Year* 2007–08 *Income* £157,798 *Grants* £89,450 *Assets* £4,859,342

TRUSTEES R J Corben; J Fletcher; L J Martin; R N Hext; D T B Wigg; M W Hardcastle; S W L Brice.

HOW TO APPLY In writing to the correspondent. The trustees meet quarterly.

WHO TO APPLY TO John Stewart, Secretary, 4 Barnes Street Cottages, Three Elm Lane, Golden Green, Kent TN11 0BQ

CC NO 208455   **ESTABLISHED** 1951

■ The Denise Cohen Charitable Trust

WHERE FUNDING CAN BE GIVEN UK.

WHO CAN BENEFIT Registered charities.

WHAT IS FUNDED Jewish; education; health and welfare of older people, infirm people and children; humanities; arts and culture.

SAMPLE GRANTS Nightingale (£9,250); Chai Cancer Care (£8,000); Child Resettlement Fund and Community Security Trust (£5,000 each); British Technion Society (£3,000); Central Synagogue (£2,750); Marie Curie Cancer Care (£2,000); Magen David Adom (£1,500); Donmar Warehouse Projects and Tate Gallery (£1,000 each); British Friends of Zaka (£750); Jewish Book Council (£500); Jewish Care (£400); Salvation Army (£200); and Jewish Children's Holiday Fund (£100).

FINANCES *Year* 2007–08 *Income* £83,904 *Grants* £98,305 *Assets* £1,040,188

TRUSTEES Denise Cohen; Martin Paisner; Sara Cohen.

HOW TO APPLY In writing to the correspondent.

WHO TO APPLY TO Martin Paisner, Trustee, Berwin Leighton and Paisner, Adelaide House, London Bridge, London EC4R 9HA

CC NO 276439   **ESTABLISHED** 1977

■ The Vivienne and Samuel Cohen Charitable Trust

WHERE FUNDING CAN BE GIVEN UK and Israel.

WHO CAN BENEFIT Charitable organisations.

WHAT IS FUNDED Particular emphasis is given to Jewish causes; general charitable purposes, mainly education, culture and medical causes including research.

WHAT IS NOT FUNDED No grants to individuals.

SAMPLE GRANTS Chai Cancer Care (£26,000 in two grants); University College London (£10,000); Ariel (£7,000); British Friends of Herzog Hospital (£5,000); SPNI Jerusalem (£4,700 in two grants); Yakar (£3,000); the Spiro Ark (£2,500 in two grants); Hamifal Education Children's Homes and University Jewish Chaplaincy Board (£2,000 each); Elimination of Leukaemia Fund, JNF Charitable Trust and Norwood Child Care (£1,000 each).
FINANCES *Year* 2007–08 *Income* £184,079 *Grants* £154,531 *Assets* £2,784,262
TRUSTEES Dr V L L Cohen; M Y Ben-Gershon; J S Lauffer; Dr G L Lauffer.
HOW TO APPLY In writing only, to the correspondent.
WHO TO APPLY TO Dr Vivienne Cohen, Trustee, 9 Heathcroft, Hampstead Way, London NW11 7HH
CC NO 255496   **ESTABLISHED** 1965

■ The R and S Cohen Fondation

WHERE FUNDING CAN BE GIVEN Worldwide.
WHO CAN BENEFIT Charitable organisations.
WHAT IS FUNDED Education and relief-in-need.
TYPE OF GRANT One-off and recurrent.
RANGE OF GRANTS £500 to £30,000.
SAMPLE GRANTS Bridges Charitable Trust (£500,000); The Portland Trust (£265,000); The Prince's Foundation for Children/Art (£62,500); Refuge (£45,000); Responsible Action (£30,000); Chief Rabbinate Trust (£25,000); Jewish Leadership Council (£20,000); National Portrait Gallery (£10,000); Jewish Book Council (£5,000); Down Syndrome Education International (£3,000); and Trickle Up (£2,500).
FINANCES *Year* 2007–08 *Income* £99,565 *Grants* £1,480,562 *Assets* £6,380,259
TRUSTEES Lady Sharon Harel-Cohen; Sir Ronald Cohen; Tamara Harel-Cohen; David Marks; Jonathan Harel-Cohen.
HOW TO APPLY In writing to the correspondent.
WHO TO APPLY TO Mel Holland, 42 Portland Place, London W1B 1NB *email* mel@nottinghillfilms.com
CC NO 1078225   **ESTABLISHED** 1999

■ The John S Cohen Foundation

WHERE FUNDING CAN BE GIVEN Worldwide.
WHO CAN BENEFIT Registered charities.
WHAT IS FUNDED General charitable purposes but particularly supporting education, music and the arts and the environment, both built and natural.
TYPE OF GRANT One-off and recurring.
RANGE OF GRANTS Typically £5,000 or less; larger grants up to around £20,000.
SAMPLE GRANTS Southbank Centre (£48,000); Royal National Theatre (£20,000); Glyndebourne Festival and the National Gallery (£15,000 each); Royal Parks Foundation, Natural History Museum and Cambridge University Library (£10,000 each); RVW Trust (£9,000); Scottish Opera (£7,500); Public Catalogue Foundation (£7,000); British School at Rome, English National Opera and Jewish Literary Trust (£5,000); Royal College of Music (£4,500); Edinburgh International Book Festival (£3,500); English Pen, INDEX on Censorship and Volunteer Reading Help (£3,000 each); British Museum, National Life Story Collection and Shelter (£2,000 each); Community of the Holy Fire – Herefordshire, Music of Life, Scottish Seabird Centre and Wildfowl and Wetlands Trust (£1,000 each).

FINANCES *Year* 2007–08 *Income* £508,355 *Grants* £393,106 *Assets* £8,400,857
TRUSTEES Dr David Cohen; Ms Imogen Cohen; Ms Olivia Cohen; Ms Veronica Cohen.
HOW TO APPLY In writing to the correspondent.
WHO TO APPLY TO Mrs Diana Helme, Foundation Administrator, PO Box 21277, London W9 2YH *Tel* 020 7286 6921
CC NO 241598   **ESTABLISHED** 1965

■ Col-Reno Ltd

WHERE FUNDING CAN BE GIVEN UK and Israel.
WHO CAN BENEFIT Religious and educational institutions benefiting children, young adults, students and Jewish people.
WHAT IS FUNDED Jewish religion and education.
SAMPLE GRANTS Agudas Yisrael of California (£20,000); Hasmonean High School (£10,000); Society of Friends of the Torah (£8,000); Friends of Beis Yisrael Trust (£7,500); Jerusalem Library Fund (£1,900); Friends of Lubavitch Scotland (£1,000); Emuna (£750); Friends of Shabbaten Choir (£600); UK Friends of Meir Panim (£300); Chinuch Atzmai in Israel and Shaare Zedek UK (£200 each); and British Friends of Atid (£100).
FINANCES *Year* 2007–08 *Income* £91,492 *Grants* £53,245 *Assets* £533,957
TRUSTEES M H Stern; A E Stern; K Davis; Mrs R Davis; C A Stern; Mrs L Goldstein.
HOW TO APPLY In writing to the correspondent.
WHO TO APPLY TO The Trustees, 15 Shirehall Gardens, Hendon, London NW4 2QT
CC NO 274896   **ESTABLISHED** 1977

■ The Colchester Catalyst Charity

WHERE FUNDING CAN BE GIVEN North east Essex.
WHO CAN BENEFIT Health organisations.
WHAT IS FUNDED Provision of support by direct contributions to health organisations for specific and well-designed projects in order to improve healthcare.
WHAT IS NOT FUNDED No support for general funding, staff or running costs (usually). Retrospective funding is not considered.
TYPE OF GRANT One-off.
SAMPLE GRANTS Previous beneficiaries have included Balkerne Gardens Trust, Clacton Family Support, Colchester League of Friends Scanner Appeal, Colchester Toy Library, Headway Essex, St Anne's Clacton, St Helena Hospice and Tendring Shop Mobility.
FINANCES *Year* 2007–08 *Income* £360,654 *Grants* £475,095 *Assets* £7,959,435
TRUSTEES A H Frost, Chair; C Hayward; P W E Fitt; Dr E Hall; Dr M P Hickman; A W Livesley; R W Whybrow.
HOW TO APPLY In writing to the correspondent.
WHO TO APPLY TO Peter Fitt, Company Secretary, 7 Coast Road, West Mersea, Colchester CO5 8QE *email* colcat@btinternet.com
CC NO 228352   **ESTABLISHED** 1959

■ John Coldman Charitable Trust

WHERE FUNDING CAN BE GIVEN UK, with a preference for Edenbridge in Kent.
WHO CAN BENEFIT Registered charities.
WHAT IS FUNDED General charitable purposes, particularly community and Christian groups and UK organisations whose work benefits the community such as children's and medical charities and schools.

Think carefully about every application. Is it justified?

439

RANGE OF GRANTS £250 upwards.

SAMPLE GRANTS Oasis Community Learning (£290,000); Oasis International – India (£30,000); Institute of Cancer Research (£25,000); Hever C of E Primary School (£23,000); NSPCC (£20,000); Great Ormond Street Hospital (£10,000); National Gardens Scheme – Kent (£6,900); Falkland Islands Memorial Chapel Appeal (£5,000); Africa Foundation (£4,000); the Avenues Trust (£2,500); National Autistic Society (£500 each); and Cancer Research UK (£250).

FINANCES *Year* 2007–08 *Income* £572,178 *Grants* £516,000 *Assets* £362,365

TRUSTEES D J Coldman; G E Coldman; C J Warner.

OTHER INFORMATION During 2007–08 an additional £39,000 went towards the running of the Holcot Residential Centre, which operates as a hostel, holiday centre and community centre for the use of young people and others.

HOW TO APPLY In writing to the correspondent.

WHO TO APPLY TO C J Warner, Trustee, Polebrook, Hever, Edenbridge, Kent TN8 7NJ *Tel* 01732 770660 *email* charles.warner@ warners-solicitors.co.uk

CC NO 1050110   **ESTABLISHED** 1995

■ The Cole Charitable Trust

WHERE FUNDING CAN BE GIVEN Greater Birmingham, Kent and Cambridge.

WHO CAN BENEFIT Local community projects or local branches of larger organisations. Individuals are also supported.

WHAT IS FUNDED General charitable purposes. Grants were given in the following categories: care and social welfare; children and young people; disability; health; arts, culture and heritage; education and training; personal and community empowerment; international aid and development; and archaeology.

WHAT IS NOT FUNDED No grants for large national organisations, religion, education, animal welfare, or to individuals not backed by a charity.

TYPE OF GRANT Small capital or project grants; normally one-off.

RANGE OF GRANTS Up to £1,000.

SAMPLE GRANTS Cerebral Palsy Midlands, East Kent Cyrenians, Life Education Centre West Midlands, Prisoners' Advice Service, Weoley Castle Community Church and Wolverhampton Asylum Seekers and Refugee Service (£1,000 each); Relate Kent (£700); the Albright Trust, Birmingham Centre for Art Therapies, Birmingham Clubs for Young People and Freshwinds (£500 each); Trescott Primary School (£400); and Britten Sinfonia and Dover Sea Cadet Corps (£300 each).

FINANCES *Year* 2007–08 *Income* £57,195 *Grants* £45,000 *Assets* £1,322,177

TRUSTEES Prof. T J Cole; G N Cole; Dr J G L Cole; T E C Cole; Dr J N Cole; A Frewin; K Hebron.

HOW TO APPLY In writing to the correspondent, and must include recent annual accounts. An sae should not be sent. Two meetings per year; deadlines for applications are mid-March and mid-September.

WHO TO APPLY TO The Administrator, PO Box 51, Cambridge CB3 9QL *Tel* 01223 312374 *email* coletrust@btinternet.com

CC NO 264033   **ESTABLISHED** 1972

■ The Colefax Charitable Trust

WHERE FUNDING CAN BE GIVEN Hampshire and Berkshire.

WHO CAN BENEFIT Registered charities.

WHAT IS FUNDED General charitable purposes.

WHAT IS NOT FUNDED No grants to individuals.

SAMPLE GRANTS Previous beneficiaries have included: Church on the Heath, Homestart, Jumbulance, Living Paintings Trust, Newbury District OAP Association, Newbury Spring Festival, Prospect Educational Trust, Reading Voluntary Action, Reliance Cancer Foundation, Southend Residents' Association and Watership Brass.

FINANCES *Year* 2007–08 *Income* £281,587 *Grants* £112,927 *Assets* £9,757,281

TRUSTEES J E Heath; H J Krohn.

HOW TO APPLY 'The trustees decide jointly which charitable institutions are to receive donations from the trust. No invitations are sought from eligible institutions.'

WHO TO APPLY TO Hans J Krohn, Trustee, Westbrook House, St Helens Gardens, The Pitchens, Wroughton, Wiltshire SN4 0RU

CC NO 1017285   **ESTABLISHED** 1993

■ The John and Freda Coleman Charitable Trust

WHERE FUNDING CAN BE GIVEN Hampshire and Surrey and surrounding areas.

WHO CAN BENEFIT Education and training centres.

WHAT IS FUNDED The trust aims to provide: 'an alternative to an essentially academic education, to encourage and further the aspirations of young people with talents to develop manual skills and relevant technical knowledge to fit them for satisfying careers and useful employment. The aim is to develop the self-confidence of individuals to succeed within established organisations or on their own account and to impress upon them the importance of service to the community, honesty, good manners and self discipline.'

WHAT IS NOT FUNDED No grants are made to students.

TYPE OF GRANT Loans not given. Grants to 'kick start' relevant projects, capital costs other than buildings and core costs are all considered. Recurrent grants are given.

RANGE OF GRANTS Up to £20,000.

SAMPLE GRANTS Surrey SATRO (£11,000); Surrey Care Trust (£10,000); Surrey Community Development Trust (£8,000); Prince's Trust (£7,500); Guildford YMCA, Historic Royal Palaces and Treloar Trust (£5,000 each); Reigate and Redhill YMCA and Surrey Clubs for Young People (£3,000 each); Sayers Croft and Surrey Family Mediation Service (£2,500 each); and Surrey Council for Voluntary Youth Service (£2,000).

FINANCES *Year* 2007–08 *Income* £37,328 *Grants* £70,100 *Assets* £905,916

TRUSTEES I Williamson; Mrs J L Bird; P H Coleman; B R Coleman.

HOW TO APPLY In writing to the correspondent. Telephone calls are not welcome.

WHO TO APPLY TO Paul Coleman, Chair, Alderney House, 58 Normandy Street, Alton, Hampshire GU34 1DE

CC NO 278223   **ESTABLISHED** 1979

■ The Bernard Coleman Trust

WHERE FUNDING CAN BE GIVEN Worldwide.

WHO CAN BENEFIT Charitable organisations.

WHAT IS FUNDED 'The objects of the charity are to provide coaching facilities to young sportsmen and sportswomen and to give donations to other similar sporting charities and grants to sporting clubs and associations. It also makes grants to medical services and to youth projects.'

RANGE OF GRANTS £500–£10,000.

SAMPLE GRANTS Chance to Shine Charity (£10,000); Sri Lanka Cricket Club (£7,500); the Hornsby Trust, Surrey Care Trust and the Royal Hospital for Neurodisability (£5,000 each); Wimbledon Cricket Club (£3,500); and Ashtead Cricket Club, the Merton Park Explorer Scout Unit, Prostate Research Campaign, Sportability and UCL Hospitals – lung cancer research (£3,000 each).

FINANCES *Year* 2007–08 *Income* £111,272 *Grants* £87,100 *Assets* £581,989

TRUSTEES B Coleman; D Newton; J Fairclough; M Courtness.

HOW TO APPLY In writing to the correspondent.

WHO TO APPLY TO The Secretary, Moonstone, Pilgrims Way, Westhumble, Dorking, Surrey RH5 6AP

CC NO 1075731   **ESTABLISHED** 1999

■ The George Henry Collins Charity

WHERE FUNDING CAN BE GIVEN Within a 50-mile radius of Birmingham, or overseas.

WHO CAN BENEFIT Local charities and local branches of registered national charities in Birmingham benefiting older people, the socially isolated, or people who are ill.

WHAT IS FUNDED Wide, but the relief of illness, infirmity, old age or loneliness take preference. Trustees will consider donating one-tenth of annual income to charities for use overseas.

WHAT IS NOT FUNDED No grants to individuals.

TYPE OF GRANT One-off project funding.

RANGE OF GRANTS £250–£2,000. Mostly under £250.

SAMPLE GRANTS Sutton Coldfield YMCA and Agape (£500 each); EEIBA (£400); Shelter, Woodland Trust, Birmingham Cathedral Music Endowment Fund and Swinfen Charitable Trust (£250 each); Crisis Point and Concern Worldwide (£200 each); and Howley Grante Scout Group (£100).

FINANCES *Year* 2008–09 *Income* £58,848 *Grants* £31,080 *Assets* £1,150,933

TRUSTEES Anthony Collins, Chair; Elizabeth Davies; Andrew Waters; Roger Otto; Peter Coggan.

HOW TO APPLY In writing to the correspondent. The trustees usually meet in March, July and November.

WHO TO APPLY TO Chrissy Norgrove, c/o Martineau, No. 1 Colmore Square, Birmingham B4 6AA *Tel* 0870 763 2000

CC NO 212268   **ESTABLISHED** 1959

■ The E Alec Colman Charitable Fund Ltd

WHERE FUNDING CAN BE GIVEN UK and worldwide.

WHO CAN BENEFIT Charitable organisations, particular favour is given to those benefiting Jewish people and children.

WHAT IS FUNDED Relief of poverty; advancement of education; social welfare; and advancement of religion. The trust aims to pinpoint areas of interest and take the initiative in funding organisations working in these fields.

WHAT IS NOT FUNDED No grants to individuals.

RANGE OF GRANTS £150–£5,000.

SAMPLE GRANTS World Jewish Relief (£5,000); Send a Cow (£2,500); Army Cadet Force Association, the Royal British Legion and RNIB (£2,000 each); Practical Action (£1,500); the Smile Train UK (£1,200); British Friends of Ohel Sarah, the Salvation Army and Yad Vashem UK Foundation (£1,000 each); Brighton and Hove Parents and Children Group (£850); Operation New World (£750); 3H Fund (£500); At Risk Teenagers (£250); and 95th Birmingham Scout Group (£150).

FINANCES *Year* 2007–08 *Income* £60,275 *Grants* £44,466 *Assets* £1,032,550

TRUSTEES S H Colman; Mrs E A Colman; M Harris.

HOW TO APPLY In writing to the correspondent; however, the trust has stated that new beneficiaries are only considered in exceptional circumstances.

WHO TO APPLY TO A N Carless, Secretary, Colman House, 6–10 South Street, Harborne, Birmingham B17 0DB *Tel* 0121 427 7700

CC NO 243817   **ESTABLISHED** 1965

■ The Sir Jeremiah Colman Gift Trust

WHERE FUNDING CAN BE GIVEN UK, with a preference for Hampshire, especially Basingstoke.

WHO CAN BENEFIT Projects with well-established needs for support; the trust has already established priority beneficiaries.

WHAT IS FUNDED Advancement of education and literary scientific knowledge; moral and social improvement of people; maintenance of churches of the Church of England and gifts and offerings to the churches; financial assistance to past and present employees/members of Sir Jeremiah Colman at Gatton Park or other institutions associated with Sir Jeremiah Colman.

WHAT IS NOT FUNDED Grants are not made to individuals requiring support for personal education, or to individual families for welfare purposes.

FINANCES *Year* 2007–08 *Income* £134,147 *Grants* £109,350 *Assets* £4,327,317

TRUSTEES Sir Michael Colman; Lady Colman; Oliver Colman; Hon. Mrs Colman; Jeremiah Colman.

OTHER INFORMATION In 2007–08 grants were broken down as follows: 'annual' donations (£57,000); 'special' donations (£49,000); and 'extra' donations (£3,500).

HOW TO APPLY The trust has stated that funds are fully committed – unsolicited applications are therefore not welcomed.

WHO TO APPLY TO Mrs V R Persson, Secretary to the Trustees, Malshanger, Basingstoke, Hampshire RG23 7EY

CC NO 229553   **ESTABLISHED** 1920

■ The Colt Foundation

WHERE FUNDING CAN BE GIVEN In practice UK.

WHO CAN BENEFIT Universities and research establishments benefiting research workers and students taking higher degrees.

WHAT IS FUNDED Research projects at universities and other independent research institutions into occupational and environmental health.

WHAT IS NOT FUNDED Grants are not made for the general funds of another charity, directly to individuals or projects overseas.

TYPE OF GRANT Research, project.

RANGE OF GRANTS £20,000–£100,000.

SAMPLE GRANTS National Heart and Lung Institute (£124,500); University of Aberdeen (£87,000); University of Central London (£38,000); University of Edinburgh (£22,000); and ELEGI – Poland (£8,400).

FINANCES *Year* 2008 *Income* £821,479 *Grants* £801,965 *Assets* £17,880,586

TRUSTEES Prof. David Coggon; Clare Gilchrist; Prof. A J Newman Taylor; Juliette O'Hea; Peter O'Hea; Alan O'Hea; Jerome O'Hea; Natasha Lebus; Patricia Lebus.

OTHER INFORMATION £89,000 was awarded to an unspecified number of students.

HOW TO APPLY In writing to the correspondent. Initial applications should contain sufficient information for the scientific advisers to be able to comment, and include a lay summary for the trustees' first appraisal. This lay summary is regarded as important, as the majority of the trustees do not have a medical or scientific background and this helps them with their decision making. The trustees meet twice each year, normally in May and November. Applications should reach the correspondent by 23 March and 1 October in time for these meetings so that advice can be obtained from external assessors beforehand. However, applicants can submit a single sheet 'lay summary' at any time during the year, so that advice can be given on whether the work is likely to fall within the remit of the foundation, prior to working on a full application. The foundation does not have application forms. Applicants are asked to read the following guidelines carefully and follow them when preparing an application: What is the work you would like to do; why does the work need doing; who is doing or has done similar work, and how will your work add to it; how do you intend to carry out the work, and why do you think this is the right approach; what resources will you need to do the work, and are these resources available; who will do the work, and how much time will each of the people involved devote to it; how long will the work take; how much money do you need to complete the work; and when do you plan to start?

WHO TO APPLY TO Mrs Jacqueline Douglas, Director, New Lane, Havant, Hampshire PO9 2LY *Tel* 023 9249 1400 *Fax* 023 9249 1363 *email* jackie. douglas@uk.coltgroup.com *Website* www. coltfoundation.org.uk

CC NO 277189   **ESTABLISHED** 1978

....

■ The Coltstaple Trust

WHERE FUNDING CAN BE GIVEN Worldwide.

WHO CAN BENEFIT Charitable organisations.

WHAT IS FUNDED 'The relief of persons in need, poverty or distress in third world countries and the relief of persons who are homeless or in housing need in the UK or any other part of the world.'

TYPE OF GRANT Recurrent.

SAMPLE GRANTS Oxfam (£400,000); St Mungo's (£150,000); Opportunity International (£40,000); North West University Whole School Development Programme, Portsmouth Housing Charity – E C Roberts Centre and Students Partnership (£20,000 each); and Sport for Life (£10,000).

FINANCES *Year* 2007–08 *Income* £234,103 *Grants* £660,000 *Assets* £5,032,853

TRUSTEES Lord Oakshott of Seagrove Bay; Dr P Oakshott; Lord Newby of Rothwell; B R M Stoneham; Mrs E G Colville.

HOW TO APPLY In writing to the correspondent.

WHO TO APPLY TO Lord Oakshott of Seagrove Bay, Trustee, c/o Pollen House, 10–12 Cork Street, London W1S 3NP

CC NO 1085500

....

■ Colwinston Charitable Trust

WHERE FUNDING CAN BE GIVEN Mostly Wales.

WHO CAN BENEFIT UK registered charities.

WHAT IS FUNDED The trustees seek to support charitable organisations working in the fields of opera/music theatre, classical music, and the visual arts. They will also consider specific project proposals for the assistance of libraries and archives. Opera/music theatre – the trust aims to widen the opportunities to enjoy and appreciate performances of opera and music theatre, especially by assisting organisations to develop new audiences for performances of the highest quality; classical music – the trust aims to widen the opportunities to enjoy and to appreciate traditional classical music, and is especially interested to support projects that deliver high quality performances to areas where provision is limited; visual arts – the trust aims to widen the opportunities to enjoy and to be stimulated by the visual arts, to foster creative endeavour and to help develop new audiences; and libraries and archives – the trust will consider applications for specific projects but are unlikely to support capital projects. 'The trust is especially interested in *exceptional* projects that demonstrate *excellence* in terms of the creative ambition of the project, the quality of the artistic product, the calibre of the participating artists, and the value of the artistic experience for audiences and/or participants.'

WHAT IS NOT FUNDED The trust will not consider applications for capital building projects, for general appeals, for retrospective funding, for conferences and seminars, websites, publications, or from individuals.

SAMPLE GRANTS Welsh National Opera (£70,000); Music Theatre Wales (£25,000); Chapter Arts (£20,000); Wales Millennium Centre (£17,000); the Circuit (£16,000); Mid Wales Opera (£12,000); Gregynog Festival and Mousetrap Theatre Projects (£10,000 each); Presteigne Festival of Music and the Arts (£8,000); Sound Affairs (£7,900); Taliesin Theatre/Swansea University (£5,000); and Lower Machen Festival (£3,000).

FINANCES *Year* 2008–09 *Grants* £230,055

TRUSTEES Mrs A Clementson; M D Paisner; J C Prichard; M C T Prichard; R J Maskrey.

OTHER INFORMATION The trust derives its income from the royalties from the West End production of *The Mousetrap*, the Agatha Christie play, which opened in 1952.

HOW TO APPLY Full and detailed guidelines are available on the trust's website. 'In the first instance, and prior to sending any application to the trust, organisations should make contact with the Consultant Director, preferably by email, supplying a brief summary of the project and indicating the grant level being sought.' The trustees meet twice yearly (usually March and October) to consider applications and to make decisions on grants.

WHO TO APPLY TO Amanda McMurray, Consultant Director, 14 Hanover Court, Midhope Road,

Woking, Surrey GU22 7UX *email* colwinston.
trust@ntlworld.com *Website* www.colwinston.
org.uk

cc no 1049189   ESTABLISHED 1995

■ Colyer-Fergusson Charitable Trust

WHERE FUNDING CAN BE GIVEN Churches and registered charities in Kent.

WHO CAN BENEFIT Charities and churches aiming to improve quality of life, tackle poverty, social isolation or exclusion, promote the arts and protect the natural resources and heritage of the local areas for their inhabitants.

WHAT IS FUNDED Current priority areas are: safer communities; protecting and supporting older vulnerable people; refugees and asylum seekers; caring for carers; transition to independence for young people leaving care; encouraging active living.

WHAT IS NOT FUNDED No grants to the following: animal welfare charities; individuals directly; research (except practical research designed to benefit the local community directly); hospitals or schools; political activities; commercial ventures or publications; the purchase of vehicles including minibuses; overseas travel or holidays; retrospective grants or loans; direct replacement of statutory funding or activities that are primarily the responsibility of central or local government; large capital, endowment or widely distributed appeals; applications from churches and charities outside Kent.

TYPE OF GRANT One-off, recurring, capital, core, running and start-up costs will all be considered, as will salaries, buildings, project and research costs. Funding may be given for up to three years.

RANGE OF GRANTS £500–£75,000.

SAMPLE GRANTS Minster Abbey (£75,000); Deal Town Football Club (£40,000); St Gile's Trust (£30,000); Alkham Valley Community Project (£21,000); Capel-le-Fern Village Hall (£15,000); Thanington Neighbourhood Community Centre (£12,500); Betteshanger Social Club & Community Centre (£10,000); and Volunteer Reading Help (£5,000).

FINANCES *Year* 2008–09 *Income* £831,496 *Grants* £601,500 *Assets* £26,904,738

TRUSTEES Jonathan Monckton, Chair; Nicholas Fisher; Robert North; Ruth Murphy.

HOW TO APPLY All applicants must complete the on-line application form. There is no deadline for applications and all applications will be acknowledged. Trustees meet regularly during the year and decisions are usually processed within six months. All applicants will be notified in writing. The trust requests applicants, where possible, to submit any supporting material by email as scanned documents or files to: admin@cfct.org.uk

WHO TO APPLY TO Jacqueline Rae, Director, Hogarth House, 34 Paradise Road, Richmond, Surrey TW9 1SE *Tel* 020 8948 3388 *email* grantadmin@cfct.org.uk *Website* www.cfct.org.uk

cc no 258958   ESTABLISHED 1969

■ Comic Relief

WHERE FUNDING CAN BE GIVEN UK and overseas (mainly Africa).

WHO CAN BENEFIT UK registered charities; voluntary organisations; and self-help groups.

WHAT IS FUNDED For the period 2009–2012 the charity's UK grants programmes are focusing on the following areas: mental health; domestic and sexual abuse (young people aged 11 to 25); refugee and asylum seeking women; sport for change; sexually exploited and trafficked young people (aged 11 to 25); young people and alcohol (aged 11 to 25); young people with mental health problems (aged 11 to 25); 'local communities' – this programme is being administered by the Community Foundation Network. Contact your local community foundation for further information.

WHAT IS NOT FUNDED There are certain types of work and organisations that Comic Relief does not fund. If your proposal falls into one of these categories, please do not apply: grants to individuals; medical research or hospitals; churches or other religious bodies where the monies will be used for religious purposes; work where there is statutory responsibility to provide funding; projects where the work has already taken place; statutory bodies, such as local authorities or Primary Care Trusts or organisations seeking funding to replace cuts by statutory bodies; profit-making organisations, except social enterprises. The charity is also unable to fund minibuses.

TYPE OF GRANT Capital or revenue. One-off or spread over up to three years.

RANGE OF GRANTS Grants average between £25,000 and £40,000, and rarely exceed this upper limit.

FINANCES *Year* 2007–08 *Income* £45,521,000 *Grants* £51,979,000 *Assets* £76,863,000

TRUSTEES Peter Benett-Jones, Chair; Albert Tucker; Alec McGivan; Claudia Lloyd; Colin Howes; Duncan Bannatyne; Emma Freud; Harry Cayton; Jana Bennett; Jim Hytner; J K Rowling; Laurence Newman; Lenny Henry; Matthew Freud; Mike Harris; Mike Soutar; Nalini Varma; Richard Curtis; Sir Steve Redgrave.

PUBLICATIONS Essential Information for applicants; Grants Strategy.

HOW TO APPLY Please ensure that you have read the charity's 'Grant Making Principles and Essential Information' for applicants. An application form is available via the charity's website.

WHO TO APPLY TO Gilly Green, Head of UK Grants, 5th Floor, 89 Albert Embankment, London SE1 7TP *Tel* 020 7820 5555 *Minicom* 020 7820 5500 *email* ukgrants@comicrelief.com *Website* www.comicrelief.com

cc no 326568   ESTABLISHED 1985

■ The Comino Foundation

WHERE FUNDING CAN BE GIVEN UK.

WHO CAN BENEFIT Organisations benefiting young adults and academics.

WHAT IS FUNDED Support of educational activities which encourage and enable individuals and groups to motivate and empower themselves; progressively develop their potential for the benefit of themselves and others; and encourage a culture which affirms and celebrates both achievement and responsible practice in industry and commerce.

WHAT IS NOT FUNDED No grants to individuals or for or research projects.

TYPE OF GRANT One-off.

SAMPLE GRANTS Sheffield Hallam University (£90,000); PACE Centre (£75,000); Liverpool John Moores University, University of Winchester and Wigan Borough Partnership (£50,000 each); Homeground Project – Liverpool (£23,000); Institute for Global Ethics UK Trust (£48,000); RSA Tipton Academy (£25,000); Ideas Foundation (£10,000); Potential Trust (£12,000); Youth Leaders in STEM (£7,000); Bailey Comino Scholarship (£6,000); and Compass (£1,000).

FINANCES *Year* 2007–08 *Income* £325,486 *Grants* £330,182 *Assets* £5,860,701

TRUSTEES Mrs A Comino-Jones; Dr W E Duckworth; Sir Mike Tomlinson; S Bailey; J E Slater.

OTHER INFORMATION The trust meets these aims through its patented GRASP approach, which offers a structure for thinking in a results-driven manner through a greater pattern, design and method of thinking. Most of the funds are given towards centres which promote the GRASP approach. Further information on this can be gathered from a leaflet prepared from the trust or on their extensive website.

HOW TO APPLY Requests for support should initially be sent to the administrator by e-mail.

WHO TO APPLY TO A C Roberts, Administrator, 29 Hollow Way Lane, Amersham, Buckinghamshire HP6 6DJ *Tel* 01494 722595 *email* enquire@ cominofoundation.org.uk *Website* www. cominofoundation.org.uk

CC NO 312875   **ESTABLISHED** 1971

·········

■ Community Foundation for Calderdale

WHERE FUNDING CAN BE GIVEN Calderdale, with ability to manage funds outside of this area.

WHO CAN BENEFIT Constituted voluntary, community and faith groups, run for and by local people and registered charities working in Calderdale.

WHAT IS FUNDED General. Each scheme has different criteria but priority tends to be given to projects which: achieve outstanding community impact; help people living in communities identified as being particularly disadvantaged; benefit people from black and minority ethnic communities; help people with special needs; benefit older people; and/or benefit young people under the age of 19.

WHAT IS NOT FUNDED The foundation will not fund any of the following: general appeals; projects which have already taken place or for retrospective funding; projects which would normally be funded from statutory sources, i.e., Calderdale MBC, the local education authority, social services or central government; projects for the advancement of religion; projects where the main beneficiaries are animals; projects that do not directly benefit people living in Calderdale; political activities; applications made up entirely of core and/or running costs (exceptions may be made in extraordinary circumstances).

TYPE OF GRANT Revenue, capital, one-off.

RANGE OF GRANTS Up to £10,000.

FINANCES *Year* 2007–08 *Income* £843,199 *Grants* £873,691 *Assets* £6,016,487

TRUSTEES Dr Rose Wheeler; Leigh-Anne Stradeski; Brenda Hodgson; Mike Payne; Alison Roberts; Kate Hinks; Susan Fisher; Rod Hodgson; Russell Earnshaw; Juliet Chambers; Jennifer Feather; Roger Moore; Anne Clare Townley.

HOW TO APPLY The foundation's website has details of the grant schemes currently being administered. Application packs for all of the programmes are available to download from the

website. Alternatively, contact the foundation directly and they will send a pack in the post. If you wish to discuss your project before applying, the grants team are always happy to answer any queries (Tel: 01422 438738). The foundation also runs a monthly drop-in, where groups can go for advice and support on their applications.

WHO TO APPLY TO Megan Vickery, Grants Manager, Community Foundation House, 162a King Cross Road, Halifax HX1 3LN *Tel* 01422 349 700 *Fax* 01422 350 017 *email* enquiries@cffc.co.uk *Website* www.cffc.co.uk

CC NO 1002722   **ESTABLISHED** 1991

··········

■ The Community Foundation for Greater Manchester

WHERE FUNDING CAN BE GIVEN Greater Manchester.

WHO CAN BENEFIT Registered charities and small, locally run community or voluntary groups who seek to improve the circumstances in economically and socially excluded areas in Greater Manchester facing disadvantage.

WHAT IS FUNDED General charitable purposes including health; welfare; education; people with disabilities; older people; young people and children. Improving the quality of life and helping to build stronger communities across Greater Manchester.

WHAT IS NOT FUNDED The foundation will not support: organisations and projects outside the Greater Manchester area; organisations trading for profit or intending to redistribute grant awards; major capital requests, i.e. building and construction work; requests that will replace or enhance statutory provision; academic or medical research & equipment; overseas travel; primary purpose of request is to promote religious or political beliefs; retrospective grants – (projects/ activities that have already taken place); projects that fall within statutory sector responsibility; sponsorship or fundraising events; contributions to larger/major appeals. (Where the application sum would not cover at least 75% of the total project cost); holidays and social outings. (Except in cases of specific disablement or proven benefit to a community or group of people); local branches of national charities unless locally managed, financially autonomous and not beneficiaries of national marketing or promotion; more than one application at a time for the same project.

TYPE OF GRANT One-off; project. Start-up costs will be considered.

RANGE OF GRANTS Mostly under £5,000.

FINANCES *Year* 2007–08 *Income* £6,147,368 *Grants* £4,300,240 *Assets* £3,431,788

TRUSTEES Dr Tom Manion, Chair; John Sandford; Chris Hirst; Richard Hogben; Tony Burns; Gary Newborough; David Dickman; Simon Webber; Jo Farrell; Han-Son Lee; Sandra Lindsay; Natalie Qureshi; Laura Harper.

PUBLICATIONS Guidelines; information packs.

HOW TO APPLY The foundation's website provides full guidelines for each of the programmes for which organisations can apply. It also provides application and monitoring forms for each programme. If you are applying for a grant for the first time, or if you would like advice before making an application, call the foundation on 0161 214 0940. Applications will only be accepted if submitted on the foundation's application form. All sections of the form must be completed even if the information is supplied in the form of a report, leaflet and so on. The foundation prefers not to receive applications by fax; completed forms should be returned by post. The decision of the foundation's trustees is final and no discussion will be entered into. The foundation will, however, try to provide helpful feedback to both successful and unsuccessful applicants.

Applicants are requested to provide copies of the constitution, and a copy of the latest, relevant annual accounts and the last two bank statements with their applications. Decisions are almost always given within three months but the exact time will often depend on a number of factors and not just when the appropriate committee next meets. One of the foundation's grants administrators may contact you for further information or to discuss your application with you. The Community Foundation operates a 24-hour grant line where application forms can be obtained at any time. The grant line telephone number is 0161 214 0951. Contact the foundation directly for up-to-date information on deadlines for programmes and the dates of panel meetings.

WHO TO APPLY TO Julie Langford, Deputy Chief Executive, 1st Floor, Beswick House, Beswick Row, Manchester M4 4LA *Tel* 0161 214 0940 *Fax* 0161 214 0941 *email* enquiries@communityfoundation.co.uk *Website* www.communityfoundation.co.uk
CC NO 1017504   **ESTABLISHED** 1993

■ The Community Foundation for Northern Ireland

WHERE FUNDING CAN BE GIVEN Northern Ireland and the six border counties of the Republic of Ireland.
WHO CAN BENEFIT Community groups, self-help organisations and voluntary organisations benefiting young adults, women, and unemployed people.
WHAT IS FUNDED Priority areas: peace-building; community development; social justice; cross-border development; active citizenship; poverty, social inclusion. Open programmes include: The Turkington Fund; Community Arts Small Grants; Telecommunity Programme; Local Community Fund; and One Small Step Grant Fund.
WHAT IS NOT FUNDED Each open programme has its own exclusions, but in general no grants are given for: ongoing running costs of organisations; major capital building programmes; travel; vehicles; holiday schemes; play groups; sports activities; housing associations; promotion of religion; paying off debts; retrospective grants; general appeals. Neither will the trust fund projects where there is a statutory responsibility or to replace statutory funding; or individuals.
TYPE OF GRANT One-off.
RANGE OF GRANTS £100–£150,000.
FINANCES *Year* 2007–08 *Income* £4,380,134 *Grants* £3,299,207 *Assets* £17,403,960
TRUSTEES Tony McCusker, Chair; Les Allamby; Mike Bamber; Barbary Cook; Sammy Douglas; Dr Jeremy Harbison; Noreen Kearney; Julie Knight; Dr Mike Morrissey; Dr Duncan Morrow; Stephanie Morrow; Conal McFeely; Tayra McKee; Anne McReynolds; Hilary Sidwell; Colin Stutt.
HOW TO APPLY As the application procedure varies depending on the fund being applied to and not all funds are 'open' all of the time, please refer to the foundation's website.
WHO TO APPLY TO Avila Kilmurray, Director, Community House, Citylink Business Park, 6a

Albert Street, Belfast BT12 4HQ *Tel* 028 9024 5927 *Fax* 028 9032 9839 *email* info@communityfoundationni.org *Website* www.communityfoundationni.org
IR NO XN45242   **ESTABLISHED** 1979

■ The Company of Tobacco Pipe Makers' and Tobacco Blenders' Benevolent Fund

WHERE FUNDING CAN BE GIVEN City of London, and Sevenoaks School.
WHO CAN BENEFIT Educational establishments benefiting children, young adults, students, and people disadvantaged by poverty.
WHAT IS FUNDED To assist in the education of those who would not otherwise be able to afford it. To support only those charities with which the company can have an active relationship.
WHAT IS NOT FUNDED No grants to individuals.
TYPE OF GRANT Ongoing scholarships.
SAMPLE GRANTS Guildhall School of Music awards and the Speech and Language Hearing Centre (£8,000 each); Sevenoaks School – Tobacco Pipemakers awards (£4,200); CHICKS, Arundel Castle Cricket Foundation and Riding for the Disabled – Barrow Farm (£4,000 each); the London Regiment Welfare Fund (£2,500); Headway (£1,000); the Lord Mayor's Appeal and St Botolph's Church – Aldgate (£500); the Corporation of the Sons of the Clergy (£250); and Royal British Legion (£100).
FINANCES *Year* 2008–09 *Income* £119,462 *Grants* £41,923 *Assets* £1,857,688
TRUSTEES Derek P C Harris, Chair; Stephen L Preedy; J Alec G Murray; Nigel M S Rich; Fiona J Adler; George E C Lankester.
HOW TO APPLY The trust has stated that it is not seeking additional beneficiaries.
WHO TO APPLY TO Simon G Orlik, Clerk, Simon G Orlik, 23 Downsview Gardens, Dorking, Surrey RH4 2DX
CC NO 200601   **ESTABLISHED** 1961

■ The Compton Charitable Trust

WHERE FUNDING CAN BE GIVEN Northamptonshire.
WHO CAN BENEFIT Charitable organisations, with a preference for those with a connection to the family estates of the Marquess of Northampton as well as those which the Marquess is a patron of.
WHAT IS FUNDED General charitable purposes.
SAMPLE GRANTS Dogs Trust and Help for Heroes (£5,000 each); the Compton Wynyates Church Trust and Feldon Church Trust (£2,000 each); King Edwards VII Hospital Midhurst and St Michael Steiner School (£1,000 each); the Leukaemia Care Society (£500); NSPCC (£250); Royal British Legion – Poppy Appeal (£150); and Ghurkha Welfare Trust (£100).
FINANCES *Year* 2007–08 *Income* £28,202 *Grants* £18,616 *Assets* £786,569
TRUSTEES Marquess of Northampton; Lady Pamela Northampton; Earl Daniel Compton.
HOW TO APPLY In writing to the correspondent. Unsolicited applications are considered, but are usually unsuccessful.
WHO TO APPLY TO The Trustees, Moore Stephens, St Paul's House, Warwick Lane, London EC4M 7BP
CC NO 280404   **ESTABLISHED** 1980

■ The Douglas Compton James Charitable Trust

WHERE FUNDING CAN BE GIVEN Northamptonshire.

WHO CAN BENEFIT Registered charities.

WHAT IS FUNDED General, education and social welfare. Some preference is given for Masonic charities.

TYPE OF GRANT One-off and recurrent.

RANGE OF GRANTS £2,000–£37,000.

SAMPLE GRANTS Provincial Grand Charity (£37,000); Perse School Fees (£17,000); Grand Charity and Air Ambulance (£10,000 each); Cransley Hospice (£7,000); Friends of Kettering and District Hospitals, Headway and Macmillan Nurses (£5,000 each); and Friars School (£2,000).

FINANCES *Year* 2007–08 *Income* £147,885 *Grants* £135,552 *Assets* £4,631,907

TRUSTEES Jim Higham; John Humphrey; Patrick Marlow; Richard Ongley.

HOW TO APPLY In writing to the correspondent.

WHO TO APPLY TO Louise Davies, Montague House, Chancery Lane, Thrapston, Northamptonshire NN14 4LN *Tel* 01832 732161

CC NO 1091125   **ESTABLISHED** 2002

■ The Congleton Inclosure Trust

WHERE FUNDING CAN BE GIVEN The town of Congleton and the parishes of Hulme Walfield and Newbold with Astbury.

WHO CAN BENEFIT Local organisations; UK organisations with projects in the area.

WHAT IS FUNDED The relief of people who are older, impotent and poor; the relief of distress and sickness; the provision and support of facilities for recreation or other leisure-time activities; the provision and support of educational facilities; and any other charitable purpose.

WHAT IS NOT FUNDED No grants to individuals outside the beneficial area or to organisations not benefiting exclusively to the people in the area of benefit.

TYPE OF GRANT Buildings, capital, core costs, feasibility studies, salaries and start-up costs will be considered. Funding may be given for up to one year.

SAMPLE GRANTS Congleton High School (£5,300); Congleton Pentecostal Hall (£3,000); Congleton Museum Trust (£2,600); Eaton Bank School (£2,500); Astbury Mere Trust and Visyon (£2,000 each); Congleton Coronation Bowling Club (£1,500); Wellspring Church (£1,400); Buglawton Scouts, Dane Valley Swimming Club and East Cheshire Cross Roads (£1,000 each); Beartown Belles (£900); Churches Together (£750); Quinta School (£450); and Macclesfield Hospital (£100).

FINANCES *Year* 2008 *Income* £68,195 *Grants* £55,447 *Assets* £1,551,967

TRUSTEES K P Boon, Chair; J W Beardmore; Mrs J Goodier; G Humphreys; A B McCormick; Mrs J Moore; R J Moore; E G Pedley; M A S Roy; Revd D Taylore; J S Wainwright; A B Watson.

HOW TO APPLY On a form available from the correspondent. The trustees meet in January, April, July and October. Applications should be submitted by the first day of the month in which the trustees meet.

WHO TO APPLY TO D A Daniel, Clerk, PO Box 138, Congleton, Cheshire CW12 3SZ *email* daviddaniel@uwclub.net

CC NO 244136   **ESTABLISHED** 1795

■ The Congregational and General Charitable Trust

WHERE FUNDING CAN BE GIVEN UK.

WHO CAN BENEFIT Protestant churches and community projects, in particular those associated with United Reformed and Congregational denominations.

WHAT IS FUNDED (i) Funds for building or property projects to churches and charities of the United Reformed and Congregational denominations or other Protestant churches. (ii) Church community projects seeking funding towards their capital costs.

TYPE OF GRANT One-off for property projects and capital costs.

FINANCES *Year* 2008–09 *Income* £73,000 *Grants* £186,000 *Assets* £8,943,000

TRUSTEES Robert B Copleton, Chair; David J Collett; Revd. Anthony G Burnham; Maurice Dyson; Revd Arnold Harrison; Revd Michael R Heaney; Revd Ifan Rh Roberts; Barrie E Smith.

HOW TO APPLY In a form which can be downloaded from the trust's website. 'When sending your application please attach any supporting documentation – such as your church's or organisation's accounts, the project's accounts, appeal leaflets or project literature – along with your signed application form.' The closing dates for applications are 31 January and 31 July each year.

WHO TO APPLY TO David Collett, Secretary of the Trustees, Currer House, Currer Street, Bradford, West Yorkshire BD1 5BA *email* trust@congregational.co.uk *Website* www.congregational.co.uk

CC NO 297013   **ESTABLISHED** 1987

■ The Conscience Trust

WHERE FUNDING CAN BE GIVEN UK.

WHO CAN BENEFIT Charitable organisations.

WHAT IS FUNDED 'The charity provides grants to other registered charities and organisations, primarily to assist with projects of a horticultural and eco-friendly nature.'

SAMPLE GRANTS Torbay Coast and Countryside Trust (£119,000).

FINANCES *Year* 2007–08 *Income* £25,655 *Grants* £119,000 *Assets* £665,008

TRUSTEES Adrian Miller; Will Michelmore; Simon Whewell; Prof. Jo Anderson.

HOW TO APPLY 'Please apply in writing, with applications to be limited to 500 words.'

WHO TO APPLY TO The Trustees, c/o Michelmores, Woodwater House, Pynes Hill, Exeter EX2 5WR

CC NO 1044136

■ The Conservation Foundation

WHERE FUNDING CAN BE GIVEN UK and overseas.

WHO CAN BENEFIT Registered charities.

WHAT IS FUNDED Creation and management of environmental and conservation orientated projects funded by sponsorship. Income is generated to pay for the costs of managing charitable projects and supporting activities.

FINANCES *Year* 2008 *Income* £1,379,900

TRUSTEES J Senior, Chair; D A Shreeve; Prof. D J Bellamy; J B Curtis; W F Moloney; Mrs E A Kinmonth; Mrs L Dunn; Ms D Fennell.

OTHER INFORMATION Information about the foundation's current projects can be found on its website.

HOW TO APPLY In writing to the correspondent.

WHO TO APPLY TO W F Moloney, Trustee, 1 Kensington Gore, London SW7 2AR *Tel* 020 7591 3111 *email* info@conservationfoundation. co.uk *Website* www.conservationfoundation.co. uk

CC NO 284656   **ESTABLISHED** 1982

■ The Consolidated Charities for the Infirm – Merchant Taylors' Company

WHERE FUNDING CAN BE GIVEN Lewisham, Southwark, Tower Hamlets, Hackney and environs; occasionally Greater London.

WHO CAN BENEFIT Charitable organisations.

WHAT IS FUNDED Relief of need, people with disabilities, infirm, older people and children, sheltered housing and residential care homes.

TYPE OF GRANT Between one and three years.

SAMPLE GRANTS Sense (£40,000); Demelza (£36,000); Tall Ships Youth Trust (£10,000); Combat Stress (£6,000); Spitalfield Crypt Trust (£5,000); and Stable Family Home Trust (£2,500).

FINANCES *Year* 2008 *Income* £450,943 *Grants* £203,284 *Assets* £8,407,577

TRUSTEES Christopher M Keville; R W E Charlton; The Earl of Stockton; P T E Massey.

HOW TO APPLY In writing using the appropriate application form which is available from the correspondent or by visiting www.merchanttaylors.co.uk. The charity states that emailed enquiries are preferred and responded to quickest.

WHO TO APPLY TO Matthew Dear, Charities Officer, Merchant Taylors' Hall, 30 Threadneedle Street, London EC2R 8JB *Tel* 020 7450 4447 *Fax* 020 7588 2776 *email* charities@merchant-taylors. co.uk *Website* www.merchanttaylors.co.uk

CC NO 214266   **ESTABLISHED** 1960

■ The Construction Industry Trust for Youth

WHERE FUNDING CAN BE GIVEN UK.

WHO CAN BENEFIT Any youth organisation for building projects benefiting young people aged 14 to 30 who are unemployed or disadvantaged by poverty, and those living in both rural and urban areas.

WHAT IS FUNDED To improve the condition of life, by sponsorship of youth training in the construction industry and by assisting in providing buildings for recreational use and occupational training.

WHAT IS NOT FUNDED Training outside of the construction industry and its associated trades and professions is not considered. Applications for build grants or the refurbishment of youth centres are not considered.

TYPE OF GRANT One-off for buildings. Funding can be given for up to three years for training.

FINANCES *Year* 2008 *Income* £768,181 *Grants* £24,140 *Assets* £787,823

TRUSTEES Rod Bennion, Chair; Douglas A Barrat; Michael A Brown; Norman Critchlow; Martin K Davis; Anthony J Furlong; Richard B Haryott; Richard Laudy; Liz Male; Peter Marchant; Rob Oldham; Martin P W Scarth; John C M Taylor; Alistair H C Voaden; Andy Wates.

OTHER INFORMATION In 2008 a further £612,000 was spent on it own community based projects.

HOW TO APPLY In writing, or via email, to the correspondent for an application form, with an outline of the request. Forms can be downloaded from the trust's website.

WHO TO APPLY TO The Trust Director, 55 Tufton Street, London SW1P 3QL *Tel* 020 7227 4563 *email* cyt@thecc.org.uk *Website* www. constructionyouth.org.uk

CC NO 1094323   **ESTABLISHED** 1961

■ The Cook and Wolstenholme Charitable Trust

WHERE FUNDING CAN BE GIVEN Bournville and the surrounding area just south of Birmingham City Centre.

WHO CAN BENEFIT Charitable organisations.

WHAT IS FUNDED General charitable purposes, with a preference for organisations supporting young and older people.

SAMPLE GRANTS SENSE (£3,000); Pavilion Christian Community (£2,500); British Heart Foundation, County Air Ambulance and St Mary's Hospice (£2,000 each); Alderbrook School (£1,500); Birmingham Children's Hospital, Birmingham Women's Foundation NHS Trust, Brain Tumour UK, Brandwood Centre and Mobility Trust (£1,000 each); Cockshutt Hill Technical College and RNLI (£500 each); and Wychall Primary School (£250).

FINANCES *Year* 2007–08 *Income* £21,840 *Grants* £28,550 *Assets* £518,545

TRUSTEES Peter Barber; Dennis Carson; Patrick Beasley.

HOW TO APPLY In writing to the correspondent. The trustees meet about every six months, although applications for grants are considered all year round.

WHO TO APPLY TO Dennis Carson, Clerk, c/o Mills & Reeve, 78–84 Colmore Row, Birmingham B3 2AB

CC NO 1091984   **ESTABLISHED** 2000

■ Gordon Cook Foundation

WHERE FUNDING CAN BE GIVEN UK.

WHO CAN BENEFIT Charities benefiting children and young adults.

WHAT IS FUNDED The foundation is dedicated to the advancement of all aspects of education and training which are likely to promote character development and citizenship. In recent years the foundation has adopted the term 'Values Education' to denote the wide range of activity it seeks to support.

WHAT IS NOT FUNDED Individuals are unlikely to be funded.

TYPE OF GRANT One-off and recurring for projects and research. Funding may be given for more than three years.

RANGE OF GRANTS £1,000–£30,000.

SAMPLE GRANTS Previous beneficiaries include Norham Foundation, Health Education Board for Scotland, Citizen Foundation, North Lanarkshire Council and Northern College.

FINANCES *Year* 2008 *Income* £360,433

TRUSTEES G Ross, Chair; D A Adams; Prof. B J McGettrick; Dr P Clarke; Dr W Gatherer; J Marshall; C P Skene.

OTHER INFORMATION Previous research indicates that grants are made totalling around £200,000 each year.

HOW TO APPLY The trustees are proactive in looking for projects to support; however, unsolicited applications may be considered if they fall within the foundation's criteria and are in accordance with current programmes. Forms may be obtained from the correspondent.

Think carefully about every application. Is it justified?

447

WHO TO APPLY TO Mrs Irene B Brown, Foundation Secretary, 3 Chattan Place, Aberdeen AB10 6RB *Tel* 01224 571010 *Fax* 01224 571010 *email* gordoncook@btconnect.com *Website* www.gordoncook.org.uk
SC NO SC017455   **ESTABLISHED** 1974

....

■ The Ernest Cook Trust

WHERE FUNDING CAN BE GIVEN Worldwide, in practice UK.

WHO CAN BENEFIT Charitable or not for profit organisations working through education or training in three main areas of activity, being the environment and the countryside, the arts, crafts and architecture and literacy and numeracy.

WHAT IS FUNDED Grants are given for educational work only, focusing on children and young people in the fields of countryside and environment, arts and crafts, architecture, literary and numeracy, research and other educational projects.

WHAT IS NOT FUNDED Applicants must represent either registered charities or not-for-profit organisations. Grants are normally awarded on an annual basis and will not be awarded retrospectively. Grants are not made to: individuals; agricultural colleges; education work which is part of social support, therapy or medical treatment; building and restoration work; sports and recreational activities; work overseas. Support for wildlife trusts and for farming and wildlife advisory groups is largely restricted to those based in counties in which the trust owns land (Gloucestershire, Buckinghamshire, Leicestershire, Dorset and Oxfordshire).

TYPE OF GRANT Conditional; annual; one-off. Project; research; salaries; and start-up costs. Funding may be given for up to three years.

SAMPLE GRANTS Edward Barnsley Trust (£25,000), to cover the cost of an apprentice; Chetham's School of Music (£21,000), towards an early years music project; Year of Food and Farming (£20,000), towards educational work in the North East and South West; National Library of Wales (£10,000), towards the cost of 2,000 education packs; Royal Entomological Society (£9,600), to cover the cost of the school and farm wildlife programme; Scottish Ensemble (£7,500), to help with the school based element of the Lifelong Learning Programme; Withywood Community School (£6,800), towards the cost of ten music lessons for 60 pupils; and Scottish Seabird Centre (£5,000), towards educational resources for the website.

FINANCES *Year* 2007–08 *Income* £4,696,941 *Grants* £1,597,264 *Assets* £83,043,097

TRUSTEES Anthony Bosanquet, Chair; Harry Henderson; Andrew Christie-Miller; Patrick Maclure; Miles C Tuely; Victoria Edwards.

HOW TO APPLY There is no application form. Applicants are asked to send a covering letter addressed to the grants administrator as well as describing their educational project clearly on no more than two additional sheets of A4, specifying how any grant will be spent. A simple budget for that project should be included, noting any other funding applications. The latest annual report and accounts for the organisation should also be provided. Please do not send further supporting material or e mail applications. Successful applicants will be asked to complete an Agreement which includes the ability to pay the grant by the BACS. The Agreement also requires the applicant to submit a report on the funded project; failure to do so will ensure the rejection of any further application and may result in a request to repay the award. The full board of Trustees meets twice a year, in April and October, to consider grants in excess of £4,000; applications for these meetings should be submitted by 31 January and 31 August respectively. Meetings to consider grants of £4,000 or less are normally held in February, May, July, September and December. Notification about the date of payment of grants is given when the offer is made. If necessary, please contact the Grants Office to discuss a potential application: staff will be pleased to assist you.

WHO TO APPLY TO Mrs Ros Leigh, Grants administrator, Fairford Park, Fairford, Gloucestershire GL7 4JH *Tel* 01285 712492 *Fax* 01285 713417 *email* grants@ernestcooktrust.org.uk *Website* www.ernestcooktrust.org.uk
CC NO 313497   **ESTABLISHED** 1952

....

■ The Cooks Charity

WHERE FUNDING CAN BE GIVEN UK, especially City of London.

WHO CAN BENEFIT Charities and individuals.

WHAT IS FUNDED Projects concerned with catering. Any charitable purpose (with some sort of catering connection) in the City of London.

SAMPLE GRANTS Academy of Culinary Arts (£55,000); Food Education At Schools Today (£42,000); Hackney Community College (£30,000); Springboard (£25,000); Ironbridge Museum (£15,000); Crisis Skylight Cafe (£12,000); Bournemouth University (£10,000); Broadway, Pembroke House and Treloar Trust (£5,000 each); City University (£4,500); and Corpus Christi College (£3,400).

FINANCES *Year* 2007–08 *Income* £372,353 *Grants* £189,490 *Assets* £4,012,057

TRUSTEES H F Thornton; G A V Rees; B E G Puxley.

HOW TO APPLY In writing to the correspondent. Applications are considered in spring and autumn.

WHO TO APPLY TO Michael C Thatcher, Clerk and Solicitor, Coombe Ridge, Thursley Road, Churt, Farnham, Surrey GU10 2LQ *email* clerk@cookslivery.org.uk
CC NO 297913   **ESTABLISHED** 1987

....

■ The Cookson Charitable Trust

WHERE FUNDING CAN BE GIVEN UK.

WHO CAN BENEFIT Charitable organisations.

WHAT IS FUNDED General charitable purposes.

RANGE OF GRANTS £30–£20,000.

SAMPLE GRANTS Amber Foundation (£20,000); King's College Cambridge (£5,000); Besom Foundation (£1,000); Bishopstone PCC, CPRE, Marie Curie Cancer Care, Holburne Museum, Live Music Now! and Royal Marsden Hospital (£500 each); International Musicians Seminar (£400); Youth Clubs Hampshire and the Isle of Wight (£300); Help for Heroes (£200); St Margaret's Somerset Hospice (£100); the National Art Collections Fund (£50); and National Trust (£30).

FINANCES *Year* 2007–08 *Income* £34,484 *Grants* £30,080 *Assets* £236,042

TRUSTEES H R Cookson; C M Cookson.

HOW TO APPLY In writing to the correspondent.

WHO TO APPLY TO H R Cookson, Trustee, Manor Farm, Stratford Tony, Salisbury SP5 4AT
CC NO 265207   **ESTABLISHED** 1972

■ The Catherine Cookson Charitable Trust

WHERE FUNDING CAN BE GIVEN UK, with some preference for the north east of England.
WHO CAN BENEFIT Charitable organisations.
WHAT IS FUNDED General charitable purposes.
RANGE OF GRANTS Mostly £1,000 or less. A few large grants are made.
SAMPLE GRANTS St Paul's Church – Jarrow (£80,000); Kidney Research UK (£50,000); Royal Grammar School Newcastle (£35,000); Bubble Appeal (£30,000); Heart Research UK and Riding for the Disabled Association (£10,000 each); Berwick Upon Tweed Preservation Trust, Beadnell Parish Council, Leukaemia Research and Riding Mill Village Hall Trust (£5,000 each); Mining Museum – Cleveland and Royal Blind Society West Sussex (£2,000 each); Beadnell Village Playground, Help the Aged, Kings Church Darlington and Sunderland and North Durham Royal Society for the Blind (£1,000 each); Chernobyl Children Lifeline, Grove Hill Methodist Church – Middlesbrough, Hebburn Sea Scouts, National Missing Persons Helpline and Newcastle PROPS (£500 each); the Meningitis Trust (£400); Wildfowl and Wetlands Trust (£250); the Royal Regiment of Fusiliers (£200); and Albany Youth Project, All Saints Monkwearmouth, Children Community Safety Group, Hastings Writers' Group, the Royal British Legion and Spital Estate Community Association (£100 each).
FINANCES *Year* 2007–08 *Income* £1,078,833 *Grants* £291,765 *Assets* £21,989,645
TRUSTEES David S S Hawkins; Peter Magnay; Hugo F Marshall; Daniel E Sallows; Jack E Ravenscroft.
HOW TO APPLY In writing to the correspondent.
WHO TO APPLY TO Peter Magnay, Trustee, Thomas Magnay and Co, 13 Regent Terrace, Gateshead, Tyne and Wear NE8 1LU *Tel* 0191 488 7459
CC NO 272895   **ESTABLISHED** 1977

■ Harold and Daphne Cooper Charitable Trust

WHERE FUNDING CAN BE GIVEN UK.
WHO CAN BENEFIT National charities.
WHAT IS FUNDED Medical research, health and Jewish charities.
WHAT IS NOT FUNDED No grants to individuals.
TYPE OF GRANT Capital (buildings considered), project and research. Core costs and running costs are considered. Funding available for up to three years.
RANGE OF GRANTS One large grant; the remainder for smaller amounts.
SAMPLE GRANTS Jewish Care (£75,000); Blond McIndoe Research Foundation (£5,000); Whizz Kidz (£3,000); Aidis Trust, Elimination of Leukaemia Fund and Macmillan Cancer Support (£2,000 each); Marie Curie Cancer Care (£1,500); and 3H Fund, Breast Cancer Campaign, Deafblind UK and the Shooting Star Children's Hospice (£1,000 each).
FINANCES *Year* 2007–08 *Income* £157,787 *Grants* £137,500 *Assets* £1,759,762
TRUSTEES Mrs S Roter; Miss Judith Portrait; T Roter; Miss A Roter; Ms M V Hockley.
HOW TO APPLY In writing to the correspondent; applications are not acknowledged.
WHO TO APPLY TO T Miles, c/o Portrait Solicitors, 1 Chancery Lane, London WC2A 1LF
CC NO 206772   **ESTABLISHED** 1962

■ Mabel Cooper Charity

WHERE FUNDING CAN BE GIVEN UK, with a possible interest in South Devon.
WHO CAN BENEFIT Registered charities.
WHAT IS FUNDED General charitable purposes. Preference is given to projects with low overheads.
WHAT IS NOT FUNDED No grants to individuals.
RANGE OF GRANTS £100–£15,000.
SAMPLE GRANTS East Portlemouth Village Hall (£19,000).
FINANCES *Year* 2007–08 *Income* £62,851 *Grants* £19,000 *Assets* £1,179,037
TRUSTEES A E M Harbottle; J Harbottle; I A Harbottle; D J Harbottle.
HOW TO APPLY The trust states that it does not welcome, or reply to, unsolicited applications.
WHO TO APPLY TO The Secretary, Lambury Cottage, East Portlemouth, Salcombe, Devon TQ8 8PU
CC NO 264621   **ESTABLISHED** 1972

■ The Alice Ellen Cooper Dean Charitable Foundation

WHERE FUNDING CAN BE GIVEN Worldwide, with a preference for UK charities in Dorset and west Hampshire.
WHO CAN BENEFIT Registered charities.
WHAT IS FUNDED Registered charities supporting health, humanitarian causes, social disadvantage, education, religion, community, arts and culture, amateur sport and disability.
WHAT IS NOT FUNDED No grants to individuals.
TYPE OF GRANT One-off and recurring.
RANGE OF GRANTS Mostly £1,000–£10,000.
SAMPLE GRANTS Cherry Tree Nursery – Sheltered Work Opportunities Project (£50,000); West of England School & College (£36,000); Piers Simon Appeal and the Wessex Autistic Society (£25,000 each); East Holton Church and the Royal British Legion – Dorset (£20,000 each); Water Aid (£15,000); Action for Kids, Dorset & Somerset Air Ambulance Trust and the Spinal Injuries Association (£10,000 each); Child Aid (£8,000); Dorset Blind Association (£7,500); Beaminster School, Coping with Chaos, Huntington's Disease Association and SOS Children's Villages UK (£5,000 each); Jubilee Sailing Trust and Dorset Action on Abuse (£3,000 each); The Seeing Ear and Special Toys Educational Postal Service (£2,000 each); and Foundation for the Study of Infant Deaths and the War Memorial Trust (£1,000 each).
FINANCES *Year* 2007–08 *Income* £917,527 *Grants* £790,500 *Assets* £16,644,391
TRUSTEES John R B Bowditch; Mrs Linda J Bowditch; Rupert J A Edwards; Douglas J E Neville-Jones; Emma Blackburn.
HOW TO APPLY In writing to the correspondent. Each application should include: name and address of organisation; charity registration number; details of the project; details of the community, including area covered and numbers who will benefit from the project; details of fund raising activities and other anticipated source of grants; a copy of the latest financial accounts.
WHO TO APPLY TO Rupert J A Edwards, Trustee, Edwards and Keeping, Unity Chambers, 34 High East Street, Dorchester, Dorset DT1 1HA *Tel* 01305 251333 *Fax* 01305 251465 *email* office@edwardsandkeeping.co.uk
CC NO 273298   **ESTABLISHED** 1977

■ The Marjorie Coote Animal Charity Trust

WHERE FUNDING CAN BE GIVEN Worldwide.

WHO CAN BENEFIT Registered charities for the benefit of animals.

WHAT IS FUNDED The care and protection of horses, dogs and other animals and birds. It is the policy of the trustees to concentrate on research into animal health problems and on the protection of species, whilst continuing to apply a small proportion of the income to general animal welfare, including sanctuaries.

WHAT IS NOT FUNDED No grants to individuals.

TYPE OF GRANT One-off and recurrent.

RANGE OF GRANTS Grants are usually in the range of £500–£10,000.

SAMPLE GRANTS RSPCA Sheffield's Rebuild Project (£90,000); Animal Health Trust (£10,000); PDSA (£8,000); WWF-UK (£6,000); the Whiteley Wildlife Conservation Trust (£4,000); Sheffield Wildlife Trust and the Wildfowl and Wetlands Trust (£3,000 each); Mill House Sanctuary (£2,500); FRAME and Tusk Trust (£2,000 each); Devon Horse and Pony Sanctuary (£1,500); Save the Rhino International (£1,000); and Dog Lost and Yorkshire Swan Rescue (£500 each).

FINANCES *Year* 2007–08 *Income* £123,749 *Grants* £173,500 *Assets* £3,117,818

TRUSTEES Sir Hugh Neill; Mrs J P Holah; Lady Neill; Mrs S E Browne.

HOW TO APPLY In writing to the correspondent. Applications should reach the correspondent during September for consideration in October/November.

WHO TO APPLY TO Mrs J P Holah, Trustees, Dykelands Farm, Whenby, York YO61 4SF *email* info@mcacharity.org.uk

CC NO 208493   **ESTABLISHED** 1954

■ The Marjorie Coote Old People's Charity

WHERE FUNDING CAN BE GIVEN South Yorkshire.

WHO CAN BENEFIT Old people of small means.

WHAT IS FUNDED The established charitable organisations which work actively for the benefit of old people in the area of jurisdiction.

WHAT IS NOT FUNDED No grants to individuals.

SAMPLE GRANTS Age Concern Sheffield, the Cavendish Centre and St Luke's Hospice (£15,000 each); and the Extracare Charitable Trust, Sheffield Dial-A-Ride and Voluntary Action Sheffield (£10,000 each).

FINANCES *Year* 2007–08 *Income* £110,500 *Grants* £97,200 *Assets* £2,915,292

TRUSTEES Sir Hugh Neill; Mrs J A Lee; Lady Neill; N J A Hutton.

HOW TO APPLY In writing to the correspondent during May. Appeals received at other times of the year are deferred unless for an urgent grant for a specific one-off project.

WHO TO APPLY TO Sir Hugh Neill, Trustee, Barn Cottage, Lindrick Common, Worksop, Nottinghamshire S81 8BA *Tel* 01909 562806

CC NO 226747   **ESTABLISHED** 1958

■ The Helen Jean Cope Trust

WHERE FUNDING CAN BE GIVEN Mostly Leicestershire, but also Derbyshire and Nottinghamshire.

WHO CAN BENEFIT Registered charities only.

WHAT IS FUNDED General charitable purposes, supporting single projects.

WHAT IS NOT FUNDED No grants to individuals or unregistered charities.

TYPE OF GRANT Generally single projects.

SAMPLE GRANTS Leicestershire & Rutland Wildlife Trust (£30,000); Abbeyfield Loughborough Society Ltd and Help the Aged (£10,000 each); Canine Partners, Long Cawson Recreation Ground, Motor Neurone Disease Association and Thorpe Sachville Village Hall (£5,000 each); The Braille Chess Association, Charnwood Christmas Toy Appeal, Derby Playhouse, Perthes Association and the Public Catalogue Foundation (£2,500 each); Dayax Development Centre, Friends of Grace Dieu Priory, Prison Fellowship, and Starlight Children's Foundation (£1,000 each); and Act One, Christ in the Centre and Leicestershire North Neighbourhood Watch (£500 each).

FINANCES *Year* 2007–08 *Income* £138,273 *Grants* £357,550 *Assets* £2,293,401

TRUSTEES K J Brydson; D N Murphy; J M Savage; L A Brydson; G S Freckelton.

HOW TO APPLY In writing to the correspondent.

WHO TO APPLY TO Mrs M M Savage, Secretary, 39 Farndale Drive, Loughborough, Leicestershire LE11 2RG

CC NO 1071203   **ESTABLISHED** 1998

■ The J Reginald Corah Foundation Fund

WHERE FUNDING CAN BE GIVEN Leicestershire and Rutland.

WHO CAN BENEFIT Charitable organisations. However, particular favour is given to hosiery firms carrying out their business in the city or county of Leicester and Rutland.

WHAT IS FUNDED General charitable purposes, particularly for the benefit of employees and ex-employees of hosiery firms carrying on business in the city or county of Leicester and Rutland.

WHAT IS NOT FUNDED Applications from individuals are not considered unless made by, or supported by, a recognised charitable organisation.

TYPE OF GRANT One-off and recurrent.

RANGE OF GRANTS Up to £11,000.

SAMPLE GRANTS Leicester Charities Organisation (£11,000); Leicester Children's Holiday Centre (£8,000); Whizz-Kidz and Eyres Monsell Club for Young People (£6,000 each); LOROS (£5,000); Dove Cottage Day Hospice (£4,000); Army Benevolent Fund (£3,000); Special Effects (£2,500); Leicester Clubs for Young People (£2,000); Age Concern (£1,500); and Leicestershire Autistic Society, Worldwide Volunteering for Young People and Leicestershire Scouts (£1,000 each).

FINANCES *Year* 2007–08 *Income* £132,657 *Grants* £103,068 *Assets* £3,930,961

TRUSTEES D P Corah; Roger Bowder; G S Makings.

HOW TO APPLY In writing to the correspondent. Trustees meet about every two months.

WHO TO APPLY TO Mrs P Fowle, Clerk, c/o Harvey Ingram Owston, 20 New Walk, Leicester LE1 6TX *Tel* 0116 254 5454

CC NO 220792   **ESTABLISHED** 1953

■ The Gershon Coren Charitable Foundation

WHERE FUNDING CAN BE GIVEN UK and the developing world.

WHO CAN BENEFIT Registered charities, particularly Jewish organisations.

WHAT IS FUNDED General charitable purposes, social welfare and Jewish causes.

RANGE OF GRANTS £500–£40,000.

SAMPLE GRANTS Gategi Village Self Help Group (£40,000); Magen David Adom UK (£28,000); Aish UK and UJS Hillel (£6,000 each); Hadassah Medical Relief Association UK, Jewish Care and Nightingale House (£5,000 each); B'nai B'rith UK and St Joseph's Hospice (£2,500 each); Smile Train (£1,100); Barnabas Fund, JAMI, Jewish Music Institute, One Voice and Zionist Federation (£1,000 each); and NSPCC, Spiro Ark and Whizz Kids (£500 each).

FINANCES *Year* 2007–08 *Income* £113,951 *Grants* £130,650 *Assets* £2,506,430

TRUSTEES Muriel Coren; Anthony Coren; Walter Stanton.

HOW TO APPLY In writing to the correspondent.

WHO TO APPLY TO The Trustees, 3rd Floor, 7–10 Chandos Street, London W1G 9DQ

CC NO 257615   **ESTABLISHED** 1968

■ The Corinthian Trust

WHERE FUNDING CAN BE GIVEN UK and overseas.

WHO CAN BENEFIT Evangelical Christianity.

WHAT IS FUNDED The trust makes grants only to evangelical Christian organisations and individuals who are known to, or recommended to, the trustees. Nearly all the trust's grants are ongoing.

WHAT IS NOT FUNDED No grants to individuals or organisations not known to the trustees.

TYPE OF GRANT Recurrent.

RANGE OF GRANTS Up to £7,000.

SAMPLE GRANTS Children Alone Trust (£6,900); International Nepal Fellowship (£5,400); Esher Green Baptist Church (£5,100); Avishek Church – Nepal (£3,000); SAGOAL – Nepal (£2,500); Central Asia Fellowship (£1,200); and Asal Chimeki – Nepal (£1,000).

FINANCES *Year* 2007–08 *Income* £47,509 *Grants* £52,637 *Assets* £680,278

TRUSTEES John S Bradley; Mrs Judith M Bradley; James N Bradley; David N Price.

OTHER INFORMATION The 2007–08 grant total includes £5,100 given directly to individual Christian workers.

HOW TO APPLY In writing to the correspondent, only if recommended to apply.

WHO TO APPLY TO John S Bradley, Trustee, Oregon, Avenue Road, Cobham, Surrey KT11 3HW *Tel* 01932 864665 *email* j.bradley@btinternet.com

CC NO 278531   **ESTABLISHED** 1979

■ Edwin Cornforth 1983 Charity Trust

WHERE FUNDING CAN BE GIVEN UK.

WHO CAN BENEFIT Christian Science organisations.

WHAT IS FUNDED Eight charities as stated in the will. Preference is given to certain Christian Science organisations and in practice, other charities are not considered.

WHAT IS NOT FUNDED No grants to individuals.

TYPE OF GRANT Recurrent.

SAMPLE GRANTS Previous beneficiaries included Auxiliary Committee for Retirement Homes, Claremount Fan Court Foundation Ltd, First Church of Christ – Sutton Coldfield, The Pison Trust and Vermont Trust Ltd.

FINANCES *Year* 2007–08 *Income* £23,483 *Grants* £10,000

TRUSTEES Lloyds TSB Private Banking Ltd.

HOW TO APPLY In writing to the correspondent.

WHO TO APPLY TO Lloyds TSB Private Banking Ltd, UK Trust Centre, The Clock House, 22–26 Ock Street, Abingdon, Oxfordshire OX14 5SW *Tel* 01235 232769

CC NO 287196   **ESTABLISHED** 1983

■ Michael Cornish Charitable Trust

WHERE FUNDING CAN BE GIVEN Lincolnshire and overseas.

WHO CAN BENEFIT Preference for registered charities in the Lincolnshire area and charities involving children.

WHAT IS FUNDED General, community, young people, medical, overseas aid.

SAMPLE GRANTS 3D Youth Services (£10,000); Epilepsy Research UK, Family Welfare Association, Happy Days, Queen Alexandra Hospital Home and The Smile Train (£5,000 each); and break, Jobs 4 All, St John Ambulance and Lincoln & Lindsey Blind Association (£2,500 each). £5,000 went overseas to Children of the Andes and a further £500 went to individuals.

FINANCES *Year* 2008 *Income* £178,987 *Grants* £79,500 *Assets* £13,094,403

TRUSTEES Michael J Cornish, Chair; Susan M Cornish; Richard L J Vigar.

HOW TO APPLY In writing to the correspondent.

WHO TO APPLY TO Richard L J Vigar, Trustee, 15 Newland, Lincoln LN1 1XG *Tel* 01522 531341

CC NO 1107890   **ESTABLISHED** 2005

■ The Evan Cornish Foundation

WHERE FUNDING CAN BE GIVEN UK and developing countries.

WHO CAN BENEFIT Charitable organisations.

WHAT IS FUNDED General charitable purposes; overseas aid.

SAMPLE GRANTS Alzheimer's Society and Survival International (£15,000 each); Afghan Connection, Amnesty International UK, Field Studies Council, Jessie's Fund, Médecins Sans Frontières, Orbis UK, Tools for Self Reliance and the Treehouse Trust – Parent Support Project (£10,000 each); and Asylum Seeker Support Initiative and Fydell House Centre (£5,000 each).

FINANCES *Year* 2007–08 *Income* £427,974 *Grants* £120,000 *Assets* £7,299,712

TRUSTEES Ethel Cornish; Barbara Ward; Mary Cornish; Sally Cornish; Rachel Cornish.

HOW TO APPLY The trustees will consider applications as well as seeking out causes to support. They normally meet at least four times a year.

WHO TO APPLY TO The Trustees, c/o Provincial House, Solly Street, Sheffield S1 4BA *email* contactus@evancornishfoundation.org.uk

CC NO 1112703   **ESTABLISHED** 2005

Think carefully about every application. Is it justified?

451

■ Cornwall Community Foundation

WHERE FUNDING CAN BE GIVEN Cornwall and the Isles of Scilly.

WHO CAN BENEFIT Local projects in Cornwall and the Isles of Scilly that engage local people in making their communities better places to live. This includes groups, projects and individuals.

WHAT IS FUNDED Community-based causes.

RANGE OF GRANTS Usually up to £10,000.

FINANCES *Year* 2008 *Income* £1,207,918 *Grants* £535,172 *Assets* £1,138,816

TRUSTEES James Williams, Chair; Oliver Baines; Mrs M Bickford-Smith; David Bishop; Hon Evelyn Boscawen; Paul Davies; John Ede; Lady Mary Holborow; Michael Miles; Ian Pawley; Daphne Skinnard; Peter Stethridge.

HOW TO APPLY On a form available from the foundation. For general information about grants contact the grants team (tel: 01566 779333 or email: grants@cornwallfoundation.com).

WHO TO APPLY TO The Orchard, Market Street, Launceston, Cornwall PL15 8AU *Tel* 01566 779333 *email* info@cornwallfoundation.com *Website* www.cornwallfoundation.com

CC NO 1099977   **ESTABLISHED** 2003

■ The Cornwall Historic Churches Trust

WHERE FUNDING CAN BE GIVEN Cornwall.

WHO CAN BENEFIT Places of Christian worship.

WHAT IS FUNDED The repair and restoration of churches, with particular regard to those of architectural or historical merit.

WHAT IS NOT FUNDED The trust is unlikely to consider the following: routine maintenance and repair work which the church community could be expected to deal with themselves; re-decoration – other than when it follows from a major restoration scheme; introduction of domestic or similar facilities within the church building; schemes which damage or adversely affect the basic building, especially its external appearance; replacement or installation of heating systems required for the comfort of the congregations; redesign and layout of the churchyard and work on tombstones – other than the restoration of specific tombstones with some significant historic connections; repair and/or maintenance of associated buildings (e.g. school rooms and church halls).

TYPE OF GRANT One-off grants.

RANGE OF GRANTS Up to £4,000. When determining the level of grant support, the trust operates a points system which takes the following factors into account: the age of the church or chapel; the merit of the building; the church's effort in two respects – (i) its participation in the CHCT's annual sponsored event and (ii) other church efforts to raise funds for the project; financial need; the church's own financial resources.

FINANCES *Year* 2007 *Income* £47,612 *Grants* £39,200 *Assets* £50,682

TRUSTEES Mrs H Briggs, Chair; The Lord Lieutenant for Cornwall; The Lord Bishop of Truro; Sir Richard Rashleigh; The Viscountess Boyd of Medon; A H Foot; C F Hall; G J Holborow; Mrs M R C Parr.

PUBLICATIONS Leaflet on Cornish church conservation.

OTHER INFORMATION Donations were approved to 18 churches and chapels.

HOW TO APPLY In writing to the correspondent for an application form, guidelines and booklet.

WHO TO APPLY TO Simon Coy, Hon. Secretary, Dipper Bridge, Ruthernbridge, Bodmin PL30 5LU

email secretary@cornwallhistoricchurchestrust. org *Website* www.cornwallhistoricchurchestrust. org

CC NO 218340   **ESTABLISHED** 1955

■ The Duke of Cornwall's Benevolent Fund

WHERE FUNDING CAN BE GIVEN UK, with a number of grants made in the Cornwall area.

WHO CAN BENEFIT Registered charities.

WHAT IS FUNDED The relief of people in need of assistance because of sickness, poverty or age; the provision of almshouses, homes of rest, hospitals and convalescent homes; the advancement of education; the advancement of the arts and religion; and the preservation for the benefit of the public of lands and buildings.

RANGE OF GRANTS Up to £100,000. Typically under £5,000 each.

SAMPLE GRANTS The Prince's Regenerations Trust (£105,000); the Prince's Foundation (£15,000); Bryher Community Association and Cornwall Buildings Preservation Trust (£5,000 each); Soil Association (£4,000); St Breward Parish Church Appeal (£2,500); Lifebuoy Charitable Trust (£2,000); and All Saints Church – Curry Mallet, Launceston College, the Merchant Venturers, Royal Cornwall Agricultural Association and St Endellion Festival (£1,000 each).

FINANCES *Year* 2007–08 *Income* £139,316 *Grants* £195,544 *Assets* £2,828,566

TRUSTEES Hon. James Leigh-Pemberton; W R A Ross.

HOW TO APPLY In writing to the correspondent. Applicants should give as much detail as possible, especially information on how much money has been raised to date, what the target is and how it will be achieved. Applications can be made at any time. Trustees meet quarterly.

WHO TO APPLY TO Robert Mitchell, 10 Buckingham Gate, London SW1E 6LA *Tel* 020 7834 7346

CC NO 269183   **ESTABLISHED** 1975

■ The Cornwell Charitable Trust

WHERE FUNDING CAN BE GIVEN The south west of England, with a preference for Cornwall.

WHO CAN BENEFIT Registered charities.

WHAT IS FUNDED General charitable purposes, funding projects and individuals specifically and primarily in the Cornwall area.

WHAT IS NOT FUNDED No support for travel, expeditions or university grants.

TYPE OF GRANT Project and capital.

SAMPLE GRANTS The Constant Gardener Trust (£18,000).

FINANCES *Year* 2007–08 *Income* £39,163 *Grants* £40,312 *Assets* £870,129

TRUSTEES David Cornwell; Valerie Cornwell; Gordon Smith; Matthew Bennett.

OTHER INFORMATION The grant total in 2007–08 included 900 given to individuals.

HOW TO APPLY In writing to the correspondent.

WHO TO APPLY TO G C Smith, Trustee, Devonshire House, 1 Devonshire Street, London W1W 5DR

CC NO 1012467   **ESTABLISHED** 1992

■ The Sidney and Elizabeth Corob Charitable Trust

WHERE FUNDING CAN BE GIVEN UK.

WHO CAN BENEFIT Charitable organisations.

WHAT IS FUNDED General charitable purposes, supporting a range of causes including education, arts, welfare and Jewish charities.

WHAT IS NOT FUNDED No grants to individuals or non-registered charities.

RANGE OF GRANTS Up to £90,000.

SAMPLE GRANTS Oxford Centre for Hebrew and Jewish Studies (£47,000); Autism Speaks (£20,000); United Synagogue (£10,000); and British Technion Society, the HOPE Charity, Jewish Care, Magen David Adom UK, (£10,000 each).

FINANCES *Year* 2007–08 *Income* £33,836 *Grants* £216,242 *Assets* £610,648

TRUSTEES A L Corob; E Corob; C J Cook; J V Hajnal; S A Wechsler; S Wiseman.

HOW TO APPLY In writing to the correspondent. The trustees meet at regular intervals.

WHO TO APPLY TO The Trustees, 62 Grosvenor Street, London W1K 3JF

CC NO 266606   **ESTABLISHED** 1973

■ The Corona Charitable Trust

WHERE FUNDING CAN BE GIVEN UK and overseas.

WHO CAN BENEFIT Jewish people.

WHAT IS FUNDED Jewish religious education and relief-in-need.

SAMPLE GRANTS Cosmos Belz Limited (£12,000); Hasmonean High School (£5,800); Friends of Tashbar Chazon Ish (£4,500); Raleigh Close Charitable Trust (£3,000); WST Charity Limited (£3,200); Ahavas Shalom Charity Fund (£800); Chana (£1,500); and Aish Hatorah, Emunah, the G M Trust, Gateshead Jewish Academy, Sasson Vesimcha Charitable Trust and Yeshivas Beis Hillel (£1,000 each).

FINANCES *Year* 2007–08 *Income* £42,583 *Grants* £42,110 *Assets* £80,021

TRUSTEES A Levy; A Levy; B Levy.

HOW TO APPLY In writing to the correspondent.

WHO TO APPLY TO A Levy, Trustee and Secretary, 16 Mayfield Gardens, Hendon, London NW4 2QA

CC NO 1064320   **ESTABLISHED** 1997

■ The Costa Family Charitable Trust (formerly the Morgan Williams Charitable Trust)

WHERE FUNDING CAN BE GIVEN UK.

WHO CAN BENEFIT Christian organisations.

WHAT IS FUNDED Charities with which the trustees have some connection.

SAMPLE GRANTS Alpha International (£500,000); Great Ormond Street Hospital (£25,000); 24–7 Prayer (£10,000); The Message, Hope HIV and The Chasah Trust (£7,000 each); The Philo Trust (£5,000); Breakthrough Breast Cancer (£3,000); and St David's CTR (£1,000).

FINANCES *Year* 2007–08 *Income* £655,852 *Grants* £575,972 *Assets* £101,367

TRUSTEES K J Costa; Mrs A F Costa.

HOW TO APPLY The trust states that only charities personally connected with the trustees are supported and absolutely no applications are either solicited or acknowledged.

WHO TO APPLY TO K J Costa, Trustee, 50 Stratton Street, London W1J 8LL *Tel* 020 7352 6592

CC NO 221604   **ESTABLISHED** 1964

■ The Cotton Industry War Memorial Trust

WHERE FUNDING CAN BE GIVEN UK.

WHO CAN BENEFIT Individuals and organisations.

WHAT IS FUNDED This trust makes grants to educational bodies to assist eligible students in furtherance of their textile studies, to other bodies which encourage recruitment into or efficiency in the industry or organisations otherwise researching or benefiting the cotton industry. Major support has also been given to other causes, including those related to young people and people with disabilities.

SAMPLE GRANTS Adventure Farm Trust (£35,000); Texprint – Contribution to Operating Costs of Exhibition (£30,000); Royal School for the Deaf and Communication Disorders (£20,000); Samuel Crompton Fellowship Award – Bursaries (£11,000); the Society of Dyers and Colourists (£10,000); Fusiliers Museum Bury (£9,800); the Jack Brown Scholarship Awards – Bursaries (£6,500); and Glasgow School of Art (£2,500).

FINANCES *Year* 2008 *Income* £367,110 *Grants* £130,839 *Assets* £5,369,969

TRUSTEES P Booth; C Trotter; Prof. A P Lockett; K Lloyd; K R Garbett; P Reid; D Babbs.

HOW TO APPLY In writing to the correspondent.

WHO TO APPLY TO The Trustees, c/o 42 Boot Lane, Heaton, Bolton BL1 5SS

CC NO 242721   **ESTABLISHED** 1947

■ The Cotton Trust

WHERE FUNDING CAN BE GIVEN UK and overseas.

WHO CAN BENEFIT UK-registered charities.

WHAT IS FUNDED Relief of suffering; elimination and control of disease; people who have disabilities and disadvantaged people.

WHAT IS NOT FUNDED Grants are only given to UK-registered charities that have been registered for at least one year. No grants to animal charities, individuals, students, further education, travel, expeditions, conservation, environment, arts, new building construction, the purchase of new buildings or 'circular' appeals. The trustees will only support the purchase of computer systems and equipment if it is to be directly used by people who are disadvantaged or have disabilities, but not general IT equipment for the running of organisations.

TYPE OF GRANT Grants are primarily awarded for capital expenditure for specific projects or items of specialist equipment. A limited number of grants are awarded for running costs where the grant will provide direct support for a clearly identifiable charitable project.

RANGE OF GRANTS Usually £250–£5,000.

SAMPLE GRANTS Leicester Charity Link towards support/equipment for families (£41,000); CamFed (£15,000); Merlin (£10,000); Africa Now (£5,000); Angels International (£4,000); International Medical Corps and Leukaemia Research (£2,500 each); Harvest Help (£2,250); Edinburgh Young Carers Project (£1,500); Shelter, St Giles Trust and Village Service Trust (£1,000 each); People for Animal Care Trust (£750); and Youth Action Wiltshire (£580).

FINANCES *Year* 2007–08 *Income* £198,322 *Grants* £227,435 *Assets* £5,663,858

TRUSTEES J B Congdon; T E Cotton; E S Cotton; C B Cotton.

HOW TO APPLY In writing to the correspondent with latest accounts, evidence of charitable status, detailed budget, timetable and details of funds raised. Guidelines are available with an sae. Deadlines for applications are the end of July and the end of January, with successful applicants being notified within three months of these dates. It is regretted that only successful applications can be answered. The trustees only accept one application in a 12-month period.

WHO TO APPLY TO Mrs J B Congdon, Trustee, PO Box 6895, Earl Shilton, Leicester LE9 8ZE *Tel* 01455 440917
CC NO 1094776 **ESTABLISHED** 1956

■ Country Houses Foundation

WHERE FUNDING CAN BE GIVEN England.
WHO CAN BENEFIT Registered charities, building preservation trusts and private owners.
WHAT IS FUNDED The preservation of buildings of historic or architectural significance together with their gardens and grounds, for the public benefit. 'We aim to give grants for repairs and restoration work required to prevent loss or damage to historic buildings located in England, their gardens, grounds and any outbuildings. We would normally expect your building to be listed, scheduled, or in the case of a garden included in the English Heritage Register of Parks and Gardens. However, we may also make grants to projects which involve an unlisted building of sufficient historic or architectural significance or importance if it is within a conservation area.'
WHAT IS NOT FUNDED 'As a general rule we do not offer grants for the following: projects which do not have a heritage focus; alterations and improvements; routine maintenance and minor repairs; general running costs; demolitions; rent, loan or mortgage payments; buying furniture, fittings and equipment except where they have an historic relationship with the site and are relevant to the project; work carried out before a grant offer has been made in writing and accepted. We aim to give grants for repairs and restoration work required to prevent loss or damage to historic buildings located in England, their gardens, grounds and any outbuildings. We would normally expect your building to be listed, scheduled, or in the case of a garden included in the English Heritage Register of Parks and Gardens. However, we may also make grants to projects which involve an unlisted building of sufficient historic or architectural significance or importance if it is within a conservation area.' Full guidelines are available on the foundation's website.
FINANCES *Year* 2007–08 *Income* £1,414,692 *Grants* £231,131 *Assets* £14,378,068
TRUSTEES Oliver Pearcey; Nicholas Barber; Michael Clifton; Norman Hudson; Christopher Taylor; Sir John Parsons.
HOW TO APPLY *Pre-Application Forms* can be completed online, or in a hard copy and returned by post. The foundation tries to respond to within 28 days of receipt. If a project fits the criteria then a unique reference number will be issued which must be quoted on the *Full Application Form*. Applications can be made at anytime.
WHO TO APPLY TO David Price, Company Secretary, The Manor, Sheephouse Farm, Uley Road, Dursley, Gloucestershire GL11 5AD *Tel* 0845 402 4102 *Fax* 0845 402 4103 *email* david@ countryhousesfoundation.org.uk *Website* www. countryhousesfoundation.org.uk
CC NO 1111049 **ESTABLISHED** 2005

■ County Durham Foundation

WHERE FUNDING CAN BE GIVEN Durham and Darlington.
WHO CAN BENEFIT Community groups and grassroots organisations seeking to improve the quality of life in their local area, particularly those aiming to combat poverty and disadvantage or promote a more equitable and just society. Applications from branches of UK organisations will only be considered if they are able to demonstrate financial independence.
WHAT IS FUNDED The foundation encourages applications from groups working in the following areas: children and young people – groups and projects that help children and young people access activities and services where they play a key role in the decision making; vulnerable people – groups and projects working with disadvantaged people, in particular providing increased access to services and facilities for people with disabilities, the homeless and older people; community regeneration – local partnerships plus residents and tenants' associations that aim to improve health, education, reduce crime levels (and improve community safety) and to regenerate employment, housing and the physical environment with the support of their local community; self-help groups – community based, small self-help groups who deliver basic services; environmental improvements – small-scale environmental projects particularly improvements to community held land; education, capacity and skills development – group and community-based training and education programmes, particularly for those who have had no previous access to training opportunities; health – groups and community based projects providing access to healthy eating, increased physical activity and self-help services, which aim to improve the health and well being of communities; and in particular applications from groups working in rural areas.
WHAT IS NOT FUNDED The foundation will not fund: projects outside County Durham and Darlington; national or regional charities with no independent office in County Durham or Darlington; groups that have more than one year's running costs held as free reserves; projects which should be funded by a statutory body; sponsored events; improvements to land that is not open to the general public at convenient hours; projects promoting political activities; deficit or retrospective funding; faith groups promoting religious, community based activities. Funding is not normally given for: medical research and equipment; school projects; animal welfare; general contributions to large appeals (but specific items can be funded); building or buying premises and freehold or leasehold land rights; minibuses or other vehicles; overseas travel; grants for more than one year. Some of the programmes have other exclusions. If your project is at all unusual please contact the foundation to discuss your application before submitting it.
TYPE OF GRANT Various depending on funding criteria.
FINANCES *Year* 2007–08 *Income* £3,009,349 *Grants* £1,849,509 *Assets* £6,398,151
TRUSTEES Andrew Martell; David Watson; Lady Sarah Nicholson; Katherine Welch; John Hamilton; Mark I'anson; Michele Armstrong; David Martin; Christopher Lendrum; Richard Tonks; Ada Burns; Prof. Tim Blackman; Alex Worrall; Gerald Osborne; George Garlick.

PUBLICATIONS Newsletter, information leaflets, grant guidelines and application forms.

OTHER INFORMATION The grant total includes £205,000 given in individual grants.

HOW TO APPLY An expression of interest form should be completed in the first instance instead of a full application form. This can be downloaded, completed online or requested from the foundation by post or telephone. If the foundation feels that the project meets the criteria for one of its funds applicants will then be asked to complete a full application form. This system is designed to save organisations time in completing a detailed application for a project that may not be supported. There are exceptions to this procedure and applicants should view the website or contact the correspondent for further information. The foundation has a variety of grant programmes running, with new ones being added all the time. It supports groups, projects and individuals mainly in County Durham and Darlington, and in some circumstances, individuals in the north east. Organisations which are not registered charities are considered but must be a not-for-profit organisation that is benevolent, charitable or philanthropic and established to alleviate disadvantage in the community.

WHO TO APPLY TO Barbara Gubbins, Chief Executive, Jordan House, Forster Business Centre, Finchale Road, Durham DH1 5HL *Tel* 0191 383 0055 *Fax* 0191 383 2969 *email* info@countydurhamfoundation.co.uk *Website* www.countydurhamfoundation.co.uk

CC NO 1047625   **ESTABLISHED** 1995

■ The Augustine Courtauld Trust

WHERE FUNDING CAN BE GIVEN UK, with a preference for Essex.

WHO CAN BENEFIT Registered charities benefiting people in Essex and explorers.

WHAT IS FUNDED General charitable purposes, but mostly organisations in Essex working with young people who are disadvantaged and conservation. Exploration of the Arctic and Antarctic regions are also supported. Preference is given to charities which the trust has a special interest in, knowledge of or association with.

WHAT IS NOT FUNDED No grants to individuals. No grants to individual churches for fabric repairs or maintenance.

TYPE OF GRANT One-off grants for projects and core costs, which may be made for multiple years if an application is submitted for each year.

RANGE OF GRANTS £500–£8,000. Normally in the range of £500–£2,000.

SAMPLE GRANTS Friends of Essex Churches (£7,000); Essex Association of Boys Clubs (£4,500); the Cirdan Sailing Trust (£4,000); Rural Community Council of Essex (£2,400); Stubbers (£2,500); College of St Mark – Audley End and Prader Willi Syndrome Association UK (£2,000 each); Depaul Trust, RNLI – Eastern Region and St Luke's Hospice – Basildon (£1,000 each); and Acorn Villages and Colchester Emergency Night Shelter (£500 each).

FINANCES *Year* 2007–08 *Income* £56,059 *Grants* £63,650 *Assets* £1,198,033

TRUSTEES Revd. A C C Courtauld; The Lord Lieutenant of Essex; The Bishop of Chelmsford; Julien Courtauld; D E Fordham; Lieutenant General Sir Anthony Denison-Smith; T J R Courtauld; W M Courtauld.

OTHER INFORMATION This trust was founded in 1956 by Augustine Courtauld, an Arctic explorer who was proud of his Essex roots. His charitable purpose was simple: 'my idea is to make available something that will do some good.'

HOW TO APPLY Applications must be submitted via the online form on the trust's website. Written applications will not be accepted.

WHO TO APPLY TO Bruce Ballard, Clerk, Birkett Ballard, No. 1 Legg Street, Chelmsford, Essex CM1 1JS *Website* www.augustinecourtauldtrust.org

CC NO 226217   **ESTABLISHED** 1956

■ Coutts Charitable Trust

WHERE FUNDING CAN BE GIVEN UK, preference is given to areas where Coutts and Co. has a physical presence, specifically London.

WHO CAN BENEFIT UK registered charities.

WHAT IS FUNDED 'Charities supported include those involved with helping the homeless, rehabilitation and teaching self-help (drug; alcohol; young offenders), disabled (both physically and mentally) disadvantaged adults and children, youth organisations, older people, medical research, heritage, education and the relief of poverty.'

WHAT IS NOT FUNDED No response to circular appeals. No support for appeals from individuals or overseas projects.

TYPE OF GRANT Regular annual grants and one-off for specific projects.

RANGE OF GRANTS Most donations are in the range of £500–£1,000 'where a comparatively small amount can still make a great difference'. Many donations are between £1,000 and £2,000 with a portion of the charitable budget being used for larger donations.

FINANCES *Year* 2007–08 *Income* £876,497 *Grants* £869,703 *Assets* £133,704

TRUSTEES The Earl of Home, Peregrine Banbury, Mrs Sally Doyle, Gerald L Bailey; Mrs Wendy Butler

HOW TO APPLY In writing to the correspondent, at any time. Applications should include clear details of the purpose for which the grant is required. Grants are made regularly where amounts between £500 and £1,000. are deemed to be appropriate. The trustees meet quarterly to consider larger donations.

WHO TO APPLY TO Mrs C Attwater, Trust Administrator, 440 Strand, London WC2R 0QS *Tel* 020 7753 1000 *email* carole.attwater@coutts.com

CC NO 1000135   **ESTABLISHED** 1987

■ General Charity of Coventry

WHERE FUNDING CAN BE GIVEN Within the boundary of the City of Coventry.

WHO CAN BENEFIT People in need, children, young and older people, disabled (physically or mentally), people in need of social or health care and organisations that would benefit such people in the City of Coventry.

WHAT IS FUNDED Welfare.

WHAT IS NOT FUNDED No grants to organisations outside Coventry, or for holidays unless of a recuperative nature.

TYPE OF GRANT Pensions, relief in need and educational award bursaries.

RANGE OF GRANTS Up to £50,000.

SAMPLE GRANTS Myton Hospice Coventry (£50,000); David Scott's Coventry Jubilee Community Care Trust (£45,000); Tiny Tim's Children's Centre (£35,000); Community Transport and Air

Ambulance Service (£30,000 each); Enterprise Club for Disabled People (£20,000); Coventry Cathedral (£10,000); the West Midlands Special Schools Team Championship (£8,000); University Hospital – Coventry (£5,000); and the Lighthouse Christian Care Ministry (£2,500).

FINANCES *Year* 2008 *Income* £1,341,403 *Grants* £1,220,931 *Assets* £7,392,960

TRUSTEES D J Evans (Chair); M J Harris; Dr C A Rhodes; Mrs M Weitzel; D Mason; T Proctor; R Barker; Mrs E Eaves; E Curtis; H Richards; W Thompson; Cllr N Lee; Mrs H Johnson; P Robinson; Cllr J Harrison; Cllr G Crookes; Mrs H Machlachlan; Cllr M Lapsa.

OTHER INFORMATION During the year, £266,000 was awarded in grants to individuals.

HOW TO APPLY In writing to the correspondent. Applications are not accepted directly from the general public for relief in need (individuals).

WHO TO APPLY TO Mrs V A Tosh, Clerk to the Trustees, General Charities Office, Old Bablake, Hill Street, Coventry CV1 4AN *Tel* 024 7622 2769 *Fax* 024 7622 2769 *email* cov.genchar@virgin.net

CC NO 216235   **ESTABLISHED** 1983

■ Coventry Building Society Charitable Foundation

WHERE FUNDING CAN BE GIVEN The Midlands.

WHO CAN BENEFIT Registered charities.

WHAT IS FUNDED A wide range of causes based, or active, in the Midlands, with a preference for smaller local charities.

WHAT IS NOT FUNDED No grants can be given outside of the Midlands area. The following are not eligible for support: large charities which enjoy national coverage; charities with no base within the branch area; charities with an annual donated income in excess of £2500,000; charities with assets over £500,000; projects requiring ongoing commitment; large capital projects; maintenance or building works for buildings, gardens or playgrounds; major fundraising; projects which are normally the responsibility of other organisations such as NHS and local authorities; sponsorship of individuals; requests from individuals; replacing funds which were the responsibility of another body; educational institutions, unless for the relief of disadvantage; promotion of religious, political or military causes; sporting clubs or organisations, unless for the relief of disadvantage; medical research or equipment; more than one donation to the same organisation in a year – further applications will be considered after a period of three years; animal welfare.

TYPE OF GRANT One-off.

RANGE OF GRANTS Up to £3,000, but, generally £500–£2,000.

SAMPLE GRANTS The Albrighton Trust, Bereavement Cruse Care, Dream Maker's Children's Charity and Kings Community Church (£3,000 each); Tettenhall Wood School (£2,500); Abacus Counselling Services (£2,400); Children with Cystic Fibrosis Dream Holidays, City of Coventry Scout Association and Victim Support Warwickshire (£2,000); Birmingham Centre for Arts Therapies and Sport 4 Life UK (£1,500 each); and Citizen Advocacy Solihull (£1,000).

FINANCES *Year* 2007 *Income* £52,334 *Grants* £75,200 *Assets* £13,037

TRUSTEES M Judge; J Rushton; Ms Y J White; Ms C Arnold; P Walters.

HOW TO APPLY On an application form available online or from the correspondent. This should be returned together with any supporting documentation. In some circumstances the foundation may request further information before considering the application. The trustees meet quarterly, in February, May, August and November.

WHO TO APPLY TO Anna Cuskin, Oakfield House, Po Box 600, Binley, Coventry CV3 9YR *Website* www.coventrybuildingsociety.co.uk

CC NO 1072244   **ESTABLISHED** 1998

■ The John Cowan Foundation

WHERE FUNDING CAN BE GIVEN UK (national charities) and Surrey (community projects).

WHO CAN BENEFIT Charitable organisations.

WHAT IS FUNDED The foundation makes grants to purely local causes apart from national established charities. Charitable support will be considered for: oncology, hospices, hospices at home, medical transport, youth work, almshouses, community and social centres, Alzheimer's disease, arthritis and rheumatism, cancers, heart disease, motor neurone disease, terminal illness and sight loss. Grants range from £25 to £20,000.

WHAT IS NOT FUNDED No support for individuals, community projects outside Surrey area, or overseas projects.

RANGE OF GRANTS Usually up to £5,000.

SAMPLE GRANTS Surrey Air Ambulance (£5,000); Chelsham Field Project (£4,700); Surrey Community Development Trust, The Prince's Trust, British Wheelchair Sports Foundation and South East Cancer Help Centre (£2,000 each); Marie Curie Centre (£1,500); War Memorials Trust, the Orpheus Centre and the Blue Cross (£1,000 each); and Open Door Youth Counselling Service and Deafblind UK (£500 each).

FINANCES *Year* 2007–08 *Income* £39,533 *Grants* £46,577 *Assets* £691,555

TRUSTEES C E Foster; S J Arkoulis; J C Arkoulis

HOW TO APPLY In writing to the correspondent.

WHO TO APPLY TO Mrs C E Foster, Trustee, 12 Kingswood Place, 119 Croydon Road, Caterham, Surrey CR3 6DJ *Tel* 01883 344930 *email* joram@freenet.co.uk

CC NO 327613   **ESTABLISHED** 1987

■ The Sir Tom Cowie Charitable Trust

WHERE FUNDING CAN BE GIVEN City of Sunderland and County Durham.

WHO CAN BENEFIT Young people, older people, the infirm and disabled, poor or needy people due to social and/or economic circumstances.

WHAT IS FUNDED General charitable purposes.

RANGE OF GRANTS £500–£20,000.

SAMPLE GRANTS Villa Real School (£20,000); Variety Club – Durham Trinity Sunshine Bus (£19,000); Children's Hope Foundation (£12,000); Sunderland Laverneo (£7,000); Starlight Children's Foundation (£3,000); and Durham Association of Clubs for Young People (£1,000).

FINANCES *Year* 2008–09 *Income* £256,162 *Grants* £70,924 *Assets* £3,634,865

TRUSTEES Sir Tom Cowie; Peter Blackett; David Gray; Lady Diana Cowie.

HOW TO APPLY In writing to the correspondent.

WHO TO APPLY TO Loraine Maddison, Estate Office, Broadwood Hall, Lanchester, Durham DH7 0TN
Tel 01207 529 663 *email* lorraine@sirtomcowie.com
CC NO 1096936   **ESTABLISHED** 2003

■ Cowley Charitable Foundation

WHERE FUNDING CAN BE GIVEN Worldwide, with some preference for south Buckinghamshire and the Aylesbury area.
WHO CAN BENEFIT Registered charities.
WHAT IS FUNDED General charitable purposes.
WHAT IS NOT FUNDED No grants to non-registered charities. No grants to individuals, or for causes supposed to be serviced by public funds or with a scope considered to be too narrow.
TYPE OF GRANT One-off donations for development, capital projects and project funding.
RANGE OF GRANTS Usually £1,000–£2,000.
SAMPLE GRANTS Thinking Foundation (£11,000); International Dark Sky Association – USA (£9,000); Chase – Christopher's Children's Hospice and War Memorials Trust (£5,000 each); Against Malaria Foundation, Médecins Sans Frontières and Wordsworth Trust (£1,500 each); Age Concern Buckinghamshire, Live Music Now! and John Soames Museum (£1,000 each); Pere Jean Zambe (£800); Trinity Hospice and YMCA (£500 each); and Artists General Benevolent Fund (£200).
FINANCES *Year* 2007–08 *Income* £48,951 *Grants* £54,000 *Assets* £866,414
TRUSTEES 140 Trustee Co. Ltd; Mrs H M M Cullen.
HOW TO APPLY The trust states that unsolicited applications are not invited, and that the trustees carry out their own research into charities.
WHO TO APPLY TO The Secretary, 140 Trustee Co. Ltd, 36 Broadway, London SW1H 0BH
CC NO 270682   **ESTABLISHED** 1973

■ The Sir William Coxen Trust Fund

WHERE FUNDING CAN BE GIVEN England.
WHO CAN BENEFIT Hospitals or charitable institutions carrying out orthopaedic work.
WHAT IS FUNDED Hospitals and other charitable institutions in England carrying out orthopaedic work, particularly in respect of children.
WHAT IS NOT FUNDED No grants to individuals or non-charitable institutions.
TYPE OF GRANT One-off grants and research fellowships.
SAMPLE GRANTS Action for Kids, Brainwave, Motability, Neuromuscular Centre, SCAT and Torch (£5,000 each); Bobath Centre, DEMAND, the Foundation for Conductive Education and Strongbones (£4,000 each); MERU and Pace Centre (£3,000 each); St Luke's Hospital (£2,900); and Daisy Chain Children's Trust (£2,100).
FINANCES *Year* 2007–08 *Income* £70,523 *Grants* £79,000 *Assets* £1,831,052
TRUSTEES Six Aldermen appointed by the Court of Aldermen, together with the Lord Mayor.
HOW TO APPLY In writing to the correspondent.
WHO TO APPLY TO The Trustees, The Town Clerk's Office, City of London, PO Box 270, Guildhall, London EC2P 2EJ
CC NO 206936   **ESTABLISHED** 1940

■ The Lord Cozens-Hardy Trust

WHERE FUNDING CAN BE GIVEN UK with a preference for Merseyside and Norfolk.
WHO CAN BENEFIT Registered charities.
WHAT IS FUNDED General charitable purposes with a particular interest in supporting medical and education causes.
WHAT IS NOT FUNDED No grants to individuals.
TYPE OF GRANT One-off and recurrent.
RANGE OF GRANTS Up to £20,000, mostly for smaller amounts of £5,000 or less.
SAMPLE GRANTS Norfolk and Norwich Association for the Blind (£20,000); East Anglian Air Ambulance, North West Air Ambulance and YESU (£5,000 each); Raleigh International Trust (£1,250); Breast Cancer Campaign, Liverpool School of Tropical Medicine, Norfolk and Norwich Association for the Blind, The Prince's Trust, Hospital of St John, Salvation Army and World Association of Girl Guides and Girl Scouts (£1,000).
FINANCES *Year* 2007–08 *Income* £144,253 *Grants* £78,050 *Assets* £2,744,980
TRUSTEES Hon. Beryl Cozens-Hardy; J E V Phelps; Mrs L F Phelps; J J P Ripman.
HOW TO APPLY In writing to the correspondent. Applications are reviewed quarterly.
WHO TO APPLY TO The Trustees, PO Box 28, Holt, Norfolk NR25 7WH
CC NO 264237   **ESTABLISHED** 1972

■ The Craignish Trust

WHERE FUNDING CAN BE GIVEN UK, with a preference for Scotland.
WHO CAN BENEFIT Charitable organisations.
WHAT IS FUNDED Projects that promote the welfare of the local community, particularly through the arts, education and the environment. Projects of special interest to the trustees.
WHAT IS NOT FUNDED Running costs are not normally supported.
TYPE OF GRANT Project grants.
RANGE OF GRANTS £500–£7,500.
SAMPLE GRANTS Previous beneficiaries have included Art in Healthcare, Boilerhouse Theatre Company Ltd, Butterfly Conservation – Scotland, Cairndow Arts Promotions, Centre for Alternative Technology, Edinburgh International Book Festival, Edinburgh Royal Choral Union, Friends of the Earth Scotland, Human Rights Watch Charitable Trust and Soil Association Scotland.
FINANCES *Year* 2007–08 *Income* £171,251
TRUSTEES Ms M Matheson; J Roberts; Ms C Younger.
HOW TO APPLY There is no formal application form; applicants should write to the correspondent. Details of the project should be included together with a copy of the most recent audited accounts.
WHO TO APPLY TO The Trustees, c/o Geoghegan and Co, 6 St Colme Street, Edinburgh EH3 6AD
SC NO SC016882   **ESTABLISHED** 1961

■ The Craps Charitable Trust

WHERE FUNDING CAN BE GIVEN UK, Israel.
WHO CAN BENEFIT Charitable organisations.
WHAT IS FUNDED General charitable purposes, particularly Jewish organisations. It is not the policy of the trustees to make grants in response to appeals addressed to them, and applications will not be acknowledged.
RANGE OF GRANTS Up to £25,000.

SAMPLE GRANTS British Technion Society (£25,000); Jewish Care (£20,000); British WIZO (£16,000); Friends of the Hebrew University (£14,000); JNF Charitable Trust (£13,000); the New Israel Fund (£12,000); and Jerusalem Foundation (£11,000); CBF World Jewish Relief (£5,000); British Friends of Haifa University (£4,000); Motor Neurone Disease Association (£2,000); Amnesty International (£1,000); and B'nai B'rith Hillel Foundation (£1,000).

FINANCES *Year* 2007–08 *Income* £258,860 *Grants* £177,000 *Assets* £3,640,920

TRUSTEES J P M Dent; Miss C S Dent; Miss L R Dent.

HOW TO APPLY The trust states that 'funds of the trust are fully committed and the trust does not invite applications for its funds'.

WHO TO APPLY TO The Trustees, 3rd Floor, Bryanston Court, Selden Hill, Hemel Hempstead, Hertfordshire HP2 4TN

CC NO 271492   **ESTABLISHED** 1976

■ Michael Crawford Children's Charity

WHERE FUNDING CAN BE GIVEN UK.

WHO CAN BENEFIT Children and young adults, especially those disadvantaged by poverty and/or illness.

WHAT IS FUNDED Children and young people, and in particular the relief of sickness and the relief of poverty.

WHAT IS NOT FUNDED No grants for school fees and living expenses, travel and other expenses for 'year out' projects, conferences and so on.

TYPE OF GRANT Mainly capital grants.

SAMPLE GRANTS Previously £13,500 to Sick Children's Trust.

FINANCES *Year* 2007–08 *Income* £290,486 *Grants* £81,996 *Assets* £2,804,218

TRUSTEES M P Crawford, Chair; M D Paisner; K P Dias; A Clark.

HOW TO APPLY In writing to the correspondent. Grants are made half yearly and are considered in April and October of each year. Only successful applicants will be notified.

WHO TO APPLY TO K P Dias, Trustee, Regina House, 124 Finchley Road, London NW3 5JS *Tel* 020 7433 2400 *Fax* 020 7433 2491

CC NO 1042211   **ESTABLISHED** 1994

■ The Cray Trust

WHERE FUNDING CAN BE GIVEN Mainly the east of Scotland.

WHO CAN BENEFIT Charitable organisations.

WHAT IS FUNDED General charitable purposes.

WHAT IS NOT FUNDED No support for political appeals and large UK or international charities. No grants to individuals.

RANGE OF GRANTS £100–£260,000. Average grant size in 2008–09 was £2,337.

SAMPLE GRANTS Charitable Assets Trust (£260,000); Canine Partners, Equibuddy and Equine Grass Sickness Fund (£5,000 each); Princess Royal Trust for Carers (£4,500); Alzheimer's Scotland (£2,000); Cherish India (£1,400); Backup Trust and Barnardos Scotland (£1,300 each); the Priory Church (£1,200); and Rainbow RDA (£1,000).

FINANCES *Year* 2008–09 *Income* £76,900 *Grants* £313,180 *Assets* £1,076,636

TRUSTEES P R Gammell; J E B Gammell.

HOW TO APPLY This trust does not accept unsolicited applications.

WHO TO APPLY TO The Trustees, c/o Springfords Accountants, Dundas House, Westfield Park, Eskbank, Midlothian EH22 3FB

SC NO SC005592   **ESTABLISHED** 1976

■ The Crescent Trust

WHERE FUNDING CAN BE GIVEN UK.

WHO CAN BENEFIT Charitable organisations.

WHAT IS FUNDED The arts (especially larger museums), heritage and ecology. Smaller grants are mainly given in the medical field. Only specific charities of which the trustees have personal knowledge are supported.

TYPE OF GRANT One-off and recurrent.

RANGE OF GRANTS £250–£43,000.

SAMPLE GRANTS The Fitzwilliam Museum (£45,000); National Gallery of Scotland (£40,000); the Louvre Museum (£10,000); the Attingham Trust and the Watts Gallery (£5,000 each); Museum of Garden History (£1,500); Broadway Central Office and Over the Wall (£1,000 each); Chase Hospice Care for Children, Chelsea Pensioners and Save the Children (£250 each); and AIDS Ark (£100).

FINANCES *Year* 2007–08 *Income* £42,706 *Grants* £109,430 *Assets* £332,893

TRUSTEES J C S Tham; R A F Lascelles.

HOW TO APPLY This trust states that it does not respond to unsolicited applications.

WHO TO APPLY TO Ms C Akehurst, 9 Queripel House, 1 Duke of York Square, London SW3 4LY

CC NO 327644   **ESTABLISHED** 1987

■ Criffel Charitable Trust

WHERE FUNDING CAN BE GIVEN UK and overseas.

WHO CAN BENEFIT Registered charities.

WHAT IS FUNDED The advancement of Christianity and the relief of poverty, sickness and other needs.

SAMPLE GRANTS St Giles Hospice (£61,000); Four Oaks Methodist Church (£28,000); Tear Fund (£11,000); and the Monkton Campaign (£10,000).

FINANCES *Year* 2007–08 *Income* £74,357 *Grants* £164,130 *Assets* £1,415,721

TRUSTEES J C Lees; Mrs J E Lees; Mrs J I Harvey.

HOW TO APPLY All funds are fully committed. The trust states that no applications are considered or acknowledged. Please do not apply.

WHO TO APPLY TO Mr and Mrs J C Lees, Trustees, Hillfield, 4 Wentworth Road, Sutton Coldfield, West Midlands B74 2SG

CC NO 1040680   **ESTABLISHED** 1994

■ Cripplegate Foundation

WHERE FUNDING CAN BE GIVEN London borough of Islington and part of the City of London.

WHO CAN BENEFIT Charitable organisations, schools and organisations working with schools and individuals.

WHAT IS FUNDED Grants which aim to improve the quality of life in the area of benefit and provide opportunities for local residents. There are three main themes: social cohesion, reducing poverty and inequality and increasing access to opportunities and making connections.

WHAT IS NOT FUNDED In the main grants programme no funding is given for: national charities or organisations outside the area of benefit; schemes or activities which would relieve central or local government of their statutory responsibilities; grants to replace cuts in funding made by the local authority or others; medical research or equipment; national fundraising appeals; advancement of religion unless the applicant also offers non-religious services to the community; animal welfare; retrospective grants; commercial or business activities; grants for events held in the church of St Giles-without Cripplegate; grants to organisations recruiting volunteers in south Islington for work overseas. In the individuals programme the following will not be funded: funeral costs; the purchase of computers; child care costs; money that has been stolen; items already bought or ordered; housing costs or council tax; repayment of debts; education needs (apart from school uniforms); wheelchairs or disability vehicles and scooters; grants for students not normally resident in the area of benefit.

TYPE OF GRANT Grants for core costs, project funding, salary costs and capital costs, often over more than one year.

RANGE OF GRANTS Up to £169,000.

SAMPLE GRANTS Mary Ward Legal Centre (£169,000); Islington Voluntary Action Council (£65,000); Urban Hope (£45,000); Writers in Schools Project (£32,000); Industrial Trust (£16,000); Clod Ensemble (£11,000); Step Together Dance Project and the Garden Classroom (£5,000 each); Inner City Films (£4,000); Golden Lane Campus (£2,700); and Islington Cyclists Action Group (£280).

FINANCES *Year* 2008 *Income* £2,541,510 *Grants* £1,518,462 *Assets* £26,333,697

TRUSTEES John Tomlinson; David Graves; Barbara Riddell; Paula Kahn; Judith Moran; Revd Katharine Rumens; Tom Jupp; Barry Edwards; John Gilbert; Lucy Watt; David Sulkin; Heather Lamont; Rob Hull; Mark Yeadon; Anne- Marie Ellis; Rob Abercrombie.

OTHER INFORMATION The grant total includes £136,000 given to individuals.

HOW TO APPLY Each programme has a different application form and deadline dates. Applicants are encouraged to telephone or email the foundation to discuss their project before making a full application. Full details of the application process are available on the foundation's helpful website.

WHO TO APPLY TO Kristina Glenn, Director, 76 Central Street, London EC1V 8AG *Tel* 020 7549 8181 *Fax* 020 7549 8180 *email* grants@cripplegate. org.uk *Website* www.cripplegate.org

CC NO 207499   **ESTABLISHED** 1891

■ The Violet and Milo Cripps Charitable Trust

WHERE FUNDING CAN BE GIVEN UK.

WHO CAN BENEFIT Charitable organisations.

WHAT IS FUNDED Prison and human rights organisations.

SAMPLE GRANTS Prison Reform Trust (£115,000); European Educational Research Trust (£50,000); Corpus Christi College (£35,000); the Prison Advice and Care Trust (£25,000); the New Bridge and Trinity Hospice (£20,000 each); and St Bernadette's Church (£6,500).

FINANCES *Year* 2007–08 *Income* £457,613 *Grants* £271,500 *Assets* £1,363,645

TRUSTEES Anthony J R Newhouse; Richard J Lithenthal; Jennifer Beattie.

OTHER INFORMATION The trust often gives more in grants than it receives in income.

HOW TO APPLY The trust states that unsolicited applications will not receive a response.

WHO TO APPLY TO The Trustees, 52 Bedford Row, London WC1R 4LR

CC NO 289404   **ESTABLISHED** 1984

■ The Cromarty Trust

WHERE FUNDING CAN BE GIVEN UK, with a preference for the Parish of Cromarty and Kent.

WHO CAN BENEFIT Charitable organisations.

WHAT IS FUNDED The trust supports organisations mainly concerned with: the preservation, maintenance or improvement of any buildings of beauty or historical or architectural interest; the conservation of natural features, the landscape, ecology and character of the area; the furtherance of general educational, religious and social amenities; the stimulation of public interest in the history, character, beauty and wildlife of the area.

SAMPLE GRANTS Cromarty Arts Trust (£7,000); Friends of Christ Church Spitalfields and North Down Society (£3,000 each); Cromarty and District Community Council (£2,000); Cromarty 2007 (£1,500); Somerville College (£1,000); Romney Marsh Historic Churches Trust (£400); and Friends of Wormshill Church (£350).

FINANCES *Year* 2007–08 *Income* £32,852 *Grants* £22,206 *Assets* £733,766

TRUSTEES John Nightingale of Cromarty; Alexander Nightingale; Rebecca Homfray.

HOW TO APPLY Applications are not invited as the trustees take a proactive approach to grantmaking and the development of projects which they wish to support.

WHO TO APPLY TO John Nightingale, Trustee, 25 West Square, London SE11 4SP

CC NO 272843   **ESTABLISHED** 1976

■ The Harry Crook Foundation

WHERE FUNDING CAN BE GIVEN Bristol.

WHO CAN BENEFIT Registered charities.

WHAT IS FUNDED In 2007 the trust informed us that it had decided to 'close' the fund to external application until further notice, with all available funds directed towards a single identified charity [Redland High School].

WHAT IS NOT FUNDED Medical research charities and charities serving need outside the boundaries of the City of Bristol. No grants to individuals.

SAMPLE GRANTS Redland High School (£31,000); All Hallows Restoration Fund (£5,000); and Exeter Cathedral Third Millennium Appeal (£1,000).

FINANCES *Year* 2007–08 *Income* £39,723 *Grants* £37,000 *Assets* £1,175,822

TRUSTEES R G West, Chair; J O Gough; D J Bellew; M C Manisty.

HOW TO APPLY In light of the foundation's 2007 resolution to 'close' the trust to external applications until further notice, any future applications to the trust will be ignored, 'no acknowledgement will be given, and, in particular, no consideration will be given to them.'

WHO TO APPLY TO D J Bellow, Trustee, Veale Wasbrough Lawyers, Orchard Court, Orchard Lane, Bristol BS1 5WS

CC NO 231470   **ESTABLISHED** 1963

Think carefully about every application. Is it justified?

459

■ The Cross Trust

WHERE FUNDING CAN BE GIVEN UK and overseas.

WHO CAN BENEFIT Individuals, and organisations benefiting Christians.

WHAT IS FUNDED Christian work.

TYPE OF GRANT One-off grants for core, capital and project support.

SAMPLE GRANTS The Areopagus Trust (£100,000); and the Kingham Hill Trust (£7,600). Previous beneficiaries included: Oakhill College, Friends of St Ebbe's Trust, Proclamation Trust, Friends International, Rock Foundation, Agape Missionaries, OMF Asia Interactive and St Andrews Partnership.

FINANCES *Year* 2007–08 *Income* £239,354 *Grants* £726,343 *Assets* £315,931

TRUSTEES Michael S Farmer; Mrs Jenny D Farmer; Douglas J Olsen.

HOW TO APPLY The trust has previously stated that no unsolicited applications are considered, and that funds are fully committed.

WHO TO APPLY TO David Stephenson, Cansdales, Bourbon Court, Nightingale Corner, Little Chalfont, Buckinghamshire HP7 9QS *Tel* 01494 765428 *email* davids@cansdales.co.uk

CC NO 298472   **ESTABLISHED** 1987

■ The Cross Trust

WHERE FUNDING CAN BE GIVEN Scotland.

WHO CAN BENEFIT Individuals and organisations.

WHAT IS FUNDED About 80% of the grants are given to individuals for educational purposes (including travel for their courses). Grants to organisations are normally made for music, drama or outdoor activities to benefit young people.

WHAT IS NOT FUNDED No retrospective applications will be considered.

TYPE OF GRANT Normally one-off, occasionally for longer periods.

FINANCES *Year* 2007–08 *Grants* £175,000

TRUSTEES Revd Hon R D Buchanan-Smith; Dr R H MacDougall; Dr A R MacGregor; Mrs Clare Orr; Dougal Philip; Mark Webster.

HOW TO APPLY Application forms and guidance notes are available from the correspondent.

WHO TO APPLY TO The Secretary, McCash and Hunter Solicitors, 25 South Methven Street, Perth PH1 5ES *Tel* 01738 620451 *email* crosstrust@mccash.co.uk *Website* www.thecrosstrust.org.uk

SC NO SC008620   **ESTABLISHED** 1943

■ The Croydon Relief in Need Charities

WHERE FUNDING CAN BE GIVEN The borough of Croydon.

WHO CAN BENEFIT Local charities and individuals.

WHAT IS FUNDED General, health and welfare.

TYPE OF GRANT Recurrent.

SAMPLE GRANTS Croydon Welcare (£100,000); the Garwood Foundation and Kick London – Croydon (£25,000 each); Croydon Drop In (£17,000); Age Concern – Croydon (£15,000); Darby & Joan Club (£12,500); RASASC (£10,000); Macmillan Cancer Support (£7,500); South East Cancer Help Centre (£5,000); Nightwatch (£3,500); and Thornton Heath District Girl Guides (£1,000).

FINANCES *Year* 2007 *Income* £239,155 *Grants* £225,426 *Assets* £29,572

TRUSTEES N P Hepworth, Chair; Mrs M Adigun-Boaye; Mrs B E Cripps; D J Cripps; Mrs T G Stewart; Mrs L A Talbot; Mrs C D A Trower;

Hon Alderman J L Aston; C P Clementi; Revd Canon C J L Boswell; A Galer; Mrs M Bourne.

OTHER INFORMATION In 2007 a grant was made to an individual via Aidis Trust.

HOW TO APPLY In writing to the correspondent.

WHO TO APPLY TO W B Rymer, Clerk, Elis David Almshouses, Duppas Hill Terrace, Croydon CR0 4BT

CC NO 810114   **ESTABLISHED** 1962

■ The Mayor of Croydon's Charity Fund

WHERE FUNDING CAN BE GIVEN Croydon.

WHO CAN BENEFIT Registered charities.

WHAT IS FUNDED General charitable purposes. The grantmaking of this trust is the prerogative of whichever mayor is in office in any particular year.

FINANCES *Year* 2007–08 *Income* £47,970 *Grants* £26,750 *Assets* £27,698

TRUSTEES Lea Goddard

HOW TO APPLY Unsolicited applications cannot be considered.

WHO TO APPLY TO Lea Goddard, Head of Registration Services, The Town Hall, Katharine Street, Croydon, Surrey CR9 1DE *Tel* 020 8760 5730 *email* lea.goddard@croydon.gov.uk *Website* www.croydon.gov.uk

CC NO 1042479   **ESTABLISHED** 1994

■ The Peter Cruddas Foundation

WHERE FUNDING CAN BE GIVEN UK, with a particular interest in London.

WHO CAN BENEFIT Registered charities, hospitals and other institutions.

WHAT IS FUNDED Children and young people. 'The foundation gives priority to programmes designed to help disadvantaged and disengaged young people to pursue their education (including vocational) and more generally develop their potential whether through sport or recreation, voluntary programmes or otherwise. Preference will be given to the support of projects undertaken by charitable organisations for the benefit of such people. Consideration may be also given in certain circumstances for individual support but only on referral from appropriate sponsor organisations.'

TYPE OF GRANT One-off and recurrent grants for capital and revenue costs.

SAMPLE GRANTS The Dean and Canons of Windsor – College of St George (£1.49 million); The Prince's Trust (£500,000); Duke of Edinburgh Awards (£499,500); The National Osteoporosis Society (£375,000); Royal Opera House Foundation (£241,000); Harris Manchester College (£224,000); Policy Exchange Limited (£140,000); The Royal Hospital Chelsea and Coram (£100,000 each); Tick Tock Club – Great Ormond Street Children's Hospital (£75,000); The Chichester Festival Theatre (£50,000); Young Adult Trust (£20,000); Heart Cells Foundation (£12,000); Dementia (£10,000); and the Willow Foundation (£2,000).

FINANCES *Year* 2007–08 *Income* £3,077,991 *Grants* £3,882,462

TRUSTEES Lord David Young, Chair; Peter Cruddas; Martin Paisner.

HOW TO APPLY On an application form available to download from the foundation's website. The foundation provides guidance on how to complete the application form, also available on the website.

WHO TO APPLY TO Stephen D Cox, Administrator, 66 Prescot Street, London E1 8HG *Tel* 020 3003 8360 *Fax* 020 3003 8580 *email* s.cox@ pcfoundation.org.uk *Website* www. petercruddasfoundation.org.uk
CC NO 1117323   **ESTABLISHED** 2006

■ Cruden Foundation Ltd

WHERE FUNDING CAN BE GIVEN Mainly Scotland.
WHO CAN BENEFIT Registered charities.
WHAT IS FUNDED General charitable purposes.
WHAT IS NOT FUNDED No grants to individuals.
TYPE OF GRANT Recurrent and one-off.
RANGE OF GRANTS Up to £15,000.
SAMPLE GRANTS Edinburgh International Festival (£15,000); Friends of Carberry and Gartmore (£10,000); Edinburgh Headway Group (£8,000); Marie Curie Cancer Care Scotland (£5,000); Edinburgh Academy Foundation (£2,500); Children 1st (£2,000); and Glasgow School of Art (£2,000).
FINANCES *Year* 2007–08 *Income* £386,140 *Grants* £314,145 *Assets* £5,180,477
TRUSTEES N Lessels, Chair; M R A Matthews; J G Mitchell; A Johnston; M J Rowley; D D Walker; K D Reid.
HOW TO APPLY In writing to the correspondent.
WHO TO APPLY TO M R A Matthews, Secretary, Baberton House, Juniper Green, Edinburgh EH14 3HN
SC NO SC004987   **ESTABLISHED** 1956

■ The Ronald Cruickshanks' Foundation

WHERE FUNDING CAN BE GIVEN UK, with some preference for Folkestone, Faversham and the surrounding area.
WHO CAN BENEFIT Individuals and organisations, including various local churches.
WHAT IS FUNDED General charitable purposes, but particularly for the benefit of people in financial and other need within the stated beneficial area.
TYPE OF GRANT Recurrent.
RANGE OF GRANTS £250–£7,000.
SAMPLE GRANTS Demelza House Children's Hospice and the Pilgrims Hospice – Canterbury (£7,000 each); Kent Air Ambulance (£3,500); Folkestone Town Mayor's Christmas Fund (£3,000); Jesuit Missions (£2,500); Canterbury Cathedral Appeal (£2,000); Age Concern – Folkestone (£1,500); British Red Cross and St Joseph's – Cheriton (£1,000 each); St Nicholas Church – Newington (£750); Hospice in the Weald (£500); and Home-Start Shepway (£250).
FINANCES *Year* 2007–08 *Income* £222,926 *Grants* £122,750 *Assets* £1,777,008
TRUSTEES I F Cloke, Chair; J S Schilder; Mrs S E Cloke.
HOW TO APPLY In writing to the correspondent. Applications should be received by the end of September for consideration on a date coinciding closely with the anniversary of the death of the founder, which was 7 December.
WHO TO APPLY TO I F Cloke, Trustee, 34 Cheriton Gardens, Folkestone, Kent CT20 2AX
CC NO 296075   **ESTABLISHED** 1987

■ Cuby Charitable Trust

WHERE FUNDING CAN BE GIVEN UK, overseas.
WHO CAN BENEFIT Registered charities.
WHAT IS FUNDED Jewish causes.
FINANCES *Year* 2007–08 *Income* £311,014 *Grants* £267,045 *Assets* £233,835
TRUSTEES S S Cuby, Chair; Mrs C B Cuby.
HOW TO APPLY In writing to the correspondent.
WHO TO APPLY TO C B Cuby, Secretary, 16 Mowbray Road, Edgware, Middlesex HA8 8JQ
CC NO 328585   **ESTABLISHED** 1990

■ Cullum Family Trust

WHERE FUNDING CAN BE GIVEN UK.
WHO CAN BENEFIT Registered charities and institutions.
WHAT IS FUNDED Social welfare, education and general charitable purposes.
SAMPLE GRANTS Kids Company (£166,000); City of Norwich School (£105,000); Sussex Community Foundation (£75,000); and the Born Free Foundation (£50,000).
FINANCES *Year* 2007–08 *Income* £11,087,824 *Grants* £406,350 *Assets* £17,893,744
TRUSTEES Peter Geoffrey Cullum; Ann Cullum; Claire Louise Cullum; Simon Timothy Cullum.
HOW TO APPLY In writing to the correspondent.
WHO TO APPLY TO Peter Geoffrey Cullum, Trustee, Wealden Hall, Parkfield, Sevenoaks, Kent TN15 0HX
CC NO 1117056   **ESTABLISHED** 2006

■ The Culra Charitable Trust

WHERE FUNDING CAN BE GIVEN UK.
WHO CAN BENEFIT Registered charities only.
WHAT IS FUNDED General charitable purposes.
WHAT IS NOT FUNDED Grants are not given to non-registered charities or individuals.
SAMPLE GRANTS Royal Air Force Benevolent Fund (£6,000); and Birchfield Educational Trust Ltd (£3,000).
FINANCES *Year* 2007–08 *Income* £29,206 *Grants* £26,750 *Assets* £589,483
TRUSTEES C Byam-Cook; P J Sienesi; G Needham; G Francis.
HOW TO APPLY The trust tends to support organisations known to the trustees, rather than responding to unsolicited applications. The trustees meet twice a year.
WHO TO APPLY TO Stephen Tuck, 1 College Hill, London EC4R 2RA
CC NO 274612   **ESTABLISHED** 1977

■ The Cumber Family Charitable Trust

WHERE FUNDING CAN BE GIVEN Worldwide, with a preference for the developing world and Berkshire and Oxfordshire.
WHO CAN BENEFIT Individuals and organisations.
WHAT IS FUNDED Health, homelessness, disability, welfare, rural development, housing, overseas aid, Christian aid, agricultural development, young people's and children's welfare and education. About 50% of the funding given is for work overseas.
WHAT IS NOT FUNDED No grants for animal welfare. Only very few to individuals with local connections and who are personally known to the trustees are supported. Local appeals outside Berkshire and Oxfordshire are not usually supported.

TYPE OF GRANT Usually single grant, not repeated within three years. Occasionally support up to three years for a project.

RANGE OF GRANTS £250–£3,000.

SAMPLE GRANTS RABI (£5,000); Vale and Ridgeway Trust (£3,000); Alzheimer's Research Trust and Maggie's Cancer Caring Centres (£2,000 each); Build Africa, Home Start Southern Oxfordshire, the Respite Association and Tools for Self Reliance (£1,000 each); Sunningwell School of Art (£600); Independence at Home, Microloan Foundation, Oxfordshire Playbus and Slough Furniture Project (£500 each); and the Titus Trust (£250).

FINANCES *Year* 2007–08 *Income* £51,489 *Grants* £55,600 *Assets* £827,277

TRUSTEES A R Davey; W Cumber; Mrs M J Cumber; Mrs M J Freeman; Mrs M E Tearney; Mrs J E Mearns.

HOW TO APPLY In writing to the correspondent. The trustees usually meet twice a year.

WHO TO APPLY TO Mrs M E Tearney, Trustee, Manor Farm, Marcham, Abingdon, Oxfordshire OX13 6NZ *Tel* 01865 391327

CC NO 291009   **ESTABLISHED** 1985

■ Cumberland Building Society Charitable Foundation

WHERE FUNDING CAN BE GIVEN Cumbria, Dumfries and Galloway, Lancashire (Preston area) and Northumberland (Haltwhistle area).

WHO CAN BENEFIT Registered charities.

WHAT IS FUNDED General charitable purposes in areas where the trustees determine Cumberland Building Society operates.

WHAT IS NOT FUNDED No grants to non-registered charities and those working outside the operating area.

RANGE OF GRANTS Up to £1,000.

SAMPLE GRANTS Previous beneficiaries have included Children's Heart Federation, Community Action Furness, Community Transport South Lakeland, Currock House Association, DebRA, the Food Train, the Genesis Appeal, Hospice at Home, L'Arche Preston and St John Ambulance.

FINANCES *Year* 2007–08 *Income* £28,657 *Grants* £35,795 *Assets* £24,212

TRUSTEES Rev J Libby, Chair; E Amos; Mrs J Thomson; W R Wilkinson; Mrs C Graham; J R Carr.

HOW TO APPLY In writing to the correspondent.

WHO TO APPLY TO The Administrator, Cumberland House, Castle Street, Carlisle CA3 8RX *Tel* 01228 541341 *email* charitablefoundation@cumberland.co.uk *Website* www.cumberlandbanking. com/about/community/charitable-foundation

CC NO 1072435   **ESTABLISHED** 1998

■ Cumbria Community Foundation

WHERE FUNDING CAN BE GIVEN Cumbria.

WHO CAN BENEFIT Organisations and individuals under several different programmes.

WHAT IS FUNDED Improving the quality of the community life of people in Cumbria, and in particular those in need by reason of disability, age, low-income or other disadvantage.

WHAT IS NOT FUNDED The following are not supported: animal welfare; deficit funding; general large appeals; boxing clubs; medical research and equipment; non-Cumbrian projects; sponsored events; replacement of statutory funding; projects that have already happened;

applications where you have had a grant from that fund within the last year (except Grassroots Grants); and individuals (except for specific funds). Please contact the foundation for information on any individual restrictions on any of the grant programmes.

TYPE OF GRANT One off and recurring.

RANGE OF GRANTS About £500–£13,000.

SAMPLE GRANTS Salterbeck Alliance for Community Enterprise Ltd – two grants (£13,000); Cumbria Alcohol and Drug Advisory Service and Interchoc Co-operative Society Ltd (£10,000 each); Works 4 You Ltd – Cleator Moor (£8,000); Allerdale YouthBank and Cumbria Federation of Young Farmers' Clubs (£7,000 each); Kendal School of Gymnastics (£6,300); Lakeland Orienteering Club (£6,000); Belle Vue Church – Carlisle (£5,600); and South Tynedale Railway Preservation Society, Alston Producers' Markets, Pitstop Project Barrow, West Cumbria Carers and Allerdale Disability Association (£5,000 each).

FINANCES *Year* 2007–08 *Income* £1,641,407 *Grants* £1,024,266 *Assets* £3,350,448

TRUSTEES Peter Hensman; Ian Brown; Derek Lyon; Eric Apperley; June Chapman; Susan Aglionby; David Brown; James Carr; Chris Coombes; Rob Cairns; Elaine Woodburn; Trevor Hebdon; Bob Mather; Robin Burgess; Heike Horsburgh; Sarah Dunning; Shirley Williams; Dick Raaz; Stewart Young; Peter Stybelski; Catherine Alexander; Christine Hughes; Mike Casson.

HOW TO APPLY Application forms and clear and full guidelines for each of the foundation's programmes are available to download on the foundation's website or by contacting the correspondent directly. Applications should include the following supporting information: a copy of the organisation's governing document (not required for registered charities); a copy of the latest accounts (or bank statements covering the last quarter if the organisation has been operating for less than a year); details of an independent referee; a copy of the organisation's child protection or safeguarding policy (if the project will involve working with children and/or young people). The foundation prefers to receive applications via email, even if the supporting documents have to be sent by post. Applicants are encouraged to contact the foundation prior to making an application in order to confirm their eligibility. Applications are accepted throughout the year and decisions are usually taken within two months. Some programmes offer a faster process for small urgent projects.

WHO TO APPLY TO Andrew Beeforth, Director, Dovenby Hall, Dovenby, Cockermouth, Cumbria CA13 0PN *Tel* 01900 825 760 *Fax* 01900 826 527 *email* enquiries@cumbriafoundation.org *Website* www.cumbriafoundation.org

CC NO 1075120   **ESTABLISHED** 1999

■ The Cunningham Trust

WHERE FUNDING CAN BE GIVEN Scotland.

WHO CAN BENEFIT Mostly universities.

WHAT IS FUNDED Grants are made to university departments which are carrying out academic research in the field of medicine.

WHAT IS NOT FUNDED Grants are unlikely to be made available to non-regular beneficiaries.

TYPE OF GRANT Revenue and project funding for up to two years.

SAMPLE GRANTS Previous beneficiaries have included Aberdeen University – Department of Zoology, Aberdeen University – Department of

Ophthalmology, Department of Biomedical Sciences, Edinburgh University's Centre of Tropical Veterinary Medicine and St Andrew's University – School of Biomedical Sciences.
FINANCES *Year* 2007–08 *Income* £416,950
TRUSTEES Prof. C Blake; A C Caithness; Dr D McD Greenhough.
HOW TO APPLY All applications must be submitted on the standard form.
WHO TO APPLY TO The Trustees, Murray Donald and Caithness Solicitors, Kinburn Castle, St Andrews, Fife KY16 9DR
SC NO SC013499   **ESTABLISHED** 1984

■ The Harry Cureton Charitable Trust

WHERE FUNDING CAN BE GIVEN The area covered by Peterborough and Stamford hospitals.
WHO CAN BENEFIT Individuals and organisations.
WHAT IS FUNDED Medical, Health and Sickness.
FINANCES *Year* 2007–08 *Income* £38,366
Grants £260,138 *Assets* £2,976,054
TRUSTEES T P S Bhullar; R C Cooper; C N Monsell; N D Plumb; S D Richards.
HOW TO APPLY On a form which can be downloaded from the trust's website.
WHO TO APPLY TO C N Monsell, Trustee, c/o Greenwoods Solicitors LLP, Monkstone House, Peterborough PE1 1JE *email* info@harrycureton.org.uk *Website* www.harrycureton.org.uk
CC NO 1106206   **ESTABLISHED** 2005

■ The D J H Currie Memorial Trust

WHERE FUNDING CAN BE GIVEN Essex.
WHO CAN BENEFIT Registered charities.
WHAT IS FUNDED General charitable purposes. The trust continues to support causes which the founder had an interest in including charities supporting people with disabilities (particularly children), conservation of the countryside, homes for the aged and sporting activities in the county.
WHAT IS NOT FUNDED No grants to individuals.
SAMPLE GRANTS BTCV, Independence at Home, Mid Essex Hospitals and Vitalise.
FINANCES *Year* 2007–08 *Income* £56,179
Grants £6,000 *Assets* £1,257,514
TRUSTEES National Westminster Bank plc.
HOW TO APPLY In writing to the correspondent. The trustees consider applications in June each year and all applications should be submitted by the end of May. Annual accounts/last annual report to be enclosed with application. No recipient may benefit more than once every four years.
WHO TO APPLY TO The Trust Secretary, Natwest Trust Services, 5th Floor, Trinity Quay 2, Avon Street, Bristol BS2 0PT
CC NO 802971   **ESTABLISHED** 1990

■ The Dennis Curry Charitable Trust

WHERE FUNDING CAN BE GIVEN UK.
WHO CAN BENEFIT Charitable organisations.
WHAT IS FUNDED General, particular interest in conservation/environment and education. Occasional support is given to churches and cathedrals.
RANGE OF GRANTS £500–£20,000.
SAMPLE GRANTS Natural History Museum (£27,000); Durrell Wildlife Conservation Trust (£12,000); Galapagos Conservation Trust and University of

Oxford – Wildlife Conservation Research Unit (£10,000 each); the Council for National Parks, New Hall and Royal Naval Museum (£5,000 each); British Trust for Ornithology (£2,000); University of Glasgow Trinidad Expedition (£1,500); and Médecins Sans Frontières (£1,000).
FINANCES *Year* 2007–08 *Income* £94,172
Grants £83,500 *Assets* £2,952,572
TRUSTEES M Curry; Mrs A S Curry; Mrs M Curry-Jones; Mrs P Edmond.
HOW TO APPLY In writing to the correspondent.
WHO TO APPLY TO N J Armstrong, Secretary to the Trust, Alliotts, 5th Floor, 9 Kingsway, London WC2B 6XF
CC NO 263952   **ESTABLISHED** 1971

■ The Raymond Curtis Charitable Trust

WHERE FUNDING CAN BE GIVEN UK.
WHO CAN BENEFIT Registered charities.
WHAT IS FUNDED Organisations supporting children under 18 and older people.
RANGE OF GRANTS Up to £5,600.
SAMPLE GRANTS Maidenhead Synagogue (£5,600); Variety Club of Great Britain (£5,500); and Central Church of England, Hezon Yeshaya and Wizo (£1,000 each).
FINANCES *Year* 2008 *Income* £16,000
Grants £15,000
TRUSTEES Richard Curtis
HOW TO APPLY In writing to the correspondent.
WHO TO APPLY TO R Curtis, Administrator, 8 Horseshoe Park, Pangsbourne, Berkshire RG8 7JW *Tel* 01189 844 881 *Fax* 01189 844853
CC NO 1050295   **ESTABLISHED** 1995

■ The Manny Cussins Foundation

WHERE FUNDING CAN BE GIVEN Mainly UK, with some emphasis on Yorkshire.
WHO CAN BENEFIT Organisations.
WHAT IS FUNDED Welfare and care of older people and children at risk; Jewish causes; healthcare in Yorkshire and overseas; general in Yorkshire and the former county of Humberside.
WHAT IS NOT FUNDED No grants to individuals.
SAMPLE GRANTS Donisthorpe Hall (£100,000).
FINANCES *Year* 2007–08 *Income* £124,803
Grants £129,242 *Assets* £837,411
TRUSTEES A Reuben; A Cussins; A J Cussins; J R Cussins; Mrs A Reuben.
HOW TO APPLY The correspondent states that applications are not sought as the trustees carry out their own research.
WHO TO APPLY TO Arnold Reuben, Trustee, c/o Ford Campbell Freedman, 34 Park Cross Street, Leeds, LS 1 2QH
CC NO 219661   **ESTABLISHED** 1962

■ The Cutler Trust (the Worshipful Company of Makers of Playing Cards)

WHERE FUNDING CAN BE GIVEN UK and City of London.
WHO CAN BENEFIT Organisations and individuals.
WHAT IS FUNDED 'The aims and objectives of the trust are: to support the City of London ('civic') charities/connected charities and City of London schools and colleges and, where relevant, inner London schools; to assist specific deserving students in their education; to support relevant,

smaller charities in which Liverymen are actively involved and which they support; to support smaller charities where the trustees are able to establish an ongoing relationship.'

SAMPLE GRANTS Demelza Hospice Care for Children (£23,000).

FINANCES *Year* 2007–08 *Income* £98,298 *Grants* £48,700 *Assets* £582,413

TRUSTEES D M Ladd; P M Cregeen; R A Howells; D C Warner; K T Heather; A J Carter.

OTHER INFORMATION The grant total in 2007–08 included £1,000 given in annuities. 'The Cutler Trust was set up on 25 October 1943 by two card manufacturers, John Waddington Limited and De La Rue Company Limited and named after the then Master, Lindsay Cutler, (whose grandsons have been apprenticed to the Livery and are now Liverymen). Consistent to the original Livery concept, it was initially for beneficiaries and dependants of those who were or had been employed in the manufacture of Playing Cards.'

HOW TO APPLY 'The trust invites applications for funding of grants from members of the Worshipful Company of Makers of Playing Cards, from educational bodies connected with the City of London, and from members of the public. The Marshall of Appeals considers the merits of the applications and seeks further information before submitting recommendations to the trustees' meeting.'

WHO TO APPLY TO P Bowen, Clerk to the Trustees, 8 Capell Avenue, Chorleywood, Hertfordshire WD3 5HX *Website* www.makersofplayingcards.co.uk

CC NO 232876   ESTABLISHED 1943

....

■ The Cwmbran Trust

WHERE FUNDING CAN BE GIVEN Cwmbran.

WHO CAN BENEFIT Local groups.

WHAT IS FUNDED Grants are made to provide social amenities for the advancement of education and the relief of poverty and sickness in the urban area of Cwmbran town. Particular support is given to local groups for older people and people who are disabled.

WHAT IS NOT FUNDED No grants are made outside of Cwmbran or to organisational running costs.

RANGE OF GRANTS £100–£10,000.

FINANCES *Year* 2007–08 *Income* £83,171 *Grants* £54,206 *Assets* £1,511,813

TRUSTEES Four co-opted Trustees; two nominated trustees; R C Grieg Nominees Ltd.

OTHER INFORMATION The grant total in 2007–08 includes £18,000 donated to 19 individuals.

HOW TO APPLY In writing to the correspondent. Trustees usually meet five times a year in March, May, July, October and December. Where appropriate, applications are investigated by the grants research officer. When the trustees judge it would be helpful, applicants are invited to put their case to the trustees in person. Where an application has to be dealt with urgently, for example, because of the pressure of time or of need, trustees may be contacted by letter or telephone in order that an early decision may be made.

WHO TO APPLY TO K L Maddox, Arvin Meritor HVBS (UK) Ltd, H V B S (UK) Ltd, Grange Road, Cwmbran, Gwent NP44 3XU *Tel* 01633 834040 *Fax* 01633 834051 *email* cwmbrantrust@arvinmeritor.com

CC NO 505855   ESTABLISHED 1976

■ Itzchok Meyer Cymerman Trust Ltd

WHERE FUNDING CAN BE GIVEN Worldwide.

WHO CAN BENEFIT Registered charities and occasional small grants to individuals – both mainly of the Jewish faith.

WHAT IS FUNDED Advancement of the orthodox Jewish faith, education, social welfare, relief of sickness, medical research and general.

TYPE OF GRANT Mostly recurrent.

RANGE OF GRANTS Up to £100,000.

SAMPLE GRANTS Centre for Torah Education (£100,000); Friends of Ohr Akiva Institute (£90,000); Telz Talmudical Academy Trust (£50,000); Kolel Breslaw (£43,000); Beth Hamedrash Gur (£38,000); Beis Aaron Trust (£25,000); Pardes Chana Institutions (£15,000); Yeshivat Kollel Breslov (£10,000); and TAT Family Relief Fund (£5,000).

FINANCES *Year* 2007–08 *Income* £850,918 *Grants* £856,395 *Assets* £2,177,147

TRUSTEES Mrs H F Bondi; I M Cymerman; M D Cymerman; Mrs R Cymerman; Mrs S Heitner.

HOW TO APPLY In writing to the correspondent.

WHO TO APPLY TO I M Cymerman, 15 Riverside Drive, Golders Green Road, London NW11 9PU *Tel* 020 7272 2255

CC NO 265090   ESTABLISHED 1972

■ The D'Oyly Carte Charitable Trust

WHERE FUNDING CAN BE GIVEN UK.

WHO CAN BENEFIT Registered charities only, or where it is clear the objects of the appeal are for charitable purposes.

WHAT IS FUNDED Mainly the arts, medical/welfare charities and the environment.

WHAT IS NOT FUNDED The trust is unlikely to support the following: animal welfare; applications from individuals, or for the benefit of one individual; charities requiring funding for statutory requirements; charities operating outside the UK; conferences or seminars; exhibitions; expeditions and overseas travel; general appeals; large national charities which enjoy widespread support; maintenance of religious buildings; medical research; NHS Trust hospitals for operational or building costs; recordings and commissioning of new works; religious activities; schools, nurseries and playgroups (other than those for children with special needs); support and rehabilitation from drug or alcohol misuse. Due to the volume of appeals received, the trustees have decided not to consider requests from charities that have had an application turned down until two years have elapsed after the date of rejection.

TYPE OF GRANT Mainly one-off.

RANGE OF GRANTS Up to £20,000 but mostly under £5,000.

SAMPLE GRANTS The Royal Academy of Dramatic Art (£20,000); Help the Hospices (£15,000); Samling Foundation (£10,000); Trees for Life (£6,500); Academy of Ancient Music Trust, Gazen Salts Nature Reserve and Challenging Behaviour Foundation (£5,000 each); and Nash Concert Society (£4,500).

FINANCES *Year* 2007–08 *Income* £1,412,858 *Grants* £1,094,468 *Assets* £41,051,729

TRUSTEES Jeremy Leigh Pemberton, Chair; Francesca Radcliffe; Julia Sibley; Henry Freeland; Andrew Jackson; Michael O'Brien.

HOW TO APPLY Potential applicants should write to the correspondent with an outline proposal of no more than two A4 pages. This should cover the work of the charity, its beneficiaries and the need for funding. Applicants qualifying for consideration will then be required to complete the trust's application form. The form should be returned with a copy of the latest annual report and accounts. Applications for specific projects should also include clear details of the need the intended project is designed to meet and an outline budget. The majority of applications are considered in March, July and November. The trust states that it is happy to discuss potential applications on the telephone.

WHO TO APPLY TO Jane Thorne, Secretary, 1 Savoy Hill, London WC2R 0BP *Tel* 020 7420 2600

CC NO 1112457   **ESTABLISHED** 1972

■ The Roald Dahl Foundation

WHERE FUNDING CAN BE GIVEN UK.

WHO CAN BENEFIT Registered charities and individuals. In general, the trust aims to provide help to organisations where funds are not readily available. Preference for small or new organisations rather than long-established, large or national organisations.

WHAT IS FUNDED Haematology: help for children and young people up to the age of 25 with blood disorders which are not cancer related – most commonly haemophilia, sickle cell and thalassaemia. Neurology: help for children and young people up to the age of 25 who have epilepsy, acquired brain injury or neuro-degenerative conditions where there is progressive intellectual and neurological deterioration; literacy: work to assist children and young people who may need extra help to achieve this essential basic skill. There is a small grants scheme to give individual assistance to children and young people (and their families) who fall within the medical categories. Within the medical fields specifically, grants may be made for pump-priming funding of specialist paediatric nursing and other care, especially where there is an emphasis on community care, for a maximum of two years; assistance to residential and day care centres for children and young people who come into the above medical categories; small items of medical equipment that will allow the patient to be cared for in the home with community care/ hospital back-up.

WHAT IS NOT FUNDED The foundation does not consider grant applications for: general appeals from large, well-established charities or national appeals for large building projects; research in any field; any organisations which do not have charitable status or exclusively charitable aims; statutory bodies; projects outside the UK; school or higher education fees; arts projects; organisations for people with blood disorders which are cancer related due to the relatively large number of charities helping in the oncological field; or core funding.

TYPE OF GRANT One-off, start-up costs, salaries, projects for up to two years; the range is wide.

RANGE OF GRANTS Individual: £50–£500. Organisations: up to £25,000.

SAMPLE GRANTS Whittington Hospital, London (£42,500), towards establishing a specialist nurse position; Bradford Teaching Hospitals NHS Foundation Trust (£32,000), towards establishing a specialist nurse position; King's College Hospital Charity (£30,000), to provide a portable EEG system for the paediatric unit of the hospital; NHS Greater Glasgow and Clyde (£18,400), towards establishing a new nursing post; Brain and Spine Foundation (£12,500), for a pilot project on how to support pupils with ABI; National Society for Epilepsy (£6,500), towards an awareness project in Buckinghamshire and Hertfordshire; and Royal Belfast Hospital (£4,000), for books and toys for the children's haematology outpatients department.

FINANCES *Year* 2007–08 *Income* £813,704 *Grants* £409,600 *Assets* £1,798,029

TRUSTEES Felicity Dahl, Chair; Martin Goodwin; Roger Hills.

HOW TO APPLY 'First, make sure that your project or application falls within the criteria listed. Then request (or download) and complete the appropriate application form providing all the required information and, if you feel that any other information is relevant, a covering letter.

However if you have queries or are unsure if the proposed application falls within our criteria, you are strongly encouraged to telephone first. Application forms should be sent, together with a copy of the organisation's accounts and annual report for each of the last two years, to the Grants Director. Applications for posts should include a copy of the proposed job description and person specification. Applications for nursing posts must include information about how the post will be funded after the end of the pump-priming period. When completing the form you should clearly demonstrate how your project fits our eligibility criteria and funding priorities. You should also clearly tell us what activities you would undertake with the funding, who will benefit (including the number of beneficiaries, their age ranges and whether they are from a specific area or community), how they will benefit (e.g. what the project will do to help, support or empower them) and how you will measure the outcomes of the project. We endeavour to visit as many organisations applying for funds as possible, but we may simply telephone for more information.'

WHO TO APPLY TO The Grants Director, 81a High Street, Great Missenden, Buckinghamshire HP16 0AL *Tel* 01494 890465 *Fax* 01494 890459 *email* enquiries@roalddahlfoundation.org *Website* www.roalddahlfoundation.org **CC NO** 1004230   **ESTABLISHED** 1991

....

■ The Daily Prayer Union Charitable Trust Ltd

WHERE FUNDING CAN BE GIVEN UK.
WHO CAN BENEFIT Christians and evangelists.
WHAT IS FUNDED Evangelical Christian purposes.
WHAT IS NOT FUNDED No grants for bricks and mortar.
RANGE OF GRANTS £1,000–£7,000.
SAMPLE GRANTS Monkton Combe School (£14,000); UCCF (£6,700); Jerusalem Trust (£2,800); Anglican Mainstream, CARE, Careforce, Claypath Trust and Martyr's Memorial Trust (£2,000 each); London City Missions and Titus Trust (£1,400); Crosslinks, This Way Up and Wycliffe Bible Group (£1,200 each); and Adventure Plus, All Souls Clubhouse, IFES, Torbay Hospital and UCCF (£1,000 each).
FINANCES *Year* 2007–08 *Income* £60,311 *Grants* £98,655 *Assets* £226,382
TRUSTEES Revd G C Grinham; Mrs F M Ashton; Mrs E D Bridger; Revd D J Jackman; Revd T J Sterry; Mrs A V Tompson.
OTHER INFORMATION In 2007–08 the sum of £43,000 was paid in 12 grants to individuals
HOW TO APPLY The trust supports causes already known to the trustees. Unsolicited applications are unlikely to be successful. Trustees meet at different times throughout the year, usually around March, June and October.
WHO TO APPLY TO Mrs C Palmer, Secretary, 12 Weymouth Street, London W1W 5BY **CC NO** 284857   **ESTABLISHED** 1983

....

■ The Daiwa Anglo-Japanese Foundation

WHERE FUNDING CAN BE GIVEN UK, Japan.
WHO CAN BENEFIT Individuals and institutions (UK or Japanese) benefiting young adults, students and Japanese people – including schools, universities, grass roots and professional groups.
WHAT IS FUNDED The education of citizens of the UK and Japan in each other's culture, institutions, arts, and so on. Scholarships, bursaries and awards to enable students and academics in the UK and Japan to pursue their education abroad. Grants to charitable institutions promoting education in the UK or Japan, and research.
WHAT IS NOT FUNDED Daiwa Foundation Small Grants cannot be used for: general appeals; capital expenditure (e.g., building refurbishment, equipment acquisition, etc); consumables (e.g., stationery, scientific supplies, etc); school, college or university fees; research or study by an individual school/college/university student; salary costs or professional fees; commissions for works of art; retrospective grants; replacement of statutory funding; commercial activities.Daiwa Foundation Awards cannot be used for: any project that does not involve both a British and a Japanese partner; general appeals; capital expenditure (e.g., building refurbishment, equipment acquisition, etc); salary costs or professional fees; commissions for works of art; retrospective grants; replacement of statutory funding; commercial activities.
TYPE OF GRANT Outright or partnership grants, paid in sterling or Japanese yen. One year funding.
RANGE OF GRANTS £5,000–£15,000 for collaborative projects; £1,000–£5,000 for small grants.
FINANCES *Year* 2007–08 *Income* £1,772,706 *Grants* £616,012 *Assets* £36,420,119
TRUSTEES Sir Michael Perry; Hiroaki Fujii; Lady Lucy Adrian; Nicholas Clegg; Sir John Whitehead; Mr Dozen; Mr Hara; Mr Everett; Merryn Somerset Webb; Sir David Brewer; Lord Brittan; Sir Peter Williams; Andrew Smithers; Akira Kyota.
HOW TO APPLY Application forms are available to download at: www.dajf.org.uk. Applicants should submit three completed forms. Japanese applications for the Small Grants fund should be sent to the Tokyo office. All other applications should be sent to the address listed here. There are two application deadlines each year: 31 March (for a decision by 31 May) and 30 September (for a decision by 30 November). The foundation encourages applicants to submit their application as early as possible.
WHO TO APPLY TO Prof. Marie Conte-Helm, Director General, Daiwa Foundation, Japan House, 13/14 Cornwall Terrace, London NW1 4QP *Tel* 020 7486 4348 *Fax* 020 7486 2914 *email* office@dajf.org.uk *Website* www.dajf.org.uk **CC NO** 299955   **ESTABLISHED** 1988

....

■ Oizer Dalim Trust

WHERE FUNDING CAN BE GIVEN UK and overseas.
WHO CAN BENEFIT Registered charities.
WHAT IS FUNDED The alleviation of poverty amongst members of the Orthodox Jewish faith and the furtherance of Orthodox Jewish education.
FINANCES *Year* 2007–08 *Income* £194,928 *Grants* £243,405 *Assets* £6,379
TRUSTEES B Berger; M Freund; M Cik.
HOW TO APPLY In writing to the correspondent.
WHO TO APPLY TO M Cik, Trustee, 68 Osbaldeston Road, London N16 7DR **CC NO** 1045296   **ESTABLISHED** 1994

■ The Dr and Mrs A Darlington Charitable Trust

WHERE FUNDING CAN BE GIVEN Devon, in particular Sidmouth and East Devon.

WHO CAN BENEFIT Only registered charities.

WHAT IS FUNDED The trust mainly supports medical causes; people who are disabled; older people; and socially isolated people. Grants also given in the fields of nature conservation and preservation.

WHAT IS NOT FUNDED Applications from individuals, including students, are unlikely to be successful. Applications for donations to be used outside Devon (particularly outside Sidmouth and East Devon) are also unlikely to be successful.

TYPE OF GRANT One-off, some recurring.

RANGE OF GRANTS Up to about £15,000.

SAMPLE GRANTS Previous beneficiaries include: Peninsula Medical School Foundation, Children's Health and Exercise Research Centre, Salcombe Regis Church, Vitalise, Freedomwheels, Listening Books, Motability, West of England School and College, MS Therapy Centre, Brainwave, SSAFA, St Loyes, UBS and Countryside Foundation.

FINANCES *Year* 2007–08 *Income* £181,583 *Grants* £113,481

TRUSTEES Lloyds TSB Bank plc.

HOW TO APPLY In writing to the correspondent. The trustees regret that they cannot send replies to unsuccessful applicants. The trustees meet quarterly in March, June, September and December; applications should be received the previous month.

WHO TO APPLY TO The Trust Manager, Lloyds TSB Bank plc, UK Trust Centre, The Clock House, 22–26 Ock Street, Abingdon, Oxfordshire OX14 5SW *Tel* 01235 232734

CC NO 283308   **ESTABLISHED** 1981

■ Baron Davenport's Charity

WHERE FUNDING CAN BE GIVEN Warwickshire, Worcestershire, Staffordshire, Shropshire and West Midlands.

WHO CAN BENEFIT Individuals and charitable organisations and institutions, benefiting children, young adults, retired people, widows, and people disadvantaged by poverty.

WHAT IS FUNDED Social welfare, children and young people under the age of 25.

WHAT IS NOT FUNDED There are no exclusions, providing the applications come within the charity's objects and the applying organisation is based within the charity's beneficial area, or the organisation's project lies within or benefits people who live in the beneficial area.

TYPE OF GRANT One-off or annual grants, for capital or revenue costs.

RANGE OF GRANTS Mostly £2,500 or less.

SAMPLE GRANTS Previous beneficiaries included: Birmingham St Mary's Hospice; Donna Louise Trust; Acorns Children's Hospice; Almshouse Charity Birmingham; Beacon Centre for the Blind; Compton Hospice; Job's Close Residential Home for the Elderly; Trinity Hospital; Primrose Hospice; Cancer Help Centre; Berrow Cottage Homes; Coventry and District Free Church Homes for the Elderly; Gracewell Homes Foster Trust.

FINANCES *Year* 2008 *Income* £1,152,000 *Grants* £1,149,000

TRUSTEES Christopher Hordern, Chair; Sue M Ayres; William M Colacicchi; Paul Dransfield; Philip A Gough; Rob Prichard.

OTHER INFORMATION Unfortunately, although submitted to the Charity Commission, the charity's 2008 accounts were not yet available to view at the time of writing (November 2009).

HOW TO APPLY In writing to the correspondent, accompanied by the latest accounts and any project costs. Distributions take place twice a year at the end of May and November and applications should be received at the charity's office by 15 March or 15 September. All applications are acknowledged and those not within the charity's objects are advised.

WHO TO APPLY TO Mrs Marlene Keenan, Administrator, Portman House, 5–7 Temple Row West, Birmingham B2 5NY *Tel* 0121 236 8004 *Fax* 0121 233 2500 *email* enquiries@ barondavenportscharity.org *Website* www. barondavenportscharity.org

CC NO 217307   **ESTABLISHED** 1930

■ The Davidson (Nairn) Charitable Trust

WHERE FUNDING CAN BE GIVEN Nairn area.

WHO CAN BENEFIT Social welfare organisations and all charities recognised in Scottish Law.

WHAT IS FUNDED Grants may be made towards the provision of leisure and recreation facilities, relieving poverty, assisting older people and educational concerns.

WHAT IS NOT FUNDED Only registered charities are supported or charities recognised in Scottish law.

FINANCES *Year* 2007 *Income* £62,314 *Grants* £50,000

TRUSTEES Ian A Macgregor and others.

OTHER INFORMATION Recent up-to-date information has not been available on this trust.

HOW TO APPLY On a form available from the correspondent.

WHO TO APPLY TO The Trustees, Messrs R and R Urquhart, Incorporating MacGregor and Co Solicitors, Royal Bank of Scotland Buildings, 20 High Street, Nairn IV12 4AX

SC NO SC024273   **ESTABLISHED** 1995

■ Davidson Charitable Trust

WHERE FUNDING CAN BE GIVEN UK.

WHO CAN BENEFIT Jewish organisations.

WHAT IS FUNDED Jewish and charitable purposes.

SAMPLE GRANTS Hampstead Synagogue Building Fund (£625,000); Holburne Museum (£24,000); Emunah (£20,000); Friends of Ohel Torah (£16,000); Royal Opera House (£10,000); Lubavitch UK, Maccabi GB, Magen David Adom UK and Shaare Zedek UK (£5,000 each); the Fairly House School (£4,000); and the Ashmolean Museum and Sarah Charitable Trust (£1,000).

FINANCES *Year* 2007–08 *Income* £1,059,575 *Grants* £926,522 *Assets* £207,012

TRUSTEES G A Davidson; M Y Davidson; Mrs E Winer.

HOW TO APPLY In writing to the correspondent.

WHO TO APPLY TO Eve Winer, Trustee, 58 Queen Anne Street, London W1G 8HW

CC NO 262937   **ESTABLISHED** 1971

■ The Alderman Joe Davidson Memorial Trust

WHERE FUNDING CAN BE GIVEN UK, with a preference for Hampshire.

WHO CAN BENEFIT Local and specific national organisations and individuals benefiting: children; older people, nominated by Age Concern; and Jewish people.

WHAT IS FUNDED Charities that are named in the trust deed, people who are in need and the provision of Christmas parties. The trust also presents watches to school children for regular attendance.

TYPE OF GRANT Recurring grants given to specific organisations.

FINANCES *Year* 2007–08 *Income* £32,636 *Grants* £13,145 *Assets* £728,800

TRUSTEES K Crabbe; J Stock.

OTHER INFORMATION The trust was established to provide 'dwellings for persons over 70 years of age in necessitous circumstances preferably resident in Portsmouth for more than 25 years'.

HOW TO APPLY The trustees are only permitted to make grants to individuals or organisations that are specified in the Trust Deed.

WHO TO APPLY TO The Secretary to the Trustees, Portsmouth City Council, Civic Offices, Guildhall Square, Portsmouth PO1 2QR

CC NO 202591   **ESTABLISHED** 1962

■ Michael Davies Charitable Settlement

WHERE FUNDING CAN BE GIVEN UK.

WHO CAN BENEFIT Organisations.

WHAT IS FUNDED General charitable purposes.

RANGE OF GRANTS Up to £15,000.

SAMPLE GRANTS BTYC Sailsports Club (£15,000); Camden Arts Centre, Camp and Trek, Marie Curie Cancer Care, North London Hospice, School Aid India and Tools for Training Overseas (£10,000 each); Médecins du Monde and the Study Gallery (£5,000 each); Architects For Aid (£3,500); Thames Wharf Charity (£2,000); the Langford Trust for Animal Health and Welfare (£1,000); and the Architectural Association Inc. (£750).

FINANCES *Year* 2007–08 *Income* £30,701 *Grants* £94,249 *Assets* £554,708

TRUSTEES M J P Davies; K A Hawkins.

HOW TO APPLY In writing to the correspondent.

WHO TO APPLY TO K Hawkins, Administrator, Lee Associates, 5 Southampton Place, London WC1A 2DA

CC NO 1000574   **ESTABLISHED** 1990

■ The Gwendoline and Margaret Davies Charity

WHERE FUNDING CAN BE GIVEN UK, with particular favour given to Wales.

WHO CAN BENEFIT Registered charities only. Welsh charities are particularly favoured.

WHAT IS FUNDED General charitable purposes, with special consideration given to the arts, health and young people. Organisations in the fields of education, medical research, community care services environment and faith activities may also be considered.

WHAT IS NOT FUNDED Grants are made to registered charities only.

TYPE OF GRANT Mainly one-off, occasionally recurrent for specific capital projects.

RANGE OF GRANTS £100–£100,000, typical grant £5,000–£10,000.

SAMPLE GRANTS National Museum and Galleries (£35,000); The Prince's Trust – Cymru (£15,000); Gregynog Festival (£10,000); David Davies Memorial Institute (£6,000); Valley Kids (£2,000); Centre for Alternative Technology (£1,500); and Gwasg Gregynog (£1,000).

FINANCES *Year* 2007–08 *Income* £278,958 *Grants* £126,164 *Assets* £6,252,835

TRUSTEES Rt Hon. David Davies; Dr James A Davies; Dr Denis Balsom.

HOW TO APPLY The trustees consider appeals on an individual basis. There are no application forms as the trustees prefer to receive letters from applicants setting out the following information: whether the organisation is a registered charity; details of the reason for the application – the type of work and so on; the cost; how much has been raised so far towards the cost; the source of the sums raised; a copy of the last audited accounts if available; and any other information that the applicant may consider would help the application. Unsuccessful appeals are not informed unless an sae is enclosed.

WHO TO APPLY TO Mrs Susan Hamer, Secretary, The Offices, Plas Dinam, Llandinam, Powys SY17 5DQ *Tel* 01686 689172 *Fax* 01686 689172

CC NO 235589   **ESTABLISHED** 1934

■ The Hamilton Davies Trust

WHERE FUNDING CAN BE GIVEN Irlam and Cadishead (in Salford) and Rixton with Glazebrook (in Warrington).

WHO CAN BENEFIT Community organisations.

WHAT IS FUNDED '(1) Youth – Supporting youth leaders and developing the youth movement with the aim of promoting links to education, sports and community initiatives and encouraging organised activities. (2) Education – Adding value to existing provision and raising children's expectations. (3) Sport – Sport is particularly important in the development of young people and the trust has supported projects by providing funds for equipment and kit, holiday programmes and competitions. (4) Community – Support for the community by way of rebuilding and refurbishment of community buildings, supporting group work, festivals and enhancing communication between local facilities and residents.'

SAMPLE GRANTS I & C Young People's Project (£18,000); Salford City Council (£14,000); Cheshire Police Authority (£11,000); St Helen's School Governors (£10,000); Salford Community Leisure (£7,500); Relate (£6,000); Moorfield Primary School (£3,000); Bridgewater School, Poorlots Allotment and St Mary's Parent Guild (£2,000 each); Fiddlers Lane Primary (£1,500); Friendly Faces, Irlam Hornets and Triton Hockey Club (£1,000 each); Friends of St Josephs (£700); St Mary's School (£500); Fridays (£300); St Mary's Parent Guild (£250); Irlam Royalettes (£225); Phoenix Gem Dance Troupe (£200); and Salford Community Leisure (£60).

FINANCES *Year* 2007–08 *Income* £1,462,318 *Grants* £155,778 *Assets* £4,055,283

TRUSTEES N McArthur; G Chisnall; F Cocker.

HOW TO APPLY In writing to the correspondent. Applications should include a brief outline of the project for which support is requested, the amount of funding required and details of any other funding applications that have been made. The trustees will consider all applications, with applicants being informed of their decision in writing. The trust welcomes initial telephone calls to discuss potential projects.

WHO TO APPLY TO Colette Fairfax, Secretary to the Trust, 117c Liverpool Rd, Cadishead, Manchester M44 5BG *Tel* 0161 222 4003 *email* info@hamiltondavies.org.uk

CC NO 1106123   **ESTABLISHED** 2004

■ The Wilfrid Bruce Davis Charitable Trust

WHERE FUNDING CAN BE GIVEN UK, but mainly Cornwall; India.

WHO CAN BENEFIT Voluntary groups and registered charities.

WHAT IS FUNDED The trust presently concentrates on 'improving the quality of life for those who are physically disadvantaged and their carers'. The geographical area covered is almost exclusively Cornwall, however the main thrust of the trust's activities is now focused on India.

WHAT IS NOT FUNDED No applications from individuals are considered.

SAMPLE GRANTS Pallium India (£35,000); Pain and Palliative Care Society Calicut (£15,000); Guwahati Pain Clinic (£5,000); Helford River Children's Sailing Trust and Jubilee Sailing Trust (£1,000 each); Cornwall Community Foundation (£525); Chernobyl Children's Holidays, Cornwall Blind Association and United Church of Zambia (£250 each); and NSPCC (£200).

FINANCES *Year* 2008–09 *Income* £31,144 *Grants* £59,551 *Assets* £198,174

TRUSTEES W B Davis; Mrs D F Davis; Mrs D S Dickens; Mrs C A S Pierce.

HOW TO APPLY No replies are made to unsolicited applications. The correspondent has stated that the budget for many years to come is fully committed and that the trust receives hundreds of applications, none of which can be supported.

WHO TO APPLY TO W B Davis, Trustee, La Feock Grange, Feock, Truro, Cornwall TR3 6RG

CC NO 265421   **ESTABLISHED** 1967

■ Davis-Rubens Charitable Trust

WHERE FUNDING CAN BE GIVEN UK.

WHO CAN BENEFIT Registered charities with a preference for UK-wide and Jewish charities.

WHAT IS FUNDED General charitable purposes.

WHAT IS NOT FUNDED No grants to individuals.

TYPE OF GRANT Mainly recurrent.

RANGE OF GRANTS £50–£1,000, mostly under £500.

SAMPLE GRANTS Jewish Care (£1,000); Vitalise (£750); Jewish Deaf Association (£600); Diabetes UK (£500); Musician's Benevolent Fund (£400); Trinity Hospice (£350); Greater London Fund for the Blind (£250); British Friends of the Hebrew University of Jerusalem (£200); Butler Trust (£100); and Universal Beneficent Society – UBS (£50).

FINANCES *Year* 2007–08 *Income* £25,637 *Grants* £23,381 *Assets* £663,791

TRUSTEES Enid Rubens; Giles Rubens; Edward Checkley.

HOW TO APPLY In writing to the correspondent, however, the trust states that applications from new charities are rarely considered.

WHO TO APPLY TO Renny Clark, Gilbert Allen and Co., Churchdown Chambers, Bordyke, Tonbridge, Kent TN9 1NR *Tel* 01732 770100

CC NO 263662   **ESTABLISHED** 1971

■ The Dawe Charitable Trust

WHERE FUNDING CAN BE GIVEN Cambridgeshire, national, international.

WHO CAN BENEFIT Charitable organisations.

WHAT IS FUNDED Disadvantaged people and homelessness.

RANGE OF GRANTS £1,000–£100,000.

SAMPLE GRANTS The Prince's Trust (£50,000); St Theresa Charity and Manda Wilderness Agricultural Project (£5,000 each).

FINANCES *Year* 2007–08 *Income* £149,753 *Grants* £62,400 *Assets* £2,982,822

TRUSTEES Dr Peter Dawe; Lindsay Dawe; David Kerr.

HOW TO APPLY In writing to the correspondent, outlining ideas and needs.

WHO TO APPLY TO Dr Peter Dawe, Fen View, 17a Broad Street, Ely, Cambridgeshire CB7 4AJ *Tel* 0845 345 8999

CC NO 1060314   **ESTABLISHED** 1997

■ The De Clermont Charitable Company Ltd

WHERE FUNDING CAN BE GIVEN UK, with a preference for north east England.

WHO CAN BENEFIT Headquarters organisations, and local organisations in the north east of England.

WHAT IS FUNDED General charitable purposes, particularly those charities of special interest to the founders of this company, i.e. medical research, children and young people, service organisations and overseas disaster appeals.

WHAT IS NOT FUNDED No grants for organisations concerned with drugs and alcohol misuse.

RANGE OF GRANTS Up to £3,000.

SAMPLE GRANTS Previous beneficiaries have included: Sedburgh School Foundation, Borders Support Group, Alzheimer's Research Trust, Lowick Village Hall and Universal Beneficent Society, Brooke Hospital for Animals and Haydn Bridge High School and CLIC Sargent.

FINANCES *Year* 2007–08 *Income* £32,102 *Grants* £20,137 *Assets* £846,344

TRUSTEES Elizabeth de Clermont; Caroline Orpwood; Herbert Orpwood.

OTHER INFORMATION No grants list was available from the latest accounts.

HOW TO APPLY In writing to the correspondent.

WHO TO APPLY TO Elizabeth de Clermont, Bowmonthill, Mindrum, Northumberland TD12 4QW

CC NO 274191   **ESTABLISHED** 1977

■ The Helen and Geoffrey De Freitas Charitable Trust

WHERE FUNDING CAN BE GIVEN UK.

WHO CAN BENEFIT Charitable organisations and voluntary umbrella bodies registered in the UK.

WHAT IS FUNDED The conservation of the countryside and environment in rural Britain; the preservation of Britain's cultural heritage; assistance to people who are underprivileged through community facilities and services, advice centres and community arts and recreation. Once a year the trustees may respond to a national or international humanitarian crisis which may be outside the terms of reference of the trust.

WHAT IS NOT FUNDED No grants to non-registered charities, individuals, or to charities on behalf of individuals. Definitely no support for charities concerned with medical or health matters, or with physical, mental or sensory impairments.

TYPE OF GRANT Usually one-off for feasibility studies, project and occasionally for start-up costs.

RANGE OF GRANTS £500–£5,000.

SAMPLE GRANTS Staffordshire Wildlife Trust and GINA (£5,000 each); Tarka Country Trust (£3,000); Dartington Hall Trust (£2,800); the Grasslands Trust, Marine Conservation Society, Nailsea Tithe Barn Trust and Suffolk Building Preservation Trust (£2,500 each); Devon Wildlife Trust (£1,500); St Michael and All Angels – London Fields (£1,500); and Community Can Cycle (£500).

FINANCES *Year* 2007–08 *Income* £25,007 *Grants* £33,800 *Assets* £658,879

TRUSTEES Richard Kirby; Frances de Freitas; Roger de Freitas.

HOW TO APPLY In writing to the correspondent at the following address: PO Box 18667, London, NW3 5WB. Trustees meet quarterly.

WHO TO APPLY TO Richard Kirby, Trustee, Speechly Bircham LLP, 6 New Street Square, London EC4A 3LX

CC NO 258597   **ESTABLISHED** 1969

■ Peter De Haan Charitable Trust

WHERE FUNDING CAN BE GIVEN UK.

WHO CAN BENEFIT Charitable organisations.

WHAT IS FUNDED General charitable purposes, including organisations connected with children and young people. The current focus of the trust is social welfare, the environment and the arts.

WHAT IS NOT FUNDED 'We will not accept applications for grants: that directly replace or subsidise statutory funding; from individuals or for the benefit of one individual; for work that has already taken place; which do not have a direct benefit to the UK; for medical research; for adventure and residential courses, expeditions or overseas travel; for holidays and respite care; for endowment funds; for the promotion of a specific religion; that are part of general appeals or circulars; from applicants who have applied to us within the last 12 months. In addition to the above, we are unlikely to support: large national charities which enjoy widespread support; local organisations which are part of a wider network of others doing similar work; individual pre-schools, schools; out-of-school clubs, supplementary schools, colleges, universities or youth clubs; websites, publications, conferences or seminars.'

TYPE OF GRANT Project grants or core costs.

RANGE OF GRANTS Mostly up to £20,000.

SAMPLE GRANTS London Wildlife Trust (£400,000); Leicestershire & Rutland Wildlife Trust (£275,000); Missing People (£250,000); YouthNet (£200,000); Rainbow Trust (£100,000); New Horizon Centre (£80,000); L'Ouverture (£60,000); Bede Home Association and Cardinal Hume Centre (£30,000 each); Dandelion Trust for Children, Noah's Ark Community Café and Twelves Company (£23,000 each); Walsall Street Teams (£20,000); Accept, Exodus Project and Perthes Association (£15,000 each); Theatre in Education (£5,000); Sarum Orchestra (£4,000); Full Body and the Voice, Ice and Fire Theatre Company and the Whitechapel Art Gallery (£2,000 each); and Ascendance Repertory Company Ltd, Children's Discovery Centre and Sudden Productions (£1,000 each).

FINANCES *Year* 2007–08 *Income* £417,000 *Grants* £2,600,000 *Assets* £23,300,000

TRUSTEES Peter Charles De Haan; David Peter Davies; Janette McKay; Paul Vaight; Opus Corporate Trustees Limited.

HOW TO APPLY In writing or via email to the correspondent. Grants may be for project-based applications or to subsidise core costs. The following information should be included: a statement that you have made reference to the website; a description of the charity's aims and achievements; charity registration number; an outline and budget for the project for which funding is sought; a copy of the latest financial statements; details of funds raised and the current shortfall. Applications are considered on a continuing basis throughout the year. Major grants are awarded at the trustee meeting held quarterly in March, June, September and December. Notification of the outcome of applications will be by email. Where an email address is not available, no notification will be possible. The charity states that it is not seeking applications from wildlife trusts.

WHO TO APPLY TO Mrs Sam Tuson Taylor, 1 China Wharf, 29 Mill Street, London SE1 2BQ *Tel* 020 7232 5471 *email* stusontaylor@pdhct.org.uk *Website* www.pdhct.org.uk

CC NO 1077005   **ESTABLISHED** 1999

■ The De Laszlo Foundation

WHERE FUNDING CAN BE GIVEN UK and worldwide.

WHO CAN BENEFIT Arts organisations and registered charities.

WHAT IS FUNDED Promotion of the arts; general charitable purposes.

RANGE OF GRANTS It is increasingly the policy of the trustees to make a small number of targeted large grants.

SAMPLE GRANTS The De Laszlo Archive Trust (£188,000); Gordonstoun School Arts Centre (£20,000); Royal Marsden (£10,000); Foundation for Liver Research (£8,000); City and Guilds of London Art School (£6,500); Treloar Trust (£5,500); European Foundation (£5,000); Federation of British Artists (£3,000); National Youth Orchestra (£1,500); Worldwide Volunteering (£1,000); Cardboard Citizens (£500); and Chelsea Open Air Nursery School (£250).

FINANCES *Year* 2007–08 *Income* £773,660 *Grants* £366,180 *Assets* £2,284,805

TRUSTEES Damon de Laszlo, Chair; Lucy Birkbeck; Robert de Laszlo; William de Laszlo.

OTHER INFORMATION The foundation was set up to promote the advancement and promotion of education and interest in the visual arts with special reference to encouraging knowledge of the works of contemporary painters, in particular those of the late Philip de Laszlo.

HOW TO APPLY The foundation informs us at the moment that fund are fully committed to existing long term projects.

WHO TO APPLY TO Christabel Wood, 5 Albany Courtyard, London W1J 0HF

CC NO 327383   **ESTABLISHED** 1978

■ The Leopold De Rothschild Charitable Trust

WHERE FUNDING CAN BE GIVEN UK.

WHO CAN BENEFIT Registered charities only.

WHAT IS FUNDED General charitable purposes, particularly the arts and Jewish organisations.

SAMPLE GRANTS Exbury Gardens Limited (£400,000); Countess of Munster Musical Trust and Solti Foundation (£10,000 each); Royal National Theatre and Trinity College Cambridge (£5,000 each); Jewish Music Institute and Royal

College of Music (£2,000 each); Aldeburgh Foundation, Black Watch Heritage Appeal, English Chamber Orchestra and Music Society and London Philharmonic Orchestra (£1,000 each); Holly Lodge Centre, Interact (£500); Willow Trust (£250); and Friends of Holland Park and Streetwise Opera (£100 each).

FINANCES *Year* 2007–08 *Income* £70,987 *Grants* £475,351 *Assets* £1,440,706

TRUSTEES Rothschild Trust Corporation Ltd.

HOW TO APPLY In writing to the correspondent.

WHO TO APPLY TO The Clerk, Rothschild Trust Corporation Ltd, New Court, St Swithin's Lane, London EC4P 4DU

CC NO 212611 **ESTABLISHED** 1959

■ The Deakin Charitable Trust

WHERE FUNDING CAN BE GIVEN Mainly Surrey with a preference for Woking.

WHO CAN BENEFIT Mainly local charities including hospices and various religious organisations, and students seeking to extend their music education.

WHAT IS FUNDED General charitable purposes.

SAMPLE GRANTS Woking Hospice (£12,000); Methodist Church – Gambia and Epworth Choir (£2,000 each); Woking Choral Society and Woking Sixth Form College (£1,500 each); Marjorie Richardson Appeal and Hillview Surgery Appeal (£500 each); Christian Aid (£30); and Methodist Publishing House (£8). Musical bursaries amounted to £2,700.

FINANCES *Year* 2007–08 *Income* £51,015 *Grants* £22,285 *Assets* £840,679

TRUSTEES Walter Deakin; Geraldine Lawson; Paul Deakin; William Hodgetts.

HOW TO APPLY In writing to the correspondent.

WHO TO APPLY TO William Hodgetts, c/o Herbert Parnell, Kingsway House, 123–125 Goldsworth Road, Woking, Surrey GU21 1LR *Tel* 01483 885 700

CC NO 258001 **ESTABLISHED** 1968

■ William Dean Countryside and Educational Trust

WHERE FUNDING CAN BE GIVEN Principally Cheshire; also Derbyshire, Lancashire, Staffordshire and the Wirral.

WHO CAN BENEFIT Individuals and organisations.

WHAT IS FUNDED The trust gives grants towards enterprises in its immediate locality which promote education in natural history, ecology and the conservation of the natural environment. For example, wildlife trusts; schools for ecological and conservation projects; and parks and pleasure grounds for similar purposes.

WHAT IS NOT FUNDED Education is not funded, unless directly associated with one of the stated eligible categories.

TYPE OF GRANT Capital, core costs, feasibility studies, one-off, project, research, and start-up costs. Funding may be given for up to two years.

RANGE OF GRANTS £100–£25,000.

SAMPLE GRANTS Cheshire Wildlife Trust (£16,000 in three grants); One Earth Festival (£2,000 in two grants); Friends of Westminster Park (£1,500); and Garden Organic, the Woodland Trust and St Stephens Church (£1,000 each); Rossendale Trust (£750); Shropshire Barn Owls (£600 in two grants); Chester Cathedral Garden (£500); Believe to Achieve (£300); Congleton Cricket

Club (£250); Butterfly Conservation (£200); and St Luke's Hospice (£100).

FINANCES *Year* 2007 *Income* £81,420 *Grants* £47,900 *Assets* £1,277,477

TRUSTEES David Daniel, Chair; William Crawford; John Ward; David Crawford; Margaret Williamson.

HOW TO APPLY In writing to the correspondent.

WHO TO APPLY TO Mrs Brenda Bell, St Mary's Cottage, School Lane, Astbury, Congleton, Cheshire CW12 4RG *Tel* 01260 290194 *email* bellstmarys@hotmail.com

CC NO 1044567 **ESTABLISHED** 1995

■ The Debmar Benevolent Trust

WHERE FUNDING CAN BE GIVEN UK and Israel.

WHO CAN BENEFIT Jewish organisations.

WHAT IS FUNDED Jewish charitable purposes.

RANGE OF GRANTS Up to £30,000, but mostly under £1,000.

SAMPLE GRANTS Previous beneficiaries included: Beis Hamedrash Hachodosh, Chasdei Belz, Chevras Mauous Lador, Gevurath Ari, Telz Talmudical Academy, Friends of Assos Chesed, Pardes Chana, ATLIB, Bobov Institutions, Ohr Akiva Institute, Tomchei Shaarei Zion, Ponivitch Institutions, Yeshiva Shaarei Zion, Beis Yoel High School, Format Charity Trust and Manchester Kollel.

FINANCES *Year* 2007–08 *Income* £3,817,873 *Grants* £813,188 *Assets* £9,138,090

TRUSTEES Martin Weisz; Gella Klein; Hilary Olsberg; Rosalind Halpern; Vivienne Lewin.

OTHER INFORMATION A list a grants was not provided in the trust's latest accounts.

HOW TO APPLY In writing to the correspondent.

WHO TO APPLY TO Martin Weisz, Trustee, 3rd Floor, Manchester House, 86 Princess Street, Manchester M1 6NP *Tel* 0161 236 4107

CC NO 283065 **ESTABLISHED** 1979

■ The Delfont Foundation

WHERE FUNDING CAN BE GIVEN UK.

WHO CAN BENEFIT Registered charities.

WHAT IS FUNDED General charitable purposes.

TYPE OF GRANT Usually one-off for specific purposes.

RANGE OF GRANTS Up to £5,000.

SAMPLE GRANTS Entertainment Artistes' Benevolent Fund (£2,000); JAMI (£1,500); Brainwave, Dogs Trust, Liberal Jewish Synagogue and Royal Academy of Arts (£1,000 each); and Jewish Marriage Council, Second Chance and Police Dependents Trust (£500 each).

FINANCES *Year* 2006 *Income* £27,103 *Grants* £18,540 *Assets* £567,382

TRUSTEES David Delfont; Jennifer Morse; Susan Meddings; Guy Parsons; Mary Connor; John Sykes.

HOW TO APPLY In writing to the correspondent.

WHO TO APPLY TO John Sykes, Secretary, 8 Ashburnham Road, Eastbourne, East Sussex BN21 2HU *Tel* 01323 645 820

CC NO 298047 **ESTABLISHED** 1987

■ The Delius Trust

WHERE FUNDING CAN BE GIVEN UK.

WHO CAN BENEFIT Organisations.

WHAT IS FUNDED 'The trust promotes the music of Frederick Delius and of British composers born since 1860, by giving help towards the cost of performances, publications and recordings. In addition, assistance is occasionally offered to organisations and institutions active in this field. Priority is always given to the promotion of the works of Delius, especially those that are rarely performed.'

WHAT IS NOT FUNDED The trust will not usually make retrospective grants, nor does it consider support for capital projects. Grants are not generally made for individual performance, recording or publishing projects.

FINANCES *Year* 2007 *Income* £143,974 *Grants* £61,620 *Assets* £2,488,841

TRUSTEES Musicians' Benevolent Fund (Representative: William Parker); David Lloyd-Jones; Martin Williams.

HOW TO APPLY In writing for consideration by the trustees and the advisers. See the trust's website for further details. The trust meets three times a year, in February, June and October. Applications should be received early in the month before each meeting. The trust will not usually make retrospective grants. There is no standard application form.

WHO TO APPLY TO Helen Faulkner, Secretary to the Trust, 7–11 Britannia Street, London WC1X 9JS *Tel* 020 7239 9143 *email* DeliusTrust@mbf.org.uk *Website* www.delius.org.uk

CC NO 207324   **ESTABLISHED** 1935

■ The Dellal Foundation

WHERE FUNDING CAN BE GIVEN UK.

WHO CAN BENEFIT Registered charities only.

WHAT IS FUNDED Mostly 'the welfare and benefit of Jewish people'.

WHAT IS NOT FUNDED No grants to individuals.

TYPE OF GRANT One-off.

FINANCES *Year* 2007–08 *Income* £30,097 *Grants* £119,017 *Assets* £603,601

TRUSTEES J Dellal; E Azouz; J Azouz; G Dellal.

HOW TO APPLY In writing to the correspondent.

WHO TO APPLY TO The Administrator, 25 Harley Street, London W1G 9BR

CC NO 265506   **ESTABLISHED** 1973

■ The Delves Charitable Trust

WHERE FUNDING CAN BE GIVEN UK.

WHO CAN BENEFIT General approved charities.

WHAT IS FUNDED General charitable purposes. To support approved charities by annual contributions.

WHAT IS NOT FUNDED The trust does not give sponsorships or personal educational grants.

SAMPLE GRANTS British Heart Foundation (£25,000); Action Medical Research (£10,000); Sequal Trust (£8,000); Survival International (£7,500); MacMillan Cancer Support (£6,500); Médecins Sans Frontières(£6,000); Liverpool School of Tropical Medicine (£5,500); Medical Foundation for the Care of Victims of Torture and Save the Children (£5,000 each); Servite Sisters (£4,000); International Childcare Trust, National Association for Colitis and Crohn's Disease (£3,000 each); Big Issue Foundation (£2,500); Amnesty International, Charterhouse-in-Southwark and Council for Music in Hospitals (£1,000 each); and SightSavers International (£250).

FINANCES *Year* 2007–08 *Income* £279,215 *Grants* £170,200 *Assets* £6,311,760

TRUSTEES Elizabeth Breeze; John Breeze; George Breeze; Charles Breeze; Edward Breeze; Mark Breeze; Catharine Mackey.

HOW TO APPLY 'The funds of the trust are currently fully committed and no unsolicited requests can therefore be considered by the trustees.'

WHO TO APPLY TO The Trust Administrator, Luminary Finance LLP, PO Box 135, Longfield, Kent DA3 8WF

CC NO 231860   **ESTABLISHED** 1922

■ The Demigryphon Trust

WHERE FUNDING CAN BE GIVEN UK, with a preference for Scotland.

WHO CAN BENEFIT Registered charities only.

WHAT IS FUNDED General charitable purposes. The trust supports a wide range of organisations and appears to have a preference for education, medical, children and Scottish organisations.

WHAT IS NOT FUNDED No grants to individuals; only registered charities are supported.

TYPE OF GRANT Mainly one-off grants.

RANGE OF GRANTS Mostly up to £5,000.

SAMPLE GRANTS The Third Viscount Cowdray's Charity Trust (£43,000); the A-Z Trust and the Game Conservancy Trust (£5,000 each); Teenage Cancer Trust (£1,000); the Rainbow Trust Children's Charity, Royal Northern Countryside Initiative, Royal Scottish Agricultural Benevolent Institution and WCRF UK (£500 each); Breakthrough Breast cancer (£250); Children with Leukaemia (£200); and Cancer Research UK (£50).

FINANCES *Year* 2007–08 *Income* £81,712 *Grants* £56,500 *Assets* £2,583,178

TRUSTEES The Cowdray Trust Ltd.

OTHER INFORMATION In 2007–08 a further 31 payments were made to pensioners.

HOW TO APPLY In writing to the correspondent, including an sae. No application forms or guidelines are issued and there is no deadline. Only successful applications are acknowledged.

WHO TO APPLY TO The Secretary, Pollen House, 10–12 Cork Street, London W1S 3LW

CC NO 275821   **ESTABLISHED** 1978

■ The Denman Charitable Trust

WHERE FUNDING CAN BE GIVEN Bristol area and South Gloucestershire.

WHO CAN BENEFIT Organisations benefiting research workers, at- risk groups, people disadvantaged by poverty, and socially isolated people.

WHAT IS FUNDED Medical research, health and welfare.

WHAT IS NOT FUNDED No grants to individuals and non charitable organisations.

TYPE OF GRANT Pump priming rather than running costs.

SAMPLE GRANTS Empire and Commonwealth Museum (£25,000); St. Mary Redcliff Organ Appeal (£20,000); Childtime (£15,000); Alzheimers Society and Jessie May Trust (£2,000 each); Meningitis UK, RNLI and Avon Outward Bound (£1,000 each); Triumph over Phobia (£500); Disabled Travel Service (£300); and Cransley Hospice (£120).

FINANCES *Year* 2007–08 *Income* £59,554 *Grants* £80,359

TRUSTEES Arnold Denman; Dorothy Denman; David Marsh; Sue Denman; Joanna Denman.

HOW TO APPLY In writing to the correspondent.

WHO TO APPLY TO Dorothy Denman, PO Box 1881, Old Sodbury, Bristol BS37 6WS *email* dorothydenman@camers.org

CC NO 326532   **ESTABLISHED** 1983

■ The Denton Charitable Trust

WHERE FUNDING CAN BE GIVEN UK, with a preference for West Yorkshire.

WHO CAN BENEFIT Small local and UK organisations particularly interested in benefiting children and young people, older people, people with disabilities and people with cancer.

WHAT IS FUNDED Particular interest in social welfare projects rather than arts, music, environmental or historical appeals.

WHAT IS NOT FUNDED No grants for sponsorship, educational projects funded by the state, or students looking for grants to support further education, exchange visit or overseas course.

TYPE OF GRANT One-off preferred.

RANGE OF GRANTS Up to £5,000.

SAMPLE GRANTS Vizion Youth Cafe and Wesley Housing Project (£1,000 each); Shipley Women's Aid, ASBAH, International Voluntary Service, New Hope Leeds, Sangat Centre and Bradford Toy Library (£500 each); and Wharfe Valley Community Project (£100).

FINANCES *Year* 2007–08 *Income* £28,981 *Grants* £7,100 *Assets* £212,434

TRUSTEES Fiona Wood; John Wood; Susan Wood; Timothy Wood.

OTHER INFORMATION Individuals may also be supported in cases of direct need.

HOW TO APPLY In writing to the correspondent. The trustees meet in May and November and applications should be submitted in good time.

WHO TO APPLY TO Susan Wood, Trustee, Crook Farm, Denton, Ilkley LS29 0HD *Tel* 01943 603 457

CC NO 1054546   **ESTABLISHED** 1996

■ The Denton Wilde Sapte Charitable Trust

WHERE FUNDING CAN BE GIVEN Preference for the City of London and Milton Keynes.

WHO CAN BENEFIT Normally registered charities.

WHAT IS FUNDED General charitable purposes with a preference for organisations with a legal connection, such as community law centres, or children's charities, medical charities or the arts. Preference is also given to organisations which have a connection with Denton Wilde Sapte LLP or are local to the company's offices.

WHAT IS NOT FUNDED No grants to individuals. Education and scholarships will not be funded.

TYPE OF GRANT One-off and recurrent.

RANGE OF GRANTS Mainly £250–£1,000.

SAMPLE GRANTS Social Committee (£5,000); Richard House Hospice (£3,000); London Legal Support Trust (£2,000); Birbeck College (£1,500); Kids in Action and Drama Expression (£1,000 each); Essex Air Ambulance (£750); Independence at Home, Action for Blind People and Animal Foundation (£500 each); Southend Toy Library (£250); and Waltham New Town Brownies (£50).

FINANCES *Year* 2007–08 *Income* £98,295 *Grants* £77,010 *Assets* £48,715

TRUSTEES Mark Andrews; Virginia Glastonbury; Howard Morris.

HOW TO APPLY In writing only, to the correspondent. Trustees meet quarterly.

WHO TO APPLY TO Kathy Vanderhook, Administrator, 1 One Fleet Place, London EC4M 7WS *Tel* 020 7320 6048 *email* kathy.vanderhook@ dentonwildesapte.com

CC NO 1041204   **ESTABLISHED** 1994

■ The Earl of Derby's Charitable Trust

WHERE FUNDING CAN BE GIVEN Merseyside.

WHO CAN BENEFIT Local charitable organisations, predominantly within the beneficial area.

WHAT IS FUNDED Grant giving is categorised as follows: (a) age, disablement and sickness; (b) education and young people; (c) religion; (d) racing charities; (e) general.

WHAT IS NOT FUNDED No grants to individuals.

RANGE OF GRANTS £100–£1,000; generally £750.

SAMPLE GRANTS The Colonel's Fund and Liverpool University Equine Appeal (£10,000 each); Royal National Institute for the Blind – Liverpool (£5,000); Cameron House School Foundation (£2,500); Local Solutions (£1,000); St Michael's Church – Huyton, Anfield Youth Club, British Racing School and Willowbrook Hospice (£750 each); and Liver Research Trust (£500).

FINANCES *Year* 2007–08 *Income* £108,443 *Grants* £49,800 *Assets* £808,677

TRUSTEES Rt Hon. The 19th Earl of Derby; C J Allan.

HOW TO APPLY In writing to the correspondent. Trustees meet twice a year in January and July; applicants should apply two months before the meetings.

WHO TO APPLY TO The Trustees, Knowsley, Prescot, Merseyside L34 4AF *email* charity@knowsley. com

CC NO 515783   **ESTABLISHED** 1984

■ The Derbyshire Churches and Chapels Preservation Trust

WHERE FUNDING CAN BE GIVEN Derbyshire.

WHO CAN BENEFIT Churches and chapels of any Christian denomination.

WHAT IS FUNDED The preservation, repair and improvement of churches and chapels in Derbyshire.

SAMPLE GRANTS St. John the Baptist – Dronfield and Christ Church – Burbage (£10,000 each); St. Lawrence – Shottle (£5,500); All Saints – Elton (£3,700); St. Margaret Clitherow – Duffield (£1,000); and St. Margaret – Wormhill, Holy Trinity – Dinting Vale and Holy Trinity – Middleton by Wirksworth (£500 each).

FINANCES *Year* 2007–08 *Income* £196,261 *Grants* £63,167 *Assets* £217,592

TRUSTEES Alan Bemrose, Chair; David Garnett; Canon M A B Mallender; Dr Patrick Strange; Christopher Cunliffe.

HOW TO APPLY On a form available from the correspondent. The grants panel meets quarterly.

WHO TO APPLY TO Dr Patrick Strange, 1 Greenhill, Wirksworth, Derbyshire DE4 4EN *Tel* 01629 824 904

CC NO 1010953   **ESTABLISHED** 1992

■ Derbyshire Community Foundation

WHERE FUNDING CAN BE GIVEN Derbyshire and the city of Derby.

WHO CAN BENEFIT Voluntary groups and volunteers and the people they work with in Derbyshire across a wide spectrum of activity tackling disadvantage and promoting quality of life.

WHAT IS FUNDED Community groups and voluntary organisations working to tackle disadvantage and improve quality of life. Likely priority themes are as follows: supporting families; getting back to work; health and wellbeing; young people; helping groups work; and creative community.

WHAT IS NOT FUNDED The foundation's general exclusions are: profit-making organisations where individual members benefit financially (legitimate social enterprises & community interest companies can receive funding but the foundation asks that you read the additional guidelines related to this type of group structure); medical equipment; animal charities; any project which promotes faith or involves the refurbishment/building of a place of worship; statutory bodies including schools, hospitals, police etc; any project which directly replaces statutory obligations; any project which promotes a political party; projects which benefit people outside of Derbyshire; retrospective funding (grants for activities which have already taken place); and sponsored events.

TYPE OF GRANT Usually one-off, though depending on the programme and donor's wishes, the trust may give more than one grant to the same group for different projects or items. Capital, core costs, feasibility studies, research, running costs, salaries and start-up costs. Funding for up to one year will be considered.

RANGE OF GRANTS Mainly between £100 to £5,000; possibly more for managed programmes depending on their criteria.

SAMPLE GRANTS Derbyshire Rural Community Centre (£147,000); Derby CVS (£84,000); South Normanton and Pinxton Development Project (£63,000); LINKS Chesterfield and North East Derbyshire Council for Voluntary Service (£32,000); SCILLS – Sherwater Community for Independent Living (£15,000); Viva Chamber Orchestra and SAIL – Sexual Abuse and Incest Line (£10,000 each); Hollingwood After School Club (£9,900); Shipley Hall Cricket Club (£8,700); and Woodville Parish Council (£7,200).

FINANCES *Year* 2007–08 *Income* £3,973,944 *Grants* £1,465,008 *Assets* £6,117,388

TRUSTEES Helen Bishop; Arthur Blackwood; David Coleman; Kjell Karlsen; Nick Mirfin; Matthew Montague; Clive Moesby; David Moss; Lucy Palmer; Rt Rev. Alastair Redfern; Pat Taylor; David Walker; Robin Wood.

HOW TO APPLY The foundation offers several different funds, each offering funding for a maximum of twelve months and each with a specific focus or set of criteria. Please visit the foundation's website for full details of the current grant programmes and the relevant application documents. If you require any further help in deciding which fund to apply for contact the grants team on 01773 514850. Applicants should download and complete the appropriate application form from the website and send it to the correspondent with the following supporting documents: annual accounts; bank statements; group constitution; management committee form (please download this from the website); and minutes from the last management committee meeting. Applications are passed to a member of the grants team for assessment and to prepare all of the information ready to present to the award making panel. During this time, applicants are likely to be contacted by the grants team for an informal chat about their application and their group, which helps the foundation to understand the background of the project and gives the best chance of a successful bid. The decision on whether to award a grant is made by, either a panel of independent people from the local community, who meet every eight weeks, or by a panel set up by the fund-holder, who will usually meet

once every three months. Please note: the grants team are entirely independent and will not make any funding recommendations to the panels. Applicants will be informed of the decision date for their application and are invited to call the grants team or check the website, to find out the decision, two days after the panel date. You will also receive the panel decision in writing within one week of the panel date. The foundation also states that it is willing to provide full, honest feedback on all decisions and is happy to discuss any outcome with applicants.

WHO TO APPLY TO The Grants Team, Foundation House, Unicorn Business Park, Wellington Street, Ripley, Derbyshire DE5 3EH *Tel* 01773 514 850 *Fax* 01773 741 410 *email* info@derbyshirecommunityfoundation.co.uk *Website* www.derbyshirecommunityfoundation.co.uk

CC NO 1039485   **ESTABLISHED** 1996

....

■ The J N Derbyshire Trust

WHERE FUNDING CAN BE GIVEN Mainly Nottingham and Nottinghamshire.

WHO CAN BENEFIT Organisations with charitable status.

WHAT IS FUNDED General charitable purposes, including: the promotion of health; the development of physical improvement; the advancement of education; and the relief of poverty, distress and sickness. Local charities receive preferential consideration.

WHAT IS NOT FUNDED No grants to individuals. Costs of study are not supported.

TYPE OF GRANT Buildings, capital, core costs, project, research, recurring and running costs, salaries, and start-up costs will be considered. Funding may be given for up to three years.

RANGE OF GRANTS Up to £15,000.

SAMPLE GRANTS Stonebridge City Farm and NORSACA (£15,000 each); Age Concern – Nottingham and Nottinghamshire (£7,000); Elizabeth Finn Care (£5,600); I CAN, Macmillan Cancer Support, Action for ME and the Army Benevolent Fund (£5,000 each); Whizz Kidz and Motability (£4,000 each); Beeston Youth and Community Centre and Relate Nottinghamshire (£3,000 each); and Broxtowe Womens Project and YWCA – Nottingham (£2,000 each).

FINANCES *Year* 2007–08 *Income* £238,952 *Grants* £212,300 *Assets* £4,542,253

TRUSTEES Mrs A L Carver, Chair; S J Christophers; P R Moore; Mrs L Whittle; C J George; Mrs B Lawrie.

OTHER INFORMATION In 2007/08, grants were broken down into the following categories: physical health and disability (£57,000); youth organisations (£37,000); older people (£15,000); protection and welfare of women and children (£13,000); general medical and ambulance (£6,000); miscellaneous (£86,000).

HOW TO APPLY On a form available from the correspondent. Applications can be made at any time but trustees usually only meet to consider them twice a year in March and September. Details of the project are required. A reply is only given to unsuccessful applicants if they enclose an sae.

WHO TO APPLY TO David Parish, Secretary, The Poynt, 45 Wollaton Street, Nottingham NG1 5FW *Tel* 0115 948 9589 *email* david.parish@tenongroup.com

CC NO 231907   **ESTABLISHED** 1944

■ Devon Community Foundation

WHERE FUNDING CAN BE GIVEN County of Devon.

WHO CAN BENEFIT Voluntary and community groups.

WHAT IS FUNDED Support primarily for voluntary and community organisations, particularly those working to relieve the effects of poverty and disadvantage.

WHAT IS NOT FUNDED The foundation does not fund: statutory organisation's including schools; regional or local offices of national organisations; projects promoting political activities; commercial ventures; individuals; projects for the sole benefit of animals or plants; other grant making organisations; and churches. Individual programmes may have further eligibility criteria. Please check the website or contact the foundation directly to confirm that your organisation is eligible to apply.

TYPE OF GRANT Predominantly one-off small grants for projects. Running costs and start-up costs will be considered. Funding may be given for up to one year, and very occasionally for two years.

RANGE OF GRANTS £50–£10,000.

FINANCES *Year* 2007–08 *Income* £1,458,440 *Grants* £1,229,562 *Assets* £430,472

TRUSTEES David Stevens; Michael Gee; Dr Katherine Gurney; Steve Hindley; Mike Bull; Tim Legood; Anthony Melville; Mark Haskell; Dr Anne Mildmay White; Michael Hockin; Chris Hill; Arthur Ainslie; Martin Lamb; David Searle; Peter Keech; Paul Ellis; Jane McCloskey.

HOW TO APPLY The foundation's website has details of the grant schemes currently being administered.

WHO TO APPLY TO Kathy Beechen, Deputy Chief Executive, The Factory, Leat Street, Tiverton, Devon EX16 5LL *Tel* 01884 235887 *Fax* 01884 243824 *email* grants@devoncf.com *Website* www.devoncf.com

CC NO 1057923   **ESTABLISHED** 1996

■ The Devon Educational Trust

WHERE FUNDING CAN BE GIVEN Devon.

WHO CAN BENEFIT Primarily individuals living in Devon, or whose parents live in Devon. Individuals, and organisations benefiting children, young adults and students.

WHAT IS FUNDED The education of people under the age of 25.

WHAT IS NOT FUNDED No grants for school fees and help is not normally given to people starting a second or higher degree.

RANGE OF GRANTS Up to £4,000.

SAMPLE GRANTS Sir Francis Chichester Trust (£4,000); Castle Primary School (£1,200); Chance to Shine (£500); Ide Primary School (£250); and Fairbanks Family Centre (£220).

FINANCES *Year* 2008 *Income* £38,352 *Grants* £7,475 *Assets* £815,262

TRUSTEES Prof. W J Forsythe, Chair; Mrs J A E Cook; H B Evans; Dr C M Gillet; F J Rosamond; B W Wills-Pope; D R Wakinshaw.

OTHER INFORMATION Grants were made to 122 individuals totalling £26,000.

HOW TO APPLY In writing to the correspondent for an application form. Two referees will be approached for letters of support for each applicant. The trustees meet three times a year in March, July and November with a closing date four weeks before each meeting.

WHO TO APPLY TO The Clerk, PO Box 86, Teignmouth TQ14 8ZT *email* jc.matthews@tiscali.co.uk

CC NO 220921   **ESTABLISHED** 1988

■ The Devon Historic Churches Trust

WHERE FUNDING CAN BE GIVEN Devon and diocese of Exeter.

WHO CAN BENEFIT Churches and chapels.

WHAT IS FUNDED The trust gives grants/loans for 'the preservation, repair, maintenance, improvement and upkeep of churches in the County of Devon and the diocese of Exeter.'

WHAT IS NOT FUNDED Redundant churches/chapels, bells, plumbing, disabled facilities and routine maintenance.

TYPE OF GRANT Grants and loans.

RANGE OF GRANTS Around £500–£5,000.

SAMPLE GRANTS Diptford – St Mary (£4,500); Chudleigh Knighton (£4,000); Marldon and Crediton Congregational (£3,000 each); Mary Tavy (£2,000); Bridford (£1,500); Inwardleigh (£1,000); and East Budleigh (£500).

FINANCES *Year* 2007–08 *Income* £238,163 *Grants* £51,645 *Assets* £1,113,195

TRUSTEES Lady Anne Boles, Chair; Earl of Devon; Nicholas Maxwell-Lawford; Carol Plumstead; Lt Cdr Christopher Tuke; Lt Col James Michie; Rosemary Howell; Judith Kauntze; John Malleson; Philip Tuckett; Penelope Dudgeon; Christopher Hewetson; Rev Dr David Keep; Lt Col Charles Rich.

HOW TO APPLY In writing to the correspondent. The trustees meet quarterly to receive reports from officers and committees and to consider grant applications.

WHO TO APPLY TO John Malleson, Clifford Lodge, Drewsteignton, Exeter EX6 6QE *Tel* 01647 24104 *email* contact@devonhistoricchurches.co.uk *Website* www.devonhistoricchurches.co.uk

CC NO 265594   **ESTABLISHED** 1973

■ The Duke of Devonshire's Charitable Trust

WHERE FUNDING CAN BE GIVEN UK, with a preference for Derbyshire.

WHO CAN BENEFIT Registered charities only.

WHAT IS FUNDED General charitable purposes.

WHAT IS NOT FUNDED Grants are only given to registered charities and not to individuals.

RANGE OF GRANTS £100–£8,000.

SAMPLE GRANTS Treasures Nursery (£8,000); Bolton Abbey PCC and Royal Agricultural Benevolent Fund (£7,000 each); and Atlantic Salmon Fishing Trust, Contact the Elderly, Hearing Dogs for Deaf People and Wilsthorpe Business and Enterprise College (£5,000 each); Pilsley C of E Trust Account (£2,500); Chesterfield and District Shopmobility (£2,000); and Ashgate Hospice, Matlock Hospitals League of Friends and St John Ambulance Derbyshire (£1,000 each).

FINANCES *Year* 2007–08 *Income* £290,484 *Grants* £102,384 *Assets* £10,425,147

TRUSTEES Duke of Devonshire; Duchess of Devonshire; Earl of Burlington; Sir Richard Beckett.

HOW TO APPLY In writing to the correspondent.

WHO TO APPLY TO The Trustees, Chatsworth, Bakewell, Derbyshire DE45 1PP

CC NO 213519   **ESTABLISHED** 1949

■ The Sandy Dewhirst Charitable Trust

WHERE FUNDING CAN BE GIVEN UK, with a strong preference for East and North Yorkshire.

WHO CAN BENEFIT Charitable organisations and individuals connected with I J Dewhirst Holdings Limited.

WHAT IS FUNDED General and relief-in-need.

SAMPLE GRANTS Samaritans (£10,000); St Mary's Church – Rievaulx (£5,000); Committee of Huby and Weeton Pre-School and Shrewsbury Drapers Co. (£2,000 each); Army Benevolent Fund (£1,500); Driffield Agricultural Society and York Minster Fund (£1,000); All Saints Church Nafferton, All Saints Church – Kilham, Driffield Children's Outing Fund, Filey Sea Cadets, Hull Sea Cadets Corps and St Catherine's Hospice (£500 each); and Cancer Research (£250).

FINANCES *Year* 2007 *Income* £70,551 *Grants* £37,750 *Assets* £1,881,980

TRUSTEES T C Dewhirst; P J Howell; J A R Dewhirst.

OTHER INFORMATION The grant total in 2007 included £6,000 distributed in two grants to individuals.

HOW TO APPLY The trust does not accept unsolicited applications.

WHO TO APPLY TO The Secretary, Addleshaw Goddard, 100 Barbirolli Square, Manchester M2 3AB

CC NO 279161 **ESTABLISHED** 1979

■ DG Charitable Settlement

WHERE FUNDING CAN BE GIVEN UK.

WHO CAN BENEFIT Registered charities.

WHAT IS FUNDED General charitable purposes.

RANGE OF GRANTS £500–£200,000.

SAMPLE GRANTS Previous beneficiaries have included Age Concern, Amnesty International, Battersea Home for Dogs, Crisis, Cancer Research UK, Environmental Investigation Agency Charitable Trust, Great Ormond Street Hospital, Greenpeace, IPPF Europe, Terrence Higgins Trust, Medical Foundation for Victims of Torture, Oxfam, Prisoners Abroad, Prisoners of Conscience Appeal Fund, Scope, St Richard's Hospital Charitable Trust and Shelter.

FINANCES *Year* 2007–08 *Income* £17,414

TRUSTEES D J Gilmour; P Grafton-Green; Ms P A Samson.

HOW TO APPLY This trust does not consider unsolicited applications.

WHO TO APPLY TO Joanna Nelson, PO Box 62, Heathfield, East Sussex TN21 8ZE

CC NO 1040778 **ESTABLISHED** 1994

■ The Laduma Dhamecha Charitable Trust

WHERE FUNDING CAN BE GIVEN UK and overseas.

WHO CAN BENEFIT Organisations only.

WHAT IS FUNDED General charitable purposes including the relief of sickness and education in rural areas.

FINANCES *Year* 2007–08 *Income* £278,676 *Grants* £68,335 *Assets* £1,685,583

TRUSTEES K R Dhamecha; S R Dhamecha; P K Dhamecha.

HOW TO APPLY In writing to the correspondent.

WHO TO APPLY TO Pradip Dhamecha, Trustee, 2 Hathaway Close, Stanmore, Middlesex HA7 3NR

CC NO 328678 **ESTABLISHED** 1990

■ Diabetes UK

WHERE FUNDING CAN BE GIVEN UK.

WHO CAN BENEFIT Organisations which benefit people with diabetes.

WHAT IS FUNDED To promote and fund research into the causes and effects of diabetes, and the treatment and alleviation of the effects of diabetes to minimise the potential serious complications that can arise.

TYPE OF GRANT Equipment, fellowships, research grants, small grants, and studentships will be considered.

RANGE OF GRANTS £5,000–£40,000.

SAMPLE GRANTS Grants to institutions were broken down as follows: cause and prevention – £3.21 million; care and treatment – £1.65 million; cure – £170,000.

FINANCES *Year* 2008 *Income* £30,154,000 *Grants* £5,032,000 *Assets* £10,309,000

TRUSTEES Rekha Wadhwani; Alison Finney; David McCance; John Grumitt; Ian Powell; Dr Niti Pall; Graham Spooner; Renata Drinkwater; Frank Moxon; Susan Browell; Gerard Tosh; Prof. Sir George Alberti.

HOW TO APPLY Potential applicants are first advised to read the 'Diabetes UK's research strategy' and the 'General guide to applicants', both available on the trust's website. Further information on the application process and deadlines for each specific scheme is also available on the website or by contacting the trust directly.

WHO TO APPLY TO Tanya Bernstein, Administrator, 10 Parkway, London NW1 7AA *Tel* 020 7424 1000 *Fax* 020 7424 1001 *email* info@diabetes.org. uk *Website* www.diabetes.org.uk

CC NO 215199 **ESTABLISHED** 1934

■ Alan and Sheila Diamond Charitable Trust

WHERE FUNDING CAN BE GIVEN UK.

WHO CAN BENEFIT Registered charities only, particularly Jewish charities.

WHAT IS FUNDED Jewish causes and general charitable purposes.

WHAT IS NOT FUNDED No grants to individuals.

SAMPLE GRANTS Norwood (£7,000); British WIZO (£5,300); Anglo Israel Association, British School of Osteopathy and Community Security Trust (£4,000 each); Sidney Sussex College and UJIA (£3,000 each); Youth Aliyah Child Rescue (£2,500); and Magen David Adorn (£2,100); British Friends of Bar-Ilan University and Holocaust Educational Trust (£1,000 each); British Technion Society (£600); British ORT and St Mary's Hospital (£500 each); Jewish Care (£250); and Demelza Hospice Care for Children, Jewish Marriage Council, Kisharon, Weiner Library Endowment Trust and ZSV Trust (£100 each).

FINANCES *Year* 2007–08 *Income* £68,537 *Grants* £57,357 *Assets* £1,512,580

TRUSTEES A Diamond, Chair; Mrs S Diamond; J R Kropman; Ms K Goldberg.

HOW TO APPLY The trust states that it will not consider unsolicited applications. No preliminary telephone calls. There are no regular trustees' meetings. The trustees frequently decide how the funds should be allocated. The trustees have their own guidelines, which are not published.

WHO TO APPLY TO The Trustees, Regency House, 3 Grosvenor Square, Southampton SO15 2BE

CC NO 274312 **ESTABLISHED** 1977

■ The Diana, Princess of Wales Memorial Fund

WHERE FUNDING CAN BE GIVEN Unrestricted, mainly the UK and Africa.

WHO CAN BENEFIT Registered charities working with the most disadvantaged people in the UK and around the world.

WHAT IS FUNDED 'From 2007 to 2012, the fund's grant-making activities will be grouped under three initiatives: Palliative Care – under which the trust is committed to spending up to £10 million over five years to promote the scale-up of palliative care in Ethiopia, Malawi, Kenya, Rwanda, South Africa, Tanzania, Uganda, Zambia and Zimbabwe, and its integration into their governments' health policies; Refugee and Asylum Seekers – under which the trust is committed to spending up to £10 million over five years to raise awareness and highlight the needs and issues of young refugees and asylum seekers; Partnership – under which the trust is committed to spending up to £5 million over five years to follow-up and add leverage to its previous investments into penal affairs in the UK, and internationally into its programme on eradicating explosive remnants of war.'

WHAT IS NOT FUNDED The trust will not fund individuals or projects outside its funding priorities.

TYPE OF GRANT Full project funding. Campaigning. Multi-year grants available.

RANGE OF GRANTS £2,000 and over.

SAMPLE GRANTS The Church of England Children's Society (£907,000); Bail for Immigration Detainees (£345,000); Landmine Action – Cluster Munitions Coalition (£266,000); Hereford Muheza Link Society (£231,000); Island Hospice and Bereavement Service (£155,000); PASADA (£95,000); Kenya Hospices and Palliative Care Association (£61,000); Wits Health Consortium (£45,000); Refugee Action (£25,000); Catholic Diocese of Mansa Home Based Care (£20,000); Zambia Ministry of Health (£5,000); and University of Dundee (£2,000).

FINANCES *Year* 2008 *Income* £2,290,000 *Grants* £3,775,000 *Assets* £21,545,000

TRUSTEES The Diana, Princess of Wales Memorial Fund Trustee Company.

OTHER INFORMATION In November 2004, a $25 million joint grants scheme between the Diana, Princess of Wales Memorial Fund and the Franklin Mint was announced as part of their out-of-court settlement of a legal dispute. Under the joint grants scheme, some £13.5 million of grants have been made to a jointly agreed list of excellent charitable causes that resonate with the memory of the late Diana, Princess of Wales.

HOW TO APPLY 'Grants are provided on an 'invitation-to-bid' basis or through negotiated partnerships with selected organisations that have the capacity to deliver the initiatives' desired outcomes. Projects will be rigorously assessed against the initiatives' strategic objectives, and to maximise impact grants are awarded for up to five years with a mid-term review.'

'As the fund is engaged in pro-active grant-making, providing grants on 'invitation to bid' basis, the fund is unable to accept general requests for funding from either organisations or individuals. The demand for funds is always greater than the money available, and the fund is of the belief that we can help more people by distributing grants to organisations that have the capacity to deliver the desired outcomes of our three initiatives.'

WHO TO APPLY TO Helen Jones, Office Manager, The County Hall, Westminster Bridge Road, London SE1 7PB *Tel* 020 7902 5500 *Fax* 020 7902 5511 *email* memorial.fund@memfund.org.uk *Website* www.theworkcontinues.org
CC NO 1064238 **ESTABLISHED** 1997

■ The Dibden Allotments Charity

WHERE FUNDING CAN BE GIVEN Hythe, Fawley and Marchwood.

WHO CAN BENEFIT Grants can be made to individuals as well as organisations, including students and unemployed people.

WHAT IS FUNDED To relieve need, hardship or distress, and to invest in the community's future. Grants are awarded to individuals in need, to voluntary and charitable organisations, and to schemes benefiting children, particularly under-fives, older people and young people.

WHAT IS NOT FUNDED Scholarships to 'Schools of Excellence', such as those for the performing arts.

RANGE OF GRANTS Up to £21,000.

SAMPLE GRANTS Handy Trust (£21,000); Hythe and Dibden Mini Buses (£20,000); Waterside CAB (£9,000); Oakhaven Hospice (£5,000); Applemore College (£1,600); Waterside Primary (£1,500); Theodora Childrens Trust (£1,000); Students Exploring Marriage Trust (£550); and Waterside Baton Twirlers (£500).

FINANCES *Year* 2007–08 *Income* £404,249 *Grants* £364,698 *Assets* £8,014,587

TRUSTEES Mike Harvey, Chair; Maureen McLean; Judy Saxby; Martin Cox; Malcolm Fidler; Joan Shewry; Jennifer Barrow; Patricia Hedges; Peter Parrott.

OTHER INFORMATION £189,000 was given to individuals.

HOW TO APPLY In writing to the correspondent who will supply guidelines and application forms. A third party, such as social services, teachers, and so on, must support applications from individuals.

WHO TO APPLY TO Barrie Smallcalder, Clerk to the Trustees, 7 Drummond Court, Hythe, Southampton, Hampshire SO45 6HD *Tel* 023 8084 1305 *Fax* 023 8084 1305 *email* dibdenallotmentscharity@btconnect.com
CC NO 255778 **ESTABLISHED** 1995

■ The Gillian Dickinson Trust

WHERE FUNDING CAN BE GIVEN County Durham, Northumberland and Tyne and Wear.

WHO CAN BENEFIT Registered charities, museums, arts and theatre groups.

WHAT IS FUNDED Arts and general charitable purposes.

RANGE OF GRANTS Up to £75,000.

SAMPLE GRANTS £75,000 each to Durham University and Live Theatre; £10,000 each to Tyne and Wear Museums, Calvert Trust and National Glass Centre; £5,000 to Frosterley Community School; £2,500 to Bailey Theatre Company; and £2,400 to Magic Lantern.

FINANCES *Year* 2007–08 *Income* £82,477 *Grants* £189,900 *Assets* £2,332,523

TRUSTEES Alexander Dickinson; Piers Dickinson; Adrain Gifford; James Ramsbotham.

HOW TO APPLY In writing to the correspondent.

WHO TO APPLY TO Patrick Evans, St Ann's Wharf, 112 Quayside, Newcastle Upon Tyne NE1 3DX *Tel* 0191 2799628 *Fax* 0191 2799100
CC NO 1094362 **ESTABLISHED** 2002

■ The Dickon Trust

WHERE FUNDING CAN BE GIVEN North East England and Scotland.

WHO CAN BENEFIT Registered charities.

WHAT IS FUNDED General charitable purposes.

WHAT IS NOT FUNDED No support for individuals, unregistered charities or churches.

TYPE OF GRANT One-off.

RANGE OF GRANTS £500–£2,000.

SAMPLE GRANTS Burns Group Unit Support, Edinburgh Young Carers Project and MS Research Fund Newcastle University (£2,000 each); Alexandra Rose Day, British Red Cross – Northumbria Branch, Calvert Trust, Changing Faces, the Children's Charity, Headway, Mitford Church, National Talking Newspapers, Northumberland Association of Clubs for Young People, React, Spinal Injuries Association, the Yard and Whizz Kidz (£1,000 each); and Lothian Autistic Society Tyneside Challenge (£500 each).

FINANCES *Year* 2007–08 *Income* £57,038 *Grants* £38,000 *Assets* £1,443,713

TRUSTEES Mrs D L Barrett; Major-General R V Brims; R Y Barrett; M L Robson; A Copeman.

HOW TO APPLY Applications can be made online at the trust's website. The trustees meet twice a year in summer and winter to consider appeals. Any applications received by the end of October will be considered at the winter meeting and any applications made after that time, up to the end of May, will be considered at the summer meeting.

WHO TO APPLY TO Helen Tavroges, Dickinson Dees, St Anne's Wharf, 112 Quayside, Newcastle NE99 1SB *Tel* 0191 279 9698 *Website* www.dickontrust.org.uk

CC NO 327202   **ESTABLISHED** 1986

■ The Digbeth Trust

WHERE FUNDING CAN BE GIVEN West Midlands, principally Birmingham.

WHO CAN BENEFIT Smaller local, new and emerging voluntary and community groups, particularly those addressing exclusion and disadvantage.

WHAT IS FUNDED The trust manages a number of grant programmes that are generally targeted by area or theme, or both. See its website for current schemes.

WHAT IS NOT FUNDED General appeals, capital core costs, medical research, project running costs and grants for individuals.

TYPE OF GRANT One-off grants to enable groups to access specialist advice and services.

FINANCES *Year* 2007–08 *Income* £449,133 *Grants* £198,785 *Assets* £122,319

TRUSTEES Eddie Currall, Chair; Christopher Burrows; John Copping; Michael Woolton; David Williams-Masinda; Karen Garry; Polly Goodwin; Safaraz Ali; Claire Barton; Graham Mitchell; Nigel Potter.

HOW TO APPLY The trust welcomes direct contact with groups. Application forms and guidance notes are available for the programmes it manages (this changes from time to time). Development worker support is offered to eligible groups.

WHO TO APPLY TO Kate Hazlewood, Manager, Unit 321, The Custard Factory, Gibb Street, Digbeth, Birmingham B9 4AA *Tel* 0121 753 0706 *Fax* 0121 248 3323 *email* info@digbethtrust.org.uk *Website* www.digbethtrust.org.uk

CC NO 517343   **ESTABLISHED** 1984

■ The Dinwoodie Settlement

WHERE FUNDING CAN BE GIVEN UK.

WHO CAN BENEFIT Organisations benefiting academics and postgraduate research workers.

WHAT IS FUNDED Postgraduate medical education centres (PMCs) and research fellowships for suitably qualified medical practitioners of registrar status in general medicine or general surgery.

WHAT IS NOT FUNDED Anything falling outside the main areas of work referred to above. The trustees do not expect to fund consumable or equipment costs or relieve the NHS of its financial responsibilities.

TYPE OF GRANT Building projects will be considered. The trust's funds can be committed for three years when supporting major projects.

RANGE OF GRANTS Maximum of £1 million towards no more than one postgraduate medical centre project in an area. No more than the salary of two research workers in any one year.

SAMPLE GRANTS Wolverhampton Medical Institute (£85,000); and Imperial College London (£76,000).

FINANCES *Year* 2007–08 *Income* £483,473 *Grants* £160,938 *Assets* £4,660,332

TRUSTEES William A Fairbairn; Dr John M Fowler; Miss Christian Webster; Rodney B N Fisher; John A Gibson.

OTHER INFORMATION Annual figures for grants versus income may vary substantially as payments towards building costs of each project usually absorb more than one year's available income.

HOW TO APPLY The trustees state they are proactive rather than reactive in their grant-giving. Negotiating for new PMCs and monitoring their construction invariably takes a number of years.

WHO TO APPLY TO The Clerk to the Trustees, c/o Thomas Eggar, The Corn Exchange, Baffins Lane, Chichester, West Sussex PO19 1GK

CC NO 255495   **ESTABLISHED** 1968

■ Disability Aid Fund (The Roger and Jean Jefcoate Trust)

WHERE FUNDING CAN BE GIVEN UK.

WHO CAN BENEFIT People with physical, mental or multiple disabilities or hearing or visual impairment.

WHAT IS FUNDED 'In partnership with other national, regional and local grantmakers the trust provides a wide range of technology like adapted computers and communication aids for people with physical, mental or multiple disabilities or hearing or visual impairment. People with poorly understood conditions are especially welcome to apply; examples include fibromyalgia, chronic fatigue syndrome or ME (myalgic encephalomyelitis), multiple chemical sensitivity, upper limb disorder or RSI (repetitive strain injury), dyslexia, post traumatic stress disorder, mental illness and similar, often hidden, disabilities which lack the compassion factor. The trustees are also keen to help people with progressive neurological conditions like muscular dystrophy, multiple sclerosis, Parkinson's disease, Friedreich's ataxia or motor neurone disease where there is often a total loss of speech. Providing an adapted portable computer or communication aid at this crucial time, when remaining lifespan is limited, can be truly vital. The trust co-operates closely with local voluntary agencies and statutory services, usually arranging a personal visit by a specialist technology assessor who works with the disabled person and their family and local education and healthcare professionals to select and cost the most suitable equipment. The trustees also support small and well run local, regional and national organisations with strong support from volunteers and with only modest expenditure on fundraising and administration, especially those where service users actively help to run the group.'

SAMPLE GRANTS Cancer and Bio-detection Dogs – Aylesbury, Canine Partners, ME Research UK – Perth and West Cumbria Society for the Blind (£10,000 each); British Sjogren's Association – Birmingham (£7,000); Cancer and Bio-detection Dogs – Aylesbury (£6,000); PACE – Aylesbury, SHARE Community – Wandsworth, Therapy Centre – Bedford and Woodrow High House – Amersham (£5,000 each); DIAL Northamptonshire – Daventry (£4,000); Multiple Sclerosis National Therapy Centres (£3,500); and MS Therapy Centre – Hereford (£1,000).

FINANCES *Year* 2007–08 *Income* £228,570
Grants £187,671 *Assets* £2,492,596

TRUSTEES Vivien Dinning, Chair; Roger Jefcoate; Valerie Henchoz; Rosemary McCloskey; Carol Wemyss.

OTHER INFORMATION The grant total in 2007–08 included £47,000 given in 45 grants to individuals.

HOW TO APPLY In writing to the correspondent.

WHO TO APPLY TO Roger Jefcoate, Trustee, 2 Swanbourne Road, Mursley, Milton Keynes MK17 0JA

CC NO 1096211   **ESTABLISHED** 2002

■ Dischma Charitable Trust

WHERE FUNDING CAN BE GIVEN Worldwide, with a strong preference for London and the south east of England.

WHO CAN BENEFIT Charitable organisations.

WHAT IS FUNDED General charitable purposes, with a preference for education, arts and culture, conservation and human and animal welfare.

WHAT IS NOT FUNDED Medical research charities.

RANGE OF GRANTS £500–£5,000.

SAMPLE GRANTS British Association for Adopting and Fostering, Treloars, Trinity Hospice and World Wildlife Fund (£5,000 each); Happy Days Children's Charity and SANE (£3,500 each); Epic Arts and Acid Survivors Trust International (£3,000 each); International Animal Rescue (£2,500); and UK Sports Association (£2,000).

FINANCES *Year* 2007 *Income* £82,568
Grants £135,000 *Assets* £5,157,878

TRUSTEES Simon Robertson; Edward Robertson; Lorna Robertson Timmis; Virginia Robertson; Robertson; Arabella Brooke.

HOW TO APPLY The trustees meet half-yearly to review applications for funding. Only successful applicants are notified of the trustees' decision. Certain charities are supported annually, although no commitment is given.

WHO TO APPLY TO Linda Cousins, The Secretary, Rathbone Trust Company Ltd, c/o 159 New Bond Street, London W15 2UD *Tel* 020 7399 0820 *email* linda.cousins@rathbones.com

CC NO 1077501   **ESTABLISHED** 1999

■ The Djanogly Foundation

WHERE FUNDING CAN BE GIVEN Worldwide.

WHO CAN BENEFIT Registered charities.

WHAT IS FUNDED Developments in medicine, education, social welfare and the arts. Welfare of older and younger people. Jewish charities.

RANGE OF GRANTS £15–£200,000.

SAMPLE GRANTS Great Ormond Street Children's Hospital and British Museum Development Trust (£200,000 each); Weizmann Institute Foundation (£175,000); Jerusalem Foundation (£161,000); University of Nottingham (£100,000); National Gallery Trust (£83,000); Nottingham Playhouse (£50,000); Royal Anglican Benevolent Fund (£30,000); Jewish Care (£12,000); St Nicholas School (£8,000); Norwood (£5,000); Imperial War Museum (£2,000); and WIZO (£500).

FINANCES *Year* 2007–08 *Income* £1,390,235
Grants £1,123,865 *Assets* £14,788,065

TRUSTEES Sir Harry Djanogly; Michael S Djanogly; Lady Djanogly.

HOW TO APPLY In writing to the correspondent.

WHO TO APPLY TO Christopher Sills, Secretary, 3 Angel Court, London SW1Y 6QF *Tel* 020 7930 9845

CC NO 280500   **ESTABLISHED** 1980

■ The DLA Piper Rudnick Gray Cary Charitable Trust (previously known as the DLA Charitable Trust)

WHERE FUNDING CAN BE GIVEN UK.

WHO CAN BENEFIT Charitable organisations.

WHAT IS FUNDED General charitable purposes.

WHAT IS NOT FUNDED No grants to individuals.

TYPE OF GRANT Mainly single donations.

RANGE OF GRANTS £1,000–£10,000.

SAMPLE GRANTS The Cutty Sark Trust (£10,000); Solicitors' Benevolent Association (£8,500); Christie's Hospital, Green Belt Movement International and The Prince's Trust (£5,000 each); Yorkshire Air Ambulance and South Yorkshire Community Foundation Flood Disaster Relief Fund, The University of Michigan Law School (£51,000).

FINANCES *Year* 2008 *Income* £131,693
Grants £131,611 *Assets* £235,779

TRUSTEES N G Knowles; P Rooney.

HOW TO APPLY In writing to the correspondent, for consideration every three months.

WHO TO APPLY TO G J Smallman, Secretary, Fountain Precinct, Balm Green, Sheffield S1 1RZ *Tel* 0114 267 5594 *email* godfrey.smallman@ wrigleys.co.uk

CC NO 327280   **ESTABLISHED** 1986

■ The DLM Charitable Trust

WHERE FUNDING CAN BE GIVEN UK, especially the Oxford area.

WHO CAN BENEFIT Organisations benefiting: children; young adults; older people; medical professionals, nurses and doctors; and people with head and other injuries, heart disease or blindness.

WHAT IS FUNDED Charities operating in Oxford and the surrounding areas, particularly charities working in the fields of: arts, culture and recreation; religious buildings; self-help groups; the conservation of historic buildings; memorials; monuments and waterways; schools; community centres and village halls; parks; various community services and other charitable purposes.

WHAT IS NOT FUNDED No grants to individuals.

TYPE OF GRANT Feasibility studies, one-off, research, recurring costs, running costs and start-up costs. Funding of up to three years will be considered.

SAMPLE GRANTS The Ley Community (£20,000); Wildlife Research Conservation Unit and Pathway Workshop (£10,000 each); Prostate Cancer Charity and Bayworth Baptist Charity (£5,000 each); Oxford Youth Works (£2,500); Harvest Trust Holidays for Children and Christians Against Poverty (£2,000); Oxfordshire Mind and Guide Dogs for the Blind (£1,000).

FINANCES *Year* 2007–08 *Income* £150,184 *Grants* £105,500 *Assets* £4,931,005

TRUSTEES Dr E A de la Mare; Mrs P Sawyer; J A Cloke; Miss J E Sawyer.

HOW TO APPLY In writing to the correspondent. Trustees meet in February, July and November to consider applications.

WHO TO APPLY TO J A Cloke, Trustee, Cloke and Co., Warnford Court, Throgmorton Street, London EC2N 2AT *Tel* 020 7638 8992

CC NO 328520   **ESTABLISHED** 1990

■ The DM Charitable Trust

WHERE FUNDING CAN BE GIVEN England and Wales and Israel.

WHO CAN BENEFIT Registered charities.

WHAT IS FUNDED General charitable purposes.

FINANCES *Year* 2007–08 *Income* £1,885,880 *Grants* £2,376,084 *Assets* £1,455,043

TRUSTEES S J Goldberg, Chair; D Cohen; P Klein.

HOW TO APPLY In writing to the correspondent.

WHO TO APPLY TO S J Goldberg, Trustee, Ground Floor, Sutherland House, 70–78 West Hendon Broadway, London NW9 7BT

CC NO 1110419   **ESTABLISHED** 2005

■ Louise Dobson Charitable Trust

WHERE FUNDING CAN BE GIVEN UK, with some preference for West Sussex.

WHO CAN BENEFIT Children, people with mental disabilities, religious groups and general poverty relief.

WHAT IS FUNDED General charitable purposes with some preference for causes local to the trust.

SAMPLE GRANTS Previous beneficiaries have included: CAFOD (£1,000); Worth Abbey Lay Community (£700); HCPT (£650); Worth Abbey Parish (£500); A and B Lourdes Fund (£450); Inside Trust (£350); St Catherine's Hospice (£300); and Catherington School, Catenian Association and SASBA (£200 each).

FINANCES *Year* 2007–08 *Income* £5,159 *Grants* £5,000

TRUSTEES Christopher Dobson, Chair; Stephen Leach.

HOW TO APPLY In writing to the correspondent.

WHO TO APPLY TO C N Y Dobson, Sopers Ride, Selsfield Road, Turners Hill, Crawley, West Sussex RH10 4PP *Tel* 01342 715345

CC NO 1022659   **ESTABLISHED** 1986

■ The Derek and Eileen Dodgson Foundation

WHERE FUNDING CAN BE GIVEN In practice, Brighton and Hove.

WHO CAN BENEFIT Individuals and organisations.

WHAT IS FUNDED Welfare of older people.

SAMPLE GRANTS No details of grant beneficiaries were available.

FINANCES *Year* 2007–08 *Income* £113,653 *Grants* £87,118 *Assets* £1,936,716

TRUSTEES C C K Butler, Chair; P E Goldsmith; R Prater; E Squires.

HOW TO APPLY In writing to the correspondent. Trustees meet quarterly, or more frequently if necessary to assess grant applications.

WHO TO APPLY TO Ian W Dodd, Clerk, 8 Locks Hill, Portslade, Brighton and Hove, East Sussex BN41 2LB *Tel* 01273 419 802 *email* ianw.dodd@ntlworld.com

CC NO 1018776   **ESTABLISHED** 1993

■ The Dollond Charitable Trust

WHERE FUNDING CAN BE GIVEN UK and Israel.

WHO CAN BENEFIT Jewish organisations.

WHAT IS FUNDED Jewish communities; general charitable purposes.

TYPE OF GRANT One-off and recurrent.

RANGE OF GRANTS Typically £5,000–£10,000.

SAMPLE GRANTS Yavneh College, Borehamwood (£400,000); British Friends of Shuvu/Return (£135,000 in total); Jerusalem College of Technology (£56,000); Yeshivas Ateret Shlomo (£20,000); Beis Sorah Schneiver School, Great Ormond Street Hospital, Kol Torah College Jerusalem, Norwood Ravenswood, Side by Side and WST Charity Limited (£10,000 each); and British Friends of Ariel, Cancer Research UK, Jewish Deaf Association, Menorah Foundation, Torah Vodaas Ltd and Yeshiva Brisk (£5,000 each).

FINANCES *Year* 2007–08 *Income* £1,989,080 *Grants* £1,003,000 *Assets* £26,816,818

TRUSTEES Adrian Dollond; Jeffery Milston; Mellisa Dollond; Brian Dollond; Rina Dollond.

HOW TO APPLY In writing to the correspondent.

WHO TO APPLY TO Jeffery Milston, Trustee, c/o FMCB, Hathaway House, Popes Drive, Finchley, London N3 1QF *Tel* 020 8346 6446 *email* gwz@fmcb.co.uk

CC NO 293459   **ESTABLISHED** 1986

■ Domepride Ltd

WHERE FUNDING CAN BE GIVEN UK and overseas.

WHO CAN BENEFIT To benefit Jewish people, at risk groups, and people who are disadvantaged by poverty or socially isolated.

WHAT IS FUNDED Jewish causes, especially those in the welfare field. General charitable purposes.

RANGE OF GRANTS About £500– £5,000.

SAMPLE GRANTS Previous beneficiaries include: Belz, Agudas Israel Housing Association, Chasdei Yoel, Asos Chesed, Bnos Yisroel Schools, Merkaz Torah Vochesed, Nitra and Ahavas Chesed.

FINANCES *Year* 2007–08 *Income* £128,173 *Grants* £44,491 *Assets* £39,092

TRUSTEES J Padwa; G Padwa; A J Cohen; E Padwa; N Padwa.

OTHER INFORMATION No grants list was available from the latest accounts.

HOW TO APPLY In writing to the correspondent.

WHO TO APPLY TO The Trustees, c/o 3rd Floor, Manchester House, 86 Princess Street, Manchester M1 6NG

CC NO 289426   **ESTABLISHED** 1983

■ The Dorcas Trust

WHERE FUNDING CAN BE GIVEN UK.

WHO CAN BENEFIT Designated charities specified by the trustees, benefiting children, young adults, students, Christians, and people disadvantaged by poverty.

WHAT IS FUNDED Advancement of the Christian religion, relief of poverty and advancement of education.

SAMPLE GRANTS Previous beneficiaries have included: Dorcas Developments Limited (£103,000); Navigators (£15,000); Newmarket Day Centre (£14,000); World Vision (£5,000); Mildmay Mission (£3,000); Integra (£2,000); Shaftesbury Society and Moorlands Bible College (£1,000 each); Send a Cow (£500); Chernobyl Children's Lifeline (£100); and RNIB (£50).

FINANCES *Year* 2008–09 *Income* £47,375 *Grants* £33,521 *Assets* £1,183,477

TRUSTEES J C L Broad; J D Broad; P L Butler.

OTHER INFORMATION The trustees will also consider making loans to organisations and individuals

HOW TO APPLY In writing to the correspondent, although the trust stated that applications cannot be considered as funds are already committed.

WHO TO APPLY TO I Taylor, Port of Liverpool Building, Pier Head, Liverpool L3 1NW *Tel* 0151 236 6666

CC NO 275494 **ESTABLISHED** 1978

■ The Dorema Charitable Trust

WHERE FUNDING CAN BE GIVEN UK.

WHO CAN BENEFIT Organisations benefiting children, young adults, older people, at-risk groups and socially isolated people.

WHAT IS FUNDED Medicine, health, welfare, education and religion.

TYPE OF GRANT One off and recurrent.

SAMPLE GRANTS A list of beneficiaries was not available.

FINANCES *Year* 2008 *Income* £63,040 *Grants* £27,500 *Assets* £233,808

TRUSTEES D S M Nussbaum; Mrs K M Nussbaum; S Murray-Williams.

HOW TO APPLY The trust strongly stated that unsolicited applications are not considered, describing such appeals as a waste of charitable resources.

WHO TO APPLY TO D S M Nussbaum, Trustee, 4 Church Grove, Amersham, Buckinghamshire HP6 6SH

CC NO 287001 **ESTABLISHED** 1983

■ Dorfred Charitable Trust

WHERE FUNDING CAN BE GIVEN Worldwide.

WHO CAN BENEFIT Small UK-registered charities working in Africa, Asia and South America.

WHAT IS FUNDED Projects working to alleviate the many problems of peoples in 'poorer' countries and emergency aid in response to, for example, natural disasters or war.

TYPE OF GRANT Mainly small one-off grants.

SAMPLE GRANTS Previous beneficiaries include: U.C.S. The Griffin Trust, Tree Aid, Starfish Greathearts Foundation, Consortium for Street Children, Excellent Development, Interhealth, Power International, International Nepal Fellowship and Voluntary Missionary Movement.

FINANCES *Year* 2007–08 *Income* £18,536 *Grants* £40,000

TRUSTEES Roger E Dean; Patricia J Fulker; Philip G Gardam; Rev Father Wood.

HOW TO APPLY In writing to the correspondent.

WHO TO APPLY TO Philip Gardam, Trustee, 9 Bailey Mews, Auckland Road, Cambridge CB5 8DR *Tel* 01233 510914 *email* info@dorfred-trust.org.uk *Website* www.dorfred-trust.org.uk

CC NO 1092347 **ESTABLISHED** 2001

■ The Dorset Historic Churches Trust

WHERE FUNDING CAN BE GIVEN Dorset.

WHO CAN BENEFIT Churches.

WHAT IS FUNDED The trust gives grants for 'the preservation, repair, maintenance and improvement of churches in Dorset.'

TYPE OF GRANT One-off grants, mainly, but also interest-free loans for up to four years will be considered.

RANGE OF GRANTS Governed by funds available and by need.

SAMPLE GRANTS Buckhorn Weston (£10,000); Branksome (£5,000); Cheselbourne (£2,000); and Margaret Marsh (£1,500).

FINANCES *Year* 2008 *Income* £99,879 *Grants* £79,000 *Assets* £447,762

TRUSTEES Capt. N T L L Thimbleby, Chair; Sir M Hanham; Lady May; Sir P Williams; G A L F Pitt-Rivers; A C Stuart; Archdeacon of Dorset; Bishop of Sherbourne; P F Moule; R D Allan; J O C Alexander; Viscount Hood; S R V Pomeroy; Archdeacon of Sherbourne; R F Adeney; T Hobson; Lord Bishop of Salisbury; Lord Digby.

HOW TO APPLY In writing to the correspondent.

WHO TO APPLY TO P F Moule, Hon. Secretary, Ryall's Ground, Yetminster, Sherborne, Dorset DT9 6LL *email* pandfmoule@yahoo.co.uk *Website* www.dorsethistoricchurchestrust.co.uk

CC NO 282790 **ESTABLISHED** 1960

■ The Dorus Trust

WHERE FUNDING CAN BE GIVEN Mainly UK.

WHO CAN BENEFIT Registered UK charities with a national focus benefiting people of all ages, homeless people, people with addictions, physical disabilities, cancer or diabetes, and underprivileged children.

WHAT IS FUNDED Support is given to projects including hostels, hospices, holiday accommodation, respite care, care in the community, health counselling and some environmental issues.

WHAT IS NOT FUNDED No grants to individuals, expeditions, research, scholarships, charities with a local focus, local branches of UK charities or towards running costs.

TYPE OF GRANT Projects and one-off grants. Funding for one year or less.

RANGE OF GRANTS £500–£15,000.

SAMPLE GRANTS Dogs for the Blind (£13,000); British Liver Trust (£11,000); Epsom Medical Research, SeeAbility and Hearing Research Trust (£10,000 each); Heartline Association (£7,500); Tall Ships Youth Trust (£6,000); Crisis UK (£5,000); National Deaf Childrens' Society (£4,500); Exeter University Foundation (£3,000); Christian Lewis Foundation (£2,500).

FINANCES *Year* 2007 *Income* £157,072 *Grants* £148,350 *Assets* £3,068,285

TRUSTEES C H Peacock; Mrs B Bond; A M Bond.

HOW TO APPLY This trust no longer accepts applications.

WHO TO APPLY TO C H Peacock, Trustee, c/o Charities Aid Foundation, Kings Hill, West Malling, Kent ME19 4TA *Tel* 01732 520028

CC NO 328724 **ESTABLISHED** 1990

■ Double 'O' Charity Ltd

WHERE FUNDING CAN BE GIVEN UK and overseas.

WHO CAN BENEFIT Registered charities and individuals.

WHAT IS FUNDED Primarily, grants towards the relief of poverty, preservation of health and the advancement of education. However, the charity considers all requests for aid.

WHAT IS NOT FUNDED No grants to individuals towards education or for their involvement in overseas charity work.

TYPE OF GRANT Preferably one-off.

RANGE OF GRANTS £1,000–£50,000.

SAMPLE GRANTS The National Association for People Abused in Childhood (NAPAC) (£36,000); Bedales School (£32,000); Spirit of Recovery (£30,000); Richmond Bridge Friendship Club (£16,000); The Arvon Foundation (£5,000); Elton John AIDS Foundation (£1,000).

FINANCES *Year* 2007–08 *Income* £234,720 *Grants* £134,443 *Assets* £113,206

TRUSTEES P D B Townshend; Mrs K Townshend; N R Goderson.

OTHER INFORMATION Grants were also given to individuals totalling £31,000.

HOW TO APPLY In writing to the correspondent.

WHO TO APPLY TO The Trustees, c/o 4 Friars Lane, Richmond, Surrey TW9 1NL

CC NO 271681   **ESTABLISHED** 1976

■ The Doughty Charity Trust

WHERE FUNDING CAN BE GIVEN England, Israel.

WHO CAN BENEFIT Jewish organisations benefiting people who are disadvantaged by poverty or who are sick.

WHAT IS FUNDED To promote (a) the orthodox Jewish Religion, (b) orthodox Jewish education and (c) institutions for Jewish people who are poor, ill and/or elderly.

WHAT IS NOT FUNDED No grants to individuals.

TYPE OF GRANT Loan or grant, usually £1,000 or less.

RANGE OF GRANTS £250–£23,000.

SAMPLE GRANTS Tomchai Shaarie Zion (£23,000); Bobor Institute and Keren Haschesed Trust (£10,000 each); Tiferes Ivi (£9,600); Friend of Kiryat Sefer (£5,000); Sinai Synagogue (£4,600); Beis Yaakov School (£3,400); Jewish Rescue and Relief (£1,000).

FINANCES *Year* 2007 *Income* £244,313 *Grants* £208,418 *Assets* £74,945

TRUSTEES G Halibard, Chair; Mrs M Halibard.

OTHER INFORMATION Other grants of less than £250 each totalled £2,600.

HOW TO APPLY In writing to the correspondent.

WHO TO APPLY TO Gerald B Halibard, Trustee, 22 Ravenscroft Avenue, Golders Green, London NW11 0RY *Tel* 020 8209 0500

CC NO 274977   **ESTABLISHED** 1977

■ The R M Douglas Charitable Trust

WHERE FUNDING CAN BE GIVEN UK with a preference for Staffordshire.

WHO CAN BENEFIT Registered charities already in receipt of support from the trust.

WHAT IS FUNDED The relief of poverty (including provision of pensions) especially for present and past employees (and their families) of Robert M Douglas (Contractors) Ltd, and general charitable purposes especially in the parish of St Mary, Dunstall.

TYPE OF GRANT Mostly small grants, including buildings, capital, core costs, one-off, research, and recurring costs.

RANGE OF GRANTS £200–£5,000. Typically £200–£500.

SAMPLE GRANTS Previous beneficiaries have included Bible Explorer for Christian outreach, British Red Cross for general purposes, Burton Graduate Medical College to equip a new lecture theatre, Four Oaks Methodist Church for its centenary appeal, Lichfield Diocesan Urban Fund for Christian mission, St Giles Hospice – Lichfield for development, SAT-7 Trust for Christian outreach and John Taylor High School – Barton in Needwood for a performing arts block.

FINANCES *Year* 2007–08 *Income* £44,218 *Grants* £34,750 *Assets* £1,128,795

TRUSTEES J R T Douglas; Mrs J E Lees; F W Carder.

OTHER INFORMATION In 2007–08, grants totalling £6,250 were distributed to individuals connected with the company.

HOW TO APPLY The trust has previously stated that its funds were fully committed.

WHO TO APPLY TO J R T Douglas, Trustee, 68 Liverpool Road, Stoke-on-Trent ST4 1BG

CC NO 248775   **ESTABLISHED** 1966

■ The Drapers' Charitable Fund

WHERE FUNDING CAN BE GIVEN UK, with a special interest in the City and adjacent parts of London and Moneymore and Draperstown in Northern Ireland.

WHO CAN BENEFIT Registered or exempt charities.

WHAT IS FUNDED General charitable purposes including education, heritage, the arts, prisoner support and textile conservation.

WHAT IS NOT FUNDED Grants are not usually made for: individuals; schools; colleges and universities (except in North Wales and Greenwich & Lewisham through The Thomas Howell's Education Fund for North Wales and Sir William Boreman's Foundation); churches; almshouses; animal welfare; counselling or advocacy; medical research/relief, hospitals or medical centres; children's disabilities, physical disabilities or medical conditions; holidays or general respite care; organisations solely assisting refugees, asylum seekers or specific cultural or ethnic groups within the UK; organisations that are not registered charities, unless exempt from registration; funds that replace or subsidise statutory funding; local branches of national charities, associations or movements; work that has already taken place; general appeals or circulars; loans or business finance.

TYPE OF GRANT One-off or recurrent grants for capital and core costs.

RANGE OF GRANTS Mostly for £10,000 or less.

SAMPLE GRANTS Bancroft's School (£85,000); Help for Heroes (£51,000); Queen Mary – University of London (£50,000); Hertford College – Oxford (£34,000); Project Trust (£20,000); Hanover Foundation (£15,000); Zimbabwe Farmers Trust Fund (£11,000); Women's Aid – Orkney (£10,000); Butler Trust (£7,500); Blundell's School (£6,000); and Beatbullying (£5,000).

FINANCES *Year* 2007–08 *Income* £1,714,862 *Grants* £1,043,629 *Assets* £26,302,773

TRUSTEES The Drapers' Company.

HOW TO APPLY Applications can be made at any time during the year. The charities committee meets four times a year (October, January, April and July). Applicants should complete the 'application summary sheet' (available to download from the website) and submit it together with a document on proposed funding. This should include detailed information about the organisation and the project/activity to be funded; full costings and project budget for the proposed work for which the grant is requested, or the organisation's income and expenditure budget for the current year (whichever is appropriate); and the most recent audited financial statements and trustees report. Applications should be submitted by post only. For full details of the application process and the trust's current priorities, applicants are advised to refer to the trust's website.

WHO TO APPLY TO Andy Mellows, Head of Charities, The Drapers' Company, Drapers' Hall, Throgmorton Avenue, London EC2N 2DQ *Tel* 020 7588 5001 *Fax* 020 7628 1988 *email* charities@thedrapers.co.uk *Website* www. thedrapers.co.uk

cc no 251403   ESTABLISHED 1959

....
■ **The Drayson Foundation**

WHERE FUNDING CAN BE GIVEN UK.

WHO CAN BENEFIT Children who are sick and in need, including social welfare services and medical welfare and research charities.

WHAT IS FUNDED relief of sickness, with particular emphasis on children and the advancement of education.

RANGE OF GRANTS up to £33,000.

SAMPLE GRANTS National Centre for Young People with Epilepsy (£33,000); Children's Fire and Burn Trust (£10,000); Macmillan Cancer Relief (£3,500).

FINANCES *Year* 2007–08 *Income* £91,606 *Grants* £46,833 *Assets* £3,267,198

TRUSTEES Lord Drayson, Lady Drayson, Clare Maurice

HOW TO APPLY In writing to the correspondent.

WHO TO APPLY TO Clare Maurice, c/o Allen and Overy, One Bishops Square, London E1 6AO

cc no 1076700   ESTABLISHED 1999

....
■ **Dromintee Trust**

WHERE FUNDING CAN BE GIVEN Worldwide.

WHO CAN BENEFIT Charitable organisations.

WHAT IS FUNDED General charitable purposes.

RANGE OF GRANTS up to £30,000.

SAMPLE GRANTS Consolata Fathers (£30,000); CAFOD (£28,000); InterCare (£20,000); Loros and Rainbows Childrens Hospital (£10,000 each); The Little Way Association (£5,000); Breast Cancer Campaign, The MedicAlert Foundation, Mencap, Powerful Information and the World Medical Fund (£2,000 each).

FINANCES *Year* 2007–08 *Income* £239,504 *Grants* £112,493 *Assets* £1,223,765

TRUSTEES Hugh Murphy; Margaret Murphy; Robert Smith; Paul Tiernan; Mary Murphy; Patrick Murphy

HOW TO APPLY In writing to the correspondent.

WHO TO APPLY TO Hugh Murphy, Trustee, The Manor House, Main Street, Thurnby, Leicester LE7 9PN *Tel* 0116 241 5100

cc no 1053956   ESTABLISHED 1996

....
■ **The Dugdale Charitable Trust**

WHERE FUNDING CAN BE GIVEN UK, with a preference for Hampshire and West Sussex, and overseas.

WHO CAN BENEFIT Christians and Christian organisations who are personally known to the trustees.

WHAT IS FUNDED General charitable purposes.

SAMPLE GRANTS New Life Church (£10,000); Winchester Family Church (£9,000); Waltham Chase Methodist Church; Great Lakes Outreach, Christians Against Poverty Mission Aviation Fellowship, Open Doors and Oriental Missionary Society International (£5,000 each); Christian Action Research and Education (CARE) (£2,000).

FINANCES *Year* 2007–08 *Income* £93,621 *Grants* £109,571 *Assets* £496,820

TRUSTEES R A Dugdale; Mrs B Dugdale; J Dugdale; S Dugdale.

HOW TO APPLY This trust only supports causes known personally to the trustees. Unsolicited applications are not considered.

WHO TO APPLY TO R Dugdale, Trustee, Harmsworth Farm, Botley Road, Curbridge, Hampshire SO30 2HB

cc no 1052941   ESTABLISHED 1995

....
■ **The Duis Charitable Trust**

WHERE FUNDING CAN BE GIVEN Worldwide.

WHO CAN BENEFIT Children, medical, general.

WHAT IS FUNDED The trust makes grants benefiting groups largely concerned with children and Jewish causes, although this incorporates support of social welfare, education, capital library and hospital appeals.

WHAT IS NOT FUNDED No grants to individuals.

SAMPLE GRANTS Previous beneficiaries have included Norwood Ravenswood, Great Ormond Street Hospital, BINOH Norwood Childcare, Dulwich Picture Gallery, National Playing Fields, Down's Syndrome Association, Joint Jewish Charitable Trust, Hillel Special Purposes Fund, Breakaway Charity Committee, Children's Wish Foundation and Jewish Care.

FINANCES *Year* 2007–08 *Income* £56,468 *Grants* £40,000 *Assets* £515,609

TRUSTEES Julian Michael Fellerman.

HOW TO APPLY In writing to the correspondent.

WHO TO APPLY TO Robert Gore, 14 New Street, London EC2M 4HE

cc no 800487   ESTABLISHED 1987

....
■ **The Dulverton Trust**

WHERE FUNDING CAN BE GIVEN Unrestricted. Mainly UK in practice. An interest in the Cotswolds. Limited support to parts of Africa. Few grants for work in London or Northern Ireland.

WHO CAN BENEFIT Mainly UK projects, some regional and local projects at a minor level.

WHAT IS FUNDED Young people and education, conservation, general welfare and to a lesser extent activities in preservation and peace and humanitarian support.

WHAT IS NOT FUNDED Grants rarely given for: individuals; museums, galleries, libraries, exhibition centres and heritage attractions; individual churches, cathedrals and other historic buildings; individual schools, colleges, universities or other educational establishments; hospices, hospitals, nursing or residential care homes; expeditions or research projects; activities outside the stated geographical scope. Support is rarely given to charities whose main beneficiaries live within Greater London or Northern Ireland. No support for the following areas of activity: health and medicine, including drug and alcohol addiction, therapy and counselling; support for people with disabilities; the arts, including theatre, music and drama; sport, including sports centres and

Think carefully about every application. Is it justified?

483

individual playing field projects; animal welfare or projects concerning the protection of single species; expeditions and research projects; individuals volunteering overseas; conferences, cultural festivals, exhibitions and events; salaries for specific posts; major building projects, including the purchase of property or land; endowments; retrospective funding; appeals which seek to replace statutory funding.

TYPE OF GRANT Project and one-off funding. Also capital and core costs. Funding is rarely given for more than one year.

RANGE OF GRANTS £1,000–£130,000; typically £20,000.

SAMPLE GRANTS Combat Stress (£40,000); Book Aid International (£36,000); Encompass (£32,000); Right Track Scotland (£30,000); St Ethelburga's and Marine Stewardship Council (£25,000 each); TreeAid (£17,000); Westcountry Rivers Trust (£11,000); One Plus One (£10,000); and Ocean Youth Trust South (£5,000).

FINANCES *Year* 2008–09 *Income* £1,448,375 *Grants* £2,966,436 *Assets* £58,521,028

TRUSTEES Col. David Fanshawe, Chair; Christopher Wills; Sir John Kemp-Welch; Lord Carrington; Tara Douglas-Home; Lord Dulverton; Lord Gowrie; Dr Catherine Wills; Richard Fitzalan Howard; Sir Malcolm Rifkind; Dame Mary Richardson.

HOW TO APPLY Applications should be made in writing to the director. Trustees meetings are held four times a year – in February, May, July and October (though decisions on small grants can be made more rapidly – if essential, very rapidly). Initial enquiries by telephone, for example to establish eligibility, are welcomed. Applications should, if possible, be restricted to a letter and maximum of two sheets of paper, and should include the applicant's registered charity number, a brief description of the background, aims and objectives of the charity, details of the specific appeal for which funding is sought together with the funding target, and the balance of funding outstanding at the time of application. Initial applications should always include a copy of the previous year's annual report and accounts. All applications will receive a reply as soon as possible, although research and consultation may delay a response. All rejected applications will receive notification and an explanation for an appeal's rejection will be given. The selection procedure can take between three to six months, so applicants are advised to apply in plenty of time if funding is required by a certain date.

WHO TO APPLY TO Col. Christopher Bates, Director, 5 St James's Place, London SW1A 1NP *Tel* 020 7629 9121 *Fax* 020 7495 6201 *email* trust@dulverton.org *Website* www.dulverton.org

CC NO 206426   **ESTABLISHED** 1949

■ The P B Dumbell Charitable Trust

WHERE FUNDING CAN BE GIVEN Occasionally worldwide, but mostly the Wolverhampton and Shropshire area.

WHO CAN BENEFIT Institutions and individuals.

WHAT IS FUNDED General charitable purposes.

WHAT IS NOT FUNDED No educational grants are given.

RANGE OF GRANTS Up to £5,000.

SAMPLE GRANTS Beacon Centre for the Blind and Compton Hospice (£5,000 each); St Peter's Church – Worfield (£3,500); Ironbridge Gorge Museum Trust (Rose Hill House Trust) (£2,500);

Ludlow Festival 2008 (£2,000); Clunbury Church (£1,750); County Air Ambulance Trust (£1,500); Believe to Achieve and South Shropshire Furniture Scheme (£500 each); and Brickkiln Dunstall Gateway Club and The Rest Room – Madeley (£250 each).

FINANCES *Year* 2007–08 *Income* £43,791 *Grants* £34,900 *Assets* £1,014,542

TRUSTEES M H Gilbert; C F Dumbell.

OTHER INFORMATION Grants were made to four individuals totalling £400.

HOW TO APPLY In writing to the correspondent. The trustees meet annually in June when most grants are considered. Some applications will be considered at other times. Telephone calls are not welcomed.

WHO TO APPLY TO C F Dumbell, Trustee, Lower Hall, Worfield, Bridgnorth, Shropshire WV15 5LH *Tel* 01746 716 607

CC NO 232770   **ESTABLISHED** 1964

■ The Dumbreck Charity

WHERE FUNDING CAN BE GIVEN Worldwide, especially the West Midlands.

WHO CAN BENEFIT Charitable organisations. New applications are restricted to Midlands organisations.

WHAT IS FUNDED Animal welfare and conservation; children's welfare; people who are older or who have mental or physical disabilities; medical causes; and general charitable purposes.

WHAT IS NOT FUNDED No grants to individuals.

TYPE OF GRANT Recurring and one-off grants.

RANGE OF GRANTS £500–£3,000, but mainly for amounts around £1,000 each.

SAMPLE GRANTS Spear (£4,000); Brooke Animal Hospital (£3,000); International League for the Protection of Horses (£2,000); and Redwing Horse Sanctuary and Worcester Farming (£1,000 each).

FINANCES *Year* 2007–08 *Income* £103,320 *Grants* £119,000 *Assets* £3,360,051

TRUSTEES A C S Hordern; H B Carslake; Mrs J E Melling.

HOW TO APPLY In writing to the correspondent. The trustees meet annually in April/May. Unsuccessful applications will not be acknowledged. Organisations operating in the UK outside Worcestershire, Warwickshire or the West Midlands will not be supported.

WHO TO APPLY TO A C S Hordern, Trustee, 7 Bridge Street, Pershore, Worcestershire WR10 1AJ

CC NO 273070   **ESTABLISHED** 1976

■ Dunard Fund

WHERE FUNDING CAN BE GIVEN Worldwide, in practice UK with a particular interest in Scotland.

WHO CAN BENEFIT Arts, environment and humanitarian causes.

WHAT IS FUNDED Principally to the training for and performance of classical music at the highest standard and to education and display of the visual arts, also at international standard. A small percentage of the fund is dedicated to environmental and humanitarian projects.

WHAT IS NOT FUNDED Grants are only given to charities recognised in Scotland or charities registered in England and Wales.

TYPE OF GRANT The Trustees prefer to engage with recipients to enable long-term development of projects and initiatives which have major and lasting significance; they are therefore less inclined to provide one-off donations.

RANGE OF GRANTS £50–£500,000.

SAMPLE GRANTS (£286,000); Festival City Theatres Trust (£250,000); Oxford University Development Trust and Edinburgh Sculpture Workshop (£150,000 each); Scottish Opera (£125,000); Scottish Chamber Orchestra (£101,000); The Prince's Charities Foundation (£100,000); Welsh National Opera (£75,000); The English Concert (£60,000); Royal Scottish National Orchestra and English National Opera (£50,000 each); Napier University (£40,000); The Handel House Trust (£25,000); Royal Opera House and Aldeburgh Music (£20,000 each); Perth Festival of the Arts (£6,000); Appeal of the Arts/Stewart's Melville College and the Art Fund (£5,000 each); The Cockburn Association (£1,000); and Deeside Suzuki Piano Festival and Innerpeffray Library (£500 each).

FINANCES *Year* 2007–08 *Income* £1,281,726 *Grants* £1,960,621 *Assets* £4,616,248

TRUSTEES Carol Colburn Høgel; Elisabeth Høgel; Catherine Høgel; Erik Høgel; Colin Liddell.

HOW TO APPLY In writing to the correspondent.

WHO TO APPLY TO Mrs Carol Colburn Høgel, Trustee, 4 Royal Terrace, Edinburgh EH7 5AB *Tel* 0131 556 4043 *Fax* 0131 556 3969

CC NO 295790   **ESTABLISHED** 1986

··

■ Ronald Duncan Literary Foundation

WHERE FUNDING CAN BE GIVEN UK.

WHO CAN BENEFIT Theatre and the arts.

WHAT IS FUNDED Arts and culture, general.

TYPE OF GRANT One-off and recurrent.

RANGE OF GRANTS £250–£24,000.

SAMPLE GRANTS Ronald Duncan Archive (£24,000); Ledbury Poetry Festival (£1,250); The Plough Arts Centre – Torrington (£900); Contact Theatre, Firefly Youth Project, Ludlow Assembly Rooms, New Writing South and Queens Theatre (£500 each); and Polka Theatre (£250).

FINANCES *Year* 2007–08 *Income* £14,454 *Grants* £30,827 *Assets* £382,222

TRUSTEES Krysia Cairns; Briony Lawson; Valerie Poulter; Anna Trussler.

HOW TO APPLY In writing to the correspondent.

WHO TO APPLY TO Peter Reeves, Willow Byre, Abingdon Road, Tubney, Abingdon OX13 5QL *Tel* 05601 782 976

CC NO 266559

··

■ The Dunhill Medical Trust

WHERE FUNDING CAN BE GIVEN UK.

WHO CAN BENEFIT Registered charities particularly those benefiting older people and academic institutions undertaking medical research.

WHAT IS FUNDED The trust's current charitable priorities are: care of older people; research into diseases and issues of ageing; projects related to disabilities and rehabilitation in respect of the elderly. These priorities are reviewed every three years (or more often if deemed appropriate by the trustees), and may be changed in accordance to the trustees' view of the most effective application of available funds.

WHAT IS NOT FUNDED The trust will not fund: organizations based outside the UK, or whose work primarily benefits people outside the UK; large national charities, with an income in excess of £10 million, or assets exceeding £100 million; issues that are already well-funded in the UK, such as heart disease, cancer or HIV/AIDS; sponsorship of individuals; sponsorship of conferences or charitable events; services or equipment that would be more appropriately provided by the National Health Service; charities representing specific professions or trade associations; grants to cover the revenue or capital costs of hospices (although, research undertaken within a hospice setting is eligible for consideration); travel or conference fees (except where these items are an integral part of a project); new or replacement vehicles (unless an integral part of a community-based development); general maintenance; institutional overheads associated with research activity (i.e. the trust will not pay the full economic cost of research activities).

TYPE OF GRANT Project grants to research groups, as well as some grants for salaries and building or equipment costs for specific projects.

SAMPLE GRANTS Previous beneficiaries include: Royal College of Physicians, University of East Anglia, University of Leeds, Stroke Association, St. Georges Hospital Medical School, Age Concern Kirklees, Alzheimer's Support, Deafway, Age Care and Schonfeld Square Foundation.

FINANCES *Year* 2007–08 *Income* £3,312,183 *Grants* £3,064,069 *Assets* £86,054,653

TRUSTEES Ronald E Perry; Timothy Sanderson; Prof. Roger Boyle; The Rt Revd Christopher Chessun; Prof. Martin Severs; Kay Glendinning; Prof. James McEwen; Prof. Roderick Hay; Richard Nunneley.

OTHER INFORMATION The Dunhill Medical trust is a member of the Association of Medical Research Charities.

HOW TO APPLY By post or email to the secretary to the trustees. All applicants for general or research grants are asked to provide an initial outline, including a brief description of the organisation and of the project/work or research to be carried out. Once the initial application has been assessed, eligible applicants will be sent a formal grant application form which will request additional and supporting information. As the application procedure differs depending upon whether you are apply for a general or research grant, you are strongly advised to visit the trust's website before making an application to ensure that you have all the relevant information. Once you have done so, if you still require any specific advice regarding your application, please contact the trust's office. Full applications are considered by the Grants and Research Committee which meets quarterly (normally in February, May, July and November). The committee makes recommendations on whether applications should be supported and decisions are then referred to the board of trustees for approval at their quarterly meetings (normally held in March, June, September and December). Applications approved are normally notified within one week of the meeting. Generally, decisions are made within about three months, although research applications may take longer, due to the requirements of the peer review process.

WHO TO APPLY TO Claire Large, Administrative Director, 3rd Floor, 16–18 Marshalsea Road, London SE1 1HL *Tel* 020 7403 3299 *Fax* 020 7403 3277 *email* info@dunhillmedical.org.uk *Website* www.dunhillmedical.org.uk

CC NO 294286   **ESTABLISHED** 1951

■ The Harry Dunn Charitable Trust

WHERE FUNDING CAN BE GIVEN UK, with a strong preference for Nottinghamshire.

WHO CAN BENEFIT Organisations benefiting people with multiple sclerosis; environmental charities.

WHAT IS FUNDED Charities working in the fields of health facilities and buildings; support to voluntary and community organisations; MS research; conservation; bird sanctuaries and ecology.

WHAT IS NOT FUNDED Only organisations known to the trustees are supported. No grants to individuals.

TYPE OF GRANT Core costs and one-off; funding for one year or less will be considered.

RANGE OF GRANTS £100–£5,000.

SAMPLE GRANTS St Lukes Hospice (£4,500); Nottingham Multiple Sclerosis Therapy Centre Limited (£4,000); Disability Aid Fund (£3,500); Wildfowl and Wetlands Trust, Support Dogs and Friends of Brancaster Church (£3,000 each); Multiple Sclerosis Trust and National Association for Colitis and Crohns Disease (£2,500 each); Seafarers UK and Nottinghamshire Wildlife Trust (£2,000 each); Rainbow Children's Hospice and Parkinson's Disease Society (£1,500 each); Age Concern and Macmillan Cancer Support (£1,000 each).

FINANCES *Year* 2007–08 *Income* £73,978 *Grants* £60,000 *Assets* £1,876,230

TRUSTEES A H Dunn; N A Dunn; R M Dunn.

HOW TO APPLY In writing to the correspondent.

WHO TO APPLY TO The Trustees, Rushcliffe Developments, Tudor House, 13–15 Rectory Road, West Bridgford, Nottingham NG2 6BE *Tel* 0115 945 5300 *email* nad@rushcliffe.co.uk

CC NO 297389   **ESTABLISHED** 1987

■ The Houghton Dunn Charitable Trust

WHERE FUNDING CAN BE GIVEN UK, with an interest in Lancashire.

WHO CAN BENEFIT Registered charities only, especially those working in Lancashire.

WHAT IS FUNDED Medical, health, welfare, environment, wildlife, churches and heritage.

WHAT IS NOT FUNDED No grants to individuals.

TYPE OF GRANT Cash grants, mostly recurring. Occasional large grants for capital purposes.

SAMPLE GRANTS Previous beneficiaries have included: AMEND, Arthritis Research Campaign, Cancer BACUP, Cancer Research UK, Christie Hospital NHS Trust, East Lancashire Hospice Fund, Lancashire Wildlife Trust, Marie Curie Cancer Care, Macmillan Cancer Relief, National Eczema Society, National Trust Lake District Appeal and National Youth Orchestra.

FINANCES *Year* 2007–08 *Income* £327,718 *Grants* £326,000 *Assets* £7,122,992

TRUSTEES D H Dunn; Mrs E Dunn; A M H Dunn; R C H Dunn.

HOW TO APPLY In writing to the correspondent. There is no set time for the consideration of applications, but donations are normally made in March each year.

WHO TO APPLY TO D H Dunn, Trustee, 25 Clitheroe Road, Whalley, Clitheroe BB7 9AD

CC NO 261685   **ESTABLISHED** 1967

■ The W E Dunn Trust

WHERE FUNDING CAN BE GIVEN Midlands.

WHO CAN BENEFIT Charitable organisations and individuals.

WHAT IS FUNDED The funding priorities are to benefit people who are sick or in adversity and resident in the Midlands area, particularly in Wolverhampton, Wednesbury, North Staffordshire and neighbouring localities. The trustees have full discretion and in addition to dealing with local personal requests through social services departments, they make donations to local charities and occasionally to UK charities. The trustees particularly wish to assist older people and the very young, but they will not make grants to settle or reduce debts already incurred. The trust will consider funding: accommodation and housing; infrastructure, support and development; community arts and recreation; health; environmental issues; education and training; costs of study; community facilities and services; and other charitable purposes.

WHAT IS NOT FUNDED No grants to settle or reduce debts already incurred.

TYPE OF GRANT Buildings, capital, core costs, one-off, project and start-up costs. All funding is for up to three years.

RANGE OF GRANTS Up to £1,000.

SAMPLE GRANTS University of Birmingham (£5,000); Cure Leukaemia and St Mary's Hospice (£2,000 each); and Beacon Centre for the Blind, British Dental Health Foundation, Kidderminster Cookley Scout Group, North Staffordshire Polish Day Care Centre and the Teenage Cancer Trust (£1,000 each).

FINANCES *Year* 2007–08 *Income* £157,935 *Grants* £127,436 *Assets* £4,078,048

TRUSTEES David J Corney, Chair; Leita H Smethurst; C Paul King; Jennifer A Warbrick.

OTHER INFORMATION The grant total in 2007–08 included £48,000 to 355 individuals.

HOW TO APPLY In writing to the correspondent giving the name and address, some idea of the income/outgoings and any other necessary particulars of the grantee. Organisations should always enclose accounts. Grants to individuals are considered every week; grants to organisations, every three or four months.

WHO TO APPLY TO David J Corney, Trustee, The Trust Office, 30 Bentley Heath Cottages, Tilehouse Green Lane, Knowle, Solihull B93 9EL *Tel* 01564 773407

CC NO 219418   **ESTABLISHED** 1958

■ The Charles Dunstone Charitable Trust

WHERE FUNDING CAN BE GIVEN UK and overseas.

WHO CAN BENEFIT Registered charities.

WHAT IS FUNDED General charitable purposes.

WHAT IS NOT FUNDED The trustees do not normally make grants to individuals.

RANGE OF GRANTS Previously up to £55,000.

SAMPLE GRANTS Previous beneficiaries have included: Burnham Overy Harbour Trust; Get Connected; Serpentine Trust; Sail for Gold; Holkham Opera; Hounslow Action for Youth Association; RNLI; Thames Valley & Chiltern Air Ambulance; National Autistic Society, Prostate Research Campaign UK, Sail 4 Cancer and the Wellbeing Trust.

FINANCES *Year* 2007–08 *Income* £140,586 *Grants* £1,971,051 *Assets* £3,905,845

TRUSTEES Denis Dunstone; Adrian Bott; Nicholas Folland.

HOW TO APPLY Proposals are usually requested by the trustees and unsolicited applications are not likely to be successful.

WHO TO APPLY TO The Trustees, H W Fisher and Company, 11–15 William Road, London NW1 3ER *Tel* 020 7388 7000

CC NO 1085955 **ESTABLISHED** 2001

■ Dushinsky Trust Ltd

WHERE FUNDING CAN BE GIVEN Mainly Israel.

WHO CAN BENEFIT Jewish and Israeli charities.

WHAT IS FUNDED Alleviation of poverty and the furtherance of orthodox Jewish education.

SAMPLE GRANTS Previous beneficiaries have included: United Institutes of Dushinsky, Minchat Yitzchok Institutions and Ish Lerehu Fund.

FINANCES *Year* 2008 *Income* £432,002 *Grants* £432,503 *Assets* £17,577

TRUSTEES S Reisner; Z Levine; M Schischa.

HOW TO APPLY The trust does not accept unsolicited applications.

WHO TO APPLY TO S Reisner, Secretary, 23 Braydon Road, London N16 6QL *Tel* 020 8802 7144

CC NO 1020301 **ESTABLISHED** 1992

■ Mildred Duveen Charitable Trust

WHERE FUNDING CAN BE GIVEN Worldwide.

WHO CAN BENEFIT Charitable organisations.

WHAT IS FUNDED General charitable purposes.

RANGE OF GRANTS up to £5,000.

SAMPLE GRANTS Whizz Kidz (£5,000); Monica Cantwell Trust (£4,000); Whittington Babies and Masterclass Trust (£2,500 each); National Deaf Children's Society, Tavistock Clinic Foundation, Almeida Theatre (£2,000 each); Help for Heroes (£1,500); St Catherine's Hospice, PDSA, Brighton and Hove Parents Group and Sussex Air Ambulance (£1,000 each).

FINANCES *Year* 2007–08 *Income* £43,065 *Grants* £39,500 *Assets* £1,223,927

TRUSTEES P Holgate; A Houlstoun; P Loose; J Shelford.

HOW TO APPLY In writing to the correspondent.

WHO TO APPLY TO Peter Holgate, Trustee, Devonshire House, 60 Goswell Road, London EC1M 7AD *Tel* 020 7566 4000

CC NO 1059355 **ESTABLISHED** 1996

■ The Annette Duvollet Charitable Trust

WHERE FUNDING CAN BE GIVEN UK and overseas.

WHO CAN BENEFIT Charities supporting young people aged 14–25.

WHAT IS FUNDED General charitable purposes.

RANGE OF GRANTS up to £10,000.

SAMPLE GRANTS Norfolk and Norwich Scope Association (NANSA) (£7,400); Depaul Trust and SPEAR (£5,000 each); Centrepoint and Neuromuscular Centre (£3,000 each); Children's Trust (£1,750); and Island Trust (£1,050).

FINANCES *Year* 2007–08 *Income* £35,895 *Grants* £24,860 *Assets* £729,356

TRUSTEES Peter Clarke; Caroline Dawes; Richard Shuttleworth.

HOW TO APPLY In writing to the correspondent.

WHO TO APPLY TO Peter Clarke, Trustee, 18 Nassau Road, London SW13 9QE *Tel* 020 8748 5112

CC NO 326505 **ESTABLISHED** 1984

■ The Dwek Family Charitable Trust

WHERE FUNDING CAN BE GIVEN UK, with a preference for the Greater Manchester area.

WHO CAN BENEFIT Individuals and small charities without a large fundraising profile. In previous years mainly Jewish charities have been supported.

WHAT IS FUNDED People who are in need, disabled or disadvantaged.

FINANCES *Year* 2007–08 *Income* £92,874 *Grants* £53,150 *Assets* £622,296

TRUSTEES J C Dwek; J V Dwek; A J Leon.

HOW TO APPLY In writing to the correspondent.

WHO TO APPLY TO J C Dwek, Trustee, Suite One, Courthill House, 66 Water Lane, Wilmslow, Cheshire SK9 5AP

CC NO 1001456 **ESTABLISHED** 1989

■ The Dyers' Company Charitable Trust

WHERE FUNDING CAN BE GIVEN UK.

WHO CAN BENEFIT Registered charities only.

WHAT IS FUNDED General charitable purposes.

WHAT IS NOT FUNDED No grants to individuals.

RANGE OF GRANTS Up to £25,000, in practice around £500–£5,000.

SAMPLE GRANTS Heriot-Watt University (£22,000); Royal College of Art (£6,000); Help for Heroes (£5,000); Speak Ability and Royal Overseas League Music Competition (£2,000 each); Historic Churches Preservation Trust and Guildhall School of Music and Drama (£1,000 each); and Helen Arkell Dyslexia Trust and Frensham Pond Sailability (£500 each).

FINANCES *Year* 2007–08 *Income* £875,891 *Grants* £317,675 *Assets* £5,790,571

TRUSTEES The court of The Dyers' Company.

OTHER INFORMATION The trust also funds a bursary school for a school in Norwich, for which it gave £58,000 in 2007/08.

HOW TO APPLY The trust does not welcome unsolicited applications.

WHO TO APPLY TO The Clerk, Dyers Hall, Dowgate Hill, London EC4R 2ST

CC NO 289547 **ESTABLISHED** 1984

■ The James Dyson Foundation

WHERE FUNDING CAN BE GIVEN UK, local community around the Dyson company's UK headquarters, in Malmesbury, Wiltshire.

WHO CAN BENEFIT Registered charities and educational institutions.

WHAT IS FUNDED Educational institutions working in the field of design, technology and engineering; charities carrying out medical or scientific research; and projects which aid the local community around Dyson, in Malmesbury, Wiltshire.

TYPE OF GRANT One-off and recurrent.

RANGE OF GRANTS £3,000–£1.3 million.

SAMPLE GRANTS Bath Technology Centre (£1.3 million); Target Pink (£552,000); Dyson Design Awards (£246,000); Bath Royal United Hospital – Opera Night (£50,000); Pompidou Project (£24,000); D and T Show (£17,000); Royal College of Art (£12,000); The Prince's Trust (£5,000); and CLIC (£3,000).

FINANCES *Year* 2007–08 *Income* £2,952,045 *Grants* £2,466,278 *Assets* £7,333,824

HOW TO APPLY Applications in writing on headed paper to the correspondent. Organisations can also apply via email or through the foundation's website.

WHO TO APPLY TO The Dyson Press Office, Tetbury Hill, Malmesbury, Wiltshire SN16 0RP
Tel 01666 827 205
email jamesdysonfoundation@dyson.com
Website www.jamesdysonfoundation.com
CC NO 1099709   **ESTABLISHED** 2003

488

Does the trust you have chosen match your needs? Haphazard applications waste postage and time

■ EAGA Partnership Charitable Trust

WHERE FUNDING CAN BE GIVEN UK.

WHO CAN BENEFIT Organisations and institutions benefiting research workers, academics and medical professionals.

WHAT IS FUNDED The trust currently provides grants to fund research and other projects within two grant programmes: the first programme aims to clarify the nature, extent and consequences of fuel poverty and offer insights into the energy efficient and cost-effective relief of fuel poverty; the second programme aims to explore issues related to vulnerable consumers and their multiple needs and preferences. It explores the overlap between fuel poverty and wider deprivation, in order to develop a better understanding of different groups of vulnerable and/or deprived consumers. The trust gives priority to funding proposals that have the potential to inform or influence national perceptions and policies and have a wide geographic focus. A project that operates at a local level will only be considered for a grant if it: clearly demonstrates innovation; identifies the policy relevance of the project; has wide applicability; and has well developed and accurately costed evaluation and dissemination plans.

WHAT IS NOT FUNDED No grants to individuals. No grants for general fund-raising appeals; no grants for projects that comprise solely of capital works; no retrospective funding; no funding for energy advice provision materials; no funding towards the maintenance of websites; no grants for local energy efficiency/warm homes initiatives.

TYPE OF GRANT One-off for projects and research. Funding is available for up three years.

RANGE OF GRANTS Up to £70,000.

SAMPLE GRANTS Centre for Sustainable Energy (£70,000); Leeds Animation Workshop (£61,000); Changeworks (£52,000); Attend (£38,000); and Pett Projects (£24,000).

FINANCES *Year* 2007–08 *Income* £152,037 *Grants* £245,995 *Assets* £1,232,417

TRUSTEES J Clough; V Graham; A Harvey; Prof. G Manners; G Ritzema; Dr J Wade; Prof. D Gordon.

HOW TO APPLY 'Applicants are requested to complete an application form. All applications that are completed in full and fulfil the main aims of [the trust] will be assessed at a formal meeting of trustees. Meetings are held three times a year. The trustees review applications against specific criteria and objectives.'

WHO TO APPLY TO Dr Naomi Brown, Trust Manager, EAGA House, Archbold Terrace, Jesmond, Newcastle upon Tyne NE2 1DB *Tel* 0191 247 3800 *email* eagact@aol.com *Website* www. eagagroup.com

CC NO 1088361   **ESTABLISHED** 2001

■ The Eagle Charity Trust

WHERE FUNDING CAN BE GIVEN UK, in particular Manchester, and overseas.

WHO CAN BENEFIT UK, international and local charities.

WHAT IS FUNDED The trust stated it supports a wide variety of charities, especially those concerned with welfare.

TYPE OF GRANT One-off, with no commitment to providing ongoing funding.

RANGE OF GRANTS Around £500–£3,000.

SAMPLE GRANTS Oxfam – Darfur and Chad (£2,500); Medecines Sans Frontiers, UNICEF and Shelter (£2,000 each); British Red Cross – Bangladesh and MacMillan Cancer Support (£1,500 each); Amnesty International, Sight Savers International and Samaritans (£1,000 each); and Turning Point, Claire House and Wateraid (£500 each).

FINANCES *Year* 2007 *Income* £35,342 *Grants* £38,500 *Assets* £968,214

TRUSTEES Mrs L A Gifford; Miss D Gifford; Mrs E Y Williams; Mrs S A Nowakowski; R M E Gifford.

HOW TO APPLY In writing to the correspondent. However, please note, unsolicited applications are not invited.

WHO TO APPLY TO The Trustees, Nairne Son and Green, 477 Chester Road, Cornbrook, Manchester M16 9HF *Tel* 0161 872 1701

CC NO 802134   **ESTABLISHED** 1989

■ Audrey Earle Charitable Trust

WHERE FUNDING CAN BE GIVEN UK.

WHO CAN BENEFIT Registered charities.

WHAT IS FUNDED General charitable purposes with some preference for animal welfare and conservation charities.

TYPE OF GRANT Mostly recurrent.

RANGE OF GRANTS up to £10,000, in practice, £500–£2,000.

SAMPLE GRANTS Wells and Hospital Hospice Trust (£10,000); Burnham Market and Norton Village Hall (£5,000); Action for Blind People, Age Concern England and British Red Cross Society and Blue Cross Animal Hospital (£2,000 each); and East Anglia Air Amublance, RSPB and Wildfowl and Wetlands Trust (£1,000 each).

FINANCES *Year* 2007–08 *Income* £62,387 *Grants* £56,886 *Assets* £3,608,186

TRUSTEES Paul Andrew Shiels; Roger James Weetch.

HOW TO APPLY In writing to the correspondent.

WHO TO APPLY TO Paul Sheils, Trustee, 24 Bloomsbury Square, London WC1A 2PL *Tel* 020 7637 0661 *Fax* 020 7436 4663 *email* psheils@mail.com

CC NO 290028   **ESTABLISHED** 1984

■ The Earley Charity

WHERE FUNDING CAN BE GIVEN The liberty of Earley, the central, eastern and southern part of Reading borough, Earley and the immediate surrounding area.

WHO CAN BENEFIT Individuals in need and charitable and community organisations.

WHAT IS FUNDED To give aid to: the relief of distress and sickness; the relief of people who are elderly, disabled or living in poverty; the provision and support (with the object of improving the conditions of life in the interests of social welfare) of facilities for recreation and other leisure time occupation; the provision and support of educational facilities; and any other charitable purpose for the benefit of the community.

WHAT IS NOT FUNDED No nationwide appeals are considered. The trust has previously stated that it would prefer applications from local offices of national organisations.

TYPE OF GRANT One-off, project and start-up costs. Funding is available for up to one year.

RANGE OF GRANTS £250–£40,000 for organisations. £30–£2,500 for individuals.

SAMPLE GRANTS RVA (£38,000); RISC (£35,000); Earley Crescent Community Association (£32,000); BWA (£31,000); RCWRU (£20,000); Age Concern (£18,000); MAPP Partnership (£17,000); Bicycle Helmet Awareness (£5,000); Trinity Church Building Fund (£3,500); and Reading U3A (£1,500).

FINANCES *Year* 2007 *Income* £1,153,425 *Grants* £239,914 *Assets* £13,617,980

TRUSTEES R F Ames, Chair; Mrs M Eastwell; Dr D G Jenkins; Mrs L Owen; L G Norton; D C Sutton; P Hooper.

OTHER INFORMATION A further £14,000 was paid in grants individuals.

HOW TO APPLY In writing to the correspondent; applications are considered at any time. The trustees meet in February, May, August and November and applications should be submitted in the preceding month. No response is given to applicants from outside the beneficial area. Telephone calls or emails are welcome from applicants who wish to check their eligibility.

WHO TO APPLY TO Jane Wittig, The Liberty of Earley House, Strand Way, Earley, Reading, Berkshire RG6 4EA *Tel* 0118 975 5663 *email* enquiries@earleycharity.org.uk *Website* www.earleycharity.org.uk

CC NO 244823   **ESTABLISHED** 1820

■ Earls Colne and Halstead Educational Charity

WHERE FUNDING CAN BE GIVEN The catchment area of the former Earls Colne and Halstead grammar schools.

WHO CAN BENEFIT Organisations for the furtherance of education, individuals and local schools.

WHAT IS FUNDED Furtherance of the education of local children and young adults.

RANGE OF GRANTS Up to £6,000.

SAMPLE GRANTS Hedingham School (£6,100); Honywood School (£4,900); Ramsey School (£3,300); Richard De Clare School (£1,700); and Earls Colne Primary School (£1,000).

FINANCES *Year* 2007–08 *Income* £49,785 *Grants* £34,057 *Assets* £1,272,050

TRUSTEES Mrs P R Taylor, Chair; Ms S Thurgate; Mrs M M James; J M Carter; O S Forder; G C Waterer; A H Frost; Mrs A Paramor; R N Firth; J Panayi; Mrs F Murray.

OTHER INFORMATION A further £14,000 was given in grants to individuals.

HOW TO APPLY In writing to the correspondent.

WHO TO APPLY TO Kaveri Woodward, Clerk to the Trustees, St Andrew's House, 2 Mallows Field, Halstead, Essex CO9 2LN *Tel* 01787 479960 *email* earlscolnehalstead.edcharity@yahoo.co.uk

CC NO 310859   **ESTABLISHED** 1975

■ The Earmark Trust

WHERE FUNDING CAN BE GIVEN UK, with a preference for charities based in Kent.

WHO CAN BENEFIT Charitable organisations, usually those personally known to the trustees.

WHAT IS FUNDED People with disabilities, children, cancer research, the arts, Christian causes and general charitable purposes.

WHAT IS NOT FUNDED Applications from individuals are seldom considered. Applications from large-scale charities, church/cathedral restoration schemes or organ rebuilding projects are also not considered.

RANGE OF GRANTS £250–£5,000.

SAMPLE GRANTS Rochdale Special Needs Cycling Club (£5,000); St Luke's Hospital for the Clergy (£2,200); Laine Theatre Arts (£1,500); Willow Trust, Jubilee Sailing Trust and Kent Air Ambulance (£500); and Pestolazzi International Village Trust, Russian Immigrant Aid Fund, Scripture Union and Two Tim Two Trust (£250 each).

FINANCES *Year* 2007–08 *Income* £41,016 *Grants* £25,611 *Assets* £923,677

TRUSTEES F C Raven; A C M Raven.

HOW TO APPLY In writing to the correspondent.

WHO TO APPLY TO The Trustees, 8 Bidborough Court, Penshurst Road, Bidborough, Tunbridge Wells, Kent TN3 0XJ

CC NO 267176   **ESTABLISHED** 1974

■ East Kent Provincial Charities

WHERE FUNDING CAN BE GIVEN UK, with a preference for Kent.

WHO CAN BENEFIT Individuals and organisations.

WHAT IS FUNDED Relief of poverty of children and older people; advancement of education; care of people who are sick and older people; and general charitable purposes.

RANGE OF GRANTS Usually up to £10,000.

SAMPLE GRANTS Provincial Grand Masters Lodge (£9,300); Kent Masonic Library and Museum (£7,500); Royal Masonic Benevolent Institution (£7,300); Kent Mark Benevolent Fund (£4,300); Canterbury Masonic Charities (£4,200); and New Masonic Samaritan Fund (£1,100); Kent Air Ambulance (£6,400); Pahar Trust (£4,000); Margate Swimming Club (£1,500); and Dover War Memorial, Sheppey Sea Cadets and Whitstable Umbrella Community Centre (£1,000 each).

FINANCES *Year* 2007–08 *Income* £469,525 *Grants* £80,425 *Assets* £27,885

TRUSTEES Patrick Thomas, Chair; Graham Smith; John Edmondson; Peter Daniels; Peter Rodd; Brian Powell; Keith Pavey; Patrick Flanagan; Thomas Denne.

HOW TO APPLY In writing to the correspondent.

WHO TO APPLY TO Patrick Flanagan, Secretary, 11 Boorman Way, Estuary View Business Park, Whitstable, Kent CT5 3SE *Tel* 01227 272944 *email* office@ekpca.org.uk *Website* www.ekpca.org.uk

CC NO 1023859   **ESTABLISHED** 1993

■ East London Community Foundation

WHERE FUNDING CAN BE GIVEN North East London, including Barking and Dagenham, Hackney, Havering, Newham, Redbridge, Tower Hamlets and Waltham Forest.

WHO CAN BENEFIT The community in north east London, including people who are disabled, older people and people disadvantaged by poverty; people involved in arts and cultural activities and multi-cultural groups.

WHAT IS FUNDED The foundation has a range of different funds designed for small community and voluntary groups working to help local people across East and North East London. For example, Grassroots Grants, Comic Relief and the Fair Share programme. It is important to note that grant schemes can change frequently. Please consult the foundation's website for details of current programmes and their deadlines.

WHAT IS NOT FUNDED No grants to individuals or to activities that are primarily religious or party political.

TYPE OF GRANT One-off small grants.

RANGE OF GRANTS Mostly £500–£5,000.

SAMPLE GRANTS African Youth League (£25,000); Chain Reaction (£10,000); Heart of Oak Judo (£7,000); Seedtime Project (£6,600); Upminster Cricket Club (£5,000); Bonny Downs (£3,900); Club Bana Yolo (£2,300); Ilford and District Bereavement Care (£1,000); the Friendship Club Café (£700); and Buxton Bear Pre-School (£410).

FINANCES *Year* 2007–08 *Income* £711,868 *Grants* £617,758 *Assets* £69,540

TRUSTEES Sanjay Mazumder; David Harris; Alan Thompson; John D'Abbro; Ram Bhandari; Sharon Hanoomansingh; Steve Carters; Jonathan Caton.

HOW TO APPLY The foundation's website has details of the grant schemes currently being administered. Application forms and guidance notes can be downloaded from the website or requested by telephone or letter.

WHO TO APPLY TO Anja Beinroth, Grant Manager/ Acting Director, LCCM House, Kemp Road RM8 1ST *Tel* 0300 303 1203 *email* enquiries@elcf.org.uk *Website* www.elcf. org.uk

CC NO 1000540   **ESTABLISHED** 1990

■ Eastern Counties Educational Trust Limited

WHERE FUNDING CAN BE GIVEN Preference for Essex, Suffolk, Norfolk, Cambridgeshire and Hertfordshire.

WHO CAN BENEFIT Those with special educational needs, particularly those under 25 who have emotional and behavioural difficulties.

WHAT IS FUNDED Activities, projects or equipment which will assist the above.

WHAT IS NOT FUNDED No grants to individuals. Normally no grants are given for recurring costs.

TYPE OF GRANT One-off and recurring.

RANGE OF GRANTS £500–£10,000.

SAMPLE GRANTS Red Balloon Learner Centre – Norwich (£20,000); Manningtree High School (£16,000); Chantry High School – Ipswich (£13,000); Adventure Playgrounds for People with Special Needs (£10,000); Lexden Springs School – Colchester (£7,500); London Mozart Players (£6,000); Felixstowe Level Two Youth Project and Essex Association of Boys Clubs (£5,000 each); and Happy Days Children's Charity (£4,000).

FINANCES *Year* 2007–08 *Income* £158,571 *Grants* £124,713 *Assets* £2,955,957

TRUSTEES H Anderson; Mrs V L d'Angibau; P G Glossop; L M Lepper; F V Morgan; Mrs K E Norman-Butler; A J Willis; Mrs G Campbell; Mrs D M Reed; Lady Singleton; Miss J S Clark.

HOW TO APPLY An application form should be obtained from the correspondent. This provides details of information to be submitted with it. Unsuccessful applicants will not be informed unless an sae is provided.

WHO TO APPLY TO Mr A H Corin, Company Secretary, Brook Farm, Wet Lane, Boxted, Colchester, Essex CO4 5TN *Tel* 01206 273295

CC NO 310038   **ESTABLISHED** 1922

■ The Sir John Eastwood Foundation

WHERE FUNDING CAN BE GIVEN UK, but mainly Nottinghamshire in practice.

WHO CAN BENEFIT Local organisations, particularly those concerned with disabled and older people and children with special needs.

WHAT IS FUNDED General charitable purposes.

WHAT IS NOT FUNDED No grants to individuals.

RANGE OF GRANTS Mostly £5,000 or less.

SAMPLE GRANTS Meden Charitable Trust (£20,000); Newark and Notts Agricultural Society, Nottingham University and Bilsthorpe Miners Welfare Scheme (£10,000 each); and Bluebell Wood Children's Hospice and Bridge St Methodist Church (£5,000 each); RNID (£4,000); Warsop United Charities and Alzheimer's Society (£3,000 each); Nottingham Hospice Limited, Army Benevolent Fund and Literacy Volunteers (£2,000 each); and National Talking Newspaper, No Panic, Aspley Methodist Church and Balderton Resource Centre (£1,000 each).

FINANCES *Year* 2007–08 *Income* £4,679,075 *Grants* £377,260 *Assets* £8,959,252

TRUSTEES Gordon G Raymond, Chair; Diana M Cottingham; Valerie A Hardingham; Constance B Mudford; Peter M Spencer.

HOW TO APPLY In writing to the correspondent.

WHO TO APPLY TO Gordon G Raymond, Trustee, Burns Lane, Warsop, Mansfield, Nottinghamshire NG20 0QG *Fax* 01623 847955

CC NO 235389   **ESTABLISHED** 1964

■ The Ebenezer Trust

WHERE FUNDING CAN BE GIVEN UK and overseas.

WHO CAN BENEFIT Registered charities.

WHAT IS FUNDED Advancement of Protestant and Evangelical tenets of the Christian faith. Activities in which the trustees are personally interested or involved.

WHAT IS NOT FUNDED No grants to individuals.

TYPE OF GRANT Occasionally interest-free loans.

RANGE OF GRANTS Up to around £10,000, in practice, between £500 and £5,000.

SAMPLE GRANTS Brentwood Baptist Church (£11,000); TEAR Fund (£6,000); Baptist Missionary Society, Barnabas Trust, and Viz a Viz (£5,000 each); Brentwood Schools Christian Worker Trust (£4,000); Evangelical Alliance and Shatesbury Society (£2,000 each); Ethiopian Graduates School of Technology, Africa Inland Mission, Care Trust and Salvation Army (£1,000 each); and Stepping Stones Trust, London City Mission and Far Eastern Broadcasting Association (£500 each).

FINANCES *Year* 2007–08 *Income* £47,328 *Grants* £74,423 *Assets* £713,227

TRUSTEES Nigel Davey; Ruth Davey.

HOW TO APPLY The trust states that they 'are most unlikely to consider unsolicited requests for grants'.

WHO TO APPLY TO Nigel Davey, Trustee, Longwood Lodge, Whites Hill, Stock, Ingatestone, Essex CM4 9QB *Tel* 01277 829893
CC NO 272574   ESTABLISHED 1976

■ The EBM Charitable Trust

WHERE FUNDING CAN BE GIVEN UK.
WHO CAN BENEFIT Charitable organisations.
WHAT IS FUNDED General charitable purposes, especially animal welfare and research, youth development and the relief of poverty.
TYPE OF GRANT Recurring and one-off.
RANGE OF GRANTS £2,500–£250,000.
SAMPLE GRANTS Home of Horseracing Trust (£250,000); British Racing School (£125,000); Injured Jockey's Fund (£100,000); Royal Veterinary College (£75,000); Animal Health Trust (£70,000); Cardinal Hume Centre (£40,000); Macmillan Cancer Support (£30,000); Treloar Trust (£20,000); Brain Research Trust (£10,000); Dogs for the Disabled (£8,500); RNIB (£5,000); and New Astley Club (£3,500).
FINANCES *Year* 2007–08 *Income* £898,081 *Grants* £1,153,000 *Assets* £37,791,452
TRUSTEES Richard Moore; Michael Macfadyen; Stephen Hogg.
HOW TO APPLY 'Unsolicited applications are not requested as the trustees prefer to support donations to charities whose work they have researched and which is in accordance with the wishes of the settlor. The trustees do not tend to support research projects as research is not a core priority but there are exceptions. The trustees' funds are fully committed. The trustees receive a very high number of grant applications which are mostly unsuccessful.'
WHO TO APPLY TO Keith Lawrence, Moore Stephens, St Paul's House, 8–12 Warwick Lane, London EC4M 7BP *Tel* 020 7334 9191 *Fax* 020 7651 1953
CC NO 326186   ESTABLISHED 1982

■ The Ecology Trust

WHERE FUNDING CAN BE GIVEN Mainly UK.
WHO CAN BENEFIT Registered charities working on ecological and environmental initiatives, particularly, in the areas of agriculture, energy, and climate change.
WHAT IS FUNDED Support is given to projects that prevent environmental degradation and that change values and attitudes, both amongst the public and with people in positions of power. In general the trust seeks to address the causes of the environmental crisis that we face, and to tackle these, rather than to make the consequences of this crisis easier to live with.
WHAT IS NOT FUNDED The trust is unlikely to make grants to the following kinds of projects: work that has already taken place; part of general appeals or circulars; outward-bound courses, expeditions and overseas travel; capital projects (i.e. buildings and refurbishment costs); conservation of already well-supported species or of non-native species; and furniture, white goods, computer, paint, timber and scrap recycling projects.
TYPE OF GRANT One-off and recurring grants for project and core costs.
RANGE OF GRANTS Up to £464,000.
SAMPLE GRANTS Marie Curie Cancer Care (£464,000); Fundacion Ecologica De Cuixmala (£45,000); UK Waste Incineration Network

(£15,000); and Highland Foundation for Wildlife (£6,500).
FINANCES *Year* 2007–08 *Income* £1,167,508 *Grants* £530,866 *Assets* £632,910
TRUSTEES Jeremy Faull, Chair; Charles Filmer; Kenneth Richards.
HOW TO APPLY In writing to the correspondent.
WHO TO APPLY TO Jon Cracknell, Hon. Secretary, Unicorn Administration Ltd, 30–36 King Street, Maidenhead SL6 1NA
CC NO 1099222   ESTABLISHED 2003

■ Eden Arts Trust

WHERE FUNDING CAN BE GIVEN The Eden district of Cumbria.
WHO CAN BENEFIT Individuals and organisations benefiting: young adults and older people; artists; actors and entertainment professionals; musicians; textile workers and designers; volunteers; and writers and poets.
WHAT IS FUNDED To promote and develop the arts and art projects involving the community, and to encourage new groups.
WHAT IS NOT FUNDED Only projects/groups in the Eden district can be funded.
TYPE OF GRANT Local arts and crafts projects, days and events, feasibility studies.
RANGE OF GRANTS Up to £5,000.
SAMPLE GRANTS Appleby Jazz Festival (£2,000); Highlights Rural Touring and Craft Tour (£2,000); and Storytelling Festival (£500). Smaller grants amounted to £8,100, but beneficiaries were not listed.
FINANCES *Year* 2007–08 *Income* £131,979 *Grants* £12,563 *Assets* £114,841
TRUSTEES Ifor Freeman; Barbara Slack; Keith Morgan; Mary Warburton; Terence Smith; Jeremy Latimer; Heather Heron.
HOW TO APPLY Contact the trust by telephone or email for further information.
WHO TO APPLY TO Irene Faith, Executive Officer, 1 Sandgate, Penrith, Cumbria CA11 7TP *Tel* 01768 899444 *Fax* 01768 895920 *email* enquiries@edenarts.co.uk *Website* www.edenarts.co.uk
CC NO 1000476   ESTABLISHED 1990

■ EDF Energy Trust (EDFET)

WHERE FUNDING CAN BE GIVEN UK.
WHO CAN BENEFIT Individuals and families and voluntary and not-for-profit organisations.
WHAT IS FUNDED The trust offers two types of grants: *individual grants* – to cover the payment of gas and electricity debts and other essential household debts or costs (applicants must be EDF Energy account holders); and *organisational grants* – for organisations working in the field of money advice, debt counselling or energy efficiency advice.
WHAT IS NOT FUNDED No grants for: fines for criminal offences; educational or training needs; debts to central government departments; medical equipment, aids and adaptations; holidays; business debts; catalogues; credit cards; personal loans; deposits for secure accommodation; or overpayment of benefits.
TYPE OF GRANT Contracts and full project funding for up to three years.
SAMPLE GRANTS A list of organisational grants was not provided in the accounts but previous beneficiaries include: Hammersmith and Fulham Citizens Advice Bureau (CAB), Medway CAB, Blackfriars Advice Centre, East London Financial Inclusion Unit, Truro Citizens Advice, Age

Concern – Exeter, Bristol Debt Advice Centre, Cheltenham Housing Aid Centre and Direct Debt Line.

FINANCES *Year* 2007–08 *Income* £3,026,983 *Grants* £189,432 *Assets* £610,959

TRUSTEES Yvonne Constance; Jane Guy; Bob Jackson; Denice Fennell; Steve Meakin; Peter Privett.

OTHER INFORMATION Please note: the trust's latest accounts cover the period from 1 October 2007 to 31 December 2008. In addition to the grant figure above a further £2.3 million was given to individuals.

HOW TO APPLY Organisational grants: it is advisable to contact the foundation for further information on future grant programmes and deadlines. Individual grants: applications can be submitted throughout the year. Applications must be made on a standard application form, which can be downloaded from the website, obtained from local advice centres such as citizen's advice bureau or by writing to the trust. The trust also has an online application form, accessible via the website.

WHO TO APPLY TO The Trustees, Freepost RLXG-RBYJ-USXE, EDF Energy Trust, PO Box 42, Peterborough PE3 8XH *Tel* 01733 421 021 *Fax* 01733 421 020 *email* edfet@charisgrants. com *Website* www.edfenergytrust.org.uk

CC NO 1099446   **ESTABLISHED** 1996

■ The Gilbert and Eileen Edgar Foundation

WHERE FUNDING CAN BE GIVEN UK (and a few international appeals).

WHO CAN BENEFIT Smaller organisations.

WHAT IS FUNDED Medical Research – the promotion of medical and surgical science in all forms; care and support – helping people who are young, old and in need; fine arts – raising the artistic taste of the public in music, drama, opera, painting, sculpture and the fine arts; education in the fine arts – the promotion of education in the fine arts; religion – the promotion of religion; recreation – the provision of facilities for recreation or other leisure time activities.

WHAT IS NOT FUNDED Grants for education in the fine arts are made by way of scholarships awarded by academies and no grants are made directly to individuals in this regard.

RANGE OF GRANTS Usually £250–£5,000.

SAMPLE GRANTS Atlantic Salmon Trust, Landmine Action and Reading Chinese School, Children in Crisis, Operation New World and NSPCC (£1,000); and Reading Voluntary Action, Victim Support, Wells for India, Survival for Tribal Peoples, Marine Conservation Society and Ghurkha Welfare Trust (£500 each).

FINANCES *Year* 2005 *Income* £59,399 *Grants* £107,600 *Assets* £1,080,175

TRUSTEES A E Gentilli; R S Parker.

HOW TO APPLY In writing to the correspondent. There are no application forms.

WHO TO APPLY TO Penny Tyson, c/o Chantrey Vellacott DFK, Prospect House, 58 Queens Road, Reading RG1 4RP *Website* www.cvdfk. com

CC NO 241736   **ESTABLISHED** 1965

■ Gilbert Edgar Trust

WHERE FUNDING CAN BE GIVEN Predominantly UK, limited overseas.

WHO CAN BENEFIT Registered charities, educational or cultural bodies benefiting children, medical professionals and research workers.

WHAT IS FUNDED Only charities which the trustees find worthwhile will be supported. Grants are given in the following categories: homeless; hospice; medical; overseas; research; social; and young people.

WHAT IS NOT FUNDED No grants to individuals or non-registered charities.

RANGE OF GRANTS Up to £10,000, however the trust states that it gives most grants at around £500–£1,500.

SAMPLE GRANTS The Not Forgotten Association and Marylebone Project (£10,000 each); NSPCC, Mind and Shelter (£3,000 each); Macmillan Cancer Relief and National Institute of Conductive Education (£2,000 each); and Samaritans and Police Foundation and Prisoners Abroad (£1,000 each).

FINANCES *Year* 2007–08 *Income* £59,399 *Grants* £107,600 *Assets* £1,080,175

TRUSTEES S C E Gentilli; A E Gentilli; Dr R E B Solomons.

HOW TO APPLY In writing to the correspondent, with a copy of a brochure describing your work.

WHO TO APPLY TO The Trustees, c/o Cave Harper and Co., North Lee House, 66 Northfield End, Henley-on-Thames, Oxfordshire RG9 2BE *Tel* 01491 572565

CC NO 213630   **ESTABLISHED** 1955

■ Edinburgh Children's Holiday Fund

WHERE FUNDING CAN BE GIVEN Edinburgh and the Lothians.

WHO CAN BENEFIT Children.

WHAT IS FUNDED Grants are awarded to charitable and voluntary organisations that are concerned with children's welfare and provide holidays for children who are disadvantaged.

WHAT IS NOT FUNDED No grants directly to individuals.

TYPE OF GRANT One-off grants.

SAMPLE GRANTS Previous beneficiaries have included Acorn Christian Centre, Castleview Primary School, Children 1st, Drug Prevention Group, Forthview Primary School, Mother's Union Holiday Scheme, the Roses Charitable Trust, Scottish Spina Bifida Association, Stepping Stones and Uphill Ski Club.

FINANCES *Year* 2007–08 *Income* £84,401

HOW TO APPLY On a form available from the correspondent. Trustees meet to consider grants in January and May. Applications should be sent in mid-December and mid-April respectively.

WHO TO APPLY TO The Secretaries, Bryce, Wilson and Co. Chartered Accountants, 22 Walker Street, Edinburgh EH3 7HR *Tel* 0131 225 5111 *Fax* 0131 220 0283

SC NO SC010312

■ The Edinburgh Trust, No 2 Account

WHERE FUNDING CAN BE GIVEN UK and worldwide.

WHO CAN BENEFIT Registered charities only.

WHAT IS FUNDED General charitable purposes, but the trust fund and the income may be applied for the promotion and advancement of education and of the efficiency of the armed services.

WHAT IS NOT FUNDED No grants to individuals; only scientific expeditions are considered with the backing of a major society. No grants to non-registered charities.

RANGE OF GRANTS Usually £500–£3,000.

SAMPLE GRANTS Edwina Mountbatten Trust (£2,750); Federation of London Youth Clubs and Royal Marines General Fund (£2,500 each); Outward Bound Trust and The Award Scheme (£2,000 each); Burman Star Association, The Maritime Trust and Royal Life Saving Society (£1,500 each); and British Heart Foundation, Interact Worldwide and The British Trust for Conservation Volunteers (£1,000 each).

FINANCES *Year* 2007–08 *Income* £94,134 *Grants* £66,062 *Assets* £2,236,851

TRUSTEES Sir Brian McGrath; C Woodhouse; Sir Miles Hunt-Davis.

HOW TO APPLY In writing to the correspondent. The trustees meet to consider grants in April each year. Applications must be submitted by January.

WHO TO APPLY TO The Secretary, Buckingham Palace, London SW1A 1AA *Tel* 020 7930 4832

CC NO 227897   **ESTABLISHED** 1959

··

■ Edinburgh Voluntary Organisations' Trust Funds

WHERE FUNDING CAN BE GIVEN Edinburgh and the Lothians.

WHO CAN BENEFIT Organisations and individuals. Organisations should have an annual turnover of under £200,000. Priority is given to local charitable organisations so that a national organisation will be required to indicate need and a local presence in Edinburgh and the Lothians according to the agreed policy.

WHAT IS FUNDED The trustees have revised their grant-aid policies with effect from April 2006 recognising the difficulty that local voluntary organisations face in attaining regular funding for their main activities. Consequently, for the period 2006 to 2010 the trustees will provide grants to voluntary organisations properly constituted and registered as charitable for purposes of social welfare and especially for local initiatives which benefit people in Edinburgh and the Lothians and when the organisation's aims and objectives are within trust policies, it is solvent and not in debt, and where the plan is imaginative and sound. The trustees may support main core-funding to assist progress and a grant for a genuine new development, after the first three years, may also be provided to a local organisation. Priority is given to organisations that combat inequalities and promote voluntary action. Arts or environmental tasks will only be considered where a significant social service or therapeutic intent is the main aim.

WHAT IS NOT FUNDED No grants are given to or for: non-registered charities; general appeals; statutory agencies or to replace statutory funding; salaries; commercial organisations or purposes; private schools and colleges; distribution by other agencies; repairs, extensions and alterations for property or for new buildings (grants can be given for essential equipment as part of a project); organisations concerned solely with the arts (although consideration will be given to applications for work with the trust's priority groups i.e. learning

difficulties, physical disability, older people and substance misuse).

TYPE OF GRANT One-off and recurrent for a maximum of three years.

RANGE OF GRANT Organisations: up to £2,000 annually.

SAMPLE GRANTS Previous beneficiaries include: LIBRA, Midlothian Befriending Scheme, Lothian Autistic Society, Northfield and Willowbrae Community Services Group, Loan Head Community Services Association, Senior Action Group, Positive Help, Reality to Work and Drake Music Project in Scotland.

FINANCES *Year* 2008–09 *Income* £828,158

TRUSTEES Penny Richardson; Helen Berry; Graeme Thom; Geoffrey Lord; Monica Langa.

OTHER INFORMATION Despite making a written request for the accounts of this trust (including an sae) these were not provided. The following entry is based on information filed with the Office of the Scottish Charity Regulator and available on the trust's useful website. Please note: at present the Edinburgh Voluntary Organisations Council is the administrative structure for the following trusts: Miss A Beveridge's Trust, William Thyne Trust and Edinburgh Voluntary Organisations' Trust. It now administers these together and there is one application form for organisations. In addition, the trust also administers grants on behalf of Children in Need and Ponton House.

HOW TO APPLY Application forms are available from the correspondent. Applications must be submitted to Edinburgh Voluntary Organisations' Trust (EVOT) and not to the individual trusts.

WHO TO APPLY TO Janette Scappaticcio, Trust Fund Administrator, 14 Ashley Place, Edinburgh EH6 5PX *Tel* 0131 555 9100 *Fax* 0131 555 9101 *email* janettescappaticco@evoc.org.uk *Website* www.evoc.org.uk

SC NO SC031561   **ESTABLISHED** 1868

··

■ Educational Foundation of Alderman John Norman

WHERE FUNDING CAN BE GIVEN Norwich and Old Catton.

WHO CAN BENEFIT Individuals who are descendants of Alderman Norman, and organisations benefiting children, young adults and students.

WHAT IS FUNDED The trust primarily supports the education of the descendants of Alderman Norman, but also supports young people, local schools and educational establishments in the area.

WHAT IS NOT FUNDED No grants to non-registered charities. No applications from outside Norwich and Old Catton will be considered.

RANGE OF GRANTS £500–£6,000.

SAMPLE GRANTS Norwich Cathedral Choir Endowment Fund (£6,000); The How Hill Trust (£5,000); Norfolk County Council EWS Activity Fund and West Norwich Partnership (£3,000 each); Mancroft Advice Project (£2,000); The Claimants Unity Trust (£1,700); and Football in the Community, Leeway Norwich Womens Aid and Norwich Sea Cadets (£1,000 each).

FINANCES *Year* 2007–08 *Income* £274,543 *Grants* £28,820 *Assets* £6,051,801

TRUSTEES Revd J Boston; R Sandall; Dr J Leach; Revd Canon M Smith; D S Armes; C D Brown; C I H Mawson; Mrs C I H Mawson; Mrs T Hughes; S Slack; J Hawkins; R Hughes; F Whymark.

OTHER INFORMATION In 2007–08, grants were given to descendants (£179,000); Old Catton

Residents (£6,300); and organisations (£29,000).

HOW TO APPLY In writing to the correspondent. Grants to organisations are considered at the trustees meeting in May/June, however the trustees usually meet three times each year, in February, May and October.

WHO TO APPLY TO N F Saffell, Clerk, Brown and Co, Old Bank of England Court, Queen Street, Norwich NR2 4TA *Tel* 01603 629871 *email* n. saffell@brown-co.com

CC NO 313105 **ESTABLISHED** 1962

■ Edupoor Limited

WHERE FUNDING CAN BE GIVEN Worldwide.

WHO CAN BENEFIT Registered charities.

WHAT IS FUNDED Projects in line with the trust's objects of, 'the advancement in education and training through the world, the relief of poverty, old age, illness, both mental and physical and the relief of persons suffering from any disability, and such other charitable purpose as the association may time to time authorise'.

FINANCES *Year* 2007–08 *Income* £490,691 *Grants* £453,095 *Assets* £41,861

TRUSTEES Michael Shelton; Richard Fraser.

OTHER INFORMATION Accounts were on file at the Charity Commission, without a list of grants.

HOW TO APPLY In writing to the correspondent.

WHO TO APPLY TO Michael Shelton, Trustee, Flat 10, 125 Clapton Common, Stamford Hill, London E5 9AB

CC NO 1113785 **ESTABLISHED** 2006

■ The W G Edwards Charitable Foundation

WHERE FUNDING CAN BE GIVEN UK.

WHO CAN BENEFIT Projects benefiting older people.

WHAT IS FUNDED The provision of care for older people through existing charities.

WHAT IS NOT FUNDED No grants to individuals.

TYPE OF GRANT Principally capital projects. Trustees currently prefer to give towards a named item rather than into a pool building fund.

RANGE OF GRANTS £1,000 to £10,000. Average grant about £4,000.

SAMPLE GRANTS Beneficiaries included: Age Concern Sevenoaks (£16,000); Deptford Action Group for the Elderly (£10,000); Action on Elder Abuse (£8,400); Extracare Charitable Trust, Coventry (£6,000); London Mozarts Players and Northumberland Wildlife Trust (£5,000 each); Henshaws Society for Blind People (Northwest) and Age Exchange (£4,000 each); and Music in Hospitals, Scotland (£2,000).

FINANCES *Year* 2007–08 *Income* £145,054 *Grants* £102,000 *Assets* £3,050,751

TRUSTEES Mrs Margaret E Offley Edwards; Prof. Wendy D Savage; Mrs G Shepherd Coates; Ms Yewande Savage.

HOW TO APPLY In writing to the correspondent, including: confirmation of charitable status (charity number on letterhead will suffice); brief details of the project; budget statement for the project; current fundraising achievements and proposals for future fundraising; items of expenditure within project costing approx £1,000 to £5,000 – trustees currently prefer to give towards a named item rather than into a pool building fund; copy of latest accounts if available. There are no forms or deadlines for applications. If your project fulfils the Foundation's policy criteria, your details will be passed on to the trustees for consideration at their next meeting.

WHO TO APPLY TO Janet Brown, Clerk to the Trustees, c/o 123a Station Road, Oxted, Surrey RH8 0QE *Tel* 01883 714412 *Fax* 01883 714433 *email* janetbrown@ wgedwardscharitablefoundation.org.uk *Website* www.wgedwardscharitablefoundation. org.uk

CC NO 293312 **ESTABLISHED** 1985

■ The William Edwards Educational Charity

WHERE FUNDING CAN BE GIVEN Kenilworth.

WHO CAN BENEFIT Schools and colleges benefiting children, young adults, academics and students under the age of 25.

WHAT IS FUNDED The education of young people.

TYPE OF GRANT One-off and recurrent grants.

RANGE OF GRANTS Generally around £500 to £10,000.

SAMPLE GRANTS Kenilworth School (£40,000); St Nicholas' Community Primary School (£11,000); Park Hill Junior School (£7,000); St John's County Primary School (£4,000); Abbotsford School (£3,000); and Crackley Hall School (£1,800).

FINANCES *Year* 2007–08 *Income* £186,168 *Grants* £108,740 *Assets* £6,041,760

TRUSTEES K Rawnsley; Cllr Mrs P Edwards; Cllr J Hatfield; Capt. S C Harrison; Cllr H A Thomas; Dr G Raper; J A Cooke; Cllr M Coker; Cllr N J Vincent.

OTHER INFORMATION The 2007–08 grant total includes: grants to schools (£103,000); grants to individuals (£34,000); and bursaries for post-graduate study (£21,000).

HOW TO APPLY In writing to the correspondent. Trustees meet four times a year.

WHO TO APPLY TO J M P Hathaway, Clerk to the Trustees, Messrs Heath and Blenkinsop, 42 Brook Street, Warwick CV34 4BL

CC NO 528714 **ESTABLISHED** 1981

■ Dr Edwards' and Bishop King's Fulham Endowment Fund

WHERE FUNDING CAN BE GIVEN Fulham: specifically the post code areas of SW6, part of W14 and part of W6.

WHO CAN BENEFIT Organisations or local groups that help people on low incomes who live in Fulham. Grants are also made to individuals in need.

WHAT IS FUNDED One-off projects and summer schemes.

WHAT IS NOT FUNDED 'The charity does not respond to general funding appeals but will consider matching funding raised from other sources, but not for any purpose for which statutory funding is available.'

TYPE OF GRANT Running costs, one off project grants.

RANGE OF GRANTS Up to £5,000.

SAMPLE GRANTS Furnish Community Furniture Store (£26,000); Hammersmith and Fulham Play Association (£5,900); Bishop Creighton House Settlement (£5,000); Fulham Legal Advice Centre (£4,800); Active Planet Ltd – Summer scheme (£3,500); Rampage Holiday Project (£3,000); Brunswick Club – Summer scheme (£2,000); Hammersmith and Fulham Caring for Carers (£1,700); and Hammersmith Bengali Project – Summer project (£1,000).

FINANCES *Year* 2007–08 *Income* £413,546 *Grants* £140,614 *Assets* £8,331,664

TRUSTEES Michael Clein; David C Cole; Ian Gray; Ron Lawrence; Susan O'Neill; Allen Russell Smith; Kofi Sunu; Charles Treloggan; Michael Waymouth; Carole Bailey; Cllr Adronie Alford; Patricia Phillips; Bobbie Richards; Rev Mark Osborne.

OTHER INFORMATION Grants made directly to individuals totalled £144,000, from which, the majority of grants were made for relief in need purposes.

HOW TO APPLY On an application form available from the correspondent or the trust's website. The trust also requests that the following documents be included with your application: a copy of the organisation's constitution or rules; the most recent annual report and accounts or a financial statement and a brief description of your activities and a financial statement; a list of the members of your management committee; a list (if applicable) of the streets and postcodes of the people you are working with; a summary outline of the project; a budget for the project; and any appropriate estimates for materials, equipment or work. Grants to organisations are considered bi-monthly. The clerk to the trustees may ask to visit your organisation before your application is considered.

WHO TO APPLY TO Vivienne Robb, Clerk to the Trustees, Percy Barton House, 33–35 Dawes Road, Fulham, London SW6 7DT *Tel* 020 7386 9387 *Fax* 020 7610 2856 *email* clerk@debk. org.uk *Website* www.debk.org.uk

CC NO 1113490   **ESTABLISHED** 1981

■ The Elephant Trust

WHERE FUNDING CAN BE GIVEN UK.

WHO CAN BENEFIT Individual artists, arts organisations and publications concerned with the visual arts.

WHAT IS FUNDED Visual arts. The priorities are to extend the frontiers of creative endeavour, to promote the unconventional and the imaginative and, within its limited resources, to make it possible for artists and arts organisations to realise and complete specific projects.

WHAT IS NOT FUNDED No education or other study grants.

TYPE OF GRANT One-off contributions to specific projects.

RANGE OF GRANTS Up to £3,500, but larger grants may be considered.

SAMPLE GRANTS Atlas Press and Studio Voltaire (£3,500 each); Camden Arts Centre and Matt's Gallery (£3,000 each); Book Works, The Common Guild and Ikon Birmingham, Institute of Contemporary Arts and S1 Art Space (£2,000 each); City Projects London Ltd (£1,800); and The Showroom (£1,000).

FINANCES *Year* 2007–08 *Income* £65,665 *Grants* £63,018 *Assets* £1,669,083

TRUSTEES Dawn Ades; Antony Forwood; Matthew Slotover; Tony Penrose; Richard Wentworth; Sarah Whitfield.

OTHER INFORMATION The trustees also administer the George Melhuish Bequest which has similar objectives.

HOW TO APPLY In writing to the correspondent. Guidelines are available. The trustees meet four times a year.

WHO TO APPLY TO Ruth Rattenbury, 512 Bankside Lofts, 65 Hopton Street, London SE1 9GZ *email* ruth@elephanttrust.org.uk

CC NO 269615   **ESTABLISHED** 1975

■ The George Elias Charitable Trust

WHERE FUNDING CAN BE GIVEN Some preference for Manchester.

WHO CAN BENEFIT Mostly Jewish organisations.

WHAT IS FUNDED Mainly Jewish causes, some smaller donations (£100–£750) to more general charitable causes, including educational needs, healthcare and the fight against poverty.

TYPE OF GRANT Capital.

RANGE OF GRANTS Usually up to £20,000, with some larger amounts considered.

SAMPLE GRANTS Ahavat Shalom (£43,000); Hale and District Hebrew Congregation (£26,000); Lubavitch South Manchester (£13,000); Jewish Humanitarian Foundation (£7,200); The Jewish Learning Exchange (£5,000); Chai Network (£4,700); South Manchester Mikva Trust (£4,000); Manchester Jewish Chaplaincy (£3,000); Christie Hospital (£1,900); and Jewish Agency (£1,000).

FINANCES *Year* 2007–08 *Income* £262,869 *Grants* £251,194 *Assets* £157,276

TRUSTEES E C Elias; S E Elias.

HOW TO APPLY In writing to the correspondent. Trustees meet monthly.

WHO TO APPLY TO N G Denton, Charity Accountant, Elitex House, 1 Ashley Road, Altrincham, Cheshire WA14 2DT *Tel* 0161 928 7171 *email* textiles@kshaw.com

CC NO 273993   **ESTABLISHED** 1977

■ The Gerald Palmer Eling Trust Company

WHERE FUNDING CAN BE GIVEN Berkshire.

WHO CAN BENEFIT Charitable organisations.

WHAT IS FUNDED Christian religion, particularly the Orthodox Church; medical research and the study of medicine; and relief of sickness and poverty.

WHAT IS NOT FUNDED No grants to individuals.

TYPE OF GRANT One-off.

RANGE OF GRANTS Up to £10,000.

SAMPLE GRANTS Russian Orthodox Church (£10,000); Action on Addiction and Tall Ships Youth Trust (£5,000 each); Bucklebury Memorial Hall (£4,000); Barnados, International Spinal Research Trust and St George's Centre (£3,000 each); St Matthews Church – Midgham (£2,000); Holy Trinity PCC (£1,000); and Friends of HM Prison (£500).

FINANCES *Year* 2007–08 *Income* £1,024,748 *Grants* £197,500 *Assets* £34,115,555

TRUSTEES Jasper Clutterbuck; Desmond Harrison; Robin Broadhurst; James Gardiner.

OTHER INFORMATION The trust is responsible for the long term maintenance of the character and qualities of the Eling Estate, which is the principal asset of the original endowment, and the protection and sustenance of its environment. The sum of £438,000 went towards running the estate during the year.

HOW TO APPLY In writing to the correspondent.

WHO TO APPLY TO K McDiarmid, Englefield Estate Office, Englefield Road, Theale, Reading RG7 5DU *Tel* 0118 930 2504 *email* mcd@ englefield.co.uk

CC NO 1100869   **ESTABLISHED** 2003

■ The Elizabeth Frankland Moore and Star Foundation

WHERE FUNDING CAN BE GIVEN UK.

WHO CAN BENEFIT Charitable organisations.

WHAT IS FUNDED General charitable purposes.

SAMPLE GRANTS Beneficiaries included: The Not Forgotten Association and Accord (£10,000 each); Prisoners Abroad and Riverside Museum Appeal (£5,000 each); Special Forces Benevolent Fund (£2,500); The Friends of Barnes Hospital (£2,000); The Barton Trust, Wiltshire Air Ambulance Appeal and Revive Scotland (£1,000 each); Scottish SPCA, Plan International UK and Wessex Multiple Sclerosis Therapy Centre (£500 each).

FINANCES *Year* 2007–08 *Income* £197,605 *Grants* £90,000 *Assets* £6,873,751

TRUSTEES Mrs J Cameron; R A Griffiths; J D Hewens; Dr David Spalton.

HOW TO APPLY In writing to the correspondent. Trustees meet twice a year.

WHO TO APPLY TO c/o Claydons Barns, 11 Towcester Road, Whittlebury, Northamptonshire, NN 12 8XU

CC NO 257711   **ESTABLISHED** 1968

■ The Wilfred and Elsie Elkes Charity Fund

WHERE FUNDING CAN BE GIVEN Staffordshire and especially Uttoxeter, including UK-wide charities benefiting the area.

WHO CAN BENEFIT Organisations benefiting children and older people.

WHAT IS FUNDED The trustees have a particular interest in child welfare, the welfare of older people, organisations working with deaf people, and medical charities involved with deafness, Alzheimer's disease, Parkinson's disease and a range of other diseases. Animal welfare; infrastructure development; charity or voluntary umbrella bodies; accommodation and housing; and community facilities and services, are also considered.

WHAT IS NOT FUNDED Grants are normally made to organisations rather than to individuals.

TYPE OF GRANT Recurrent grants are given in a number of cases but more normally the grant is a one-off payment. Grants can be made for buildings, capital, core costs, project, research, running costs, salaries and start-up costs. Funding is available for up to and over three years.

SAMPLE GRANTS Peter Pan Nursery (£8,000); The Children's Heart Federation and Broadway Methodist Church (£5,000 each); Dr Charles Bamford Convalescent Home (£4,000); The Brainwave Centre and British Dyslexics (£3,000 each); Stafford Samaritans and 1st Uttoxeter Scout Group (£2,000); Deafblind UK and North Staffs Youth for Christ (£1,000 each); and Henshaws Society for Blind People (£500).

FINANCES *Year* 2007–08 *Income* £307,165 *Grants* £88,930 *Assets* £2,210,722

TRUSTEES Royal Bank of Scotland plc.

HOW TO APPLY In writing to the correspondent.

WHO TO APPLY TO The Trust Section Manager, RBS Trust Services, Eden, Lakeside, Chester Business Park, Wrexham Road, Chester CH4 9QT

CC NO 326573   **ESTABLISHED** 1984

■ The Maud Elkington Charitable Trust

WHERE FUNDING CAN BE GIVEN Mainly Desborough, Northamptonshire and Leicestershire.

WHO CAN BENEFIT Registered charities, particularly local, and local branches of UK charities and individuals through established bodies such as NHS trusts.

WHAT IS FUNDED General charitable purposes including health and welfare, especially of older people, young people and community.

WHAT IS NOT FUNDED No grants to individuals.

TYPE OF GRANT One-off and recurrent.

SAMPLE GRANTS Northamptonshire County Council Social Services (£33,000, comprising 91 individual payments); Leicester Charity Link (£21,000, comprising 17 individual payments); Leicester Grammar School – bursaries (£8,800); Age Concern – Wigston and Oadby (£7,500); Mayday Trust (£5,000); SSAFA Forces Help (£3,300); Charnwood 20–20 and National Autistic Society – Leicester (£2,000 each); Carers Centre – Leicestershire and Rutland (£1,500); and MENCAP (£1,300).

FINANCES *Year* 2007–08 *Income* £697,085 *Grants* £467,856 *Assets* £20,140,999

TRUSTEES Roger Bowder, Chair; Allan A Veasey; Caroline A Macpherson.

OTHER INFORMATION 193 grants below £1,000 were made totalling £140,000; these were not individually listed.

HOW TO APPLY In writing to the correspondent. There is no application form or guidelines. The trustees meet every seven or eight weeks.

WHO TO APPLY TO Mrs Paula Fowle, Administrator, c/o Harvey Ingram Owston, 20 New Walk, Leicester LE1 6TX *Tel* 0116 257 6129 *Fax* 0116 255 3318 *email* paula.fowle@harveyingram.co.uk

CC NO 263929   **ESTABLISHED** 1972

■ Ellador Ltd

WHERE FUNDING CAN BE GIVEN UK.

WHO CAN BENEFIT Jewish people.

WHAT IS FUNDED The trust supports organisations benefiting Jewish people and also Jewish individuals.

FINANCES *Year* 2007–08 *Income* £43,349 *Grants* £42,953 *Assets* £395,743

TRUSTEES J Schrieber; S Schrieber; Mrs H Schrieber; Mrs R Schrieber.

HOW TO APPLY In writing to the correspondent.

WHO TO APPLY TO J Schrieber, Trustee and Governor, Ellador Ltd, 20 Ashstead Road, London E5 9BH *Tel* 020 7242 3580

CC NO 283202   **ESTABLISHED** 1981

■ The Ellerdale Trust

WHERE FUNDING CAN BE GIVEN Worldwide.

WHO CAN BENEFIT Charitable organisations.

WHAT IS FUNDED Relief of poverty, distress or suffering in any part of the world, particularly amongst children.

RANGE OF GRANTS In practice, around £1,000–£20,000.

SAMPLE GRANTS Sense (£18,000); Action for Kids (£10,000); Mind (£7,000); Psychiatric Research Trust and Nelson's Journey (£5,000 each); Fairbridge Merseyside and Martin Sailing Project (£3,000 each); Nightingales Romania (£2,000); and Music Alive (£1,000).

FINANCES *Year* 2007–08 *Income* £284,990 *Grants* £57,000 *Assets* £6,345,296

TRUSTEES A T R Macfarlane; P C Kurthausen; S P Moores.

HOW TO APPLY In writing to the correspondent.

WHO TO APPLY TO The Trustees, c/o Macfarlane and Co., Cunard Building, Water Street, Liverpool L3 1DS *Tel* 0151 236 6161

CC NO 1073376   ESTABLISHED 1998

■ The John Ellerman Foundation

WHERE FUNDING CAN BE GIVEN Mainly UK.

WHO CAN BENEFIT UK registered charities which operate nationally or across England; local/regional charities should not apply.

WHAT IS FUNDED Health and disability – preventive medicine, support for those with serious medical conditions, physical disability, mental illness and for carers; social welfare – children, youth work, families and older people; arts – music, opera, museums, galleries, theatre and dance; conservation – the natural environment; overseas – social welfare, development and health.

WHAT IS NOT FUNDED Grants are made only to registered charities, and are not made for the following purposes: medical research; for or on behalf of individuals; individual hospices; local branches of national organisations; 'Friends of' groups; education or educational establishments; religious causes; conferences and seminars; sports and leisure facilities; purchase of vehicles; the direct replacement of public funding; deficit funding; domestic animal welfare; drug or alcohol misuse; prisons and offenders. Because of the volume of appeals which are received, the trustees do not consider further requests from charities which have had an application turned down until at least two years have elapsed since the letter of rejection. Similarly, funded charities can expect to wait two years from the last grant payment before a further application will be considered.

TYPE OF GRANT One-off or recurring. Core costs, project, running costs, salaries, and start-up costs. Funding may be given for up to three years.

RANGE OF GRANTS £10,000 minimum.

SAMPLE GRANTS Volunteer Reading Help (£51,000); Bletchley Park Trust, Place2Be and University of Cape Town Trust (£50,000 each); Woodland Trust (£40,000); STOP – Trafficking UK (£30,000); Haemophilia Society (£28,000); Grandparent's Association (£25,000); Buglife (£20,000); Unicorn Theatre (£15,000); and York Minster Fund (£10,000).

FINANCES *Year* 2008–09 *Income* £1,866,000 *Grants* £4,333,676 *Assets* £92,856,000

TRUSTEES Richard Edmunds; Dr John Hemming; Sue MacGregor; David Martin-Jenkins; Surgeon Vice-Admiral Anthony Revell; Lady Sarah Riddell; Beverley Stott; Dominic Caldecott.

HOW TO APPLY In writing to the correspondent following the foundation's guidelines available from its website.

WHO TO APPLY TO Eileen Terry, Appeals Manager, Aria House, 23 Craven Street, London WC2N 5NS *Tel* 020 7930 8566 (general) 020 7451 1471 (direct) *Fax* 020 7839 3654 *email* enquiries@ellerman.org.uk *Website* www.ellerman.org.uk

CC NO 263207   ESTABLISHED 1971

■ The Ellinson Foundation Ltd

WHERE FUNDING CAN BE GIVEN Worldwide.

WHO CAN BENEFIT Jewish organisations, especially boarding schools teaching the Torah. The trust usually supports the same organisations each year.

WHAT IS FUNDED Hospitals, education and homelessness, usually with a Jewish teaching aspect.

WHAT IS NOT FUNDED No grants to individuals.

TYPE OF GRANT Capital and recurring grants.

RANGE OF GRANTS Usually up to £10,000.

SAMPLE GRANTS Keser Yeshua Refua Uparnosa (£80,000); Kolel Ohel Torah (£9,000); British Friends of Jaffa Institute (£7,500); Friends of Yeshivas Brisk (£6,000); Institute of Torah and Charity (£3,000); and Rosecare Foundation (£1,000).

FINANCES *Year* 2007–08 *Income* £1,014,367 *Grants* £357,830 *Assets* £2,911,635

TRUSTEES C O Ellinson; A Ellinson; A Z Ellinson; U Ellinson.

HOW TO APPLY In writing to the correspondent. However, the trust generally supports the same organisations each year and unsolicited applications are not welcome.

WHO TO APPLY TO The Trustees, Messrs Robson Laidler and Co, Fernwood House, Fernwood Road, Jesmond, Newcastle upon Tyne NE2 1TJ *Tel* 0191 281 8191

CC NO 252018   ESTABLISHED 1967

■ The Edith Maud Ellis 1985 Charitable Trust

WHERE FUNDING CAN BE GIVEN UK, Ireland and overseas.

WHO CAN BENEFIT Registered charities benefiting Quakers, at risk groups, and people who are disadvantaged by poverty or socially isolated. Support is also given to victims of disasters, famine and war, and refugees.

WHAT IS FUNDED General charitable purposes including religious and educational projects (but not personal grants for religious or secular education nor grants for church buildings) and projects in international fields especially related to economic, social and humanitarian aid to developing countries.

WHAT IS NOT FUNDED No grants to individuals.

RANGE OF GRANTS Up to £10,000.

SAMPLE GRANTS Project Trust (£5,000); Friends World Committee for Consultation (£3,800); Dr Williams Charity, Women's International League and the Irish School of Ecumenics (£1,500 each); Wyndham Place Trust, Cape Town Peace Centre and Corrymeela Community (£1,000 each); and Dystonia Society and Budiriro Trust (£750 each).

FINANCES *Year* 2007–08 *Income* £93,932 *Grants* £33,750

TRUSTEES A P Honigmann; E H Milligan.

HOW TO APPLY In writing to the correspondent.

WHO TO APPLY TO Mrs H Fuff, Administrator, c/o Heckford Norton, 18 Hill Street, Saffron Walden, Essex CB10 1JD *Tel* 01799 522636 *email* hf@heckfordnorton.co.uk

CC NO 292835   ESTABLISHED 1985

■ The Ellis Campbell Foundation

WHERE FUNDING CAN BE GIVEN Hampshire, Perth and Kinross/Tayside.

WHO CAN BENEFIT Organisations benefiting young disadvantaged people. Maintenance and preservation of buildings is also considered.

WHAT IS FUNDED Education of disadvantaged people under 25; preservation/protection/improvement of items of architectural/structural/horticultural/mechanical heritage; encouragement of community based projects.

WHAT IS NOT FUNDED No grants to individuals. Other than the grants made annually over a period, no grants will be made more regularly than every other year. No funding for annual running costs.

TYPE OF GRANT Usually one-off funding, though grants may be given for over three to five years.

RANGE OF GRANTS Average grants of £1,300.

SAMPLE GRANTS Grants have been given previously to: Anvil Trust; Scottish Community Foundation; Prince's Trust; Bhutan Society; Meridian Trust Association; Hampshire Scouting; Hampshire Country Learning; Martin Sailing Project; Ro Ro Sailing Project; and Wheatsheaf Trust.

FINANCES *Year* 2008 *Income* £59,633 *Grants* £112,236 *Assets* £1,695,826

TRUSTEES M D C C Campbell, Chair; L F Campbell; Miss L G Campbell; J L C Campbell; Mrs A J Andrew.

HOW TO APPLY In writing to the correspondent. Trustees meet in April and November. Applications should be submitted before the preceding month and will only be acknowledged if they fall strictly within the trust's eligibility guidelines.

WHO TO APPLY TO Michael Campbell, Chair, Shalden Park Steading, Shalden, Alton, Hampshire GU34 4DS *Tel* 01256 381821 *email* office@elliscampbell.co.uk

CC NO 802717   **ESTABLISHED** 1989

■ James Ellis Charitable Trust

WHERE FUNDING CAN BE GIVEN UK.

WHO CAN BENEFIT Registered medical research charities and organisations involved with health issues.

WHAT IS FUNDED The trust gives in the areas of medical research and the relief of serious illness.

TYPE OF GRANT One-off.

RANGE OF GRANTS £500–£5,000.

SAMPLE GRANTS Previous beneficiaries include: Coronary Artery Disease Research Association, Fight for Sight, International Spinal Research Trust, Meningitis Research Foundation, Arthritis Research Campaign, Dermatitis and Allied Diseases Research Trust, Cystic Fibrosis Trust and Muscular Dystrophy Campaign.

FINANCES *Year* 2007–08 *Income* £23,804 *Grants* £25,000

TRUSTEES S J Ellis; J N Sheard; E Lord.

HOW TO APPLY In writing to the correspondent between November and January, for consideration in February.

WHO TO APPLY TO S J Ellis, Settlor, Barn Cottage, Botany Lane, Lepton, Huddersfield HD8 0NE *Tel* 01484 602066 *Fax* 01484 313577 *email* rukuhia@aol.com

CC NO 1055617   **ESTABLISHED** 1996

■ The Elm House Trust

WHERE FUNDING CAN BE GIVEN North Yorkshire and the north east of England.

WHO CAN BENEFIT Organisations and educational establishments in Durham and N E Yorkshire.

WHAT IS FUNDED Education and general charitable purposes.

SAMPLE GRANTS Citizens Advice Bureau (£10,000); UK Melorheostosis Association (£5,000); Burton-cum-Walden Parish Council (£1,400); and Vacation Chamber Orchestra (£1,000). £1.34 million was donated to VOLT as the trust directly finances the building and development of the learning centre in Durham.

FINANCES *Year* 2007 *Income* £397,397 *Grants* £17,415 *Assets* £4,638,519

TRUSTEES J O Ritchie; J P W Ritchie; R Whiteley.

HOW TO APPLY In writing to the correspondent.

WHO TO APPLY TO R Whiteley, 2 Greengate, Cardale Park, Harrogate HG3 1GY

CC NO 1109073   **ESTABLISHED** 2005

■ The Elmgrant Trust

WHERE FUNDING CAN BE GIVEN UK, with a preference for the south west of England.

WHO CAN BENEFIT Individuals and organisations.

WHAT IS FUNDED Encouragement of local life through education, the arts and the social sciences.

WHAT IS NOT FUNDED The following are not supported: large scale UK organisations; postgraduate study, overseas student grants, expeditions and travel and study projects overseas; counselling courses; renewed requests from the same (successful) applicant within a two-year period.

TYPE OF GRANT Primarily one-off, occasionally recurring (but not within a two-year period); core funding; no loans.

RANGE OF GRANTS £50–£5,000 (very occasionally over this). Typically £500.

SAMPLE GRANTS Second Chance Trust for Devon and Cornwall (£3,000); Dartington International Summer School (£2,000); Wren, The Dartington Hall Trust and Exeter Homeless Action Group (£1,000); The Prison Phoenix Trust (£700); National Coastwatch Institution, St Peter's Hospice, Life Cycle UK and Refugee Support Group Devon (£500); and Apollo Football Club and Anglo-Asian Cultural Centre (£200).

FINANCES *Year* 2007–08 *Income* £59,544 *Grants* £47,729 *Assets* £1,939,526

TRUSTEES Marian Ash, Chair; Sophie Young; Paul Elmhirst; Mark Sharman.

OTHER INFORMATION In 2007–08 the grant total included £2,125 paid to ten individuals.

HOW TO APPLY In writing to the correspondent, giving full financial details and, where possible, a letter of support. Initial telephone calls are welcome if advice is needed. There are no application forms. Guidelines are issued. An sae would be very helpful, although this is not obligatory. Currently, meetings are held three times a year in March, June and October. Applications need to be received one clear month prior to meeting.

WHO TO APPLY TO Angela Taylor, Secretary, The Elmhirst Centre, Dartington Hall, Totnes, Devon TQ9 6EL *Tel* 01803 863160

CC NO 313398   **ESTABLISHED** 1936

Think carefully about every application. Is it justified?

499

■ The Elmley Foundation

WHERE FUNDING CAN BE GIVEN Herefordshire and Worcestershire.

WHO CAN BENEFIT Individuals and organisations benefiting: actors and entertainment professionals; musicians; writers and poets; and textile workers and designers; students of the arts.

WHAT IS FUNDED Arts activity.

WHAT IS NOT FUNDED No grants for endowments, loans or general appeals.

TYPE OF GRANT Capital, core costs, contracts and full project funding. Funding of up to, and over, three years will be considered.

RANGE OF GRANTS £500–£10,000.

SAMPLE GRANTS Huntingdon Arts Ltd and Rural Media Company (£10,000 each); Meadow Gallery (£9,000); Worcester Arts Workshop (£6,000); Wolverly High School (£5,000); Dancefest (£3,000); Malvern Chase Brass Band (£4,000); and Redditch Music Society (£500).

FINANCES *Year* 2007–08 *Income* £329,983 *Grants* £244,869 *Assets* £4,939,373

TRUSTEES Deborah Ann Swallow; Diana Johnson; Sam Driver White.

OTHER INFORMATION The total grants included £23,000 for individuals.

HOW TO APPLY In writing to the correspondent, including a budget and showing other possible or existing sources of funding.

WHO TO APPLY TO Samuel Driver White, Secretary, West Aish, Morchard Bishop, Crediton, Devon EX17 6RX *Tel* 01363 877433 *email* foundation@elmley.org.uk *Website* www.elmley.org.uk

CC NO 1004043　　　　**ESTABLISHED** 1991

■ Elshore Ltd

WHERE FUNDING CAN BE GIVEN Worldwide.

WHO CAN BENEFIT Jewish organisations.

WHAT IS FUNDED Advancement of religion and relief of poverty.

FINANCES *Year* 2007–08 *Income* £451,964 *Grants* £378,823 *Assets* £260,340

TRUSTEES H M Lerner; A Lerner; S Yanofsky.

HOW TO APPLY In writing to the correspondent.

WHO TO APPLY TO c/o Michael Pasua & Co., 220 The Vale, Golders Green, London NW11 8SR

CC NO 287469　　　　**ESTABLISHED** 1983

■ The Vernon N Ely Charitable Trust

WHERE FUNDING CAN BE GIVEN Worldwide, with a preference for London borough of Merton.

WHO CAN BENEFIT Organisations.

WHAT IS FUNDED Christian causes, welfare, disability, children, young people and overseas grants.

WHAT IS NOT FUNDED No grants to individuals.

RANGE OF GRANTS Around £4,000.

SAMPLE GRANTS Age Concern, Cardiac Risk in the Young, The Samaritans, London Sports Forum for Disabled People, Christchurch URC, Polka Children's Theatre and Community Housing Therapy (£4,000 each); British Tennis Foundation (£1,750); and West Barnes Singers and Sobell Hospice (£500 each).

FINANCES *Year* 2007–08 *Income* £73,208 *Grants* £78,750 *Assets* £1,601,011

TRUSTEES J S Moyle; D P Howorth; R S Main.

HOW TO APPLY In writing to the correspondent.

WHO TO APPLY TO Derek Howorth, Trustee, Grosvenor Gardens House, 35–37 Grosvenor Gardens, London SW1W 0BY *Tel* 020 7828 3156 *email* dph@helmores.co.uk

CC NO 230033　　　　**ESTABLISHED** 1962

■ The Embleton Trust

WHERE FUNDING CAN BE GIVEN UK.

WHO CAN BENEFIT Organisations.

WHAT IS FUNDED Nearly all of the funds are committed to long-term projects relating to legal education and free legal advice centres.

TYPE OF GRANT One off and recurrent.

RANGE OF GRANTS Up to £15,000.

SAMPLE GRANTS City Solicitors Educational Trust (£15,000); Cambridge House Legal Centre (£10,000); Beating Bowel Cancer (£6,700); Princess Alliance Hospice (£2,000); St Christopher's Hospice (£1,000); London Legal Support Trust and BPP Law School (£500 each); and Charterhouse-in-Southwark (£200).

FINANCES *Year* 2007–08 *Income* £35,787 *Grants* £35,865 *Assets* £4,325

TRUSTEES Simon Martin; Charles Martin.

OTHER INFORMATION The trust is associated with and funded by partners in Macfarlanes, a firm of solicitors.

HOW TO APPLY Unsolicited applications are not accepted.

WHO TO APPLY TO Simon Martin, Macfarlanes Solicitors, 20 Cursitor Street, London EC4A 1LT *Tel* 020 7831 9222 *email* simon.martin@macfarlanes.com

CC NO 285274

■ The Emerton-Christie Charity

WHERE FUNDING CAN BE GIVEN UK.

WHO CAN BENEFIT Registered charities only.

WHAT IS FUNDED General charitable purposes. Preference is given to assist older and younger people, particularly those with disabilities or who are disadvantaged.

WHAT IS NOT FUNDED Generally no grants to individuals; religious organisations; restoration or extension of buildings; start-up costs; animal welfare and research; cultural heritage; or environmental projects.

TYPE OF GRANT Donations for capital projects and/or income requirements.

RANGE OF GRANTS Usually up to £5,000.

SAMPLE GRANTS RNLI and Trinity College of Music (£4,000 each); Medecins Sans Frontieres and Westnell Nursery (£3,000 each); The Life Centre (£2,500); Alzheimers Research Trust, Cameroon Gardens Project, Roots and Shoots, National Eye Research Centre and British Forces Foundation (£2,000 each).

FINANCES *Year* 2007–08 *Income* £68,741 *Grants* £48,500 *Assets* £2,389,688

TRUSTEES A F Niekirk; Dr N A Walker; Dr C Mera-Nelson; Lt Col W D Niekirk; Dr S E Walker.

HOW TO APPLY In writing to the correspondent. A demonstration of need based on budgetary principles is required and applications will not be acknowledged unless accompanied by an sae. Trustees normally meet once a year in the autumn to select charities to benefit.

WHO TO APPLY TO The Trustees, c/o Cartmell Shepherd, Viaduct House, Carlisle CA3 8EZ *Tel* 01228 516666 *email* jmj@cartmells.co.uk

CC NO 262837　　　　**ESTABLISHED** 1971

■ EMI Music Sound Foundation

WHERE FUNDING CAN BE GIVEN UK and Ireland.

WHO CAN BENEFIT Individuals and organisations benefiting: children and young adults; musicians; music students; and music teachers.

WHAT IS FUNDED Non-specialist schools to fund music education; music students in full time education to fund instrument purchase; music teachers to fund courses and training. Every year EMI Music Sound Foundation awards bursaries to students at seven music colleges in the UK and Ireland. These bursaries are distributed at each college's discretion, based on criteria provided by the foundation. For more information, please contact the colleges directly (Birmingham Conservatoire, Drumtech/Vocaltech/GuitarX – London, Institute of Popular Music – Liverpool, Irish World Music Centre – Limerick, Royal Scottish Academy of Music and Drama – Glasgow, Royal Academy – London and Royal Welsh College of Music and Drama – Cardiff).

WHAT IS NOT FUNDED No support for: applications from outside the United Kingdom and Ireland; non-school based community groups, music therapy centres, and so on; applications over £2,500.

RANGE OF GRANTS Maximum award £2,500 (for schools, individuals and music teachers). Bursaries: annual donation of £5,000 to each college.

SAMPLE GRANTS Previous beneficiaries include North Leamington School, Churchfield School, Brentwood Ursulie Convent, Egglescliffe School, Guthlaxton College, Focus Events for the String of Pearls Millennium Festival, King William's College, Young Persons Concert Foundation and Music Wheel.

FINANCES *Year* 2007–08 *Income* £362,738 *Grants* £196,841 *Assets* £7,851,764

TRUSTEES Eric Nicoli, Chair; Jim Beach; John Deacon; Paul Gambaccini; Leslie Hill; David Hughes; Rupert Perry; Tony Wadsworth; Christine Walter; Charles Ashcroft.

OTHER INFORMATION 'EMI Music Sound Foundation is an independent music education charity, established in 1997 to celebrate the centenary of EMI Records and to improve young peoples' access to music education in the UK and Ireland.'

HOW TO APPLY On a form which can be downloaded from the foundation's website.

WHO TO APPLY TO Janie Orr, Chief Executive, 27 Wrights Lane, London W8 5SW *Tel* 020 7795 7000 *Fax* 020 7795 7296 *email* enquiries@musicsoundfoundation.com *Website* www.musicsoundfoundation.com

CC NO 1104027　　　　**ESTABLISHED** 1996

■ The Emilienne Charitable Trust

WHERE FUNDING CAN BE GIVEN Not defined.

WHO CAN BENEFIT Charitable organisations.

WHAT IS FUNDED The trustees are particularly interested in support for charities involved in the treatment of addiction and in promoting education.

FINANCES *Year* 2007–08 *Income* £41,000 *Grants* £36,000 *Assets* £684,000

TRUSTEES M Howson-Green; B M Baxendale; Mrs M A Howson-Green.

HOW TO APPLY In writing to the correspondent.

WHO TO APPLY TO M Howson-Green, Trustee, Ashton House, 12 The Precinct, Winchester Road, Chandlers Ford, Eastleigh, Hampshire SO53 3AP

CC NO 327849　　　　**ESTABLISHED** 1988

■ The Emmandjay Charitable Trust

WHERE FUNDING CAN BE GIVEN UK, with a special interest in West Yorkshire.

WHO CAN BENEFIT Charities and individuals.

WHAT IS FUNDED General charitable purposes, with particular favour given to helping disadvantaged people. Many different projects are supported; for example, caring for people who are physically and mentally disabled or terminally ill, work with young people and medical research. Projects which reach a lot of people are favoured.

WHAT IS NOT FUNDED 'The trust does not pay debts, does not make grants to individual students, and does not respond to circulars.' Grants are only given, via social services, to individuals if they live in Bradford.

RANGE OF GRANTS Usually £50–£10,000 (higher grants are exceptional).

SAMPLE GRANTS Previous beneficiaries have included: Abbeyfield Bradford Society, Bradford's War on Cancer, British Heart Foundation, British Red Cross, Cancer Support Centre, Caring for Life – Leeds, Marie Curie Cancer Centre, Research into Ageing and West Yorkshire Youth Association.

FINANCES *Year* 2007–08 *Income* £228,956 *Grants* £388,750 *Assets* £3,831,823

TRUSTEES Mrs Sylvia Clegg; John A Clegg; Mrs S L Worthington; Mrs E A Riddell.

HOW TO APPLY In writing to the correspondent.

WHO TO APPLY TO Mrs A E Bancroft, Administrator, PO Box 88, Otley, West Yorkshire LS21 3TE

CC NO 212279　　　　**ESTABLISHED** 1962

■ The Worshipful Company of Engineers Charitable Trust Fund

WHERE FUNDING CAN BE GIVEN UK.

WHO CAN BENEFIT Individuals and registered charities.

WHAT IS FUNDED The trust's main aim is to support professional engineers who are in need and in the final stages of their educational qualification. Grants are also made to organisations, especially those with an engineering bias for educational purposes.

SAMPLE GRANTS Previous beneficiaries have included Engineers for Disaster Relief and Ironbridge Development Trust.

FINANCES *Year* 2008 *Income* £54,145 *Grants* £7,000 *Assets* £429,120

TRUSTEES Rear Admiral D K Bawtree; Cdr Bryan Gibson; Dr Robert Hawley; Major General Edward G Willmott.

HOW TO APPLY In writing to the correspondent.

WHO TO APPLY TO Air Vice Marshall G Skinner, Clerk, The Worshipful Company of Engineers, Wax Chandlers Hall, 6 Gresham Street, London EC2V 7AD *Tel* 020 7726 4830 *Fax* 020 7726 4820 *email* clerk@engineerscompany.org.uk *Website* www.engineerscompany.org.uk

CC NO 289819

■ The Englefield Charitable Trust

WHERE FUNDING CAN BE GIVEN Worldwide, in practice UK and local charities in Berkshire.

WHO CAN BENEFIT Mainly registered charities; some local schools and churches are supported.

WHAT IS FUNDED Particularly charities working in the fields of: infrastructure development; religion; residential facilities and services; arts, culture and recreation; health; conservation; education and training; and various community facilities and services.

WHAT IS NOT FUNDED Individual applications for study or travel are not considered.

TYPE OF GRANT Buildings, capital, interest-free loans, research, running costs, salaries and start-up costs. Funding for one year or less will be considered.

RANGE OF GRANTS Mainly £5,000 or less.

SAMPLE GRANTS St Mary the Virgin Church, Reading (£96,000); Englefield PCC (£18,200); Ufton Court Education Trust (£12,500); Newbury & District Agricultural Society (£10,500); Reading YMCA (£6,000); Policy Exchange (£5,000); Multiple Sclerosis Therapy Centre (£4,700); Friends of Victoria Park (£4,000); Swings and Smiles (£3,000); Thatcham Relief in Need Charity and St Matthew's Church, Midgham (£2,000 each); and ARC Addington Fund, Christian Solidarity Worldwide, Miriam Dean Fund and Thatcham & District Rotary Club (£1,000 each).

FINANCES *Year* 2007–08 *Income* £326,359 *Grants* £404,681 *Assets* £10,933,556

TRUSTEES Sir William Benyon; James Shelley; Lady Elizabeth Benyon; Richard H R Benyon; Mrs Catherine Haig; Zoe Benyon.

HOW TO APPLY In writing to the correspondent enclosing the latest accounts, stating the charity's registered number and the purpose for which the money is to be used. Applications are considered in March and September. Only applications going before the trustees will be acknowledged.

WHO TO APPLY TO Alexander S Reid, Secretary to the Trustees, Englefield Estate Office, Englefield Road, Theale, Reading RG7 5DU *Tel* 0118 930 2504 *Fax* 0118 932 3748 *email* sandyreid@englefield.co.uk

CC NO 258123   ESTABLISHED 1968

....

■ The English Schools' Football Association

WHERE FUNDING CAN BE GIVEN England.

WHO CAN BENEFIT Members of the association, and organisations benefiting children and young adults, sportsmen and women and teachers.

WHAT IS FUNDED Mental, moral and physical development of schoolboys through association football. Assistance to teacher charities.

WHAT IS NOT FUNDED Grants are restricted to membership and teacher charities.

FINANCES *Year* 2007 *Income* £1,113,007 *Grants* £247,750 *Assets* £992,012

TRUSTEES P J Harding, Chair; G Smith; M R Duffield.

HOW TO APPLY In writing to the correspondent.

WHO TO APPLY TO Dawn Howard, Finance Officer, 4 Parker Court, Staffordshire Technology Park, Stafford, Staffordshire ST18 0WP *Tel* 01785 785970 *Fax* 01785 256246 *email* dawn.howard@schoolsfa.com *Website* www.esfa.co.uk

CC NO 306003   ESTABLISHED 1904

....

■ The Enkalon Foundation

WHERE FUNDING CAN BE GIVEN Northern Ireland.

WHO CAN BENEFIT Grants made only to organisations for projects inside Northern Ireland.

WHAT IS FUNDED Improving the quality of life in Northern Ireland. Funding is given to cross-community groups, self help, assistance to unemployed people and groups helping people who are disadvantaged.

WHAT IS NOT FUNDED No grants to individuals unless ex-employees. No grants are given outside Northern Ireland or for travel outside Northern

Ireland. Normally grants are not made to playgroups or sporting groups outside the Antrim borough area or for medical research.

TYPE OF GRANT Mainly for starter finance, single projects or capital projects.

RANGE OF GRANTS Up to £6,000 maximum but usually for around £500.

SAMPLE GRANTS Previous beneficiaries have included Council for the Homeless – Northern Ireland, Dungiven Community Resource Centre, Steeple Community Association, Tools for Solidarity and Youth Initiatives Northern Ireland.

FINANCES *Year* 2006–07 *Grants* £125,000

TRUSTEES Dr R L Schierbeek, Chair; J A Freeman; D H Templeton.

HOW TO APPLY In writing to the correspondent. There are no closing dates or application forms. Guidance notes are available from the foundation's offices. Applications, by letter, should provide the following information: description of the organisation and a copy of the constitution and rules; proposed budget and details of the project; audited accounts (if available) or statement of accounts for the most recent; completed financial year and a copy of the latest annual report; details of charitable status; other sources of finance for the organisation at present and for the proposed project; experience and/or qualifications of staff and committee members; a list of officers and committee members; contact address and telephone number. Trustees meet four times a year and applicants will be advised as soon as practical after a meeting has taken place. All applicants, successful or unsuccessful, will be advised of the trustees' decision. Applications will not be acknowledged unless accompanied by an sae.

WHO TO APPLY TO J W Wallace, Secretary, 25 Randalstown Road, Antrim, Northern Ireland BT41 4LJ *Tel* 028 9446 3535 *Fax* 028 9446 5733 *email* enkfoundation@lineone.net

IR NO XN62210   ESTABLISHED 1985

....

■ Entindale Ltd

WHERE FUNDING CAN BE GIVEN Unrestricted.

WHO CAN BENEFIT Organisations benefiting Orthodox Jews.

WHAT IS FUNDED Orthodox Jewish charitable organisations.

TYPE OF GRANT Capital.

RANGE OF GRANTS £500–£80,000.

SAMPLE GRANTS Jewish Learning Exchange (£80,000); Yesodey HaTorah Schools (£70,000); Chevras Machzikei Mesivta (£60,000); Chevras Maoz LaDol (£48,000); Vaad Ho Rabbonim Leinyonei Tzodokoh (£35,000); Notzar Chesed (£27,000); Boinei Olom (£12,000); Chasdel Cohen (£9,000); Achieve Trust (£5,000); Ihud Mosdos Gur (£1,000); Finchley Central Synagogue (£750); and Friends of Yeshivas Brisk (£500).

FINANCES *Year* 2007–08 *Income* £1,478,877 *Grants* £1,277,306 *Assets* £14,545,400

TRUSTEES Allan Becker; Barbara Bridgeman; Stephen Goldberg.

HOW TO APPLY In writing to the correspondent.

WHO TO APPLY TO Barbara Bridgeman, Secretary, 8 Highfield Gardens, London NW11 9HB *Tel* 020 8458 9266 *Fax* 020 8458 8529

CC NO 277052   ESTABLISHED 1978

■ The Epigoni Trust

WHERE FUNDING CAN BE GIVEN UK.

WHO CAN BENEFIT Registered UK charities with a national remit benefiting people of all ages, homeless people, those with addictions, physical disabilities, cancer, diabetes, and underprivileged children.

WHAT IS FUNDED Support is given to projects including hostels, hospices, holiday accommodation, respite care, care in the community, health counselling and some environmental issues.

WHAT IS NOT FUNDED No grants to individuals, expeditions, research, scholarships, charities with a local focus, local branches of UK charities or towards running costs.

TYPE OF GRANT Project and one-off. Funding for one year or less.

RANGE OF GRANTS £500–£10,000.

SAMPLE GRANTS Refuge, Macmillan Cancer Support and Talking Books (£10,000 each); Family Matters (£9,400); Kidney Research UK (£8,100); Reality Adventure Works in Scotland Ltd (£7,700); Samaritans (£5,500); Treloar Trust (£4,700); and Winston's Wish and Sussex Snowdrop Trust (£4,000 each).

FINANCES *Year* 2007–08 *Income* £159,338 *Grants* £146,800 *Assets* £3,122,601

TRUSTEES C H Peacock; Mrs B Bond; A M Bond.

HOW TO APPLY This trust no longer accepts applications.

WHO TO APPLY TO Charles Peacock, Trustee, c/o Charities Aid Foundation, King's Hill, West Malling, Kent ME19 4TA *Tel* 01732 520028

CC NO 328700   **ESTABLISHED** 1990

■ Epilepsy Research UK

WHERE FUNDING CAN BE GIVEN UK.

WHO CAN BENEFIT Researchers conducting studies that will benefit people with epilepsy.

WHAT IS FUNDED 'Epilepsy Research UK annually invites applications for grants to support basic, clinical and scientific research work in the UK into the causes, treatment and prevention of epilepsy. We encourage applications on all aspects of epilepsy including basic and social science, clinical management and holistic management of patients.'

WHAT IS NOT FUNDED Research not undertaken within a recognised institute in the UK.

TYPE OF GRANT Projects, fellowship, research and equipment. Funding is for up to three years.

RANGE OF GRANTS Up to £80,000.

FINANCES *Year* 2007–08 *Income* £1,331,326 *Grants* £1,130,431 *Assets* £411,274

TRUSTEES Dr R Appleton; B Akin; Prof C Binnie; Rt Hon D Cameron; Dr J H Cross; Dr R Elwes; J Hirst; S Lanyon; Dr J Mumford; Dr L Nashef; Prof B Neville; P Newman; Dr J Oxley; H Salmon; M Stevens; Dr H Wilkins.

OTHER INFORMATION The grant total figure in 2007–08 represents awards committed.

HOW TO APPLY Applications are invited by advertisement in journals and through the Research Register (interested parties can register for updates at www.epilepsyresearch.org.uk).

WHO TO APPLY TO Isabella von Holstein, Research and Information Executive, PO Box 3004, London W4 4XT *Tel* 020 8995 4781 *Fax* 020 8995 4781 *email* info@eruk.org.uk *Website* www.epilepsyresearch.org.uk

CC NO 1100394   **ESTABLISHED** 1985

■ The Equitable Charitable Trust

WHERE FUNDING CAN BE GIVEN Mainly UK: overseas projects can sometimes be supported.

WHO CAN BENEFIT Schools and other organisations benefiting disabled or disadvantaged children.

WHAT IS FUNDED Specific projects for the educational needs of disabled or disadvantaged young people. The trust has three specific priorities: education projects or services that support the learning and development of disabled children and young people in the UK; formal education projects for disadvantaged children and young people in the UK that support delivery of the National Curriculum (i.e. curriculum enrichment projects) or that deliver accredited vocational learning that will increase employability; education projects that will help increase participation in, or improve the quality of, education for disadvantaged or disabled children and young people in developing countries.

WHAT IS NOT FUNDED 'The trust does not make grants towards the following: general appeals or mail shot requests for donations; informal education projects and those that are only loosely educational; projects felt to be more akin to social work than education; therapeutic treatments; supplementary schooling and homework clubs; mother tongue language classes; state maintained or voluntary aided schools, colleges or universities, either directly or via another charity (e.g. Friends, PTAs); local authorities; public schools or independent schools that are not specifically for children and young people with disabilities or special educational needs; sports education, facilities or activities (e.g. playing fields, sports clubs, or projects that are delivered through the medium of sport); projects or work related to the Olympic Games or Cultural Olympiad; salaries for posts that are not directly related to service delivery (we would not make a grant towards the salary of a fundraiser or book-keeper, for instance); minibuses; pre-school education projects (unless these are solely for the benefit of children with disabilities or special needs); individuals; bursary schemes; projects that promote religious belief or practice; holidays; recreational activities or overseas trips; capital applications for equipment or facilities that will be only partly used for education or by under 25s from disadvantaged or disabled backgrounds (e.g. outdoor education centres that also deliver recreational activities, or that are not exclusively for the use of disadvantaged or disabled children and young people).'

TYPE OF GRANT Project costs, capital expenditure, equipment and the salary costs of a post.

RANGE OF GRANTS Up to £55,000.

SAMPLE GRANTS Voluntary Services Overseas (£55,000) for year three of a three year grant towards a volunteer education project in Eritrea; Sunfield (£50,000) a capital grant towards building costs of an independent residential school in Worcestershire for profoundly disabled children and young people; Prior's Court Foundation (£30,000) a capital grant towards the cost of improving facilities at an independent special school providing early intervention for children with severe autism; Afghan Connection (£27,000) a capital grant towards the cost of building and equipping a new girls' school in Afghanistan; Birmingham Focus on Blindness (£20,000) a one year grant towards specialist ICT equipment for blind and partially sighted school children in Birmingham; Drake Music Project (£15,000) a one year grant towards an Assistive Music Technology project

Think carefully about every application. Is it justified?

503

for disabled young people in Manchester and the North West; Lambourne End (£10,000) for year one of a two year grant towards the salary of a Farm & Environment Education Worker at a centre in Essex; FARA (£5,000) a capital grant towards a new specialist residential education centre for young people with learning disabilities in Romania; and Hampstead Theatre (£1,200) a one year grant towards a scriptwriting project for young people with disabilities from the Royal Free Hospital School in London.

FINANCES *Year* 2008 *Income* £724,722 *Grants* £892,038 *Assets* £6,782,922

TRUSTEES Brian McGeough; Roy Ranson; Peter Goddard.

HOW TO APPLY The trust offers the following application guidance on its website.
'Applications can be submitted at any time and are considered monthly by the trustees. The trust does not have an application form, but recommends that organisations follow the guidelines outlined below when applying for a grant. Applications should be no longer than four A4 sides, in font size no smaller than 11 point and should begin with a short (half page) summary. Your budget and accounts are additional to this. Applications should: describe your organisation clearly, its background and track record, what it does and who it seeks to benefit or help; provide details of your organisation's status (e.g. registered charity, company limited by guarantee) and its trustees; state the name of the project you are asking us to fund, and clearly and succinctly describe it; explain what the structure of the project will be; why it is needed; the number of people who will benefit from it; their ages; how you will ensure it is cost effective; provide details of any partners (other organisations, statutory bodies etc.), and say what stage the project has so far reached. If young people are involved in the development or monitoring of the project please provide details; explain which of our priorities your project addresses and how it meets the priority; say what the aims of the project are and what outcomes (practical results, changes and/or improvements) it hopes to achieve. If you are seeking funding to continue an existing project or a pilot, it is important that you are able to demonstrate the effectiveness of the work and what the outcomes have been to date; describe how the aims, progress and outcomes of the project will be monitored and evaluated and, where appropriate, how you will disseminate good practice to others; describe how the project will be managed and name the people who will be in charge of it and their relevant experience or qualifications. If the application is for a salary, please include a copy of the job description for the post; ask for a specific amount; enclose a detailed budget for the full duration of the project (i.e. if it is a three year project don't just send us a one year budget!), together with a full copy of your organisation's most recent audited or independently inspected accounts. It is important that if the accounts show a significant surplus or deficit of income, you explain the reason for this; state what funds have already been raised for the project and list any other funding you have applied for; explain where ongoing funding (if required) will be obtained when the trust's grant ends; provide the names and addresses of two independent referees that know your organisation's work. Tell us who these individuals are and how they/their organisations are connected to yours. Trustees, current volunteers or beneficiaries are not suitable referees.'

'Please keep your application as simple as possible and avoid the use of technical terms and jargon. Applications should be addressed to Brian McGeough and Peter Goddard, the Joint Managing Trustees. The trust receives a large number of applications each year and application numbers have increased significantly in the past year. Regrettably, this means we have to decline many good applications. The trust is normally able to provide a decision within eight weeks of receipt of an application. In some cases an in-principle decision is made by trustees pending receipt of references, further information or a visit being arranged. All grants are subject to the trust's terms and conditions of grant. A copy of these can be downloaded from the website. Applicants who are unsuccessful will be notified in writing and cannot re-apply for at least six months from the date of notification.'

WHO TO APPLY TO Jennie Long, Grants Officer, Sixth Floor, 65 Leadenhall Street, London EC3A 2AD *Tel* 020 7264 4995 *Fax* 020 7488 9097 *email* jlong@equitablecharitabletrust.org.uk *Website* www.equitablecharitabletrust.org.uk

CC NO 289548   **ESTABLISHED** 1984

··

■ The Equity Trust Fund

WHERE FUNDING CAN BE GIVEN UK.

WHO CAN BENEFIT Theatres, theatre companies and professional theatre performers in genuine need, with special reference to members, past and present, of the union Equity.

WHAT IS FUNDED Welfare and educational grants to individuals and work performed by theatres and theatre companies.

WHAT IS NOT FUNDED No grants to non-professional performers, drama students, non-professional theatre companies, multi-arts venues, community projects or projects with no connection to the professional theatre.

TYPE OF GRANT Grants and loans.

RANGE OF GRANTS Up to £50,000, in practice, around £5,000–£10,000.

SAMPLE GRANTS Dancers' Career Development (£45,000); Stage One (£15,000); The Mousetrap Foundation (£7,000); Bristol Old Vic Theatre and Kings Theatre Southsea (£5,000 each); Oval House Theatre (£2,000); Sherman Youth Theatre (£1,200).

FINANCES *Year* 2007–08 *Income* £364,422 *Grants* £271,074 *Assets* £9,050,909

TRUSTEES Colin Baker; Glen Barnham; James Bolam; Annie Bright; Jo Cameron Brown; Robin Browne; Oliver Ford Davies; Graham Hamilton; Frank Hitchman; Barbara Hyslop; Milton Johns; Harry Landis; Ian McGarry; Frederick Pyne; Gillian Raine; Jean Rogers; John Rubinstein; Rosalind Shanks; Ian Talbot; Josephine Tewson; Jeffry Wickham; Frank Williams; Johnny Worthy.

HOW TO APPLY In the first instance please call the office to ascertain if the application is relevant. Failing that, submit a brief letter outlining the application. A meeting takes place about every six to eight weeks. Ring for precise dates. Applications are required at least two weeks beforehand.

WHO TO APPLY TO Keith Carter, Secretary, 222 Africa House, 64 Kingsway, London WC2B 6AH *Tel* 020 7404 6041

CC NO 328103   **ESTABLISHED** 1989

■ The Eranda Foundation

WHERE FUNDING CAN BE GIVEN UK.

WHO CAN BENEFIT Registered charities.

WHAT IS FUNDED The promotion of original research, and the continuation of existing research into medicine and education, fostering of the arts, and promotion of social welfare.

WHAT IS NOT FUNDED No grants to individuals.

TYPE OF GRANT Capital, project, running costs and recurring costs for up to three years.

RANGE OF GRANTS About £500–£150,000.

SAMPLE GRANTS Cambridge Business School (£1.9 million); Cystic Fibrosis Trust (£350,000); Outward Bound Trust (£250,000); Royal Academy of Dramatic Art (£271,000); British Technion Society (£100,000); Integrated Rural Development Centre (£76,000); Index on Censorship (£60,000); Jewish Music Institute (£15,000); Cancer Bacup (£10,000); and Wellbeing of Women (£5,000).

FINANCES *Year* 2007–08 *Income* £5,134,522 *Grants* £5,730,405 *Assets* £57,009,790

TRUSTEES Sir Evelyn de Rothschild; Renée Robeson; Leopold de Rothschild; Miss Jessica de Rothschild; Anthony de Rothschild; Sir Graham Hearne; Lady Lynn de Rothschild.

HOW TO APPLY In writing to the correspondent. Trustees usually meet in March, July and November and applications should be received two months in advance.

WHO TO APPLY TO Gail Devlin-Jones, Secretary, PO Box 6226, Wing, Leighton Buzzard, Bedfordshire LU7 0XF *Tel* 01296 689 157 *email* eranda@btconnect.com

CC NO 255650   **ESTABLISHED** 1967

■ The Ericson Trust

WHERE FUNDING CAN BE GIVEN UK, developing countries, Eastern and Central Europe.

WHO CAN BENEFIT Registered charities only, benefiting: middle-aged and older people; researchers; people disadvantaged by poverty; ex-offenders and those at risk of offending; homeless people; immigrants and refugees.

WHAT IS FUNDED Older people; community projects/local interest groups, including arts; prisons, prison reform, mentoring projects, and research in this area; refugees; mental health; environmental projects and research; aid to developing countries only if supported and represented or initiated and administered by a UK registered charity.

WHAT IS NOT FUNDED No grants to individuals or to non-registered charities. Applications from the following areas are generally not considered unless closely connected with one of the above: children's and young people's clubs, centres and so on; schools; charities dealing with illness or disability (except psychiatric); or religious institutions, except in their social projects.

TYPE OF GRANT Project. Requests for core funding, running costs or particular items are considered.

RANGE OF GRANTS Up to £6,000, with most grants made at £3,000.

SAMPLE GRANTS Anti-Slavery International and Umalini Mary Brahma Charitable Trust (£6,000 each); Minority Rights Group (£4,000); Action on Elder Abuse, Ashram International, Bhopal Medical Appeal, Headway East London, Howard League for Penal Reform, The Koestler Trust, Psychiatric Rehabilitation Association, The Rainforest Foundation, The Relatives and Residents Association and Tools for Self

Reliance (£3,000 each); and Quaker Social Action (£2,000).

FINANCES *Year* 2007–08 *Income* £249,952 *Grants* £48,000 *Assets* £810,485

TRUSTEES Miss R C Cotton; Mrs V J Barrow; Mrs A M C Cotton.

HOW TO APPLY Unsolicited applications cannot be considered as the trust has no funds available. The correspondent stated: 'We are increasingly worried by the waste of applicants' resources when they send expensive brochures at a time when we are unable to consider any new appeals and have, indeed, reduced some of our long standing grants due to the bad economic situation. It is particularly sad when we receive requests from small charities in Africa and Asia.'

WHO TO APPLY TO The Trustees, Flat 2, 53 Carleton Road, London N7 0ET *email* claudia.cotton@googlemail.com

CC NO 219762   **ESTABLISHED** 1962

■ The Ernest Hecht Charitable Foundation

WHERE FUNDING CAN BE GIVEN England and Wales.

WHO CAN BENEFIT Registered charities.

WHAT IS FUNDED Support is given for: the advancement of education; relief of poverty; and advancement of religion.

FINANCES *Year* 2007–08 *Income* £20,611

TRUSTEES E Hecht; A P Rose; R Ward.

OTHER INFORMATION Grants average around £36,000 each year.

HOW TO APPLY In writing to the correspondent.

WHO TO APPLY TO Robert Ward, Trustee, Summit House, 170 Finchley Road, London NW3 6BP

CC NO 1095850   **ESTABLISHED** 2002

■ The Erskine Cunningham Hill Trust

WHERE FUNDING CAN BE GIVEN Scotland.

WHO CAN BENEFIT Organisations registered in Scotland benefiting older people, young people, ex-service men and women, seamen, and the Church of Scotland.

WHAT IS FUNDED The Church of Scotland is the largest single focus of the trust's interest (50% of annual income). Other grants are restricted to charitable work in Scotland with older people; young people; ex-servicemen and women; seamen; Scottish interests; with priority given to charities administered by voluntary or honorary officials.

WHAT IS NOT FUNDED No grants to individuals.

TYPE OF GRANT Recurring grants to the Church of Scotland; one-off grants to individual Scottish charities.

RANGE OF GRANTS Approximately £1,000 each to individual charities.

SAMPLE GRANTS Beneficiaries have included ChildLine and Cruse Bereavement Care, The Sailors' Family Society and Venture Trust.

FINANCES *Year* 2008 *Income* £61,313 *Grants* £60,000 *Assets* £302,224

TRUSTEES R M Maiden; Very Revd Dr A McDonald; I W Grimmond; Very Revd J Cairns; Very Revd A McLellan; Dr A Elliot; The Church of Scotland Trust.

HOW TO APPLY In writing to the correspondent at the above address. An application form is available via e-mail from the correspondent. There is a two-year time bar on repeat grants. The trustees do not consider applications from outside Scotland.

WHO TO APPLY TO Fred Marsh, Secretary, Department of National Mission, Church of Scotland Offices, 121 George Street, Edinburgh EH2 4YN *Tel* 0131 225 5722 *email* fmarsh@cofscotland. org.uk

SC NO SC001853 **ESTABLISHED** 1955

....

■ The Esfandi Charitable Foundation

WHERE FUNDING CAN BE GIVEN UK and overseas.
WHO CAN BENEFIT Registered charities.
WHAT IS FUNDED Jewish causes.
RANGE OF GRANTS Usually up to £50,000.
SAMPLE GRANTS Norwood (£110,000); British Friends of Migdal Ohr (£51,000); Colnel Chabad (£30,000); Winnicot Foundation (£27,000); Community Security Trust, Jewish Care and Lubavitch Foundation (£25,000 each); Association Des Israelites (£17,000); Jewish World Relief (£10,000); Western Marble Arch Synagogue (£7,100); Jerusalem Foundation and One Family UK (£5,000 each); National Hospital Development Foundation (£2,500); and Nightingale, TRIBE and UNICEF (£1,000 each).
FINANCES *Year* 2007–08 *Income* £354,790 *Grants* £467,824 *Assets* £88,666
TRUSTEES J Esfandi; Mrs D Esfandi.
HOW TO APPLY In writing to the correspondent.
WHO TO APPLY TO J Esfandi, Trustee, 36 Park Street, London W1K 2JE
CC NO 1103095 **ESTABLISHED** 2004

....

■ Essex Community Foundation

WHERE FUNDING CAN BE GIVEN Essex, Southend and Thurrock.
WHO CAN BENEFIT Any voluntary and community organisations, or any non-profit-making organisation working for the benefit of people living in Essex, Southend and Thurrock. The foundation is particularly interested in small grass-roots groups.
WHAT IS FUNDED Support generally falls under the broad heading of social welfare. The foundation distributes grants through various funds. Information on current funds and their criteria is available on the foundation's website.
WHAT IS NOT FUNDED The foundation does not support the following: political activities; statutory bodies undertaking their statutory obligations, including schools; general appeals; activities which support animal welfare; projects that operate outside of Essex, or benefit non-Essex residents; retrospective funding.
TYPE OF GRANT Core costs/revenue costs, new or continuing projects, one-off initiatives and capital costs.
RANGE OF GRANTS £50–£100,000.
SAMPLE GRANTS Beacon Project (£70,000); Inclusion Ventures (£65,000) Basildon, Billericay and Wickford CVS (£52,000); The Prince's Trust (£16,000); Chelmsford Agency for Volunteering (£12,000); Kemp-Welch Partnership Project (£10,000); Mistley Cricket Club (£7,000); Whatever Youth Club (£6,500); Theatre Resource (£5,500); and Maldon Carers Centre (£5,200).
FINANCES *Year* 2007–08 *Income* £2,837,023 *Grants* £1,172,557 *Assets* £8,937,951
TRUSTEES John Spence; Charles Clark; Christopher Holmes; John Stanger; David Boyle; Margaret Hyde; Stephen Packham; Carol Golbourn;

Rhiannedd Pratley; Martin Hopkins; John Barnes; Jason Bartella.
HOW TO APPLY Essex Community Foundation manages a number of funds, many of which are tailored to the individual wishes of the donors. However, with the exception of the four funds listed below, all you have to do is complete a general application form and the foundation will find the right fund for you. Application forms are available from the foundation's office or can be downloaded from the website. Deadlines are usually twice a year on 9 January and 9 September; please contact the foundation for exact dates. Grants are awarded within three months of the deadlines. If in doubt about the suitability of your project for funding, call the foundation's grants team on 01245 356018, or email: grants@essexcf.org.uk. The four funds which use a specific application form are: Grassroots Grants, Crimebeat, High Sheriff's Award, Marion Ruth Courtauld Educational Fund. They may also have different application deadlines. Further information about each of these funds is available from the foundation's website, or by contacting the grants team, as above.
WHO TO APPLY TO Grants Team, 121 New London Road, Chelmsford, Essex CM2 0QT *Tel* 01245 355 947 *Fax* 01245 246 391 *email* general@ essexcf.org.uk *Website* www. essexcommunityfoundation.org.uk
CC NO 1052061 **ESTABLISHED** 1996

....

■ The Essex Fairway Charitable Trust

WHERE FUNDING CAN BE GIVEN South east England, with a preference for Essex.
WHO CAN BENEFIT Registered charities, particularly those directly benefiting people in need. Small charities in south east England, particularly Essex, will be favoured.
WHAT IS FUNDED General charitable purposes.
WHAT IS NOT FUNDED No grants for medical research, animal welfare, the environment and political and religious purposes. No grants to large UK charities. Individuals are only considered in very exceptional circumstances.
TYPE OF GRANT One-off grants for capital and revenue costs and full project funding. Replacement of statutory funding also available.
SAMPLE GRANTS Previous beneficiaries have included Awareness of Down's Syndrome, CHESS, East Essex District Scouts Council, Fair Haven Hospice, Farleigh Hospice, Felixstowe Youth Development Group, Hamelin Trust, Headway Essex, Anne Lloyd Memorial Trust, Macmillan Cancer Relief, Martha Trust, St Christopher's School, Stepney Children's Fund and St Patrick's Trust.
FINANCES *Year* 2008 *Income* £46,278 *Grants* £168,880 *Assets* £1,266,790
TRUSTEES P W George; C J Holmes.
PUBLICATIONS A full grants list is available on request to the trust.
HOW TO APPLY Please note the following statement from the trust: 'The trust very rarely gives donations in response to applications from charities that it has not previously supported and will not reply to such applications'.
WHO TO APPLY TO K H Larkman, c/o Birkett Long, Essex House, 42 Crouch Street, Colchester, Essex CO3 3HH *Tel* 01206 217300
CC NO 1066858 **ESTABLISHED** 1997

■ The Essex Heritage Trust

WHERE FUNDING CAN BE GIVEN Essex.

WHO CAN BENEFIT Any organisation, body or individual whose project will be to the benefit of the people of Essex.

WHAT IS FUNDED Grants to bodies or individuals undertaking specific work in accord with the objects of the trust, including publication or preservation of Essex history and restoration of monuments, significant structures, artefacts and church decorations and equipment.

TYPE OF GRANT Mostly one-off grants for revenue and capital costs.

RANGE OF GRANTS Up to £5,000.

SAMPLE GRANTS Ashdon Windmill Trust Ltd and St Margaret of Antioch – Toppesfield (£4,000 each); Colchester Archaeological Trust (£3,500); Brightlingsea Town Council (£3,000); Thomas Plume Library – Maldon (£2,500); Essex Place Names Project (£2,000); Chelmsford Museum (£1,000); St Mary the Virgin – Strethall (£800); and Kingsway Hall – Dovercourt (£500).

FINANCES *Year* 2007–08 *Income* £84,227 *Grants* £55,100 *Assets* £1,267,754

TRUSTEES Lord Petre; Richard Wollaston; Mark Pertwee; Peter Mamelok; James Bettley; Brian Moody; Susan Brice; Elizabeth Hart; Jonathan Douglas-Hughes.

PUBLICATIONS Annual newsletter.

OTHER INFORMATION The trust has been able to keep its governance costs low due to the continuing sponsorship of the salary and payroll costs of the trust's administrator by Essex County Council.

HOW TO APPLY In writing or by telephone to the correspondent by letter in the first instance. An application form will be returned for detailed completion with estimates if it is considered that the project falls within the trust's objectives. The trustees meet three times a year in March, July and November, when grant awards will be made.

WHO TO APPLY TO Sharon Hill, Administrator, Cressing Temple, Braintree, Essex CM77 8PD *Tel* 01376 585794 *Fax* 01376 585794 *email* eht@dsl.pipex.com *Website* www.essexheritagetrust.co.uk

CC NO 802317   **ESTABLISHED** 1989

■ Essex Provincial Charity Fund

WHERE FUNDING CAN BE GIVEN Essex.

WHO CAN BENEFIT Essex Freemasons; their dependants; central Masonic charities, and other charities.

WHAT IS FUNDED Preference for charities with a medical bias and, primarily in Essex, that assist the community in general.

WHAT IS NOT FUNDED No grants to individuals, other than those who are dependants of freemasons.

SAMPLE GRANTS Previous beneficiaries have included Broomfield Hospital – St Andrew's Centre, Grand Charity, London Chest Hospital, Macmillan Cancer Relief, Royal Masonic Trust for Girls and Boys, New Masonic Samaritan Fund and Royal Masonic Benevolent Fund.

FINANCES *Year* 2007–08 *Income* £234,683 *Grants* £37,587 *Assets* £1,005,763

TRUSTEES John Rundlett; Frederick Harris; Allan Kemp; Christopher Williams; Andrew Bishop.

OTHER INFORMATION Grants totalling £172,000 were administered by the trust on behalf of the Grand Charity.

HOW TO APPLY In writing to the correspondent.

WHO TO APPLY TO Andrew Bishop, Trustee, 11 Olivia Drive, Leigh-On-Sea SS9 3EF

CC NO 215349   **ESTABLISHED** 1932

■ The Essex Youth Trust

WHERE FUNDING CAN BE GIVEN Essex.

WHO CAN BENEFIT Beneficiaries include schools, youth clubs and organisations giving advice, help and information.

WHAT IS FUNDED The advancement of education for people under the age of 25 who are in need of assistance. Preference is given to those who are in need owing to 'being temporarily or permanently deprived of normal parental care or who are otherwise disadvantaged'. 'The trustees favour organisations which develop young people's physical, mental and spiritual capacities through active participation in sports and indoor and outdoor activities. As a result they are particularly supportive of youth clubs and other organisations which provide facilities for young people to take active part in an assortment of activities as well as single activity organisations.'

WHAT IS NOT FUNDED No grants to individuals.

RANGE OF GRANTS Up to £25,000.

SAMPLE GRANTS Cirdan Sailing Trust (£50,000 in two grants); Essex Association on Boys Clubs (£49,000 in four grants); Havering Crossroads (£10,000); Christian Adventure Trust (£6,000); Voice for the Child in Care and Depaul Trust (£5,000 each); Listening Books (£4,500); Whizzkids (£3,300); Dream Holidays and Strongbones Children's Charitable Trust (£1,000 each).

FINANCES *Year* 2007–08 *Income* £490,437 *Grants* £385,072 *Assets* £7,931,677

TRUSTEES Richard Wenley; Julien Courtauld; Michael Dyer; Raymond Knappett; Revd Duncan Green; David Robson; Julia Denison-Smith; Claire Coltwell; Michael Biegel.

OTHER INFORMATION The grant total figure for 2007–08 represents grants paid during the year.

HOW TO APPLY On a form available from the correspondent. The trustees meet on a quarterly basis.

WHO TO APPLY TO J P Douglas-Hughes, Gepp and Sons, 58 New London Road, Chelmsford, Essex CM2 0PA *Tel* 01245 493939 *Fax* 01245 493940 *email* douglas-hughesj@gepp.co.uk

CC NO 225768   **ESTABLISHED** 1963

■ The Estelle Trust

WHERE FUNDING CAN BE GIVEN UK and Zambia.

WHAT IS FUNDED Overseas aid and general charitable purposes in the UK.

RANGE OF GRANTS Usually up to £10,000.

SAMPLE GRANTS Wind pump materials in Africa (£12,000); International Rescue Society (£10,000); Hand Around the World (£7,500); Malaysia Future Leap Project (£3,500); Chisamba Orphans Training Centre (£2,000); British Red Cross Disaster Fund, Action for Blind People, Shelter and Action Aid (£1,000 each); and Help for Heroes, Prostate Research Campaign UK and Sight Savers (£500 each).

FINANCES *Year* 2007–08 *Income* £301,938 *Grants* £68,929 *Assets* £1,379,233

TRUSTEES N AN E Farrow; G R Ornstein; Mrs K-M Britain; Mrs S Farrow; D Wise.

HOW TO APPLY In writing to the correspondent.

Think carefully about every application. Is it justified?

507

WHO TO APPLY TO Ged Ornstein, Trustee, Fisher Phillips, 170 Finchley Road, London NW3 6BP
Tel 020 7483 6100
CC NO 1101299   **ESTABLISHED** 2003

■ Euro Charity Trust

WHERE FUNDING CAN BE GIVEN Worldwide, mainly India, Africa, Bangladesh and the UK.
WHO CAN BENEFIT Registered charities.
WHAT IS FUNDED The relief of poverty; to assist the vulnerable; and to assist in the advancement of education in the UK and the rest of the world.
FINANCES *Year* 2007 *Income* £422,537
Grants £5,498,518 *Assets* £3,528,600
TRUSTEES Ahmed Omer; Nasir Awan; Abdul Malik; Abdul Alimahomed.
HOW TO APPLY In writing to the correspondent.
WHO TO APPLY TO Ahmed Omer, Trustee, 284C High Street, Smethwick, West Midlands E66 3NN
CC NO 1058460   **ESTABLISHED** 1996

■ The Evangelical Covenants Trust

WHERE FUNDING CAN BE GIVEN UK, with a preference for Devon.
WHO CAN BENEFIT Christian organisations of an evangelical nature and general charitable purposes.
WHAT IS FUNDED Grants are distributed on a UK basis, but with the majority of donors living in Devon – in 1999–2000 44% of all gifts were distributed to churches in the county.
SAMPLE GRANTS 32% of all gifts were distributed to churches in Devon.
FINANCES *Year* 2007–08 *Income* £90,685
Grants £89,760 *Assets* £23,054
TRUSTEES C Desmond Gahan; Alfred W Tarring; Kathleen M Tarring.
HOW TO APPLY The trust stressed that unsolicited applications are not considered: 'Grants are made only on the request and recommendation of donors of the trust.'
WHO TO APPLY TO Alfred W Tarring, Trustee, Mardon, 188b Exeter Road, Exmouth, Devon EX8 3DZ
Tel 01395 273287
CC NO 285224   **ESTABLISHED** 1982

■ The Alan Evans Memorial Trust

WHERE FUNDING CAN BE GIVEN UK.
WHO CAN BENEFIT Registered charities only.
WHAT IS FUNDED The purchase of land and the planting of trees, shrubs and plants. The restoration of cathedrals, churches and other buildings of beauty or historical interest, to which the public can have access.
WHAT IS NOT FUNDED No grants to individuals or for management or running expenses, although favourable consideration is given in respect of the purchase of land and restoration of buildings. Grants are given to registered charities only. Appeals will not be acknowledged.
RANGE OF GRANTS £1,000–£5,000.
SAMPLE GRANTS Cathedral Church of the Holy Spirit, Guildford, Surrey, The Peterborough Cathedral Development and Preservation Trust, Wells Cathedral – Somerset, Lincoln Cathedral – Lincolnshire, and The Church of Our Lord, St Mary and St Germaine – Selby Abbey (£5,000 each); The English Hedgerow Trust, The Landmark Trust and The Zoological Society of London (£1,000 each); St Wilfid's Church – Leeds (£1,500); and Berkshire,

Buckinghamshire and Oxfordshire Wildlife Trust and The Thatcham Charity;.
FINANCES *Year* 2007–08 *Income* £67,658
Grants £264,500 *Assets* £1,805,670
TRUSTEES Coutts and Co.; D J Halfhead; Mrs D Moss.
HOW TO APPLY There is no formal application form, but appeals should be made in writing to the correspondent, stating why the funds are required, what funds have been promised from other sources (for example, English Heritage) and the amount outstanding. The trust also told us that it would be helpful when making applications to provide a photograph of the project. Trustees normally meet four times a year, although in urgent cases decisions can be made between meetings.
WHO TO APPLY TO The Trust Manager, Coutts and Co., Trustee Department, 440 Strand, London WC2R 0QS
CC NO 326263   **ESTABLISHED** 1979

■ Sir John Evelyn's Charity

WHERE FUNDING CAN BE GIVEN Ancient parishes of St Nicholas Deptford and St Luke Deptford.
WHO CAN BENEFIT Charities benefiting people disadvantaged by poverty.
WHAT IS FUNDED Pensions and grants to organisations working to relieve poverty.
SAMPLE GRANTS Armada Community project (£71,000); Evelyn 190 Centre (£30,000); Exodus Youth Scheme (£21,000); Twinkle Park Trust (£19,000); 192 Music, Media and Education (£11,000); Deptford Churches (£10,000); Herb Garden (£5,000); and Leapfrog Toddler Group (£3,000).
FINANCES *Year* 2008 *Income* £88,553
Grants £199,846 *Assets* £2,298,570
TRUSTEES Bridget Perry, Chair; Revd J K Lucas; Jasmine Barnett; Kay Ingledew; Mrs J Miller; Cllr M O'Mara; Revd Patrick Doel; Cllr Margaret Mythen.
OTHER INFORMATION Grants to individuals totalled £5,000.
HOW TO APPLY In writing to the correspondent.
WHO TO APPLY TO Mrs Colette A Saunders, Clerk's Office, Armada Court Hall, 21 McMillan Street, Deptford, London SE8 3EZ *Tel* 020 8694 8953
CC NO 225707   **ESTABLISHED** 1974

■ The Eventhall Family Charitable Trust

WHERE FUNDING CAN BE GIVEN Preference for north west England.
WHO CAN BENEFIT Institutions and individuals.
WHAT IS FUNDED General charitable purposes.
WHAT IS NOT FUNDED No grants to students.
SAMPLE GRANTS Previous beneficiaries have included Aish Hatorah, ChildLine, Clitheroe Wolves Football Club, Community Security Trust, Greibach Memorial, Guide Dogs for the Blind, Heathlands Village, International Wildlife Coalition, JJCT, MB Foundation Charity, Only Foals and Horses Sanctuary, Red Nose Day, RNLI, Sale Ladies Society, Shelter and South Manchester Synagogue.
FINANCES *Year* 2007–08 *Income* £134,758
Grants £245,000 *Assets* £3,015,704
TRUSTEES Julia Eventhall; David Eventhall.
HOW TO APPLY In writing to the correspondent. Please note, however, previous research highlighted that the trust stated it only has a very limited amount of funds available.

Telephone calls are not accepted by the trust. Trustees meet monthly to consider grants. A pre-addressed envelope is appreciated (stamp not necessary). Unsuccessful applicants will not receive a reply.

WHO TO APPLY TO The Trustees, PO Box 490, Altrincham WA14 22T

CC NO 803178   **ESTABLISHED** 1989

■ The Everard Foundation

WHERE FUNDING CAN BE GIVEN Leicestershire.

WHO CAN BENEFIT Local organisations of all sizes. Grants to UK-wide organisations must be to fund something tangibly local.

WHAT IS FUNDED General charitable purposes.

WHAT IS NOT FUNDED No grants to individuals.

TYPE OF GRANT Capital and revenue costs. Funding is available for up to three years.

RANGE OF GRANTS From £250.

SAMPLE GRANTS Riverside Community College (£25,000); Leicestershire Cares (£13,000); Age Concern – Leicestershire and Rutland (£11,000); Special Effect (£5,000); Contact and Young Enterprise (£1,000 each); Army Benevolent Fund (£750); Marie Curie Cancer Care and Turning Point Women's Centre (£500 each); and St John's Church (£250).

FINANCES *Year* 2007–08 *Income* £857,452 *Grants* £86,694 *Assets* £1,839,610

TRUSTEES Richard Everard; Serena Richards; William Swan.

HOW TO APPLY In writing to the correspondent at any time.

WHO TO APPLY TO Richard Everard, Trustee, Castle Acres, Everard Way, Enderby, Leicester LE19 1BY

CC NO 272248   **ESTABLISHED** 1976

■ The Eveson Charitable Trust

WHERE FUNDING CAN BE GIVEN Herefordshire, Worcestershire and the county of West Midlands (covering Birmingham, Coventry, Dudley, Sandwell, Solihull, Walsall and Wolverhampton).

WHO CAN BENEFIT Registered charities.

WHAT IS FUNDED People with physical disabilities, (including those who are blind or deaf); people with mental disabilities; hospitals and hospices; children who are in need, whether disadvantaged or with physical or mental disabilities; older people; homeless people; medical research into problems associated with any of these conditions.

WHAT IS NOT FUNDED Grants are not made to individuals, even if such a request is submitted by a charitable organisation.

TYPE OF GRANT Capital and revenue, recurring and one-off.

RANGE OF GRANTS From a few hundred pounds to £150,000; average grant around £8,000.

SAMPLE GRANTS Macmillan Cancer Relief (£150,000); Megan Baker House – Leominster (£60,000); Autism – West Midlands (£50,000); Age Concern – Hereford (£30,000); West Mercia Womens Aid and Herefordshire Voluntary Action (£20,000 each); Birmingham Settlement (£15,000); Depaul Trust (£10,000); Living Painting Trust (£6,000); Haven – Wolverhampton (£4,000); and City of Birmingham Orchestra (£3,800).

FINANCES *Year* 2007–08 *Income* £822,086 *Grants* £2,484,216 *Assets* £71,811,847

TRUSTEES David Pearson, Chair; Bruce Maughfling; Rt. Revd Anthony Priddis, Bishop of Hereford;

Martin Davies; Louise Woodhead; Bill Wiggin; Richard Mainwaring.

OTHER INFORMATION There were also 74 grants of £3,000 or less. These included grants to small local charities within the trust's remit and geographical area.

HOW TO APPLY The trustees meet quarterly, usually at the end of March and June and the beginning of October and January. Applications can only be considered if they are on the trust's standard, but very simple, 'application for support' form which can be obtained from the administrator at the offices of the trust in Gloucester. The form must be completed and returned (together with a copy of the latest accounts and annual report of the organisation) to the trust's offices at least six weeks before the meeting of trustees at which the application is to be considered, in order to give time for necessary assessment procedures, often including visits to applicants. Before providing support to statutory bodies (such as hospitals and schools for people with learning difficulties), the trust requires written confirmation that no statutory funds are available to meet the need for which funds are being requested. In the case of larger grants to hospitals, the trust asks the district health authority to confirm that no statutory funding is available. Where applications are submitted that clearly fall outside the grant-making parameters of the trust, the applicant is advised that the application cannot be considered and reasons are given. All applications that are going to be considered by the trustees are acknowledged in writing. Applicants are advised of the reference number of their application and of the quarterly meeting at which their application is going to be considered. The decisions are advised to applicants in writing soon after these meetings. Funded projects are monitored.

WHO TO APPLY TO Alex D Gay, Administrator, 45 Park Road, Gloucester GL1 1LP *Tel* 01452 501352 *Fax* 01452 302195

CC NO 1032204   **ESTABLISHED** 1994

■ The Beryl Evetts and Robert Luff Animal Welfare Trust

WHERE FUNDING CAN BE GIVEN UK.

WHO CAN BENEFIT Animal charities. The trust supports the same beneficiaries each year.

WHAT IS FUNDED Veterinary research and the care and welfare of animals.

TYPE OF GRANT Priority to research projects and bursaries.

RANGE OF GRANTS Up to £65,000.

SAMPLE GRANTS Animal Welfare Trust (£65,000); Royal Veterinary College (£60,000); Mayhew Animal Home (£5,500); Blue Cross (£2,500); and Greek Animal Welfare Trust, National Equine Defence League, Battersea Dogs Home, Brooke Hospitals for Animals, World Land Trust Fund (£625 each).

FINANCES *Year* 2007–08 *Income* £49,099 *Grants* £136,125 *Assets* £1,218,313

TRUSTEES Sir R Johnson; Revd M Tomlinson; Mrs J Tomlinson; R P J Price; B Nicholson; Lady Johnson; Ms G Favot; M Condon.

HOW TO APPLY 'No applications, thank you.' The trust gives grants to the same beneficiaries each year and funds are often allocated two years in advance.

WHO TO APPLY TO The Administrator, 294 Earls Court Road, London SW5 9BB

CC NO 283944   **ESTABLISHED** 1981

■ The Execution Charitable Trust

WHERE FUNDING CAN BE GIVEN Worldwide, in practice mainly UK.

WHO CAN BENEFIT Charitable organisations.

WHAT IS FUNDED Local organisations and community projects working in deprived areas in the UK, tackling the root causes, as well as the symptoms, of poverty and isolation.

TYPE OF GRANT One-off and recurring.

RANGE OF GRANTS Up to £400,000.

SAMPLE GRANTS Absolute Return for Kids; Trinity Community Centre – London; London Citizens, LondonFARE – Glasgow; ULW – Manchester; the Warren – Kingston upon Hull; Peace One Day – London; Windsor Women's Centre – Belfast; and the Strategy – Mid Glamorgan.

FINANCES *Year* 2008 *Income* £1,167,439 *Grants* £1,469,030 *Assets* £928,325

TRUSTEES Jacky Joy; John R Moore; Cheryl Mustapha Whyte; Damien Devine; Peter Ward; Neil Strong.

HOW TO APPLY The trust does not consider unsolicited applications for grants. The trust has appointed New Philanthropy Capital (NPC) to proactively identify effective organisations on its behalf. If you believe your organisation matches the funding criteria listed here and you want to provide basic contact details and a short outline of your project, go to the Execution Charitable Trust's website and fill in the online form.

WHO TO APPLY TO Cheryl Mustapha Whyte, Trustee, Block D, The Old Truman Building, 91 Brick Lane, London E1 6QL *Tel* 020 7375 2007 *email* info@executionlimited.com *Website* www.executioncharitabletrust.org/default.aspx

CC NO 1099097   **ESTABLISHED** 2003

■ The Mayor of Exeter's Appeal Fund

WHERE FUNDING CAN BE GIVEN Exeter.

WHO CAN BENEFIT One charity is supported each year, selected by the Mayor Elect.

WHAT IS FUNDED General charitable purposes.

SAMPLE GRANTS Previous beneficiaries have included Headway Exeter, Hospice Care – Exeter, St Petrox House for the Homeless and The Ellen Tinkham School for children with special needs.

FINANCES *Year* 2007–08 *Income* £21,399 *Grants* £21,399

TRUSTEES Exeter City Council

HOW TO APPLY In writing to the correspondent.

WHO TO APPLY TO Head of Treasury Services, Exeter City Council, Civic Centre, Paris Street, Exeter EX1 1JN *Tel* 01392 265241 *email* mayoralty@ exeter.gov.uk *Website* www.exeter.gov.uk

CC NO 283469

■ The Exilarch's Foundation

WHERE FUNDING CAN BE GIVEN Mainly UK.

WHO CAN BENEFIT Jewish people, at risk groups, and people who are disabled, disadvantaged by poverty or socially isolated.

WHAT IS FUNDED Mainly Jewish organisations; some medical and welfare charities.

SAMPLE GRANTS Westminster Academy (£600,000); The British Library (£150,000); The Royal Albert Trust (£125,000); and ESC Educational Charity (£100,000).

FINANCES *Year* 2007 *Income* £9,071,804 *Grants* £1,086,899 *Assets* £51,732,257

TRUSTEES N E Dangoor; D A Dangoor; E B Dangoor; R D Dangoor; M J Dangoor.

OTHER INFORMATION The foundation's annual report states that: 'The trustees have built up a designated reserve of £10 million for the specific purpose of assisting the setting up of educational and religious institutions in a future re-established Jewish community in Iraq. Once the position and security of that country has been stabilised it is anticipated that some Jews may chooses to live in Iraq when they will be free to pursue their religious faith without fear of persecution and discrimination.'

HOW TO APPLY The trust stated that it does not respond to unsolicited applications for grants.

WHO TO APPLY TO N E Dangoor, Trustee, 4 Carlos Place, Mayfair, London W1K 3AW *Tel* 020 7399 0850

CC NO 275919   **ESTABLISHED** 1978

■ Extonglen Limited

WHERE FUNDING CAN BE GIVEN UK.

WHO CAN BENEFIT Orthodox Jewish organisations.

WHAT IS FUNDED Orthodox Jewish causes.

RANGE OF GRANTS Up to £100,000.

SAMPLE GRANTS Kol Halashon Education Programme (£470,000); Ahavas Chesed (£95,000); Pikuach Nefesh (£50,000); Kupath Gemach Chaim Bechesed Viznitz Trust (£40,000); British Friends of Nishmat Yisrael (£12,000); and Children's Town Charity (£3,600).

FINANCES *Year* 2007 *Income* £1,189,129 *Grants* £672,563 *Assets* £14,448,335

TRUSTEES M Levine; Mrs C Levine; B B Rapaport; I Katzenberg.

HOW TO APPLY In writing to the correspondent.

WHO TO APPLY TO The Trustees, New Burlington House, 1075 Finchley Road, London NW11 0PU *Tel* 020 8731 0777 *email* ml@rowdeal.com

CC NO 286230   **ESTABLISHED** 1982

■ The Matthew Eyton Animal Welfare Trust

WHERE FUNDING CAN BE GIVEN Not defined.

WHO CAN BENEFIT Animal charities, mainly farm animal charities as opposed to wild or companion animals; vegetarians; and vegans.

WHAT IS FUNDED Animal charities, vegetarian/vegan.

TYPE OF GRANT One-off.

RANGE OF GRANTS £50–£51,000.

SAMPLE GRANTS PETA's Research and Education Foundation (£51,000); Compassion in World Farming (£14,000); the Vegetarians and Vegans Foundation and the Soil Association (£13,00 each); the Association for the Study of Animal Behaviour (£2,000); the Vegetarians Campaign Group (£500); and the Humane Education Research Trust (£60).

FINANCES *Year* 2007–08 *Income* £109,446 *Grants* £92,905 *Assets* £68,370

TRUSTEES Mrs Audrey Eyton; P H Cheshire.

HOW TO APPLY In writing to the correspondent.

WHO TO APPLY TO The Trustees, 7 Blackfriars Street, Canterbury, Kent CT1 2AP

CC NO 1003575   **ESTABLISHED** 1991

■ F C Charitable Trust

WHERE FUNDING CAN BE GIVEN Worldwide, but mainly the UK.

WHO CAN BENEFIT Christian and welfare organisations.

WHAT IS FUNDED The trust gives support in the areas of Christian churches, missionary societies, ministers, missionaries and welfare.

WHAT IS NOT FUNDED Individuals are not eligible for grants and the trust does not normally support a charity unless it is known to the trustees.

SAMPLE GRANTS Emmanuel Church Wimbledon (£23,000 in 13 grants); Jesus Lane Trust and Titus Trust (£1,000 each); Reform (£630); and Roman Catholic Diocese of Arundel and Brighton (£200).

FINANCES *Year* 2008–09 *Income* £30,774 *Grants* £31,608 *Assets* £378,821

TRUSTEES John Vernor Miles; The Rev Jonathan James Molyneux Fletcher.

HOW TO APPLY Applications can only be accepted from registered charities and should be in writing to the correspondent. In order to save administration costs, replies are not sent to unsuccessful applicants. For the most part, funds are fully committed.

WHO TO APPLY TO J C Vernor Miles, Trustee, Vernor Miles and Noble, 5 Raymond Buildings, Grays Inn, London WC1R 5DD *Tel* 020 7242 8688

CC NO 277686   **ESTABLISHED** 1978

■ The F P Limited Charitable Trust

WHERE FUNDING CAN BE GIVEN UK, with a possible preference for Greater Manchester.

WHO CAN BENEFIT Registered charities.

WHAT IS FUNDED This trust supports educational causes, schools, religious bodies and medical appeals, giving most of its funds to regular beneficiaries.

SAMPLE GRANTS Donations were made to a variety of schools, religious institutions and medical appeals. Unfortunately a detailed list of beneficiaries was not available.

FINANCES *Year* 2007–08 *Income* £30,000 *Grants* £27,440 *Assets* £6,429

TRUSTEES Joshua Pine; Simon Pine.

HOW TO APPLY In writing to the correspondent.

WHO TO APPLY TO Simon Pine, Trustee, Crown Mill, 1 Crown Street, Salford M3 7DH *Tel* 0161 834 0456 *Fax* 0161 832 0385

CC NO 328737   **ESTABLISHED** 1990

■ The Faber Charitable Trust

WHERE FUNDING CAN BE GIVEN UK.

WHO CAN BENEFIT Jewish causes.

WHAT IS FUNDED General charitable purposes.

FINANCES *Year* 2007–08 *Income* £20,884 *Grants* £30,802

TRUSTEES Bernard Faber; Fay Faber; Benjamin Rosefelder; Jeremy Golker.

HOW TO APPLY In writing to the correspondent.

WHO TO APPLY TO H Kramer, Trustee, c/o Devonshire House, 1 Devonshire Street, London W1W 5DR

CC NO 294820

■ Esmée Fairbairn Foundation

WHERE FUNDING CAN BE GIVEN UK.

WHO CAN BENEFIT Voluntary and charitable organisations.

WHAT IS FUNDED The Main Fund: The cultural life of the UK, education and learning, the natural environment and enabling disadvantaged people to participate more fully in society. The foundation prioritises work that: addresses a significant gap in provision; develops or strengthens good practice; challenges convention or takes a risk in order to address a difficult issue; tests out new ideas or practices; takes an enterprising approach to achieving its aims; sets out to influence policy or change behaviour more widely.

Strands: the foundation also makes grants under the following four strands:

'*Biodiversity* – Supporting practical conservation action and the science which underpins it. The strand will focus on species and habitats that are uncharismatic or hard to fund and aims to support the development of effective conservation approaches. Linking science and practical action, it will prioritise partnership applications involving research organisations, practical conservation charities and voluntary nature societies. *Food* – The aim of the Food Strand is to promote an understanding of the role of food in enhancing quality of life. It will prioritise the enjoyment and experience of food rather than its production and we seek to enable as many people in the UK as possible to access, prepare and eat nutritious, sustainable food. We are interested in work that influences policy and practice across a range of food-related areas. We expect to support a mix of practical projects that have wide significance, and some research and policy based work.

Museum & Heritage Collections – This strand will focus on time-limited collections work including research, documentation and conservation that is outside the scope of an organisation's core resources. We will prioritise proposals that are at an early stage of development where it may be difficult to guarantee tangible outcomes. We will also prioritise proposals that have the potential to share knowledge with other organisations through partnership working or dissemination.

New Approaches to Learning – Devising, testing and disseminating new approaches to teaching and learning that address current and future challenges in state schools and pre-schools.'

WHAT IS NOT FUNDED The foundation will not support the following: applications from individuals or which benefit one individual; applications from organisations which have applied within the previous 12 months; work which has already taken place; work which does not directly benefit people in the UK; work which directly replaces statutory funding; medical research; standard health services and day/residential care; animal welfare; expeditions and overseas travel; endowment funds; general appeals or circulars. The foundation will not fund routine work in the areas, or from the organisations, listed below. The only exception is that it may make occasional grants in these areas, if the work is developmental or preventive, and fulfils specific funding priorities in one or more of the sectors. If your work comes under one of these categories, telephone the foundation first to talk through whether making an application will be worthwhile: Large national charities which enjoy wide support; branches, members and affiliates of large national charities; after-school clubs; capital projects – building or major refurbishment costs; citizens' advocacy; community-based transport schemes; conferences and seminars; counselling services; furniture recycling projects; holidays/respite care; hospices; individual schools, nurseries and playgroups; information and advice service; items of equipment; maintenance of individual religious buildings (including parish churches) or projects that promote religious beliefs; rent guarantee schemes; sport; vocational training; work in prisons (unless the project is unique, or develops a new model capable of replication, or brings people without previous experience of prison into contact with an aspect of the prison system); and youth clubs.

TYPE OF GRANT Primarily core and project grants. Funding can be given for up to or over three years.

RANGE OF GRANTS The average grant from the Main Fund was £64,500.

SAMPLE GRANTS From the Main Fund: Lloyds TSB Foundation for Scotland (£750,000), towards a new £10 million fund over three years for vulnerable 14–19 years olds; The Soil Association (£398,000), towards developing membership over three years to increase unrestricted core income; ADFAM National (£384,000), towards the salaries of a stakeholder involvement co-ordinator, administrator and running costs of the new membership support project over five years, to develop ADFAM into a national umbrella organisation for self-help/peer support groups and services, and professionals working with families affected by drugs and alcohol; Forum for the Future (£240,000), towards core staff and overhead costs of the sustainable Bristol region project; Shelter (£237,000), towards the costs over three years of the pilot Knowsley Child Support Service aimed at meeting the needs of homeless children and thereby breaking the cycle of inter-generational homelessness; British Trust for Ornithology (£180,000), towards the salary and travel costs of the co-ordinator over five years for the 'Bird Atlas 2007–11'. An estimated 50,000 volunteers will assess changes in distribution and numbers of the UK's birds; Muslim Youth Helpline (£178,500), towards the salary of the helpline supervisor and contribution to core costs over four years; Children in Scotland (£103,000), towards the salary of an early years' policy officer over three years to make a lasting impact on Scottish early years policy, provision and practice; North Highland Forest Trust (£88,000), towards the salaries of the biodiversity forester and part time support staff over three years, promoting sustainable management of biodiversity-rich woodland; Positive Action for Refugees and Asylum Seekers (£53,000), towards core costs over three years of intensive support and emergency provision to destitute asylum seekers in Leeds; Sahara in Preston (£30,000), towards the salary of a project worker over two years to support a range of support services to BME women who are victims of domestic violence and forced marriage; The Oil Depletion Analysis Centre (£20,000), towards costs over two years of establishing a network to spread awareness among local authorities of peak oil and to stimulate policies to protect communities against its worst impacts; and Westminster Befriend A Family (£10,000), towards core costs to provide befriending, mentoring and family support to families with children aged 0–8 years.

FINANCES *Year* 2008 *Income* £32,006,000 *Grants* £21,484,000 *Assets* £724,804,000

TRUSTEES Tom Chandos, Chair; Felicity Fairbairn; Beatrice Hollond; James Hughes-Hallett; Thomas Hughes-Hallet; Kate Lampard; Baroness Linklater; William Sieghart.

HOW TO APPLY 'Applying for a grant from the Main Fund. Please follow these three steps: 1. Read through the guidance notes, paying careful attention to the sort of work we support – and what we do not. 2. If you think your organisation's activities could attract Esmée Fairbairn funding, go through the self-assessment checklist for eligibility [available from the foundation's website]. 3. If you can answer 'yes' to each of the self-assessment checklist questions, submit a first stage application [available from the foundation's website].

What happens next
We will then get back to you, aiming to acknowledge your first stage application within a week of receiving it. Within a month we will either suggest taking it to the second stage or decline to support it. If you are invited to proceed to the second stage, we will ask you for some additional information that will depend on what you have already told us and the size and complexity of the work you would like us to support.

How will we evaluate your application?
We receive many more applications than we can support. Therefore, we have to be selective. As part of our selection process, we look to support work that has the best chance of achieving its objectives or will leave behind knowledge and experience that could benefit others.
Every application for support is different and we examine each according to the likelihood of it making a difference in the applicant organisation's area of work. Depending on the nature of your application, these are some of the criteria we will apply: how strong are your ideas and how well equipped are your people to carry them out?; how well do you understand the issues you are addressing and what is your track record?; do you have a clear plan or idea and the capacity to deliver it?; what difference would help from us make to your work?; does your work have the potential to be applied more widely or can it influence the work of others?; would receiving our support make you more likely to attract help and engagement from others?; how would your organisation be stronger by the end of the grant and how developed are your long-term plans for sustainability? There is a different application process for the funding strands.' To learn more about the strands and how to apply, visit the foundation's website.

WHO TO APPLY TO Dawn Austwick, Chief Executive, Kings Place, 90 York Way, London N1 9AG *Tel* 020 7812 3700 *Fax* 020 7812 3701 *email* info@esmeefairbairn.org.uk *Website* www.esmeefairbairn.org.uk

CC NO 200051   **ESTABLISHED** 1961

....

■ The Fairstead Trust

WHERE FUNDING CAN BE GIVEN Worldwide.
WHO CAN BENEFIT UK registered charities and individuals.
WHAT IS FUNDED General charitable purposes.
RANGE OF GRANTS £500–£25,000.
SAMPLE GRANTS EACH (£25,000); Family Links (£15,000); Castlehaven Community Association, Nelson's Journey and St Albans Cathedral Educational Centre (£10,000 each); Cley Memorial Hall Fund (£9,000); Southwark Tigers

– Football Team (£6,500); Southwark Tigers – Rugby Team (£5,000); Chance to Shine (£5,000); Afghan Connection and NNRDA (£1,000 each); and Hopefield Animal Sanctuary (£500).

FINANCES *Year* 2007–08 *Income* £28,106 *Grants* £98,000 *Assets* £2,025,746

TRUSTEES Edward Cox; Wendy Cox; Lucinda Cox; Claire Mitchell.

HOW TO APPLY In writing to the correspondent containing the following: aims and objectives of the charity; nature of appeal; total target if for a specific project; contributions received against target; registered charity number; any other relevant factors.

WHO TO APPLY TO c/o Ms L J Stoten, Payne Hicks Beach, 10 New Square, Lincoln's Inn, London WC2A 3QG

CC NO 1096359   **ESTABLISHED** 2003

■ The Fairway Trust

WHERE FUNDING CAN BE GIVEN UK and worldwide.

WHO CAN BENEFIT Charities, universities, colleges and schools.

WHAT IS FUNDED Support of universities, colleges, and schools in UK and abroad; scholarships, grants and loans to postgraduates and undergraduates; grants to help religious purposes; support of clubs and recreational facilities for children and young people; preservation and maintenance of buildings of particular interest; and social welfare.

WHAT IS NOT FUNDED No grants to medical charities.

RANGE OF GRANTS £1,000–£10,000.

SAMPLE GRANTS Boys' and Girls' Clubs of Northern Ireland and Welsh National Opera (£2,000); Sight Savers (£1,500); Prayer Book Society (£1,300); KidsOut (£1,000); Kingston Theatre and Kingston University (£1,000 each); Grantchester PCC (£750); Petersham Trust and ZANE (£500 each).

FINANCES *Year* 2007–08 *Income* £36,189 *Grants* £33,500 *Assets* £38,309

TRUSTEES Mrs Janet Grimstone; Ms K V M Suenson-Taylor.

HOW TO APPLY In writing to the correspondent, although the trust has previously stated 'as funds and office resources are limited it cannot be guaranteed that unsolicited applications will be answered'.

WHO TO APPLY TO Mrs J Grimstone, Trustee, The Gate House, Coombe Wood Road, Kingston-upon-Thames, Surrey KT2 7JY

CC NO 272227   **ESTABLISHED** 1976

■ Faisaltex Charitable Trust

WHERE FUNDING CAN BE GIVEN Worldwide.

WHO CAN BENEFIT Charitable organisations.

WHAT IS FUNDED Organisations working internationally providing religious or other education to children who are in need; the advancement of religion or public services; the relief of sickness and the preservation of good health; and the relief of poverty.

SAMPLE GRANTS Previous beneficiaries include: Preston Guild Rotary Club; Preston Muslim Girl's High School; and St Piux X Preparatory School – Preston.

FINANCES *Year* 2008–09 *Income* £192,896 *Grants* £124,037 *Assets* £3,303,190

TRUSTEES Arif Patel; Mrs Sabina Patel; Munaf Patel; Faisal Patel; Mrs Yasmeen Patel; Arif Barber.

OTHER INFORMATION Grants total refers to grants made to organisations in the UK. £12,159 was given in grants to overseas organisations.

HOW TO APPLY In writing to the correspondent.

WHO TO APPLY TO Arif Patel, Trustee, 11 Saroe Green Park, Fulwood, Preston PR2 8HW *Tel* 01772 704440

CC NO 1085973   **ESTABLISHED** 2001

■ The Family Foundations Trust

(also known as Mintz Family Foundation)

WHERE FUNDING CAN BE GIVEN UK.

WHO CAN BENEFIT Organisations benefiting Jewish people.

WHAT IS FUNDED Jewish causes; general charitable purposes.

SAMPLE GRANTS CIVITAS: Institute for the Study of Civil Society (£35,000); UK Jewish Israel Appeal (£30,000); UK Friends of AWIS (£25,000); World Jewish Relief and Community Security Trust (£10,000 each); Wellbeing of Women, Chai Cancer Care and Holocaust Education Trust (£5,000 each); Jewish Women's Aid (£3,500); The Roundhouse Trust (£3,000); National Hospital Development Foundation (£2,000); and Disability Foundation (£500).

FINANCES *Year* 2007–08 *Income* £208,474 *Grants* £198,600 *Assets* £563,716

TRUSTEES R B Mintz; P G Mintz.

HOW TO APPLY In writing to the correspondent.

WHO TO APPLY TO The Accountant to the Trustees, Gerald Edelman, 25 Harley Street, London W1G 9BR *Tel* 020 7299 1400

CC NO 264014   **ESTABLISHED** 1972

■ The Family Rich Charities Trust

WHERE FUNDING CAN BE GIVEN UK and, to a limited extent, overseas.

WHO CAN BENEFIT Medical, welfare, arts and music charities.

WHAT IS FUNDED Beneficiaries include hospitals; organisations specialising in disease research such as epilepsy, leukaemia, cancer, Parkinson's disease and diabetes; care of people with disabilities; and disaster relief.

WHAT IS NOT FUNDED No grants to individuals.

SAMPLE GRANTS Previous beneficiaries have included the British Heart Foundation, Colon Cancer Concern, the British Epilepsy Association, Computer Aid International, the Diabetes Trust Research Fund, the Leprosy Relief Association, Marie Curie Cancer Care, Medecins Sans Frontiers and Scannappeal, the Multiple Sclerosis Society and the Royal Star and Garter Home.

FINANCES *Year* 2008–09 *Income* £39,540 *Grants* £42,806

TRUSTEES Barbara Anderman; Margaret Fruchter; Tessa Goldstein; Jean Rich.

HOW TO APPLY In writing to the correspondent.

WHO TO APPLY TO Margaret Ann Fruchter, Trustee, 6 Forge Lane, Petersham Road, Richmond-upon-Thames, Surrey TW10 7BF *Tel* 020 8948 7982

CC NO 264192   **ESTABLISHED** 1972

■ Famos Foundation Trust

WHERE FUNDING CAN BE GIVEN UK and overseas.

WHO CAN BENEFIT Small local projects and established organisations benefiting children, young adults, clergy and Jewish people.

WHAT IS FUNDED Education, religion, international organisations, and general charitable purposes. The trust will consider funding: the advancement of the Jewish religion; synagogues; Jewish umbrella bodies; church schools; cultural and religious teaching and religious studies.

WHAT IS NOT FUNDED No grants to individuals.

TYPE OF GRANT One-off, core costs and running costs. Funding is given for one year or less.

RANGE OF GRANTS Up to £5,000.

SAMPLE GRANTS Medical (£1,418); education (£38,583); relief of poverty £42,841); and places of worship (£19,265).

FINANCES *Year* 2007–08 *Income* £311,855 *Grants* £102,107 *Assets* £1,530,449

TRUSTEES Rabbi S M Kupetz; Mrs F Kupetz.

HOW TO APPLY In writing to the correspondent, at any time. The trust does not accept telephone enquiries.

WHO TO APPLY TO Rabbi S M Kupetz, Trustee, 4 Hanover Gardens, Salford, Lancashire M7 4FQ *Tel* 0161 740 5735

CC NO 271211 **ESTABLISHED** 1976

■ The Lord Faringdon Charitable Trust

WHERE FUNDING CAN BE GIVEN UK.

WHO CAN BENEFIT Registered charities only.

WHAT IS FUNDED Educational grants and scholarships; hospitals and the provision of medical treatment for people who are ill; purchase of antiques and artistic objects for museums and collections which have public access; care and assistance of people who are older or infirm; community and economic development and housing; development and assistance of arts and sciences, physical recreation and drama; research into matters of public interest; relief of poverty; support of matters of public interest; animal care and conservation; maintaining and improving the Faringdon Collection.

WHAT IS NOT FUNDED No grants to individuals, just to registered charities.

TYPE OF GRANT Core, capital and project support considered.

SAMPLE GRANTS Garsington Opera (£35,000); Faringdon Skateboard Track (£15,000); Cantebury Cathedral Development Ltd (£10,000 each); Faringdon Youth Centre, The James Wentworth-Stanley Memorial Fund, Oxford Playhouse Trust, Ashmolean Museum and Royal Choral Society (£5,000 each); Pembroke House Mission (£2,500); Stroke Association, Samaritans and Derma Trust (£2,000 each); and Migraine Trust, Listening Books and Prisoner's Advice Service (£1,000 each).

FINANCES *Year* 2007–08 *Income* £186,470 *Grants* £126,500 *Assets* £6,431,497

TRUSTEES A D A W Forbes, Chair; Hon. J H Henderson; R P Trotter.

HOW TO APPLY In writing to the correspondent.

WHO TO APPLY TO J R Waters, Secretary to the Trustees, The Estate Office, Buscot Park, Oxfordshire SN7 8BU *Tel* 01367 240786 *email* estbuscot@aol.com

CC NO 1084690 **ESTABLISHED** 2000

■ Samuel William Farmer's Trust

WHERE FUNDING CAN BE GIVEN Mainly Wiltshire.

WHO CAN BENEFIT Registered charities benefiting children and older people.

WHAT IS FUNDED Charities working in the fields of residential facilities and services, infrastructure development, churches, hospices, healthcare, medical studies and research, conservation, environmental and animal sciences, education and various community facilities and services.

WHAT IS NOT FUNDED No grants to students, or for schools and colleges, endowments, inner-city welfare or housing.

TYPE OF GRANT One-off and recurrent. Buildings, project, research, running costs, salaries and start-up costs. Funding is available for up to three years.

RANGE OF GRANTS £250–£15,000.

SAMPLE GRANTS Devizes District Guiding Building Fund and The Community Foundation for Wiltshire and Swindon (£10,000 each); Wiltshire Air Ambulance Appeal (£7,000); Avon Wildlife Trust (£5,000); STARS Appeal and The Oundle School Mencap Holiday (£2,500 each); Fluency Trust, Helen and Douglas House Hospice, The Oundle School Foundation (£2,000); and Spinal Injuries Association, Larkrise Community Farm and National Osteoporosis Society (£1,000).

FINANCES *Year* 2007 *Income* £81,235 *Grants* £81,000 *Assets* £2,402,441

TRUSTEES Mrs J A Liddiard; W J Rendell; P G Fox-Andrews; B J Waight; C K Brockis.

OTHER INFORMATION In 2007 an additional £6,000 was distributed in 'annual' grants: Royal Agricultural Benevolent Institution and Royal United Kingdom Beneficent (£3,000 each).

HOW TO APPLY In writing to the correspondent. Trustees meet half-yearly.

WHO TO APPLY TO Mrs M Linden-Fermor, Secretary, 71 High Street, Market Lavington, Devizes, Wiltshire SN10 4AG *Tel* 01380 813299

CC NO 258459 **ESTABLISHED** 1929

■ The Farmers' Company Charitable Fund

WHERE FUNDING CAN BE GIVEN UK.

WHO CAN BENEFIT Individuals and organisations benefiting students, and members of the Farmers' Company who are disadvantaged by poverty or in distress, socially isolated or at risk.

WHAT IS FUNDED Promotion of agriculture research and education, including scholarships; providing relief to members of the Farmers' Company in hardship or distress; providing funds for UK students travelling abroad to study agriculture; environmental issues.

RANGE OF GRANTS Usually up to £2,000.

SAMPLE GRANTS Previously: Wye College; Seale Hayne College; the Royal Agricultural Benevolent Institution; the Lord Mayor's Appeal.

FINANCES *Year* 2007–08 *Income* £171,071 *Grants* £30,843 *Assets* £1,387,650

TRUSTEES The Court of Assistants of the Worshipful Company of Farmers.

OTHER INFORMATION Grants were made to individuals totalling £16,000.

HOW TO APPLY In writing to the correspondent.

WHO TO APPLY TO David King, Clerk, Red Copse End, Red Copse Lane, Boars Hill, Oxford OX1 5ER *Tel* 01865 321580 *Fax* 01865 321580 *email* clerk@farmerslivery.org.uk *Website* www.farmerslivery.org.uk

CC NO 258712 **ESTABLISHED** 1969

■ The Thomas Farr Charitable Trust

WHERE FUNDING CAN BE GIVEN UK, especially Nottinghamshire.

WHO CAN BENEFIT Registered charities only.

WHAT IS FUNDED General charitable purposes.

WHAT IS NOT FUNDED No grants to individuals.

RANGE OF GRANTS Up to £25,000; usually for £5,000 or less.

SAMPLE GRANTS Nottingham High School (£150,000); Nottingham Arts Theatre (£25,000); Edward Lane Community Association (£12,200); NSPCC and Beeston Youth and Community Centre (£5,000 each); Age Concern and the Sea Cadets (£3,000 each); Help the Aged and Army Benevolent Fund (£2,000 each); Literacy Volunteers and the Place2Be (£1,000 each).

FINANCES *Year* 2007–08 *Income* £384,418 *Grants* £314,568 *Assets* £6,670,539

TRUSTEES Rathbone Trust Company Ltd; Henry J P Farr; Mrs Amanda M Farr; Barry Davys; Mrs P K Myles.

HOW TO APPLY In writing to the correspondent. Applications are considered in March and September/November.

WHO TO APPLY TO Kevin J Custis, Rathbone Trust Company Ltd, 159 New Bond Street, London W1S 2UD *Tel* 020 7399 0807

CC NO 328394   **ESTABLISHED** 1989

■ Walter Farthing (Trust) Limited

WHERE FUNDING CAN BE GIVEN Mid Essex.

WHO CAN BENEFIT Organisations enlarging the range (including innovative projects) and/or volume of charitable services provided in the locality.

WHAT IS FUNDED Initiation or assistance of the development of projects by undertaking or grant aiding the acquisition, erection or adaptation of buildings and the provision of initial equipment.

WHAT IS NOT FUNDED The trust does not ordinarily support the headquarters of national charities, services which public authorities are empowered to provide, individuals or current expenditure of any nature or description.

TYPE OF GRANT Capital grants.

RANGE OF GRANTS £250–£20,000.

SAMPLE GRANTS Broomfield Hospital Charity Office (£5,000); Brainwave (£3,000); Guinness Independence at Home (£2,000); Acorn Villages and Friends of Edith Borthwick School (£1,000 each); and Essex Association of Boys Clubs and Children's Hope Foundation (£500 each).

FINANCES *Year* 2007–08 *Income* £41,842 *Grants* £27,175 *Assets* £816,321

TRUSTEES Geoffrey Chivas; Christine E Sands; Michael Vandome; Francis V Whitbread; Anthea Tilsley; D J Wisbey; K M Webb.

HOW TO APPLY In writing to the correspondent. Please note that the trust states that it receives many applications that fall outside its area of interest, which cannot be considered.

WHO TO APPLY TO Michael Vandome, Trustee, Fir Tree Lane, Little Baddow, Chelmsford CM3 4SS *Tel* 01245 223465 *Fax* 01245 227810

CC NO 220114   **ESTABLISHED** 1957

■ Farthing Trust

WHERE FUNDING CAN BE GIVEN UK and overseas.

WHO CAN BENEFIT Individuals and charitable organisations which are personally known to the trustees.

WHAT IS FUNDED General charitable purposes.

TYPE OF GRANT One-off and recurring grants.

SAMPLE GRANTS During the year grants were broken down into the following categories: Christian causes (£46,000); churches (£30,000); missionary work (£26,000); education (£20,000); individuals in need (£12,000); general charities (£4,500); local grants (£1,300).

FINANCES *Year* 2007–08 *Income* £117,766 *Grants* £139,226 *Assets* £2,993,775

TRUSTEES C H Martin; Mrs E Martin; Miss J Martin; Mrs A White.

HOW TO APPLY Applications and enquiries should be made in writing to the correspondent. Applicants, and any others requesting information, will only receive a response if an sae is enclosed. There would seem little point in applying unless a personal contact with a trustee is established.

WHO TO APPLY TO The Trustees, PO Box 277, Cambridge CB7 9DE

CC NO 268066   **ESTABLISHED** 1974

■ The Fassnidge Memorial Trust

WHERE FUNDING CAN BE GIVEN London borough of Hillingdon, especially the former urban district of Uxbridge.

WHO CAN BENEFIT Individuals and organisations benefiting children, older people, parents and children, carers, people with disabilities, people disadvantaged by poverty, and victims of domestic violence.

WHAT IS FUNDED Welfare of older people and families, particularly charities working in the fields of care in the community, day centres and meals provision.

WHAT IS NOT FUNDED Applications from people or organisations outside the London borough of Hillingdon are not considered.

TYPE OF GRANT Small one-off grants and start-up costs. Funding of one year or less will be considered.

RANGE OF GRANTS Up to £10,000.

SAMPLE GRANTS 60+Fair; Sipson Community Association; and Hillingdon Homelessness Comfort Fund.

FINANCES *Year* 2008–09 *Income* £34,129 *Grants* £5,001 *Assets* £780,696

TRUSTEES David Bishop; Brian Fredericks; David Horne; Paul Harmsworth; Andrew Retter; David Routledge; David Williams; David Herriott; Richard Walker; Peter Curling; Peter Ryerson; David Yarrow.

HOW TO APPLY In writing to the correspondent.

WHO TO APPLY TO Paul Cowan, 119 Cannonbury Avenue, Pinner, Middlesex HA5 1TR *Tel* 020 8248 3372

CC NO 303078   **ESTABLISHED** 1963

■ Joseph Fattorini Charitable Trust 'B' Account

WHERE FUNDING CAN BE GIVEN UK, including Guernsey.

WHO CAN BENEFIT Roman Catholic, older and younger people.

WHAT IS FUNDED General charitable purposes.

RANGE OF GRANTS Up to £12,000, but in practice, between £500 and £2,000.

SAMPLE GRANTS Stonyhurst College (£12,000); Raes Charitable Trust and Bridge Steel (£2,000 each); Greenbury Cheshire Home, First Meeting and Les Bourges Hospice Development (£1,000

Think carefully about every application. Is it justified?

515

each); and Grassington Festival and Hebden Hood (£500 each).

FINANCES *Year* 2007–08 *Income* £33,491 *Grants* £19,631 *Assets* £643,917

TRUSTEES Joseph Fattorini; Peter Fattorini.

HOW TO APPLY In writing to the correspondent.

WHO TO APPLY TO Peter Fattorini, Trustee, White Abbey, Linton in Craven, Skipton, North Yorkshire BD23 5HQ

CC NO 200032   **ESTABLISHED** 1960

■ The Fawcett Charitable Trust

WHERE FUNDING CAN BE GIVEN UK with a preference for Hampshire and West Sussex.

WHO CAN BENEFIT Work aimed at increasing the quality of life of people with disabilities by facilitating and providing recreation opportunities.

WHAT IS NOT FUNDED Large national charities are excluded as a rule.

SAMPLE GRANTS Chichester Harbour Trust (£75,000); RYA Sailability (£65,000); Naomi House (£50,000); Wessex Children's Hospice (£30,000); St Wilfred's Hospice (£25,000); NSPCC (£20,000); Portsmouth Cathedral (£15,000); Sailing Academy and Jubilee Sailing Trust (£5,000 each); Bikeability (£1,000).

FINANCES *Year* 2007–08 *Income* £21,059 *Grants* £292,000 *Assets* £593,897

TRUSTEES D J Fawcett; Mrs F P Fawcett; D W Russell.

HOW TO APPLY In writing to the correspondent.

WHO TO APPLY TO Céline Lecomte, Blake Lapthorn, Harbour Court, Compass Road, North Harbour, Portsmouth, Hampshire PO6 4ST

CC NO 1013167   **ESTABLISHED** 1990

■ The February Foundation

WHERE FUNDING CAN BE GIVEN UK and overseas.

WHO CAN BENEFIT Charitable organisations and institutions.

WHAT IS FUNDED The foundation will consider the following organisations for the receipt of grants, equity investment or loans: charities for the benefit of persons who are making an effort to improve their lives; charities for the benefit of persons no longer physically or mentally able to help themselves; charities which protect tie environment; charities offering formal education resulting in recognised qualifications; small or minority charities where small grants will have a significant impact; companies where the acquisition of equity would be in line with the foundation's investment policy.

TYPE OF GRANT One-off grants for capital and revenue costs. Loans are also considered.

FINANCES *Year* 2008–09 *Income* £646,475 *Grants* £2,323,486 *Assets* £10,349,206

TRUSTEES Richard Pierce-Saunderson; James Carleton; The February Foundation (Cayman).

OTHER INFORMATION The foundation made 30 grants to 25 organisations. A list of beneficiaries was not available.

HOW TO APPLY Email applications are preferred, and such applications will be processed in advance of hardcopy applications. Due to a high volume of applications, the foundation expects response times to be around 12 weeks from the date of the original application. Please ensure that the subject field of any communication you send contains the name of your organisation or cause. Emails with empty subject fields will be automatically deleted, whilst those with incomplete subject fields will experience a delay

in processing. All applications should be accompanied by full accounts for your most recent completed financial year (audited or unaudited). This is essential.

WHO TO APPLY TO Richard Pierce-Saunderson, Trustee, Chantala, Wilby Road, Stradbroke, Suffolk IP21 5JN *email* rps@ thefebruaryfoundation.org *Website* www.thefebruaryfoundation.org

CC NO 1113064   **ESTABLISHED** 2006

■ Federation of Jewish Relief Organisations

WHERE FUNDING CAN BE GIVEN Mainly Israel.

WHO CAN BENEFIT Jewish people, particularly those disadvantaged by poverty, socially isolated or in at risk groups, and those who are victims of war.

WHAT IS FUNDED Relief of Jewish victims of war and persecution; help wherever Jewish need exists.

SAMPLE GRANTS Grants included £28,000 for clothing shipped to Israel; £24,000 in grants and donations for distribution by the Israel office of the charity.

FINANCES *Year* 2007–08 *Income* £79,718 *Grants* £92,158 *Assets* £218,273

TRUSTEES M Katz, Chair; A M Garfield; Mrs A Lando.

OTHER INFORMATION Founded in 1919 to assist victims of war and persecution in Europe and the Eastern Bloc. Since 1948 it has been concerned mainly in Israel with the rehabilitation, clothing, feeding and education of children of immigrant families.

HOW TO APPLY In writing to the correspondent.

WHO TO APPLY TO Alfred Garfield, Trustee, 143 Brondesbury Park, London NW2 5JL *Tel* 020 8451 3425 *Fax* 020 8459 8059

CC NO 250006   **ESTABLISHED** 1919

■ Feed the Minds

WHERE FUNDING CAN BE GIVEN Developing countries and Eastern Europe.

WHO CAN BENEFIT Christian organisations.

WHAT IS FUNDED Grants are given to support Christian literature and communication programmes.

TYPE OF GRANT Capital and project grants to develop new work and increase overall potential of organisations, for periods from one to three years.

RANGE OF GRANTS Up to £25,000.

SAMPLE GRANTS Narowal Rural Development Fund – Pakistan (£25,000); Rural Welfare Association – India (£17,000); Cliff College – UK (£10,000); Simli-Aid – Ghana (£8,400); Uzima Publishing (£7,200); CCSFU – Fudan University, China (£4,000); and SHARE – India (£1,000).

FINANCES *Year* 2007–08 *Income* £732,948 *Grants* £297,334 *Assets* £188,205

TRUSTEES John Clark; Dr Frances Shaw; Rev Canon Mark Oxbrow; Paul Langridge; Rev Jonathan Kerry; Edward Duffield; David Docherty; Rev Joanna Yates; Roger Jack Cann; Dr David Goodbourn; Rogelio Prieto-Duran; Rev George Lind; Robin Thomas.

OTHER INFORMATION www.feedtheminds.org

HOW TO APPLY On a form available from the correspondent.

WHO TO APPLY TO The Trustees, 36 Causton Street, London SW1P 4AU *Tel* 0845 121 2102 *Fax* 020 7592 3939 *email* info@feedtheminds.org *Website* www.feedtheminds.org

CC NO 291333   **ESTABLISHED** 1964

■ The John Feeney Charitable Bequest

WHERE FUNDING CAN BE GIVEN Birmingham.

WHO CAN BENEFIT Charitable organisations benefiting the Birmingham area.

WHAT IS FUNDED Benefit of public charities in Birmingham only; promotion of art in Birmingham only; acquisition and maintenance of open spaces near Birmingham.

WHAT IS NOT FUNDED Applications will not be accepted: from, or on behalf of, individuals; which do not directly benefit the Birmingham area or Birmingham charitable organisations; which could be considered as political or denominational. Additionally, applications from large national charities, even with a Birmingham base, are unlikely to succeed.

TYPE OF GRANT Capital.

RANGE OF GRANTS Generally £200–£5,000.

SAMPLE GRANTS Farmhurst Ballet School (£10,000); Birmingham Opera Company (£2,000); Lighthouse Group (£1,000); and Carrs Lane Counselling Centre Limited (£500).

FINANCES *Year* 2007 *Income* £72,012 *Grants* £60,000 *Assets* £1,641,032

TRUSTEES C R King-Farlow; D M P Lea; S J Lloyd; Mrs M F Lloyd; H B Carslake; J R L Smith; M S Darby; Mrs S R Wright.

HOW TO APPLY In writing to the correspondent by March of each year. There is no application form and no sae is required. However, letters in support must clearly set out for what purpose, or purposes, the funding is being sought and must enclose a copy of the charity's latest accounts.

WHO TO APPLY TO Martin J Woodward, Secretary, Cobbetts Solicitors, One Colmore Square, Birmingham B4 6AJ *Tel* 0845 404 2404 *email* martin.woodward@cobbetts.co.uk

CC NO 214486   **ESTABLISHED** 1906

■ The George Fentham Birmingham Charity

WHERE FUNDING CAN BE GIVEN City of Birmingham.

WHO CAN BENEFIT Individuals and organisations benefiting young adults and people disadvantaged by poverty.

WHAT IS FUNDED Educational grants to bona fide residents of Birmingham (three-year minimum) aged 16 to 25 years of age. Particularly charities working in the fields of tertiary and higher education, and various community services and facilities, will be considered.

WHAT IS NOT FUNDED Only registered charities are supported. West Midlands organisations outside the city of Birmingham are not eligible.

RANGE OF GRANTS Up to £4,000.

FINANCES *Year* 2008 *Income* £145,056 *Grants* £111,423 *Assets* £4,233,451

TRUSTEES H Malik; M Holcombe; M Martin; D Ridgeway; S Bowen.

OTHER INFORMATION In 2008, an additional £9,500 was paid in grants to individuals.

HOW TO APPLY On a form available from the correspondent. General grants are made in April and October, while education grants are made from September to April.

WHO TO APPLY TO Mrs Anne Holmes, c/o Cobbetts Solicitors, One Colmore Square, Birmingham B4 6JA *Tel* 0845 404 2404 *email* ann.holmes@cobbetts.co.uk

CC NO 214487   **ESTABLISHED** 1907

■ The A M Fenton Trust

WHERE FUNDING CAN BE GIVEN UK, preference for North Yorkshire, and overseas.

WHO CAN BENEFIT Registered charities.

WHAT IS FUNDED General charitable purposes.

WHAT IS NOT FUNDED The trust is unlikely to support local appeals, unless they are close to where the trust is based.

TYPE OF GRANT Mostly one-off.

RANGE OF GRANTS £100–£20,000.

SAMPLE GRANTS Dewsbury League of Friendship (£7,500); Yorkshire Dales Sailing Home (£5,000); Kenmore Leonard Cheshire Homes and St John of Jerusalem Eye Hospital (£2,500 each) Deaf Way, Disability Action Yorkshire, Ghurkha Welfare Trust and NSPCC (£2,000 each); Marie Curie Cancer Care and National Childrens Home (£1,500); and National Animal Welfare Trust, Crime Stoppers Trust and Arthritis Research Campaign (£1,000 each).

FINANCES *Year* 2007–08 *Income* £155,926 *Grants* £132,054 *Assets* £4,397,546

TRUSTEES J L Fenton; C M Fenton.

HOW TO APPLY In writing to the correspondent.

WHO TO APPLY TO J L Fenton, Trustee, 14 Beech Grove, Harrogate, North Yorkshire HG2 0EX *Tel* 01423 504442

CC NO 270353   **ESTABLISHED** 1975

■ The Allan and Nesta Ferguson Charitable Settlement

WHERE FUNDING CAN BE GIVEN Unrestricted, with a local interest in Birmingham and Bishop's Stortford.

WHO CAN BENEFIT Organisations and individuals.

WHAT IS FUNDED Education, overseas development and world peace.

SAMPLE GRANTS The Open University and the Cambridge Foundation (£500,000 each); Coventry University (£468,000); Royal Academy of Music (£45,000); Microloan Foundation (£35,000); Christian Aid and Coterie Trust (£30,000 each); Garden Africa (£25,000); New Vision Development Organisation Kenya (£20,000); Concords International Trust and Fellowship of Reconciliation (£15,000 each).

FINANCES *Year* 2008 *Income* £1,362,170 *Grants* £3,756,756 *Assets* £23,251,110

TRUSTEES Elizabeth Banister; David Banister; Lesley Roff; Richard Tee.

OTHER INFORMATION Grants are also made towards the fees of postgraduate students who are in their final year of a postgraduate course, subject to evidence of financial hardship. In 2008, grants to individuals totalled £106,000.

HOW TO APPLY Applications by charities for small to medium grants (up to a maximum of £50,000) may be submitted at any time and will be considered on a regular basis. Applications for larger grants will be considered at bi-annual meetings held in March and October and applications should be submitted at the very latest in the previous months i.e. February or September. Grants to charities will be on a matching funding basis only so that if the applicant has raised 50% of their budget the trustees will consider awarding matching funding up to a maximum of 50%. However, if the applicant has raised less than 50% of their budget the trustees will only consider awarding a maximum of 30% funding. Evidence of actively seeking funds from other sources is seen by the trustees as being a beneficial addition to any application. No repeat applications will be considered within three years of the conclusion of the grant term. The trust prefers applications to be submitted online. Alternatively, forms can be downloaded and sent by post. Please do not extend the length of the forms, or add any attachments. Applications must not exceed three pages. Please use text size 12. If you are applying for more than one project, please use a separate form for each project. All applications by email will be acknowledged and a decision will usually be given within three months of the application. No progress reports will be given and no correspondence will be entered into in the meantime.

WHO TO APPLY TO Richard Tee, Trustee, Stanley Tee Solicitors, High Street, Bishops Stortford, Hertfordshire CM23 2LU *Tel* 01279 755200 *email* jrt@stanleytee.co.uk *Website* www.fergusontrust.co.uk

CC NO 275487   **ESTABLISHED** 1977

■ Elizabeth Hardie Ferguson Charitable Trust Fund

WHERE FUNDING CAN BE GIVEN UK, with some interest in Scotland.

WHO CAN BENEFIT Organisations benefiting children and young people, particularly those who are sick.

WHAT IS FUNDED The welfare and wellbeing of children and young people. Also charities involved in medical research and hospitals where special medical equipment is needed.

WHAT IS NOT FUNDED Non-registered charities and individuals are not supported. The trust does not make grants overseas.

RANGE OF GRANTS £250–£10,000.

SAMPLE GRANTS Previous beneficiaries have included the Govan Initiative and Harmony Row Boys' Club.

FINANCES *Year* 2007–08 *Income* £402,303 *Grants* £300,000

TRUSTEES Sir Alex Ferguson; Cathy Ferguson; Huw Roberts; Ted Way; Les Dalgarno; Paul Hardman; Jason Ferguson.

HOW TO APPLY An application form and guidelines should be requested in writing from the correspondent. The committee meets to consider grants at the end of January and July. Applications should be received by December and June respectively.

WHO TO APPLY TO The Trustees, c/o 27 Peregrine Crescent, Droylsden, Manchester M43 7TA

SC NO SC026240   **ESTABLISHED** 1988

■ The Fidelity UK Foundation

WHERE FUNDING CAN BE GIVEN Unrestricted, in practice particular preference is given to projects in Kent, Surrey, London and continental Europe.

WHO CAN BENEFIT Not for profit organisations, charities.

WHAT IS FUNDED General, giving is primarily allocated for charitable purposes in the following areas: community development, health, arts and culture and education. The trust seeks to support projects undertaken by organisations to increase proficiency, achieve goals and reach long-term self-sufficiency. Most often, funding is given for projects such as capital improvements, technology upgrades, organisational development and planning initiatives.

WHAT IS NOT FUNDED Grants are not generally made to: start-up, sectarian, or political organisations; private schools, and colleges or universities;

individuals. Grants are not made for: sponsorships or benefit events; scholarships; corporate memberships; advertising and promotional projects; exhibitions. Generally grants are not made for running costs, but may be considered on an individual basis through the foundation's small grant scheme. Grants will not normally cover the entire cost of a project. Grants will not normally be awarded to an organisation in successive years. The foundation receives many more applications for grants than it is able to fund so not all applications that fall within the guidelines will receive grants.

TYPE OF GRANT Buildings, capital, IT development, one-off grants to develop infrastructure. Funding for less than one year is considered.

SAMPLE GRANTS The Mary Rose Trust (£300,000); Great Dixter Charitable Trust (£250,000); Watts Gallery (£200,000); Chatham Historic Dockyard Trust (£162,000); Trinity Hospice (£100,000); Breakthrough Breast Cancer (£93,000); Muscular Dystrophy Campaign (£80,000); Albert Ludwig's Universtat Frieburg (£79,000); Broadway Homelessness and Support (£64,000); and Latitude Global Volunteering (£25,000).

FINANCES *Year* 2008 *Income* £7,055,682 *Grants* £4,126,906 *Assets* £82,649,041

TRUSTEES Edward C Johnson; Barry Bateman; Anthony Bolton; Robert Milotte; Richard Millar; John Owen.

HOW TO APPLY In writing to the correspondent. The following documentation is required: Fidelity UK Foundation summary form (form can be downloaded from the foundation's website); organisation history and objectives; description of request and rationale, see below; itemised project budget; list of other funders and status of each request; list of directors and trustees with their backgrounds; current management accounts; most recently audited financial statements. When writing the description of your request and your rationale, please address the following questions: How does the project fit into the larger strategic plan of your organisation? What will a grant allow your organisation to achieve? How will a grant change or improve the long-term potential of your organisation? What is the implementation plan and timeline for the project? How will the project be evaluated? There are no deadlines for submitting grant proposals. All applications will normally receive an initial response within three months. The volume of requests as well as diligence of review process require a three to six month period, which should be factored into the applicant's funding plan. Please note that the Fidelity UK Foundation accepts no liability for any costs incurred by a charitable organisation when preparing an application to submit to the foundation.

WHO TO APPLY TO Susan Platts-Martin, Chief Executive, Oakhill House, 130 Tonbridge Road, Hildenborough, Tonbridge, Kent TN11 9DZ *Tel* 01732 361144 *Fax* 01732 834143 *Website* www.fidelityukfoundation.org

CC NO 327899   **ESTABLISHED** 1988

■ The Bluff Field Charitable Trust

WHERE FUNDING CAN BE GIVEN UK.

WHO CAN BENEFIT Charitable organisations.

WHAT IS FUNDED General charitable purposes.

SAMPLE GRANTS Previous beneficiaries have included Emmanuel Church Billericay, Leukaemia Research Fund, Risk Waters' World Trade

Centre UK Appeal, St George's Hospital Medical School and Wigmore Hall Trust.

FINANCES *Year* 2008 *Income* £501 *Grants* £8,000

TRUSTEES Peter Field; Sonia Field; Stanley Salter.

OTHER INFORMATION In 2008 this trust had an income of just £501 and a total expenditure of £8,000. In previous years it has received substantial income from donations and Gift Aid.

HOW TO APPLY In writing to the correspondent.

WHO TO APPLY TO Peter Field, Trustee, 8 The Little Boltons, London SW10 9LP *Tel* 020 7373 1863 *email* bfct@btinternet.com

CC NO 1057992 **ESTABLISHED** 1996

....

■ The Doris Field Charitable Trust

WHERE FUNDING CAN BE GIVEN UK, with a preference for Oxfordshire.

WHO CAN BENEFIT Large UK and small local organisations benefiting children and young adults; at risk groups; people who are disadvantaged by poverty or socially isolated.

WHAT IS FUNDED Medical, welfare, education and general charitable purposes.

WHAT IS NOT FUNDED It is unlikely that grants would be made for overseas projects or to individuals for higher education.

TYPE OF GRANT One-off and recurrent.

RANGE OF GRANTS £50–£50,000, mostly £5,000 or less.

SAMPLE GRANTS Ucare (£45,000); Maintenance of Doris Field Memorial Park (£18,000); Oxford Radcliffe Hospital – Cancer Campaign (£10,000); and The Unicorn School (£5,000); Adventure Plus Limited (£3,000); Marie Curie Cancer Care, Jubilee Sailing Trust and Oxfordshire Samaritans (£2,000 each) Autism Speaks, Alzheimers Research Trust and Relate Oxfordshire (£1,000 each); and Abingdon Concert Band, British Blind Sport and Wellbeing of Women (£500 each).

FINANCES *Year* 2007–08 *Income* £397,357 *Grants* £242,050 *Assets* £7,693,373

TRUSTEES N A Harper; J Cole; Mrs W Church.

HOW TO APPLY On a form available from the correspondent. Applications are considered three times a year or as and when necessary.

WHO TO APPLY TO The Trustees, c/o Morgan Cole, Buxton Court, 3 West Way, Oxford OX2 0SZ *Tel* 01865 262183

CC NO 328687 **ESTABLISHED** 1990

....

■ Fife Council/Common Good Funds and Trusts

WHERE FUNDING CAN BE GIVEN East Fife.

WHO CAN BENEFIT Individuals in need and local community groups such as community councils and sports clubs.

WHAT IS FUNDED Arts, buildings, conservation/environment, disability, education/training, heritage, hospitals/hospices, social welfare of people of all ages and sports and recreation.

WHAT IS NOT FUNDED The following causes are not supported: animal welfare; medical/health; medical research; overseas projects; political appeals; and religious appeals.

TYPE OF GRANT One-off grants for capital and revenue costs.

RANGE OF GRANTS Mostly under £2,000.

FINANCES *Year* 2007–08 *Grants* £70,000

OTHER INFORMATION Despite making a written request for the accounts of this trust (including an sae) these were not provided. The following

entry is based on the information available on the council website.

HOW TO APPLY Contact the correspondent for further details. An application form and guidelines are available for the Common Good Funds but not for the trusts. Applications can be made at any time.

WHO TO APPLY TO Linda Purdie, Team Leader (Democratic Services), Fife Council, Fife House, North Street, Glenrothes, Fife KY7 5LT *Tel* 08451 555555 (Ext 442175) *Fax* 01592 583155 *Website* www.fife.gov.uk

SC NO SC019393

....

■ The Fifty Fund

WHERE FUNDING CAN BE GIVEN Nottinghamshire and surrounding area.

WHO CAN BENEFIT Individuals and organisations benefiting retired people; unemployed people; those in care, fostered and adopted; parents and children; one-parent families; widows and widowers; carers; disabled people; and people disadvantaged by poverty.

WHAT IS FUNDED Relief of poverty, infrastructure development, charity or voluntary umbrella bodies, advice and information on housing, respite care, and various community services.

WHAT IS NOT FUNDED No grants for education, expeditions or travel.

TYPE OF GRANT Mostly one-off grants for revenue costs and project funding.

RANGE OF GRANTS £100–£10,000.

SAMPLE GRANTS Shelter NHAS (£10,000); Salvation Army (£7,500); Cheshire Homes (£6,500); Army Benevolent Fund (£4,500); Cares for Kids Breakfast Club (£3,000); Friary Drop In (£2,000); Youth at Risk (£1,000); and Gateway Trust (£500).

FINANCES *Year* 2007 *Income* £334,875 *Grants* £218,537 *Assets* £7,710,479

TRUSTEES E W Whiles; E A Randall; Revd Canon G B Barrodale.

OTHER INFORMATION The fund also made grants to individuals totalling £51,000.

HOW TO APPLY In writing to the correspondent. The trustees meet twice a year to consider grant applications.

WHO TO APPLY TO Stephen Moore, Clerk, Nelsons Solicitors, Pennine House, 8 Stanford Street, Nottingham NG1 7BQ *Tel* 0115 989 5251

CC NO 214422 **ESTABLISHED** 1963

....

■ Dixie Rose Findlay Charitable Trust

WHERE FUNDING CAN BE GIVEN UK.

WHO CAN BENEFIT Charitable organisations. Especially those concerned with children, seafarers and the blind.

WHAT IS FUNDED General charitable purposes.

SAMPLE GRANTS Cassell Hospital, The Children's Society, Leukaemia Research, The Mission to Seafarers, Royal National Lifeboat Institution and Royal National Mission to Deep Sea Fishermen (£8,000 each); and Association of Wheelchair Children, Demand, Elizabeth Finn Care, Fighting Blindness, Motability and Treetops Hospice (£2,000 each).

FINANCES *Year* 2006–07 *Income* £130,994 *Grants* £152,311 *Assets* £4,331,022

TRUSTEES HSBC Trust Co. (UK) Ltd.

HOW TO APPLY In writing to the correspondent.

WHO TO APPLY TO Samantha D'Ambrosio, Trust Manager, HSBC Trust Co. (UK) Ltd, 10th Floor,

Think carefully about every application. Is it justified?

519

Norwich House, Nelson Gate, Commercial Road, Southampton SO15 1GX *Tel* 023 8072 2231
cc no 251661   **established** 1967

■ Finnart House School Trust

where funding can be given Worldwide.

who can benefit Organisations benefitting Jewish children and young people in need of care and/or education.

what is funded Bursaries and scholarships are given, to Jewish secondary school pupils and university entrants who are capable of achieving, but would probably not do so because of family and economic pressures. Also supported is work concerned with people who are disaffected, disadvantaged socially and economically through illness or neglect or in need of care and education.

type of grant Buildings, capital, one-off and project. Funding is available for up to two years.

range of grants Typical grant £5,000.

sample grants Jewish Free School (£12,000); King Solomon High School (£9,000); Hasmonean High School and The Club House (£3,000).

finances *Year* 2007–08 *Income* £178,372 *Grants* £148,886 *Assets* £4,322,090

trustees Dame Hilary Blume and David Fobel (co-Chairs); Robert Cohen; Lilian Hochhauser; Linda Paterson; Sue Leifer; Gideon Lyons; Dr Louis Marks; Mark Sebba.

other information In 2007–08, a further £102,000 was given in total in 63 scholarships to individuals.

how to apply By application form, which needs to be submitted together with a copy of the latest annual report and accounts.

who to apply to Peter Shaw, Clerk, PO Box 603, Edgware, Middlesex HA8 4EQ *Tel* 020 3209 6006 *email* info@finnart.org *Website* www.finnart.org

cc no 220917   **established** 1901

■ Gerald Finzi Charitable Trust

where funding can be given UK.

who can benefit Organisations and individuals.

what is funded The trustees aim to reflect the ambitions and philosophy of the composer Gerald Finzi (1901–56), which included the general promotion of 20th century British music through assisting and promoting festivals, recordings and performances of British music. A limited number of modest grants are also offered to young musicians towards musical training.

range of grants Up to £6,000.

sample grants National Youth Orchestra – composers course (£5,600); Bournemouth Symphony Orchestra (£3,000); Kenneth Leighton Trust (£1,600); Three Choirs Festival (£1,250); Music at Tradebigge and Ex Cathedra (£600 each); Percy Young Scholarship (£500).

finances *Year* 2007–08 *Income* £65,820 *Grants* £37,269 *Assets* £89,692

trustees Robert Gower, Chair; Christian Alexander; Andrew Burn; Jean Finzi; Nigel Finzi; Jeremy Dale Roberts; Paul Spicer.

how to apply In writing to the correspondent.

who to apply to Elizabeth Pooley, Administator, P O Box 137, Shaftesbury, Dorset SP7 0WX *Tel* 01244 320300 *Fax* 01244 341200 *email* admin@finzi.org.uk *Website* www.geraldfinzi.org

cc no 313047   **established** 1969

■ Firtree Trust

where funding can be given UK and abroad.

who can benefit Christian organisations.

what is funded Religious education and the advancement of the Protestant and Evangelical tenets of the Christian faith.

type of grant One year grants for capital and revenue costs.

range of grants Up to £3,000.

sample grants Warlingham Methodist Church (£3,100); Open Doors (£2,000); Fear Found and International Needs (£1,800 each); Operation Mobchsalton (£1,400); and Bible Lands, Far East Broadcasting Association, Hope Now and Lifewords (£1,000 each).

finances *Year* 2007–08 *Income* £47,266 *Grants* £41,055 *Assets* £12,053

trustees Maurice John Turner; Margaret Helen Turner; James Stephen Turner; Paul Turner; Elizabeth Turner.

other information Grants totalling £11,000 were given to individuals.

how to apply In writing to the correspondent.

who to apply to The Trust Department, Jacob Cavenagh and Skeet, 5 Robin Hood Lane, Sutton, Surrey SM1 2SW *Tel* 020 8643 1166 *email* andrew@jcssutton.co.uk

cc no 282239

■ The Sir John Fisher Foundation

where funding can be given UK, with a preference for charities in the Furness peninsula and adjacent area and local branches of national charities.

who can benefit Registered charities.

what is funded General charitable purposes with a preference for the shipping industry, medicine, the navy or military and music and theatre.

what is not funded The trustees will generally not fund: individuals; sponsorship; expeditions; promotion of religion; places of worship; animal welfare; retrospective funding; pressure groups; community projects outside Barrow-in-Furness and surrounding area (except occasional projects in Cumbria or North Lancashire or if they fall within one of the other categories supported by the foundation).

range of grants £25–£25,000.

sample grants National Maritime Museum – Cornwall (£70,000 in total); Barrow Sea Cadet Corps (£32,000); Lancaster University (£30,000); Barrow & District Society for the Blind (£25,000); University of Dundee and RNLI Crew Training (£20,000 each); Cancer Research UK (£15,000); Anglo-Austrian Music Society and London Handel Society Ltd (£10,000 each); Citizens Advice Bureau South Lakeland (£8,000); Ulverston International Music Festival (£7,000); Tall Ships Youth Trust and NSPCC (£5,000 each); Mission to Seafarers and the Fire Services National Benevolent Fund (£1,000 each); and John Rylands University Library (£500).

finances *Year* 2007–08 *Income* £924,563 *Grants* £723,041 *Assets* £47,120,994

trustees Diane S Meacock; Sir David Hardy; Daniel Purser Tindall; Rowland Frederick Hart Jackson.

how to apply The foundation's trustees fund projects requiring either capital or revenue support. There is no general limit to the grant which can be awarded to any one project. Most grants given are for less than £10,000. In the past the trustees have given larger grants to major one-off projects or for research projects over defined periods. The trustees are, in appropriate cases, willing to express an intention to commit funds for up to three years, if it can be shown that substantial benefit will result from an extended period of funding. An intention to commit funds for future years is always subject to funds being available at the time. Urgent grants for small (less than £4,000) amounts can be considered between meetings, but the trustees would expect an explanation as to why the application could not be considered at a normal meeting. Applications should be made by submitting a completed application form, either by email or post, together with all relevant information (set out on the application form) to the secretary at least six weeks in advance of the trustees' meeting. The trustees meet at the beginning of May and the beginning of November each year. You are always welcome to contact the secretary for an informal discussion before submitting an application for funding. The trustees expect to receive feedback from the organisations they support, to help in their decision making process. Organisations are asked to provide a brief one page report about nine months after receipt of a grant (or when the specific project assisted has been completed). A feedback form is available from the foundation's website.

WHO TO APPLY TO Dr David Hart Jackson, Trust Secretary, Heaning Wood, Ulverston, Cumbria LA12 7NZ *Tel* 01229 580349 *email* info@ sirjohnfisherfoundation.org.uk *Website* www. sirjohnfisherfoundation.org.uk

CC NO 277844   **ESTABLISHED** 1979

■ Fisherbeck Charitable Trust

WHERE FUNDING CAN BE GIVEN Worldwide.

WHO CAN BENEFIT Registered charities worldwide.

WHAT IS FUNDED The advancement of the Christian religion; support for the provision of accommodation for the homeless; the relief of poverty; the advancement of education; conservation of the environment and the preservation of heritage.

WHAT IS NOT FUNDED Grants are only made to individuals known to the trust or in exceptional circumstances.

TYPE OF GRANT One-off and recurrent.

RANGE OF GRANTS Up to £50,000.

SAMPLE GRANTS Tear Fund (£48,000); Urban Saints (£44,500); Bible Society (£28,000); Release International (£24,000); National Trust (£19,000); Hope for Lugazi (£12,000); Scripture Union (£9,000); and Sustrans (£6,000).

FINANCES *Year* 2007–08 *Income* £483,958 *Grants* £456,100 *Assets* £176,399

TRUSTEES I R Cheal; Mrs J Cheal; M Cheal.

HOW TO APPLY Grants are given in accordance with the wishes of the Cheal family.

WHO TO APPLY TO The Trustees, Home Farm House, 63 Ferringham Lane, Ferring, Worthing, West Sussex BN12 5LL *Tel* 01903 241027 *email* ian@roffeyhomes.com

CC NO 1107287   **ESTABLISHED** 2004

■ The Fishmongers' Company's Charitable Trust

WHERE FUNDING CAN BE GIVEN UK, however this refers to charities whose objects extend throughout England. In practice, mainly the City of London and its adjacent boroughs.

WHO CAN BENEFIT Registered charities and individuals (for educational grants only).

WHAT IS FUNDED General. In practice, education, relief of poverty and disability, in particular assistance to almshouses, fishery related bodies, environment and heritage.

WHAT IS NOT FUNDED No grants to individuals except for educational purposes.

RANGE OF GRANTS Up to £350,000.

SAMPLE GRANTS Gresham's School (£331,000); Marion Richardson School (£30,000); Jesus Hospital Almshouses (£28,000); City and Guilds of London Art School (£25,000); Lord Mayor's Appeal (£9,000); Atlantic Salmon Trust (£8,800); Billingsgate Seafood Training School (£5,000); Harrietsham Almshouse (£4,900); Help for Heroes (£3,000); St Magnus the Martyr (£1,500); and Nancy Oldfield Trust, Broadway and Airbourne Forces Museum (£1,000 each).

FINANCES *Year* 2008 *Income* £874,848 *Grants* £660,963 *Assets* £12,119,525

TRUSTEES K S Waters; P T R Woodward; Court of the Worshipful Company of Fishmongers.

OTHER INFORMATION £76,000 was distributed to individuals during the year.

HOW TO APPLY In writing to the correspondent. Meetings take place three times a year, in March, June/July and November, and applications should be received a month in advance. No applications are considered within three years of a previous grant application being successful. Unsuccessful applications are not acknowledged.

WHO TO APPLY TO Peter Woodward, Clerk, The Fishmongers' Company, Fishmongers' Hall, London Bridge, London EC4R 9EL *Tel* 020 7626 3531 *Fax* 020 7929 1389 *email* clerk@ fishhall.co.uk

CC NO 263690   **ESTABLISHED** 1972

■ Marc Fitch Fund

WHERE FUNDING CAN BE GIVEN UK.

WHO CAN BENEFIT Both individuals and societies benefiting young adults, research workers and students.

WHAT IS FUNDED Publication and research in archaeology, historical geography, history of art and architecture, heraldry, genealogy, surnames, catalogues of and use of archives (especially ecclesiastical) and other antiquarian, archaeological or historical studies. In many cases, the awards enable work to be undertaken, or the results published either in print or on-line form, which would not otherwise be achieved.

WHAT IS NOT FUNDED No grants are given towards foreign travel or for research outside the British Isles, unless the circumstances are very exceptional; no awards are made in connection with vocational or higher education courses or to people reading for higher degrees.

RANGE OF GRANTS Institutions: up to £15,000.

SAMPLE GRANTS Victoria County History (£33,000); Bodleian Library (£28,000); Newcastle University (£17,000); and The Wallace Collection and Public Catalogue Foundation (£15,000 each); Berkshire Records Society (£10,000); Calendar of Papal Registers (£9,000); Henley Archaeological and Historical Group (£5,000); Royal Irish Academy (£3,000); Royal Albert Memorial Museum Exeter (£2,500); Ashmolean Museum (£2,000); National Museums Liverpool (£1,500); Watts Gallery (£1,250); The Trimontium Trust (£1,000); and Devonshire Association for Advancement of Science, Literature and Arts (£600).

FINANCES *Year* 2007–08 *Income* £245,749 *Grants* £199,309 *Assets* £4,531,716

TRUSTEES A S Bell, Chair; Prof. D M Palliser; Prof. J Blair; Dr H Forde; A Murison; L Allason-Jones; Prof. D Hey.

HOW TO APPLY In writing to the correspondent. The Council of Management meets twice a year, usually in April and September, to consider applications. The deadlines for receipt of completed applications and references are 1 March and 1 August.

WHO TO APPLY TO The Director, PO Box 207, Chipping Norton OX7 3ZQ *Tel* 01608 811944 *email* admin@marcfitchfund.org.uk *Website* www.marcfitchfund.org.uk

CC NO 313303   **ESTABLISHED** 1956

■ The Fitton Trust

WHERE FUNDING CAN BE GIVEN UK.

WHO CAN BENEFIT Registered charities only.

WHAT IS FUNDED General charitable purposes.

WHAT IS NOT FUNDED No grants to individuals.

RANGE OF GRANTS Usually £100–£250; occasionally £1,000 or more.

SAMPLE GRANTS King's Medical Research Trust (£2,100); and Young Peoples Trust for the Environment, Cancer Resource Centre and Sheffield Institute Foundation for Motor Neurone Disease (£1,000 each).

FINANCES *Year* 2007–08 *Income* £125,713 *Grants* £106,800 *Assets* £1,798,339

TRUSTEES Dr R P A Rivers; D V Brand; R Brand; K J Lumsden; E M Lumsden; L P L Rivers.

HOW TO APPLY In writing to correspondent. The trustees meet three times each year, usually in April, August and December. The trust states: 'No application considered unless accompanied by fully audited accounts. No replies will be sent to unsolicited applications whether from individuals, charities or other bodies.'

WHO TO APPLY TO Mrs Rosalind Gordon-Cumming, The Secretary, PO Box 649, London SW3 4LA

CC NO 208758   **ESTABLISHED** 1928

■ The Earl Fitzwilliam Charitable Trust

WHERE FUNDING CAN BE GIVEN UK, with a preference for areas with historical family connections, chiefly in Cambridgeshire, Northamptonshire and Yorkshire.

WHO CAN BENEFIT Organisations benefiting: children and young adults; clergy; ex-service and service people; volunteers; Christians; Church of England; at risk groups; disabled people; people living in rural areas; victims of abuse and crime; victims of man-made or natural disasters; and people with cancer, diabetes, head and other injuries, leprosy, mental illness, spina bifida and hydrocephalus. Projects and charities connected in some way with or which will benefit rural life and communities including churches.

WHAT IS FUNDED Preference for charitable projects in areas with historical family connections, chiefly in Cambridgeshire, Northamptonshire and Yorkshire. Particularly charities working in the fields of: accommodation and housing; infrastructure, support and development; Christian outreach; churches; religious umbrella bodies; arts, culture and recreation; health facilities and buildings; cancer research; conservation and environment; schools and colleges; and various community facilities and services.

WHAT IS NOT FUNDED No grants to individuals.

TYPE OF GRANT Buildings, capital, endowments, one-off, project and research. Funding of one year or less will be considered.

RANGE OF GRANTS Usually £100–£5,000.

SAMPLE GRANTS York Minster Fund, Peterborough Cathedral Trust and Liver Research Trust (£5,000 each); Ryedale In-Touch Group, Macmillan Cancer Support, Deafblind UK and Addenbrooke's Charitable Trust (£2,500 each); East Anglia's Children's Hospice, Northamptonshire Association for the Blind and Prince's Trust (£2,000 each); Helpston and Etton Community Association and Nene Valley Archaeological Trust (£1,000 each); Renewable Heritage Trust and Farm Crisis Network (£500); and Habitat for Humanity and Historic Churches Trust (£250 each).

FINANCES *Year* 2007–08 *Income* £217,623 *Grants* £90,925 *Assets* £8,063,726

TRUSTEES Sir Philip Naylor-Leyland; Lady Isabella Naylor-Leyland.

HOW TO APPLY In writing to the correspondent. Trustees meet about every three months.

WHO TO APPLY TO R W Dalgleish, Secretary to the Trustees, Estate Office, Milton Park, Peterborough PE6 7AH *Tel* 01733 267740 *email* agent@miltonestate.co.uk

CC NO 269388   **ESTABLISHED** 1975

■ Bud Flanagan Leukaemia Fund

WHERE FUNDING CAN BE GIVEN UK.

WHO CAN BENEFIT Hospitals and similar organisations carrying out research, diagnosis and treatment of leukaemia and allied diseases; people with leukaemia and their families and dependants.

WHAT IS FUNDED Promotion of clinical research into the treatment and possible cure of leukaemia and allied diseases and the publication of the results of all such research. Relief of people with leukaemia and allied diseases and the relief of poverty and distress among their families and dependants. The policy is to make donations to hospitals and similar institutions for equipment or research into leukaemia and allied diseases so that as many people as possible benefit.

WHAT IS NOT FUNDED The fund does not normally make grants to welfare charities or to individuals.

TYPE OF GRANT Capital (including buildings), project and research. Funding can be for up to three years.

RANGE OF GRANTS Usually up to £10,000.

SAMPLE GRANTS The Royal Marsden Hospital (£10,000); St Christophers Hospice (£500); and St Catherines Hospice (£200).

FINANCES *Year* 2007 *Income* £204,438 *Grants* £10,700 *Assets* £561,858

TRUSTEES S Coventry; K Kaye; A Rowden; G Till.

HOW TO APPLY In writing to the correspondent.

WHO TO APPLY TO Sandra Clark, General Secretary, c/o Abbots, Printing House, 66 Lower Road, Harrow HA2 0DH *Website* www.bflf.org.uk

CC NO 1092540   **ESTABLISHED** 1969

■ The Rose Flatau Charitable Trust

WHERE FUNDING CAN BE GIVEN UK.

WHO CAN BENEFIT Registered charities.

WHAT IS FUNDED Jewish causes; and other organisations which particularly attract the interest of the trustees.

WHAT IS NOT FUNDED No grants to individuals.

RANGE OF GRANTS £100–£15,000.

SAMPLE GRANTS World Jewish Relief (£10,000); Jewish Blind and Disabled (£5,500); Multiple Sclerosis Society and Brantwoods Trust (£5,000 each); British Red Cross (£4,500); Institute of Cancer Research and The Childrens Trust (£2,500 each); Princess Alice Hospital and National Listening Library (£2,000 each); and Spinal Research (£1,000).

FINANCES *Year* 2007–08 *Income* £49,963 *Grants* £80,629 *Assets* £1,749,629

TRUSTEES M E G Prince; A E Woolf; N L Woolf.

HOW TO APPLY The trust stated: 'Our funds are fully committed to the foreseeable future'. Speculative applications will therefore be fruitless.

WHO TO APPLY TO M E G Prince, Trustee, 5 Knott Park House, Wrens Hill, Oxshott, Leatherhead KT22 OHW

CC NO 210492   **ESTABLISHED** 1959

■ The Ian Fleming Charitable Trust

WHERE FUNDING CAN BE GIVEN UK.

WHO CAN BENEFIT Individual musicians, and registered charities benefiting medical professionals, research workers and scientists. Support is also given to at risk groups, and people who are disabled, disadvantaged by poverty or socially isolated.

WHAT IS FUNDED Income is allocated equally between: national charities actively operating for the support, relief and welfare of men, women and children who are disabled or otherwise in need of help, care and attention, and charities actively engaged in research on human diseases; and music education awards under a scheme administered by the Musicians Benevolent Fund and advised by a committee of experts in the field of music.

WHAT IS NOT FUNDED No grants to individuals except under the music education award scheme. No grants to purely local charities.

RANGE OF GRANTS £1,000–£3,000.

SAMPLE GRANTS Bowel and Cancer Research (£3,000); Arthritis Research Campaign, Dystonia Society, Royal British Legion and Gurkha Welfare Trust (£2,000 each); and British Forces Foundation, Epilepsy Action, Scottish Society for Autism, Motability and Spinal Injuries Association (£1,500).

FINANCES *Year* 2007–08 *Income* £114,134 *Grants* £109,000 *Assets* £1,983,478

TRUSTEES A A I Fleming; N A M McDonald; A W W Baldwin; A H Isaacs.

OTHER INFORMATION The grant total in 2007–08 consisted of £48,000 to organisations and £61,000 to individuals through the music educational awards scheme.

HOW TO APPLY In writing to the correspondent.

WHO TO APPLY TO A A I Fleming, Trustee, haysmacintyre, Fairfax House, 15 Fulwood Place, London WC1V 6AY *Tel* 020 7969 5500 *email* mjones@haysmacintyre.com

CC NO 263327   **ESTABLISHED** 1971

■ The Joyce Fletcher Charitable Trust

WHERE FUNDING CAN BE GIVEN England, almost entirely South West.

WHO CAN BENEFIT England/wide and south west charities. This trust will consider funding for the benefit of all ages; musicians; volunteers; those in care, fostered and adopted; one-parent families; parents and children; people with disabilities; those living in rural areas; and socially isolated people.

WHAT IS FUNDED Music in the community and in a special needs context; children's welfare; and charities in the south west. Currently main areas of interest are institutions and organisations specialising in music education and performance, special needs education and performance involving music, and charities for children's welfare. Arts, culture and recreation; art galleries and cultural centres; community centres and village halls; theatres' and opera houses' education programmes; and other charitable purposes are all considered for funding.

WHAT IS NOT FUNDED Grants to individuals and students are exceptionally rare; applications are not sought. No support for areas which are the responsibility of the local authority. No support is given to purely professional music/arts promotions. No support for purely medical research charities.

TYPE OF GRANT Recurring expenses; capital; or new projects.

RANGE OF GRANTS £250–£2,000, occasionally more.

SAMPLE GRANTS Live Music Now! (£5,500); Welsh National Opera (£4,000); Bath Festivals (£3,500); Iford Arts and Wiltshire Music Centre (£3,000 each); English Speak Union and Bath Area Play Project (£2,000 each); Project Trust and Hope and Homes for Children (£1,000 each); and Supporting Disabled in Need (£600).

FINANCES *Year* 2007–08 *Income* £82,688 *Grants* £70,600 *Assets* £2,196,990

TRUSTEES R A Fletcher; W D R Fletcher; S C Sharp; S P Fletcher.

HOW TO APPLY In writing to the correspondent before 1 November each year. There are no application forms. Letters should include the purpose for the grant, an indication of the history and viability of the organisation and a summary of accounts. Preliminary telephone calls are accepted. Acknowledgements are only given if the application is being considered or if an sae is sent.

WHO TO APPLY TO R A Fletcher, Trustee and Correspondent, 17 Westmead Gardens, Upper Weston, Bath BA1 4EZ *Tel* 01225 314355

CC NO 297901   **ESTABLISHED** 1987

■ The Roy Fletcher Charitable Trust

WHERE FUNDING CAN BE GIVEN Shropshire.

WHO CAN BENEFIT Local organisations.

WHAT IS FUNDED Children and young people; older people; disadvantage. The trust also established The Roy Fletcher Centre to house caring agencies and provide office space, meeting and counselling rooms; this is now run independently of the trust.

WHAT IS NOT FUNDED The trust is unlikely to fund projects eligible for statutory funding, applicants not seeking funds from elsewhere, UK charities, operating costs, building repairs or educational grants. The trust no longer supports individuals.

SAMPLE GRANTS The Prince's Trust (£5,000).

FINANCES *Year* 2007–08 *Income* £97,075 *Grants* £5,000 *Assets* £3,120,462

TRUSTEES Mrs R A Coles; Mrs G M Mathias; Mrs E J Fletcher-Cooper; D N Fletcher.

HOW TO APPLY In writing to the correspondent only. The trustees meet three times a year in early January, May and October, and requests for funding should be received at least four weeks before each meeting. The trust does not welcome telephone enquiries to The Roy Fletcher Centre (which is a separate organisation).

WHO TO APPLY TO Mrs I Cowen, c/o Roy Fletcher Centre, 12–17 Cross Hill, Shrewsbury, Shropshire SY1 1JE *email* info@royfletchertrust.org.uk *Website* www.royfletchertrust.org.uk

CC NO 276498   **ESTABLISHED** 1978

■ **Florence's Charitable Trust**

WHERE FUNDING CAN BE GIVEN UK, with a preference for Rossendale in Lancashire.

WHO CAN BENEFIT Mainly local organisations, or local branches of UK organisations, benefiting employees or former employees of the shoe trade and older people or people disadvantaged by poverty. Support may be given to children and young adults.

WHAT IS FUNDED General charitable purposes, especially establishment, maintenance and support of places of education; relief of sickness of infirmity for older people; and relief of poverty of anyone employed or formerly employed in the shoe trade.

WHAT IS NOT FUNDED No grants to individuals educational fees, exchange visits or gap year activities.

TYPE OF GRANT Mainly recurrent grants.

RANGE OF GRANTS £50–£30,000.

SAMPLE GRANTS Pioneer Community Club (£28,000); Whitworth Water Ski (£6,000); North West Air Ambulance and Bacup Family Centre (£5,000 each); Rossendale United Junior Football Club (£2,500); British Heart Foundation, Rossendale Search and Rescue and Heart of Lancashire appeal (£1,000 each); Rochdale Special Needs (£750); Macmillan Cancer Support and All Black Netball Fund (£500 each); Children with AIDS and SENSE (£250 each); and Sport Relief and Tenovus (£100).

FINANCES *Year* 2007–08 *Income* £59,557 *Grants* £98,989 *Assets* £1,102,465

TRUSTEES C C Harrison; A Connearn; G D Low; J Mellows; R D Uttley; K Duffy; S Holding.

HOW TO APPLY In writing only to the correspondent (no telephone calls allowed). To save on administration costs, unsuccessful applications will not be acknowledged even if an sae is provided.

WHO TO APPLY TO The Secretary to the Trustees, E Suttons and Sons, PO Box 2, Riverside, Bacup, Lancashire OL13 0DT

CC NO 265754   **ESTABLISHED** 1973

■ **The Florian Charitable Trust**

WHERE FUNDING CAN BE GIVEN UK.

WHO CAN BENEFIT Individuals and organisations.

WHAT IS FUNDED General charitable purposes – 'particular emphasis has been placed on funding specific projects, and where possible supporting those charities geographically local to one or more of the trustees, so there can be personal contact between a trustee and the charity benefited. The majority, but by no means all, of the donations have supported medical and allied charities, with a particular focus on those helping disabled children'.

RANGE OF GRANTS Around £1,000 to £3,000.

SAMPLE GRANTS The Addenbrooke's Charitable Trust, Alzheimers Research Trust, Arthritis Research Campaign, BIME, the Brain Research Trust, Deafness Research Trust, Epilepsy Research UK, The Migraine Trust, Meningitis

Research Campaign and Multiple Sclerosis Society (£3,000 each).

FINANCES *Year* 2007–08 *Income* £53,955 *Grants* £27,000 *Assets* £1,159,166

TRUSTEES V J Treasure; G A Treasure; R M G Thornely; S Treasure.

HOW TO APPLY In writing to the correspondent. The trustees meet bi-annually.

WHO TO APPLY TO Sarah Fraser, Thomas Eggar LLP, The Corn Exchange, Baffins Lane, Chichester, West Sussex PO19 1GE *email* sarah.fraser@thomaseggar.com

CC NO 1043523   **ESTABLISHED** 1995

■ **The Flow Foundation**

WHERE FUNDING CAN BE GIVEN UK.

WHO CAN BENEFIT Registered charities.

WHAT IS FUNDED The trust makes grants to support child welfare, education, environment, Jewish, and medical causes.

RANGE OF GRANTS Up to £20,000.

SAMPLE GRANTS Previous beneficiaries have included After Adoption, Brain Research Trust, British Friends of Haifa University, British ORT, Chicken Shed Theatre Company, Honey Pot Charity, International Centre for Child Studies, Jewish Care, Norwood, Royal Pharmaceutical Society, Tate Gallery Foundation, Toynbee Hall Foundation, Unite for the Future, Variety Club Children's Charity, Weizmann Institute Foundation and West London Synagogue.

FINANCES *Year* 2007–08 *Income* £19,861

TRUSTEES Mrs N Shashou; Mrs Nina Sowerbutts; H Woolf; Mrs J Woolf.

HOW TO APPLY In writing to the correspondent on one sheet of paper only.

WHO TO APPLY TO Mrs Nita Sowerbutts, Trustee, 22 Old Bond Street, London W1S 4PY *Tel* 020 7499 9099

CC NO 328274   **ESTABLISHED** 1989

■ **The Gerald Fogel Charitable Trust**

WHERE FUNDING CAN BE GIVEN UK.

WHO CAN BENEFIT Mainly headquarters organisations benefiting: children and older people, those in care, fostered and adopted, Jewish people and homeless people.

WHAT IS FUNDED Charities working in the fields of: the advancement of the Jewish religion; synagogues; and cultural and religious teaching. The trust may also fund residential facilities, arts activities, care in the community, hospices, hospitals, cancer research and campaigning on health issues.

WHAT IS NOT FUNDED No grants to individuals or non-registered charities.

TYPE OF GRANT One-off and recurrent.

SAMPLE GRANTS Chai Cancer Care (£12,000); Jewish Care (£10,000); Jewish Child's Day (£6,000); Nightingale House and Yad Vashem Foundation UK (£2,500 each); Alzheimers Society (£2,000); United Jewish Israel Appeal, London Jewish Cultural Centre and Oxfam (£1,000 each).

FINANCES *Year* 2007–08 *Income* £83,902 *Grants* £60,315 *Assets* £907,836

TRUSTEES J G Fogel; B Fogel; S Fogel; D Fogel.

HOW TO APPLY In writing to the correspondent.

WHO TO APPLY TO J Clay, Accountant, Morley and Scott, Lynton House, 7–12 Tavistock Square, London WC1H 9LT

CC NO 1004451   **ESTABLISHED** 1991

■ The Follett Trust

WHERE FUNDING CAN BE GIVEN UK and overseas, with a preference for Stevenage in the UK.

WHO CAN BENEFIT Individuals and organisations benefiting children and young adults, actors and entertainment professionals, musicians, textile workers and designers, writers and poets, at risk groups and people disadvantaged by poverty; medical research and hospital projects; people with disabilities.

WHAT IS FUNDED Education; individual students in higher education (including theatre); disability and health; trusts for writers and publishers; and international relief work.

RANGE OF GRANTS Usually up to £20,000.

SAMPLE GRANTS Canon Collins Trust (£21,000); Stevenage Citizens Advice Bureau (£14,000); Charities Aid Foundation, Dyslexia Action and Impilo Place of Safety (£10,000 each); Stevenage Community Trust (£7,000); National Campaign For The Arts (£5,000); MacMillan Cancer Relief (£3,400); Bedwell Community Centre (£3,000); Relate North Hertfordshire (£2,100); Stevenage Women's Resource Centre (£2,000); Stevenage Credit Union and International Medical Corps (£1,500 each); and Deafness Research, Tradecraft Exchange and One World Action (£1,000 each).

FINANCES *Year* 2008–09 *Income* £123,393 *Grants* £140,382 *Assets* £45,386

TRUSTEES Martin Follett; Ken Follett; Barbara Follett.

OTHER INFORMATION In 2008–09 the grant total included £7,200 given to individuals.

HOW TO APPLY The trust states: 'a high proportion of donees come to the attention of the trustees through personal knowledge and contact rather than by written application. Where the trustees find it impossible to make a donation they rarely respond to the applicant unless a stamped addressed envelope is provided'.

WHO TO APPLY TO M D Follett, Trustee, 17 Chescombe Road, Yatton, North Somerset BS49 4EE

CC NO 328638   **ESTABLISHED** 1990

■ The Football Association National Sports Centre Trust

WHERE FUNDING CAN BE GIVEN UK.

WHO CAN BENEFIT County football associations, football clubs and other sports associations.

WHAT IS FUNDED The provision, maintenance and improvement of facilities for use in recreational and leisure activities.

TYPE OF GRANT One-off grants towards community-based projects.

RANGE OF GRANTS £5,000–£25,000.

FINANCES *Year* 2007 *Income* £254,579 *Grants* £42,051 *Assets* £4,928,409

TRUSTEES G Thompson; W T Annable; R G Berridge; B W Bright; M M Armstrong.

HOW TO APPLY In writing to the correspondent.

WHO TO APPLY TO Mike Appleby, Secretary to the Trustees, 25 Soho Square, London W1D 4FA *Tel* 020 7745 4589 *Fax* 020 7745 5589 *email* mike.appleby@thefa.com

CC NO 265132   **ESTABLISHED** 1972

■ The Football Association Youth Trust

WHERE FUNDING CAN BE GIVEN UK.

WHO CAN BENEFIT County football associations, schools, universities and other sports associations benefiting young people who play football or other sports.

WHAT IS FUNDED The organisation or provision of facilities which will enable young people under the age of 21 in the UK to play association football or other games and sports including the provision of equipment, lectures, training colleges, playing fields or indoor accommodation.

TYPE OF GRANT One-off.

FINANCES *Year* 2007–08 *Income* £216,464 *Grants* £611,636 *Assets* £4,340,772

TRUSTEES Raymond G Berridge; Barry W Bright; Geoff Thompson; Jack Perks.

HOW TO APPLY In writing to the correspondent. Grants are made throughout the year. There are no application forms, but a copy of the most recent accounts should be sent.

WHO TO APPLY TO Mike Appleby, Secretary, Football Association Ltd, 25 Soho Square, London W1D 4FA *Tel* 020 7745 4589 *Fax* 020 7745 5589 *email* mike.appleby@thefa.com

CC NO 265131   **ESTABLISHED** 1972

■ The Football Foundation

WHERE FUNDING CAN BE GIVEN England.

WHO CAN BENEFIT Grass roots of football. It also funds educational and community projects.

WHAT IS FUNDED The grass roots advisory group works at an infrastructure level to deliver modern facilities in parks, local leagues and schools throughout the country. Local football partnerships have been established to ensure that all relevant groups have a voice in how football is delivered in their communities. The community and education panel aims to promote community and education initiatives and enhance football's role as a positive force in society.

FINANCES *Year* 2007–08 *Income* £67,706,000 *Grants* £82,133,000 *Assets* £5,422,000

TRUSTEES Richard Scudamore; Roger Burden; Peter McCormick; Philip Smith.

OTHER INFORMATION See the foundation's website for full details of the current schemes.

HOW TO APPLY Application forms and guidance notes are available on request directly from the foundation or downloadable from the website.

WHO TO APPLY TO Robert Booker, Director of Finance, 30 Gloucester Place, London W1U 8FF *Tel* 08453 454 555 *Fax* 08453 457 057 *email* enquiries@footballfoundation.org.uk *Website* www.footballfoundation.org.uk

CC NO 1079309   **ESTABLISHED** 2000

■ The Forbes Charitable Foundation

WHERE FUNDING CAN BE GIVEN UK.

WHO CAN BENEFIT Charities benefiting adults with learning disabilities.

WHAT IS FUNDED Welfare causes.

TYPE OF GRANT Capital rather than revenue projects.

RANGE OF GRANTS Usually up to £10,000.

SAMPLE GRANTS Orchard Trust and L'Arche – Inverness (£5,000 each); Scope and Acorn Services – North Yorkshire (£2,500 each); Brain and Spinal Injuries Centre and the Fircroft Trust

(£2,000 each); Break and the Norman Laud Association (£1,500 each); the Mayfield Trust (£1,250); Merseyside Tuesday and Thursday Clubs and Peter le Marchant Trust (£1,000 each); Cornerstone Community Care (£500); and Scope (£250).

FINANCES *Year* 2007–08 *Income* £89,654 *Grants* £37,900 *Assets* £2,310,848

TRUSTEES Col. R G Wilkes, Chair; Major Gen. R L S Green; I Johnson; J C V Lang; C G Packham; N J Townsend; J M Waite; R Warburton.

HOW TO APPLY In writing to the correspondent. Applications are considered in June and November.

WHO TO APPLY TO The Secretary to the Trustees, 9 Weir Road, Kibworth, Leicestershire LE8 0LQ

CC NO 326476   **ESTABLISHED** 1983

■ Forbesville Limited

WHERE FUNDING CAN BE GIVEN UK and overseas.

WHO CAN BENEFIT Children, young adults, students and Jewish people will be considered.

WHAT IS FUNDED Support for orthodox Jewish organisations, educational and charitable institutions.

FINANCES *Year* 2007 *Income* £20,451 *Grants* £38,000

TRUSTEES M Berger, Chair; Mrs J S Kritzler; D B Kritzler.

HOW TO APPLY In writing to the correspondent.

WHO TO APPLY TO M Berger, Chair, Holborn House, 219 Golders Green Road, London NW11 9DD *Tel* 020 8209 0355

CC NO 269898   **ESTABLISHED** 1975

■ The Forces Trust

WHERE FUNDING CAN BE GIVEN UK.

WHO CAN BENEFIT Registered military charities.

WHAT IS FUNDED Military charities. The trustees prefer to assist people (disabled, injured and disadvantaged) rather than institutions or the preservation of buildings.

WHAT IS NOT FUNDED No grants to any non-naval or military charities, individuals, scholarships or education generally.

TYPE OF GRANT Capital, one-off, project, research and recurring costs. Funding of up to two years.

RANGE OF GRANTS £500–£25,000, typically £2,500.

SAMPLE GRANTS British Limbless Ex-Service Men's Association (£16,000); St David's Nursing Home (£8,000); League of Remembrance (£5,000); Erskine Hospital and Sir Oswald Stoll Foundation (£4,000 each); Scottish National Institution for the War Blinded (£2,000); and SSAFA-Forces Help Cumbria and Gordon Highlanders London Association Benevolent Fund (£1,000 each).

FINANCES *Year* 2007–08 *Income* £51,749 *Grants* £40,944 *Assets* £1,086,954

TRUSTEES Col. A F Niekirk; Capt. A P C Niekirk; Lieu. Col. W D Niekirk; Brig. R E Nugee; B E V Bowater.

HOW TO APPLY In writing to the correspondent at any time, preferably on one side of A4.

WHO TO APPLY TO Col. A F Niekirk, Trustee, c/o Hunters, 9 New Square, London WC2A 3QN

CC NO 211529   **ESTABLISHED** 1924

■ Ford Britain Trust

WHERE FUNDING CAN BE GIVEN Local to the areas in close proximity to Ford Motor Company Limited's locations in the UK. These are Essex, East London, South Wales, Southampton, Daventry and Leamington Spa.

WHO CAN BENEFIT Organisations benefiting: children; young adults; older people; unemployed people; volunteers; at risk groups; carers; disabled people; people disadvantaged by poverty; ex-offenders and those at risk of offending; homeless people; and victims of crime, domestic violence and abuse.

WHAT IS FUNDED Currently the main areas of interest are children and young people (with emphasis on education, special needs children, youth organisations); community service; disability; social welfare; community arts and recreation; cultural heritage; accommodation and housing; respite care for carers; support and self-help groups; ambulances and mobile units; hospices; and social advice centres.

WHAT IS NOT FUNDED National charities are assisted rarely and then only when the purpose of their application has specific benefit to communities located in close proximity to Ford locations. Applications in respect of sponsorship, individuals, research, overseas projects, travel, religious or political projects are not eligible. Applications for core funding and/or salaries, revenue expenses, and major building projects are rarely considered.

TYPE OF GRANT Capital, buildings, one-off, and start-up costs. Funding is available for one year or less.

RANGE OF GRANTS Most grants range between £250 and £3,000.

SAMPLE GRANTS Thames Gateway Youth Football Programme, London Borough of Barking and Dagenham (£20,000); and West Billericay Community Association (£5,000).

FINANCES *Year* 2007–08 *Income* £171,502 *Grants* £136,660 *Assets* £186,708

TRUSTEES R M Blenkinsop; M J Brophy; M J Callaghan; J Calvert-Lee; S Dalvi; D S Russell; J L Tottingham.

HOW TO APPLY In writing to the correspondent. Applications should include the following: purpose of the project; whom it is intended to help and how; why the project is important and necessary (how things were done before); how the project is to be carried out; the project's proposed starting time and time of completion; total cost of the project; how much has been raised so far, sources of funding obtained and expected; examples of fundraising activities by the organisation for the project; the amount being asked for. A brief résumé of the background of the charity is appreciated. Where appropriate copies of accounts should be provided. Trustees meet in June and November each year. Applications are considered in order of receipt and it may take several months before an application is considered. The trust receives many more applications than it can help.

WHO TO APPLY TO Andy Taylor, Room 1/619, Ford Motor Company Limited, Eagle Way, Brentwood, Essex CM13 3BW *Tel* 01277 252551 *email* fbtrust@ford.com *Website* www.ford.co.uk/fbtrust

CC NO 269410   **ESTABLISHED** 1975

■ The Oliver Ford Charitable Trust

WHERE FUNDING CAN BE GIVEN UK.

WHO CAN BENEFIT Neighbourhood-based community projects, students and institutions. Children, young persons or adults who have learning disabilities or learning difficulties.

WHAT IS FUNDED The trust aims to educate the general public and advance knowledge of the history and techniques of interior decoration, the design of fabrics and other decorative materials and landscape gardening. Charities providing housing, educational or training facilities for children, young persons or adults who have learning disabilities or learning difficulties.

TYPE OF GRANT One-off.

RANGE OF GRANTS Usually up to £10,000.

SAMPLE GRANTS The Victoria and Albert Museum (£17,000); Mencap (£7,000); Fircroft Trust (£6,300); Fortune Centre of Riding Therapy, Norman Laud Association and Orchard Vale Trust (£5,000 each); Spadwork and Cornerstone Community Care (£3,000 each); Robert Owen Foundation (£2,300); Rose Road Association (£2,000); and the Furniture and History Society (£1,800).

FINANCES *Year* 2007–08 *Income* £99,251 *Grants* £70,879 *Assets* £2,480,716

TRUSTEES Derek Hayes; Lady Wakeham; Martin Levy.

OTHER INFORMATION Grants are given each year to students studying at the Victoria and Albert Museum (£17,000 in 2007–08).

HOW TO APPLY In writing to the correspondent. Trustees meet in March and October.

WHO TO APPLY TO Matthew Pintus, Macfarlanes, 10 Norwich Street, London EC4A 1BD *Tel* 020 7831 9222

CC NO 1026551   **ESTABLISHED** 1993

■ Fordeve Ltd

WHERE FUNDING CAN BE GIVEN UK.

WHO CAN BENEFIT Organisations benefiting Jews, at risk groups and people who are unemployed, disadvantaged by poverty or socially isolated. Support may also be given to people who are disabled, homeless, immigrants or refugees.

WHAT IS FUNDED Jewish causes and relief of need.

SAMPLE GRANTS Previous beneficiaries have included: the Gertner Charitable Trust; Lubavitch Foundation; the Yom Tov Assistance Fund; the Society of Friends of the Torah; Lolev Charitable Trust; Beth Jacob Grammar School for Girls.

FINANCES *Year* 2007–08 *Income* £435,000 *Grants* £278,011 *Assets* £735,229

TRUSTEES J Kon; Mrs H Kon.

HOW TO APPLY In writing to the correspondent.

WHO TO APPLY TO J Kon, Trustee, c/o Gerald Kreditor & Co, Hallswelle House, 1 Hallswelle Road, London NW11 0DH *Tel* 020 8209 1535

CC NO 1011612   **ESTABLISHED** 1992

■ The Forest Hill Charitable Trust

WHERE FUNDING CAN BE GIVEN UK and overseas.

WHO CAN BENEFIT Organisations and individuals.

WHAT IS FUNDED Christian causes.

RANGE OF GRANTS Grants usually range between £1,000 and £2,000.

SAMPLE GRANTS LINX – two individual grants (£21,000); Great Parks Chapel – four individual grants (£12,000); Viz-a-Viz – two individual grants (£6,000); Leprosy Mission, Prison Fellowship and Life for the World (£2,000 each);

Bible Network (£1,500); and Cambodian Trust, United Mission Nepal, Karen Hill Tribes Trust, World Villages Child and Farm Crisis Network (£1,000 each).

FINANCES *Year* 2007 *Income* £194,325 *Grants* £195,800 *Assets* £3,406,624

TRUSTEES H F Pile, Chair; Mrs P J Pile; R S Pile; Mrs M S Tapper; M Thomas.

HOW TO APPLY The trustees have previously stated that their aim was to maintain regular and consistent support to the charities they are currently supporting. New requests for funding are therefore very unlikely to succeed and unsolicited applications are rarely considered.

WHO TO APPLY TO Mrs P J Pile, Secretary to the Trustees, 104 Summercourt Way, Brixham, Devon TQ5 0RB *Tel* 01803 852857 *email* horacepile@tiscali.co.uk

CC NO 1050862   **ESTABLISHED** 1995

■ The Lady Forester Trust

WHERE FUNDING CAN BE GIVEN Shropshire.

WHO CAN BENEFIT Primarily, the residents of the Parish of Wenlock and then the inhabitants of the County of Shropshire.

WHAT IS FUNDED Residents who are sick, convalescent, disabled or infirm where help is not readily available to them from other sources.

RANGE OF GRANTS Up to £30,000.

SAMPLE GRANTS Friendly Transport Service (£25,000); County Air Ambulance Trust and Severn Hospice (£10,000 each); Pioneer Centre (£5,000); Community Foundation for Shropshire & Telford (£2,000); and Breast Cancer Haven and Down's Syndrome Association (£1,000 each).

FINANCES *Year* 2008 *Income* £160,535 *Grants* £103,693 *Assets* £3,399,201

TRUSTEES Lady Forester, Chair; Mrs Alice Stoker; Mrs Libby Collinson; John Simpson; John Michael Dugdale; Mrs Kathleen Mason; Henry Carpenter; Lord Forester.

OTHER INFORMATION The grant total included grants to individuals totalling £23497.

HOW TO APPLY Trustees meet on a quarterly basis to consider applications and will consider unsolicited applications. Grants for individuals are usually recommended by GPs or social workers. Application should be made in writing to the correspondent.

WHO TO APPLY TO Lady Forester, Chair, Willey Estates, The Estate Office, Willey Park, Willey, Broseley, Shropshire TF12 5JJ *Tel* 01952 882146 *Fax* 01952 883680

CC NO 241187   **ESTABLISHED** 1979

■ The Foresters' Fund for Children

WHERE FUNDING CAN BE GIVEN UK.

WHO CAN BENEFIT Non-profit-making organisations, charities and agencies.

WHAT IS FUNDED Projects related to improving the quality of life of children and for specific education needs.

SAMPLE GRANTS Childwatch and Gone Forever (£2,000 each); and Nottingham Police (£1,700).

FINANCES *Year* 2007–08 *Income* £53,921 *Grants* £26,728 *Assets* £77,224

TRUSTEES Tom Ball, Chair; Alex Clark; Darren Hanney; Jenna Cox.

HOW TO APPLY In writing to the correspondent, or via an application form available from the fund's website. Applications are considered by the trustees at their quarterly meetings.

Think carefully about every application. Is it justified?

527

WHO TO APPLY TO The Grants Secretary, PO Box 29429, Cumbernauld, Glasgow G67 9AL *Tel* 01236 736192 *email* grants@ forestersfundforchildren.org.uk *Website* www.forestersfundforchildren.org.uk
CC NO 327449   **ESTABLISHED** 1987

■ The Foresters' Charity Stewards UK Trust

WHERE FUNDING CAN BE GIVEN UK.
WHO CAN BENEFIT Individuals and institutions benefiting older people, disabled people and communities as a whole.
WHAT IS FUNDED To improve quality of life and the environment of the community at large.
TYPE OF GRANT One-off grants for capital and revenue costs.
RANGE OF GRANTS £50–£750.
SAMPLE GRANTS Previous beneficiaries have included: Abbeyfield, AOF Education Awards Fund, AOF Foresters' Home, AOF Yorkshire Convalescent Home, Mayor of Scarborough's Charity, North Middlesex Hospital, RNLI and Taste for Adventure.
FINANCES *Year* 2008 *Income* £31,414 *Grants* £20,000
TRUSTEES Graham D Lloyd; Barbara Lloyd; Rita Overington; Carole Shuttle; Derek Shuttle; Bill Runagall.
HOW TO APPLY In writing to the correspondent.
WHO TO APPLY TO Graham D Lloyd, Trustee, Littlecroft, 8 The Marches, Kingsfold, Horsham, West Sussex RH12 3SY
CC NO 328604   **ESTABLISHED** 1990

■ Gwyneth Forrester Trust

WHERE FUNDING CAN BE GIVEN England and Wales.
WHO CAN BENEFIT Charitable organisations.
WHAT IS FUNDED The trustees support a specific charitable sector each year. In 2009/10 the focus of the trust's grantmaking was strokes and heart disease.
WHAT IS NOT FUNDED No grants to individuals.
TYPE OF GRANT One-off.
SAMPLE GRANTS The Stroke Association and the British Heart Foundation (£100,000 each); and Cardiac Risk in the Young, CORDA, Different Strokes, Heart Research UK and Speakability (£50,000 each).
FINANCES *Year* 2008–09 *Income* £467,462 *Grants* £450,000 *Assets* £17,036,862
TRUSTEES Wendy J Forrester; Anthony J Smee; Michael B Jones; Christopher Perkins.
HOW TO APPLY The trust has previously stated that 'applications for aid cannot be considered'.
WHO TO APPLY TO Christopher Perkins, Trustee, Lancaster House, 7 Elmfield Road, Bromley, Kent BR1 1LT *Tel* 020 8461 8014
CC NO 1080921   **ESTABLISHED** 2000

■ The Donald Forrester Trust

WHERE FUNDING CAN BE GIVEN UK and overseas.
WHO CAN BENEFIT Charities benefiting people who are sick or disabled, particularly older people and children.
WHAT IS FUNDED Medical Welfare and Relief; Overseas; Children and young people; Old People's Welfare; Hospitals and Hospices; Physical Disability; Blind and Deaf; Community Care and Social Welfare; Medical Research; Animal and Bird Welfare, Services and Ex-

Services; Religious Organisations; Maritime, Mental Health; the Homeless; Arts, Culture and Sport; Environmental Heritage; Trades and Professions; Education.
WHAT IS NOT FUNDED No grants to individuals.
TYPE OF GRANT One off and recurrent.
RANGE OF GRANTS £5,000 to £15,000.
SAMPLE GRANTS Cambridge Foundation – to finance a Research Fellowship in the Department of Clinical Neurosciences, Cambridge University (£180,000 over three years); British Red Cross Flood Appeal (£20,000); Agents of Change, Canine Partners, Churcher's College 1722 Society and Rowans Hospice (£15,000 each); Barnardos, Camphill Village Trust, Children's Society, EIA Charitable Trust, Help for Heroes and Kenward Trust (£10,000 each); and Women's Royal Voluntary Service Trust, the Passage and Guideposts Trust (£5,000 each).
FINANCES *Year* 2007–08 *Income* £831,295 *Grants* £980,000 *Assets* £7,827,671
TRUSTEES Wendy J Forrester, Anthony J Smee; Michael B Jones; Hilary J Porter; Christopher A Perkins.
HOW TO APPLY The trust supports a substantial number of charities on a regular basis. We are informed that regrettably, detailed applications, which place 'an intolerable strain' on administrative resources, cannot be considered. It is suggested that very brief details of an application should be submitted to the correspondent on one side of A4. The trustees normally meet twice a year to consider and agree on the grants which are paid half yearly. There are no specific requirements under the trust deed and over the years the trustees have supported a wide range of national and international charities and endeavoured to achieve a balance between the large institutions and the smaller charities that experience greater difficulty in fund raising. The trustees have developed a fairly substantial list of charities that are supported on a regular basis, but new proposals, both regular and 'one-off' are considered at each meeting.
WHO TO APPLY TO Christopher A Perkins, Trustee, Lancaster House, 7 Elmfield Road, Bromley, Kent BR1 1LT *Tel* 020 8461 8014
CC NO 295833   **ESTABLISHED** 1986

■ The Anna Rosa Forster Charitable Trust

WHERE FUNDING CAN BE GIVEN Worldwide.
WHO CAN BENEFIT Charitable organisations.
WHAT IS FUNDED Medical research, animal welfare, famine relief.
RANGE OF GRANTS Usually between £2,500 and £3,500.
SAMPLE GRANTS Cats Protection League, the Dogs Trust, the Donkey Sanctuary, PDSA, Farm Africa, Oxfam, Feed the Children and CARE International UK (£3,400 each); and Prostate Research Campaign UK, British Cancer Research Trust, British Heart Foundation, International Spinal Research Trust, Arthritis Research Trust and Brain Research Trust (£2,700 each).
FINANCES *Year* 2007–08 *Income* £85,757 *Grants* £82,180 *Assets* £2,062,633
TRUSTEES R Napier; Mr A Morgan.
HOW TO APPLY In writing to the correspondent.
WHO TO APPLY TO R Napier, Trustee, Floor E, Milburn House, Dean Street, Newcastle upon Tyne NE1 1LF *Tel* 0191 230 1819
CC NO 1090028   **ESTABLISHED** 1996

■ The Forte Charitable Trust

WHERE FUNDING CAN BE GIVEN UK and overseas.

WHO CAN BENEFIT Community-based projects and national organisations and institutions.

WHAT IS FUNDED The Roman Catholic faith, Alzheimer's disease and senile dementia.

FINANCES *Year* 2007–08 *Income* £580 *Grants* £120,000

TRUSTEES Hon. Sir Rocco Forte; Hon. Mrs Olga Polizzi di Sorrentino; G F L Proctor; Lowndes Trustees Ltd.

OTHER INFORMATION Information was provided by the trust.

HOW TO APPLY In writing to the correspondent.

WHO TO APPLY TO Mrs Heather McConville, Lowndes House, Lowndes Place, London SW1X 8DB *Tel* 020 7235 6244 *email* hmcconville@ roccofortehotels.com

CC NO 326038   **ESTABLISHED** 1982

■ Lord Forte Foundation

WHERE FUNDING CAN BE GIVEN UK.

WHO CAN BENEFIT Educational establishments benefiting those carrying out research in the fields defined below.

WHAT IS FUNDED Educational establishments providing training courses or carrying out research in the field of hotel management and training, and the travel and tourism industries.

RANGE OF GRANTS Usually from £5,000 up to £30,000.

SAMPLE GRANTS Training for Life – the Hoxton Apprentice (£30,000); Thames Valley University (£10,000); and Leeds Thomas Danby, Llandrillo College, the Bournemouth and Poole College Foundation and Westminster Kingsway College (£5,000 each). U.

FINANCES *Year* 2007–08 *Income* £67,894 *Grants* £60,125 *Assets* £2,048,130

TRUSTEES Lord Janner, Chair; Hon Sir Rocco Forte; Hon. Mrs Olga Polizzi di Sorrentino; Viscount Montgomery of Alamein; G F L Proctor; T N Scade.

HOW TO APPLY In writing to the correspondent.

WHO TO APPLY TO Mrs Heather McConville, Lowndes House, Lowndes Place, Belgrave Square, London SW1X 8DB *Tel* 020 7235 6244 *email* hmcconville@roccofortecollection.com

CC NO 298100   **ESTABLISHED** 1987

■ Foundation for Management Education

WHERE FUNDING CAN BE GIVEN UK.

WHO CAN BENEFIT UK business schools and management studies departments benefiting young adults, older people and students.

WHAT IS FUNDED Improvement of quality and relevance of management education and development, by encouraging and supporting innovation in management education in the leading UK business schools and colleges; enhancing the supply and quality of management teachers; encouraging the development of research into management education and teaching methods; and supporting innovative developments in management education for managers operating within a highly competitive environment.

WHAT IS NOT FUNDED Individual applications for further studies cannot be supported.

FINANCES *Year* 2007–08 *Income* £390,794 *Grants* £706,028 *Assets* £365,837

TRUSTEES Geoffrey Armstrong; Valerie Boakes; Tim Boswell; Mary Chapman; Dr Charles Constable; Paula Graham; Prof. A G Hopwood; J L James; Robert Lintott; G C Olcott; David Thomas; C G C Vyvyan; Lord J E Tomlinson of Walsall; James Watson; John Wybrew.

HOW TO APPLY Unsolicited applications are not encouraged.

WHO TO APPLY TO The Director, TBAC Business Centre, Avenue Four, Station Lane, Witney OX28 4BN *Tel* 01993 848722 *email* fme@ lineone.net *Website* www. management-education.org.uk

CC NO 313388   **ESTABLISHED** 1960

■ Four Acre Trust

WHERE FUNDING CAN BE GIVEN Worldwide.

WHO CAN BENEFIT Charities benefiting at risk groups and carers, and people who are disadvantaged by poverty, disabled, homeless, socially isolated people or living in urban areas. There is a strong preference for groups benefiting young people.

WHAT IS FUNDED Mainly registered charities that provide a service to individuals, particularly for respite breaks and holidays; school holiday activity schemes; mentoring schemes; and youth work in local communities.

WHAT IS NOT FUNDED The trust does not support the following: advice services; advocacy; alcohol projects; animal welfare; applications from charities/organisations based abroad; arts; basic services (as opposed to imaginative new projects) for people with disabilities or older people; branches of national charities; commercial publications; conferences or seminars; counselling; direct replacement of statutory funding; drop-ins; drugs, HIV/AIDS projects; establishing funds for scholarships or loans; general appeals; heritage; individuals; IT training/projects; individual parish churches; large UK-charities which enjoy wide support, including local branches of UK-charities; medical (including research), general healthcare or costs of individual applicants; mental health care; overseas projects other than eye care and water provision; overseas travel, conference attendance or exchanges; performances, exhibitions or festivals; prisoner and offender projects; refugee projects; religious activities; research projects; school related projects; science; sports; stage, film or television production costs; and university or similar research. The trust does not pay off deficits or loans, replace withdrawn or reduced statutory funding or give grants retrospectively. Grants are not given towards any large capital, endowment or widely distributed appeal.

TYPE OF GRANT Provision of premises; project; capital; interest-free loans; repeat and one-off funding.

RANGE OF GRANTS £3,000–£105,000, mostly less than £5,000.

SAMPLE GRANTS Room to Read (£105,000); Visions for the Future (£77,000); International Childcare Trust (£71,000); Essex Assn Boys Club (£60,000); Tarabai Hospital (£53,000); Sight Savers (£48,000); Fostering Network (£33,000); Centre 63 Church of England Youth (£29,000); Whitehaven Harbour Project (£25,000); Let Us Play schemes (19,000); John Fawcett Foundation (£10,000); and Belfast Activity Centre (£7,500).

FINANCES *Year* 2007–08 *Income* £985,828 *Grants* £2,358,480 *Assets* £9,657,595

TRUSTEES Mary A Bothamley; John P Bothamley; Robert L Carruthers; Stephen Ratcliffe; Taymour Ezzat.

OTHER INFORMATION Around 25% of the trust's grant aid is given to charities that are registered in the UK but which operate abroad. Support in this area is currently focused on water and sanitation projects and eye care services.

HOW TO APPLY Application forms are available from the trust's website and should be submitted by email. Telephone calls prior to application are welcomed. The trustees meet in February, April, June, August, October and December. All applications are replied to, and are usually processed within three months. All applicants are visited by one of the trust's field officers to discuss how the trust may best offer support. A brief but full report is required on the outcome of the funding. Rejected lottery bids will be considered, but organisations are asked to telephone the trust to discuss the project before making an application. Please note: the trust always receives more applications than it has funds to support and even if a project fits the trust's policy priorities, it may not be possible to make a grant.

WHO TO APPLY TO June Horton, Trust Administrator, Treferanon, St Weonards, Hereford HR2 8QF *Tel* 01981 580 002 *email* info@fouracretrust. org.uk *Website* www.fouracretrust.org.uk

CC NO 1053884   **ESTABLISHED** 1996

■ The Four Winds Trust

WHERE FUNDING CAN BE GIVEN Worldwide.

WHO CAN BENEFIT Registered charities and people working in religion.

WHAT IS FUNDED Christian and overseas aid organisations, but grants are also given to retired evangelists and to missionaries and their dependants.

RANGE OF GRANTS Up to £4,500.

SAMPLE GRANTS Ashbury Free Church (£4,500); Counties Evangelistic Work (£3,000); Forest Hill Community Church (£1,500); Swindon Youth for Christ (£1,100).

FINANCES *Year* 2008–09 *Income* £68,491 *Grants* £36,113 *Assets* £610,037

TRUSTEES Philip Charters; Mary Charters; Peter John Charters; Simon Charters; Frances Charters.

OTHER INFORMATION The grant total includes grants made to individual evangelists and missionaries totalling £5,700.

HOW TO APPLY The trust was set up for purposes in which the trustees have a personal interest and the funds are earmarked for these purposes. Unsolicited requests are unlikely to be considered.

WHO TO APPLY TO Philip Charters, Trustee, Four Winds, Church Lane, Ashbury, Swindon SN6 8LZ *Tel* 01793 710431

CC NO 262524   **ESTABLISHED** 1971

■ The Fowler, Smith and Jones Charitable Trust

WHERE FUNDING CAN BE GIVEN Essex.

WHO CAN BENEFIT New grants limited to Essex-based projects.

WHAT IS FUNDED Churches, UK organisations, some overseas charities.

WHAT IS NOT FUNDED No grants to individuals.

TYPE OF GRANT One-off and limited recurrent grants.

RANGE OF GRANTS Most grants given up to £10,000.

SAMPLE GRANTS PARC (£70,000); First Site (£65,000); and Brentwood Theatre (£25,000); Special Needs and Parents Charity (£10,000); Depaul Trust (£5,000); Age Concern – Southend (£4,000); Maldon Mind and Hamelin Trust (£3,000 each); Salesian Convent Welfare Centre (£2,500); Maldon District CVS and Soundabout (£2,000 each); Lupus UK and Motor Neurone Disease (£1,500); and St Katherine's Little Bardfield (£1,000).

FINANCES *Year* 2007–08 *Income* £581,750 *Grants* £483,100 *Assets* £11,249,275

TRUSTEES P J Tolhurst, Chair; W J Tolhurst; E C Watson.

HOW TO APPLY In writing to the correspondent.

WHO TO APPLY TO Mrs A Mason, Secretary, c/o Tolhurst Fisher, Malbrough House, Victoria Road South, Chelmsford, Essex CM1 1LN *Tel* 01245 216123 *email* amason@tolhurstfisher.com

CC NO 259917   **ESTABLISHED** 1969

■ The Foyle Foundation

WHERE FUNDING CAN BE GIVEN UK.

WHO CAN BENEFIT Registered charities and state schools.

WHAT IS FUNDED Arts and learning.

WHAT IS NOT FUNDED No grants to individuals, organisations which are not registered charities or for international work. No retrospective funding.

RANGE OF GRANTS £10,000–£50,000.

SAMPLE GRANTS Royal National Theatre (£250,000); National Museums and Galleries of Northern Ireland (£150,000); Opera North and Leeds Grand Theatre Development Trust (£125,000); World Monuments Fund in Britain (£100,000); Cambridge Foundation (£75,000); Royal Aeronautical Society (£50,000); Yorkshire Sculpture Park (£40,000); Worcester Cathedral Development and Restoration Trust (£30,000); Friends of Colnbrook School and the Manchester Museum (£25,000 each); North of England Institute of Mining and Mechanical Engineers (£20,000); Cheltenham Festivals (£16,000); Children's Discovery Centre (£15,000); Oxford Centre for Hebrew and Jewish Studies (£14,000); Swaffham Museum Limited (£12,000); and Northern Actors Centre and Scottish Borders Community Orchestra (£10,000 each).

FINANCES *Year* 2007–08 *Income* £3,763,343 *Grants* £5,151,250 *Assets* £68,461,581

TRUSTEES Michael Smith; Kathryn Skoyles; Sir Peter Duffell.

HOW TO APPLY 'All applicants should complete and return the Main Grants Scheme application form together with supporting information. Applicants should provide additional information, where relevant, as detailed in the Supplementary Information and Building Project Checklists (below). The application form and documentation is to be sent to [the correspondent]. Applications are accepted all year round. We have no deadlines. Except for capital projects, it may take up to four months, occasionally longer, to receive a decision from the trustees, so apply well in advance. Please note that competition is intense; we receive many more applications than we are able to fund.

Capital Projects

Please note for capital projects seeking more than £50,000 the foundation will now only consider these twice a year in the spring and autumn. Therefore it could be up to six months before we take a decision on your project. It is expected that all applications will be acknowledged within two weeks including applications which do not qualify for consideration which will be rejected. The Chief Executive may wish to discuss the application, request further information and visit the applicant, in order to appraise the application before it is presented to trustees. The Chief Executive will report to the trustees at the first available meeting and will notify the applicant of the trustees' decision.

Supplementary Information – c*hecklist of supplementary information where an application is submitted for a specific project (including building projects), to be provided in addition to the Main Grants Scheme application form* Applicants should submit a summary covering the following points: name of project; description of the project or funding request; why the project is needed; when the project will start; how long the project will take; how many people will benefit from/participate in the project; total cost of project (please provide a project budget); amount of grant sought; when the funding is required; amount to be raised from other sources (if applicable) and how will this be raised; will the project proceed without funding from the foundation?; how will the project/service be sustainable in the future (if ongoing)?; who will manage the project from within the organisation; how will the project be monitored and evaluated and how and when would progress reports be provided to the foundation (if required).

Additional Information – Building Projects –*the following issues should be addressed and summarised: i*f your project is one phase of a larger project then please provide a summary of the cost, aims and timescales of the entire project, as part of the context for your application; to what level of the RIBA design stages has the project progressed? Please note that usually we will not accept an application if the design has not reached RIBA Stage D; has the project obtained outline, or full, planning permission and listed building consent (if relevant)?; please detail the indicative project timescale from start to completion; has a robust project budget including contingency been allowed for? (please provide details). Please demonstrate why you consider that your contingency budget is sufficient; what risk factors have been considered and how will these be minimised?; has a realistic strategy/timescale for raising the project funding been devised?; please describe your project management structure and state why this is considered adequate; has a professional technical team been recruited? How were they chosen? Were EU procurement regulations followed? If not, why not?; who are or will be *(if known),*the architects and technical team, the project managers and the main contractors. New building projects should also provide an outline business plan, including income/expenditure projections.'

WHO TO APPLY TO David Hall, Chief Executive, Rugby Chambers, 2 Rugby Street, London WC1N 3QU *Tel* 020 7430 9119 *Fax* 020 7430 9830 *email* info@foylefoundation.org.uk *Website* www.foylefoundation.org.uk
CC NO 1081766   **ESTABLISHED** 2000

■ The Isaac and Freda Frankel Memorial Charitable Trust

WHERE FUNDING CAN BE GIVEN UK and overseas, particularly Israel.
WHO CAN BENEFIT Established organisations benefiting children, young adults and people disadvantaged by poverty. People of many different religions and cultures will be funded, but preference is given to Jewish people.
WHAT IS FUNDED Jewish charities, medicine and health, education, religion and the relief of poverty.
WHAT IS NOT FUNDED No grants to individuals or students, for expeditions or scholarships.
TYPE OF GRANT One-off and recurrent grants.
RANGE OF GRANTS £1,000 or less.
FINANCES *Year* 2007–08 *Income* £107,754 *Grants* £133,507 *Assets* £535,914
TRUSTEES M D Frankel; G Frankel; J Steinhaus; J Silkin.
HOW TO APPLY In writing to the correspondent.
WHO TO APPLY TO M D Frankel, Secretary, 33 Welbeck Street, London W1G 8LX *Tel* 020 7872 0023
CC NO 1003732   **ESTABLISHED** 1991

■ Sydney E Franklin Deceased's New Second Charity

WHERE FUNDING CAN BE GIVEN Worldwide. Priority, but not exclusively, to developing world projects.
WHO CAN BENEFIT Smaller charities with low overheads dealing with developing world self-help projects or endangered species. Funding may be given to people disadvantaged by poverty and victims of famine, man-made or natural disasters and war.
WHAT IS FUNDED Mainly small charities with low overheads; focusing on developing world self-help projects, endangered species and people disadvantaged by poverty.
TYPE OF GRANT One-off and project grants.
RANGE OF GRANTS Typical grant £500–£3,000.
SAMPLE GRANTS Previous beneficiaries have included: Kerala Federation for the Blind; Water for Kids; Narwhal/Niaff; United Charities Fund; Ashram International, Books Abroad, Children of the Andes, Kaloko Trust, Microloan Foundation, Tools for Self Reliance, Tree Aid and Window for Peace UK.
FINANCES *Year* 2007–08 *Income* £26,316 *Grants* £35,500 *Assets* £540,835
TRUSTEES Dr R C G Franklin; Ms T N Franklin; Ms C Holliday.
HOW TO APPLY Donations may only be requested by letter, including a copy of latest accounts, and these are placed before the trustees at their meeting which is normally held at the end of each year. Applications are not acknowledged.
WHO TO APPLY TO Dr R C G Franklin, Trustee, c/o 39 Westleigh Avenue, London SW15 6RQ
CC NO 272047   **ESTABLISHED** 1973

■ The Jill Franklin Trust

WHERE FUNDING CAN BE GIVEN Worldwide.
WHO CAN BENEFIT Charitable organisations, not necessarily registered charities, benefiting: disabled people; carers; ex-offenders and those at risk of offending; people with a mental illness; refugees and asylum-seekers.
WHAT IS FUNDED Current concerns are: self-help groups, advice, training, and employment; to support people with a mental illness or learning

Think carefully about every application. Is it justified?

531

difficulties, and their carers (parents etc); respite care, and holidays in the UK only (grants for holidays are only given where there is a large element of respite care and only to registered charities, not to individuals); organisations helping and supporting refugees and asylum-seekers coming to or in the UK; the restoration (not 'improvement') of churches of architectural importance (half a page in Pevsner's *Buildings*) and occasionally to other buildings of architectural importance (the church should be open to visitors every day).

WHAT IS NOT FUNDED Grants are not given to: appeals for building work; endowment funds; branches of a national organisations, and to the centre itself (unless it is a specific grant, probably for training in the branches); replace the duties of government, local authorities or the NHS; encourage the 'contract culture', particularly where authorities are not funding the contract adequately; religious organisations set up for welfare, education etc. of whatever religion, unless the service is open to and used by people from all denominations; overseas projects; 'heritage schemes' animal charities; students, nor to any individuals nor for overseas travel; medical research.

TYPE OF GRANT One-off, project, recurring costs, running costs and start-up costs. Funding for up to three years will be considered.

RANGE OF GRANTS Typically £500–£1,000.

SAMPLE GRANTS Camden City Islington & Westminster Bereavement Services (£10,000); Prisoners Education Trust (£8,800); Marie Curie Cancer Cure (£5,600); Princess Royal Trust for Carers (£5,000); Buildings Book Trust (£3,000); Woodland Trust (£2,000); and Powerhouse; Medical Foundation for Victims of Torture; North Somerset Crossroads Carers; and Respite Association (£1,000 each).

FINANCES *Year* 2007–08 *Income* £78,445 *Grants* £65,532 *Assets* £1,621,592

TRUSTEES Andrew Franklin; Norman Franklin; Sally Franklin; Sam Franklin; Tom Franklin.

HOW TO APPLY In writing to the correspondent, enclosing a copy of the latest annual report and accounts and a budget for the project. Organisations based outside the UK should provide the name, address and telephone number of a correspondent or referee in the UK. 'The trustees tend to look more favourably on an appeal which is simply and economically prepared: glossy, 'prestige' and mail sorted brochures do not impress the trustees.' Unsolicited enquiries are not usually acknowledged. 'We have very little uncommitted cash, and so most applications are rejected, for the only reason that we have insufficient money.'

WHO TO APPLY TO N Franklin, Trustee, Flat 5, 17–19 Elsworthy Road, London NW3 3DS *Tel* 020 7722 4543 *email* info@jill-franklin-trust.org.uk *Website* www.jill-franklin-trust.org.uk

CC NO 1000175   **ESTABLISHED** 1988

····································

■ The Gordon Fraser Charitable Trust

WHERE FUNDING CAN BE GIVEN UK, with a preference for Scotland.

WHO CAN BENEFIT Registered charities.

WHAT IS FUNDED At present the trustees are particularly interested in help for children and young people, the environment and in assisting organisations associated with the arts. Other charitable purposes will also be considered.

WHAT IS NOT FUNDED No grants are made to organisations which are not recognised charities, or to individuals.

TYPE OF GRANT Grants are usually one-off, though funding for up to three years may be considered.

RANGE OF GRANTS £100–£12,000, typical grant £250–£750.

SAMPLE GRANTS Ballet West (£9,000); the MacRoberts Arts Centre (£7,000); the Aberlour Child Care Trust and Scottish Museums Council (£6,000 each); Scottish International Piano Competition (£5,500); Mull Theatre (£3,000); KilMartin House Trust and National Library of Scotland (£2,000 each); Paisley Festival Company, the Hebridean Trust and Sense Scotland (£1,000 each).

FINANCES *Year* 2007–08 *Income* £239,144 *Grants* £134,700 *Assets* £2,853,932

TRUSTEES Mrs Margaret A Moss; William F T Anderson.

HOW TO APPLY In writing to the correspondent. Applications are considered in January, April, July and October. Grants towards national or international emergencies can be considered at any time. All applicants are acknowledged; an sae would, therefore, be appreciated.

WHO TO APPLY TO Mrs Margaret A Moss, Trustee, Holmhurst, Westerton Drive, Bridge of Allan, Stirling FK9 4QL

CC NO 260869   **ESTABLISHED** 1966

····································

■ The Hugh Fraser Foundation

WHERE FUNDING CAN BE GIVEN UK, especially western or deprived areas of Scotland.

WHO CAN BENEFIT Registered charities working in many different sectors principally hospitals, schools and universities, arts organisations and organisations working with the handicapped, the underprivileged and the aged.

WHAT IS FUNDED Medical facilities and research; relief of poverty and assistance for older and infirm people; education and learning; provision of better opportunities for people who are disadvantaged; music and the arts; encouragement of personal development and training of young people.

WHAT IS NOT FUNDED Grants are not usually awarded to individuals.

TYPE OF GRANT Capital and revenue grants for up to three years, sometimes longer. Start-up costs.

RANGE OF GRANTS Up to £100,000.

SAMPLE GRANTS Previous beneficiaries include Scottish Science Trust and Capability Scotland.

FINANCES *Year* 2007–08 *Income* £4,923,376 *Grants* £813,840 *Assets* £51,857,761

TRUSTEES Dr Kenneth Chrystie; Belinda Ann Hanson; Patricia Fraser; Blair Smith.

OTHER INFORMATION Note: the Hugh Fraser Foundation has recently merged with the Emily Fraser Trust, a related charity. As a result the trustees will, in exceptional circumstances, also help individuals and the dependents of individuals who were or are engaged in the drapery and allied trades and the printing, publishing, books and stationary, newspaper and allied trades in the UK.

HOW TO APPLY In writing to the correspondent. The trustees meet on a quarterly basis to consider applications.

WHO TO APPLY TO Katrina Muir, Trust Administrator, Turcan Connell WS, Princes Exchange, 1 Earl Grey Street, Edinburgh EH3 9EE *Tel* 0131 228 8111

SC NO SC009303   **ESTABLISHED** 1960

■ The Joseph Strong Frazer Trust

WHERE FUNDING CAN BE GIVEN Unrestricted, in practice, England and Wales.

WHO CAN BENEFIT Registered charities only.

WHAT IS FUNDED General charitable purposes, with broad interests in the fields of medical and other research, social welfare, people with disabilities, children, hospitals, education, maritime, young people, religion and wildlife.

WHAT IS NOT FUNDED No grants to individuals.

TYPE OF GRANT One-off, capital and recurring costs.

SAMPLE GRANTS Alzheimer's Society and Royal National Institute for the Deaf (£5,500 each); Cancer Research – Wales and Covent Garden Cancer Research Trust (£5,000 each); Barnet Bereavement Project and the Prisoners' Education Trust (£4,000 each); and Arthritis Research Campaign and St Mungo Association (£3,000 each).

FINANCES *Year* 2007–08 *Income* £506,785 *Grants* £590,330 *Assets* £11,628,689

TRUSTEES Sir William A Reardon Smith, Chair; David A Cook; R M H Read; William N H Reardon Smith; William I Waites.

HOW TO APPLY In writing to the correspondent. Trustees meet twice a year, usually in March and September. Application forms are not necessary. It is helpful if applicants are concise in their appeal letters, which must include an sae if acknowledgement is required.

WHO TO APPLY TO The Trustees, Floor A, Milburn House, Dean Street, Newcastle upon Tyne NE1 1LE *Tel* 0191 232 8065 *Fax* 0191 222 1554 *email* uf@joseph-miller.co.uk

CC NO 235311   **ESTABLISHED** 1939

■ The Louis and Valerie Freedman Charitable Settlement

WHERE FUNDING CAN BE GIVEN UK, especially Buckinghamshire.

WHO CAN BENEFIT National and local (Burnham in Buckinghamshire) charities.

WHAT IS FUNDED Health, welfare and equine interests in which the Freedman family have a particular interest. Local education and youth charities are also supported.

WHAT IS NOT FUNDED No grants to individuals. Only registered charities are considered for support.

RANGE OF GRANTS Usually around £5,000 to £10,000.

SAMPLE GRANTS Burnham Health Promotion Trust (£50,000); Tavistock Aphasia Tryst, Prostate Research Campaign UK, British Heart Foundation, and Blakebrook School (£10,000 each); and Vitalise (£5,000 each).

FINANCES *Year* 2007–08 *Income* £143,027 *Grants* £95,000 *Assets* £3,798,534

TRUSTEES M A G Ferrier; F H Hughes.

HOW TO APPLY There is no application form. Applications should be in writing to the correspondent and they will not be acknowledged. Notification of a failed application will only be given if a sae is enclosed.

WHO TO APPLY TO F H Hughes, Trustee, c/o Bridge House, 11 Creek Road, East Molesey, Surrey KT8 9BE

CC NO 271067   **ESTABLISHED** 1976

■ The Freemasons' Grand Charity

WHERE FUNDING CAN BE GIVEN England, Wales and overseas.

WHO CAN BENEFIT Charities benefiting freemasons and their dependants; medical research, hospices and other charities concerned with general welfare especially of young and older people and overseas emergency aid.

WHAT IS FUNDED Consideration is only given to charities whose work covers the whole of England and Wales; London charities (no other local charities should apply); freemasons of the United Grand Lodge of England, their widows and certain other dependants; hospices; social welfare organisations, organisations supporting vulnerable people including the young and older people, medical research and emergency aid.

WHAT IS NOT FUNDED Those not eligible for a grant are: individuals (other than for the relief of 'poor and distressed freemasons and their poor and distressed dependants'); charities that serve an individual region or city, for example, a regional hospital, local church, day centre or primary school; organisations not registered with the Charity Commission, except some exempt charities; activities that are primarily the responsibility of central or local government or some other responsible body; organisations or projects outside of England and Wales; and charities that are deemed to hold funds in excess of their requirements. Grants are not normally given to: activities that are primarily the responsibility of central or local government; animal welfare; arts; capital building costs; environment; organisations with political objectives.

RANGE OF GRANTS £500–£500,000.

SAMPLE GRANTS Ovarian Cancer Action (£1 million over five years); The Scout Association (£500,000 over five years); SSAFA (£100,000); Deafness Research UK (£83,000); RNLI (£72,000); Epilepsy Research UK (£25,000); British Red Cross (£20,000).

FINANCES *Year* 2007–08 *Income* £15,838,100 *Grants* £3,881,900 *Assets* £57,484,100

TRUSTEES The council, consisting of the president, deputy president, vice president, and 30 council members, listed in the annual reports.

PUBLICATIONS Booklet, *Information on Masonic Charities.*

HOW TO APPLY Application forms are available from the charity's office or from its website. This form must be completed in full accompanied by a copy of the latest annual report and full audited accounts; these must be less than 18 months old. Hospice grant applications are made on a separate form, available from either the appropriate provincial grand lodge (listed in telephone directories, usually under 'freemasons' or 'masons') or the trust's office. Applications may be submitted at any time throughout the year. Applications are not accepted for 'emergency grants' which are made as 'the need arises' and at the trustees' discretion.

WHO TO APPLY TO Ms Laura Chapman, Chief Executive, 60 Great Queen Street, London WC2B 5AZ *Tel* 020 7395 9261 *Fax* 020 7395 9295 *email* info@the-grand-charity.org *Website* www.grandcharity.org

CC NO 281942   **ESTABLISHED** 1980

■ The Thomas Freke and Lady Norton Charity

WHERE FUNDING CAN BE GIVEN Only within the parishes of Hannington, Inglesham, Highworth, Stanton Fitzwarren, Blunsdon St Leonards and Castle Eaton.

WHO CAN BENEFIT Local communities and organisations benefiting children, young adults and Christians.

WHAT IS FUNDED Buildings or equipment for churches, schools, youth and community facilities. The trust is willing to consider emergency or unforeseen expenditure. Funding may also be given to community centres, village halls, recreation grounds and sports centres.

WHAT IS NOT FUNDED No grants are given for ordinary running expenses. No applications from outside the beneficial area can be considered.

TYPE OF GRANT Capital.

FINANCES *Year* 2007–08 *Income* £99,373 *Grants* £75,941 *Assets* £3,297,871

TRUSTEES Mrs Lorna Wallace; Mrs Valerie J Davies; Dr Keith T Scholes; John M E Scott; Edwin R Cole.

HOW TO APPLY In writing to the correspondent for help with capital projects such as building improvements development or, provision of specialist equipment. Clear outline details of the project and accurate estimated costs are required. Trustees meet four times a year to consider applications. The correspondent has previously stated that: 'There have been many applications from outside the beneficial area that cannot be supported.'

WHO TO APPLY TO Barry T Compton, Clerk, 23 Chedworth Gate, Broome Manor, Swindon SN3 1NE *email* barry.compton@btinternet.com

CC NO 200824   **ESTABLISHED** 1990

■ The Charles S French Charitable Trust

WHERE FUNDING CAN BE GIVEN North east London and south west Essex.

WHO CAN BENEFIT Registered charities.

WHAT IS FUNDED General charitable purposes, including community services and facilities.

WHAT IS NOT FUNDED Only registered charities are supported.

RANGE OF GRANTS £1,000–£10,000.

SAMPLE GRANTS Chigwell School Astroturf (£15,000); St Mary's Laughton (£10,000); Essex Yeomanry (£5,000); CREST, Laughton Youth and Marie Curie Cancer Care (£3,000 each); Glass Sellers Charity Fund and the Worshipful Company of Actuaries Charitable Fund (£2,500 each); Homerton Hospital, Open Road Colchester, Richard House Children's Hospice and Vitalise (£2,000 each); Michael Roberts Charitable Trust (£1,500); and Calvert Trust, Kings Cross Homelessness and Quaker Social Action (£1,000 each);.

FINANCES *Year* 2007–08 *Income* £261,008 *Grants* £154,703 *Assets* £7,469,196

TRUSTEES W F Noble; M P W Scarth; J Thomas; R Foster.

HOW TO APPLY In writing to the correspondent, including a copy of the latest accounts. The trustees meet four times a year. The trust invites applications for grants and donations from local charities and these applications are reviewed against the trust's objects, with grants and donations being awarded at the trustee's discretion.

WHO TO APPLY TO W F Noble, Trustee, 169 High Road, Loughton, Essex IG10 4LF *email* csfct@waitrose.com

CC NO 206476   **ESTABLISHED** 1959

■ The Anne French Memorial Trust

WHERE FUNDING CAN BE GIVEN Diocese of Norwich (Norfolk and north Suffolk).

WHO CAN BENEFIT Christians, clergy and local charities.

WHAT IS FUNDED Any charitable purpose in the beneficial area, especially church-related causes.

TYPE OF GRANT One-off, project, research and feasibility.

RANGE OF GRANTS Up to £15,000.

FINANCES *Year* 2007–08 *Income* £155,132 *Grants* £237,225 *Assets* £5,662,230

TRUSTEES Lord Bishop of Norwich.

HOW TO APPLY The trust states that 'under no circumstances does the Bishop wish to encourage applications for grants.'

WHO TO APPLY TO C H Dicker, c/o Lovewell Blake, Sixty Six, North Quay, Great Yarmouth, Norfolk NR30 1HE

CC NO 254567   **ESTABLISHED** 1963

■ The Freshfield Foundation

WHERE FUNDING CAN BE GIVEN UK.

WHAT IS FUNDED Environment, climate change and, to a less extent, healthcare.

SAMPLE GRANTS Friends of the Earth (£80,000); Sustrans (£70,000); New Economics Foundation (£55,000); Forestry Stewardship Council (£50,000); Osteopathic Centre for Children (£40,000); Centre for Tomorrow's Company (£35,000); Transport 2000 Trust and Cambridge University (£30,000 each); Soil Association (£20,000); Cree Valley Community Woodland Trust (£15,000); Global Canopy Foundation (£10,000); and the Ecology Trust (£3,000).

FINANCES *Year* 2007–08 *Income* £205,244 *Grants* £438,000 *Assets* £6,173,700

TRUSTEES Paul Kurthausen; Patrick A Moores; Mrs Elizabeth J Potter.

HOW TO APPLY In writing to the correspondent, although the trust states that 'the process of grant making starts with the trustees analysing an area of interest, consistent with the charity's aims and objectives, and then proactively looking for charities that they think can make the greatest contribution'. With this in mind, a letter of introduction to your organisation's work may be more appropriate than a formal application for funding.

WHO TO APPLY TO Paul Kurthausen, Trustee, 2nd Floor, MacFarlane and Co., Cunard Building, Water Street, Liverpool L3 1DS *Tel* 0151 236 6161 *Fax* 0151 236 1095 *email* paulk@macca.co.uk

CC NO 1003316   **ESTABLISHED** 1991

■ The Freshgate Trust Foundation

WHERE FUNDING CAN BE GIVEN Mainly Sheffield and South Yorkshire.

WHO CAN BENEFIT Organisations benefiting: people of all ages; actors and entertainment professionals; musicians; textile workers and designers; writers and poets; at risk groups; people disadvantaged by poverty and socially isolated people. Both innovatory and established bodies may be considered.

WHAT IS FUNDED Local appeals working in the fields of: education (including travel and training); medical (both psychological and physical); recreation; music and arts; welfare and social care; heritage.

WHAT IS NOT FUNDED The trust restricts its grants to UK charitable organisations and does not deal with applications from individuals, national appeals or for church fabric unless used for a wider community purpose.

TYPE OF GRANT Capital (including buildings), core costs, endowments, feasibility studies, interest free loans, one-off, project, research, running costs, recurring costs, salaries and start-up costs. Funding for up to three years will be considered.

FINANCES *Year* 2008 *Income* £127,497 *Grants* £89,525 *Assets* £2,300,909

TRUSTEES J F B Hopkins; J E Parkin; Miss E Murray; D R Stone; Dr F W Wright; J C Mould; Mrs V A Linnemann; Ms H Dobson; P Else; U Fitch.

HOW TO APPLY In writing to the correspondent, by early February, June and October each year. Applications are not normally acknowledged.

WHO TO APPLY TO Jonathan Robinson, Secretary, The Hart Shaw Building, Europa Link, Sheffield Business Park, Sheffield, South Yorkshire S91 1XU *Tel* 0114 251 8850 *Fax* 0114 251 8851

CC NO 221467   **ESTABLISHED** 1962

■ The Friarsgate Trust

WHERE FUNDING CAN BE GIVEN UK, with a strong preference for West Sussex, especially Chichester.

WHO CAN BENEFIT UK and East and West Sussex organisations, especially those already supported by the trust.

WHAT IS FUNDED General charitable purposes, especially education and welfare of children and young people and care of older people and those in need.

WHAT IS NOT FUNDED Local organisations outside Sussex are unlikely to be supported.

RANGE OF GRANTS Up to £20,000, with most grants ranging between £500–£2,000.

SAMPLE GRANTS West Sussex Association for Disabled People (£18,000); 12th Chichester Scout Group (£8,000); and Chichester Youth Adventure Trust (£5,200); Christian Care Association, Fernhurst Youth Club and Chichester Community Transport (£2,000 each); Samaritans (£1,500); Remix Project and Impact Initiative (£1,100 each); The Dystonia Society, Independent Age and Southbourne Sea Scout Group (£1,000 each); and Farms for City Children, the National Society for Epilepsy and East Sussex Association for the Blind (£500 each).

FINANCES *Year* 2007–08 *Income* £107,527 *Grants* £71,465 *Assets* £3,055,394

TRUSTEES A C Colenutt; T J Bastow; Mrs V Higgins.

HOW TO APPLY In writing to the correspondent. Applicants are welcome to telephone first to check they fit the trust's criteria.

WHO TO APPLY TO Miss Amanda King-Jones, The Corn Exchange, Baffins Lane, Chichester, West Sussex Po19 1GE *Tel* 01243 786111 *Fax* 01243 775640

CC NO 220762   **ESTABLISHED** 1955

■ The Friends Hall Farm Street Trust

WHERE FUNDING CAN BE GIVEN Birmingham and district.

WHO CAN BENEFIT Charitable organisations.

WHAT IS FUNDED Religion and education, primarily Quaker concerns.

WHAT IS NOT FUNDED Applications from outside the beneficial area cannot be considered.

FINANCES *Year* 2007–08 *Income* £15,372

TRUSTEES Eric Adams; John Bodycote; Roger Gough; Mary Goodyear; Barbara Richardson.

HOW TO APPLY In writing to the correspondent. Applications should be submitted between March and October for consideration in October/November. Ineligible applications will not receive a reply.

WHO TO APPLY TO Eric Adams, Trustee, 36 Grove Avenue, Moseley, Birmingham B13 9RY

CC NO 209818   **ESTABLISHED** 1893

■ Friends of Biala Ltd

WHERE FUNDING CAN BE GIVEN UK and overseas.

WHO CAN BENEFIT Jewish organisations and registered charities.

WHAT IS FUNDED Religious institutions of the orthodox Jewish faith, and the relief of poverty.

SAMPLE GRANTS Friends of Biala Israel (£227,000); Aguda Hadadit (£100,000); Yeshiva Beis Ephraim (£49,000); Gemach Ezra Hadadit (£27,000); and Freebee Foundation Limited (£10,000).

FINANCES *Year* 2007–08 *Income* £426,004 *Grants* £413,374 *Assets* £3,179,313

TRUSTEES B Z Rabinovitch; Mrs T Weinberg.

HOW TO APPLY In writing to the correspondent.

WHO TO APPLY TO The Secretary, c/o Sugarwhite Associates, 5 Windus Road, London N16 6UT

CC NO 271377   **ESTABLISHED** 1964

■ Friends of Boyan Trust

WHERE FUNDING CAN BE GIVEN Worldwide.

WHO CAN BENEFIT Orthodox Jews.

WHAT IS FUNDED Jewish causes.

SAMPLE GRANTS Gomlei Chesed of Chasidei Boyan (£84,000); Mosdot Tiferet Yisroel Boyan (£31,000); Kimcha De'Pischa Boyan (£21,000); Kimcha De'Pischa Beitar Ilit (£13,000); Chevras Mo'oz Ladol (£12,000); Kolel Avrechim Boyan, Betar Ilit (£6,000); Ezer Mikoidesh Foundation (£2,000); Beis Rizhin Trust (£1,500); and Yad Vochessed (£1,000).

FINANCES *Year* 2007 *Income* £209,085 *Grants* £206,920 *Assets* £6,553

TRUSTEES J Getter; M Freund; N Kuflik.

HOW TO APPLY In writing to the correspondent.

WHO TO APPLY TO Jacob Getter, Trustee, 23 Durley Road, London N16 5JW *Tel* 020 8809 6051

CC NO 1114498   **ESTABLISHED** 2006

■ The Friends of Kent Churches

WHERE FUNDING CAN BE GIVEN County of Kent, particularly the dioceses of Canterbury and Rochester.

WHO CAN BENEFIT Churches of architectural merit and historical interest.

WHAT IS FUNDED The upkeep of their fabric and the preservation of fixtures of importance.

WHAT IS NOT FUNDED No grants for reordering, new extensions, toilets and kitchens; heating, redecorating and rewiring; bells, clocks and organs.

TYPE OF GRANT Building. Interest-free loans are considered.

RANGE OF GRANTS £250–£20,000.

SAMPLE GRANTS All Saints – Snodland (£13,000); St Nicholas – St Nicholas at Wade (£10,000); St Giles – Shipbourne (£8,000); St Mildred – Tenterden (£7,000); St Mary – Riverhead (£3,000); St Mary – Stelling (£2,000); URC – Staplehurst (£500); and Victoria Road Baptist – Deal (£300).

FINANCES *Year* 2008 *Income* £198,399 *Grants* £154,800 *Assets* £462,026

TRUSTEES Charles Banks; Charles Oliver; Margaret Prevett; The Hon Jennifer Raikes; Paul Smallwood; Angela Parish; Leslie Smith; William Wells; Nigel Whitehead; Richard Latham; Jane Boucher; Mary Colvile.

HOW TO APPLY In writing to the correspondent.

WHO TO APPLY TO Marion Hanbury, The Old Rectory, Ruckinge, Ashford, Kent TN26 2PE *Tel* 01233 732328 *Website* www.friendsofkentchurches. co.uk

CC NO 207021   **ESTABLISHED** 1950

■ Friends of Muir Group

WHERE FUNDING CAN BE GIVEN UK.

WHO CAN BENEFIT Individuals, community groups and charitable organisations benefiting Muir Group residents in areas where they live or work.

WHAT IS FUNDED Priority is given to young people, older people and communities.

WHAT IS NOT FUNDED No grants for: the settling of debts; the promotion of political activities; general public appeals; the ongoing costs for Credit Unions (although start up grants are considered); the support of individual religions to the exclusion of other religions (however initiatives that promote tolerance and understanding of different faiths and cultures are actively supported).

TYPE OF GRANT Capital grants, revenue costs and full project funding.

FINANCES *Year* 2007–08 *Income* £54,215 *Grants* £45,642 *Assets* £91,527

TRUSTEES Richard Hoffman, Chair; David Booth; Adrienne Berkson; Martyn Delaney; David Inight; Leslie Patterson; Robert Robertson.

OTHER INFORMATION A list of grant beneficiaries was not included in the trust's accounts.

HOW TO APPLY Please note the following statement from the trust: 'We receive many applications from organisations that have failed to read our application guidelines and criteria. We also insist that applications are made through our application forms and not in the form of a letter.' Guidance notes and application forms are available on request from the correspondent and can also be downloaded from the trust's website.

WHO TO APPLY TO Andrew Hunt, Secretary, Old Government House, Dee Hills Park, Chester, Cheshire CH3 5AR *Tel* 01244 313613 *email* andrew.hunt@muir.org.uk *Website* www. muir.org.uk

CC NO 1100471   **ESTABLISHED** 2002

■ Friends of Wiznitz Limited

WHERE FUNDING CAN BE GIVEN UK and overseas.

WHO CAN BENEFIT Registered charities.

WHAT IS FUNDED Jewish education in the UK and overseas.

SAMPLE GRANTS Igud Mosdos Wiznitz (£209,000); Mosdos Winitz (£280,000); Tzemach Tzadik (£35,000); LeHacahzicom V LeHachayosom (£198,000); and Kehal Ahavat Yisroel (£30,000).

FINANCES *Year* 2007–08 *Income* £1,447,859 *Grants* £826,870 *Assets* £1,009,319

TRUSTEES H Feldman; E Kahan; R Bergmann; S Feldman.

OTHER INFORMATION In 2007–08 grants were divided between: education (£589,000); and relief of poverty (£237,000).

HOW TO APPLY In writing to the correspondent.

WHO TO APPLY TO E Gottesfeld, 8 Jessam Avenue, London E5 9UD

CC NO 255685   **ESTABLISHED** 1948

■ Friends Provident Charitable Foundation

WHERE FUNDING CAN BE GIVEN UK.

WHO CAN BENEFIT Groups and organisations working with disadvantaged people.

WHAT IS FUNDED The foundation 'currently works to create the conditions throughout the UK for improved access to appropriate financial services for those who are currently excluded, particularly those on low incomes or otherwise vulnerable to market failure'. Friends Provident Tradition- 'The foundation also carries forward a legacy of giving by the Friends Provident Group. Trustees have determined that a proportion (currently up to 15%) of the foundation's funds may be committed in line with previous gifts to charity made by the Group. The current criteria for giving are: medical research aimed at preventative medicine; charities/causes that were related to the regions where Friends Provident operated as an employer, including the City of London; Quaker initiatives.'

SAMPLE GRANTS Royal College of Psychiatrists (£109,000); Institute of Public Policy research (£100,000); Bristol Debt Advice Centre (£86,000); Queen of Mary and Westfield College (£70,000); Daycare Trust (£58,000); National Housing Federation and University of Birmingham (£50,000 each); University of Salford – Insurance Provision Models (£30,000); Roehampton University (£21,000); Rocket Science UK Ltd (£20,000); THRIVE (£15,000); East End Fair Finance (£8,000); and Money Advice Trust (£5,000).

FINANCES *Year* 2007–08 *Income* £1,060,669 *Grants* £747,000 *Assets* £20,939,074

TRUSTEES Brian Sweetland, Chair; Kate Green; Nick Perks; Jenny Shellens; Ashley Taylor; Whitni Thomas; Mike Hampton.

OTHER INFORMATION In 2007–08 a further £2,500 was given in Friends Provident Tradition grants.

HOW TO APPLY See the foundation's website for up-to-date details of their giving policy.

WHO TO APPLY TO The Company Secretary, Pixham End, Surrey, Dorking, Surrey RH4 1QA *Tel* 0845 268 3388 *email* foundation.enquiries@ friendsprovident.co.uk *Website* www. friendsprovidentfoundation.org

CC NO 1087053   **ESTABLISHED** 2002

■ The Frognal Trust

WHERE FUNDING CAN BE GIVEN UK.

WHO CAN BENEFIT Registered charities benefiting older people, children and people with disabilities or sight loss.

WHAT IS FUNDED The trustees' current grant-making policy is to make relatively small grants to as many qualifying charities as possible. Particularly charities working in the fields of: residential facilities and services; cultural heritage; hospices; nursing homes; ophthalmological research; conservation; heritage; parks; and community services. Other charitable purposes will be considered.

WHAT IS NOT FUNDED The trust does not support: any animal charities; the advancement of religion; charities for the benefit of people outside the UK; educational or research trips; branches of national charities; general appeals; individuals.

TYPE OF GRANT Buildings, capital, one-off, research and start-up costs will be considered.

RANGE OF GRANTS £200–£3,500.

SAMPLE GRANTS Previous beneficiaries include: Canniesburn Research Trust, Samantha Dickson Research Trust, Royal Liverpool and Broad Green University Hospitals, Aireborough Voluntary Services to the Elderly, Elderly Accommodation Counsel, Leeds Society for Deaf and Blind People, Action Medical Research, Friends of the Elderly, Gloucestershire Disabled Afloat Riverboat Trust, National Rheumatoid Arthritis Society, Stubbers Adventure Centre, Wireless for the Bedridden Society, and Yorkshire Dales Millennium Project.

FINANCES *Year* 2007–08 *Income* £79,849 *Grants* £75,033 *Assets* £2,010,501

TRUSTEES Philippa Blake-Roberts; Jennifer Helen Fraser; P Fraser.

HOW TO APPLY In writing to the correspondent. Applications should be received by February, May, August and November, for consideration at the trustees' meeting the following month.

WHO TO APPLY TO Donor Grants Officer, Steynings House, Summerlock Approach, Salisbury, Wiltshire SP2 7RJ

CC NO 244444   **ESTABLISHED** 1964

■ T F C Frost Charitable Trust

WHERE FUNDING CAN BE GIVEN UK and overseas.

WHO CAN BENEFIT Research associates of recognised centres of excellence in ophthalmology.

WHAT IS FUNDED Research in ophthalmology by establishing research fellowships and supporting specific projects.

WHAT IS NOT FUNDED There are no available resources for the relief of blind people or people suffering from diseases of the eye.

RANGE OF GRANTS £5,000–£35,000.

SAMPLE GRANTS University of Southampton – Professor Andrew Lotery and University of Bristol – Chair in Experimental Ophthalmology (£10,000 each); and the Rayne Institute St Thomas' Hospital – Professor John Marshall (£5,000).

FINANCES *Year* 2007–08 *Income* £91,098 *Grants* £25,000 *Assets* £2,651,056

TRUSTEES T A F Frost; M D Sanders; M H Miller.

HOW TO APPLY In writing to the correspondent. Trustees meet twice a year.

WHO TO APPLY TO John Holmes, Holmes and Co Accountants, 10 Torrington Road, Claygate, Esher, Surrey KT10 0SA *Tel* 01372 465378

CC NO 256590   **ESTABLISHED** 1966

■ The Patrick Frost Foundation

WHERE FUNDING CAN BE GIVEN Worldwide, but only through UK charities.

WHO CAN BENEFIT Registered charities.

WHAT IS FUNDED The relief and welfare of people of small means and the less fortunate members of society, and assistance for small organisations where a considerable amount of self-help and voluntary effort is required.

WHAT IS NOT FUNDED No grants to individuals or non-UK charities.

TYPE OF GRANT One-off donations.

RANGE OF GRANTS Mainly £5,000 or less.

SAMPLE GRANTS Dogs for the Disabled, London Narrow Boat Project and Humberside Police Authority (£20,000 each); Action on Addiction, Motivation Charitable Trust and Opportunity International (£10,000 each); and Family Holiday Association, Chance for Children Trust, Medical Foundation for the Care of Victims of Torture, Naomi House Children's Hospice and Contact the Elderly (£5,000 each).

FINANCES *Year* 2007–08 *Income* £335,531 *Grants* £310,000 *Assets* £5,366,318

TRUSTEES Mrs Helena Frost; Donald Jones; Luke Valner; Dominic Tayler.

HOW TO APPLY In writing to the correspondent, accompanied by the last set of audited accounts. The trustees regret that due to the large number of applications they receive, they are unable to acknowledge unsuccessful applications.

WHO TO APPLY TO Mrs Helena Frost, Trustee, c/o Trowers and Hamlins LLP, Sceptre Court, 40 Tower Hill, London EC3N 4DX *Tel* 020 7423 8000 *Fax* 020 7423 8001

CC NO 1005505   **ESTABLISHED** 1991

■ Maurice Fry Charitable Trust

WHERE FUNDING CAN BE GIVEN UK and overseas.

WHO CAN BENEFIT Registered charities benefiting at risk groups, and people disadvantaged by poverty or socially isolated. Support is given to medical professionals, research workers, scientists, academics and writers and poets. Support may also be given to refugees, and victims of famine, man-made or natural disasters and war.

WHAT IS FUNDED General charitable purposes. Currently the main areas of interest are welfare, humanities, environmental resources, and international causes.

WHAT IS NOT FUNDED No grants to individuals.

RANGE OF GRANTS £500–£2,500.

SAMPLE GRANTS NSPCC (£2,500); Alone in London, Llanèlli Dinefwr Hospice Appeal Fund and Lymphoma Association (£2,000 each); Amnesty International and the Maypole Project (£1,500 each); and Borders Forest Trust, Northumberland County Scout Council, Tree Aid and Scottish Borders Community Orchestra (£1,000 each).

FINANCES *Year* 2007–08 *Income* £39,483 *Grants* £20,000 *Assets* £1,022,356

TRUSTEES L E A Fry; Mrs F Cooklin; Mrs L Weaks.

HOW TO APPLY The trust states that it does not respond to unsolicited applications.

WHO TO APPLY TO L E A Fry, Trustee, 98 Savernake Road, London NW3 2JR

CC NO 327934   **ESTABLISHED** 1988

■ Mejer and Gertrude Miriam Frydman Foundation

WHERE FUNDING CAN BE GIVEN UK and overseas.

WHO CAN BENEFIT Organisations benefiting children, young adults, students, teachers and governesses. Support is given to Jewish people, and particular favour is given to Jewish charities.

WHAT IS FUNDED New and established charitable projects for study and research, including scholarships, fellowships, professorial chairs, lectureships, prizes, awards and the cost of purchasing or erecting any building or land required for such projects. Support in these areas is given to organisations and institutions only. Individuals are not supported under any circumstances.

WHAT IS NOT FUNDED No grants to individuals for scholarships or any other purpose.

RANGE OF GRANTS Up to £4,000.

SAMPLE GRANTS North West London Jewish Day School (£4,000), Jewish Care and Norwood Ravenswood (£3,500 each), Kisharon (£3,000), Chai Cancer Care (£2,000); Kesser Torah (£1,700); Friends of Yeshiva O H R Elchanan (£1,500); the Merephdi Foundation (£1,000); Institute for Higher Rabbinicial Studies (£700); and Talia Trust for Children (£500).

FINANCES *Year* 2007–08 *Income* £38,659 *Grants* £33,400 *Assets* £85,036

TRUSTEES L J Frydman; G B Frydman; D H Frydman.

HOW TO APPLY In writing to the correspondent.

WHO TO APPLY TO G Frydman, Trustee, c/o Westbury Schotness and Co., 145–157 St John Street, London EC1V 4PY *Tel* 020 7253 7272

CC NO 262806   **ESTABLISHED** 1971

■ The Fulmer Charitable Trust

WHERE FUNDING CAN BE GIVEN Worldwide, especially the developing world and Wiltshire.

WHO CAN BENEFIT Registered charities worldwide, especially in the developing world and Wiltshire.

WHAT IS FUNDED General charitable purposes.

WHAT IS NOT FUNDED No support for gap year requests. Very few unsolicited applications are accepted.

RANGE OF GRANTS Up to £15,000, but mostly for £500–£3,000.

SAMPLE GRANTS Sight Savers (£14,000); Shelter, Sense and Save the Children (£12,000 each); the Sequal Trust and NSPCC (£9,000); Manna Society and Age Concern (£8,000 each); and the Brain Research Trust and Christian Aid (£7,000 each); Coventry Cathedral Development Trust and World Medical Fund (£4,000 each); British Heart Foundation and Care International (£3,000 each); Farm Africa and Pump Aid (£2,500 each); Plan UK and Army Benevolent Fund (£2,000 each); Aid for Trade and Womenkind (£1,500 each); Aid for Romanian Orphanages, Engineers without Borders UK and Medical Aid for Palestinians (£1,000 each); Zimbabwe AIDS Orphans, Listening Books and Aplastic Anaemia Trust (£500 each); and Seeds for Africa and World Jewish Relief Fund (£250 each).

FINANCES *Year* 2007–08 *Income* £442,165 *Grants* £422,091 *Assets* £8,661,606

TRUSTEES J S Reis; Mrs S Reis; Mrs C Mytum; Miss E J Reis.

HOW TO APPLY In writing to the correspondent.

WHO TO APPLY TO The Trustees, Estate Office, Street Farm, Compton Bassett, Calne, Wiltshire SN11 8SW *Tel* 01249 760410 *Fax* 01249 760410

CC NO 1070428   **ESTABLISHED** 1998

■ Worshipful Company of Furniture Makers Charitable Fund

WHERE FUNDING CAN BE GIVEN UK.

WHO CAN BENEFIT Individuals and organisations.

WHAT IS FUNDED Causes directly connected to furniture, funding design competitions, prototypes and visits to exhibitions or factories and offering bursaries to students at colleges.

FINANCES *Year* 2007–08 *Income* £462,155 *Grants* £9,233 *Assets* £1,152,036

TRUSTEES Sir John Perring; Roger H Richardson; Martin Jourdan.

OTHER INFORMATION Grants were made to organisations totalling £9,000.

HOW TO APPLY In writing to the correspondent.

WHO TO APPLY TO Mrs Jan A Wright, Clerk, Furniture Makers' Hall, 12 Austin Friars, London EC2N 2HE *Tel* 020 7256 5558 *Fax* 020 7256 5155 *email* clerk@furnituremakers.org.uk *Website* www.furnituremakers.co.uk

CC NO 270483   **ESTABLISHED** 1975

■ The Fuserna Foundation

WHERE FUNDING CAN BE GIVEN UK and overseas.

WHO CAN BENEFIT Children and older people.

WHAT IS FUNDED Relief-in-need and mental and physical illness.

WHAT IS NOT FUNDED The foundation will not generally consider projects that include the following: animals; religious activities/institutions; general appeals.

SAMPLE GRANTS Clinton Climate Initiative (£245,000); Project Walk (£172,000); Global Heritage Fund (£40,000); Amaudo UK (£10,000); Santa Monica Mountains & Seashore (£7,700); SeeSaw (£2,100); and Moving Mountains (£1,000).

FINANCES *Year* 2007–08 *Income* £697,349 *Grants* £478,122 *Assets* £263,535

TRUSTEES Ariadne Getty; Justin Williams; Fran Hollywood; Susan Bartkowiak; Owen Clutton.

HOW TO APPLY The foundation asks for all initial applications to be in writing and to include the following: 'background information about the charity or charitable project in question'; 'details of the project that currently requires funding including the objective of the project and full operational details of how that objective will be achieved.'; 'a copy of your most recent financial statutory accounts'; 'details of the budget outlined in respect of the project'; 'details of existing sources of finance, including donations from other Charitable Trusts and details of other fund raising activities in place in respect of raising the funds needed for the project.' 'Upon receipt of the above information, a member of the foundation's day to day operational staff may wish to visit the charity prior to presenting its application to the trustees or alternatively to commence discussions with you. Further to this your application will be put forward to the trustees of the Fuserna Foundation for their consideration.'

WHO TO APPLY TO The Trustees, Sixth Floor, 6
Chesterfield Gardens, Mayfair, London W1J 5BQ
Tel 020 7409 3900 *email* info@
fusernafoundation.org *Website* www.
fusernafoundation.org
CC NO 1107895   **ESTABLISHED** 2005

■ The G D Charitable Trust

WHERE FUNDING CAN BE GIVEN Worldwide.
WHO CAN BENEFIT Registered charities.
WHAT IS FUNDED Animal welfare, the environment, disability, homelessness.
WHAT IS NOT FUNDED No grants to individuals.
SAMPLE GRANTS Marine Conservation Society (£51,000); George Adamson Wildlife Preservation Trust (£25,000); Society for the Protection of Animals Abroad (£13,000); The Children's Hospice South West – Bristol (£5,000); Born Free (£3,500); and Wild Horse Welfare (£500).
FINANCES *Year* 2007 *Income* £110,439 *Grants* £97,493 *Assets* £3,675,885
TRUSTEES George Lincoln Duffield; Natasha Velvet Duffield; Alexander Seamus Fitzgibbons.
HOW TO APPLY In writing to the correspondent.
WHO TO APPLY TO The Trustees, c/o Bircham Dyson Bell LLP, 50 Broadway, Westminster, London SW1H 0BL *Tel* 020 7227 7000
CC NO 1096101   **ESTABLISHED** 2002

■ Gableholt Limited

WHERE FUNDING CAN BE GIVEN UK.
WHO CAN BENEFIT Jewish organisations.
WHAT IS FUNDED Advancement of the orthodox Jewish faith.
FINANCES *Year* 2007–08 *Income* £1,734,537 *Grants* £81,265 *Assets* £15,590,101
TRUSTEES S Noe; Mrs E Noe; C Lerner; P Noe; A E Bude.
HOW TO APPLY In the past this trust has stated that 'in the governors' view, true charitable giving should always be coupled with virtual anonymity' and for this reason they are most reluctant to be a party to any publicity. Along with suggesting that the listed beneficiaries might also want to remain unidentified, they also state that the nature of the giving (to orthodox Jewish organisations) means the information is unlikely to be of much interest to anyone else. Potential applicants would be strongly advised to take heed of these comments.
WHO TO APPLY TO Mrs E Noe, Secretary, 115 Craven Park Road, London N15 6BL *Tel* 020 8802 4782
CC NO 276250   **ESTABLISHED** 1978

■ The Galanthus Trust

WHERE FUNDING CAN BE GIVEN UK and overseas.
WHO CAN BENEFIT Registered charities and individuals.
WHAT IS FUNDED Medical, developing countries, environment, conservation.
RANGE OF GRANTS UK and overseas.
FINANCES *Year* 2007 *Income* £50,965 *Grants* £105,850 *Assets* £870,675
TRUSTEES S F Rogers; Mrs J M Rogers.
HOW TO APPLY In writing to the correspondent. 'All requests for grants are considered carefully by the trustees. The trustees decide whether to donate and the amount to donate.'

WHO TO APPLY TO Mrs J M Rogers, Trustee, West Farm House, Newton Tony, Salisbury SP4 0HF *Tel* 01980 629345 *email* galanthustrust@yahoo.co.uk
CC NO 1103538   **ESTABLISHED** 2004

■ The Galbraith Trust

WHERE FUNDING CAN BE GIVEN The administrative area of Lancaster City Council.
WHO CAN BENEFIT Charitable organisations.
WHAT IS FUNDED General charitable purposes.
RANGE OF GRANTS £250–£2,000.
SAMPLE GRANTS Archbishop Hutton After School Fun Club, Bare Necessities Pre-School Playgroup, Bolton-le-Sands Village Hall, Lancashire Outward Bound Association and Night Owls (£1,500 each); Friendship Centre (£1,000); 1st Heysham Guides and Community Learning Network (£800 each); St Barnabas Housebound Club (£600); Lancaster and Garstang Division Girl Guiding and Stage Struck Youth Theatre (£500 each); and Greenfield Court residents Association (£300).
FINANCES *Year* 2008–09 *Income* £27,999 *Grants* £33,337 *Assets* £347,898
TRUSTEES Ms K F Gordon, Chair; J W Wilson; M V L Harris; Mrs I E Bowker; M W Burrow; P G Crowther.
HOW TO APPLY Application forms may be obtained from the Lancaster District Council for Voluntary Service at the following address: Trinity Community Centre, Middle Street, Lancaster LA1 1JZ.
WHO TO APPLY TO David Marsden, Blackhurst Swainson Goodier, Aalborg Square, Lancaster LA1 1GG
CC NO 1086717   **ESTABLISHED** 2001

■ The Gale Family Charitable Trust

WHERE FUNDING CAN BE GIVEN UK, mainly Bedfordshire.
WHO CAN BENEFIT Registered charities, with a preference for Bedfordshire-based charities.
WHAT IS FUNDED Churches and church ministries, community life in Bedfordshire and general charitable purposes.
WHAT IS NOT FUNDED Grants are rarely given to individuals.
SAMPLE GRANTS Bunyan Meeting Free Church (£17,000); Baptist Union (£8,000); St Paul's Church – Bedford (£7,000); Prebend Day Centre (£5,000); North Beds. Hospice Day Care (£4,000); Bedford Home Start and Keech Cottage (£3,000 each); RNLI, Road Victim Support, Spinal Injuries Association and Starlight Children's Foundation (£2,000 each); 3H Fund, Barnardos, Cancer Research UK, Odell Parish Council, St Owen's Church – Bromham and War Memorials Trust (£1,000 each); and Bedfordshire Youth Theatre and Clapham Methodist Church (£500 each).
FINANCES *Year* 2006–07 *Income* £166,159 *Grants* £164,500 *Assets* £4,162,735
TRUSTEES G D Payne, Chair; J Tyley; J Williams; A J Ormerod; Mrs D Watson; P H Tyler; W Browning; K Fletcher.
HOW TO APPLY In writing to the correspondent. Grants are distributed once a year and applications should be made by May for consideration in July.

WHO TO APPLY TO G Garner, Garner Associates, Northwood House, 138 Bromham Road, Bedford MK40 2QW *Tel* 01234 354 508 *Fax* 01234 349 588 *email* ggg@garnerassociates.co.uk
CC NO 289212   **ESTABLISHED** 1984

■ The Angela Gallagher Memorial Fund

WHERE FUNDING CAN BE GIVEN UK and international organisations based in the UK.
WHO CAN BENEFIT Registered charities benefiting: children; Christians; Roman Catholics; and those suffering from paediatric diseases. Support will also go to people disadvantaged by poverty; people with disabilities; victims of famine and disasters; and victims of abuse.
WHAT IS FUNDED The aim of the fund is to help children within the UK. The fund will also consider Christian, humanitarian and educational projects worldwide. Particularly charities working in the fields of: special needs education; day centres; holidays and outings; and Catholic bodies. Small charities which do not have access to large corporate donors are given priority. International disasters are aided by way of CAFOD and Red Cross only.
WHAT IS NOT FUNDED Donations will not be made to the following: older people; scientific research; hospitals and hospices; artistic and cultural appeals; animal welfare; or building and equipment appeals. No grants to individuals.
TYPE OF GRANT One-off grants for core costs.
RANGE OF GRANTS Usually £500–£1,000.
SAMPLE GRANTS Anglo-Peruvian Child Care Mission, Kidz R Us, Dream Holidays Handicapped Children and Order of the Assumption – India (£1,000 each); and Rochdale Cycling Club, Penguins Playgroup, Alliance Youth Works, Rutland Sailability, Wells for India, Sussex Autistic Society, Seeds of Hope and Combat Stress (£500 each).
FINANCES *Year* 2007 *Income* £38,450 *Grants* £33,750 *Assets* £1,186,913
TRUSTEES N A Maxwell-Lawford; P Mostyn; A Swan.
HOW TO APPLY In writing to the correspondent, for consideration at trustees' meetings twice a year. Applicants must include a set of accounts or the appeal will not be considered. Applications are not acknowledged without an sae.
WHO TO APPLY TO Mrs D R Moss, Secretary, Church Cott, The Green, Mirey Lane, Woodbury, Devon EX5 1LT *Tel* 01395 232097
CC NO 800739   **ESTABLISHED** 1989

■ The Gamlen Charitable Trust

WHERE FUNDING CAN BE GIVEN UK.
WHO CAN BENEFIT Organisations benefiting law students and trainee solicitors.
WHAT IS FUNDED Legal education, general charitable purposes.
TYPE OF GRANT Grants for scholarships, bursaries and prizes.
RANGE OF GRANTS Up to £7,500.
SAMPLE GRANTS Newbury Spring Festival (£7,500); City Solicitors Educational Trust (£2,700); and Cancer Research UK and Bampton Classical Opera (£500 each).
FINANCES *Year* 2007–08 *Income* £250,699 *Grants* £11,195 *Assets* £1,547,685
TRUSTEES R G Stubblefield; P G Eaton; J W M Chadwick.
HOW TO APPLY In writing to the correspondent.

WHO TO APPLY TO R G Stubblefield, Trustee, c/o Penningtons, Newbury House, 20 Kings Road West, Newbury, Berkshire RG14 5XR *Tel* 01635 571000
CC NO 327977   **ESTABLISHED** 1988

■ The Gamma Trust

WHERE FUNDING CAN BE GIVEN UK, with a possible preference for Scotland.
WHO CAN BENEFIT Registered charities.
WHAT IS FUNDED General charitable purposes.
WHAT IS NOT FUNDED No grants to individuals.
TYPE OF GRANT Project, research and recurring costs.
SAMPLE GRANTS Previous beneficiaries have included British Red Cross, British Heart Foundation, Cancer Research Campaign and Erskine Hospital.
FINANCES *Year* 2009 *Income* £81,658 *Grants* £60,000
HOW TO APPLY In writing to the correspondent for consideration quarterly.
WHO TO APPLY TO The Trust Secretary, c/o Mazars CYB Services Limited, 90 St Vincent Street, Glasgow G2 5UB
SC NO SC004330

■ The Gannochy Trust

WHERE FUNDING CAN BE GIVEN Scotland, with a preference for the Perth and Kinross area.
WHO CAN BENEFIT Organisations which meet the OSCR Charity Test.
WHAT IS FUNDED The trust's grant-making mission is: 'to make a positive difference for the benefit of people living in Scotland, with a preference for Perth and Kinross'. It has four grant-making themes: (1) inspiring young people; (2) improving the quality of life of the disadvantaged and vulnerable; (3) supporting and developing community amenities; (4) care for the natural and man-made environment. NOTE: Themes 3 and 4 are restricted to Perth and Kinross.
WHAT IS NOT FUNDED 'General applications for funds will not be considered – applications must be specific, and preferably for a project with a defined outcome, not general running costs; donations will not be made to individuals; donations will only be made to organisations which meet the OSCR Charity Test; projects where the benefit of a donation will be realised outside Scotland; donations will rarely be made to projects that do not demonstrate an element of self or other funding; donations will not be made that contribute to an organisation's healthy reserves or endowments; applications will seldom be considered for more than a three-year commitment; applications will not be considered for holidays, with the exception of those for the disabled and disadvantaged living in Perth & Kinross where the project has a tangible recreational or educational theme; applications will not be considered for animal welfare projects, with the exception of wildlife projects within Perth & Kinross that meet the sub-themes within theme 4; applications will not be considered from schools for recreational facilities unless there will be a demonstrable and sustained community involvement, preferably for the disadvantaged or vulnerable; applications from pre-school groups, play schemes, after school clubs and parent-teacher associations; applications will not be considered from cancer and other health-related charities unless they demonstrate that their project

directly provides tangible relief from suffering and direct patient benefit; applications from places of worship will not be considered unless there is a distinct community benefit through use as a community centre or village hall, and where there is not a similar facility nearby; applications will not be considered from charities re-applying within a year of their previous appeal or award, or instalment thereof; applications will not be considered where funding would normally be provided by central or local government; waste disposal/landfill, pollution control and renewable energy projects will not be considered if they are the sole purpose of the project, and unless they meet the criteria within theme 4; applications will not be considered for political or lobbying purposes.

SAMPLE GRANTS University of Dundee – Diabetes Clinical Research (£500,000); Perth and Kinross Leisure – Bell's Sports Centre (£360,000); Riverside Museum Appeal Trust (£350,000); University of Dundee – Ninewells (£200,000); Greenock Arts Guild Limited and Perth and Kinross Heritage Trust (£100,000 each); Scottish Veteran's Garden City Association – Scone House Project (£80,000); and Glenfarg Public Hall Association (£60,000).

FINANCES Year 2007–08 Income £5,863,373 Grants £1,587,857 Assets £132,428,096

TRUSTEES Dr Russell Leather, Chair; Mark Webster; Dr James H F Kynaston; Ian W McMillan; Stewart N Macleod.

HOW TO APPLY On a form which can be downloaded from the trust's website. Full guidelines are available.

WHO TO APPLY TO Fiona Russell, Secretary, Kincarrathie House Drive, Pitcullen Crescent, Perth PH2 7HX Tel 01738 620653 email admin@gannochytrust.org.uk Website www.gannochytrust.org.uk

SC NO SC003133   **ESTABLISHED** 1937

....

■ The Ganzoni Charitable Trust

WHERE FUNDING CAN BE GIVEN Suffolk.
WHO CAN BENEFIT Registered charities.
WHAT IS FUNDED General charitable purposes.
WHAT IS NOT FUNDED Grants to individuals will not be considered. Applications from outside Suffolk are not normally considered and will not be acknowledged.
TYPE OF GRANT A number of the grants are recurring, the remainder will normally be one-off.
RANGE OF GRANTS £50–£10,000.
SAMPLE GRANTS St Edmundsbury and Ipswich Diocese (£10,000); St Francis Church (£5,000); the Anglican Centre in Rome and Elizabeth Finn Care (£2,000 each); the CYDS Project, the Royal Anglican Regiment and Monks Eleigh School Community Hall (£1,000 each); and SCOPE and Christians Against Poverty (£500 each).
FINANCES Year 2008–09 Income £232,167 Grants £87,345 Assets £2,564,867
TRUSTEES Hon. Mary Jill Ganzoni; Hon. Charles Boscawen; Nicholas Ridley.
HOW TO APPLY In writing to the correspondent. Telephone calls are not encouraged. There are no application forms, guidelines or deadlines. No sae is required unless material is to be returned.
WHO TO APPLY TO Hon. C R Boscawen, Trustee, Birketts LLP, 24–26 Museum Street, Ipswich IP1 1HZ Tel 01473 232300
CC NO 263583   **ESTABLISHED** 1971

....

■ The Worshipful Company of Gardeners of London

WHERE FUNDING CAN BE GIVEN Mainly City of London.
WHO CAN BENEFIT Horticultural organisations.
WHAT IS FUNDED The fund supports charitable activities connected with horticulture in all its forms and within the City of London.
RANGE OF GRANTS £100–£5,500.
SAMPLE GRANTS City and Guilds of London Institution (£5,300); London Children's Flower Society and Gardening for the Disabled (£5,000 each); London Gardens Society and Royal Gardeners Orphan Fund (£4,000 each); London in Bloom (£2,500); Spitalfields Crypt Trust and Mudchute Farm and Park (£1,000 each); and Peter Bedford Housing Association, Christ's Hospital Foundation, Kisharon Charitable Trust, Broadway Homelessness and Support and Trees for Cities (£500 each).
FINANCES Year 2007–08 Income £69,372 Grants £58,300 Assets £394,544
TRUSTEES N A Chalmers, Chair; Alan D Wiltshire; W B Fraser; Mrs N L Robinson; Guy R C Petty; Ramsay Shewell-Cooper; Sir Gavin Arthur; Venerable P A Delaney; M L E Dowlen; B S Porter.
HOW TO APPLY In writing to the correspondent.
WHO TO APPLY TO Trevor Faris, Clerk, 25 Luke Street, London EC2A 4AR Tel 020 7739 6404 (PA to the Clerk) or ext. 6696 (Assistant Clerk) Fax 020 7613 3412 email paclerk@gardenerscompany.org.uk Website www.gardenerscompany.org.uk
CC NO 222079   **ESTABLISHED** 1962

....

■ The Samuel Gardner Memorial Trust

WHERE FUNDING CAN BE GIVEN Harrow on the Hill.
WHO CAN BENEFIT Organisations and charitable groups.
WHAT IS FUNDED Music and music education; the arts and heritage; preservation of landscaped public spaces. There is an emphasis on the encouragement of young people.
WHAT IS NOT FUNDED No grants to individuals.
SAMPLE GRANTS Arthur Gardner Scholarship (£22,000).
FINANCES Year 2007–08 Income £42,227 Grants £44,500 Assets £1,405,173
TRUSTEES Timothy Brown; Marion Friend; Ms Ursula Jones; Timothy J Lines; John A Stenhouse.
HOW TO APPLY In writing to the correspondent.
WHO TO APPLY TO Mrs Pauline McAlpine, SBM & Company, 117 Fentman Road, London SW8 1JZ Tel 020 7582 9473 email pauline@sbmandco.com
CC NO 261059   **ESTABLISHED** 1970

....

■ The Garnett Charitable Trust

WHERE FUNDING CAN BE GIVEN South west England and Northern Ireland.
WHO CAN BENEFIT Registered charities.
WHAT IS FUNDED Health, hospices, environmental causes and animal welfare groups, arts, culture and recreation.
WHAT IS NOT FUNDED No grants to individuals.
RANGE OF GRANTS £5–£10,000.
SAMPLE GRANTS Previous beneficiaries included: All Hallows' School – Cranmore, CARE International, Design Museum, Ireland Fund of Great Britain, National Gallery Trust, St Michael's Parish and Save the Children.

FINANCES *Year* 2007–08 *Income* £14,567
TRUSTEES A J F Garnett; Mrs P Garnett; Mrs
S Brown; Fiona Vincent.
HOW TO APPLY In writing to the correspondent.
WHO TO APPLY TO Sandra Brown, Osborne Clarke
Solicitors, 2 Temple Back East, Bristol
BS1 6EG *Tel* 0117 917 3022
CC NO 327847   ESTABLISHED 1988

■ Garrick Charitable Trust

WHERE FUNDING CAN BE GIVEN UK.
WHO CAN BENEFIT Registered charities.
WHAT IS FUNDED Institutions which are seeking to
further theatre (including dance), literature or
music.
RANGE OF GRANTS Usually £2,500, exceptionally up
to £10,000.
SAMPLE GRANTS Montiverdi Choir and Orchestra Ltd
(£11,000); Music in Prisons, Young Concert
Artists Trust and Manchester Camerata (£5,000
each); Voices of British Ballet (£4,000); Cherub
Company London, Talawa Theatre Company and
Shakespeare at the Tobacco Factory (£2,500
each); Stonecrabs Productions Ltd (£2,000);
and Yorkshire Bach Choir (£1,000).
FINANCES *Year* 2007–08 *Income* £181,928
Grants £192,018 *Assets* £4,805,923
TRUSTEES A Hammond, Chair; N Newton; G Palmer;
Sir S Waley-Cohen; A H Doggart.
HOW TO APPLY Initial applications are reviewed by
the trustees who decide whether or not to send
an application form. Trustees meet quarterly.
WHO TO APPLY TO The Secretary, 15 Garrick Street,
London WC2E 9AY *Tel* 020 7395 4136
email alans@garrickclub.co.uk
CC NO 1071279   ESTABLISHED 1998

■ Garvan Limited

WHERE FUNDING CAN BE GIVEN UK.
WHO CAN BENEFIT Jewish organisations.
WHAT IS FUNDED Jewish charitable purposes.
FINANCES *Year* 2007–08 *Income* £459,616
Grants £227,840 *Assets* £839,071
TRUSTEES A Ebert; L Ebert.
HOW TO APPLY In writing to the correspondent.
WHO TO APPLY TO The Trustees, Flat 9, Windsor
Court, Golders Green Road, London NW11 9PP
CC NO 286110   ESTABLISHED 1980

■ The Gatsby Charitable Foundation

WHERE FUNDING CAN BE GIVEN Unrestricted.
WHO CAN BENEFIT Registered charities only. Many
beneficiary organisations are specialist research
institutes.
WHAT IS FUNDED 'Plant Science: to develop basic
research in fundamental processes of plant
growth and development and molecular plant
pathology, to encourage young researchers in
the field of plant science in the UK;
Neuroscience: to support world-class research
in the area of neural circuits and behaviour, and
in the area of theoretical neuroscience; and to
support activities which enhance our
understanding in this field; Science and
Engineering Education: to support improvement
in educational opportunity in the UK for a
workforce that can better apply technology for
wealth creation by incubating innovative
programmes in the field of science and
engineering education and promoting excellence

in teaching and learning; Africa: to promote
economic development and income generation
through selected programmes supporting small
scale manufacturing and enterprise and market
sector development in selected African
countries; Institute for Government: an
independent centre available to politicians and
the civil service, focused on making government
more effective; The Arts: to support the fabric
and programming of institutions with which
Gatsby's founding family has long connections;
Mental Health: to improve the quality of life for
people with long-term problems by improved
delivery of services.'
WHAT IS NOT FUNDED Generally, the trustees do not
make grants in response to unsolicited
applications or to individuals.
TYPE OF GRANT One-off and recurring grants.
SAMPLE GRANTS Royal Shakespeare Company
(£5.25 million); Gatsby Technical Education
Projects (£3 million); Kilimo Trust (£2.1 million);
University College London (£1.7 million);
Science and Plants for Schools (£327,000).
Under 'General' (other charitable work which
falls outside the trustees' main fields of
interest): National Children's Bureau
(£1 million), for the Children's Residential Care
Unit, Research Department and related
programmes on children's personal health and
social development; Centre for Cities
(£809,000), towards core costs; London
Borough of Greenwich (£475,000), towards a
collaborative project to develop a new model of
care for families where a parent has a long-term
mental health problem; I CAN (£330,000),
towards core costs and towards extending the
Early Years accreditation programme and to
start up more Early Years nurseries for children
with speech disorders; Manchester College of
Arts & Technology (£142,400), towards the
development of the enterprise support
programme; National Centre for Social Research
(£90,300), towards continued funding of the
annual British Social Attitudes Survey; University
of Oxford (£60,000), towards the 'Options for
Britain' public policy research project;
Association of Young People with ME (£25,000);
and Auditory Verbal UK (£17,500).
FINANCES *Year* 2007–08 *Income* £198,685,000
Grants £40,866,068 *Assets* £464,715,000
TRUSTEES Bernard Willis; Sir Andrew Cahn; Miss
Judith Portrait.
OTHER INFORMATION The trust is one of the
Sainsbury Family Charitable Trusts which share
a common administration. An application to one
is taken as an application to all.
HOW TO APPLY Proposals are generally invited by the
trustees or initiated at their request. Unsolicited
applications are not encouraged and are unlikely
to be successful.
WHO TO APPLY TO Peter Hesketh, Director, Allington
House, 1st Floor, 150 Victoria Street, London
SW1E 5AE *Tel* 020 7410 0330 *Fax* 020 7410
0332 *email* contact@gatsby.org.uk
Website www.gatsby.org.uk
CC NO 251988   ESTABLISHED 1967

■ Gatwick Airport Community Trust

WHERE FUNDING CAN BE GIVEN Parts of East and West
Sussex, Surrey and Kent but particularly
communities directly affected by operations at
Gatwick Airport. A map of the area of benefit
can be seen on the website.

WHO CAN BENEFIT Environmental and community projects in the area of benefit.

WHAT IS FUNDED Priority categories for support are: the development of young people; art projects including amateur drama, music and art; sporting facilities; environmental improvement and conservation; improvements to community facilities such as village halls; support for people who are disabled; support for older people; and the encouragement of additional volunteering or giving in the area.

WHAT IS NOT FUNDED The trustees will not consider projects that involve any of the following categories: projects or beneficiaries that are completely or largely outside the area of benefit (less attention is given to applications from areas not directly affected by the airport); recurrent expenditure or running costs, ongoing maintenance or deficits; salaries or training costs, except start-up costs in relation to an additional amenity or service being established that will be self-sustaining thereafter; costs that should be funded from other sources, e.g. public bodies; applications from organisations that have statutory responsibilities such as local authorities, hospitals, schools, unless it is a project that is over and above their core activities; the purchase of land or buildings. Grants will not be made to organisations that are working to make a profit for shareholders, partners or sole owners, nor to individuals. Grants will not normally be made where it is evident that little or no effort has been made to raise funds elsewhere.

TYPE OF GRANT The trust favours applications that involve one-off capital or project costs, rather than ongoing maintenance, salaries or training costs.

RANGE OF GRANTS £250–£5,000.

SAMPLE GRANTS Crawley Community Transport (£5,000); WRVS Crawley Centre (£4,500); Brambles Respite Care Centre – Horley (£3,000); Reigate and Redhill YMCA (£2,500); Fairway Infant School – Copthorne and Sussex Oakleaf Housing Association (£2,000 each); British Wireless for the Blind (£1,500); Art Matters – Horley (£1,200); East Grinstead Cricket Club (£1,000); and Cranleigh Young People's Theatre (£200).

FINANCES *Year* 2008 *Income* £183,057 *Grants* £166,350 *Assets* £28,987

TRUSTEES Christopher Lowe, Chair; Kay Hammond; Neil Matthewson; John Mortimer; Mike Roberts; Michael Sander; James Smith; Christopher Chadburn-Hersey; Andy Kynoch.

HOW TO APPLY Application forms are available during the period each year when applications are being accepted (see below) by contacting the trust by telephone or writing to: GACT, PO Box 464, Tunbridge Wells, Kent TN2 9PU. Forms can also be downloaded from the website. Applications are invited once a year, usually between January and March. Grants are paid by the end of May. Further information can be found on the trust's website. Telephone queries are welcomed.

WHO TO APPLY TO Rosamund Quade, Trust Secretary, c/o Public Affairs, 7th Floor, Destinations Place, Gatwick Airport, West Sussex RH6 0NP *Tel* 01892 826088 *Website* www.gact.org.uk

CC NO 1089683   **ESTABLISHED** 2001

■ The Robert Gavron Charitable Trust

WHERE FUNDING CAN BE GIVEN Mainly UK.

WHO CAN BENEFIT Mainly small charities.

WHAT IS FUNDED The principal fields of interest continue to include health and welfare (including charities for people with disabilities), prisons and prison reform, arts and arts education, education and social policy and research. Much of the funding follows the trustees' own charitable involvement. The trust generally makes a small number of substantial grants together with a larger number of smaller donations.

WHAT IS NOT FUNDED The trust does not give donations to individuals or to large national charities.

TYPE OF GRANT One-off; project; research; recurring cost; and salaries. Funding can be given for up to three years.

RANGE OF GRANTS £25–£100,000.

SAMPLE GRANTS King Alfred School (£100,000); St Peter's College Foundation, Arab Israel Children's Tennis and Young Foundation (£50,000 each); University of York (£40,000); Barbados Cricket Association (£31,000); Friends of Highgate Cemetery (£15,000); Sadler's Wells Development Trust (£10,000); Rainbow Drama Group (£5,000); University of the Arts – London (£2,500); Youth at Risk (£1,000); and ZSV Trust (£100).

FINANCES *Year* 2007–08 *Income* £1,031,669 *Grants* £863,358 *Assets* £8,861,784

TRUSTEES Lord Robert Gavron; Charles Corman; Lady Katharine Gavron; Jessica Gavron; Sarah Gavron.

HOW TO APPLY Although the trust indicates that its funds are fully committed and that it would have difficulty in considering further appeals, particularly due to the current financial climate, some new projects may be supported. Organisations should apply in writing only to the correspondent. Please enclose a stamped addressed envelope and latest accounts. There are no regular dates for trustees' meetings, but they take place about five times a year.

WHO TO APPLY TO Mrs Dilys Ogilvie-Ward, Secretary, 44 Eagle Street, London WC1R 4FS *Tel* 020 7400 4300 *Fax* 020 7400 4245

CC NO 268535   **ESTABLISHED** 1974

■ Jacqueline and Michael Gee Charitable Trust

WHERE FUNDING CAN BE GIVEN UK.

WHO CAN BENEFIT Charitable organisations, with a preference for Jewish groups.

WHAT IS FUNDED Almost exclusively health and educational charities. Arts and social welfare causes may be considered.

TYPE OF GRANT Project grants, one-off or long-term.

RANGE OF GRANTS Usually up to £10,000.

SAMPLE GRANTS SJP Charity Trust Ltd (£10,000); Chai Lifeline Cancer-Care (£7,800); Sheffield Institute Foundation for Motor Neurone Disease (£5,000); St Georges Medical School (£3,000); Tel Aviv Foundation and the Treehouse Trust (£2,000); and Almeida Theatre Company Limited and Hampstead Theatre Limited (£1,000 each).

FINANCES *Year* 2007–08 *Income* £100,706 *Grants* £60,378 *Assets* £64,376

TRUSTEES M J Gee; J S Gee.

HOW TO APPLY In writing to the correspondent.

WHO TO APPLY TO Michael J Gee, Trustee, 27 Berkeley House, Hay Hill, London W1J 8NS *Tel* 020 7493 1904 *Fax* 020 7499 1470 *email* trust@sherman.co.uk
CC NO 1062566   ESTABLISHED 1997

■ The General Nursing Council for England and Wales Trust

WHERE FUNDING CAN BE GIVEN England and Wales.
WHO CAN BENEFIT Universities and other public bodies benefiting nurses.
WHAT IS FUNDED Public bodies undertaking research into matters directly affecting nursing or the nursing profession.
TYPE OF GRANT One-off or annually towards revenue costs.
SAMPLE GRANTS Florence Nightingale Foundation – for promoting research and investigation into matters relating to nursing (£60,000); University of Swansea – for advancing the science and art of nursing (£35,000); Sacred Space Foundation – for assisting in the furtherance of nurses' welfare (£5,000); and University of Manchester – for advancing the science and art of nursing (£2,800).
FINANCES *Year* 2008–09 *Income* £119,739 *Grants* £102,855 *Assets* £2,013,693
TRUSTEES Sir Ron de Witt; Prof. Dame Betty Kershaw; Prof. Dickon Weir-Hughes; Dame Jacqueline Docherty.
HOW TO APPLY In writing to the correspondent, by 30 April for June meeting, by 30 September for November meeting.
WHO TO APPLY TO Dr Sam Koroma, Secretary, 83 Victoria Road, Lower Edmonton, London N9 9SU *Tel* 020 8345 5379 *email* gnct@koroma5824.fsnet.co.uk
CC NO 288068   ESTABLISHED 1983

■ Generations Charitable Trust

WHERE FUNDING CAN BE GIVEN London Borough of Merton and overseas.
WHO CAN BENEFIT 'Children who need it the most; those who have disabilities, disadvantaged, or struggle with ill health. The trust supports local causes in the Borough of Merton where the family are resident and also works abroad in developing countries. The trust also supports projects for environmental protection and conservation; the central aim being to leave a gift for future generations.'
WHAT IS FUNDED Local causes in the Borough of Merton and also in developing countries.
SAMPLE GRANTS Previous beneficiaries have included Born Free Foundation, The Friends of the Mothers Programme, Hampton House – Northampton, Hopes and Homes for Children, Kids Company, Mothers2Mothers, Over the Wall, Royal Institute for the Blind, the Spring Centre, Youth Cancer Trust and Velocity Wheelchair Racing.
FINANCES *Year* 2007–08 *Income* £12,778 *Grants* £147,044
TRUSTEES Robert Finch, Stephen Finch; Rohini Finch.
HOW TO APPLY In writing to the correspondent
WHO TO APPLY TO Rohini Finch, Trustee, 36 Marryat Road, Wimbledon, London SW19 5BD *Tel* 020 8946 7760 *email* rfinch@rfinch.plus.com *Website* www.generationsct.co.uk
CC NO 1110565   ESTABLISHED 2005

■ J Paul Getty Jr Charitable Trust

WHERE FUNDING CAN BE GIVEN UK, mainly England.
WHO CAN BENEFIT Mainly registered charities. Priority is likely to be given to projects in the less prosperous parts of the country, particularly outside London and the south east, and to those which cover more than one beneficial area.
WHAT IS FUNDED Projects to do with poverty and misery in general and unpopular causes in particular. The trusts current areas of interest are: *Reducing Re-offending*: projects aiming to improve the lot of people in prison and smooth the transition for those leaving prison, maximising their chances of successful resettlement; *Improving Prospects*: projects providing meaningful occupation for young people aged 14–19 to improve their employability and diminish the risk of social exclusion; work to improve the treatment of refugees and asylum seekers; *Repairing Communities*: projects led from within the community with the aim of integrating different social and ethnic groups in pursuit of worthwhile goals; *Repairing Lives*: projects making a lasting impact on the lives of people with substance misuse problems; projects helping people who are homeless or at risk of homelessness; *Preserving Heritage*: conserving or restoring buildings and landscapes which are of national value and accessible to the public; saving from export art and manuscripts of national importance; developing conservation skills, especially among disadvantaged groups; *Sustaining the Arts:* nurturing and developing artistic endeavour of the highest quality.
WHAT IS NOT FUNDED Grants are not given for: individuals; organisations based outside of the UK; schools; universities or public sector organisations; routine maintenance, repairs, refurbishment or modernisation costs, or large-scale development projects, such as church restoration work or the construction of new village halls and local community centres; medical care or general health and wellbeing programmes; one-off events, residential or adventure trips. Priority is likely to be given to projects in the less prosperous parts of the country, particularly outside London and the south east, and to those which cover more than one beneficial area. Please remember this trust has no connection with the Getty Foundation in the USA.
TYPE OF GRANT Capital or recurrent; core funding and salaries are considered. Grants for salaries or running costs are for a maximum of three years. Some small grants of up to £1,000 can be made between meetings of the trustees.
RANGE OF GRANTS Up to £250,000 (over three years).
SAMPLE GRANTS Church Urban Fund and Emmaus UK (£150,000 each); Local Solutions – Liverpool (£111,000); Trail Blazers – Aylesbury (£90,000); Prison Reform Trust (£50,000); Barnstaple Poverty Action Group (£38,000); the Green Team – Edinburgh (£30,000); Asian Advisory Service – Derby (£14,000); Stepney Bank Stables – Newcastle Upon Tyne (£10,000); and Moor Trees – Devon (£8,100).
FINANCES *Year* 2008 *Income* £1,999,104 *Grants* £3,049,449 *Assets* £44,433,210
TRUSTEES Christopher Gibbs, Chair; Lady Getty; Vanni Treves; Christopher Purvis.
OTHER INFORMATION This trust has no connection with the Getty Foundation in the USA.
HOW TO APPLY Applications must be submitted using the online form, accessible through the trust's

website. There are no 'closing dates', and all applicants should receive an initial response within six weeks. The form will ask you to provide: information on the work of the organisation; details of the organisation's size and income; an overview of the project/work for which funding is required; the daytime contact details of someone with whom the trust can discuss the application. When starting an application for the first time applicants will be asked to complete a short 'eligibility quiz' to check that their project falls within the trust's criteria. If successful you will be able to begin the full application (guidance on completing the form is given within the form itself). If the project is short-listed for a grant of over £5,000, the trust will request more detailed information about the charity and the specific project. The trustees meet quarterly to consider applications, usually in April, July, September and December. It usually takes between three and six months for larger grants to be awarded. For requests of £5,000 or less it may be possible for the trustees to award a grant between meetings.

WHO TO APPLY TO Elizabeth Rantzen, Director, 1 Park Square West, London NW1 4LJ *Tel* 020 7486 1859 *Website* www.jpgettytrust.org.uk

cc no 292360   **established** 1985

■ The Gibbs Charitable Trust

WHERE FUNDING CAN BE GIVEN UK with a preference for the south of England and worldwide.

WHO CAN BENEFIT Organisations benefiting Methodists are given particular attention.

WHAT IS FUNDED Primarily to support Methodist charities; also areas of social or educational concern. Grants are normally made to projects of which the trustees have personal knowledge. Also supported are international causes and creative arts, especially those which use the arts for personal development.

WHAT IS NOT FUNDED A large number of requests are received by the trust from churches undertaking improvement, refurbishment and development projects, but only a few of these can be helped. In general, Methodist churches are selected, sometimes those the trustees have particular knowledge of. Individuals and animal charities are not supported.

TYPE OF GRANT Buildings, capital and project grants will be considered.

RANGE OF GRANTS Almost all grants in the range £500–£10,000.

SAMPLE GRANTS Christian Aid – Afghanistan and Climate Change and Oxfam Mozambique (£10,000 each); Biblical Illiteracy, St John's College, Durham (£5,000); Tree Aid (£4,000); Blackheath Conservatoire (£3,000); Solar Aid (£2,500); Hope and Homes for Children – Sierra Leone (£2,000); World Medical Fund, Harvest Help, YCare – Education in Southern Sudan and Appropriate Technology Asia (£1,000 each).

FINANCES *Year* 2007–08 *Income* £78,537 *Grants* £130,050 *Assets* £2,170,723

TRUSTEES John N Gibbs, Chair; James Gibbs; Andrew Gibbs; Celia Gibbs; Elizabeth Gibbs; Jessica Gibbs; John E Gibbs; Juliet Gibbs; Patience Gibbs; Rebecca Gibbs; William Gibbs; James D Gibbs.

HOW TO APPLY The trust has no application forms, although an application cover sheet is available on the trust's website along with a policy and guidelines page. Requests should be made in writing to the correspondent. The trustees meet three times a year, after Christmas, near Easter and late summer. Unsuccessful applicants are not normally notified. The trustees do not encourage telephone enquiries or speculative applications. They also state that they are not impressed by applicants that send a huge amount of paperwork.

WHO TO APPLY TO Dr James M Gibbs, Trustee, 8 Victoria Square, Clifton, Bristol BS8 4ET *email* jamesgibbs@btinternet.com *Website* www.gibbstrust.org.uk

cc no 207997   **established** 1946

■ Simon Gibson Charitable Trust

WHERE FUNDING CAN BE GIVEN UK and local charities in East Anglia and South Wales.

WHO CAN BENEFIT Registered or exempt charities.

WHAT IS FUNDED General.

WHAT IS NOT FUNDED No grants to individuals.

TYPE OF GRANT One-off or recurring, core costs, running costs, project, research, buildings and capital. Funding may be given for up to three years.

RANGE OF GRANTS £1,000 to £10,000, but most grants fall in the range £3,000 to £5,000.

SAMPLE GRANTS Ely Cathedral Appeal Fund, Prostate Cancer Charity and The Prince's Trust (£10,000 each). Other beneficiaries included: Action on Addiction, Barnardo's, Breast Cancer Campaign Wales, Jubilee Sailing Trust, Save the Rhino, the Suffolk Foundation and the Welsh Livery Guild Charitable Trust (£5,000 each); RNLI and Welsh National Opera (£4,000 each); Air Training Corp, Barry YMCA, Gurkha Welfare Trust, National Eye Research Centre, Welsh School in London and Wildlife Trust of South and West Wales (£3,000 each); Amelia Trust Farm and Brecon International Festival of Jazz (£2,000 each); and Exning Methodist Church Trustees (£1,000).

FINANCES *Year* 2007–08 *Income* £588,817 *Grants* £488,000 *Assets* £12,482,471

TRUSTEES Bryan Marsh; Angela Homfray; George Gibson; Deborah Connor.

HOW TO APPLY 'There are no application forms. Charities applying to the trust should make their application in writing in whatever way they think best presents their cause.' It acknowledges all applications but does not enter into correspondence with applicants unless they are awarded a grant. The trustees meet in May and applications should be received by March.

WHO TO APPLY TO Bryan Marsh, Trustee, Wild Rose House, Llancarfan, Vale of Glamorgan CF62 3AD *email* marsh575@btinternet.com

cc no 269501   **established** 1975

■ The G C Gibson Charitable Trust

WHERE FUNDING CAN BE GIVEN Unrestricted, in practice mainly UK with interests in Suffolk, Wales and Scotland.

WHO CAN BENEFIT Registered charities and 'authorities'.

WHAT IS FUNDED General charitable purposes, in practice, mainly art, music & education; health, hospices & medical research; community & other social projects; religion.

WHAT IS NOT FUNDED No grants to individuals.

TYPE OF GRANT Capital, research, running and core costs.

RANGE OF GRANTS £1,000–£20,000; mostly £1,000–£3,000.

SAMPLE GRANTS Botanic Garden Conservation International, Help for Heroes and Royal Welsh College of Music & Drama (£10,000 each); Weston Spirit (£8,000); New Astley Club – Newmarket (£6,000); Friends of Llandaff, St

David's Cathedral, Addenbrooks Hospital, Dorset Health Wish Trust and Medical Foundation (£5,000 each); British Youth Opera, Royal National College for the Blind – Hereford and Parish Church of All Saints – Slawston (£4,000 each); Wales Millennium Centre and Starlight Children's Foundation (£3,000 each); Scripture Union (£2,000); and RNIB (£1,000).

FINANCES *Year* 2007–08 *Income* £634,764 *Grants* £556,000 *Assets* £13,353,467

TRUSTEES Simon Gibson; Jane M Gibson; Robert D Taylor; Martin Gibson; Lucy Kelly.

HOW TO APPLY In writing to the correspondent by October each year. Trustees meet in November/ December. Successful applicants will receive their cheques during January. Organisations that have already received a grant should re-apply describing how the previous year's grant was spent and setting out how a further grant would be used. In general, less detailed information is required from national charities with a known track record than from small local charities that are not known to the trustees. NB 'Due to the volume of applications, it is not possible to acknowledge each application, nor is it possible to inform unsuccessful applicants.'

WHO TO APPLY TO Karen Griffin, c/o Deloitte and Touche, Blenheim House, Fitzalan Court, Newport Road, Cardiff CF24 0TS *Tel* 029 2048 1111

CC NO 258710   **ESTABLISHED** 1969

■ The Harvey and Hilary Gilbert Charitable Trust

WHERE FUNDING CAN BE GIVEN UK.
WHO CAN BENEFIT Registered charities.
WHAT IS FUNDED General charitable purposes.
SAMPLE GRANTS Community Security Trust (£10,000); Cancer Backup (£5,000); Gentlemen's Night Out (£1,000); Great Ormond Street Hospital (£500); and Wessex Cancer Trust (£150).
FINANCES *Year* 2007–08 *Income* £25,658 *Grants* £35,816 *Assets* £7,470
TRUSTEES Harvey Gilbert; Claire Abrahams.
HOW TO APPLY In writing to the correspondent.
WHO TO APPLY TO Harvey Gilbert, Trustee, 7 Spaniards Park, Columbas Drive, Hampstead, London NW3 7JD
CC NO 296293   **ESTABLISHED** 1986

■ The Girdlers' Company Charitable Trust

WHERE FUNDING CAN BE GIVEN UK, with a preference for City and East End of London, and Hammersmith and Peckham.
WHO CAN BENEFIT Registered charities benefiting children, young adults, academics, students and teachers.
WHAT IS FUNDED Medicine and health, education, welfare, youth welfare, heritage, environment, humanities and Christian religion.
WHAT IS NOT FUNDED Applications will only be considered from registered charities. Whilst it is extremely rare for grants to be made to individuals, the trustees will consider applications from, or on behalf of, a person who is disabled or disadvantaged needing financial support to enable their participation in a course of training or study leading to employment.
TYPE OF GRANT One-off and recurrent.
RANGE OF GRANTS Mostly up to £10,000.

SAMPLE GRANTS London Youth (£48,000); Leyton Orient Community Sports Programme (£28,600); Westminster House Youth Club (£15,000); Gordon's School (£14,000); Royal School of Needlework (£11,000); Guildhall School of Music and Drama (£10,000); The Oval Trust and Royal Star & Garter Homes (£9,000 each); Queen Elizabeth's Foundation for the Disabled (£7,500); The Cancer Treatment and Research Trust (£6,000); Haven House Foundation (£5,000); and The Food Chain (£1,000).

FINANCES *Year* 2007–08 *Income* £355,994 *Grants* £590,498 *Assets* £3,600,755

TRUSTEES Court of the Company of Girdlers.

HOW TO APPLY Applicants should write to the correspondent. To be considered for a donation please cover each of the following points: the beneficial area under which a grant is sought; a brief summary of the organisation's background and aims; the specific nature of the request, highlighting the change you wish to bring about; how you will know if you have achieved these changes; your charity registration number. Applications from charities whose beneficiaries reside in Hammersmith or Peckham are considered annually. Donations are in the order of £1,000. Each April and November the trustee considers general applications with ten donations of approximately £1,000 being made on each occasion. The closing dates are the last Friday in January and August. Successful applicants are unlikely to be awarded a further donation within the following five years. Successful applicants will be informed in May and December.

WHO TO APPLY TO John Gahan, Charities Manager, Girdlers' Hall, Basinghall Avenue, London EC2V 5DD *Tel* 020 7448 4851 *Fax* 020 7628 4030 *email* clerk@girdlers.co.uk

CC NO 328026   **ESTABLISHED** 1988

■ The Glass-House Trust

WHERE FUNDING CAN BE GIVEN Unrestricted, but UK in practice.
WHO CAN BENEFIT Registered charities and institutions.
WHAT IS FUNDED Housing, the built environment, art and child development.
WHAT IS NOT FUNDED Grants are not normally made to individuals.
RANGE OF GRANTS £1,200–£176,000.
SAMPLE GRANTS Glass-House Community-led Design (£176,000), for a further grant towards this project's core costs. This project was established by Trustees in 2000 and provides design advice to residents participating in the regeneration of social housing; A Space (£70,000), towards the director's salary for A Space in the London Borough of Hackney, an innovative project providing emotional support for children within a number of the Borough's primary and secondary schools; London Musicians Collective (£40,000), towards the costs of Resonance FM; Tate Millbank (£10,000), towards the major retrospective of the paintings of Peter Doig; Arts Educational School Trust, Tring Park School (£5,000), towards the Robert Cohan project, a collaboration with the Rambert School of Ballet and Contemporary Dance to document Cohan's dance and choreographic methods in association; Intoart Projects (£5,000), towards provision of a free studio space and materials for a learning disability arts project; and Paintings in Hospitals (£2,500), towards running

Think carefully about every application. Is it justified?

547

costs; The Sainsbury Archive (£1,200), towards running costs.

FINANCES *Year* 2007–08 *Income* £600,508 *Grants* £358,311 *Assets* £12,160,042

TRUSTEES Alexander Sainsbury; Timothy Sainsbury; Jessica Sainsbury; Elinor Sainsbury; Miss Judith Portrait.

OTHER INFORMATION The trust is one of the Sainsbury Family Charitable Trusts which share a common administration. An application to one is taken as an application to all.

HOW TO APPLY See the guidance for applicants in the entry for the Sainsbury Family Charitable Trusts. A single application will be considered for support by all the trusts in the group. However, in the case of this trust, 'trustees initiate proposals to be considered and do not encourage unsolicited approaches'.

WHO TO APPLY TO Alan Bookbinder, Director, Allington House, 1st Floor, 150 Victoria Street, London SW1E 5AE *Tel* 020 7410 0330 *Fax* 020 7410 0332 *Website* www.sfct.org.uk

CC NO 1017426   **ESTABLISHED** 1993

■ The B and P Glasser Charitable Trust

WHERE FUNDING CAN BE GIVEN UK and worldwide.

WHO CAN BENEFIT Registered charities.

WHAT IS FUNDED General charitable purposes, particularly health and disability charities, and Jewish organisations.

WHAT IS NOT FUNDED No grant to individuals or students.

RANGE OF GRANTS £500–£7,000.

SAMPLE GRANTS Practical Action (£8,000), Nightingale House (£7,500), RNIB adn Sight Savers International (£5,000 each): British Council Shaare Zedek Medical Centre, Jewish Deaf Association, Macmillan Cancer Relief – Hertfordshire and UNICEF (£2,000 each); Action Aid, British Red Cross and Friends of St Francis Hospice (£1,000 each); and Tring and District Patients Medical Fund (£500).

FINANCES *Year* 2007–08 *Income* £84,872 *Grants* £64,750 *Assets* £1,672,545

TRUSTEES J D H Cullingham; M J Glasser; J A Glasser.

HOW TO APPLY In writing to the correspondent. To keep administrative costs to a minimum the trust is unable to reply to unsuccessful applicants.

WHO TO APPLY TO B S Christer, Stafford Young Jones, The Old Rectory, 29 Martin Lane, London EC4R OAU

CC NO 326571   **ESTABLISHED** 1984

■ The Glastonbury Trust Limited

WHERE FUNDING CAN BE GIVEN UK.

WHO CAN BENEFIT Individuals, schools and other community groups in providing learning experiences that focus on emotional well-being and spiritual growth.

WHAT IS FUNDED Projects that address the needs of the wider community, particularly those that support family and community cohesion.

TYPE OF GRANT One-off.

RANGE OF GRANTS Up to about £10,000.

SAMPLE GRANTS Isle of Avalon Foundation (£9,600); Avalon Library (£3,900); and Goddess Temple (£3,700). In addition to the above grants, £12,000 was given under the category 'secondary schools', £1,900 to 'primary

schools' and a further £1,500 to 'other' causes.

FINANCES *Year* 2008 *Income* £70,337 *Grants* £32,942 *Assets* £576,007

TRUSTEES Godfrey Bishop; Martin Jones; Revd Judith Lawrence; Sheila Martin; Gareth Mills; Susan Strong; Robin Weelen.

OTHER INFORMATION The trust states that: 'The donations to the Isle of Avalon Foundation, Avalon Library and the Goddess Temple; an educational company and a religious body, have been made to help them pay their rents to Glastonbury Courtyard Limited (a wholly owned subsidiary).'

HOW TO APPLY Please note the following advice on the trust's website: 'The trust can consider applications for grants at any of its quarterly meetings. The grant process begins with potential applicants contacting the Executive Director, Chris Trwoga, by telephone or email to discuss the proposed project and to see whether it is likely to fall within the trust's funding criteria and is either charitably educational or charitably religious. Trustee meetings are held in March, June, September and December, so it is important that applicants contact the trust at least six weeks before the next trustees meeting in order to prepare the application for possible consideration at the meeting. The trust does not insist on match funding or partnership with other organisations in grant applications. If the trust agrees to fund a project, successful applicants will sign a contract agreeing to timescale and agreed outputs. Payment will generally be made in arrears on completion of specific targets, although advance payments can be made if the trust can be ensured that this money can be returned in the case of non-completion of the project.'

WHO TO APPLY TO Chris Trwoga, Executive Director, 2–4 High Street, Glastonbury BA6 9DU *Tel* 01458 831399 *email* glastonburytrust@ukonline.co.uk *Website* www.glastonburytrust.co.uk

CC NO 1078170   **ESTABLISHED** 1999

■ Global Care

WHERE FUNDING CAN BE GIVEN Overseas.

WHO CAN BENEFIT Children and families in one world's poorest countries through relief and development. People of many religions, cultures and social circumstances will be supported.

WHAT IS FUNDED Trustees favour children's charities already supported by them working in the poorest countries and the advancement of Christian education.

FINANCES *Year* 2008–09 *Income* £855,917 *Grants* £757,603 *Assets* £881,559

TRUSTEES Norman Lochhead; Rachel Murrill; Paul Slater; Sue Matejtschuk; Margaret Patterson; Raymond Neal; Mark Curran.

HOW TO APPLY Applications are not recommended. Trustees seek out projects to support, as appropriate, and new grants cannot be considered.

WHO TO APPLY TO John White, Chief Executive Officer, 2 Dugdale Road, Coventry CV6 1PB *Tel* 024 7660 1800 *Fax* 024 7660 1444 *email* info@globalcare.org.uk *Website* www.globalcare.org.uk

CC NO 1054008   **ESTABLISHED** 1996

■ Global Charities (formally GCap Charities)

WHERE FUNDING CAN BE GIVEN UK (Classic FM), London (Capital Radio), Cardiff (Red Dragon FM), Crawley (Mercury FM), London (Choice FM) and Peterborough, Colchester, Suffolk, Norwich, Cambridgeshire, Berkshire and North Hampshire, Bristol, Wiltshire, Oxfordshire, Gloucestershire, Exeter and East Devon, Plymouth, Somerset, Sussex, Hampshire and West Sussex, Dorset and New Forest, Essex and Kent (Heart Network).

WHO CAN BENEFIT Community organisations and registered charities.

WHAT IS FUNDED Projects supporting children, young people and adults, who: are experiencing poverty and disadvantage; have/are experiencing abuse, neglect, homelessness, violence or crime; or have an illness or disability.

WHAT IS NOT FUNDED Each individual branch has specific exclusions, generally however the charities will not fund: individual children or families; retrospective funding; statutory funding – funding for schools or health projects that would otherwise be covered by designated statutory funding from the local authority; salaried posts; deficit funding or repayment of loans; medical research; purchase of a minibus; trips abroad; distribution to other organisations; religious activities; political groups; general structural changes to buildings; projects which are part of a larger charity and are not separately constituted; core funding for a national or regional charity.

TYPE OF GRANT Capital; core costs; one-off; project; running costs.

RANGE OF GRANTS Mostly under £10,000. Larger grants are made very occasionally.

SAMPLE GRANTS Sixth Sense Theatre (£7,500); Cambourne Youth Partnership (£5,000); Havens Hospices – Essex (£3,000); Bangladeshi Parents Association (£2,100); Howbury Friends (£1,800); and Centrepoint – Hammersmith and Fulham (£1,600). Beneficiaries of the large grants programme included: Prince's Foundation for Children and the Arts (£100,000); Missing People (£61,000); and Impact Initiatives (£25,000). The charity has also distributed 66 grants totalling £401,000 to eligible groups in the year as part of its V project to develop youth volunteering activities.

FINANCES *Year* 2008–09 *Income* £3,375,862 *Grants* £2,039,619 *Assets* £1,354,529

TRUSTEES Martin George, Chair; Nigel Atkinson; David Briggs; Moira Swinbank; Paul Soames; Peter Williams.

HOW TO APPLY The charity provides the following guidance on its website: 'If you have a general enquiry regarding how to apply for funds please contact us (Tel: 020 7054 8391). We are always glad to answer questions from any organisation, charity or group on our grants process. Each station has at least one round of grant awards in the year. We attempt to fund as many eligible applications as possible, although this is always limited to the funds raised in the year. Details are given on each of our stations' websites [. . .] as well as how to apply for application forms. These forms are reviewed and updated by local grants panel in conjunction with the overall Board to ensure the application process is as accessible as possible and to ensure applicants are guided though our funding criteria.'

WHO TO APPLY TO Simon Knapp, Head of Operations and Finance, 30 Leicester Square, London WC2H 7LA *Tel* 020 7054 8389 *email* charities@thisisglobal.com *Website* www.thisisglobal.com/charities

CC NO 1091657   **ESTABLISHED** 1978

■ Gloucestershire Community Foundation

WHERE FUNDING CAN BE GIVEN Gloucestershire.

WHO CAN BENEFIT Charitable organisations and social enterprises.

WHAT IS FUNDED Combating disadvantage in Gloucestershire.

TYPE OF GRANT Revenue and full project funding.

FINANCES *Year* 2008 *Income* £794,454 *Grants* £438,000 *Assets* £2,812,684

TRUSTEES Simon Preston; Johnathan Carr; Lesley Archer; Ian Brothwood; Graham Bruce; Anne Chambers; Jonathan Carr; Harjit Gill; Richard Graham; Tania Hitchins; Andrew Stone; Brian Thornton; Chris Wakeman.

PUBLICATIONS Children in the Community – Making Things Better teachers' pack.

HOW TO APPLY Information sheets, guidelines and an application forms are avilable from the correpsondent. Staff are pleased to discuss any potential project applications. The foundation operates other funds and administers a number of grant making trusts. Please see its website for up-to-date details.

WHO TO APPLY TO The Grants Development Manager, British Energy, Barnett Way, Barnwood, Gloucester GL4 3RS *Tel* 01452 656386 *email* jane.jarman@british-energy.com or darien.parkes@british-energy.com *Website* www.gloucestershirecommunityfoundation.co.uk

CC NO 900239   **ESTABLISHED** 1989

■ The Gloucestershire Historic Churches Trust

WHERE FUNDING CAN BE GIVEN Gloucestershire.

WHO CAN BENEFIT Churches and chapels.

WHAT IS FUNDED 'GHCT is a charity which raises funds to help places of Christian worship of all denominations with repairs and improvements to the fabric of the buildings and their contents, as well as to their surrounding churchyards. Our aim is to help keep the 500 plus churches and chapels in the county alive, not only as places of worship and active centres of community life, but also as buildings which make a huge impact on the landscape of Gloucestershire and help to draw visitors to the county.'

WHAT IS NOT FUNDED No grants are made for routine maintenance.

TYPE OF GRANT One-off, but repeat applications will be considered.

RANGE OF GRANTS £250–£10,000, typical grant £2,500.

FINANCES *Year* 2008 *Income* £155,740 *Grants* £100,000 *Assets* £1,043,651

TRUSTEES Ian Phillips; Ben Woods; Richard Steel; Philip Kendell.

HOW TO APPLY Application forms and full guidelines can be downloaded from the trust's website.

WHO TO APPLY TO B Woods, Chair of Grants Committee, 2 Shepherds Way, Cirencester, Gloucestershire GL7 2EY *Tel* 01285 659159 *email* grants@ghct.org.uk *Website* www.ghct.org.uk

CC NO 1120266   **ESTABLISHED** 1980

■ Worshipful Company of Glovers of London Charity Fund

WHERE FUNDING CAN BE GIVEN UK with a preference for the City of London.

WHO CAN BENEFIT Glovers and glove-related projects; general charitable purposes.

WHAT IS FUNDED The trust makes grants mainly towards the provision of gloves, or to causes that are related to the City of London.

RANGE OF GRANTS Up to £3,000.

SAMPLE GRANTS City of London School (£6,300); King Edwards School (£3,500); British Glove Association prizes and Guildhall School of Music and Drama (£2,000 each); Crisis (£1,600); Jubilee Sailing Trust (£1,300); Church of St Margaret in Lothbury (£1,500); and the Passage (£1,000).

FINANCES *Year* 2007–08 *Income* £52,144 *Grants* £34,093 *Assets* £690,844

TRUSTEES S Brooker; J Brown; O Holmes; R Jennings; B Wicks.

HOW TO APPLY In writing to the correspondent.

WHO TO APPLY TO Mrs Monique Hood, Clerk, 73 Clapham Manor Street, London SW4 6ds *Tel* 020 7622 2167 *Fax* 020 7622 0316

CC NO 269091   **ESTABLISHED** 1975

■ GMC Trust

WHERE FUNDING CAN BE GIVEN UK, predominantly in the West Midlands.

WHO CAN BENEFIT Organisations benefiting children, young adults and older people.

WHAT IS FUNDED Primarily medical research, also causes related to inner city deprivation. Income is substantially committed to a range of existing beneficiaries.

WHAT IS NOT FUNDED No grants to individuals, or to local or regional appeals outside the West Midlands. The trust does not respond to national appeals, except where there are established links.

TYPE OF GRANT One-off.

RANGE OF GRANTS Grants of up to £50,000.

SAMPLE GRANTS Cancer Research UK and Mental Health Foundation (£50,000 each); ZANE (£11,000); Mind and Prostate Cancer Research Centre (£10,000 each); CORE – Digestive Disorders Foundation (£5,000); Age Concern (£2,500); Schools Outreach and King's Lynn Arts Centre (£2,000 each); NSPCC, Depaul Trust and Birmingham Royal Ballet (£1,000 each); British Lung Foundation and Musicians Benevolent Fund (£500 each); and British-Nigeria Educational Trust and Lymphoma Association (£100 each).

FINANCES *Year* 2007–08 *Income* £166,801 *Grants* £231,650 *Assets* £2,480,082

TRUSTEES Sir Adrian Cadbury; B E S Cadbury; M J Cadbury.

HOW TO APPLY In writing to the correspondent. The trust will only consider written applications, and applications outside the trust's remit will not be acknowledged.

WHO TO APPLY TO Rodney Pitts, Secretary, 4 Fairways, 1240 Warwick Road, Knowle, Solihull, West Midlands B93 9LL *Tel* 01564 779971 *Fax* 01564 770499

CC NO 288418   **ESTABLISHED** 1965

■ The GNC Trust

WHERE FUNDING CAN BE GIVEN UK, with preferences for Birmingham and Cornwall.

WHO CAN BENEFIT Registered charities.

WHAT IS FUNDED To support those charities which the trustees have special interest in, knowledge of or association with.

WHAT IS NOT FUNDED No grants are made to national appeals, London-based charities or to individuals.

RANGE OF GRANTS £20–£10,000; mostly for £1,000 or less.

SAMPLE GRANTS Downing College (£250,000); Oxford Research Group (£10,000); Oxford Peace Research Trust (£5,000); Grace of God Church (£4,000); Orthodox Church (£2,500); Marie Curie Cancer Care and Association for International Cancer Research (£1,000 each); and Overseas Mission Fellowship (£750).

FINANCES *Year* 2007 *Income* £72,681 *Grants* £312,105 *Assets* £1,500,869

TRUSTEES G T E Cadbury; R N Cadbury; Mrs J E B Yelloly.

HOW TO APPLY In writing to the correspondent at any time. There are no application forms and applications are not acknowledged.

WHO TO APPLY TO Mrs P M Spragg, c/o PricewaterhouseCoopers, Cornwall Court, 19 Cornwall Street, Birmingham B3 2DT *Tel* 0121 265 5000

CC NO 211533   **ESTABLISHED** 1960

■ The Mrs Godfrey-Payton Trust

WHERE FUNDING CAN BE GIVEN Warwick Town only.

WHO CAN BENEFIT Registered charities.

WHAT IS FUNDED Particular interests are: projects that benefit Warwick Town and the inhabitants thereof, for example, arts, almshouses and youth clubs; projects (non-medical) designed to help older people retain their independence; and projects known to the trustees.

WHAT IS NOT FUNDED Grants are not given for medical purposes or to individuals.

TYPE OF GRANT Usually one-off. Buildings, capital, core costs, feasibility studies, projects and funding for up to one year will be considered.

SAMPLE GRANTS Previous beneficiaries have included Elizabeth Finn Trust, Friendship Project for Children, South Warwickshire Carers' Support Service, Warwick Arts Society and Warwick District CVS.

FINANCES *Year* 2008 *Income* £72,688 *Grants* £104,250

TRUSTEES Richard David Creed; Matthew George Life.

HOW TO APPLY In writing to the correspondent. The trustees will accept unsolicited applications but cannot and support or reply to them all.

WHO TO APPLY TO Richard D Creed, Trustee, Foresters House, Sherston, Malmesbury, Wiltshire SN16 0LQ

CC NO 1005851   **ESTABLISHED** 1991

■ The Meir Golda Trust

WHERE FUNDING CAN BE GIVEN UK.

WHO CAN BENEFIT Particular favour is given to Jewish charities, but charities benefiting followers of all faiths are considered. People with illnesses of any kind are a priority.

WHAT IS FUNDED General charitable purposes; the arts; conservation; animal facilities and services; synagogues and Jewish bodies.

RANGE OF GRANTS £18–£40,500.

SAMPLE GRANTS No beneficiary list was available.
FINANCES *Year* 2007–08 *Income* £13,357
Grants £2,272
TRUSTEES J Gutstein
HOW TO APPLY In writing to the correspondent.
WHO TO APPLY TO J Gutstein, 17 Highfield Road,
London NW11 9LS *Tel* 020 8731 9393
CC NO 1041256   **ESTABLISHED** 1994

■ The Sydney and Phyllis Goldberg Memorial Charitable Trust

WHERE FUNDING CAN BE GIVEN UK.
WHO CAN BENEFIT Organisations benefiting, research
workers, at risk groups, and people who are
disabled, disadvantaged by poverty or socially
isolated.
WHAT IS FUNDED Medical research, welfare and
disability.
TYPE OF GRANT One-off, some recurrent.
RANGE OF GRANTS Usually up to £15,000.
SAMPLE GRANTS Children of St Mary's Intensive Care
Department of Child Health, the British
Stammering Association, the Dystonia Society,
Children with Special Needs Foundation, Life
Centre and the Prostate Cancer Charity
(£13,500 each); and Isaac Goldberg Charity
Trust (£7,500).
FINANCES *Year* 2007–08 *Income* £544,073
Grants £102,000 *Assets* £3,055,515
TRUSTEES H G Vowles; M J Church; C J Pexton.
HOW TO APPLY In writing to the correspondent.
Telephone requests are not appreciated.
Applicants are advised to apply towards the end
of the calendar year.
WHO TO APPLY TO M J Church, Trustee, Coulthards
Mackenzie, 17 Park Street, Camberley, Surrey
GU15 3PQ *Tel* 01276 65470
CC NO 291835   **ESTABLISHED** 1985

■ The Golden Bottle Trust

WHERE FUNDING CAN BE GIVEN Worldwide.
WHO CAN BENEFIT Registered charities.
WHAT IS FUNDED General charitable purposes with a
preference for charities supporting the
environment, health, education, religion, the
arts and developing countries.
WHAT IS NOT FUNDED No grants for individuals or
organisations that are not registered charities.
TYPE OF GRANT 'One-off' and recurring.
RANGE OF GRANTS Up to £10,000.
SAMPLE GRANTS The Bulldog Trust (£230,000);
China Oxford Scholarship Fund (£100,000);
Eton College (£50,000); Henry C Hoare
Charitable Trust (£30,000); Jesus College
Cambridge (£20,000); Trinity Hospice
(£14,000); Migratory Salmon Fund, Theatre of
Memory Trust, Ahoy Centre, Royal Academy and
Wells Cathedral Girl Choristers' Trust (£10,000
each); RIDA Drawings and Archives (£7,500);
Royal College of Surgeons (£7,000); and Flora
& Fauna International (£5,200).
FINANCES *Year* 2007–08 *Income* £1,157,372
Grants £942,667 *Assets* £7,095,481
TRUSTEES Messrs Hoare Trustees (H C Hoare;
D J Hoare; R Q Hoare; A S Hoare; V E Hoare;
S M Hoare; A S Hopewell.)
HOW TO APPLY In writing to the correspondent.
Applications are considered from bank staff and
external registered charities.

WHO TO APPLY TO Miss J Moore, Messrs Hoare
Trustees, 37 Fleet Street, London EC4P 4DQ
Tel 020 7353 4522 *Fax* 020 7353 4521
email enquiries@hoaresbank.co.uk
CC NO 327026   **ESTABLISHED** 1985

■ Golden Charitable Trust

WHERE FUNDING CAN BE GIVEN UK with a preference
for West Sussex.
WHO CAN BENEFIT Registered charities.
WHAT IS FUNDED Literature, English Literature, the
conservation of printed books and manuscripts,
and libraries and museums, church restoration
and medical research.
WHAT IS NOT FUNDED No grants to individuals.
TYPE OF GRANT Endowment, sometimes recurring.
RANGE OF GRANTS Up to £20,000, usually between
£100–£2,500.
SAMPLE GRANTS Westminster Synagogue
(£100,000); Petworth Cottage Nursing Home
(£20,000) the Music Mind Spirit Trust
(£10,000); The Wordsworth Trust (£2,500); The
Langdon Foundation (£2,000); Chichester
Cathedral Trust (£1,800); Royal School of
Needlework and Inter-Cultural Youth Exchange
(£1,000 each); Reform Foundation Trust (£700);
the Macmillan Cancer Trust and Dermatitis and
Allied Diseases Research Trust (£500 each);
Helen and Douglas House (£250); and Cancer
Research UK (£100).
FINANCES *Year* 2007–08 *Income* £116,007
Grants £154,638 *Assets* £1,023,281
TRUSTEES Mrs S J F Solnick; J M F Golden.
HOW TO APPLY In writing to the correspondent.
WHO TO APPLY TO Lewis Golden, Secretary to the
Trustees, Little Leith Gate, Angel Street,
Petworth, West Sussex GU28 0BG *Tel* 01798
342434
CC NO 263916   **ESTABLISHED** 1972

■ The Jack Goldhill Charitable Trust

WHERE FUNDING CAN BE GIVEN UK.
WHO CAN BENEFIT Registered charities benefiting
those in need.
WHAT IS FUNDED Human need causes and visual
arts.
WHAT IS NOT FUNDED No support for individuals or
new applications.
SAMPLE GRANTS Previous beneficiaries have included
CST, City and Guilds of London School of Art,
Jack Goldhill Award Fund, JNF Charitable Trust,
Jewish Care, Joint Jewish Charitable Trust,
Nightingale House, Royal Academy of Arts, Royal
London Hospital, Tate Gallery, Tricycle Theatre
Co., West London Synagogue and Atlantic
College.
FINANCES *Year* 2007 *Income* £112,859
Grants £104,070 *Assets* £285,825
TRUSTEES G Goldhill; J A Goldhill; M L Goldhill.
OTHER INFORMATION A list of grants has not been
included with the accounts filed at the Christy
Commission in recent years.
HOW TO APPLY The trustees have a restricted list of
charities to whom they are committed and no
unsolicited applications can be considered.
WHO TO APPLY TO Jack Goldhill, Trustee, 85
Kensington Heights, Campden Hill Road, London
W8 7BD *Tel* 020 7727 4326
CC NO 267018   **ESTABLISHED** 1974

■ The Goldmark Trust

WHERE FUNDING CAN BE GIVEN UK.

WHO CAN BENEFIT Registered charities.

WHAT IS FUNDED General charitable purposes.

RANGE OF GRANTS Typically up to £5,000.

SAMPLE GRANTS Sight Savers International – Eye Care programme in Sierra Leone and After Adoption (£5,000 each); Rainbow Trust, Fostering Network and Diabetes UK (£2,500 each); Noah's Ark Trust (£2,000); and Tuberous Sclerosis Association, British Blind Sport, Bikeability and Jubilee Sailing Trust (£1,000 each).

FINANCES *Year* 2007–08 *Income* £135,177 *Grants* £60,000 *Assets* £2,283,815

TRUSTEES A O M Goldsmith; P L Luckett; M J Snell.

HOW TO APPLY In writing to the correspondent. The trustees meet at least twice a year.

WHO TO APPLY TO Graham Cole, 30 St Giles, Oxford OX1 3LE

CC NO 1072901   **ESTABLISHED** 1998

■ The Goldsmiths' Arts Trust Fund

WHERE FUNDING CAN BE GIVEN UK.

WHO CAN BENEFIT Registered charities.

WHAT IS FUNDED The arts by the encouragement of the art of design and good craftsmanship.

SAMPLE GRANTS Goldsmiths' Craft and Design Council (£34,000); University College for the Creative Arts (£20,000); City of London Festival (£10,000); Royal College of Art (£7,000); University of Central England (£2,500); London Metropolitan University (£1,600); and Yorkshire Arts Space (£1,000).

FINANCES *Year* 2007–08 *Income* £1,258,318 *Grants* £108,650 *Assets* £73,257

TRUSTEES Court of Assistants of the Goldsmiths' Company; Susan Bailey.

HOW TO APPLY In writing to the correspondent.

WHO TO APPLY TO The Clerk, The Goldsmiths' Company, Goldsmiths' Hall, Foster Lane, London EC2V 6BN *Tel* 020 7606 7010 *Fax* 020 7606 1511 *email* the.clerk@ thegoldsmiths.co.uk *Website* www. thegoldsmiths.co.uk

CC NO 313329

■ The Goldsmiths' Company Charity

WHERE FUNDING CAN BE GIVEN UK, with a special interest in London charities.

WHO CAN BENEFIT Registered charities, individuals connected with the trade of goldsmithing, silversmithing and jewellery, and Londoners in need. Grants are made to London-based or national charities, but not to local provincial charities. Where charities are members, branches or affiliates of an association, appeals are accepted from the governing body or head office of that association only. In the case of church restoration, block grants are made to the Historic Churches Preservation Trust and therefore appeals from individual churches will not normally be considered.

WHAT IS FUNDED Support of the goldsmiths' craft, education, and general charitable purposes (including general welfare, medical welfare, young people, heritage, church, and arts.).

WHAT IS NOT FUNDED Applications are not normally considered on behalf of medical research; animal welfare; memorials to individuals; overseas projects; individual housing

associations; endowment schemes; charities with a turnover of more than £10 million.

TYPE OF GRANT Buildings, capital, salaries, core, project, start-up and running costs. Funding is occasionally three year, but usually one-off.

RANGE OF GRANTS £500 upwards.

SAMPLE GRANTS 7th Rifles Welfare Fund – to provide combined mess facilities at Dalton barracks (£100,000); Somerset Community Foundation – for the rural deprivation project (£60,000); National Churches Trust – for general funds (£30,000); City Music Society – for sponsorship of a series of concerts (£19,000); Federation of London Youth Clubs (London Youth) – for general funds and Chemistry Olympiad – to provide medals for the 2009 event (£10,000 each); Strawberry Hill Trust – towards regilding the state rooms (£6,000); Council for Music in Hospitals – for work in Northern Ireland (£5,000); Core Arts – for the poetry tutor's costs (£3,000); and CMO Productions – for the 2008 summer school holiday project (£1,000).

FINANCES *Year* 2007–08 *Income* £3,839,384 *Grants* £2,991,325 *Assets* £80,961,765

TRUSTEES The Court of Assistants of the Goldsmiths' Company. The Charity Advisory Committee consists of: D A E R Peake, Chair; S A Shepherd; A M J Galsworthy; Hon. Mark Bridges; Revd D Paton; W H C Montgomery; Dr C Mackworth-Young; Mrs S Hamilton; J R Polk; Mrs V R Beverley; R O'Hara.

HOW TO APPLY Applications should be made by letter, no more than two sides of A4 in length, highlighting the case for the company to give its support. The letter should be accompanied by the completed application form, which can be downloaded from the company's website. The form may be retyped, but should follow the same format and length (three sides of A4). All questions should be answered. Do not cut and paste information on the form. Legible handwritten applications are acceptable. The charity's most recent annual report and audited accounts (or financial report required by the Charities Act) should also be included. Applications are considered monthly, except in August and September, and there is usually a three to four month delay between receipt of an appeal and a decision being made. Applications from any organisation, whether successful or not, are not normally considered more frequently than every three years. Any enquiries should be addressed to the correspondent.

WHO TO APPLY TO Miss H Erskine, Charity Administrator, Goldsmiths' Hall, Foster Lane, London EC2V 6BN *Tel* 020 7606 7010 *Fax* 020 7606 1511 *email* charity@ thegoldsmiths.co.uk *Website* www. thegoldsmiths.co.uk/charities

CC NO 1088699   **ESTABLISHED** 1961

■ The Golsoncott Foundation

WHERE FUNDING CAN BE GIVEN UK.

WHO CAN BENEFIT Arts organisations.

WHAT IS FUNDED The trust states its objects as follows: 'to promote, maintain, improve and advance the education of the public in the arts generally and in particular the fine arts and music. The fostering of the practice and appreciation of the arts, especially amongst young people and new audiences, is a further specific objective.'

WHAT IS NOT FUNDED No grants to individuals.

TYPE OF GRANT One-off and some recurring grants.

RANGE OF GRANTS £200–£5,000.

....

■ Golubovich Foundation

....

■ The Good Neighbours Trust

■ Goodfund

WHERE FUNDING CAN BE GIVEN North east of England.

WHO CAN BENEFIT Children and young people and those who are social disadvantaged.

WHAT IS FUNDED Children's wellbeing, poverty, nature and wildlife conservation, community development.

WHAT IS NOT FUNDED Initiatives of a political; mainstream educational or religious nature are generally excluded.

SAMPLE GRANTS Help the Aged, Northumberland Wildlife Trust and Mencap (£29,000 each); Percy Hedley School (£25,000); and the National Missing Persons Helpline (local initiatives) and Daisy Chain (£15,000 each).

FINANCES *Year* 2008 *Income* £1,334,755 *Grants* £343,746 *Assets* £55,889

TRUSTEES D W Midgley, Chair; J Chexal; F Raglan.

HOW TO APPLY A nominated form can either be download from the Goodfund website, or requested by telephone. It can also be completed online.

WHO TO APPLY TO A R Turner, Company Secretary, Fabriam Centre, Atmel Way, Silverlink, Newcastle upon Tyne NE28 9NZ *Tel* 0191 280 4349 *Fax* 0191 280 5411 *email* applications@goodfund.org *Website* www.goodfund.org

CC NO 1107024   **ESTABLISHED** 2004

■ Nicholas and Judith Goodison's Charitable Settlement

WHERE FUNDING CAN BE GIVEN UK.

WHO CAN BENEFIT Registered charities.

WHAT IS FUNDED Arts and arts education; mostly commitments to previously supported charities. Other causes may be considered.

WHAT IS NOT FUNDED No grants to individuals.

TYPE OF GRANT Recurrent capital grants. One-off grants may be considered.

RANGE OF GRANTS £200–£40,000, although most grants are for £2,000 or less.

SAMPLE GRANTS Wigmore Hall and Handel House Trust (£25,000); V and A – Medieval (£20,000); and The Courtauld Institute (£15,000); Fitzwilliam (£6,900); Academy of Ancient Music, English National Opera and London Library (£5,000 each); Victoria and Albert Museum (£2,700); British Museum (£2,000); Attingham Trust, Royal Academy Exhibitions and Tate Foundation (£1,000 each); National Life Story Collection (£850); Crafts Council (£500); and World Monuments Fund (£350).

FINANCES *Year* 2007–08 *Income* £217,040 *Grants* £153,189 *Assets* £1,820,980

TRUSTEES Sir Nicholas Goodison; Lady Judith Goodison; Miss Katharine Goodison.

HOW TO APPLY The trust states that it cannot respond to unsolicited applications.

WHO TO APPLY TO Sir N Goodison, Trustee, PO Box 2512, London W1A 5ZP

CC NO 1004124   **ESTABLISHED** 1991

■ The Everard and Mina Goodman Charitable Foundation

WHERE FUNDING CAN BE GIVEN UK and Israel.

WHO CAN BENEFIT Registered charities only.

WHAT IS FUNDED As well as supporting causes related to the Jewish faith, this trust also makes grants for: the relief of poverty; the advancement of education; children and young people; medicine and health; and rehabilitation and training.

WHAT IS NOT FUNDED No grants to individuals.

SAMPLE GRANTS Previous beneficiaries include: British Friends of Bar-Ilan University – Life Sciences Faculty, Variety Club – Sunshine Coach Appeal, British Friends of Laniado Hospital, Child Resettlement Fund, Institute for Jewish Policy Research, Western Marble Arch Synagogue, Smile Train UK, Jewish Women's Aid, National Autistic Society and High Blood Pressure Foundation.

FINANCES *Year* 2007–08 *Income* £59,401 *Grants* £272,674 *Assets* £1,806,883

TRUSTEES Dr Everard Goodman; Mina Goodman; Michael Goodman; Suzanne Goodman; David Goodman.

OTHER INFORMATION In 2006 the foundation's income increased significantly due to a substantial donation from the settlor, Everard Goodman, former chief executive of property company Tops Estates. Although, a substantial part of this went to the Faculty of Life Sciences at Bar-Ilan University in Israel (£2 million), the foundation's increase in income has allowed the level of general grantmaking to rise significantly.

HOW TO APPLY In writing to the correspondent.

WHO TO APPLY TO Dr Everard Goodman, Trustee, Flat 5, 5 Bryanston Court, London W1H 7HA *Tel* 020 7355 3333

CC NO 220474   **ESTABLISHED** 1962

■ The Goodman Foundation

WHERE FUNDING CAN BE GIVEN UK, excluding Scotland.

WHO CAN BENEFIT Registered charities.

WHAT IS FUNDED General, social welfare, older people, health and disability.

FINANCES *Year* 2007–08 *Income* £516,634 *Grants* £336,372 *Assets* £1,510,415

TRUSTEES L J Goodman; C Goodman; R M Cracknell; L Tidd.

OTHER INFORMATION In 2007–08 grants were given in the following categories: 'Poor, sick, elderly and disabled' (£159,000); 'Third world and disasters' (£93,000); 'other' (£53,000); 'children's charities' (£31,000).

HOW TO APPLY In writing to the correspondent.

WHO TO APPLY TO The Trustees, c/o APB, Unit 6290, Bishops Court, Solihull Parkway, Birmingham Business Park, Birmingham B37 7YB

CC NO 1097231   **ESTABLISHED** 2003

■ Mike Gooley Trailfinders Charity

WHERE FUNDING CAN BE GIVEN UK.

WHO CAN BENEFIT Charitable organisations.

WHAT IS FUNDED Medical research and general charitable purposes.

WHAT IS NOT FUNDED Grants are not made to overseas charities or to individuals.

RANGE OF GRANTS £100–£500,000.

SAMPLE GRANTS Previous grants include: Alzheimer's Society (£400,000); Prostate Cancer Charity (£100,000); and Second World War Experience Centre (£40,000).

FINANCES *Year* 2007–08 *Income* £1,104,140 *Grants* £439,500 *Assets* £9,847,244

TRUSTEES Mark Bannister; Michael D W Gooley; Bernadette M Gooley; Tristan P Gooley; Fiona Gooley; Louise Breton.

OTHER INFORMATION A list of grants was not included in the charity's recent accounts.

HOW TO APPLY In writing to the correspondent.

WHO TO APPLY TO Louise Breton, Trustee, Trailfinders Ltd, 9 Abingdon Road, London W8 6AH *Tel* 020 7938 3143 *Fax* 020 7937 6059
CC NO 1048993   ESTABLISHED 1995

■ Leonard Gordon Charitable Trust

WHERE FUNDING CAN BE GIVEN England and Wales.
WHO CAN BENEFIT Jewish organisations.
WHAT IS FUNDED Religion, education and welfare.
FINANCES *Year* 2007–08 *Income* £30,045 *Grants* £86,991 *Assets* £195,615
TRUSTEES Leonard Gordon, Chair; Michael Gordon; Ian Fidler.
HOW TO APPLY In writing to the correspondent.
WHO TO APPLY TO Leonard Gordon, Chair, 17 Park Street, Salford M7 4NJ *Tel* 0161 792 3421
CC NO 1075185   ESTABLISHED 1999

■ The Gosling Foundation Limited

WHERE FUNDING CAN BE GIVEN Worldwide. In practice UK.
WHO CAN BENEFIT Registered charities.
WHAT IS FUNDED The relief of poverty, suffering and distress; provision of facilities for recreation and other leisure-time occupation (in the interests of social welfare); naval and service charities; advancement of education; furtherance of other charitable purposes.
RANGE OF GRANTS Mainly £100–£5,000, but up to £300,000.
SAMPLE GRANTS Armed Forces Memorial Trust (two grants totalling £350,000); White Ensign Association (three grants totalling £205,000); Princes' Foundation (two grants totalling £102,000); Greater London Fund for the Blind (£100,000); Maritime Reserve Centenary Fund (2 grants totalling £60,000); Special Boat Service Association (£50,000); HMS Ark Royal (Central Fund) (two grants totalling (£35,000); Royal Marine Band (£30,000); Tennis Foundation (two grants totalling £25,000); Seafarers UK (£21,000); Twickenham Sea Cadets (two grants totalling £20,000); HMS Heron CAF – Church Fund (two grants totalling £8,000); Darlmouth Baptist Church and St Paul's Trust Centre (£5,000 each); Hands Around the World (£2,000); and St Paul's Church Knightsbridge (£500).
FINANCES *Year* 2007–08 *Income* £4,286,044 *Grants* £1,930,050 *Assets* £92,433,632
TRUSTEES Sir Donald Gosling; Ronald F Hobson; R J Knight; A P Gosling.
HOW TO APPLY In writing to the correspondent. The grant making policies of the foundation are 'regularly reviewed' and currently are: applications should fall within the objects of the foundation; there is no minimum limit for any grant; all grants will be approved unanimously; the charity will only make grants to individuals in exceptional circumstances.
WHO TO APPLY TO Miss Anne Yusof, Secretary, 21 Bryanston Street, Marble Arch, London W1H 7PR *Tel* 020 7495 5599
CC NO 326840   ESTABLISHED 1962

■ The Gough Charitable Trust

WHERE FUNDING CAN BE GIVEN UK, with a possible preference for Scotland.
WHO CAN BENEFIT Registered charities only, usually working in the areas outlined below, benefiting children, young adults and the Church of England.
WHAT IS FUNDED Youth projects; Episcopal or Church of England projects; preservation of the countryside.
WHAT IS NOT FUNDED No support for non-registered charities and individuals including students.
TYPE OF GRANT Usually one-off but some ongoing.
SAMPLE GRANTS Irish Guards Lieutenant Colonels Fund, Prince of Wales Lodge No 259 Benevolent Fund, The Lifeboat Service Memorial Book Trust, National Army Development Trust, Household Brigade Benevolent Fund, Lloyds Charities Fund, Lloyds Benevolent Fund, Crown and Manor Boys Club and Trinity Hospice.
FINANCES *Year* 2007–08 *Income* £43,307 *Grants* £7,100
TRUSTEES Lloyds Bank plc.
HOW TO APPLY In writing to the correspondent at any time. No acknowledgements are sent. Applications are considered quarterly.
WHO TO APPLY TO The Trust Manager, Lloyds TSB Private Banking Ltd, UK Trust Centre, 22–26 Ock Street, Abingdon OX14 5SW *Tel* 01235 232712
CC NO 262355   ESTABLISHED 1970

■ The Gould Charitable Trust

WHERE FUNDING CAN BE GIVEN UK.
WHO CAN BENEFIT Registered charities only.
WHAT IS FUNDED General charitable purposes, with a preference for charities working in the field of self-help.
WHAT IS NOT FUNDED No grants to individuals.
RANGE OF GRANTS Usually up to £5,000.
SAMPLE GRANTS One to One (£5,000); Alzheimers Research Trust, NSPCC and FCED Foundation Philippines (£2,000 each); Child Hope (£600); Medecins Sans Frontiers, Friends of Hebrew University, and New Israel Fund (£500 each); SOS Children and Jewish World Relief (£300 each); and Project Trust and Hackney Quest (£200 each).
FINANCES *Year* 2007–08 *Income* £52,618 *Grants* £61,915 *Assets* £951,184
TRUSTEES Mrs J B Gould; L J Gould; M S Gould; S Gould; S H Gould.
HOW TO APPLY In writing to the correspondent, although the trust states: 'We never give donations to unsolicited requests on principle.'
WHO TO APPLY TO S Gould, Trustee, Cervantes, Pinner Hill, Pinner, Middlesex HA5 3XU
CC NO 1035453   ESTABLISHED 1993

■ The Grace Charitable Trust

WHERE FUNDING CAN BE GIVEN UK.
WHO CAN BENEFIT Registered charities, including Christian organisations.
WHAT IS FUNDED General charitable purposes, Christian, education, medical and social welfare.
RANGE OF GRANTS £1,000–£10,000.
SAMPLE GRANTS Alpha (£25,000); the International Christian College (£25,000); and Euroevangelism (£52,000).
FINANCES *Year* 2007–08 *Income* £80,051 *Grants* £311,406 *Assets* £3,465,621
TRUSTEES Mrs G J R Payne; E Payne; Mrs G M Snaith; R B M Quayle.
OTHER INFORMATION In 2007–08, a further £8,900 was given in grants to individuals.
HOW TO APPLY The trust states: 'Grants are made only to charities known to the settlors and unsolicited applications are, therefore, not considered.'
WHO TO APPLY TO Mrs G J R Payne, Trustee, Rhuallt House, Rhuallt, St Asaph, Sir Ddinbych

Think carefully about every application. Is it justified?

555

LL17 0TG *Tel* 01745 583141 *Fax* 01745
585243
cc no 292984 **ESTABLISHED** 1985

■ A B Grace Trust

WHERE FUNDING CAN BE GIVEN Garstang and Preston.
WHO CAN BENEFIT Charitable organisations.
WHAT IS FUNDED General charitable purposes.
TYPE OF GRANT Recurrent.
SAMPLE GRANTS Christ Church – Over Wyresdale,
RNLI, RSPB and St Peter's Parish Church –
Scorton (£6,500 each); and Guide Dogs for the
Blind, RSPCA, St Helen's Church, Churchtown,
St Mary's and St Michael's Church – Bonds and
United Reformed Church – Garstang (£5,200).
FINANCES *Year* 2007–08 *Income* £42,202
Grants £52,000 *Assets* £992,298
TRUSTEES Anthony H Blunt; Thomas I Balmain;
Valerie M Wilson.
HOW TO APPLY 'The charity's trust deed sets out very
specifically who are beneficiaries are to be and
consequently we are unable to consider any
grant applications.'
WHO TO APPLY TO Antony Blunt, Trustee, 31
Yewlands Drive, Garstang, Preston PR3 1JP
cc no 504332 **ESTABLISHED** 1975

■ The Graff Foundation

WHERE FUNDING CAN BE GIVEN UK and worldwide.
WHO CAN BENEFIT Charitable organisations.
WHAT IS FUNDED General charitable purposes.
TYPE OF GRANT One-off and recurrent.
SAMPLE GRANTS Raisa Gorbachev Foundation
(£6,000); Beis Yisrael Trust and the Tate
Foundation (£5,000); Elton John AIDS
Foundation (£2,500); and White Ribbon Alliance
and Laniado Hospital – Israel (£2,000 each).
FINANCES *Year* 2008 *Income* £182,384
Grants £21,500 *Assets* £3,254,551
TRUSTEES Laurence Graff; Francois Xavier Graff;
Anthony D Kerman.
HOW TO APPLY In writing to the correspondent.
WHO TO APPLY TO Anthony D Kerman, Trustee,
Kerman and Co LLP, 200 Strand, London
WC2R 1DJ
cc no 1012859 **ESTABLISHED** 1991

■ The Grahame Charitable Foundation Limited

WHERE FUNDING CAN BE GIVEN UK and overseas.
WHO CAN BENEFIT Organisations benefiting: children,
young adults, older people and Jewish people.
WHAT IS FUNDED The advancement of the Jewish
religion; health facilities and buildings, medical
studies and research; special schools; cultural
and religious teaching; and community services.
WHAT IS NOT FUNDED No grants to individuals.
TYPE OF GRANT Capital, core costs, interest-free
loans, one-off, recurring costs and start-up
costs. Funding for up to two years may be
considered.
RANGE OF GRANTS £100–£60,000.
SAMPLE GRANTS British Friends of the Shaare Zedek
Medical Centre (£60,000); and United Jewish
Israel Appeal (£38,000).
FINANCES *Year* 2008 *Income* £205,993
Grants £311,272 *Assets* £1,383,911
TRUSTEES A Grahame; J M Greenwood.
HOW TO APPLY The trustees allocate funds on a long-
term basis and therefore have none available
for other applicants.

WHO TO APPLY TO Mrs G Grahame, Secretary, 5
Spencer Walk, Hampstead High Street, London
NW3 1QZ *Tel* 020 7794 5281
cc no 1102332 **ESTABLISHED** 1969

■ Grampian Police Diced Cap Charitable Fund

WHERE FUNDING CAN BE GIVEN Within the Grampian
police force area only.
WHO CAN BENEFIT Charitable organisations.
WHAT IS FUNDED General charitable purposes.
WHAT IS NOT FUNDED National charities and those
outside the beneficial area cannot be
supported.
FINANCES *Year* 2008–09 *Income* £155,613
Grants £35,000
HOW TO APPLY In writing to the correspondent.
WHO TO APPLY TO The Secretary, Queen Street,
Aberdeen AB10 1ZA
sc no SC017901

■ The Granada Foundation

WHERE FUNDING CAN BE GIVEN North west England.
WHO CAN BENEFIT Organisations.
WHAT IS FUNDED Encouragement and promotion of
the study, practice and appreciation of the fine
arts and the methods and means of their
dissemination; encouragement and promotion of
the study and application of the sciences;
promotion and advancement of education;
promotion and provision of facilities for
recreation or other leisure time occupation in
the interests of social welfare.
WHAT IS NOT FUNDED No grants will be given for
general appeals, individuals (including for
courses of study), expeditions, overseas travel
or youth clubs/community associations.
RANGE OF GRANTS £500–£15,000.
SAMPLE GRANTS Chetham's School of Music
(£75,000); Buxton Festival (£20,000); Tate
Liverpool (£5,000); Bollington Festival (£4,000);
Comma Press, Momentum Theatre, Liverpool
Lantern Company and North West Disability Arts
Forum (£2,000 each); and Boojum Theatre
Company (£1,000).
FINANCES *Year* 2008–09 *Income* £147,557
Grants £151,000 *Assets* £2,619,266
TRUSTEES Advisory Council: Sir Robert Scott, Chair;
Lord Bernstein; Lady Manduell; Prof. Denis
McCaldin; Mrs Margaret Kenyon; Philip
Ramsbottom; Miss Kathy Arundale; Prof.
Jennifer Latto; Christopher Kerr.
HOW TO APPLY On an application form, available in
writing from the correspondent, giving an outline
of the project. Detailed information can be
added when the formal application is submitted.
Details of the next trustees' meeting will be
given when an application form is sent (trustees
meet three times a year at irregular intervals).
All letters are acknowledged. 'The Advisory
Council interprets the guidelines in a flexible
way, realising that it cannot hope to achieve a
true balance across all the areas of activity. The
council does, however, examine the context of
each application and tries to make grants in
areas where the benefit will be most widely felt.'
WHO TO APPLY TO Mrs Irene Langford, Administrator,
PO Box 3430, Chester CH1 9BZ *Tel* 01244
661867 *email* irene.langford@btconnect.com
Website www.granadafoundation.org
cc no 241693 **ESTABLISHED** 1965

■ Grand Charitable Trust of the Order of Women Freemasons

WHERE FUNDING CAN BE GIVEN UK and overseas.

WHO CAN BENEFIT Registered charities.

WHAT IS FUNDED General charitable purposes. This trust donates about half its grant total to causes related to the Order of Women Freemasons, including individual members and their dependants. The remaining half is donated to external charities.

SAMPLE GRANTS Cancer Research UK and Macmillan Nurses (£250,000 each); Adelaide Litten Charitable Trust (£49,000); and grants were also made to individuals totalling £15,000.

FINANCES *Year* 2007–08 *Income* £310,922 *Grants* £557,176 *Assets* £690,876

TRUSTEES B I Fleming-Taylor; M J P Masters; B Wildman; H I Naldrett; J S Brown; Z D Penn.

HOW TO APPLY In writing to the correspondent. Applications should be submitted by the end of July each year for consideration by the trustees.

WHO TO APPLY TO Mrs Joan Sylvia Brown, Trustee, 27 Pembridge Gardens, London W2 4EF *Tel* 020 7229 2368 *Website* www.owf.org.uk

CC NO 1059151　　**ESTABLISHED** 1996

■ The Grand Order of Water Rats' Charities Fund

WHERE FUNDING CAN BE GIVEN UK.

WHO CAN BENEFIT Organisations benefiting: actors and entertainment professionals and their dependants.

WHAT IS FUNDED Assistance to members of the variety and light entertainment profession who are in need. Also supplying medical equipment to certain hospitals and institutions.

WHAT IS NOT FUNDED No grants to students.

TYPE OF GRANT One-off and recurrent.

FINANCES *Year* 2007 *Income* £198,739 *Grants* £83,382 *Assets* £1,515,741

TRUSTEES Wyn Calvin; Roy Hudd; Kaplan Kaye; Keith Simmons; Ken Joy.

HOW TO APPLY In writing to the correspondent. The trustees meet once a month.

WHO TO APPLY TO John Adrian, Secretary, 328 Gray's Inn Road, London WC1X 8BZ *Tel* 020 7407 8007 *email* charities@gowr.net *Website* www.gowr.net

CC NO 292201　　**ESTABLISHED** 1889

■ The Grange Farm Centre Trust

WHERE FUNDING CAN BE GIVEN The London Metropolitan Police District and Epping Forest.

WHO CAN BENEFIT Charitable organisations, including scout groups etc.

WHAT IS FUNDED Recreation and leisure activities.

WHAT IS NOT FUNDED No grants to individuals and usually no grants to applications received from local authorities.

RANGE OF GRANTS £550–£20,000.

SAMPLE GRANTS Copped Hall Trust (£60,000); Chigwell Community Trust (£30,000); St Mary's Catholic School (£20,000); Epping Forest Community Church (£10,000); Flash Musicals (£5,000); Toynbee Hall (£3,000); Panthion Foundation (£1,000); and West Hatch School (£500).

FINANCES *Year* 2007–08 *Income* £376,351 *Grants* £182,041 *Assets* £9,621,818

TRUSTEES A Pelican; R D Neville; Mrs E Webster; M Woollard; M Tomkin; C Huckle; R E Flaxman; Mrs A Wheeler; S Barnes

HOW TO APPLY In writing to the correspondent giving a brief outline of what the grant will be used for. After initial consideration that the application falls within both the area of benefit and the objects of the trust, an application form will be sent to the applicant for completion which will then be considered in greater detail by the trustees.

WHO TO APPLY TO N E Gadsby, Clerk, c/o 181 High Street, Epping, Essex CM16 4BQ *Tel* 01992 578642 *Fax* 01992 572586

CC NO 285162　　**ESTABLISHED** 1984

■ Grantham Yorke Trust

WHERE FUNDING CAN BE GIVEN The (old) West Midlands metropolitan county area.

WHO CAN BENEFIT People under the age of 25 who are in need and were born within the old West Midlands metropolitan county area, and youth organisations benefiting such people.

WHAT IS FUNDED Education, including providing outfits, clothing, tools, instruments, equipment or books to help such people on leaving school, university and so on, to prepare for, or enter a profession or trade.

WHAT IS NOT FUNDED No grants are given towards anybody aged 25 and over.

RANGE OF GRANTS Generally £50–£5,000.

SAMPLE GRANTS Quinzone (£8,000); All Saints Youth Project, Krunch and Youthwise (£5,000 each); Anawin (£3,000); and Deep Impact Theatre Company and Wellchild (£2,500 each).

FINANCES *Year* 2007–08 *Income* £296,297 *Grants* £165,233 *Assets* £5,738,113

TRUSTEES Howard Belton, Chair; Peter Jones; Tim Clarke; Miss Elspeth Insch; Sam Monaghan; Fred Rattley; Philip Smiglarski; Barbara Welton; Rev Pamela Ogilvie.

HOW TO APPLY In writing to the correspondent. The trustees meet four times a year, in March, June, September and December.

WHO TO APPLY TO Mrs Christine Norgrove, Appeals Clerk, Martineau Johnson, No. 1 Colmore Square, Birmingham B4 6AA *Tel* 0870 763 2000

CC NO 228466　　**ESTABLISHED** 1975

■ GrantScape

WHERE FUNDING CAN BE GIVEN UK.

WHO CAN BENEFIT Environmental and community-based projects.

WHAT IS FUNDED Its generic grant-making policy is as follows: GrantScape will only make grants in line with its charitable objectives; grants will be made on a justifiable and fair basis to projects which provide best value; grants will be made to projects that improve the life of communities and the environment; GrantScape will make available specific criteria for each of the grant programmes that it manages. All grants are subject to meeting the generic grant-making criteria as well as the specific grant programme criteria.

WHAT IS NOT FUNDED Specific exclusions apply to each programme – see General for details.

FINANCES *Year* 2008–09 *Income* £999,312 *Grants* £2,516,656 *Assets* £2,996,714

TRUSTEES Dave Bramley; Doug De Freitas; Jacqueline Rae; Chris Brown; Alan Loynes; Alastair Singleton; Sheila Torrance

OTHER INFORMATION New grant programmes are introduced from time to time – check the charity's website for up-to-date information.

HOW TO APPLY Applications are made electronically via the charity's website.

WHO TO APPLY TO Mr S Hargreaves, Contact, Office E, Whitsundoles, Broughton Road, Salford, Milton Keynes MK17 8BU *Tel* 01908 545780 *Fax* 01908 545799 *email* helpdesk@grantscape.org.uk *Website* www.grantscape.org.uk

CC NO 1102249   **ESTABLISHED** 2004

....

■ The J G Graves Charitable Trust

WHERE FUNDING CAN BE GIVEN Mainly Sheffield.

WHO CAN BENEFIT Registered charities.

WHAT IS FUNDED Charities working in the fields of: provision of parks and open spaces; libraries and art galleries; advancement of education; general benefit of people who are sick or poor; and such other charitable purposes as the trustees see fit. The income is mainly applied to local (Sheffield) charities for capital purposes rather than running costs.

WHAT IS NOT FUNDED Grants are generally not made to or for the benefit of individuals.

TYPE OF GRANT Mainly for capital and one-off for start-ups. Some for running costs.

RANGE OF GRANTS Up to £5,000.

SAMPLE GRANTS Sheffield Royal Society for the Blind and Sheffield Galleries & Museum Trust (£5,000 each); SVP Furniture Store and Cathedral Archer Project (£3,000 each); County of Sheffield Guide Association and Flower Estate Community Association (£2,500 each); Macmillan Cancer and Lost Chord (£2,000 each); Meersbrook Park Users Trust and Sheaf Domestic Abuse (£1,500 each); and Shopmobility Sheffield (£1,300).

FINANCES *Year* 2008 *Income* £174,162 *Grants* £83,550 *Assets* £3,535,899

TRUSTEES T H Reed, Chair; R S Sanderson; R T Graves; S Hamilton; D S W Lee; Mrs A C Womack; G W Bridge; P Price; Mrs J Lee; Dr D R Cullen; J C Bramah.

HOW TO APPLY In writing to the correspondent, to reach the secretary by 31 March, 30 June, 30 September or 31 December. Applications should indicate whether the applicant is a registered charity, include audited accounts and include a statement giving such up-to-date information as is available with regard to the income and any commitments the organisation has.

WHO TO APPLY TO R H M Plews, Secretary, 2nd Floor, Fountain Precinct, Balm Green, Sheffield S1 2JA *Tel* 0114 276 7991 *Fax* 0114 223 1717

CC NO 207481   **ESTABLISHED** 1930

....

■ The Gray Trust

WHERE FUNDING CAN BE GIVEN Nottinghamshire, especially Linby and Southall.

WHO CAN BENEFIT Organisations benefiting older people, retired people, ex-service and service people, and people who are disadvantaged by poverty or disability.

WHAT IS FUNDED General charitable purposes, primarily for the benefit of older people, charitable purposes in the parishes of Linby and Papplewick and the surrounding area, and to provide sheltered accommodation for older people in Sherwood House and cottages.

WHAT IS NOT FUNDED Grants are not made to individuals and seldom for applications from outside Nottinghamshire.

SAMPLE GRANTS Age Concern Nottingham (£10,000); Papplewick & Linby Village Hall and St John's Day Centre for the Elderly (£2,000 each); Aspley

Methodist Church, Family Care and Radford Visiting Scheme (£1,000 each); and Portland College, Prince of Paste Anglers, the Eyeless Trust and Camphill Village Trust (£500 each).

FINANCES *Year* 2007–08 *Income* £145,024 *Grants* £155,048 *Assets* £5,317,522

TRUSTEES Clare Hardstaff; Bella St Clair Harlow; Richard B S Stringfellow; Rev. Can. Keith H Turner.

HOW TO APPLY In writing to the correspondent by letter of application together with most recent accounts.

WHO TO APPLY TO Kelly Boorman, Trust Co-ordinator, 309–329 Haydn Road, Sherwood, Nottingham NG5 1HG *Tel* 0115 960 7111 *Fax* 0115 969 1313 *email* kelly.boorman@smithcooper.co.uk

CC NO 210914   **ESTABLISHED** 1962

....

■ The Great Britain Sasakawa Foundation

WHERE FUNDING CAN BE GIVEN UK and Japan.

WHO CAN BENEFIT Voluntary, educational and cultural organisations and registered charities benefiting citizens of UK and Japan. Emphasis on younger people and on projects benefiting groups of people rather than individuals.

WHAT IS FUNDED Advancement of the education of the citizens of the UK and Japan in each other's institutions, people, history, language, culture, and society and in each other's intellectual, artistic and economic life. Research, exchanges, seminars, courses, publications and cultural events may all be funded. The foundation has a special scheme for joint research in medicine and health (the Butterfield Awards).

WHAT IS NOT FUNDED Grants are not made to individuals applying on their own behalf. The foundation will consider proposals from organisations that support the activities of individuals, provided they are citizens of the UK or Japan. No grants are awarded for the construction, conservation or maintenance of land and buildings, student fees or travel in connection with study for a qualification.

TYPE OF GRANT Mainly one-off; also project and research, maximum term three years. No funding for core-costs.

RANGE OF GRANTS £500–£30,000.

SAMPLE GRANTS National Institute for Japanese Studies – two grants (£30,000); Japan Experience Study Tour 2007: Allerton Grange High School – Leeds (£22,000); Dr T Ogi, Sussex University with Professor Y Miki and Dr K Takenaka, Tokyo Medical and Dental University (£12,000); Asia Pacific Technology Network (£10,000); University College for the Creative Arts (£8,000); British Association for Teaching Japanese as a Foreign Language – two grants (£7,000); Community Links, GLOBE / NCY Trust (£6,000); Clifton Scientific Trust (£5,000); President Kennedy Youth Club – Coventry (£3,000); Aikido Union England (£2,700); and Northern Gallery for Contemporary Art (£1,500).

FINANCES *Year* 2007 *Income* £690,328 *Grants* £664,877 *Assets* £23,668,495

TRUSTEES Earl of St Andrew, Chair; Hiroaki Fujii; Prof Nozomu Hayashi; Michael French; Jeremy Brown; Prof. Harumi Kimura; Yohei Sasakawa; Prof. Shoichi Watanabe; Sir John Boyd; Prof. Peter Mathias; Prof. David Cope; Taysuya Tanami.

OTHER INFORMATION The foundation is rarely able to consider grants for the total cost of any project and encourages applicants to seek additional support from other donors.

HOW TO APPLY The foundation expresses a strong preference for emailed applications. A form will be emailed on request, and is also available from the foundation's website where detailed information is given about the foundation's grant giving and application procedures. Application forms are also available from both the London headquarters or from the Tokyo office at: The Nippon Foundation Bldg 4F, 1–2–2 Akasaka Minato-ku, Tokyo 107–0052. The application form requires the following information: a summary of the proposed project and its aims, including dates, its likely impact and long-term sustainability; the total cost of the project and the amount of the desired grant, together with a note of other expected sources of funds; and a description of what elements of the project grant funding has been requested for (the foundation prefers to support identifiable activities rather than general overheads). Organisations should be registered charities, recognised educational institutions, local or regional authorities, churches, media companies, publishers or other bodies that the foundation may approve. Telephone enquiries or personal visits are welcomed by the foundation's staff to discuss eligibility in advance of any formal application. The awards committee meets in London in February, May and October. Applications should be received by December, March and August. Awards meetings in Tokyo are held in April and October, with applications to be submitted by February and September. School applicants are requested to first file an application with Connect Youth International, Japan Exchange Programme, 10 Spring Gardens, London SW1A 2BN (which is part of the British Council), to which the foundation grants external finance, aimed at encouraging exchanges (both ways) for schools in Great Britain and Japan, (their website is: www.connectyouthinternational.com). All applicants are notified shortly after each awards committee meeting of the decisions of the trustees. Those offered grants are asked to sign and return an acceptance form and are given the opportunity to say when they would like to receive their grant. Please note: the foundation receives requests for two to three times the amount of money it actually has available for grants and many applicants receive much less than they asked for.

WHO TO APPLY TO Stephen McEnally, Chief Executive, Dilke House, 1 Malet Street, London WC1E 7JN *Tel* 020 7436 9042 *Fax* 020 7355 2230 *email* grants@gbsf.org.uk *Website* www.gbsf. org.uk

CC NO 290766   **ESTABLISHED** 1985

■ The Great Stone Bridge Trust of Edenbridge

WHERE FUNDING CAN BE GIVEN The parish of Edenbridge.

WHO CAN BENEFIT Organisations, and individuals under 25 for educational purposes.

WHAT IS FUNDED Education and general charitable purposes in the parish of Edenbridge.

TYPE OF GRANT Some recurrent.

FINANCES *Year* 2007–08 *Income* £125,840 *Grants* £77,862 *Assets* £2,973,653

TRUSTEES Mrs R Parsons, Chair; Richard Davison; Peter Deans; Roy Cunnington; Dennis Leigh;

Mrs C Burges; John Hodson; Dr Andrew Russell; Alan Dell; Giles Jackman.

OTHER INFORMATION The grant total also includes £1,500 in grants to schools in Edenbridge.

HOW TO APPLY In writing to the correspondent.

WHO TO APPLY TO William Ross, Clerk, 8 Church Lane, East Grinstead, West Sussex RH19 3BA

CC NO 224309   **ESTABLISHED** 1964

■ The Great Torrington Town Lands Charity

WHERE FUNDING CAN BE GIVEN Great Torrington, Devon.

WHO CAN BENEFIT Individuals and organisations, including clubs, societies and churches.

WHAT IS FUNDED People in need and general charitable purposes.

FINANCES *Year* 2007–08 *Income* £267,521 *Grants* £57,838 *Assets* £5,683,732

TRUSTEES Mrs T Batty; S M Blake; Dr H E Cramp; B M Davies; Rev J D Hummerstone; E W J Kelly; Mrs S Lambert; G Lee; J B Nash; Mrs E Norridge; R Rumbold; A J Stacey; T R Sutton; Mrs E Weeks.

HOW TO APPLY In writing to the correspondent.

WHO TO APPLY TO Chris Styles, Town Hall Office, High Street, Torrington, Devon EX38 8HN *Tel* 01805 623517 *Fax* 01805 623517

CC NO 202801   **ESTABLISHED** 1971

■ The Constance Green Foundation

WHERE FUNDING CAN BE GIVEN England, with a preference for West Yorkshire.

WHO CAN BENEFIT Registered charities, and organisations recognised as charitable, benefiting children; young adults and older people; service and ex-service people; seafarers and fishermen; unemployed people; those in care, fostered and adopted; at risk groups; disabled people; people disadvantaged by poverty; homeless people; victims of famine and war; and people with autism, cancer, epilepsy, head and other injuries, multiple sclerosis, prenatal conditions, terminal illness or tropical diseases.

WHAT IS FUNDED Some preference is given to charities operating in Yorkshire. In previous years grants have been made mainly, but not exclusively, to national organisations in the fields of social welfare and medicine, with special emphasis on support of young people in need and mentally and physically disabled people. Preference for charities working in the fields of residential facilities and services, health and social care professional bodies, councils for voluntary service, special schools and special needs education, medical research and various community facilities and services.

WHAT IS NOT FUNDED Sponsorship of individuals is not supported.

TYPE OF GRANT Capital, special project, buildings and one-off funding of one year or less.

RANGE OF GRANTS Typically up to £10,000.

SAMPLE GRANTS Avalon Breakaway, Teenage Cancer Trust and Martin House – Wetherby (£10,000 each); Salvation Army and Leonard Cheshire (£7,500 each); Act4Africa, Children of the Andes, British Association for Adopting and Fostering and Save The Children – Bangladesh Cyclone Appeal (£5,000 each); Sports Aid and the Olice Branch (£3,000 each); West Yorkshire Playhouse, Older Peoples Action in the Locality

Think carefully about every application. Is it justified?

559

and Huntingdon's Disease Association (£1,500 each); and Autism Initiatives UK, British Red Cross and Chernobyl Children in Need (£1,000 each).

FINANCES *Year* 2007–08 *Income* £355,752 *Grants* £296,780 *Assets* £7,536,450

TRUSTEES M Collinson; Col. H R Hall; Mrs M L Hall; Mrs S Collinson.

OTHER INFORMATION During the year grants were broken down into the following categories: medical and social care (£106,000); 'disabled and aged' (£79,000); children and young persons (£67,000); homeless (£26,000); church and community projects (£20,000).

HOW TO APPLY At any time in writing to the correspondent (no special form of application required). Applications should include clear details of the need the intended project is designed to meet, plus an outline budget.

WHO TO APPLY TO Mrs S Hall, FCM Limited, Centenary House, La Grande Route de St Pierre, St Peter, Jersey JE3 7AY *Tel* 01534 487757 *Fax* 01534 485261 *email* management@fcmtrust.com

CC NO 270775   **ESTABLISHED** 1976

....

■ The Barry Green Memorial Fund

WHERE FUNDING CAN BE GIVEN UK, with a preference for Yorkshire and Lancashire.

WHO CAN BENEFIT There is a preference towards smaller charities working at grassroots level.

WHAT IS FUNDED Preference for smaller charities rescuing and caring for cruelly treated animals; animal homes; animal welfare; cats, catteries and other facilities for cats; dogs, kennels and other facilities for dogs; and horses, stables and other facilities for horses.

WHAT IS NOT FUNDED No expeditions, scholarships, work outside the UK or individuals.

TYPE OF GRANT Buildings, core costs, one-off, recurring costs, running costs and start-up costs. Funding available for more than three years.

RANGE OF GRANTS £500–£8,000.

SAMPLE GRANTS Assisi Animal Sanctuary (£8,000); Brooke Hospital for Animals and HACK (£5,000 each); Dumfries & Galway Canine Rescue Centre (£4,000); Animal Health Trust and Hearing Dogs for the Deaf (£3,000 each); Albert's Horse Sanctuary and Greyhound Awareness League (£2,000 each); Hollyfield Wild Bird Hospital and Margaret Green Foundation Trust (£1,000); and Cotton Tails Rabbit and Guinea Pig Rescue and London Wildlife Trust (£500 each).

FINANCES *Year* 2006–07 *Income* £196,661 *Grants* £62,500 *Assets* £1,463,260

TRUSTEES Richard Fitzgerald-Hart; Mark Fitzgerald-Hart.

HOW TO APPLY In writing to the correspondent including a copy of the accounts.

WHO TO APPLY TO The Clerk to the Trustees, c/o Fitzgerald-Harts, Claro Chambers, Bridge Street, Boroughbridge, York YO51 9LD *Tel* 01423 322 312

CC NO 1000492   **ESTABLISHED** 1990

....

■ The Philip Green Memorial Trust

WHERE FUNDING CAN BE GIVEN UK and overseas, with a preference for Israel and Nepal.

WHO CAN BENEFIT Charitable organisations.

WHAT IS FUNDED Young and older people, people with disabilities, people in need.

SAMPLE GRANTS Community Security Trust (£14,000); Ayrshire Hospice (£11,000); Sail Africa (£10,000); Namaste Children's Home – Nepal and Jewish Care (£5,000 each); Chai Lifeline Cancer Care Centre, Human Development and Community Services – Nepal and Searchlight Educational Trust (£3,000 each); Project Harar and London ExBoxers Association (£2,000 each); and National Hospital Development Fund and Cancer Research UK (£1,000 each).

FINANCES *Year* 2007–08 *Income* £570,396 *Grants* £355,455 *Assets* £193,078

TRUSTEES C Paskin; M Campbell; S Paskin; I Rondel; M Epstein; M Parsons; D Kosky.

HOW TO APPLY In writing to the correspondent.

WHO TO APPLY TO The Committee, 301 Trafalgar House, Grenville Place, Mill Hill, London NW7 3SA *Tel* 020 8906 8732 *email* info@pgmt.org.uk *Website* www.pgmt.org.uk

CC NO 293156

....

■ Philip and Judith Green Trust

WHERE FUNDING CAN BE GIVEN UK and Africa.

WHO CAN BENEFIT Registered charities.

WHAT IS FUNDED Christian and missionary work.

SAMPLE GRANTS Lambeth Partnership and the Bible Society (£10,000 each); Africa Enterprises (£9,300); Greyfriars Church (£7,200); Stewardship SVS (£6,200); and Mission Aviation (£2,400).

FINANCES *Year* 2007–08 *Income* £100,605 *Grants* £61,055 *Assets* £189,430

TRUSTEES P N Green; J A Green.

OTHER INFORMATION Other grants of smaller amounts were made totalling £16,000; however these were not listed in the charity's accounts.

HOW TO APPLY In writing to the correspondent.

WHO TO APPLY TO Philip Green, Trustee, Marchfield, Flowers Hill, Pangbourne, Berkshire RG8 7BD

CC NO 1109933   **ESTABLISHED** 2005

....

■ Mrs H R Greene Charitable Settlement

WHERE FUNDING CAN BE GIVEN UK, with a preference for Norfolk and Wistanstow in Shropshire.

WHO CAN BENEFIT Individuals and institutions, particularly those benefiting at risk groups, and people who are disadvantaged by poverty or socially isolated.

WHAT IS FUNDED Welfare and general charitable purposes.

FINANCES *Year* 2007–08 *Income* £78,612 *Grants* £72,530 *Assets* £2,131,914

TRUSTEES A C Briggs; Revd J B Boston; D A Moore.

OTHER INFORMATION A recent list of grants has not been included in the accounts filed at the Charity Commission.

HOW TO APPLY The trust states that it does not respond to unsolicited applications.

WHO TO APPLY TO N G Sparrow, Birketts, Kingfisher House, 1 Gilder's Way, Norwich NR3 1UB

CC NO 1050812   **ESTABLISHED** 1845

....

■ Greenham Common Community Trust Limited

WHERE FUNDING CAN BE GIVEN West Berkshire and northern Hampshire with particular interest in Newbury.

WHO CAN BENEFIT Community organisations and individuals.

WHAT IS FUNDED General charitable purposes.

WHAT IS NOT FUNDED Grants are only made within the trust's geographical area of operation.

RANGE OF GRANTS £37,000–£100.

SAMPLE GRANTS West Berkshire Youth Offending Team (£33,000); North Hampshire Medical Fund (£25,000); 14–21 Time to Talk (£10,000); Newbury Family Counselling Service (£8,500); Berkshire County Blind Society (£7,000); West Berkshire Learning (£6,000); Newbury Operatic Society and Community Gardening Club (£4,000 each); Pathways to Employment (£3,000); 1st Kingsclere Scout Group and Berkshire Multiple Sclerosis Therapy Centre (£2,000 each); Watership Down Choir (£1,000); Newbury Nomads and Mental Health Advocacy Service (£500 each); and Newbury Ringing Group (£300).

FINANCES *Year* 2007–08 *Income* £4,998,820 *Grants* £1,233,936 *Assets* £47,054,044

TRUSTEES Sir P Michael, Chair; D Bailey; G Mather; P Bryant; M Morris; P Pockney; J Robinson; Ms O Ni-Chionna.

HOW TO APPLY On a form available by telephoning the trust. Grants should be submitted by December/January for consideration in February. Applications can also be made via the trust website.

WHO TO APPLY TO Stuart Tagg, Chief Executive, Liberty House, The Enterprise Centre, New Greenham Park, Newbury, Berkshire RG19 6HW *Tel* 01635 817444 *Fax* 01635 817555 *email* enquiries@greenham-common-trust.co.uk *Website* www.greenham-common-trust.co.uk

CC NO 1062762   **ESTABLISHED** 1997

....

■ Naomi and Jeffrey Greenwood Charitable Trust

WHERE FUNDING CAN BE GIVEN UK.

WHO CAN BENEFIT Mainly Jewish organisations.

WHAT IS FUNDED General charitable purposes.

RANGE OF GRANTS £25–£10,000.

SAMPLE GRANTS Previous beneficiaries have included B'nai B'rith of England, Community Security Trust, Conquer and Learn, Friends of the Sick, National Jewish Chaplaincy Board, Hillel House Manchester, Jewish Care, Jewish Literary Trust, Sunderland Kolel, UJIA, Walk the Walk Worldwide, World Jewish Relief and ZSV Trust – Food Lifeline.

FINANCES *Year* 2007–08 *Income* £10,027 *Grants* £7,799

TRUSTEES J M Greenwood; Mrs N Greenwood.

HOW TO APPLY In writing to the correspondent.

WHO TO APPLY TO J M Greenwood, Trustee, Flat 6, Summit Lodge, 9 Lower Terrace, London NW3 6RF *Tel* 020 7431 5779

CC NO 275633   **ESTABLISHED** 1978

....

■ Greggs Foundation (formerly Greggs Trust)

WHERE FUNDING CAN BE GIVEN UK, with a preference for the North East of England, and in the regions of Greggs Plc's Divisional Charity Committees.

WHO CAN BENEFIT The trustees are committed to equal opportunities and anti-discriminatory practice and wish to encourage applications from disadvantaged groups of all kinds including ethnic minorities, people with disabilities and other minorities, without prejudice as to racial origin, religion, age, gender or sexual orientation. Recent grants have included support for work with homeless people, older people, young people, children and women, including unemployed people, for people with disabilities and ethnic and multi-cultural groups.

WHAT IS FUNDED Applications from small community-led organisations and self-help groups are more likely to be successful than those from larger and well-staffed organisations and those that have greater fundraising capacity. Projects in the fields of the arts, the environment, conservation, education and health will be considered so long as they have a social welfare focus and/or are located in areas of deprivation.

WHAT IS NOT FUNDED Major grants are not made for: animal welfare; capital projects including the purchase, construction and refurbishment of buildings; events such as conferences, seminars and exhibitions, expeditions and overseas travel, fee-charging residential homes, nurseries and care facilities; festivals, performance and other entertainment activities; fundraising events; holidays and outings; hospitals, health service trusts, medically related appeals and medical equipment; individuals other than through the Hardship Fund; large, well-staffed organisations with a greater fundraising capacity; loans or repayments of loans; national organisations and their regional branches; mini-buses other than community transport schemes; research – academic and medical; religious promotion; replacement of statutory funds; retrospective grants; schools other than for pre-school and after school clubs and activities promoting parental and community involvement; sponsorship – organisations and individuals; sports kit equipment; uniformed organisations such as Scouts, Guides and Sea Cadets. The following are not supported through the hardship fund: payment of debt; computer equipment; sponsorship; overseas expeditions.

TYPE OF GRANT Core costs, running costs, project, start-up costs, recurring costs, salaries, one-off. Funding may be given for up to three years.

RANGE OF GRANTS Major grant for core costs and salaries between £10,000–£15,000. One off grants to small organisations or low cost budget grants between £1,000–£10,000. Hardship Fund grants for necessities between £50–£150.

SAMPLE GRANTS Major grants included: Newcastle-upon-Tyne Community Foundation (£40,000); Pennywell Neighbourhood Project, North Sunderland and Seahouses Development Trust and Moving On – Durham (£15,000 each); Escape Family Support – Blythe (£12,000); Newcastle Advocacy Project and North Tyneside Disability Forum (£10,000 each); Consett Churches Detached Youth Project (£7,500); Manor Residents Association – Hartlepool (£5,000); and Newcastle Women's Aid (£1,000).

FINANCES *Year* 2008 *Income* £1,065,150 *Grants* £904,296 *Assets* £7,924,775

TRUSTEES Andrew Davison, Chair; Felicity Deakin; Richard Hutton; Peter McKendrick; Fiona Nicholson; Annemarie Norman; Lesley Spuhler; Melanie Nicholson.

HOW TO APPLY In writing to the correspondent. Applicants for major grants are asked to set out their application briefly in a letter, giving full address, phone/fax number and a contact name, the purpose of the application, the amount requested, and details of other applications for the same purposes. More information about the project may be provided in supporting documents. The following should be included: a copy of your latest audited annual report and accounts/financial statement; a budget for the organisation for the current year and a budget for which the application is made; details of your organisation's bank account in which you would like us to pay any grant which might be approved and a copy of a recent bank statement. The trust advises that you do not overload you application with attachments. Send only relevant information and check that your envelope has the correct postage. It is advisable to take a copy of your application and retain it for your own records. Full guidelines are available on request from the trust or downloaded from the website. Requests for major grants are assessed in March, June, September and November and applications should be sent in two months prior to meeting dates. The trust aims to respond to applications for small grants within approximately two months and to acknowledge applications for major grants in the same period. Applicants will be informed if their applications have not been selected for further consideration.

WHO TO APPLY TO Foundation Manager, Fernwood House, Clayton Road, Jesmond, Newcastle upon Tyne NE2 1TL *Tel* 0191 212 7626 *Fax* 0191 281 9536 *email* greggstrust@greggs.co.uk *Website* www.greggstrust.org.uk

CC NO 296590   **ESTABLISHED** 1987

■ The Greys Charitable Trust

WHERE FUNDING CAN BE GIVEN UK and locally in Oxfordshire.

WHO CAN BENEFIT Charitable organisations.

WHAT IS FUNDED 'The trustees seek to make donations to other charities and voluntary bodies for the benefit of Church of England preservation projects, other charities dealing with historical preservation, both local to Oxfordshire and nationally, and may seek to make donations to the arts.'

SAMPLE GRANTS Trinity College – Oxford (£20,000); Conservation International and Oxfordshire Historic Churches Trust (£10,000 each); Rotherfield Greys PCC (£6,000); St Mary's Church – Henley-on-Thames (£5,000); the Landmark Trust (£3,500 in two grants); the Royal Opera House (£1,500); the Art Fund, Ripon College Cuddesdon (£1,000); and Army Benevolent Fund (£500).

FINANCES *Year* 2007–08 *Income* £30,646 *Grants* £73,500 *Assets* £1,151,181

TRUSTEES J S Brunner; T B H Brunner.

HOW TO APPLY In writing to the correspondent, the trustees usually meet twice a year.

WHO TO APPLY TO The Trustees, c/o Lawrence Graham LLP, 4 More London, Riverside, London SE1 2AU

CC NO 1103717   **ESTABLISHED** 2004

■ Grimmitt Trust

WHERE FUNDING CAN BE GIVEN Birmingham and district and areas where trustees have a personal connection.

WHO CAN BENEFIT Local charities and local branches of UK charities.

WHAT IS FUNDED Culture and education, disability, community, children and young people, medical and health, overseas, and older people.

RANGE OF GRANTS Up to £20,000 each. Mostly less than £500 each.

SAMPLE GRANTS Beneficiaries included: Go Africa – Sudan schools and Lench's Trust (£20,000 each); Birmingham County Scout Council (£12,000); the Methodist Art Collection and

WaterAid (£10,000 each); Birmingham Bach Choir (£6,000); Birmingham Childrens Hospital, Birmingham Law Centre, Komera Project and Barnardo's Midlands (£5,000 each); Edwards Trust (£3,500); Barton Training Trust and Prisoners Education Trust (£3,000 each); and Lozells Project (£2,500).

FINANCES *Year* 2007–08 *Income* £293,661 *Grants* £234,329 *Assets* £6,943,417

TRUSTEES P W Welch; Mrs M E Welch; T N P Welch; Revd C Hughes Smith; Dr A D Owen; Mrs S L Day; L Murray; J M Dickens; Mrs S J Wilkey.

OTHER INFORMATION In 2007–08, smaller grants of less than £2,500 were made to 167 organisations, totalling £82,000, and a grant was made to one individual during the year.

HOW TO APPLY In writing to the correspondent.

WHO TO APPLY TO The Secretary, The Grimmitt Trust, 4a St Catherines Road, Blackwell, Worcestershire B60 1BN *Tel* 0121 445 2197 *email* admin@grimmitt-trust.org.uk

CC NO 801975   **ESTABLISHED** 1989

■ The Grocers' Charity

WHERE FUNDING CAN BE GIVEN UK.

WHO CAN BENEFIT Registered charities only.

WHAT IS FUNDED The charity's charitable aims are broad-ranging, encompassing education, the church, the relief of poverty, medicine, support for the arts, heritage, older people, young people and those with disabilities.

WHAT IS NOT FUNDED Only UK-registered charities are supported. Individuals cannot receive grants directly, although grants can be given to organisations on their behalf. Support is rarely given to the following unless there is a specific or long-standing connection with the Grocers' Company: cathedrals, churches and other ecclesiastical bodies, hospices, schools and other educational establishments, research projects.

TYPE OF GRANT Both capital and revenue projects. Non-recurring grants of limited value. Core costs, one-off, running costs and salaries will be considered. Funding may be given for up to one year.

RANGE OF GRANTS £1,500–£132,000.

SAMPLE GRANTS Oundle School for bursaries (£83,000) and scholarships (£49,000); St Paul's Cathedral Foundation – major grant (£75,000) and fabric fund (£5,000); Rheumatology Discretionary Fund UCL (£78,000); Trinity Sailing Trust (£31,000); Veterans Aid (£26,000); Mossbourne Community Academy (£15,000); St Peter's – Ugborough (£7,000); Fulham Palace Trust and Royal Artillery Museums (£5,000 each); he Young Vic (£2,000); and the Multiple Sclerosis Resource Centre (£1,500).

FINANCES *Year* 2007–08 *Income* £1,640,647 *Grants* £1,186,900 *Assets* £11,429,378

TRUSTEES Directors of The Grocers' Trust Company Ltd (about 30).

HOW TO APPLY Applications for grants can be considered from UK registered charities only and must comply with current guidelines, including restrictions, as detailed in the Grocers' Charity Annual Review and on the Grocers' Company website: www.grocershall.co.uk. Applications should be made on a form available from the correspondent and include the latest audited accounts of the applicant, together with its annual report should accompany the application. Applications can be submitted at any time of the year. They will not be acknowledged, but all will receive notification of the outcome in due course. (This may take several months depending on the time of year when the application is submitted). The charity's financial year runs from 1 August to 31 July, and applications are considered at meetings held four times during that period – November (September), January (November), April (February) and June (May). **NB:** Applications for consideration in a given period must be received by the beginning of the month shown in brackets, e.g. applications for the November meeting must be received at latest by the beginning of September.

WHO TO APPLY TO Anne Blanchard, Charity Administrator, Grocers' Hall, Princes Street, London EC2R 8AD *Tel* 020 7606 3113 *Fax* 020 7600 3082 *email* anne@grocershall. co.uk *Website* www.grocershall.co.uk
CC NO 255230   **ESTABLISHED** 1968

....

■ The M and R Gross Charities Limited

WHERE FUNDING CAN BE GIVEN UK and overseas.
WHO CAN BENEFIT Jewish organisations.
WHAT IS FUNDED Organisations supporting the orthodox Jewish religion and Jewish education.
SAMPLE GRANTS Previous beneficiaries include: Atlas Memorial Limited (£3 million); United Talmudical Associates Limited, a grant making organisation which distributes smaller grants made by the trust (£1.3 million); Chevras Tsedokoh Limited (£530,000); Kolel Shomrei Hachomoth (£75,000); Telz Talmudical Academy & Talmud Torah Trust (£50,000 each); Gevurah Ari Torah Academy Trust (£40,000); Friends of Yeshivas Brisk (£30,000); Beis Ruchel Building Fund (£25,000); Beth Hamedresh Satmar Trust (£26,000); Kehal Chareidim Trust (£12,000); Daas Sholem (£10,000); Craven Walk Beis Hamedrash and Union of Orthodox Hebrew Congregations (£5,000 each); and Yetev Lev Jerusalem (£2,400).
FINANCES *Year* 2007–08 *Income* £9,135,075 *Grants* £3,106,093 *Assets* £25,968,374
TRUSTEES Mrs Rifka Gross; Mrs Sarah Padwa; Michael Saberski.
OTHER INFORMATION A recent list of grants was not available.
HOW TO APPLY In writing to the organisation. Applications are assessed on a weekly basis and many of the smaller grants are dealt with through a grant making agency, United Talmudical Associates Limited.
WHO TO APPLY TO Mrs Rivka Gross, Secretary, Cohen Arnold and Co., New Burlington House, 1075 Finchley Road, London NW11 0PU *Tel* 020 8731 0777 *Fax* 020 8731 0778
CC NO 251888   **ESTABLISHED** 1967

....

■ The Grove Charitable Trust

WHERE FUNDING CAN BE GIVEN UK and overseas.
WHO CAN BENEFIT Jewish people and people disadvantaged by poverty.
WHAT IS FUNDED Organisations advancing education in and the religion of orthodox Jewish faith, and the relief of poverty.
RANGE OF GRANTS £50–£10,000.
SAMPLE GRANTS Previous beneficiaries include: Friends of Laniado Hospital, Pardes House School, Achisomoch Aid Co. Ltd, Society of Friends of the Torah, Friends of Mir Yeshiva, Beth Shmnel Synagogue, Keren Hatorah,

Friends of Bobor and Gertner Charitable Trust and Emuua Education Centre.
FINANCES *Year* 2007 *Income* £84,926 *Grants* £18,410 *Assets* £69,985
TRUSTEES Mrs R Bodner, Chair; M Bodner; Mrs S Bodner; A Denderowicz.
HOW TO APPLY In writing to the correspondent.
WHO TO APPLY TO Mrs R Bodner, Chair, 40 Highfield Gardens, London NW11 9HB
CC NO 279110   **ESTABLISHED** 1979

....

■ The GRP Charitable Trust

WHERE FUNDING CAN BE GIVEN UK.
WHO CAN BENEFIT Organisations already known to the trust.
WHAT IS FUNDED Jewish, general.
WHAT IS NOT FUNDED No grants to individuals.
RANGE OF GRANTS Typically up to £80,000.
SAMPLE GRANTS Oxford Centre for Hebrew & Jewish Studies (£80,000); Traditional Alternatives Foundation (£25,000); Wallace Collection (£18,000); Jerusalem Foundation (£14,000); Trinity College (£10,000); Politics and Economics Research Trust and Council of Christians and Jews, British Friends of the Israel Philharmonic Orchestra (£5,000); Community Security Trust (£3,000); Anglo-Israel Association (£2,000); Friends of Courtauld Institute of Art and Gurkha Regimental Trust; Simon Marks Jewish Primary School Trust (£1,000); Royal British Legion, Chicken Shed Theatre Company and Woolf Institute British Friends of Haifa University (£500); and Arrhythmia Alliance (£200).
FINANCES *Year* 2007–08 *Income* £166,281 *Grants* £172,000 *Assets* £4,464,033
TRUSTEES Kleinwort Benson Trustees Ltd.
OTHER INFORMATION The GRP of the title is George Richard Pinto, a London banker who established the trust.
HOW TO APPLY In writing to the correspondent. However, the trustees prefer to provide medium-term support for a number of charities already known to them, and unsolicited applications are not acknowledged. Trustees meet annually in March.
WHO TO APPLY TO The Secretary, Kleinwort Benson Trustees Ltd, PO Box 57005, 30 Gresham Street, London EC2V 7PG *Tel* 020 3207 7356
CC NO 255733   **ESTABLISHED** 1968

....

■ The David and Marie Grumitt Foundation

WHERE FUNDING CAN BE GIVEN UK, with a preference for London.
WHO CAN BENEFIT Registered charities, with a preference for charities supporting homeless people.
WHAT IS FUNDED General charitable purposes.
RANGE OF GRANTS £500–£5,000.
SAMPLE GRANTS Jesuit Missions (£5,000); St Ann's Church (£3,000); CAFOD and Catholic Children's Society (£2,000 each); Passage Day Centre (£1,500); and Cardinal Hume Centre, DePaul Trust and the Cancer Vaccine Institute (£1,000 each).
FINANCES *Year* 2007–08 *Income* £28,715 *Grants* £19,500 *Assets* £710,500
TRUSTEES The Governor and Company of the Bank of Scotland; Marie Grumitt.
HOW TO APPLY This trust has stated that the income of the foundation is fully committed for the

foreseeable future and it does not respond to unsolicited applications.

WHO TO APPLY TO Marion Bisset, Trustee Tax Manager, Donaldson House, 97 Haymarket Terrace, Edinburgh EH12 5HD *Tel* 0131 313 7908 *Fax* 0131 313 7950 *email* marion. bisset@mazars.co.uk

CC NO 288826   **ESTABLISHED** 1984

....

■ The Bishop of Guildford's Foundation

WHERE FUNDING CAN BE GIVEN Diocese of Guildford.

WHO CAN BENEFIT Voluntary and community groups who are linked with a church or faith community, or engaged in a project working in partnership with a church or faith community. Organisations don't have to be registered charities but do have to have a constitution or set of rules, and a bank account, or be supported by an organisation that has these.

WHAT IS FUNDED Community projects. The purpose of the foundation's grants programme is to support projects and partnerships through which church or faith linked groups meet local needs or get involved in community development and regeneration. Priority will be given to projects and partnerships which build communities' own capacity to meet local needs, especially in relation to those who are excluded or vulnerable. It normally expects those funded to obtain funding and/or support in kind from other sources and will only fund the entire costs of a project on an exceptional basis. It aims to help projects access funding from other sources. It will act as a first funder, enabling new projects to unlock other funds. It aims to achieve a balance between strategic grants, which make an impact on project development and sustainability, and small grants, which enable particular activities to take place.

WHAT IS NOT FUNDED Funding is not normally given to assist individuals directly, or for capital costs, or for projects which have already occurred.

TYPE OF GRANT Small grants, usually up to £2,000 and larger strategic grants, usually up to £10,000. Applications for funding for more than one year can be considered, especially where this enables projects to apply for other funding.

RANGE OF GRANTS £500–£8,000.

SAMPLE GRANTS Partnership Development Project (£32,000); North East Hampshire Development (£27,000); Faith Communities Capacity (£21,000); Camberley Churches and Lakeview (£10,000 each); South East England Faiths Forum (£7,000); the Vine and Watts Gallery (£4,200 each); Ebbisham Association (£2,000); Emmaus House (£400); and Thames Housing Project (£350).

FINANCES *Year* 2007–08 *Income* £151,770 *Grants* £147,196 *Assets* £61,961

TRUSTEES Rt Revd Christopher Hill, Bishop of Guildford; Revd Canon Christopher Rich; Revd Canon Nigel Nicholson; Geoffrey Riggs; Abby Thomas; Nasir Virji; Martin Lee.

OTHER INFORMATION The foundation works in partnership with staff from the diocesan Department for Social Responsibility, including a development team assigned to work with the foundation.

HOW TO APPLY On a form available either as a paper copy or by email. There are two application forms; one for grant applications for up to £2,000; and another for applications for larger projects. Applications are welcomed at any time. The foundation's development team can provide

advice and assistance in making an application. Beneficiaries must have a bank or building society account. Full guidelines are available from the foundation.

WHO TO APPLY TO Mrs Jane Schofield, Diocesan House, Quarry Street, Guildford, Surrey GU1 3XG *Tel* 01483 790324 *email* jane. schofield@cofeguildford.org.uk *Website* www. bgf.co.uk

CC NO 1017385   **ESTABLISHED** 1993

....

■ The Guildry Incorporation of Perth

WHERE FUNDING CAN BE GIVEN Perth, Guildtown and surrounding areas.

WHO CAN BENEFIT Members of the Guildry; residents of Perth and surrounding area who are in need.

WHAT IS FUNDED The main purpose of the trust is to provide support for its members and their families. Charitable donations are also made to local causes at the discretion of the committee.

WHAT IS NOT FUNDED Any appeals outside Perth.

SAMPLE GRANTS Previous beneficiaries included: the Diabetes Research Campaign; Guildtown Community Association; Perth Access Cars; Perthshire Rugby Club; and Family Mediation.

FINANCES *Year* 2008–09 *Income* £227,716

TRUSTEES Gordon Bannerman; Michael Norval; Alastair Anderson; Alexander Sneddon; Ian Nicol; Rae Pattillo; Alistair Barn; Louis Flood; Dr Ronald McDougall.

OTHER INFORMATION A further £76,000 was given in grants to individuals.

HOW TO APPLY In writing to the correspondent. 'Requests for charitable donations may be made tot he Guildry by members and close members of their family. Additionally, any other individuals living in, or organisations located in, either Perth or Guildtown, may apply for a donation.' The trust meets to consider grants on the last Tuesday of every month.

WHO TO APPLY TO Lorna Peacock, Secretary, 42 George Street, Perth, Perthshire PH1 5JL *Tel* 01738 623195

SC NO SC008072   **ESTABLISHED** 1210

....

■ The Walter Guinness Charitable Trust

WHERE FUNDING CAN BE GIVEN UK with a preference for Wiltshire and overseas.

WHO CAN BENEFIT Charitable organisations only.

WHAT IS FUNDED The trust is unlikely to be able to support anything it is not already in touch with, but would be interested to hear from charities concerned with research, education, communities and ecology.

WHAT IS NOT FUNDED No grants to individuals.

TYPE OF GRANT Normally one-off.

SAMPLE GRANTS British Red Cross, Fairbridge and Textile Conservation Centre Foundation (£5,000 each); Andover Mind, Ludgershall Scouts Hall and National Children's Homes (£3,000); Friends of he Elderly, Help for Heroes, Inspire Foundation and Prospect Hospice (£2,000 each); and Octobus Project, Reach Inclusive Arts, Refugee Therapy Centre, RNIB and SCOPE (£1,000 each).

FINANCES *Year* 2007–08 *Income* £134,884 *Grants* £116,750 *Assets* £6,024,498

TRUSTEES Hon. F B Guinness; Hon. Mrs R Mulji; Hon. Catriona Guinness.

HOW TO APPLY In writing to the correspondent. Replies are only sent when there is a positive

564

Does the trust you have chosen match your needs? Haphazard applications waste postage and time

decision. Initial telephone calls are not possible. There are no application forms, guidelines or deadlines. No sae is required.

WHO TO APPLY TO The Secretary, Biddesden House, Andover, Hampshire SP11 9DN

CC NO 205375   **ESTABLISHED** 1961

■ The Gulbenkian Foundation

WHERE FUNDING CAN BE GIVEN UK and the Republic of Ireland.

WHO CAN BENEFIT Registered charities or tax exempt organisations concerned with the arts, education, social change or Anglo-Portuguese cultural relations.

WHAT IS FUNDED The foundation is organised around programmes in four areas: cultural understanding; fulfilling potential; environment; innovation. The foundation develops its own work, initiatives and partnerships, and is not generally open to applications, with the exception of its Innovation Fund.

WHAT IS NOT FUNDED 'The UK Branch of the foundation gives grants only for proposals of a charitable kind, from registered charities or similar not-for-profit organisations. It does not fund individuals. It deals only with grant applications from organisations in the UK and the Republic of Ireland and only with projects which benefit people in these countries. Please note we do not give grants for: housing or the purchase, construction, repair or furnishing of buildings; equipment, including vehicles, IT, or musical instruments; student grants or the education, training fees, maintenance or medical costs of individual applicants; establishing funds for scholarships or loans; teaching or research posts or visiting fellowships; support for gap year activities; commercial publications; festivals; UK cultural or other work in Portugal; scientific research; medicine or related therapies; religious activities; sports; holidays of any sort; animal welfare. We never make loans or retrospective grants, nor help to pay off deficits or loans, nor can we remedy the withdrawal or reduction of statutory funding. We do not give grants in response to any large capital, endowment or widely distributed appeal.'

TYPE OF GRANT Generally one-off grants, occasionally recurring for a maximum of three years.

RANGE OF GRANTS Average £5,000, with notional limit of £15,000.

FINANCES *Year* 2007 *Grants* £1,895,000

TRUSTEES The foundation's Board of Administration in Lisbon. UK resident trustee: Martin Essayan.

PUBLICATIONS Advice to Applicants for Grants; publications catalogue. The UK Branch commissions and publishes a number of reports and books connected with its programmes of work in the arts, education and social change.

HOW TO APPLY Innovation Fund *only*

How and when to apply

'Outline ideas should be submitted by email using the Initial Enquiry Form which is available from the foundation's website. Initial Enquiries can be sent in at any time of the year, but you should allow at least three months between this and the proposed starting date of your research period. Initial Enquiries will be assessed in the context of other applications and, if short-listed, fuller information will be requested and applicants invited to discuss their project with us. We will specify the additional information we need and the date we require it by. After completion of this stage, final applications will be considered at one of our three annual Trustee Meetings. Please

email the completed Initial Enquiry Form to: info@gulbenkian.org.uk'

WHO TO APPLY TO Andrew Barnett, Director, 50 Hoxton Square, London N1 6PB *Tel* 020 7012 1400 *Fax* 020 7908 7580 *email* info@ gulbenkian.org.uk *Website* www.gulbenkian.org. uk

ESTABLISHED 1956

■ The Gunter Charitable Trust

WHERE FUNDING CAN BE GIVEN UK.

WHO CAN BENEFIT Local and UK organisations.

WHAT IS FUNDED General charitable purposes including the countryside, medical and wildlife causes.

WHAT IS NOT FUNDED No support for unsolicited applications.

RANGE OF GRANTS Typically up to £20,000.

SAMPLE GRANTS Disaster Emergency Committee – Bangladesh Cyclone Appeal and Darfur and Chad Crisis Appeal (£18,000 each); Liverpool School of Tropical Medicine (£9,500); Dandelion Trust (£9,000); Marie Stopes International (£7,000); Medical Foundation for the Care of Victims of Torture (£5,800); Friends of Doctor Peary Lal Hospital (£3,900); Medecins Sans Frontiers (£3,000); St Nicholas Church – Charlwood, Sense and Alzheimer's Disease Society (£2,000 each); Work Aid and the Prostate Cancer Charity (£1,000 each); and Plantlife International and Rainforest Concern (£500 each).

FINANCES *Year* 2007–08 *Income* £133,095 *Grants* £129,626 *Assets* £2,369,342

TRUSTEES J de C Findlay; R G Worrall.

HOW TO APPLY Applications are considered by the trustees twice a year. No unsolicited applications are accepted, and all such applications are immediately returned to the applicant.

WHO TO APPLY TO The Trustees, c/o Forsters, 31 Hill Street, London W1J 5LS *Tel* 020 7863 8333

CC NO 268346   **ESTABLISHED** 1974

■ The Gur Trust

WHERE FUNDING CAN BE GIVEN Worldwide.

WHO CAN BENEFIT Individuals and organisations benefiting children, young adults, students and Jewish people.

WHAT IS FUNDED Advancement of education and the orthodox Jewish religion.

FINANCES *Year* 2007–08 *Income* £59,219 *Grants* £45,619 *Assets* £1,371,953

TRUSTEES I M Cymerman; M Mandel; S Morgenstern.

HOW TO APPLY In writing to the correspondent. The trust has previously stated that: 'Funds are raised by the trustees. All calls for help are carefully considered and help is given according to circumstances and funds then available.'

WHO TO APPLY TO The Trustees, 5 Windus Road, London N16 6UT *Tel* 020 8880 8910

CC NO 283423   **ESTABLISHED** 1961

■ Gurunanak

WHERE FUNDING CAN BE GIVEN North west England.

WHO CAN BENEFIT Individuals and organisations.

WHAT IS FUNDED The relief of poverty in north west England; welfare; and general charitable purposes.

TYPE OF GRANT One-off and recurrent.

RANGE OF GRANTS £25–£1,500.

FINANCES *Year* 2007–08 *Income* £295,382
Grants £282,249 *Assets* £24,478
TRUSTEES B S Kohli; J S Kohli; H S Chadha;
A S Dhody.
HOW TO APPLY In writing to the correspondent.
WHO TO APPLY TO B S Kohli, Trustee, Livingstone &
Co, 9 King Edward Buildings, Bury Old Road,
Salford M7 4QJ *Tel* 0161 7400411 *Fax* 0161
7214279
CC NO 1017903   ESTABLISHED 1993

....

■ Dr Guthrie's Association

WHERE FUNDING CAN BE GIVEN Scotland, with a
preference for Edinburgh.
WHO CAN BENEFIT Not-for-profit organisations
benefiting disadvantaged children and young
people under 22 years of age.
WHAT IS FUNDED The care and welfare of young
people.
WHAT IS NOT FUNDED No grants to individuals, or in
support of: projects of an environmental nature;
mainstream activities and statutory
requirements of schools, universities and
hospitals; large-scale building projects; historic
restoration; retrospective funding.
RANGE OF GRANTS £250–£1,000.
SAMPLE GRANTS Abernethy Trust, Citylife Ministries
Ltd, City Youth Café, Glasgow City Mission,
Happy Days Children's Charity, Reality Adventure
Works in Scotland, Riptide Music Studios, Tall
Ships Youth Trust, Turning Point Scotland and
Visibility (£1,000 each); Childline Scotland
(£750); Red School Youth Centre (£700); and
Bibles for Children (£500).
FINANCES *Year* 2007–08 *Income* £44,342
Grants £60,400 *Assets* £1,428,870
TRUSTEES J M P Galbraith, Chair; Mrs S Crane; Mrs
R Derby; P J Derby; Mrs A M G Hepburn; Ms
E Marquis.
HOW TO APPLY Applications are considered by the
trustees three times a year (approximately) in
February, June and October.
WHO TO APPLY TO Fiona Watson, Secretary and
Treasurer, Scott-Moncrieff, 17 Melville Street,
Edinburgh EH3 7PH
SC NO SC009302

The H and J Spack Charitable Trust

WHERE FUNDING CAN BE GIVEN Worldwide.

WHO CAN BENEFIT Charities and organisations working in the worldwide community.

WHAT IS FUNDED Jewish and general charitable purposes.

RANGE OF GRANTS Up to £3,000.

SAMPLE GRANTS Previous beneficiaries include Jewish Care United Jewish Israel Appeal, New London Synagogue, Defending Jewish Community Security Trust, Royal Mencap Society, Dementia Relief Trust, Langdon Foundation, Nightingale Care for Life, Prostate Cancer, Cancer Research UK and Care of China's Orphaned & Abandoned.

FINANCES *Year* 2008–09 *Income* £20,177

TRUSTEES Arvind Raichand Shah; Harvey Montague Spack; Mrs Judith Anne Spack.

HOW TO APPLY In writing to the correspondent.

WHO TO APPLY TO Harvey Montague Spack, 28 Hill Street, London W1J 5NW

CC NO 1087689 **ESTABLISHED** 2001

The H and M Charitable Trust

WHERE FUNDING CAN BE GIVEN UK, with some preference for Kent.

WHO CAN BENEFIT Charities concerned with seamanship, including welfare education.

WHAT IS FUNDED 'Resources are committed on a regular annual basis to organisations who have come to rely upon [the trust] for their funding.'

SAMPLE GRANTS Arethusa Venture Centre (£36,000); Jubilee Sailing Trust (£15,000); Royal Engineers Association, North London Hospice and Guide Dogs for the Blind (£10,000 each); Fairbridge – Kent (£6,000); Royal Star and Garter Home, R.S.P.C.A and Royal National Lifeboat Association (£5,000 each); Kent Air Ambulance (£4,000); and Hand in Gillingham (£2,000).

FINANCES *Year* 2007–08 *Income* £36,840 *Grants* £124,008 *Assets* £2,649,075

TRUSTEES Mrs P M Lister; D Harris; J Lister.

HOW TO APPLY The trustees said they do not wish their trust to be included in this guide since it leads to disappointment for applicants. Unsolicited applications will not be successful.

WHO TO APPLY TO David Harris, Trustee, Abbey House, 342 Regents Park Road, London N3 2LJ *Tel* 020 8445 9104

CC NO 272391 **ESTABLISHED** 1976

H and T Clients Charitable Trust

WHERE FUNDING CAN BE GIVEN Undefined.

WHO CAN BENEFIT Organisations.

WHAT IS FUNDED General charitable purposes.

FINANCES *Year* 2007–08 *Income* £299,218 *Grants* £34,056 *Assets* £109,424

TRUSTEES H M Lask; R M Harris; M Webber.

HOW TO APPLY In writing to the correspondent.

WHO TO APPLY TO H M Lask, Trustee, 65 New Cavendish Street, London W1G 7LS

CC NO 1104345 **ESTABLISHED** 2004

H C D Memorial Fund

WHERE FUNDING CAN BE GIVEN Worldwide.

WHO CAN BENEFIT Organisations benefiting the environment and people who are in need. Especially, people disadvantaged by poverty, education or ill-health and people with disabilities.

WHAT IS FUNDED Health, education, community, environment, development aid abroad, and other social and educational work in the UK and the Republic of Ireland.

WHAT IS NOT FUNDED The following are unlikely to be supported: evangelism or missionary work; individuals; nationwide emergency appeals; animal charities.

TYPE OF GRANT Can be one-off or recurring, including core costs, buildings and start-up costs. Funding may be given for up to three years.

RANGE OF GRANTS £1,000–£154,000; average grant: £10,000–£20,000.

SAMPLE GRANTS San Carlos Hospital – Mexico, for health purposes (£66,000); St Nicholas Church – Bristol, for community purposes (£70,000); Woodland Trust, for environmental purposes (£50,000); Operation Noah, for climate change (£40,000); Practical Action – Peru and Nepal, for development (£30,000); Refugee Support Group Devon, for refugees (£20,000); Tanzania Development Trust – Tanzania, for education (£16,000); Turntable Furniture, for community purposes (£15,000); Country Trust, for environment and education (£10,000); Meath Epilepsy Trust, for health (£5,000); and Mpora Orphanage Fund – Uganda, for education (£3,000).

FINANCES *Year* 2007–08 *Income* £959,079 *Grants* £841,500 *Assets* £615,946

TRUSTEES Nicholas Debenham, Chair; Bill Flinn; Dr Millie Sherman; Jeremy Debenham; Catherine Debenham.

HOW TO APPLY In writing to the correspondent, although please note that the trust has a preference for seeking out its own projects and only very rarely responds to general appeals. 'Unsolicited applications are not encouraged. They are acknowledged, but extremely rarely receive a positive response. No telephone enquiries, please.'

WHO TO APPLY TO Harriet Lear, Secretary, Knowlands Farm Granary, Barcombe, Lewes, East Sussex BN8 5EF

CC NO 1044956 **ESTABLISHED** 1995

The H P Charitable Trust

WHERE FUNDING CAN BE GIVEN UK.

WHO CAN BENEFIT Orthodox Jewish charities.

WHAT IS FUNDED Jewish charitable purposes.

SAMPLE GRANTS Previous beneficiaries included: Craven Walk Charities, Emuno Educational Centre Ltd, Gur Trust, Ponivez, Yad Eliezer, Yeshuas Caim Synagogue and Yetev Lev.

FINANCES *Year* 2007–08 *Income* £361,162 *Grants* £351,915 *Assets* £1,423,472

TRUSTEES A Piller; Mrs H Piller; A Zonszajn.

HOW TO APPLY In writing to the correspondent.

WHO TO APPLY TO Aron Piller, Trustee, 26 Lingwood Road, London E5 9BN *Tel* 020 8806 2432

CC NO 278006 **ESTABLISHED** 1979

■ The Hackney Parochial Charities

WHERE FUNDING CAN BE GIVEN The London Borough of Hackney.

WHO CAN BENEFIT Organisations benefiting children, young adults and people disadvantaged by poverty may be considered. Community organisations can also benefit.

WHAT IS FUNDED Community and education projects which benefit people in Hackney who are poor.

TYPE OF GRANT One-off and recurrent.

RANGE OF GRANTS Up to £40,000.

SAMPLE GRANTS London Borough of Hackney (£6,000); Anna Fiorentini Theatre & Film School (£4,500); Hoxton Health Group and St Mungos (£3,000 each); Studio Upstairs and Single Parent Housing (£2,000 each); S Pinter Youth Group (£1,000); and Community Housing Group (£500).

FINANCES *Year* 2007–08 *Income* £224,520 *Grants* £131,826 *Assets* £4,766,691

TRUSTEES D Field, Chair; G R Bell; Rev R Wickham; Miss P Hibbs; Cllr G N Taylor; Mrs V Edwards; Mrs M Cannon; Ms N Baboneau; H Deadman; P Ottino.

OTHER INFORMATION Other grants under £2,000 amounted to £80,000.

HOW TO APPLY In writing to the correspondent. The trustees will consider written applications for grants and project funding from individuals and organisations that are in line with the charity's objectives and are within the area of benefit at their discretion.

WHO TO APPLY TO Robin Sorrell, Clerk to the trustees, Messrs Craigen Wilders Sorrell, 2 The Broadway, High Street, Chipping Ongar, Essex CM5 9JD *Tel* 01277 899006 *Fax* 01277 899067 *email* robinsorrellcws@aol.com

CC NO 219876   **ESTABLISHED** 1904

■ The Hadfield Trust

WHERE FUNDING CAN BE GIVEN Cumbria.

WHO CAN BENEFIT Organisations benefiting children, young adults and older people; unemployed people; parents and children; one parent families; and widows and widowers.

WHAT IS FUNDED Charities concerned with social needs, youth employment, help for older people, the arts and the environment. Particularly supported are those working in the fields of accommodation and housing; support and development; arts, culture and recreation; health; conservation; education and training; and social care and development.

WHAT IS NOT FUNDED The following would not normally be considered for a grant: applicants from outside the county of Cumbria; individuals; any form of sponsorship; religious bodies; political organisations; pressure groups; feasibility studies; schools seeking specialist status; where funding from statutory bodies is, or should be available.

TYPE OF GRANT Capital projects preferred; buildings will be considered and funding is generally for one year or less.

RANGE OF GRANTS Minimum £500.

SAMPLE GRANTS Beneficiaries included: Shap Bowling Club; the Outward Bound Trust; Lowes Court Gallery; Greystoke Church; Breath of Life Foundation; Rose Theatre Group; the Ruskin Society; Cumbria Youth Alliance; Volunteer Centre Eden; Cumbria Cerebal Palsy; Cockermouth Georgian Fair; Lancrost Festival; and Egremont Cricket Club.

FINANCES *Year* 2007–08 *Grants* £207,748

TRUSTEES R A Morris; A T Morris; W Rathbone; A W Forsyth.

PUBLICATIONS A leaflet setting out the aims and objectives of the trust (available on request).

HOW TO APPLY A completed application form is always required and is available from the trust's website or offices. The completed application form should be sent to the dministrator together with a copy of the applicant's most recent accounts to reach the trust not later than the deadline for the relevant meeting. The deadlines are always the 1st of the month preceding that of the trustees' meeting i.e. 1 February, 1 June and 1 October. If the application form gives insufficient space for your project to be described, up to two sheets of A4 paper can be accepted. The policy of the trust is that capital funding is strongly preferred but some revenue requests will be accepted in particular circumstances. If in any doubt about the best way to complete the application form, including the size of the grant to be requested, applicants are strongly advised to telephone the Administrator who will be glad to advise. In reaching their decision the trustees have the benefit of advice from the Advisory Panel which meets some weeks before them to discuss in detail the applications. The Advisory Panel, chaired by Alan Forsyth, is made up of people resident in Cumbria and drawn from all parts of the county who have wide experience and knowledge of the charitable sector.

WHO TO APPLY TO Michael Hope, Administrator, 3 College Path, Formby, Liverpool L37 1LH *Tel* 01704 834887 *Fax* 01704 879736 *email* admin@hadfieldtrust.org.uk *Website* www.hadfieldtrust.org.uk

CC NO 1067491   **ESTABLISHED** 1998

■ The Hadley Trust

WHERE FUNDING CAN BE GIVEN UK, especially London.

WHO CAN BENEFIT Registered charities.

WHAT IS FUNDED The trust's objects allow it to assist in creating opportunities for people who are disadvantaged as a result of environmental, educational or economic circumstances or physical or other handicap to improve their situation, either by direct financial assistance, involvement in project and support work, or research into the causes of and means to alleviate hardship.

SAMPLE GRANTS The largest grant recipients during the year were New Economics Foundation, Prison Reform Trust, Policy Exchange, British Urological Foundation; and Second Chance. Grant amounts were not stated.

FINANCES *Year* 2007–08 *Income* £4,190,855 *Grants* £2,320,460 *Assets* £69,414,363

TRUSTEES Janet Hulme; Philip Hulme.

HOW TO APPLY In writing to the correspondent.

WHO TO APPLY TO Carol Biggs, Trust Administrator, Gladsmuir, Hadley Common, Barnet, Hertfordshire EN5 5QE *Tel* 020 8447 4577 *Fax* 020 8447 4571 *email* carol@hadleytrust.org

CC NO 1064823   **ESTABLISHED** 1997

■ The Hadrian Trust

WHERE FUNDING CAN BE GIVEN Within the boundaries of the old counties of Northumberland and Durham, this includes Tyne and Wear and the former county of Cleveland (north of the Tees).

WHO CAN BENEFIT Organisations benefiting people of all ages; unemployed people; volunteers; people in care, or who are fostered or adopted; one-parent families; and widows and widowers. Typical grants in 2004 were to councils of voluntary service, advice and counselling services, women's projects, youth clubs and schools, charities for people who are disabled, older people, arts and environmental projects, church restoration and block grants for individuals in need.

WHAT IS FUNDED Social welfare and other charitable projects within the boundaries of the old counties of Northumberland and Durham (this includes Tyne and Wear). The main headings under which applications are considered are: social welfare; young people; women; older people; people with disabilities; ethnic minorities; the arts; the environment; education and churches.

WHAT IS NOT FUNDED General appeals from large UK organisations and smaller bodies working outside the beneficial area are not considered.

TYPE OF GRANT Usually one-off for a special project or part of a project. The average grant is £1,000. Buildings, capital, project, research, recurring costs, as well as running costs, salaries and start-up costs will be considered. Funding of up to three years will be considered.

RANGE OF GRANTS £250–£5,000.

SAMPLE GRANTS Beneficiaries included: Six Townships History Group; Northumbria Coalition Against Crime; Get Hooked on Fishing Charitable Trust; Women's Health and Wellbeing Group – Hartlepool; Huntingdon's Disease Association; North East Polish Community Association; the Voices Foundation; Friends of Prudhoe Woods; Hexham Abbey Festival; Northern Roots-Gateshead; and Sunderland Youth Orchestra.

FINANCES *Year* 2007–08 *Income* £225,578 *Grants* £215,075 *Assets* £5,082,318

TRUSTEES B J Gillespie, Chair; J B Parker; P A Dodgson; R H M Hargreave.

HOW TO APPLY In writing to the correspondent setting out details of the project, the proposed funding, a list of any other applications being made (with the result if known) and a copy of the latest annual report/accounts. Applications are considered at meetings usually held in October, January, March and July each year, or as otherwise required. There is no application form but an information sheet is available on request. Eligible applications will be acknowledged and given a date when the application will be considered. Successful applicants will hear within two weeks of the meeting; no further correspondence is sent to unsuccessful applicants. To help assess the effectiveness of their grantmaking the trustees welcome reports from successful applicants on how the grant has been spent and how it has helped the project, especially if a repeat application is being considered. Applications for individuals should be sent to: Greggs Charitable Trust, Fernwood House, Clayton Road, Jesmond, Newcastle upon Tyne NE2 1TL.

WHO TO APPLY TO John Parker, 36 Rectory Road, Gosforth, Newcastle upon Tyne NE3 1XP *Tel* 0191 285 9553

CC NO 272161   **ESTABLISHED** 1976

■ The Alfred Haines Charitable Trust

WHERE FUNDING CAN BE GIVEN Birmingham and West Midlands (including Staffordshire and Warwickshire).

WHO CAN BENEFIT Mainly smaller charities.

WHAT IS FUNDED Christian social action. Grants were broken down into the following categories: family support and counselling; young people's and children's work; humanitarian and overseas aid; medically disadvantaged; care for older people and people with disabilities; homeless; and holidays for disadvantaged children and teenagers.

WHAT IS NOT FUNDED No support for activities which are primarily the responsibility of central or local government or some other responsible body; animal welfare; church buildings – restoration, improvements, renovations or new ones; environmental – conservation and protection of wildlife and landscape; expeditions and overseas trips; hospitals and health centres; individuals, including students (on the rare occasions that individuals are supported, the person has to be recommended by someone known to the trustees and the funding should be of long-term benefit to others); large national charities; it is unusual for the trust to support large national charities even where there is a local project; loans and business finance; medical research projects; promotion of any religion other than Christianity; or school, universities and colleges. Projects overseas or outside the West Midlands, whether Christian or not, will only be considered where the applicants are known to a trustee or are recommended by someone known to a trustee who has first hand knowledge of the work.

TYPE OF GRANT Generally one-off. Specific projects rather than general running costs.

FINANCES *Year* 2007–08 *Income* £38,708 *Grants* £127,455 *Assets* £1,242,308

TRUSTEES A L Gilmour; G L H Moss.

HOW TO APPLY In writing to the trustees, quoting ref: DSC. Applications should include a brief description of the activities of the organisation; details of the project and its overall cost; what funds have already been raised and how the remaining funds are to be raised; a copy of the latest accounts including any associated or parent organisation; any other leaflets or supporting documentation. When considering whether to apply for funding, advice (if needed) can be obtained from the administrator prior to writing. Replies are only sent where further information is required. No telephone calls or correspondence will be entered into for any proposed or declined applications. Successful applicants are required to complete an official receipt and produce a report on the project, usually after ten months. Successful applicants are advised to leave at least ten months before applying for further support.

WHO TO APPLY TO Mrs J A Gilmour, Administrator, Dale Farm, Worcester Lane, Sutton Coldfield B75 5PR

CC NO 327166   **ESTABLISHED** 1986

■ The Hale Trust

WHERE FUNDING CAN BE GIVEN Surrey, Sussex, Kent and Greater London.

WHO CAN BENEFIT Individuals and registered charities in the area defined above. The trust will consider children and young adults (up to the age of 25) who have disabilities and students for recognised courses who are disadvantaged by poverty, including unemployed people and volunteers.

WHAT IS FUNDED There is a tendency to support local projects where the trust can see the use the money is put to.

WHAT IS NOT FUNDED The trust does not give grants for: the purchase, repair or furnishing of buildings; basic equipment or teachers' salaries, which by law are the responsibility of the education authorities; performances, exhibitions or festivals; youth projects or foreign travel; conferences or seminars; university or medical research; establishing funds for bursary or loan schemes; stage, film or video production costs, or commercial publications; supplementary schools or mother tongue teaching; general fundraising campaigns or appeals; or retrospective grants to help pay off overdrafts or loans. The trust will not remedy the withdrawal or reduction of statutory funding.

TYPE OF GRANT One-off grants funded for up to one year.

RANGE OF GRANTS £80–£5,000.

SAMPLE GRANTS Hindleap Warren, in bursaries (£5,000); Edenbridge Holiday Activities Scheme (£1,700); Brighton and Hove Parents and Children's Group and Arts for All (£600 each); and Spitalfields Farm Association, the Paddocks Riding for All and Summer Dreams (£500 each).

FINANCES *Year* 2007–08 *Income* £58,766 *Grants* £29,967 *Assets* £1,115,114

TRUSTEES J Burns, Chair; Mrs J M Broughton; J E Tuke; Mrs S A Henderson; A Stephens; Mrs D Whitmore; Mrs J Cole.

OTHER INFORMATION Grants to individuals cannot exceed £1,200 each year or last for more than three years and the total amount allocated from the income of the trust for this purpose in any one year is strictly limited.

HOW TO APPLY In writing to the correspondent. The trustees meet in February, June and October so it is advisable to apply in time for these meetings.

WHO TO APPLY TO Mrs J M Broughton, Secretary, Rosemary House, Woodhurst Park, Oxted, Surrey RH8 9HA

CC NO 313214　　　　**ESTABLISHED** 1970

■ E F and M G Hall Charitable Trust

WHERE FUNDING CAN BE GIVEN South east England.

WHO CAN BENEFIT Charities concerned with children and older people; disability and medical charities; churches; and others.

WHAT IS FUNDED General charitable purposes.

WHAT IS NOT FUNDED No grants to individuals.

TYPE OF GRANT One-off and recurrent.

RANGE OF GRANTS Up to £2,000.

SAMPLE GRANTS Mercy Ships and Friends of Edenbridge Hospital (£1,000 each); Shelter (£600); and Unicef, Barnardo's, Canterbury Cathedral, Cheshire Homes and Bread and Water for Africa (£500 each).

FINANCES *Year* 2007–08 *Income* £45,187 *Grants* £26,417 *Assets* £1,023,627

TRUSTEES Anthony E F Hall; Moira G Hall; Ian F Hall.

HOW TO APPLY In writing to the correspondent, although the trust had previously stated that its funds are already allocated to selected charities.

WHO TO APPLY TO Moira Hall, Trustee, Holmsley House, Holtye Common, Cowden, Edenbridge, Kent TN8 7ED

CC NO 256453　　　　**ESTABLISHED** 1968

■ The Edith Winifred Hall Charitable Trust

WHERE FUNDING CAN BE GIVEN UK, with a preference for Northamptonshire.

WHO CAN BENEFIT Registered charities.

WHAT IS FUNDED General charitable purposes.

SAMPLE GRANTS Northamptonshire Association of Youth Clubs (£300,000); Age Concern Northamptonshire and St Peter's School (£250,00 each); the Countryside Alliance Foundation (£150,000); University of Northampton Foundation (£138,000); Creation Theatre Company (£80,000); St Peter's Church – Walgrave and Luton Churches Education Trust (£35,000); St Mary Magdelene (£7,200); and Northamptonshire Community Foundation (£5,000).

FINANCES *Year* 2007–08 *Income* £141,062 *Grants* £1,255,772 *Assets* £3,375,001

TRUSTEES D Reynolds; D Endicott; P P Reynolds; L C Burgess-Lumsden.

HOW TO APPLY In writing to the correspondent.

WHO TO APPLY TO D Endicott, Trustee, Spratt Endicott, 52–54 South Bar Street, Banbury, Oxfordshire OX16 9AB *Tel* 01295 204000

CC NO 1057032　　　　**ESTABLISHED** 1996

■ Robert Hall Charity

WHERE FUNDING CAN BE GIVEN West Walton, Wisbech and Walsoken in Cambridgeshire.

WHO CAN BENEFIT Organisations particularly those benefiting children and young adults.

WHAT IS FUNDED General charitable purposes, including charities working with hospices and hospitals, medical research, conservation and campaigning, education and various community services and facilities.

WHAT IS NOT FUNDED No grants to individuals.

TYPE OF GRANT Range of grants including buildings, capital, recurring costs and start-up costs. Funding for up to three years may be available.

SAMPLE GRANTS West Walton Parish Church (£19,000); Angles Theatre (£10,000); Cancer Research UK and Friends of Wisbech Hospitals (£7,000 each); St Peter's Church of England Junior School (£5,000); West Walton Village Hall (£4,000); Alzheimer's Society (£3,000); Fenland Mencap (£2,000); Downham Market High School (£1,500); and 3rd Wisbech Guides Group (£1,000).

FINANCES *Year* 2007–08 *Income* £41,845 *Grants* £70,029

TRUSTEES David William Ball; Colin Neil Arnold; D C Burall; Miss E A Plater.

HOW TO APPLY In writing to the correspondent. Applications are considered at twice yearly trustees' meetings.

WHO TO APPLY TO D Ball, Trustee, Frasers Solicitors, 29 Old Market, Wisbech, Cambridgeshire PE13 1ND *Tel* 01945 468 700 *Fax* 01945 468 709 *email* d.ball@frasers-solicitors.com

CC NO 1015493　　　　**ESTABLISHED** 1992

■ The Hamamelis Trust

WHERE FUNDING CAN BE GIVEN UK, but with a special interest in the Godalming and Surrey areas.

WHO CAN BENEFIT UK charities involved in medical research or conservation projects.

WHAT IS FUNDED Medical research in the UK; and specific projects for conservation of the countryside in the UK.

WHAT IS NOT FUNDED Projects outside the UK are not considered. No grants to individuals.

TYPE OF GRANT Project.

RANGE OF GRANTS Up to £10,000.

SAMPLE GRANTS Chiddingfold PCC St Marys Church (£50,000); Bedfordshire, Cambridge and Northantshire Wildlife Trust (£25,000); Berkshire, Buckinghamshire and Oxfordshire Wildlife Trust (£2,500); and Rodborough Technology School (£500).

FINANCES *Year* 2007–08 *Income* £100,835 *Grants* £77,750 *Assets* £2,275,228

TRUSTEES Mrs L Dadswell; Dr A F M Stone; Ms L J Stone.

HOW TO APPLY In writing to the correspondent. All applicants are asked to include a short summary of the application along with any published material and references. Unsuccessful appeals will not be acknowledged. Dr Adam Stone, one of the trustees, who is medically qualified, assesses medical applications.

WHO TO APPLY TO Mrs L Dadswell, Trustee, c/o Penningtons Solicitors LLP, Highfield, Brighton Road, Godalming, Surrey GU7 1NS *Tel* 01483 791800

CC NO 280938 **ESTABLISHED** 1980

....

■ Hamilton Wallace Trust

WHERE FUNDING CAN BE GIVEN UK.

WHO CAN BENEFIT Registered charities.

WHAT IS FUNDED General charitable purposes.

RANGE OF GRANTS £500–£1,000.

SAMPLE GRANTS Previous beneficiaries included: Diabetes UK; Brainwave, Crohns in Childhood Research Association, Dyslexia Action, Independent Age, Motor Neurone Disease Association and Young Minds; and Disabled Living Foundation, Nightstop UK and Step by Step.

FINANCES *Year* 2008–09 *Income* £25,315

TRUSTEES Timothy James Lindsay Calder; Bryan James Weir.

HOW TO APPLY In writing to the correspondent. Trustees meet twice a year to consider appeals, in November and May of each year, and it would be helpful for any appeals to be received about a month before the meetings.

WHO TO APPLY TO B J Weir, Trustee, Travers Smith and Braithwaite and Co., 10 Snow Hill, London EC1A 2AL *Tel* 020 7295 3000 *Fax* 020 7295 3500 *email* Bryan.Weir@TraversSmith.com

CC NO 1052453 **ESTABLISHED** 1996

....

■ Paul Hamlyn Foundation

WHERE FUNDING CAN BE GIVEN UK and India.

WHO CAN BENEFIT Registered charities and organisations.

WHAT IS FUNDED The foundation aims to address issues of inequality and disadvantage, particularly in relation to children and young people. Its main areas of interest are arts, education and learning in the UK and local organisations supporting vulnerable groups of people, especially children, in India.

WHAT IS NOT FUNDED In the UK the foundation does not support: individuals or proposals for the benefit of one individual; funding for work that has already started; general circulars/appeals; proposals about property or which are mainly about equipment or other capital items; overseas travel, expeditions, adventure and residential courses; promotion of religion; animal welfare; medical/health/residential or day care; proposals from organisations outside the UK, except under the India programme;

proposals that benefit people living outside the UK, except under the India programme. The foundation is unlikely to support: endowments; organisations that use funding to make grants; websites, publications, seminars unless part of a wider proposal. In India, the foundation does not support: individuals or proposals for the benefit of one individual; retrospective (funding for work that has already started); general circulars/appeals; proposals that solely concentrate on the purchasing of property, equipment or other capital items; overseas activities, including travel, expeditions, adventure and residential courses.

TYPE OF GRANT Grants are usually one-off, for a specific project or for a specific part of a project, and funding is normally given for one year only.

RANGE OF GRANTS Usually up to £30,000 each.

SAMPLE GRANTS I CAN (£300,000), to support the development phase of a national initiative; Sistema Scotland (£234,000), core support over two years to grow children's orchestras in Raploch, on the outskirts of Stirling; Dance United (£200,000), for support for the Artistic Management Team in order for it to focus on new areas of work. This will include creating new work through partnerships with organisations in the social exclusion sector; Levenmouth YMCA (£150,000), for an initiative tackling anti-social behaviour, delivering changes of behaviour and attitude through positive young person centred activities; Citizenship Foundation (£120,000), to bring together local young asylum seekers/refugee groups and youth groups involving established residents, in order to empower them to jointly engage in positive community action; National Children's Bureau (£89,000), to explore and record the views of children and young people in Northern Ireland, especially marginalised children, to ensure these are heard and taken seriously; South Warwickshire Carers Support Service (£39,000), for the Educational Support Project to work with young carers in education whose caring responsibilities at home lead to educational underachievement, truancy and exclusion; and Learning Away (£34,000), towards school residentials; and Shetland Arts Development Agency (£7,500), for a restorative arts project with marginalised young people who have been referred to the Community Mediation Team due to interpersonal difficulties.

FINANCES *Year* 2008–09 *Income* £14,223,000 *Grants* £13,417,000 *Assets* £466,265,000

TRUSTEES Jane Hamlyn, Chair; Michael Hamlyn; Robert Boas; James Lingwood; Baroness Estelle Morris; Claus Moser; Anthony Salz; Peter Wilson-Smith.

HOW TO APPLY The foundation's guidance on its application procedure is particularly detailed and helpful:

'Applicants should submit an application using the outline application form which can be completed online. It will be acknowledged automatically by email. You will hear from us within four weeks whether or not we accept your outline application and wish to take it forward. If we accept your outline application, a member of our staff will contact you to progress your proposal. You will normally be asked to send further details about the proposed work which should include the following information–in this order and up to a maximum of eight pages in total: what do you aim to achieve? (please describe in approx 50 words); how will you achieve your aim(s)? (please describe in approx 50 words); how your specific objectives link with the aims of the scheme to which you are applying;

Think carefully about every application. Is it justified?

571

job description (if you are applying for funding for a post); anticipated problems and how you will address them; start date and length of work; who will undertake the work?; number of beneficiaries; total budget for this work; exact breakdown of how PHF money would be spent; other funders/fundraising; monitoring and evaluation plans; dissemination strategy; sustainability/future funding; independent referee; appropriate letters of support.'

'Please ensure that the above information reaches us by email. You can send any additional supporting information by post if necessary. In addition to the details requested above, we would also like you to send us: an annual report and audited financial statements or equivalent (ideally electronically); name of your organisation's Chief Executive or equivalent. We will then assess your application. This may involve correspondence and meetings between our staff and your representatives, and may also include consultation with our trustees, advisers and independent referees. We will normally complete the assessment within two to three months of receiving the further details as listed above. The assessed proposal will then go to a decision making meeting. Applications for up to £10,000 are normally considered by staff. Applications over £10,000 and up to £150,000 are normally considered by the relevant programme committee. Applications for over £150,000, or applications which are novel or potentially contentious, are considered first by the relevant programme committee and then by the full board of trustees. The programme committees and the full board of trustees meet four times a year. We do not publish meeting dates. Please allow six months between making an outline application and the start date for the work you propose to carry out with our funding, or longer if the proposal is particularly large or complex. We will not consider applications from organisations outside the UK, or applications to help people who live outside the UK. This does not apply to our India programme.'

WHO TO APPLY TO Tony Davey, Information and Resources Officer, 18 Queen Anne's Gate, London SW1H 9AA *Tel* 020 7227 3500 *Fax* 020 7222 0601 *email* information@phf.org. uk *Website* www.phf.org.uk
CC NO 1102927   **ESTABLISHED** 1987

....

■ The Helen Hamlyn Trust

WHERE FUNDING CAN BE GIVEN Worldwide.
WHO CAN BENEFIT Organisations working in the fields of: medical, the arts and culture, education and welfare, heritage and conservation in India, international humanitarian affairs and healthy ageing. Within these areas of activity the trust also supports a number of projects with a design focus which are undertaken by the Helen Hamlyn Research Centre at the Royal College of Art, London.
WHAT IS FUNDED Support for individual projects aim to: encourage innovation in the medical arena; increase access to the arts and support the professional development of artists from the fields of music and the performing arts; increase intercultural understanding, provide opportunities for young people to develop new interests and practical skills which will contribute to their education and their future lives and to create opportunities for young offenders to acquire practical skills which will support their personal development for their future lives; conserve heritage in India; improve

international relations; provide practical support to enable older people to maintain their independence for as long as possible.
SAMPLE GRANTS Helen Hamlyn Centre at the Royal College of Art for the Chair of Design (£2 million over five years); The Royal Opera House (£594,000 in total); Fight for Sight (£240,000); Design Dimension Educational Trust (£210,500); Royal Horticultural Society (£196,000 in total); Indian National Trust for Conservation and Heritage (£11,000 in total); and St Wilfred's Care Home (£6,000).
FINANCES *Year* 2008–09 *Income* £3,164,539 *Grants* £4,082,767 *Assets* £4,262,217
TRUSTEES Lady Hamlyn; Dr Kate Gavron; Dr Shobita Punja; Brendan Cahill; Margaret O'Rorke; Anthony Edwards; Dr Deborah Swallow; Mark Bolland.
HOW TO APPLY The trustees bring forward recommendations for projects to support.
WHO TO APPLY TO Andrew P Gray, Trust Administrator and Secretary, 129 Old Church Street, London SW3 6EB *Tel* 020 7351 5057 *Fax* 020 7352 3284 *email* andrew.gray@helenhamlyntrust.org
CC NO 1084839   **ESTABLISHED** 2000

....

■ Sue Hammerson's Charitable Trust

WHERE FUNDING CAN BE GIVEN UK, with a slight preference for London.
WHO CAN BENEFIT Registered charities benefiting people disadvantaged by poverty, medical professionals, research workers and scientists.
WHAT IS FUNDED General charitable purposes. Particular consideration is given to the advancement of medical learning and research and to the relief of sickness and poverty. Substantial support is given to Lewis W Hammerson Memorial Home.
WHAT IS NOT FUNDED No grants to individuals.
RANGE OF GRANTS £50–£200,000, most grants are under £1,000.
SAMPLE GRANTS Royal Albert Hall and WLS Jewish Futures (£5,000 each); Royal Opera House (£4,400); National Theatre (£3,500); Hampstead Synagogue, Musequality, and the Rix Centre (£2,000 each); Youth Cancer Trust (£1,500); Tate Foundation and Royal Academy of Arts (£1,000 each); and World Emergency Relief, Holocaust Educational Trust, Ethiopiaid and British Heart Foundation (£250 each).
FINANCES *Year* 2007–08 *Income* £264,118 *Grants* £260,700 *Assets* £7,483,519
TRUSTEES Sir Gavin Lightman; A J Thompson; A J Bernstein; Mrs P A Beecham; D B Hammerson; P S Hammerson.
HOW TO APPLY In writing to the correspondent. The trust states, however, that its funds are fully committed.
WHO TO APPLY TO R Watson, H W Fisher and Co, Acre House, 11–15 William Road, London NW1 3ER *Tel* 020 7388 7000
CC NO 235196   **ESTABLISHED** 1957

....

■ The Hammonds Charitable Trust

WHERE FUNDING CAN BE GIVEN Mainly Birmingham, London, Leeds, Bradford and Manchester.
WHO CAN BENEFIT Registered charities only.
WHAT IS FUNDED General charitable purposes.
RANGE OF GRANTS Usually up to £10,000.
SAMPLE GRANTS Business in the Community (£8,800); Janes Appeal (£4,200); Crisis UK (£3,600); Cancer Research UK (£2,300);

Eureka The National Children's Museum, Global Angels Foundation and Orchid Cancer Appeal (£1,000 each); Leukaemia Research Fund and Cross-Cultural Solutions (£500); and Shelter, Oxfam and Acorns Children's Hospice (£250 each).

FINANCES *Year* 2007–08 *Income* £79,717 *Grants* £71,641 *Assets* £137,884

TRUSTEES S M Gordon; J S Forrest; S R Miller; S Kelly

OTHER INFORMATION This trust was formerly known as The Hammond Suddards Edge Charitable Trust.

HOW TO APPLY This trust does not accept unsolicited applications.

WHO TO APPLY TO Linda Sylvester, Hammonds Solicitors, Rutland House, 148 Edmund Street, Birmingham B3 2JR *email* linda.sylvester@ hammonds.com *Website* www.hammonds.com

CC NO 1064028   **ESTABLISHED** 1997

■ The Hampshire and Islands Historic Churches Trust

WHERE FUNDING CAN BE GIVEN Hampshire, Isle of Wight and the Channel Islands.

WHO CAN BENEFIT Churches.

WHAT IS FUNDED The restoration, preservation, repair, maintenance and improvement of churches, including monuments, fittings and furniture, in the area specified above.

RANGE OF GRANTS Up to £3,000.

SAMPLE GRANTS Previous beneficiaries include: Gosport Holy Trinity, Swanmore – St Michael & All Angels and Swaythling – St Albarn; Hospital of St Cross; Hambledon – St Peter & St Paul and Meonstoke – St Andrew; Cowes – St Mary the Virgin; Farringdon – All Saints; Hurstbourne Priors – St Andrew, Portsea – St George, Wymering – St Peter & St Paul.

FINANCES *Year* 2008 *Income* £53,799

TRUSTEES Nick Jonas, Chair; Corinne Bennett; Revd John Cranmer; Ven. Adrian Harbidge; John Steel; Lady Joan Applecart.

OTHER INFORMATION From the grant total, the trust also paid out £20,212 to churches as a result of the annual Bike Ride fundraising event.

HOW TO APPLY In writing to the correspondent. Grants are paid out only on submission of architects' certificates and receipted fee accounts, so there is sometimes a considerable delay between the trust offering a grant and actually making the payment.

WHO TO APPLY TO The Secretary, 19 St Peter Street, Winchester, Hampshire SO23 8BU *Tel* 01962 760872 *Website* www. hampshirehistoricchurches.org.uk

CC NO 299633   **ESTABLISHED** 1988

■ Hampshire and Isle of Wight Community Foundation

WHERE FUNDING CAN BE GIVEN Hampshire and Isle of Wight.

WHO CAN BENEFIT Individuals and organisations.

WHAT IS FUNDED General charitable purposes.

RANGE OF GRANTS £1,000–£10,000.

FINANCES *Year* 2008 *Grants* £424,882

TRUSTEES Michael Campbell, Chair; Will Godfrey; Pat James; Jonathan Whiticar; Revd Trevor Wilmott; Lena Samuels; Carole Damper; Marcelle Speller; Jim Iles; Robin Freeman; Chris Freeman.

HOW TO APPLY Application forms can be downloaded from the foundation's website.

WHO TO APPLY TO Toni Shaw, Chief Executive Officer, Sun Alliance House, Wote Street, Basingstoke, Hampshire RG21 1LU *Tel* 01256 776101 *email* info@hantscf.org.uk *Website* www. hantscf.org.uk

CC NO 1100417   **ESTABLISHED** 2002

■ The Hampstead Wells and Campden Trust

WHERE FUNDING CAN BE GIVEN The former metropolitan borough of Hampstead; organisations covering a wider area but whose activities benefit Hampstead residents among others may also apply.

WHO CAN BENEFIT Organisations, institutions and individuals in Hampstead and Camden, benefiting children, young adults and older people, parents and children, ethnic minority groups, at risk groups, people who are disabled or disadvantaged by poverty, ex-offenders and those at risk of offending, refugees, homeless people, socially isolated people, and victims of abuse and domestic violence.

WHAT IS FUNDED The relief of people in need who are sick, convalescent, have disabilities or are infirm, and the relief generally of people in need or distress.

WHAT IS NOT FUNDED Grants may not be made towards the payment of rates or taxes, or in principle where statutory bodies have the responsibility to help.

TYPE OF GRANT One-off to individuals and organisations, some recurring.

SAMPLE GRANTS Previous beneficiaries include: Royal Free Hospital (£44,000); Camden Community Law Centre (£19,000); Kingsgate Community Association (£15,000); Macmillan Cancer Relief (£6,000); the Brandon Centre and Treehouse Speech & Language Programme (£5,000 each); and Volunteer Reading Help (£2,000).

FINANCES *Year* 2007–08 *Income* £712,507 *Grants* £263,300 *Assets* £14,421,520

TRUSTEES Geoff Berridge, Chair; Ms Gaynor Bassey; Dr Diana Dick; Mrs Francoise Findlay; Dennis Finning; Michael Bieber; Ian Harrison; Mrs Margaret Hepburn; Mrs Gaynor Humphreys; Margaret Little; John Smithard; Mrs Jocelyne Tobin; Revd Stephen Tucker; Alistair Voaden; Dr Christina Williams; Andrew Way; George Webster.

OTHER INFORMATION In 2007/08 a further £83,757 was given to individuals and £94,770 in pensions.

HOW TO APPLY Applications may be made at any time. The trustees meet eight times a year and in addition requests for smaller grants are considered at more frequent intervals. There is no application form (for organisations), but 'it is imperative to show, preferably with statistical information, how many people in the former metropolitan borough of Hampstead have been or will be helped by the project [. . .] Applications may be discussed with the staff of the trust prior to their submission'.

WHO TO APPLY TO Mrs Sheila A Taylor, Director/Clerk to the Trustees, 62 Rosslyn Hill, London NW3 1ND *Tel* 020 7435 1570 *Fax* 020 7435 1571 *email* grant@hwct.fsnet.co.uk *Website* www.hwct.org.uk

CC NO 1094611   **ESTABLISHED** 1971

■ Hampton Fuel Allotment Charity

WHERE FUNDING CAN BE GIVEN Hampton, the former borough of Twickenham, and the borough of Richmond (in that order).

WHO CAN BENEFIT Community groups, voluntary organisations and individuals.

WHAT IS FUNDED A percentage of fuel bills of individuals in need; to provide essential equipment for individuals in need or distress; to support organisations which deliver services for people in need; general medical support; organisations supporting people who have disabilities, physical or mental; organisations which support social or medical welfare and housing needs; educational, youth and community projects; and organisations which provide recreation and leisure activities.

WHAT IS NOT FUNDED The charity is unlikely to support grants to individuals for private and post-compulsory education; adaptations or building alterations for individuals; holidays, except in cases of severe medical need; decoration, carpeting or central heating; anything which is the responsibility of a statutory body; national general charitable appeals; animal welfare; religious groups, unless offering a non-religious service to the community; commercial and business activities; endowment appeals; political projects; retrospective capital grants. The trustees have decided for the present to limit grants towards major 'one-off' projects generally to £30,000. Applicants are advised to contact the clerk prior to formally submitting such applications. The trustees are also reluctant to support ongoing revenue costs of organisations unless they can show clearly that within the area of benefit a substantial number of people are being charitably assisted. They also expect organisations to show that other support will be forthcoming and that the organisation will become self-reliant over an identified period of years.

TYPE OF GRANT Various including capital, one-off and loans.

SAMPLE GRANTS Richmond Fellowship Foundation International (£60,000); Age Concern – Richmond upon Thames (£49,000); Shooting Star Children's Hospice (£35,000); Hampton War Memorial Charity (£18,000); Twickenham and Thames Valley Bee-Keepers' Association (£15,000); Crossway Pregnancy Crisis Centre (£10,000); Environment Trust for Richmond upon Thames (£5,500); Vietnamese Community Association in South West London (£1,800); Young Scientists Event in Richmond (£1,000); and Churches Together in Teddington (£450).

FINANCES *Year* 2007–08 *Income* £2,064,336 *Grants* £1,098,000 *Assets* £3,900,000

TRUSTEES Reverend D N Winterburn, Chair; R Ellis; G Hunter; Mrs M T Martin; J Mortimer; Dr J Young; Reverend G Clarkson; S Leamy; J Cardy; D Cornwell; D Parish.

OTHER INFORMATION A further £662,000 was awarded to individuals in fuel grants and equipment.

HOW TO APPLY In writing to the clerk on the application form available from the trust or its website. Please do not send requests by email. On receipt of your application form the clerk will review it and may wish to ask further questions before submitting it to the trustees for consideration. All eligible applications will be considered. The general grants panel meets every two months, considers all project grants and for over £25,000 and makes a recommendation to the quarterly meeting of the trustees. The clerk will be pleased to inform organisations about the dates of meetings when their application is to be considered. Organisations are advised to put in their applications well in advance of meeting dates. In the case of major capital or other large projects, it may be, that on occasions, a small group of trustees are asked to discuss the scheme with the organisation and its advisors. It may also involve a site visit or an independent evaluation by an assessor. Conditions may be attached to any grant and the trust should be kept regularly informed as to the progress and effectiveness of a project. In certain cases, where conditions have been attached to the grant, written confirmation of acceptance of these by the organisation will be required prior to the grant being paid. 'The trustees accept no liability for any commitment by an applicant to expenditure for which a grant is requested until the applicant has been informed in writing that the trustees have approved a grant.' Major capital projects on a 'once and for all' basis are paid in instalments as work progresses. Applicants may like to discuss their project with the clerk prior to completion of an application form. Due to the volume of applications received it is not always possible to fund organisations even though they may fall within the trust's criteria.

WHO TO APPLY TO M J Ryder, Clerk, 15 High Street, Hampton, Middlesex TW12 2SA *Tel* 020 8941 7866 *Fax* 020 8979 5555 *email* info@hamptonfuelcharity.co.uk *Website* www.hfac.co.uk

CC NO 211756   **ESTABLISHED** 1811

■ The W A Handley Charitable Trust

WHERE FUNDING CAN BE GIVEN Northumberland and Tyneside.

WHO CAN BENEFIT Registered charities only.

WHAT IS FUNDED General charitable purposes with preference for the alleviation of distress, crisis funding, pump-priming finance and operating expenses.

WHAT IS NOT FUNDED No grants to individuals. Grants are only made to registered charities.

TYPE OF GRANT Buildings; capital; core costs; endowments; feasibility studies; one-off; project; research; running costs; recurring costs; salaries; and start-up costs. Funding is available for up to one year.

SAMPLE GRANTS The Alnwick Garden (£25,000); Northumberland Institute for Cancer Research (£20,000); Northumberland Wildlife (£12,000); Prostate Research Campaign UK and Game & Wildlife Conservation (£5,000 each); and Northumberland Association of Clubs for Young People (£4,000).

FINANCES *Year* 2007–08 *Income* £383,537 *Grants* £347,300 *Assets* £9,208,555

TRUSTEES Anthony Glenton; David Milligan; William Dryden; David Irvin.

HOW TO APPLY In writing to the correspondent, quoting the applicant's official charity number and providing full back-up information. Grants are made quarterly in March, June, September and December.

WHO TO APPLY TO David Milligan, Trustee, c/o Ryecroft Glenton, 32 Portland Terrace, Jesmond, Newcastle upon Tyne NE1 1QP *email* davidmilligan@ryecroft-glenton.co.uk

CC NO 230435   **ESTABLISHED** 1963

■ Beatrice Hankey Foundation Ltd

WHERE FUNDING CAN BE GIVEN UK and overseas.

WHO CAN BENEFIT Institutions benefiting Christians.

WHAT IS FUNDED The advancement of the Christian religion, especially training missionaries. Study and training courses in Eastern Europe.

WHAT IS NOT FUNDED No grants for buildings or equipment.

TYPE OF GRANT Recurrent.

RANGE OF GRANTS Up to £14,000.

SAMPLE GRANTS Lagan College (£14,000); Corrymeela Community (£3,500); St Alfege's School Project (£3,000); Cornerstone Community (£2,000); the Dalitso Trust and Community Meeting Point – Harpenden (£1,000); Christian Solidarity Worldwide, the Light House and Hope in Christ (£500); and Rugby Youth for Christ (£200).

FINANCES *Year* 2007 *Income* £47,888 *Grants* £28,182 *Assets* £1,154,059

TRUSTEES Rev S Barnes; H W Bright; E F Dawe; J G Green; Rev Canon P Gompertz; L Grafin zu Lynar; T Halliday; P Sargeant; Revd D Saville; A Y Stewart; H Walker; G Vye; R Woodcock

HOW TO APPLY Unsolicited applications cannot be considered.

WHO TO APPLY TO Mrs M Churchill, Secretary, 11 Staverton Road, Werrington, Peterborough, Cambridgeshire PE4 6LY *Tel* 01733 571794

CC NO 211093   **ESTABLISHED** 1949

■ The Hanley Trust

WHERE FUNDING CAN BE GIVEN UK, with a preference for Corby and Rutland.

WHO CAN BENEFIT Registered charities benefiting at-risk groups, people disadvantaged by poverty and socially isolated people.

WHAT IS FUNDED Organisations concerned with social welfare and disadvantage.

WHAT IS NOT FUNDED Grants are not made to individuals or to non-registered charities.

RANGE OF GRANTS Up to a maximum of £4,000, with most grants made between £250 and £2,500.

SAMPLE GRANTS Butler Trust and Irene Taylor Trust (£2,500 each); Helen Arkell Dyslexia Centre, Howard League for Penal Reform, Pembroke College Cambridge and Shelter (£1,000 each); Amnesty International, Deafness Research UK, Mind, Project Trust and Kurdish Aid Foundation (£500 each).

FINANCES *Year* 2007 *Income* £36,087 *Grants* £29,400 *Assets* £1,092,573

TRUSTEES Hon. Sarah Price, Chair; Hon. James Butler; Nicholas Smith.

HOW TO APPLY In writing to the correspondent.

WHO TO APPLY TO Hon. Mrs Sarah Price, Trustee, 21 Buckingham Gate, London SW1E 6LS

CC NO 299209   **ESTABLISHED** 1987

■ The Hanlye Charitable Trust

WHERE FUNDING CAN BE GIVEN UK.

WHO CAN BENEFIT People who are poor and sick, have disabilities or who are convalescing, poor children who are sick, the advancement of the education of such children and the welfare of animals.

WHAT IS FUNDED Registered charities.

SAMPLE GRANTS Manchester Jewish Community Centre (£3,750); Medequip4kids (£1,000); Rainscough Trust (£750); and Langdon Foundation (£500).

FINANCES *Year* 2007–08

TRUSTEES J R Bostock; I A Ross; T K Saunders; S L Goodman.

HOW TO APPLY In writing to the correspondent. Trustees meet bi-annually.

WHO TO APPLY TO I A Ross, Trust Secretary, Aberdeen House, South Road, Haywards Heath, West Sussex RH16 4HG *Tel* 01444 414125

CC NO 1107470   **ESTABLISHED** 2004

■ The Kathleen Hannay Memorial Charity

WHERE FUNDING CAN BE GIVEN UK.

WHO CAN BENEFIT Registered charities, universities and schools.

WHAT IS FUNDED General charitable purposes, particularly Christian causes, health, social welfare and education. The trust will consider funding, for example: community development; support to voluntary and community organisations; support to volunteers; social care professional bodies; the advancement of the Christian religion; churches including conservation of church buildings; Anglican and Free Church umbrella bodies; music; health; church schools; special schools; education and training; medical research; religion; social sciences; specialist research; and social care and development.

WHAT IS NOT FUNDED No grants to individuals or non-registered charities.

TYPE OF GRANT One-off grants for capital and revenue costs.

RANGE OF GRANTS £4,000 – £150,000.

SAMPLE GRANTS Monkton Combe School – to establish a bursary fund at the pre-Prep School (£150,000); Children's Fire and Burn Trust – towards work with children affected by scalds and burns (£40,000); St Mary Magdalene, Hullavington PCC – towards the renewal and renovation of the church (£30,000); and the Reverend JPR Saunt – towards sponsoring the education of 'Lilian Lwanga' in Uganda (£4,000).

FINANCES *Year* 2007–08 *Income* £291,510 *Grants* £222,220 *Assets* £14,584,380

TRUSTEES Jonathan F Weil; Simon P Weil; Christian Alison K Ward.

OTHER INFORMATION The trustees were unable to meet before the end of the financial year so the majority of the donations agreed were not made until early in the following financial year. At a meeting held in May 2008 the trustees sanctioned further donations totalling £206,000, for which provision has not been made in these accounts.

HOW TO APPLY In writing to the correspondent. The trustees usually meet in March.

WHO TO APPLY TO G Fincham, Administrator, 15 Suffolk Street, London SW1Y 4HG *Tel* 020 7036 5685

CC NO 299600   **ESTABLISHED** 1988

■ The Doughty Hanson Charitable Foundation

WHERE FUNDING CAN BE GIVEN Unrestricted.

WHO CAN BENEFIT Registered charities.

WHAT IS FUNDED The relief of poverty distress and suffering, advancing education and appreciation in the arts and science, furthering religious work and other charitable purposes in any part of the world.

SAMPLE GRANTS Parchment Trust (£50,000); Snowdon Award (£11,000); NSPCC (£5,000);

Brainwave (£4,000); Independent Age (£3,000); Downside Fisher Club and Prostate Cancer (£1,000 each); and UNICEF (£200).

FINANCES *Year* 2007 *Income* £202,264 *Grants* £203,838

TRUSTEES Nigel Doughty; Richard Hanson; Max Lever; Stephen Marquardt.

HOW TO APPLY In writing to the correspondent – the grants committee meets about four times a year. Only successful applicants receive a response.

WHO TO APPLY TO Julie Foreman, Secretary, PO Box 31064, London SW1Y 5ZP

CC NO 1080755   **ESTABLISHED** 2000

■ Lord Hanson Foundation

WHERE FUNDING CAN BE GIVEN Worldwide.

WHO CAN BENEFIT Charitable organisations.

WHAT IS FUNDED General charitable purposes.

RANGE OF GRANTS Up to £13,000.

SAMPLE GRANTS Hanson Research Trust (£10,000); Raisa Gorbachev Foundation (£9,000); The Children's Trust (£5,000); Temi Charitable Union (£2,500); and Royal College of Radiologists and Skill Force (£1,000 each).

FINANCES *Year* 2007–08 *Income* £65,499 *Grants* £36,500 *Assets* £1,138,754

TRUSTEES Jonathan Azis; Alan Hagdrup; The Hon Robert Hanson.

HOW TO APPLY In writing to the correspondent.

WHO TO APPLY TO Miss Gillian Ryan, 31 Wilton Row, London SW1X 7NS *Tel* 020 7245 6996

CC NO 1077014   **ESTABLISHED** 1999

■ The Haramead Trust

WHERE FUNDING CAN BE GIVEN Worldwide, in practice, developing countries, UK and Ireland and locally in the east Midlands.

WHO CAN BENEFIT Registered charities and individuals and families in need of direct assistance.

WHAT IS FUNDED Children, social welfare, education, people with disabilities, homeless people, medical assistance, victims and oppressed people and religious activities.

TYPE OF GRANT Core support, building/renovation, equipment, vehicles and project support will all be considered.

RANGE OF GRANTS £1,000–£120,000.

SAMPLE GRANTS CAFOD (£120,000); British Red Cross (£100,000); Shelter (£60,000); Leicestershire and Rutland Organisation for the Relief of Suffering (£25,000); Love & Share (£20,000); Intercare and Menphys (£15,000 each); and Dove Cottage Day Hospice, Leicester Charity Link, Phoenix Futures and Streetwise (£10,000 each).

FINANCES *Year* 2007–08 *Income* £1,340,406 *Grants* £1,226,100 *Assets* £1,105,219

TRUSTEES Simon P Astill; Mrs Winifred M Linnett; Michael J Linnett; Robert H Smith; David L Tams; Revd Joseph A Mullen.

HOW TO APPLY In writing to the correspondent. The trustees meet every couple of months and may visit funded projects for monitoring purposes or to assess for future grants.

WHO TO APPLY TO Michael J Linnett, Trustee, Park House, Park Hill, Gaddesby, Leicestershire LE7 4WH *Tel* 01664 840908 *Fax* 01664 840908

CC NO 1047416   **ESTABLISHED** 1995

■ Miss K M Harbinson's Charitable Trust

WHERE FUNDING CAN BE GIVEN UK and developing countries.

WHO CAN BENEFIT Development organisations.

WHAT IS FUNDED International development.

RANGE OF GRANTS £1,000–£9,000.

SAMPLE GRANTS Previous beneficiaries have included ActionAid, British Red Cross Worldwide Fund for Nature, Breadline Africa, Care Britain, Ethopiaid Intermediate Technology, Marie Stopes International, Oxfam, Romanian Orphanage Trust, Sight Savers International, UNICEF.

FINANCES *Year* 2008 *Grants* £150,000

TRUSTEES A Maguire; G L Harbinson; R Harbinson.

OTHER INFORMATION Up-to-date information was unavailable for this trust.

HOW TO APPLY In writing to the correspondent.

WHO TO APPLY TO The Secretary, 190 St Vincent Street, Glasgow G2 5SP *Tel* 0141 204 2833

■ Harbo Charities Limited

WHERE FUNDING CAN BE GIVEN UK.

WHO CAN BENEFIT Charities, and scholastic and religious institutions.

WHAT IS FUNDED General charitable purposes and Jewish causes.

SAMPLE GRANTS Beis Chinuch Lebonos Girls School, Beth Rochel d'Satmar, Bobov Trust, Chevras Maoz Ladol, Craven Walk Charitable Trust, Edgware Yeshiva Trust, Keren Yesomim, Kollel Shomrei HaChomoth, Tevini Limited, Tomchei Shabbos, Yad Eliezer, Yesode Ha Torah School and Yeshiva Chachmay Tsorpha.

FINANCES *Year* 2007–08 *Income* £86,650 *Grants* £92,099 *Assets* £759,230

TRUSTEES Harry Stern; Barbara J Stern; Harold Gluck.

HOW TO APPLY In writing to the correspondent.

WHO TO APPLY TO The Trustees, c/o Cohen Arnold and Co., New Burlington House, 1075 Finchley Road, London NW11 0PU

CC NO 282262   **ESTABLISHED** 1981

■ The Harborne Parish Lands Charity

WHERE FUNDING CAN BE GIVEN The ancient parish of Harborne, which includes parts of Harborne, Smethwick, Bearwood and Quinton.

WHO CAN BENEFIT All grants must benefit people living within the parish.

WHAT IS FUNDED Charities working in the fields of: accommodation and housing; infrastructure and technical support; infrastructure development; healthcare; health facilities and buildings; physical and mental disability organisations; schools; education and training; community centres and village halls; playgrounds and community services; individual need and other charitable purposes.

TYPE OF GRANT Buildings, capital, core costs, interest-free loans, one-off, project, running costs, salaries and start-up costs. Funding for up to one year will be considered.

SAMPLE GRANTS Previous beneficiaries include: Quinzone (£85,000); Central Mediation Services and Community Resource Info Service (£29,000 each); Women Acting in Today's Society (£20,000); Cape Community Care Day Centre (£10,000); Welsh House Farm Community Project and the Friendship Club (£8,000 each);

Smethick Pakistani Muslims Association and Central Africa Refugee Link (£3,000 each); and Langley Parochial Church Council and Tividale Tigers Jazz Band (£1,000 each).

FINANCES *Year* 2007–08 *Income* £876,201 *Grants* £299,000 *Assets* £862,028

TRUSTEES Cllr J E C Alden; Cllr P Hollingworth; P W Lawrence; M Lloyd; J S Gregory; I McArdle; Mrs V Montague-Smith; F Jephcott; R Horton; Mrs R Silber; Mrs J Lawrence; Cllr V Silvester.

HOW TO APPLY In writing to the correspondent. An exact map of the beneficial area can be obtained from the trust (or on its website) and should be consulted before an application is submitted. Further information can be obtained from the trust's website.

WHO TO APPLY TO Miss L J Bending, Clerk to the Trustees, 109 Court Oak Road, Harborne, Birmingham B17 9AA *Tel* 0121 426 1600 *Fax* 0121 428 2267 *email* theclerk@hplc. fednet.org.uk *Website* www. harborneparishlandscharity.org.uk

CC NO 219031   **ESTABLISHED** 1699

■ The Harbour Charitable Trust

WHERE FUNDING CAN BE GIVEN UK.

WHO CAN BENEFIT Organisations benefiting children, young adults and students. Support may also be given to teachers and governesses, medical professionals, research workers, parents and children and one-parent families.

WHAT IS FUNDED Childcare, education and healthcare, and other charitable organisations.

WHAT IS NOT FUNDED Grants are given to registered charities only.

SAMPLE GRANTS Grants were broken down as follows: Joint Jewish Charitable Trust (£39,000); education (£16,000); healthcare (£2,000); childcare (£900); and 'other' donations (£2,000).

FINANCES *Year* 2007–08 *Income* £157,219 *Grants* £61,703 *Assets* £2,964,480

TRUSTEES Mrs B B Green; Mrs Z S Blackman; Mrs T Elsenstat; Mrs E Knobil.

HOW TO APPLY In writing to the correspondent.

WHO TO APPLY TO The Trustees, c/o Barbican House, 26–34 Old Street, London EC1V 9QQ

CC NO 234268   **ESTABLISHED** 1962

■ The Harbour Foundation

WHERE FUNDING CAN BE GIVEN Worldwide, with a preference for London.

WHO CAN BENEFIT Organisations and individuals.

WHAT IS FUNDED There is a preference for at risk groups, people disadvantaged by poverty, people who are homeless, refugees and people who are socially isolated. Support may also be given to research workers and students.

TYPE OF GRANT Recurring costs.

SAMPLE GRANTS Previous beneficiaries include: Israel Guide Dog Center for the Blind, Westminster Synagogue, SRF UK, Les Azuriales Opera Trust, Tel Aviv Foundation, East London Business Alliance, Reform Club Conservation, UCLH and World Jewish Relief, Save the Children and Wigmore Hall Trust.

FINANCES *Year* 2007–08 *Income* £1,159,970 *Grants* £291,150 *Assets* £29,462,388

TRUSTEES S R Harbour; A C Humphries; D Harbour; Rex Harbour.**HOW TO APPLY** In writing to the correspondent. Applications need to be received by February, as trustees meet in March.

WHO TO APPLY TO The Trustees, The Courtyard Building, 11 Curtain Road, London EC2A 3LT *Tel* 020 7456 8180

CC NO 264927   **ESTABLISHED** 1970

■ The Harding Trust

WHERE FUNDING CAN BE GIVEN Mainly, but not exclusively, north Staffordshire and surrounding areas.

WHO CAN BENEFIT To benefit actors and entertainment professionals; musicians; textile workers and designers; writers and poets; at risk groups; people who are ill or disadvantaged by poverty; and socially isolated people. Consideration will be given to national charities if there is a good reason for doing so.

WHAT IS FUNDED To give to smaller rather than larger charities. Charities supported are in most cases connected with music and the arts but local welfare charities and hospices are also given support.

TYPE OF GRANT One-off and recurrent.

SAMPLE GRANTS Stoke on Trent Festival (£30,000); Harding Trust Piano Recitals (£17,000); Wolverhampton Civic Hall Orchestra (£10,000); Stoke on Trent Music School – Education Scheme (£5,000); Patrons Victoria Hall Organ (£2,500); Douglas Macmillan Hospice, Katharine House Hospice and Donna Louise Trust (£1,500 each); and St Johns Ambulance (£1,000).

FINANCES *Year* 2007–08 *Income* £171,282 *Grants* £116,750 *Assets* £3,826,675

TRUSTEES G G Wall; J P C Fowell; M N Lloyd; G B Snow.

HOW TO APPLY In writing to the correspondent. The trustees meet annually in spring/early summer. Accounts are needed for recurrent applications.

WHO TO APPLY TO The Administrator, Brabners Chaffe Street, 1 Dale Street, Liverpool L2 2ET *Tel* 0151 600 3000

CC NO 328182   **ESTABLISHED** 1989

■ William Harding's Charity

WHERE FUNDING CAN BE GIVEN Aylesbury in Buckinghamshire.

WHO CAN BENEFIT Older people, those in the charity's almshouse accommodation and young people under the age of 25 to further their education.

WHAT IS FUNDED To assist young people in education, including at an individual level, by providing scholarships, maintenance allowances, travel awards and grants for equipment. At a wider level, grants are made to the LEA for Aylesbury schools to fund equipment in addition to that which can be provided by the authority. The charity also provides relief in need and for the general benefit of Aylesbury residents.

WHAT IS NOT FUNDED 'All persons and organisations not based in Aylesbury Town.'

TYPE OF GRANT One-off and capital.

RANGE OF GRANTS £500–£200,000 (organisations).

SAMPLE GRANTS Previous beneficiaries have included: the Buckingham Foundation (£18,000); Aylesbury Youth Action, Excellence in Aylesbury Schools and Queen Park Art Centre (£10,000 each); Aylesbury Youth Forum (£5,000); Aylesbury United Sports Development (£4,500); Broughton Infant School and DPEAP (£3,000 each); British Dyslexics and the Dove Centre (£2,000 each); and Aylesbury Town

Bowles Club and Mandeville Youth Dance (£1,500 each).
FINANCES *Year* 2007 *Income* £643 *Grants* £180,000
TRUSTEES Bernard Griffin, Chair; William Chapple; Mrs Freda Roberts; Leslie Sheldon; Mrs Betty Foster; John Vooght; Mrs Kathleen Brooker; Mrs Penni Thorne; Roger Evans.
HOW TO APPLY In writing to the correspondent. Trustees meet on a monthly basis to consider and determine applications for charitable assistance.
WHO TO APPLY TO J Leggett, c/o Parrott and Coales, 14 Bourbon Street, Aylesbury, Buckinghamshire HP20 2RS *Tel* 01296 318500 *Website* www.whardingcharity.org.uk
CC NO 310619   **ESTABLISHED** 1978

■ The Hare of Steep Charitable Trust

WHERE FUNDING CAN BE GIVEN UK, with preference for the south of England, especially Petersfield and East Hampshire.
WHO CAN BENEFIT Registered charities only.
WHAT IS FUNDED Charities which benefit the community, in particular the advancement of social, cultural, medical, educational and religious projects.
WHAT IS NOT FUNDED No funding for overseas charities, students, visits abroad or political causes.
TYPE OF GRANT Mainly annual contributions but one-off grants are made for special projects.
RANGE OF GRANTS £250–£2,000.
SAMPLE GRANTS Previous beneficiaries include: Alzheimer's Disease Society, Arthritis and Rheumatism Council – Petersfield, British Heart Foundation, Rainbow House Trust and SSAFA.
FINANCES *Year* 2007–08 *Income* £102,315 *Grants* £49,750 *Assets* £127,619
TRUSTEES P L F Baillon; J S Grenfell; J R F Fowler; S M Fowler; S E R Johnson-Hill.
HOW TO APPLY 'The trustees already support as many charities as they could wish and would certainly not welcome any appeals from others. Unsolicited requests are not acknowledged.'
WHO TO APPLY TO Mrs S M Fowler, Hon. Secretary, 56 Heath Road, Petersfield, Hampshire GU31 4EJ *Tel* 01730 267953
CC NO 297308   **ESTABLISHED** 1987

■ The Harebell Centenary Fund

WHERE FUNDING CAN BE GIVEN UK.
WHO CAN BENEFIT UK and small charitable organisations benefiting children, older people, carers, people who are disabled and animals.
WHAT IS FUNDED Neurological research and animal welfare. This includes charities working in the fields of health, medical studies and research, conservation, heritage, special needs education and holidays and outings.
WHAT IS NOT FUNDED No grants are made towards infrastructure or to individuals.
TYPE OF GRANT One-off, core costs, research, recurring costs, running costs and funding for one year or less will be considered.
RANGE OF GRANTS Up to £4,000.
SAMPLE GRANTS Crathie School (£2,500); the Cats Protection League, Bluebell Hospice, Motor Neurone Disease Association and Ro-Ro Sailing Project (£2,000 each); and Trinity Hospice, Martin's House Children's Hospice and Helen House Hospice (£1,500 each).

FINANCES *Year* 2007 *Income* £77,623 *Grants* £54,000 *Assets* £2,183,624
TRUSTEES Ms P J Chapman; M I Goodbody; F M Reed.
HOW TO APPLY In writing to the correspondent. Unsolicited applications are not requested, as the trustees prefer to make donations to charities whose work they have come across through their own research.
WHO TO APPLY TO Ms P J Chapman, 50 Broadway, London SW1H 0BL *Tel* 020 7227 7000 *email* pennychapman@bdb-law.co.uk
CC NO 1003552   **ESTABLISHED** 1991

■ The Hargrave Foundation

WHERE FUNDING CAN BE GIVEN Worldwide.
WHO CAN BENEFIT Registered charities.
WHAT IS FUNDED General, medical, welfare.
RANGE OF GRANTS Up to £10,000.
SAMPLE GRANTS Journalism Education and Reform (£10,000 each); St Giles Hospice (£6,000); and Rainforest Concern and The Gentlemen's 'Night Out' (£5,000 each).
FINANCES *Year* 2007–08 *Income* £165,643 *Grants* £43,336 *Assets* £2,751,279
TRUSTEES Stephen Hargrave; Dominic Moseley; Mark Parkin.
HOW TO APPLY In writing to the correspondent.
WHO TO APPLY TO Stephen Hargrave, Trustee, 47 Lamb's Conduit Street, London WC1N 3NG
CC NO 1106524   **ESTABLISHED** 2004

■ The Kenneth Hargreaves Charitable Trust

WHERE FUNDING CAN BE GIVEN UK, with a preference for Wetherby area of Leeds.
WHO CAN BENEFIT Registered charities benefiting children, young adults, students, medical professionals, community workers, research workers, teachers and project workers.
WHAT IS FUNDED Health, social welfare, arts, education, the environment and conservation.
WHAT IS NOT FUNDED No grants to individuals. Applications for core funding or salaries are rarely considered.
TYPE OF GRANT Preference is given to capital rather than revenue funding.
RANGE OF GRANTS Usually £100–£2,000.
SAMPLE GRANTS Yorkshire Cancer Centre (£25,000); Children with Leukaemia (£2,000); Selby Abbey Trust (£1,000); Hepworth Art Gallery (£500); Yorkshire Foundation For Conservation & Craftsmen (£250); and Barn Owl Trust (£100).
FINANCES *Year* 2007–08 *Income* £33,587 *Grants* £56,742 *Assets* £766,063
TRUSTEES Dr Ingrid Roscoe; Mrs M Hargreaves-Allen; Mrs Sheila Holbrook; P R P Chadwick.
HOW TO APPLY In writing to the correspondent including clear details of the intended project, an outline budget and an annual report. The trustees meet quarterly. Only successful applicants will be acknowledged.
WHO TO APPLY TO Mrs Sheila Holbrook, Hon. Treasurer, The Hollies, 28 Hookstone Drive, Harrogate HG2 8PP *Tel* 01423 885676 *Fax* 01423 885676 *email* holbrook58@aol.com *Website* www.dsc.org.uk
CC NO 223800   **ESTABLISHED** 1957

■ The Harris Charitable Trust

WHERE FUNDING CAN BE GIVEN UK, with a preference for Merton.

WHO CAN BENEFIT Registered charities known to the trustees.

WHAT IS FUNDED General charitable purposes.

RANGE OF GRANTS £50–£3,000.

SAMPLE GRANTS Grants for over £1,000 each included those made to: the British Heart Foundation; Freeways Trust; MS Society – Merton; Noah's Ark Trust and UCL Development Fund.

FINANCES *Year* 2007–08 *Income* £29,349 *Grants* £29,135

TRUSTEES Diana Harris; Colin Harris; Dr Andrew Harris; Thomas Harris.

HOW TO APPLY The trust does not respond to unsolicited applications.

WHO TO APPLY TO Mrs Diana Harris, 101 Church Road, Wimbledon, London SW19 5AL

CC NO 292652   **ESTABLISHED** 1966

■ The Harris Charity

WHERE FUNDING CAN BE GIVEN Lancashire, with a preference for the City of Preston (formally the borough of Preston.).

WHO CAN BENEFIT Young people.

WHAT IS FUNDED Charities benefiting individuals, children and young people under 25, in the Lancashire area.

TYPE OF GRANT Capital projects and provision of equipment are preferred.

RANGE OF GRANTS £40 to £5,000.

SAMPLE GRANTS Grants included those made to: the Army Cadet Association, Pear Tree School, Pendle View Primary School, SENCE, Deepdale Football Club, Young Enterprise Preston and Live Music Now North West.

FINANCES *Year* 2008–09 *Income* £136,393 *Grants* £58,709 *Assets* £2,934,257

TRUSTEES W S Huck; E J Booth; Miss B Banks; S R Fisher; T Scott; S B R Smith; S Huck; Mrs R Jolly; K Mellalieu; Mrs A Scott; Mrs N Fielden; Rev R Lane.

OTHER INFORMATION During the year, £9,770 was given in grants to individuals.

HOW TO APPLY Application forms are available from the trustees, on which the applicant is invited to submit a summary of their proposal. The trustees meet quarterly to discuss grant applications that are approved twice a year in March and September. Each candidate is informed of the outcome of their application and if successful will be asked to provide the trustees with the relevant documents and/or invoices so that the funds can be released.

WHO TO APPLY TO P R Metcalf, Secretary, Richard House, 9 Winckley Square, Preston, Lancashire PR1 3HP *Tel* 01772 821021 *Fax* 01772 259441 *email* harrischarity@mooreandsmalley. co.uk

CC NO 526206   **ESTABLISHED** 1883

■ The Harris Family Charitable Trust

WHERE FUNDING CAN BE GIVEN UK.

WHO CAN BENEFIT Charitable organisations.

WHAT IS FUNDED Health issues and the alleviation of sickness.

FINANCES *Year* 2007–08 *Income* £570,000 *Grants* £132,000 *Assets* £1,300,000

TRUSTEES R M Harris; L Harris; C E Harris.

HOW TO APPLY 'The charity invites applications for funding of projects through various sources. The applications are reviewed by the trustees who ensure that they are in accordance with the charity's objectives.'

WHO TO APPLY TO R M Harris, Trustee, Cavendish Street, London W1G 7LS

CC NO 1064394   **ESTABLISHED** 1997

■ The Harrison and Potter Trust

WHERE FUNDING CAN BE GIVEN Leeds (pre-1974 boundary).

WHO CAN BENEFIT Individuals, or organisations supporting people in need who are resident in Leeds.

WHAT IS FUNDED Individuals can be given grants for heat, lighting, equipment, clothing and holidays. Organisations or projects concerned with homeless, older people, young mothers and unemployed people are supported.

WHAT IS NOT FUNDED The trust cannot commit to repeat grants.

TYPE OF GRANT One-off and project.

RANGE OF GRANTS Individuals: £100–£200. Organisations: £1,000–£30,000.

SAMPLE GRANTS Caring Together in Woodhouse (£7,000); Caring for Life (£5,000); Older Active People (£3,000); OPAL (£1,000); and Leeds Society for Deaf and Blind (£700).

FINANCES *Year* 2008 *Income* £338,788 *Grants* £45,754 *Assets* £5,047,569

TRUSTEES G Whitehead, Chair; Dr I A Blomfield; P G Wooler; W J A Smith; Mrs H A Vinall; Mrs J V White; Lord Mayor of Leeds; Vicar of Leeds; Local Authority Representative.

OTHER INFORMATION During the year grants made to individuals totalled £9,393.

HOW TO APPLY In writing to the correspondent to be considered in February, May, August and November. Individuals must write requesting an application form and these will be considered monthly.

WHO TO APPLY TO Miss A S Duchart, Clerk, Wrigleys Solicitors, 19 Cookridge Street, Leeds LS2 3AG *Tel* 0113 204 5710

CC NO 224941   **ESTABLISHED** 1970

■ The John Harrison Charitable Trust

WHERE FUNDING CAN BE GIVEN UK.

WHO CAN BENEFIT Organisations concerned with multiple sclerosis.

WHAT IS FUNDED Multiple sclerosis support and research.

FINANCES *Year* 2007–08 *Income* £23,132 *Grants* £10,000

TRUSTEES Judy Sebba; Iris Sebba; Sian Crookes.

HOW TO APPLY In writing to the correspondent.

WHO TO APPLY TO David Hull, PO Box 326, Bedford MK40 3XU *Tel* 01234 266657

CC NO 277956   **ESTABLISHED** 1979

■ The Peter Harrison Foundation

WHERE FUNDING CAN BE GIVEN UK and south east England.

WHO CAN BENEFIT Registered charities, community amateur sports clubs, friendly or provident societies and organisations in Scotland and Northern Ireland recognised by the Inland Revenue.

WHAT IS FUNDED Charitable activities capable of demonstrating an existing high level of committed voluntary members with strong self-help activities together with well-planned and thought out projects under the following categories: Opportunities Through Sport Programme – support for sporting activities or projects which provide opportunities for children and young people who have disabilities or those who are disadvantaged, to fulfil their potential, and for other personal and life skills to be developed; Special Needs and Care Programme for Children and Young People – only for organisations in south east England; Opportunities Through Education Programme – applications not invited. Grants are also made through the Trustees' Discretionary Programme – again, invitations are not invited.

WHAT IS NOT FUNDED General appeals; retrospective funding; individuals; other grant-making bodies to make grants on its behalf; projects that replace statutory funding; projects that are the responsibility of the central or local government; holidays in the UK or abroad and expeditions; outdoor activity projects such as camping or outward bound expeditions; overseas projects; projects solely for the promotion of religion.

RANGE OF GRANTS £100–£850,000.

SAMPLE GRANTS Old Reigatians Rugby Football Club (£850,000); Children's Trust (£250,000); Loughborough University (£150,000); Harrison Scholars – six awards (£101,000); Spinal Injuries Association (£70,000); Cricket Foundation (£50,000); Medical Engineering Resource Unit – MERU (£45,000); Lifelites (£36,000); Burned Children's Club (£23,000); British Polio Fellowship (£15,000); Yvonne Arnaud Theatre Management (£11,000); Erb's Palsy Group (£5,000); and Right to Play Limited (£500).

FINANCES *Year* 2007–08 *Income* £2,345,257 *Grants* £2,133,610 *Assets* £30,284,682

TRUSTEES Peter Harrison, Chair; Joy Harrison; Julia Harrison-Lee; Peter Lee.

HOW TO APPLY The foundation has a two stage application process. Step 1: Initial enquiry. Potential applicants are asked to first read the information on eligibility and grant programmes available on the foundation's website. If your project meets the criteria for one of the open programmes (i.e. Opportunities through Sport or Special Needs and Care for Children and Young People), then complete the online initial enquiry form. This can be found in the 'application process' section of the foundation's website. Applications are processed as quickly as possible, but please be aware that the foundation receives a large number of applications and it may sometimes take up to two months for an initial enquiry form to be considered. Applications are first assessed by the foundation's staff. If it is felt the project will be of interest, they will arrange either to visit the project or to conduct a telephone discussion with the applicant about it. Depending on the outcome of these discussions, you may then be invited to submit a full application. If your initial enquiry is not successful you will be notified by email. The foundation receives many more applications than it is able to support and unfortunately have turn down many good proposals, even though they meet the criteria. No feedback is given on unsuccessful applications. Step 2: Full application. Applicants should only submit a full application form if their initial enquiry has been successful. Completed forms should be sent by post to the correspondent. If an application is successful the applicant will normally be contacted by telephone followed by a grant offer letter. The letter will explain the conditions which apply to all grant awards and also set out any special conditions which apply to your organisation. It will also confirm details of how and when you will receive the grant and how payment is made. If an application is unsuccessful the applicant will be informed by letter. The main reason for not funding projects is the volume of applications received. Organisations supported by the foundation are required to show how they have used the grant and, depending on the grant amount and the nature of the project, may be asked to undertake a review and evaluation of the project being funded. This will normally be on completion of the project, but for charities receiving their grant in several instalments, interim reports may be requested. Full details of the monitoring information required are given in the foundation's grant offer letter. The foundation aims to ensure that all grant applications that are eligible for consideration within the foundation's grants criteria are given equal consideration, irrespective of gender, sexual orientation, race, colour, ethnic or national origin, or disability.

WHO TO APPLY TO John Ledlie, Director, Foundation House, 42–48 London Road, Reigate, Surrey RH2 9QQ *Tel* 01737 228 000 *Fax* 01737 228 001 *email* enquiries@peterharrisonfoundation.org *Website* www.peterharrisonfoundation.org

CC NO 1076579   **ESTABLISHED** 1999

■ The Spencer Hart Charitable Trust

WHERE FUNDING CAN BE GIVEN UK and overseas.

WHO CAN BENEFIT Registered charities.

WHAT IS FUNDED General charitable purposes.

RANGE OF GRANTS Most grants made in region of £100 to £5,000.

SAMPLE GRANTS The League of the Helping Hand (£30,000); Norwood (£5,000); Wigmore Hall Trust (£2,000); World Jewish Relief (£1,000); Weston Turville Wells for Tanzania and the British Heart Foundation (£500 each); The Rainbow Trust, Race for Life and Kenward Trust (£250 each); and RSAUK and Breathe Easy Windsor (£100 each).

FINANCES *Year* 2008–09 *Income* £28,598 *Grants* £39,950

TRUSTEES J S Korn; I A Burman.

HOW TO APPLY In writing to the correspondent.

WHO TO APPLY TO J S Korn, Trustee, Laytons, Carmelite, 50 Victoria Embankment, Blackfriars, London EC4Y OLS *Tel* 020 7842 8000

CC NO 800057   **ESTABLISHED** 1988

■ The Hartley Charitable Trust

WHERE FUNDING CAN BE GIVEN Unrestricted.

WHO CAN BENEFIT Organisations.

WHAT IS FUNDED General charitable purposes.

WHAT IS NOT FUNDED No grants to individuals.

TYPE OF GRANT One-off and recurrent grants for core costs, projects, research and salaries, for one year or less.

SAMPLE GRANTS Alzheimer's Society (£15,000); Brain Research Trust (£10,000); Leukemia Research Fund and Ley Community Drug Services (£5,000 each); Prostate Cancer Charity (£4,000); Soil Association Limited (£3,000); and St Michael's Hospice (£2,000).

FINANCES Year 2007–08 Income £68,474 Grants £95,000 Assets £1,741,311
TRUSTEES Charles Richard Hartley; Jane Hartley; Peta Hyland.
HOW TO APPLY In writing to the correspondent. Telephone requests are not considered. Aggressive or expensive 'glossy' funding requests are not considered.
WHO TO APPLY TO Mr Rick Hartley, Sunnyside Farm, Brearton, Harrogate, Yorkshire HG3 3BX Tel 01423 869369 Fax 01423 525313 email hartleycharitabletrust@hotmail.com
CC NO 800968   **ESTABLISHED** 1989

■ The N and P Hartley Memorial Trust

WHERE FUNDING CAN BE GIVEN Unrestricted with a preference for West Yorkshire.
WHO CAN BENEFIT Organisations benefiting people who are terminally ill, people with disabilities, older people, children and young people, medical research and the environment.
WHAT IS FUNDED The trust supports individuals and community organisations benefiting people who have disabilities, older people, young people and people who are sick, including the provision of medical facilities and care for all age groups. Particular attention is given to smaller charities and individuals in need where relatively small donations may have the greatest impact. It will support both old and new causes.
WHAT IS NOT FUNDED The trust does not support the arts or animal welfare. Grants are not made for non-vocational higher education.
TYPE OF GRANT One-off and recurring.
SAMPLE GRANTS St George's Crypt and South Yorkshire Community (£10,000 each); and Mercy Ships and Hainworth Wood Community Centre (£5,000).
FINANCES Year 2007–08 Income £26,203 Grants £160,904 Assets £513,224
TRUSTEES Mrs V B Watson; Dr James Jason Procter; John Kirman; Mrs Gwen Procter.
OTHER INFORMATION During the year grants were made to individuals totalling £3,576.
HOW TO APPLY In writing to the correspondent. Applications are considered at meetings held twice a year, although urgent cases can be considered outside these meetings. Relevant accounts or budget should be enclosed. Reapplications from previous beneficiaries are welcomed.
WHO TO APPLY TO J E Kirman, c/o Arabesque House, Monkscross Drive, Huttington, York YO32 9GW Tel 01904 341200 Fax 01904 464111 email jkirman@garbutt-elliott.co.uk
CC NO 327570   **ESTABLISHED** 1987

■ The Alfred And Peggy Harvey Charitable Trust

WHERE FUNDING CAN BE GIVEN UK.
WHO CAN BENEFIT Older people, children and young people with disabilities or living in difficult socio-economic circumstances, blind and deaf people.
WHAT IS FUNDED Medical and surgical studies and research.
RANGE OF GRANTS Usually up to £25,000.
SAMPLE GRANTS Children's Adventure Farm Trust (£24,000); Country Holidays For Inner City Kids (£23,000); Starlight Children's Foundation (£20,000); Lighthouse Educational Scheme (£7,200); Beat Bullying (£7,000); The Eyeless Trust (£5,000); Deafblind UK (£4,000); Learning

Through Action (£3,000); Action for Kids (£2,000); and Sunflower Trust (£1,000).
FINANCES Year 2007–08 Income £118,909 Grants £78,614 Assets £500,294
TRUSTEES Colin John Russell; John Duncan; Kevin James Custis.
HOW TO APPLY In writing to the correspondent.
WHO TO APPLY TO The Trustees, c/o Manches LLP, Aldwych House, 81 Aldwych, London WC2B 4RP
CC NO 1095855   **ESTABLISHED** 2003

■ William Geoffrey Harvey's Discretionary Settlement

WHERE FUNDING CAN BE GIVEN Unrestricted with some preference for north west England.
WHO CAN BENEFIT Registered charities.
WHAT IS FUNDED Animal facilities and services to promote the well-being of, and prevent cruelty to, animals and birds.
TYPE OF GRANT Running costs and capital expenditure.
RANGE OF GRANTS £13,000–£25,000.
SAMPLE GRANTS Previous beneficiaries include the Dogs Trust, Three Owls Bird Sanctuary & Reserve, Wildfowl & Wetlands Trust and PDSA.
FINANCES Year 2007–08 Income £140,188 Grants £90,000
TRUSTEES F R Shackleton; F A Sherring; G J Hull.
HOW TO APPLY Previously the trust has stated that the settlor Mrs Harvey gave them 'a clear indication of the causes she favoured and [they] are guided by that for the moment at least', therefore new applicants will not be considered.
WHO TO APPLY TO F A Sherring, 1A Gibsons Road, Stockport, Cheshire SK4 4JX Tel 0161 432 8307
CC NO 800473   **ESTABLISHED** 1968

■ The Edward Harvist Trust Fund

WHERE FUNDING CAN BE GIVEN The London boroughs of Barnet, Brent, Camden, Harrow and the City of Westminster.
WHO CAN BENEFIT Registered charities.
WHAT IS FUNDED General charitable purposes.
RANGE OF GRANTS Up to £15,000.
SAMPLE GRANTS PACE (£15,000); Ijad Dance Company (£8,000); Camden Somali Forum (£5,000); Mary Ward Legal Centre (£4,100); St Johns Wood Crypt Youth Club (£3,000); Barnet Play Association (£1,500); Iran Institute (£1,100); Friends of Canons Park (£500); and Carramea (£260).
FINANCES Year 2007–08 Income £287,659 Grants £250,239 Assets £7,423,040
TRUSTEES Leslie Sussman (London borough of Barnet); Gwyneth Hampson (City of Westminster); Owen Cock (London borough of Harrow); Richard Eden (London borough of Camden); Alan Mendoza (London borough of Brent).
OTHER INFORMATION Income is distributed to the local authorities in proportion to the length of the Edgware Road passing through their area. In 2007–08 this was as follows: London borough of Barnet – (31%) £78,000; London borough of Brent – (27%) £69,000; City of Westminster – (25%) £63,000; London borough of Camden – (11%) £27,000; London borough of Harrow – (6%) £14,000.
HOW TO APPLY In writing to the relevant local authority. Do not write to the correspondent.

WHO TO APPLY TO Jennifer Hydari, London Borough of Harrow, Finance Department, PO Box 21, Civic Centre, Harrow HA1 2UJ *Tel* 020 8424 1393
CC NO 211970   ESTABLISHED 1994

■ Haskel Family Foundation

WHERE FUNDING CAN BE GIVEN UK.
WHO CAN BENEFIT Jewish people and research workers.
WHAT IS FUNDED The charity is currently funding projects concerned with social policy research and Jewish communal life.
RANGE OF GRANTS Usually up to £12,000.
SAMPLE GRANTS Aldeburgh Music (£12,000); The Orange Tree Theatre (£5,000); Liberal Judaism and the Jewish Quarterly (£3,000 each); Aldeburgh Productions (£2,000); and Rainford Trust and Watford Mencap (£500 each).
FINANCES *Year* 2007 *Income* £33,475 *Grants* £26,000 *Assets* £555,526
TRUSTEES A M Davis; J Haskel; M Nutman; Lord Haskel.
HOW TO APPLY **This trust states that it does not respond to unsolicited applications.**
WHO TO APPLY TO The Trustees, 12 Rosemont Road, Richmond-upon-Thames, Surrey TW10 6QL *Tel* 020 8948 7711
CC NO 1039969   ESTABLISHED 1993

■ Hasluck Charitable Trust

WHERE FUNDING CAN BE GIVEN UK.
WHO CAN BENEFIT Children and young people, people with disabilities.
WHAT IS FUNDED Health, welfare, disability, young people, overseas aid.
RANGE OF GRANTS Up to £10,000.
SAMPLE GRANTS Beneficiaries included: International Fund for Animal Welfare, Barnados and Macmillan Cancer Relief (£6,200 each); World Vision Bangladesh Appeal, Sustrans and Give Youth a Break (£2,000 each); The Stroke Association, Age Concern and Survival International (£1,700 each); and Marie Curie Cancer Care, Survive MIVA and the Joh Aspinall Foundation (£1,000 each).
FINANCES *Year* 2007–08 *Income* £151,540 *Grants* £102,500 *Assets* £1,070,624
TRUSTEES Matthew James Wakefield; John Philip Billing.
HOW TO APPLY In writing to the correspondent. 'Distributions are generally made in January and July, although consideration is given to appeals received at other times of the year.'
WHO TO APPLY TO John Billing, Trustee, Thring Townsend Lee & Pembertons, Kinnaird House, 1 Pall Mall East, London SW1Y 5AU *Tel* 020 7766 5600 *email* solicitors@ttuk.com
CC NO 1115323   ESTABLISHED 2006

■ The Hathaway Trust

WHERE FUNDING CAN BE GIVEN Unrestricted.
WHO CAN BENEFIT Registered charities and individuals.
WHAT IS FUNDED The trust tends to support Jewish organisations and causes.
SAMPLE GRANTS Toimchei Shabbos Manchester (£14,000); Kol Yom Trust Ltd (£6,000); Keren Hashviis (£3,000); and Ahavas Tzdedoka Vochesed (£1,000).
FINANCES *Year* 2007–08 *Income* £117,299 *Grants* £104,413 *Assets* £74,537

TRUSTEES N Younger; Mrs M Younger; Rabbi S Schwalbe.
HOW TO APPLY The trustees have stated previously that they have adopted a proactive approach to funding and now only fund projects with which they have a personal connection, therefore unsolicited requests will not be considered.
WHO TO APPLY TO The Trustees, 12 Hereford Drive, Prestwich, Manchester M25 0JA
CC NO 1064086   ESTABLISHED 1997

■ The Maurice Hatter Foundation

WHERE FUNDING CAN BE GIVEN Unrestricted.
WHO CAN BENEFIT Educational bodies, particularly those with Jewish links, and registered charities.
WHAT IS FUNDED Education, medical research and social welfare.
TYPE OF GRANT Grants, often recurring; loans.
SAMPLE GRANTS University College Hospital Charity Fund (£50,000); Ray Tye Medical Aid Foundation (£48,000); Civitas Limited (£25,000); British Friends of Haifa University (£21,000); British ORT (£10,000); and the Reform Foundation Trust (£5,000).
FINANCES *Year* 2007–08 *Income* £2,630,290 *Grants* £391,735 *Assets* £8,622,033
TRUSTEES Sir Maurice Hatter; Ivor Connick; Jeremy S Newman; Richard Hatter.
HOW TO APPLY Unsolicited applications will not be considered.
WHO TO APPLY TO Jeremy S Newman, Trustee, Ivan Sopher & Co, Unit 5, Elstree Gate, Elstree Way, Borehamwood WD6 1JD *Tel* 020 8207 0602
CC NO 298119   ESTABLISHED 1987

■ The M A Hawe Settlement

WHERE FUNDING CAN BE GIVEN UK, with a preference for the north west of England, particularly the Fylde coast area.
WHO CAN BENEFIT UK and local organisations and schemes benefiting people of all ages, women, at-risk groups, and children who are ill or disabled, people who are socially isolated, homeless or disadvantaged by poverty.
WHAT IS FUNDED Welfare of older people, women and children, disability, homelessness and other charitable purposes.
TYPE OF GRANT One-off, some recurrent.
RANGE OF GRANTS Usually up to £1,000.
SAMPLE GRANTS Kensington House Trust Ltd (£251,000); Holy Cross Church and Soup Kitchen (£860); Clarenden Street School (£240); and Impulse Dance Troup (£60).
FINANCES *Year* 2007–08 *Income* £314,205 *Grants* £254,305 *Assets* £5,402,612
TRUSTEES M A Hawe; Mrs G Hawe; M G Hawe.
OTHER INFORMATION The trust established the Kensington House Trust Ltd which provides accommodation for young homeless people; it receives substantial support from the trust. This project will be closing in 2008, however the trust will continue to use the proportionate funding to continue activities in a different accommodation.
HOW TO APPLY In writing to the correspondent.
WHO TO APPLY TO M A Hawe, Trustee, 94 Park View Road, Lytham St Annes, Lancashire FY8 4JF *Tel* 01253 796888
CC NO 327827   ESTABLISHED 1988

■ The Hawthorne Charitable Trust

WHERE FUNDING CAN BE GIVEN UK, especially Hereford and Worcester.

WHO CAN BENEFIT Organisations benefiting young people and older people, medical professionals and people disadvantaged by poverty.

WHAT IS FUNDED The trustees make donations, generally on an annual basis, to a large number of charities mainly concerned with the care of young people and older people, the relief of pain, sickness and poverty, the advancement of medical research, particularly into the various forms of cancer, research into animal health, the arts, disability and heritage.

WHAT IS NOT FUNDED Grants are given to registered charities only. No grants to individuals.

TYPE OF GRANT Often recurring.

RANGE OF GRANTS Usually up to £8,000.

SAMPLE GRANTS The Dyson Perrins Museum Trust (£8,000); Army Benevolent Fund and Welland pre-school (£5,000 each); Motor Neurone Disease Association, Battersea Dogs and Cats Home and National Trust (£3,000 each); London Library, Combat Stress and Hospice Care Kenya (£2,500 each); Woodland Trust, Crusaid and Mobility Trust (£2,000 each); Dogs Trust, S.P.A.C.E. and Music Space West Midlands (£1,000 each); and Cambridge Cancer Research Fund, Prostate Appeal and Herefordshire Mind (£250 each).

FINANCES *Year* 2007–08 *Income* £206,467 *Grants* £196,480 *Assets* £6,667,381

TRUSTEES Mrs A S C Berington; R J Clark; T P M Berington; R White.

HOW TO APPLY In writing to the correspondent, including up-to-date accounts. Applications should be received by October for consideration in November.

WHO TO APPLY TO Roger Clark, Trustee, c/o Baker Tilly, Lancaster House, 7 Elmfield Road, Bromley BR1 1LT *Tel* 020 8461 8068

CC NO 233921   **ESTABLISHED** 1964

■ The Dorothy Hay-Bolton Charitable Trust

WHERE FUNDING CAN BE GIVEN UK, with a preference for the south east of England and overseas.

WHO CAN BENEFIT Charities working with people who are blind or deaf, particularly children, young people and older people.

WHAT IS FUNDED Welfare needs.

WHAT IS NOT FUNDED The trust states that it does not generally give to individuals.

TYPE OF GRANT One-off and ongoing.

RANGE OF GRANTS Up to £3,500.

FINANCES *Year* 2007–08 *Income* £30,601 *Grants* £35,750 *Assets* £854,948

TRUSTEES Brian E Carter; Stephen J Gallico.

HOW TO APPLY In writing to the correspondent.

WHO TO APPLY TO Brian E Carter, Trustee, c/o F W Stephens, 3rd Floor, 24 Chiswell Street, London EC1Y 4YX *Tel* 020 7382 1820 *email* brian. carter@fwstephens.co.uk

CC NO 1010438   **ESTABLISHED** 1992

■ The Haydan Charitable Trust

WHERE FUNDING CAN BE GIVEN UK.

WHO CAN BENEFIT Charitable organisations.

WHAT IS FUNDED General charitable purposes and Jewish causes.

WHAT IS NOT FUNDED No grants are given for projects overseas.

TYPE OF GRANT Mainly recurrent.

SAMPLE GRANTS Previous beneficiaries include: Jewish Communal Fund, Babes in Arms, Greater London Fund for the Blind and Anthony Nolan Trust, Beth Jacob Grammar School for Girls, Leukaemia Research Fund and Nordoff Robbins Music Trust and Cancer Research UK.

FINANCES *Year* 2008 *Income* £52,478 *Grants* £33,000

TRUSTEES Christopher Smith; Irene Smith; Anthony Winter; Neil Bradley.

HOW TO APPLY Unsolicited applications are not considered.

WHO TO APPLY TO Neil Bradley, 1 Manchester Square, London W1U 3AB *Tel* 020 3219 2600

CC NO 1003801   **ESTABLISHED** 1991

■ The Haymills Charitable Trust

WHERE FUNDING CAN BE GIVEN UK, but particularly the west of London and Suffolk, where the Haymills group is sited.

WHO CAN BENEFIT Organisations benefiting children and young adults; former employees of Haymills; at-risk groups, people who are disadvantaged by poverty and socially isolated people.

WHAT IS FUNDED The trust seeks to support projects which are not widely known, and therefore likely to be inadequately funded. Main support is given to registered charities operating in areas lying in and to the west of London and in Suffolk. Grants fall into four main categories: *education* – schools, colleges and universities; *medicine* – hospitals, associated institutions and medical research; *welfare* – primarily to include former Haymills staff, people in need, or who are otherwise distressed or disadvantaged; and *youth* – support for schemes to assist in the education, welfare and training of young people. A limited number of applications will be considered which can show they are committed to further education and training, preferably for employment in the construction industry.

WHAT IS NOT FUNDED No personal applications will be considered unless endorsed by a university, college or other appropriate authority.

SAMPLE GRANTS Youth and welfare – £108,000; Medical – £55,000; Education – £33,000.

FINANCES *Year* 2007–08 *Income* £218,805 *Grants* £195,000 *Assets* £5,857,221

TRUSTEES W G Underwood, Chair; E F C Drake; I W Ferres; K C Perryman; J A Sharpe; J L Wosner.

HOW TO APPLY In writing to the correspondent, but note the comments in the general section. Trustees meet at least twice a year, usually in March and October. Applications are not acknowledged.

WHO TO APPLY TO I W Ferres, Secretary, 7 Wildwood, Northwood HA6 2DB *email* ian.w.ferres@ btinternet.com

CC NO 277761   **ESTABLISHED** 1979

■ The Charles Hayward Foundation

WHERE FUNDING CAN BE GIVEN Worldwide, in practice mainly UK with some overseas funding.

WHO CAN BENEFIT Registered charities.

WHAT IS FUNDED Predominantly capital costs for organisations undertaking projects which are preventative or provide early intervention; developmental or innovative; promote or continue good practice and add value to existing services. Priority areas: People with disabilities, early intervention, medical research, medical, older people, art, preservation & environment,

Think carefully about every application. Is it justified?

583

community, hospices, criminal justice, overseas, young people at risk.

WHAT IS NOT FUNDED Grants are not made for: academic chairs; bursaries; church restoration; computers; education; endowment funds; environmental and animal sciences; fund-raising activities; general repairs; non-medical academic research; paying off loans; revenue funding or core costs, general funding, continuing funding and replacement funding; replacement of government or lottery funding or activities primarily the responsibility of central or local government or any other responsible body; travel, outings or holidays.

TYPE OF GRANT Capital cost of buildings, extensions, adaptations, equipment and furnishings. Occasionally project funding for start-up or development.

RANGE OF GRANTS Generally £1,000–£50,000.

SAMPLE GRANTS Previous beneficiaries include: Combat Stress – London, Alzheimer's Research Trust – Cambridge, Cystic Fibrosis Trust – Bromley, Little Ouse Headwaters Project – Norfolk, Sibs for brothers and sisters – Yorkshire, Number 8 – Pershore Community and Arts Centre, Salvation Army – London Headquarters, Send a Cow – Bath, St. Richard's Hospice – Worcester and the Philippine Trust.

FINANCES *Year* 2007 *Income* £2,290,138 *Grants* £1,853,161 *Assets* £53,095,599

TRUSTEES A D Owen, chair; I F Donald; Sir William Asscher; Mrs J M Chamberlain; Sir Jack Hayward; Mrs S J Heath; B D Insch; J N van Leuven; Miss A T Rogers; Ms J Streather.

OTHER INFORMATION The trustees amend their policy from time to time. Up-to-date guidelines for applicants can be downloaded from the foundation's website. They may also be obtained by sending an sae to the foundation's offices specifying either 'General Guidelines' or 'Overseas Guidelines'.

HOW TO APPLY 'There is no application form. Your initial application should be made in writing to the Administrator, Dorothy Napierala. It should provide the details listed below. You may add any enclosures that help to describe your organisation or the project. We will advise you whether more information is required. All applications will receive an acknowledgement. However, as there is often a waiting list, and the trustees meet only four times a year to consider applications, you may have a wait of several months before you receive a decision. Please note that there are always many more applications than we are able to fund out of our limited resources. On average, our trustees approve one in twenty applications. You are advised to read these guidelines very carefully, as inappropriate applications waste time. Details required in your application:

Name and location of Organisation– The official name of your organisation and its location

Contact details – Give your name and position within the organisation, contact telephone number and address.

Description of Organisation – Provide a description of your present work and the priorities you are addressing. Quantify the scale of your operation – how many people do you help and how?

Description of Proposed Project – Describe the project you are undertaking, detailing the number of people and groups who will benefit and how. Specify how life will be improved for the target group.

Project Cost – For larger projects give a breakdown of the costs. Capital and revenue costs should be kept separate. For a capital project, include only information on the capital costs.

Funds raised and pledged – Give a breakdown of the funds raised to date towards your target, separating capital and revenue, where applicable. Include the amount of any of your own funds or reserves going into the project, and any money you intend to borrow.

Outstanding Shortfall – Specify the amount of money you still need for capital and revenue separately.

Timetable – State the timetable for the project; when it will start and be finished.

Accounts – Include one set of your latest audited accounts.'

WHO TO APPLY TO Dorothy Napierala, Administrator, Hayward House, 45 Harrington Gardens, London SW7 4JU *Tel* 020 7370 7063/7067 *Website* www.charleshaywardfoundation.org.uk

CC NO 1078969 **ESTABLISHED** 1961

....

■ Headley-Pitt Charitable Trust

WHERE FUNDING CAN BE GIVEN Mainly Ashford, Kent.

WHO CAN BENEFIT Older people and those in need.

WHAT IS FUNDED Quaker projects. The trust also administers ten bungalows for the benefit of older people.

WHAT IS NOT FUNDED Sport or animal projects.

TYPE OF GRANT One-off.

RANGE OF GRANTS Up to £2,000.

FINANCES *Year* 2008–09 *Income* £68,527 *Grants* £24,963 *Assets* £2,259,638

TRUSTEES S D Pitt; H C Pitt; J R Pitt; R W Pitt.

OTHER INFORMATION During the year grants to individuals totalled £29,300.

HOW TO APPLY In writing to the correspondent.

WHO TO APPLY TO Mrs T E M Pitt, Summerville, Ulley Road, Kennington, Ashford, Kent TN24 9HX *Tel* 01233 626189

CC NO 252023 **ESTABLISHED** 1955

....

■ The Headley Trust

WHERE FUNDING CAN BE GIVEN Unrestricted.

WHO CAN BENEFIT Registered charities working in the areas listed. The trust prefers to support innovative schemes that can be successfully replicated or become self-sustaining.

WHAT IS FUNDED Arts and heritage – UK: support for a wide variety of built conservation or heritage projects. Arts and heritage – overseas – restoration of buildings, statuary or paintings, primarily in Central and Eastern Europe, supporting the capacity of new heritage NGOs, and training the next generation of conservation and heritage professionals. Developing countries: priority is given to projects in sub-Saharan Anglophone Africa and Ethiopia. Focus areas include water/sanitation projects, environmental projects, education and literacy projects, health projects and community and voluntary sector development. Education: provision of bursary support, particularly for artistic or technical skills training, or performing opportunities for talented young artists, including the disadvantaged or disabled. Health and social welfare: support for a broad range of health and social welfare projects, particularly supporting older people of limited means, especially with their housing needs, or help carers of an ill or disabled relative. Also, parenting education projects; and occasional health research into specialist areas of particular interest to the trustees.

WHAT IS NOT FUNDED Grants are not normally made to individuals.

TYPE OF GRANT One-off, capital and project over three years or less.

SAMPLE GRANTS Brighton & Sussex Medical School (£150,000); the Passage – Victoria (£120,000); HACT – Housing Association Charitable Trust (£90,000); Hove Museum (£70,000); Common Ground (£60,000); Law Society of Zimbabwe (£50,000); Cutty Sark Trust (£40,000); National Trust for Scotland (£30,000); Bowes Museum Trust (£25,000); National Trust – Slovakia (£18,000); and Bishopsland Educational Trust (£10,000).

FINANCES *Year* 2007 *Income* £2,584,000 *Grants* £2,186,742 *Assets* £78,909,000

TRUSTEES Sir Timothy Sainsbury; Lady Susan Sainsbury; Timothy James Sainsbury; J R Benson; Judith Portrait.

OTHER INFORMATION The trust is one of the Sainsbury Family Charitable Trusts which share a common administration. An application to one is taken as an application to all.

HOW TO APPLY The Museums' Treasure Acquisition Scheme has its own application form, available from the Headley Museums Archaeological Acquisition Fund website, www.headley-archaeology.org.uk. For information on the small Aids for Disabled Fund, ring the trust on 020 7410 0330. Otherwise, see the guidance for applicants in the entry for the Sainsbury Family Charitable Trusts. A single application will be considered for support by all the trusts in the group. However, for this as for many of the trusts, 'proposals are generally invited by the trustees or initiated at their request. Unsolicited applications are discouraged and are unlikely to be successful, even if they fall within an area in which the trustees are interested'.

WHO TO APPLY TO Alan Bookbinder, Director, Allington House, 1st Floor, 150 Victoria Street, London SW1E 5AE *Tel* 020 7410 0330 *Fax* 020 7410 0332 *Website* www.sfct.org.uk

CC NO 266620   **ESTABLISHED** 1973

■ Heagerty Charitable Trust

WHERE FUNDING CAN BE GIVEN UK and overseas.

WHO CAN BENEFIT Catholic organisations and registered charities.

WHAT IS FUNDED General charitable purposes.

WHAT IS NOT FUNDED The trust says it identifies causes it wishes to support itself and unsolicited applications are not considered.

RANGE OF GRANTS Up to £5,000.

FINANCES *Year* 2007–08 *Income* £31,625 *Grants* £41,000 *Assets* £711,870

TRUSTEES J S Heagerty; Miss P Smith; P J P Heagerty; Mrs V C M Heagerty.

HOW TO APPLY The trust says it identifies causes it wishes to support itself and unsolicited applications are not considered.

WHO TO APPLY TO J S Heagerty, Trustee, Walstead Grange, Lindfield, Surrey RH16 2QQ

CC NO 1033543   **ESTABLISHED** 1994

■ The Heald Charitable Trust

WHERE FUNDING CAN BE GIVEN UK.

WHO CAN BENEFIT Registered charities benefiting children, young adults and older people; research workers; volunteers; people in care or who are fostered or adopted; parents and children; one parent families; disabled people; people who are disadvantaged by poverty,

homeless or socially isolated people; and victims of man-made or natural disasters.

WHAT IS FUNDED Registered charities concerned with the welfare of children overseas.

TYPE OF GRANT One-off, project, research and recurring costs.

RANGE OF GRANTS £325–£10,000.

SAMPLE GRANTS Previous beneficiaries include: Alistar Roberts Memorial, Care International, Leonard Cheshire International and Save the Children.

FINANCES *Year* 2008–09 *Income* £24,492

TRUSTEES Natwest private banking.

HOW TO APPLY In writing to the correspondent.

WHO TO APPLY TO The Manager – Charities, NatWest Trusts and Estates, Brighton Branch, 153 Preston Road, Brighton, East Sussex BN1 6BD *Tel* 01273 545119 *Fax* 01273 545006

CC NO 1045914   **ESTABLISHED** 1995

■ Healthsure Group Ltd

WHERE FUNDING CAN BE GIVEN Manchester and surrounding areas, Northampton and Norwich.

WHO CAN BENEFIT Health authorities and welfare charities benefiting disabled people, at-risk groups, people disadvantaged by poverty, and socially isolated people.

WHAT IS FUNDED Priority is given to health authorities and NHS trusts, with hospices, homes for people with disabilities and welfare organisations also within the trust's scope.

SAMPLE GRANTS Previous beneficiaries included: Age Concern Norwich; Bolton Hospice; Booth Hall Children's Hospital; Children's Society; Disabled Living; Friends of Northampton General Hospital; Genesis Appeal; George House Trust; Little Sisters of the Poor; Rainbow Family Trust; Royal Manchester Children's Hospital Research; Royal School for the Deaf; Stockport Community Transport; and Willow Wood Hospice.

FINANCES *Year* 2008 *Income* £77,495 *Grants* £209,426 *Assets* £2

TRUSTEES J W Cameron, Chair; J E Barnard; R T H Sear; L Pattison.

HOW TO APPLY In writing to the correspondent.

WHO TO APPLY TO J W Cameron, Trustee, 43–45 Lever Street, Manchester M60 7HP

CC NO 260031   **ESTABLISHED** 1969

■ May Hearnshaw's Charity

WHERE FUNDING CAN BE GIVEN UK, particularly South Yorkshire, North Nottinghamshire, Derbyshire, East Lancashire or Cheshire areas.

WHO CAN BENEFIT Registered charities concerned with the relief of poverty and sickness, advancement of religion and education.

WHAT IS FUNDED There is a preference for work with children.

TYPE OF GRANT One-off, with grants for buildings, core costs, research, recurring costs, running costs and salaries all considered. Funding may be given for up to three years.

RANGE OF GRANTS £500–£10,000.

SAMPLE GRANTS Alzheimers Society Sheffield, Ripley Methodist Church and Whirlow Hall Farm Trust (£5,000 each); Mind (£4,000); Culcheth Methodist Church, Dore Youth Worker Trust and St Laurence Education Trust (£3,000 each); Derbyshire Children's Holiday Centre, Dyslexic Action and Cystic Fibrosis Trust (£2,000 each): the Living Paintings Trust, the Mercian Trust and Royal British Legion (£1,000 each); and the Elizabeth Foundation (£500).

FINANCES *Year* 2007–08 *Income* £81,184 *Grants* £72,855 *Assets* £1,805,152

TRUSTEES J Rowan; D C Law; Mrs M West; M Ferreday; R Law; W Munro.

HOW TO APPLY 'The trustees usually decide on and make grants to charitable organisations at least once a year but may decide to make grants at any time. They do not include in their consideration appeals received direct from individuals.'

WHO TO APPLY TO J Rowan, Trustee, Barber Harrison and Platt, 2 Rutland Park, Sheffield S10 2PD

CC NO 1008638   **ESTABLISHED** 1992

■ The Heart of England Community Foundation

WHERE FUNDING CAN BE GIVEN The city of Coventry and Warwickshire.

WHO CAN BENEFIT Community-based groups and activities benefiting a wide range of social circumstances.

WHAT IS FUNDED General charitable purposes, in particular for the benefit of the local community in Warwickshire and the city of Coventry and people who are disabled, and to promote social and economic development. This includes residential facilities and services, community arts and recreation, respite care and care for carers, support and self-help groups, community services, social issues advice and information and health advocacy.

WHAT IS NOT FUNDED Grants will not usually be considered for the following: general and major fundraising; individuals; educational institutions except where the institution or project is aimed at the relief of disadvantage; promotion of religious causes except where the institution or the project is aimed at relief of disadvantage; medical research; organisations with no permanent presence in the beneficial area; animal welfare; political activity; organisations with substantial reserves relative to turnover; sports clubs except where the institution or the project is aimed at relief of disadvantage; salaries and other core costs.

TYPE OF GRANT Buildings, capital, core costs, feasibility studies, one-off, project, research, development costs, salaries, and start-up costs. Funding is available for up to one year.

RANGE OF GRANTS £100–£7,000.

FINANCES *Year* 2007–08 *Income* £1,437,663 *Grants* £1,025,696 *Assets* £1,818,802

TRUSTEES John Atkinson, Chair; Peter Deeley; Mrs Margaret Backhouse; Mrs Sally Carrick; Andrew Corner; Stewart Fergusson; David Green; Brian Holt; Donald Hunter; Zamurad Hussain; Lady Jane Liggins; Susan Ong; Ven. Michael Paget-Wilkes; Peter Shearing; John Taylor

OTHER INFORMATION The priorities of the trustees are reviewed annually; applicants are encouraged to contact the foundation by telephone to obtain up-to-date information on current priorities. Only one grant will be given to an organisation in any one year from the foundation.

HOW TO APPLY An application form may be downloaded from the foundation's website (www.heartofenglandcf.co.uk – located under 'Forms and reports') or, you can call on 024 7688 4386 and a copy will be sent it to you. Although guidance on how to complete the application form is included within the form itself, you are encouraged to telephone the foundation to discuss your project in advance of applying. Grants Officers, who cover specific geographical areas and funds, will be able to assist you.

WHO TO APPLY TO Ms Kate Mulkern, Director, Pinley House, Sunbeam Way, PO BOX 227, Coventry CV3 1ND *Tel* 024 7688 4386 *Fax* 024 7688 4640 *email* info@heartofenglandcf.co.uk *Website* www.heartofenglandcf.co.uk

CC NO 1117345   **ESTABLISHED** 1995

■ The Heathcoat Trust

WHERE FUNDING CAN BE GIVEN Local causes in and around Tiverton, Devon.

WHO CAN BENEFIT Local organisations to Tiverton and individual grants to employees and pensioners of the Heathcoat group of companies.

WHAT IS FUNDED Welfare, educational.

TYPE OF GRANT Recurring and one-off.

RANGE OF GRANTS Usually less than £1,000.

FINANCES *Year* 2007–08 *Income* £612,325 *Grants* £560,475 *Assets* £18,973,917

TRUSTEES Sir Ian Heathcoat Amory; M J Gratton; J Smith; Mr C Dunster; Mr S Butt.

OTHER INFORMATION A further £483,000 was distributed to individuals in 2007–08.

HOW TO APPLY In writing to the correspondent. There are application forms for certain education grants.

WHO TO APPLY TO Mr E W Summers, Secretary, The Factory, Tiverton, Devon EX16 5LL *Tel* 01884 254949 *Website* www.heathcoat.co.uk

CC NO 203367   **ESTABLISHED** 1945

■ Heathside Charitable Trust

WHERE FUNDING CAN BE GIVEN UK.

WHO CAN BENEFIT Charitable organisations, especially Jewish groups.

WHAT IS FUNDED General charitable purposes.

RANGE OF GRANTS £1,000–£141,100.

SAMPLE GRANTS Previous beneficiaries include: Joint Jewish Charitable Trust (£141,100); Raft (£35,000); Jewish Education Defence Trust (£25,000); Community Security Trust (£21,300); Jewish Care (£15,000); British Friends of Jaffa Institute, GRET, and Motivation (£10,000 each).

FINANCES *Year* 2007 *Income* £946,968 *Grants* £373,223 *Assets* £4,275,423

TRUSTEES Sir Harry Solomon; Lady Judith Solomon; Geoffrey Jayson; Louise Jacobs; Juliet Solomon; Daniel Solomon.

OTHER INFORMATION Accounts for 2008 were overdue at the Charity Commission. In recent years, a list of grants has not been included in the trust's accounts.

HOW TO APPLY In writing to the correspondent, at any time.

WHO TO APPLY TO Sir Harry Solomon, Trustee, Hillsdown House, 32 Hampstead High Street, London NW3 1QD *Tel* 020 7431 7739

CC NO 326959   **ESTABLISHED** 1985

■ The Charlotte Heber-Percy Charitable Trust

WHERE FUNDING CAN BE GIVEN Worldwide, with a preference for Gloucestershire.

WHO CAN BENEFIT Registered charities.

WHAT IS FUNDED General charitable purposes.

WHAT IS NOT FUNDED No grants to individuals.

RANGE OF GRANTS Mostly between £500–5,000.

■ Percy Hedley 1990 Charitable Trust

WHERE FUNDING CAN BE GIVEN UK with a preference
for Northumberland and Tyne and Wear.
WHO CAN BENEFIT Charitable organisations.
WHAT IS FUNDED General charitable purposes.
RANGE OF GRANTS Up to £5,000, with most grants
made in the range of £250–£500.
SAMPLE GRANTS Previous beneficiaries have
included: Newcastle Theatre Royal Trust
(£5,000); Percy Hedley Foundation and
Newcastle Royal Grammar School – Bursary
Fund (£3,000 each); National Playing Fields
Association, the Anaphylaxis Campaign,
Samaritans of Tyneside and Marie Curie
Foundation – Newcastle (£1,000 each);
Salvation Army and Northumberland Wildlife
Trust (£500 each); and Listening Books and
Pets as Therapy (£250 each).
FINANCES *Year* 2007–08 *Income* £52,474
Grants £40,256 *Assets* £1,377,531
TRUSTEES G W Meikle; J R Armstrong; Mrs
F M Ruffman.
HOW TO APPLY In writing to the correspondent.
Trustees meet twice a year.
WHO TO APPLY TO J Armstrong, Trustee, 10 Castleton
Close, Newcastle upon Tyne NE2 2HF *Tel* 0191
281 5953
CC NO 1000033   ESTABLISHED 1990

■ The Hedley Denton Charitable Trust

WHERE FUNDING CAN BE GIVEN North east England.
WHO CAN BENEFIT Charitable organisations, including
those operating overseas.
WHAT IS FUNDED General charitable purposes.
RANGE OF GRANTS £250–£2,000.
SAMPLE GRANTS Partners in the Community Trust
(£2,000); NEPAC and Rift Valley Newcastle
Justice Project (£1,000 each); Chillingham Wild
Cattle Association, Fishermans Mission and
Henshaws Society for the Blind (£500 each);
and Action Medical Research, Morpeth Music
Society and Nakuru Baby Orphanage (£250
each).
FINANCES *Year* 2007–08 *Income* £44,999
Grants £32,400 *Assets* £889,230
TRUSTEES I H Nicholson, Chair; Miss D M Wild;
C M Watts.
HOW TO APPLY In writing to the correspondent.
WHO TO APPLY TO I H Nicholson, Trustee, 5 West
Road, Ponteland, Newcastle upon Tyne

NE20 9ST *Tel* 01661 823863 *Fax* 01661
823724 *email* law@iainnicholson.co.uk
CC NO 1060725   ESTABLISHED 1996

■ The Hedley Foundation

WHERE FUNDING CAN BE GIVEN UK only.
WHO CAN BENEFIT Registered charities benefiting
young people, their education, training, health
and welfare; disabled people and the terminally-
ill.
WHAT IS FUNDED Organisations working with young
people, local church and community projects,
organisations concerned with people who are
disabled or seriously ill and medical equipment.
WHAT IS NOT FUNDED Grants are made to UK
registered charities only. No support for
individuals, churches and cathedrals, core
revenue costs, salary or transport funding, or for
very large appeals.
TYPE OF GRANT Grants for specific projects only,
mostly one-off but a limited number of recurring
grants for up to three years are given. No
revenue or salary funding.
RANGE OF GRANTS £1,000–£15,000; average grant
£3,000.
SAMPLE GRANTS Colonel's Fund (£26,000 in two
grants); Action on Addiction (£20,000); Combat
Stress (£18,000 in three grants); Marchant
Holiday School (£15,000); Bag Books
(£10,000); British Youth Opera (£5,000);
Yorkhill Children's Foundation (£4,000);
Butterwick Hospice (£3,000); Rochford Trust
(£1,500); and Kinmos Volunteer Group Ltd
(£500).
FINANCES *Year* 2007–08 *Income* £1,444,392
Grants £949,327 *Assets* £28,100,833
TRUSTEES John F Rodwell, Chair; Patrick R Holcroft;
George R Broke; Lt Col. Peter G Chamberlin;
Lorna B Stuttaford; Angus Fanshawe.
HOW TO APPLY Application forms are downloadable
from the foundation's website. Once completed
in typescript, the form should be printed off and
sent by post to the appeals secretary named
above, accompanied by your e-mail address, or
a self-addressed envelope (not necessarily
stamped). The trustees meet six times a year.
The closing date for a meeting is three weeks
beforehand. All applications will be
acknowledged, but, in the case of those short-
listed, not until after they have been considered
by the trustees. The trustees usually meet in
January, March, May, July, September and
November. A list of meeting dates for the
current year is published on the foundation's
website. In 2007–08 the foundation received
nearly 1,500 applications, of which less than
two-thirds were within the stated criteria. As a
result, the foundation made 348 grants and
urges that applicants should not be surprised,
or too disappointed, if they are unsuccessful.
WHO TO APPLY TO Pauline Barker, Appeals Secretary,
1–3 College Hill, London EC4R 2RA *Tel* 020
7489 8076 *email* pbarker@hedleyfoundation.
org.uk *Website* www.hedleyfoundation.org.uk
CC NO 262933   ESTABLISHED 1971

■ The H J Heinz Company Limited Charitable Trust

WHERE FUNDING CAN BE GIVEN UK.
WHO CAN BENEFIT Organisations benefiting children
and young adults, at-risk groups, people
disadvantaged by poverty and socially isolated
people.

Think carefully about every application. Is it justified?

587

WHAT IS FUNDED The trust typically supports medicine, welfare, education (food technology and nutrition in particular), conservation, community relations and the arts. UK bodies are more likely to be favoured than local groups unless local applicants operate in the immediate vicinity of the company's main operating locations.

WHAT IS NOT FUNDED No grants to individuals. Requests for political or denominational causes or for advertising are not considered.

TYPE OF GRANT One-off.

RANGE OF GRANTS £1,000–£8,000.

SAMPLE GRANTS Previous beneficiaries include: Royal Academy of Arts, Muscular Dystrophy Campaign, English Speaking Union, Baby Lifeline, the Association of Post-Natal Illness and Manna House.

FINANCES *Year* 2008 *Income* £91,467

TRUSTEES Mrs D Heinz; S Bailey; B R Purgavie; N Perry.

HOW TO APPLY In writing to the address below, no follow-up telephone calls. Applications are considered once or twice a year. Applicants whether successful or unsuccessful are informed of the trustees' decisions.

WHO TO APPLY TO Elizabeth Keane, Trust Secretary, Hayes Park South Building, Hayes End Road, Hayes, Middlesex UB4 8AL *Website* www.heinz.co.uk

CC NO 326254   **ESTABLISHED** 1982

■ The Hellenic Foundation

WHERE FUNDING CAN BE GIVEN UK.

WHO CAN BENEFIT Organisations and individuals, to advance education in the cultural tradition and heritage of Greece, particularly in the subjects of education, philosophy, the arts and science.

WHAT IS FUNDED Projects involving education, research, music and dance, books and library facilities, and university symposia.

WHAT IS NOT FUNDED The foundation is unable to offer scholarships or grants to cover tuition fees and living expenses.

RANGE OF GRANTS Up to £15,000.

SAMPLE GRANTS Royal Academy Byzantine exhibition (£15,000); Theatro Technis (£1,000); and Aghia Shophia School (£200).

FINANCES *Year* 2007 *Income* £25,664 *Grants* £16,675 *Assets* £469,743

TRUSTEES Tryphon E Kendros, Hon. Chair; Stamos J Fafalios, Chair; George A Tsavliris; Nicos H Sideris; Irene M Monios; Dr Eleni Yannakakis; Zenon K Mouskos; Constantinos I Caroussis; Mary Bromley; Irene J Fafalios-Zannas; Angela K Kulukundis; George A Lemos; George D Lemos; Louisa Williamson; Despina M Moschos; Anna S Polemis-Alisafakis.

HOW TO APPLY In writing to the correspondent.

WHO TO APPLY TO The Secretary, St Paul's House, Warwick Lane, London EC4M 7BP *Tel* 020 7251 5100

CC NO 326301   **ESTABLISHED** 1982

■ The Michael and Morven Heller Charitable Foundation

WHERE FUNDING CAN BE GIVEN Worldwide.

WHO CAN BENEFIT Organisations benefiting academics, medical professionals, research workers, scientists, students and teachers.

WHAT IS FUNDED Medical, education and scientific research.

WHAT IS NOT FUNDED No support for individuals.

RANGE OF GRANTS £5,000–£100,000.

SAMPLE GRANTS Education (£140,521); Research (£16,870); Humanitarian (£46,512).

FINANCES *Year* 2007–08 *Income* £304,520 *Grants* £203,903 *Assets* £4,636,828

TRUSTEES Michael Heller; Morven Heller.

HOW TO APPLY In writing to the correspondent.

WHO TO APPLY TO M A Heller, Trustee, Carlton House, 22a St James's Square, London SW1Y 4JH *Tel* 020 7415 5000 *Fax* 020 7415 0611

CC NO 327832   **ESTABLISHED** 1988

■ The Simon Heller Charitable Settlement

WHERE FUNDING CAN BE GIVEN Worldwide.

WHO CAN BENEFIT Organisations benefiting academics, medical professionals, research workers, scientists, students and teachers.

WHAT IS FUNDED Medical research and scientific and educational research.

WHAT IS NOT FUNDED No grants to individuals.

SAMPLE GRANTS Education (£71,541); Humanitarian (£152,677); Research (£67,500).

FINANCES *Year* 2007–08 *Income* £399,649 *Grants* £291,718 *Assets* £8,600,641

TRUSTEES M A Heller; Morven Heller; W S Trustee Company Limited.

HOW TO APPLY In writing to the correspondent.

WHO TO APPLY TO The Trustees, Carlton House, 22a St James' Square, London SW1Y 4JH *Tel* 020 7415 5000

CC NO 265405   **ESTABLISHED** 1972

■ Help the Aged

WHERE FUNDING CAN BE GIVEN UK and overseas.

WHO CAN BENEFIT Voluntary and charitable groups which offer a range of resources to support vulnerable or disadvantaged older people live independently in their communities. This includes minority ethnic groups, carers, homeless people, and people living in urban and rural areas.

WHAT IS FUNDED Local projects providing services which are needed in their communities, where the services in question (a) meet needs that are defined by older people themselves, and (b) clearly target disadvantage.

WHAT IS NOT FUNDED The charity does not support funding for loans, or to reduce deficits already incurred by projects, or to make up a shortfall due to underbidding for a service contract; commercial companies or statutory agencies; organisations artificially created as trusts, designed to meet the needs of community care proposals or to realise European funding; holidays; residential or nursing homes, except to support independent living of older people and where the benefits extend to the wider community; registered social landlords except where there is a clearly defined project focusing on a vulnerable group, for example, homeless older people; individual members of the public; replacing spending cuts made by local or central government.

TYPE OF GRANT Capital; one-off; running costs; salaries; and start-up costs. Funding is available for up to three years.

RANGE OF GRANTS About £200–£50,000.

FINANCES *Year* 2007–08 *Income* £71,907,000 *Grants* £4,953,000 *Assets* £18,928,000

TRUSTEES Dr Beverly Castleton; Henry Cathcart; Dr June Crown; Brian Fox; Rosemary Kelly; Janet

Lord; Tony Rice; Michael Roberts; Len Sanderson; Prof. John Williams; Christopher Woodbridge; Angus Young; Josephine Connell; Simon Waugh; Hilary Wiseman.

PUBLICATIONS Publications include: *Tackling Older People's Fear of Crime; Future Communities;* and *Debt and Older People: how age affects attitudes to borrowing.*A full list of publications is available on the charity's website.

HOW TO APPLY For more information on how to apply for community grants contact the Grants Unit by emailing grants.unit@ace.org.uk or calling 020 8765 7738. For further information on the SeniorMobility programme contact Graham Lale, SeniorMobility Manager on telephone: 020 7239 1825 or email: grahamlale@helptheaged. org.uk.

WHO TO APPLY TO Grants Unit, York House, 207–221 Pentonville Road, London N1 9UZ *Tel* 020 7278 1114 *Fax* 020 7278 1116 *email* info@ helptheaged.org.uk *Website* www.helptheaged. org.uk

CC NO 272786   **ESTABLISHED** 1977

....

■ Help the Homeless Ltd

WHERE FUNDING CAN BE GIVEN UK only.
WHO CAN BENEFIT Voluntary agencies benefiting single homeless people.
WHAT IS FUNDED To help any voluntary residential project which has made every endeavour, unsuccessfully, to raise funds from other known sources.
WHAT IS NOT FUNDED Charities with substantial funds are not supported. No grants to individuals.
TYPE OF GRANT Usually one-off for buildings, capital and projects.
RANGE OF GRANTS Normally up to £3,000. Trustees will also consider applications for larger pump priming grants for major and innovative projects. Applicants should enquire about the status of the Large Grants Programme before making an application.
SAMPLE GRANTS Emmaus Sheffield (£50,000); Slough Homeless Our Concern (£10,000); Emmaus Cambridge and Byker Bridge Housing Association (£5,000 each); Oasis Church Trust, Save the Family and Healthy Living Projects (£3,000 each); Freedom Centre (£2,500); Nightsafe (£2,000); and Harlow Homeless Centre (£560).
FINANCES *Year* 2007–08 *Income* £102,379 *Grants* £119,836 *Assets* £1,151,216
TRUSTEES F J Bergin; T S Cookson; L A Bains; T Rogers; P Fullerton; J Rose.
HOW TO APPLY Application forms can be downloaded from the trust's website. Trustees meet to consider grants four times a year.
WHO TO APPLY TO The Secretary, 6th Floor, 248 Tottenham Court Road, London W1T 7QZ *email* hth@help-the-homeless.org.uk *Website* www.help-the-homeless.org.uk
CC NO 271988   **ESTABLISHED** 1975

....

■ Help the Hospices

WHERE FUNDING CAN BE GIVEN UK.
WHO CAN BENEFIT Organisations benefiting people who are disabled, and medical professionals in hospices.
WHAT IS FUNDED Grants are given to local voluntary hospices, in-patient, day care and home care teams, and for equipment for patient care and improved services; training for hospice staff (NHS and voluntary); research funding and advisory services to hospices.

TYPE OF GRANT One-off and recurrent.
FINANCES *Year* 2007–08 *Income* £6,130,000 *Grants* £996,000 *Assets* £4,949,000
TRUSTEES Dr Helen Clayson; Rt Hon Lord Newton; Sally Taylor; David Clark; Bay Green; Beverley Brooks; Graham Elderfield; Gary Hawkes; Judith Hodgson; Peter Holliday; Marina Phillips; Sheila Tonge; Isabel Whaite.
OTHER INFORMATION In 2007–08 a further £409,000 was distributed among 1,067 individuals.
HOW TO APPLY Generally on a form available from the Grants Officer, from whom further information is also available. For major grant programmes, potential applicants should request details first as policies change. The trust's website contains detailed information of the grant-making policy and should be viewed before an application is considered. For emergency grants, applicants should write directly to the chief executive.
WHO TO APPLY TO David Praill, Chief Executive, 34–44 Britannia Street, London WC1 9JG *Tel* 020 7520 8200 *email* grants@helpthehospices.org. uk *Website* www.helpthehospices.org.uk
CC NO 1014851   **ESTABLISHED** 1984

....

■ The Helping Foundation

WHERE FUNDING CAN BE GIVEN Greater London and Greater Manchester.
WHO CAN BENEFIT Institutions and registered charities.
WHAT IS FUNDED The advancement of education according to the tenets of the Orthodox Jewish Faith; the advancement of the Orthodox Jewish Religion and the relief of poverty amongst the older people or people in need, hardship or distress in the Jewish Community.
TYPE OF GRANT Recurrent grants.
RANGE OF GRANTS Mostly up to around £50,000.
SAMPLE GRANTS Talmud Education Trust (£1.9 million); Notzar Chesed (£731,000); Friends of Mir (£360,000); Asser Bishvil Foundation (£290,000); TTT (£68,000); Bourne Heights (£35,000); Jewish Rescue & Relief Committee (£26,000); Chirat Devora & Chochmat Sholom (£15,000); and Talmud Torah Chinuch Norim (£2,000).
FINANCES *Year* 2008–09 *Income* £6,898,772 *Grants* £3,567,426 *Assets* £38,773,329
TRUSTEES Benny Stone; David Neuwirth; Rabbi Aubrey Weis; Mrs Rachel Weis.
HOW TO APPLY In writing to the correspondent.
WHO TO APPLY TO Benny Stone, Trustee, 1 Allandale Court, Waterpark Road, Salford M7 4JN
CC NO 1104484   **ESTABLISHED** 2004

....

■ The Hemby Trust

WHERE FUNDING CAN BE GIVEN Merseyside and Wirral.
WHO CAN BENEFIT Charitable organisations.
WHAT IS FUNDED Social needs, community facilities and services, young people and employment, schools and colleges, help for older people, health, the arts, culture and recreation, the environment and church buildings.
WHAT IS NOT FUNDED Grants will not be given to political organisations, pressure groups or individuals, feasibility studies, organisations outside Merseyside or Wirral, or to replace statutory funding.
TYPE OF GRANT Capital grants.
RANGE OF GRANTS £300 to £5,000.
SAMPLE GRANTS Alder Hey Imagine Appeal (£25,000); St John's Hospice – Wirral (£2,500); Halton Autistic Family Support and Merseyside

Holiday Service (£2,000 each); Granby Toxteth Activities Club (£1,500); Brighter Living Partnership, Fire Fighters Charity, Liverpool Somali Cultural Heritage and Sola Arts (£1,000 each); North Liverpool Citizen's Advice and Sefton OPERA (£750 each); and Roundabout Centre and Goyararu Contemporary Arts (£500 each).

FINANCES *Year* 2008–09 *Income* £108,809 *Grants* £119,012 *Assets* £1,888,368

TRUSTEES R A Morris; P T Furlong; A T Morris; N A Wainwright.

HOW TO APPLY Applicants should write to the correspondent for a leaflet which sets out the aims and objectives of the trust and an application form which should be returned with a copy of the applicant's latest accounts. A date will be given for the return of the form if it is to be discussed by the trustees at their next meeting. The trustees meet at the end of March, July and November. Applications are not acknowledged, but the applicant is welcome to telephone the administrator (01704 834887) to check it has been received.

WHO TO APPLY TO Michael Hope, 3 College Path, Formby, Liverpool L37 1HW *Website* www. hembytrust.org.uk

CC NO 1073028   **ESTABLISHED** 1998

■ The Christina Mary Hendrie Trust for Scottish and Canadian Charities

WHERE FUNDING CAN BE GIVEN Scotland and Canada.

WHO CAN BENEFIT Charities benefiting young people and older people.

WHAT IS FUNDED Charities connected with young people and older people. Cancer charities are also supported.

WHAT IS NOT FUNDED Grants are not given to individuals. Only organisations known to the trustees can be considered.

RANGE OF GRANTS Typical grants £1,000–£5,000.

SAMPLE GRANTS Beneficiaries of grants included: Outfit Moray (£150,000); Beannachar Ltd (£50,000); Lilias Graham Trust (£35,000); Erskine (£30,000); Combat Stress and Prison Phoenix Trust (£15,000 each); Lord Roberts Workshop (£10,000); Rock Trust (£5,000); and Scottish Cot Death (£2,500).

FINANCES *Year* 2007–08 *Income* £124,415 *Grants* £272,000 *Assets* £6,442,307

TRUSTEES Sir Alistair Irwin, Chair; Anthony Cox; Arabella Cox; Charles Cox; Mary-Rose Grieve; Susie Hendrie; Miss Caroline Irwin; John K Scott-Moncrieff.

HOW TO APPLY In writing to the correspondent.

WHO TO APPLY TO Alan Sharp, Secretary, Anderson Strathern Solicitors, 1 Rutland Court, Edinburgh EH3 8EY *Tel* 0131 270 7700 *Fax* 0131 270 7788

SC NO SC014514   **ESTABLISHED** 1975

■ The Henley Educational Charity

WHERE FUNDING CAN BE GIVEN Henley-on-Thames and the parishes of Bix and Rotherfield Greys in Oxfordshire and Remenham in Berkshire only.

WHO CAN BENEFIT Individuals and organisations concerned with the education of children, young adults and people who are disadvantaged. State-maintained schools and colleges in the area defined above.

WHAT IS FUNDED Grants are given to alleviate financial hardship, to support particular educational initiatives and courses and to help meet the cost of educational visits, books and equipment at a local school or college.

WHAT IS NOT FUNDED Applicants for individual grants must be under 25 years of age, and must either be resident in the area of benefit or have attended a state-maintained school in the area for at least two years.

TYPE OF GRANT Mainly one-off grants for core and capital support; also project funding.

RANGE OF GRANTS All applications considered individually.

SAMPLE GRANTS Henley Youth Centre (£10,000); Henley Cricket Club (£6,000); and Nomad (£4,000).

FINANCES *Year* 2008–09 *Income* £155,976 *Grants* £85,032 *Assets* £2,798,327

TRUSTEES T Buckett, Chair; A Follet; Mrs M S T Hall; Mrs E Hodgkin; W Parrish; Mrs M Smith; Mrs R G Whittaker; the Mayor of Henley; the Rector of Henley.

HOW TO APPLY Apply in writing to the correspondent for an application form.

WHO TO APPLY TO Mrs Claire Brown, Clerk, 9 Damer Gardens, Henley-on-Thames, Oxfordshire RG9 1HX

CC NO 309237   **ESTABLISHED** 1604

■ The Tim Henman Charitable Foundation

WHERE FUNDING CAN BE GIVEN UK.

WHO CAN BENEFIT Registered charities.

WHAT IS FUNDED General charitable purposes and medical research.

SAMPLE GRANTS Previous beneficiaries include Brainwave, Brain Tumour Research and Give it Your Max.

FINANCES *Year* 2006–07 *Income* £46,581 *Grants* £24,000 *Assets* £7,420

TRUSTEES Jan Felgate; Lucy Henman; Tim Henman.

HOW TO APPLY The trustees tend to select charities for support based on their own experience and knowledge. It receives a high number of requests which have to be refused.

WHO TO APPLY TO Neil Grainger, Talent Financial Ltd, Chiswick Gate, 3rd Floor, 598–608, Chiswick High Road, London W4 5RT *Tel* 020 8104 1002

CC NO 1083055   **ESTABLISHED** 2001

■ Philip Henman Trust

WHERE FUNDING CAN BE GIVEN Worldwide.

WHO CAN BENEFIT UK-registered charities concerned with long term overseas development.

WHAT IS FUNDED Grants are aimed at established major UK registered charity (normally defined as having an income of over £100,000 per annum). The funding from the trust should be important to the project, normally accounting for between 20% and 80% of the total project budget. The project should be partly funded by other sources, voluntary work and central office administration costs can be counted as other source funding.

WHAT IS NOT FUNDED The trust does not fund ongoing concerns.

TYPE OF GRANT Long-term grants. Projects starting and finishing within five years.

RANGE OF GRANTS £3,000–£5,000 per year. A maximum of £25,000 over the course of the project.

SAMPLE GRANTS Overseas aid (£29,000); Social welfare (£5,000); Child aid (£5,000); Medical and community work (£5,000); Other (£220).

FINANCES *Year* 2007–08 *Income* £65,058 *Grants* £44,573 *Assets* £1,854,407

TRUSTEES J C Clark; D J Clark; J Duffey.

HOW TO APPLY Applications are only considered once a year – the deadline is always 10 September. Applications are no longer accepted by post. Please use the online form to submit applications.

WHO TO APPLY TO D J Clark, Trustee, 16 Pembury Road, Tonbridge TN9 2HX *Tel* 01732 362227 *email* info@pht.org.uk *Website* www.pht.org.uk

CC NO 1054707　　　　**ESTABLISHED** 1986

■ Esther Hennell Charitable Trust

WHERE FUNDING CAN BE GIVEN UK.
WHO CAN BENEFIT Registered charities.
WHAT IS FUNDED General.
WHAT IS NOT FUNDED No grants to individuals.
SAMPLE GRANTS Previous beneficiaries include: Emmanuel Church Wimbledon, Strangers' Rest Mission, Shaftesbury Society, Whitefield Christian Trust, Barnabas Fund, Interserve, Tear Fund, AIM, South Asian Concern and Crosslinks UK.

FINANCES *Year* 2007–08 *Income* £25,443 *Grants* £25,000 *Assets* £571,495

TRUSTEES Esther J Hennell; Jane Ann Hunt; Nicholas W Smith.

HOW TO APPLY In writing to the correspondent.

WHO TO APPLY TO Nicholas W Smith, Trustee, Currey and Co, 21 Buckingham Gate, London SW1E 6LS *Tel* 020 7802 2700

CC NO 261477

■ The G D Herbert Charitable Trust

WHERE FUNDING CAN BE GIVEN UK.
WHO CAN BENEFIT Registered charities.
WHAT IS FUNDED The trust supports medicine, health, welfare and environmental resources. It mainly gives regular grants to a set list of charities, with a few one-off grants given each year.

TYPE OF GRANT Mainly recurrent.
RANGE OF GRANTS Up to £2,500.
SAMPLE GRANTS Beneficiaries of 'special donations' included: Ashford and Tenterden Samaritans, Children's Fire and Burn Trust, The Queen Alexandra Hospital Home, National ME Centre for Fatigue Syndromes, The Rainbow Centre, St Raphael's Hospice and Deafness Research UK (£2,000 each). Beneficiaries of 'regular donations' included: The National Trust, Friends of the Elderly, Marie Curie Cancer Care, PDSA, Royal College of Surgeons of England, Royal Hospital for Neuro-Disability and The Woodland Trust (£2,500 each); Ogbourne St Georges PCC and Wiltshire Wildlife Trust (£500 each).

FINANCES *Year* 2007–08 *Income* £59,843 *Grants* £72,500 *Assets* £1,836,462

TRUSTEES M E Beaumont; J J H Burden.

OTHER INFORMATION 'Regular donations' were made to 25 organisations in 2007–08

HOW TO APPLY In writing to the correspondent. No applications are invited other than from those charities currently supported by the trust.

WHO TO APPLY TO J J H Burden, Trustee, Barnards Inn, 86 Fetter Lane, London EC4A 1EN *Tel* 020 7405 1234

CC NO 295998　　　　**ESTABLISHED** 1986

■ The Joanna Herbert-Stepney Charitable Settlement (also known as The Paget Charitable Trust)

WHERE FUNDING CAN BE GIVEN Worldwide, with an interest in Loughborough.

WHO CAN BENEFIT Normally only British registered charities.

WHAT IS FUNDED Sheer need is paramount, and, in practice, nothing else can be considered. There is a preference for the unglamorous, for maximum achievement with minimal resources. Priorities include the developing world, deprived children, old age, 'green' projects, and animal welfare. The trust does sometimes give ongoing support, thus leaving fewer funds for new applicants.

WHAT IS NOT FUNDED The trust states that 'sheer need is paramount, in practice, nothing else is considered'. Grants are only given to registered UK charities. Overseas projects can only be funded via UK charities; no money can be sent directly overseas. The trust does not support individuals (including students), projects for people with mental disabilities, medical research or AIDS/HIV projects.

RANGE OF GRANTS £50–£5,000.

SAMPLE GRANTS Belton Church Restoration (£50,000); and Dawson and Fowler Foundation (£20,000).; Second Chance (£5,000); Oxfam (£4,000); Farms for City Children and Soil Association (£3,000 each); Childhood First, Ethiopiaid, and Pattaya Orphanage Trust (£2,000 each); the Organic Research Centre, World Medical Fund, Task Brasil, Southwark Community Education Council and Mission Romania (£1,000 each); and Coventry City Farm, Asthma UK and Anglo-Peruvian Child Care Mission (£500 each).

FINANCES *Year* 2007–08 *Income* £309,663 *Grants* £243,196 *Assets* £6,776,787

TRUSTEES Joanna Herbert-Stepney; Lesley Mary Blood; Meg Williams.

HOW TO APPLY In writing to the correspondent; there is no application form. The trustees meet in spring and autumn. The trust regrets that it cannot respond to all applications.

WHO TO APPLY TO Joanna Herbert-Stepney, Trustee, Old Village Stores, Dippenhall Street, Crondall, Farnham, Surrey GU10 5NZ

CC NO 327402　　　　**ESTABLISHED** 1986

■ The Anne Herd Memorial Trust

WHERE FUNDING CAN BE GIVEN Scotland, with a preference for Tayside, the City of Dundee and Broughty Ferry.

WHO CAN BENEFIT People who are visually impaired.

WHAT IS FUNDED Organisations working in the beneficial area with visually impaired individuals.

RANGE OF GRANTS Up to £20,000.

FINANCES *Year* 2007–08 *Income* £46,242

TRUSTEES B Neil Bowman; Mrs Pamela M M Bowman; Mrs Elizabeth N McGillivray; Rory W H Hudson; Mrs Elizabeth M Breckon; Robert J Wild.

HOW TO APPLY In writing to the correspondent. Trustees meet once a year to consider grants, usually in June. Applications should be received by March/April.

WHO TO APPLY TO The Trustees, Bowman Scottish Lawyers, 27 Bank Street, Dundee DD1 1RP

SC NO SC014198

■ The Herefordshire Community Foundation

WHERE FUNDING CAN BE GIVEN Herefordshire.

WHO CAN BENEFIT Community and voluntary groups and individuals in Herefordshire.

WHAT IS FUNDED General charitable purposes.

RANGE OF GRANTS Up to £10,000.

SAMPLE GRANTS Carer's Support and Megan Baker House (£10,000 each); Deaf Direct (£9,800); Burghill and Tillington Cricket Club and Northolme Community Centre Association (£7,000 each); Herefordshire Nature Trust (£6,500); Slow Food Herefordshire (£5,900); Beyond Wild Art (£5,600); and Hopscotch Playgroup and Illuminate (£5,200 each).

FINANCES *Year* 2007–08 *Income* £380,259 *Grants* £359,699 *Assets* £155,651

TRUSTEES Mrs J Perridge; R S Kelly; W L Banks; Mrs C J Forrester; W Lindesay.

HOW TO APPLY In writing to the correspondent.

WHO TO APPLY TO David Barclay, Director, The Fred Bulmer Centre, Wall Street, Hereford HR4 9HP *Tel* 01432 272550

CC NO 1094935   **ESTABLISHED** 2002

■ The Herefordshire Historic Churches Trust

WHERE FUNDING CAN BE GIVEN Old county of Herefordshire.

WHO CAN BENEFIT All Christian places of worship.

WHAT IS FUNDED The restoration, preservation, repair, maintenance and improvement of churches, their contents and their churchyards in Herefordshire.

TYPE OF GRANT Buildings.

RANGE OF GRANTS Up to £5,000.

SAMPLE GRANTS Beneficiaries included the following parishes: Peterchurch and Titley (£10,000 each); Norton Canon (£8,500); Wellington (£7,000); Leinthall Earls (£6,500); Kings Caple (£4,000); Ross (£2,000); Leominster Priory (£1,500); and Withington (£1,000).

FINANCES *Year* 2008 *Income* £129,554 *Grants* £64,050 *Assets* £621,546

TRUSTEES Earl of Darnley, Chair; David Furnival; H C Moore; Archdeacon of Hereford; Miss Susan Bond; R H Peers; S Arbuthnott; Ven Malcolm Colmer; Ali Hayden Jones.

HOW TO APPLY In writing to the correspondent. Deadlines for applications are 15 March and 15 September.

WHO TO APPLY TO David Furnival, The Woodhouse, Staplow, Ledbury, Herefordshire HR8 1NP *Tel* 01531 640030 *email* furnivald@aol. com/davidfurnival@tiscali.co.uk *Website* www. herefordhistoricchurchestrust.org.uk

CC NO 511181   **ESTABLISHED** 1954

■ The Heritage of London Trust Ltd

WHERE FUNDING CAN BE GIVEN All 33 London boroughs.

WHO CAN BENEFIT Listed buildings in London.

WHAT IS FUNDED The restoration of buildings of architectural importance. Grants are mainly given for skilled restoration of notable features of listed buildings, generally (though not exclusively) external work. Examples of buildings assisted are churches, community centres, almshouses, theatres, hospitals, museums and educational establishments.

RANGE OF GRANTS Up to £20,000.

FINANCES *Year* 2007–08 *Income* £427,955 *Grants* £98,973 *Assets* £862,164

TRUSTEES Hon. Nicholas Assheton, Chair; Sir John Lambert, Ronald Barden; Nicholas Bell; Mrs Bridget Cherry; Cllr Robert Davies; Martin Drury; John Dudley Fishburn; Katharine Goodison; Jonathan Gestetner; Norman Howard; Cllr Denise Jones; Frances Lloyd; Derek Lutyens; Michael Medlicott; Cllr Bob Skelly; Dame Valerie Strachan; Cllr Nigel Sumner.

PUBLICATIONS Map: *Historic Buildings in Covent Garden.*

HOW TO APPLY Initial contact should be by telephone. If the project seems eligible, guidance notes will be sent to the applicant who should make a formal application in writing. Board meetings are held in January, May and September.

WHO TO APPLY TO Diana Beattie, Director, 38 Elbury Street, London SW1W 0LU *Tel* 020 7730 9472 *Fax* 020 7117 1125 *email* info@ heritageoflondon.com *Website* www. heritageoflondon.com

CC NO 280272   **ESTABLISHED** 1980

■ The Hertfordshire Community Foundation

WHERE FUNDING CAN BE GIVEN Hertfordshire.

WHO CAN BENEFIT Individuals and organisations which benefit local people. Many are smaller, less well-known groups or less 'popular' causes that often find it extremely difficult to obtain funds elsewhere.

WHAT IS FUNDED To support the work of local charities and voluntary groups for the benefit of the community, with the following particular concerns: disadvantaged children and families; developing young people; access to education, training and employment; the needs of older people; and other community needs. Grants are made for a variety of needs including: running costs; training; staff costs; equipment; and new initiatives.

WHAT IS NOT FUNDED No grants are made towards: UK or general appeals, or those with no specific Hertfordshire focus; statutory or public bodies, or to replace withdrawn statutory funding; religious or political causes, medical research, holidays, overseas travel or full-time education; or individuals, except within the terms of special funds, e.g. the Children's Fund.

TYPE OF GRANT Development grants, revenue or capital, not long-term funding or as part of a large building project. Maximum £5,000 for one-off grants, or £15,000 over three years; usually smaller amounts. Project grants up to £5,000 for specific purpose, start-up or development. Small grants of £500 on a one-off basis – usually for small groups. Small individual grants up to £300 for children within very specific areas.

RANGE OF GRANTS £100–£10,000 per year for up to three years.

SAMPLE GRANTS Citizens Advice Bureau Hertfordshire (£15,000); Broxbourne and East Hertfordshire Credit Union (£8,000); Hertfordshire PASS (£6,000); Satsang Mandal (£5,000); Hitchin Town Bowls Club (£2,900); Age Concern Hertfordshire (£2,500); Hertfordshire Area Rape Crisis and Sexual Abuse Centre (£1,500); Dacorum Indian Society and Neomari Beadcraft Training Services (£500 each); Grandparents' Association (£490); and Alzheimer's Disease Society (£175).

FINANCES *Year* 2007–08 *Income* £1,533,668 *Grants* £1,238,121 *Assets* £3,394,505

TRUSTEES J Stuart Lewis, Chair; John Peters; Kate Belinis; Caroline McCaffrey; Betty Goble; William Tudor John; David Fryer; Michael Master; Richard Roberts.

PUBLICATIONS Leaflets; newsletter; guidelines for applicants.

HOW TO APPLY Application packs are available from the foundation. An initial telephone call or e-mail to check eligibility is welcomed.

WHO TO APPLY TO David Fitzpatrick, Chief Executive, Foundation House, 2–4 Forum Place, Fiddlebridge Lane, Hatfield, Hertfordshire AL10 0RN *Tel* 01707 251 351 *email* grants@hertscf.org.uk *Website* www.hertscf.org.uk

CC NO 299438   **ESTABLISHED** 1988

■ The Hesed Trust

WHERE FUNDING CAN BE GIVEN UK and overseas.

WHO CAN BENEFIT Christian charities benefiting children, young adults, older people, clergy, students, Christians and evangelists.

WHAT IS FUNDED Christian charitable purposes. The trust will consider funding the advancement of religion and the Free Church umbrella bodies.

WHAT IS NOT FUNDED No support for expeditions and individual requests.

TYPE OF GRANT One-off grants, for one year or less.

RANGE OF GRANTS Up to £45,000.

SAMPLE GRANTS Ministries Without Borders (45,000); Aquila Ministries (£14,000); Iglesia Cuba (£11,000); Scripture Knowledge (£3,000); and Rainbow Africa (£100).

FINANCES *Year* 2007–08 *Income* £172,941 *Grants* £73,000 *Assets* £94,207

TRUSTEES P Briggs; R Eagle; G Rawlings; J C Smith.

HOW TO APPLY The trust states that no applications are now being considered.

WHO TO APPLY TO G Rawlings, Secretary, 14 Chiltern Avenue, Cosby, Leicestershire LE9 1UF *Tel* 0116 286 2990 *email* glynrawlings@btopenworld.com

CC NO 1000489   **ESTABLISHED** 1990

■ The Hesslewood Children's Trust (Hull Seamen's and General Orphanage)

WHERE FUNDING CAN BE GIVEN East Yorkshire and North Lincolnshire.

WHO CAN BENEFIT Individuals and organisations in the area defined above, benefiting children and young adults under 25. Support will be given to people in care, or who are fostered or adopted; people who are disabled; people disadvantaged by poverty; ex-offenders and people at risk of offending; homeless people; people living in both rural and urban areas; socially isolated people; and victims of abuse and crime.

WHAT IS FUNDED To provide aid for young individuals in need and to support youth organisations for holidays. Particularly supported are charities working in the fields of education, housing and accommodation, and arts, culture and recreation.

WHAT IS NOT FUNDED No grants to benefit people over the age of 25 will be made.

TYPE OF GRANT One-off. Funding may be given for up to one year.

RANGE OF GRANTS Up to £17,000.

SAMPLE GRANTS Hull Compact (£16,800); Bude Park Primary School, Dyslexia in Action, Ganton Special School, Prince's Trust and Sidney Smith

School (£5,000 each); and Andrew Marvell Youth Centre and Barnado's (£1,000 each).

FINANCES *Year* 2007–08 *Income* £108,198 *Grants* £118,668 *Assets* £2,480,171

TRUSTEES I D Graham, Chair; R M S Allenby; Dr C Woodyatt; Capt. E Howlett; D Turner; Revd T Boyns; Mrs G Munn; M Mitchell; E W Gilbert; Dr C Jones; Mrs D Lidgett; Dr D Nicholas; P Evans.

OTHER INFORMATION Payments to individuals totalled £36,000.

HOW TO APPLY On a form available from the correspondent, with a telephone number if possible. The trustees meet to consider applications at least three times a year. No replies are given to ineligible organisations. This trust informed us that it promotes its work through its own avenues, receiving more applications than it can support.

WHO TO APPLY TO R E Booth, Secretary, c/o Graham and Rosen Solicitors, 8 Parliament St, Hull HU1 2BB *Tel* 01482 323123

CC NO 529804   **ESTABLISHED** 1982

■ The Bernhard Heuberger Charitable Trust

WHERE FUNDING CAN BE GIVEN Worldwide.

WHO CAN BENEFIT Jewish organisations benefiting Jewish people.

WHAT IS FUNDED Jewish charitable purposes.

SAMPLE GRANTS Beis Ahron Trust, Tchabe Kollel Limited and C.M.M (£25,000 each); Notzar Chesed Central Aid Fund (£20,000); Shuvo Yisroel, WST Charity Limited and Yesoday Hatorah Schools (£10,000 each); Enzer North West, Down's Syndrome Association, C.M.Z. Limited (£5,000); JFS School and Kemble Charitable Trust (£3,500); Emunah (£2,500); Hendon United Synagogue (£2,400); Institute for Higher Rabbinical Studies (£2,000); Beth Yaakov Seminary for Girls (£1,000); and other small charitable donations (£5,800).

FINANCES *Year* 2007–08 *Income* £110,657 *Grants* £160,699 *Assets* £2,326,775

TRUSTEES D H Heuberger; S N Heuberger.

HOW TO APPLY In writing to the correspondent.

WHO TO APPLY TO The Trustees, 12 Sherwood Road, London NW4 1AD

CC NO 294378   **ESTABLISHED** 1986

■ Hexham and Newcastle Diocesan Trust (1947)

WHERE FUNDING CAN BE GIVEN Diocese of Hexham and Newcastle, overseas.

WHO CAN BENEFIT Roman Catholic organisations.

WHAT IS FUNDED This trust supports the advancement of the Roman Catholic religion in Hexham and Newcastle by both initiating its own projects and giving grants to other organisations.

RANGE OF GRANTS Up to £300,000.

SAMPLE GRANTS CAFOD Development and emergency aid (£268,000); Mission Charities (£127,000); Sick and Retired Priests (£101,000); National Catholic Fund (£90,000); Peru Mission (£59,000); Catholic Education Service (£45,000); Holy Places (£29,000); World Communications (£16,000); Carmelite Convent (£10,000); and Catholic Agency for Social Concerns (£3,000).

FINANCES *Year* 2007–08 *Income* £21,300,000 *Grants* £1,136,000 *Assets* £63,627,000

TRUSTEES Revd Canon Seamus Cunningham; Monsignor Gerard Lavender; Revd James O'Keefe; Revd Philip Quinn; Revd Martin Stempczyk; Revd Christopher Jackson.

HOW TO APPLY At the time of writing recent information was not available. Therefore, potential applicants are strongly advised to contact the trust for further information before making an application.

WHO TO APPLY TO Mrs Kathleen M Smith, Bishop's House, 800 West Road, Newcastle upon Tyne NE5 2BJ *Tel* 0191 243 3300 *Fax* 0191 243 3309 *email* finance@edurcdhn.org.uk *Website* rcdhn.org.uk

CC NO 234071   **ESTABLISHED** 1867

■ The P and C Hickinbotham Charitable Trust

WHERE FUNDING CAN BE GIVEN UK, with a preference for Leicestershire and Rutland.

WHO CAN BENEFIT Registered charities only. Particular favour is given to Quakers.

WHAT IS FUNDED The trust generally supports local (Leicester, Leicestershire and Rutland) charities and Quaker activities in a wider field.

WHAT IS NOT FUNDED No grants to individuals applying for bursary-type assistance or to large UK charities.

TYPE OF GRANT Usually one-off grants.

RANGE OF GRANTS Up to £15,000, most grants made between £1,000 and £2,000.

SAMPLE GRANTS Voluntary Action – Rutland (£15,000); Worgan Trust and Rainbows Children's Hospice (£10,000 each); Belgrave Playhouse (£2,500); National Trust for Egryn – North Wales and the Woodland Trust (£2,000 each); Society of Friends – Leicester PM (£1,400); and Cruise Bereavement Care, RSPB and New Futures Project (£1,000 each).

FINANCES *Year* 2007–08 *Income* £636,145 *Grants* £71,455 *Assets* £3,213,803

TRUSTEES Catherine Hickinbotham; Roger Hickinbotham; Rachel Hickinbotham; Anna Hickinbotham.

HOW TO APPLY In writing to the correspondent, giving a brief outline of the purpose of the grant. Replies will not be sent to unsuccessful applicants.

WHO TO APPLY TO Roger Hickinbotham, Trustee, 9 Windmill Way, Lyddington, Oakham, Leicestershire LE15 9LY *Tel* 01572 821236 *email* rogerhick@gmail.com

CC NO 216432   **ESTABLISHED** 1947

■ The Rosalind Hicks Charitable Trust

WHERE FUNDING CAN BE GIVEN Devon.

WHO CAN BENEFIT Charitable organisations.

WHAT IS FUNDED General charitable purposes.

RANGE OF GRANTS £500–£5,000.

SAMPLE GRANTS South Devon College – Write Here, Write Now project (£5,300); Age Concern – Torbay, Chew Lake Association of Disabled Sailors and Starlight Children's Foundation (£2,000 each); Hope UK (£1,600); Happy Days and Rowcroft Hospice (£!,500 each); Blue Cross Tiverton and Devon Wildlife Trust (£1,000 each); and Susanna Harvey Trust (£500).

FINANCES *Year* 2007–08 *Income* £31,357 *Grants* £23,970 *Assets* £681,801

TRUSTEES N J Wollen; T A W Gregory; Mrs A Clementson; Lady J F Cassels.

HOW TO APPLY In writing to the correspondent.

WHO TO APPLY TO The Trustees, c/o Hooper & Wollen, 30 The Terrace, Torquay TQ1 1BS *Tel* 01803 213251 *Fax* 01803 296871

CC NO 1050135   **ESTABLISHED** 1995

■ The Higgs Charitable Trust

WHERE FUNDING CAN BE GIVEN UK, with a preference for the former county of Avon.

WHO CAN BENEFIT Mostly medical research trusts or foundations. Organisations benefiting children, young adults, older people and people who are disadvantaged by poverty or homeless.

WHAT IS FUNDED Mainly research into deafness carried out by private charitable foundations. Also considered are charities working in the fields of religious buildings; housing and accommodation; animal facilities and services; conservation and campaigning; and education and training.

TYPE OF GRANT One-off and research. Funding for more than three years will be considered.

RANGE OF GRANTS Up to £25,000.

SAMPLE GRANTS TWJ Foundation (£25,000).

FINANCES *Year* 2008 *Income* £31,985 *Grants* £25,000 *Assets* £674,893

TRUSTEES D W M Campbell; T W Higgs; Mrs L Humphris; P Humphris.

HOW TO APPLY In writing to the correspondent, not less than two months before the annual general meeting in November.

WHO TO APPLY TO Anthony Nash, Mogers, 24 Queen Square, Bath BA1 2HY *Tel* 01225 750 000

CC NO 267036   **ESTABLISHED** 1982

■ Alan Edward Higgs Charity

WHERE FUNDING CAN BE GIVEN Within 25 miles of the centre of Coventry only.

WHO CAN BENEFIT Registered charities where their activity will benefit young people either directly, through their family, or through the provision of facilities or services to the community.

WHAT IS FUNDED Activities or projects that contribute to the amelioration of deprivation.

WHAT IS NOT FUNDED Applications from individuals are not entertained. No grants for the funding of services usually provided by statutory services, medical research, travel outside the UK or evangelical or worship activities.

TYPE OF GRANT One-off capital for buildings and equipment; will consider both core and revenue funding of projects.

RANGE OF GRANTS Typically £500–£30,000.

SAMPLE GRANTS Alan Higgs Centre Trust (£460,000); Coventry Institute of Creative Enterprise (£40,000); The Living Environment Trust (£28,000); Belgrave Theatre (£20,000); Family Holiday Association (£10,000); Shakespeare Hospice Appeal (£5,000); Guideposts Trust (£3,000); and the RSPB (£1,000).

FINANCES *Year* 2007–08 *Income* £574,420 *Grants* £572,000 *Assets* £17,754,814

TRUSTEES Peter J Davis; Marilyn F Knatchbull-Hugessen; Andrew Young.

HOW TO APPLY In writing to the clerk to the trustees, along with: a copy of the latest audited accounts; charity number (if registered); a detailed description of the local activities for the benefit of which the grant would be applied; the specific purpose for which the grant is sought; a copy of the organisation's policy that ensures the protection of young or vulnerable people and a clear description of how it is implemented and monitored.

....

■ The High Sheriff's Police Trust for the County of West Midlands

WHERE FUNDING CAN BE GIVEN West Midlands Police catchment area.

WHO CAN BENEFIT Children and young people in all matters relating to alcohol, drug and solvent misuse.

WHAT IS FUNDED Crime prevention projects in partnership with the police.

WHAT IS NOT FUNDED No grants towards personal applications, circular and capital appeals.

RANGE OF GRANTS Up to £10,000.

SAMPLE GRANTS Previous grant recipients included Dudley Lifeskills Partnership; Smethwick Sound; The Orb Project; Youth Safety in Schools; Arts Film Project; A Sporting Chance; Safe Water – Sea Cadet Corps; Arson Task Force – Firestarter Project, and 'Trouble' – Special Needs Version.

FINANCES *Year* 2007–08 *Income* £27,319 *Grants* £0 *Assets* £190,869

TRUSTEES C Birchall; J Hesketh; P Gormley; D Smith; Mrs A Worley.

HOW TO APPLY In writing to the correspondent. Applicants must have a police partner or a statement of support for the project. The trustees consider applications three times a year.

WHO TO APPLY TO Ann Penfold, Lloyd House, Colmore Circus, Queensway, Birmingham B4 6NQ *Tel* 0121 428 6196 *Fax* 0121 626 5285 *email* a.penfold@west-midlands.pnn.police.uk
CC NO 1075800   **ESTABLISHED** 1999

....

■ Highcroft Charitable Trust

WHERE FUNDING CAN BE GIVEN UK and overseas.

WHO CAN BENEFIT Organisations benefiting Jewish people, especially people disadvantaged by poverty.

WHAT IS FUNDED The advancement and study of the Jewish faith and the Torah. The relief of poverty and advancement of education among people of the Jewish faith.

RANGE OF GRANTS Up to £10,000.

SAMPLE GRANTS Previous beneficiaries include Chevras Maoz Ladal, Kol Yaacov, SOFT, Tevini, Friends of Beer Miriam, Institute For Higher Rabbinic Studies, Kollel Ohr Yechiel, Kollel Chibas Yerushalayim, Craven Walk Charity Trust and London Friends of Kamenitzer.

FINANCES *Year* 2007–08 *Income* £101,665 *Grants* £75,649 *Assets* £434,027

TRUSTEES Rabbi R Fischer; Mrs S L Fischer.

HOW TO APPLY In writing to the correspondent.

WHO TO APPLY TO Rabbi R Fischer, Trustee, 15 Highcroft Gardens, London NW11 0LY
CC NO 272684   **ESTABLISHED** 1975

....

■ The Hilden Charitable Fund

WHERE FUNDING CAN BE GIVEN UK and developing countries.

WHO CAN BENEFIT Charities, voluntary organisations and NGOs. Preference is given to smaller organisations rather than large national charities. Scottish charities are only funded through a block grant to Scottish Community Foundation which they distribute to the sector.

WHAT IS FUNDED Homelessness, minority groups and race relations, penal affairs and overseas development.

WHAT IS NOT FUNDED Grants are not normally made for well established causes or to individuals, and overseas grants concentrate on development aid in preference to disaster relief.

TYPE OF GRANT Capital, revenue and recurring. Also running costs and project costs.

RANGE OF GRANTS Average grant £4,000.

SAMPLE GRANTS Scottish Community Foundation (£33,000); Joint Council for the Welfare of Immigrants (£15,000); WOMANKIND Worldwide (£8,000); Mityana Charity (£7,000); Counselling and Prayer Trust (£6,500); Centre Project (£5,000); North London Action for the Homeless (£4,000); and Open Door (£3,000).

FINANCES *Year* 2007–08 *Income* £462,324 *Grants* £443,000 *Assets* £12,262,672

TRUSTEES Ms M E Baxter; A J M Rampton; Prof. D S Rampton; Prof. M B H Rampton; J R A Rampton; Ms C S L Rampton; Mrs E K Rodeck; Prof. C H Rodeck; H B Woodd; C H Younger; E J Rodeck; Miss E M C Rampton.

HOW TO APPLY When making an application, grant seekers should bear in mind the points below. 'We expect all applicants to complete the application form. Your case for funds should be concise (no more than two sides of A4), but supporting documentation is essential. Please ensure your application includes enclosures of: your most recent independently inspected accounts; your most recent annual report; projected income and expenditure for the current financial year. Please be clear in your application form about when the proposed work is to commence, and give the relevant timetable. Your application for funds should cover the following: clear explanation about who is responsible for managing the project; a coherent plan of how the work is going to be carried out together with relevant budgets. Project budgets should be presented in the context of the overall income and expenditure of the applicant NGO/Charity; a plan of how the work is going to be maintained and developed in the future by involving relevant agencies and attracting money and resources; an explanation of why the local project seeks the help of a UK agency; details of local costs (e.g. salaries of state-employed teachers and medical personnel, cost of vehicles, petrol etc) and notes of any problems over exchange rates or inflation; an account of the political, economic, religious and cultural situation in the country/area; a brief comment on the extent to which the project can rely on government and local state funding in the country concerned; details of monitoring and evaluation.'

Overseas applications

Applicants applying direct from outside the UK must complete the Overseas Application Form. IMPORTANT: Applicants from the UK applying for funds for their project partners, must complete both the UK Application Form and the Overseas Application Form. Application forms, including one for Summer Playschemes, are available from the trust's website or offices. Please note that forms must be submitted to the secretary by post as hard copies; forms submitted by email or other electronic means are not accepted. Applicants are advised to ensure that they have read the application guidelines at the top of the form prior to completion.

Potential applicants in Scotland should contact the Scottish Community Foundation, 22 Carlton

Think carefully about every application. Is it justified?

....

595

Road, Edinburgh EH8 8DP; Tel: 0131 524 0300; website: www.scottishcf.org

WHO TO APPLY TO Rodney Hedley, Secretary, 34 North End Road, London W14 0SH *Tel* 020 7603 1525 *Fax* 020 7603 1525 *email* hildencharity@hotmail.com *Website* www. hildencharitablefund.org.uk

CC NO 232591 **ESTABLISHED** 1963

■ The Joseph and Mary Hiley Trust

WHERE FUNDING CAN BE GIVEN The West Riding of Yorkshire.

WHO CAN BENEFIT Registered charities.

WHAT IS FUNDED General charitable purposes, medical, religious and educational causes.

WHAT IS NOT FUNDED No grants to individuals, expeditions or travel bursaries. Grants to churches are usually only given to those once attended by Joseph or Mary Hiley.

TYPE OF GRANT Capital, core costs, research and recurring costs.

RANGE OF GRANTS Usually up to £200.

SAMPLE GRANTS Past recipients have included Action Medical Research, RNLI, groups for people with disabilities and hospices.

FINANCES *Year* 2007–08 *Income* £14,002

TRUSTEES Elizabeth Hjort; Mary Browning; Anne Palmer.

HOW TO APPLY In writing to the correspondent. Rejected applications are not notified unless an sae is enclosed.

WHO TO APPLY TO Anne Palmer, Old Vicarage House, Vicarage Lane, Bramham, Wetherby, Leeds LS23 6QG *Tel* 01937 842850 *email* palmeranneb@hotmail.com

CC NO 248301 **ESTABLISHED** 1966

■ The Holly Hill Charitable Trust

WHERE FUNDING CAN BE GIVEN UK and developing countries.

WHO CAN BENEFIT Registered charities.

WHAT IS FUNDED Environmental conservation work and education for environmental conservation. Most grants are made directly to educational institutions which accounts for most of the income – little is available for other applications.

WHAT IS NOT FUNDED No grants to individuals.

RANGE OF GRANTS £1,000–£40,000.

SAMPLE GRANTS Rainforest Concern (£65,000); Eden River Trust (£30,000); Devon Wildlife Trust (£20,000); West Country Rivers Trust and Kasanka Trust (£15,000 each); Cuenca Limon Costa Rica (£7,700); True Nature Films, Aberdeen University and St Columban's Environmental Report (£5,000 each); Sussex University (£4,000); Ecology Project (£2,600); and Ecuador Community Workshop (£1,500).

FINANCES *Year* 2007–08 *Income* £28,686 *Grants* £201,232 *Assets* £985,675

TRUSTEES M D Stanley; A Lewis.

HOW TO APPLY In writing to the correspondent. Applications need to be received in April and September, and trustees meet in June and November.

WHO TO APPLY TO The Trustees, Unit No. 525, Citibox Kensington Ltd, 2 Old Brompton Road, London SW7 3DQ

CC NO 1044510 **ESTABLISHED** 1994

■ The Derek Hill Foundation

WHERE FUNDING CAN BE GIVEN UK.

WHO CAN BENEFIT Organisations and individuals.

WHAT IS FUNDED The promotion of arts and culture.

TYPE OF GRANT Bursaries and travel costs.

SAMPLE GRANTS Artes Mundi – funding to provide education and develop public interest in contemporary visual art (£10,000); the British School at Rome – scholarship (£8,000); Future Talent – to fund opportunities for young musicians in state sector education and Welsh National Opera – contribution to the Songlines 2008 project (£7,500 each); Festival of Muslim Cultures – funding to promote a better understanding between Muslims and Memorial Arts Charity – to fund part of the living costs of an apprentice (£5,000); Royal Northern College of Music – travel bursaries and Watts Gallery Summer School – bursaries (£3,000 each); and Royal Academy of Music – travel bursaries (£1,500).

FINANCES *Year* 2007–08 *Income* £54,898 *Grants* £75,778 *Assets* £1,571,645

TRUSTEES Northern Trust Fiduciary Services (UK) Limited; Rt Hon. Alexander Patrick Greysteil Hore Ruthven, Earl of Gowrie; Lord Armstrong of Ilminster; Mrs Josephine Batterham.

OTHER INFORMATION Grants to seven individuals totalled £13,798.

HOW TO APPLY In writing to the correspondent.

WHO TO APPLY TO The Trustees, c/o Northern Trust Fiduciary Services UK Ltd, 50 Bank Street, Canary Wharf, London E14 5NT

CC NO 801590 **ESTABLISHED** 1989

■ The Charles Littlewood Hill Trust

WHERE FUNDING CAN BE GIVEN UK, with a preference for Nottinghamshire and Norfolk.

WHO CAN BENEFIT Charitable organisations in the UK, particularly those in Norfolk and Nottinghamshire.

WHAT IS FUNDED General charitable purposes.

WHAT IS NOT FUNDED Applications from individuals are not considered. Grants are seldom made for repairs of parish churches outside Nottinghamshire.

TYPE OF GRANT Applications for starter finance are encouraged. Grants are seldom made to endowment or capital funds.

RANGE OF GRANTS £1,000–£15,000, but usually of £5,000 or less.

SAMPLE GRANTS The Norfolk and Norwich Association for the Blind (£13,000); Catholic Cathedral of East Anglia (£10,000); St John Waterwing (£6,000); Beaumond House Community Hospice, Nottinghamshire Wildlife Trust and Peter Le Marchant Trust (£5,000 each); Family Care (£3,000); Royal Anglian Regiment Museum Appeal (£2,500); National Centre for Young People with Epilepsy (£2,000); and Brainwave, British Lung Foundation, The Gurkha Welfare Trust, The Prostate Cancer Charity, Tiny Tickers and the Queen Alexandra Hospital Home (£1,000 each).

FINANCES *Year* 2008 *Income* £199,952 *Grants* £167,227 *Assets* £3,347,386

TRUSTEES C W L Barratt; W F Whysall; T H Farr; N R Savory.

HOW TO APPLY In writing to the correspondent, including the latest set of audited accounts, at least one month before trustees' meetings in March, July and November. Unsuccessful applications will not be notified.

WHO TO APPLY TO W F Whysall, Trustee, Berryman Shacklock LLP, Park House, Friar Lane,

Nottingham NG1 6DN *Tel* 0115 945 3700
Fax 0115 948 0234
cc no 286350　　　　　established 1978

■ The Hillingdon Community Trust

where funding can be given The London borough of Hillingdon.

who can benefit Community organisations.

what is funded Supports community projects, education, the relief of poverty and advocacy in the beneficial area.

what is not funded No grants to individuals, public bodies, religious bodies or organisations that have already received funding in respect of a completed project.

type of grant One-off; recurrent.

range of grants Small grants: £500–£7,500. Main grants: Above £7,500.

finances *Year* 2008–09 *Income* £1,123,276 *Grants* £798,693 *Assets* £1,376,683

trustees David Brough, Chair; Tony Eginton; Tim Hughes; Elaine Jacobs; Douglas Mills; Christine Taylor; Ian Campbell; Jody Hawley; Isabel King; Colin Lowen.

other information Grants approved for the year were: Small grants – £118,011 and Main grants – £680,682

how to apply Small grants scheme – Application forms are available from the trust or can be can downloaded from the trust's website. Main grants scheme – This is a two-stage process. Initially, applicants complete a two-sided expression of interest form. These are considered by the Main Grants Sub-Committee and the trustees, who shortlist applicants with a reasonable likelihood of being funded. These applicants are then invited to complete and submit a full application for a main grant. Forms are available from the trust or can be can downloaded from the trust's website, which also has details of application deadlines.

who to apply to Christine Little, Trust Administrator, Barra Hall, Wood end, Green Road, Hayes, Middlesex UB3 2SA *Tel* 020 8581 1676 *email* info@ hillingdoncommunitytrust.org.uk *Website* www. hillingdoncommunitytrust.org.uk

cc no 1098235　　　　　established 2003

■ The Hillingdon Partnership Trust

where funding can be given The London borough of Hillingdon.

who can benefit Organisations benefiting people of all ages, at risk groups, people disadvantaged by poverty and socially isolated people.

what is funded The trust aims: to build links between the local community and the business sector to secure funding for community initiatives and projects; to relieve people resident in Hillingdon who are sick, disabled, elderly, poor or in other social and economic circumstances; to provide, or assist in providing, equipment and facilities not normally provided by the local authority for the purpose of advancing education or relieving people in need.

finances *Year* 2007–08 *Income* £355,569 *Grants* £331,701 *Assets* £122,484

trustees Dr D Neave; M J Taylor; J H Crowe; Air Cmdr P Thomas, Chair; J A Watts; M A Wisdom; Prof. H S Wolff; Ann Banks; A Kanjee; N Smith; Miranda Clarke; Nicholas Hurd; John Randall; Peter O'Reilly; David Routledge; Prof. Linda Thomas.

other information 'In general the trust does not itself make grants. It does make appeals to its business supporters on behalf of needy organisations and exceptionally, individuals, and the business partners may then provide funds direct to the applicant. Exceptionally, the trust may meet a need by arranging the purchase of necessary items and delivering the essential items to an applicant.' In 2007–08 £11,000 was paid in grants to organisations with the trust stating that £332,000 was delivered in cash or kind.

how to apply On a form available from the correspondent.

who to apply to John Matthews, Chief Executive, Room 22–25 Building 219, Epsom Square, London Heathrow Airport, Hillingdon, Middlesex TW6 2BW *Tel* 020 8897 3611 *Fax* 020 8897 3613 *email* johnmatthewshpt@lineone.net

cc no 284668　　　　　established 1982

■ R G Hills Charitable Trust

where funding can be given UK and overseas.

who can benefit Registered charities.

what is funded General charitable purposes.

range of grants Up to £5,000.

sample grants Canterbury Theatre and Festival Trust, Arthritis Care and Disability Challengers Ltd (£5,000 each); Health for All and Leonard Cheshire (£4,000 each); Hope UK and Sumatran Orangutan Society (£3,000 each); Build Africa, Kent Wildlife Trust and Macmillan Cancer Support (£2,000 each); and British Blind Sport and Bowland Pennine Mountain Rescue Team (£1,000 each).

finances *Year* 2007–08 *Income* £119,892 *Grants* £120,000 *Assets* £2,838,017

trustees D J Pentin; H M S Barrett

how to apply In writing to the correspondent.

who to apply to H M S Barrett, Trustee, Furley Page, 39 St Margaret's Street, Canterbury, Kent CT1 2TX *Tel* 01227 763939

cc no 1008914　　　　　established 1982

■ Hinchley Charitable Trust

where funding can be given UK and overseas.

who can benefit Mainly evangelical Christian organisations.

what is funded General charitable purposes, with particular reference to evangelical Christian work.

type of grant One-off and recurring, usually for projects, but capital and core costs are considered.

range of grants £100–£12,000.

sample grants Associated Bus Ministries (£12,000); International Needs and Lighthouse Group (£10,000 each); Central Eurasian Partners, Wycliffe Bible Translators and Nehemiah Project (£5,000 each); Scripture Union (£3,000); Mission Aviation Fellowship and Kids Church (£2,500 each); Cross Roads Christian Counselling (£2,000); Reach for Rwanda (£1,500); and Timios Trust (£1,000).

finances *Year* 2007–08 *Income* £166,106 *Grants* £141,569 *Assets* £2,723,961

trustees Dr B Stanley; J D Levick; S P Dengate; R Northcott.

how to apply The trust states that it does not respond to unsolicited applications. Replies will rarely, if ever, be made to applications for grants by post or on the telephone, as existing funds are all fully committed to charities which are regularly supported.

WHO TO APPLY TO Dr Brian Stanley, Chair,
Watersmeet, 56 Barton Road, Haslingfield,
Cambridge CB3 7LL *Tel* 01223 741120
email bs217@cam.ac.uk
CC NO 1108412   ESTABLISHED 1973

■ Lady Hind Trust

WHERE FUNDING CAN BE GIVEN England and Wales,
with a preference for Nottinghamshire and
Norfolk.
WHO CAN BENEFIT Charitable organisations in
England and Wales.
WHAT IS FUNDED General charitable purposes with
some preference for health and disability related
charities.
WHAT IS NOT FUNDED Grants are not awarded to
individuals.
TYPE OF GRANT Core and project support.
RANGE OF GRANTS Up to £20,000, but mostly
£1,000 to £5,000.
SAMPLE GRANTS St Martin's Housing Trust
(£25,000); Nottingham Almshouse Charity
(£20,000); Norwich Cathedral (£13,000);
Southwell Minster (£10,000); Lincolnshire &
Nottinghamshire Air Ambulance (£7,500); True's
Yard Fishing Heritage Museum (£5,000); St
John the Baptist and All Saints Churches,
Collingham (£3,000);
Elizabeth Finn Trust (£2,500); East Anglia's
Children's Hospices and the Huntington's
Disease Association (£2,000 each); and the
Alzheimer's Society, British Polio Fellowship,
Contact the Elderly, Independence at Home,
Parkinson's Disease Society, Starlight Children's
Foundation and Association of Wheelchair
Children (£1,000 each).
FINANCES *Year* 2007 *Income* £399,297
Grants £328,287 *Assets* £12,492,014
TRUSTEES Charles W L Barratt; Tim H Farr; Nigel
R Savory; Bill F Whysall.
HOW TO APPLY Applications, in writing and with latest
accounts, must be submitted at least one
month in advance of trustee meetings held in
March, July and November. Unsuccessful
applicants are not notified.
WHO TO APPLY TO Bill F Whysall, Trustee, c/o
Berryman Shacklock, Park House, Friar Lane,
Nottingham NG1 6DN *Tel* 0115 945 3700
Fax 0115 948 0234
CC NO 208877   ESTABLISHED 1951

■ The Hinduja Foundation

WHERE FUNDING CAN BE GIVEN Worldwide.
WHO CAN BENEFIT Registered charities.
WHAT IS FUNDED Health-care, educational charities,
scarcity relief, poverty alleviation, art and
culture, sports, social, economic and
international development-related research.
RANGE OF GRANTS Up to £50,000.
SAMPLE GRANTS Hinduja Cambridge Trust
(£106,000); India Art Event (£9,000); Lord
Mayors Appeal and Kings College London
(£5,000 each); University of Warwick (£2,500);
Sindhi Association of UK (£2,000); Anglo Arab
Organisation (£1,500); and Malayalee
Association of UK (£500).
FINANCES *Year* 2008 *Income* £178,884
Grants £151,830 *Assets* £17,635
TRUSTEES S P Hinduja; G P Hinduja; P P Hinduja.
HOW TO APPLY In writing to the correspondent.
WHO TO APPLY TO The Trustees, c/o New Zealand
House, 80 Haymarket, London SW1Y 4TE
Website hindujagroup.com
CC NO 802756   ESTABLISHED 1989

■ Stuart Hine Trust

WHERE FUNDING CAN BE GIVEN UK and overseas.
WHO CAN BENEFIT Evangelical Christian
organisations, supported by Stuart Hine during
his lifetime or by the trustees since his death.
WHAT IS FUNDED The support of Christian ministry.
SAMPLE GRANTS £99,000 to Wycliff Bible
Translators.
FINANCES *Year* 2007–08 *Income* £163,084
Grants £129,933 *Assets* £221,990
TRUSTEES Raymond Bodkin; Nigel Coltman; Amelia
Gardner; Philip Johnson.
OTHER INFORMATION The trust receives its income
mainly from royalties from the song 'How Great
Thou Art' written by Stuart Hine.
HOW TO APPLY The trust states that 'unsolicited
requests for funds will not be considered'.
Funds are basically distributed in accordance
with the wishes of the settlor.
WHO TO APPLY TO Raymond Bodkin, Trustee,
'Cherith', 23 Derwent Close, Hailsham, East
Sussex BN27 3DA *Tel* 01323 843948
CC NO 326941   ESTABLISHED 1985

■ The Hinrichsen Foundation

WHERE FUNDING CAN BE GIVEN UK.
WHO CAN BENEFIT Organisations benefiting
musicians; individual musicians.
WHAT IS FUNDED Assisting contemporary composition
and its performance, and musicological
research. The trustees are aware that financial
assistance is often necessary to create the
opportunities for both composition and
research. They are equally aware that the
results of composition or research need to be
made known and that financial assistance is
often necessary for the production of
performance materials, for the publication of the
results of research and for performances of new
compositions to take place.
WHAT IS NOT FUNDED The trust does not support
study courses, including those at postgraduate
level. Grants are not given for instruments,
equipment or recordings.
TYPE OF GRANT Usually one-off for a specific project
or part of a project.
RANGE OF GRANTS Variable, generally between £500
and £2,000.
SAMPLE GRANTS Huddersfield Contemporary Music
Festival (£5,000); Dartington International
Summer School and Spitalfields Festival
(£2,000 each); Birmingham Contemporary
Music Group and Kettle's Yard (£1,500 each);
Swaledale Festival and York Late Music Festival
(£1,000 each); The Red Violin (£750); Dmitri
Ensemble (£500); and Pro Nobis Singers
(£450).
FINANCES *Year* 2007 *Income* £32,320
Grants £41,983
TRUSTEES P Standford, Chair; T Berg; Dr J Cross; Dr
Linda Hirst; Sue Lubbock; K Potter; P Strang;
Prof S Walsh; Mrs T Estell.
HOW TO APPLY On a form that can be downloaded
from the foundation's website.
WHO TO APPLY TO The Secretary, PO Box 309,
Leatherhead, Surrey KT22 2AT
email hinrichsen.foundation@editionpeters.com
Website www.hinrichsenfoundation.org.uk
CC NO 272389   ESTABLISHED 1976

■ The Hintze Family Charitable Foundation

WHERE FUNDING CAN BE GIVEN England and Wales.

WHO CAN BENEFIT Churches, museums, galleries, libraries, schools and charitable organisations.

WHAT IS FUNDED The trust operates in the following areas: promoting access to museums, libraries and art galleries; supporting Christian churches in England and Wales, particularly the Diocese of Southwark; the relief of sickness and people with terminal illnesses; and, the provision of resources and equipment for schools, colleges and universities (in particular to enable the acquisition and retention of antiquarian books to be used as a learning resource).

TYPE OF GRANT Capital and revenue funding, mostly over two to five years.

RANGE OF GRANTS Up to £1.4 million.

SAMPLE GRANTS The Princes' Foundations (1.4 million); Lockwood Charitable Foundation (£1 million); Friends of the University of Sydney (£680,000); the National Gallery (£500,000); and International Theological Institute (£119,000).

FINANCES *Year* 2008 *Income* £3,901,003 *Grants* £4,361,460 *Assets* £1,489,122

TRUSTEES Michael Hintze; Nick Hunt; David Swain; Steven Walters.

HOW TO APPLY The trust offers the following application guidance in its latest accounts: 'The foundation invites applications for grants or commitments from charities which serve the objects of the foundation. No specific format is required for applications. Applications, along with potential donations and commitments identified by the Chief Executive and the trustees, are considered in formal trustee meetings.'

WHO TO APPLY TO Oliver Hylton, Trustee, 5th Floor, 33 Chester Street, London SW1X 7BL *Tel* 020 7201 6862

CC NO 1101842   **ESTABLISHED** 2003

■ The Hitchin Educational Foundation

WHERE FUNDING CAN BE GIVEN Unrestricted, in practice, Hertfordshire.

WHO CAN BENEFIT Individuals and local organisations benefiting children, young adults and students under the age of 25 years.

WHAT IS FUNDED The advancement of education and training.

WHAT IS NOT FUNDED No support for second degrees or the purchase of certain books.

TYPE OF GRANT One-off.

RANGE OF GRANTS Up to £15,000.

SAMPLE GRANTS Hitchin Boys' School, the Priory School and Hitchin Girls' School (£15,000 each); and Hertfordshire Educational Foundation (£300).

FINANCES *Year* 2008 *Income* £114,260 *Grants* £63,097 *Assets* £1,290,955

TRUSTEES A F Kingston-Splatt; D Hitchcock; D Ashley; D Miller; Mrs L A L Greenwood; N Brook; C Minton; C Lacey; Revd M Roden; D Chapallaz; Mrs S J Wren; Mrs P Cherry; Dr R Lee; Mrs S Cracknell; Mrs J Wood.

OTHER INFORMATION Applicants must have lived in Hitchin or attended a Hitchin school for at least two years. In 2008, a further £16,000 was given in miscellaneous grants.

HOW TO APPLY Apply in writing to the correspondent for an application form.

WHO TO APPLY TO Brian Frederick, Clerk, c/o Chaplin Frobisher Welling, Icknield House, Eastcheap, Letchworth, Hertfordshire SG6 3YY *Tel* 01462 631717 *Fax* 01462 681509

CC NO 311024   **ESTABLISHED** 1965

■ The Henry C Hoare Charitable Trust

WHERE FUNDING CAN BE GIVEN UK.

WHO CAN BENEFIT Charitable organisations.

WHAT IS FUNDED General charitable purposes.

TYPE OF GRANT One-off and annual donations.

SAMPLE GRANTS Trinity College Cambridge (£25,000); Transform Drug Policy Foundation (£20,000); Autism Research Centre, European Squirrel Initiative, Mental health Foundation, Prospect Burma and Reform Research Trust (£10,000 each); Tree Aid (£7,500); and Okeford Fitzpaine C of E Primary School (£7,000).

FINANCES *Year* 2007–08 *Income* £186,023 *Grants* £181,250 *Assets* £3,137,026

TRUSTEES Henry C Hoare; Messrs Hoare Trustees.

HOW TO APPLY In writing to the correspondent.

WHO TO APPLY TO C Hoare and Co, 37 Fleet Street, London EC4P 4DQ

CC NO 1088669   **ESTABLISHED** 2001

■ The Eleemosynary Charity of William Hobbayne

WHERE FUNDING CAN BE GIVEN Support is first given to causes in Hanwell and any surplus is then donated to causes in the borough of Ealing.

WHO CAN BENEFIT Specific beneficiaries as stated in the trust's deed; Organisations and individuals in (a) Hanwell, then (b) borough of Ealing.

WHAT IS FUNDED General charitable purposes, including the relief of need and hardship.

RANGE OF GRANTS Up to about £5,000.

SAMPLE GRANTS Previous beneficiaries include: Hanwell Neighbourly Care Scheme, Copley Close Summer Outings, Log Cabin Adventure Playground, North Hanwell Baptist Church and Ealing, Hammersmith and Hounslow Samaritans.

FINANCES *Year* 2007–08 *Income* £157,411 *Grants* £24,251 *Assets* £2,379,802

TRUSTEES Revd Matthew Grayshon, Chair; Mark Cosstick; Roy Price; Allison Rockley; John Sawyer; Susan Stiff; Angela Wallis; Nicholas Robinson; Robert Coomber; David Muir.

OTHER INFORMATION In addition, £15,713 was paid in grants to individuals.

HOW TO APPLY In writing to the correspondent.

WHO TO APPLY TO Caroline Lumb, Clerk, The William Hobbayne Community Centre, St. Dunstans Road, London W7 2HB *Tel* 020 8579 2921 *Fax* 020 8579 2921

CC NO 211547   **ESTABLISHED** 1962

■ The Hobson Charity Limited

WHERE FUNDING CAN BE GIVEN UK.

WHO CAN BENEFIT Registered charities only, particularly those benefiting people of all ages, students, teachers, at risk groups, people disadvantaged by poverty and socially isolated people.

WHAT IS FUNDED Relief of poverty and distress among older people and the poor. The provision of recreation and leisure facilities. The advancement of education and other charitable purposes.

WHAT IS NOT FUNDED No grants to individuals, except in exceptional circumstances.

TYPE OF GRANT One-off and recurrent.

RANGE OF GRANTS £1,000–£100,000.

SAMPLE GRANTS Woodard Corporation Limited (£1 million in total); Armed Forces Memorial Trust (£350,000 in total); White Ensign Association (£120,000); Royal Marines Museum (£100,000); Army Benevolent Fund (£80,000); Coram Foundation (£70,000); Moorfields Eye Hospital (£50,000); Opera North (£25,000); Diabetes UK (£20,000); North London Hospice (£16,000 in total); Gloucestershire Emergency Accommodation Resource and the Polar Extreme Foundation (£10,000 each); Children with Leukaemia (£5,000); Hendon Band of the Salvation Army (£2,000); and Pentland Finchley Carnival (£1,000).

FINANCES *Year* 2007–08 *Income* £3,881,469 *Grants* £2,699,358 *Assets* £591,057

TRUSTEES Deborah Hobson; Sir Donald Gosling; Sir Ronald F Hobson; Lady Hobson; J Richardson.

HOW TO APPLY In writing to the correspondent. The trustees meet quarterly.

WHO TO APPLY TO Deborah Hobson, Trustee and Secretary, 21 Bryanston Street, Marble Arch, London W1H 7PR *Tel* 020 7495 5599

CC NO 326839   **ESTABLISHED** 1985

....

■ Hockerill Educational Foundation

WHERE FUNDING CAN BE GIVEN UK, with a preference for the dioceses of Chelmsford and St Albans.

WHO CAN BENEFIT Organisations benefiting young adults, older people, academics, students, teachers and educational support staff Christians and the Church of England.

WHAT IS FUNDED The foundation's current priorities are: (i) Grants to individual teachers and others in an educational capacity, either training to teach or seeking to develop their professional abilities and qualifications, particularly in Religious Education. (ii) Grants to individuals taking other first degree or further education courses, excluding courses which lead directly to careers other than teaching. (iii) Training and support for the church's educational work in the dioceses of Chelmsford and St Albans. (iv) Research, development and support grants to organisations in the field of religious education. Grants are also made to organisations for projects and research likely to enhance the Church of England's contribution to higher and further education or religious education in schools.

WHAT IS NOT FUNDED Grants are not given for general appeals for funds, 'bricks and mortar' building projects or purposes that are the clear responsibility of another body. With regard to individuals, grants will not normally be considered from teachers who intend to move out of the profession; those in training for ordination or for other kinds of mission; clergy who wish to improve their own qualifications, unless they are already engaged in teaching in schools and/or intend to teach in the future; students of counselling, therapy or social work; undergraduates or people training for other professions, such as accountancy, business, law or medicine; people doing courses or visits abroad, including 'gap' year courses (except as an integral part of a course, or a necessary part of research); children at primary or secondary school.

FINANCES *Year* 2007–08 *Income* £304,538 *Grants* £245,936 *Assets* £5,636,470

TRUSTEES Revd C W Herbert; Ven T P Jones. Four ex-officio trustees; four diocesan trustees; seven nominative trustees; one co-opted trustee.

OTHER INFORMATION In 2007–08 grants to individuals totalled £42,466.

HOW TO APPLY On a form available from the correspondent, to be submitted by 30 April each year. Results of applications will be communicated in June. Receipt of applications are not acknowledged. Applications which do not fit the criteria do not normally receive a reply

WHO TO APPLY TO Derek J Humphrey, Secretary, 3 The Swallows, Harlow, Essex CM17 0AR *Tel* 01279 420855 *Fax* 0560 3140931 *email* info@hockerillfoundation.org.uk *Website* www.hockerillfoundation.org.uk

CC NO 311018   **ESTABLISHED** 1977

....

■ Matthew Hodder Charitable Trust

WHERE FUNDING CAN BE GIVEN Worldwide.

WHO CAN BENEFIT Organisations and individuals.

WHAT IS FUNDED The trust's charitable concern is with: book publishing; literacy and literature; reading; the book trade (including the provision of books); arts education (including music); Christian endeavour.

WHAT IS NOT FUNDED Health (unless reading related); social welfare; environment; politics.

TYPE OF GRANT One-off only.

FINANCES *Year* 2008 *Income* £36,509 *Grants* £29,200 *Assets* £948,389

TRUSTEES Mark Hodder-Williams, Chair; Tim Biggs-Davison; Roger Spurling; Timothy Ford; Anthony Brown.

OTHER INFORMATION The trust has no geographical limits and makes grants to individuals and organisations.

HOW TO APPLY In writing to the correspondent.

WHO TO APPLY TO Mark Hodder-Williams, Chair of Trustees, Little Birches, 38 Greenhill Road, Otford, Sevenoaks, Kent TN14 5RS *Tel* 01959 522180

CC NO 1042741   **ESTABLISHED** 1994

....

■ The Sir Julian Hodge Charitable Trust

WHERE FUNDING CAN BE GIVEN UK.

WHO CAN BENEFIT Registered charities benefiting people of all ages. Support may also be given to people who are disabled, medical professionals, research workers, scientists, students and teachers and governesses. Support may also be given to people with cancer, paediatric diseases, polio and tuberculosis.

WHAT IS FUNDED General charitable purposes, especially medical research in cancer, polio, tuberculosis and diseases of children. General advancement of medical and surgical science, the advancement of education, religion, and the relief of older people and people who are disabled.

WHAT IS NOT FUNDED No grants to individuals or companies.

RANGE OF GRANTS £500–£5,000.

SAMPLE GRANTS Techniquest (£3,000); Royal Vetenary College and Dogs for the Disabled (£2,500 each); Brittle Bone Society, Deafblind UK and Royal School for the Deaf & Communication Disorders (£2,000 each); the

Firefighters Charity (£1,500); Watford & Three Rivers Furniture Recycling Scheme, The Royal National Institute for Deaf People and SENSE (£1,000 each).

FINANCES *Year* 2007–08 *Income* £81,416 *Grants* £73,000 *Assets* £1,346,455

TRUSTEES Lady Hodge; Robert J Hodge; Joyce Harrison; Derrek L Jones; Margaret Cason; Eric M Hammonds.

HOW TO APPLY In writing to the correspondent.

WHO TO APPLY TO Margaret Cason, Trustee, Ty Gwyn, Lisvane Road, Lisvane, Cardiff CF14 0SG

CC NO 234848　　　**ESTABLISHED** 1964

■ The Jane Hodge Foundation

WHERE FUNDING CAN BE GIVEN Unrestricted, in practice UK with a preference for Wales.

WHO CAN BENEFIT UK registered charities.

WHAT IS FUNDED Medical and surgical science, studies and research; education; religion; and general charitable purposes.

WHAT IS NOT FUNDED No grants to individuals.

TYPE OF GRANT One-off and recurring grants and loans.

RANGE OF GRANTS Up to around £140,000.

SAMPLE GRANTS Cardiff Business School (£139,000 in three grants); George Thomas Hospice Care (£58,000 in two grants); Archdiocese of Cardiff (£50,000); Wallich Clifford Community (£26,000); Bobath Cymru (£10,000 in two grants); Race Equality First (£7,000); Vale of Glamorgan Railway and Morriston Orpheus Choir (£5,000 each); Education in World Citizenship (£4,500); Welsh Heritage Schools Initiative (£3,500); and Llanishen Methodist Church (£3,000).

FINANCES *Year* 2007–08 *Income* £1,315,670 *Grants* £1,111,886 *Assets* £26,921,205

TRUSTEES Lady Moira Hodge; Eric Hammonds; Robert Hodge; Joyce Harrison; Derek L Jones; Ian Davies; Margaret Cason.

HOW TO APPLY In writing to the correspondent. Applications for grants are considered by the trustees at regular meetings throughout the year. Applications are acknowledged.

WHO TO APPLY TO Margaret Cason, Secretary, Ty Gwyn, Lisvane Road, Lisvane, Cardiff CF14 0SG *Tel* 029 2076 6521 *email* dianne.lydiard@janehodgefoundation.co.uk

CC NO 216053　　　**ESTABLISHED** 1962

■ The J G Hogg Charitable Trust

WHERE FUNDING CAN BE GIVEN UK.

WHO CAN BENEFIT To benefit people in need and animals in need.

WHAT IS FUNDED Humanitarian causes, overseas charities, wild and domestic animal welfare causes.

WHAT IS NOT FUNDED No grants to individuals. Registered charities only are supported.

SAMPLE GRANTS Kids Company and Oxfam (£15,000 each); Medicinema and Teddy Bear Air Care (£10,000 each); and Addiction Recovery Foundation (£7,000).

FINANCES *Year* 2007–08 *Income* £23,834 *Grants* £57,000 *Assets* £724,383

TRUSTEES Sarah Jane Houldsworth; Joanna Wynfreda Turvey.

HOW TO APPLY In writing to the correspondent. To keep administration costs to a minimum, the trust is unable to reply to unsuccessful applicants.

WHO TO APPLY TO C M Jones, Trustees' Accountant, Chantrey Vellacott DFK, Russell House,

10 -12 Russell Square, London WC1B 5LF *Tel* 020 75099000 *email* cjones@cvdfk.com

CC NO 299042　　　**ESTABLISHED** 1987

■ The Holbeck Charitable Trust

WHERE FUNDING CAN BE GIVEN Worldwide, preference for York.

WHO CAN BENEFIT Registered charities, universities and schools.

WHAT IS FUNDED (1) The advancement of medical research; (2) the advancement of education; (3) the advancement of the Christian religion; (4) people in need; (5) the preservation of buildings or sites of historic or architectural importance. 'The trust receives both solicited and unsolicited applications for funding. The trustees are also encouraged to identify suitable charities, including local organisations as well as national organisations in need of funding for specific projects.'

WHAT IS NOT FUNDED No grants to animal charities. Unsolicited applications for large capital projects or medical research projects are not supported.

FINANCES *Year* 2008–09 *Income* £334,000 *Grants* £223,000 *Assets* £5,381,000

TRUSTEES G C Horsfield; F A Horsfield; J R Lane; V A Denman; C L Horsfield.

HOW TO APPLY In writing to the correspondent including the latest annual report and accounts. The trustees meet quarterly.

WHO TO APPLY TO The Trustees, c/o Rollits, Rowntree Wharf, Navigation Road, York YO1 9WE

CC NO 1113089　　　**ESTABLISHED** 2006

■ The Holden Charitable Trust

WHERE FUNDING CAN BE GIVEN UK, with a preference for the Manchester area.

WHO CAN BENEFIT Organisations benefiting Jewish people. Children, young adults and students may benefit.

WHAT IS FUNDED Jewish charitable purposes with emphasis on the advancement of education.

SAMPLE GRANTS Friends of Beis Eliyohu Trust (£23,000); Broughton Jewish Cassel Fox Primary School (£20,000); Broom Foundation (£18,000); Talmud Torah Trust (£11,000); Yeshayh Adler Memorial Fund (£10,000); King David Schools (£7,400); Manchester Jewish Grammar School (£5,000); Ohr Yerushalayim (£4,300); Manchester Eruv Committee (£3,000); The Forum (£2,500); Manchester Junior Girls School (£2,000); and Aish UK (£1,000).

FINANCES *Year* 2007–08 *Income* £157,682 *Grants* £212,640 *Assets* £1,037,358

TRUSTEES David Lopian; Marion Lopian; Michael Lopian.

HOW TO APPLY In writing to the correspondent.

WHO TO APPLY TO The Clerk, c/o Lopian Gross Barnett and Co., Cardinal House, 20 St Mary Parsonage, Manchester M3 2IG *Tel* 0161 832 8721

CC NO 264185　　　**ESTABLISHED** 1972

■ John Holford's Charity

WHERE FUNDING CAN BE GIVEN The parishes of Clutton and Middlewich, the borough of Congleton and that part of Astbury that lies outside the borough.

WHO CAN BENEFIT Mostly individuals, also organisations including schools.

WHAT IS FUNDED Relief in need and educational visits and trips.
FINANCES *Year* 2007–08 *Income* £82,725 *Grants* £26,653
TRUSTEES Mrs Anita Lockett; Revd Ian Bishop; Revd Canon Nigel Elbourne; Mrs Rosamund Mahon; Revd Dr J C Cuttell; E S Tudor Evans; Revd David Taylor; Mrs Jane Shelmerdine.
OTHER INFORMATION Up to five percent of the income can be used for relief-in-need in the parish of Clutton, with the remainder divided equally between the parish of Middlewich, the borough of Congleton and the part of Astbury outside the borough of Congleton.
HOW TO APPLY In writing to the correspondent.
WHO TO APPLY TO The Clerk, Birch Cullimore, Friars, White Friars, Chester CH1 1XS *Tel* 01244 356789 *email* kerris.owen@cullimoredutton.co.uk
CC NO 223046   **ESTABLISHED** 1984

··

■ **The Hollands-Warren Fund**

WHERE FUNDING CAN BE GIVEN Maidstone.
WHO CAN BENEFIT Residents of the borough of Maidstone who are in genuine need.
WHAT IS FUNDED Temporary medical and nursing services and/or domestic help for residents.
RANGE OF GRANTS Up to £43,000.
SAMPLE GRANTS Twilight Nursing Service (£43,000); and Heart of Kent Hospice (£13,000).
FINANCES *Year* 2008 *Income* £69,941 *Grants* £55,550 *Assets* £2,199,610
TRUSTEES Kim Harrington; D W H Bell; A S Palmer; J C M Sankey.
HOW TO APPLY In writing to the correspondent.
WHO TO APPLY TO Kim Harrington, Somerfield House, 59 London Road, Maidstone, Kent ME16 8JH *Tel* 01622 690691 *email* kimharrington@brachers.co.uk
CC NO 279747   **ESTABLISHED** 1977

··

■ **The Hollick Family Charitable Trust**

WHERE FUNDING CAN BE GIVEN UK and overseas.
WHO CAN BENEFIT Registered charities.
WHAT IS FUNDED General charitable purposes.
TYPE OF GRANT One-off and recurrent.
SAMPLE GRANTS AMREF (£12,000); London Citizens (£7,500); Real Action and the Westside Independent School (£5,000 each); VSO (£4,000); Leaders Quest – China Earthquake Fund (£1,500); and Kingsdale School, Prisoners Abroad, Saving Faces and West Kent Branch Alzheimer's Society (£1,000 each).
FINANCES *Year* 2008–09 *Income* £163,384 *Grants* £66,857 *Assets* £1,074,033
TRUSTEES Lord Hollick; Lady Hollick; Hon. C D Hollick; C M Kemp; D W Beech; Hon. G L Hollick; Hon. A M Hollick; T Kemp.
HOW TO APPLY In writing to the correspondent.
WHO TO APPLY TO D W Beech, Solicitor, c/o Peter Bryan and Co, Foxglove House, 166 Piccadilly, London W1J 9EF *Tel* 020 7493 4932
CC NO 1060228   **ESTABLISHED** 1997

··

■ **The Holliday Foundation**

WHERE FUNDING CAN BE GIVEN UK.
WHO CAN BENEFIT Organisations and individuals.
WHAT IS FUNDED General charitable purposes.
WHAT IS NOT FUNDED BEAT and Michael Palin Centre (£5,000 each); Charsfield Recreation Ground,

Little Brig Sailing Trust and Portsmouth Renal Fund (£2,500 each); and Child Hope (£1,000).
FINANCES *Year* 2007–08 *Income* £72,794 *Grants* £21,630 *Assets* £1,293,515
TRUSTEES D W J Garrett; Mrs J M Garrett; J A Cave; A R Wilson; A W MacDonald.
HOW TO APPLY In writing to the correspondent.
WHO TO APPLY TO The Trustees, Salisbury Partners LLP, 25 Hill Street, London W1J 5LW *Minicom* ichael
CC NO 1089931   **ESTABLISHED** 2002

··

■ **The Dorothy Holmes Charitable Trust**

WHERE FUNDING CAN BE GIVEN UK, with a preference for Dorset.
WHO CAN BENEFIT UK registered charities benefiting young adults and older people; people who are sick; clergy; ex-service and service people; legal professionals; unemployed people; volunteers; parents and children; one-parent families; widows and widowers; at risk groups; carers; and people who are disabled.
WHAT IS FUNDED Charities working in the fields of advice and information on housing; emergency and short-term housing; residential facilities; respite and sheltered accommodation; information technology and computers; civil society development; support of voluntary and community organisations; health professional bodies; and religion will be considered. Support is also given to healthcare; hospices and hospitals; cancer research; church buildings; heritage; secondary schools and special schools; counselling on social issues; and income support and maintenance.
WHAT IS NOT FUNDED Only applications from registered charities will be considered.
TYPE OF GRANT Buildings; capital; core costs; one-off; project; research; recurring costs; running costs; salaries; and start-up costs. Funding for up to and over three years will be considered.
RANGE OF GRANTS Up to £6,000.
SAMPLE GRANTS Wallingford School (£6,000); Children in Touch, Crisis and Christmas and RNLI (£5,000 each); Hyman Cen Foundation (£4,000); Army Benevolent Fund (£3,000); Action on Elder Abuse and Clic Sargeant Cancer Fund (£2,000 each); National Autistic Society and Raleigh International (£1,000 each); and Royal Free Hospital Retirement Fellowship (£300).
FINANCES *Year* 2007–08 *Income* £28,592 *Grants* £64,600 *Assets* £753,948
TRUSTEES Mrs B M Cody; Miss M Cody; Dr S Roberts; J Roberts.
HOW TO APPLY In writing to the correspondent, preferably in January to March each year.
WHO TO APPLY TO Michael Kennedy, Smallfield Cody and Co, 5 Harley Place, Harley Street, London W1G 8QD *Tel* 020 7636 6100
CC NO 237213   **ESTABLISHED** 1964

··

■ **The Holst Foundation**

WHERE FUNDING CAN BE GIVEN UK.
WHO CAN BENEFIT Mainly musicians.
WHAT IS FUNDED To promote public appreciation of the musical works of Gustav and Imogen Holst and to encourage the study and practice of the arts. Funds are almost exclusively for the performance of music by living composers.
WHAT IS NOT FUNDED No support for the recordings or works of Holst that are already well supported,

nor for capital projects. No grants to individuals for educational purposes.

RANGE OF GRANTS Usually up to £30,000.

SAMPLE GRANTS NMC Recordings (£120,000); Aldeburgh Music (£30,000); BCMG (£8,800); Aldeburgh Productions (£6,000); Andre Heller (£5,000); BMIC (£3,000); Tete a Tete Productions and Opera North (£2,500); Huddersfield Festival and Spitalfield Festival (£2,000 each); and Cheltenham Music Society, Chandos Records, Pro Corda Trust and Prestiegne Festival (£1,000 each).

FINANCES *Year* 2007–08 *Income* £96,790 *Grants* £212,600 *Assets* £1,892,693

TRUSTEES Rosamund Strode, Chair; Noel Periton; Prof. Arnold Whittall; Peter Carter; Andrew Clements; Julian Anderson.

OTHER INFORMATION Royalties from the Holst Estate have largely ceased since the copyright expired at the end of 2004. From 2006 both the number and the size of grants have been greatly reduced as a result.

HOW TO APPLY In writing to the correspondent. Trustees meet four times a year. There is no application form. Seven copies of the application should be sent. Applications should contain full financial details and be as concise as possible. Funding is not given retrospectively.

WHO TO APPLY TO The Grants Administrator, 179 Great Portland Street, London W1W 5LS *Tel* 020 8673 4215 (answerphone only) *email* holst@dpmail.co.uk

CC NO 283668   **ESTABLISHED** 1981

■ P H Holt Foundation

WHERE FUNDING CAN BE GIVEN UK, with a preference for Merseyside.

WHO CAN BENEFIT Charitable organisations.

WHAT IS FUNDED General charitable purposes in the UK, especially Merseyside, particularly when original work or work of special excellence is being undertaken.

WHAT IS NOT FUNDED No grants to individuals. Grants are not usually given to organisations outside Merseyside.

TYPE OF GRANT One-off and recurrent.

RANGE OF GRANTS Up to £10,000.

SAMPLE GRANTS Rotters Community Composting (£7,000); Plaza Community Cinema (£6,000); Fuse New Theatre for Young People, Liverpool Arts Interface, Liverpool Carnival Company and Merseyside Dance Initiative (£5,000 each); Merseyside Family Support Association and Toxteth Community College (£3,000 each); the Basement Drop Night Drop-in Centre and Yambi Africa (£2,000 each); and Bluecoat, China Pearl and Urban Strawberry Lunch (£1,000 each).

FINANCES *Year* 2007–08 *Income* £262,316 *Grants* £129,700 *Assets* £12,928,841

TRUSTEES Neil Kemsley, Chair; Tilly Boyce; Martin Cooke; Paige Earlam; Nikki Eastwood; Anthony Hannay; Derek Morris; Ken Ravenscroft.

HOW TO APPLY In writing to the correspondent at any time. Full and detailed guidance notes are available from the trust.

WHO TO APPLY TO Roger Morris, Secretary, India Buildings, Liverpool L2 0RB *Tel* 0151 473 4693 *Fax* 0151 473 4693

CC NO 1113708   **ESTABLISHED** 1955

■ The Edward Holt Trust

WHERE FUNDING CAN BE GIVEN UK with a preference for Greater Manchester.

WHO CAN BENEFIT Charitable projects.

WHAT IS FUNDED Primarily the maintenance of a block of ten flats in Didsbury, Manchester, for retired people. Preference to charities which the trustees have special interest in, knowledge of or association with, including cancer, neurological and ageing research.

TYPE OF GRANT Buildings, capital, project and research. Funding is available for up to three years.

SAMPLE GRANTS Christie Hospital NHS Trust – Communication Skills Training Unit (£83,000).

FINANCES *Year* 2007–08 *Income* £220,523 *Grants* £83,334 *Assets* £6,631,003

TRUSTEES Richard Kershaw, Chair; Mike Fry; David Tully; Edward Tudor-Evans; Angela Roden.

HOW TO APPLY 'This trust no longer responds to unsolicited grant requests.'

WHO TO APPLY TO Bryan Peak, Secretary, 22 Ashworth Park, Knutsford, Cheshire WA16 9DE *Tel* 01565 651086 *email* edwardholt@ btinternet.com

CC NO 224741   **ESTABLISHED** 1955

■ The Holywood Trust

WHERE FUNDING CAN BE GIVEN Dumfries and Galloway.

WHO CAN BENEFIT Young people in Dumfries and Galloway. Grants are made both to individuals and to organisations.

WHAT IS FUNDED 'The Holywood Trust assists organisations working with or for young people in Dumfries and Galloway. It does this by means of secondment of staff, management and administrative support, assisting with fund-raising activity as well as direct financial support.

TYPE OF GRANT One-off, capital and recurring (usually limited to three years) depending on need.

RANGE OF GRANTS £10–£50,000.

FINANCES *Year* 2007–08 *Income* £1,112,879

TRUSTEES Mrs E A Nelson, Chair; C A Jencks; J J G Brown; A M McLeod; B J K Weatherall; Ms L L Fox.

HOW TO APPLY On a form available from the correspondent. Applications are considered by the trustees at least three times a year.

WHO TO APPLY TO Richard Lye, Trust Administrator, Mount St Michael, Craigs Road, Dumfries DG1 4UT *Tel* 01387 269176 *Website* www. holywood-trust.org.uk

SC NO SC009942   **ESTABLISHED** 1981

■ The Homelands Charitable Trust

WHERE FUNDING CAN BE GIVEN UK.

WHO CAN BENEFIT Registered charities benefiting children, particularly people in at risk groups, or who are victims of abuse or domestic violence. Support may also be given to clergy, medical professionals and research workers.

WHAT IS FUNDED General charitable purposes in accordance with the settlor's wishes. Special emphasis is given to the General Conference of the New Church, medical research and the care and protection of children. Hospices are also supported.

WHAT IS NOT FUNDED No grants to individuals.

SAMPLE GRANTS Previous beneficiaries include: General Conference of the New Church (£45,000); Bournemouth Society of the New Church (£20,000); Broadfield Memorial

Think carefully about every application. Is it justified?

603

Benevolent Trust (£11,000); New Church College (£7,500); Asbah (£5,000); RNLI (£4,000); Action Medical Research, Fellowship Afloat, Jubilee Sailing Trust, Manic Depression Fellowship and National Children Homes (£3,000 each); and Action for the Blind, Bliss, Child Accident Prevention Trust, Dreams Come True, Hope House, Mencap, RNID, Seeability, Survival International, Trinity Hospice, University College London, Wessex Children Hospice Trust and YMCA (£2,000 each).

FINANCES *Year* 2007–08 *Income* £259,713 *Grants* £270,000 *Assets* £6,581,587

TRUSTEES D G W Ballard; N J Armstrong; Revd C Curry; R J Curry.

HOW TO APPLY In writing to the correspondent.

WHO TO APPLY TO N J Armstrong, Trustee, c/o Alliotts, 4th Floor, Imperial House, 15 Kingsway, London WC2B 6UN *Tel* 020 7240 9971

CC NO 214322 **ESTABLISHED** 1962

■ **The Homestead Charitable Trust**

WHERE FUNDING CAN BE GIVEN UK.

WHO CAN BENEFIT Actors and entertainment professionals, musicians, textile workers and designers, writers and poets, Christians, at risk groups, people disadvantaged by poverty, and socially isolated people.

WHAT IS FUNDED Medical, health and welfare, animal welfare, Christianity and the arts.

TYPE OF GRANT Some recurring.

RANGE OF GRANTS Up to £10,000.

SAMPLE GRANTS City of Joy Foundation (£10,000); Crusade, PAVA Foundation and Angel Covers USA (£5,000 each); EKTA Project (£3,600); Hope and Homes for Children, Vedanta Institute and Francis Home Hospice (£2,000 each); and Vet Aid, CRY and Gwalior Children's Home (£1,000 each).

FINANCES *Year* 2007–08 *Income* £240,553 *Grants* £54,008 *Assets* £4,995,160

TRUSTEES Sir C Bracewell-Smith; Lady N Bracewell-Smith.

OTHER INFORMATION The trust fund of the Sir Charles Bracewell-Smith Voluntary Settlement worth £1.6 million was transferred to the trust in October 2004.

HOW TO APPLY In writing to the correspondent.

WHO TO APPLY TO Lady Nina Bracewell-Smith, Trustee, Flat 7, Clarence Gate Gardens, Glentworth Street, London NW1 6AY *Tel* 020 7258 1051

CC NO 293979 **ESTABLISHED** 1986

■ **Sir Harold Hood's Charitable Trust**

WHERE FUNDING CAN BE GIVEN Worldwide.

WHO CAN BENEFIT Roman Catholic charities and churches.

WHAT IS FUNDED Charities dealing with the advancement of the Roman Catholic faith through religious buildings, religious umbrella bodies and other Roman Catholic organisations.

WHAT IS NOT FUNDED No grants to individuals.

TYPE OF GRANT One-off and recurring.

SAMPLE GRANTS Individual beneficiaries are not listed in the 2007–08 accounts. Grants were categorised as follows: Churches (£74,000); Single grants (£69,000); Education (£54,000); Youth (£46,000); Special grants (£43,000); Missionary work (£37,000); Prisoners (£25,000); Homeless and Retreat centres (£20,000 each); Services (£15,000); Leprosy,

Hospitals and Schools (£12,000 each); Seminary (£7,000); Aid (£6,000); Nursing (£5,000); Vatican (£4,000).

FINANCES *Year* 2007–08 *Income* £569,650 *Grants* £460,750 *Assets* £14,332,164

TRUSTEES Dom James Hood; Anne-Marie True; Nicholas True; Margaret Hood; Christian Elwes.

HOW TO APPLY In writing to the correspondent. The trustees meet once a year to consider applications, usually in November.

WHO TO APPLY TO Margaret Hood, Trustee, Haysmacintyre, Fairfax House, 15 Fulwood Place, London WC1V 6AY *Tel* 020 7722 9088

CC NO 225870 **ESTABLISHED** 1962

■ **The Hope Trust**

WHERE FUNDING CAN BE GIVEN Worldwide, with a preference for Scotland.

WHO CAN BENEFIT Individuals and organisations benefiting Christians; Church of England; evangelists; Methodists; Quakers; Unitarians and people with a substance addiction.

WHAT IS FUNDED The provision of education and the distribution of literature to combat the misuse and effects of drink and drugs and to promote the principles of Reformed Churches; charities concerned with the advancement of the Christian religion, Anglican bodies, Free Church, rehabilitation centres and health education.

WHAT IS NOT FUNDED No grants to gap year students, scholarship schemes or to any individuals, with the sole exception of PhD students of theology studying at Scottish universities. No grants for the refurbishment of property.

TYPE OF GRANT Core costs, one-off funding, project, research, recurring costs, running costs, salaries, start-up costs and funding for more than three years will be considered.

RANGE OF GRANTS £100–£6,000.

SAMPLE GRANTS Previous beneficiaries have included Church of Scotland Priority Areas Fund, World Alliance of Reformed Churches, National Bible Society for Scotland, Feed the Minds and Waldensian Mission Aid.

FINANCES *Year* 2008 *Income* £187,168 *Grants* £150,000

TRUSTEES Prof. G M Newlands; Prof. D A S Ferguson; Revd G R Barr; Revd Dr Lyall; Carole Hope; Revd Gillean McLean.

HOW TO APPLY In writing to the correspondent. The trustees meet to consider applications in June and December each year. Applications should be submitted by mid-May or mid-November each year.

WHO TO APPLY TO The Secretary, Drummond Miller, 31–32 Moray Place, Edinburgh EH3 6BZ *Tel* 0131 226 5151 *email* rmiller@drummond-miller.co.uk

SC NO SC000987 **ESTABLISHED** Late nineteenth century

■ **HopMarket Charity**

WHERE FUNDING CAN BE GIVEN The city of Worcester.

WHO CAN BENEFIT 'Needy' people in the city of Worcester. 'Needy' is defined as those 'who, by reason of poverty, sickness or infirmity, whether young or old, are in need of financial assistance, care or attention'. People of all ages, volunteers, and people who are disabled or disadvantaged by poverty.

WHAT IS FUNDED The trust has adopted the following guidelines: 'That as a general principle the funds should be allocated to either capital or revenue projects which fall within the purposes of the charity and which will generate further support for the community. Where revenue funding is made, such support should not imply any ongoing commitment except where the trustees specifically indicate otherwise. Emphasis should be placed on assisting applications which have an affinity to matters which are within the council's sphere of activity.'

WHAT IS NOT FUNDED No grants to, or on behalf of, individuals.

RANGE OF GRANTS £2,500–£15,000.

SAMPLE GRANTS Worcester Play Council (£15,000); Worcester Citizens Advice, Worcester Housing & Benefits Advice and Noah's Ark Trust (£13,000 each); Perdiswell Young People's Club (£10,000); DIAL South Worcestershire (£7,700); Maggs Day Centre (£5,100); Ethic Access Link (£4,000); and Armchair (£2,500).

FINANCES *Year* 2007–08 *Income* £286,758 *Grants* £83,505 *Assets* £1,200,057

TRUSTEES The City Council.

HOW TO APPLY On a form available from the correspondent. Applications should be submitted by the beginning of January or August for consideration in March or September respectively.

WHO TO APPLY TO Ms D Porter, Administrator, Worcester City Council, Guildhall, Worcester WR1 2ZB *Tel* 01905 722019 *Fax* 01905 722028 *email* corporateservices@ cityofworcester.gov.uk

CC NO 244569   **ESTABLISHED** 1964

■ The Cuthbert Horn Trust

WHERE FUNDING CAN BE GIVEN UK.

WHO CAN BENEFIT Organisations benefiting older people and the environment.

WHAT IS FUNDED Older people, the environment and general charitable purposes.

WHAT IS NOT FUNDED No grants are made to individuals.

TYPE OF GRANT One-off and recurrent.

RANGE OF GRANTS £1,000–£10,000.

SAMPLE GRANTS Farms for City Children (£6,000); Progressive Farming Trust (£5,000) International Bee Research Association, Norfolk Wherry Trust and Sevenoaks Symphony Orchestra (4,000 each); Ovingdean Hall School, The Charleston Trust, The Fishermans Mission and MS National Therapy Centres (£3,000 each); Norwegian Locomotive Trust (£2,500); and the Grasslands Trust (£2,000).

FINANCES *Year* 2007 *Income* £343,267 *Grants* £55,000 *Assets* £1,354,920

TRUSTEES Alliance Assurance Company Ltd; A H Flint.

HOW TO APPLY There are no application forms to complete; applicants should provide in writing as much background about their charity or cause as possible. Applications need to be received by December as the trustees meet as soon as possible after the financial year end. Only successful applications will be notified.

WHO TO APPLY TO Laurie Wilson, Trust Manager, Capita Trust Company Limited, Phoenix House, 18 King William Street, London EC4N 7HE *Tel* 020 7800 4126 *email* trusts@capitatrust. co.uk

CC NO 291465   **ESTABLISHED** 1985

■ The Antony Hornby Charitable Trust

WHERE FUNDING CAN BE GIVEN Unrestricted with a preference for London and the Home Counties.

WHO CAN BENEFIT Registered charities.

WHAT IS FUNDED General charitable purposes, in particular supporting charities involved in medical activities, education and welfare.

WHAT IS NOT FUNDED No grants to individuals. Only registered charities are supported. No grants to localised building projects.

RANGE OF GRANTS Mainly £100–£1,000.

SAMPLE GRANTS Charities Aid Foundation (£24,000 redistributed to 39 organisations); Army Benevolent Fund, David Rattray Memorial Trust, REGAIN, Save Canterbury Cathedral, St Albans Education Trust, Samaritans, Shelter and University College Hospitals Charities (£1,000 each); Trinity College of Music (£750); Ashmolean Museum, British Limbless Ex-Servicemen Association, British Neurological Research Trust, Mary Rose Trust, PACE Centre and St Albans Cathedral Music Trust (£500 each); Friends of Chelsea and Westminster Hospital (£250); and Elizabeth Finn Care (£100).

FINANCES *Year* 2007–08 *Income* £38,006 *Grants* £39,375 *Assets* £1,191,180

TRUSTEES Marie Antoinette Hall; Mark Antony Loveday; Michael Wentworth-Stanley; Jane Wentworth-Stanley.

HOW TO APPLY The trust has stated that it is fully committed and does not usually add new names to its list of beneficiaries unless it is a charity known to the trustees, or a very special appeal.

WHO TO APPLY TO Paul Langdon, Saffrey Champness, Lion House, 72–75 Red Lion Street, London WC1R 4GB *Tel* 020 7841 4000

CC NO 263285   **ESTABLISHED** 1971

■ The Horne Foundation

WHERE FUNDING CAN BE GIVEN Mainly Northamptonshire.

WHO CAN BENEFIT Preference is given to local organisations benefiting young adults, children and older people, especially people disadvantaged by poverty, with occasional grants also made to UK organisations.

WHAT IS FUNDED Predominantly large grants towards major educational projects that involve new buildings and regular smaller donations to local projects in the Northampton and Oxfordshire area and student bursaries for higher education through Northampton schools.

WHAT IS NOT FUNDED The foundation prefers organisations without religious affiliation.

TYPE OF GRANT Capital and project grants.

RANGE OF GRANTS Up to £15,000.

SAMPLE GRANTS Boys Brigade, Northamptonshire Association of Youth Clubs Octopus Project and Prince's Trust LCIN (£10,000 each); Corby Furniture Project (£5,000); Forum Cinema (£3,000); Volunteer Reading Help and Northampton Festival Opera (£2,000 each); and Daventry Contact (£1,200).

FINANCES *Year* 2007–08 *Income* £278,351 *Grants* £155,996 *Assets* £6,807,614

TRUSTEES E J Davenport; Mrs R M Harwood; C A Horne.

OTHER INFORMATION In 2007/08, 57 grants were given to individual students totalling £111,000.

HOW TO APPLY In writing to the correspondent at any time.

WHO TO APPLY TO Mrs R M Harwood, Secretary, PO Box 6165, Newbury RG14 9FY
email hornefoundation@googlemail.com
CC NO 283751   ESTABLISHED 1981

....

■ The Horne Trust

WHERE FUNDING CAN BE GIVEN UK and the developing world.
WHO CAN BENEFIT Charities, hospices and charitable projects.
WHAT IS FUNDED Homelessness, hospices (particularly children's hospices), medical support and development of self-reliant technology in Africa and the developing world.
RANGE OF GRANTS £1,000–£40,000.
SAMPLE GRANTS Demelza House Children's Hospice, Humberstone Hydrotherapy Pool and World Medical Fund (£10,000 each); AbilityNet, Share Community and Woodlands Hospice – Liverpool (£7,500); Laura Campbell-Preston Trust (£6,700); Deafblind UK, FACT, and Young Minds (£5,000 each); Winfield Trust, Disability Aid Fund Whitby Dog Rescue (£1,000 each).
FINANCES *Year* 2007–08 *Income* £211,701 *Grants* £415,700 *Assets* £6,599,296
TRUSTEES J T Horne; J L Horne; N J Camamile.
HOW TO APPLY Normally in writing to the correspondent, although the trust has stated that currently unsolicited applications cannot be supported.
WHO TO APPLY TO J T Horne, Trustee, Kingsdown, Warmlake Road, Chart Sutton, Maidstone, Kent ME17 3RP *Tel* 01622 842638 *email* mail.jh@horne-trust.org.uk
CC NO 1010625   ESTABLISHED 1992

....

■ The Worshipful Company of Horners' Charitable Trusts

WHERE FUNDING CAN BE GIVEN Mainly in London.
WHO CAN BENEFIT Registered charities, educational establishments and individuals.
WHAT IS FUNDED General charitable purposes; education in plastics; and scholarships and bursaries in education.
SAMPLE GRANTS Motor Neurone Disease Research (£15,000); Design Innovation in Plastic (£10,000); Royal Armories (£5,000); Epic Arts, the Pirate Club and Quaker Social Action (£3,000 each); Plastic Historical Society (£2,500); and Orpheus Centre (£2,000).
FINANCES *Year* 2008 *Income* £138,664 *Grants* £96,739 *Assets* £1,494,332
TRUSTEES R Anstis; D F Oxley; M Hart; B J Ridgewell; I A McColl; E M Hunt; C W Welch; C K Howe; D Beynon; R Leader.
OTHER INFORMATION Other grants for under £1,000 each amounted to £9,000.
HOW TO APPLY In writing to the correspondent.
WHO TO APPLY TO Raymond Layard, Clerk to the trustees, The Horners Company, The Clergy House, Hide Place, London SW1P 4NJ *email* horners.clerk@btinternet.com
Website www.horners.org.uk
CC NO 292204

....

■ The Hornsey Parochial Charities

WHERE FUNDING CAN BE GIVEN Ancient parish of Hornsey in part of the boroughs of Hackney and Haringey.
WHO CAN BENEFIT Individuals and organisations benefiting people disadvantaged by poverty.

WHAT IS FUNDED General benefit of poor people residing in Old Hornsey.
WHAT IS NOT FUNDED Residential qualification needed (must have lived in ancient parish of Hornsey for at least a year). No commitment to continuous grants.
SAMPLE GRANTS The charities administered a combined grants total of £82,000 given to numerous causes in the beneficial area. Full details of grants were withheld on the grounds of protecting the confidentiality of the recipients.
FINANCES *Year* 2008 *Income* £99,044 *Grants* £82,385 *Assets* £2,468,807
TRUSTEES Revd P Henderson; E Griffiths; J Hudson; A Jones; P Kenyon; V Manheim; L Marshall; B Simon; Revd G Seabrook; K Jones; A Gillespie; C O'Brien; A Casale.
HOW TO APPLY In writing to the correspondent. Initial enquiries by e-mail are welcome.
WHO TO APPLY TO The Clerk to the Trustees, PO Box 22985, London N10 3XB *Tel* 020 8352 1601 *Fax* 020 8352 1601 *email* hornseypc@blueyonder.co.uk
CC NO 229410   ESTABLISHED 1890

....

■ The Hospital of God at Greatham

WHERE FUNDING CAN BE GIVEN Darlington, Durham, Gateshead, Hartlepool, Newcastle upon Tyne, Northumberland, North Tyneside, South Tyneside, Stockton on Tees and Sunderland.
WHO CAN BENEFIT Charities, voluntary organisations and individuals. Grants are only made to individuals when the application originates from social service offices. The trust supports children, young adults, older people, at risk groups, carers, people who are disabled, disadvantaged by poverty, homeless or socially isolated, victims of abuse and domestic violence, and people with Alzheimer's disease, epilepsy and hearing loss.
WHAT IS FUNDED Preference is given to projects concerned with local initiatives aimed at disadvantaged people, particularly charities working in the field of social care and with local communities.
WHAT IS NOT FUNDED No grants for: capital projects; building work; education, travel or adventure projects; hospices; work outside the beneficial area; UK organisations with no base in the north east of England; training, conferences or feasibility studies.
TYPE OF GRANT One-off, capital, core funding, running costs and salaries. Funding for one year or more will be considered.
RANGE OF GRANTS £500–£8,000.
SAMPLE GRANTS Bishop of Durham Discretionary Fund (£7,700); Newcastle Diocese Discretionary Fund (£6,500); Opendoor North East and Blue Sky Trust (£4,000 each); After Adoption (£3,000); Rainbow Trust, St Pauls Community Project and South Area Parent Support (£2,000 each); Families in Care and Baby Equipment Loan Service (£1,700 each); Northumbrian Day Break (£1,500); Lifeline (£1,200); The Learning Library, Motor Neurone Disease Association and Ashington Amateur Boxing (£1,000 each).
FINANCES *Year* 2008 *Income* £2,835,404 *Grants* £113,697 *Assets* £32,965,241
TRUSTEES Mrs S Mitchell, Chair; Ven I Jagger; Ven G Miller; B Winter; J Allen; S Croft; J De Martino; M Poole; P Shields; P Sinclair.
OTHER INFORMATION The charity's main work is the provision of almshouse accommodation and residential care. Grants are made from surplus funds.

HOW TO APPLY Applications should be made to the correspondent in writing. The grants committee meets three times a year. Applications should include in no more than two pages giving the following information: the objects of the charity; description of, and budget for the project and the specific work for which funding is sought; a copy of the latest audited accounts. The correspondent is happy to answer initial telephone enquiries.

WHO TO APPLY TO David Granath, The Estate Office, Greatham, Hartlepool TS25 2HS *Tel* 01429 870247 *Fax* 01429 871469 *email* david. granath@hospitalofgod.org.uk *Website* www. hospitalofgod.org.uk

CC NO 1123540　　　**ESTABLISHED** 1973

....

■ The Hospital Saturday Fund

WHERE FUNDING CAN BE GIVEN UK, the Republic of Ireland and overseas.

WHO CAN BENEFIT Hospitals, hospices, medically-associated charities and welfare organisations providing similar services worldwide, but mostly in the UK and Republic of Ireland. Individuals can also be directly supported.

WHAT IS FUNDED Medical care and research to organisations; specialist equipment, welfare and scholarships to individuals.

WHAT IS NOT FUNDED Unless there are exceptional circumstances, organisations are not supported in successive years.

TYPE OF GRANT One-off grants. Organisations are rarely supported in successive years.

RANGE OF GRANTS Usually up to £3,000.

FINANCES *Year* 2008 *Income* £166,091 *Grants* £328,640

TRUSTEES John Greenwood; Jane Laidlaw Dalton; Michael Boyle; John Randel; Graham Hind; David Thomas; Keith Lawrey.

OTHER INFORMATION In 2008 the trust made grants to individuals totalling £21,799.

HOW TO APPLY Hospitals, hospices and medically-related charities are invited to write detailed letters or to send a brochure with an accompanying letter. There is a form for individuals to complete available from the personal assistant to the trust administrator.

WHO TO APPLY TO K R Bradley, Chief Executive, 24 Upper Ground, London SE1 9PD *Tel* 020 7928 6662 *email* charity@hsf.eu.com

CC NO 1123381　　　**ESTABLISHED** 1987

....

■ The Sir Joseph Hotung Charitable Settlement

WHERE FUNDING CAN BE GIVEN Worldwide.

WHO CAN BENEFIT Charitable organisations.

WHAT IS FUNDED General charitable purposes.

SAMPLE GRANTS Various grants totalling £275,000 were made to the School of Oriental and African Studies for the Sir Joseph Hotung Programme for Law, Human Rights and Peace Building in the Middle East; various grants totalling £816,000 were paid to St George's Hospital Medical School to fund the Chairs in Molecular Vaccinology, Immunology and Rheumatology. St Martin-in-the-Fields Church (£250,000); London Symphony Orchestra (£50,000); Oriental Ceramic Society (£25,000); International Spinal Research Trust (£1,200); Victoria & Albert Museum (£500).

FINANCES *Year* 2007–08 *Income* £1,688,824 *Grants* £1,418,159 *Assets* £1,561,928

TRUSTEES Sir Joseph E Hotung; Sir Robert D H Boys; Victoria F Dicks; Michael Gabriel; Joseph S Lesser.

HOW TO APPLY In writing to the correspondent.

WHO TO APPLY TO Sir Joseph Hotung, Trustee, c/o HSBC Private Bank (UK) Ltd, 78 St James' Street, London, SW1A 1EJ

CC NO 1082710　　　**ESTABLISHED** 2000

....

■ Houblon-Norman/George Fund

WHERE FUNDING CAN BE GIVEN UK.

WHO CAN BENEFIT Organisations benefiting academics and research workers.

WHAT IS FUNDED Research into the interaction and function of financial and business institutions, the economic conditions affecting them, and the dissemination of knowledge thereof. Fellowships are tenable at the Bank of England. The research work to be undertaken is intended to be full-time work, and teaching or other paid work must not be undertaken during the tenure of the fellowship, without the specific consent of the trustees. In considering applications the trustees will pay particular regard to the relevance of the research to current problems in economics and finance.

TYPE OF GRANT Research fellowship.

FINANCES *Year* 2007–08 *Income* £115,669 *Grants* £81,202 *Assets* £2,001,747

TRUSTEES C R Bean; Brendan Barber; Hon. Peter Jay.

HOW TO APPLY On an application form available from the website.

WHO TO APPLY TO The Secretary, MA Business Support Unit HO-2, Bank of England, Threadneedle Street, London EC2R 8AH *Tel* 020 7601 3778 *Fax* 020 7601 4423 *email* ma-hngfund@bankofengland.co.uk *Website* www.bankofengland.co.uk/about/ fellowships

CC NO 213168　　　**ESTABLISHED** 1944

....

■ The House of Industry Estate

WHERE FUNDING CAN BE GIVEN Borough of Bedford.

WHO CAN BENEFIT People who are in need and local organisations.

WHAT IS FUNDED Local organisations concerned with unemployed people, young people, counselling and housing.

WHAT IS NOT FUNDED Funds are not given in relief of taxes or other public funds. No recurrent grants are given.

TYPE OF GRANT One-off.

SAMPLE GRANTS Previous beneficiaries included: Bedford Community Rights; Bedfordshire Garden Carers; Bedford Pilgrims Housing Association; Kempston Summer School; and King's Arms Project.

FINANCES *Year* 2007–08 *Income* £160,995 *Grants* £147,636 *Assets* £3,439,405

TRUSTEES Cllr A Bagchi; Cllr T Hill; Cllr M Headley; Cllr P Merryman; Cllr P Olney; Cllr R Rigby; Cllr S Oliver.

HOW TO APPLY In writing to the correspondent.

WHO TO APPLY TO Director of Finance, Bedford Borough Council, Town Hall, St Paul's Square, Bedford MK40 1SJ *Tel* 01234 267422

CC NO 257079　　　**ESTABLISHED** 1968

■ The Reta Lila Howard Foundation

WHERE FUNDING CAN BE GIVEN UK and Republic of Ireland.

WHO CAN BENEFIT Children up to the age of 16.

WHAT IS FUNDED Innovative projects that benefit children, and projects concerned with 'the education of young people or to ameliorate their physical and emotional environment'.

WHAT IS NOT FUNDED Grants are not given to individuals, organisations which are not registered charities, or towards operating expenses, budget deficits, (sole) capital projects, annual charitable appeals, general endowment funds, fundraising drives or events, conferences, or student aid.

RANGE OF GRANTS £5,000 –£45,000.

SAMPLE GRANTS Countryside Education Trust (£70,000); Barnardo's (£68,500); Civitas (£60,000); The Tree Council (£53,000); Farms for City Children (£40,000); Children's Hospice Association Scotland (£35,000); Teach First (£30,000); New Forest Museum & Library (£20,000); The Bridge End Community Centre (£15,000); and Bibles for Children (£10,000).

FINANCES *Year* 2007–08 *Income* £268,000 *Grants* £718,000 *Assets* £14,000,000

TRUSTEES Emma Adamo; Nicolas Bauta; Alannah Weston; Charles Burnett; Graham Weston; Garfield Mitchell; Tara Rebanks; Kim Abell.

HOW TO APPLY The trust states that it does not accept unsolicited applications, since the trustees seek out and support projects they are interested in.

WHO TO APPLY TO The Company Secretary, Jamestown Investments Ltd, 4 Felstead Gardens, Ferry Street, London E14 3BS *Tel* 020 7537 1118 *email* jamestown@btinternet.com

CC NO 1041634   **ESTABLISHED** 1994

■ The Daniel Howard Trust

WHERE FUNDING CAN BE GIVEN UK and Israel.

WHO CAN BENEFIT Charities benefiting: children; young adults; actors and entertainment professionals; musicians; textile workers and designers; and writers and poets.

WHAT IS FUNDED Culture, education, the environment and welfare. Particularly Jewish causes.

WHAT IS NOT FUNDED Grants are only made to registered charities. No grants to individuals.

TYPE OF GRANT Recurrent and one-off.

SAMPLE GRANTS World Jewish Relief – Metuna (£30,000); The Israel Family Therapy Advancement Fund (£25,000); Friends of Daniel for Rowing (£20,000); International Scholarship Foundation Charitable Trust (£20,000 in two grants); British Friends of the IGDCB and The British Friends of Israel Philharmonic (£15,000 each); and Tel Aviv University and Weizmann Institute Foundation (£10,000 each).

FINANCES *Year* 2005–06 *Income* £264,001 *Grants* £178,343 *Assets* £10,759,214

TRUSTEES Dame Shirley Porter; Mrs Linda Streit; Steven Nigel Porter; Brian Padgett; Andrew Peggie.

OTHER INFORMATION No accounts received at the Charity Commission since those for 2005/06.

HOW TO APPLY In writing to the correspondent.

WHO TO APPLY TO Mrs Sarah Hunt, c/o Principle Capital, 9 Savoy Street, London WC2E 7ER *Tel* 020 7340 3222

CC NO 267173   **ESTABLISHED** 1974

■ The Clifford Howarth Charity Settlement

WHERE FUNDING CAN BE GIVEN UK, with a preference for Lancashire (Burnley/Rossendale).

WHO CAN BENEFIT Local and UK-registered charities which were supported by the founder.

WHAT IS FUNDED General charitable purposes.

WHAT IS NOT FUNDED Only registered charities will be supported. No grants to individuals, for scholarships or for non-local special projects.

TYPE OF GRANT One-off.

RANGE OF GRANTS £1,000–£20,000.

SAMPLE GRANTS Cumbria Cerebral Palsy (£15,000); St Marys Hospice (£5,000); St Nicholas Church – Newchurch (£3,000); Hospice in Rossendale (£2,500); and Ulverstone Inshore Rescue, Beaver Scouts, Spurgeons and Burnley Garrick Club (£2,000 each).

FINANCES *Year* 2007–08 *Income* £27,689 *Grants* £33,500 *Assets* £592,619

TRUSTEES James Howarth; Judith Howarth; Mary Fenton.

HOW TO APPLY The charity states that grants are only made to organisations known to the trustees, and that applications are unlikely to be successful.

WHO TO APPLY TO James Howarth, Trustee, 14A Hall Garth, Kelbeck, Barrow in Furness, Cumbria LA13 0QT

CC NO 264890   **ESTABLISHED** 1972

■ HSBC Global Education Trust

WHERE FUNDING CAN BE GIVEN Worldwide.

WHO CAN BENEFIT Charitable organisations.

WHAT IS FUNDED The charity's aims are to 'promote and advance education generally and in particular to promote and support primary and secondary education in areas of social and economic deprivation'. Projects generally benefit individuals between the ages of 3 and 25 and are normally funded for one year, although occasionally longer.

FINANCES *Year* 2008 *Income* £898,060 *Grants* £3,037,762 *Assets* £4,870,370

TRUSTEES Lord Brockwell; Gerard Davis; Prof. Steve Hodkinson.

HOW TO APPLY The trust invites applications for funding, however many approaches are received direct or via departments of HSBC Bank plc.

WHO TO APPLY TO The Trust Secretary, Level 16, 8 Canada Square, London E14 5HQ *Tel* 020 7992 1561 *email* globaleducation@hsbc.com *Website* www.hsbc.com

CC NO 1084542   **ESTABLISHED** 2001

■ The Huddersfield Medical Trust Fund

WHERE FUNDING CAN BE GIVEN The Huddersfield district of the Kirklees area health authority.

WHO CAN BENEFIT Patients treated by the NHS.

WHAT IS FUNDED Equipment used by a number of patients.

WHAT IS NOT FUNDED Support is not provided for salaries or ongoing maintenance.

SAMPLE GRANTS Grants have previously been given for hospital equipment and educational material, presumably for Huddersfield Royal Infirmary.

FINANCES *Year* 2007–08 *Income* £5,730

TRUSTEES Dr A Hamilton; Mrs D Melluish; Ms M Atkinson; Dr M Wybrew; Dr R Heaton; Dr S Gurney; B Bottomley.

HOW TO APPLY In writing to the correspondent.

WHO TO APPLY TO Dr A H Hamilton, Trustee, c/o Huddersfield Royal Infirmary, Acre Street, Lindley, Huddersfield HD3 3EA *Tel* 01484 342484 *Fax* 01484 342121
CC NO 512734   **ESTABLISHED** 1982

....
■ The Hudson Foundation
WHERE FUNDING CAN BE GIVEN UK, with a preference for the Wisbech area.
WHO CAN BENEFIT Individuals and organisations benefiting older people and those who are infirm, especially in the Wisbech area.
WHAT IS FUNDED The relief of older people and people who are infirm.
RANGE OF GRANTS Up to £80,000.
SAMPLE GRANTS Wisbech Parish Church of St Peter and St Paul (£80,000); Ely Diocesan Board of Finance (£64,000); Wisbech St Mary Sports and Community Centre (£30,000); Wisbech Grammar School (£29,000); Wisbech Swimming Club (£8,400); Methodist Homes for the Aged (£6,200); Alzheimer's Society (£1,200); Wisbech and Fenland Museum (£250); and Wisbech Music Society (£150).
FINANCES *Year* 2007–08 *Income* £913,457 *Grants* £218,357 *Assets* £1,707,851
TRUSTEES H A Godfrey; D W Ball; S G Layton.
HOW TO APPLY In writing to the correspondent. Trustees meet quarterly.
WHO TO APPLY TO David W Ball, 1–3 York Road, Wisbech, Cambridgeshire PE13 1EA
CC NO 280332   **ESTABLISHED** 1980

....
■ The Huggard Charitable Trust
WHERE FUNDING CAN BE GIVEN UK, with a preference for South Wales.
WHO CAN BENEFIT Older people, people who are disabled, people who are disadvantaged by poverty.
WHAT IS FUNDED Advancement of religion, the relief of poverty, disability and the welfare of older people.
RANGE OF GRANTS Up to £12,000.
SAMPLE GRANTS Bro Morgannwg NHS Trust (£12,000); Whitton Rosser Trust – Vale of Glamorgan (£8,000); Laparoscopy Laser Fund – UHW (£6,000); SWS Cymru (£5,000); Amelia Methodist Trust, Vale of Glamorgan (£4,500); and CURE Fund, Cardiff (£4,000).
FINANCES *Year* 2007–08 *Income* £52,370 *Grants* £82,450 *Assets* £1,803,107
TRUSTEES Mrs A Helme; S J Thomas.
OTHER INFORMATION In 2007–08, donations under £4,000 each totalled £43,000.
HOW TO APPLY The trustees are not inviting applications for funds.
WHO TO APPLY TO S J Thomas, Trustee, Blacklands Farm, Five Mile Lane, Bonvilston, Cardiff CF5 6TQ
CC NO 327501   **ESTABLISHED** 1987

....
■ The Geoffrey C Hughes Charitable Trust
WHERE FUNDING CAN BE GIVEN UK.
WHO CAN BENEFIT Actors and entertainment professionals and musicians.
WHAT IS FUNDED This trust is essentially interested in two areas: nature conservation/environment and performing arts, particularly ballet or opera with a bias towards modern work.
WHAT IS NOT FUNDED No grants to individuals.

FINANCES *Year* 2007–08 *Income* £14,887 *Grants* £16,370
TRUSTEES J R Young; P C M Solon; W A Bailey.
HOW TO APPLY In writing to the correspondent.
WHO TO APPLY TO P C M Solon, Trustee, c/o Mills & Reeve, Francis House, 112 Hills Road, Cambridge CB2 1PH *Tel* 01223 222290
CC NO 1010079   **ESTABLISHED** 1992

....
■ The Hull and East Riding Charitable Trust
WHERE FUNDING CAN BE GIVEN Hull and the East Riding of Yorkshire.
WHO CAN BENEFIT Registered charities only, with a possible preference for organisations working with children/young people, medical/disability and welfare.
WHAT IS FUNDED General charitable purposes.
WHAT IS NOT FUNDED Grants are not normally given to individuals. No grants to organisations or causes of a political nature, or for religious purposes, although requests for maintenance of significant religious buildings may be considered. If a donation has been made the trustees would not expect to receive a further request from the recipient in the immediate future.
TYPE OF GRANT The trust prefers to fund the capital costs of a project, but will consider funding revenue costs over a limited period of time.
RANGE OF GRANTS £100–£20,000.
SAMPLE GRANTS Previous beneficiaries have included: Action for Children in Conflict, Bridlington Community Transport Consortium, Deafblind UK, Hornsea Scout Group Council and Relate – Hull and East Yorkshire; and Hull Community Transport, Hull Boys Club and Hull Social Services, Hull Compact Limited and Community Focus, Macmillan Cancer Relief, Manna Project and York Minster Fund and Sobriety and King's School Brunton.
FINANCES *Year* 2008–09 *Income* £267,398 *Grants* £200,000
TRUSTEES M J Hollingbery; Mrs M R Barker; A M Horsley.
HOW TO APPLY In writing to the correspondent, including the aims of the project and benefits hoped for, the costs involved with budgets/ accounts as appropriate, the contribution sought from the trust and details of other funds raised. The trustees meet in May and November and requests for donations will only be considered at those meetings. Applications must be received by 30 April and 31 October. The trust states: 'It is unlikely that the trustees would support the total cost of a project and applicants should be able to demonstrate that funds have been raised or are in the process of being raised from other sources.'
WHO TO APPLY TO J R Barnes, Secretary and Administrator, Greenmeades, Kemp Road, Swanland, East Yorkshire HU14 3LY *Tel* 01482 634664 *email* john@barnes1939.karoo.co.uk
CC NO 516866   **ESTABLISHED** 1985

....
■ Hulme Trust Estates (Educational)
WHERE FUNDING CAN BE GIVEN Greater Manchester.
WHO CAN BENEFIT Educational establishments.
WHAT IS FUNDED This trust supports educational establishments in the Greater Manchester area; 12% of the income is given to William Hulmes'

Grammar School, with the residue going to local schools.

SAMPLE GRANTS Brasenose College (£91,000); Manchester University (£46,000); Schools Committee (£30,000); William Hulmes Grammar School, Bury Grammar School and Hulme Grammar School – Oldham (£6,000 each); Manchester High School for Girls (£5,000); and Manchester Grammar School (£1,000).

FINANCES *Year* 2008 *Income* £251,361 *Grants* £216,870 *Assets* £6,801,047

TRUSTEES D J Claxton, Chair; J R Leigh; T A Hoyle; I Thompson; Dr J S Knowland; Prof R. Cashmore; Mrs R Brierley; P Sidwell.

HOW TO APPLY In writing to the correspondent.

WHO TO APPLY TO J M Shelmerdine, Secretary, Butcher Barlow, 205 Moss Lane, Bramhall, Cheshire SK7 1BA *Tel* 0161 439 8228

CC NO 532297   **ESTABLISHED** 1964

■ Human Relief Foundation

WHERE FUNDING CAN BE GIVEN Iraq, Jordan, Ethiopia and other regions requiring urgent relief/aid.

WHO CAN BENEFIT Organisations benefiting at risk groups, carers, people who are disabled, people disadvantaged by poverty, refugees, victims of famine, man-made or natural disasters and war. Medical professionals, scientists, unemployed people and volunteers will be supported.

WHAT IS FUNDED General charitable purposes for the relief of poverty, sickness and to protect and preserve good health, and advance education of those in need from impoverished countries, in particular Somalia, Bosnia, Iraq, Bangladesh and Lebanon. Infrastructure, support and development and cultural activity are also funded.

WHAT IS NOT FUNDED No grants to individuals, or for medical expenses, tutors or examination fees.

SAMPLE GRANTS Previous beneficiaries have included: Red Crescent U A E; Qatar Charitable Society, Muslim Aid; Islamic Trust; Elrahm Trust; Saudi Arabia (Muslim World League).

FINANCES *Year* 2008 *Income* £970,483

TRUSTEES Dr Nabeel Al Rahmadhani, Chair; Dr Saad Mustafa; Dr Ali Al-Quirbi; Dr Haytham Al-Kaffaf; Wael Musabbah; Fared Sabre; Osama Shaban Abdalla; Dr Nooh Al-Kaddo.

HOW TO APPLY In writing to the correspondent.

WHO TO APPLY TO The Chair, PO Box 194, Bradford, West Yorkshire BD7 1BQ *Tel* 01274 392727 *Website* www.hrf.co.uk

CC NO 1043676   **ESTABLISHED** 1995

■ The Humanitarian Trust

WHERE FUNDING CAN BE GIVEN Worldwide, mainly Israel.

WHO CAN BENEFIT Organisations and individuals.

WHAT IS FUNDED 'The trustees consider grant applications from organisations and individuals in the UK and abroad, especially in the fields of education, health, social welfare, civil society, Jewish communal life and general charitable purposes.'

TYPE OF GRANT One-off grants.

RANGE OF GRANTS up to £10,000.

SAMPLE GRANTS The two largest grants went to one organisation, Friends of the Hebrew University of Jerusalem towards: the Humanitarian Trust Fellowship and the M Gunsbourg Memorial Scholarships (£10,000 each). Other beneficiaries included: New Israel Fund (£6,000); Institute for Jewish Policy Research (£5,000); University of Oxford (£4,500);

Jerusalem Foundation Bilingual School, Association for Civil Rights in Israel and The Samaritans (£2,000 each); King's College London, University of Dundee and University of Birmingham (£500 each).

FINANCES *Year* 2007–08 *Income* £121,010 *Grants* £79,850 *Assets* £4,136,657

TRUSTEES Jacques Gunsbourg; Pierre Halban; Anthony Lerman.

HOW TO APPLY In writing to the correspondent, including annual report and accounts, projected budgets and future plans. Applications are considered at trustees' meetings in March and October.

WHO TO APPLY TO Mrs M Myers, Secretary, 27 St James's Place, London SW1A 1NR *Tel* 020 7409 1376

CC NO 208575   **ESTABLISHED** 1946

■ The Humberside Charitable Health Trust

WHERE FUNDING CAN BE GIVEN Kingston upon Hull, East Yorkshire and North East Lincolnshire.

WHO CAN BENEFIT Organisations.

WHAT IS FUNDED Healthcare provision (including facilities and equipment), medical research and medical education.

SAMPLE GRANTS Daisy Appeal (£100,000); Hull University (£60,000); Hull and east Yorkshire Hospitals NHS Trust (£48,000); CASE (£39,000); Humber Mental Health Trust (£28,000); Barnardos and Macmillan Cancer Relief (£10,000 each); Frederick Holmes School (£8,800); KIDS (£6,000); and Dove House (£2,200).

FINANCES *Year* 2007–08 *Income* £247,410 *Grants* £64,947 *Assets* £4,933,813

TRUSTEES R D King; K Gorton; Mrs J Bielby; F M Burton; Prof. P W R Lee; A Milner; S L Smith; Mrs W Thomas.

HOW TO APPLY In writing to the correspondent. The trustees meet bi-monthly.

WHO TO APPLY TO Roger King, Secretary, Baker Tilly, Wilberforce Court, Alfred Gelder Street, Hull HU1 1YH

CC NO 1091814   **ESTABLISHED** 2002

■ The Michael and Shirley Hunt Charitable Trust

WHERE FUNDING CAN BE GIVEN UK and overseas.

WHO CAN BENEFIT Prisoners and/or their families, and people charged with criminal offences and held in custody. Also, animals which are unwanted, sick or ill-treated.

WHAT IS FUNDED Relief of need, hardship or distress of prisoners and/or their families; animal welfare.

WHAT IS NOT FUNDED No grants for fines, bail, legal costs, rent deposits and so on.

TYPE OF GRANT One-off.

RANGE OF GRANTS £50–£10,000.

SAMPLE GRANTS Martletts Hospice Hove (£6,000); CNCF and St Barnabus Hospice (£5,000 each); Prisoners Abroad (£3,000); Action for Prisoners Families (£2,500); Animal Care and Sheffield Animal Shelter (£2,000 each); and Hack Horse Sanctuary, Yorkshire Swan Rescue Hospital and British Divers Marine Life Rescue (£1,000 each).

FINANCES *Year* 2007–08 *Income* £337,676 *Grants* £54,199 *Assets* £5,140,623

TRUSTEES W J Baker; C J Hunt; S E Hunt; D S Jenkins; K D Mayberry.

HOW TO APPLY In writing to the correspondent.
WHO TO APPLY TO Mrs D S Jenkins, Trustee, Ansty House, Henfield Road, Small Dole, West Sussex BN5 9XH *Tel* 01903 817116 *Fax* 01903 879995
CC NO 1063418   **ESTABLISHED** 1997

....

■ The Albert Hunt Trust

WHERE FUNDING CAN BE GIVEN UK.
WHO CAN BENEFIT Registered charities.
WHAT IS FUNDED Projects that enhance the physical and mental welfare of individuals, or group of individuals.
WHAT IS NOT FUNDED No grants for research or overseas work.
RANGE OF GRANTS Usually up to £50,000.
SAMPLE GRANTS Spectrum Safe Centre (£104,000); Demelza House Children's Hospice and the Home Farm Trust (£50,000 each); the Meath Epilepsy Trust and White Lodge Centre (£30,000 each); Phyllis Tuckwell Hospice and the Tree House Trust (£25,000 each); Dorward House (£20,000); SENSE (£16,000); Age Concern – Seven Oaks and District (£15,000); Linden Lodge Charitable Trust (£12,000); Chilterns MS Centre, Cornwall Multiple Sclerosis Therapy Centre Ltd, Farleigh Hospice and the Nelson Trust (£10,000 each); and Bedfordshire and Northamptonshire Multiple Sclerosis Therapy Centre, British Limbless Ex-Servicemen's Association, ChildLine and Friends of the Elderly (£5,000 each).
FINANCES *Year* 2007–08 *Income* £1,550,191 *Grants* £1,650,478 *Assets* £44,533,090
TRUSTEES Coutts and Co; R J Collis; Mrs B McGuire.
HOW TO APPLY In writing to the correspondent. All appeals should be by letter containing the following: aims and objectives of the charity; nature of appeal; total target if for a specific project; contributions received against target; registered charity number; any other relevant factors. The correspondent has stated that no unsolicited correspondence will be acknowledged, unless an application receives favourable consideration. Trustees meet in March, July and November although appeals are considered on an ongoing basis.
WHO TO APPLY TO Steve Harvey, Senior Trust Manager, Coutts and Co., Trustee Department, 440 Strand, London WC2R 0QS *Tel* 020 7663 6825 *Fax* 020 7663 6794
CC NO 277318   **ESTABLISHED** 1979

....

■ The Hunter Foundation

WHERE FUNDING CAN BE GIVEN UK and overseas.
WHO CAN BENEFIT Charitable organisations.
WHAT IS FUNDED Educational initiatives aimed largely at children; relief of poverty; community development. Focus in the developed world is to invest in national educational programmes that challenge the system wide issues which prevent children from achieving their potential. In the developing world the focus is on investing in holistic developments that embed solutions within communities and countries, again with education being central.
RANGE OF GRANTS £10,000 £750,000.
SAMPLE GRANTS Previous beneficiaries include: Determined to Succeed, the Children's Charity, Make Poverty History, Band Aid for Village Reach Mozambique, Cash for Kids at Christmas Charitable Trust, Maggie Care Centre, Retail Trust, Variety Club, NCH Action for Children

Scotland, Cancer Research, Prince's Scottish Youth Business Trust and Children in Need.
FINANCES *Year* 2007–08 *Income* £11,443,749
TRUSTEES Sir Tom Hunter, Chair; Lady Marion Hunter; Jim McMahon; Robert Glennie; Vartan Gregorian.
OTHER INFORMATION Despite making a written request for the accounts of this foundation (including an sae) these were not provided. The following entry is based on the details filed with the Office of the Scottish Charity Regulator and information on the foundation's website.
HOW TO APPLY The foundation offers the following application guidance on its website: 'The Hunter Foundation proactively sources programmes for investment, or works with partners to develop new programmes where a gap or clear need is identified. As such it is very rare indeed for THF to fund unsolicited bids, however if you wish to apply please complete a maximum two-page summary outlining how your project fits with our aims and objectives and email it to info@thehunterfoundation.co.uk. This summary should include: summary of project; impact of project; any independent evaluation undertaken of your project/programme; if this is a local programme how it could be scaled to become a national programme; current sources of funding; and funding sought from the Hunter Foundation. Please note: we do not have a large staff and thus we will not consider meetings in advance of this information being provided. If your project appears to be of initial interest, we will then contact you to discuss this further.'
WHO TO APPLY TO Sir Tom Hunter, Trustee, Marathon House, Olympic Business Park, Drybridge Road, Dundonald, Ayrshire KA2 9AE *email* info@thehunterfoundation.co.uk *Website* www.thehunterfoundation.co.uk
SC NO SC027532   **ESTABLISHED** 1998

....

■ Miss Agnes H Hunter's Trust

WHERE FUNDING CAN BE GIVEN Scotland (apart from specified medical research).
WHO CAN BENEFIT Organisations benefiting people of all ages, including unemployed people, volunteers, people who are in care, fostered or adopted, parents and children, and one-parent families. Also supported are carers, people who are disabled, people disadvantaged by poverty, homeless people, socially isolated people and people who are ill. These areas were under review at the time of writing (November 2009).
WHAT IS FUNDED Charities assisting people who are blind; people with disabilities; training and education for disadvantaged people; those working towards an established cause, relief or cure for cancer, tuberculosis or rheumatism. These aims are also pursued in the fields of children and family support; youth development; older people; homelessness; mental illness; and the environment. These areas were under review at the time of writing (November 2009).
WHAT IS NOT FUNDED No grants to individuals, or to organisations under the control of the UK government.
TYPE OF GRANT Mainly one-off, buildings, capital, core costs, feasibility studies, projects, research and start-up costs will be considered.
RANGE OF GRANTS £500–£8,000; typical grant £1,000–£5,000.
SAMPLE GRANTS Previous beneficiaries included: Alzheimer's Research Trust Arthritis Care in Scotland; Cancer Bacup; Dementia Services Development Trust, Fairbridge in Scotland,

Macmillan Cancer Relief, RNIB and Shelter and Waverley Care.

FINANCES *Year* 2007–08 *Income* £670,575 *Grants* £389,077 *Assets* £17,990,752

TRUSTEES N D S Paterson; W F MacTaggart; A P Gray; Mrs A M Campbell.

OTHER INFORMATION In late 2009 the trust stated that it was reviewing its grant-making policies and would be making new guidelines available via a new website. No website was available at the time of writing (November 2009), so please check for up-to-date information before making an application, perhaps under previous interests or ways of operating.

HOW TO APPLY Please check the trust's record with the Office of the Scottish Charity Regulator for details of the trust's new website, which will include information on new grant-making policies and guidance.

WHO TO APPLY TO Mrs Jane Paterson, Grants Administrator, Robson McLean WS, 28 Abercromby Place, Edinburgh EH3 6QF *Tel* 0131 538 5496 (mornings only)

SC NO SC004843   **ESTABLISHED** 1954

■ The Huntingdon Foundation

WHERE FUNDING CAN BE GIVEN Mainly UK, some giving in the US.

WHO CAN BENEFIT Organisations benefiting Jewish people.

WHAT IS FUNDED Jewish organisations, particularly schools.

WHAT IS NOT FUNDED Individuals.

RANGE OF GRANTS About £1,000 to £60,000.

SAMPLE GRANTS Bais Medrash Gevoha L'Torah Ateres Yisrael, Torah Temima Primary School, Tikun, JNF, Noam Primary School, Edgware Jewish Primary School, American Friends of Hala and Bais Yaccov Primary School.

FINANCES *Year* 2007–08 *Income* £736,978 *Grants* £460,808 *Assets* £10,589,015

TRUSTEES Benjamin Perl, Chair; Dr Shoshana Perl; R Jeidel (USA); Jonathan Perl; Naomi Sorotzkin; Joseph Perl.

OTHER INFORMATION The accounts do not list the amounts given to individual recipient organisations.

HOW TO APPLY In writing to the correspondent. The trustees meet several times a year.

WHO TO APPLY TO Benjamin Perl, 8 Goodyers Gardens, London NW4 2HD *Tel* 020 8202 2282

CC NO 286504   **ESTABLISHED** 1984

■ Huntingdon Freemen's Charity

WHERE FUNDING CAN BE GIVEN Huntingdon.

WHO CAN BENEFIT Individuals and organisations.

WHAT IS FUNDED Relief in need (including sickness and healthcare provision); provision of pensions; educational needs; and recreational needs.

WHAT IS NOT FUNDED No applications from outside the boundaries of Huntingdon.

SAMPLE GRANTS Huntingdon Olympic Gymnastics Club (£100,000); Commemoration Hall Refurbishment (£25,000); Sport Huntingdon (£15,000); St Barnabus Furniture Project (£7,000); and towards Christmas meals for older people (£2,000).

FINANCES *Year* 2008–09 *Income* £504,940 *Grants* £364,846 *Assets* £10,565,934

TRUSTEES Edward G Bocking; Michael A Bloomfield; Brian S Bradshaw; James D Fell, Jonathon Hampstead; John R Hough; Laine Kadic.

HOW TO APPLY In writing to the correspondent.

WHO TO APPLY TO David Kerr, Clerk to the Trustees, 37 High Street, Huntingdon, Cambridgeshire PE29 3AQ *Tel* 01480 414909 *email* huntingdonfreemens@tiscali.co.uk

CC NO 1044573   **ESTABLISHED** 1993

■ John Huntingdon's Charity

WHERE FUNDING CAN BE GIVEN The parish of Sawston.

WHO CAN BENEFIT This charity makes grants for the relief of need, hardship and distress in the parish of Sawston.

WHAT IS FUNDED The charity provides housing and family support services. Grants are made to both organisations and individuals.

RANGE OF GRANTS Up to £10,000.

SAMPLE GRANTS Cogwheel Trust and Family Mediation (£10,000 each); Locality Youth Provision and Bellbird School (£5,000 each); Sawston Nursery (£4,800); Cambridge Joint Playschemes (£2,200); Centre 33 (£2,000); Camsight (£1,500); and Roundabout (£500).

FINANCES *Year* 2008 *Income* £379,582 *Grants* £65,396 *Assets* £6,782,774

TRUSTEES R C Cullum, Chair; Mrs E Clapp; T Butler; Dr A Gelson; Mrs K Gilmore; Mrs S Hatton; Mrs C Ingham; E Murray; Mrs S Reynolds.

HOW TO APPLY In writing to the correspondent.

WHO TO APPLY TO Revd Mary Irish, Clerk to the Trustees, John Huntingdon House, Tannery Road, Sawston, Cambridge CB22 3UW *Tel* 01223 830599 *email* office@johnhuntingdon.org.uk

CC NO 203795   **ESTABLISHED** 1972

■ Hurdale Charity Limited

WHERE FUNDING CAN BE GIVEN Worldwide.

WHO CAN BENEFIT Organisations benefiting Jewish people.

WHAT IS FUNDED Jewish organisations that promote the Orthodox Jewish way of life.

WHAT IS NOT FUNDED In writing to the trustees.

TYPE OF GRANT One-off and recurring.

RANGE OF GRANTS Up to £250,000.

SAMPLE GRANTS Previous beneficiaries include: UTA, Mesifta, Chevras Moaz Ladol, Vyoel Moshe Trust, Beis Ruchel, Kollel Rabinow, Mosdos Belz Bnei Brak, Pesach Project Trust, Kehal Chasidei Bobov, Hachzakos Torah V'chesed, Medical Aid Trust, Yeshiva Law of Trust and Zichron Yechezkal Trust.

FINANCES *Year* 2007–08 *Income* £2,232,193 *Grants* £1,615,825 *Assets* £17,937,868

TRUSTEES M Oestreicher, Chair; Mrs E Oestreicher; P Oestreicher; D Oestreicher; A Oestreicher; J Oestreicher; B Oestreicher.

HOW TO APPLY In writing to the correspondent.

WHO TO APPLY TO Abraham Oestreicher, Correspondent, New Burlington House, 1075 Finchley Road, London NW11 0PU

CC NO 276997   **ESTABLISHED** 1978

■ The Hutton Foundation

WHERE FUNDING CAN BE GIVEN Worldwide.

WHO CAN BENEFIT Charitable organisations.

WHAT IS FUNDED Christian causes.

SAMPLE GRANTS Catholic Trust for England and Wales and Hampshire (£100,000 each); NSPCC (£34,000); Catholic Bishops Conference (£25,000); Aid to the Church in Need (£25,000); and International Theologies Institute (£21,000).

FINANCES *Year* 2007 *Income* £2,808,280
Grants £365,938 *Assets* £2,449,985
TRUSTEES Graham Hutton; Amanda Hutton; Richard Hutton; James Hutton.
HOW TO APPLY In writing to the correspondent.
WHO TO APPLY TO Graham Hutton, Trustee, Spring Cottage, Cranes Road, Sherborne St John, Hampshire RG24 9HY
CC NO 1106521   ESTABLISHED 2004

■ The Huxham Charitable Trust

WHERE FUNDING CAN BE GIVEN Mainly Albania and Kosova.
WHO CAN BENEFIT Registered UK charities; Christian organisations, refugees.
WHAT IS FUNDED Development work.
FINANCES *Year* 2007–08 *Income* £50,128
Grants £37,732 *Assets* £151,184
TRUSTEES Revd Deryck Markham; Revd Percy; Mr Corney; Mrs Angela Huxham.
HOW TO APPLY The trust stated it is has been unable to support any new organisations in recent years.
WHO TO APPLY TO Adrian W Huxham, Thatcher Brake, 37 Whidborne Avenue, Torquay TQ1 2PG *Tel* 01803 380399
CC NO 1000179   ESTABLISHED 1990

■ The Nani Huyu Charitable Trust

WHERE FUNDING CAN BE GIVEN UK, particularly but not exclusively within 50 miles of Bristol.
WHO CAN BENEFIT Welfare organisations.
WHAT IS FUNDED 'To assist people who are underprivileged, disadvantaged or ill, young people in matters of health, accommodation and training and those requiring assistance or medical care at the end of their lives.'
FINANCES *Year* 2007–08 *Income* £153,429
Grants £137,000 *Assets* £2,920,864
TRUSTEES S Whitmore; Ben Whitmore; Charles Thatcher; Maureen Whitmore.
HOW TO APPLY In writing to the correspondent.
WHO TO APPLY TO The Trustees, Rusling House, Butcombe BS40 7XQ *Tel* 01275 474433 *email* maureensimonwhitmore@btinternet.com
CC NO 1082868   ESTABLISHED 2000

■ The P Y N and B Hyams Trust

WHERE FUNDING CAN BE GIVEN Worldwide.
WHO CAN BENEFIT Organisations, especially those benefiting Jewish people.
WHAT IS FUNDED Jewish organisations and general charitable purposes.
FINANCES *Year* 2007–08 *Income* £105,066
Grants £330,575 *Assets* £1,264,930
TRUSTEES Mrs M Hyams; D Levy; N Shah.
HOW TO APPLY In writing to the correspondent, but please note, the trust states that funds are fully committed and unsolicited applications are not welcomed.
WHO TO APPLY TO Mrs M Hyams, Trustee, Lubbock Fine, Russell Bedford House, City Forum, 250 City Road, London EC1V 2QQ *Tel* 020 7490 7766
CC NO 268129   ESTABLISHED 1974

■ The Hyde Charitable Trust – Youth Plus

WHERE FUNDING CAN BE GIVEN The areas in which the Hyde Group operates (currently London, Kent, Surrey, Sussex and Hampshire).
WHO CAN BENEFIT Schools and registered charities.
WHAT IS FUNDED Youth Plus is 'mainly interested in innovative projects seeking to address problems faced by children and young people in areas typified by social deprivation. These areas will often have high levels of unemployment and disenchantment within the community and offer very few prospects for young people.
WHAT IS NOT FUNDED No funding for: projects outside of the area where Hyde is working – no areas outside the South East of England; sporting, social or fund-raising events; medical research, hospices, residential homes for older people; any other projects which the trustees deem to fall outside its main criteria.
SAMPLE GRANTS Young Pride Awards (£26,000); Holiday Play Fund (£19,000); and Sports Fund (£12,000).
FINANCES *Year* 2007–08 *Income* £314,000
Grants £307,000 *Assets* £2,799,000
TRUSTEES Peter Matthew; Stephen Hill; Patrick Elliott; Geron Walker; Martin Wheatley; Derek Biggs.
OTHER INFORMATION 'Youth Plus is supported by Hyde Plus, Hyde's economic and community regeneration arm. Hyde Plus administers the grants and supports groups in the development of projects seeking Youth Plus funding.'
HOW TO APPLY The trust has recently informed us that it can no longer accept unsolicited applications.
WHO TO APPLY TO Janet Grant, Youth Plus, Hyde Charitable Trust, Hollingsworth House, 181 Lewisham High Street, London SE13 6AA *Tel* 020 8297 7575 *email* youthplus@hyde-housing.co.uk *Website* www.youthplus.co.uk
CC NO 289888   ESTABLISHED 1984

The Idlewild Trust

WHERE FUNDING CAN BE GIVEN UK.

WHO CAN BENEFIT Registered charities only.

WHAT IS FUNDED The encouragement of excellence in the performing and fine arts and the preservation for the benefit of the public of buildings and items of historical interest or national importance. Occasional support is given to bodies for educational bursaries in these fields and for conservation of the natural environment.

WHAT IS NOT FUNDED Grants to registered charities only. No grants are made to individuals. The trust will not give to: repetitive UK-wide appeals by large charities; appeals where all, or most, of the beneficiaries live outside the UK; local appeals unless the artistic significance of the project is of more than local importance; appeals whose sole or main purpose is to make grants from the funds collected; endowment or deficit funding.

TYPE OF GRANT Buildings, core costs, endowments, feasibility studies, one-off, projects, research and start-up costs.

RANGE OF GRANTS £500–£5,000. Average grant £2,000.

SAMPLE GRANTS National Children's Orchestra, Tate Gallery and the Council for Music in Hospitals (£3,000 each); National Youth Theatre of Great Britain (£2,500); London SYmphony Orchestra and Young Musicians Symphony Orchestra (£2,000 each) Edinburgh World Heritage (£1,800); Nottinghamshire Wildlife Trust and Spitalfields Festival (£1,500 each); and Tree for Cities (£1,000).

FINANCES *Year* 2008 *Income* £187,886 *Grants* £123,450 *Assets* £3,305,096

TRUSTEES Lady Judith Goodison, Chair; J A Ford; M Wilson; J Ouvry; Dr T Murdoch.

HOW TO APPLY On a form available from the correspondent, or as a download from the trust's website. This can be sent via post or e-mailed as a Microsoft Word file. Applications should include the following information: Applications should include the following information: budget breakdown (one page); most recent audited accounts; a list of other sponsors, including those applied to; other relevant information. Potential applicants are welcome to telephone the trust on Tuesdays or Wednesdays between 10am and 4pm to discuss their application and check eligibility. Trustees meet twice a year, usually in March and November. All eligible applications, which are put forward to the trustees, are acknowledged; other applications will not be acknowledged unless an sae is enclosed. Applications from organisations within 18 months of a previous grant will not be considered.

WHO TO APPLY TO Mrs Angela Hurst, Administrator, 1a Taylors Yard, 67 Alderbrook Street, London SW12 8AD *Tel* 020 8772 3155 *email* info@idlewildtrust.org.uk *Website* www.idlewildtrust.org.uk

CC NO 268124   **ESTABLISHED** 1974

The Iliffe Family Charitable Trust

WHERE FUNDING CAN BE GIVEN UK and Worldwide.

WHO CAN BENEFIT The majority of donations are made to charities already known to the trustees. Thereafter, preference is given to charities in which the trust has a special interest.

WHAT IS FUNDED Medical, activities for people who are disabled, heritage organisations, and education.

WHAT IS NOT FUNDED No grants to individuals and rarely to non-registered charities.

RANGE OF GRANTS Usually up to £40,000.

SAMPLE GRANTS Yattendon PCC (£40,000); Marine Society & Sea Cadets (£25,000); Royal Shakespeare Company (£20,000); Game Conservancy Trust (£15,000); Royal Horticultural Society and Belgrade Theatre (£10,000 each); Douai Library Appeal (£6,000); Tennis Foundation (£5,000); Yattendon and Frilsham Christian Stewardship (£3,000); North Atlantic Salmon Fund (£1,000).

FINANCES *Year* 2007–08 *Income* £195,250 *Grants* £254,141 *Assets* £1,248,785

TRUSTEES N G E Petter; G A Bremner; Lord Iliffe; Hon. Edward Iliffe.

HOW TO APPLY In writing to the correspondent. Only successful applications will be acknowledged. Grants are considered at ad hoc meetings of the trustees, held throughout the year.

WHO TO APPLY TO The Secretary to the Trustees, Barn Close, Yattendon, Berkshire RG18 0UX *Tel* 01635 203929

CC NO 273437   **ESTABLISHED** 1977

Impetus Trust

WHERE FUNDING CAN BE GIVEN Worldwide, in practice UK.

WHO CAN BENEFIT Charities which work with people who are disadvantaged, are at a critical stage in their strategic development, have an income of between £250,000 and £10,000,000 a year, have operated and produced accounts for the last three years and have a headquarters and a significant portion of its management in England.

WHAT IS FUNDED Work which will: tackle the greatest need by focusing on: unfashionable, under-resourced sectors where management capacity needs strengthening; and people-focused medium-sized UK-based charities with a minimum of three years operations; maximise impact by selecting a small number of charities which: make a demonstrable difference to the lives of a substantial number of disadvantaged people; are capable of achieving high and sustainable impact; keenly want and need the distinctive investment package that the trust offers; facilitate step change in these charities' performance with three to five year funding of agreed core costs, capacity building, hands-on management support through monthly meetings and active monitoring.

WHAT IS NOT FUNDED Grants are not made to: organisations focusing on animals, culture and heritage rather than people; organisations whose services are conditional upon the acceptance, profession or observance of a particular religious position; organisations substantially/exclusively working in the areas of research or advocacy (unless impact on people's lives is demonstrable); umbrella organisations.

TYPE OF GRANT Long-term funding for core costs.

RANGE OF GRANTS £100,000–£500,000 over three to five years.

SAMPLE GRANTS St Giles Trust and Naz Project London (£67,500 each); beat (£56,000); LEAP Confronting Conflict (£45,000); CamFed International (£40,000); Key Fund (£30,000); IntoUniversity (£25,000); and Acumen and Street League (£12,500 each).

FINANCES *Year* 2007–08 *Income* £1,851,667 *Grants* £356,250 *Assets* £1,762,460

TRUSTEES Stephen Dawson, Chair; Nat Sloane; Andy Hinton; Ian Meakins; Craig Dearden-Phillips; Louis Elson; Chris Underhill; Amelia Howard; Stephen Lambert.

HOW TO APPLY In writing to the correspondent including the following information: how long the charity has been running; what you see as the charity's unique positioning in your sector; the charity's annual income; the charity's main achievements over the past five years (e.g. income generation; social impact, etc.); the charity's aims and goals for the next three to five years; why the charity is applying for Impetus investment; how you heard about Impetus. Your application must also include: a copy of your current strategic/business plan; the charity's latest audited accounts; a summary of the charity's strengths, weaknesses, opportunities and threats. We will consider the information provided and respond as soon as possible. If you fit our criteria and we believe that your charity could become one of those we hope to work with, we will invite your Chief Executive and Chair for a meeting with us. It will take a minimum of four months from that meeting for an investment to be agreed. The decision-making process will include meetings with your trustees and management as well as site visits and analysis of your financial data. We carry out this due diligence to ensure long-term success in our partnership with you. If we decide not to form a partnership with you, we hope that you still find that you have benefited substantially from the process. We would like to stress that, throughout this process, the decision to proceed is as much for you as for us. Our approach is not right for everyone and you should only proceed if you are convinced that you need this full venture philanthropy package.

WHO TO APPLY TO Stephen Dawson, Trustee, 20 Flaxman Terrace, London WC1H 9PN *Tel* 020 3384 3940 *email* info@impetus.org.uk *Website* www.impetus.org.uk

CC NO 1094681   **ESTABLISHED** 2002

■ The Indigo Trust

WHERE FUNDING CAN BE GIVEN UK and overseas.

WHO CAN BENEFIT Organisations or programmes that have the potential to bring about systematic change both in prisons and within the criminal justice system more widely.

WHAT IS FUNDED Prisons and criminal justice. The trust wishes to fund programmes in the areas of: improved use of resources in the sector, particularly in resettlement and education; the development of innovation and best practice in the sector, particularly in terms of the use of the web and new technologies; research and dissemination to support the areas above.

WHAT IS NOT FUNDED Grants are not usually made to individuals.

SAMPLE GRANTS Anne Peaker Centre for Arts in Criminal Justice and We Are What We Do (£40,000 each); Ashden Awards (£20,000); and HM YOI Huntercombe (£9,400).

FINANCES *Year* 2007–08 *Income* £391,025 *Grants* £30,775 *Assets* £8,092,506

TRUSTEES Francesca Sainsbury; Dominic Flynn; Bernard Chi-Chung Fung.

OTHER INFORMATION Note: cancelled grants and changes in date of payment meant that a total of £79,000 was not actually paid during the year.

HOW TO APPLY See the guidance for applicants in the entry for the Sainsbury Family Charitable Trusts. A single application will be considered for support by all the trusts in the group. However, please see comments above regarding the selection of beneficiaries.

WHO TO APPLY TO Alan Bookbinder, Director, Allington House, 1st Floor, 150 Victoria Street, London SW1E 5AE *Tel* 020 7410 0330 *Fax* 020 7410 0332 *Website* www.sfct.org.uk

CC NO 1075920   **ESTABLISHED** 1999

■ The Ingram Trust

WHERE FUNDING CAN BE GIVEN UK and overseas, especially Surrey.

WHO CAN BENEFIT Established registered charities only.

WHAT IS FUNDED General charitable purposes. The trust prefers to support specific projects including special services and equipment. It will support major UK charities together with some local ones in the county of Surrey. Normally the policy is to support a limited number of charities (usually less than 20), but with a longer-term commitment to each.

WHAT IS NOT FUNDED No grants to non-registered charities or to individuals. No charities specialising in overseas aid are considered except those dedicated to encouraging self help or providing more permanent solutions. No animal charities except those concerned with wildlife conservation.

RANGE OF GRANTS Up to £75,000.

SAMPLE GRANTS The Centre of the Cell (£75,000); Shelter and ActionAid (£50,000 each); The Prince's Trust (£30,000); Almeida Theatre Company Limited (£25,000); Farm Africa (£20,000); CHASE (£17,000); Childline, Disability Challengers and the Woodland Trust (£10,000 each); and The Princess Alice Hospice Trust Ltd (£3,000).

FINANCES *Year* 2007–08 *Income* £366,080 *Grants* £745,500 *Assets* £13,665,502

TRUSTEES C J Ingram; Mrs J E Ingram; Ms C M Maurice.

HOW TO APPLY In writing to the correspondent, although the trust states that it receives far more worthy applications than it is able to support.

WHO TO APPLY TO Joan Major, Administrator, c/o 8th Floor, 101 Wigmore Street, London W1U 1QU *email* theingramtrust@sandaire.com

CC NO 1040194   **ESTABLISHED** 1994

■ The Inland Waterways Association

WHERE FUNDING CAN BE GIVEN UK and Ireland.

WHO CAN BENEFIT Organisations promoting the restoration of inland waterways (such as canal and river navigations).

WHAT IS FUNDED (1) Construction, especially works relating to the restoration of navigation such as locks, bridges, aqueducts, culverts, weirs, pumps, excavation, dredging, lining, and so on; (2) administration – support for a particular purpose, such as a project officer, a funding appeal or for promotional literature or events;

Think carefully about every application. Is it justified?

615

(3) professional services, such as funding of feasibility studies or detailed work on engineering, economic or environmental issues; (4) land purchase; (5) research on matters affecting waterway restoration, including original research, reviews of research undertaken by others and literature reviews; (6) education, such as providing information to local authorities or agencies to promote the nature and benefits of waterway restoration.

WHAT IS NOT FUNDED No grants to individuals. No retrospective grants for projects where expenditure has already been incurred or committed.

TYPE OF GRANT Capital, feasibility studies, one-off grants, project and research grants. Funding can be given over a number of years.

RANGE OF GRANTS Up to £15,000. In exceptional cases, larger grants can be made.

SAMPLE GRANTS Driffield Navigation Trust (£7,500); Lichfield & Hatherton Canals Restoration Trust and Caldon & Uttoxeter Canal Trust (£5,000 each); British Waterways (£2,500); Rolle Canal and North Devon Waterways Society, Wiltshire and Berkshire Canal Trust and Foxton Locks Partnership (£2,000 each); and River Gipping Trust (£1,000).

FINANCES *Year* 2008 *Income* £1,455,466 *Grants* £27,000 *Assets* £2,096,273

TRUSTEES The Council of the Association; Doug Beard; Ray Carter; Leslie Etheridge; John Fletcher; Anthony Harrison; Michael Palmer; John Pomfret; Paul Strudwick; Vaughan Welch; Ian West.

HOW TO APPLY In writing to the correspondent. Applications should comply with the 'Guidelines for Applicants', also available from the correspondent. Each applicant should provide a full description of its proposal, show that the organisation can maintain a satisfactory financial position and demonstrate that it is capable of undertaking the proposed project. Applications for up to £2,000 are assessed under a simplified procedure – each application should demonstrate that the grant would be used to initiate or sustain a restoration scheme or significantly benefit a specific small project. Applications for over £2,000 should demonstrate that the grant would be applied to one of the types of projects (1–6). Applicants should also demonstrate the extent to which the project satisfies one or more of the following conditions: the grant would unlock (lever) a grant several times larger from another body; the grant would not replace grants available from other sources; the project does not qualify for grants from major funding sources; the grant would enable a key project to be undertaken which would have a significant effect on the prospect of advancing the restoration and gaining funds from other sources for further restoration projects; the result of the project would have a major influence over the progress of a number of other restoration projects; The Inland Waterways Association Restoration Committee would have a major influence in the management of the project, including monitoring of expenditure.

WHO TO APPLY TO The Chairman of the IWA Restoration Committee, Island House, Moor Road, Chesham, Buckinghamshire, HP5 1WA *Tel* 01923 711114 *Fax* 01923 897000 *email* iwa@waterways.org.uk *Website* www.waterways.org.uk

CC NO 212342   **ESTABLISHED** 1946

■ The Inlight Trust

WHERE FUNDING CAN BE GIVEN UK.

WHO CAN BENEFIT Registered charities benefiting people from many different religions.

WHAT IS FUNDED Donations are made on a non-denominational basis to charities providing valuable contributions to spiritual development and charities concerned with spiritual healing and spiritual growth through religious retreats.

WHAT IS NOT FUNDED Grants are made to registered charities only. Applications from individuals, including students, are ineligible. No grants are made in response to general appeals from large national organisations. Grants are seldom available for church buildings.

TYPE OF GRANT Usually one-off for a specific project or part of a project. Bursary schemes eligible. Core funding and/or salaries are rarely considered.

RANGE OF GRANTS Up to £20,000.

SAMPLE GRANTS Samye Ling Rokpa Trust – (four grants totalling £60,000); White Eagle Lodge – (two grants totalling £31,000); Kagyu Samye Dzong (£20,000); Burrswood, Tunbridge Wells (10,000); White Eagle Lodge (£7,500); FWBO – Buddhafield, Meditation Centre and the Magga Bhavaka Trust (5,000 each); Christians in Care (£3,000); and Manchester Reform Synangogue (£1,500).

FINANCES *Year* 2007–08 *Income* £237,380 *Grants* £148,000 *Assets* £5,312,005

TRUSTEES Sir T Lucas; Mrs W Collett; S Neil; R Wolfe; D Hawkins; Mrs J Hayward.

HOW TO APPLY In writing to the correspondent including details of the need the intended project is designed to meet plus an outline budget and the most recent available annual accounts of the charity. Only applications from eligible bodies are acknowledged. Applications must be accompanied by a copy of your trust deed or of your entry in the Charity Commission register. They are considered four times a year. Only successful applicants are informed.

WHO TO APPLY TO The Trustees, PO Box 2, Liss, Hampshire GU33 6YP *Tel* 01730 894120

CC NO 236782   **ESTABLISHED** 1957

■ The Inman Charity

WHERE FUNDING CAN BE GIVEN UK.

WHO CAN BENEFIT 'The directors operate a grant giving policy, providing funds for such charitable object or institution as the directors think fit. In addition to supporting a wide range of charitable organisations, the charity makes a regular payment (normally £15,000 per annum) to the Victor Inman Bursary Fund at Uppingham School of which the settlor had been a lifelong supporter.'

WHAT IS FUNDED Previously, the main areas of interest have been older people, medical research, hospices and disability.

WHAT IS NOT FUNDED No grants to individuals.

RANGE OF GRANTS Most grants were of £5,000 or less.

SAMPLE GRANTS Victor Inman Bursary Fund at Uppingham School (£20,000); Vitalise and Help the Hospices (£8,000 each); the Roy Castle Lung Cancer Research, Bowel Disease Research Foundation and the Inspire Foundation (£5,000 each); the Anthony Nolan Trust, DeafBlind UK and Gurkha Welfare Trust (£4,000 each); The Manna Society and West Suffolk Voluntary Association for the Blind (£3,000 each); Tax Volunteers (£2,000); Mind (£1,500); and Tools for Self Reliance (£1,000).

FINANCES *Year* 2008 *Income* £203,627 *Grants* £242,000 *Assets* £4,430,504

TRUSTEES A L Walker; Miss B M A Strother; M R Matthews; Prof. J D Langdon.

HOW TO APPLY In writing to the correspondent accompanied by the charity's latest report and full accounts. Applications should contain the following: aims and objectives of the charity; nature of the appeal; total target if for a specific project; contributions received against target; registered charity number; any other relevant factors.

WHO TO APPLY TO The Trustees, Payne Hicks Beech, 10 New Square, Lincoln's Inn, London WC2A 3QG

CC NO 261366   **ESTABLISHED** 1970

■ The Inner London Magistrates Court Poor Box Charity and Feeder Charity

WHERE FUNDING CAN BE GIVEN Inner London.

WHO CAN BENEFIT Individuals and organisations.

WHAT IS FUNDED Relief of need, hardship or distress.

WHAT IS NOT FUNDED Not directly for the relief of rates, taxes or other public funds. No recurrent grants.

SAMPLE GRANTS Inner London Probation Services – Christmas Donations (£15,000) and Relief Payments (£3,300); Centrepoint – Frederick Street Project (£6,000); Apex Charity Trust, Broadway Day Centre, Clean Break, Crisis, Prisoners' Family and Friends and Women's Link (£5,000 each); Tower Hamlets Mission (£4,000); St Giles Trust, West London Churches Homeless Concern and Spitalfields Crypt Trust (£3,000 each); 999 Club and U Turn (£2,000 each); and Victim Support (£1,000).

FINANCES *Year* 2008–09 *Income* £133,762 *Grants* £75,305 *Assets* £2,568,390

TRUSTEES T Workman; R Mangnall; Ms B Morse; N Evans; Mrs P Sinclair; Q Purdy; K Griffiths.

OTHER INFORMATION Under a Charity Commission scheme of 1995, this new charity now administers the amalgamated assets of the poor box funds of 16 previous London magistrates' courts, as well as a number of other associated trusts. These old trusts covered the courts of Bow Street, Camberwell Green, Clerkenwell, Greenwich, Hampstead, Highbury Corner, Horseferry Road, Inner London, Marlborough Street, Marylebone, Old Street, South Western, Thames, Tower Bridge, West London and Woolwich.

HOW TO APPLY In writing to the correspondent.

WHO TO APPLY TO Paula Carter, Administrator, City of Westminster Courts, 7th Floor, 65 Romney Street, London SW1P 3RD *Tel* 020 7805 1132

CC NO 1046214   **ESTABLISHED** 1995

■ The Worshipful Company of Innholders General Charity Fund

WHERE FUNDING CAN BE GIVEN UK.

WHO CAN BENEFIT Registered charities and voluntary organisations.

WHAT IS FUNDED Children and young people, older people and education and training, particularly regarding the hotel industry.

WHAT IS NOT FUNDED No grants to individuals.

TYPE OF GRANT Mainly one-off, but also recurrent.

FINANCES *Year* 2007–08 *Income* £23,643 *Grants* £30,000

TRUSTEES The Worshipful Company of Innholders.

HOW TO APPLY In writing to the correspondent, including the reason for applying and current financial statements and so on.

WHO TO APPLY TO The Clerk, Innholders' Hall, 30 College Street, London EC4R 2RH *Tel* 020 7236 6703 *Fax* 020 7236 0059 *email* mail@innholders.co.uk

CC NO 270948   **ESTABLISHED** 1976

■ The Innocent Foundation

WHERE FUNDING CAN BE GIVEN India, Indonesia, Ecuador, Guatemala, Brazil, Colombia and Costa Rica.

WHO CAN BENEFIT Community based projects and non-government organisations.

WHAT IS FUNDED Helping to sustain long-term projects benefiting the community. Innovative projects that make best use of natural resources to create a better future.

WHAT IS NOT FUNDED No grants to individuals.

TYPE OF GRANT Most funds are allocated in three year partnerships.

SAMPLE GRANTS Find your Feet (£27,000); Farm Africa (£20,000); Action Aid (£16,000); Practical Action (£14,000); War on Want (£11,000); Microloan Foundation (£9,400); Plan International (£7,200); Kaloko Trust (£4,500); ATWT (£3,000); and WOMANKIND (£2,000).

FINANCES *Year* 2008 *Income* £69,386 *Grants* £171,236 *Assets* £1,176,232

TRUSTEES Adam Balon; Jon Wright; Richard Reed.

OTHER INFORMATION 'The foundation was established by innocent drinks and was registered with the Charity Commission in June 2004. Each year it gives at least 10% of its profits to charity.

HOW TO APPLY Information on how to apply can be found on the foundation's website.

WHO TO APPLY TO The Secretary, The Goldhawk Estate, Brackenbury Road, London W6 0BA *Website* www.innocentfoundation.org

CC NO 1104289   **ESTABLISHED** 2004

■ The International Bankers Charitable Trust (The Worshipful Compnay of Interntional Bankers)

WHERE FUNDING CAN BE GIVEN UK with preference for inner London.

WHO CAN BENEFIT Registered charities only.

WHAT IS FUNDED 'The company will seek to promote recruitment and development of employees in the financial services industry with particular emphasis on those younger people in the immediate area of the city who would not normally be able to aspire to a city job.'

WHAT IS NOT FUNDED The following areas are excluded from company grants: large projects towards which any contribution from the company would have limited impact; general appeals or circulars; replacement of statutory funds; salaries; counselling; course fees for professionals; medical research; fundraising events and sponsorship.

TYPE OF GRANT The company may support: (a) specific projects where a donation from the Company would cover either a significant proportion of the cost or an identified element of it; (b) Long-term funding of scholarships and/or bursaries.

SAMPLE GRANTS Brokerage Citylink Grant (£30,000); Chinese Earthquake Donation (£6,400); City of London School for Boys and City of London School for Girls (£5,000 each); Lord Mayor's

Appeal and Mansion House Scholarship Scheme (£2,500 each); and CHICKS and Reed's School Helping Hands Scheme (£1,000).

FINANCES *Year* 2007–08 *Income* £179,732 *Grants* £72,724 *Assets* £796,238

TRUSTEES The Worshipful Company of International Bankers.

OTHER INFORMATION 'As a representative of the major commercial activity in the city, banking and financial services, the company combines the traditions of the City Livery Companies with a modern outlook on the financial services sector. With more than 600 members, drawn from over 250 companies and institutions and with almost 50 nationalities represented, the company has a truly international character.'

HOW TO APPLY On a form with can be downloaded from the trust's website. Previous grant recipients must allow two years from the date the original grant was awarded to reapply.

WHO TO APPLY TO Tim Woods, Clerk, 3rd Floor, 12 Austin Friars, London EC2N 2HE *Tel* 020 7374 0214 *email* tim.woods@internationalbankers.co.uk *Website* www.internationalbankers.co.uk

CC NO 1087630   **ESTABLISHED** 2001

....

■ International Spinal Research Trust

WHERE FUNDING CAN BE GIVEN UK and overseas.

WHO CAN BENEFIT Academic institutions undertaking research into spinal cord injury.

WHAT IS FUNDED A wide range of research activities are funded, with the sole aim of ending the permanence of paralysis caused by spinal cord injury, such as clinical-based programmes and PhD studentships.

WHAT IS NOT FUNDED No commercial organisations or private individuals are funded.

FINANCES *Year* 2007–08 *Income* £1,676,358 *Grants* £759,889 *Assets* £578,679

TRUSTEES David Allan; Frances Blois; Martin Curtis; Diana Garnham; Prof. Charles Greenough; Philippa Herbert; John Hick; Dr Lee Illis; Jane Pelly; Dr Ruth McKernan; Prof. Frank Walsh.

HOW TO APPLY The trust advertises in publications such as the British Medical Journal, The Lancet, Nature and Science for people to apply to work on specific research topics. Applications should be made in the form of a letter of intent, of approximately two sides of A4 in length. All applications are reviewed by the Scientific Committee, assisted where appropriate by other scientists in the field. Some applicants will then be invited to make a full application. Unsolicited applications will not be considered.

WHO TO APPLY TO The Head of Research, Unit 8a Bramley Business Centre, Station Road, Bramley, Guildford, Surrey GU5 0AZ *Tel* 01483 898786 *email* research@spinal-research.org *Website* www.spinal-research.org

CC NO 281325   **ESTABLISHED** 1980

....

■ The Inverforth Charitable Trust

WHERE FUNDING CAN BE GIVEN UK.

WHO CAN BENEFIT UK-wide charities only.

WHAT IS FUNDED 'For the three year period commencing January 2008, the trustees have decided to support 12 selected charities with annual donations. The charities concerned have been notified. Charities supported in the past who have not been selected have also been notified, and for the next three years the funds of the Inverforth Charitable Trust will be fully

committed. Charities which have not been selected for donations should not apply to the Inverforth Charitable trust; any unsolicited applications made in 2008 and thereafter will be discarded and no acknowledgement will be sent.'

RANGE OF GRANTS All grants given ranged from £500 to £5,000.

SAMPLE GRANTS Help for Heroes (£5,000); Helriot Hospice Homecare and CHASE Hospice Care for Children (£2,000 each); the ART Fund, British Lung Foundation, Voluntary Services Overseas and National Youth Orchestra of Great Britain (£1,500 each); National Playbus Association, Kidscape, Contact the Elderly and Farms for City Children (£1,000 each); and Book Aid International, Bowel Cancer UK and the Gurkha Welfare Trust (£500 each).

FINANCES *Year* 2007 *Income* £195,262 *Grants* £154,500 *Assets* £3,871,078

TRUSTEES Elizabeth Lady Inverforth; Dr Andrew Weir; Mrs C Kane.

HOW TO APPLY No applications are being accepted for the three year period commencing January 2008.

WHO TO APPLY TO The Secretary, 58a Flood Street, London SW3 5TE *Tel* 0870 770 2657

CC NO 274132   **ESTABLISHED** 1977

....

■ Investream Charitable Trust

WHERE FUNDING CAN BE GIVEN In practice the UK and Israel.

WHO CAN BENEFIT Registered charities.

WHAT IS FUNDED Jewish, education, relief of poverty, medical and community.

SAMPLE GRANTS Beneficiaries included: Jewish Care, Cosmon Belz, Chana, Project Seed, Menorah High School for Girls, Train for Employment, Woodstock Sinclair Trust and Chai Cancer Care. Individual grant amounts were not disclosed in the accounts.

FINANCES *Year* 2007–08 *Income* £4,234,496 *Grants* £2,644,470 *Assets* £1,768,019

TRUSTEES M Morris; M Golker; G S Morris.

HOW TO APPLY In writing to the correspondent.

WHO TO APPLY TO The Trustees, 38 Wigmore Street, London W1U 2RU *Tel* 020 7486 2800

CC NO 1097052   **ESTABLISHED** 2003

....

■ The Ireland Fund of Great Britain

WHERE FUNDING CAN BE GIVEN Ireland and Great Britain.

WHO CAN BENEFIT Organisations benefiting people disadvantaged by poverty.

WHAT IS FUNDED Peace, reconciliation, cultural activity and the alleviation of poverty among Irish communities north and south of the border and in the UK.

WHAT IS NOT FUNDED Grants are generally not given for: general administration costs; travel or accommodation costs; payments for buildings or land; general appeals i.e. applications must be made for clearly specified purposes; other grant making trusts; payments for vehicles; medical expenses. No multi-annual awards.

SAMPLE GRANTS Louvain Trust (£175,000); GOAL International (£140,000); Wexford Festival Foundation (£84,000); Young Christian Workers (£25,000); Linacre (£20,000); Alfaner (£15,000); All Hallows College (£14,000); Lifestart (£10,000); and Belvedere College (£2,000).

FINANCES *Year* 2007 *Income* £1,141,073 *Grants* £489,130 *Assets* £643,134

....

618

TRUSTEES Peter Sutherland, Chair; Kingsley Aikins; Seamus McGarry; Basil Geoghegan; Peter Kiernan; John Rowan; Hon Kevin Pakenham; Ruth McCarthy.

HOW TO APPLY Application forms and full details of how to apply are available from the IFGB website.

WHO TO APPLY TO 2nd Floor, Wigglesworth House, 69 Southwark Bridge Road, London SE1 9HH *Tel* 0845 872 5401 *email* greatbritain@irlfunds.org *Website* www.irlfunds.org/great_britain

CC NO 327889   **ESTABLISHED** 1988

....

■ The Irish Youth Foundation (UK) Ltd (incorporating The Lawlor Foundation)

WHERE FUNDING CAN BE GIVEN UK.

WHO CAN BENEFIT Community-based organisations working directly with young Irish people.

WHAT IS FUNDED Projects benefiting young Irish people or enhancing their personal and social development, especially if they are disadvantaged or in need. A wide range of projects are supported which include: help for the homeless; employment and training schemes; help for women and children escaping violence; repatriation schemes; help for young offenders; cross community initiatives; help to combat discrimination; professional counselling and advocacy; educational, cultural and social activities; and drug rehabilitation.

WHAT IS NOT FUNDED The foundation generally does not support: projects for people over 25; general appeals; large/national charities; academic research; alleviating deficits already incurred; individuals; capital bids; or overseas travel.

TYPE OF GRANT Programme development grants; seeding grants; grants to upgrade premises and/or equipment and small grants.

RANGE OF GRANTS Grants for organisations in England, Scotland and Wales fall into the following three categories: Small grants for up to £2,500; Medium grants for over £2,500 and under £12,000; Large grants for one year or more ranging from £12,000–£25,000. The Irish Youth Foundation (UK) and the Irish Youth Foundation (Ireland) have established a joint fund to provide support for community and voluntary groups in Northern Ireland. Grants for organisations in Northern Ireland are up to £5,000.

SAMPLE GRANTS Brent Adolescent Centre – London (£15,000 in two grants for three years); Irish Community Care – Merseyside (£12,000); London Gypsy and Traveller Unit (£9,000); The National Deaf Children's Society – Northern Ireland (£4,500); Artillery Youth Centre – Belfast and Irish Arts Foundation – Leeds (£4,000 each); Drake Music Project – Newry (£3,500); Warwickshire Schools Gaelic Athletics Association (£2,000); Down Community Arts – Downpatrick (£3,000); Headliners – Derry (£2,500); and Our Lady Queen of Peace Youth Club – Belfast and Liverpool Irish Festival Society (£1,000 each).

FINANCES *Year* 2008 *Income* £274,264 *Grants* £252,850 *Assets* £2,255,542

TRUSTEES John O'Neill, Chair; John Dwyer; Fred Hucker; Virginia Lawlor; Mary Clancy; Mark Gilbert; David Murray; Jim O'Hara.

OTHER INFORMATION Irish Youth Foundation (UK) Ltd merged with the Lawlor Foundation (effective from 30 June 2005). The work of the Lawlor Foundation towards the advancement of education in Northern Ireland continues with support for Irish students and educational organisations.

HOW TO APPLY Applications are assessed on an annual basis and application forms are only available during the annual round either on the website or by request. The application period is short as forms are only available during December and January, with grant awards being made the following April. Applications are assessed on the following requirements: need; continuity; track record/evaluation; disadvantaged young people; innovativeness; funding sources; and budgetary control. Faxed or emailed applications are not considered. Unsolicited applications outside the annual round of grant applications will not be considered or acknowledged.

WHO TO APPLY TO Linda Tanner, The Irish Centre, Blacks Road, Hammersmith, London W6 9DT *Tel* 020 8748 9640 *email* info@iyf.org.uk *Website* www.iyf.org.uk

CC NO 328265   **ESTABLISHED** 1989

....

■ The Ironmongers' Foundation

WHERE FUNDING CAN BE GIVEN UK with some preference for inner London.

WHO CAN BENEFIT 'The Ironmongers' Company aims to help people who are disadvantaged to improve their ability to make the most of life. We wish to support projects that develop and nurture the motivation and skills necessary to take advantage of opportunities.'

WHAT IS FUNDED Projects benefiting: children and young people up to the age of 25; educational activities; specific projects with clear aims and objectives to be met within a planned timescale. The company's support should make a recognisable difference; therefore preference will be given to requests which cover a significant element of the cost and to those from smaller organisations.

WHAT IS NOT FUNDED No grants towards: large projects towards which any contribution from the Company would have limited impact; general appeals or circulars; replacement of statutory funds; general running costs (a reasonable proportion of overheads will be accepted as part of project costs); counselling; course fees for professionals; medical research; fundraising events and sponsorship; retrospective appeals and projects starting before the date of the relevant Committee meeting.

TYPE OF GRANT The trustees will consider making grants over more than one year to longer term projects, subject to a satisfactory evaluation of progress at the end of each year.

RANGE OF GRANTS Mostly £1,000–£10,000.

SAMPLE GRANTS King Edward's School (£75,000); Chelsea Pensioners' Appeal (£12,000); St Paul's Cathedral (£10,000); Westminster Bangladeshi Association (£7,000); Friends of Arnold Circus (£5,900); Shoots and Roots (£5,000); Crossness Engines Trust (£4,000); Guildhall School Trust (£3,200); Sea Cadets (£2,400); Museum of London (£2,000); and Chapel Street Nursery (£1,300).

FINANCES *Year* 2007–08 *Income* £167,167 *Grants* £283,646 *Assets* £2,091,334

TRUSTEES Worshipful Ironmongers' Company.

HOW TO APPLY The company's 'Grant Application Summary Sheet' must be completed and returned including a description of the project, of no more than three A4 pages. Summary sheets can be downloaded from the fund's website. The Appeals Committee meets twice a year in March and October. The deadlines for receipt of applications are 31 January and 31 August respectively. Please note that applications are not accepted by e-mail. Grants must be spent within twelve months from the date of the award.

WHO TO APPLY TO Helen Sant, Charities Administrator, Ironmongers' Hall, Barbican, London EC2Y 8AA *Tel* 020 7776 2311 *Fax* 020 7600 3519 *email* helen@ironhall.co.uk *Website* www.ironhall.co.uk

CC NO 238256   **ESTABLISHED** 1964

■ Irshad Trust

WHERE FUNDING CAN BE GIVEN UK and overseas.

WHO CAN BENEFIT Institutions involved in Islamic research and similar educational activities.

WHAT IS FUNDED Promotion of education in an Islamic environment.

SAMPLE GRANTS £719,355 to Islamic College for Advanced Studies; £72,950 in donations to similar organisations.

FINANCES *Year* 2008 *Income* £1,584,259 *Grants* £792,305 *Assets* £1,731,569

TRUSTEES Mohsen Mohammadi Araghi; Abolhossein Moezi; Mohammed Saeed Bahmanpour; Prof. Abolfazl Ezzati; Dr Mohammed Jafar Elmi; Dr Syed Naqi Hassan Kirmani.

HOW TO APPLY Beneficiaries are selected by the trustees who make personal contact with potential donors.

WHO TO APPLY TO The General Secretary, 133 High Road, Willesden, London NW10 2SW *Website* www.islamic-college.ac.uk

CC NO 1056468   **ESTABLISHED** 1996

■ The Charles Irving Charitable Trust

WHERE FUNDING CAN BE GIVEN Mainly Gloucestershire.

WHO CAN BENEFIT Charitable organisations.

WHAT IS FUNDED Disability, mental health, older people in the local community, local community projects, homelessness, victim support and the resettlement of offenders.

WHAT IS NOT FUNDED Research, expeditions, computers or equipment are not supported unless benefiting people who are disabled.

TYPE OF GRANT Capital, project and recurring.

RANGE OF GRANTS Mostly in the rage of £50–£1,000. Larger grants are sometimes made.

SAMPLE GRANTS The Willow Trust (£10,000).

FINANCES *Year* 2007–08 *Income* £79,373 *Grants* £74,287 *Assets* £1,661,149

TRUSTEES A P Hilder; Mrs J E Lane; D J Oldham; P W Shephard.

HOW TO APPLY In writing to the correspondent, giving details of the proposed project, its total cost and the amount (if any) already raised or promised from other sources. In 2007–08 the trusted noted 'a decline in the number of grants awarded because of a decline in the number of applications received'.

WHO TO APPLY TO Mrs J E Lane, Trustee and Secretary, PO Box 868, Cheltenham, Gloucestershire GL53 9WZ

CC NO 297712   **ESTABLISHED** 1987

■ Irwin Trust

WHERE FUNDING CAN BE GIVEN UK and overseas.

WHO CAN BENEFIT Charities concerned with Christianity, relief of sickness, promotion of health, advancement of education and benefit to the community.

WHAT IS FUNDED General charitable purposes.

SAMPLE GRANTS Goldhill Baptist Church (£10,000); The School of Pharmacy and LICC (£5,000 each); Barnabas Fund and Relief for Oppressed People Everywhere (£4,000 each); Release International (£3,000); Worldshare (£2,000); Global Connections (£1,000); and DCI Trust and Moorlands College (£500 each).

FINANCES *Year* 2007–08 *Income* £27,401 *Grants* £39,500 *Assets* £223,796

TRUSTEES T R Irwin; Mrs E J Irwin.

HOW TO APPLY In writing to the correspondent.

WHO TO APPLY TO T R Irwin, Trustee, Kleinwort Benson, PO Box 57005, 30 Gresham Street, London EC2P 2US *Tel* 020 3207 7338 *Fax* 0203 207 7665

CC NO 1061646   **ESTABLISHED** 1997

■ The ISA Charity

WHERE FUNDING CAN BE GIVEN UK.

WHO CAN BENEFIT Registered charities only.

WHAT IS FUNDED Causes related to the arts, health and education in the broadest sense. This can include both UK and overseas initiatives. The charity selects various organisations which help to find the individual beneficiaries.

FINANCES *Year* 2007–08 *Income* £194,855 *Grants* £45,825 *Assets* £1,478,914

TRUSTEES R Paice; Mrs M Paice; Miss A Paice.

HOW TO APPLY The charity's website included the following statement: 'The charity adopts a venture philanthropy approach and identifies its own projects. It does not accept funding requests from individuals, organisations or other charities. As a consequence it will not acknowledge any unsolicited funding requests.'

WHO TO APPLY TO R Paice, Trustee, Bourton House, Bourton On The Hill, Moreton-In-Marsh, Gloucestershire GL56 9AE *Tel* 01386 700121 *Website* www.isacharity.org

CC NO 326882   **ESTABLISHED** 1985

■ The Isaacs Charitable Trust

WHERE FUNDING CAN BE GIVEN UK and Israel.

WHO CAN BENEFIT Registered charities.

WHAT IS FUNDED Jewish charities and general charitable purposes, particularly medical causes. The trustees tend to support favoured projects.

TYPE OF GRANT Recurrent and one-off.

RANGE OF GRANTS £500–£6,000.

SAMPLE GRANTS Previous beneficiaries have included Jewish Care, the Child Resettlement Fund Emunah, the Marie Curie Foundation, Friends of Laniado UK, Norwood Children and Families Trust, Nightingale House, Cancer Research UK, British Heart Foundation, Furniture Trades Benevolent Association, North Western Reform Synagogue, Royal National Lifeboat Institution and Scope.

FINANCES *Year* 2007–08 *Income* £24,658

TRUSTEES J E Isaacs; N D Isaacs; M C Sefton-Green.

HOW TO APPLY This trust's income is fully committed to its current list of donees. New applications are not considered.

WHO TO APPLY TO Nathan David Isaacs, Trustee, Flat 26 Leamington House, 23 Stonegrave, Edgware HA8 7TN *Tel* 020 8958 7854
CC NO 264590   ESTABLISHED 1972

■ The J Isaacs Charitable Trust

WHERE FUNDING CAN BE GIVEN England and Wales.
WHO CAN BENEFIT Charitable organisations.
WHAT IS FUNDED General charitable purposes.
RANGE OF GRANTS Up to £100,000.
SAMPLE GRANTS Jewish Museum London and Trinity Hospice (£50,000 each); Lehman Brothers Foundation Europe (£40,000); Oxford Centre for Hebrew Jewish Studies and Greenhouse Schools Project (£25,000 each); Norwood (£14,000); One Family UK (£11,000); Hospital for Special Surgery (£7,600); London Jewish Forum and the Children Foundation (£5,000 each); Young People Foundation, Alone in London, Cancer Research UK and Cystic Fibrosis Foundation (£2,500 each); and Myeloma UK (£1,500).
FINANCES *Year* 2007–08 *Income* £7,969,083 *Grants* £456,907 *Assets* £14,473,935
TRUSTEES Jeremy Isaacs: Joanne Isaacs; Helen Eastwick.
HOW TO APPLY In writing to the correspondent.
WHO TO APPLY TO Peter Katz, c/o Touch Group plc, Saffron House, 6–10 Kirby Street, London EC1N 6TS *email* peter.katz@touchgroupplc.com
CC NO 1059865   ESTABLISHED 1996

■ The Island Health Trust

WHERE FUNDING CAN BE GIVEN Tower Hamlets and Newham.
WHO CAN BENEFIT Individuals, charitable organisations and non-profit-making organisations, providing that they are working/studying within primary care.
WHAT IS FUNDED Consideration is given to any project that will improve and benefit residents and visitors to Newham and Tower Hamlets which to not have to be supplied by statutory organisations and which fall within primary care.
WHAT IS NOT FUNDED Projects that would not directly benefit the inhabitants of Newham and Tower Hamlets which do not fall into 'primary care'.
TYPE OF GRANT Either a one-off grant, or grants over a one year, two and/or three year period.
SAMPLE GRANTS The Island Health Practice (£12,000); Crossroads Christian Counselling Service (£8,700); Richard House Children's Hospice (£6,000); WHCM (£5,000); Newham Music Trust (£5,200); Macmillan Cancer Support (£4,500); St Hilda's East Community Centre (£2,500); and Whizz-Kidz (£750).
FINANCES *Year* 2007–08 *Income* £280,358 *Grants* £48,016 *Assets* £2,759,786
TRUSTEES Ms Kate Priestley, Chair; Roger Squire; Doris Penn; Sunny Crouch; Stephen Molyneaux; Andrew Ridley; Alan Holman; Alex Macdonald.
OTHER INFORMATION The trust also became a company limited by guarantee in 2009.
HOW TO APPLY Requests should be made on an application form available from the correspondent. The trustees meet four times a year.
WHO TO APPLY TO Mrs Sonia Lapwood, Clerk, 43 Caledonian Wharf, London E14 3EN *Tel* 020 7538 1494 *email* info@islandhealthtrust.org *Website* www.islandhealthtrust.org
CC NO 1009795   ESTABLISHED 1992

■ The Isle of Anglesey Charitable Trust

WHERE FUNDING CAN BE GIVEN Isle of Anglesey.
WHO CAN BENEFIT Organisations in Anglesey.
WHAT IS FUNDED General.
WHAT IS NOT FUNDED Individuals.
TYPE OF GRANT One-off and recurring.
RANGE OF GRANTS 1,000–£257,000.
SAMPLE GRANTS Oriel Ynys Mon Gallery (£257,000); Moelfre Boat Club and Tabernacl Church Menai Bridge (£6,000 each); CM Chapel Aberffraw (£3,700); Rhosmeirch Community Centre (£3,300); Llanfaelog Village Hall (£2,200); Riding for the Disabled (£1,500); Glannau Ffraw Hall (£1,300); and Holyhead Gateway Club (£1,000).
FINANCES *Year* 2006–07 *Income* £438,898 *Grants* £376,931 *Assets* £15,856,057
TRUSTEES Anglesey County Council.
OTHER INFORMATION The sum of £1.8 million has also been earmarked towards 'regeneration schemes' from the trust's capital fund, although this has not yet been allocated in full. Two large grants were made to Menter Mon Monased (£300,000) and Ymddiriedolaeth Syr Kyffin Williams (£150,000) from this fund during the year.
HOW TO APPLY In writing to the correspondent, following advertisements in the local press in February. The trust considers applications once a year: 'we will take details of any prospective applicants during the year, but application forms are sent out annually in February'.
WHO TO APPLY TO David Elis-Williams, Treasurer, Isle of Anglesey County Council, County Offices, Llangefni, Anglesey LL77 7TW *Tel* 01248 752607 *Fax* 01248 752696 *email* gvwfi@anglesey.gov.uk
CC NO 1000818   ESTABLISHED 1990

■ Isle of Dogs Community Foundation

WHERE FUNDING CAN BE GIVEN The Isle of Dogs (i.e. the wards of Blackwall, Millwall, Limehouse, East India and Lansbury).
WHO CAN BENEFIT Community and voluntary organisations serving the area defined above or having direct impact on the area.
WHAT IS FUNDED General, including community development, education and training and employment.
WHAT IS NOT FUNDED IDCF will not fund: individuals; projects with primarily religious activities; projects with primarily political activities; projects or activities that are a statutory service; activities that are the responsibility of the local or health authorities; activities that have already taken place.
TYPE OF GRANT The foundation's current policy is to offer: 'Fast track' grants up to £800 – normally for one-off projects or capital needs; 'Standard' grants of between £800 and £10,000 – for general purposes, capital items, or running costs; and 'Large' grants over £10,000 per annum for multiple years, for larger, well established organisations.
RANGE OF GRANTS Mainly £100–£10,000.
FINANCES *Year* 2007–08 *Income* £1,072,920 *Grants* £995,755 *Assets* £4,770,136
TRUSTEES Sister Christine Frost; Mark Bensted; David Chesterton; Gabrielle Harrington; Mohammed Shahid Ali; Stella Bailey; Howard Dawber; Jeffrey Hennessey; Elizabeth Passey;

Shiria Khatun; Timothy Archer; Adrian
Greenwood; Ava Sam.

HOW TO APPLY The foundation's website has details
of the grant schemes currently being
administered. Please note: the foundation asks
that grant seekers discuss their potential
applications with the director, Tracey Betts,
before the forms are submitted.

WHO TO APPLY TO Tracy Betts, Director, Jack Dash
House, 2 Lawn House Close, Isle of Dogs,
London E14 9YQ *Tel* 020 7345 4444 *Fax* 020
7538 4671 *email* admin@idcf.org
Website www.idcf.org

CC NO 802942   **ESTABLISHED** 1990

....

■ The ITF Seafarers Trust

WHERE FUNDING CAN BE GIVEN UK and overseas.

WHO CAN BENEFIT Seafarers of all nations and their
dependants.

WHAT IS FUNDED Seafaring organisations; and the
social welfare of seafarers of all nations, their
families and dependants.

TYPE OF GRANT Buildings, capital, one-off, project,
training and education.

RANGE OF GRANTS Up to £1,500,000.

FINANCES *Year* 2007–08 *Income* £2,258,737
Grants £2,453,849 *Assets* £28,582,144

TRUSTEES T Broome; D Cockroft; R Crow; P Crumlin;
D Heindel; R Howard; L Lindgren; B Orrell;
G Stevenson.

HOW TO APPLY On a form available from the
correspondent. Applications must be supported
by an ITF affiliated seafarers' or dockers' trade
union and have a proven record of dealing with
seafarers' welfare.

WHO TO APPLY TO Tom Homer, Head of Dept., 49–60
Borough Road, London SE1 1DS *Tel* 020 7403
2733 *Fax* 020 7357 7871 *email* trust@itf.org.
uk *Website* www.itfglobal.org.uk

CC NO 281936   **ESTABLISHED** 1981

■ J A R Charitable Trust

WHERE FUNDING CAN BE GIVEN Worldwide.

WHO CAN BENEFIT Organisations benefiting older people, students, Roman Catholics, missionaries, and people disadvantaged by poverty.

WHAT IS FUNDED The advancement of the Roman Catholic faith; education for people under 30; and the provision of food, clothing and accommodation for people in need over 55.

WHAT IS NOT FUNDED The trust does not normally support a charity unless it is known to the trustees and it does not support individuals.

TYPE OF GRANT One-off and recurring.

RANGE OF GRANTS £1,000–£5,000.

SAMPLE GRANTS Westminster Cathedral (£5,000); The Passage (£4,000); Liverpool Archdiocesan Youth Pilgrimage, Venerable English College and St Joseph's Hospice (£3,000 each); Anchor House, Jesuit Volunteers and Aid to the Church in Need (£2,000 each); and Tongabezi Trust School, Marriage Care and Dans La Rue (£1,000 each).

FINANCES *Year* 2007–08 *Income* £75,418 *Grants* £64,000 *Assets* £2,241,658

TRUSTEES Philip R Noble; Revd William Young; Revd Paschal Ryan.

HOW TO APPLY In writing to the correspondent. Please note that the trust's funds are fully committed to regular beneficiaries and it states that there is very little, if any, for unsolicited appeals. In order to save administration costs replies are not sent to unsuccessful applicants.

WHO TO APPLY TO Philip R Noble, Trustee, c/o Vernor Miles and Noble, 5 Raymond Buildings, Gray's Inn, London WC1R 5DD *Tel* 020 7242 8688

CC NO 248418   **ESTABLISHED** 1966

■ The J J Charitable Trust

WHERE FUNDING CAN BE GIVEN Unrestricted.

WHO CAN BENEFIT Charities benefiting children with learning difficulties particularly dyslexia, ex-offenders and people at risk of offending.

WHAT IS FUNDED Literacy: to improve the effectiveness of literacy teaching in the primary and secondary education sectors for children with general or specific learning difficulties, including dyslexia, and to do the same through agencies working with ex-offenders or people at risk of offending. Also helping those who have become disaffected from education and who now find themselves homeless or in prison. Environment UK: to support environmental education, particularly supporting projects displaying practical ways of involving children and young adults. Support is rarely given to new educational resource packs in isolation from the actual process of learning and discovering. More interest is shown to programmes which help pupils and teachers develop a theme over a time, perhaps combining IT resources for data gathering and communication, with exchange visits and the sharing of information and ideas between schools. There is also an interest in the sustainable transport, energy efficiency and renewable energy in the wider society. Environment overseas: to support community-based agriculture projects which aim to help people to help themselves in an environmentally sustainable way. General: especially the education and social welfare of children who are disadvantaged.

RANGE OF GRANTS £600–£80,000.

SAMPLE GRANTS London Libraries Development Agency (£80,000), towards Opening the Doors, a partnership between libraries and homelessness charities to encourage people at risk to benefit from library and educational services; KPMG Foundation (£70,000), towards the voluntary sector monitoring of the government-funded roll out phase of Every Child a Reader; Shannon Trust (£60,000), towards the employment costs of a volunteer development manager; The Ashden Awards (£50,000), towards the 2008 awards; British Dyslexia Association (£30,000), towards the consolidation of the rescue plan; Hampshire Development Education Centre (£18,000), towards the second and third years of the pilot project for a model of sustainable development in nine Hampshire schools; and Dyslexia Association of Staffordshire (£10,000), a final grant towards core costs in 2008/09.

FINANCES *Year* 2007–08 *Income* £2,443,266 *Grants* £533,976 *Assets* £29,070,473

TRUSTEES John Julian Sainsbury; Mark Sainsbury; Miss Judith Portrait; Ms Lucy Guard.

OTHER INFORMATION The trust is one of the Sainsbury Family Charitable Trusts which share a common administration. An application to one is taken as an application to all.

HOW TO APPLY See the guidance for applicants in the entry for the Sainsbury Family Charitable Trusts. A single application will be considered for support by all the trusts in the group. However, for this as for many of the trusts, 'proposals are generally invited by the trustees or initiated at their request. Unsolicited applications are discouraged and are unlikely to be successful, even if they fall within an area in which the trustees are interested'.

WHO TO APPLY TO Alan Bookbinder, Director, Allington House, 1st Floor, 150 Victoria Street, London SW1E 5AE *Tel* 020 7410 0330 *Fax* 020 7410 0332 *Website* www.sfct.org.uk

CC NO 1015792   **ESTABLISHED** 1992

■ The J R S S T Charitable Trust

WHERE FUNDING CAN BE GIVEN UK.

WHO CAN BENEFIT Organisations or individuals undertaking research or action in fields which relate directly to the non-charitable work of the Joseph Rowntree Reform Trust Ltd. Academics and research workers may benefit.

WHAT IS FUNDED The trust works in close association with the Joseph Rowntree Reform Trust Ltd, which is a non-charitable trust of which all the trustees of The JRSST Charitable Trust are directors, in supporting the development of an increasingly democratic and socially just UK.

WHAT IS NOT FUNDED No student grants are funded.

TYPE OF GRANT Specific project finance in particular fields of trust interest.

SAMPLE GRANTS IDASA/Zimbabwe Institute (£104,000); British Documentary Film Foundation (£49,000); Democratic Audit (£29,000); Reuters Institute for the Study of Journalism (£24,000); Foreign Policy Centre and Scottish Votepods (£5,000 each); Centre for Women & Democracy (£4,800); Scottish Social Enterprise Coalition (£4,400); and Lesbian & Gay Foundation (£2,400).

Think carefully about every application. Is it justified?

623

FINANCES *Year* 2007 *Income* £167,028 *Grants* £67,218 *Assets* £3,457,981

TRUSTEES Christine J Day; Christopher J Greenfield; David T Shutt (Lord Shutt of Greetland); Paedar Cremin; Mandy Cormack; Danny G Alexander; Pam Giddy; Andrew Neal.

OTHER INFORMATION Examples of beneficiaries given are of grants that have been approved, rather than paid.

HOW TO APPLY The trustees meet quarterly. They do not invite applications.

WHO TO APPLY TO Tina Walker, The Garden House, Water End, York YO30 6WQ *Tel* 01904 625744 *Fax* 01904 651502 *email* info@jrrt.org.uk *Website* www.jrrt.org.uk

CC NO 247498   **ESTABLISHED** 1955

■ Elizabeth Jackson Charitable Trust

WHERE FUNDING CAN BE GIVEN Warwickshire and surrounding areas, particularly Barston (Solihull) and Great Rollright (Oxfordshire).

WHO CAN BENEFIT Organisations and individuals.

WHAT IS FUNDED General charitable purposes.

RANGE OF GRANTS Grants averaged between £500 and £2,000.

SAMPLE GRANTS Previous beneficiaries include: Jobs Close, Dogs for the Disabled, Hunt Servants Fund, Injured Jockeys Fund, Warwick Arts Society, Age Concern, Association for Spina Bifida and Hydrocephalus, British Red Cross, Marie Curie Cancer Care, Meningitis Trust of Stroud, Meningitis Research Foundation of Thornbury, Motor Neurone Disease Association, Royal Veterinary College Animal Care Trust, Scope, and Warwickshire and Northamptonshire Air Ambulance.

FINANCES *Year* 2007–08 *Income* £40,963 *Grants* £43,000 *Assets* £946,808

TRUSTEES Robin S Ogg; James P H Davy; Jeremy S Seel.

HOW TO APPLY In writing to the correspondent.

WHO TO APPLY TO Charles McKenzie, Olympus House, Olympus Avenue, Tachbrook Park, Warwick CV34 6RJ *Tel* 01926 886688

CC NO 1083421   **ESTABLISHED** 1999

■ Jacobs Charitable Trust

WHERE FUNDING CAN BE GIVEN Unrestricted.

WHO CAN BENEFIT Voluntary and community groups.

WHAT IS FUNDED Jewish charities and arts organisations are supported.

SAMPLE GRANTS Previous beneficiaries include: Central Synagogue Central Charities Fund, Jewish Care, London School of Economics, Haifa University, Norton Museum of Art, Tate Foundation, Community Security Trust, Israel Philharmonic Orchestra Foundation, Royal Opera House and Royal Academy of Arts.

FINANCES *Year* 2007–08 *Income* £3,556 *Grants* £264,108

TRUSTEES Lord Jacobs, Chair; Lady Jacobs.

HOW TO APPLY In writing to the correspondent.

WHO TO APPLY TO The Rt Hon the Lord Jacobs, Chair, 9 Nottingham Terrace, London NW1 4QB *Tel* 020 7486 6323

CC NO 264942   **ESTABLISHED** 1972

■ The Ruth and Lionel Jacobson Trust (Second Fund) No 2

WHERE FUNDING CAN BE GIVEN UK, with a preference for north east England.

WHO CAN BENEFIT Organisations benefiting people of all ages, medical professionals, parents and children, people with disabilities, people who are sick, people who have had strokes or who are terminally ill, homeless people, refugees and victims of famine.

WHAT IS FUNDED Organisations working in the fields of holiday accommodation and residential facilities, support for voluntary organisations, the Jewish religion, health, animal/bird sanctuaries and nature reserves, special needs education and speech therapy and various community facilities and services.

WHAT IS NOT FUNDED No grants for individuals. Only registered charities will be supported.

TYPE OF GRANT One-off, project and research. Funding is available for one year or less.

RANGE OF GRANTS £50–£10,000; typical grant £100–£500.

SAMPLE GRANTS United Jewish Israel Appeal (£25,000); Lupus UK (£5,000); and WIZO UK (£3,000).

FINANCES *Year* 2007–08 *Income* £50,914 *Grants* £37,950 *Assets* £1,164,565

TRUSTEES Anne Jacobson; Malcolm Jacobson.

HOW TO APPLY In writing to the correspondent. Please enclose an sae. Applications are considered every other month.

WHO TO APPLY TO The Trustees, 14 The Grainger Suite, Dobson House, The Regent Centre, Newcastle upon Tyne NE3 3PF

CC NO 326665   **ESTABLISHED** 1984

■ Jaffe Family Relief Fund

WHERE FUNDING CAN BE GIVEN UK.

WHO CAN BENEFIT Registered charities.

WHAT IS FUNDED People in need.

WHAT IS NOT FUNDED No grants to charities for anything which is not direct relief of poverty in UK.

SAMPLE GRANTS Previously grants have been made to: Bryson House, Catholic Children's Society, Campden Charities, Central Family Service Units, Providence Row, SSAFA Forces Help, West London Action for Children and West London Family Service Unit.

FINANCES *Year* 2007–08 *Income* £43,089 *Grants* £27,809 *Assets* £1,248,904

TRUSTEES Dr B P Levitt; Dr R R Jacobson; Mrs G A Haworth.

HOW TO APPLY In writing to the correspondent, but the trust states 'funds are unlikely to allow us to add to the list of beneficiaries'.

WHO TO APPLY TO Robin Jacobson, Trustee, 24 Manor Way, Beckenham, Kent BR3 3LJ *Tel* 020 0650 8125

CC NO 208560   **ESTABLISHED** 1970

■ John James Bristol Foundation

WHERE FUNDING CAN BE GIVEN Worldwide, in practice the city of Bristol, UK.

WHO CAN BENEFIT Usually only charitable bodies that can clearly show that they are benefiting Bristol residents.

WHAT IS FUNDED Educational, medical causes and the welfare of older people are the key focus areas.

WHAT IS NOT FUNDED No grants to individuals.

RANGE OF GRANTS £50–£250,000.

SAMPLE GRANTS Penny Brohn Cancer Care (£200,000); FareShare Community Food Network (£36,000); Red Maids' School and Redland High School (£30,000 each); Barton Hill Settlement (£28,000); Re: Work (£20,000); Marie Curie Cancer Care (£14,000); Hammer Out and Motability (£10,000 each); Southville Community Development Association (£4,000); Relate Avon and Merchants' Academy (£3,000); Gay Elms Primary School (£2,900); Bristol and District Tranquiliser Project (£2,200); and Pensioners Voice (£1,000).

FINANCES *Year* 2007–08 *Income* £1,956,694 *Grants* £1,123,204 *Assets* £43,703,919

TRUSTEES Joan Johnson; David Johnson; Elizabeth Chambers; John Evans; Andrew Jardine; Andrew Webley; John Haworth.

HOW TO APPLY The trustees meet quarterly in February, May, August and November to consider appeals received by the end of January, April, July and October. There is no application form and appeals should be submitted by post, to the chief executive on no more than two sides of A4. Applications **must be submitted by post**, email applications will not be considered.

If further information is required it will be requested and a visit to the applicant may be made by a representative of the foundation. Grants are normally only given to charitable bodies who can clearly show that they are benefiting Bristol residents, and working within the foundation's key focus areas of education, health and older people. The grant making policy is reviewed annually.

WHO TO APPLY TO Julia Norton, Chief Executive, 7 Clyde Road, Redland, Bristol BS6 6RG *Tel* 0117 923 9444 *Fax* 0117 923 9470 *email* info@johnjames.org.uk *Website* www.johnjames.org.uk

CC NO 288417   **ESTABLISHED** 1983

....

■ **The Susan and Stephen James Charitable Settlement** (also known as the Stephen James Charitable Trust)

WHERE FUNDING CAN BE GIVEN UK.

WHO CAN BENEFIT Registered charities; Jewish organisations.

WHAT IS FUNDED General charitable purposes.

RANGE OF GRANTS £60–£20,000.

SAMPLE GRANTS Hadassah Medical Relief Association UK (£20,000); Norwood Ravenswood (£17,000); Jewish Care (£13,000); Community Security Trust (£6,500); World Jewish Relief (£6,00); and Nightingale (£5,00); Tree House (£1,000); Deaf Child Worldwide (£500); Prostate Cancer Charity (£350); Brent Adolescent Centre (£250); Heart Cells Foundation (£200); and Chai Cancer Care (£60).

FINANCES *Year* 2008 *Income* £87,296 *Grants* £85,283 *Assets* £15,944

TRUSTEES S M James; Mrs S R James.

HOW TO APPLY In writing to the correspondent.

WHO TO APPLY TO S M James, Trustee, 4 Turner Drive, London NW11 6TX *Tel* 020 7486 5838

CC NO 801622   **ESTABLISHED** 1988

....

■ **The James Trust**

WHERE FUNDING CAN BE GIVEN UK and overseas.

WHO CAN BENEFIT Principally Christian organisations benefiting Christians, young adults, older people, people disadvantaged by poverty, disaster victims, and refugees.

WHAT IS FUNDED Churches, Christian organisations and individuals. Support is primarily to Christian causes, the advancement of the Christian religion and Anglican diocesan and Free Church umbrella bodies.

WHAT IS NOT FUNDED No grants to individuals not personally known to the trustees.

TYPE OF GRANT One-off, capital, projects, recurring costs, salaries and start-up costs. Funding is available for up to three years.

RANGE OF GRANTS Usually up to £10,000.

SAMPLE GRANTS Previously, Archbishops Council (£10,000); Above Bar Church (£7,700); Food For the Hungry (£5,000); UCCF (£3,600); Crusaders (£4,100); TearFund (£1,900); Christian Aid (£1,300); Bible Society (£800); Church Missionary Society (£500); and Cancer Research (£200).

FINANCES *Year* 2008–09 *Income* £49,775 *Grants* £82,318 *Assets* £191,632

TRUSTEES R J Todd; G Blue.

HOW TO APPLY In writing to the correspondent. Unsolicited applications are not acknowledged.

WHO TO APPLY TO R J Todd, Trustee, 27 Radway Road, Upper Shirley, Southampton, Hampshire SO15 7PL *Tel* 023 8078 8249

CC NO 800774   **ESTABLISHED** 1989

....

■ **The Jarman Charitable Trust**

WHERE FUNDING CAN BE GIVEN Birmingham and district.

WHO CAN BENEFIT Organisations benefiting children, young adults, older people, one-parent families, at-risk groups, people who are disabled and homeless people. Also supported are people with Alzheimer's disease, arthritis and rheumatism, asthma, autism, cancer, cystic fibrosis, diabetes, head and other injuries, heart disease, multiple sclerosis, muscular dystrophy, spina bifida and hydrocephalus and people who have had strokes.

WHAT IS FUNDED Welfare work, church building extension schemes and general social services in the Birmingham district. This includes convalescent homes, hospices, hospitals, nursing homes, rehabilitation centres, cancer research, community centres and village halls, day centres, holidays and outings, youth work and playschemes.

WHAT IS NOT FUNDED There is a preference for registered charities. No grants to individuals.

TYPE OF GRANT Annual donations and one-off payments.

RANGE OF GRANTS £30–£275.

SAMPLE GRANTS Previous beneficiaries include Coventry Day Centre for the Homeless, Friendship Project for Children, St Anne's Hostel for Men, St Paul's Church, Samaritans – Birmingham, Shakespeare Hospice and Victim Support – East Birmingham.

FINANCES *Year* 2007–08 *Income* £12,359 *Grants* £36,746 *Assets* £954,449

TRUSTEES Dr G M Jarman; Mrs S Chilton; Mrs B J Jarman; Mrs I Jarman.

HOW TO APPLY In writing to the correspondent by the first week in February or the first week in September. Trustees meet in spring and autumn. The trust does not want telephone calls and will not acknowledge applications even if an sae is enclosed. Accounts and/or budgets should be included.

WHO TO APPLY TO Mrs S M Chilton, Trustee, 52 Lee Crescent, Edgbaston, Birmingham, West Midlands B15 2BJ

CC NO 239198   **ESTABLISHED** 1964

....

■ The John Jarrold Trust

WHERE FUNDING CAN BE GIVEN UK and overseas, but mostly Norfolk.

WHO CAN BENEFIT Organisations benefiting academics, research workers and students.

WHAT IS FUNDED General charitable purposes of all kinds and in particular of education and research in all or any of the natural sciences. Social welfare, arts, education, environment/ conservation, medical research, churches. Funds currently very limited.

WHAT IS NOT FUNDED Educational purposes that should be supported by the state will not be helped by the trust. Local groups outside Norfolk are very unlikely to be supported unless there is a personal connection to the trust. Individual educational programmes and gap year projects are not supported.

TYPE OF GRANT One-off.

RANGE OF GRANTS Usually up to £4,000.

FINANCES *Year* 2007–08 *Income* £129,284 *Grants* £132,103 *Assets* £1,425,315

TRUSTEES A C Jarrold, Chair; R E Jarrold; P J Jarrold; Mrs D J Jarrold; Mrs J Jarrold; K W Jarrold; Mrs W A L Jarrold; L C Jarrold.

HOW TO APPLY Trustees meet in January and June each year and applications should be made in writing by the end of November and April respectively. Grants of up to £250 can be made between meetings.

WHO TO APPLY TO Caroline Jarrold, Secretary, Jarrold and Sons Ltd, Whitefriars, Norwich NR3 1SH *Tel* 01603 677360 *email* caroline.jarrold@ jarrold.com *Website* www.jarrold.com

CC NO 242029   **ESTABLISHED** 1965

■ Jay Education Trust

WHERE FUNDING CAN BE GIVEN Worldwide.

WHO CAN BENEFIT Jewish organisations.

WHAT IS FUNDED 'The objects of the charity are: the relief of poverty in the Jewish Community worldwide; the advancement of religious education according to the beliefs and values of the Jewish Faith worldwide and any charitable purpose at the discretion of the trustees for the benefit of the community.'

SAMPLE GRANTS Mifalei Tzedoko Vochesed (£200,000); United Talmudical Associates (£82,000); British Friends Of Igud Hakolelim B'Yerushalayim (£70,000); Lolev Charitable Trust and Toldos Aharon Israel (£50,000 each); Edupoor Ltd (£35,000); Chachmei Tzorfat Trust (£34,000); Heichel Aharon (£25,000); Friends of Sanz Institutions (£16,000); Yad Vochessed (£14,000); Zedokoh Bechol Eis (£2,700); Belz Yeshiva London (£2,500); Jewish Seminary For Girls (£2,000); and Comet Charities Ltd (£1,250).

FINANCES *Year* 2007–08 *Income* £2,039,550 *Grants* £1,880,016 *Assets* £2,954,484

TRUSTEES Rabbi A Schechter; G Gluck; S Z Stauber.

HOW TO APPLY In writing to the correspondent.

WHO TO APPLY TO Rabbi A Schechter, Trustee, 37 Filey Avenue, London N16 6JL

CC NO 1116458   **ESTABLISHED** 2006

■ JCA Charitable Foundation

WHERE FUNDING CAN BE GIVEN Israel.

WHO CAN BENEFIT Projects benefiting Jewish people, particularly children and those living in rural areas.

WHAT IS FUNDED The foundation helps the development of new settlements in Israel, the Kibbutzim and Moshavim, contributes to the resettlement of Jewish people in need, fosters viable agricultural and rural life to support them, and encourages other trusts and foundations to join it in partnership to fulfil its ideals. New projects in education and agricultural research are now the main interests of the JCA.

WHAT IS NOT FUNDED Grants are not awarded for individual students' tuition fees in Israel or elsewhere.

TYPE OF GRANT Loans, grants and feasibility studies. Funding may be given for one year or less.

SAMPLE GRANTS Tel Hai Academic College ($2 million); Migal Galilee Technology Centre ($163,000); Eshel Hanasi Youth Village ($94,000); the Mariculture Centre ($71,000); Kibbutz Shomria ($50,000); Kibbutz Contemporary Dance Centre ($40,000); Ben Gurion Heritage Institute ($30,000); Ein Shemer Greenhouse ($24,000); Keshet Eilon Music Centre ($19,000); Ran Munitz Model Farm ($14,000); Or National Missions ($9,000); and Dvir Butterfly Farm ($4,000).

FINANCES *Year* 2008 *Income* £2,603,000 *Grants* £1,999,000 *Assets* £31,046,000

TRUSTEES Sir Stephen Waley-Cohen, President; A Philippson; A Wormser; Y Admoni; R Brickner; J Capelluto; Prof Yona Chen; Efraim Halevy; J Jakobi; Mme Beatrice Jouan; Issac Lidor; Dr Shimon Ravid; Mark Sebba; Mrs Hana Smouha; Guy Wallier.

OTHER INFORMATION The amounts given in Sample Grants relate to US dollars.

HOW TO APPLY Full proposals should be sent to the office in Israel. For further information contact the correspondent.

WHO TO APPLY TO Timothy R Martin, Company Secretary, The Victoria Palace Theatre, Victoria Street, London SW1E 5EA *Tel* 020 7828 0600 *Fax* 020 7828 6882 *email* thejcafoundation@ aol.com *Website* www.ica-is.org.il

CC NO 207031   **ESTABLISHED** 1891

■ The Jeffrey Charitable Trust

WHERE FUNDING CAN BE GIVEN Scotland and elsewhere.

WHO CAN BENEFIT Organisations benefiting seafarers and fishermen, volunteers, and people in care, or who are fostered or adopted.

WHAT IS FUNDED Primarily this trust is concerned with medical research, and carer organisations. It also considers holiday and respite accommodation; health; conservation; independent and special schools; tertiary, higher and special needs education; community facilities and transport; and emergency care for refugees and their families.

WHAT IS NOT FUNDED Animal-related charities, medical electives and projects eligible for statutory support are not considered.

TYPE OF GRANT One-off and recurring grants are most commonly made for capital, buildings, core costs, endowment, project, research, running costs, salaries and start-up costs. Funding is available for up to three years.

RANGE OF GRANTS £250–£20,000; typical grant £1,000–£1,500.

SAMPLE GRANTS £20,000 to Glasgow Royal Infirmary for HTR project – diabetes centre; £5,000 to Dunstans Home for the War-blinded for general purposes; £2,500 each to Morrison's Academy Appeal for bursary provision and Donaldson School for the Deaf for a development project; £2,000 each to Erskine Hospital for general purposes, Princess Royal Trust for Carers for general purposes, and Edinburgh Breast Cancer

Foundation for general purposes; £1,359 to Salvation Army for general purposes; £1,000 each to Capability Scotland for general purposes and Crieff Parish Church for hall refurbishment.

FINANCES *Year* 2008–09 *Income* £73,898

TRUSTEES R B A Bolton; R S Waddell; Mrs M E Bolton; Dr A C MacCuish.

HOW TO APPLY In writing to the correspondent, although due to continuing support to long-term projects and anticipated repeat grants to other organisations, new requests for assistance are unlikely to be successful.

WHO TO APPLY TO Robert B A Bolton, 29 Comrie Street, Crieff, Perthshire PH7 4BD *Tel* 01764 652224 *Fax* 01764 653999

SC NO SC015990   **ESTABLISHED** 1972

....

■ Rees Jeffreys Road Fund

WHERE FUNDING CAN BE GIVEN UK.

WHO CAN BENEFIT Universities, research bodies, academic staff and students, as well as proposals for roadside rest projects.

WHAT IS FUNDED The trustees will consider funding lectureships and postgraduate bursaries over an academic year; research projects; roadside rests; and transport and alternative transport. Only subjects directly related with road and transportation will be considered.

WHAT IS NOT FUNDED Grants are not given to environmental projects not related to highways, individual works for cycle tracks or works of only local application. Also, Operational and administrative staff costs are rarely considered.

TYPE OF GRANT Some one-off capital, some bursaries and others for research and lectureships including salaries and, in some cases, running costs and endowments. Funding is available for up to five years.

RANGE OF GRANTS Up to £24,000.

SAMPLE GRANTS 'Education' (£92,000); 'Research and general' (£89,000); 'Physical Projects' (£28,000); and 'Other Education Projects' (£23,000).

FINANCES *Year* 2008 *Income* £127,990 *Grants* £210,555 *Assets* £5,196,882

TRUSTEES David Bayliss, Chair; M N T Cottell; T Depledge; A Frye; Prof S Glaister; D Hutchinson; M Shaw; Prof J Wootton.

HOW TO APPLY There is no set form of application for grants; brief details should be submitted initially to the trustees either by telephone or post. The trustees meet five times in the year, usually in January, April, July, September and November; Trustees 'favour proposals where the outcome will have a national impact rather than local application and where costs are shared with other funding partners'. In general, 'project expenditure (excluding overheads and core funding) is grant aided.'

WHO TO APPLY TO Brian Smith, Fund Secretary, Merriewood, Horsell Park, Woking, Surrey GU21 4LW *Tel* 01483 750758 *email* briansmith@reesjeffreys.co.uk *Website* www.reesjeffreys.org

CC NO 217771   **ESTABLISHED** 1950

....

■ The Jenour Foundation

WHERE FUNDING CAN BE GIVEN UK, with a special interest in Wales.

WHO CAN BENEFIT Registered charities only.

WHAT IS FUNDED General charitable purposes. Both UK charities and local charities in Wales are supported.

WHAT IS NOT FUNDED No support for individuals.

RANGE OF GRANTS Usually up to £8,000.

SAMPLE GRANTS Atlantic College and Cancer Research Wales (£8,000 each); Welsh National Opera and British Heart Foundation (£7,000 each); Red Cross International and Army Benevolent Fund (£6,000 each); Wales Council for the Blind and George Thomas Society (£4,000 each); Wales Millenium Centre and Bath Institute of Medical Engineering (£3,000 each); the Gurkha Welfare Trust and Multiple Sclerosis Society (£2,000 each); and Society for Welfare of Horses and Ponies (£1,000).

FINANCES *Year* 2007–08 *Income* £156,840 *Grants* £118,750 *Assets* £3,062,866

TRUSTEES Sir P J Phillips; G R Camfield; D M Jones.

HOW TO APPLY Applications should be in writing and reach the correspondent by February for the trustees' meeting in March.

WHO TO APPLY TO The Trustees, Deloitte and Touche, Blenhein House, Fitzalan Court, Newport Road, Cardiff CF24 0TS *Tel* 02920 264348

CC NO 256637   **ESTABLISHED** 1968

....

■ The Jephcott Charitable Trust

WHERE FUNDING CAN BE GIVEN UK, developing countries.

WHO CAN BENEFIT 'We like to make grants which will make a difference, preference will be given to charities or projects which are having difficulty getting started, or raising funds from other sources.' The financial situation of the organisation is taken into account (85% of income should be directly applied to advancing its charitable objectives).

WHAT IS FUNDED Funding priorities: population control – support for schemes, particularly educational ones, which help to control excessive growth in population; the natural environment – projects involved in conserving the natural environment (it does not support projects involving animal welfare or heritage sites or buildings); education – projects will be considered benefiting people of all ages and backgrounds; healthcare projects; population control; the natural environment; education; health.

WHAT IS NOT FUNDED The trust does not support: organisations whose administrative expenses form more than 15% of their annual income; individuals; animal welfare; heritage; projects which require long-term funding are not normally considered.

TYPE OF GRANT Pump-priming – helping to get an organisation up and running, or make a significant step forward. Project costs – capital rather than running costs are preferred.

RANGE OF GRANTS Grants are made in the range of £2,000–£10,000, and in exceptional cases only, up to £20,000. The trust prefers to make one-off donations to get many projects started, rather than support fewer projects charities over a long period.

SAMPLE GRANTS Riding School for the Disabled of Cornwall (£25,000); African Child Education Programme and Depaul Foundation (£15,000 each); Hailer Foundation (£12,500); Ugandan Rural School Initiative (£11,000); China Candlelight Education Fund (£10,000); Green Light Trust (£8,000); Youth Education Service and Berkeley Reforestation Trust (£6,600 each); Action Water (£5,100); and African Village Support (£4,000); and Lowe Syndrome Trust (£1,500).

FINANCES *Year* 2007–08 *Income* £289,549 *Grants* £200,379 *Assets* £4,806,894

Think carefully about every application. Is it justified?

627

TRUSTEES Lady Jephcott, Chair; Judge A North; Mrs D Adler; K Morgan; M L Jephcott; Mrs C Thomas.

HOW TO APPLY Full and detailed guidelines and application forms can be downloaded from the trust's website. Trustees meet twice a year (in April and October) and must have detailed financial information about each project before they will make a decision. Only applications from eligible bodies are acknowledged, when further information about the project may be requested. Monitoring of grant expenditure is usually required. It is not usual to make more than one grant to any organisation.

WHO TO APPLY TO Mrs Meg Harris, Secretary, Cotley, Streatham Rise, Exeter, Devon EX4 4PE *Tel* 01392 841160 *Website* www.jephcottcharitabletrust.org.uk

CC NO 240915   **ESTABLISHED** 1965

....

■ The Jerusalem Trust

WHERE FUNDING CAN BE GIVEN Unrestricted.

WHO CAN BENEFIT Organisations working for the promotion of Christianity in the fields detailed below.

WHAT IS FUNDED Christian evangelism and relief work overseas, particularly for indigenous training and support and production of appropriate literature and resource materials for Christians in Anglophone Africa, central and eastern Europe, and the former Soviet Union; Christian media, particularly supporting training and networking projects for Christians working professionally in all areas of the media and for those considering media careers; Christian education, particularly the development of Christian school curriculum resource materials for RE and other subjects, support and training of Christian teachers of all subjects and lay training; Christian art, focused mainly on a small number of pro-active commissions of works of art for places of worship; Christian evangelism and social responsibility work at home, particularly Christian projects which develop new ways of working with children and young people and projects which promote Christian marriage and family life. Also church planting and evangelistic projects and those which undertake Christian work with prisoners, ex-prisoners and their families.

WHAT IS NOT FUNDED Trustees do not normally make grants towards building or repair work for churches. Grants are not normally made to individuals.

SAMPLE GRANTS Jerusalem Productions Ltd (£250,000), for disbursement by Jerusalem Productions during the calendar year of 2008; Transforming Lives (£220,000), towards core costs; St John's College – Nottingham (£135,000), towards costs of the Story of the Church of England; Stapleford Centre (£110,000), towards core costs; Youth for Christ in Britain (£80,000), towards the cost of a staff development programme; Global Day of Prayer London (£50,000), towards the Global Day of Prayer 2008; Carlile College (£35,000), towards the salary costs of the head of training, specifically to work with smaller organisations in Nairobi's informal settlements; Matheteuo (£22,500), towards the costs of a programme of Theological Education by Extension in the Anglican Province of Uganda; and Alliance of Religions and Conservation (£10,000), towards the Green Gospels.

FINANCES *Year* 2008 *Income* £3,221,000 *Grants* £2,308,000 *Assets* £67,102,000

TRUSTEES Rt Hon. Sir Timothy Sainsbury; Lady Susan Sainsbury; Dr V E Hartley Booth; Phillida Goad; Dr Peter Frankopan.

OTHER INFORMATION The trust is one of the Sainsbury Family Charitable Trusts which share a common administration. An application to one is taken as an application to all.

HOW TO APPLY See the guidance for applicants in the entry for the Sainsbury Family Charitable Trusts. A single application will be considered for support by all the trusts in the group. However, for this as for many of the trusts, 'proposals are generally invited by the trustees or initiated at their request'.

WHO TO APPLY TO Alan Bookbinder, Director, Allington House, 1st Floor, 150 Victoria Street, London SW1E 5AE *Tel* 020 7410 0330 *Fax* 020 7410 0332 *email* jerusalemtrust@sfct.org.uk *Website* www.sfct.org.uk

CC NO 285696   **ESTABLISHED** 1982

....

■ Jerwood Charitable Foundation

WHERE FUNDING CAN BE GIVEN UK.

WHO CAN BENEFIT Organisations benefiting young adults, actors, artists, musicians, research workers, writers, dancers and choreographers, directors, producers and film makers.

WHAT IS FUNDED Principally education in its broadest sense and the visual and performing arts, but the foundation also funds design, science, engineering and other areas of human endeavour.

WHAT IS NOT FUNDED The Jerwood charitable Foundation will not consider applications on behalf of: individuals; building or capital costs (including purchase of equipment); projects in the fields of religion or sport; animal rights or welfare; cover study fees or course fees; general fundraising appeals which are likely to have wide public appeal; appeals to establish endowment funds for other charities; appeals for matching funding for National Lottery applications; grants for the running and core costs of voluntary bodies; projects which are of mainly local appeal or identified with a locality; medical or mental health projects; social welfare, particularly where it may be considered a government or local authority responsibility; retrospective awards; projects outside Great Britain; schools which are trying to attain Special Schools Status; touring or production costs; environmental or conservation projects. The foundation may, where there are very exceptional circumstances, decide to waive an exclusion.

TYPE OF GRANT Principally one-off, usually incorporating challenge funding, but will sometimes be prepared to maintain support if consistency will secure better results.

RANGE OF GRANTS Lower range will be around £5,000–£10,000, and the more substantial grants usually ranging between £10,000–£50,000.

SAMPLE GRANTS Jerwood Moving Images (£125,000); Jerwood Creative Studio at Sadlers Wells (£120,000); Artangel (£100,000); Glyndebourne Young Singers (£70,000); Music Theatre Wales (£37,000); Royal Society of Literature (£28,000); Manchester International Festival (£20,000); Aldeburgh Poetry Festival (£13,000); Sequences and Repetitions (£5,000); and Liederkreis (£1,000).

FINANCES *Year* 2007 *Income* £1,131,751 *Grants* £1,563,625 *Assets* £28,223,715

Does the trust you have chosen match your needs? Haphazard applications waste postage and time

TRUSTEES Tim Eyles, Chair; Edward Paul; Julia Wharton; Anthony Palmer; Sarah Vine; Thomas Grieve; Rupert Tyler.

HOW TO APPLY Applications should be by letter to the director, outlining the aims and objectives of the organisation and the aims and objectives of the specific project or scheme for which assistance is sought. The following supporting documents should be sent with the application: a detailed budget for the project, identifying administrative, management and central costs; details of funding already in place for the project, including any other trusts or sources which are being or have been approached for funds. If funding is not in place, details of how the applicant plans to secure the remaining funding; details of the management and staffing structure, including trustees; the most recent annual report and audited accounts of the organisation, together with current management accounts if relevant to the project.
The foundation may wish to enter into discussions and/or correspondence with the applicant which may result in modification and/or development of the project or scheme. Any such discussion or correspondence will not commit the foundation to funding that application. Successful applicants will be invited to report to the foundation at the completion of their project and to provide photographs of the work or project supported. As the foundation receives a large number of applications, it is not possible to have preliminary meetings to discuss possible support before a written application is made.

WHO TO APPLY TO Shonagh Manson, Director, 171 Union Street, Bankside, London SE1 OLN *Tel* 020 7261 0279 *email* shonagh.manson@ jerwood.org *Website* www. jerwoodcharitablefoundation.org
CC NO 1074036   ESTABLISHED 1999

....

■ Jesus Hospital Charity

WHERE FUNDING CAN BE GIVEN Barnet.

WHO CAN BENEFIT Individuals; and local organisations benefiting people of all ages, academics, research workers, scientists, students, unemployed people, volunteers, families, at risk groups, carers, people who are disabled, people with a medical condition or disease, people who are disadvantaged by poverty or who are socially isolated, and victims of abuse, crime and domestic violence.

WHAT IS FUNDED This trust will consider funding: almshouses; support to voluntary and community organisations; support to volunteers; respite care and care for carers; support and self-help groups; ambulances and mobile units; special needs education; training for work; costs of study; academic subjects, sciences and research; and community services.

WHAT IS NOT FUNDED No grants for relief of rates, taxes or other public funds.

TYPE OF GRANT Capital and one-off. Funding is available for one year or less. Each case is considered on its merits.

RANGE OF GRANTS Up to £700.

FINANCES *Year* 2008 *Income* £571,084 *Grants* £12,200 *Assets* £7,424,703

TRUSTEES Michael Holford; Neil Kobish; Brenda Sandford; P J Mellows; William Carrington; Ian Lawless; Revd Canon Hall Speers; Catherine Cavanagh; Stephen Payne; Dr I Johnston; M Bye.

HOW TO APPLY In writing to the correspondent. Trustees meet six times a year to consider grants.

WHO TO APPLY TO Simon Smith, Clerk to the Visitors (Trustees), Ravenscroft Lodge, 37 Union Street, Barnet, Hertfordshire EN5 4HY *Tel* 020 8440 4374
CC NO 1075889   ESTABLISHED 1679

....

■ Jewish Child's Day

WHERE FUNDING CAN BE GIVEN Worldwide. In practice, mainly Israel and UK.

WHO CAN BENEFIT Organisations caring for Jewish children.

WHAT IS FUNDED Charitable purposes of direct benefit to Jewish children who are disadvantaged, suffering or in need of special care.

WHAT IS NOT FUNDED Individuals are not supported. Grants are not given towards general services, building or maintenance of property or staff salaries.

TYPE OF GRANT 'One-off' and recurring.

RANGE OF GRANTS Up to £150,000.

SAMPLE GRANTS Children of Chernobyl (£151,000); Micha Haifa (£101,000); Manchester Jewish Federation (£37,500); Eilya (£14,000); Alyn Hospital (£9,000); Step by Step (£8,400); Gan Hayeled (£7,000); Shema and Roots for Generations (£5,000 each); Kfar Hayarok Youth Village (£4,500); Cystic Fibrosis Foundation of Israel (£3,500); Ezra Youth Movement (£3,000); Shilo Israel Children's Fund and Schneider (£500 each).

FINANCES *Year* 2007–08 *Income* £1,025,307 *Grants* £717,369 *Assets* £649,455

TRUSTEES Joy Moss, Chair; June Jacobs; Stephen Moss; Virginia Campus; David Clayton; Francine Epstein; Rhonda Marcus; Susie Olins; Suellen Winer; Amanda Ingram; Gaby Lazarus.

HOW TO APPLY If your organisation meets JCD's criteria, you could apply for a grant ranging from £500 to £5,000 towards the cost of small or medium size items of equipment or a project that will directly benefit children. The committee considers applications in February, June and September each year. Completed application forms should be sent together with a set of audited accounts by 31 December, 30 April and 31 July accordingly. To apply for a grant from JCD please contact Jackie Persoff on 020 8446 8804 or jackie.persoff@jcd.uk.com.

WHO TO APPLY TO Daniel Burger, Executive Director, 5th Floor, 707 High Road, North Finchley, London N12 0BT *Tel* 020 8446 8804 *Fax* 020 8446 7370 *email* info@jcd.uk.com *Website* www.jcd.uk.com
CC NO 209266   ESTABLISHED 1947

....

■ The Jewish Youth Fund

WHERE FUNDING CAN BE GIVEN UK.

WHO CAN BENEFIT Jewish youth clubs, centres, movements and groups.

WHAT IS FUNDED Jewish youth work projects, equipment and premises.

WHAT IS NOT FUNDED Grants are not made in response to general appeals. Formal education is not supported.

TYPE OF GRANT Grants are made for a whole variety of Jewish youth work projects. Loans are sometimes offered towards the cost of building.

RANGE OF GRANTS Up to £50,000.

FINANCES *Year* 2007–08 *Income* £92,530 *Grants* £162,450 *Assets* £3,756,879

TRUSTEES Jonathan Gestetner; Richard McGratty; Lady Morris of Kenwood; Miss Wendy

F Pollecoff; Adam D Rose; Stephen B Spitz; Phillipa Strauss.

HOW TO APPLY On an application form available from the correspondent, enclosing a copy of the latest accounts and an annual report.

WHO TO APPLY TO Peter Shaw, Secretary, 24 Chiswell Street, London EC1Y 4YX *Tel* 020 7443 5169 *email* info@jyf.org.uk

CC NO 251902   **ESTABLISHED** 1937

■ The JMK Charitable Trust

WHERE FUNDING CAN BE GIVEN Worldwide.

WHO CAN BENEFIT Registered charities only, benefiting the appreciation of art and music, also assisting religious organisations to help relations with other faiths.

WHAT IS FUNDED There is a preference for charities concerned with Art and Music.

RANGE OF GRANTS £500–£10,000.

SAMPLE GRANTS The two largest grants went to: Royal College of Music (£30,000); and English Touring Opera (£9,000). Other beneficiaries included: National Theatre (£7,500); Les Azuriales Opera House (£4,500); Royal Opera House (£4,200); Magen David Adom UK (£3,000); Get Kids Going, Philharmonia Trust, Starlight and West London Synagogue (£1,000 each); Classic Opera Company and RCR Cancer Appeal (£500 each).

FINANCES *Year* 2007–08 *Income* £83,262 *Grants* £75,199 *Assets* £1,994,696

TRUSTEES Mrs J M Karaviotis; J Karaviotis.

HOW TO APPLY In writing to the correspondent. No acknowledgement of receipt is given.

WHO TO APPLY TO The Trustees, Chantrey Vellacott DFK, Prospect House, 58 Queen's Road, Reading, Berkshire RG1 4RP *Tel* 0118 952 4700

CC NO 274576   **ESTABLISHED** 1977

■ The Joanies Trust

WHERE FUNDING CAN BE GIVEN UK.

WHO CAN BENEFIT Registered charities.

WHAT IS FUNDED Grants are given to organisations working with young people aged 11 to 25, especially projects that lead to employment, accreditation, further education, training and integration. In particular the trust looks for innovation and entrepreneurship. The event can be one-off or part of a programme. The trust looks for strong evidence of how closely applicants consult young people in developing their service, and for any community involvement or local financial support.

WHAT IS NOT FUNDED Funding is not given for: national organisations, even if the project is local; general appeals and activities which collect funds for subsequent redistribution; individuals; promotion of religion; services run by statutory or public authorities, or that replace statutory funding; minibuses; UK organisations; animal charities; projects that have taken place or have started before the deadline; projects that are based outside the UK; outings, trips, or fun days.

TYPE OF GRANT Grants for running costs, both project and core costs, and capital costs.

SAMPLE GRANTS Rape Crisis Lancaster (£1,900); Warrington Wolves (£1,300); Walsall Youth Arts and Music Pool (£1,200 each); Sudanese Development Programme, Central Africa Refugee Link and Neuromuscular Centre (£1,000 each); Seaford Lifeguards (£800); Community Action

(£750); and Islay & Jura Community Enterprises (£500).

FINANCES *Year* 2008 *Income* £35,469 *Grants* £33,704 *Assets* £652,568

TRUSTEES Alan Lloyd; Peter Arscott; Vivien Arscott.

HOW TO APPLY The trustees will only consider applications which are submitted on the trust's application form; this is now only available to download as a PDF file from the trust's website in order to keep administration and postage costs as low as possible. Applicants are asked to print out and fill in the application form, and send it to the trust's address for the attention of 'the administrator', along with a copy of their annual accounts. 'Applications will benefit by showing how a project supports this particular age group. Those that are succinct and that give direct answers to the questions in the application form stand a greater chance of success.'

WHO TO APPLY TO Peter Arscott, Secretary, PO Box 42, Ledbury, Herefordshire HR8 1WH *Tel* 01531 633345 *email* info@joaniestrust.org. uk *Website* www.joaniestrust.org.uk

CC NO 1097803   **ESTABLISHED** 2003

■ The Harold Joels Charitable Trust

WHERE FUNDING CAN BE GIVEN UK and US.

WHO CAN BENEFIT Jewish organisations only, with a possible preference for USA.

WHAT IS FUNDED General charitable purposes.

RANGE OF GRANTS £50–£20,000.

SAMPLE GRANTS In the US: Womens Resource Centre of Sarasota County (£20,000); Young Judea (£15,000); Florida Studio Theatre (£12,000); Jewish Family and Children's Service (£6,300); Emunah of America (£3,000); Florida Holocaust Museum (£2,000); Temple Beth Sholom (£1,600); Gocio Elementary School (£1,000); Family Law Connection (£250); World Jewish Congress (£170); and the American Jewish Committee (£100); In the UK: Jewish Care (£5,200); World Jewish Relief (£5,000); the Tel Aviv Foundation (£2,000); Bet Elazraki Home (£1,500); United Synagogue (£1,400); National Theatre (£1,300); Royal Academy of Arts (£1,000); I Rescue (£500); Tricycle Theatre Co Ltd (£400); Hampstead Synagogue and British Friend of the Hebrew University (£300 each); and Chai Cancer Care (£100).

FINANCES *Year* 2007–08 *Income* £36,088 *Grants* £55,686 *Assets* £777,857

TRUSTEES H Joels; Dr N Joels; Mrs V Joels; N E Joels

HOW TO APPLY In writing to the correspondent.

WHO TO APPLY TO H Joels, Trustee, 11a Arkwright Road, London NW3 6AA *email* hjoles7@aol.com

CC NO 206326   **ESTABLISHED** 1957

■ The Jonathan Joels Charitable Trust

WHERE FUNDING CAN BE GIVEN UK and overseas.

WHO CAN BENEFIT Registered charities.

WHAT IS FUNDED General charitable purposes.

RANGE OF GRANTS Up to $18,000.

SAMPLE GRANTS Previously, figures provided by the trust on grants awarded were quoted in US dollars and included: UJA Federation of Bergen County and North Hudson ($34,800); Congregation Ahavath Torah ($8,500); Moriah School of Englewood ($8,000); Ramaz School ($6,700); Ramaz Special Educational Fund

($3,600); Jewish Community Center on the Palisades ($3,300); Emunah of America ($2,200); and Shaare Zedek Medical Center in Jerusalem ($1,900). Grants of less than $1,000 included: Sinai Special Needs Institute, Jewish Home and Rehabilitation Center, Boys Town Jerusalem Foundation of America, Jewish Family Service, East Hill Synagogue, United Lifeline/Kav Lachayim, Yeshiva Chanoch Lenaar, Yeshiva Ohr Hatalmud of Englewood, Chai Lifeline, AZTUM, League for the Hard of Hearing, National Jewish Council for the Disabled, SCAT, Keser Dovid Inc, Chabad Center of Fort Lee, Friends of the Israeli Defence Forces, Lakewood Cheder School and Friends of the Lubavitch of Bergen County.

FINANCES *Year* 2007–08 *Income* £24,404

TRUSTEES J Joels; N E Joels; H Joels; Debra Joels.

HOW TO APPLY In writing to the correspondent.

WHO TO APPLY TO The Trustees, EBK Partnership, 1 Beauchamp Court, Victors Way, Barnet, Herts EN5 5TZ *Tel* 020 8216 2520 *Fax* 020 8216 2521

CC NO 278408   **ESTABLISHED** 1978

■ The Nicholas Joels Charitable Trust

WHERE FUNDING CAN BE GIVEN UK and overseas.

WHO CAN BENEFIT Registered charities only, with a preference for Jewish charities.

WHAT IS FUNDED General charitable purposes.

RANGE OF GRANTS Up to £9,000.

SAMPLE GRANTS World Jewish Relief (£9,000); Norwood (£5,300); Emunah (£4,300); United Jewish Israel Appeal (£3,800); Jewish Care (£2,000); Zionist Federation (£1,000); United Synagogue (£900); I Rescue (£750); Chinese Disaster Fund (£500); Jewish Women's Aid (£200); and Friends of the Tate Gallery (£100).

FINANCES *Year* 2007–08 *Income* £25,890 *Grants* £33,350 *Assets* £494,025

TRUSTEES N Joels; H Joels; Mrs A Joels.

HOW TO APPLY In writing to the correspondent.

WHO TO APPLY TO N Joels, Trustee, 66 Wigmore Street, London W1U 2SB *Tel* 01923 841376

CC NO 278409   **ESTABLISHED** 1978

■ The Norman Joels Charitable Trust

WHERE FUNDING CAN BE GIVEN UK, Israel and the Middle East.

WHO CAN BENEFIT Registered charities only.

WHAT IS FUNDED General charitable purposes.

RANGE OF GRANTS £100–£3,500.

SAMPLE GRANTS Previous beneficiaries have included: Friends of Magen David Action in Great Britain, Jewish Aid Committee, Jewish Care, Joint Jewish Charitable Trust, New London Synagogue, Norwood Ravenswood, The Spiro Institute and World Jewish Relief.

FINANCES *Year* 2007–08 *Income* £56,540 *Grants* £44,969 *Assets* £1,276,918

TRUSTEES Jessica L Joels; Norman Joels; Harold Joels; Myriam Joels.

HOW TO APPLY In writing to the correspondent.

WHO TO APPLY TO Henry Freedman, Grunberg and Co, 10 – 14 Accommodation Road, London NW11 8EY *Tel* 020 8458 0083 *Fax* 0208 458 0783

CC NO 206325   **ESTABLISHED** 1957

■ The Joffe Charitable Trust

WHERE FUNDING CAN BE GIVEN Worldwide, in practice, developing countries.

WHO CAN BENEFIT Registered charities with good quality leadership and clear objectives.

WHAT IS FUNDED The alleviation of poverty and protection/advancement of human rights mainly in the developing world, (poverty for this purpose could include some forms of suffering such as mental or physical disability and lack of education).

WHAT IS NOT FUNDED Likely exclusions are humanitarian assistance; large charities except perhaps for important projects which might not otherwise happen; the arts; charities likely to exclusively benefit causes in the developed world.

TYPE OF GRANT 'One-off', occasionally recurring. Loans may also be available.

RANGE OF GRANTS Around £1,000–£50,000.

SAMPLE GRANTS Acid Survivors Trust International (£50,000); War on Want (£38,000); Microloan Foundation (£35,000); Africa Now (£30,000); Global Witness and Charities Aid Foundation (£25,000 each); New Economics Foundation (£20,000); Alive and Kicking (£15,000); International Commission of Jurists (£10,000); and David Astor Trust (£7,500). Smaller grants of less than £5,000 totalled £66,000.

FINANCES *Year* 2007–08 *Income* £512,905 *Grants* £430,591 *Assets* £13,561,582

TRUSTEES Lord Joel Joffe; Lady Vanetta Joffe; Deborah Mila Joffe.

HOW TO APPLY In writing to the correspondent. It should be noted that funds are often committed to charities of special interest to the trustees. The trust does not acknowledge unsuccessful applications due to a lack of resources, nor will reasons for the application being turned down be given.

WHO TO APPLY TO Lord Joffe, Trustee, Liddington Manor, The Street, Liddington, Swindon SN4 0HD *Tel* 01793 790203 *email* joffetrust@ mail.com

CC NO 270299   **ESTABLISHED** 1968

■ The Elton John AIDS Foundation

WHERE FUNDING CAN BE GIVEN Unrestricted.

WHO CAN BENEFIT Organisations helping those people living with HIV/AIDS, or running AIDS prevention programmes.

WHAT IS FUNDED Projects concerned with the alleviation of the physical, emotional and financial hardship of people living with HIV/ AIDS, and AIDS prevention programmes.

WHAT IS NOT FUNDED For both UK and international grants the foundation will not fund: academic or medical research; conferences; grants to individuals; repatriation costs; retrospective funding.

TYPE OF GRANT Revenue and specific projects. Core costs; one-off, running costs; and salaries. Funding may be given for one year or up to three years.

RANGE OF GRANTS From £250.

FINANCES *Year* 2008 *Income* £15,694,237 *Grants* £6,900,000 *Assets* £23,478,275

TRUSTEES Sir Elton John, Chair; David Furnish; Lynette Jackson; Frank Presland; Anne Aslett; Marguerite Littman; Johnny Bergius; James Locke; Rafi Manoukian; Scott Campbell.

HOW TO APPLY The foundation's website has an interactive map which you can use to click on a country you are interested in. This will take you to a page containing an overview of the country and the foundation's work within it, some examples of previous projects, details of the current grant strategy for that country and the application procedure. Interested organisations should complete a 'concept note' (available to download from the website) and email it to grants@ejaf.com.

WHO TO APPLY TO Robert Key, Executive Director, 1 Blythe Road, London W14 0HG *Tel* 020 7603 9996 *Fax* 020 7348 4848 *email* admin@ejaf.com *Website* www.ejaf.com

CC NO 1017336   ESTABLISHED 1993

■ The Michael John Trust

WHERE FUNDING CAN BE GIVEN UK.

WHO CAN BENEFIT Scientific research, education, health, disability – UK.

WHAT IS FUNDED Registered charities.

SAMPLE GRANTS Previous beneficiaries have included: Contaminated Blood Independent Public Enquiry, the Snowdon Award Scheme, the Science and Technology Foundation Trust and Help the Aged.

FINANCES *Year* 2008–09 *Income* £244,252 *Grants* £190,950 *Assets* £2,177,400

TRUSTEES Dr H P Jost; Mrs M J Jost; M J O Kettle; R Worby.

HOW TO APPLY In writing to the correspondent. The trustees meet quarterly.

WHO TO APPLY TO Dr Peter Jost, Trustee, Angel Chambers, 57 London Road, Enfield, Middlesex EN2 6SW

CC NO 293571   ESTABLISHED 1986

■ The Lillie Johnson Charitable Trust

WHERE FUNDING CAN BE GIVEN UK, with a preference for the West Midlands.

WHO CAN BENEFIT Charities concerned with children, young people and medical causes.

WHAT IS FUNDED Medical and welfare causes.

WHAT IS NOT FUNDED No support for individuals.

FINANCES *Year* 2007–08 *Income* £275,253 *Grants* £204,077 *Assets* £5,555,510

TRUSTEES V M C Lyttle; P W Adams; J W Desmond; Mrs V C Adams.

HOW TO APPLY Applications are only considered from charities which are traditionally supported by the trust. The trust stated that it is inundated with applications it cannot support and feels obliged to respond to all of these.

WHO TO APPLY TO J W Desmond, Trustee, Heathcote House, 136 Hagley Road, Edgbaston, Birmingham B16 9PN *Tel* 0121 454 4141

CC NO 326761   ESTABLISHED 1985

■ The Johnson Group Cleaners Charity

WHERE FUNDING CAN BE GIVEN Merseyside only.

WHO CAN BENEFIT Registered local charities benefiting: children, young adults and older people; at risk groups; carers; people disadvantaged by poverty; ex-offenders and those at risk of offending; homeless people; victims of abuse and domestic violence; and people with substance misuse problems.

WHAT IS FUNDED Merseyside charities, including Councils for Voluntary Service, care in the community and holidays and outings.

WHAT IS NOT FUNDED No grants to national charities or individuals.

TYPE OF GRANT Core costs, one-off, project and running costs.

RANGE OF GRANTS Up to £80,000, usually £5,000 or less.

SAMPLE GRANTS Johnson Group Welfare Charity (£80,000); Bootle YMCA, Stroke Association, Salvation Army and Claire House (£5,000 each); Royal School for the Blind, Slightline Vision and Merseyside Holiday Services (£3,000 each); Rainbow Charity Children's Hospice (£750); Halton Haven Hospice and Merseyside Gymnastic Club (£500 each); and Wellchild (£250).

FINANCES *Year* 2007–08 *Income* £104,824 *Grants* £127,474 *Assets* £190,386

TRUSTEES Johnson Group Cleaners Trustee Co. (No. 1) Ltd.

HOW TO APPLY In writing only to the correspondent.

WHO TO APPLY TO Dennis A Hargreaves, Abbots Park, Monks Way, Preston Brook, Cheshire WA7 3GH *Tel* 0151 933 6161

CC NO 802959   ESTABLISHED 1990

■ The Johnnie Johnson Trust

WHERE FUNDING CAN BE GIVEN UK, with a preference for the West Midlands.

WHO CAN BENEFIT To benefit children and young adults.

WHAT IS FUNDED Heritage and training/adventure breaks for children, youth and welfare organisations.

SAMPLE GRANTS Johnnie Johnson Adventure Trust (£130,000); and 1st Shirley Scouts (£200).

FINANCES *Year* 2008 *Income* £139,097 *Grants* £135,200 *Assets* £2,749,803

TRUSTEES P V Johnson; P E T Johnson; Mrs J S Fordham; G W Ballard; S G Kitchen.

OTHER INFORMATION Over the last few years, the trust's funds have mostly been given to Johnnie Johnson Adventure Trust, which provides adventure/training for children.

HOW TO APPLY In writing to the correspondent. Please note that most funds go to the trust's sister charity and very little is available to other organisations.

WHO TO APPLY TO Christopher R Jackson, Newtown House, Hewell Road, Enfield, Redditch, Worcestershire B97 6AY *Tel* 01527 584458

CC NO 200351   ESTABLISHED 1961

■ The Johnson Wax Ltd Charitable Trust

WHERE FUNDING CAN BE GIVEN 20-mile radius of Frimley Green, Surrey.

WHO CAN BENEFIT Local charities.

WHAT IS FUNDED Health, education, local community, environment, arts, sports.

WHAT IS NOT FUNDED No grants to individuals.

RANGE OF GRANTS £4,000 average.

FINANCES *Year* 2007–08 *Income* £313,370 *Grants* £144,379 *Assets* £276,213

TRUSTEES Mrs R Gillingham; Mrs C Hyde; Mrs N Bandtock.

HOW TO APPLY In writing to the correspondent including the following information: the amount requested and what it is needed for; – details of how the grant will benefit a broad cross-section of the Frimley Green community and meet a clear social need within it.

WHO TO APPLY TO Jan Jewers, S C Johnson Wax Ltd, Frimley Green, Camberley, Surrey GU16 7AJ *Tel* 01276 852422 *email* jjewers@scj.com

CC NO 200332   ESTABLISHED 1961

■ The Joicey Trust

WHERE FUNDING CAN BE GIVEN Unrestricted, but in practice, the county of Northumberland and the old metropolitan county of Tyne and Wear.

WHO CAN BENEFIT Registered charities operating in Northumberland and Tyne and Wear or groups with a specific project within the area defined above. The trust will consider funding organisations benefiting people of all ages, seafarers and fishermen, people who are in care, fostered or adopted and one-parent families.

WHAT IS FUNDED This trust will consider funding activities within the following fields: residential facilities and services; a range of infrastructure, technical support and development; charity or voluntary umbrella bodies; religious buildings; music, dance and theatre; healthcare, facilities and buildings; conservation; education and training; and community facilities and services. UK appeals are not normally supported unless there is specific evidence of activity benefiting the local area.

WHAT IS NOT FUNDED The trust states that it will not support 'bodies not having registered charitable status; personal applications; individuals; groups that do not have an identifiable project within the beneficial area'.

TYPE OF GRANT One-off for capital and revenue projects, with preference for discrete projects over running costs. Also start-up costs, buildings, core costs, projects and salaries.

RANGE OF GRANTS Up to £5,000 with very occasional larger grants.

SAMPLE GRANTS Diocese of Newcastle PICA Appeal (£10,000); Dame Allan's Development Trust, Adventure Holidays and the Chillingham Wild Cattle Association (£5,000 each); Greggs Trust (£4,500); Northumberland Toy Library and Children's Resource Centre (£3,500); RNIB and Percy Hedley Foundation (£3,000 each); Rainbow Trust Children's Charity and Disability North (£2,500 each); Young Enterprise North East and REHAB UK (£2,000 each); National Rheumatoid Arthritis Society and Sunderland Juvenile Service (£1,500 each); and Red Squirrels in South Scotland and the Sailors' Families Society (£1,000 each).

FINANCES *Year* 2007–08 *Income* £269,502 *Grants* £239,700 *Assets* £6,823,565

TRUSTEES Rt Hon. Lord Joicey; Rt Hon. Lady Joicey; Hon. A H Joicey; R H Dickinson.

HOW TO APPLY There is no application form and applications should be made in writing to the correspondent. Trustees' meetings are held in January and July and applications should be received not later than the end of November and the end of May respectively. Applications should include a brief description of the project and must include a copy of the previous year's accounts and, where possible, a copy of the current year's projected income and expenditure. In the case of large projects, an indication should be given of how the major sources of funding are likely to be secured, including reference to any Community Fund grant applied for/received. Unsuccessful applicants will not be informed unless an sae is provided.

WHO TO APPLY TO N A Furness, Appeals Secretary, Dickinson Dees LLP, St Ann's Wharf, 112 Quayside, Newcastle Upon Tyne NE99 1 SB *Tel* 0191 279 9683 *Fax* 0191 230 8921 *email* sylvia.hepplewhite@dickinson-dees.com

CC NO 244679   **ESTABLISHED** 1965

■ The Jones 1986 Charitable Trust

WHERE FUNDING CAN BE GIVEN UK, mostly Nottinghamshire.

WHO CAN BENEFIT Registered charities.

WHAT IS FUNDED People with disabilities, welfare of older people, welfare of younger people, education and purposes beneficial to the community.

WHAT IS NOT FUNDED No grants to individuals.

RANGE OF GRANTS Up to around £200,000, but mostly between £4,000 and £25,000.

SAMPLE GRANTS Queen's Medical Centre – Nottingham University Hospital NHS Trust (£193,000); Cope Children's Trust (£40,000); Prince of Paste Anglers (£30,000); Age Concern – Nottingham and Nottinghamshire (£25,000); Nottingham Arts Theatre (£20,000); Southwell Care Project (£18,000); Long Eaton Society for Mentally Handicapped Children and Adults (£10,000); Nottingham Historic Churches Trust (£6,500); Fun Days – Shepherd School (£5,000); and Nottinghamshire Scouts (£4,000).

FINANCES *Year* 2007–08 *Income* £4,401,236 *Grants* £768,710 *Assets* £19,108,891

TRUSTEES Robert Heason; Richard Stringfellow; John David Pears.

HOW TO APPLY In writing to the correspondent. The trust invites applications for grants by advertising in specialist press. Applications are considered for both capital and/or revenue projects as long as each project appears viable.

WHO TO APPLY TO David Lindley, Smith Cooper, Haydn House, 309–329 Haydn Road, Sherwood, Nottingham NG5 1HG *Tel* 0115 960 7111 *Fax* 0115 969 1313

CC NO 327176   **ESTABLISHED** 1986

■ Dezna Robins Jones Charitable Foundation

WHERE FUNDING CAN BE GIVEN Preference for Wales.

WHO CAN BENEFIT Local medical charities.

WHAT IS FUNDED Medical, general charitable purposes.

SAMPLE GRANTS Cancer Care Cymru (£462,000); University Hospital of Wales – Cardiff (£138,000); Cory band (£72,000); and Performance Arts Education (£48,000).

FINANCES *Year* 2007–08 *Income* £128,719 *Grants* £720,000 *Assets* £4,723,331

TRUSTEES B W R Jones; A C Cooke; A L C Boobyer.

HOW TO APPLY In writing to the correspondent. Trustees meet at least twice a year.

WHO TO APPLY TO Bernard Jones, Trustee, Greenacres, Laleston, Bridgend, Mid Glamorgan CF32 0HN *Tel* 01656 768584

CC NO 1104252   **ESTABLISHED** 2004

■ The Marjorie and Geoffrey Jones Charitable Trust

WHERE FUNDING CAN BE GIVEN UK, preference south west of England.

WHO CAN BENEFIT Registered charities.

WHAT IS FUNDED General charitable purposes.

RANGE OF GRANTS £1,000–£5,000.

SAMPLE GRANTS Torbay Coast and Countryside Trust (£4,000); Pilgrim BM45 Trust Ltd, Living Paintings and Teign Heritage (£3,000 each); Children's Hospice South West and Fire Services Benevolent Fund (£2,500); DeafBlind UK and West Country Rivers (£2,000 each); and

Rural Stress South West, The Two Moors Festival and Apollo Football Club (£1,000 each).

FINANCES *Year* 2007–08 *Income* £73,601 *Grants* £48,500 *Assets* £1,968,852

TRUSTEES N J Wollen; W F Coplestone Boughey; P M Kay.

HOW TO APPLY In writing to the correspondent. The trustees meet four times a year to consider applications.

WHO TO APPLY TO N J Wollen, Trustee, Carlton House, 30 The Terrace, Torquay, Devon TQ1 1BS *Tel* 01803 213251 *email* nigel. wollen@hooperwollen.co.uk

CC NO 1051031 **ESTABLISHED** 1995

■ The Jordan Charitable Foundation

WHERE FUNDING CAN BE GIVEN UK national charities, Herefordshire and Sutherland, Scotland.

WHO CAN BENEFIT UK national charities and local charities and community groups in Herefordshire and Sutherland, Scotland.

WHAT IS FUNDED General charitable purposes.

TYPE OF GRANT One-off, capital and core costs will be considered.

RANGE OF GRANTS £1,000–£200,000.

SAMPLE GRANTS Hereford Cathedral Perpetual Trust (£215,000); Herefordshire Mind (£26,000); Blue Cross (£25,000); and CLD Youth Counselling Trust and County Air Ambulance Trust (£15,000 each); Brooke Hospital for Animals, the Samaritans and the Stroke Association (£10,000 each); Sutherland Schools Pipe Band (£6,000); Age Concern, British Heart Foundation, Injured Jockeys' Fund and Herefordshire Nature Trust (£5,000 each); Children's Hospital Association – Scotland (£2,000); and Prostate Cancer Charity (£1,000).

FINANCES *Year* 2008 *Income* £1,243,835 *Grants* £602,500 *Assets* £35,729,105

TRUSTEES Sir Ronald Miller; Sir George Russell; Ralph Stockwell; Christopher Jan Andrew Bliss; Simon Paul Jennings; David Geoffrey Barker.

HOW TO APPLY In writing to the correspondent.

WHO TO APPLY TO Ralph Stockwell, Trustee, 8th Floor, 6 New Street Square, New Fetter Land, London EC4A 3AQ *Tel* 020 7842 2000 *email* jordan@rawlinson-hunter.com

CC NO 1051507 **ESTABLISHED** 1995

■ The Joron Charitable Trust

WHERE FUNDING CAN BE GIVEN UK.

WHO CAN BENEFIT Registered charities.

WHAT IS FUNDED 'The charity's policy is to make grants to registered charities in the fields of education, medical research and other charities who can demonstrate that the grants will be used effectively.'

SAMPLE GRANTS Roan Charitable Trust (£1 million); A & E Bunker Charitable Settlement (£200,000); Jewish Care (£100,000); the Wilderness Foundation (£60,000); Child's Dream Foundation (£51,000); Theodora Children's Trust (£25,000); Scleroderma Society (£20,000); Rainbow Trust Children's Charity (£15,000); the Ian Rennie Hospice at Home (£10,000); and Hope and Homes for Children (£1,500).

FINANCES *Year* 2007–08 *Income* £1,931,406 *Grants* £1,865,712 *Assets* £834,974

TRUSTEES Bruce D G Jarvis; Mrs Sandra C Jarvis; Joseph R Jarvis.

HOW TO APPLY 'There is no formal grants application procedure. The trustees retain the services of a charitable grants advisor and take account of the advice when deciding on grants.'

WHO TO APPLY TO Bruce D G Jarvis, Chair, 115 Wembley Commercial Centre, East Lane, North Wembley, Middlesex HA9 7UR

CC NO 1062547 **ESTABLISHED** 1997

■ The J E Joseph Charitable Fund

WHERE FUNDING CAN BE GIVEN London, Manchester, Israel, India and Hong Kong.

WHO CAN BENEFIT Jewish people who are poor and in need.

WHAT IS FUNDED Jewish community organisations, especially those catering for people who are socially disadvantaged and young people.

WHAT IS NOT FUNDED No grants to individuals. No support for capital projects.

TYPE OF GRANT Outright cash grants frequently on an annual basis. Very occasionally loans.

RANGE OF GRANTS £500–£10,000.

SAMPLE GRANTS The Future Generation Fund (£15,000); University Jewish Chaplaincy Board (£5,500); Spanish and Portuguese Synagogue Welfare Board and Tishma School Centre for Autistic Children (£5,000 each); Edinburgh House and Alyn Pediatric & Adolescence Rehabilitation Centre (£4,500 each); Jacob Benjamin Elias Synagogue, Simon Marks Jewish Primary School, Jewish Free School and Jewish Preparatory School (£3,000 each); Or Hachayim Girls College (£2,500); and Jewish Lads & Girls Brigade (£1,500).

FINANCES *Year* 2007–08 *Income* £151,541 *Grants* £122,071 *Assets* £4,236,661

TRUSTEES F D A Mocatta, Chair; P Sheldon; J H Corre; P S Gourgey; J S Horesh; S Frosh.

HOW TO APPLY In writing to the correspondent, including a copy of the latest accounts. The trustees respond to all applications which are first vetted by the secretary. The trust stated that many applications are unsuccessful as the number of appeals exceeds the amount available from limited income.

WHO TO APPLY TO Roger J Leon, Secretary, Flat 10, Compass Close, Edgware, Middlesex HA8 8HU *Tel* 020 8958 0126

CC NO 209058 **ESTABLISHED** 1946

■ The Lady Eileen Joseph Foundation

WHERE FUNDING CAN BE GIVEN UK.

WHO CAN BENEFIT Mainly UK organisations benefiting at-risk groups and people who are disadvantaged by poverty or socially isolated.

WHAT IS FUNDED Largely welfare and medical causes. General charitable purposes are also supported.

TYPE OF GRANT One-off.

RANGE OF GRANTS Up to £10,000.

SAMPLE GRANTS Second Chance (£7,500); Coldstream Guards Association (£6,500); Alzheimers Research Trust and Friends of the Home Physiotherapy Service (£5,000 each); Havens Hospices (£4,500); Ellenor Foundation and Queen Alexandra Hospital (£3,000 each); Independent Age and Wellbeing of Women (£2,000 each); and Cystic Fibrosis Trust, Foundation for the Prevention of Blindness and Action for Kids (£1,000 each).

FINANCES *Year* 2007–08 *Income* £39,265 *Grants* £115,500 *Assets* £943,414

TRUSTEES Mrs J Sawdy; T W P Simpson; Mrs N J Thornton.

HOW TO APPLY In writing to the correspondent, although the trust states that unsolicited requests will not be considered.

WHO TO APPLY TO Thurlstan W Simpson, Colbrans Farm, Cow Lane, Laughton, East Sussex BN8 6BZ

CC NO 327549   **ESTABLISHED** 1987

■ The Josh Charitable Trust

WHERE FUNDING CAN BE GIVEN UK and Israel.

WHO CAN BENEFIT Registered charities.

WHAT IS FUNDED General charitable purposes.

FINANCES *Year* 2007–08 *Income* £90,986 *Grants* £86,774 *Assets* £17,612

TRUSTEES J Cope; Mrs S Cope; S D Cope.

HOW TO APPLY In writing to the correspondent.

WHO TO APPLY TO The Trustees, 1 Lancaster Drive, Prestwich, Manchester M25 0HZ

CC NO 1107060

■ JTH Charitable Trust

WHERE FUNDING CAN BE GIVEN Scotland, in particular west Scotland and Glasgow.

WHO CAN BENEFIT Individuals and organisations.

WHAT IS FUNDED Grants are given to a range of organisations, including universities, cultural bodies and those caring for people who are sick. Support may also be given to charities working in the fields of community services, community centres and village halls, special needs education, voluntary and community organisations and volunteers.

WHAT IS NOT FUNDED The following are not usually supported: medical electives, second or further qualifications, payment of school fees or costs incurred at tertiary educational establishments.

TYPE OF GRANT Some grants are made to individuals for educational purposes. Core costs, one-off, project, research, running costs and start-up costs will be considered.

RANGE OF GRANTS £100–£10,000.

SAMPLE GRANTS Previous beneficiaries have included Crossroads (Scotland) Care Attendance Scheme and East Park Home for Inform Children, Royal Blind Asylum and School, University of Glasgow and University of Strathclyde.

FINANCES *Year* 2008–09 *Income* £222,154 *Grants* £198,450 *Assets* £3,344,979

TRUSTEES Gordon M Wyllie; Christine C Howat.

HOW TO APPLY In writing to the correspondent. There is no application form for organisations. Applications should contain a summary not longer than one side of A4, backed up as necessary with schedules. A copy of the latest accounts and/or business plan should be included. Costs and financial needs should be broken down where possible. It should be clear what effect the grant will have and details of other grants applied for or awarded should be given. Evidence that the project will enhance the quality of life of the clients and that they are involved in the decision making must be included. 'Applications should include evidence of charitable status, current funding, and the use you are making of that. Projects should be demonstrated to be practical and business-like. It is a condition of any grant given that a report be made as to how the funds have been used. Grants not used for the purposes stated must be returned.' Successful applicants should not reapply in the following year. Unsuccessful applicants are not acknowledged due to the large number of applications received by the trust. The trustees meet to consider grants in March, June, September and December. Applications should be received in the preceding month.

WHO TO APPLY TO Lynne Faulkner, Biggart Baillie LLP, Dalmore House, 310 St Vincent Street, Glasgow G2 5QR *Tel* 0141 228 8000 *Fax* 0141 228 8310 *email* lfaulkner@biggartbaillie.co.uk

SC NO SC000201   **ESTABLISHED** 1989

■ The Judith Trust

WHERE FUNDING CAN BE GIVEN UK.

WHO CAN BENEFIT Organisations concerned with people with a learning disability and mental health needs.

WHAT IS FUNDED Multi-disciplinary preventative and innovative approaches to help those with learning disabilities and mental health problems, especially women, children and Jewish people.

WHAT IS NOT FUNDED No grants to individuals.

TYPE OF GRANT One-off, project and research. Funding may be given for up to three years.

SAMPLE GRANTS Living in the Community Project (£26,000); and 'Healthcare needs and experiences of care' (£11,000).

FINANCES *Year* 2007–08 *Income* £27,723 *Grants* £36,524 *Assets* £581,489

TRUSTEES Dr Annette Lawson; Peter Lawrence; George Lawson; Charlotte Collins; Geraldine Holt; Colin Samson.

PUBLICATIONS Joined Up Care: good practice in services for people with learning disabilities and mental health needs.

HOW TO APPLY In writing to the correspondent; however, please note that most grants are made through experts and advisors. The trust does not accept unsolicited applications for funding, but is pleased to hear from organisations who wish the Trust to be aware of their work

WHO TO APPLY TO Dr A R Lawson, Trustee, 5 Carriage House, 88–90 Randolph Avenue, London W9 1BG *Tel* 020 7266 1073 *Fax* 020 7289 5804 *email* judith.trust@lineone.net *Website* www.judithtrust.org.uk

CC NO 1063012   **ESTABLISHED** 1997

■ The Cyril and Eve Jumbo Charitable Trust

WHERE FUNDING CAN BE GIVEN Worldwide.

WHO CAN BENEFIT Charitable organisations.

WHAT IS FUNDED The objectives of the trust are: fresh water projects; projects that deal with grass roots and front line action, and that set up sustainable, ongoing projects so that people can increase their independence and create their own livelihoods; projects that help children (particularly those in countries recovering from war and trauma), older people and people with disabilities/special needs.

SAMPLE GRANTS Wherever the Need (£7,200); Friends of Manjushree Vidyapith School and Orphanage (£3,700); and Association Espanola Contra el Cancer, Agoonoree (Greater London) Trust Fund, Clinic Nepal, Excellent Development, Humanity first, Speech Language and Hearing Centre and WellBeing of Women (£2,200 each).

FINANCES *Year* 2006–07 *Income* £34,912 *Grants* £26,500 *Assets* £374,170

TRUSTEES Geoffrey Allan Margolis; Rafiq Ahmed Hayat; Michaela Justice; Fred Kindall.

Think carefully about every application. Is it justified?

635

HOW TO APPLY Unsolicited applications are not always accepted. Please check the trust's website for up-to-date details.

WHO TO APPLY TO The Trustees, 56a Poland Street, London W1F 7NN *email* info@ mumbojumboworld.com

CC NO 1097209   **ESTABLISHED** 2003

....

■ The Anton Jurgens Charitable Trust

WHERE FUNDING CAN BE GIVEN UK with a preference for the south east of England.

WHO CAN BENEFIT UK registered charities.

WHAT IS FUNDED The welfare of children and young people; youth organisations; centres, clubs and institutions; community organisations; day centres and nurseries; and general welfare organisations.

TYPE OF GRANT Generally one-off.

RANGE OF GRANTS £1,000–£15,000.

SAMPLE GRANTS Silcester Parochial Council (£25,000); Highland Hospice (£15,000); Ability Net, Kid's Company and Royal School for Deaf Children – Margate (£10,000 each); child Link Adoption Society (£8,000); the Fifth Trust (£6,000); Bucks Disability Information Network and Queen Alexandra Hospital Home (£5,000 each); Hope House (£4,000); Haemophilia Society (£3,000); Barnabas Adventure Centres and Vitalise (£2,000 each); and Bury Shopmobility (£1,000).

FINANCES *Year* 2007–08 *Income* £298,774 *Grants* £380,300 *Assets* £6,877,794

TRUSTEES Eric M C Deckers; R Jurgens; Frans A V Jurgens; John F M Jurgens; Maria E Edge-Jurgens; M A J Jurgens.

HOW TO APPLY In writing to the correspondent. The trustees meet twice a year in June and October. The trustees do not enter into correspondence concerning grant applications beyond notifying successful applicants.

WHO TO APPLY TO Mrs Maria E Edge-Jurgens, Trustee, Saffrey Champness, Lion House, 72–75 Red Lion Street, London WC1R 4GB *Tel* 020 7841 4000 *Fax* 020 7841 4100

CC NO 259885   **ESTABLISHED** 1969

....

■ Jusaca Charitable Trust

WHERE FUNDING CAN BE GIVEN UK, overseas and Israel.

WHO CAN BENEFIT Registered charities.

WHAT IS FUNDED Jewish, arts, research, religion, housing.

FINANCES *Year* 2007–08 *Income* £1,412,452 *Grants* £131,950 *Assets* £1,350,830

TRUSTEES Ralph Neville Emanuel; Sara Jane Emanuel; Carolyn Leonora Emanuel; Maurice Seymour Emanuel; Diana Clare Franklin; Donald Franklin; Rachel Paul.

OTHER INFORMATION The trust aims to distribute at least 50% of donations to Jewish charities in the UK, overseas and Israel, and of the remainder about 40% to be donation to charities operating in the UK and about 60% outside the UK.

HOW TO APPLY Grants are made at the discretion of the trustees.

WHO TO APPLY TO The Trustees, 17 Ashburnham Grove, London SE10 8UH

CC NO 1012966   **ESTABLISHED** 1992

The Bernard Kahn Charitable Trust

WHERE FUNDING CAN BE GIVEN UK and Israel.

WHO CAN BENEFIT Organisations benefiting Jewish people, children and young adults, people disadvantaged by poverty, teachers, governesses and rabbis.

WHAT IS FUNDED Relief of, and assistance to, Jewish people to alleviate poverty; the advancement of religion and education.

RANGE OF GRANTS £25–£45,000.

SAMPLE GRANTS Achisomoch Aid Company Ltd (£10,000); the Menorah Primary School (£4,800); Whinney House Limited (£4,500); Arachim Limited (£3,000); Beth Hamedrash Elyon Golders Green Limited (£2,100); Shaare Zedek UK (£500); Society for the Transmission of the Jewish Heritage (£200); and Manchester Jewish Grammar School (£100).

FINANCES *Year* 2007–08 *Income* £118,284 *Grants* £130,495 *Assets* £1,751,963

TRUSTEES Mrs C B Kahn; S Fuehrer, Y E Kahn.

HOW TO APPLY In writing to the correspondent.

WHO TO APPLY TO The Trustees, 18 Gresham Gardens, London NW11 8PD

CC NO 249130   **ESTABLISHED** 1965

The Stanley Kalms Foundation

WHERE FUNDING CAN BE GIVEN UK and overseas.

WHO CAN BENEFIT Organisations and individuals involved with: orthodox Jewish education in the UK and Israel; the arts; medicine; and other secular and religious programmes.

WHAT IS FUNDED Encouragement of orthodox Jewish education in the UK and Israel, particularly by providing scholarships, fellowships and research grants. Other areas supported include the arts, medicine and other programmes, both secular and religious.

TYPE OF GRANT One-off, research, project, bursaries and scholarships.

SAMPLE GRANTS Previous beneficiaries include: Dixons City Academy, Milliken Community High, Royal Opera House Foundation, Jewish Care, Jewish National Fund, Norwood Ltd, British Friends of Haifa University, Keren Klita, Spirituality for Kids and Jewish Policy Research.

FINANCES *Year* 2007–08 *Income* £15,204 *Grants* £198,970

TRUSTEES Lord Stanley Kalms; Lady Pamela Kalms; Stephen Kalms.

HOW TO APPLY In writing to the correspondent, but note that most of the trust's funds are committed to projects supported for a number of years.

WHO TO APPLY TO Mrs Jane Hunt-Cooke, 84 Brook Street, London W1K 5EH *Tel* 020 7499 3494

CC NO 328368   **ESTABLISHED** 1989

The Karenza Foundation

WHERE FUNDING CAN BE GIVEN UK.

WHO CAN BENEFIT Charitable organisations.

WHAT IS FUNDED General charitable purposes.

RANGE OF GRANTS Larger grants can be up to £20,000.

SAMPLE GRANTS Previously: Charities Aid Foundation, Liver Cancer Surgery Appeal, Aid to Children Everywhere and St Catherine's Hospice.

FINANCES *Year* 2007–08 *Income* £32,646 *Grants* £30,000

TRUSTEES Mrs E L R Uren; Edward Uren; Mrs A F Uren.

HOW TO APPLY In writing to the correspondent.

WHO TO APPLY TO The Trustees, Suite A, Gostrey House, Union Road, Farnham, Surrey GU9 7PT

CC NO 264520   **ESTABLISHED** 1972

The Boris Karloff Charitable Foundation

WHERE FUNDING CAN BE GIVEN Worldwide.

WHO CAN BENEFIT UK and local charities benefiting actors, musicians and people disadvantaged by mental or physical illness.

WHAT IS FUNDED General charitable purposes.

WHAT IS NOT FUNDED Charities with large resources are not supported.

RANGE OF GRANTS £100–£10,000.

SAMPLE GRANTS RADA – Boris Karloff Scholarship Fund, Royal Theatrical Fund and Cinema and Television Fund (£10,000 each); Shakespeare Globe Trust (£6,500); and Cambridge Film Festival, Surrey County Cricket (two grants), the English Touring Theatre and LAMDA (£5,000 each).

FINANCES *Year* 2007–08 *Income* £81,604 *Grants* £66,000 *Assets* £2,190,617

TRUSTEES Ian D Wilson; P A Williamson; O M Lewis.

HOW TO APPLY In writing to the correspondent.

WHO TO APPLY TO The Trustees, Peachey and Co., 95 Aldwych, London WC2B 4JF *Tel* 020 7316 5200

CC NO 326898   **ESTABLISHED** 1985

The Ian Karten Charitable Trust

WHERE FUNDING CAN BE GIVEN Great Britain and Israel, with some local interest in Surrey and London.

WHO CAN BENEFIT People with disabilities attending CTEC Centres, and students who have been awarded Karten Scholarships by universities or conservatoires.

WHAT IS FUNDED The establishment by suitable charities of centres for computer-aided training, education and communication (CTEC Centres) for people with severe physical, sensory or cognitive disabilities, or with mental health problems; scholarships for postgraduate study and research in selected subjects at selected universities and for postgraduate training of musicians of outstanding talent at selected conservatoires; and the trust makes occasional small donations to some charities in Surrey and London.

WHAT IS NOT FUNDED No grants to individuals.

TYPE OF GRANT Projects: sometimes funded over a period of two years; charities: normally one-off, but in some cases repeated annually; universities: scholarships.

RANGE OF GRANTS £50–£150,000.

FINANCES *Year* 2007–08 *Income* £312,454 *Grants* £274,480 *Assets* £7,732,615

TRUSTEES Ian H Karten, Chair; Mrs Mildred Karten; Tim Simon; Angela Hobbs.

OTHER INFORMATION In 2007–08 a further £52,000 was distributed to six institutions for scholarships.

HOW TO APPLY The trust currently only considers grants to charities supported in the past. Individual scholarships are no longer available directly to students, instead the trust's chosen universities select the Karten Scholarships themselves. The trustees meet every six weeks to consider applications.

WHO TO APPLY TO Timothy Simon, The Mill House, Newark Lane, Ripley, Surrey GU23 6DP *Tel* 01483 225020 *Fax* 01483 222420 *email* iankarten@btinternet.com *Website* www. karten-network.org.uk

CC NO 281721   **ESTABLISHED** 1980

■ The Kasner Charitable Trust

WHERE FUNDING CAN BE GIVEN UK and Israel.
WHO CAN BENEFIT Jewish organisations.
WHAT IS FUNDED Jewish charitable purposes.
RANGE OF GRANTS £25–£10,000.
SAMPLE GRANTS Previous beneficiaries include: Friends of Bar Ilan University and UJIA, UTA, Gateshead Academy for Jewish Studies, RS Trust, Yeshivat Maharash Engel Radomshitz, Beth Abraham Synagogue, Emunoh Educational Trust, British Friends of Bnei Brak Hospital, Friends of Arad and Society of Friends of Torah.
FINANCES *Year* 2007–08 *Income* £126,985 *Grants* £94,793 *Assets* £741,364
TRUSTEES Elfreda Erlich; Baruch Erlich; Josef Kasner; Judith Erlich.
HOW TO APPLY In writing to the correspondent.
WHO TO APPLY TO Josef Kasner, Trustee, 1a Gresham Gardens, London NW11 8NX *Tel* 020 8455 7830

CC NO 267510   **ESTABLISHED** 1974

■ The Kass Charitable Trust

WHERE FUNDING CAN BE GIVEN UK.
WHO CAN BENEFIT Organisations.
WHAT IS FUNDED The trust now focuses on 'poverty and education for disadvantaged children'.
RANGE OF GRANTS Up to £11,000.
SAMPLE GRANTS Torah Temimah School (£11,000).
FINANCES *Year* 2007–08 *Income* £92,205 *Grants* £66,176 *Assets* £27,516
TRUSTEES David Elliot Kass; Mrs Shulamith Malkah Sandler.
HOW TO APPLY In writing to the correspondent.
WHO TO APPLY TO D E Kass, Trustee, 37 Sherwood Road, London NW4 1AE *Tel* 020 8371 3111

CC NO 1006296   **ESTABLISHED** 1991

■ The Kathleen Trust

WHERE FUNDING CAN BE GIVEN UK, with a preference for London.
WHO CAN BENEFIT Organisations benefiting young musicians.
WHAT IS FUNDED Typically course fees or instrument costs for outstanding young musicians.
SAMPLE GRANTS Oxford Chamber Music Festival (£10,000); and British Kidney Patient Association – Young Clarinetist (£1,000).
FINANCES *Year* 2007–08 *Income* £31,485 *Grants* £34,500 *Assets* £1,173,523
TRUSTEES E R H Perks; Sir O C A Scott; Lady P A Scott; Mrs CN Withington.
OTHER INFORMATION The trusts main grant-making priority is individuals. In 2007–08, grants were given to 16 students totalling £24,000.
HOW TO APPLY In writing to the correspondent.
WHO TO APPLY TO E R H Perks, Trustee, Currey and Co, 21 Buckingham Gate, London SW1E 6LS *Tel* 020 7828 4091

CC NO 1064516   **ESTABLISHED** 1997

■ The Michael and Ilse Katz Foundation

WHERE FUNDING CAN BE GIVEN Worldwide.
WHO CAN BENEFIT International and UK schemes and organisations benefiting Jewish people, at risk groups, and people who are disadvantaged by poverty or socially isolated.
WHAT IS FUNDED Primarily Jewish organisations. Medical/disability and welfare charities are also supported.
TYPE OF GRANT One-off and recurring.
RANGE OF GRANTS Up to £20,000.
SAMPLE GRANTS Jewish Care (£20,000); University College London (£15,000); Community Security Trust (£12,000); Norwood Children and Families First and Bournemouth Orchestral Society (£10,000 each); The Worshipful Company of Butchers (£5,000); Nightingale House for Aged Jews (£3,000); New Israel Fund of Great Britain and Magen David Adorn UK (£2,000 each); Bournemouth Reform Synagogue and Hannah Levy House Trust (£1,200 each); MacMillan Cancer Relief, Holocaust Education Trust and Tel Aviv Sourasky Medical Centre (£1,000 each).
FINANCES *Year* 2007–08 *Income* £108,811 *Grants* £108,500 *Assets* £867,343
TRUSTEES Norris Gilbert; Osman Azis.
HOW TO APPLY In writing to the correspondent
WHO TO APPLY TO Osman Azis, Trustee, The Counting House, Trelill, Bodmin, Cornwall PL30 3HZ *Tel* 01208 851814

CC NO 263726   **ESTABLISHED** 1971

■ The Katzauer Charitable Settlement

WHERE FUNDING CAN BE GIVEN UK, but mainly Israel.
WHO CAN BENEFIT Jewish people.
WHAT IS FUNDED Jewish organisations, predominantly in Israel.
RANGE OF GRANTS Up to £30,000.
SAMPLE GRANTS Beneficiaries were: Chabad Ra'anana (£26,000); Moriah Community and Meir Hospital (£10,000); Nahalat Yehiel (£6,000); Mercaz Hatorah (£4,000); Rabbi K Gross (£3,800); KollelRalanana (£3,200); Friends of Lubavitch (£2,900); Beit Hatavshil (£1,000).
FINANCES *Year* 2007–08 *Income* £97,584 *Grants* £76,617 *Assets* £921,418
TRUSTEES G C Smith; Mrs E Moller; M S Bailey; W Lian.
HOW TO APPLY In writing to the correspondent.
WHO TO APPLY TO Gordon Smith, Trustee, c/o Devonshire House, 1 Devonshire Street, London W1W 5DR *Tel* 020 7304 2000 *email* walter. lian@citroenwells.co.uk

CC NO 275110   **ESTABLISHED** 1977

■ The C S Kaufman Charitable Trust

WHERE FUNDING CAN BE GIVEN UK.
WHO CAN BENEFIT Organisations benefiting Jewish people.
WHAT IS FUNDED Mainly Jewish organisations.
WHAT IS NOT FUNDED No grants to individuals.
RANGE OF GRANTS Up to £30,000.
SAMPLE GRANTS Vaad Lehatzole and Mifalei Tzedoko Vochesed Israel (£30,000 each); Centre for Torah Educational Trust (£25,000); Matono (£20,000); Kollel Sha'arei Schlomo and Association Cerfi (£4,000 each); Achiezer

(£2,500); Jewish Teachers Training Course
(£1,700); and TAT Family Relief Fund (£1,500).
FINANCES *Year* 2007–08 *Income* £76,457
Grants £132,525 *Assets* £863,133
TRUSTEES I I Kaufman; Mrs L L Kaufman;
J J Kaufman; S Kaufman.
HOW TO APPLY In writing to the correspondent.
WHO TO APPLY TO C S Kaufman, 162 Whitehall Road,
Gateshead, Tyne and Wear NE8 1TP
CC NO 253194   **ESTABLISHED** 1967

■ The Geoffrey John Kaye Charitable Foundation

WHERE FUNDING CAN BE GIVEN UK and overseas.
WHO CAN BENEFIT Jewish people.
WHAT IS FUNDED Jewish organisations and other
charitable purposes.
TYPE OF GRANT Largely recurrent.
SAMPLE GRANTS WJA (£4,900); and Friends of
Nightingale House (£1,000).
FINANCES *Year* 2007–08 *Income* £51,379
Grants £16,529 *Assets* £855,150
TRUSTEES G J Kaye; Mrs S Rose; J Pears.
OTHER INFORMATION In 2007–08, a donation
totalling £11,000 was also given to one
individual.
HOW TO APPLY In writing to the correspondent.
Please note the foundation has previously
stated that funds were fully committed.
WHO TO APPLY TO R J Freebody, Accountant, 7 St
John's Road, Harrow, Middlesex HA1 2EY
Tel 020 8863 1234 *email* charity@mmrca.co.uk
CC NO 262547   **ESTABLISHED** 1971

■ The Emmanuel Kaye Foundation

WHERE FUNDING CAN BE GIVEN UK and overseas.
WHO CAN BENEFIT Organisations benefiting medical
professionals, research workers, scientists,
Jewish people, at-risk groups, people who are
disadvantaged by poverty and socially isolated
people.
WHAT IS FUNDED Medical research, welfare and
Jewish organisations.
WHAT IS NOT FUNDED Organisations not registered
with the Charity Commission are not supported.
RANGE OF GRANTS £50–£25,000.
SAMPLE GRANTS St James Conservation Trust
(£6,000); Imperial College London and
Nightingale (£5,000 each); Royal Academy of
Arts and St Michaels Hospice – North
Hampshire (£2,500 each); Jewish Care, the
Holocaust Education Trust, Shaare Zedek UK,
Community Links Trust, Laniado UK and UK
Friends of Magen David Adom (£2,000 each);
and Caius (£1,500).
FINANCES *Year* 2007–08 *Income* £57,011
Grants £59,350 *Assets* £1,018,754
TRUSTEES David Kaye; Lady Kaye; John Forster;
Michael Cutler.
HOW TO APPLY In writing to the correspondent.
WHO TO APPLY TO The Secretary to the Trustees,
Oakleigh House, High Street, Hartley Wintney,
Hampshire RG27 8PE *Tel* 01252 843773
CC NO 280281   **ESTABLISHED** 1980

■ The Caron Keating Foundation

WHERE FUNDING CAN BE GIVEN UK.
WHO CAN BENEFIT Professional carers,
complimentary healing practitioners, cancer
charities and support groups dealing with cancer
patients, as well as individuals and families who
are affected by the disease.
WHAT IS FUNDED Support for cancer patients.
SAMPLE GRANTS Jersey Hospice Care (£30,000);
Action Cancer (£25,000); and SCAT Bone
Cancer (£20,000).
FINANCES *Year* 2007–08 *Income* £274,720
Grants £173,350 *Assets* £526,952
TRUSTEES M Keating; G Hunniford.
HOW TO APPLY In writing to the correspondent.
WHO TO APPLY TO The Secretary, PO Box 122,
Sevenoaks, Kent TN13 1UM *email* info@
caronkeating.org *Website* www.caronkeating.org
CC NO 1106160   **ESTABLISHED** 2004

■ The Soli and Leah Kelaty Trust Fund

WHERE FUNDING CAN BE GIVEN England and Wales.
WHO CAN BENEFIT Registered charities.
WHAT IS FUNDED General, education, overseas aid,
religion.
FINANCES *Year* 2007–08 *Income* £60,487
Grants £57,139 *Assets* £820,482
TRUSTEES David Lerer; Fredrick Kelaty; Sharon
Mozel Kelaty.
HOW TO APPLY In writing to the correspondent.
WHO TO APPLY TO F S Kelaty, Secretary, Block O,
OCC Building, London N4 1TJ *Tel* 020 8800
2000 *email* freddy.kelaty@asiatic.co.uk
CC NO 1077620   **ESTABLISHED** 1999

■ Kelsick's Educational Foundation

WHERE FUNDING CAN BE GIVEN Lakes parish
(Ambleside, Grasmere, Langdale and part of
Troutbeck).
WHO CAN BENEFIT Organisations and individuals
under 25 years of age.
WHAT IS FUNDED Educational needs of individuals;
organisations providing educational benefit to
those under 25. School activities such as
educational visits, field trips, music lessons.
Academic courses and apprenticeships including
equipment.
WHAT IS NOT FUNDED Holidays, course items without
receipts.
TYPE OF GRANT Capital and project support, for
longer than three years.
RANGE OF GRANTS £50–£3,000.
SAMPLE GRANTS £121,000 to individuals; and
£96,000 to organisations.
FINANCES *Year* 2007–08 *Income* £309,874
Grants £217,424 *Assets* £5,931,563
TRUSTEES N Hutchinson, Chair; N M Tyson; Mrs
E M Braithwaite; Mrs L A Dixon; Mrs H M Fuller;
P Jackson; J O Halstead; Mrs J Renouf;
N C Martin; W R F Coke; R Jenkinson; R Curphey.
OTHER INFORMATION The Kelsick Foundation office is
open Monday-Friday: 9.30 to 12.30.
HOW TO APPLY Application forms are available from
the correspondent and from the website.
WHO TO APPLY TO P G Frost, Clerk, Kelsick Centre, St
Mary's Lane, Ambleside, Cumbria LA22 9DG
Tel 01539 431289 *Fax* 01539 431292
email john@kelsick.plus.com *Website* www.
kelsick.org.uk
CC NO 526956   **ESTABLISHED** 1723

■ The Kemp–Welch Charitable Trust

WHERE FUNDING CAN BE GIVEN UK.

WHO CAN BENEFIT National and local charities.

WHAT IS FUNDED Medical research, parochial church councils, care and welfare of both children and older people and educational establishments, arts and culture, wildlife and the environment.

RANGE OF GRANTS Up to £2,500.

SAMPLE GRANTS Game Conservancy Scottish Research Trust (£2,500); Little Hallingbury Parochial Church Council (£1,500); Cancer Vaccine Institute, Every Child and National Portrait Gallery (£1,000 each); Childhood First, Macmillan Cancer Relief and Scottish Countryside Alliance Educational Trust (£500 each); and Rainbow Trust Childrens Charity, Essex Association of Boys Clubs and Community Links Trust (£250 each).

FINANCES *Year* 2007–08 *Income* £155,627 *Grants* £42,200 *Assets* £926,156

TRUSTEES Sir John Kemp–Welch; Lady Diana Elisabeth Kemp–Welch.

HOW TO APPLY No unsolicited applications.

WHO TO APPLY TO Sir John Kemp–Welch, Trustee, Little Hallingbury Place, Wrights Green Lane, Little Hallingbury, Bishop's Stortford, Hertfordshire CM22 7RE *Tel* 01279 722455

CC NO 263501

■ The Kay Kendall Leukaemia Fund

WHERE FUNDING CAN BE GIVEN Unrestricted.

WHO CAN BENEFIT Organisations conducting research into and treatment of leukaemia.

WHAT IS FUNDED Medical research into and treatment of leukaemia.

WHAT IS NOT FUNDED Circular appeals for general support are not funded.

TYPE OF GRANT Research, capital, equipment.

SAMPLE GRANTS Institute of Cancer Research (£410,000 in total); University of Cambridge (£385,000 in total); Imperial College School of Medicine (£287,000 in total); and University of Manchester (£214,000 in total).

FINANCES *Year* 2007–08 *Income* £2,090,000 *Grants* £2,040,000 *Assets* £50,105,000

TRUSTEES Judith Portrait; Timothy J Sainsbury; Christopher Stone.

OTHER INFORMATION The trust is one of the Sainsbury Family Charitable Trusts which share a common administration. An application to one is taken as an application to all.

HOW TO APPLY A preliminary letter or telephone call to the administration offices of the Kay Kendall Leukaemia Fund may be helpful to determine whether or not a proposal is likely to be eligible. Application forms are available by contacting the trust's office. Research Proposal: 'Applicants should complete the approved application form and include a research proposal (aims, background, plan of investigation, justification for budget). The research proposal should be three to five single-spaced pages for project grants (excluding references, costings and CV) and up to ten single-spaced pages for programme grants. Applications should be submitted by email in addition to the provision of a hard copy with original signature. The trustees will take account of annual inflation and of salary increases related to nationally negotiated pay scales and these should not be built into the application. Salaries should generally be on nationally agreed scales.

Tenured or non time-limited appointments will not be supported. The trustees may, from time to time, set special conditions for the award of a grant. Final decision on the award of a grant is made by the trustees, having taken into account advice from their scientific advisers. The trustees consider proposals twice each year, normally May and October. To allow for the refereeing process, new full proposals for the May meeting should be received by 28 February and for the October/November meeting by 15 July. Late applications may be deferred for six months.

WHO TO APPLY TO Alan Bookbinder, Director, Allington House, 1st Floor, 150 Victoria Street, London SW1E 5AE *Tel* 020 7410 0330 *Fax* 020 7410 0332 *email* info@kklf.org.uk *Website* www.kklf.org.uk

CC NO 290772   **ESTABLISHED** 1984

■ William Kendall's Charity (Wax Chandlers' Company)

WHERE FUNDING CAN BE GIVEN Greater London and the London borough of Bexley.

WHO CAN BENEFIT Charitable organisations in Greater London working for relief of need; in Bexley, charitable organisations generally.

WHAT IS FUNDED Most donations are for relief of need in London.

WHAT IS NOT FUNDED Grants are not normally made to large charities, charities whose accounts disclose substantial reserves or non-registered charities. Grants are not made to replace cuts in funding made by local authorities or others, schemes or activities which would be regarded as relieving central or local government of their statutory responsibilities or cover deficits already incurred.

TYPE OF GRANT One-off or recurring.

RANGE OF GRANTS £500–£20,000, typical grant £5,000.

SAMPLE GRANTS Grants from the Bexley Fund included those made to: Bexley Accessible Transport Scheme (£5,000); Bexley Trust for Adult Students and Bexley Womens Aid (£2,000 each); and Carers' Support Bexley (£1,000).

FINANCES *Year* 2007–08 *Income* £99,296 *Grants* £23,554 *Assets* £2,925,652

TRUSTEES Wax Chandlers' Company.

OTHER INFORMATION Grants to six individuals from the Persons in Need Fund totalled £5,000.

HOW TO APPLY The company undertakes its own research and does not respond to unsolicited applications.

WHO TO APPLY TO The Clerk to the Wax Chandlers' Company, Wax Chandlers' Hall, 6 Gresham Street, London EC2V 7AD *Tel* 020 7606 3591 *Fax* 020 7600 5462 *email* info@chandlers.ndonet.com *Website* www.waxchandlers.org.uk/charity

CC NO 228361   **ESTABLISHED** 1559

■ The Kennedy Charitable Foundation

WHERE FUNDING CAN BE GIVEN Unrestricted, but mainly Ireland with a preference for County Mayo and County Sligo.

WHO CAN BENEFIT Registered charities and individuals.

WHAT IS FUNDED Predominantly organisations connected with the Roman Catholic faith, mainly in Ireland.

RANGE OF GRANTS £200–£50,000; typical grant £1,000–£5,000.

SAMPLE GRANTS Short Strand Community Forum (£41,000); Pontifical Irish College Trust (£34,000); Ireland Health Foundation (£23,500); Little Sisters of the Poor (£20,000); Diocese of Hexham & Newcastle (£15,000); Trafford New Diabetes Unit (£11,000); Society of African Missions (£10,000); Cornerstone (£3,500); Bridge Project (£2,500); Children with Leukaemia (£2,000); and Cancer Research UK (£1,000).

FINANCES *Year* 2007–08 *Income* £589,575 *Grants* £468,500 *Assets* £498,539

TRUSTEES Patrick James Kennedy; Kathleen Kennedy; John Gerard Kennedy; Patrick Joseph Francis Kennedy; Anna Maria Kelly.

HOW TO APPLY The foundation says that 'unsolicited applications are not accepted'.

WHO TO APPLY TO Alan Pye, 12th Floor, Bank House, Charlotte Street, Manchester M1 4ET *Tel* 0161 236 8191 *Fax* 0161 236 4814 *email* kcf@pye158.freeserve.co.uk

CC NO 1052001   **ESTABLISHED** 1995

■ The Kennel Club Charitable Trust

WHERE FUNDING CAN BE GIVEN UK.

WHO CAN BENEFIT Registered charities or research bodies benefiting dogs; research workers and vets; and people who are disabled blind or deaf where dogs are involved (e.g. in support of human beings).

WHAT IS FUNDED The trust describes its objects as 'science, welfare and support'. It supports the furthering of research into canine diseases and hereditary disorders of dogs and also organisations concerned with the welfare of dogs in need and those which aim to improve the quality of life of humans by promoting dogs as practical or therapeutic aids.

WHAT IS NOT FUNDED The trust does not give grants directly to individuals; veterinary nurses can apply to the British Veterinary Nursing Association where bursaries are available. The trustees tend not to favour funding the costs of building work.

TYPE OF GRANT One-off and recurring for set periods.

RANGE OF GRANTS The trust gives both ongoing and one-off grants, generally up to £35,000 each a year for research and of up to £10,000 each for support of dogs and those who care for them or benefit from them.

FINANCES *Year* 2008 *Income* £1,388,388 *Grants* £824,253 *Assets* £2,609,804

TRUSTEES M Townsend, Chair; M Herrtage; W H King; J Spurling; Mrs J Ziman.

OTHER INFORMATION Further information is available at the trust's website.

HOW TO APPLY In writing to the administrator, including latest accounts. Please state clearly details of the costs for which you are requesting funding, and for what purpose and over what period the funding is required. The trustees meet three or four times a year.

WHO TO APPLY TO Doug Holford, 1–5 Clarges Street, Piccadilly, London W1J 8AB *Tel* 020 7518 1037 *email* dholford@the-kennel-club.org.uk *Website* www.mad4dogs.org.uk

CC NO 327802   **ESTABLISHED** 1988

■ Kent Community Foundation

WHERE FUNDING CAN BE GIVEN Kent.

WHO CAN BENEFIT Local charities, community groups and voluntary organisations and individuals.

WHAT IS FUNDED Improving the quality of life for people in Kent. The foundation administers a number of funds established by individuals, families and companies. In addition it has its own general fund which enables it to support voluntary groups which fall outside the stated criteria of these funds.

FINANCES *Year* 2007–08 *Income* £3,074,565 *Grants* £2,601,152 *Assets* £1,838,373

TRUSTEES Peter Hardy, Chair; Barry Jones; Annabel Campbell; Mike Angell; Laura Jones; Eric Watts; Alan Rogers; Amanda Cottrell; Tracey Reddings.

OTHER INFORMATION A member of the Community Foundation Network, Kent Community Foundation is a charitable foundation set up to encourage philanthropy for the benefit of the people of Kent. In 2007–08 grants were made to almost 600 groups.

HOW TO APPLY Further information on applications can be obtained from the Grants Team.

WHO TO APPLY TO The Grants Team, Evegate Park Barn, Evegate Business Park, Evegate, Ashford, Kent TN25 6SX *Tel* 01303 814500 *email* admin@kentcf.org.uk *Website* www.kentcf.org.uk

CC NO 1084361   **ESTABLISHED** 2001

■ The Nancy Kenyon Charitable Trust

WHERE FUNDING CAN BE GIVEN UK.

WHO CAN BENEFIT Registered charities only.

WHAT IS FUNDED General charitable purposes. Primarily for people and causes known to the trustees.

WHAT IS NOT FUNDED Grants not usually made to individuals.

RANGE OF GRANTS Up to £11,000.

SAMPLE GRANTS Nancy Oldfield Trust (£11,000); the Rainbow Farm Trust (£8,500); St Nicholas Church – Ashchurch (£3,500); Essex Association of Boys' Clubs and the Nehemiah Project (£3,000 each); Cheltenham Youth for Christ and the Starfish Cafe – Cambodia (£2,000 each); and The Family Haven, National Star Centre for Disabled Youth and EmthonjeniTrust (£1,000 each).

FINANCES *Year* 2007–08 *Income* £45,147 *Grants* £45,400 *Assets* £1,433,479

TRUSTEES Lucy Phipps; Maureen Kenyon; Christopher Kenyon; Sally Kenyon; Peter Kenyon.

HOW TO APPLY In writing to the correspondent at any time. Applications for causes not known to the trustees are considered annually in December.

WHO TO APPLY TO The Trustees, Meads Barn, Ashwell Business Park, Ilminster, Somerset TA19 9DX *Tel* 01460 259852

CC NO 265359   **ESTABLISHED** 1972

■ Keren Association

WHERE FUNDING CAN BE GIVEN UK.

WHO CAN BENEFIT Organisations benefiting children, young adults and Jewish people.

WHAT IS FUNDED The advancement of education; the provision of religious instruction and training in traditional Judaism; general charitable purposes.

SAMPLE GRANTS Previous beneficiaries include: Beis Aharon Trust, Yeshivah Belz Machnovke, U T A,

Yetev Lev Jerulalem, Lomdei Tom h Belz Machnovke, Friends of Beis Yaakov, Yeshlvat Lom dei Torah, Friends of Arad, Kupat Gmach Vezer Nlsuin, Clwk Yaakov and British Heart Foundation.

FINANCES *Year* 2007–08 *Income* £8,479,179 *Grants* £6,467,420 *Assets* £19,275,539
TRUSTEES E Englander, Chair; Mrs S Englander; P N Englander; S Z Englander; B Englander; J S Englander; Mrs H Z Weiss; Mrs N Weiss.
OTHER INFORMATION A list of grant recipients was not included in the accounts.
HOW TO APPLY In writing to the correspondent.
WHO TO APPLY TO Mrs S Englander, Trustee, 136 Clapton Common, London E5 9AG
CC NO 313119   **ESTABLISHED** 1961

■ Kermaville Ltd

WHERE FUNDING CAN BE GIVEN UK.
WHO CAN BENEFIT Organisations benefiting Jewish people.
WHAT IS FUNDED Advancement of religion according to the orthodox Jewish faith and general charitable purposes.
SAMPLE GRANTS Previous beneficiaries include Yeshivas Imrei Chaim Spinka, Bais Rochel D'Satmar, Keren Tzedoka Vechessed, Kollel Congregation Yetev Lev, Kollel Atzei Chaim, United Talmudical Association, Ponevez Beth Hamedrash and Lolev Charitable Trust.
FINANCES *Year* 2007–08 *Income* £26,814 *Grants* £26,000 *Assets* £228,414
TRUSTEES L Rabinowitz.
HOW TO APPLY In writing to the correspondent.
WHO TO APPLY TO M Freund, 3 Overlea Road, London E5 9BG *Tel* 020 8806 5783
CC NO 266075   **ESTABLISHED** 1973

■ E and E Kernkraut Charities Limited

WHERE FUNDING CAN BE GIVEN UK.
WHO CAN BENEFIT Charitable organisations.
WHAT IS FUNDED General charitable purposes, Jewish and education.
FINANCES *Year* 2007–08 *Income* £1,003,543 *Grants* £735,927 *Assets* £5,996,160
TRUSTEES E Kernkraut, Chair; Mrs E Kernkraut; Joseph Kernkraut; Jacob Kernkraut.
HOW TO APPLY In writing to the correspondent.
WHO TO APPLY TO E Kernkraut, Chair, c/o New Burlington House, 1075 Finchley Road, London NW11 0PU *Tel* 020 8806 7947
CC NO 275636   **ESTABLISHED** 1978

■ The Peter Kershaw Trust

WHERE FUNDING CAN BE GIVEN Manchester and the surrounding district only.
WHO CAN BENEFIT Registered charities benefiting young adults and older people, carers and people who are disadvantaged by poverty, homeless or socially isolated.
WHAT IS FUNDED Medical research, grants to medical and other institutions, bursaries for schools.
WHAT IS NOT FUNDED No grants to individuals or for building projects.
TYPE OF GRANT One-off or core costs. Also research, running costs, salaries and start-up costs. Funding may be given for up to three years.
RANGE OF GRANTS Up to £25,000.
SAMPLE GRANTS Chorlton Youth Project (£25,000); Charnley Research Institute – hip replacement

surgery research (£21,000); Reach Out (£20,000); Royal School for Deaf and Communications Disorder (£15,000); Copperdale Trust (£14,000); Fairbridge, Life Share, Jigsaw and Broughton House (£10,000 each); Stockport Cerebral Palsy Society (£8,000); Mosses Centre (£7,500); King's School – Macclesfield (£5,500); and Bury Grammar Schools and Manchester Grammar School (£3,300 each); Knutsford Methodist Church (£3,000); Farms for City Children (£2,300); Independent Options (£1,500); and Bobby Moore Fund (£250).
FINANCES *Year* 2007–08 *Income* £300,510 *Grants* £269,174 *Assets* £6,450,572
TRUSTEES R P Kershaw, Chair; Mrs H F Kershaw; Mrs M L Rushbrooke; D Tully; Mrs R Adams; T Page.
HOW TO APPLY In writing to the correspondent, however the trust is always oversubscribed. The trustees normally meet twice a year in May and November to consider recommendations for grant aid which will be disbursed in June and December respectively.
WHO TO APPLY TO Bryan Peak, Secretary, 22 Ashworth Park, Knutsford, Cheshire WA16 9DE *Tel* 01565 651086 *email* pkershawtrust@btinternet.com
CC NO 268934   **ESTABLISHED** 1974

■ The Kessler Foundation

WHERE FUNDING CAN BE GIVEN UK.
WHO CAN BENEFIT Charitable organisations, with a preference for Jewish organisations.
WHAT IS FUNDED The foundation will assist organisations which may be devoted to: the advancement of Jewish religion, learning, education and culture; the improvement of inter-faith, community and race relations, and the combating of prejudice; the alleviation of the problems of minority and disadvantaged groups; the protection, maintenance and monitoring of human rights; the promotion of health and welfare; the protection and preservation of records and objects with special significance to the Jewish and general community; or the encouragement of arts, literature and science including archaeology, natural history and protection of the environment with special reference to the Jewish community.
WHAT IS NOT FUNDED In general the foundation will not support the larger well-known charities with an income in excess of £100,000, and will not provide grants for social, medical and welfare projects which are the responsibility of local or national government.
RANGE OF GRANTS Up to £2,000.
SAMPLE GRANTS Jewish Council for Racial Equality, Asylum Aid and Bedouin Women for Themselves (£2,000 each); International Council of Jewish Women (£1,500); Project Harar Ethiopia (£1,200); Peace Child Israel, Makor Charitable Trust, Jewish Bereavement Counselling Service and Theatre Objektiv (£1,000 each); Friends of Israel Educational Foundation and Quest New London Synagogue (£750 each); Ipswich Community Playbus and Aid for Romanian Orphanages (£500 each); and Arts to Share (£250).
FINANCES *Year* 2007–08 *Income* £29,092 *Grants* £46,438 *Assets* £238,439
TRUSTEES L Blackstone, Chair; Mrs J Jacobs; Prof. M Geller; Mr N P J Saphir; Mrs J F Mayers; P Morgenstern.
HOW TO APPLY On a form available from the correspondent. The trustees meet at least twice

a year in June and December. Applicants will be notified of decisions as soon as possible after then.

WHO TO APPLY TO L R Blackstone, 25 Furnival Street, London EC4A 1JT

CC NO 290759   **ESTABLISHED** 1984

....

■ Keswick Hall Charity

WHERE FUNDING CAN BE GIVEN East Anglia.

WHO CAN BENEFIT University of East Anglia, its teachers and students (especially student teachers) and corporate organisations in the dioceses of Ely, Norwich and St Edmundsbury and Ipswich.

WHAT IS FUNDED Grants to support the education and training of religious education (RE) teachers and students, corporate grants to support the teaching of RE, and research and development grants in that subject.

WHAT IS NOT FUNDED The trust does not make grants for buildings, courses in pastoral work or courses which are purely for personal interest. Retrospective applications will not be considered. If an application is received from a student who has already started a course, but has not yet completed it, the application will not be regarded as a retrospective application. The trustees state that they give priority to their own initiatives.

RANGE OF GRANTS Up to £8,000.

FINANCES *Year* 2008–09 *Income* £227,825 *Grants* £3,500 *Assets* £3,067,603

TRUSTEES Right Revd D Atkinson; Revd C Davidson; Revd Canon T Elbourne; R Evans; Revd C Everett; Revd Canon A R Heawood; T Haydn; A Mash; Revd Canon S Pettitt; Revd Canon Sanders.

OTHER INFORMATION In 2008–09 £3,500 was given to organisations and £2,847 to individuals

HOW TO APPLY Grant applications should be received by the beginning of the months of January, May or September each year and must be made using the forms obtained either from the website (www.keswickhalltrust.org.uk) or fromthe correspondent.

WHO TO APPLY TO Phil Filer, Executive Secretary, PO Box 202, Wymondham NR18 8AE *Tel* 01603 882376 *Fax* 01603 882378 *email* admin@keswickhalltrust.org.uk *Website* www.keswickhalltrust.org.uk

CC NO 311246   **ESTABLISHED** 1968

....

■ The Ursula Keyes Trust

WHERE FUNDING CAN BE GIVEN Chester, but occasionally other areas.

WHO CAN BENEFIT Individuals and institutions benefiting at risk groups, and people who are disadvantaged by poverty, socially isolated or sick.

WHAT IS FUNDED The purpose of the trust is to support the financial needs of various organisations and individuals in the Chester area, particularly in the fields of health and social care. A wide range of causes are supported, including cultural and leisure projects, particularly when matched by other fundraising efforts. Funds are mainly directed at the cost of capital projects and equipment rather than as a source of funding for ongoing running costs or salaries. National charities are also considered for support if there is a clear link to a local beneficiary.

WHAT IS NOT FUNDED No support for students or political groups.

TYPE OF GRANT Small and large grants.

RANGE OF GRANTS Mostly under £10,000.

SAMPLE GRANTS Hospice of the Good Shepherd (£32,000); Save the Family (£16,500); Macmillan Cancer Support (£15,000); the Wingate Centre (£10,000); Belgrave Infant School (£6,000); Tarporley War Memorial Hospital Trust (£5,000); Brain Injury Rehabilitation & Development (£4,200); British Red Cross (£3,000); Chester Rape Crisis (£2,000); and Kids Konnect (£1,000).

FINANCES *Year* 2007 *Income* £346,794 *Grants* £185,741 *Assets* £5,813,301

TRUSTEES J F Kane, Chair; Dr R A Owen; H M Shaw; Dr A E Elliot; J R Leaman; J D Brimelow.

OTHER INFORMATION Grants were also made to individuals totalling £11,000.

HOW TO APPLY In writing to the correspondent.

WHO TO APPLY TO Sharon Bakewell, Administrator to the Trustees, c/o Baker Tilly, Steam Mill, Chester, Cheshire CH3 5AN *Tel* 01244 505100 *Fax* 01244 505101 *Website* www.ursula-keyes-trust.org.uk

CC NO 517200   **ESTABLISHED** 1985

....

■ The Kiawah Charitable Trust

WHERE FUNDING CAN BE GIVEN Primarily sub Saharan Africa and southern India.

WHO CAN BENEFIT Charitable organisations.

WHAT IS FUNDED Young people whose lives are vulnerable due to health and/or education issues.

SAMPLE GRANTS Hope and Homes for Children (£177,000); Playpumps (£50,000); Sight Savers International (£45,000); Noah and Railway Children (£30,000 each); Pratham UK Limited (£10,000); EOPD (£7,500); and Dreamnight and Walk the Walk Worldwide (£1,000 each).

FINANCES *Year* 2007–08 *Income* £285,328 *Grants* £353,856 *Assets* £1,021,802

TRUSTEES Peter Smitham; Lynne Smitham; Vic Miles.

HOW TO APPLY 'The trustees consider any applications received for grants and adopt a proactive approach in seeking worthy causes requiring support.'

WHO TO APPLY TO The Trustees, c/o Farrer and Co., 65–66 Lincoln's Inn Fields, London WC2A 3LH

CC NO 1107730   **ESTABLISHED** 2005

....

■ The Robert Kiln Charitable Trust

WHERE FUNDING CAN BE GIVEN UK, with a special interest in Hertfordshire and Bedfordshire. Occasionally overseas.

WHO CAN BENEFIT Organisations benefiting archaeologists and small environmental organisations.

WHAT IS FUNDED General charitable purposes with a preference for small organisations.

WHAT IS NOT FUNDED Applications from individuals, large national appeals, churches, schools or artistic projects (such as theatre groups) will not be considered.

TYPE OF GRANT Usually one-off, or instalments for particular projects.

RANGE OF GRANTS £250–£2,500. Mostly £500.

SAMPLE GRANTS Hertford Symphony Orchestra (£2,750); Groundwork – Hertfordshire (£2,000); University of Sheffield (£1,600); University of Nottingham (£1,500); Afghan Training Foundation, Computer Aid International, Hadrian's Wall Pilgrimage, Orkney Archaeology

Think carefully about every application. Is it justified?

643

Trust, Ware Museum and Welwyn Archaeology Society (£1,000 each).

FINANCES *Year* 2007–08 *Income* £53,307 *Grants* £44,036 *Assets* £904,840

TRUSTEES S W J Kiln; Mrs B Kiln; Dr N P Akers; Mrs J Akers.

OTHER INFORMATION The trust stated: 'Most of the income is allocated to regular beneficiaries, where relationship has been built up over many years (55%). The trustees are keen to support new projects, particularly those from small local organisations. The trustees support many charities where they have a particular interest.'

HOW TO APPLY In writing to the correspondent, setting out as much information as seems relevant and, if possible, costings and details of any other support. The trust no longer has twice-yearly distribution meetings and will endeavour to distribute funds within one month of receiving applications, subject to funds being available. The trust does not acknowledge receipt of applications unless an sae is enclosed.

WHO TO APPLY TO Mrs Sarah Howell, Secretary to the trustees, 15a Bull Plain, Hertford SG14 1DX *Tel* 01992 554962 *email* kilntrust@hemscott. net

CC NO 262756   ESTABLISHED 1970

■ The King Henry VIII Endowed Trust – Warwick

WHERE FUNDING CAN BE GIVEN The former borough of Warwick only.

WHO CAN BENEFIT Half the income goes to Warwick churches, 30% to Warwick Independent Schools Foundation and 20% for the 'Town Share' – general charitable purposes for the inhabitants of the town of Warwick.

WHAT IS FUNDED General charitable purposes in the former borough of Warwick (in effect now covered by the postcode area CV34). (The grant total in this entry only applies to the grants for general charitable purposes.).

RANGE OF GRANTS £300–£75,000.

SAMPLE GRANTS Beneficiaries of the Town Share of the trust's income included: (£75,000), Warwick Hospital Cancer Ward Appeal, (£36,000), Newburgh Primary School(£15,000) Warwick Tennis Club, (£9,000) Senior Citizens Holiday Club, (£3,000) Warwick International Festival (£3,000).

FINANCES *Year* 2008 *Income* £1,756,545 *Grants* £309,759 *Assets* £24,534,685

TRUSTEES Trustees names not disclosed – dispensation given.

HOW TO APPLY In writing to the correspondent. Trustees meet to make grants six times a year.

WHO TO APPLY TO R J Wyatt, Clerk, 12 High Street, Warwick CV34 4AP *Tel* 01926 495533 *Fax* 01926 401464

CC NO 232862   ESTABLISHED 1964

■ The King/Cullimore Charitable Trust

WHERE FUNDING CAN BE GIVEN UK.

WHO CAN BENEFIT Charitable organisations.

WHAT IS FUNDED General charitable purposes.

RANGE OF GRANTS Up to £25,000.

SAMPLE GRANTS Amerderm Research Trust (£25,000); Countryside Foundation for Education (£15,000); Music in Hospitals (£11,000); Duke of Edinburgh Award, Thames Valley Hospice, Lorica St Patrick's, Crisis, Age

Concern (£10,000 each); and Practical Action in Nepal and Orangutan Foundation (£5,000 each).

FINANCES *Year* 2007–08 *Income* £316,660 *Grants* £110,650 *Assets* £5,101,105

TRUSTEES P A Cullimore; C Gardner; C J King; A G McKechnie.

HOW TO APPLY In writing to the correspondent.

WHO TO APPLY TO P A Cullimore, Trustee, 52 Ledborough Lane, Beaconsfield, Buckinghamshire HP9 2DF *Tel* 01494 678811

CC NO 1074928   ESTABLISHED 1999

■ The King's Fund

WHERE FUNDING CAN BE GIVEN London.

WHO CAN BENEFIT Voluntary or statutory organisations in the health sector in or serving Greater London.

WHAT IS FUNDED Through the Partners for Health in London funding and development programme, focusing initially on four areas: end-of-life care, sexual health, mental health advocacy and integrated health care; delivering, on behalf of the Department of Health, the current Enhancing the Healing Environment programmes and developing new areas of application; delivering a national awards scheme to identify and promote best practice in community organisations working to improve health; developing analytical tools to be used throughout the National Health Service.

FINANCES *Year* 2008 *Income* £12,761,000 *Grants* £1,171,000 *Assets* £114,414,000

TRUSTEES Sir Cyril Chantler; Strone Macpherson; Jude Goffe; David Wootton; Dr Penelope Dash; Simon Stevens; Jacqueline Docherty; Prof Julian Le Grand.

OTHER INFORMATION The King's Fund is a leading independent health care charity, set up in 1897 by the Prince of Wales, later King Edward VII, to support the improvement of the health of Londoners and health care in London. Today it fulfils this mission through a range of activities, including research and policy analysis as well as grantmaking – which accounts for about one-quarter of its charitable expenditure.

HOW TO APPLY Applicants are advised to check the fund's website or contact them directly for the latest information on current funding programmes.

WHO TO APPLY TO Kate Batlin, The Funding and Development Department, 11–13 Cavendish Square, London W1G 0AN *Tel* 020 7307 2400 *Fax* 020 7307 2809 *email* grants@kingsfund. org.uk *Website* www.kingsfund.org.uk

CC NO 1126980   ESTABLISHED 1897

■ The Mary Kinross Charitable Trust

WHERE FUNDING CAN BE GIVEN UK.

WHO CAN BENEFIT Registered charities benefiting research workers, young people and people disadvantaged by poverty.

WHAT IS FUNDED General charitable purposes. Donations confined to projects which the trust promotes and manages, particularly in the areas of medical research, to benefit the communities of which trustees have direct knowledge: young people, mental health and penal affairs. Grants made under the heading of youth are often made with crime prevention in mind.

WHAT IS NOT FUNDED No grants to individuals.

TYPE OF GRANT Capital projects, core costs and recurring.

SAMPLE GRANTS Moseley Community Development Trust (£190,000); Juvenile Diabetes Research Foundation (£97,000); Queen's Medical Research Institute – University of Edinburgh (£50,000); Hepatitis C Trust (£30,000); Peninsula Medical School Foundation (£25,000); Prospex (£20,000); Bendrigg Trust (£11,000); Prison Radio Association (£5,000); Skye and Lochalsh Mental Health Association (£2,000); and West Midlands Charity Trusts Group (£900).

FINANCES Year 2008–09 Income £736,785 Grants £868,235 Assets £20,861,168

TRUSTEES Elizabeth Shields, Chair; Fiona Adams; Neil Cross; Jonathan Haw; Robert McDougall.

HOW TO APPLY 'Because the trustees have no office staff and work from home, they prefer dealing with written correspondence rather than telephone calls from applicants soliciting funds.' Please note: unsolicited applications to this trust are very unlikely to be successful.

WHO TO APPLY TO Fiona Adams, Trustee, 36 Grove Avenue, Moseley, Birmingham B13 9RY

CC NO 212206   ESTABLISHED 1957

■ Kinsurdy Charitable Trust

WHERE FUNDING CAN BE GIVEN UK.

WHO CAN BENEFIT Charitable organisations.

WHAT IS FUNDED General charitable purposes.

RANGE OF GRANTS Up to £5,000.

SAMPLE GRANTS R.N.L.I. and Alzheimer's Society (£5,000 each); Parkinson's Disease Society, Help the Aged, MacMillan Cancer Support, the Childrens Trust, the British Red Cross and Save the Children (£4,000 each); and League of friends – West Berkshire Hospice (£2,000 each).

FINANCES Year 2007–08 Income £270,151 Grants £73,000 Assets £1,371,470

TRUSTEES R P Tullett; A H Bartlett.

HOW TO APPLY In writing to the correspondent.

WHO TO APPLY TO The Trustees, Cheviot Asset Management Limited, 90 Long Acre, London WC2E 9RA

CC NO 1076085   ESTABLISHED 1999

■ Kirkley Poor's Land Estate

WHERE FUNDING CAN BE GIVEN The parish of Kirkley and the former borough of Kirkley.

WHO CAN BENEFIT Individuals and organisations.

WHAT IS FUNDED Welfare and disability. The trust administers a grocery voucher scheme enabling people of pensionable age in Kirkley to receive a grant each winter to purchase groceries. It cooperates with Kirkley High School to make grants to former pupils whose parents have low incomes to help with their expenses at university or other further education establishments. All funding has to be calculated to reduce identified need, hardship or distress.

WHAT IS NOT FUNDED No grants to well known charities or only to local branches.

TYPE OF GRANT One-off.

RANGE OF GRANTS Up to £3,575.

SAMPLE GRANTS Grants made to organisations included the following: St. John's Housing Trust and the Waveney Womens Refuge (£3,575), Waveney Counselling Service (£2,750), Kirkley Church – St. Peter & St. John, Pakefield Church and Waveney Rape & Abuse (£1,650 each), Waveney Crossroads (£1,550), Salvation Army – Kirkley Branch (£900), Lowestoft Club for the Elderly and Kirkley Pre-school (£500 each).

FINANCES Year 2007–08 Income £78,359 Grants £42,002 Assets £1,873,327

TRUSTEES Mrs J Van-Pelt, Chair; Mr M Cook; Mr R Castleton; Mr A Shepherd; Rev R Wormald.

OTHER INFORMATION In total, individuals received £2,650; 744 vouchers of £20 each were also given to older people in Kirkely for the purchase of groceries in the winter.

HOW TO APPLY In writing to the correspondent.

WHO TO APPLY TO Lucy Walker, Clerk, 4 Station Road, Lowestoft, Suffolk NR32 4QF Tel 01502 514964

CC NO 210177   ESTABLISHED 1976

■ The Richard Kirkman Charitable Trust

WHERE FUNDING CAN BE GIVEN UK, with a preference for Hampshire.

WHO CAN BENEFIT Registered charities and individuals.

WHAT IS FUNDED General charitable purposes, however the trustees are considering financing various plans for alleviating drug addiction.

RANGE OF GRANTS Up to £3,000.

SAMPLE GRANTS Vermont School (£7,000); Streetscene, Rose Road Association, British Limbless Ex-Servicemen Association (£4,000 each); Leukeamia Busters, Marwell Preservation Trust and Alresford Citizens Advice Bureau (£3,000 each); British Diabetic Association, Jubilee Sailing Trust and Stroke Association (£2,000 each); and Wessex Childrens Hospice Trust, Haemophilia Society and Police Dependants Trust (£1,500 each).

FINANCES Year 2007–08 Income £70,442 Grants £86,223 Assets £1,603,239

TRUSTEES M Howson-Green; Mrs F O Kirkman; B M Baxendale; D A Hoare.

OTHER INFORMATION In 2007–08 there were 50 further grants given to institutions of £1,000 or less totalling £33,000.

HOW TO APPLY The trust carries out its own research for beneficiaries and does not respond to applications by post or telephone.

WHO TO APPLY TO M Howson-Green, Trustee, Ashton House, 12 The Precinct, Wincester Road, Chandlers Ford, Eastleigh, Hampshire SO53 2GB Tel 023 8027 4555 Fax 023 8027 5766

CC NO 327972   ESTABLISHED 1988

■ Kirschel Foundation

WHERE FUNDING CAN BE GIVEN UK.

WHO CAN BENEFIT Registered charities.

WHAT IS FUNDED The trust states that its aims and objectives are 'to provide benefits to underprivileged persons, who may be either disabled or lacking resources'. In practice this includes many Jewish organisations.

RANGE OF GRANTS Up to £50,000.

SAMPLE GRANTS Ahavat Shalom Charity Fund (£50,000); Jewish Learning Exchange (£46,000); Moracha Limited (£40,000); Treehouse Trust (£25,000); Friends of Lubavitch Scotland (£17,000); Yakar Education Foundation (£10,000); Evelina Children's Hospital Appeal (£8,000); Friends of Yeshiva Hazon Mei (£5,000); Noam Primary School (£4,300); National Autistic Society (£3,500); Rays of Sunshine (£3,000); Cholel Chabad (£2,500); WST Charity Limited (£2,000); and the BST Charitable Trust, Jewish Care and Kisharon (£1,000 each).

FINANCES *Year* 2007–08 *Income* £537,104
Grants £385,710 *Assets* £844,704

TRUSTEES Laurence Grant Kirschel; Ian Lipman; Stephen Pinshaw.

OTHER INFORMATION In 2007/08, the total of all other donations, individually less than £1,000 each was £7,800.

HOW TO APPLY In writing to the correspondent.

WHO TO APPLY TO 131 Edgware Road, London W2 2AP *Tel* 020 7437 4372

CC NO 1067672   **ESTABLISHED** 1998

....

■ Robert Kitchin (Saddlers' Company)

WHERE FUNDING CAN BE GIVEN City of London and contiguous boroughs.

WHO CAN BENEFIT Organisations and student welfare.

WHAT IS FUNDED Education and general charitable purposes.

SAMPLE GRANTS City University London (£76,000); Hindleap Warren (£30,000); St Ethelburga's Centre for Reconciliation and Peace (£23,000); London Borough of Tower Hamlets – maths project (£10,000); Beormund Primary School (£5,400); St Andrew's Youth Club – Westminster (£5,000); and City of London School, City of London School for Girls, City of London Freemen's School and Reed's School (£650 each).

FINANCES *Year* 2008–09 *Income* £158,619
Grants £152,188 *Assets* £2,487,506

TRUSTEES Saddlers' Company.

OTHER INFORMATION Each year the charity gives a fixed percentage to two organisations – City University receives 50% of net income, while St Ethelburga's Centre for Reconciliation and Peace receives 15% of net income. The remaining 35% is distributed at the discretion of the trustees.

HOW TO APPLY In writing to the correspondent. However, the discretionary element of the trust's income is fully committed each year and the trustees are unable to respond to applications.

WHO TO APPLY TO The Clerk to the Trustees, Saddlers' Company, Saddlers' Hall, 40 Gutter Lane, London EC2V 6BR *Tel* 020 7726 8661 *email* clerk@saddlersco.co.uk

CC NO 211169   **ESTABLISHED** 1891

....

■ Ernest Kleinwort Charitable Trust

WHERE FUNDING CAN BE GIVEN UK, mainly Sussex and overseas.

WHO CAN BENEFIT Registered charities.

WHAT IS FUNDED The main fields of work are wildlife and environmental conservation, disability, medical research, welfare of older people and welfare of young people.

WHAT IS NOT FUNDED Individuals and local charities outside Sussex are normally excluded. Very small, narrowly specialised activities and unfocussed causes are also avoided.

TYPE OF GRANT Grants for start-up, capital costs and ongoing expenses for up to five years.

RANGE OF GRANTS Up to £70,000 but mostly between £100 and £2,000.

SAMPLE GRANTS River Trust (£70,000); Tusk Trust and WWF – UK (£50,000 each); Interact Worldwide (£40,000); Brendoncare Foundation Development Trust (£15,000); Sussex Community Foundation (£12,000); Froglife (£6,500); Amberly Working Museum (£5,000);

Pathways to Health (£2,000); Miracles (£1,000); Blind in Business (£500); Sussex Supreme Twirlers (£300); and Rowan's Hospice (£50).

FINANCES *Year* 2007–08 *Income* £1,471,336
Grants £952,087 *Assets* £51,040,916

TRUSTEES Kleinwort Benson Trustees Ltd; Madeleine, Lady Kleinwort; Richard Ewing; Simon Robertson; Sir Christopher Lever; Sir Richard Kleinwort; Marina Kleinwort; Alexander Kleinwort.

HOW TO APPLY In writing to the correspondent, enclosing a copy of the most recent annual report and financial statements. Trustees meet in March and October, but applications are considered throughout the year, normally within two to three months of receipt. Consideration of appeals received is undertaken by small groups of trustees to whom authority has been delegated to make individual grants of up to £10,000 each. These groups meet quarterly so applications for smaller grants can be dealt with quickly. Only successful applicants are notified of the trustees' decision.

WHO TO APPLY TO Nick Kerr-Sheppard, Secretary, Kleinwort Benson, 30 Gresham Street, London EC2V 7PG *Tel* 020 3207 7338

CC NO 229665   **ESTABLISHED** 1963

....

■ The Marina Kleinwort Charitable Trust

WHERE FUNDING CAN BE GIVEN UK.

WHO CAN BENEFIT Arts organisations.

WHAT IS FUNDED Arts projects.

WHAT IS NOT FUNDED No grants to individuals.

SAMPLE GRANTS National Theatre (£6,000); Old Vic (£5,500); Almeida Theatre Co Ltd, Central School of Ballet, Dance Umbrella and Music Theatre Wales (£5,000 each); Gate Theatre Company Limited (£4,000); English Chamber Orchestra and Music Society (£3,200); Blindart, Bonachela Dance Company, Conquest Art, Endymion Ensemble Ltd and London Children's Ballet (£3,000 each); and Chickenshed and Classical Road Show (£2,000 each).

FINANCES *Year* 2007–08 *Income* £65,110
Grants £57,700 *Assets* £1,371,670

TRUSTEES Miss Marina Rose Kleinwort, Chair; David James Roper Robinson; Miss Zenaida Yanowsky; Mrs Tessa Elizabeth Bremmer.

HOW TO APPLY In writing to the correspondent.

WHO TO APPLY TO The Secretary, 30 Gresham Street, London EC2V 7PG

CC NO 1081825   **ESTABLISHED** 2000

....

■ The Sir James Knott Trust

WHERE FUNDING CAN BE GIVEN Tyne and Wear, Northumberland, County Durham inclusive of Hartlepool but exclusive of Darlington, Stockton-on-Tees, Middlesbrough, Redcar and Cleveland.

WHO CAN BENEFIT Registered charities only.

WHAT IS FUNDED Support of the welfare of people who are disadvantaged, the young, older people, people with disabilities, education and training, medical care, historic buildings, the environment, music and the arts and seafarers' and services' charities.

WHAT IS NOT FUNDED Individuals, replacement of funding withdrawn by local authorities or organisations that do not have an identifiable project within the beneficial area.

SAMPLE GRANTS Academy School – Ashington and TS Northumbria (£50,000 each); Northumbria

Historic Churches Trust (£18,000); Diocese of Durham and Diocese of Newcastle (£15,000 each); Scout Association – Durham County (£11,000); Sage Gateshead (£10,000); YMCA – North East (£8,000); NSPCC and Greggs Trust (£5,000 each); Southwick Neighbourhood Youth Project (£3,000); Sea Cadets – Jarrow (£2,500); Tomorrow's People (£2,000); and Simonburn Village Hall (£1,500).

FINANCES *Year* 2008–09 *Income* £1,336,737 *Grants* £1,114,689 *Assets* £30,010,970

TRUSTEES Prof. Oliver James; Charles Baker-Cresswell; Sarah Riddell; Ben Speke.

HOW TO APPLY In writing to the correspondent, giving a brief description of the need, with relevant consideration to the following points: what type of organisation you are and how you benefit the community; how you are organised and managed; how many staff/volunteers you have; if a registered charity, please provide your registered number, if not you will need to submit the name and registered number of a charity which is prepared to administer funds on your behalf; what relationship, if any, do you have with similar or umbrella organisations; please provide details of your main funding source; please provide full details of the project you are currently fundraising for, including the cost, the amount required and when the funds are needed; please give details of who else you have approached and what response have you had; please confirm whether you have you applied to the Big Lottery Fund (if not, state why not); and please enclose a copy of your latest trustee report and accounts (if you are a new organisation then provide a copy of your latest bank statement). Not all the questions/points may apply to you, but they give an idea of what the trustees may ask when considering applications. Applicants may be contacted for further information. Trustees normally meet in spring, summer and autumn. Applications need to be submitted at least three months before a grant is required. However, if your application is for a grant of less than £1,000, this can usually be processed outside meetings and usually within one month.

WHO TO APPLY TO Vivien Stapeley, Secretary, 16–18 Hood Street, Newcastle upon Tyne NE1 6JQ *Tel* 0191 230 4016 *Fax* 0191 230 2817 *email* info@knott-trust.co.uk *Website* www. knott-trust.co.uk

CC NO 1001363   **ESTABLISHED** 1990

■ **The Kobler Trust**

WHERE FUNDING CAN BE GIVEN UK.

WHO CAN BENEFIT Registered charities. Grants given to individuals only in exceptional circumstances.

WHAT IS FUNDED General charitable purposes with emphasis on the arts and Jewish causes.

WHAT IS NOT FUNDED Grants are only given to individuals in exceptional circumstances.

TYPE OF GRANT No restrictions. These vary from small grants on a one-off basis for a specific project to a continuing relationship.

RANGE OF GRANTS £500–£50,000.

SAMPLE GRANTS Beth Shalom (£50,000); Jewish AIDS Trust (£20,000); Chicken Shed Theatre Company, Royal Academy of Music and UK Jewish Film Festival (£10,000 each); Naz Project London (£6,000); Cued Speech Association and South West London Law Centre (£5,000 each); Action for Blind People and St Giles Trust (£2,000 each); DEMAND (£2,000); Guildhall School Trust (£5,000); Happy Days (£2,000); Kisharon, Merseyside Thursday Club

and Surrey Care Trust (£1,000 each); and Age Concern (£500).

FINANCES *Year* 2007–08 *Income* £148,397 *Grants* £242,511 *Assets* £3,339,804

TRUSTEES A Xuereb; A H Stone; Ms J L Evans; J W Israelsohn.

HOW TO APPLY Applications should be in writing and incorporate full details of the charity for which funding is requested. Acknowledgements are not generally sent out to unsuccessful applicants.

WHO TO APPLY TO Ms J L Evans, Trustee, c/o Lewis Silkin LLP, 5 Chancery Lane, Clifford's Inn, London EC4A 1BL

CC NO 275237   **ESTABLISHED** 1963

■ **The Kohn Foundation**

WHERE FUNDING CAN BE GIVEN UK and overseas.

WHO CAN BENEFIT Registered charities.

WHAT IS FUNDED General charitable purposes, especially education, Jewish religion, relief of poverty, care of people who are sick or who have a mental illness, medical research, and the arts (particularly music).

SAMPLE GRANTS The Royal Society (£275,000); Royal Academy of Music (£114,000); Wigmore Hall Song Contest (£81,000); Chai Cancer Care (£20,000); and Imperial College Ernst Chain Prize (£18,000) Israel Philharmonic Orchestra Foundation (£12,000); Emunah (£10,000); and Hasmonean High School (£6,000).

FINANCES *Year* 2007 *Income* £46,255 *Grants* £620,416 *Assets* £1,169,451

TRUSTEES Dr Ralph Kohn, Chair; Zahava Kohn; Anthony A Forwood.

HOW TO APPLY In writing to the correspondent.

WHO TO APPLY TO Dr R Kohn, Trustee, c/o Wilkins Kennedy, Bridge House, London Bridge, London SE1 9QR

CC NO 1003951   **ESTABLISHED** 1991

■ **Kollel and Co. Limited**

WHERE FUNDING CAN BE GIVEN Worldwide.

WHO CAN BENEFIT Jewish organisations.

WHAT IS FUNDED The objects of the charity are the: advancement of education and religion in accordance with the doctrines of the Jewish religion; and the relief of poverty.

FINANCES *Year* 2007–08 *Income* £1,280,166 *Grants* £1,481,273 *Assets* £2,161,711

TRUSTEES S Low; J Lipschitz; Z Rothschild.

HOW TO APPLY 'Grants are made upon application by the charity concerned. Grants are made in amounts thought appropriate by the directors/trustees.'

WHO TO APPLY TO A Low, Secretary, Lieberman and Co, 2L Cara House, 339 Seven Sisters Road, London N15 6RD

CC NO 1077180   **ESTABLISHED** 1999

■ **The KPMG Foundation**

WHERE FUNDING CAN BE GIVEN UK.

WHO CAN BENEFIT Refugees, young offenders, children and young people who have been in care, children and young people with dyslexia/literacy difficulties.

WHAT IS FUNDED Registered charities.

SAMPLE GRANTS Beneficiaries included: Every Child a Chance Trust (£143,000); Youth at Risk (£134,000); University of Cambridge – Institute of Criminology (£61,000); North of England Refugee Service (£55,000); Helena Kennedy

Foundation (£37,000); British Association for Adoption and Fostering (£28,000); Young Vic (£13,000); Youth Enterprise Scotland (£12,000); Chichester Festival Theatre (£5,000); and Tate Gallery (£3,000).

FINANCES *Year* 2007–08 *Income* £838,819 *Grants* £732,337 *Assets* £6,268,838

TRUSTEES John Griffith-Jones, Chair; Gerry Acher; Sir John Cassels; Helena Kennedy; Robin Oakley; Dr Ashley Steel; Neil Sherlock.

HOW TO APPLY Application forms can be downloaded from KPMG the website in pdf and Word format. 'The KPMG Foundation considers applications for the General Grants programme once a year. Throughout the year, we capture all organisations keen to apply for funding on a database. When the Trustees agree their funding date at the end of each year for the following year, we write to all organizations on our database providing them with details of the funding date, when applications must be submitted and any specific criteria defined by the Trustees. If you would like your details added to our database then please email us at kpmg@kpmg.co.uk'
'The trustees meet four times a year. Once a year the trustees will assess all applications and make their funding decisions. If the trustees are keen to progress your application a project/site visit may be undertaken by either one of the trustees or one of the support team. In addition, the trustees may request that a Financial due diligence assessment be undertaken, by the Foundation Treasurer, of the charitable organisation seeking funding.'

WHO TO APPLY TO Jo Clunie, Director, KPMG, Salisbury Square House, 8 Salisbury Square, London EC4Y 8BB *email* kpmgfoundation@kpmg.co.uk *Website* www.kpmg.co.uk/about/foundation

CC NO 1086518   **ESTABLISHED** 2001

■ The Kreditor Charitable Trust

WHERE FUNDING CAN BE GIVEN UK, with preferences for London and North East England.

WHO CAN BENEFIT Jewish organisations and UK welfare organisations benefiting Jewish people, at risk groups, and people who are disadvantaged by poverty or socially isolated.

WHAT IS FUNDED Jewish organisations working in education and social and medical welfare.

SAMPLE GRANTS Previous beneficiaries have included: Academy for Rabbinical Research, British Diabetic Association, British Friends of Israel War Disabled, Fordeve Ltd, Jerusalem Ladies' Society, Jewish Care, Jewish Marriage Council Kosher Meals on Wheels, London Academy of Jewish Studies, NW London Talmudical College, Ravenswood, RNID and UNICEF UK.

FINANCES *Year* 2007–08 *Income* £69,272 *Grants* £68,387 *Assets* £87,896

TRUSTEES P M Kreditor; M P Kreditor.

HOW TO APPLY In writing to the correspondent.

WHO TO APPLY TO Paul M Kreditor, Gerald Kreditor and Co., Chartered Accountants, Hallswelle House, 1 Hallswelle Road, London NW11 0DH *Tel* 020 8209 1535 *Fax* 020 8209 1923 *email* admin@gerald-kreditor.co.uk

CC NO 292649   **ESTABLISHED** 1985

■ The Kreitman Foundation

WHERE FUNDING CAN BE GIVEN UK.

WHO CAN BENEFIT Registered charities and other tax exempt charitable organisations benefiting children, young adults and older people, people who are disabled and people disadvantaged by poverty.

WHAT IS FUNDED Education, health and welfare and animal conservation.

WHAT IS NOT FUNDED No grants to individuals.

TYPE OF GRANT Capital and core costs.

SAMPLE GRANTS Social welfare activities (£51,000); educational activities (£10,000); and health activities (£5,000). The foundation has also entered into two funding projects in the field of medical research. The Royal Marsden Hospital received quarterly payments of £25,000 and Myeloma UK received quarterly payment s of £15,000.

FINANCES *Year* 2008–09 *Income* £44,233 *Grants* £66,250 *Assets* £4,030,040

TRUSTEES Mrs Jill Luck-Hille; P M Luck-Hille; J W Prevezer.

HOW TO APPLY To the correspondent in writing. The trustees seem to have a list of regular beneficiaries and it may be unlikely that any new applications will be successful.

WHO TO APPLY TO J W Prevezer, Trustee, Landau Baker Limited, Mountcliff House, 154 Brent Street, London NW4 2DR *Tel* 020 8359 9988

CC NO 269046   **ESTABLISHED** 1975

■ The Neil Kreitman Foundation

WHERE FUNDING CAN BE GIVEN Worldwide, in practice UK, USA and Israel.

WHO CAN BENEFIT Registered or exempt charities.

WHAT IS FUNDED Arts and culture; education; health and social welfare; and Jewish charities.

WHAT IS NOT FUNDED No grants to individuals.

TYPE OF GRANT Primarily general funds with some small capital grants and core costs.

RANGE OF GRANTS Generally £500–£30,000.

SAMPLE GRANTS British Museum (£120,000); Crocker Art Museum (£66,000); Ancient India and Iran Trust (£28,000); Release (£20,000); Yale University (£10,000); Hindu Kuch Conservation Society (£7,000); and Cambridge University (£5,000).

FINANCES *Year* 2007–08 *Income* £846,501 *Grants* £539,686 *Assets* £20,660,736

TRUSTEES N R Kreitman; G C Smith.

HOW TO APPLY In writing to the correspondent.

WHO TO APPLY TO Gordon C Smith, Trustee, Citroen Wells & Partners, Devonshire House, 1 Devonshire Street, London W1W 5DR *Tel* 020 7304 2000 *Fax* 020 7304 2020 *email* gordon.smith@citreonwells.co.uk

CC NO 267171   **ESTABLISHED** 1974

■ The Heinz, Anna and Carol Kroch Foundation

WHERE FUNDING CAN BE GIVEN UK.

WHO CAN BENEFIT Individuals with chronic illnesses; disabled people; people who are disadvantaged by poverty; homeless people; victims of abuse and domestic violence; and victims of war.

WHAT IS FUNDED The foundation exists to further medical research, support people who have suffered injustice and relieve hardship amongst people with medical conditions.

WHAT IS NOT FUNDED No grants are made to students or for holidays. Overseas applications or projects are not considered.

TYPE OF GRANT Research and funding of up to three years will be considered.

RANGE OF GRANTS Up to £10,000.

SAMPLE GRANTS Previous beneficiaries include: Bath Institute of Medical Engineering, Brainwave, Breakthrough Breast Cancer, Eyeless Trust, Northern Friends of ARMS, VISCERAL and University College London.

FINANCES *Year* 2008–09 *Income* £171,499 *Grants* £98,179 *Assets* £2,919,681

TRUSTEES Mrs M Cottam; Dr A Kashti; D Lang; X Lang; Ms A Page; C Rushbrook; J Seagrim.

HOW TO APPLY Appeals are considered monthly. Applications on behalf of individuals must be submitted through a recognised body, such as social services, GP/consultant, CAB or welfare rights. Applications for medical research should include details of the research, the cost of the project and any further relevant information, which should be no more than four pages long. Research applications are considered monthly. Applications always receive a reply. Please include an sae.

WHO TO APPLY TO Mrs H Astle, PO Box 5, Bentham, Lancaster LA2 7XA *Tel* 01524 263001 *Fax* 01524 262721 *email* hakf50@hotmail.com

CC NO 207622   **ESTABLISHED** 1962

....

■ Kupath Gemach Chaim Bechesed Viznitz Trust

WHERE FUNDING CAN BE GIVEN UK and Israel.

WHO CAN BENEFIT Registered charities.

WHAT IS FUNDED Jewish causes.

RANGE OF GRANTS Up to £33,000.

SAMPLE GRANTS Yesodey Hatorah School (£10,000); and Kehal Chasidei Wiznitz (£32,000).

FINANCES *Year* 2008–09 *Income* £236,808 *Grants* £114,689 *Assets* £180,842

TRUSTEES I Kahan; S Weiss; A Pifko.

HOW TO APPLY In writing to the correspondent.

WHO TO APPLY TO S Weiss, Trustee, 171 Kyverdale Road, London N16 6PS *Tel* 020 8442 9604

CC NO 1110323   **ESTABLISHED** 2005

....

■ The Kyte Charitable Trust

WHERE FUNDING CAN BE GIVEN UK.

WHO CAN BENEFIT Organisations benefiting medical professionals and research workers. Support may go to at risk groups, and people who are disadvantaged by poverty or socially isolated.

WHAT IS FUNDED Medical research, community services.

RANGE OF GRANTS Up to £25,000.

SAMPLE GRANTS United Jewish Israel Appeal (£25,000); Jewish Care (£20,000); Myeloma UK (£15,000); and Community Security Trust (£12,000).

FINANCES *Year* 2007–08 *Income* £146,998 *Grants* £126,141 *Assets* £27,313

TRUSTEES D M Kyte; T M Kyte; J L Kyte; I J Kyte.

HOW TO APPLY In writing to the correspondent.

WHO TO APPLY TO The Trustees, Business Design Centre, 52 Upper Street, London N1 0QH

CC NO 1035886   **ESTABLISHED** 1994

■ Lacims-Maclis Charitable Trust

WHERE FUNDING CAN BE GIVEN UK.

WHO CAN BENEFIT Charitable organisations.

WHAT IS FUNDED General charitable purposes.

RANGE OF GRANTS £100–£4,000.

SAMPLE GRANTS TBA Tour de Racing and Leukaemia Research (£3,000 each); Colonels Fund Grenadier Guards, Interhealth, Nicholls Spinal Injury Foundation and the Prostate Cancer Charity (£2,000 each); The Watermill Theatre (£1,000); and NSPCC (£250).

FINANCES *Year* 2007–08 *Income* £26,895 *Grants* £31,500 *Assets* £443,605

TRUSTEES R P Tullett; A H Bartlett; M N C Kerr-Dineen; R Leigh Wood.

HOW TO APPLY In writing to the correspondent.

WHO TO APPLY TO R P Tullett, Trustee, Robert Philip Tullett, Cheviot Asset Management, 90 Long Acre, London WC2E 9RA *Tel* 020 7438 5666

CC NO 265596   **ESTABLISHED** 1973

■ The Late Sir Pierce Lacy Charity Trust

WHERE FUNDING CAN BE GIVEN UK and overseas.

WHO CAN BENEFIT The trust only supports the Roman Catholic Church or associated institutions which are registered charities and does not fund requests from individuals.

WHAT IS FUNDED Medicine and health, welfare, education, religion and general charitable purposes. Particularly charities working in the field of infrastructure development, residential facilities and services, Christian education, Christian outreach, Catholic bodies, charity or voluntary umbrella bodies, hospices, rehabilitation centres, advocacy, education and training, community services and community issues.

WHAT IS NOT FUNDED The trust only supports the Roman Catholic Church or associated institutions.

TYPE OF GRANT Recurrent small grants of £1,000 or less, buildings, capital, core costs, project, research, start-up costs and funding for more than three years may be considered.

RANGE OF GRANTS Most are less than £500.

SAMPLE GRANTS Previously: Crusade of Rescue, St Francis Children's Society, Poor Mission Fund, St Cuthbert's Mayne RC School, Society of St Vincent De Paul, Poor Mission Fund, Catholic Children's Society and St Francis's Leprosy Guild.

FINANCES *Year* 2007–08 *Income* £24,438 *Grants* £23,520 *Assets* £576,857

TRUSTEES CGU Insurance plc

HOW TO APPLY In writing to the correspondent, at any time.

WHO TO APPLY TO P Burke, Head of Trustee Management, Norwich Union, Trustee Department, Pitheavlis, Perth PH2 0NH *Tel* 01738 895590 *Fax* 01738 895903

CC NO 1013505   **ESTABLISHED** 1992

■ The K P Ladd Charitable Trust

WHERE FUNDING CAN BE GIVEN UK and overseas.

WHO CAN BENEFIT Churches and other organisations.

WHAT IS FUNDED 'It is the trustees' present intention that the fund will be applied to support Christian charities and other charitable organisations involved in religious activities. This will be done by supporting churches, missionary work and other organisations both in the UK and overseas.'

SAMPLE GRANTS London Institute for Contemporary Christianity (£25,000); Eastbury Church Northwood Trust (£17,000); Kepplewray Trust (£6,000); Tonbridge Church (£5,000); SOS Bosnia (£4,000); London City Mission (£3,000); Emmanuel Church Northwood (£2,500); Mercy Ships (£2,000); and Keswick Ministries, Salvation Army and Wycliffe Bible Translators (£1,000 each).

FINANCES *Year* 2007–08 *Income* £103,045 *Grants* £79,000 *Assets* £1,660,531

TRUSTEES Roger Cooper; Brian Ladd; Kenneth Ladd.

HOW TO APPLY In writing to the correspondent.

WHO TO APPLY TO Roger Cooper, Trustee, 2 Wolsey Road, Northwood HA6 2HS

CC NO 1091493   **ESTABLISHED** 2002

■ John Laing Charitable Trust

WHERE FUNDING CAN BE GIVEN UK.

WHO CAN BENEFIT Existing and former employees of John Laing plc who are in need; 'charitable organisations, or in exceptional circumstances from not-for-profit companies'.

WHAT IS FUNDED More recently, the trust has concentrated its support on charities which support the following main themes: education; community regeneration; disadvantaged young people; homelessness with a particular emphasis on day centres; and environment.

WHAT IS NOT FUNDED No grants to individuals (other than to Laing employees and/or their dependants).

TYPE OF GRANT Usually one-off, but a small number are supported for an agreed period, often up to three years.

RANGE OF GRANTS £250–£25,000.

SAMPLE GRANTS National Communities Resource Centre (£50,000); Countin You (£35,000); National Literacy Trust (£20,000); Atlantic College (£18,000); Tomorrow's People (£10,000); Essex Wildlife Trust (£6,000); and Scarborough Homeless Support Services (£2,500).

FINANCES *Year* 2008 *Income* £2,047,000 *Grants* £2,161,000 *Assets* £42,300,000

TRUSTEES C M Laing; Sir Martin Laing; D C Madden; R I Sumner; P Jones; D Whipp; L Krige.

OTHER INFORMATION In 2008 the grant total included £741,000 distributed to about 645 individuals whom were either current or former employees of John Laing plc.

HOW TO APPLY In writing to the correspondent. The trust does not have an application form and applicants are asked to keep the initial request as brief as possible. There is no deadline for receipt of applications. All applications are dealt with on a rolling basis. The trust says that all applications are acknowledged.

WHO TO APPLY TO Michael Hamilton, Secretary, 33 Bunns Lane, Mill Hill, London NW7 2DX *Tel* 020 8959 7321 *email* michael.a.hamilton@laing.com *Website* www.laing.com/lct.htm

CC NO 236852   **ESTABLISHED** 1962

■ Maurice and Hilda Laing Charitable Trust

WHERE FUNDING CAN BE GIVEN UK and overseas.

WHO CAN BENEFIT Registered charities.

WHAT IS FUNDED The advancement of the Christian religion and the relief of poverty both in the UK and overseas. In practice grants awarded fall into three main categories: to organisations seeking to promote Christian faith and values through evangelistic, educational and media activities at home and overseas; to organisations seeking to express Christian faith through practical action to help people in need, for example, those with disabilities, the homeless, the sick, young people, prisoners and ex-offenders; to organisations working to relieve poverty overseas, with a particular emphasis on helping children who are vulnerable or at risk. In most cases these grants to overseas projects are made through UK registered charities who are expected to monitor and evaluate the projects on behalf of the trust, providing progress reports at agreed intervals.

WHAT IS NOT FUNDED No grants to groups or individuals for the purpose of education, travel, attendance at conferences or participation in overseas exchange programmes. No grants towards church restoration or repair.

TYPE OF GRANT Usually one-off grants to capital costs or project funding on a one-off or recurring basis. A few grants towards the core costs of national organisations.

RANGE OF GRANTS Most grants are under £10,000 but larger awards are available.

SAMPLE GRANTS Lambeth Fund (£185,000); Ethiopian Graduate School of Theology (£175,000); Charities Aid Foundation (£170,000); SAT-7 Trust Ltd (£150,000); St Martin-in-the-Fields (£100,000); Workaid (£50,000); YMCA UK National Trust (£25,000); Hope UK (£10,000); and Children in Crisis, Cutting Edge Ministries and Jesus Army Charitable Trust (£5,000 each).

FINANCES *Year* 2008 *Income* £1,628,396 *Grants* £2,154,366 *Assets* £32,279,832

TRUSTEES Andrea Currie; Peter Harper; Robert Harley; Ewan Harper; Charles Laing; Stephen Ludlow.

OTHER INFORMATION See the entry for the Laing Family Foundations for the work of the group as a whole.

Please note: in 2006 the trust made the decision to work towards winding up the trust over a 10–15 year period. As such, there will be a controlled increase in the level of future grant expenditure.

HOW TO APPLY In writing to the correspondent. One application only is needed to apply to this or the Kirby Laing Foundation, Martin Laing Foundation or Beatrice Laing Charitable Trust. Multiple applications will still only elicit a single reply, even then applicants are asked to accept non-response as a negative reply on behalf of all these trusts, unless a stamped addressed envelope is enclosed. After the initial sifting process, the Maurice and Hilda Laing Trust follows its own administrative procedures. These trusts make strenuous efforts to keep their overhead costs to a minimum. As they also make a very large number of grants each year, in proportion to their income, the staff must rely almost entirely on the written applications submitted in selecting appeals to go forward to the trustees. Each application should contain all the information needed to allow such a decision to be reached, in as short and straightforward a way as possible. Specifically, each application should say: what the money is for; how much is needed; how much has already been found; and where the rest of the money is to come from. The trustees meet quarterly to consider applications for grants above £10,000. In most cases the trust's administrators will have met with applicants and prepared reports and recommendations for the trustees. Applications for smaller amounts are considered on an ongoing basis throughout the year. The administrators are authorised to make such grants without prior consent up to a maximum of £100,000 in each quarter, the grants to be reported to the trustees and approved retrospectively at the following quarterly meeting. All recipients of grants over £5,000 are asked to report on how the money has been spent and what has been achieved.

WHO TO APPLY TO Elizabeth Harley, Secretary, 33 Bunns Lane, Mill Hill, London NW7 2DX *Tel* 020 8238 8890 *Fax* 020 8238 8897

CC NO 1058109   **ESTABLISHED** 1996

■ The Laing Family Foundations

WHERE FUNDING CAN BE GIVEN UK and overseas.

WHAT IS FUNDED There is an evangelical Christian background to the group, but collectively the grants lists cover most fields of welfare and health as well as the promotion of Christianity, at home and overseas. Support for medical research, of the scientific sort is limited, and there is no general support for the arts (though one trust has a limited interest in this field).

WHAT IS NOT FUNDED No grants to groups or individuals for the purpose of education, travel, attendance at conferences or participation in overseas exchange programmes. In general the trusts rarely make grants towards the running costs of local organisations, which they feel have to be raised from within the local community.

TYPE OF GRANT One-off and recurrent.

OTHER INFORMATION The following trusts (except the Rufford Maurice Laing Foundation) are administered from a common office in north London and an application to one is seen as an application to all. However, they have different funding patterns and each has its own entry. They are: The Kirby Laing Foundation; The Rufford Maurice Laing Foundation; The Beatrice Laing Trust; The Maurice and Hilda Laing Charitable Trust.

HOW TO APPLY None of the trusts issue application forms and an application to one is seen as an application to all. An application for a grant towards a specific capital project should be in the form of a short letter giving details of the project, its total cost, the amount raised and some indication of how it is to be financed. A copy of the organisation's latest annual report and accounts, together with a stamped addressed envelope, should be enclosed. Unless an sae is enclosed applicants are asked to accept non-response as a negative reply. Applications for small amounts are considered on an ongoing basis.

WHO TO APPLY TO Miss Elizabeth Harley, 33 Bunns Lane, Mill Hill, London NW7 2DX *Tel* 020 8238 8890 *Fax* 020 8238 8897

Think carefully about every application. Is it justified?

651

■ The Christopher Laing Foundation

WHERE FUNDING CAN BE GIVEN UK, with a particular interest in Hertfordshire.

WHO CAN BENEFIT Applications from headquarter organisations and local organisations will be considered.

WHAT IS FUNDED General charitable purposes, arts and culture, environment, health and sport, with a preference for local projects in Hertfordshire.

WHAT IS NOT FUNDED Donations are only made to registered charities.

TYPE OF GRANT Recurrent and one-off. Grants are given for core support, capital funding and project, seed and feasibility funding. Loans may be given.

SAMPLE GRANTS Charities Aid Foundation (£30,000);The Lord's Taverners and Fields in Trust – National Playing Fields Association (£25,000 each); Groundwork, Hertfordshire and Hertfordshire Community Foundation (£20,000 each); Global Action Plan and Hertfordshire Air Ambulance (£10,000 each); NCH – Action for Children, The Orpheus Centre and Youth Create (£5,000 each); and Forum for the Future and St Peter's Church (£2,500 each).

FINANCES *Year* 2007–08 *Income* £177,202 *Grants* £160,000 *Assets* £6,468,968

TRUSTEES Christopher M Laing; John Keeble; Peter S Jackson; Diana C Laing.

HOW TO APPLY In writing to the correspondent.

WHO TO APPLY TO Sarah Martin, Trust Consultant, c/o TMF Management UK Ltd, 400 Capability Green, Luton LU1 3AE *Tel* 01582 439200 *email* sarah.martin@tmf-group.com

CC NO 278460   **ESTABLISHED** 1979

■ The David Laing Foundation

WHERE FUNDING CAN BE GIVEN Worldwide.

WHO CAN BENEFIT Organisations benefiting children, including those who are in care, fostered or adopted; one-parent families; and people who are disabled.

WHAT IS FUNDED The policy is to support charities aiding children, people from broken homes, and people who are physically and mentally disabled; with further donations to bodies supporting the improvement of the arts, education and training, overseas aid, social welfare and, sports and recreation.

WHAT IS NOT FUNDED No grants to individuals.

TYPE OF GRANT Grants are not normally recurrent on a regular annual basis unless forming phases of a larger donation. Some charities are closely associated with the foundation and would benefit more frequently. Starter finance, recurring expenses or single projects are considered. Sometimes a small grant plus an interest-free loan.

SAMPLE GRANTS Northamptonshire Community Foundation (£120,000 in three grants); Grove House Hospice (£21,000); International Organ Festival (£15,000); Lord's Taverners (£6,500 in four grants); St John Ambulance (£6,000); Peterborough Cathedral (£5,000); British Olympic Foundation (£4,700 in three grants); Firfield Primary School PTA, Game Conservancy Trust, Hertfordshire Agricultural Society and Interact Reading Service (£2,000 each).

FINANCES *Year* 2007–08 *Income* £152,612 *Grants* £179,077 *Assets* £4,741,708

TRUSTEES David Eric Laing; John Stuart Lewis; Richard Francis Dudley Barlow; Frances Mary Laing.

OTHER INFORMATION When supporting larger charities the support will be at headquarters and local levels as, for instance, in support of Save the Children Fund where donations to headquarters will aid the African famine appeal, but support is also given to local branches.

HOW TO APPLY In writing to the correspondent. Trustees meet in March, June, October and December, although applications are reviewed weekly. Due to the large number of applications received, and the relatively small number of grants made, the trust is not able to respond to all requests.

WHO TO APPLY TO David E Laing, Trustee, Fermyn Woods Hall, Brigstock, Northamptonshire, NN 14 3JA *Tel* 01536 373886

CC NO 278462   **ESTABLISHED** 1979

■ The Kirby Laing Foundation

WHERE FUNDING CAN BE GIVEN Unrestricted, but mainly UK.

WHO CAN BENEFIT Registered charities benefiting disadvantaged sections of the community including people with disabilities or mental illness, people disadvantaged by poverty, and socially isolated people; UK and overseas mission societies.

WHAT IS FUNDED Advancement of the Christian faith, youth development, medical research, care and health organisations, social welfare.

WHAT IS NOT FUNDED No grants to individuals; no travel grants; no educational grants. The foundation rarely gives grants for the running costs of local organisations.

TYPE OF GRANT Usually capital costs or project funding on a one-off or recurring basis.

RANGE OF GRANTS Most grants are between £1,000 and £10,000, some significantly larger grants.

SAMPLE GRANTS Cambridge Foundation (£1.2 million); Royal Academy of Engineering (£250,000); Royal Hospital Chelsea (£100,000); Oxford Radcliffe Hospitals NHS Trust Charitable Funds (£75,000); Restoration of Appearance and Function Trust (£45,000); Wells Cathedral (£25,000); Norwich Theatre Royal and Youth for Christ (£20,000 each); Mines Advisory Group (£15,000); Youth Sport Trust (£10,000); and Justice First (£5,000).

FINANCES *Year* 2007 *Income* £1,828,211 *Grants* £2,789,479 *Assets* £55,492,201

TRUSTEES Lady Isobel Laing; David E Laing; Simon Webley; Rev Charles Burch.

OTHER INFORMATION See the entry for the Laing Family Foundations for the work of the group as a whole.

HOW TO APPLY One application only is needed to apply to this or the Beatrice Laing Trust or Maurice and Hilda Laing Charitable Trust. Multiple applications will still only elicit a single reply. These trusts make strenuous efforts to keep their overhead costs to a minimum. As they also make a very large number of grants each year, in proportion to their income, the staff must rely almost entirely on the written applications submitted in selecting appeals to go forward to the trustees. Each application should contain all the information needed to allow such a decision to be reached, in as short and straightforward a way as possible. Specifically, each application should say: what the money is for; how much is needed; how much has already been found; where the rest is to come from. Unless there is reasonable assurance on the last point the grant is unlikely to be recommended. The trustees meet four times a year to consider the award of grants of over £20,000. Decisions on smaller grants are made on an ongoing basis.

For all grants above £5,000 the foundation asks for a report from the charity one year after the grant has been made, describing briefly how the grant has been spent and what has been achieved. For larger and multi-year grants more detailed reports may be required. Where a grant is paid in instalments the usual practice is not to release the second and subsequent instalments until a review of progress has been satisfactorily completed.

WHO TO APPLY TO Elizabeth Harley, 33 Bunns Lane, Mill Hill, London NW7 2DX *Tel* 020 8238 8890 *Fax* 020 8238 8897

CC NO 264299   **ESTABLISHED** 1972

....

■ The Martin Laing Foundation

WHERE FUNDING CAN BE GIVEN UK and worldwide.
WHO CAN BENEFIT Registered charities.
WHAT IS FUNDED General charitable purposes, including environment and conservation, young people and older people, but most grants go to charities and projects which the trustees have a personal connection to.
SAMPLE GRANTS Foundation for the College of St George (£40,000); Charities Aid Foundation (£25,000); Coptic Orthodox Church Centre (£20,000); Student Education Trust (£8,000); John Laing' Charitable Trust (£7,500); and Diabetes UK, St Loys C of E Primary School and the Pushkin Prizes (£5,000 each).
FINANCES *Year* 2007–08 *Income* £260,481 *Grants* £130,500 *Assets* £7,078,985
TRUSTEES Sir John Martin Laing; Colin Fletcher; Edward Charles Laing; Nicholas Gregory; Lady Stephanie Stearn Laing.
HOW TO APPLY The trust states: 'The trustees receive an enormous and increasing number of requests for help. Unfortunately the trustees are only able to help a small proportion of the requests and consequently they limit their support to those charities where they have a personal connection or interest in their activities.'
WHO TO APPLY TO Ms Elizabeth Ann Harley, 33 Bunns Lane, London NW7 2DX *Tel* 020 8238 8890
CC NO 278461   **ESTABLISHED** 1979

....

■ The Beatrice Laing Trust

WHERE FUNDING CAN BE GIVEN UK and overseas.
WHO CAN BENEFIT Mainly registered charities.
WHAT IS FUNDED The welfare of people who are homeless, children, older people, socially excluded and people with physical, mental or learning disabilities. Grants to projects overseas are concentrated upon building the capacity to provide long-term solutions to the problems faced by countries in the developing world, rather than emergency aid. Grants towards the advancement of the evangelical Christian faith are made by the trustees through the JW Laing Trust.
WHAT IS NOT FUNDED No grants to individuals; no travel grants; no educational grants.
RANGE OF GRANTS Most grants are between £1,000 and £5,000, occasionally larger.
SAMPLE GRANTS Impact Foundation (£40,000 in three grants); Echoes of Service (£30,000 in four grants); North London Hospice and Trinity Centre Winchester (£25,000 each); Methodist Homes for the Aged (£10,000); Book Aid International (£7,500); Red Balloon Learner

Centre Group (£5,000); Kingwood Trust (£3,500); After Adoption (£2,500); Operation Youth Quake (£2,000); Spadework and Housing the Homeless Central Fund (£1,000 each); and Woodcroft Women's Fellowship (£150).

FINANCES *Year* 2007–08 *Income* £1,557,564 *Grants* £1,013,450 *Assets* £41,225,338
TRUSTEES Sir Martin Laing; David E Laing; Christopher M Laing; John H Laing; Charles Laing; Paula Blacker; Alexandra Gregory.
OTHER INFORMATION See the entry for the Laing Family Foundations for the work of the group as a whole.
HOW TO APPLY In writing to the correspondent. One application only is needed to apply to this or the Kirby Laing Foundation, Martin Laing Foundation or Maurice and Hilda Laing Charitable Trust. Multiple applications will still only elicit a single reply; even then applicants are asked to accept non-response as a negative reply on behalf of all these trusts, unless a stamped addressed envelope is enclosed. Applications are considered monthly. These trusts make strenuous efforts to keep their overhead costs to a minimum. As they also make a very large number of grants each year, in proportion to their income, the staff must rely almost entirely on the written applications submitted in selecting appeals to go forward to the trustees. Each application should contain all the information needed to allow such a decision to be reached, in as short and straightforward a way as possible. Specifically, each application should say: what the money is for; how much is needed; how much has already been found; and where the rest of the money is to come from. Unless there is reasonable assurance on the last point the grant is unlikely to be recommended. Where larger grants are contemplated, meetings and visits are often undertaken by the trust's staff.
WHO TO APPLY TO Elizabeth Harley, Secretary, c/o Laing Family Trusts, 33 Bunns Lane, Mill Hill, London NW7 2DX *Tel* 020 8238 8890
CC NO 211884   **ESTABLISHED** 1952

....

■ The Lambert Charitable Trust

WHERE FUNDING CAN BE GIVEN UK and Israel.
WHO CAN BENEFIT There is a preference for people of the Jewish faith.
WHAT IS FUNDED Each year, nominally one half of the income is given to organisations in Israel, one third to Jewish organisations based in the UK and one sixth to health and welfare charities in the UK.
TYPE OF GRANT One-off and recurrent.
RANGE OF GRANTS £250–£15,000.
SAMPLE GRANTS Jewish Care (£15,000); Action on Addiction (£4,000); Dreamstore (£3,000); Headway, Meningitis Research Foundation and Nightingale House (£2,000 each); Jewish Blind and Disabled, Friends of War Memorials and Ro-Ro Sailing Project (£1,000 each); and Sanhedria Children's Homes and Educational Centre (£500).
FINANCES *Year* 2007–08 *Income* £106,830 *Grants* £69,700 *Assets* £2,934,886
TRUSTEES M Lambert; Prof. H P Lambert; H Alexander-Passe; Jane Lambert; O E Lambert; D J R Wells.
HOW TO APPLY In writing to the correspondent before July for payment by 1 September.
WHO TO APPLY TO George Georghiou, Mercer & Hole, 72 London Road, St Albans, Hertfordshire AL1 1NS *Tel* 01727 869141
CC NO 257803   **ESTABLISHED** 1969

■ Community Foundation for Lancashire

WHERE FUNDING CAN BE GIVEN Lancashire.

WHO CAN BENEFIT Registered charities and community groups.

WHAT IS FUNDED Social welfare and general charitable purposes.

FINANCES *Year* 2008–09 *Grants* £17,600

TRUSTEES Peter Robinson; Arthur Roberts; David Sanderson; Terry Hephrun; Peter Butterfield; Pam Barker; Vijayanti Chauhan; Tom Hoyle; Ged Fitzgerald; Graham Burgess; Steve Weaver.

OTHER INFORMATION During the 2008–09 financial year a total of £1.4 million was also distributed in Lancashire by the Community Foundation for Merseyside.

HOW TO APPLY For application details, please see the foundation's website.

WHO TO APPLY TO Cathy Elliott, Chief Executive, The Bungalow, Davyfield Road, Blackburn BB1 2LX *Tel* 01254 585056 *email* glen.lockett@ lancsfoundation.org.uk *Website* www. lancsfoundation.org.uk

CC NO 1123229   **ESTABLISHED** 2005

■ Lancashire Environmental Fund

WHERE FUNDING CAN BE GIVEN Lancashire.

WHO CAN BENEFIT Environmental organisations.

WHAT IS FUNDED Environmental projects which meet the criteria of the ENTRUST scheme.

WHAT IS NOT FUNDED All projects must satisfy at least one objective of the Landfill Tax Credit Scheme. For more information about the scheme contact Entrust, the regulatory body, by visiting their website at www.entrust.org.uk or telephoning 0161 972 0074.

TYPE OF GRANT One-off and recurrent.

RANGE OF GRANTS £3,000 to £30,000.

SAMPLE GRANTS Parbold Scout Group and Holton Youth and Community Centre (£30,000 each); Lancashire Wildlife Trust (£28,000); Hawthorne Park Trust, West View Community Association and Pilling Memorial Hall (£25,000 each); Heritage Trust for the North West (££19,000); Bolton le Sands Village Hall and Saheli Community Garden (£15,000 each); Freckleton Parish Council (£8,500); and Elswick and District Village Hall (£3,000).

FINANCES *Year* 2007 *Income* £813,260 *Grants* £612,544 *Assets* £3,397,517

TRUSTEES Cllr A C P Martin, Chair; P Greijenberg; D Tattersall; P Taylor.

HOW TO APPLY Guidance notes and application forms for each funding strand are available from the correspondent or may be downloaded from the fund's website. Completed forms should contain all possible relevant material including maps, photographs, plans, and so on. The board meets quarterly in January, April, July and October. Staff are willing to have informal discussions before an application is made. Potential applicants are strongly advised to visit the website before contacting the trust.

WHO TO APPLY TO Andy Rowett, Administration Officer, The Barn, Berkeley Drive, Bamber Bridge, Preston, Lancashire PR5 6BY *Tel* 01772 317 247 *Fax* 01772 628 849 *email* andyrowett@lancsenvfund.org.uk *Website* www.lancsenvfund.org.uk

CC NO 1074983   **ESTABLISHED** 1998

■ Duchy of Lancaster Benevolent Fund

WHERE FUNDING CAN BE GIVEN The county palatine of Lancashire (in Lancashire, Greater Manchester and Merseyside), and elsewhere in the country where the Duchy of Lancaster has historical links such as land interests and church livings.

WHO CAN BENEFIT Individuals and organisations.

WHAT IS FUNDED General charitable causes, but especially young people and education, welfare of people with disabilities or older people, community help, religion.

TYPE OF GRANT Mainly one-off grants for specific projects. Recurrent grants occasionally given.

RANGE OF GRANTS Up to £10,000, but usually £50– £5,000.

SAMPLE GRANTS Monastery of St Frances and Gorton Trust (£20,000); Invalids at Home (£10,000); Lancaster University Bursary Fund (£9,000); Liverpool Cathedral and Burnley Women's Refuge (£5,000 each); L'Arche (£4,500); Toxteth Town Hall (£3,000); St Luke's Hospital for the Clergy (£2,000); North West Multi Faith Association (£1,500); Aspull ABC and Stanford Rivers Church (£1,000 each).

FINANCES *Year* 2007 *Income* £167,096 *Grants* £364,447 *Assets* £10,004,928

TRUSTEES Lord Charles Shuttleworth; Sir Alan Reid; Hon. Justice David Richards; Dame Lorna Muirhead; Robert Hildyard; Chris Adcock; Warren Smith; Alan Whittaker.

OTHER INFORMATION The Duchy of Lancaster Jubilee Trust (Charity Commission No. 1085881) is administered from the same address and mainly gives towards the Queen's Chapel of Savoy.

HOW TO APPLY In writing to the appropriate lieutenancy office (see below), at any time. Applications should be by letter, including as much information as possible. All applications are acknowledged. Lancashire lieutenancy: County Hall, Preston, Lancashire LPRI 8XJ. Greater Manchester lieutenancy: Byrum House, Quay Street, Manchester M3 30D. Merseyside lieutenancy: PO Box 144, Royal and Sun Alliance Building, New Hall Place, Old Hall Street, Liverpool L69 3EN.

WHO TO APPLY TO Chris Adcock, Duchy of Lancaster Office, 1 Lancaster Place, Strand, London WC2E 7ED *Tel* 020 7269 1707 *Fax* 020 7269 1710 *email* info@duchyoflancaster.co.uk *Website* www.duchyoflancaster.org.uk

CC NO 1026752   **ESTABLISHED** 1993

■ The Lancaster Foundation

WHERE FUNDING CAN BE GIVEN UK and overseas, with a local interest in Clitheroe.

WHO CAN BENEFIT Only charities personally known to the trustees.

WHAT IS FUNDED Christian charities only.

RANGE OF GRANTS £1,000 and over.

SAMPLE GRANTS Grand at Clitheroe (£2.6 million); Oasis Charitable Trust – the Grand (£275,000); New Generation Music and Mission (£224,000); Open Arms International (£173,000); Love and joy Ministries (£74,000); MIC South Africa (£33,000); Cornerstone Film Trust (£22,000); Christians Against Poverty (£12,000); Open Doors UK (£2,000); and Windermere Education (£1,000).

FINANCES *Year* 2007–08 *Income* £2,817,687 *Grants* £4,209,673 *Assets* £50,662,627

TRUSTEES Rosemary Lancaster; John Lancaster; Steven Lancaster; Julie Broadhurst.

HOW TO APPLY The trust has previously stated: 'We do not consider applications made to us from organisations or people unconnected with us. All our donations are instigated because of personal associations. Unsolicited mail is, sadly, a waste of the organisation's resources.'

WHO TO APPLY TO Rosemary Lancaster, Trustee, c/o Text House, 152 Bawdlands, Clitheroe, Lancashire BB7 2LA *Tel* 01200 444404

CC NO 1066850   **ESTABLISHED** 1997

■ The Lancaster-Taylor Charitable Trust

WHERE FUNDING CAN BE GIVEN UK and overseas.
WHO CAN BENEFIT Education organisations.
WHAT IS FUNDED The furtherance of 'educational excellence'.
FINANCES *Year* 2007–08 *Income* £5,992,941 *Grants* £3,035,641 *Assets* £12,032,366
TRUSTEES Steven Lloyd Edwards; Rosalind Anita Jane Smith; Lindsay Diane Dodsworth.
OTHER INFORMATION Accounts were on file at the Charity Commission without a list of grants. Full details of these grants have been given to the commission, but were not included within the accounts as 'disclosure would prejudice the purpose of these grants'.
HOW TO APPLY 'The trustees meet regularly and decisions are made at trustees' meetings.'
WHO TO APPLY TO The Trustees, Macfarlanes Solicitors, 10 Norwich Street, London EC4A 1BD
CC NO 1106035   **ESTABLISHED** 2004

■ LandAid Charitable Trust

WHERE FUNDING CAN BE GIVEN UK.
WHO CAN BENEFIT Homeless organisations.
WHAT IS FUNDED Provision of accommodation, assistance with refurbishment projects, running training and life skills programme and start-up funding for schemes that might not otherwise get off the ground.
WHAT IS NOT FUNDED No grants to individuals.
TYPE OF GRANT One-off.
RANGE OF GRANTS £5,000–£40,000.
SAMPLE GRANTS Past beneficiaries have included Marylebone Project, New Horizon Youth Centre, Upper Room, Derbyshire Housing Aid, Canaan Trust, Haven House, Emmaus Hampshire, St Mungo's, Booth Centre and the Genesis Trust.
FINANCES *Year* 2007–08 *Income* £870,069 *Grants* £50,172 *Assets* £435,618
TRUSTEES Robin Broadhurst, Chair; Steven Ossack; Michael Slade; Mike Hussey; Liz Peace; Jeremy Newsum; David Taylor; Sherin Aminossehe; Robert Bould; Lynette Lackey.
HOW TO APPLY In writing to the correspondent, setting out the aims, objectives, outputs and outcomes of the project in no more than 500 words. (Please mark the envelope 'application for funding'.) Applications should be submitted between 1 December and 31 January each year. A decision on grant allocation will be made by the committee towards the end of March. Before reaching a decision to fund the committee and/or its representatives may wish to visit the project/organisation. Information on the next round of funding will be posted on the trust's website (www.landaid.org) when it becomes available.
WHO TO APPLY TO Rosie Groves, Grants Officer, 7th Floor, 1 Warwick Row, London SW1E 5ER *Tel* 020 7802 0117 *email* enquiries@landaid. org *Website* www.landaid.org
CC NO 295157   **ESTABLISHED** 1986

■ The Jack Lane Charitable Trust

WHERE FUNDING CAN BE GIVEN Gloucestershire and Wiltshire.
WHO CAN BENEFIT Registered charities.
WHAT IS FUNDED General charitable purposes.
RANGE OF GRANTS Up to £2,500.
FINANCES *Year* 2007–08 *Income* £60,356 *Grants* £48,510 *Assets* £1,756,030
TRUSTEES Mr J A G Toogood; R White; Mrs J F Bowen; Mrs K Dorsz; D C Crampton; T G Newman; M A Wright.
HOW TO APPLY In writing to the correspondent.
WHO TO APPLY TO J A G Toogood, Trustee, Forrester & Forrester, 59 High Street, Malmesbury, Wiltshire SN16 9AH *Tel* 01666 822671 *Fax* 01666 823548 *email* admin@jacklane.co. uk
CC NO 1091675   **ESTABLISHED** 2002

■ The Allen Lane Foundation

WHERE FUNDING CAN BE GIVEN UK.
WHO CAN BENEFIT Organisations whose work is with groups who may be perceived as unpopular such as asylum seekers, lesbian, gay bisexual or transgender people, gypsies and travellers, offenders and ex-offenders, older people, people experiencing mental health problems and people experiencing violence or abuse.
WHAT IS FUNDED The provision of advice, information and advocacy; community development; neighbourhood mediation, conflict resolution and alternatives to violence; research and education aimed at changing public attitudes or policy; social welfare aimed at making a long-term difference and empowering users.
WHAT IS NOT FUNDED The foundation does not currently make grants for academic research; addiction, alcohol or drug misuse; animal welfare or animal rights; arts or cultural or language projects or festivals; work with children, young people and families; endowments or contributions to other grant-making bodies; holidays or holiday playschemes; housing; hospices and medical research; individuals; museums or galleries; overseas travel; particular medical conditions or disorders; physical or learning disabilities; private and/or mainstream education; promotion of sectarian religion; publications; purchase costs of property; refugee community groups working with single nationalities; restoration or conservation of historic buildings or sites; sports and recreation; therapy, counselling; vehicle purchase; work relating to particular medical conditions of illness; work which the trustees believe is rightly the responsibility of the state; work outside the United Kingdom; work which will already have taken place before a grant is agreed; work by local organisations with an income of more than £100,000 per annum or those working over a wider area with an income of more than £250,000. The foundation will not normally make grants to organisations which receive funding (directly or indirectly) from commercial sources where conflicts of interest for the organisation and its work are likely to arise.
TYPE OF GRANT Generally for one year only, although longer term funding of up to three years may be offered sometimes. Project or core costs.
RANGE OF GRANTS Usually £500–£15,000.
SAMPLE GRANTS STOP (Trafficking UK) – towards general costs of this national project to support trafficked people (£15,000); Northern Ireland Committee for Refugees and Asylum Seekers

Think carefully about every application. Is it justified?

655

(NICRAS) – towards staffing and running costs of an organisation supporting refugees and asylum seekers (£11,000); Caroline Walker Trust – towards a practical guide for eating well for vulnerable older people, including those with mental health problems and learning disabilities (£10,000); Kincardine and Deeside Befriending – towards volunteer expenses and core costs of befriending older people (£9,000); Norfolk Eating Disorders Association – for costs relating to a volunteer co-ordinator at this association based in Norwich (£8,500); Friends and Families of Prisoners – towards the core costs of this project in Swansea (£6,000); Dalit Solidarity Network UK – towards the core costs of raising awareness of caste discrimination (£5,000); Irish Traveller Movement in Britain – towards core costs of this organisation working to raise the capacity and social inclusion of the traveller communities (£3,000); Maitri Project – a contribution towards the core costs of the running of a drop-in centre in Leicester (£2,800); and Parents Enquiry North East – for core costs (£1,000).

FINANCES *Year* 2008–09 *Income* £666,295 *Grants* £756,000 *Assets* £12,000,000

TRUSTEES Clare Morpurgo; John Hughes; Christine Teale; Zoe Teale; Guy Dehn; Juliet Walker; Jane Walsh; Fredrica Teale.

PUBLICATIONS Every year the foundation hosts a lecture in memory of Sir Allen Lane. Since 1999 the text of each lecture each year has been published on the foundation's website.

OTHER INFORMATION The trustees regret that applications far outstrip the funds available and not all good or appropriate projects can be offered funding, even though they may fall well within current funding priorities. A rejection may be no reflection on the value of the project.

HOW TO APPLY There is no formal application form, but when sending in an application the foundation asks that you complete the registration form (available on the website) and return it with your application. Applications should be no more than four sides of A4 but the budget may be on extra pages. It should be accompanied by your last annual report and accounts (if applicable) and the budget for the whole organisation (and the project budget if they are different) for the current year.
The foundation now no longer has application deadlines. Applications are now processed continually. When the foundation has received your application they will usually be in touch within two weeks either to: ask for any further information; to tell you whether the application will be going forward to the next stage of assessment and what the timetable for a final decision will be; or to inform you that they are unable to help. The time it takes to process an application and make a grant is usually between two and six months.

WHO TO APPLY TO Tim Cutts, Executive Secretary, 90 The Mount, York YO24 1AR *Tel* 01904 613223 *Fax* 01904 613133 *email* info@allenlane.org.uk *Website* www.allenlane.org.uk

CC NO 248031   **ESTABLISHED** 1966

■ The Langdale Trust

WHERE FUNDING CAN BE GIVEN Worldwide, but with a special interest in Birmingham.

WHO CAN BENEFIT Registered charities.

WHAT IS FUNDED Youth organisations, medical, environment and social needs.

TYPE OF GRANT Annual for general and specific use.

RANGE OF GRANTS £1,000–£8,000.

SAMPLE GRANTS Barnardos – Amazon Project, Birmingham and UNICEF – Water and Wells (£8,000 each); the Leprosy Missiona and Save the Children Fund (£4,000 each); Birmingham Settlement, Fairbridge West Midlands and the Grasslands Trust (£3,000 each); National Playing Fields Association and Quaker Social Action (£2,000 each); and The Tree House Trust (£1,000).

FINANCES *Year* 2006–07 *Income* £135,387 *Grants* £140,000 *Assets* £4,159,056

TRUSTEES Jethro Elvin; Timothy R Wilson; Mrs Teresa Whiting; Martin J Woodward.

HOW TO APPLY In writing to the correspondent. The trustees meet in July.

WHO TO APPLY TO Martin J Woodward, Trustee, c/o Cobbetts Solicitors, One Colmore Square, Birmingham B4 6AJ *Tel* 0845 404 2404 *email* martin.woodward@cobbetts.co.uk

CC NO 215317   **ESTABLISHED** 1960

■ The Langley Charitable Trust

WHERE FUNDING CAN BE GIVEN UK and worldwide, with a preference for the West Midlands.

WHO CAN BENEFIT Individuals and groups benefiting Christians, at risk groups, people who are disadvantaged by poverty, socially isolated or sick.

WHAT IS FUNDED Advancement of the gospel and Christianity; welfare and health.

WHAT IS NOT FUNDED No grants to animal or bird charities.

FINANCES *Year* 2007 *Income* £892,507 *Grants* £4,060 *Assets* £5,284,475

TRUSTEES J P Gilmour; Mrs S S Gilmour.

HOW TO APPLY In writing to the correspondent. 'The trustees only reply where they require further information and so on. Neither telephone calls nor correspondence will be entered into concerning any proposed or declined applications.'

WHO TO APPLY TO The Trustees, Wheatmoor Farm, 301 Tamworth Road, Sutton Coldfield, West Midlands B75 6JP *Tel* 0121 308 0165

CC NO 280104   **ESTABLISHED** 1980

■ The Langtree Trust

WHERE FUNDING CAN BE GIVEN Gloucestershire.

WHO CAN BENEFIT Organisations benefiting the local community; occasionally to individuals if then of direct benefit to the community.

WHAT IS FUNDED General charitable purposes in Gloucestershire only. Priority is given to church projects, youth groups and people who are disabled or disadvantaged. The arts have a lower priority.

WHAT IS NOT FUNDED No grants are given in response to general appeals from large UK organisations. No grants to individuals for higher education.

TYPE OF GRANT Usually one-off for a specific project.

RANGE OF GRANTS £50–£1,000.

FINANCES *Year* 2007–08 *Income* £51,007 *Grants* £50,695 *Assets* £1,217,689

TRUSTEES Col P Haslam, Chair; Dr R E Way; G J Yates; Mrs A M Shepherd; Mrs M E Hood; Mrs K Bertram.

HOW TO APPLY In writing to the correspondent giving a simple, clear statement of the need with the costs of the project, what funding has so far been achieved and/or a recent copy of the annual accounts. Expensive, extensive, glossy appeal brochures are not appreciated. The trustees meet four to six times a year to decide the grant allocation. In exceptional circumstances a grant may be made between meetings. Please note that the address is a postal address and Randall and Payne cannot answer any telephone queries.

WHO TO APPLY TO Mrs K Bertram, Secretary, Randall & Payne, Rodborough Court, Walkley Hill, Stroud GL5 3LR

CC NO 232924   **ESTABLISHED** 1963

·····

■ The LankellyChase Foundation

WHERE FUNDING CAN BE GIVEN UK.

WHO CAN BENEFIT Charitable organisations.

WHAT IS FUNDED There are five programme areas: arts – promoting excellence and exploring the power of the arts; breaking cycles of abuse – promoting safe and protective behaviours; custody and community – promoting alternatives; free and quiet minds – seeking to restore troubled minds and lives; local people, local places – strengthening local communities and organisations. Each of these programmes contains a number of different elements. For full details please refer to the foundation's guidelines, available to download from the website or on request from the correspondent.

WHAT IS NOT FUNDED The foundation receives many more applications from worthwhile projects than it can hope to fund and as a consequence it does not support the following areas of work which are in addition to those specifically mentioned in the guidelines to the current programmes: access to buildings; advancement of religion; after school and homework clubs; animal charities; breakfast clubs; bursaries and scholarships; child befriending schemes; circular appeals; expeditions/overseas travel; festivals; formal education including schools, colleges and universities; general counselling; holidays/ holiday centres; hospitals and hospices; individual youth clubs; individuals – including students; medical care and medical research; mother and toddler groups/playgroups; museums/galleries; organisations working with particular medical conditions; other grant making organisations; research; sport; transport; vehicles; work that has already taken place; work which is primarily the responsibility of central or local government, education or health authorities.

TYPE OF GRANT Capital, revenue and full project funding for up to three years.

RANGE OF GRANTS Mainly £10,000 to £15,000. Occasionally up to £50,000.

SAMPLE GRANTS Family Welfare Association – London (£135,000); Rape Crisis England and Wales – Essex (£75,000); Arts and Minds – Essex (£60,000); Diversity Hub – Leicester (£45,000); the Forgiveness Project – London (£30,000); Fairshares – Gloucester (£21,000); Malt Cross Trust Company – Nottingham (£17,000); Villages in Action – Crediton, Devon (£10,000); and MAAN – Liverpool (£7,000).

FINANCES *Year* 2008–09 *Income* £6,384,790 *Grants* £5,449,462 *Assets* £90,222,792

TRUSTEES Nicholas Tatman (Chair); Ann Stannard; Dodie Carter; Paul Cotterill; Leo Fraser-Mackenzie; Victoria Hoskins; Marion Janner; Andrew Robinson; Kanwaljit Singh; Clive Martin.

OTHER INFORMATION This trust was created in January 2005 by the merger of The Lankelly Foundation and The Chase Charity.

HOW TO APPLY Application forms are available from the foundation's office or website. Please attach the following an itemised income and expenditure budget for the work for which funding is requested, a supporting letter (no

more than two sides of A4) and the organisation's most recent annual report. Applicants are encouraged to contact the foundation for advice if necessary.

WHO TO APPLY TO Peter Kilgarriff, Chief Executive, 1 The Court, High Street, Harwell, Didcot, Oxfordshire OX11 0EY *Tel* 01235 820044 *Fax* 01235 432720 *email* enquiries@lankellychase.org.uk *Website* www.lankellychase.org.uk

CC NO 1107583   **ESTABLISHED** 2005

·····

■ The Lanvern Foundation

WHERE FUNDING CAN BE GIVEN UK.

WHO CAN BENEFIT Organisations concerned with health and education, with a preference for children's organisations.

WHAT IS FUNDED Trustees favour registered, medical and education charities.

WHAT IS NOT FUNDED Absolutely no grants to individuals.

TYPE OF GRANT Single projects preferred. Capital expenditure.

RANGE OF GRANTS Up to £25,000.

SAMPLE GRANTS Moorfields Eye Hospital (£25,000), Childhood First, ICAN, The Joint Educational Trust, Marchant-Holliday School and Odiham Cottage Hospital Redevelopment Trust (£10,000 each); and Brathay Hall Trust, Edinburgh University – Botanic Productions, Theodora Children's Trust and Winchester Young Carers (£5,000 each).

FINANCES *Year* 2007 *Income* £124,616 *Grants* £95,000 *Assets* £3,543,542

TRUSTEES J C G Stancliffe; A H Isaacs.

HOW TO APPLY In writing to the correspondent.

WHO TO APPLY TO J C G Stancliffe, Trustee, P O Box 34475, London W6 9YB *Tel* 020 8741 2930

CC NO 295846   **ESTABLISHED** 1986

·····

■ The R J Larg Family Charitable Trust

WHERE FUNDING CAN BE GIVEN UK but generally Scotland, particularly Tayside.

WHO CAN BENEFIT Organisations benefiting children, young adults, students and people who are disabled or who have a disease or medical condition.

WHAT IS FUNDED Grants are made for cancer research, amateur music and youth organisations including university students' associations. Funding may also be given to churches, conservation, respite care, hospices, MS and neurological research, care in the community and other community facilities. Other charitable purposes will be considered.

WHAT IS NOT FUNDED Grants are not available for individuals.

TYPE OF GRANT Generally one-off, some recurring. Buildings, core costs, running costs, salaries and start-up costs will be considered. Funding may be given for up to two years.

RANGE OF GRANTS £250–£5,000; typical grant £1,000–£2,000.

SAMPLE GRANTS Previous beneficiaries include High School – Dundee, Whitehall Theatre Trust, Macmillan Cancer Relief – Dundee and Sense Scotland Children's Hospice.

FINANCES *Year* 2007–08 *Income* £140,000 *Grants* £100,000

TRUSTEES R W Gibson; D A Brand; Mrs S A Stewart.

HOW TO APPLY In writing to the correspondent. Trustees meet to consider grants in February and August.

WHO TO APPLY TO The Trustees, Whitehall House, Yeaman Shore, Dundee DD1 4BJ

SC NO SC004946   **ESTABLISHED** 1970

■ Largsmount Ltd

WHERE FUNDING CAN BE GIVEN UK and overseas.
WHO CAN BENEFIT Jewish charities.
WHAT IS FUNDED Jewish charitable purposes, mainly education.
SAMPLE GRANTS MYR Charitable Trust (£235,000).
FINANCES *Year* 2008 *Income* £1,029,858 *Grants* £540,107 *Assets* £3,219,473
TRUSTEES Z M Kaufman; Naomi Kaufman; Simon Kaufman.
HOW TO APPLY In writing to the correspondent.
WHO TO APPLY TO Simon Kaufman, Trustee, 50 Keswick Street, Gateshead NE8 1TQ *Tel* 0191 490 0140
CC NO 280509   **ESTABLISHED** 1979

■ The Lark Trust

WHERE FUNDING CAN BE GIVEN Bristol.
WHO CAN BENEFIT Registered charities benefiting people of all ages.
WHAT IS FUNDED Support in the areas of counselling, psychotherapy and the visual arts.
WHAT IS NOT FUNDED No grants to individuals.
TYPE OF GRANT Generally one-off.
RANGE OF GRANTS £100/£5,000.
SAMPLE GRANTS Royal West of England Academy (£5,000); Avon Sexual Abuse Centre (£1,500); WOMANKIND (£1,250); Bridge Foundation, Bristol Old Vic School, Broadway Trust, North Somerset Crossroads, Positive Action on Cancer and Southmead Projects (£1,000 each).
FINANCES *Year* 2007–08 *Income* £49,378 *Grants* £30,500 *Assets* £1,451,620
TRUSTEES Iris Tute; George Tute; Martin Mitchell.
HOW TO APPLY Initially in writing to the correspondent, who will check eligibility and then send a form which must be completed. Trustees do not accept information from charities wishing to build a relationship with them. Applications should be received by the end of January for consideration in March.
WHO TO APPLY TO Alice Meason, c/o Quartet Community Foundation, Royal Oak House, Royal Oak Avenue, Bristol BS1 4AH *Tel* 0117 989 7700 *Fax* 0117 989 7701
CC NO 327982   **ESTABLISHED** 1988

■ Laslett's (Hinton) Charity

WHERE FUNDING CAN BE GIVEN Worcestershire and surrounding area.
WHO CAN BENEFIT Children, older people, people who are disadvantaged by poverty and clergy.
WHAT IS FUNDED Church repairs; general benefit of people who are poor, including homes for older people and educating children; relief of sickness, hospitals and general charitable purposes in Worcestershire and surrounding area.
SAMPLE GRANTS Previous beneficiaries have included St James' – Dudley, Worcester Cathedral, All Saints – Bromsgrove, Little Malvern Priory, St James' – Dudley, St Michael's – Tenbury Wells, St Stephen's – Worcester, St Barnabas – Worcester, St George's – Kidderminster, St Michael's – Hanley Childs, Throckmorton

Chapel, St Edmund's – Dudley, St Clement's – Worcester, St Nicholas – Dormston, YMCA, Magg's Day Centre, Age Concern, Armchair, Cactus, Home-Start, Perdisell YPLC, Salvation Army, Sunfield – Stourbridge and Worcester Action for Youth.
FINANCES *Year* 2008 *Income* £38,840 *Grants* £0 *Assets* £9,557,891
TRUSTEES J B Henderson, Chair; A P Baxter; Miss E W Bonnett; Mrs A T King; Mrs E A Pugh-Cook; A D J Scott; R A F Smith; Mrs J Webb; R J R Young; J Panter; S G Taylor.
OTHER INFORMATION This trust will not be making grants in the five year period 2007 to 2011. It is planning extensive repair works on the properties that it owns, in the hope of being able to generate additional income in future years.
HOW TO APPLY Applications are not being accepted until after 2011.
WHO TO APPLY TO I C Pugh or Mary Barker, Hallmark Hulme LLP, 4 and 5 Sansome Place, Worcester WR1 1UQ
CC NO 233696   **ESTABLISHED** 1879

■ Lauchentilly Charitable Foundation 1988

WHERE FUNDING CAN BE GIVEN UK and Republic of Ireland.
WHO CAN BENEFIT Small local projects, UK and established organisations benefiting children, young adults and people disadvantaged by poverty.
WHAT IS FUNDED Advancement of education, religion, relief of poverty and general charitable purposes.
WHAT IS NOT FUNDED No grants to individuals, including students, or to non-registered charities.
TYPE OF GRANT One-off and recurrent.
RANGE OF GRANTS £50–£10,000, usually £2,500 or less.
SAMPLE GRANTS Previous grant beneficiaries have included: Prince of Wales's Charitable Foundation; Macmillan Cancer Relief; Newton Toney Memorial Hall; Recreational Ground; Friends of Newton Toney School; Museum of Garden Hospital; Archie Foundation; Chelsea Physic Garden Company; Drukpa Kargyuad Trust; Friends of the Rotunda; Grange Park Opera; Newton Toney; PCC Iveagh Trust; Alzheimer's Society; Canine Partners for Independence; Crimestoppers Trust; Ormiston Children and Families Trust; Sandy Gill Afghanistan Appeal; League of Friends of the Ipswich Hospital NHS Trust; St Gregory's Foundation; Salisbury House.
FINANCES *Year* 2007–08 *Income* £18,561 *Grants* £10,344
TRUSTEES Countess of Iveagh; Cowdray Trust Ltd.
OTHER INFORMATION Accounts had been received at the Charity Commission but were not available for viewing online
HOW TO APPLY In writing to the correspondent including an sae. Only successful applications will be acknowledged.
WHO TO APPLY TO Miss Laura Gosling, Miss Laura Gosling, Millbank Financial Services Ltd, 10 Cork Street, London W1S 3LW *Tel* 020 7439 9061 *email* charity@mfs.co.uk
CC NO 299793   **ESTABLISHED** 1988

■ Laufer Charitable Trust

WHERE FUNDING CAN BE GIVEN UK.

WHO CAN BENEFIT Jewish organisations and charities personally known to the trustees.

WHAT IS FUNDED General charitable purposes.

WHAT IS NOT FUNDED No grants to individuals, as grants are only made to registered charities.

TYPE OF GRANT Recurrent Core costs for up to one year.

RANGE OF GRANTS Any new grants made would not exceed £50 as the trust has a number of outstanding commitments which will absorb its income for the foreseeable future.

FINANCES *Year* 2007–08 *Income* £99,270 *Grants* £8,600 *Assets* £754,625

TRUSTEES S W Laufer; Mrs D D Laufer; S C Goulden; R Aarons; M Hoffman.

OTHER INFORMATION As this is a small charity, new beneficiaries are only considered in exceptional circumstances as the income is already allocated for some years to come.

HOW TO APPLY In view of the ongoing support for an existing group of charities, applications are not recommended.

WHO TO APPLY TO S W Laufer, Trustee, 342 Regents Park Road, London N3 2LJ *Tel* 020 8343 1660

CC NO 275375   **ESTABLISHED** 1961

■ The Lauffer Family Charitable Foundation

WHERE FUNDING CAN BE GIVEN Commonwealth countries, Israel and USA.

WHO CAN BENEFIT Educational and medical charities benefiting students.

WHAT IS FUNDED Education, medical and cultural causes.

WHAT IS NOT FUNDED No support for individuals.

TYPE OF GRANT Starter finance and recurrent for five years.

SAMPLE GRANTS Jewish Learning Exchange (£11,500); Society of Friends of Torah (£10,765); Spiro Ark (£9,000); United Joint Israel Appeal (£6,000); Ballet West and Jewish Deaf Association (£5,000 each); Ulpan Akiva Netanya (£3,900); Kisharon School (£2,100); Young Jewish Care (£1,275); and British Friends of the Jaffa Institute (£1,000).

FINANCES *Year* 2007–08 *Income* £148,281 *Grants* £191,541 *Assets* £4,700,115

TRUSTEES Mrs R R Lauffer; J S Lauffer; G L Lauffer; R M Lauffer.

HOW TO APPLY In writing to the correspondent; applications are considered once a year.

WHO TO APPLY TO J S Lauffer, Trustee, Clayton Stark & Co, 5th Floor, Charles House, 108–110 Finchley Road, London NW3 5JJ *Tel* 020 7431 4200

CC NO 251115   **ESTABLISHED** 1965

■ Mrs F B Laurence Charitable Trust

WHERE FUNDING CAN BE GIVEN Worldwide.

WHO CAN BENEFIT Organisations benefiting ex-service and service people, retired people, unemployed people and disadvantaged members of society within the UK or overseas to whom the UK owes a duty of care.

WHAT IS FUNDED The aid and support of people who are chronically ill and people who are disabled. The support of justice and human rights organisations and the protection of the environment and wildlife. Charities working in the fields of accommodation and housing legal services, publishing and printing, support to voluntary and community organisations, volunteer bureaux, community arts and recreation, community facilities, special schools and special needs education and literacy will also be considered.

WHAT IS NOT FUNDED No support for individuals. The following applications are unlikely to be considered: appeals for endowment or sponsorship; overseas projects, unless overseen by the charity's own fieldworkers; maintenance of buildings or landscape; provision of work or materials that are the responsibility of the state; where administration expenses, in all their guises, are considered by the trustees to be excessive; or where the fundraising costs in the preceding year have not resulted in an increase in the succeeding years donations in excess of these costs.

TYPE OF GRANT Core costs, one-off, project and start-up costs. Funding is for one year or less.

SAMPLE GRANTS Stroke Association (£15,000); St Christopher's Hospice (£5,000); Alzheimer Society – Haslemere, Breakthrough Breast Cancer, The Gurkha Welfare Trust and Halow (£2,000 each); The Brooke and Coram (£1,500 each); and CRY (£1,250).

FINANCES *Year* 2007–08 *Income* £91,747 *Grants* £91,750 *Assets* £2,388,478

TRUSTEES Mrs Caroline Fry; Mrs Camilla Carr; Ms Elizabeth Lyle.

OTHER INFORMATION Smaller grants of £1,000 or less totalled £52,000.

HOW TO APPLY In writing to the correspondent, including the latest set of accounts. Only registered charities will be considered.

WHO TO APPLY TO The Trustees, B M Box 2082, London WC1N 3XX

CC NO 296548   **ESTABLISHED** 1976

■ The Kathleen Laurence Trust

WHERE FUNDING CAN BE GIVEN UK.

WHO CAN BENEFIT General charities with specific projects and events.

WHAT IS FUNDED General charitable purposes. The trust particularly favours smaller organisations and those raising funds for specific requirements such as medical research, associations connected with disability and learning difficulties, organisations helping people who are sick, older people and children.

WHAT IS NOT FUNDED No donations are made for running costs, management expenses or to individuals.

TYPE OF GRANT One-off and recurrent grants.

RANGE OF GRANTS £400–£8,500.

SAMPLE GRANTS Arthritis Research Campaign, British Heart Foundation, MENCAP, Elizabeth Finn Trust, Battersea Dogs Home, Cancer Research Campaign and NSPCC (£8,500 each); Blood Pressure Association, Guideposts Trust and Independent Age (£2,000 each); The Dame Vera Lynn Trust and The Sick Children's Trust (£1,500 each); Action for Kids and Birmingham Settlement (£1,000 each); Endeavour Training and Second Chance (£750 each); and The Bognor Fun Bus (£400).

FINANCES *Year* 2007–08 *Income* £129,233 *Grants* £114,438 *Assets* £3,122,095

TRUSTEES Coutts and Co.

HOW TO APPLY In writing to the correspondent. Trustees meet in January and June.

Think carefully about every application. Is it justified?

659

WHO TO APPLY TO David Breach, Assistant Trust Manager, Coutts and Co, Trustee Department, 440 Strand, London WC2R 0QS *Tel* 020 7753 1000 *Fax* 020 7753 1090
CC NO 296461   **ESTABLISHED** 1987

....

■ The Law Society Charity

WHERE FUNDING CAN BE GIVEN Worldwide.
WHO CAN BENEFIT Organisations protecting people's legal rights and lawyers' welfare as well as projects from charities without an identifiable legal connection.
WHAT IS FUNDED Charitable activities in the furtherance of law and justice. This includes: charitable educational purposes for lawyers and would-be lawyers; legal research; promotion of an increased understanding of the law; and charities concerned with the provision of advice, counselling, mediation services connected with the law, welfare directly/indirectly of solicitors, trainee solicitors and other legal and Law Society staff and their families.
TYPE OF GRANT One-off and recurrent grants.
SAMPLE GRANTS The Citizenship Foundation (£90,000); LawCare Limited (£82,500); Howard League for Penal Reform (£17,500); Environmental Law Foundation and Solicitors' Benevolent Society (£15,000 each); Nottinghamshire Law Society and Working Families (£10,000 each); Asylum Support Appeals Project (£7,500); Book Aid International (£6,400); Peace Brigades International and Youthnet UK (£5,000 each).
FINANCES *Year* 2006–07 *Income* £99,208 *Grants* £319,045 *Assets* £1,872,260
TRUSTEES The Law Society Trustees Ltd.
HOW TO APPLY In writing to the correspondent. Applications are considered at quarterly trustees' meetings, usually held in April, July, September and December.
WHO TO APPLY TO Andrew Dobson, Company Secretary, 113 Chancery Lane, London WC2A 1PL *Tel* 020 7316 5597 *Website* www.lawsociety.org.uk
CC NO 268736   **ESTABLISHED** 1974

....

■ The Edgar E Lawley Foundation

WHERE FUNDING CAN BE GIVEN UK, with a preference for the West Midlands.
WHO CAN BENEFIT Older people, disability, children, community, hospices and medical in the UK.
WHAT IS FUNDED Charities involved in the provision of medical care and services to older people, children's charities, and those involved with the advancement of medicine and medical research.
WHAT IS NOT FUNDED No grants to individuals.
TYPE OF GRANT One-off.
RANGE OF GRANTS £500 upwards; typical grant £1,000–£1,500.
SAMPLE GRANTS Autism Initiative UK; Belfast Central Mission; Birmingham Boys' and Girls' Union; Birmingham St Mary's Hospice; Bolton Lads & Girls Club; Childline West Midlands; Cotswold Care Hospice; Macmillan Cancer Support (Birmingham); South Bucks Hospice; Walsall Society for the Blind; and YWCA (Wolverhampton); and Youth Action Wiltshire.
FINANCES *Year* 2007–08 *Income* £224,970 *Grants* £174,000 *Assets* £4,354,904
TRUSTEES J H Cooke, Chair; Mrs G V H Hilton; P J Cooke; F S Jackson.
HOW TO APPLY In writing to the correspondent. Applications must be received during April.

WHO TO APPLY TO F S Jackson, Trustee, Lower Wakefield, 116 Foley Road, Claygate, Surrey KT10 0NA *Tel* 01372 805 760 *email* frankjackson1945@yahoo.com *Website* www.edgarelawleyfoundation.org.uk
CC NO 201589   **ESTABLISHED** 1961

....

■ The Herd Lawson and Muriel Lawson Charitable Trust

WHERE FUNDING CAN BE GIVEN Mainly Cumbria.
WHO CAN BENEFIT Charitable organisations.
WHAT IS FUNDED This trust supports organisations benefiting older people in need, particularly those who are members of evangelical or Christian Brethren churches. A number of other named organisations receive support each year.
SAMPLE GRANTS British Red Cross Society and WWF – UK (£21,000 each); the Christian Workers Relief Fund (£15,000); West Cumbria Hospice (£7,000) the Hospice of St Mary's – Ulverston (£5,000); Ambleside Baptist Church (£4,500); Ambleside Welfare Charity and Spring Mount Fellowship (£3,000 each); the Universal Beneficient Society (£2,500); and Gospel Hall – Bowness on Windermere (£1,500).
FINANCES *Year* 2007–08 *Income* £189,782 *Grants* £84,000 *Assets* £1,620,794
TRUSTEES John Scott; Peter Matthews; Robert Holme Barker; Edmund Herd.
HOW TO APPLY The trust receives more applications than it can deal with and does not seek further unsolicited appeals.
WHO TO APPLY TO J D Scott, The Estate Office, 14 Church Street, Ambleside, Cumbria LA22 0BT
CC NO 1113220   **ESTABLISHED** 1975

....

■ The Lawson Beckman Charitable Trust

WHERE FUNDING CAN BE GIVEN UK.
WHO CAN BENEFIT Mainly headquarters organisations.
WHAT IS FUNDED Jewish organisations, welfare, education, the arts and general purposes.
WHAT IS NOT FUNDED No grants to individuals.
TYPE OF GRANT One-off and recurrent.
RANGE OF GRANTS £250–£16,000.
SAMPLE GRANTS Jewish Care (£100,000); Nightingale House (£13,500); Norwood Ravenswood (£10,000); Project SEED and UJIA (£5,000 each); Chai Lifeline Cancer Care (£3,000); Central Synagogue General Charities Fund (£2,000); UCH Hospital Charity (£1,500); Hatzola (£1,000); Bernard and Lucy Lyons Charitable Trust (£750); Juvenile Diabetes Research Foundation (£500); Heart Cells Foundation and Talking Newspapers (£250 each); and Child Resettlement Trust Fund (£150).
FINANCES *Year* 2007–08 *Income* £123,190 *Grants* £61,700 *Assets* £1,867,225
TRUSTEES M A Lawson; F C Katz; L R Stock.
HOW TO APPLY In writing to the correspondent, but please note that grants are allocated two years in advance.
WHO TO APPLY TO Melvin Lawson, Trustee, A Beckman plc, PO Box 1ED, London W1A 1ED *Tel* 020 7637 8412 *Fax* 020 7436 8599
CC NO 261378   **ESTABLISHED** 1970

■ The Raymond and Blanche Lawson Charitable Trust

WHERE FUNDING CAN BE GIVEN UK, with an interest in West Kent and East Sussex.

WHO CAN BENEFIT Registered charities benefiting children, young adults and older people, including people with disabilities.

WHAT IS FUNDED This trust will consider funding: arts activities and education; building preservation; hospice at home; nursing service; local hospices; hospitals; cancer research; community centres and village halls; guide dogs; care in the community; and armed service charities and benevolent associations.

WHAT IS NOT FUNDED No support for churches or individuals.

TYPE OF GRANT One-off, project and research. Funding is available for up to one year.

RANGE OF GRANTS £250–£5,000. Typically £500–£1,000.

SAMPLE GRANTS Hospice in the Weald (£5,000); Poppy Appeal (£4,000); Langton Green Village Hall and Heart of Kent Hospice (£3,000 each); Kent Music School and the National Trust (£2,000 each); British Lung Foundation and Childhood First (£1,000 each); Independent Age and Kent Youth (£750 each); and Micro Anophtamimic Children's Society and The Eyeless Trust (£500 each).

FINANCES *Year* 2006–07 *Income* £123,334 *Grants* £90,086 *Assets* £1,578,975

TRUSTEES John V Banks; Mrs P E V Banks; Mrs Sarah Hill.

HOW TO APPLY In writing to the correspondent.

WHO TO APPLY TO Mrs P E V Banks, Trustee, 28 Barden Road, Tonbridge, Kent TN9 1TX *Tel* 01732 352 183 *Fax* 01732 352 621

CC NO 281269   **ESTABLISHED** 1980

■ The Carole and Geoffrey Lawson Foundation

WHERE FUNDING CAN BE GIVEN Worldwide, in practice, UK.

WHO CAN BENEFIT Registered charities.

WHAT IS FUNDED Child welfare, poverty, arts, education, research and Jewish organisations.

WHAT IS NOT FUNDED In principal, no grants to individuals.

RANGE OF GRANTS £500–£115,000.

SAMPLE GRANTS World ORT Trust (£113,000); The Prince's Trust (£33,000); Chase Children's Hospice Service (£29,000); St David's Care in the Community (£15,000); Jewish Care (£13,000); Community Security Trust and World Jewish Relief (£10,000 each); Nightingale Home (£8,000); King Silver Lining Appeal (£5,000); Young Enterprise (£3,500); Meath Epilepsy Trust (£2,000); and Royal Opera House, the Sanctuary and Coexistence Trust (£1,000 each).

FINANCES *Year* 2007–08 *Income* £115,729 *Grants* £297,505 *Assets* £222,166

TRUSTEES Geoffrey C H Lawson; Carole Lawson; Harold I Connick; Edward C S Lawson; Jeremy S Lawson.

HOW TO APPLY In writing to the correspondent.

WHO TO APPLY TO Geoffrey Lawson, Trustee, Stilemans, Munstead, Godalming, Surrey GU8 4AB *Tel* 01483 420757

CC NO 801751   **ESTABLISHED** 1989

■ The Mason Le Page Charitable Trust

WHERE FUNDING CAN BE GIVEN London area.

WHO CAN BENEFIT Organisations benefiting people with cancer and medical research.

WHAT IS FUNDED General charitable purposes, with a preference for supporting charities working in cancer research and care in the London area.

WHAT IS NOT FUNDED No grants to Individuals.

SAMPLE GRANTS Previous beneficiaries include: Barry Reed Oncology Laboratory, St Barts, CORE, St Joseph's Hospice, Breast Cancer Campaign, Harlington Hospice Middlesex, Prostate Cancer Research Centre, Prostate Cancer Research Campaign UK, Dulwich Helpline, St Christopher's Hospice and Trinity Hospice.

FINANCES *Year* 2007–08 *Income* £21,590 *Grants* £42,931

TRUSTEES David Morgan; Andrew John Francis Stebbings.

HOW TO APPLY In writing to the correspondent.

WHO TO APPLY TO Andrew Stebbings, The Administrator, 45 Pont Street, London SW1X 0BX *Tel* 020 7591 3333 *Fax* 020 7591 3300

CC NO 1054589   **ESTABLISHED** 1996

■ The Leach Fourteenth Trust

WHERE FUNDING CAN BE GIVEN UK with some preference for south west England.

WHO CAN BENEFIT Grants to registered charities only.

WHAT IS FUNDED Charities working in the fields of: residential facilities and services; missionary work; conservation and environment; and community services. Support may be given to: professional bodies; councils for voluntary service; hospice at home; respite care; ambulances and mobile units; medical equipment; medical research; alternative medicine; professional and specialist training; and special needs education. Trustees mainly seek out their own ventures to support.

WHAT IS NOT FUNDED Only registered charities based in the UK are supported (the trust only gives overseas via a UK-based charity). No grants to: individuals, including for gap years or trips abroad; private schools other than for people with disabilities or learning difficulties; no pet charities.

TYPE OF GRANT Buildings, capital, core costs, one-off, project, research, running costs, recurring costs, salaries and start-up costs will be considered. Funding may be given for more than three years.

RANGE OF GRANTS £500–£5,000.

SAMPLE GRANTS Durrell Wildlife Conservation Trust (£5,000); The Princess Royal Trust for Carers (£4,000); Salvation Army (£3,000); Merlin (£2,800); Afghan Aid (£2,500); British Red Cross (£2,200); Children in Crisis (£2,000); Orbis and the Country Trust – Suffolk (£1,500 each); and UK Sports Association (£1,000).

FINANCES *Year* 2007–08 *Income* £105,301 *Grants* £87,570 *Assets* £2,830,872

TRUSTEES W J Henderson; Mrs J M M Nash; G S Ward; R Murray-Leach.

HOW TO APPLY In writing to the correspondent. Applications for a specific item or purpose are favoured. Only successful appeals can expect a reply. A representative of the trust occasionally visits potential beneficiaries. There are bi-annual meetings of trustees in summer and late autumn. Grants tend to be distributed twice a year but exceptions are made.

■ The David Lean Foundation

WHERE FUNDING CAN BE GIVEN UK.
WHO CAN BENEFIT Charitable organisations.
WHAT IS FUNDED Promotion and advancement of education and to cultivate and improve public taste in the visual arts, particularly in the field of film production, including screenplay writing, film direction and editing. The foundation supports scholarships at the National Film and Television School, Leighton Park School and other institutions.
TYPE OF GRANT One-off and recurrent grants.
SAMPLE GRANTS British Film Institute (£311,000 for film restoration); National Film and Television School (£73,000 for library/fiction direction lectures); British Academy of Film and Television Arts (£20,000 for lectures); Royal Academy of Arts (£10,000 for lectures); Literary Research (£9,000); and David Lean Trailer (£3,600).
FINANCES *Year* 2008 *Income* £317,678 *Grants* £491,744 *Assets* £334,811
TRUSTEES A A Reeves; J G Moore.
OTHER INFORMATION Of the total grants awarded, £65,000 was distributed in scholarships/ awards to individuals.
HOW TO APPLY Scholarship grants for students attending the National Film and Television School, Royal Holloway or Leighton Park School, are normally only awarded on the recommendation of the course provider with the trustees. Other applications for grants that would meet the aims of the foundation are invited in writing, enclosing full details of the project and including financial information and two references.
WHO TO APPLY TO The Trustees, KJD, Churchill House, Regent House, Stoke-on-Trent ST1 3RQ *Tel* 01782 202 020 *Fax* 01782 266060 *email* aar@kjd.co.uk *Website* www. davidleanfoundation.org
CC NO 1067074   **ESTABLISHED** 1997

■ The Leathersellers' Company Charitable Fund

WHERE FUNDING CAN BE GIVEN UK, particularly London.
WHO CAN BENEFIT Registered charities only.
WHAT IS FUNDED Charities associated with the Leathersellers' Company, the leather and hide trades, education in leather technology and for the welfare of poor and sick former workers in the industry and their dependants. Thereafter financial support is provided to registered charities associated with the City of London and its environs in the fields of education and sciences, relief of those in need, people with disabilities, children and young people, medicine and health, the arts, the church and the environment.
TYPE OF GRANT One-off and recurrent grants.
SAMPLE GRANTS University of Northampton (£63,000); Colfe's School Ltd (a related trust) (£60,000); Prendergast School (£50,000); Reach out Projects – Chellington (£25,000); Pelican Cancer Foundation (£20,000); Kids Cookery School, Prison Advise and Care Trust,

Missing People and Michael Palin Centre for Stammering Children (£15,000 each). Other aggregate grants under £15,000 totalled £483,000.
FINANCES *Year* 2007–08 *Income* £1,510,000 *Grants* £1,144,000 *Assets* £38,560,000
TRUSTEES The Leathersellers Company
HOW TO APPLY In writing to the correspondent. 'Appeals must be from registered charities operating within the UK. Priority will be given to charities connected with leather, the leather trade, and the London area due to the company's long associations there. We will also consider charities that are based throughout the United Kingdom. Please send no more than two sides of A4 in the first instance describing the charity and giving an idea of its financial situation and what you need. Do not send sets of audited accounts as these will be sought later if we require them.' Please note: the trust states that it willl soon only be accepting online applications. See the trust's website for further details.
WHO TO APPLY TO Geoffrey Russell-Jones, Administrator, 15 St Helen's Place, London EC3A 6DQ *Tel* 020 7330 1451 *Fax* 020 7330 1445 *email* grussell-jones @leathersellers.co.uk *Website* www.leathersellers.co.uk
CC NO 278072   **ESTABLISHED** 1979

■ The Leche Trust

WHERE FUNDING CAN BE GIVEN UK.
WHO CAN BENEFIT Individuals and organisations benefiting: the arts, architecture and overseas students during last six months of their PhD courses.
WHAT IS FUNDED (i) 'the promotion of amity and good relations between Britain and third world countries by financing visits to such countries by teachers or other appropriate persons, or providing financial assistance to students from overseas especially those in financial hardship during the last six months of their postgraduate doctorate study in the UK or those engaged in activities consistent with the charitable objects of the trust; (ii) assistance to academic, educational or other organisations concerned with music, drama, dance and the arts; (iii) the preservation of buildings and their contents and the repair and conservation of church furniture (including such items as monuments, but excluding structural repairs to the church fabric); preference is to be given to buildings and objects of the Georgian period; (iv) assistance to conservation in all its aspects, including in particular museums and encouraging good practice in the art of conservation by supporting investigative and diagnostic reports; (v) the support of charitable bodies or organisations associated with the preservation of the nation's countryside, towns, villages and historic landscapes.'
WHAT IS NOT FUNDED No grants are made for: religious bodies; overseas missions; schools and school buildings; social welfare; animals; medicine; expeditions; or British students other than music students.
TYPE OF GRANT For a specific purpose and not recurrent, including building costs.
RANGE OF GRANTS £800–£6,000.
SAMPLE GRANTS London Historic Parks and Gardens Trust (£6,000); Chapel at Stansted Park – Hampshire and St Patrick's Catholic Church – Soho Square, London (£5,000 each); Scottish Ballet – Glasgow (£3,400); Paxton House – Berwick upon Tweed (£3,000); British School of

Rome (£2,000); Gainsborough House – Sudbury, Suffolk (£1,500); and Wonderful Beast (£1,000).

FINANCES *Year* 2007–08 *Income* £275,187 *Grants* £215,135 *Assets* £6,040,329

TRUSTEES Dr Ian Bristow; The Hon. Mrs Felicity Guinness; Simon Jervis; Lady Greenstock; Martin Williams; Simon Wethered; Mrs Caroline Laing.

OTHER INFORMATION Included in the grant total is £28,050 given to individual students.

HOW TO APPLY In writing to the secretary. Trustees meet three times a year, in February, June and October; applications need to be received the month before.

WHO TO APPLY TO Mrs Louisa Lawson, Secretary, 84 Cicada Road, London SW18 2NZ *Tel* 020 8870 6233 *Fax* 020 8870 6233 *email* info@ lechetrust.org *Website* www.lechetrust.org
CC NO 225659   **ESTABLISHED** 1963

■ The Arnold Lee Charitable Trust

WHERE FUNDING CAN BE GIVEN UK.

WHO CAN BENEFIT Organisations benefiting children, young adults and Jewish people. Support may also be given to rabbis, medical professionals, students, teachers and governesses. Very occasional grants may be made to individuals.

WHAT IS FUNDED Established charities of high repute working in the fields of education, health and religious purposes.

WHAT IS NOT FUNDED Grants are rarely made to individuals.

SAMPLE GRANTS Previously: Joint Jewish Charitable Trust, Project SEED, Jewish Care, Lubavich Foundation, The Home of Aged Jews, Friends of Akim and Yesodey Hatorah School.

FINANCES *Year* 2007–08 *Income* £96,496 *Grants* £88,670 *Assets* £1,860,601

TRUSTEES Helen Lee; Alan Lee.

HOW TO APPLY In writing to the correspondent.

WHO TO APPLY TO Haslems Fenton LLP, Palladium House, 1–4 Argyll Street, London W1F 7LD
CC NO 264437   **ESTABLISHED** 1972

■ The William Leech Charity

WHERE FUNDING CAN BE GIVEN Northumberland, Tyne and Wear, Durham and overseas.

WHO CAN BENEFIT Volunteers, young people, disadvantaged people and Christians.

WHAT IS FUNDED Small charities with a high proportion of unpaid volunteers, organisations working in deprived areas for the benefit of local people, particularly those which encourage people to help themselves, the promotion of community involvement and Christian charitable purposes.

WHAT IS NOT FUNDED No grants for: community centres and similar (exceptionally, those in remote country areas may be supported); running expenses of youth clubs (as opposed to capital projects); running expenses of churches (this includes normal repairs, but churches engaged in social work, or using their buildings largely for 'outside' purposes, may be supported); sport; the arts; individuals or students; organisations which have been supported in the last 12 months (it would be exceptional to support an organisation in two successive years, unless support had been confirmed in advance); holidays, travel, outings; minibuses (unless over 10,000 miles a year is expected); schools; and housing associations.

TYPE OF GRANT One-off and recurring grants, loans, running costs and salaries.

RANGE OF GRANTS £100–£50,000.

SAMPLE GRANTS Peals (£50,000); Macmillan Nurses (£30,000); Central Palz (£20,000 in total); Northern Institute for Cancer Research and the People's Kitchen (£10,000 each); St John of Jerusalem Eye Hospital (£7,000); Newcastle West Methodist Circuit (£6,000); Children's Vision International and the Microloan Foundation (£5,000 each); Northumbrian Healthcare (£4,000); Durham University – Sri Lanka in Focus Project (£3,000); Haller Foundation (£2,000); and King Edward VI School – Morpeth (£1,000); and Safety Crackers (£500).

FINANCES *Year* 2007–08 *Income* £471,272 *Grants* £370,902 *Assets* £16,169,996

TRUSTEES Prof. Peter H Baylis; Cyril Davies; Adrian Gifford; Roy Leech; Richard Leech; N Sherlock; David Stabler; Barry Wallace; Prof. Chris Day.

HOW TO APPLY **The Main Fund**
'As it is the intention of the trustees to favour support for those charities who help others by utilising the generous time and skills of volunteers, they accept applications in the short form of a letter, rather than expecting the completion of a complicated application form, which may seem daunting to some applicants. In order to safe-guard our charity status, it is important that we are accountable for how funds are distributed. As such, the following protocols exist for making and investigating applications. Please note we only accept applications from registered charities, and the registered charity address must be included in the application process. For large grants and multiple grants, trustees would like to see as much supporting information as possible, and in rare cases, they may wish to interview the applicant. Your applications must include: a description of the project that the charity is undertaking, who it hopes to help, and any evidence which will support the need for this particular project; how much the project will cost, capital and revenue, with an indication of the amounts involved; how much the charity has raised so far, and where it expects to find the balance; the type of support sought; i.e. small grant, multiple grant, loan, etc.; how much does it cost to run the charity each year, including how much of the revenue is spent on salaries and employees. Where does the revenue come from? How many paid workers are there, how many volunteers are there.'

The Lady Leech Fund
'Applications to this fund should be submitted in a letter containing: the name, address and registration number of the charity; the name and contact details of the person who is authorised by the charity to apply for funding; a description of the project that the charity is undertaking, who it hopes to help, and any evidence which will support the need for this particular project; how much the project will cost, capital and revenue, with an indication of the amounts involved; how much the charity has raised so far, and where it expects to find the balance; a description of the connection between the Developing World Project, and the people in the North East of England; how much does it cost to run the charity each year, including how much of the revenue is spent on salaries and employees. Where does the revenue come from? How many paid workers are there? How many volunteers are there? Application letters can be written and submitted on the charity's website.'

WHO TO APPLY TO Mrs Kathleen M Smith, Secretary, Saville Chambers, 5 North Street, Newcastle

upon Tyne NE1 8DF *Tel* 0191 243 3300
Fax 0191 243 3309 *email* enquiries@
williamleechcharity.org.uk *Website* www.
williamleechcharity.org.uk
cc no 265491   established 1972

■ The Lord Mayor of Leeds Appeal Fund

where funding can be given Leeds.
who can benefit The charities selected by the lord mayor during her/his year of office.
what is funded Charitable causes.
sample grants Heart Research UK (£63,000); and Leeds General Infirmary (£56,000).
finances *Year* 2007–08 *Income* £68,831 *Grants* £122,619 *Assets* £61,247
trustees Lord Mayor of Leeds; Chief Executive Leeds City Council; J M Proctor; T Hanley; A Blackburn; M Hamilton.
how to apply The fund does not accept unsolicited applications.
who to apply to Stephen McHugh, The Lord Mayor's Secretary, Lord Mayor's Office, Civic Hall, Leeds LS1 1UR *Tel* 0113 247 4055
cc no 512441   established 1982

■ Leeds Building Society Charitable Foundation

where funding can be given Areas where the society's branches are located.
who can benefit Organisations benefiting the homeless, local community centres, younger people, older people, individuals with disabilities, and deaf and/or blind people.
what is funded Charities which have benefited include those working in the following areas: provision of shelter, support and resettlement programmes; for the homeless; centres offering facilities for the local community with emphasis on young and older people; provision of work experience and skills training for young people with special needs; educational and recreational projects for the deaf and blind; provision of transport for the physically disabled; practical care for the terminally ill; recreational and educational opportunities for children and young people from disadvantaged backgrounds.
what is not funded The following are not eligible for grants: restoration of buildings, including churches; playgroups, Scout or Guide associations; environmental charities (unless there is a benefit to a disadvantaged community); religious, political or military purposes; overseas charities or projects; individuals, including sponsorship; animal welfare projects; medical research or equipment.
type of grant One-off for capital projects.
range of grants £250–£1,000.
finances *Year* 2008 *Income* £114,972 *Grants* £110,367 *Assets* £28,111
trustees Paul D Taylor, Chair; Ann Shelton; Peter Marshall; Gary Brook; Karen Wint; Robert Wade.
how to apply In writing to the correspondent. The trustees meet four times a year in March, June, September and December. The trust is unable to consider applications if support has been provided in the last two years.
who to apply to Sally Smith, Secretary, 105 Albion Street, Leeds, West Yorkshire LS1 5AS

Tel 0113 216 7296 *Fax* 0113 225 7549
email ssmith@leeds-holbeck.co.uk
Website www.leedsbuildingsociety.co.
uk/foundation
cc no 1074429   established 1999

■ The Leeds Community Foundation

where funding can be given Leeds.
who can benefit Community groups and registered charities.
what is funded Social welfare and general charitable purposes.
finances *Year* 2007–08 *Income* £11,000,000 *Grants* £1,100,000
trustees John Ansbro, Chair; Martin Dean; Uell Kennedy; Brenda Redfern; Kevin O'Connor; Andrew Wriglesworth; Todd Hannula; Steve Rogers.
how to apply The foundation's website has details of the grant schemes currently being administered and how to apply.
who to apply to The Grants and Community Manager, 51a St Paul's Street, Leeds LS1 2TE *Tel* 0113 242 2426 *email* info@ leedscommunityfoundation.org.uk *Website* www. leedscommunityfoundation.org.uk
cc no 1096892   established 2005

■ Leicester Charity Link (formerly The Leicester Charity Organisation Society)

where funding can be given The city of Leicester, Leicestershire and Rutland.
who can benefit Individuals and organisations.
what is funded General charitable purposes.
sample grants Grants to: Leicestershire Palliative and Cancer Care Teams which help patients and their carers; individuals in need; grants to a few organisations through the Local Network Fund and other trusts under its administration.
finances *Year* 2007–08 *Income* £82,545 *Grants* £428,458 *Assets* £295,945
trustees Mrs R Freer; R J Hudson; C E Smith; Mrs C M Wessel; A H Jarvis; Mrs R M Ingman.
other information Of the grant total, £3,737 went to organisations and £424,721to individuals
how to apply In writing to the correspondent.
who to apply to Paul Griffiths, Chief Executive, 20a Millstone Lane, Leicester LE1 5JN *Tel* 0116 222 2200 *Fax* 0161 222 2201 *email* info@ charity-link.org *Website* www.charity-link.org
cc no 209464   established 1876

■ Leicestershire Historic Churches Trust

where funding can be given Leicestershire.
who can benefit Churches and chapels.
what is funded The restoration, preservation, repair, maintenance and improvement of churches and chapels, their churchyards and contents.
what is not funded No grants for electrical work, disability access, reordering of the interior, redecorating, toilets or kitchen facilities, extensions, school or other ancillary buildings.
finances *Year* 2007–08 *Income* £38,363 *Grants* £17,367 *Assets* £102,262
trustees R H Bloor; Hon. Lady Brooks; C B Byford; T Y Cocks; R Gill; J M Hemes; Revd D N Hole;

J Ireland; D Knowles; Dr A D McWhirr; T H Patrick; Fr Fabian Radcliffe; B W Wilford; R J Wood.

HOW TO APPLY In writing to the correspondent. The trustees meet twice a year, usually in April and October. Applications should be submitted by 1 March and 1 September. Churches and chapels have three years in which to claim a grant once a grant has been awarded.

WHO TO APPLY TO Janet Arthur, Chair, 20 Gumley Road, Smeeton Westerby, Leicester LE8 0LT *Tel* 0116 279 3995 *email* chairman@lhct.org.uk *Website* www.lhct.org.uk

CC NO 233476   **ESTABLISHED** 1964

■ The P Leigh-Bramwell Trust 'E'

WHERE FUNDING CAN BE GIVEN UK, with a preference for Bolton.

WHO CAN BENEFIT Registered charities, schools, universities and churches benefiting children, young adults, students and Methodists.

WHAT IS FUNDED Specific regular allocations, leaving little opportunity to add further charities. Support is particularly given to Methodist churches and Bolton-based organisations.

WHAT IS NOT FUNDED No grants to individuals.

TYPE OF GRANT Mainly recurrent grants to established beneficiaries.

RANGE OF GRANTS £100–£30,000.

SAMPLE GRANTS King's College School (£30,000); Leigh-Bramwell Fund (£23,000); The Methodist Church – Bolton (£11,000); Rivington Parish Church (£7,500); The Unicorn School (£7,000); and The Methodist Church – Delph Hill and The Methodist Church – Breightmet (£3,400 each); RNLI (£2,000); Barnabus, Bolton Choral Union, Bolton Deaf Society, Childline North West, NCH Bypass, West London Mission and YWCA (£500 each).

FINANCES *Year* 2007–08 *Income* £115,916 *Grants* £115,142 *Assets* £2,225,089

TRUSTEES Mrs H R Leigh-Bramwell; Mrs J Leigh Hardyment; B H Leigh-Bramwell.

HOW TO APPLY In writing to the correspondent; however, please note that previous research suggests that there is only a small amount of funds available for unsolicited applications and therefore success is unlikely.

WHO TO APPLY TO Mrs L Cooper, Secretary, W and J Leigh and Co., Tower Works, Kestor Street, Bolton BL2 2AL *Tel* 01204 521771

CC NO 267333   **ESTABLISHED** 1973

■ The Kennedy Leigh Charitable Trust

WHERE FUNDING CAN BE GIVEN Israel and UK.

WHO CAN BENEFIT Registered charities only.

WHAT IS FUNDED Projects and causes which will improve and enrich the lives of all parts of society, not least those of the young, the needy, the disadvantaged and the underprivileged. The trust's objects require three-quarters of its grant-making funds to be distributed to charitable institutions within Israel, with the remainder being distributed in the UK and elsewhere.

WHAT IS NOT FUNDED No grants to individuals.

TYPE OF GRANT Capital projects and running costs. Usually up to three years, with the possibility of renewal.

RANGE OF GRANTS £1,000 and over.

SAMPLE GRANTS Listed UK beneficiaries included: University of Cambridge Kennedy Leigh Fund

(£150,000 to fund the shortfall in the fund to allow the Kennedy Leigh Lectureship in Modern Hebrew to continue); St John Ophthalmic Eye Hospital (£27,000 a year for three years); CHAI Lifeline (£25,000 a year for three years); Oxford Centre for Hebrew Studies (£25,000 a year for three years to fund a programme for visiting Israeli academics and writers); and North London Hospice (£10,000).

FINANCES *Year* 2007–08 *Income* £681,146 *Grants* £687,786 *Assets* £18,684,529

TRUSTEES Geoffrey Goldkorn; Lesley D Berman; Carole Berman Sujo; Angela Sorkin; Michele Foux; Alexander Sorkin.

HOW TO APPLY The trust stated in its 2007/08 accounts: 'The funds available for distribution outside of Israel are all but committed for the foreseeable future to several UK charities. The trustees are therefore unable to consider applications for funding from charitable organisations outside of Israel at this time.'

WHO TO APPLY TO Naomi Shoffman, Administrator, Ort House, 126 Albert Street, London NW1 7NE *Tel* 020 7267 6500 *email* naomi@klct.org

CC NO 288293   **ESTABLISHED** 1983

■ Morris Leigh Foundation

WHERE FUNDING CAN BE GIVEN UK.

WHO CAN BENEFIT Charitable organisations, with a strong preference for Jewish/Israeli organisations.

WHAT IS FUNDED General charitable purposes, including the arts and humanities, education, culture and health and welfare causes.

TYPE OF GRANT Grants and long-term loans.

RANGE OF GRANTS £50–£6,000.

SAMPLE GRANTS Previously Royal College of Music, London Business School, Rycolewood College, Institute for Jewish Policy Research, Ronald Raven Cancer Trust, London Symphony Orchestra, London Philharmonic Orchestra, Somerset House Arts Fund, Sussex University, Community Service Trust and Chicken Shed Theatre.

FINANCES *Year* 2006–07 *Income* £47,471 *Grants* £49,861 *Assets* £1,538,806

TRUSTEES Martin D Paisner; Howard D Leigh.

HOW TO APPLY In writing to the correspondent.

WHO TO APPLY TO Tina Grant-Brook, 40 Portland Place, London W1B 1NB *Tel* 020 7908 6000

CC NO 280695   **ESTABLISHED** 1980

■ The Leigh Trust

WHERE FUNDING CAN BE GIVEN UK and overseas.

WHO CAN BENEFIT Registered charities benefiting children; young adults; older people; unemployed people; volunteers; people who are in care, fostered or adopted; ethnic minority groups; at risk groups; people disadvantaged by poverty; ex-offenders and those at risk of offending; refugees; socially isolated people; people living in urban areas; victims of abuse and crime; and people with substance misuse problems.

WHAT IS FUNDED Grants can be given to legal services, support to voluntary and community organisations, support to volunteers, health counselling, support and self-help groups, drug and alcohol rehabilitation, education and training, social counselling, crime prevention schemes, community issues, international rights of the individual, advice and information (social issues), asylum seekers, racial equality and other charitable causes.

WHAT IS NOT FUNDED The trust does not make grants to individuals.

TYPE OF GRANT Buildings, capital, core costs, one-off, project, recurring costs, running costs, salaries and start-up costs. Funding is available for up to three years.

RANGE OF GRANTS £500–£5,000.

SAMPLE GRANTS Action on Addiction, Asylum Support Appeal Project, Care for Prisoners Overseas Organisation, Church Action on Poverty, Nazareth House, New Hope Leeds and Stonebridge City Farm (£5,000 each); Ipswich Housing Action Group, New Bridge Foundation and Student Action for Refugees (£3,000 each); BID Deaf Prison Project (£2,500); Ice & Fire Theatre Company (£2,000); and Alnwick Garden Trust and Marylebone High School (£1,000 each).

FINANCES *Year* 2007–08 *Income* £93,006 *Grants* £144,430 *Assets* £2,996,546

TRUSTEES Hon. David Bernstein; Dr R M E Stone; Caroline Moorehead.

HOW TO APPLY Organisations applying for grants must provide their most recent audited accounts, a registered charity number, a cash flow statement for the next 12 months, and a stamped addressed envelope. Applicants should state clearly on one side of A4 what their charity does and what they are requesting funding for. They should provide a detailed budget and show other sources of funding for the project.

WHO TO APPLY TO The Trustees, Begbies Chettle Agar, Epworth House, 25 City Road, London EC1Y 1AR *Tel* 020 7628 5801 *Fax* 020 7628 0390

CC NO 275372   **ESTABLISHED** 1976

■ Mrs Vera Leigh's Charity

WHERE FUNDING CAN BE GIVEN UK.

WHO CAN BENEFIT Organisations only.

WHAT IS FUNDED General charitable purposes.

WHAT IS NOT FUNDED No grants to individuals.

TYPE OF GRANT One-off.

RANGE OF GRANTS £250–£500.

SAMPLE GRANTS Meath Epilepsy Trust, the Peckham Settlement, Surrey Law Centre, Abbots Hospital (£500 each); and Apec, Community Action Nepal, Action Aid and Scope (£250 each).

FINANCES *Year* 2007–08 *Income* £388,707 *Grants* £5,500 *Assets* £54,229

TRUSTEES J H Woollcombe; T A Cole.

HOW TO APPLY In writing to the correspondent, although the trust states that unsolicited applications are not considered.

WHO TO APPLY TO Thomas Eggar, Newbury House, 20 Kings Road West, Newbury, Berkshire RG14 5XR *Tel* 01635 571009

CC NO 274872   **ESTABLISHED** 1976

■ The Lennox and Wyfold Foundation

WHERE FUNDING CAN BE GIVEN Unrestricted.

WHO CAN BENEFIT Registered charities.

WHAT IS FUNDED General charitable purposes.

SAMPLE GRANTS Breakthrough Breast Cancer, towards the Generations Study (£250,000); Eton College endowment fund (£100,000); Absolute Return for Kids (£45,000); RNIB (£40,000); DeafBlind UK and Royal Marsden Cancer Campaign (£30,000 each); Amber Foundation, the Ditchley Foundation and Fight for Sight (£20,000 each); Tusk Trust (£11,000); Elephant Family and St George's Chapel –

Windsor (£10,000 each); Bucklebury Memorial Hall (£6,000); and Chipping Norton Theatre and Friends Trust, Gloucestershire Air Ambulance, Mary Hare Foundation and Reform Research Trust (£5,000 each).

FINANCES *Year* 2007–08 *Income* £474,684 *Grants* £1,111,500 *Assets* £35,664,608

TRUSTEES R J Fleming; A R Fleming; W L Hannay; C M Fleming; Mrs C F Wilmot-Sitwell.

HOW TO APPLY In writing to the correspondent.

WHO TO APPLY TO G Fincham, Secretary, c/o RF Trustee Co. Limited, Ely House, 37 Dover Street, London W1S 4NJ

CC NO 1080198   **ESTABLISHED** 2000

■ The Leonard Trust

WHERE FUNDING CAN BE GIVEN Overseas and UK, with a preference for Winchester.

WHO CAN BENEFIT Registered charities.

WHAT IS FUNDED Christian, overseas aid.

WHAT IS NOT FUNDED No grants to individuals. Medical research or building projects are no longer supported.

TYPE OF GRANT Usually one-off.

RANGE OF GRANTS £1,000–£5,000.

SAMPLE GRANTS VIVA Network – Street Children South America (£10,500); Christian Aid (£5,000); Chernobyl Children in Need (£2,300); Care in the Family, Frontier Youth, Tear Fund and Tower Hamlets (£2,000 each); L'Arche and YMCA (£1,000 each); and Brendon Care (£800).

FINANCES *Year* 2007 *Income* £35,431 *Grants* £32,600

TRUSTEES Dominic Gold; Mrs N A Gold.

HOW TO APPLY Unsolicited applications cannot be considered.

WHO TO APPLY TO Tessa E Feilden, 18 Edgar Road, Winchester, Hampshire SO23 9TW *Tel* 01962 854 800

CC NO 1031723   **ESTABLISHED** 1993

■ The Erica Leonard Trust

WHERE FUNDING CAN BE GIVEN Mainly Surrey and occasionally overseas.

WHO CAN BENEFIT Registered charities only.

WHAT IS FUNDED General charitable purposes.

WHAT IS NOT FUNDED Only able to support registered charities.

RANGE OF GRANTS Most grants are for £1,000 or less.

SAMPLE GRANTS Phoenix Trust (£9,000); Wells for India (£4,000); Leonard Trust (£2,000); Gauchers Association (£1,000); Cherry Trees (£750); Marie Curie Cancer Care (£500); and FMDM (£250).

FINANCES *Year* 2007–08 *Income* £41,950 *Grants* £41,750 *Assets* £553,127

TRUSTEES R C E Grey; A C Kemp; R Beeston.

HOW TO APPLY In writing to the correspondent.

WHO TO APPLY TO Richard C E Grey, Trustee, Old Farmhouse, Farnham Road, Elstead, Surrey GU8 6DB *Tel* 01252 702230 *email* rcegrey@aol.com

CC NO 291627   **ESTABLISHED** 1985

■ The Mark Leonard Trust

WHERE FUNDING CAN BE GIVEN Worldwide, but mainly UK.

WHO CAN BENEFIT Organisations benefiting the environment, children and young adults.

WHAT IS FUNDED Environment: environmental education, particularly supporting projects displaying practical ways of involving children and young adults, as well as sustainable transport, energy efficiency and renewable energy. Youth work: the rehabilitation of young people who have become marginalised and involved in anti-social or criminal activities, as well as extending and adding value to the existing use of school buildings and encouraging greater involvement of parents, school leavers and volunteers in extra-curricular activities. General charitable purposes.

WHAT IS NOT FUNDED Grants are not normally made to individuals.

RANGE OF GRANTS £2000–£50000.

SAMPLE GRANTS Kikass TV (£50,000); Just for Kids Law (£38,000); Ashden Awards and Small Woods Association (£30,000 each); Uniting Britain Trust (£20,000); Envision (£12,000); Plumpton College, Transport 2000 Trust and St Stevens Church – Lympne (£10,000 each); Council for Environmental Education (£5,000); Save the Rhino International (£3,300); and Devon Wildlife Trust (£2,000).

FINANCES *Year* 2007–08 *Income* £642,583 *Grants* £339,855 *Assets* £11,420,397

TRUSTEES Zivi Sainsbury; Judith Portrait; John Julian Sainsbury; Mark Sainsbury.

HOW TO APPLY 'Proposals are generally invited by the trustees or initiated at their request. Unsolicited applications are discouraged and are unlikely to be successful, unless they are closely aligned to the trust's areas of interest.' A single application will be considered for support by all the trusts in the Sainsbury family group.

WHO TO APPLY TO Alan Bookbinder, Director, Allington House, 1st Floor, 150 Victoria Street, London SW1E 5AE *Tel* 020 7410 0330 *Fax* 020 7410 0332 *Website* www.sfct.org.uk

CC NO 1040323   **ESTABLISHED** 1994

■ Lesley Lesley and Mutter Trust

WHERE FUNDING CAN BE GIVEN Dorset.

WHO CAN BENEFIT Parkinson's Disease Association, Chest Heart and Stroke Association, Multiple Sclerosis Society, Muscular Dystrophy Group of Great Britain, Royal National Institute for the Blind, Rowcroft Hospice for Torbay and Guide Dogs for the Blind (Devon Area Branch).

WHAT IS FUNDED Recipients are named in the trust deed and only those organisations can be funded.

TYPE OF GRANT Recurrent.

FINANCES *Year* 2007–08 *Income* £165,128 *Grants* £37,397 *Assets* £945,588

TRUSTEES Lloyds TSB Private Banking Ltd.

HOW TO APPLY Applications are not welcome

WHO TO APPLY TO Brian Commander, Lloyds Private Banking Limited, UK Trust Centre, The Clock House, 22–26 Ock Street, Abingdon, Oxfordshire OX14 5SW *Tel* 01235 232734 *email* brian.commander@lloydstsb.co.uk

CC NO 1018747   **ESTABLISHED** 1989

■ Leukaemia Research Fund

WHERE FUNDING CAN BE GIVEN UK.

WHO CAN BENEFIT Hospitals and university medical centres which benefit medical professionals, nurses and doctors; students; and people with leukaemia.

WHAT IS FUNDED Improving treatments, finding the cures and preventing all forms of leukaemia, Hodgkin's disease and other lymphomata, myelomata, the myelodysplasias and aplastic anaemia.

TYPE OF GRANT Capital (equipment), feasibility study, recurring costs, research and salaries.

RANGE OF GRANTS £45,000–£4.5 million.

SAMPLE GRANTS Beneficiaries included: University of Cambridge (£4.5 million); University College London (£4 million); University of Newcastle upon Tyne (£1.7 million); University of Manchester (£1.6 million); University of Southampton (£1.5 million); University of Birmingham (£1.5 million); University of Leeds and University of Oxford (£1.4 million each).

FINANCES *Year* 2007–08 *Income* £19,325,000 *Grants* £23,123,000 *Assets* £25,029,000

TRUSTEES The Earl Cadogan, Chair; P Burrell; G Brocklebank; D Cannon; A Dart; M Clarke; M Cockayne; Z Floyd; A Knowles; R Page; R Delderfield; M Williams; J Wells.

HOW TO APPLY On an application form available from the trust.

WHO TO APPLY TO Dr David Grant, Scientific Director, 43 Great Ormond Street, London WC1N 3JJ *Tel* 020 7405 0101 *Fax* 020 7242 1488 *email* info@lrf.org.uk *Website* www.lrf.org.uk

CC NO 216032   **ESTABLISHED** 1960

■ The Leverhulme Trade Charities Trust

WHERE FUNDING CAN BE GIVEN UK.

WHO CAN BENEFIT Charities connected with and benefiting commercial travellers, grocers or chemists, their wives, widows and children, especially those disadvantaged by poverty.

WHAT IS FUNDED Benevolent societies, educational institutions and research costs.

WHAT IS NOT FUNDED No capital grants. No response is given to general appeals.

TYPE OF GRANT One-off and recurrent grants.

SAMPLE GRANTS Commercial Travellers' Benevolent Institution (£240,000); Provision Trade Institution (£72,000).

FINANCES *Year* 2008 *Income* £1,539,000 *Grants* £860,000 *Assets* £38,971,000

TRUSTEES Sir Michael Perry, Chair; N W A Fitzgerald; P J-P Cescau; A S Ganguly; P Polman.

OTHER INFORMATION In 2008, a further £548,000 was disbursed in undergraduate and postgraduate bursaries.

HOW TO APPLY By letter to the correspondent. All correspondence is acknowledged. The trustees meet in February and applications need to be received by the preceding October. Undergraduate bursary applications should be directed to the relevant institution.

WHO TO APPLY TO Paul Read, Secretary, 1 Pemberton Row, London EC4A 3BG *Tel* 020 7822 6915 *email* pread@leverhulme.ac.uk *Website* leverhulme-trade.org.uk

CC NO 288404   **ESTABLISHED** 1983

Think carefully about every application. Is it justified?

667

■ The Leverhulme Trust

WHERE FUNDING CAN BE GIVEN Unrestricted.

WHO CAN BENEFIT Universities and other institutions of higher and further education; registered charities; and individuals.

WHAT IS FUNDED Grants are made to institutions for specific research undertakings, for schemes of international academic interchange and for education.

WHAT IS NOT FUNDED When submitting an application to the trust, applicants are advised that the trust does not offer funding for the following costs, and hence none of these items may be included in any budget submitted to the trust: core funding or overheads for institutions; individual items of equipment over £1,000; sites, buildings or other capital expenditure; support for the organisation of conferences or workshops, which are not directly associated with International Networks, Early Career Fellowships or Philip Leverhulme Prizes; exhibitions; contributions to appeals; endowments; a shortfall resulting from a withdrawal of or deficiency in public finance; UK student fees where these are not associated with a Research Project Grant bid or with Fine and Performing Arts schemes detailed in the Guidelines for Applicants.

TYPE OF GRANT One-off, project, research, recurring, running costs and salaries.

SAMPLE GRANTS Royal Society (£3.6 million); Mandela Rhodes Foundation (£2.5 million); Cambridge University (£2.3 million); Imperial College London (£1 million); Newcastle University (£857,000); Liverpool University (£691,000); Aberdeen University (£615,000); Durham University (£525,000); TATE (£481,000); Cardiff University (£375,000); Trinity Laban (£333,000); Royal Academy of Engineering (£300,000); and Sunderland University (£250,000).

FINANCES *Year* 2008 *Income* £51,190,000 *Grants* £48,529,000 *Assets* £1,256,110

TRUSTEES Sir Michael Perry, Chair; Patrick J P Cescau; Niall W A Fitzgerald; Dr Ashok S Ganguly; Paul Polman; Sir Iain Anderson; A C Butler.

PUBLICATIONS Full and detailed information is available in the trust's 'Guidelines for Applicants'.

HOW TO APPLY Each programme, scholarship and award has its own individual application deadline and procedure. Full guidelines and application procedures for each award scheme are available from the trust directly or via its website.

WHO TO APPLY TO Paul Read, 1 Pemberton Row, London EC4A 3BG *Tel* 020 7822 6938 *Fax* 020 7822 5084 *email* enquiries@ leverhulme.org.uk *Website* www.leverhulme.org. uk

CC NO 288371   **ESTABLISHED** 1925

■ Lord Leverhulme's Charitable Trust

WHERE FUNDING CAN BE GIVEN UK especially, Cheshire, Merseyside and surrounding areas.

WHO CAN BENEFIT Registered and exempt charities.

WHAT IS FUNDED General charitable purposes. Priority is given to certain charitable organisations and trusts in Cheshire and Merseyside, particularly educational organisations, welfare charities, youth organisations, the arts, churches, and organisations benefiting older people and people with disabilities.

WHAT IS NOT FUNDED No grants to non-charitable organisations.

TYPE OF GRANT Recurrent, one-off and capital.

RANGE OF GRANTS Up to £200,000.

SAMPLE GRANTS University of Liverpool (£200,000); Foundation of the College of St George and RNLI (£100,000 each); Royal College of Surgeons (£50,000); Royal Horticulture Society and the Lady Lever Art Gallery (£30,000 each); Princes Youth Business Trust (£27,000); and All Saints Trust (£26,000).

FINANCES *Year* 2007–08 *Income* £552,202 *Grants* £759,574 *Assets* £22,334,557

TRUSTEES A E H Heber-Percy; A H S Hannay.

HOW TO APPLY The trust states: 'Priority is given [. . .] to applications from Cheshire, Merseyside and South Lancashire and the charities supported by the settlor in his lifetime. Others who do not meet those criteria should not apply without prior invitation but should, on a single sheet, state briefly their aims and apply fully only on being asked to do so. The trustees are concerned at the continuing volume of applications which they receive despite the forgoing warning.'

WHO TO APPLY TO Mrs S Edwards, Administrator, Leverhulme Estate Office, Manor Road, Thornton Hough, Wirral CH63 1JD *Tel* 0151 336 4828 *Fax* 0151 353 0265

CC NO 212431   **ESTABLISHED** 1957

■ The Joseph Levy Charitable Foundation

WHERE FUNDING CAN BE GIVEN UK and Israel.

WHO CAN BENEFIT Registered charities benefiting children and young people, older people, health, medical research.

WHAT IS FUNDED Health and community care, religion, social welfare, education, arts, culture and sport.

WHAT IS NOT FUNDED No grants to individuals, under any circumstances.

TYPE OF GRANT Project, research, salaries and start-up costs. Funding may be given for up to and over three years.

RANGE OF GRANTS £250–£200,000.

FINANCES *Year* 2008–09 *Income* £841,750 *Grants* £132,042 *Assets* £12,971,947

TRUSTEES Mrs Jane Jason; Peter L Levy; Melanie Levy; Claudia Giat; James Jason.

OTHER INFORMATION The review was completed and it was agreed to continue to limit funding to charities with which the foundation already has a long term commitment or which is already known by the trustees. Therefore the trustees agreed to continue to keep the foundation closed to all unsolicited applications.

HOW TO APPLY No grants to unsolicited applications (see 'Information').

WHO TO APPLY TO Sue Nyfield, Director, 1st Floor, 1 Bell Street, London NW1 5BY *email* info@jlf.org. uk *Website* www.jlf.org.uk

CC NO 245592   **ESTABLISHED** 1965

■ Lewis Family Charitable Trust

WHERE FUNDING CAN BE GIVEN UK and Israel.

WHO CAN BENEFIT Charitable bodies and research institutions.

WHAT IS FUNDED Research into cancer, head injuries and birth defects; health; education; and Jewish charities.

WHAT IS NOT FUNDED No grants to individuals.

TYPE OF GRANT Up to three years funding for medical research.

RANGE OF GRANTS Up to £150,000.

SAMPLE GRANTS *Childcare* – Norwood Ravenswood (£4,500) and Action for Kids Charitable Trust (£1,500); *Education* – Citizens for True Social Justice (£39,500) and Oxford Centre for Hebrew and Jewish Studies (£10,000); *General* – The Community Security Trust (£30,000) and Demand (£5,000); *Jewish religious support* – Westminster Synagogue (£10,000) and The Jewish Leadership Council (£5,000); *Medical general* – Birth Defects Foundation (£100,000) and Meningitis UK (£2,000); *Medical research* – The Institute of Cancer Research (£40,000) and Children's Liver Disease Foundation (£5,000); *Poverty relief* – Kenya Red Cross Society (£25,000) and British WIZO (£1,000); *Support for the elderly* – Jewish Care (£106,000).

FINANCES *Year* 2007–08 *Income* £3,388,821 *Grants* £1,388,219 *Assets* £7,920,003

TRUSTEES David Lewis; Bernard Lewis.

HOW TO APPLY In writing to the correspondent.

WHO TO APPLY TO The Secretary, Chelsea House, West Gate, London W5 1DR *Tel* 020 8991 4601

CC NO 259892   **ESTABLISHED** 1962

···

■ The John Spedan Lewis Foundation

WHERE FUNDING CAN BE GIVEN UK.

WHO CAN BENEFIT The focus is on applications for small projects connected with the natural sciences, in particular horticulture, environmental education, ornithology and conservation, and from organisations benefiting, in the first instance, children, young adults and research workers.

WHAT IS FUNDED Charitable purposes, in the first instance reflecting the particular interests of John Spedan Lewis, namely horticulture, ornithology, entomology and associated educational and research projects. The trustees will also consider applications from organisations for imaginative and original educational projects aimed at developing serious interest and evident talent, particularly among young people.

WHAT IS NOT FUNDED No grants to individuals (including students), local branches of national organisations, or for salaries, medical research, welfare projects, building works or overseas expeditions.

TYPE OF GRANT Mostly one-off donations. Salaries not funded.

RANGE OF GRANTS £60–£12,000.

SAMPLE GRANTS Royal Botanic Gardens – Kew (£12,000); University of Oxford Botanic Gardens and Harcourt Arboretum (£9,000); The Tree Council, Devon Bird Watching and Preservation Society and British Trust for Ornithology (£5,000 each); Fauna and Flora International and Farming and Countryside Education (£4,500 each); The English Hedgerow Trust (£3,000); RSPB Northern Ireland (£1,000); and London Children's Flower Society (£60).

FINANCES *Year* 2007–08 *Income* £92,359 *Grants* £78,507 *Assets* £2,319,855

TRUSTEES Charlie Mayfield, Chair; Ken Temple; Dr Vaughan Southgate; Simon Fowler; Miss Tessa Colman.

HOW TO APPLY In writing to the correspondent with latest report and accounts and a budget for the proposed project.

WHO TO APPLY TO Ms Bridget Chamberlain, Secretary, Partnership House, Carlisle Place, London SW1P 1BX *Tel* 020 7592 6121 *email* bridget_chamberlain@johnlewis.co.uk

CC NO 240473   **ESTABLISHED** 1964

···

■ The Sir Edward Lewis Foundation

WHERE FUNDING CAN BE GIVEN UK and overseas, with a preference for Surrey.

WHO CAN BENEFIT Registered charities.

WHAT IS FUNDED General charitable purposes.

WHAT IS NOT FUNDED Grants are generally only given to charities, projects or people known to the trustees. No grants are given to individuals.

RANGE OF GRANTS £500–£38,000,.

SAMPLE GRANTS Fareshare (£38,000); The Children's Trust Tadworth (£10,000); and Gurkha Welfare Trust, The David Shepherd Wildlife Trust, Global Diversity Foundation and Ridgegate Home (£5,000 each); The Rugby Clubs (£4,000); Council for Music in Hospitals (£3,000); Ophthalmic Aid to Eastern Europe and Musicians Benevolent Fund (£2,500 each); UK Antarctic Heritage Trust and Telephones for the Blind (£2,000 each); Cary Dickinson Breast Cancer and Shipwrecked Fisherman's Society (£1,500); Newspaper Press Fund and Walk the Walk Worldwide (£1,000 each); and Compaid Trust and The Uphill Ski Club (£500 each).

FINANCES *Year* 2007–08 *Income* £469,708 *Grants* £190,700 *Assets* £7,168,357

TRUSTEES R A Lewis; K W Dent; Christine J A Lewis; Sarah J N Dorin.

OTHER INFORMATION The trust makes one substantial donation every two or three years, as well as smaller donations each year.

HOW TO APPLY In writing to the correspondent. The trustees meet every six months.

WHO TO APPLY TO Mrs Sandra Frankland, Messrs Rawlinson and Hunter, The Lower Mill, Kingston Road, Ewell, Surrey KT17 2AE *Tel* 020 7451 9000

CC NO 264475   **ESTABLISHED** 1972

···

■ John Lewis Partnership General Community Fund

WHERE FUNDING CAN BE GIVEN UK.

WHO CAN BENEFIT Registered charities.

WHAT IS FUNDED UK and local registered charities benefiting children and young adults, at risk groups, people who are sick or who have disabilities, people disadvantaged by poverty and those who are socially isolated. Medical professionals and research workers may be considered for funding.

WHAT IS NOT FUNDED Loans are not made and sponsorship is not undertaken. Grants are not made for the promotion of religion, political organisations, advertising or to individuals.

TYPE OF GRANT One-off and recurring grants.

RANGE OF GRANTS £250–£50,000.

SAMPLE GRANTS In 2008–09 grants were made in the following categories:

Welfare

38 grants were awarded totalling £260,000. A summary of welfare grants included British Red Cross and Retail Trust (£50,000 each); Caravan (£25,000); Hospitality Action (£15,000); Macmillan Cancer Support (£10,000); Bracknell and District CAB, Hiltingbury Community association and the Cardinal Hume Centre (£5,000 each); and Bobath Children's Therapy

Centre, Diabetes UK, Extwend Exercise Training Ltd and Gravesham Volunteer Bureau (£1,000 each).

Music

Grants were awarded to 67organisations totalling £243,000 and included Royal Academy of Music and Royal College of Music (£15,000); National Associaton of Youth Orchestras (£14,000); Chamber Music International and Hackney Youth Orchestras' Trust (£5,000 each); Brinkburn Music and Cambridge Music Festival (£3,000 each); and Banstead Musical Society (£2,500).

Arts

Grants were made to 13 organisations totalling £77,000 and included Salisbury Playhouse (£20,000); Royal Academy of Dramatic Art (£6,000); the Hepworth Wakefield Trust and Royal Exchange Theatre (£5,000 each).

Learning

Nine grants were awarded in this category totalling £27,000. Beneficiaries included the Woodfield School (£6,800); the English speaking Union, the Ruskin Museum and Lifeskills Learning for Living (£3,000 each); Oak lodge School (£1,200); Barking and Dagenham Talking Newspaper and DARE (UK) Drug, Abuse, Resistance Education (£1,000 each).

Environment

Five grants were awarded to organisations totalling £24,500 and included Relationship Foundation and Westminster Children's Society (£5,000 each); and Textile Industry Children's Trust (£1,000).

FINANCES *Year* 2008–09 *Income* £632,875 *Grants* £632,836 *Assets* £39

TRUSTEES John Lewis Partnership Trust Limited.

HOW TO APPLY In writing to the correspondent, accompanied by the latest annual report and accounts.

WHO TO APPLY TO Sandra Adrien, Partnership House, Carlisle Place, London SW1P 1BX *email* sandra_adrien@johnlewis.co.uk

CC NO 209128   **ESTABLISHED** 1961

■ The Lewis Ward Trust

WHERE FUNDING CAN BE GIVEN UK and overseas.

WHO CAN BENEFIT Children, particularly those with special needs or disabilities, are deprived or terminally ill or are lacking adequate nutrition and education.

WHAT IS FUNDED Special projects for children run locally, nationally and internationally. Hospices and special therapy units for children and organisations caring for lepers.

RANGE OF GRANTS Generally £1,000.

SAMPLE GRANTS No list of beneficiary organisations was available.

FINANCES *Year* 2007 *Income* £35,978 *Grants* £48,000 *Assets* £75,765

TRUSTEES Margaret Waugh; Revd Gareth Jones (Chair); Anne Parry; Kevin Rogers; Revd Anthony Innes; Bernard Cheetham.

HOW TO APPLY In writing to the correspondent. 'The trustees meet twice a year, when appeals for grants are considered and depending on monies available, donations are sent to those organisations it is felt are in greatest need.'

WHO TO APPLY TO Margaret Waugh, Trustee, Assisi, 11 Badgers Brook Drive, Ystradowen, Cowbridge, South Glamorgan CF71 7TX

CC NO 1100891   **ESTABLISHED** 2003

■ Lichfield Conduit Lands

WHERE FUNDING CAN BE GIVEN Lichfield.

WHO CAN BENEFIT Organisations and people under 25 who are in education.

WHAT IS FUNDED General charitable purposes.

RANGE OF GRANTS Up to £20,000.

SAMPLE GRANTS Beneficiaries included: 6th Lichfield Scout Group and Voluntary Transport for the Disabled (£20,000 each); St Giles Hospice (£11,000); St Chad's PCC (£10,000); The Lichfield Mysteries (£5,000); and Cruse Bereavement Care – Lichfield and Cannock Branch (£500).

FINANCES *Year* 2008 *Income* £37,449 *Grants* £85,982 *Assets* £866,104

TRUSTEES J Russell (Chair); J D Shaw, C P Ablitt; Revd D K Beedon; Mrs D English; A D Thompson; Mrs K Duncan Brown; B Twivey; R W White; J N Wilks; Mrs M G Boyle; M A Warfield.

OTHER INFORMATION Grants were made to individuals totalling £550.

HOW TO APPLY Application forms are available from the reception at Ansons, along with a map of the beneficial area. They are considered four times a year

WHO TO APPLY TO S R James, The Warden, Ansons LLP Solicitors, St Mary's Chambers, 5 Breadmarket Street, Lichfield WS13 6LQ *Tel* 01543 263456 *Fax* 01543 250942

CC NO 254298   **ESTABLISHED** 1982

■ Lifeline 4 Kids

WHERE FUNDING CAN BE GIVEN Worldwide.

WHO CAN BENEFIT Organisations supporting children who are disabled (up to 18 years old), such as hospitals, homes, special schools and so on. Individuals and their families are also supported.

WHAT IS FUNDED To assist children who are disabled by means of equipment and services.

WHAT IS NOT FUNDED Building projects, research grants and salaries will not be funded.

TYPE OF GRANT Equipment purchased by the trust. No cash grants are given.

SAMPLE GRANTS Previous beneficiaries include: Central Middlesex Hospital, towards equipment for its outdoor play area; Living Paintings Trust, funding the production of 20 copies of a new Living Picture Book; New Jumbulance Travel Trust, providing two portable instant resuscitation packs; Vision Aid, providing a specialised flat screen video magnifier; and the Lothian Autistic Society, for equipment for its various play schemes.

FINANCES *Year* 2008 *Income* £94,003 *Grants* £214,701 *Assets* £698,394

TRUSTEES Roger Adelman, chair; Paul Maurice; Beverley Emden; Mrs Roberta Harris; Irving Millman; Jeffrey Bonn.

HOW TO APPLY Applications for help indicating specific requirements and brief factual information must initially be made in writing, addressed to the Investigations Officer, or by email (appeals@lifeline4kids.org). Each request will be acknowledged and provided it meets the charity's criteria, an application form will be sent by post. Appeals are discussed and decided upon at monthly meetings. If appropriate, the appeal will be investigated personally by one of the charity's members. If approved, a maximum sum is allocated and we take full responsibility for the purchase and safe delivery of the approved item. Initial telephone calls from applicants are not welcome.

WHO TO APPLY TO The Investigations Officer, 215 West End Lane, West Hampstead, London NW6 1XJ *Tel* 020 7794 1661 *Fax* 020 7794 1161 *Website* www.lifeline4kids.org
CC NO 200050   **ESTABLISHED** 1961

■ The Thomas Lilley Memorial Trust

WHERE FUNDING CAN BE GIVEN UK, with some preference for the Newbury area and Isle of Man.
WHO CAN BENEFIT Individuals and organisations.
WHAT IS FUNDED General charitable purposes.
WHAT IS NOT FUNDED No grants are made to individuals for educational or gap year activities.
RANGE OF GRANTS Usually up to £2,000.
SAMPLE GRANTS All Saints Church, Cuddesdon (£2,000); Riding for the Disabled (£1,500); Samaritans, Isle of Man (£1,000); and Action Medical Research, Army Benevolent Fund, Greater London Fund for the Blind, International League for Protection of Horses, National Deaf Children's Society, Shelter and Voluntary Services Overseas (£600 each).
FINANCES *Year* 2007–08 *Income* £32,080 *Grants* £29,850 *Assets* £844,953
TRUSTEES John F Luke; Peter T A Lilley.
OTHER INFORMATION The amount available each year in individual grants in determined by the trust's income for that year.
HOW TO APPLY In writing to the correspondent.
WHO TO APPLY TO N Buckley Sharp, Littlejohn LLP, 1 Westferry Circus, London E14 4HD *Tel* 020 7516 2200
CC NO 1039529   **ESTABLISHED** 1960

■ The Limbourne Trust

WHERE FUNDING CAN BE GIVEN UK and overseas.
WHO CAN BENEFIT Communities throughout the world.
WHAT IS FUNDED Environment, welfare, and arts organisations, particularly where meeting the trust's objectives concerning the advancement of education, the protection of health, and the relief of poverty, distress and sickness.
SAMPLE GRANTS Chicks (£12,000); Journey of a Lifetime Trust and Sinfield Nature Conservation Trust (£11,000 each); the Hand Partnership and Magdalene Group (£10,000 each); Norfolk and Norwich Families House (£7,500); the Poetry Trust (£7,100); Aldeburgh Music, BEAT – the Eating Disorders Association, Whirlow Hall Farm Trust and Vauxhall City Farm (£5,000 each).
FINANCES *Year* 2007–08 *Income* £113,743 *Grants* £90,680 *Assets* £2,338,804
TRUSTEES Elisabeth Thistlethwayte; Katharine Thistlethwayte; Jennifer Lindsay; Jane Chetwynd Atkinson; Jocelyn Magnus.
HOW TO APPLY 'The trustees will seek to identify those projects where the greatest and widest benefit can be attained, and usually will only consider written applications and, where necessary, make further enquiries.' Trustees meet three times a year.
WHO TO APPLY TO Elisabeth Anne Thistlethwayte, Trustee, Downs Farm, Homersfield, Harleston, Norwich IP20 0NS
CC NO 1113796   **ESTABLISHED** 2006

■ Limoges Charitable Trust

WHERE FUNDING CAN BE GIVEN UK, with a preference for Birmingham.
WHO CAN BENEFIT Registered charities.
WHAT IS FUNDED Preference for animal and service organisations.
RANGE OF GRANTS £50–£15,000; mostly £200–£1,000.
SAMPLE GRANTS Previously: Symphony Hall (Birmingham) Ltd, Blue Coat School, University of Birmingham, Birmingham Parish Church (St Martin's) Renewal Campaign, Birmingham and Midland Limbless Ex-Servicemen's Association, MSA for Midlands People with Cerebral Palsy, Birmingham Dogs Home, West Birmingham Scout Association, Elizabeth Svendsen Trust, Arthritis Research Campaign, Dogs for the Disabled, Gloucester Three Choirs Appeal, Hope and Homes for Children and Live Music Now!.
FINANCES *Year* 2006–07 *Income* £14,127 *Grants* £55,800 *Assets* £439,668
TRUSTEES Mike Dyer; Albert Kenneth Dyer; Judy Ann Dyke; Andrew Milner.
HOW TO APPLY In writing to the correspondent.
WHO TO APPLY TO Mrs J A Dyke, Trustee, Tyndallwoods Solicitors, 29 Woodbourne Road, Edgbaston, Birmingham B17 8BY *Tel* 0121 693 2222 *Fax* 0121 693 0844
CC NO 1016178   **ESTABLISHED** 1991

■ The Linbury Trust

WHERE FUNDING CAN BE GIVEN Unrestricted.
WHO CAN BENEFIT Charities working in the fields listed below.
WHAT IS FUNDED Arts and arts education, especially support for dance and dance education. Medical research into chronic fatigue syndrome, and occasionally other 'unfashionable' areas. Drug misuse, provision of hands-on care to treat and rehabilitate drug users, particularly those which work with young people and the families of drug users. Education, especially support for best practice in the identification and teaching of children and young people with literacy problems, especially dyslexia. Environment and heritage, particularly historical buildings and major art institutions. Social welfare, especially for work helping young people disadvantaged by poverty, educational achievement or difficult family backgrounds, or who are involved in the criminal justice system. Also support for initiatives that improve quality of life of older people and through which they are helped to continue living in their own home. Developing countries, including humanitarian aid, social welfare and educational opportunities.
WHAT IS NOT FUNDED No grants to individuals.
TYPE OF GRANT Running costs, project.
SAMPLE GRANTS Ashmolean Museum (£2.4 million); Royal Ballet School (£550,000); SSAFA (£250,000); Linbury Biennial Prize for Stage Design (£177,000); St George's Chapel – Windsor (£150,000); Al Quds University Medical School Foundation and St John of Jerusalem Eye Hospital (£100,000 each); City & Guilds of London Art School (£63,000); and Foundation Training Company and Depaul Trust (£50,000 each).
FINANCES *Year* 2007–08 *Income* £9,310,000 *Grants* £5,480,000 *Assets* £159,403,000
TRUSTEES Lord Sainsbury of Preston Candover; Lady Sainsbury; Sir Martin Jacomb; Sir James Spooner.
OTHER INFORMATION The trust is one of the Sainsbury Family Charitable Trusts which share

a common administration. An application to one is taken as an application to all.

HOW TO APPLY See the guidance for applicants in the entry for the Sainsbury Family Charitable Trusts. A single application will be considered for support by all the trusts in the group. Please note: 'the trustees take a proactive approach towards grant-making; accordingly, unsolicited applications to the trust are not usually successful'.

WHO TO APPLY TO Alan Bookbinder, Director, Allington House, 1st Floor, 150 Victoria Street, London SW1E 5AE *Tel* 020 7410 0330 *Fax* 020 7410 0332 *Website* www.linburytrust.org.uk

CC NO 287077   **ESTABLISHED** 1973

■ **Lincolnshire Community Foundation**

WHERE FUNDING CAN BE GIVEN Lincolnshire.

WHO CAN BENEFIT Organisations supporting people in Lincolnshire.

WHAT IS FUNDED General charitable purposes.

SAMPLE GRANTS Grants are awarded unde the following schemes: Local Network Fund; Grassroots grants; Community Champions; Fair Share; Sport Relief & Comic Relief; Catalyst grants; Social Enterprise; Bicker Trust; Bettina Houlder Music Trust; Portugese mums; and CBIS grants.

FINANCES *Year* 2007–08 *Income* £1,809,889 *Grants* £1,288,994 *Assets* £1,184,808

TRUSTEES Jean Burton; David Close; Melanie Elwis; Richard Ferens; Jim Hopkins; Bishop of Grimsby David Rossdale; Allan Chesney; Dr Cheryle Berry.

HOW TO APPLY Please visit the foundation's website for details of current grant schemes. Application forms can be downloaded from the foundation's website or requested by phone.

WHO TO APPLY TO Gordon Hunter, Director, 4 Mill House, Carre Street, Sleaford, Lincolnshire NG34 7TW *Tel* 01529 305825 *email* lincolnshirecf@btconnect.com *Website* www.lincolnshirecf.co.uk

CC NO 1092328   **ESTABLISHED** 2002

■ **The Lincolnshire Old Churches Trust**

WHERE FUNDING CAN BE GIVEN Lincolnshire.

WHO CAN BENEFIT Churches, principally Christian churches, of any denomination.

WHAT IS FUNDED The preservation, repair and maintenance of churches over 100 years old in the area defined above, to exclude wind and weather, achieve safety and security and to ensure the preservation of those features which make old churches unique.

WHAT IS NOT FUNDED No grants for ritual or gravestone repair.

RANGE OF GRANTS £500–£10,000.

SAMPLE GRANTS Details of beneficiary churches were not available.

FINANCES *Year* 2008 *Income* £151,337 *Grants* £71,500 *Assets* £443,852

TRUSTEES P Sandberg, Chair; Baroness Willoughby de Eresby; Nevile Camamile; Mrs J Ware; D Wellman; D Lawrence; Mrs R Lindop; A Seton; C Hammant; R D Underwood; Revd C Knowles; R Critchlow; G Cook; Mrs Mona Dickinson; Mrs Henrietta Reeve; Anthony Worth; Mrs Linda Lord.

HOW TO APPLY On a form available from the correspondent.

WHO TO APPLY TO N J Camamile, Treasurer, Tower House, Lucy Tower Street, Lincoln LN1 1XW *Tel* 01522 551200

CC NO 509021   **ESTABLISHED** 1953

■ **The Lind Trust**

WHERE FUNDING CAN BE GIVEN UK.

WHO CAN BENEFIT Churches, charities and individuals involved in social action, community and Christian service.

WHAT IS FUNDED Christian service and social action.

SAMPLE GRANTS Previously: £11,236 to 'other' charities, and £10,000 to churches.

FINANCES *Year* 2007–08 *Income* £6,932,721 *Grants* £230,992 *Assets* £17,110,023

TRUSTEES Leslie C Brown; Dr Graham M Dacre; Gavin C Wilcock; Mrs Julia M Dacre; Russell B Dacre; Samuel E Dacre

OTHER INFORMATION The total given in 2007–08 covered grants to 'charities, churches and individuals'. No breakdown of this was provided.

HOW TO APPLY In writing to the correspondent at any time. However, the trust commits most of its funds in advance, giving the remainder to eligible applicants as received.

WHO TO APPLY TO Gavin Croft Wilcox, Trustee, Tithe Barn, Attlebridge, Norwich NR9 5AA *Tel* 01603 262 626

CC NO 803174   **ESTABLISHED** 1990

■ **Lindale Educational Foundation**

WHERE FUNDING CAN BE GIVEN UK and overseas.

WHO CAN BENEFIT Roman Catholic organisations benefiting children, young adults and students.

WHAT IS FUNDED Charities which aim to advance education in accordance with Christian principles and ideals within the Roman Catholic tradition, in particular those organisations that train priests. Most grants are already allocated to specific charities.

WHAT IS NOT FUNDED No grants to individuals.

TYPE OF GRANT Recurrent.

SAMPLE GRANTS Collegio Romano della Santa Croce (£35,000); Wickenden Manor and the Netherhall Educational Association Centre for Retreats and Study (three grants totalling £21,000); Thornycroft Hall (three grants totalling £23,000); and Pontifical University (£1,200).

FINANCES *Year* 2007–08 *Income* £84,033 *Grants* £85,800 *Assets* £25,850

TRUSTEES Netherhall Educational Association; Dawliffe Hall Educational Foundation; Greygarth Association.

HOW TO APPLY In writing to the correspondent, but note that most funds are already committed.

WHO TO APPLY TO J Valero, 1 Leopold Road, Ealing Common, London W5 3PB *Tel* 020 7229 7574

CC NO 282758   **ESTABLISHED** 1981

■ **The Linden Charitable Trust**

WHERE FUNDING CAN BE GIVEN UK, with a preference for West Yorkshire.

WHO CAN BENEFIT Registered charities and arts organisations.

WHAT IS FUNDED Currently, the trust's policy is to benefit charities specialising in cancer relief and research, those particularly involved with hospices, those involved in arts and also a wider range of charities based in and around Leeds.

WHAT IS NOT FUNDED No grants to individuals.

RANGE OF GRANTS Up to £20,000.

SAMPLE GRANTS Leeds International Pianoforte Competition (£20,000); Macmillan Cancer Relief (£10,000); Marie Curie Cancer Care (£7,000); Leeds Lieder, Martin House Hospice and Mission for Seafarers (£4,000 each); Caring for Life (£3,000); Opera North Foundation (£2,000); Live Music Now and York Glaziers Trust (£1,000 each); Listening Books (£600); and Second World War Experience Centre (£500).

FINANCES *Year* 2007–08 *Income* £80,379 *Grants* £113,000 *Assets* £2,570,346

TRUSTEES Miss M H Pearson.

HOW TO APPLY In writing to the correspondent.

WHO TO APPLY TO The Trustee, c/o Baker Tilly, 2 Whitehall Quay, Leeds LS1 4HG *Tel* 0113 285 5000

CC NO 326788   **ESTABLISHED** 1985

■ The Enid Linder Foundation

WHERE FUNDING CAN BE GIVEN Unrestricted.

WHO CAN BENEFIT Registered charities benefiting children, older people and people who are disabled; universities and teaching hospitals.

WHAT IS FUNDED The aims of the foundation are: to fund research and teaching related to all areas of medicine by way of medical electives and general support costs to students and chosen medical universities; to assist in the funding of chosen research fellowship schemes which are of particular interest to the trustees; to distribute in full, in accordance with the governing Trust Deed, all the income available each year; to maintain resources at a reasonable level in order to continue to provide general charitable assistance in the foreseeable future. The main objectives for the year are shaped by these strategic aims with a view to maintaining both a stable medical electives scheme at universities, to support the research fellowship schemes and to continue funding chosen general charitable causes.

TYPE OF GRANT One-off and recurrent.

SAMPLE GRANTS Royal College of Surgeons (£347,000 in total); National Children's Orchestra (£40,000); Medicins Sans Frontieres and Victoria & Albert Museum (£25,000 each); Practical Action and Bath University (£15,000 each); Bath Intensive Care Baby Unit, Kidscape, Music in Hospitals and St Christopher's Hospice (£10,000 each).

FINANCES *Year* 2007–08 *Income* £546,499 *Grants* £765,500 *Assets* £12,468,311

TRUSTEES Jack Ladeveze; Audrey Ladeveze; M Butler; C Cook; Jonathan Fountain.

OTHER INFORMATION Direct charitable expenditure, other than the trust's normal grantmaking, included £132,500 to 'teaching hospitals and universities'.

HOW TO APPLY In writing to the correspondent. Although unsolicited applications are accepted, the trust states that it prefers to support organisations whose work it has researched.

WHO TO APPLY TO Martin Pollock, Secretary, Moore Stephens LLP, St Paul's House, 8–12 Warwick Lane, London EC4M 7BP *Tel* 020 7334 9191 *Fax* 020 7651 1953 *email* martin.pollock@ moorestephens.com

CC NO 267509   **ESTABLISHED** 1974

■ The Linmardon Trust

WHERE FUNDING CAN BE GIVEN UK, with a preference for Nottinghamshire.

WHO CAN BENEFIT Registered charities.

WHAT IS FUNDED General charitable purposes.

WHAT IS NOT FUNDED Registered charities only. No grants to individuals.

RANGE OF GRANTS £500–£3,000.

SAMPLE GRANTS Association for Spina Bifida and Hydrocephalus, Changing Faces, Prostate Cancer Research Foundation, The Meningitis Trust and The Stroke Association (£3,000 each); Action Medical Research, British Institute for Brain Injured Children, Community of the Holy Fire and Leap Confronting Conflict (£1,000 each); and Get Connected, Sunny Days Children's Fund and The Manna Society (£500 each).

FINANCES *Year* 2007–08 *Income* £194,814 *Grants* £38,230 *Assets* £1,215,178

TRUSTEES HSBC Trust Company Ltd

HOW TO APPLY In writing to the correspondent. The trustees meet quarterly, generally in February, May, August and November.

WHO TO APPLY TO The Secretary, HSBC Trust Company (UK) Limited, Norwich House, Nelson Gate, Commercial Road, Southampton SO15 1GX *Tel* 023 8072 2240

CC NO 275307   **ESTABLISHED** 1977

■ The Ruth and Stuart Lipton Charitable Trust

WHERE FUNDING CAN BE GIVEN UK, with a preference for London.

WHO CAN BENEFIT Organisations benefiting Jewish people.

WHAT IS FUNDED Jewish charitable purposes.

WHAT IS NOT FUNDED No grants to individuals.

RANGE OF GRANTS £100–£30,000.

SAMPLE GRANTS Glyndebourne (£30,000); Nightingale (£15,000); Royal Opera House and Community Security Trust (£10,000 each); The Winnicot Foundation (£2,500); Cancer Research UK and The Facial Surgery Research Foundation (£1,000 each); Crafts Council (£500); Give Youth a Break (£250); and Cycle to Cannes (£100).

FINANCES *Year* 2007–08 *Income* £75,563 *Grants* £92,366 *Assets* £551,172

TRUSTEES Sir S Lipton; Lady Lipton; N W Benson.

HOW TO APPLY In writing to the correspondent.

WHO TO APPLY TO N W Benson, Trustee, Lewis Golden and Co., 40 Queen Ann Street, London W1M 9EL *Tel* 020 7580 7313

CC NO 266741   **ESTABLISHED** 1973

■ The Lister Charitable Trust

WHERE FUNDING CAN BE GIVEN UK.

WHO CAN BENEFIT Registered charities which work with young people.

WHAT IS FUNDED The advancement and the educational, physical, mental and spiritual development of children and young people under the age of 25, by providing or assisting in providing facilities for training in sailing and seamanship of children and young people who have need of such facilities by reason of poverty, social or economic circumstances (so that they may grow to full maturity as individuals and members of society). Also to provide or assist in the provision of facilities for recreation and other leisure time occupation of the general public with the object of improving their conditions of life.

WHAT IS NOT FUNDED Applications from individuals, including students, are ineligible. No grants are made in response to general appeals from large UK organisations or to smaller bodies working in areas outside its criteria.

TYPE OF GRANT Usually one-off for specific project or part of a project. Core funding and/or salaries rarely considered. Funding may be given for up to one year.

SAMPLE GRANTS The European Nature Trust (£46,000); Oak Lodge School and the Chemical Dependency Centre (£20,000 each); the Challenger Trust (£10,000); and Action of Addiction, the Children's Trust and Ray of Sunshine (£5,000 each).

FINANCES *Year* 2008–09 *Income* £230,083 *Grants* £110,500 *Assets* £5,799,454

TRUSTEES Noel A V Lister; David A Collingwood; Penny A Horne; Paul A Lister; Sylvia J Lister.

HOW TO APPLY In writing to the correspondent. Applications should include clear details of the need the intended project is designed to meet, plus an outline budget. Only applications from eligible bodies are acknowledged, when further information may be requested.

WHO TO APPLY TO Nicholas Yellowlees, c/o Apperley Limited, Market Street, Maidenhead SL6 8BE *Tel* 01628 477 879

CC NO 288730　　　**ESTABLISHED** 1981

■ Frank Litchfield Charitable Trust

WHERE FUNDING CAN BE GIVEN Mostly in and around Cambridge.

WHO CAN BENEFIT Charitable organisations.

WHAT IS FUNDED Medical services and relief of poverty amongst those involved in agriculture.

RANGE OF GRANTS Up to £10,000.

SAMPLE GRANTS Wardens of Therfield, RNID and Addenbrookes Hospital Trust (£10,000 each); Macmillan Cancer Relief (£9,000); Camread (£6,000); Deafness Research and Mary Wallace Cancer Support (£5,000 each); Our Voice (£2,500); and Bishops Stortford Helping Hands (£500).

FINANCES *Year* 2007–08 *Income* £85,575 *Grants* £85,000 *Assets* £1,919,188

TRUSTEES M T Womack; D M Chater; P Gooderham.

HOW TO APPLY In writing to the correspondent. This trust receives more applications each year than it is able to fund.

WHO TO APPLY TO Michael Womack, Trustee, 12 De Freville Avenue, Cambridge CB4 1HR *Tel* 01223 358012

CC NO 1038943　　　**ESTABLISHED** 1994

■ The Andrew and Mary Elizabeth Little Charitable Trust

WHERE FUNDING CAN BE GIVEN Mainly Glasgow and the surrounding area.

WHO CAN BENEFIT Organisations based in Scotland such as infirmaries, hospitals, homes for the aged, orphanages and other such institutions, which provide direct or indirect help to disadvantaged people.

WHAT IS FUNDED Welfare needs.

SAMPLE GRANTS Previous beneficiaries have included Ayrshire Hospice, Glasgow City Mission, Glasgow Marriage Guidance Council, Glasgow Old People's Welfare Committee, St Margaret's of Scotland Adoption Society and Strathclyde Youth Club Association.

FINANCES *Year* 2007–08 *Income* £58,507

HOW TO APPLY In writing to the correspondent. Trustees meet to consider grants once a month. Individuals should provide financial details of income support.

WHO TO APPLY TO The Trustees, Low Beaton Richmond Solicitors, Sterling House, 20 Renfield Street, Glasgow G2 5AP

SC NO SC011185

■ The Second Joseph Aaron Littman Foundation

WHERE FUNDING CAN BE GIVEN UK.

WHO CAN BENEFIT Registered charities only.

WHAT IS FUNDED General charitable purposes with special preference for academic and medical research.

WHAT IS NOT FUNDED Applications from individuals are not considered.

SAMPLE GRANTS Littman Library of Jewish Civilisation (£220,000); Foundation of Circulatory Health, Lubavitch Senior Girls School and The Spiro Ark (£5,000); University College London and Westminster Synagogue (£2,000 each); Dorset & Somerset Air Ambulance and Marie Curie Nurses (£1,500 each); and Juvenile Diabetes (£1,000).

FINANCES *Year* 2007–08 *Income* £283,001 *Grants* £255,675 *Assets* £5,260,906

TRUSTEES Mrs C C Littman; R J Littman; Glenn Hurstfield.

HOW TO APPLY The trust's funds are fully committed and no new applications are considered.

WHO TO APPLY TO R J Littman, Trustee, Manor Farm, Mill Lane, Charlton Mackrell, Somerset TA11 7BQ *Tel* 01458 223 650

CC NO 201892　　　**ESTABLISHED** 1961

■ The George John and Sheilah Livanos Charitable Trust

WHERE FUNDING CAN BE GIVEN UK.

WHO CAN BENEFIT Registered charities.

WHAT IS FUNDED Medical research and equipment, health, medical charities for children or older people, marine charities and general charitable purposes.

WHAT IS NOT FUNDED No grants to individuals or non-registered charities.

TYPE OF GRANT One-off and recurring grants. Capital grants.

SAMPLE GRANTS St Mary's Hospital in London (£200,000); The Watts Gallery (£100,000); Parkinson's Disease Society (£50,000); Fight for Sight (£47,000); University of Dundee – Child Health Studentship (£27,000); Ekklesia Project Fakenham (£18,000); Caius House – Wandsworth (£17,500); Naomi House (£15,000); Cancer Resource Centre, Headway and London Youth (£10,000 each); City University London and Listening Books (£5,000 each); Coram Family and Kidscape (£3,000 each); Colchester Furniture Project (£2,000); and Chiswick House and Gardens Project and Phab Kids (£1,000 each).

FINANCES *Year* 2008 *Income* £209,262 *Grants* £632,245 *Assets* £3,405,415

TRUSTEES Philip N Harris; Timothy T Cripps; Anthony S Holmes.

HOW TO APPLY Unsolicited applications are not requested.

WHO TO APPLY TO Philip N Harris, Trustee, Jeffrey Green Russell, Waverley House, 7–12 Noel Street, London W1F 8GQ *Tel* 020 7339 7000
CC NO 1002279   **ESTABLISHED** 1985

■ Liverpool Charity and Voluntary Services

WHERE FUNDING CAN BE GIVEN Merseyside only.
WHO CAN BENEFIT Registered charities.
WHAT IS FUNDED General charitable purposes.
SAMPLE GRANTS Grants are categorised through the CVS's main objectives as follows: Well governed: £143,000; Well resourced: £1.2 million; Well managed: £506,000; Well represented: £1.3 million.
FINANCES *Year* 2007–08 *Income* £5,105,349 *Grants* £3,166,326 *Assets* £7,497,075
TRUSTEES William Fulton; Charles Feeny; Sue Newton, Chair; Roger Morris; Philip Love; Hilary Russell; Mark Blundell; Andrew Lovelady; Christine Reeves; Dil Daly; Richard Fassam; Heather Akehurst.
OTHER INFORMATION The charity acts in a similar manner to a community foundation, administrating the giving of much smaller charitable trusts.
HOW TO APPLY In writing to the correspondent. An application should be made to the charity that will then pass it on to a relevant trust for consideration.
WHO TO APPLY TO The Grants Team, 14 Castle Street, Liverpool L2 0NJ *Tel* 0151 236 7728 *Fax* 0151 258 1153 *email* info@lcvs.org.uk *Website* www.lcvs.org.uk
CC NO 223485   **ESTABLISHED** 1970

■ The Liverpool One Foundation

WHERE FUNDING CAN BE GIVEN Liverpool and surrounding areas.
WHO CAN BENEFIT Registered charities and community groups.
WHAT IS FUNDED The prevention or relief of poverty; education and skills – especially for young people; social and community advancement; health.
RANGE OF GRANTS Mostly up to £5,000.
FINANCES *Year* 2007 *Income* £316,167 *Grants* £85,615 *Assets* £282,215
TRUSTEES Richard Mallett; Katherine Robinson; Christopher Taite.
HOW TO APPLY Contact the Community Foundation for Merseyside for details.
WHO TO APPLY TO The Trustees, Community Foundation for Merseyside, c/o Alliance and Leicester, Bridle Road, Bootle, Merseyside, GIR 0AA *Tel* 0151 966 3591 *Fax* 0151 966 3384 *email* info@cfmerseyside.org.uk *Website* www. cfmerseyside.org.uk
CC NO 1112697   **ESTABLISHED** 2005

■ Liverpool Sailors' Home Trust

WHERE FUNDING CAN BE GIVEN Merseyside.
WHO CAN BENEFIT Organisations benefiting seafarers, fishermen, ex-service and service people and sea cadets.
WHAT IS FUNDED Charities engaged in maritime activities and based in Merseyside.
WHAT IS NOT FUNDED No grants to individuals.
TYPE OF GRANT One-off and capital grants will be considered.

SAMPLE GRANTS Previous beneficiaries include: The Royal Merchant Navy School Foundation, Sail Training Association, Fairbridge Merseyside, Sea Cadet Corps – Ellesmere Port, RNLI – New Brighton, RNLI – Hoylake and West Kirby, BISS and Sea Cadet Corps – Liverpool Mersey Unit.
FINANCES *Year* 2007–08 *Income* £3,603 *Grants* £17,961
TRUSTEES D G Beazley, Chair; Mrs L P Cook; P O Copland; S Sutherland; I Higby; T Hart.
HOW TO APPLY In writing to the correspondent. Trustees meet to consider grants in March, applications should be sent by 20 January.
WHO TO APPLY TO Mrs L Gidman, Secretary, Room 19, 2 Floor, Tower Building, 22 Water Street, Liverpool L3 1AB *Tel* 0151 227 3417 *Fax* 0151 227 3417 *email* enquiries@rlsoi-uk. org
CC NO 515183   **ESTABLISHED** 1984

■ Jack Livingstone Charitable Trust

WHERE FUNDING CAN BE GIVEN UK and worldwide, with a preference for Manchester.
WHO CAN BENEFIT Registered charities benefiting Jewish people, at risk groups, and people who are ill, disadvantaged by poverty or socially isolated.
WHAT IS FUNDED Jewish charities and general charitable purposes.
TYPE OF GRANT Mostly recurrent.
SAMPLE GRANTS United Jewish Israel Appeal (331,000); Manchester City Art Gallery (£15,000); Rainscough (£6,000); The Jerusalem Foundation and Community Security Trust (£10,000 each); Bowen Trust, King David School and Royal Exchange (£5,000 each); Christies (£2,000); and Southport Jewish Aged Home, Stockdales and World Jewish Relief (£1,000 each).
FINANCES *Year* 2007–08 *Income* £94,920 *Grants* £109,480 *Assets* £1,828,978
TRUSTEES Janice Livingstone; Terence Livingstone; Brian White.
HOW TO APPLY The trust does not respond to unsolicited applications.
WHO TO APPLY TO Mrs Janice Livingstone, Trustee, Westholme, The Springs, Park Road, Bowdon, Altrincham, Cheshire WA14 3JH *Tel* 0161 928 3232
CC NO 263473   **ESTABLISHED** 1971

■ The Elaine and Angus Lloyd Charitable Trust

WHERE FUNDING CAN BE GIVEN UK, with a preference for Surrey, Kent and the south of England.
WHO CAN BENEFIT Individuals, local, regional and UK organisations benefiting children, young adults, at risk groups, people disadvantaged by poverty and socially isolated people.
WHAT IS FUNDED Health and welfare organisations, churches and education.
WHAT IS NOT FUNDED No support for overseas aid.
TYPE OF GRANT Recurrent and one-off.
RANGE OF GRANTS Below £1,000–£5,000.
SAMPLE GRANTS Rhemal Religious & Charitable Trust (£5,000); EHAS (£4,200); Alive and Kicking (£2,500); Diabetes UK and Skillway (£2,000 each); Barry Vale Community Aid, Community Life Trust, Martha Trust, Monday to Wednesday Club and Salvation Army (£1,500 each); Dandelion Trust and St Clements – Sandwich (£1,000 each).

FINANCES *Year* 2007–08 *Income* £104,941
Grants £75,259 *Assets* £2,376,200
TRUSTEES C R H Lloyd; A S Lloyd; J S Gordon; Sir
Michael Craig-Cooper; Mrs V E Best; J S Lloyd;
Mrs Philippa Satchwell Smith; Revd R J Lloyd.
OTHER INFORMATION Grants to individuals totalled
£5,600
HOW TO APPLY In writing to the correspondent. The
trustees meet regularly to consider grants.
WHO TO APPLY TO Ross Badger, Messrs Badger
Hakim Chartered Accountants, 10 Dover Street,
London W1S 4LQ
CC NO 237250   **ESTABLISHED** 1964

■ The Lloyd-Everett Trust

WHERE FUNDING CAN BE GIVEN UK and overseas.
WHO CAN BENEFIT Charitable organisations.
WHAT IS FUNDED General charitable purposes.
WHAT IS NOT FUNDED No grants to individuals or non-
UK charities.
RANGE OF GRANTS £500–£3,000.
SAMPLE GRANTS Hunter Trust for Education in
Malawi (£3,000); Frontier Youth Trust, Royal
National Institute for the Deaf, Royal Star and
Garter Home and UNICEF (£1,000 each); and
Farm Africa and Practical Action (£500 each).
FINANCES *Year* 2008 *Income* £11,539
Grants £10,035
TRUSTEES Peter Benthall Shone; Mrs Mair Elsie
Kelly; Michael Henry Everett.
OTHER INFORMATION Beneficiaries are likely to
remain the same
HOW TO APPLY The trustees allocate income each
year without reference to new appeals.
WHO TO APPLY TO P B Shone, Trustee, Teigncombe
Barn, Chagford, Devon TQ13 8ET *Tel* 01647
433235 *Fax* 01647 433053 *email* peter.
shone@btinternet.com
CC NO 264919   **ESTABLISHED** 1972

■ The Charles Lloyd Foundation

WHERE FUNDING CAN BE GIVEN The Roman Catholic
Dioceses of Menevia and Wrexham.
WHO CAN BENEFIT Roman Catholics.
WHAT IS FUNDED The upkeep of Roman Catholic
churches, houses, convents and monasteries,
the advancement of religion and the promotion
and advancement of music, either religious or
secular.
TYPE OF GRANT On-off.
SAMPLE GRANTS Caernarfon Catholic Church
(£2,000).
FINANCES *Year* 2007–08 *Income* £54,988
Grants £2,000 *Assets* £1,345,899
TRUSTEES Revd C D S Lloyd; P Walters; T V Ryan;
R C A Thorn.
HOW TO APPLY In writing to the correspondent. The
trust asks for 'evidence of hardship'.
Unsuccessful applications are not
acknowledged.
WHO TO APPLY TO Vincent Ryan, Trustee, 8–10
Grosvenor Road, Wrexham, Clwyd LL11 1BU
Tel 01978 291 000 *Fax* 01978 290493
email vincentryan@allingtonhughes.co.uk
CC NO 235225   **ESTABLISHED** 1964

■ The Lloyd Fund

WHERE FUNDING CAN BE GIVEN UK.
WHO CAN BENEFIT Charitable organisations.
WHAT IS FUNDED General charitable purposes.
SAMPLE GRANTS Previous grant recipients have
included DEC, Medecins Sans Frontieres,

Middle East Relief and Reprieve, Prospex,
Queille Music Trust and WOMANKIND.
FINANCES *Year* 2007–08 *Income* £13,415
Grants £19,227
TRUSTEES Stephen Lloyd; Lorna Lloyd; Toby Lloyd;
James Lloyd; Edward Lloyd.
HOW TO APPLY Unsolicited applications are unlikely
to be successful as the trustees have a settled
grant-making programme and funds are very
limited.
WHO TO APPLY TO Stephen Lloyd, Trustee, Bates
Wells and Braithwaite, Scandanavian House, 2–
6 Cannon Street, London EC4M 6YH *Tel* 020
7551 7711
CC NO 295018

■ Lloyd's Charities Trust

WHERE FUNDING CAN BE GIVEN UK, with particular
interest in East London.
WHO CAN BENEFIT Charitable organisations.
WHAT IS FUNDED General charitable purposes, with a
specific fund for education, training and
enterprise.
WHAT IS NOT FUNDED No grants for any appeal where
it is likely that the grant would be used for
sectarian purposes or to local or regional
branches of charities where it is possible to
support the UK organisation. Support is not
given to individuals.
SAMPLE GRANTS Coram, FARM-Africa, Samaritans
and e-Learning Foundation (£50,000 each);
Tower Hamlet Education Business Partnership
(£40,000); East London Business Alliance
(£18,000); and East London Small Business
Centre (£15,000).
FINANCES *Year* 2008 *Income* £507,245
Grants £383,372 *Assets* £1,985,860
TRUSTEES Ms Holly Bellingham; Grahame Chilton;
Brian Pomeroy; John Townsend; Graham White;
David Gittings; Lawrence Holder; John Spencer;
Iain Wilson; Ms Sue Langley.
HOW TO APPLY Funds permitting, Lloyd's Charities
Trust makes ad hoc donations. However, the
majority of funds are committed to supporting
the partnership charities the trust works with.
The trust has previously stated that as funds
are committed over a three-year period 'we are
unable to respond positively to the numerous
appeals we receive'. Applications are not
currently being invited for partner charity status.
WHO TO APPLY TO Mrs Vicky Mirfin, Secretary, One
Lime Street, London EC3M 7HA *Tel* 020 7327
6075 *Fax* 020 7327 6368
email communityaffairs@lloyds.com
Website www.lloyds.com
CC NO 207232   **ESTABLISHED** 1953

■ Lloyds TSB Foundation for England and Wales

WHERE FUNDING CAN BE GIVEN England and Wales.
WHO CAN BENEFIT Registered charities benefiting
people who are disabled or disadvantaged.
WHAT IS FUNDED Education and training and social
and community needs through the Community
Programme.
WHAT IS NOT FUNDED The foundation does not fund
the following types of organisations and
work:*Organisations:*organisations that are **not**
registered charities; second or third tier
organisations (unless there is evidence of direct
benefit to disadvantaged people); charities that
mainly work overseas; charities that mainly give
funds to other charities, individuals or other

organisations; hospitals, hospices or medical centres; rescue services; schools, colleges and universities. *Types of work*: activities which a statutory body is responsible for; capital projects, appeals, refurbishments; environmental work, expeditions and overseas travel; funding to promote religion; holidays or trips; loans or business finance; medical research, funding for medical equipment or medical treatments; sponsorship or funding towards a marketing appeal or fundraising activities; work with animals or to promote animal welfare.

TYPE OF GRANT One-off for a specific project, core funding, two or three year funding. Also capital, recurring costs, running costs and salaries.

RANGE OF GRANTS £500–£25,000.

SAMPLE GRANTS 2009: A National Voice – Nottingham (£70,000), towards the salary and on costs of the East Midlands Regional Officer and running costs; Trust Links Limited – Southend-on-Sea (£30,000), towards the Growing Together Project; BF Adventure – North Cornwall (£25,000), towards the salary and on costs of the project manager; East Lancashire Women's Refuge Association (£20,000), towards the salary of the Children's Community Support Worker; Lincoln Mind (£18,000), towards the staffing costs of the Befriending Scheme; Swansea Bay Asylum Seekers' Group (£15,000), towards the Welcome2Play Project and drop-in costs; Home Start Ceredigion (£10,000), towards the cost of travel and training for volunteers; and the Dyslexia Association Preston & District (£5,000), towards running costs and volunteer expenses.

FINANCES *Year* 2008 *Income* £28,486,000 *Grants* £23,776,000 *Assets* £9,243,000

TRUSTEES Prof. Ian Diamond, Chair; Janet Bibby; Prof. Clair Chilvers; Sarah Cooke; Pavita Cooper; Irene Evison; Mike Fairey; John Hughes; Alan Leaman; Anne Parker; Rosemary Stevenson.

OTHER INFORMATION 'At the end of 2009 the foundation, together with the foundations for Northern Ireland and the Channel Islands, was still in discussions with the Lloyds Banking Group over future funding arrangements. It is likely that the deal will involve a reduction in income for the foundations, falling from 1% to 0.5% of the group's pre-tax profits. The Lloyds TSB Foundation for Scotland has refused to accept this arrangement and has suspended its grant-making activities for the foreseeable future. Inevitably, this new arrangement will have an impact on the level of funding available from the foundation in the future.

Details of regional contacts can be found on the foundation's website. Other programmes are introduced from time to time – check the foundation's website for up-to-date information.'

HOW TO APPLY 'Step 1 – Read our guidelines: Please check our guidelines and individual criteria for the programme you are interested in so that you are clear what is and is not funded; Step 2 – Check if your charity is eligible: Before you apply you need to complete our short charity eligibility questionnaire which you can find on our website. If you don't have access to the internet or would prefer to talk to us first, please call 0870 411 1223. Please note that charity eligibility does not mean that your work meets the criteria for all of our programmes; Step 3 – We will contact you to discuss whether your work is eligible: If your charity is eligible, one of our team will contact you to discuss whether the work you are seeking funding for fits within our guidelines – and if it does to discuss the next steps; Step 4 –

Assessment: If your work is eligible for consideration and you are applying for a grant of over £5,000, your local Grant Manager will visit you to discuss your funding requirements. If you are applying for a grant of under £5,000, the Grant Manager will carry out a telephone assessment. Assessment visits take one to two hours, and your local Grant Manager will discuss a range of issues relevant to your potential application, including: your governance; your finances; your evidence of need; your work; and the difference it will make to your users/ beneficiaries. The Grant Manager will tell you whether or not to proceed with an application. If you are advised to apply, they will help you to make the best application; **Step 5 – Complete the application form:** If your local Grant Manager recommends that you complete an application form, they will give you a copy of the form. You will need to read the accompanying guidance notes and include: a copy of your most recent annual report and full signed accounts. These should be signed as approved on behalf of your Management Committee or equivalent. You must make sure your charity annual returns are up to date and registered with the Charity Commission – we will check this when we assess your application. (If your records are not up to date this could delay your application being processed); a copy of your charity's most recent bank statement so that we can verify the account details; the relevant job description if you are applying for funding towards the cost of a post, a copy of your equal opportunities policy or if you do not have one, information about your commitment to equal opportunities. We will also need to know about the other governance policies that you have in place that are relevant to your work; **Step 6 – Return your application form to us:** You will need to submit a signed copy of the form together with the supporting documents to us; **Step 7 – The decision on your application:** We respond to all applications that we receive and it takes from three to six months for a decision to be made on your application. Your local Grant Manager will tell you when you are likely to hear the decision. *Common reasons for unsuccessful applications* The foundation cannot fund all eligible applications even if they are of a high quality because each year the total amount requested by charities exceeds the money that we have available. Other reasons for the foundation not being able to make a grant include: charities' core work not being sufficiently focused on our mission; applications not falling within our guidelines; charities not filling in the application form properly; charities not having up to date annual returns or accounts filed with the Charities Commission or other relevant regulatory bodies. *When can I reapply?* If you receive a grant, you will not be eligible to apply for another grant from the Community Programme for another two years from receipt of the grant (or from receipt of the final payment if it has been two or three-year funding). If your application is unsuccessful, you must wait for a year before you apply again.'

WHO TO APPLY TO Mrs Linda Kelly, Chief Executive, Pentagon House, 52–54 Southwark Street, London SE1 1UN *Tel* 0870 411 1223 *Fax* 0870 411 1224 *email* enquiries@ lloydstsbfoundations.org.uk *Website* www. lloydstsbfoundations.org.uk

CC NO 327114 ESTABLISHED 1986

■ Lloyds TSB Foundation for Northern Ireland

WHERE FUNDING CAN BE GIVEN Northern Ireland.

WHO CAN BENEFIT Charities registered with HM Revenue and Customs, benefiting children, young adults, older people, volunteers and people who are unemployed, homeless, living in rural communities, disabled or disadvantaged by poverty. Constituted groups with charitable purposes, but not registered as a charity and have an annual income of less than £2,000, may apply for a grant of up to £1,000.

WHAT IS FUNDED Underfunded voluntary organisations which enable people who are disabled and people who are disadvantaged through social and economic circumstances, to make a contribution to the community. The trustees regret that, as the funds available are limited, they cannot support all fields of voluntary and charitable activity. The two main objectives to which funds are allocated are: (a) social and community needs; (b) education and training. For full details of the foundation's funding objectives go to the website.

WHAT IS NOT FUNDED Grants are not usually given for: organisations that are not recognised as a charity by HM Revenue and Customs; individuals, including students; animal welfare; environmental projects including those that deal with geographic and scenic issues – however, the trustees may consider projects that improve the living conditions of disadvantaged individuals and groups; activities that are normally the responsibility of central or local government or some other responsible body; schools, universities and colleges (except for projects specifically to benefit students with special needs); hospitals and medical centres; sponsorship or marketing appeals; fabric appeals for places of worship; promotion of religion; activities that collect funds for subsequent redistribution to others; endowment funds; fundraising events or activities; corporate affiliation or membership of a charity; loans or business finance; expeditions or overseas travel; construction of and extension to buildings; salary or training costs for the pre-school sector. Please note: organisations must have a total income of less than £250,000 to be eligible to apply to the Standard Grant Programme.

TYPE OF GRANT Capital, core costs, one-off, project, recurring costs, salaries and start-up costs. Funding is usually one-off, but support for two years or more is considered.

RANGE OF GRANTS Normally a maximum of £5,000, but larger amounts are considered.

SAMPLE GRANTS Beneficiaries of the standard grant programme included: CAB Fermanagh – towards the Disability Advocacy (Tribunal Representation) Project (£10,000); Ardoyne Association – to support the Outreach and Detached Advice Service (£8,500); Gingerbread Northern Ireland – towards the salary and core costs of the Lone Parent Centre (£7,000); Adapt Eating Distress Association – towards administrative support to maintain and enhance the existing service (£5,000); Ballee and District Community Group – towards the cookery school (£3,000); Women Making Waves – to provide courses and workshops for disabled and able bodied women in the group (£2,500); Churches Voluntary Work Bureau – towards awards, certificates and volunteer costs (£2,000); Carrick Preschool – towards new play equipment (£1,000); Ballybay Community Association – for community activities (£970); and GLM Silver Threads Group

– towards the Ten Years On celebration event (£200).

FINANCES *Year* 2008 *Income* £2,087,004 *Grants* £1,943,453 *Assets* £1,138,438

TRUSTEES Gary Mills, Chair; Paddy Bailie; Angela Colhoun; James Grant; David Patton; Tony Reynolds; Robert Agnew; Janet Lecky; Brian Scott.

OTHER INFORMATION Due to the current economic climate, there has been a reduction in the Lloyds Banking Group's profits, wiping out much of the income for the foundations. The Lloyds TSB Foundation for Northern Ireland has issued the following statement: 'Fortunately, the Foundation in Northern Ireland operates prudently and has a low cost base. Our rolling grant programmes focusing on Social and Community Welfare and Education and Training are ongoing, with quarterly closing dates, and continue to provide grants to underfunded local charities. However, two changes have been made to the programme, namely that the maximum amount that can be applied for is £5,000 and that to be eligible, organisations must have had an income of under £250,000 within the previous twelve months. The trustees and executive team will continue to review the parameters of this programme as, unfortunately, the funding situation could worsen in the medium term. However, we are still in receipt of very significant funding that will be allocated wisely to many voluntary and community sector organisations throughout Northern Ireland.'

HOW TO APPLY The foundation offers the following advice on applying to the Standard Grant Programme on its website:
'*Who can apply?* – The Standard Grant Programme is open to any organisation that is registered as a charity with HM Revenue and Customs. Constituted groups with charitable purpose, but not registered as a charity and have an annual income of less than £2,000, may apply for a grant of up to £1,000.'
'*How to apply?* – The application pack should be downloaded from the foundation website. The downloaded application form is in Microsoft WORD format to enable it to be completed on screen before printing off a hard copy. The application form should then be signed and dated by the three required signatories, before attaching copies of the required supporting documents.'
'*When to apply?* – The closing dates for applications are normally the second Friday of January, April, July and October. Always check the website for the latest closing dates, as they may change due to statutory holidays. Applications will be accepted until 5pm on each closing date. Applicants are required to leave one year between applications whether they are successful or unsuccessful. Organisations who have received three years consecutive funding must leave two years before reapplying. All applicants will be informed in writing of the decision approximately ten weeks from the closing date for applications. Unfortunately, demands made on the foundation always out-strip the funds available, and this means that many good applications, whilst meeting the criteria, will still be unsuccessful.'
Please note: the application process for other programmes may differ. Organisations are advised to contact the foundation for details, as appropriate.

WHO TO APPLY TO Sandara Kelso-Robb, Executive Director, 2nd Floor, 14 Cromac Place,

Gasworks, Belfast BT7 2JB *Tel* 028 9032 3000 *Fax* 028 9032 3200 *email* info@ lloydstsbfoundationni.org *Website* www. lloydstsbfoundationni.org
IR NO XN72216 **ESTABLISHED** 1986

....

■ Lloyds TSB Foundation for the Channel Islands

WHERE FUNDING CAN BE GIVEN The Channel Islands.
WHO CAN BENEFIT Organisations benefiting children and young people; older people; volunteers; at risk groups; people who are unemployed, carers, disabled, disadvantaged by poverty or homeless; and victims of abuse and domestic violence.
WHAT IS FUNDED The main aims of the foundation are to assist disadvantaged and disabled people and to promote social and community welfare within the Channel Islands. A wide range of activities are supported, and the following examples are meant as a guide only: advice services – addictions (particularly substance misuse rehabilitation), bereavement, counselling, emergency and rescue services, family support, helplines, homelessness, housing, parenting; community relations – crime prevention (particularly activities involving young people), mediation, promotion of volunteering, rehabilitation of offenders, victim support, vulnerable young people; community facilities and services – after school clubs, community centres, family centres, older people's clubs, playschemes, transport, youth organisations; cultural enrichment – improving participation in and access to the arts and national heritage; activities with an educational focus for all ages; improvements to buildings of historic or architectural value which increase their benefit to the community; projects which have a strong focus on benefit to people and the social environment; disabled people – advocacy, carers, day centres, information and advice, sheltered accommodation, transport; promotion of health – day care, information and advice, mental health, holistic medicine, home nursing, hospices. The trustees will, on an exceptional basis, also fund research projects in health related areas. The foundation also supports education and training, particularly activities which enhance learning opportunities for disabled and disadvantaged people of all ages.
WHAT IS NOT FUNDED No grants for: organisations which are not recognised charities; activities which are primarily the responsibility of the Insular authorities in the Islands or some other responsible body; activities which collect funds to give to other charities, individuals or other organisations; animal welfare; corporate subscription or membership of a charity; endowment funds; environment – conserving and protecting plants and animals, geography and scenery; expeditions or overseas travel; fabric appeals for places of worship; fundraising events or activities; hospitals and medical centres (except for projects which are clearly additional to statutory responsibilities); individuals, including students; loans or business finance; promotion of religion; schools and colleges (except for projects that will benefit disabled students and are clearly additional to statutory responsibilities); sponsorship or marketing appeals; international appeals – trustees may from time to time consider a limited number of applications from UK registered charities working abroad.

TYPE OF GRANT Depends on merit, but usually one-off for a specific project, operational costs, salaries and start-up costs. Funding of up to three years may be considered.
RANGE OF GRANTS £1,000–£180,000.
SAMPLE GRANTS Guernsey Cheshire Home (£180,000); Jersey Mencap (£140,000); Brighter Futures (£84,000); Guernsey Youth LBG (£75,000); Band of the Island for Jersey (£52,000); Dyslexia Day Centre (£35,000); St Andrews Church First and Victim Support Jersey (£20,000 each); Guernsey Scout Association (£14,000); Friends of Le Murier (£10,000); and Sark School and Community Centre Trust (£1,000). Two international grants were made to the Jubilee Sailing Trust (£40,000); and Christian Aid (£25,000). The sole general Channel Island grant went to the Council for Music in Hospitals (£10,000).
FINANCES *Year* 2008 *Income* £1,192,873 *Grants* £1,358,375 *Assets* £0
TRUSTEES Andrew Ozanne, Chair; David Christopher; Wendy Hurford; Peter Mourant; Sir Rocky Goodall; Advocate Susan Pearmain; Pauline Torode.
OTHER INFORMATION Due to the current economic climate, there has been a reduction in the Lloyds Banking Group's profits, wiping out much of the income for the foundations. The Lloyds TSB Foundation for the Channel Islands will continue its grant-making programme but has issued the following statement on the matter: 'The foundation's operations have been affected by the current economic downturn, a result of the deed of covenant with the Lloyds Banking Group being based on a three year average of the Groups profits. I expect the foundation's income to reduce in the coming years, with a need to return our reserves to a positive position. This will impact the foundation's ability to provide the volume of grants that were provided in previous years. The foundation has been working with those charities it supports on the islands, communicating this message and supporting them in seeking alternative funding, wherever possible. We will continue our commitment to Channel Island Charities, enabling them to help change peoples lives for the better. The commitment to the International Grant Giving will be retained in principle but due to reduced income levels it is unlikely that previous levels will be maintained.'
Note: at the end of 2008 the foundation had a deficit on reserves of £438,000 due to a change in its accounting policy, whereby the full cost of multi-year grants will now be recognised in the year that they are approved.
HOW TO APPLY Applications are only accepted on the foundation's own form. These, along with guidelines, are available from its website or from the foundation's office in Jersey and can be returned at any time. They must be returned by post as the foundation does not accept forms that have been emailed or faxed. All applications are reviewed on a continual basis. The trustees meet three times a year to approve donations. Decision-making processes can therefore take up to four months. Applications up to £5,000 are normally assessed within one month and all applicants are informed of the outcome of their application. Applicants are encouraged to discuss their project with one of the foundation's staff before completing an application form. This will help ensure that your project is within its criteria and that you are applying for an appropriate amount. You will also be informed of when you should hear a decision.

WHO TO APPLY TO John Hutchins, Executive Director, PO Box 160, 25 New Street, St Helier, Jersey JE4 8RG *Tel* 01534 845889 *email* john. hutchins@lloydstsbfoundations.org.uk *Website* www.ltsbfoundationci.org
CC NO 327113 ESTABLISHED 1986

....

■ Llysdinam Charitable Trust

WHERE FUNDING CAN BE GIVEN Wales.
WHO CAN BENEFIT Registered charities.
WHAT IS FUNDED General charitable purposes.
WHAT IS NOT FUNDED No grants to individuals.
TYPE OF GRANT Generally recurrent.
RANGE OF GRANTS £270–£16,000.
SAMPLE GRANTS University of Wales – Cardiff (£16,000); Central Beacons Mountain Rescue Team (£15,000); Christ College Brecon Scholarship (£8,000); Powys Art Forum (£5,000); Swansea Rugby Foundation (£4,000); Bobath Cymru Children's Therapy (£3,000); Cystic Fibrosis Unit – Singleton Hospital (£2,000); the Sequel Trust (£1,500); Fire Services National Benevolent Unit (£1,000); and Wakes Air Ambulance (£270).
FINANCES *Year* 2007–08 *Income* £194,927 *Grants* £119,038 *Assets* £4,453,245
TRUSTEES Mrs M J Elster; N O Tyler; Mrs E S Birkmyre.
HOW TO APPLY The trust stated that it was overloaded with applications and does not welcome unsolicited applications.
WHO TO APPLY TO The Trustees, Rees Richards and Partners, Druslyn House, De La Beche Street, Swansea SA1 3HH *Tel* 01792 650 705 *Fax* 01792 468 384 *email* post@reesrichards. co.uk
CC NO 255528 ESTABLISHED 1968

....

■ Localtrent Ltd

WHERE FUNDING CAN BE GIVEN UK, with some preference for Manchester.
WHO CAN BENEFIT Charities benefiting Jewish people and the advancement of the Jewish faith.
WHAT IS FUNDED The trustees will consider applications from organisations concerned with orthodox Jewish faith education and the relief of poverty.
SAMPLE GRANTS Previous beneficiaries include Chasdei Yoel Charity, Congregation Chemed, Tchabe Kollel, UTA, Asser Bishvil and Yeshiva Ohel Shimon.
FINANCES *Year* 2007–08 *Income* £80,952 *Grants* £118,240 *Assets* £270,976
TRUSTEES Mrs M Weiss; B Weiss; P Weiss; Mrs Y Weiss; Mrs Z Weiss; H Weiss.
HOW TO APPLY In writing to the correspondent.
WHO TO APPLY TO A Kahan, Lopian Gross Barnett and Co., 6th Floor, Cardinal House, 20 St Mary's Parsonage, Manchester M3 2LG *Tel* 0161 832 8721 *Fax* 0161 835 3085
CC NO 326329 ESTABLISHED 1982

....

■ The Locker Foundation

WHERE FUNDING CAN BE GIVEN UK and overseas.
WHO CAN BENEFIT Organisations benefiting Jewish people, children and young adults, students and teachers.
WHAT IS FUNDED Jewish charities, Synagogues, schools and colleges and Jewish education studies.
RANGE OF GRANTS £100–£57,000.

SAMPLE GRANTS Kahal Chassidim Bobov (£57,000); British Friends of Ezer Mizion and Magen David Adorn (£50,000 each); Supporters of Israel Dependents (£25,000); British Friends of Israel War Disabled (£21,000); British Friends of Rambam Medical Centre (£20,600); Chai Cancer Care and Wizo (£20,150 each); Emunah (£20,000 and Friends of Bnei Akiva (£18,600). Smaller grants of between £100 and £1,000 were made to Bottoms Up, Friends of Laniado UK, Jewish Child's Day, Jewish Women, Rosh Pinah Primary School and The Swaminarayan Hindu Mission.
FINANCES *Year* 2007–08 *Income* £708,328 *Grants* £476,629 *Assets* £4,313,732
TRUSTEES I Carter; M Carter; Mrs S Segal.
HOW TO APPLY In writing to the correspondent.
WHO TO APPLY TO The Trustees, 28 High Road, East Finchley, London N2 9PJ *Tel* 020 8455 9280
CC NO 264180 ESTABLISHED 1972

....

■ The Loftus Charitable Trust

WHERE FUNDING CAN BE GIVEN UK and overseas.
WHO CAN BENEFIT Jewish organisations benefiting children, young adults and students.
WHAT IS FUNDED Jewish organisations working in the areas of welfare, education and religion.
RANGE OF GRANTS £SAMPLE GRANTS South Hampstead Synagogue (£101,000); Lubavitch Foundation (£25,000); Jewish Care (£24,500); Immanuel College (£16,000); Community Security Trust (£15,000); and JNF Charitable Trust (£13,000); British Friends of Tikva Odessa, Shalom Foundation, The Holocaust Foundation, Camp Simcha, Chai Cancer Care and Nightingale House (£5,000 each).
FINANCES *Year* 2007–08 *Income* £289,400 *Grants* £355,218
TRUSTEES R I Loftus; A L Loftus; A D Loftus.
HOW TO APPLY The trustees state that all funds are committed and unsolicited applications are not welcome.
WHO TO APPLY TO Anthony Loftus, Trustee, Asher House, Blackburn Road, London NW6 1AW *Tel* 020 7604 5900
CC NO 297664 ESTABLISHED 1987

....

■ The Lolev Charitable Trust

WHERE FUNDING CAN BE GIVEN Worldwide.
WHO CAN BENEFIT Individuals and organisations.
WHAT IS FUNDED Orthodox Jewish causes.
FINANCES *Year* 2008 *Income* £3,358,804 *Grants* £3,359,576 *Assets* £58,975
TRUSTEES Abraham Tager; Eve Tager; Michael Tager.
OTHER INFORMATION The 2008 grant total included the sum of £3.1 million distributed to individuals.
HOW TO APPLY In writing to the correspondent.
WHO TO APPLY TO Abraham Tager, Trustee, 14a Gilda Crescent, London N16 6JP
CC NO 326249 ESTABLISHED 1982

....

■ London Catalyst (formerly The Metropolitan Hospital-Sunday Fund)

WHERE FUNDING CAN BE GIVEN Greater London, within the boundaries of the M25.
WHO CAN BENEFIT Hospitals, homes and medical charities outside the NHS who are also registered charities; NHS hospitals throughout

....

London; clients of social workers; individuals in need.

WHAT IS FUNDED Projects working with people on low incomes are favoured, as is work that assists adults. It is interested to hear from organisations working with minority ethnic and other faith communities, including refugees and asylum seekers. Themes the programme will fund are: community transport – such as modifications to existing or proposed transport (but not the purchase of minibuses), transportation costs to allow people to access activities and volunteer driving training; specialist equipment – such as hoists, slings, pressure mattresses, adjustable beds, special wheelchairs, mobility aids and so on; respite breaks and holidays – meeting the costs of breaks and holidays for people with health problems or disabilities and supporting respite programmes for carers; start-up costs – in exceptional cases, new organisations meeting an unmet need may receive revenue grants in their first two years to help them 'get off the ground' supporting volunteers – costs of volunteer training and involvement where this will add value to services for Londoners who are sick or have disabilities, and their carers; and arts and health – arts projects forming part of health recovery programmes, including those for older people.

WHAT IS NOT FUNDED No grants to: hospitals and homes within the NHS, including specialist clinics and appeals relating to NHS hospitals and special units; charitable organisations not registered with the Charity Commission; hospital league of friends for NHS and independent hospitals; government departments; or individuals.

TYPE OF GRANT Project and one-off.

RANGE OF GRANTS Usually £1,000–£3,000.

SAMPLE GRANTS Sundial Centre (£29,000); Kilburn Youth Centre (£20,000); Disability Advice Service Lambeth (£15,000); Rushey Green Time Bank (£12,000); Brent Mental Health Service, Barnet Care and Support Services and Real Life Parenting (£10,000 each); Alpha Grove Community Centre and Custom House & Canning Town Community Renewal Project (£4,000 each); Barnet Hospital, Adult & Elderly SW Department, Camden Assertive Outreach Team, Epsom General Hospital SW team and West London Centre for Counselling (£1,000 each); and Alternatives Trust East London and Edgware Hospital, Older Adults SW Team (£500 each).

FINANCES *Year* 2008 *Income* £408,523 *Grants* £330,669 *Assets* £9,128,445

TRUSTEES Timothy Cook; John Cornes; Canon James Cronin; Charles Davidson; Bishop Bernard Longley; Revd Paul Regen; Canon Grahame Shaw; Dr Steve Mowle; Peter Jones; Helal Uddin Abbas; Katharine Barber.

OTHER INFORMATION This entry only refers to grants made to organisations. It operates smaller funds for individuals.

HOW TO APPLY Forms and guidance can be downloaded from the charity's website or requested by phone or letter. Applications and other grant enquiries are acceptable via email. All applications are reviewed against eligibility criteria and then considered by the grants scrutiny committee before presenting to the trustees for approval.

WHO TO APPLY TO Graham Lawrence, Company Secretary, c/o The Peabody Trust, Minster Court, 45 Westminster Bridge Road, London SE1 7JB *Tel* 020 7021 4225 *email* london. catalyst@peabody.org.uk *Website* www. londoncatalyst.org.uk

CC NO 1066739   **ESTABLISHED** 1872

■ The London Law Trust

WHERE FUNDING CAN BE GIVEN UK.

WHO CAN BENEFIT Registered charities benefiting children and young people.

WHAT IS FUNDED The prevention and cure of illness and disability in children and young people; the alleviation of illness and disability in children and young people; and the encouragement in young people of the qualities of leadership and service to the community. The trust may also support charities working in the fields of education and residential facilities and services.

WHAT IS NOT FUNDED Applications from individuals, including students, are ineligible.

TYPE OF GRANT Usually one-off grants for or towards specific projects. Buildings, capital, core costs, research, running costs, recurring costs, salaries and start-up costs will also be considered. Funding may be given for up to three years.

RANGE OF GRANTS £500–£5,000; typical grant £3,000.

SAMPLE GRANTS Previous beneficiaries have included: BRIC, British Lung Foundation, Deans & Canons of Windsor, Great Ormond Street, St George's Hospital Medical School, Envision, Activenture, Swan Syndrome and Circomedia.

FINANCES *Year* 2007–08 *Income* £567,968 *Grants* £134,000 *Assets* £3,728,508

TRUSTEES Prof. Anthony R Mellows; R A Pellant; Sir Michael Hobbs; Sir Ian Gainsford.

HOW TO APPLY In writing to the correspondent. The trustees employ a grant advisor whose job is to evaluate applications. Grant applicants are requested to supply detailed information in support of their applications. The grant advisor makes on-site visits to all applicants and makes a written report The directors of the trust meet around May and December to consider the grant advisor's individual visit reports together with the application form, latest accounts and other supporting information. Most applications are considered in December, with payment being made in the following months. The best time to apply is between January and March.

WHO TO APPLY TO G D Ogilvie, Secretary, Hunters, 9 New Square, Lincoln's Inn, London WC2A 3QN *Tel* 020 7412 0050 *email* londonlawtrust@ hunters-solicitors.co.uk *Website* www. thelondonlawtrust.org

CC NO 1115266   **ESTABLISHED** 1968

■ London Legal Support Trust

WHERE FUNDING CAN BE GIVEN London and the Home Counties.

WHO CAN BENEFIT Voluntary sector legal agencies in London and the Home Counties that employ solicitors or retain the services of solicitors as volunteers to provide free legal advice to poor or disadvantaged members the public; and network organisations that support the above agencies.

WHAT IS FUNDED (i) Legal services and projects that encourage or provide co-operation between voluntary sector agencies and volunteers from private practice. (ii) Crisis intervention to 'keep the doors open' when funding cuts threaten the closure of a voluntary sector legal agency and when the trustees consider that short term

funding may lead to sustainable recovery.
(iii) One-off capital support to increase the
capacity of an agency to deliver its service.
(iv) Creation of new social welfare legal and pro
bono provision in London and the Home
Counties.

WHAT IS NOT FUNDED The trust does not fund: non
charitable activity; applications for which the
trustees feel that Legal Services Commission
funding is suitable and practical within a
reasonable time frame, except where the trust's
funding is to be used to lever matched funding.

SAMPLE GRANTS South West London Law Centre
(£38,000); Hackney Law Centre (£35,000);
Advice UK IT Bursary (£33,000); Surrey Law
Centre (£21,000); Hillingdon Law Centre
(£10,000); Enfield Law Centre (£9,600);
Paddington Law Centre (£3,500); Toynbee Hall
(£1,500); Central London Law Centre (£1,000);
Streetwise Law Centre (£860); Springfield
Advice and Law Centre (£550); Luton Law
Centre (£200); and Lewisham Law Centre
(£120).

FINANCES *Year* 2007–08 *Income* £296,169
Grants £328,288 *Assets* £86,350

TRUSTEES Julian Clark; Richard Dyton; Peter
Gardner; Graham Huntley; Steve Hynes; Joy
Julien; Michael Smyth; Marc Sosnow; Fraser
Thomas; Jeremy Thomas.

HOW TO APPLY In writing to the correspondent
stating what is needed and why. Applicants
should enclose annual accounts and annual
report. Please check the trusts's website for
availability and full guidelines.

WHO TO APPLY TO Emma Shaw, c/o Allen & Overy, 1
New Change, London EC4M 9QQ *email* chair@
londonlegalsupporttrust.org.uk
Website londonlegalsupporttrust.org.uk

CC NO 1101906

■ The London Marathon Charitable Trust

WHERE FUNDING CAN BE GIVEN Mainly London, but
also City of Birmingham and South
Northamptonshire.

WHO CAN BENEFIT Organisations involved with sports,
recreation and leisure, including schools.

WHAT IS FUNDED Recreational facilities in London.
Grants have been made towards the
establishment of play areas and nature trails;
improvements to existing leisure facilities;
provision of MUGAs (Multi Use Games Areas);
and to various rowing organisations to provide
new accommodation and boats. Grants are
aimed to benefit both the able bodied and
people with disabilities and include the sports of
athletics, cricket, tennis, gymnastics, sailing,
football, boxing, and climbing.

WHAT IS NOT FUNDED Grants cannot be made to
'closed' clubs or schools, unless the facility is
available for regular public use. No grants are
made for recurring or revenue costs. Individuals
are not supported.

SAMPLE GRANTS Charlton Athletic Community Trust
and Downside Youth Club (£100,000 each);
Royal Canoe Club (£80,000); Corbets Tey
School (£60,000); Royal Albert Dock Trust
(£41,000); Friends of Chestnuts Park
(£20,000); Bexley Cricket Club (£15,000);
Dockland Settlement (£11,000); and Charlton
Park Riding for the Disabled (£6,000).

FINANCES *Year* 2007–08 *Income* £4,684,035
Grants £1,379,283 *Assets* £12,476,198

TRUSTEES Bernard Atha; Simon Cooper; Eileen Gray;
Dame Mary Peters; Joyce Smith; John Graves;

James Dudley Henderson Clarke; John Austin;
John Disley; Sir Rodney Walker; John Bryant.

HOW TO APPLY On a form available from the
correspondent. Applications are welcomed from
London Boroughs and independent
organisations, clubs and charities. The trustees
meet once a year; the closing date is usually
the end of August.

WHO TO APPLY TO David Golton, Secretary, Kestrel
House, 111 Heath Road, Twickenham TW1 4AH
Tel 020 8892 6646 *Fax* 020 8892 6478
email lmct@ffleach.co.uk

CC NO 283813   **ESTABLISHED** 1982

■ London Masonic Charitable Trust

WHERE FUNDING CAN BE GIVEN Particular but not
exclusive focus on London.

WHO CAN BENEFIT Registered charities.

WHAT IS FUNDED General charitable purposes. The
trust coordinates donations to selected
charities.

SAMPLE GRANTS St Paul's Cathedral (£18,000);
British Red Cross, Drug and Alcohol Abuse,
Lambeth Summer Projects and St Paul's Steiner
Project (£4,000 each); and Building for Babies
and Step by Step (£3,000 each).

FINANCES *Year* 2006–07 *Income* £108,133
Grants £45,413 *Assets* £252,778

TRUSTEES Russell Race, Chair; Michael Birkett;
Andrew Henderson; Rex Thorne; Robert Corp-
Reader; Brian de Neut.

OTHER INFORMATION 'London Masonic Charitable
Trust (LMCT) exists to encourage charitable
giving among London freemasons. In
furtherance of this aim, LMCT acts as a
collection point for donations to designated
charities from London lodges, chapters and
individuals in order to relieve the designated
charity of this administrative task.'

HOW TO APPLY 'The Metropolitan Grand Lodge of
London, from time to time selects charities
where relatively small amounts of money
applied to specific projects will produce
significant results.'

WHO TO APPLY TO Michael Birkett, Trustee, 33 Great
Queen Street, PO Box 29055, London
WC2B 5UN *Website* www.metgl.com

CC NO 1081205   **ESTABLISHED** 2000

■ The William and Katherine Longman Trust

WHERE FUNDING CAN BE GIVEN UK.

WHO CAN BENEFIT Registered charities.

WHAT IS FUNDED General charitable purposes.

WHAT IS NOT FUNDED Grants are only made to
registered charities.

TYPE OF GRANT One-off and recurrent.

RANGE OF GRANTS £1,000–£30,000.

SAMPLE GRANTS Vanessa Grant Trust (£30,000);
Chelsea Festival and World Child Cancer Fund
(£20,000 each); Care (£12,000); and Hope
Education Trust and RADA (£10,000 each).
Action for ME (£5,000); The Children's Society
(£4,500); Age Concern – Kensington & Chelsea
(£3,500); RSPCA – Harmsworth Hospital
(£3,000); St Mungo's (£2,500); and Prisoners
Abroad (£1,000).

FINANCES *Year* 2007–08 *Income* £119,450
Grants £255,000 *Assets* £3,973,131

TRUSTEES W P Harriman; J B Talbot; A C O Bell.

HOW TO APPLY The trustees believe in taking a
proactive approach in deciding which charities to

support and it is their policy not to respond to unsolicited appeals.

WHO TO APPLY TO Paul Harriman, Trustee, Charles Russell LLP, 8–10 New Fetter Lane, London EC4A 1RS *Tel* 020 7203 5124

CC NO 800785   **ESTABLISHED** 1988

■ The Lord's Taverners

WHERE FUNDING CAN BE GIVEN Unrestricted, in practice, UK.

WHO CAN BENEFIT Cricket clubs affiliated to a National Governing Body, individual schools or other organisations directly involved in the organisation of youth cricket and which have a genuine need for assistance.

WHAT IS FUNDED Youth cricket, minibuses for organisations supporting young people with disabilities and sports and recreational equipment for young people with special needs.

WHAT IS NOT FUNDED Youth cricket: the following is not normally grant aided: building or renovation of pavilions; sight screens; bowling machines; mowers/rollers; overseas tours; clothing; refreshments; trophies. Sport for young people with special needs: the following will not normally be considered for a grant: capital costs; general grants; running costs including salaries; individuals (although applications will be considered for equipment to enable an individual to participate in a team/group recreational activity); holidays/overseas tours. Minibuses: homes, schools and organisations catering for young people with special needs under the age of 25 years, are entitled to only one minibus per location, although applications are accepted for a replacement.

SAMPLE GRANTS No grants list was available.

FINANCES *Year* 2008 *Income* £5,312,249 *Grants* £2,411,067 *Assets* £3,192,603

TRUSTEES John Ayling; John Barnes; Leo Callow; Mike Gatting; Richard Groom; John Hooper; Peter Johnson; Christopher Laing; Roger Oakley; Jonathan Rice; Martin Smith; Richard Stilgoe; Anthony Wreford; Simon Cleobury; Denise Horne; Nicholas Stewart; Robert Powell; Sally Surridge; Bob Bevan.

HOW TO APPLY The trust committee meets regularly to review applications for grant aid. All applications must be presented on the appropriate application forms and should be submitted to the secretary. Please see the grant-making section for further information on individual programmes. Application forms with detailed application instructions are available from the secretary or on the website.

WHO TO APPLY TO Nicky Pemberton, Head of Foundation, 10 Buckingham Place, London SW1E 6HX *Tel* 020 7821 2828 *Fax* 020 7821 2829 *email* contact@lordstaverners.org *Website* www.lordstaverners.org

CC NO 306054   **ESTABLISHED** 1950

■ The Loseley and Guildway Charitable Trust

WHERE FUNDING CAN BE GIVEN International and UK, with an interest in Guildford.

WHO CAN BENEFIT Organisations benefiting people with various disabilities and terminal illness, children and victims of natural disasters.

WHAT IS FUNDED Compassionate causes, mainly local or causes with which various members of the More-Molyneux family and trustees are associated.

WHAT IS NOT FUNDED No grants to individuals or non-registered charities.

RANGE OF GRANTS £25–£5,000. Typically £100.

SAMPLE GRANTS CHASE and Disability Challengers (£5,000 each); Brooke Hospital, Cherry Trees, Dame Vera Lynn Trust, Gurkha Welfare Trust, National Society for Epilepsy, Phyllis Tuckwell Hospice and Send a Cow (£1,000 each).

FINANCES *Year* 2007–08 *Income* £63,385 *Grants* £34,830 *Assets* £1,239,913

TRUSTEES Maj. James More-Molyneux, Chair; Mrs Susan More-Molyneux; Michael More-Molyneux; Adrian Abbott; Glye Hodson.

HOW TO APPLY In writing to the correspondent. The trustees meet in February, May and September to consider applications. However, due to commitments, new applications for any causes are unlikely to be successful.

WHO TO APPLY TO Mrs Julia Barnes, Secretary, The Estate Offices, Loseley Park, Guildford, Surrey GU3 1HS *Tel* 01483 405 114 *Fax* 01483 302 036 *email* charities@loseleypark.co.uk *Website* www.loseley-park.com/charities.asp

CC NO 267178   **ESTABLISHED** 1973

■ The Lotus Foundation

WHERE FUNDING CAN BE GIVEN UK, especially London and Surrey; occasionally overseas.

WHO CAN BENEFIT Established or newly-formed charities.

WHAT IS FUNDED The primary objectives of the trust are: 'to support those charities that fall within our aims, [i.e.] children and youth, medical, substance abuse and domestic violence, education, animal welfare and community charities'.

WHAT IS NOT FUNDED No response to circular appeals. No grants to individuals, non-registered charities, charities working outside of the foundation's areas of interest, or for research purposes.

TYPE OF GRANT One-off and Recurrent.

RANGE OF GRANTS £200–£20,000.

SAMPLE GRANTS WaterAid (£21,000); Training theTeachers' of Tomorrow (£20,000); RAPT (£16,000); Medicines Sans Frontieres (£11,000); and Shorefields School – Liverpool and Tower Hamlets Mission (£10,000 each); Fine Cell Work (£5,000); Scope (£3,000); World Horse Welfare (£2,000); The National Police Community Trust (£1,000); Children with Leukaemia (£400); and Motor Neurone Disease Association (£200).

FINANCES *Year* 2007 *Income* £172,473 *Grants* £224,192

TRUSTEES Mrs B Starkey; R Starkey; Mrs E Turner.

HOW TO APPLY In writing to the correspondent giving a brief outline of the work, amount required and project/programme to benefit. The trustees prefer applications which are simple and economically prepared rather than glossy 'prestige' and mail sorted brochures. Note: In order to reduce administration costs and concentrate its efforts on the charitable work at hand, unsolicited requests will no longer be acknowledged by the foundation.

WHO TO APPLY TO Mrs B Starkey, Trustee, c/o Startling Music Ltd, 90 Jermyn Street, London SW1Y 6JD *Tel* 020 7930 5133 *Website* www.lotusfoundation.com

CC NO 1070111   **ESTABLISHED** 1998

■ The Lowy Mitchell Foundation

WHERE FUNDING CAN BE GIVEN Worldwide.

WHO CAN BENEFIT Charitable organisations chosen at the trustees' discretion.

WHAT IS FUNDED General and Jewish charitable purposes.

SAMPLE GRANTS Grants were categorised as follows: Community and Welfare (£53,000); Arts and Culture (£35,000); Education Science and Technology (£22,000); Medical and Disability (£20,000); Children and Youth (£15,000); Religious (£13,000); and Other (£2,000). Beneficiaries included: Jewish Care (£32,500); Portobello Media (£25,000); Absolute Return for Kids and Women for Women (£10,000 each); One to One and One Voice Europe (£5,000 each); and Jewish Child's Day (£500).

FINANCES *Year* 2007–08 *Income* £25,459 *Grants* £161,347 *Assets* £757,011

TRUSTEES Lord Mitchell; Lady Mitchell; A J Weiner; A Delew.

HOW TO APPLY In writing to the correspondent.

WHO TO APPLY TO Lady Lowy Mitchell, Administrator, 3 Elm Row, London NW3 1AA *Tel* 020 7431 1534

CC NO 1094430   ESTABLISHED 2002

■ The C L Loyd Charitable Trust

WHERE FUNDING CAN BE GIVEN UK, with a preference for Berkshire and Oxfordshire.

WHO CAN BENEFIT Neighbourhood-based community projects and UK organisations benefiting at risk groups, and people who are disabled, disadvantaged by poverty or socially isolated.

WHAT IS FUNDED General charitable purposes. Local charities in Berkshire and Oxfordshire, UK health and welfare charities and UK animal welfare charities.

WHAT IS NOT FUNDED In writing to the correspondent. Grants are made several times each month.

TYPE OF GRANT One-off and recurrent.

RANGE OF GRANTS Up to £50,000; mostly £1,000 or less.

SAMPLE GRANTS Country Buildings Protection Trust (£49,000); Ashmolean Museum (£15,000); Wantage Town Governors Appeal and Wantage Vale and Downland Museum (£10,000 each); Ardington and Lockinge Tennis Club (£5,000); British Red Cross (£3,200); King Alfred Education (£3,000); Christian Aid (£2,100); Ardington and Lockinge PCC (£1,140); and East Hendred PCC and PACE (£1,000 each).

FINANCES *Year* 2007–08 *Income* £91,362 *Grants* £111,202 *Assets* £2,466,968

TRUSTEES T C Loyd; C L Loyd.

HOW TO APPLY In writing to the correspondent. Grants are made several times each month.

WHO TO APPLY TO C L Loyd, Trustee, Betterton House, Lockinge, Wantage, Oxfordshire OX12 8QL *Tel* 01235 833 265

CC NO 265076   ESTABLISHED 1973

■ LSA Charitable Trust

WHERE FUNDING CAN BE GIVEN UK.

WHO CAN BENEFIT Individuals and institutions benefiting horticultural researchers, students and people working in horticulture, and former tenants and employees of the former Land Settlement Association Ltd, who are in need.

WHAT IS FUNDED Horticultural research, the promotion of horticultural knowledge, and the relief of poverty.

SAMPLE GRANTS £34,000 to individuals for the relief of poverty; £21,000 to individuals and institutions for education.

FINANCES *Year* 2007–08 *Income* £64,346 *Grants* £54,951 *Assets* £1,297,844

TRUSTEES B E G Howe; P Hadley; C F Woodhouse; A M M Ross; S R V Pomeroy, Chair; D J P Price.

HOW TO APPLY For organisations: in writing to the correspondent. Grants to individuals for the relief of poverty are made through the Royal Agricultural Benevolent Institution.

WHO TO APPLY TO Cheryl Boyce, c/o Farrer and Co, 66 Lincoln's Inn Fields, London WC2A 3LH *Tel* 020 7242 2022

CC NO 803671   ESTABLISHED 1989

■ The Marie Helen Luen Charitable Trust

WHERE FUNDING CAN BE GIVEN UK, with a preference for Wimbledon.

WHO CAN BENEFIT Charitable organisations.

WHAT IS FUNDED The trust supports both UK and local charities concerned with cancer relief, homelessness and the relief of hardship, pain and suffering. Grants are also given to relieve developing world poverty.

RANGE OF GRANTS Up to £5,000.

SAMPLE GRANTS Kingston University Hardship Fund and Kingston and Wimbledon YMCA (£5,000 each); Headway, Alzheimer's Society, Macmillan Cancer Relief, Merton Volunteer Bureau and Sequal Trust (£2,000 each); and Good Shepherd Congregation – Columbo and Samata Sarana – Sri Lanka (£1,000 each).

FINANCES *Year* 2008 *Income* £47,612 *Grants* £57,500 *Assets* £801,033

TRUSTEES S V Perera; R R Littleton; M G Whitehead.

OTHER INFORMATION Grants to both individuals and organisations

HOW TO APPLY In writing to the correspondent.

WHO TO APPLY TO Richard R Littleton, Trustee, Hillcroft, 57 Langley Avenue, Surbiton, Surrey KT6 6QR *Tel* 020 8946 3979 *email* richard@esppos.com

CC NO 291012   ESTABLISHED 1984

■ Robert Luff Foundation Ltd

WHERE FUNDING CAN BE GIVEN UK.

WHO CAN BENEFIT Medical research charities.

WHAT IS FUNDED Medical research.

SAMPLE GRANTS Cystic Fibrosis Trust (£150,000); Royal Brompton Hospital (£110,000); Bowel Disease Research Foundation and University of Sunderland Autism Unit (£80,000 each); Wellbeing for Women (£65,000); International Spinal Research Trust and Osteopathic Centre for Children (£50,000 each); Alzheimers Society and Sheffield Health Authority Trust Fund (£40,000 each); and Blonde McIndoe Research Foundation (£25,000).

FINANCES *Year* 2007–08 *Income* £534,024 *Grants* £500,000 *Assets* £25,259,436

TRUSTEES Sir Robert Johnson; Lady Johnson; R P J Price; Ms G Favot; Mrs J Tomlinson; Revd Matthew Tomlinson; Mrs M Condon; B D Nicholson.

HOW TO APPLY The foundation makes its own decisions about what causes to support. It has stated that 'outside applications are not considered, or replied to'.

WHO TO APPLY TO Michael D Lock, Secretary, 294 Earls Court Road, Kensington, London SW5 9BB *Tel* 020 7373 7003 *email* md.lock@virgin.net
CC NO 273810   **ESTABLISHED** 1977

....
■ Henry Lumley Charitable Trust

WHERE FUNDING CAN BE GIVEN UK and overseas.
WHO CAN BENEFIT Charities which are known to at least one trustee.
WHAT IS FUNDED Medical, educational and relief of poverty/hardship.
TYPE OF GRANT Mainly recurrent.
RANGE OF GRANTS £1,000–£20,000.
SAMPLE GRANTS Royal College of Surgeons (£20,000); Eton College Foundation (£10,000); Action on Addiction, British Liver Trust, Discs, International Spinal Research, Northwick Park Institute, and Tuberous Sclerosis Association (£5,000 each); Parity, Royal British Legion and Royal Star and Garter Home for Disabled Ex-service Men and Women (£2,500 each); and Outward Bound Trust (£1,000).
FINANCES *Year* 2008 *Income* £108,562 *Grants* £135,500 *Assets* £2,861,519
TRUSTEES Henry Lumley; Peter Lumley; Robert Lumley; James Porter.
HOW TO APPLY In writing to the correspondent.
WHO TO APPLY TO Peter Lumley, Trustee, c/o Lutine Leisure Ltd, Windlesham Golf Club, Bagshot, Surrey GU19 5HY *Tel* 01276 472273
CC NO 1079480   **ESTABLISHED** 2000

....
■ Lady Lumley's Educational Foundation

WHERE FUNDING CAN BE GIVEN Pickering, Sinnington and Thornton Dale.
WHO CAN BENEFIT Lady Lumley School, schools and other places of learning, charitable organisations and individuals.
WHAT IS FUNDED Education, special benefits not provided by the LEA, provision of recreational facilities for young people and financial assistance to enable study of music or other arts.
FINANCES *Year* 2007–08 *Income* £75,603 *Grants* £57,670 *Assets* £2,112,320
TRUSTEES J H Russell, Chair; G Acomb; R Bramley; C M Cooper; R H Towler; Mrs S R Wass; A Wilson.
HOW TO APPLY The trustees meet at least three times a year to consider applications which should be made in writing to the correspondent.
WHO TO APPLY TO D C Fitzgerald, Clerk to the Governors, 1 The Mount, Thornton Dale, Pickering, North Yorkshire YO18 7TF *Tel* 01751 472121 *Fax* 01751 475132
CC NO 529625   **ESTABLISHED** 1959

....
■ Paul Lunn-Rockliffe Charitable Trust

WHERE FUNDING CAN BE GIVEN UK with a preference for Hampshire.
WHO CAN BENEFIT Organisations of UK significance and charities which may be known to the trustees, or members of their family, benefiting: people of all ages, unemployed people, Christians, at risk groups, carers, people who are disabled, people disadvantaged by poverty, ex-offenders and people at risk of offending, people who are homeless, people living in urban areas, victims of famine and disasters and people with cerebral palsy or Parkinson's disease.
WHAT IS FUNDED It is the trustees' policy not to raise income through public and private appeals. The trust's sole source of income is the dividends received from the trust's capital investments. As far as grant making is concerned the trustees' policy is to give first but not exclusive consideration to charities likely to further Christianity; to give support to charities concerned with the relief of poverty, helping the aged, supporting the infirm and disaster relief; to consider charities connected with prisons and prisoners, medical research, rehabilitation of drug addicts and youth organisations; housing and accommodation. It will also support training for work; bursaries and fees; neurological research; and holidays and outings. Finally, the trustees should not accept such new commitments that will significantly dilute the size of current grants.
WHAT IS NOT FUNDED The trustees will not fund individuals; for example, student's expenses and travel grants. Repair and maintenance of historic buildings are also excluded for support.
TYPE OF GRANT Core costs, one-off and start-up costs. Funding for more than three years will be considered.
RANGE OF GRANTS £300–£1,000.
SAMPLE GRANTS Christians Against Poverty (£1,100); Winchester Night Shelter (£1,000); Bible Society and Care (£800 each); Action for Elder Abuse, Children Country Holiday Fund, Fusion, Salvation Army, Spastics Society of India and Touchstones 12 (£500 each); Way of Life (£400); and Gateway Club (£300).
FINANCES *Year* 2007–08 *Income* £41,180 *Grants* £39,100 *Assets* £868,683
TRUSTEES Mrs Jacqueline Lunn-Rockliffe; Victor Lunn-Rockliffe; James Lunn-Rockliffe.
HOW TO APPLY The trust encourages preliminary phone calls to discuss applications. It will generally only reply to written correspondence if an sae has been included.
WHO TO APPLY TO Mrs J M Lunn-Rockliffe, Secretary, 4a Barnes Close, Winchester, Hampshire SO23 9QX *Tel* 01962 852 949 *Fax* 01962 852 949
CC NO 264119   **ESTABLISHED** 1972

....
■ C F Lunoe Trust Fund

WHERE FUNDING CAN BE GIVEN UK.
WHO CAN BENEFIT Universities and ex-employees (and their dependants) of Norwest Holst Group Ltd.
WHAT IS FUNDED Universities associated with the construction industry.
SAMPLE GRANTS ICE Quest Fund (£38,000); Leeds University (£10,000); and Leeds University – C F Lunoe Memorial Lecture (£3,000).
FINANCES *Year* 2007–08 *Income* £87,333 *Grants* £51,000 *Assets* £1,219,392
TRUSTEES J A Bosdet, Chair; P H Lunoe; R F Collins; J E Ellis; G V Smith; J A Jefkins; J A Dodson; T Parks.
OTHER INFORMATION In 2007–08 a further £27,000 was given to 16 individuals.
HOW TO APPLY In writing to the correspondent. However, the majority of the trust's funds go to organisations already known to the trustees and as a result new applications are likely to be unsuccessful.

WHO TO APPLY TO Peter Lunoe, Trustee, 29 Box
Lane, Hemel Hempstead, Hertfordshire
HP3 0DH
CC NO 214850   ESTABLISHED 1960

■ The Ruth and Jack Lunzer Charitable Trust

WHERE FUNDING CAN BE GIVEN UK.
WHO CAN BENEFIT Organisations benefiting children,
young adults and students are given priority.
WHAT IS FUNDED Jewish organisations, educational
institutions and the arts. Other charitable
purposes will be considered.
TYPE OF GRANT Mainly recurrent.
RANGE OF GRANTS £100–10,000.
SAMPLE GRANTS Kahal Chassidim Bobov (£11,000)
and Yesoday Hatorah Schools (£10,000); Chai
Cancer Care (£5,250); Hampstead Heath
(£2,900); North West London Communal Mikvah
(£2,000); Central Square Minyan and GGBH
Congregation (£1,500 each); Jerusalem
Foundation and Royal College of Music (£1,000
each); Three Faiths Forum and Lambeth Palace
Gallery (£500 each); and Glyndebourne Arts
Trust (£250).
FINANCES *Year* 2007–08 *Income* £60,005
Grants £56,749 *Assets* £43,823
TRUSTEES J V Lunzer; M D Paisner.
HOW TO APPLY In writing to the correspondent.
Unsuccessful applicants are not acknowledged.
WHO TO APPLY TO M D Paisner, Trustee, c/o Berwin
Leighton Paisner, Adelaide House, London
Bridge, London EC4R 9HA *Tel* 020 7760 1000
CC NO 276201   ESTABLISHED 1978

■ Lord and Lady Lurgan Trust

WHERE FUNDING CAN BE GIVEN UK and South Africa.
WHO CAN BENEFIT Medical charities, older people,
children and the arts.
WHAT IS FUNDED The registered objects of this trust
are: the relief and medical care of older people;
medical research, in particular cancer research
and the publication of the useful results of such
research; the advancement of education
including education in the arts for the public
benefit by the establishment of educational and
artistic bursaries; other charitable purposes at
the discretion of the trustees.
WHAT IS NOT FUNDED No support for organisations in
Scotland.
TYPE OF GRANT One-off and recurrent.
RANGE OF GRANTS £1,000–£10,000.
SAMPLE GRANTS Royal College of Music (£10,000);
English National Opera and Queen's University –
Belfast (£2,000 each); Greater Shankhill
Business Forum (£1,540); and Deafblind UK,
Help the Aged, Macmillan Cancer Relief,
Oesophageal Patients Association, St Joseph's
Hospice and Water Aid (£1,000 each).
FINANCES *Year* 2007 *Income* £45,201
Grants £60,715 *Assets* £1,448,944
TRUSTEES Simon David Howard Ladd; Andrew John
Francis Stebbings; Diana Sarah Graves.
HOW TO APPLY In writing to the correspondent.
WHO TO APPLY TO Mrs Diana Burke, c/o Pemberton
Greenish, 45 Pont Street, London SW1X 0BD
Tel 020 7591 3515 *email* charitymanager@
pglaw.co.uk
CC NO 297046   ESTABLISHED 1987

■ The Lyndhurst Trust

WHERE FUNDING CAN BE GIVEN UK and overseas, with
preferences for north east England and the
developing world.
WHO CAN BENEFIT Evangelistic Christian
organisations, especially those operating where
people have never had the opportunity of
hearing the gospel. Those involved in difficult
areas for Christian witness. Charities
ministering to the needs of the disadvantaged in
society are also funded.
WHAT IS FUNDED Charities connected with the
propagation of the gospel or the promotion of
the Christian religion; the distribution of bibles
and other Christian religious works; the support
of Christian missions; the provision of clergy;
the maintenance of churches and chapels; work
with disadvantaged people in society. Funds are
given worldwide; there is a preference for the
developing world, and in the UK a preference for
the north east of England. It tends to support
specific charities on a regular basis.
WHAT IS NOT FUNDED No support for individuals or
buildings.
TYPE OF GRANT Recurring.
RANGE OF GRANTS £500–£20,000, with most grants
for £1,000.
SAMPLE GRANTS N E 1 (Just 10) – Tyneside
(£20,000); St Aidan's Community Church –
Middlesbrough (£6,000); Bible Reading
Fellowship – Tyneside (£5,000); Friends
International (£2,000); and David Pawson
Teaching Trust and Urban Saints – Crusaders
(£1,000 each).
FINANCES *Year* 2007 *Income* £48,114
Grants £65,750 *Assets* £1,615,851
TRUSTEES Revd Dr R Ward; Mrs Jane Hinton; Ben
Hinton; Mrs Sally Tan.
OTHER INFORMATION The grants were divided into the
following areas: UK – north east England: 67%
developing world countries: 25.5% UK – general:
6% Europe and the rest of the world: 1.5%.
HOW TO APPLY In writing to the correspondent,
enclosing an sae if a reply is required. Requests
are considered half-yearly.
WHO TO APPLY TO The Secretary, PO Box 615, North
Shields, Tyne and Wear NE29 1AP
CC NO 235252   ESTABLISHED 1964

■ The Lynn Foundation

WHERE FUNDING CAN BE GIVEN UK and overseas.
WHO CAN BENEFIT Registered charities, institutions
benefiting musicians, textile workers and
designers, and artists. Older people and people
who are disabled will also benefit.
WHAT IS FUNDED Promotion and encouragement of
music, art, Masonic charities, disability, and
charities concerned with children and older
people.
TYPE OF GRANT One-off grants for core, capital and
project support. Loans are also made.
RANGE OF GRANTS Usually £500–£1,000.
SAMPLE GRANTS No grants list was available,
although support was broken down as follows:
Music and the arts – 119 grants totalling
£88,100; Disabled children – 141 grants
totalling £73,000; Disabled adults – 121 grants
totalling £63,000; Youth sponsorship – 43
grants totalling £26,500; Medical research – 35
grants totalling £17,250; Hospices – 32 grants
totalling £15,750.
FINANCES *Year* 2007–08 *Income* £396,027
Grants £283,470 *Assets* £5,937,527
TRUSTEES Guy Parsons, Chair; J F Emmott; Dr
P E Andry; P R Parsons; Ian Fair; John Sykes.

HOW TO APPLY In writing to the correspondent.

WHO TO APPLY TO Guy Parsons, Chairman of the Trustees, Blackfriars, 17 Lewes Road, Haywards Heath, West Sussex RH17 7SP *Tel* 01444 454 773 *Fax* 01444 456 192

CC NO 326944   **ESTABLISHED** 1985

··

■ The Lynwood Trust

WHERE FUNDING CAN BE GIVEN UK and overseas.

WHO CAN BENEFIT Organisations benefiting children, older people and people who are disabled.

WHAT IS FUNDED Advancement of religion and other charitable purposes including churches and missionary organisations.

WHAT IS NOT FUNDED No grants to individuals.

TYPE OF GRANT One-off and recurrent.

SAMPLE GRANTS Previous beneficiaries include: Africa Inland Mission, Amersham Christian Housing Association, Church of Christ, Evangelical Alliance, London Bible College and St Paul's Church – Rusthall.

FINANCES *Year* 2007–08 *Income* £46,331 *Grants* £61,296 *Assets* £603,182

TRUSTEES Miss J S Barling; C R Harmer.

HOW TO APPLY In writing to the correspondent.

WHO TO APPLY TO C R Harmer, Trustee, Salatin House, 19 Cedar Road, Sutton, Surrey SM2 5DA *Tel* 020 8652 2700 *Fax* 020 8652 2719 *email* colin@harmerslater.biz

CC NO 289535   **ESTABLISHED** 1984

··

■ John Lyon's Charity

WHERE FUNDING CAN BE GIVEN The London boroughs of Barnet, Brent, Camden, Ealing, Kensington and Chelsea, Hammersmith and Fulham, Harrow and the Cities of London and Westminster.

WHO CAN BENEFIT Schools and registered charities working with children and young people.

WHAT IS FUNDED Education, training, arts, sport, youth clubs, disability and counselling services, all aimed at improving the lives of children and young people in the charity's beneficial area.

WHAT IS NOT FUNDED Grants are restricted to the London boroughs of Harrow, Barnet, Brent, Ealing, Camden, City of London, City of Westminster, Hammersmith & Fulham and Kensington & Chelsea. Grants are not made: to individuals; for research, unless it is action research designed to lead directly to the advancement of practical activities in the community; for feasibility studies; for medical care and resources; in response to general charitable appeals, unless they can be shown to be of specific benefit to children and young people in one or more of the geographical areas listed; as direct replacements for the withdrawal of funds by statutory authorities for activities which are primarily the responsibility of central or local government; to umbrella organisations to distribute to projects which are already in receipt of funds from the charity; for the promotion of religion or politics; for telephone helplines; as core funding for national charities; for advice and information services; to housing associations.

TYPE OF GRANT Capital costs, revenue costs and recurring costs up to three years. Buildings, core costs, project, salaries and start-up costs.

SAMPLE GRANTS London Diocesan Board for Schools (£250,000); Harrow School Bursaries (£181,600); The John Lyon School Bursaries (£162,000); National Theatre (£100,000); Brent Play Association (£90,000); Excellence in Teaching & Learning and Phoenix Cinema

(£70,000 each); Harrow Club W10 (£54,000); West London Sports Trust, NIACE, Godolphin & Latymer School, IntoUniversity, Royal Court Young Writers Programme, Tavistock & Portman NHS Foundation Trust, H&F Partnership Against Crime, Tate Britain and Endeavour Training (£50,000 each); Harrow School Apprenticeships Programme (£48,000); Church Street Neighbourhood Management (£42,500); and English Chamber Orchestra Charitable Trust (£40,000).

FINANCES *Year* 2008–09 *Income* £5,880,696 *Grants* £4,893,444 *Assets* £169,884,879

TRUSTEES The Governors of Harrow School.

HOW TO APPLY The charity's main and small grants programmes have a two stage application process.
*Stage One – Initial Proposal:*Please write to the Grants Office with the following information: a summary of the main purpose of the project; details of the overall amount requested; the timescale of your project; some indication of how funds from the charity would be allocated.
*Stage Two – Application Form:*If your Initial Proposal is assessed positively, you will be advised whether you will need to complete an application form. Forms are required for all applications to the Main Grants Programme and for requests of over £2,000 to the Small Grants Programme. If you qualify for Stage Two you will be advised by your Grants Officer when your application form must be returned.
Applications by fax or email will not be accepted. Further details and a guide to writing a good proposal letter are available via the charity's website.
The John Lyon's Access to the Arts Fund
The John Lyon Access to the Arts Fund has a **single stage**application process and requests are made by application form. Applications can be made at any time. Application forms are available via the charity's website.

WHO TO APPLY TO The Grants Office, 45 Pont Street, London SW1X 0BX *Tel* 020 7591 3330 *Fax* 020 7589 0807 *email* info@johnlyonscharity.org.uk *Website* www.johnlyonscharity.org.uk

CC NO 237725   **ESTABLISHED** 1578

··

■ The Lyons Charitable Trust

WHERE FUNDING CAN BE GIVEN UK.

WHO CAN BENEFIT Registered charities.

WHAT IS FUNDED Health, medical research, children in need and charities concerned with animals.

TYPE OF GRANT Recurrent.

RANGE OF GRANTS £3,000–£20,000.

SAMPLE GRANTS The Royal Marsden Hospital and Macmillan Cancer Relief (£20,000 each); Helen House (£12,000); St. Thomas Hospital and Streetsmart (£10,000 each); CLIC and One25 Ltd. (£5,000 each); Cambridge Curwen Print Study Centre, Cats Protection League, Children with AIDS and Walthamstow Stadium Greyhound (£3,000 each).

FINANCES *Year* 2007–08 *Income* £393,743 *Grants* £95,000 *Assets* £1,505,879

TRUSTEES M S Gibbon; J Gibbon; G Read.

HOW TO APPLY The trust has stated that it is closed to new applications.

WHO TO APPLY TO Michael Gibbon, 74 Broad Walk, London N21 3BX *Tel* 020 8882 1336

CC NO 1045650   **ESTABLISHED** 1995

Think carefully about every application. Is it justified?

687

■ The Sir Jack Lyons Charitable Trust

WHERE FUNDING CAN BE GIVEN UK and Israel.
WHO CAN BENEFIT Charities benefiting children and young people; actors and entertainment professionals; musicians; students; textile workers and designers; writers and poets; at risk groups; those disadvantaged by poverty, and people who are socially isolated.
WHAT IS FUNDED Relief in need, arts, education and humanities. Jewish charities are also supported.
WHAT IS NOT FUNDED No grants to individuals.
TYPE OF GRANT mainly recurrent.
RANGE OF GRANTS £200–£50,000.
SAMPLE GRANTS Beer Sheva (£50,000); UJIA (£25,000); Naeh Youth Centre (£24,000); Ben-Gurion University (£7,500); London Symphony Orchestra (£7,000); the Technion Israel and University of Haifa Israel (£2,500 each); York Early Music Festival (£1,500); Aldeburgh Festival and Jewish Institute of Music (£500 each).
FINANCES *Year* 2007–08 *Income* £224,084 *Grants* £122,204 *Assets* £3,635,816
TRUSTEES Lady Roslyn Marion Lyons; M J Friedman; D S Lyons; Miss A R J Maude-Roxby; P D Mitchell.
HOW TO APPLY In writing to the correspondent. In the past the trust has stated: 'In the light of increased pressure for funds, unsolicited appeals are less welcome and would waste much time and money for applicants who were looking for funds which were not available.'
WHO TO APPLY TO Paul Mitchell, Sagars, 3rd Floor, Elizabeth House, Queen Street, Leeds LS1 2TW *Tel* 0133 297 6789
CC NO 212148   **ESTABLISHED** 1960

■ Malcolm Lyons Foundation

WHERE FUNDING CAN BE GIVEN UK.
WHO CAN BENEFIT Jewish and Israeli organisations.
WHAT IS FUNDED Jewish charitable purposes.
TYPE OF GRANT Mainly recurrent.
RANGE OF GRANTS £10–£20,000.
SAMPLE GRANTS Sage (£20,000); L'Ecole Juive du Cannes (£7,000); Chai Cancer Care (£5,500); Lubavitch Foundation (£4,000); Child Resettlement Fund (£2,300); Noam Primary School (£1,500); British Friends of Ezer Mizion and Jewish Care (£500 each); Camp Simcha (£100); and British Emunah (£10).
FINANCES *Year* 2007–08 *Income* £101,958 *Grants* £50,605 *Assets* £80,129
TRUSTEES M S Lyons; Mrs J Lyons; J S Newman.
HOW TO APPLY The trust states that it will not consider unsolicited applications.
WHO TO APPLY TO Jeremy Newman, Trustee, BDO Stoy Hayward, 55 Baker Street, London W1U 7EU *Tel* 020 7893 2602
CC NO 1050689   **ESTABLISHED** 1995

■ The Lyras Family Charitable Trust

WHERE FUNDING CAN BE GIVEN UK, Greece, worldwide.
WHO CAN BENEFIT Beneficiaries include: people disadvantaged by poverty and members of the Greek Orthodox religion.
WHAT IS FUNDED (a) Disaster funds worldwide; (b) the relief of poverty; (c) the advancement of religion, in particular within the country of Greece; and (d) other charitable purposes.
RANGE OF GRANTS Up to £5,500.

SAMPLE GRANTS Foundation for Paediatric Osteopathy and Heart Doctors Project (£5,000 each); British Red Cross (£2,500); Barnardo's and Children with Leukaemia (£1,000 each); and RNLI (£500).
FINANCES *Year* 2007 *Income* £38,135 *Grants* £28,309 *Assets* £688,246
TRUSTEES John C Lyras; John M Lyras; Richard Moore.
HOW TO APPLY In writing to the correspondent, although the trust states that its funds are fully committed and unsolicited applications are not requested.
WHO TO APPLY TO Richard Mason, Snow Hill Trustees Ltd, St Paul's House, Warwick Lane, London EC4M 7BP *Tel* 020 7334 9191
CC NO 328628   **ESTABLISHED** 1990

■ Sylvanus Lyson's Charity

WHERE FUNDING CAN BE GIVEN Diocese of Gloucester.
WHO CAN BENEFIT Individuals and organisations benefiting people of all ages, clergy, and Church of England.
WHAT IS FUNDED Religious and charitable work in the areas of youth, community, relief for widows, clergy and people in need.
WHAT IS NOT FUNDED The present policy is to make no grants for the repair or maintenance and improvement of churches or other buildings, other than in very exceptional circumstances.
TYPE OF GRANT Recurrent and one-off.
SAMPLE GRANTS Diocesan Board of Finance (£48,000); St Luke's Hospital, St Swithin's Rectory and the King's School Bursaries (£10,000 each); Gloucester Community Chaplaincy (£5,400); Cheltenham Youth for Christ (£3,750); Pioneer Minister (£3,000); Holy Trinity – Tewkesbury (£2,500); St Paul's PCC (£1,250); and Listening Post and Ripon College (£500 each).
FINANCES *Year* 2007–08 *Income* £350,856 *Grants* £129,563 *Assets* £7,806,571
TRUSTEES B V Day; G V Doswell; Rt Revd J S Went; Revd B C E Coker; Ven. Hedley Ringrose.
OTHER INFORMATION In addition grants to clergy, widows and others totalled £21,000.
HOW TO APPLY In writing to the correspondent.
WHO TO APPLY TO A Holloway, c/o Rowberry Morris Solicitors, Morroway House, Station Road, Gloucester GL1 1DW *Tel* 01452 301 903
CC NO 202939   **ESTABLISHED** 1980

■ The M and C Trust

WHERE FUNDING CAN BE GIVEN UK.

WHO CAN BENEFIT Mainly Jewish organisations benefiting Jewish people, at risk groups, people disadvantaged by poverty, and socially isolated people.

WHAT IS FUNDED Primarily Jewish and welfare organisations.

WHAT IS NOT FUNDED No grants to individuals.

TYPE OF GRANT One-off and recurrent grants.

RANGE OF GRANTS £2,500–£20,000.

SAMPLE GRANTS Jewish Care and Norwood (£20,000 each); Jerusalem Foundation (£15,000); Jewish Children's Holiday Fund, Marchant Holiday School and One Voice Europe (£10,000 each); Nightingale House (£7,500); Parentline (£7,000); Institute for Jewish Policy Research and Treehouse (£5,000 each); Break (£4,000); and Chicken Shed Theatre (£3,000).

FINANCES *Year* 2006–07 *Income* £120,026 *Grants* £118,500 *Assets* £4,186,965

TRUSTEES Lord Bernstein; Rachel J Lebus; Joyce Kemble.

HOW TO APPLY In writing to the correspondent, but the trust states that funds are currently earmarked for existing projects. In order to keep administration costs to a minimum, they are unable to reply to any unsuccessful applications.

WHO TO APPLY TO Chris Jones, Secretary, c/o Chantrey Vellacott DFK, Russell Square House, 10–12 Russell Square, London WC1B 5LF *Tel* 020 7509 9000 *Fax* 020 7509 9219

CC NO 265391   **ESTABLISHED** 1973

■ The M D and S Charitable Trust

WHERE FUNDING CAN BE GIVEN UK and Israel.

WHO CAN BENEFIT Organisations benefiting Jewish people. Support is given to rabbis, children and young adults, students, teachers and people disadvantaged by poverty.

WHAT IS FUNDED Trustees are primarily interested in Jewish causes for either the relief of poverty or the advancement of education or religion.

RANGE OF GRANTS Below £4,000–£26,000.

SAMPLE GRANTS Kolel Breslaw (£26,000); Beit Yisroel Benevolent Fund (£24,000); United Torah Institutions of Gur (£23,000); Kolel Rashbi (£21,000); Ponevez Aid and Benevolence Trust (£17,000); Chovat Hatalmidim Fund (£14,000); Gevurath Ari Academy Trust (£10,000); Kolel Polin (£9,000); TAT Family Relief Fund (£5,000); and Lovlev Trust (£4,000).

FINANCES *Year* 2007–08 *Income* £318,064 *Grants* £300,580 *Assets* £2,349,653

TRUSTEES M D Cymerman; Mrs S Cymerman.

HOW TO APPLY In writing to the correspondent.

WHO TO APPLY TO Martin D Cymerman, Trustee, 15 Riverside Drive, Golders Green Road, London NW11 9PU *Tel* 020 7272 2255

CC NO 273992   **ESTABLISHED** 1977

■ The M K Charitable Trust (formerly the Mendel Kaufman Charitable Trust)

WHERE FUNDING CAN BE GIVEN Unrestricted, in practice mainly UK.

WHO CAN BENEFIT Orthodox Jewish organisations.

WHAT IS FUNDED Support of orthodox Jewish organisations.

FINANCES *Year* 2007–08 *Income* £776,068 *Grants* £588,728 *Assets* £5,903,006

TRUSTEES Z M Kaufman; S Kaufman; A Piller; D Katz.

OTHER INFORMATION 'Grants totalling £211,000 were made during the year to six charities with which this charity has some trustees in common.'

HOW TO APPLY In writing to the correspondent. The trust accepts applications for grants from representatives of orthodox Jewish charities, which are reviewed by the trustees on a regular basis.

WHO TO APPLY TO Simon Kaufman, Trustee, c/o Cohen Arnold and Co., 1075 Finchley Road, Regent Street, Temple Fortune, London NW11 0PU *Tel* 020 8731 0777

CC NO 260439   **ESTABLISHED** 1966

■ The Madeline Mabey Trust

WHERE FUNDING CAN BE GIVEN UK and overseas.

WHO CAN BENEFIT Registered charities, including UK registered charities and international charities.

WHAT IS FUNDED Principally medical research and children's welfare and education.

WHAT IS NOT FUNDED No grants to individuals.

SAMPLE GRANTS A list of grant beneficiaries was unavailable.

FINANCES *Year* 2007–08 *Income* £877,040 *Grants* £451,505 *Assets* £568,246

TRUSTEES Alan G Daliday; Bridget A Nelson; Joanna L Singeisen.

HOW TO APPLY In writing to the correspondent. Please note, unsuccessful applications are not acknowledged.

WHO TO APPLY TO Joanna Singeisen, Trustee, Mabey House, Floral Mile, Twyford, Reading RG10 9SQ *Tel* 0118 940 3921 *Fax* 0118 940 3675

CC NO 326450   **ESTABLISHED** 1983

■ The E M MacAndrew Trust

WHERE FUNDING CAN BE GIVEN UK.

WHO CAN BENEFIT Charitable organisations.

WHAT IS FUNDED Medical and children's charities.

RANGE OF GRANTS £500–£5,000.

SAMPLE GRANTS Buckinghamshire County Agricultural Association and Buckinghamshire Foundation (£5,000 each); Action 4 Youth, Bletchley Park Trust and Calibre Audio Library (£3,000 each); Cystic Fibrosis Trust and Smile Train UK (£2,000 each); RAF Benevolent Fund and Willen Hospice (£1,000); and Crossroads (£500).

FINANCES *Year* 2007–08 *Income* £61,635 *Grants* £58,369 *Assets* £1,163,373

TRUSTEES Amanda Nicholson; J K Nicholson; Sally Grant; Verity Webster.

HOW TO APPLY The trustees state that they do not respond to any unsolicited applications under any circumstances, as they prefer to make their own decisions as to which charities to support.

WHO TO APPLY TO J P Thornton, Administrator, J P Thornton and Co., The Old Dairy, Adstockfields, Adstock, Buckingham MK18 2JE *Tel* 01296 714886 *Fax* 01296 714711

CC NO 290736   **ESTABLISHED** 1984

■ The Macdonald-Buchanan Charitable Trust

WHERE FUNDING CAN BE GIVEN UK, with a slight preference for Northamptonshire.

WHO CAN BENEFIT Registered charities, with a small preference for those benefiting young people in Northamptonshire.

WHAT IS FUNDED General charitable purposes with a preference for charities which the trust has special interest in, knowledge of or association with.

WHAT IS NOT FUNDED No grants to individuals.

TYPE OF GRANT Mainly recurrent.

RANGE OF GRANTS £50–£15,000.

SAMPLE GRANTS Carriejo Charity and Orrin Charitable Trust (£15,000 each); Ghurka Welfare, Help for Heroes and Skill Force (£5,000 each); Charities Aid Foundation (£4,000); Artists' General Benevolent Institution, Hearing Dogs for the Deaf, Migraine Trust, Order of St John, Salvation Army and Wheel Power (£500 each).

FINANCES *Year* 2008 *Income* £138,989 *Grants* £110,710 *Assets* £2,744,767

TRUSTEES Capt. John Macdonald-Buchanan, Chair; A J Macdonald-Buchanan; A R Macdonald-Buchanan; H J Macdonald-Buchanan; Mrs M C A Philipson.

HOW TO APPLY In writing to the correspondent, for consideration once a year. Appeals will not be acknowledged.

WHO TO APPLY TO Miss Linda Cousins, Rathbone Trust Co. Ltd, 159 New Bond Street, London W1S 2UD *Tel* 020 7399 0820 *email* linda.cousins@rathbone.com

CC NO 209994   **ESTABLISHED** 1952

■ The R S Macdonald Charitable Trust

WHERE FUNDING CAN BE GIVEN Scotland.

WHO CAN BENEFIT Charities and institutions working in the areas of research and support of neurological conditions, visual impairment, child welfare and animal welfare.

WHAT IS FUNDED The care and welfare of individuals suffering from neurodevelopmental or neurodegenerative disorders; the care and welfare of individuals who are either blind or suffering from visual impairment; research into neurological and ophthalmic disorders; the care and welfare of children and young persons under the age of eighteen years who have been or are in danger of being abused physically, sexually or mentally; the prevention of cruelty to animals.

WHAT IS NOT FUNDED Grants are not given to non-registered charities or individuals.

TYPE OF GRANT One-off, recurring costs, project and research will be considered. Funding may be given for up to three years and can be revenue or capital funding.

RANGE OF GRANTS Average grants are about £20,000.

SAMPLE GRANTS Capability Scotland (£120,000 in total), for various projects, with further commitments up to 2010/11; Children 1st (£100,000 in total), for work supporting survivors of abuse at various locations across Scotland; Rotary Residential & Care Centres (£50,000), towards refurbishing accommodation; Sense Scotland (£30,000); Tommy's, the Baby Charity (£25,000); RNIB Scotland (£20,000); Scottish Adoption Association (£15,000); Garvald (£8,000); and the Royal Blind Society (£2,000).

FINANCES *Year* 2008–09 *Income* £1,779,428 *Grants* £716,500 *Assets* £41,943,324

TRUSTEES Richard Sweetman, Chair; Richard K Austin; Donald Bain; Fiona Patrick; John Rafferty.

HOW TO APPLY In writing to the correspondent, including a copy of the latest audited accounts and constituting documents. Applications will normally be considered by the trustees at meetings in May and November and need to be received no later than 31 March and 30 September, respectively, to be considered at these meetings. The level of award made will vary according to the nature of the project for which funding is sought, but will not normally exceed £40,000. The average award granted is likely to be less than £20,000. The trustees will consider applications for funding over periods of up to three years. They will also consider applications both for revenue and capital funding. Applicants will be informed of the trustees' decision with regard to their application within three weeks of the trustees' meeting at which their application has been considered.

WHO TO APPLY TO Richard K Austin, Secretary, 21 Rutland Square, Edinburgh EH1 2BB *Tel* 0131 228 4681 *email* secretary@rsmacdonald.com *Website* www.rsmacdonald.com

SC NO SC012710   **ESTABLISHED** 1978

■ The Macfarlane Walker Trust

WHERE FUNDING CAN BE GIVEN UK, with priority for Gloucestershire.

WHO CAN BENEFIT Individuals, registered charities and institutions benefiting: former employees of Walker-Crosweller; musicians; actors and entertainment professionals; artists; students; and scientists.

WHAT IS FUNDED Grants to former employees, and their families, of Walker, Crosweller and Co Ltd; provision of educational facilities particularly for scientific research; encouragement of music, drama and the fine arts. Also support for community facilities and services, and charities in the fields of conservation, alternative transport, and recreation.

WHAT IS NOT FUNDED No grants for expeditions, medical expenses, nationwide appeals, animal charities or educational fees.

TYPE OF GRANT Feasibility studies, one-off, project, research, running costs and start-up costs. Funding for up to and over three years will be considered.

RANGE OF GRANTS Up to £2,000.

SAMPLE GRANTS Gloucestershire Association for Mental Health and National Star College (£2,000 each); Gloucester Choral Society, North Cotswolds Voluntary Help Centre, Prestbury & Pittville Youth and St Peters C of E Primary School (£1,000 each); CVOPHA – Home for Independent Elderly Residents (£500); and Help The Aged – Podsmead Neighbourhood Project (£100).

FINANCES *Year* 2007–08 *Income* £32,859 *Grants* £14,600 *Assets* £628,427

TRUSTEES D F Walker; N G Walker.

OTHER INFORMATION In 2007–08 grants totalling £5,381 were made to individuals.

HOW TO APPLY In writing to the correspondent giving the reason for applying, and an outline of the project with a financial forecast. An sae must accompany the initial application.

WHO TO APPLY TO Miss C Walker, Secretary, 60 Flask Walk, London NW3 1HE

CC NO 227890   **ESTABLISHED** 1963

■ The Mackay and Brewer Charitable Trust

WHERE FUNDING CAN BE GIVEN UK.

WHO CAN BENEFIT Charitable organisations.

WHAT IS FUNDED General charitable purposes.

SAMPLE GRANTS £2,750 each to Hampshire Association for the Care of the Blind, Macmillan Cancer Trust, Marie Curie Cancer Care, National Trust for Scotland, PDSA, Open Doors, Salvation Army, and St Johns Ambulance.

FINANCES *Year* 2007–08 *Income* £200,058 *Grants* £22,000 *Assets* £639,092

TRUSTEES HSBC Trust Co. (UK) Ltd

HOW TO APPLY In writing to the correspondent.

WHO TO APPLY TO The Clerk, c/o HSBC Trust Co. (UK) Ltd, 10th Floor, Norwich House, Nelson Gate, Commercial Road, Southampton SO15 1GX

CC NO 1072666   **ESTABLISHED** 1998

■ The Mackintosh Foundation

WHERE FUNDING CAN BE GIVEN Worldwide. In practice, mainly UK.

WHO CAN BENEFIT Registered charities.

WHAT IS FUNDED Priority is given to the theatre and the performing arts. Also funded are children and education; medicine; homelessness; community projects; the environment; HIV/AIDS; refugees; and other charitable purposes.

WHAT IS NOT FUNDED Religious or political activities are not supported. Apart from the foundation's drama award and some exceptions, applications from individuals are discouraged.

TYPE OF GRANT Capital, project and recurring costs up to three years.

RANGE OF GRANTS £200–£100,000.

SAMPLE GRANTS Great Ormond Street Hospital (£45,000); Highland Council (£26,000); Royal Marsden Cancer Campaign (£20,000); Theatre Investment Fund (£15,000); Royal & Derngate Theatre (£12,000); Macmillan Cancer Support (£10,500); Disasters Emergency Committee (£10,000); Tricycle Theatre Company (£7,500); Maggies' Centres (£6,300); and Motivation (£5,800).

FINANCES *Year* 2008–09 *Income* £100,000 *Grants* £411,000 *Assets* £10,300,000

TRUSTEES Sir Cameron Mackintosh, Chair; Nicholas Mackintosh; Nicholas Allott; D Michael Rose; Patricia Macnaughton; Alain Boublil; Robert Noble.

HOW TO APPLY In writing to the correspondent outlining details of the organisation, details of the project for which funding is required and a breakdown of the costs involved. Supporting documents should be kept to a minimum and sae enclosed if materials are to be returned. The trustees meet in May and October in plenary session, but a grants committee meets weekly to consider grants of up to £10,000. The foundation responds to all applications in writing and the process normally takes between four to six weeks.

WHO TO APPLY TO Nicholas Mackintosh, Appeals Director, 1 Bedford Square, London WC1B 3RB *Tel* 020 7637 8866 *Fax* 020 7436 2683 *email* info@camack.co.uk

CC NO 327751   **ESTABLISHED** 1988

■ The MacRobert Trust

WHERE FUNDING CAN BE GIVEN UK, mainly Scotland.

WHO CAN BENEFIT Recognised charitable organisations benefiting children, young adults and older people, ex-service and service people, seafarers and fishermen, and volunteers. Also artists, musicians, textile workers and designers, and writers and poets. At risk groups, carers, disabled people, people disadvantaged by poverty, and socially isolated people will also be considered.

WHAT IS FUNDED Currently, the major categories under which the trustees consider support are: science and technology; youth; services and sea; ex-servicemen's and ex-servicewomen's hospitals and homes; education; disability; community welfare. The minor categories are: agriculture and horticulture; arts and music; medical care; and Tarland and Deeside.

WHAT IS NOT FUNDED Grants are not normally provided for: religious organisations (but not including youth/community services provided by them, or projects of general benefit to the whole community, or local churches); organisations based outside the UK; individuals; endowment or memorial funds; general appeals or mail shots; political organisations; student bodies (as opposed to universities); fee-paying schools (apart from an educational grants scheme for children who are at, or need to attend, a Scottish independent secondary school and for which a grant application is made through the headteacher); expeditions; retrospective grants; or departments within a university (unless the appeal gains the support of, and is channelled through, the principal).

TYPE OF GRANT Core/revenue costs, project. Capital including buildings, feasibility studies, one-off, research, recurring and running costs, and salaries. Funding may be given for one year or more.

RANGE OF GRANTS Mostly £5,000–£10,000.

SAMPLE GRANTS National Library of Scotland (£100,000); Robert Gordon University (£47,000); Poppyscotland (£35,000); Marie Curie Cancer Care (£25,500); Association for Children's Palliative Care (£20,000); Scottish Ballet (£14,000); Centre for Science Outreach University of Durham (£10,000); Abernethy Trust (£8,000); Art in Healthcare and HIV Support Centre (£5,000 each); Caring for Life (£4,000); and Scottish Education & Action for Development (£2,000).

FINANCES *Year* 2007–08 *Income* £2,520,360 *Grants* £735,412 *Assets* £56,796,315

TRUSTEES W G Morrison, Chair; Mrs C J Cuthbert; Group Capt. D A Needham; J Swan; H Woodd; C Crole; Keith Davis; C W Pagan; J D Fowlie; H B Woodd.

PUBLICATIONS Leaflet – *Advice to Applicants for Grants*.

HOW TO APPLY The application form and full guidelines can be downloaded from the website, although applications must be posted. The trustees meet to consider applications twice a year in March and October. To be considered, applications must be received for the March meeting by the end of October previously and for the October meeting by early June previously. Applicants are informed of the trustees' decision, and if successful, payments are made immediately after each meeting.

WHO TO APPLY TO Air Comm. R W Joseph, Administrator, Cromar, Tarland, Aboyne, Aberdeenshire AB34 4UD *Tel* 01339 881444 *Website* www.themacroberttrust.org.uk

SC NO SC031346   **ESTABLISHED** 1943

Think carefully about every application. Is it justified?

691

■ The Mactaggart Third Fund

WHERE FUNDING CAN BE GIVEN UK and abroad.

WHO CAN BENEFIT Charitable organisations.

WHAT IS FUNDED General charitable purposes.

TYPE OF GRANT One-off.

RANGE OF GRANTS £100–£50,000.

SAMPLE GRANTS St Mary's Paddington Charitable Trust (£50,000); Amazon Conservation Team – Orito Sanctuary Project (£28,000); WPSI – UK (£25,000); Bahamas National Trust (£16,000); Friends of the Environment (£15,000); Mactaggart Community Cybercafe (£11,000); Ella Edgar School of Dancing (£6,300); Angling for Youth Development (£5,200); Medical Aid for Palestinians (£3,000); Scottish Countryside Alliance Education Trust (£2,000); The Red Squirrel Survival Trust (£1,000); and Seeing Ear (£750).

FINANCES *Year* 2008–09 *Income* £505,864 *Grants* £414,123 *Assets* £9,499,620

TRUSTEES Sandy Mactaggart; Robert Gore; Fiona Mactaggart; Andrew Mactaggart; Sir John Mactaggart.

HOW TO APPLY 'The trustees are solely responsible for the choice of charitable organisations to be supported. Trustees are proactive in seeking out charities to support and all projects are chosen on the initiative of the trustees. Unsolicited applications are not supported.'

WHO TO APPLY TO The Trustees, One Red Place, London W1K 6PL *Website* www.mactaggartthirdfund.org

SC NO SC014285

■ Ian Mactaggart Trust

WHERE FUNDING CAN BE GIVEN UK, with a preference for Scotland.

WHO CAN BENEFIT Charitable organisations.

WHAT IS FUNDED The trust supports education and training, culture, the relief of people who are poor, sick, in need or disabled.

WHAT IS NOT FUNDED Unsolicited requests for donations are discouraged.

RANGE OF GRANTS £30–£52,000.

SAMPLE GRANTS Robin Hood Foundation (£52,000); St Mary's Paddington Charitable Trust (£50,000); Oxfordshire Community Foundation (£22,000); Groundwork Thames Valley (£15,000); Toynbee Hall (£12,000); Islay, Jura and Community Enterprise Trust and Macmillan Cancer Support (£10,000 each); Billy's Appeal – CLIC Sargent (£8,000); Medical Foundation for the Victim's of Torture (£3,000); The English Stage Co. Ltd (£2,000); For Dementia (£1,000); Enable Glasgow (£500); and Quaker Social Action (£250).

FINANCES *Year* 2008–09 *Income* £493,557 *Grants* £321,623 *Assets* £6,701,769

TRUSTEES Sir John Mactaggart; P A Mactaggart; Jane L Mactaggart; Fiona M Mactaggart; Lady Caroline Mactaggart.

HOW TO APPLY The trustees are committed to seeking out charitable organisations that they wish to support and therefore they do not respond to unsolicited applications.

WHO TO APPLY TO The Trustees, One Red Place, London, W!K 6PL *Website* www.ianmactaggarttrust.org/index.htm

SC NO SC012502

■ James Madison Trust

WHERE FUNDING CAN BE GIVEN UK.

WHO CAN BENEFIT Charities and educational institutions.

WHAT IS FUNDED 'The objects of the charity are to support and promote studies of federal government whether within or among states and of related subjects, including the processes that may lead towards the establishment of such government, and to support or promote education and dissemination of knowledge of these subjects. These objects govern all decisions of trustees without the need for further specific annual objectives.'

TYPE OF GRANT Seminars, conferences, studies and publications.

SAMPLE GRANTS Centre for Federal Studies (£181,000); Devolution as Federalising Dynamic (£159,000); Federal Trust Projects (£105,000); Federal Solutions to State Failure (£29,000); European Foreign Policy (£15,000); European Constitutionalism (£14,000); Joint Seminar with UACES (£5,000); Cultural Europe and Culturally Vibrant but Politically Stagnant (£3,300 each); Global UK Conference (£2,100); and Young European Movement (£2,000).

FINANCES *Year* 2006–07 *Income* £95,992 *Grants* £638,965 *Assets* £879,190

TRUSTEES J H M Pinder; R Emerson; E Wistrich; R Corbett; J T Bishop.

OTHER INFORMATION In 2006–07 beneficiary institutions were the Royal Institute of International Affairs (Chatham House), One World Trust, Federal Trust for Education and Research, GLOBE-UK, the European Movement, the Wyndham Place Charlemagne Trust and the Universities of Bath, Birmingham, Bristol, Canterbury, Edinburgh, Kent, Manchester, Middlesex, London Metropolitan University and the London School of Economics.

HOW TO APPLY In writing to the correspondent. The trustees meet approximately every six weeks to approve grants.

WHO TO APPLY TO D Grace, Secretary to the Trustees, c/o 26 Bloomfield Terrace, London SW1W 8PQ

CC NO 1084835   **ESTABLISHED** 2000

■ The Magdalen and Lasher Charity

WHERE FUNDING CAN BE GIVEN Hastings.

WHO CAN BENEFIT Individuals, and organisations benefiting older and young people, and people disadvantaged by poverty.

WHAT IS FUNDED Pensions for older people in Hastings; playschemes; primary, secondary and special schools; purchase of books, travel and maintenance in schools; literacy; health care, facilities and buildings; community services.

TYPE OF GRANT One-off; one year or less.

SAMPLE GRANTS HSCTS Minibus (£13,000); Sara Lee Trust (£3,500); St John Ambulance (£3,000); St Clements Helping Hand Fund (£2,800); YMCA (£2,000); Relate South East (£1,500); Broomgrove Playscheme, Ore Church Mice Playgroup and Red Lake School(£1,000 each); and Hastings and Rother Voluntary Associaton for the Blind (£665).

FINANCES *Year* 2007–08 *Income* £1,164,567 *Grants* £106,277 *Assets* £11,365,143

TRUSTEES Ian Michael Steel, Chair; Gareth N Bendon; John H Bilsby; Keith S Donaldson; Gavin R D Kellie; Michael J Foster; Nicola J Harris; Barbara R Hobbs; Donald Burrows; Jill Cooper; Anthony Slack; John S Hayward; Gordon

L Dengate; Clive R Morris; Susan M Parsons; Terry C Soan; Joy A Waite; Trevor E Webb; Jennifer Clare Blackburn.

OTHER INFORMATION The grants total included £43,000 to organisations in general grants and eleemosynary grants.

HOW TO APPLY In writing to the correspondent.

WHO TO APPLY TO Gill Adamson, 132 High Street, Hastings, East Sussex TN34 3ET *Tel* 01424 452646 *email* mlc@oldhastingshouse.co.uk *Website* www.magdalenandlasher.co.uk

CC NO 211415   **ESTABLISHED** 1951

■ Magdalen Hospital Trust

WHERE FUNDING CAN BE GIVEN UK.

WHO CAN BENEFIT Registered charities benefiting: deprived children and young adults up to 25 years; those in care, fostered and adopted; parents and children; one-parent families; people disadvantaged by poverty; and people with HIV/AIDS.

WHAT IS FUNDED Projects for deprived and disabled children and young people, including literacy, special needs education, training for work and personal development, clubs, crime prevention, emergency care, playschemes, and counselling.

WHAT IS NOT FUNDED No grants to non-registered charities, individuals, charities with an income in excess of £150,000 or national charities.

TYPE OF GRANT One-off; project; start-up funding; one year or less.

RANGE OF GRANTS £500–£2,000; typically £1,000.

SAMPLE GRANTS Previous beneficiaries include: Brighton & Hove Parent's and Children's Group, Friends of the Family, Help & Protect Prisoners Youngsters and Open Door Youth Counselling Service Sutton (£1,500 each); Art Room Oxford, Autism Bedfordshire, Hewa Bora Community Development, Homestart, South East Essex, Hull Lighthouse Project, Kids Adventure (BUGS) and Women's Counselling Centre, Hitchin (£1,000 each); and Aid for Romanian Orphanages, Daventry Contact, Deep Impact Therapy Company, St Mary's Parish Church, Berry Pomeroy and St Stephen's Youth Work, Islington (£500 each).

FINANCES *Year* 2007–08 *Income* £13,710 *Grants* £37,000

TRUSTEES Mrs M Gregory; Mrs B Lucas; Revd R Mitchell; Ven. F R Hazell; Mrs D MacLaren; Hon. E Wood; Dr E Offerman.

HOW TO APPLY An application form and guidelines are available. A sae is required.

WHO TO APPLY TO Mrs Norma Hazell, 1 Chapelside, Clapton Row, Bourton on the Water, Gloucestershire GL54 2DN *Tel* 01451 821140 *email* fhazell@btinternet.com

CC NO 225878   **ESTABLISHED** 1963

■ The Magen Charitable Trust

WHERE FUNDING CAN BE GIVEN UK.

WHO CAN BENEFIT Registered charities.

WHAT IS FUNDED Jewish and educational organisations.

SAMPLE GRANTS Previous beneficiaries have included Manchester Yeshiva Kollel, Talmud Educational Trust, Bnos Yisroel School and Mesifta Tiferes Yisroel.

FINANCES *Year* 2007–08 *Income* £56,439 *Grants* £44,495 *Assets* £1,386,105

TRUSTEES Jacob Halpern; Mrs Rose Halpern.

HOW TO APPLY In writing to the correspondent.

WHO TO APPLY TO The Trustees, New Riverside, 439 Lower Broughton, Salford M7 2FX *Tel* 0161 792 2626

CC NO 326535   **ESTABLISHED** 1984

■ Mageni Trust

WHERE FUNDING CAN BE GIVEN UK.

WHO CAN BENEFIT Arts organisations; registered charities.

WHAT IS FUNDED General charitable purposes.

TYPE OF GRANT One-off and recurrent.

RANGE OF GRANTS Up to £5,000.

SAMPLE GRANTS LPO Thomas Beecham Group (£3,000); National Youth Orchestra (£2,500); A Feast of Music for Beckenham (£2,350); Crisis (£2,000); Extra Care, Marie Curie Cancer Care and National Theatre (£1,000 each); Opera Rara (£500); Maternity Worldwide (£370); Hope for the World (£200); Cancer Research and YMCA (£100 each).

FINANCES *Year* 2007–08 *Income* £63,072 *Grants* £22,000 *Assets* £1,168,957

TRUSTEES G L Collins; Mrs G L Collins; S J Hoare.

OTHER INFORMATION Grants to individuals totalled £6,000.

HOW TO APPLY In writing to the correspondent.

WHO TO APPLY TO Garfield Collins, Trustee, 5 Hyde Vale, Greenwich SE10 8QQ *Tel* 020 8469 2683 *email* garfcollins@gmail.com

CC NO 1070732   **ESTABLISHED** 1998

■ The Brian Maguire Charitable Trust

WHERE FUNDING CAN BE GIVEN Worldwide.

WHO CAN BENEFIT Organisations.

WHAT IS FUNDED General charitable purposes.

SAMPLE GRANTS The Peace Hospice – Starlight Walk (£5,000); Coeliac UK and Friends of Michael Sobell House (£2,000); 9 Lives Furniture, Barrow Romania Action Group, Keech Cottage Children's Hospice, the Monday Club, Paul Strickland Scanner Centre, Watford and District Talking Newspapers and Workaid (£1,000); and Watford Philharmonic (£500).

FINANCES *Year* 2007–08 *Income* £91,085 *Grants* £19,500 *Assets* £2,185,646

TRUSTEES Margaret Craik Maguire; Martin William Bennett; Burges Salmon Trustees Ltd.

HOW TO APPLY 'Applications are considered by the trustees and donations are made based on the merits of the applications.'

WHO TO APPLY TO The Trustees, Burges Salmon, Narrow Quay House, Narrow Quay, Bristol BS1 4AH

CC NO 1091978   **ESTABLISHED** 2002

■ Mahavir Trust (also known as the K S Mehta Charitable Trust)

WHERE FUNDING CAN BE GIVEN UK.

WHO CAN BENEFIT Registered charities.

WHAT IS FUNDED General, medical, welfare, relief of poverty, overseas aid, religion.

SAMPLE GRANTS Jain religion (£127,000); advancement of education in rural areas (£56,000); relief of poverty, sickness and distress (£22,000); promotion of humane behaviour towards animals and vegetarianism (£14,000); relief of financial need for victims of natural disaster (£1,000).

FINANCES *Year* 2007–08 *Income* £119,795 *Grants* £219,723 *Assets* £324,442

TRUSTEES Jay Mehta; Pravin Mehta; Kumud Mehta; Mrs Sheena Mehta Sabharwal; Nemish Mehta; Mrs P H Mehta; Mrs Sudha Mehta; Humar Mehta.

HOW TO APPLY The trust states that it does not accept unsolicited applications.

WHO TO APPLY TO Jay Mehta, 19 Hillersdon Avenue, Edgware, Middlesex HA8 7SG *Tel* 020 8958 4883 *email* mahavirtrust@googlemail.com

CC NO 298551 ESTABLISHED 1988

■ The Makin Charitable Trust

WHERE FUNDING CAN BE GIVEN Preference for Merseyside.

WHO CAN BENEFIT Registered charities.

WHAT IS FUNDED 'Learning, religion, the arts and general philanthropy.'

SAMPLE GRANTS Community Security (£15,000).

FINANCES *Year* 2007–08 *Income* £26,127 *Grants* £32,030 *Assets* £540,367

TRUSTEES E Rex Makin; Mrs S Makin; R S G Makin.

HOW TO APPLY In writing to the correspondent.

WHO TO APPLY TO c/o E Rex Makin & Co., Whitechapel, Liverpool L1 1HQ

CC NO 1089832 ESTABLISHED 2001

■ Malbin Trust

WHERE FUNDING CAN BE GIVEN Worldwide.

WHO CAN BENEFIT Organisations.

WHAT IS FUNDED Jewish, general charitable purposes.

SAMPLE GRANTS Recent grants have been made to Chasidei Belz Institutions.

FINANCES *Year* 2007–08 *Income* £115,213 *Grants* £78,228 *Assets* £502,389

TRUSTEES B Leitner; M Leitner; J Waldman.

HOW TO APPLY In writing to the correspondent.

WHO TO APPLY TO B Leitner, Trustee, 8 Cheltenham Crescent, Salford M7 4FP *Tel* 0161 792 7343

CC NO 1045174 ESTABLISHED 1995

■ The Mallinckrodt Foundation

WHERE FUNDING CAN BE GIVEN Worldwide.

WHO CAN BENEFIT Registered charities and charitable organisations.

WHAT IS FUNDED General charitable purposes.

RANGE OF GRANTS £2,000–£11,000.

SAMPLE GRANTS British Memorial Garden Trust (£11,000); Catholic Trust for England and Wales (£10,000); Vatican Library (£8,000); Companions of Windsor and Enterprise Education Trust (£5,000 each); Lambeth Partnership and Three Faiths Forum (£3,000 each); Collegio Mallinckdrodt and Royal Academy (£2,500 each); and YMSO (£2,000).

FINANCES *Year* 2007–08 *Income* £86,009 *Grants* £64,122 *Assets* £2,849,685

TRUSTEES G W Mallinckrodt; Mrs C B Mallinckrodt; L St J T Jackson.

HOW TO APPLY The foundation does not seek or respond to unsolicited applications.

WHO TO APPLY TO Sally Yates, 33 Gutter Lane, London EC2V 8AS

CC NO 1058011 ESTABLISHED 1996

■ Man Group plc Charitable Trust

WHERE FUNDING CAN BE GIVEN UK and overseas, with some preference for London.

WHO CAN BENEFIT Registered charities.

WHAT IS FUNDED General charitable purposes in the UK and overseas with some preference for causes near to or linked to the business of Man Group Plc.

WHAT IS NOT FUNDED The trust does not normally support: large national charities; charities who use outside fund-raising organisations; charities whose administration costs are thought to be excessive; animal charities; applicants who have applied within the previous 12 months; requests that directly replace statutory funding; individuals (unless under a sponsorship scheme); endowment funds; charities where the main purpose is to promote religious beliefs.

SAMPLE GRANTS KPMG Foundation – Every Child A Reader (£300,000); Historic Royal Palaces (£250,000); Merlin (£177,000); Royal Anniversary Trust (£167,000); Pianoman (£139,000); Every Child a Chance Trust, Greenhouse Schools Project and Teenage Cancer Trust (£100,000 each); Opportunity International (£55,000); Books Aid International and Camfed (£25,000 each); Almeida Theatre (£10,000); CineGuernsey (£3,000); Great Ormond Street Hospital Children's Charity (£500); and The Richard Thomas Leukaemia Fund (£300).

FINANCES *Year* 2007–08 *Income* £4,496,296 *Grants* £4,957,667 *Assets* £669,684

TRUSTEES C Brumpton; A H Scott; V W Browne; A Windham; M Chambers; P Clarke; D Fry; V Pakenham.

HOW TO APPLY The trust has stated that it does not accept unsolicited applications.

WHO TO APPLY TO L Clarke, Secretary to the Trust, Man Group Plc, Sugar Quay, Lower Thames Street, London EC3R 6DU *Tel* 020 7144 1000 *email* charitabletrust@mangroupplc.com *Website* www.mangroupplc.com

CC NO 275386 ESTABLISHED 1978

■ Manchester Airport Community Trust Fund

WHERE FUNDING CAN BE GIVEN The area which is most affected by the Manchester Airport. This includes South Manchester and Tameside, Trafford, Stockport, the borough of Macclesfield and the borough of Congleton up to but not including the towns of Macclesfield and Congleton, Vale Royal, and up to but not including Northwich.

WHO CAN BENEFIT Established groups or charities able to demonstrate clear financial records.

WHAT IS FUNDED Projects which: encourage tree planting, afforestation, landscaping and other environmental improvements or heritage conservation; promote social welfare through recreation, sport and leisure; provide better appreciation of the natural and urban environment; and promote the use of the natural environment as a safe habitat for flora and fauna. Projects must be for the benefit of the whole community or a substantial section of it, with preference given to those that have considered the needs of older people or people who have disabilities. Preference is given to those projects with volunteer involvement.

WHAT IS NOT FUNDED Applications from individuals or organisations working for profit are not considered. Projects must be over and above core activities and statutory requirements. The fund will not support applications for: running costs, salaries and expenses, general repair and maintenance, general sponsorship, office costs, office equipment, events, administration, general medical costs, uniforms, individual's sports kit, out of school clubs, or the purchase of land or buildings; projects considered by the trustees to be the statutory responsibility of local councils and government departments will not be supported; money for items already purchased or work already done; schools and churches benefiting just pupils and worshippers. Projects must demonstrate access and benefit to the wider community. Membership groups, clubs, societies and sports clubs will be considered on their own merits, particularly looking at community access and membership fees.

RANGE OF GRANTS Mostly £500–£5,000.

SAMPLE GRANTS Friends of Hesketh Park, Hope Direct and National Library for the Blind (£5,000 each); Belle Vue Brass Band, Company Fierce Academy, Wilmslow Riding Club and Wythenshawe Development Trust (£3,000 each); Poynton Ladies Hockey Club and Trafford Gingerbread (£2,000 each); Link Community Playgroup and Victoria Court Social Club (£1,000 each); and Active Longendale and Greater Manchester Riding for the Disabled Association (£500 each).

FINANCES *Year* 2007–08 *Income* £207,984 *Grants* £144,558 *Assets* £108,968

TRUSTEES Andrew Cornish, Chair; Ms Julie Armstrong; Anthony Burns; James Pearson; John N Pantall; Wilson Hamman; Peter L Kolker; Anne Hooker.

HOW TO APPLY Generally, awards are for up to £5,000 towards a project and the trustees prefer to offer part funding to complement a group's own fundraising or grant raising. Applications are considered for particular items or works that allow the project to increase community benefit. Applications from not-for-profit groups or organisations working to improve the environment or social welfare in communities within the area of benefit. The project should offer open access to all and demonstrate wide, lasting benefit to all members of the community regardless of race, gender, age, ability or religion. The items or works the group seeks funds for should clearly bring community benefit. Trustees prefer to support groups that have volunteer involvement. If you would like any advice or need an application form please contact the fund administrator. You can also get an application form online from: www.manchesterairport.co.uk. Trustees meet quarterly. You should return your completed form to the Administrator no later than the first Friday of March, June, September or December for consideration by the trustees the following month. Successful groups will usually receive a cheque a month after the trustees' meeting. Groups must send original invoices or receipts for the works or goods you purchased within three months of receiving the grant cheque.

WHO TO APPLY TO Jonathan Green, Trust Fund Administrator, The Community Relations Department, Manchester Airport Plc, 3rd Floor, Olympic House, Manchester M90 1QX *Tel* 0161 489 5281 *Fax* 0161 489 3467 *email* trust. fund@manairport.co.uk *Website* www. manchesterairport.co.uk

CC NO 1071703   **ESTABLISHED** 1997

■ The Manchester Guardian Society Charitable Trust

WHERE FUNDING CAN BE GIVEN Greater Manchester.

WHO CAN BENEFIT Preference is usually shown to smaller charities.

WHAT IS FUNDED General charitable purposes. The emphasis is very much on support in the Greater Manchester area.

WHAT IS NOT FUNDED The trust does not give to individuals.

TYPE OF GRANT Primarily small, single, capital projects.

RANGE OF GRANTS £100–£2,500.

SAMPLE GRANTS Army Cadet Force Association, Bolton Women's Aid, Help the Aged, Motability, Royal School for the Deaf and St Clements Church Ordsall and Salford Quays (£2,000 each); Austerlands Cricket Club, Beacon Counselling, Bury Parish Church, Cash Box Credit Union Limited, Manchester Adoption Society, Medical Foundation North West for Care of Victims of Torture and the Furniture Station (£1,000 each); Bradshaw Guides Stable Fund, Eser Layeled, the Avenue Methodist Church Building Fund and the Sailors' Families Society (£500 each).

FINANCES *Year* 2007–08 *Income* £91,297 *Grants* £83,540 *Assets* £3,614,172

TRUSTEES D Burton; L Worsley; W R. Lees-Jones; W J Smith; D G Wilson; J P Wainwright; P F Goddard; K Ahmed; K Hardinge; J A H Fielden; D Hawkins; P Lochery.

HOW TO APPLY On a form available from the correspondent. Applications are considered on the first Monday in March, June, September and December; they must arrive 14 days before these dates. The trustees do not welcome repeat applications within two years.

WHO TO APPLY TO J J Swift, Clerk to the Trustees, Cobbetts, 58 Mosley Street, Manchester M2 3HZ *Tel* 0845 404 2404 *Fax* 0845 404 2414

CC NO 515341   **ESTABLISHED** 1984

■ Manchester Kids

WHERE FUNDING CAN BE GIVEN Greater Manchester.

WHO CAN BENEFIT Children who are disadvantaged.

WHAT IS FUNDED Voluntary and community groups working directly with children and young people under the age of 18 experiencing, poverty, abuse, neglect and distress. Types of activities/ projects that the charity will fund include: out of school activities – after school, weekends, school holidays; educational attainment support – for example homework clubs, reading groups; sports and recreational activities; holiday and playscheme activities – including summer holiday schemes; constructive, creative and positive experiences improving self confidence and self esteem; activities designed to have an impact on youth nuisance and youth crime; and specialist equipment for children.

WHAT IS NOT FUNDED The charity will not fund: national groups or charities – except in the case of a local project connected with a national group; any group or organisations with political affiliations; any bid which does not contain corroborative evidence of genuine need; or any bid seeking to fund a salary – unless an exceptional circumstance can be proven.

RANGE OF GRANTS £100–£5,000.

SAMPLE GRANTS Bury Young Carers, Friends of Families Wigan, Oldham Young Carers, Signpost Stockport and Trafford Young Carers (£5,000

Think carefully about every application. Is it justified?

695

each); and Rochdale Special Needs Cycling Club and UEW (£2,000 each).

FINANCES *Year* 2007–08 *Income* £281,458 *Grants* £125,118 *Assets* £57,376

TRUSTEES Mike Dyble; Shirley Adams; Nick Shaw; Michelle Surrell.

OTHER INFORMATION £75,000 to individuals and £50,000 to organisations

HOW TO APPLY Applications are considered on an ongoing basis. All applications are acknowledged. The trustees meet twice a year to allocate grants and will reply to successful and unsuccessful applications shortly thereafter. Grant applications must be accompanied by the most recently audited annual accounts of the organisation seeking the grant. Applications must be received by 31st March and 30th September and decisions will be made approximately eight weeks after each deadline. Allocation of funds must be spent within twelve months of the award date. All grants will be audited and groups will be required to complete a full evaluation supplying receipts and documentation of how the grant was spent in accordance with the conditions set out by the trustees. No further grants will be considered if there is a report outstanding from a previous grant.

WHO TO APPLY TO The Charity Manager, Key 103, Castle Quay, Castlefield, Manchester M15 4PR *Tel* 0161 288 5066 *Website* www.manchesterkids.org

CC NO 1087854   **ESTABLISHED** 2001

··

■ Lord Mayor of Manchester's Charity Appeal Trust

WHERE FUNDING CAN BE GIVEN The City of Manchester.

WHO CAN BENEFIT Registered charities.

WHAT IS FUNDED General charitable purposes.

RANGE OF GRANTS Usually £500–£2,000.

SAMPLE GRANTS Family Holidays (£22,000); Afro Caribbean Care Group, College of Third Age, Ahmed Iqbal Ullah Educational Trust, Manchester Trafalgar Sea Cadet Corps, North West Pensioners and Wythenshawe Hospital Transplant Fund (£1,000 each); and Cheetham Festival Committee, Didsbury Care Group and WRVS Didsbury Over 60s (£500 each).

FINANCES *Year* 2007–08 *Income* £110,382 *Grants* £47,447 *Assets* £230,696

TRUSTEES The Mayor; The Mayor's Consort; Chief Executive; City Treasurer; W Egerton; S Silverman; A Burden.

HOW TO APPLY Application forms are available from the Mayor's office. Applications are considered quarterly.

WHO TO APPLY TO Anita Scallan, Head of Lord Mayor's Office, Lord Mayor's Suite, Town Hall, Albert Square, Manchester M60 2LA *Tel* 0161 234 3375 *Fax* 0161 274 7113

CC NO 1066972   **ESTABLISHED** 1997

··

■ The Mandeville Trust

WHERE FUNDING CAN BE GIVEN UK.

WHO CAN BENEFIT Organisations.

WHAT IS FUNDED General charitable purposes.

SAMPLE GRANTS University College London (£26,000) and Imperial College (£20,000) for research purposes; the Berkshire Community Foundation (£10,000). Other smaller grants totalled £2,500.

FINANCES *Year* 2007–08 *Income* £58,002 *Grants* £58,150

TRUSTEES Robert Cartwright Mandeville; Pauline Maude Mandeville; Peter William Murcott; Justin Craigie Mandeville.

HOW TO APPLY In writing to the correspondent.

WHO TO APPLY TO R C Mandeville, Trustee, The Hockett, Hockett Lane, Cookham Dean, Berkshire SL6 9UF *Tel* 01628 484 272

CC NO 1041880   **ESTABLISHED** 1994

··

■ The Manifold Charitable Trust

WHERE FUNDING CAN BE GIVEN UK.

WHO CAN BENEFIT Registered charities only.

WHAT IS FUNDED Education, historic buildings, environmental conservation and general. The trust has previously focused much attention on the preservation of churches, however following the death in 2007 of its founder, Sir John Smith, the trust is now allocating most of its grants for educational purposes. The trust still makes grants to the Historic Churches Preservation Trust for onward distribution to churches; however it would seem that the amount has been reduced on previous years.

WHAT IS NOT FUNDED Applications are not considered for improvements to churches as this is covered by a block grant to the Historic Churches Preservation Trust. The trust regrets that it does not give grants to individuals for any purpose.

TYPE OF GRANT One-off.

SAMPLE GRANTS Historic Churches Preservation Trust (£140,000 in total); Eton College (£78,000); Thames Hospice Care (£50,000); Historic Churches Preservation Trust (£35,000); Imperial College (£15,000); Berkeley Castle Charitable Trust and Maidenhead Heritage Trust (£10,000 each); Berkshire Medical Heritage Centre (£7,500); Gislingham PCC (£6,000); Household Cavalry Museum Trust (£5,000); Brompton Ralph PCC (£4,500); Morrab Library (£2,500); and Richmond Building Preservation Society, Askham PCC and Westray Heritage Trust (£1,000 each).

FINANCES *Year* 2007 *Income* £707,081 *Grants* £1,637,630 *Assets* £11,703,231

TRUSTEES Manifold Trustee Company Limited.

HOW TO APPLY The trust has no full-time staff, therefore general enquiries and applications for grants should be made in writing only, by post or by fax and not by telephone. The trust does not issue application forms. Applications should be made to the correspondent in writing and should: state how much money it is hoped to raise; if the appeal is for a specific project state also (a) how much it will cost (b) how much of this cost will come from the applicant charity's existing funds (c) how much has already been received or promised from other sources and (d) how much is therefore still being sought; list sources of funds to which application has been or is intended to be made (for example local authorities, or quasi-governmental sources, such as the national lottery); if the project involves conservation of a building, send a photograph of it and a note (or pamphlet) about its history; send a copy of the charity's latest income and expenditure account and balance sheet. Applications are considered twice a month, and a reply is sent to most applicants (whether successful or not) who have written a letter rather than sent a circular.

WHO TO APPLY TO Helen Niven, Studio Cottage, Windsor Great Park, Windsor, Berkshire

SL4 2HP *email* helen.niven@cumberlandlodge.
ac.uk

CC NO 229501   **ESTABLISHED** 1962

■ W M Mann Foundation

WHERE FUNDING CAN BE GIVEN Scotland.

WHO CAN BENEFIT Organisations based in Scotland or serving the Scottish community.

WHAT IS FUNDED The arts, education, music, care and so on.

RANGE OF GRANTS £100 to £10,000.

SAMPLE GRANTS House for an Art Lover (£15,000); the Pearce Institute (£7,000); Bobath – Scotland, Citizen's Theatre, Culture and Sport Glasgow and the Princess Royal Trust (£5,000 each); the National Pipeline Centre (£3,500); Scottish Opera (£3,000); Paisley Abbey Organ Appeal, the Salvation Army (£2,500); Lodging House Mission and Scottish Spina Bifida (£1,000 each); Riding for the Disabled Association – Glasgow (£750); Enterprise Education Trust and Naturedays (£500 each); Yorkhill Children's Hospital (£150); and Rangers Charity Foundation – UNICEF (£50).

FINANCES *Year* 2006–07 *Income* £187,849 *Grants* £150,000 *Assets* £3,547,830

TRUSTEES W M Mann; B M Mann; A W Mann; S P Hutcheon.

HOW TO APPLY In writing to the trustees.

WHO TO APPLY TO Bruce M Mann, Trustee, 201 Bath Street, Glasgow G2 4HY *Tel* 0141 248 4936 *Fax* 0141 221 2976 *email* mail@wmmanngroup.co.uk *Website* www.thewmmannfoundation.org.uk

SC NO SC010111

■ R W Mann Trust

WHERE FUNDING CAN BE GIVEN UK, but grants are practically all confined to organisations in Tyne and Wear, with a preference for North Tyneside.

WHO CAN BENEFIT Local activities or local branches of national charities benefiting children, young adults, older people, academics, seafarers and fishermen, students, teachers and governesses, unemployed people, volunteers, those in care, fostered and adopted, parents and children, one-parent families, widows and widowers, at risk groups, carers, people with disabilities, people disadvantaged by poverty, ex-offenders and those at risk of offending, homeless people, people living in urban areas, and victims of abuse, crime and domestic violence. People with Alzheimer's disease, autism, cancer, cerebral palsy, Crohn's disease, mental illness, motor neurone disease, multiple sclerosis, muscular dystrophy, sight loss and all terminal diseases will be considered.

WHAT IS FUNDED Charities working in the fields of: accommodation and housing; information technology and computers; infrastructure development; professional bodies; charity and umbrella bodies; arts and art facilities; theatre; the visual arts; arts activities and education; cultural activity; health; conservation and environment; education and training; and social care and development. Other charitable purposes will be considered.

WHAT IS NOT FUNDED The trust will not support: large well-established national charities; individuals; church buildings except where they are used for community groups; projects or groups which can attract public funds or which appeal to Community Fund grants or national charitable trusts or other sources except if there is a

particular part of the project which other sources would be unlikely to fund; deficits already incurred or to replace statutory funding.

TYPE OF GRANT Recurrent expenditure, capital or single expenditure. Core costs, feasibility studies, interest-free loans, one-off and project funding, recurring costs, running costs, and salaries up to two years will be considered.

RANGE OF GRANTS £100–£10,000; average £1,000.

SAMPLE GRANTS North Tyneside VODA (£6,700); Northumberland Association of Clubs for Young People (£5,250); Relate Northumberland and Tyneside (£4,500); the Cirdan Sailing Trust and Linskill and North Tyneside Community Development Trust (£4,000 each); Army Cadet Force Association (£3,500); Newcastle Women's Aid (£1,000); Burradon and Camperdown Forum (£750); Walker Challenge Group (£600); Rainbow Trust (£500); Welbeck Primary School (£350); and The Order of St John (£100).

FINANCES *Year* 2007–08 *Income* £96,545 *Grants* £156,309 *Assets* £2,455,158

TRUSTEES Mrs Judy Hamilton, Chair; Guy Javens; Mrs Monica Heath.

HOW TO APPLY In writing to the correspondent, with an sae. The Trustees meet monthly. Applicants will usually hear if their application has been successful within two months.

WHO TO APPLY TO John Hamilton, PO Box 119, Gosforth, Newcastle upon Tyne NE3 4WF *Tel* 0191 284 2158 *Fax* 0191 285 8617 *email* john.hamilton@onyx.octacon.co.uk *Website* www.rwmanntrust.org.uk

CC NO 1095699   **ESTABLISHED** 1959

■ The Leslie and Lilian Manning Trust

WHERE FUNDING CAN BE GIVEN The north east of England.

WHO CAN BENEFIT Principally charities with local affinities benefiting at risk groups, and people who are disadvantaged by poverty, socially isolated, sick or disabled.

WHAT IS FUNDED Principally health and welfare.

WHAT IS NOT FUNDED No grants to individuals.

RANGE OF GRANTS Usually £500–£2,000.

SAMPLE GRANTS St Oswald's Hospice (£2,000 in two grants); Cornerstone, Mental After Care Association, Northumbria Coalition Against Crime and RNID (£1,000 each); and Northumbria Youth Action (£500).

FINANCES *Year* 2008–09 *Income* £30,901 *Grants* £23,600 *Assets* £577,507

TRUSTEES D Jones; N Sherlock; K L Andersen.

HOW TO APPLY In writing to the correspondent by January for consideration in March.

WHO TO APPLY TO David Jones, Trustee, David Jones, 44 Midhurst Road, Newcastle upon Tyne NE12 9NU *Tel* 01912 847661

CC NO 219846   **ESTABLISHED** 1960

■ The Manoukian Charitable Foundation

WHERE FUNDING CAN BE GIVEN Worldwide.

WHO CAN BENEFIT Organisations and individuals.

WHAT IS FUNDED Social welfare, education, medical, the arts, 'Armenian matters'.

SAMPLE GRANTS Elton John AIDS Foundation (£815,000); Eurasia Program – Cambridge University (£108,000); Human Rights Watch (£103,000); Chronic Care Centre (£59,000); Mission Enfance (£46,000); Give a Child a Toy –

Lebanon (£35,000); NSPCC and English National Ballet School (£10,000 each); Chain of Hope – Mozambique (£5,000); Havens Christian Hospice (£2,000); and Westminster PHAB (£500).

FINANCES *Year* 2007–08 *Income* £2,400,000 *Grants* £1,600,000 *Assets* £990,000

TRUSTEES Mrs Tamar Manoukian; Anthony Bunker; Steven Press; Dr Armen Sarkissian.

HOW TO APPLY 'Requests for grants are received from the general public and charitable and other organisations through their knowledge of the activities of the foundation and through personal contacts of the settlor and the trustees.' The trustees meet at least once per year.

WHO TO APPLY TO The Trustees, c/o Berwin Leighton Paisners, Adelaide House, London Bridge, London EC4R 9HA

CC NO 1084065   **ESTABLISHED** 2000

■ Maranatha Christian Trust

WHERE FUNDING CAN BE GIVEN UK and overseas.
WHO CAN BENEFIT Christian organisations.
WHAT IS FUNDED The advancement of the Christian gospel.
RANGE OF GRANTS £500–£10,000.
SAMPLE GRANTS Christian Action Research and Education (£17,000 in three grants); The Vanessa Grant Memorial Trust (£10,000); Cafe Africa Trust and Micah Trust (£7,000 each); Friends of St Andrew's Church (£5,000); The Office for International Diplomacy (£3,500); Concordis International (£3,000); Cheer (£2,500); Re Source (£2,000); and Forty-Three Trust and Christians in Entertainment (£1,000).
FINANCES *Year* 2007–08 *Income* £34,338 *Grants* £99,500 *Assets* £1,006,111
TRUSTEES A C Bell; Revd L Bowring; Rt Hon. Viscount Brentford.
OTHER INFORMATION Grants were made to seven individuals. Grants to individuals of £1,000 or more totalled £9,000.
HOW TO APPLY In writing to the correspondent, but please note that the trust does not consider unsolicited applications.
WHO TO APPLY TO The Secretary, 208 Cooden Drive, Bexhill-on-Sea, East Sussex TN39 3AH *Tel* 01424 844 741
CC NO 265323   **ESTABLISHED** 1972

■ Marbeh Torah Trust

WHERE FUNDING CAN BE GIVEN UK and Israel.
WHO CAN BENEFIT Jewish charities.
WHAT IS FUNDED Furtherance of orthodox Jewish religious education and relief of poverty.
RANGE OF GRANTS £2,000–£72,000.
SAMPLE GRANTS Yeshiva Marbeh Torah (£72,000); Yad Gershon (£22,000); Kol Yaakov (£12,000); Chazon Avraham Yitzchak, Mishkenos Yaakov and Tashbar (£10,000 each); Shaarei Limud (£2,600); Beis Dovid (£2,500); and Nechomas Isser Israel (£2,000).
FINANCES *Year* 2007 *Income* £161,778 *Grants* £141,600
TRUSTEES Moishe Chaim Elzas; Jacob Naftoli Elzas; Simone Elzas.
HOW TO APPLY In writing to the correspondent.
WHO TO APPLY TO M C Elzas, Trustee, 116 Castlewood Road, London N15 6BE
CC NO 292491   **ESTABLISHED** 1985

■ The Marchday Charitable Fund

WHERE FUNDING CAN BE GIVEN UK, with a preference for south east England.
WHO CAN BENEFIT Children and young people; older people; people with disabilities; general.
WHAT IS FUNDED Education, health, social welfare, support groups and overseas disaster aid.
WHAT IS NOT FUNDED The trust generally prefers not to support local organisations outside the south east of England. No grants to individuals or towards building projects or for religious activities.
TYPE OF GRANT Capital, core costs, one-off, project, recurring costs, salaries and start-up costs. All funding is up to three years.
RANGE OF GRANTS £5,000–£11,000.
SAMPLE GRANTS Tunbridge Wells Mental Health (£11,000); Prisoners Advice Service, Refugee Support Group – Devon and Warwickshire Women's Refuge (£10,000 each); Bridewell Organic Gardens (£9,000); Kidscape (£8,000); After Adoption and Pimlico Toy Library (£7,000 each); and Magic Lantern and Red R (£5,000 each).
FINANCES *Year* 2008 *Income* £97,354 *Grants* £183,700 *Assets* £403,658
TRUSTEES Alan Mann; Lyndsey Mann; Dudley Leigh; Rose Leigh; Maureen Postles; Graham Smith; John Orchard; Priyen Gudka.
HOW TO APPLY In writing to the correspondent. Replies cannot be sent to all requests. Trustees meet quarterly.
WHO TO APPLY TO Mrs Rose Leigh, Trustee, c/o Marchday Group plc, Lingfield Point, McMullen Road, Darlington, County Durham DL1 1RW *Tel* 0845 888 7070
CC NO 328438   **ESTABLISHED** 1989

■ Marchig Animal Welfare Trust

WHERE FUNDING CAN BE GIVEN Worldwide.
WHO CAN BENEFIT Organisations and individuals that make positive contributions in protecting animals and promoting and encouraging practical work in preventing animal cruelty and suffering.
WHAT IS FUNDED There are no restrictions on the geographical area of work, types of grants or potential applicants, but all applications must be related to animal welfare and be of direct benefit to animals. Projects supported by the trust have included mobile spay/neuter clinics, alternatives to the use of animals in research, poster campaigns, anti-poaching programmes, establishment of veterinary hospitals, clinics and animal sanctuaries.
WHAT IS NOT FUNDED The trust will reject any application failing to meet its criteria. Additionally, applications relating to educational studies or other courses, expeditions, payment of salaries, support of conferences and meetings, or activities that are not totally animal welfare related, will also be rejected.
TYPE OF GRANT Based on project.
RANGE OF GRANTS Based on project.
SAMPLE GRANTS In 2007, 'projects included: the rescue and subsequent care of various species of animals in Lebanon, South Africa, Philippines, Israel, Egypt, Romania, India, Greece, Poland, Mauritius, Italy, Czech Republic and the UK; spay/neuter programmes and their promotion in Turkey, Greece, Portugal, Spain, Cyprus, South Africa, the UK, Eire, Sri Lanka, Romania, Israel, Malta, Brazil, France, Indonesia and India; providing ongoing support for the activities of a mobile clinic in Turkey and grants to establish

mobile clinic's and other veterinary/care vehicles in India, Lebanon, South Africa, Kenya, Thailand and the UK; assisting with the construction, renovation, maintenance and ongoing operations of animal shelters in Thailand, Greece, Romania, the UK, Bolivia, South Africa, Israel, India and Belgium; support was given for the promotion internationally of various education programmes relating to the care, responsible ownership and importance of animal birth control measures; in addition, support was given for the campaign against canned hunting in South Africa, investigations into the live export trade of animals from Australia to the Middle East and wildlife anti-poaching measures; veterinary medicines to relieve the suffering of animals was provided to various organisations in a number of countries. A major grant was awarded to establish 'Marchig TrustNWS Veterinary Support Teams', capable of operating internationally.'

FINANCES *Year* 2007 *Income* £499,533 *Grants* £332,223 *Assets* £14,326,050

TRUSTEES Madame Jeanne Marchig; Dr Bill Jordan; Colin Moor.

OTHER INFORMATION As well as giving grants, the trust also makes Marchig Animal Welfare Trust Awards. These awards, which take the form of a financial donation in support of the winner's animal welfare work, are given in either of the following two categories: (a) The development of an alternative method to the use of animals in experimental procedures and the practical implementation of such an alternative resulting in a significant reduction in the number of animals used in experimental procedures; (b) Practical work in the field of animal welfare resulting in significant improvements for animals either nationally or internationally.

HOW TO APPLY On an application form available from the correspondent or via the website.

WHO TO APPLY TO The Trustees, 10 Queensferry Street, Edinburgh EH2 4PG *Tel* 0131 225 6039 *Fax* 0131 220 6377 *email* info@marchigtrust. org *Website* www.marchigtrust.org

CC NO 802133   ESTABLISHED 1989

■ The Stella and Alexander Margulies Charitable Trust

WHERE FUNDING CAN BE GIVEN UK.

WHO CAN BENEFIT Institutions benefiting Jewish people.

WHAT IS FUNDED Jewish charities; the arts; general charitable purposes.

RANGE OF GRANTS Generally £50–£3,000.

SAMPLE GRANTS UJIA (£256,000); Shaare Zedek UK (£88,000); Royal Opera House Foundation (£25,000); Nightingale House (£3,000); Royal Academy Trust and Tate Foundation (£1,000 each); Enfield Centre for Natural Health (£180); NSPCC (£100); and British Heart Foundation (£50).

FINANCES *Year* 2007–08 *Income* £256,488 *Grants* £384,429 *Assets* £8,118,611

TRUSTEES Marcus J Margulies; Martin D Paisner; Sir Stuart Lipton; Alexander M Sorkin; Leslie D Michaels.

HOW TO APPLY In writing to the correspondent.

WHO TO APPLY TO M J Margulies, Trustee, c/o Time Products Ltd, 34 Dover Street, London W1S 4NG *Tel* 020 7343 7200 *Fax* 020 7343 7201 *email* marcus@timeproducts.co.uk

CC NO 220441   ESTABLISHED 1970

■ Mariapolis Limited

WHERE FUNDING CAN BE GIVEN UK and overseas.

WHO CAN BENEFIT Organisations working in the developing world.

WHAT IS FUNDED Christian ecumenism.

SAMPLE GRANTS Focolare Trust (£362,000); Pia Associazione Maschile Opera di Maria (£174,000); family welfare grants (£5,800); and Anglican Priests Training Fund (£1,500).

FINANCES *Year* 2007–08 *Income* £510,035 *Grants* £543,666 *Assets* £2,231,620

TRUSTEES Timothy M King; Manfred Kochinky; Barry Redmond.

OTHER INFORMATION This trust promotes the international Focolare Movement in the UK, and grant making is only one area of its work. It works towards a united world and its activities focus on peace and cooperation. It has a related interest in ecumenism and also in overseas development. Activities include organising conferences and courses, and publishing books and magazines.

HOW TO APPLY In writing to the correspondent.

WHO TO APPLY TO Tim King, 38 Audley Road, London W5 3ET *Tel* 020 8991 2022 *Fax* 020 8991 9053 *email* timking@focolare.org.uk

CC NO 257912   ESTABLISHED 1968

■ Market Harborough and The Bowdens Charity

WHERE FUNDING CAN BE GIVEN The parishes of Market Harborough, Great Bowden and Little Bowden.

WHO CAN BENEFIT Organisations and individuals.

WHAT IS FUNDED The trust supports a wide range of large and small projects, giving towards supporting the community, the improvement of the environment, the arts, healthcare, heritage and relief-in-need.

WHAT IS NOT FUNDED No grants towards sporting projects or to replace statutory funding.

FINANCES *Year* 2008 *Income* £610,666 *Grants* £440,532 *Assets* £13,531,588

TRUSTEES T Banks; Dr J Jones; D Battersby; J C Clare; Mrs J Hefford; B R Johnson; B Marshall; Mrs J Roberts; G Stamp; M Stamp; A F Trotter; A E Walker; I C Wells; Mrs J A Williams.

OTHER INFORMATION The trust works in informal administrative partnerships with organisations and other funding bodies to pursue schemes in line with its main areas of work. Grants were also made to 149 individuals totalling over £42,000

HOW TO APPLY On a form available from the correspondent. Potential applicants are welcome to contact the correspondent directly for further guidance.

WHO TO APPLY TO J G Jacobs, Steward, 149 St Mary's Road, Market Harborough, Leicestershire LE16 7DZ *Tel* 01858 462467 *Fax* 01858 431898 *email* mhbc@godfrey-payton.co.uk; enquiries@godfrey-payton.co.uk; or jim@godfrey-paton.co.uk.

CC NO 1041958   ESTABLISHED 1994

Think carefully about every application. Is it justified?

699

■ The Michael Marks Charitable Trust

WHERE FUNDING CAN BE GIVEN UK and overseas.
WHO CAN BENEFIT Registered charities.
WHAT IS FUNDED Conservation, environment and culture.
WHAT IS NOT FUNDED Grants are given to registered charities only. No grants to individuals or profit organisations.
RANGE OF GRANTS Generally £1,000–£25,000.
SAMPLE GRANTS Tate Britain (£25,000); The London Library (£20,000); British Library (£14,000); The De Laszlo Foundation and Zoological Society of London (£12,000 each); Norwich Theatre Royal (£10,000). St Pancras Community Trust (£8,000); Academy of Ancient Music (£7,000); Campaign for Drawing (£6,000); Oxford Philomusica Trust (£5,000); BTCV/Green Gym (£2,000); and London Song Festival (£1,000).
FINANCES *Year* 2008–09 *Income* £332,822 *Grants* £199,561 *Assets* £4,628,758
TRUSTEES Martina, Lady Marks; Prof. Sir Christopher White; Noel Annesley.
HOW TO APPLY In writing to the correspondent before July. Applications should include audited accounts, information on other bodies approached and details of funding obtained. Requests will not receive a response unless they have been successful.
WHO TO APPLY TO The Secretary, 5 Elm Tree Road, London NW8 9JY *Tel* 020 7286 4633 *Fax* 020 7289 2173
CC NO 248136   **ESTABLISHED** 1966

■ The Ann and David Marks Foundation

WHERE FUNDING CAN BE GIVEN Worldwide with a preference for Manchester.
WHO CAN BENEFIT Jewish charities.
WHAT IS FUNDED Jewish charitable purposes.
RANGE OF GRANTS Up to £3,000.
SAMPLE GRANTS 2003–04: North Cheshire Jewish Primary School (£2,600); 2004 Campaign of the United Jewish Israel Appeal (£2,500); and Manchester Jewish Federation (£2,000).
FINANCES *Year* 2007 *Income* £52,310 *Grants* £39,207 *Assets* £523,874
TRUSTEES D L Marks; Mrs A M Marks; Dr G E Marks; A H Marks; M Marks.
HOW TO APPLY Previous research suggested that the trust's funds are mostly committed and unsolicited applications are not welcome.
WHO TO APPLY TO D L Marks, Trustee, Mutley House, 1 Ambassador Place, Stockport Road, Altrincham, Cheshire WA15 8DB *Tel* 0161 941 3183 *email* davidmarks@mutleyproperties.co.uk
CC NO 326303   **ESTABLISHED** 1983

■ The Hilda and Samuel Marks Foundation

WHERE FUNDING CAN BE GIVEN UK and Israel.
WHO CAN BENEFIT Voluntary organisations and charitable groups benefiting Jewish people of all ages. Support is given to those helped by the Jewish Blind Society.
WHAT IS FUNDED General charitable purposes; the relief and assistance of poor and needy persons; education; advancement of Judaism and assistance to synagogues and Jewish bodies; community facilities and services; health.
WHAT IS NOT FUNDED No grants to individuals.

TYPE OF GRANT Buildings and other capital; core costs; project; start-up costs.
SAMPLE GRANTS ALYN Paediatric and Adolescent Rehabilitation Centre (£50,000 in two grants).
FINANCES *Year* 2007–08 *Income* £171,741 *Grants* £193,175 *Assets* £3,205,401
TRUSTEES S Marks; Mrs H Marks; D L Marks; Mrs R D Selby.
HOW TO APPLY The trust primarily supports projects known to the trustees and its funds are fully committed. Therefore unsolicited applications are not being sought.
WHO TO APPLY TO D L Marks, Trustee, 1 Ambassador Place, Stockport Road, Altrincham, Cheshire WA15 8DB *Tel* 0161 941 3183 *Fax* 0161 927 7437 *email* davidmarks@mutleyprrperties.co.uk
CC NO 245208   **ESTABLISHED** 1965

■ J P Marland Charitable Trust

WHERE FUNDING CAN BE GIVEN UK.
WHO CAN BENEFIT Registered charities.
WHAT IS FUNDED General charitable purposes.
RANGE OF GRANTS Up to £15,000.
SAMPLE GRANTS Shrewsbury School Foundation (£15,000); the Holbourne Museum (£13,000); the Harnham Water Meadows (£9,200); XT3 Media (£2,500); and Odstock Church Appeal Fund (£2,300).
FINANCES *Year* 2007–08 *Income* £88,794 *Grants* £47,126 *Assets* £297,017
TRUSTEES J P Marland; Mrs P M Marland; Mrs C J Law.
HOW TO APPLY In writing to the correspondent.
WHO TO APPLY TO J P Marland, Odstock Manor, Odstock, Salisbury SP5 4JA *Tel* 01722 329781 *email* jmarland@jltgroup.com
CC NO 1049350   **ESTABLISHED** 1995

■ The Marr-Munning Trust

WHERE FUNDING CAN BE GIVEN Worldwide, mainly developing world.
WHO CAN BENEFIT Organisations benefiting refugees, people disadvantaged by poverty, and victims of famine, war and man-made or natural disasters.
WHAT IS FUNDED Overseas aid projects, particularly those likely to improve economic and educational work. Provision of water supplies and general medical care. Refugee works and language schools are also supported.
WHAT IS NOT FUNDED No grants to individuals.
TYPE OF GRANT Recurrent and one-off.
SAMPLE GRANTS Oxfam (£21,000); Marr-Munning Asram – India (£12,000); and CAFOD – Zimbabwe (£10,000); Gram Niyojon Kendra – India (£5,140); Harvest Help – West Africa (£4,250); Homeless International – India (£4,000); Gondor University Hospital – Ethiopia (£2,000); and Action Force – Gambia, Build Africa – Kenya, Deafway – Nepal, Franciscan Missionaries Hospital, Human Need and UNICEF – African Flood Children Appeal (£1,000 each).
FINANCES *Year* 2007–08 *Income* £516,367 *Grants* £101,280 *Assets* £12,504,558
TRUSTEES Glen Barnham; Marianne Elliott; Julian Kay; Guy Perfect; Richard Tomlinson; David Strachan; Pierre Thomas.
HOW TO APPLY The trustees meet quarterly on average and usually review applications twice yearly, in the spring and autumn. Sometimes a request may be carried forward to a later meeting. However, emergency appeals may be considered at any meeting. Applications should be concise, ideally limited to no more than two sides of A4 plus a project description, budget

and summary accounts or annual report. Clear financial information is essential, and applications from small or new organisations may benefit from reference to any better-known supporters or partners. Charitable or equivalent status of the applicant organisation should be made clear. **Please note:** Any other supporting literature should be kept to a minimum. Do not waste stamps on an SAE; the trust regrets that it does not have the administrative resources at present to return papers or respond to telephone or email enquiries (a website is under consideration). A trustee has agreed to look at the requests each month and where necessary seek further information. Otherwise, applicants will normally only hear if their bid has been successful which may be more than six months from receipt of application.

WHO TO APPLY TO Donford Gleeson, 9 Madeley Road, Ealing, London W5 2LA *Tel* 020 8998 7747 *Fax* 020 8998 9593 *email* dongleeson@tiscali. co.uk

CC NO 261786   **ESTABLISHED** 1970

■ The Michael Marsh Charitable Trust

WHERE FUNDING CAN BE GIVEN Birmingham, Staffordshire, Worcestershire, Warwickshire, Coventry, Wolverhampton and associated towns in the Black Country.

WHO CAN BENEFIT Organisations benefiting children and young people, older people, at-risk groups and people who are disabled, disadvantaged by poverty or socially isolated.

WHAT IS FUNDED Health and welfare charities, community-based organisations, education and training and religious activities.

WHAT IS NOT FUNDED No grants towards animals or entertainment charities. Grants to individuals are only given through charitable institutions on their behalf.

TYPE OF GRANT Generally recurrent.

RANGE OF GRANTS Usually £300–£10,000.

SAMPLE GRANTS Cure Leukaemia (£10,000); St Basil's (£5,000); Howley Grange Scout Group (£2,500); Birmingham Institute for the Deaf, British Dyslexia Association and Where Next Association (£2,000 each); Homestart Northfield (£1,000); and Be Who You Can Be (£750).

FINANCES *Year* 2007–08 *Income* £136,716 *Grants* £103,515 *Assets* £3,743,602

TRUSTEES Peter Gary Barber; Lee Nuttall; Susan Bennett

HOW TO APPLY In writing to the correspondent. Trustees meet in June and December, considering all applications received in the preceding six months. However, they will consider on an ad-hoc basis any applications that they consider should not be retained until their next scheduled meeting.

WHO TO APPLY TO Clerk to the Trust, c/o Mills and Reeve, 78–84 Colmore Row, Birmingham B3 2AB *Tel* 0870 600 0011 *Fax* 0121 456 8483 *email* marsh.charity@mills-reeve.com

CC NO 220473   **ESTABLISHED** 1958

■ The Marsh Christian Trust

WHERE FUNDING CAN BE GIVEN UK.

WHO CAN BENEFIT Registered charities only.

WHAT IS FUNDED General charitable purposes; housing advice and information; holiday accommodation; sheltered accommodation; arts, culture and recreation; schools and colleges; education and training; day centres; emergency care; community holidays and outings; family planning clinics; support and self-help groups; well woman clinics; Christian education; missionaries and evangelicals; Quakerism; conservation of flora and fauna; historic buildings, nature reserves and woodlands; animal facilities and services; environmental and animal sciences; conservation and campaigning.

WHAT IS NOT FUNDED No grants can be made to individuals or for sponsorships. No start-up grants. No support for building funds, ordinary schools, colleges, universities or hospitals, or research.

TYPE OF GRANT Annual; more than three years.

RANGE OF GRANTS Generally £250–£4,000, with responses to new applications being at the lower end of this scale.

SAMPLE GRANTS English Speaking Union of the Commonwealth (£6,000); Industry and Parliament Trust (£5,000); Wildlife Information Network (£3,000); Refugee Council, Royal College of Music and the British Museum Friends (£2,000 each); Christians Against Poverty, Holy Trinity Brompton General Charity, National AIDS Trust and Prisoners Abroad (£1,000 each); Addaction (£800); Care (£700); Jolt (£650); Cued Speech Association UK (£600); Dystonia Society and Garden Organic (£500 each); Local Solutions (£450); Not Forgotten Association (£350); Society of Archivists (£275); and UK Antarctic Heritage Trust (£100).

FINANCES *Year* 2007–08 *Income* £214,702 *Grants* £162,332 *Assets* £5,662,545

TRUSTEES B P Marsh; R J C Marsh; Miss N C S Marsh; Mrs L Ryan.

HOW TO APPLY In writing to the correspondent, including a copy of the most recent accounts. The trustees currently receive about 8,000 applications every year, of which 7,800 are new. Decisions are made at monthly trustee meetings. The trustees attempt to visit each long-term recipient at least once every three years to review the work done, to learn of future plans and renew acquaintance with those responsible for the charity. Advice on fund-raising and other organisational problems is also offered free of charge by the trust.

WHO TO APPLY TO Brian Peter Marsh, Trustee, 2nd Floor, 36 Broadway, London SW1H 0BH *Tel* 020 7233 3112 *Website* www.marshchristiantrust. org

CC NO 284470   **ESTABLISHED** 1981

■ The Charlotte Marshall Charitable Trust

WHERE FUNDING CAN BE GIVEN UK.

WHO CAN BENEFIT Registered charities, institutions benefiting Roman Catholics, children, young adults and students.

WHAT IS FUNDED Educational and religious objects for Roman Catholics.

WHAT IS NOT FUNDED No grants are given to individuals.

RANGE OF GRANTS £300–£8,000.

SAMPLE GRANTS St Winifred's Centre – Sheffield (£8,000); St Gregory's Youth and Community Centre – Liverpool and St Mary's Star of the Sea (£6,000 each); Sacred Heart Primary School and St Mary Magdalen Catholic School (£5,000 each); Scottish Marriage Care (£4,000); St James Priory Project – Bristol and Westminster Children's Society (£3,000 each);

Speak Out Hounslow (£1,500); Independent Age (£1,000): and Birmingham Settlement and Derby TOC H (£500 each).

FINANCES *Year* 2007–08 *Income* £120,714 *Grants* £115,000 *Assets* £584,059

TRUSTEES Mrs E M Cosgrove; J Crosgrove; K B Page; J M Russell.

HOW TO APPLY On a form available from the correspondent. Completed forms must be returned by 31 December for consideration in March.

WHO TO APPLY TO The Trustees, c/o C and C Marshall Limited, Sidney Little Road, Churchfields Industrial Estate, St Leonards on Sea TN38 9PU *Tel* 01424 446 262

CC NO 211941   **ESTABLISHED** 1962

■ The Jim Marshall Charitable Trust

WHERE FUNDING CAN BE GIVEN Milton Keynes.

WHO CAN BENEFIT Charitable organisations.

WHAT IS FUNDED General charitable purposes, mainly for the benefit of children, young people, families and people who are disabled or sick.

SAMPLE GRANTS MK Victors Boxing Club, Luton and Bedfordshire Youth Association and Action 4 Youth (£25,000); Foundation for Promoting the Art of Magic (£5,000); Comedians' Golfing Society (£2,500); Hazeley School Charitable Trust (£2,000); Nathan Edwards Mobility Bike Fund (£1,100); and Music Alive, Brainwave and Music for All (£1,000 each). Grants of less than £1,000 each totalled £6,000.

FINANCES *Year* 2007 *Income* £10,927 *Grants* £94,721 *Assets* £134,855

TRUSTEES Dr James Marshall, Chair; Kenneth Saunders; Brian Charlton; Jonathon Ellery; Victoria Marshall.

HOW TO APPLY In writing to the correspondent at any time.

WHO TO APPLY TO Carl Graham, Simpson Wreford and Co, Wellesley House, Duke of Wellington Avenue, London SE18 6SS *Tel* 020 8317 6460 *email* carl.graham@simpsonwreford.co.uk

CC NO 328118   **ESTABLISHED** 1989

■ The D G Marshall of Cambridge Trust

WHERE FUNDING CAN BE GIVEN Predominantly Cambridge and Cambridgeshire.

WHO CAN BENEFIT Community projects, local appeals and local charities benefiting disabled people and people disadvantaged by poverty.

WHAT IS FUNDED Charitable causes in and around Cambridge.

WHAT IS NOT FUNDED Unsolicited applications are not supported.

SAMPLE GRANTS Air League Educational Trust (£75,000); Royal Aeronautical Society (£50,000); the Air League and University of Cambridge (£25,000 each); Fitzwilliam Museum and Horseheath Parochial Church Council (£10,000); Arkwright Scholarship Trust (£3,600); BLISS and East Anglian Air Ambulance (£2,000 each); British Red Cross, Elizabeth Foundation, Friends of Swaffham Prior School and Papworth Trust (£1,000 each); and Scope (£500).

FINANCES *Year* 2007–08 *Income* £1,166,667 *Grants* £254,950 *Assets* £2,750,457

TRUSTEES M J Marshall; J D Barker; W C M Dastur; R Marshall.

HOW TO APPLY The trust has stated that it does not respond to unsolicited applications.

WHO TO APPLY TO Ms Sarah Moynihan, Airport House, The Airport, Newmarket Road, Cambridgeshire CB5 8RY

CC NO 286468   **ESTABLISHED** 1982

■ Marshall's Charity

WHERE FUNDING CAN BE GIVEN England and Wales with preference for Kent, Surrey, Lincolnshire and Southwark.

WHO CAN BENEFIT Anglican churches and parsonage buildings.

WHAT IS FUNDED Improvement work to parsonages in England and Wales, repairs to existing Anglican churches in Kent, Surrey and Lincolnshire (as the counties were defined in 1855).

WHAT IS NOT FUNDED No grants to churches outside the counties of Kent, Surrey and Lincolnshire, as defined in 1855. No church funding for the following: cost of church halls and meeting rooms; kitchens; decorations – unless they form part of qualifying repair or improvement work; furniture and fittings; work to bells, brasses or clocks; private chapels or monuments; stained glass – although work to repair firmaments can be supported; grounds, boundary walls and fences; external lighting.

TYPE OF GRANT Building and other capital works; interest-free loans.

RANGE OF GRANTS Up to £20,000. Grants to churches usually £3,000 to £5,000. Grants to parsonages usually £1,000 to £4,000.

SAMPLE GRANTS Beneficiaries of church restoration grants included: Lincolnshire Old Churches Trust and Christ Church – Camberwell (£6,000 each); All Saints – Maidstone, Holy Trinity – Raithby and St Paul – Spalding (£5,000 each); All Saints – Bigby (£4,500); St Mary – Hainton (£3,500); Holy Trinity – Beckenham (£2,500); St Peter – Streatham (£1,000); and Friends of Kent Churches (£550).

FINANCES *Year* 2008 *Income* £1,355,628 *Grants* £1,035,658 *Assets* £16,203,504

TRUSTEES Anthea Nicholson; Colin Bird; David Lang; Michael Dudding; Colin Stenning; Stephen Clark; Gina Isaac; Bill Eason; Jeremy Hammant; John Heawood; Surbhi Malhotra; Revd Jonathan Rust; Ven Christine Hardman; Tony Guthrie; Lesley Bosman; John Murray.

HOW TO APPLY Applicants should write a letter or send an e-mail to the correspondent, giving the name and location of the Church and a brief (30 – 40 words maximum) description of the proposed work. If appropriate the charity will then send out an application form. Applications for parsonage grants should be made by the relevant Diocesan Parsonage Board. Trustees usually meet in January, April, July and October.

WHO TO APPLY TO Richard Goatcher, Clerk to the Trustees, Marshall House, 66 Newcomen Street, London SE1 1YT *Tel* 020 7407 2979 *Fax* 020 7403 3969 *email* grantoffice@ marshalls.org.uk *Website* www.marshalls.org.uk

CC NO 206780   **ESTABLISHED** 1627

■ Marshgate Charitable Settlement

WHERE FUNDING CAN BE GIVEN England and Wales.

WHO CAN BENEFIT Christian, educational and medical charities.

WHAT IS FUNDED There is an interest in work with children.

SAMPLE GRANTS Greyfriars Church (£22,000); the Philo Trust (£8,200); Stewardship and Tearfund (£5,000 each); and Bible Society, Marie Curie Cancer Care and Retrak (£500 each).

FINANCES *Year* 2007–08 *Income* £61,674 *Grants* £55,950 *Assets* £71,493

TRUSTEES C S H Hampton; M J Hampton; D E Long.

HOW TO APPLY In writing to the correspondent.

WHO TO APPLY TO Clifford Hampton, Trustee, Highmoor Hall, Henley-on-Thames, Oxfordshire RG9 5DH *Tel* 01491 641543 *Fax* 01491 641098

CC NO 1081645   **ESTABLISHED** 2000

■ Sir George Martin Trust

WHERE FUNDING CAN BE GIVEN Largely Yorkshire with particular emphasis on Leeds and Bradford.

WHO CAN BENEFIT Organisations benefiting children, young adults and older people; dance and ballet; music; theatre; opera companies; schools and colleges; education and training; community facilities and services; religious buildings; conservation.

WHAT IS FUNDED Education, social welfare, general charitable purposes, especially in Yorkshire. The trust assists a very wide range of charitable causes with a number of awards to schools and groups working with young people. Emphasis is placed on projects located in North and West Yorkshire and occasionally in Cumbria.

WHAT IS NOT FUNDED Full guidelines detailing what is and is not funded by the trust are available from the correspondent.

TYPE OF GRANT Grants for capital rather than revenue projects; reluctant to support general running costs. Grants are not repeated to any charity in any one-year; the maximum number of consecutive grants is three, though a one-off approach to grant applications is preferred. Average donation is just over £1,230.

RANGE OF GRANTS £100–£12,000.

SAMPLE GRANTS Opera North & Leeds Grand Theatre Development Trust (£12,500); Hepworth Wakefield Trust (£10,000); Safe Anchor Trust (£5,000); Ripon Cathedral (£3,000); Chopsticks – North Yorkshire (£2,000); and Woman's Holiday Centre (£350).

FINANCES *Year* 2007–08 *Income* £264,211 *Grants* £195,495 *Assets* £6,565,633

TRUSTEES T D Coates, Chair; M Bethel; R F D Marshall; P D Taylor; Ms Janet Martin.

HOW TO APPLY The trust meets in March, July and December each year to consider applications. These should be made in writing to the secretary in good time for the meetings, which usually take place in the middle of the month. Applications that are not within the guidelines cannot be answered due to substantial increase in costs. Applications that are relevant will be acknowledged and, following meetings, successful applicants will be told of the grants they are to receive. Unsuccessful applicants will not be informed. The trust is unable to consider applications from organisations without charitable status. Telephone calls are not encouraged as the office is not always staffed – it is better to write, fax or email.

WHO TO APPLY TO Peter Marshall, Secretary, Netherwood House, Skipton Road, Ilkley, West Yorkshire LS29 9RP *Tel* 01943 831 019 *Fax* 01943 831 570 *email* sirgeorgemartintrust@care4free.net

CC NO 223554   **ESTABLISHED** 1956

■ John Martin's Charity

WHERE FUNDING CAN BE GIVEN Evesham and 'certain surrounding villages' only.

WHO CAN BENEFIT Individuals and charitable or voluntary organisations benefiting the residents of Evesham.

WHAT IS FUNDED Propagation of the Christian gospel – the charity helps with the expenses of designated local clergy, PCCs and St Andrew's Church of England First School in Hampton; promotion of education – grants are made to all state schools and the college in Evesham to support special needs education, in addition to considering other educational projects; individual students – people aged 16 to 50 may apply for educational grants to support further and higher educational or vocational studies; miscellaneous education awards – given for music, arts and education visits, together with support with school uniforms; and relief in need of individuals and organisations – grants are made for the benefit of children, single parent families, people with disabilities and people who have fallen on hard times for a variety of circumstances beyond their control whilst an annual heating allowance is made to older people on limited incomes and those who benefit are invited to outings to the seaside and pantomimes.

WHAT IS NOT FUNDED No grants for the payment of rates or taxes, or otherwise to replace statutory benefits.

TYPE OF GRANT One-off, buildings, capital, core costs, start-up costs and running costs funded for one year or less. No loans are made.

RANGE OF GRANTS Individuals £5–£1,500; organisations £50–£30,000.

SAMPLE GRANTS St Peter's PCC – Bengeworth (£30,000); Wychavon Citizens Advice Bureau (£20,000); All Saints' PCC – Evesham, St Andrew's PCC – Hampton and St Richard's Hospice (£18,000 each); Prince Henry's High School (£11,000); Evesham Splash Club (£6,500); Noah's Ark Trust (£4,000); Vale of Evesham Special School (£2,500); and Youth Music Festival (£1,300).

FINANCES *Year* 2008–09 *Income* £751,034 *Grants* £640,205 *Assets* £14,551,867

TRUSTEES N Lamb, Chair; Mrs J Turner; J Smith; C Scorse; R Emson; Mrs D Raphael; Mrs F S Smith; Mrs J Westlake; J Wilson; Mrs C Evans; Revd B Collins; Revd A Spurr; Revd A Binney; Mrs G Falkner.

OTHER INFORMATION £199,000 to schools and organisations.

HOW TO APPLY Grant applications are considered from organisations in, or supporting, the town of Evesham where the requested support is considered to fit within the governing schemes of the charity. Application periods close on 1 March, 1 June, 1 September and 20 November. Forms are available from the correspondent or via the 'downloads' page at: www.johnmartins.org.uk/downloads. Details of the application procedure for individuals are also contained on the trust's website.

WHO TO APPLY TO John Daniels, Clerk, 16 Queen's Road, Evesham, Worcestershire WR11 4JP *Tel* 01386 765 440 *Fax* 01386 765 340 *email* enquiries@johnmartins.org.uk *Website* www.johnmartins.org.uk

CC NO 527473   **ESTABLISHED** 1714

■ The Mary Homfray Charitable Trust

WHERE FUNDING CAN BE GIVEN UK, with a preference for Wales.

WHO CAN BENEFIT Registered charities.

WHAT IS FUNDED General charitable purposes.

RANGE OF GRANTS Up to £3,000.

SAMPLE GRANTS Age Concern, NSPCC, Prince's Trust – Cymru, Salvation Army and Wallich Clifford Community (£3,000 each); National Botanic Garden of Wales, PDSA, Urdd Gobaith Cymru, and Wales Millennium Centre (£2,000 each); RSPB and Y Bont (£500 each).

FINANCES *Year* 2007 *Income* £63,951 *Grants* £54,000 *Assets* £1,834,047

TRUSTEES Angela Homfray; Simon Gibson.

HOW TO APPLY In writing to the correspondent. Applications should be made towards the end of the year, for consideration at the trustees' meeting in February or March each year.

WHO TO APPLY TO Angela Homfray, Trustee, c/o Blenheim House, Fitzalan Court, Newport Road, Cardiff CF24 0TS *Tel* 0292 048 1111

CC NO 273564   **ESTABLISHED** 1977

■ The Mason Porter Charitable Trust

WHERE FUNDING CAN BE GIVEN UK.

WHO CAN BENEFIT Grants are made only to charities known to the settlor.

WHAT IS FUNDED General charitable purposes, particularly Christian causes.

SAMPLE GRANTS St Luke's Methodist Church – Hoylake (£24,000); Abernethy Trust Ltd, Just Care and NXT Ministries (£10,000 each); Proclaim Trust (£5,500); St John's Hospice – Wirral and Share Jesus International (£5,000 each); the Messengers (£1,300); and the Mukuru Project (£1,000). Other grants totalled £18,300.

FINANCES *Year* 2007–08 *Income* £105,780 *Grants* £90,130 *Assets* £1,674,765

TRUSTEES Sue Newton, Chair; Mark Blundell; Dil Daly; Richard Fassam; Charles Feeny; William Fulton; Prof. Phillip Love; Andrew Lovelady; Christine Reeves; Hilary Russell; Heather Akehurst.

HOW TO APPLY The trust states that it only makes grants to charities known to the settlor and unsolicited applications are not considered.

WHO TO APPLY TO The Secretary, Liverpool Charity and Voluntary Services, 151 Dale Street, Liverpool L2 2AH *Tel* 0151 227 5177

CC NO 255545   **ESTABLISHED** 1968

■ The Nancie Massey Charitable Trust

WHERE FUNDING CAN BE GIVEN Scotland, particularly Edinburgh and Leith.

WHO CAN BENEFIT Charitable groups only.

WHAT IS FUNDED Income split between five areas: young people; older people; education; the arts; and medical research.

WHAT IS NOT FUNDED Grants are not given to individuals.

RANGE OF GRANTS £500–£2,000, but can be larger.

FINANCES *Year* 2007–08 *Grants* £130,000

TRUSTEES J G Morton; M F Sinclair; Ann Trotman.

HOW TO APPLY Write to the correspondent requesting an application form. Trustees meet three times a year in February, June and October.

Applications need to be received by January, May or September.

WHO TO APPLY TO James G Morton, Trustee, Chiene and Tait, Cairn House, 61 Dublin Street, Edinburgh EH3 6NL *Tel* 0131 558 5800 *Fax* 0131 558 5899

SC NO SC008977   **ESTABLISHED** 1989

■ The Mathew Trust

WHERE FUNDING CAN BE GIVEN City of Dundee, Angus, Perth and Kinross and Fife.

WHO CAN BENEFIT Registered charities.

WHAT IS FUNDED The advancement of education of adults; advancement of vocational and professional training; relief of poverty by providing assistance in the recruitment of people who are unemployed, or who are likely to become unemployed in the near future.

SAMPLE GRANTS University of Dundee for Angiogenesis (£50,000); Hot Chocolate Trust (£10,000); Perth College Development Trust (£8,000); Maritime Volunteer Service and Prince's Trust (£5,000 each); Young Enterprise Scotland (£4,800); Homestart – Perth (£3,000); Medicine in Malawi (£2,600); Riptide Music Studios and Scottish Chamber Orchestra (£1,000 each); and Puppet Animation Festival (£300).

FINANCES *Year* 2007–08 *Income* £232,568 *Grants* £141,462 *Assets* £7,571,094

TRUSTEES D B Grant, Chair; G S Lowden; A F McDonald; Prof. P Howie; The Lord Provost of the City of Dundee.

OTHER INFORMATION The grant total in 2007–08 includes £6,000 donated to 11 individuals.

HOW TO APPLY In writing to the correspondent.

WHO TO APPLY TO Fiona Bullions, Henderson Loggie, Chartered Accountants, Royal Exchange, Panmure Street, Dundee DD1 1DZ

SC NO SC016284   **ESTABLISHED** 1935

■ Matliwala Family Charitable Trust

WHERE FUNDING CAN BE GIVEN UK and overseas, especially Bharuch – India.

WHO CAN BENEFIT Charitable organisations.

WHAT IS FUNDED The advancement of education for pupils at Matliwala School Of Baruch in Gujerat – India, and other schools, including assisting with the provision of equipment and facilities; advancement of the Islamic religion; relief of sickness and poverty; advancement of education.

FINANCES *Year* 2007–08 *Income* £874,268 *Grants* £567,200 *Assets* £4,518,454

TRUSTEES Ayub Vali Bux; Usman Salya; Abdul Aziz Vali Patel; Yousuf Bux; Ibrahim Vali Patel.

HOW TO APPLY In writing to the correspondent.

WHO TO APPLY TO A V Bux, Trustee, 9 Brookview, Fulwood, Preston PR2 8FG *Tel* 01772 706501

CC NO 1012756   **ESTABLISHED** 1992

■ The Matt 6.3 Charitable Trust

WHERE FUNDING CAN BE GIVEN UK.

WHO CAN BENEFIT Christian organisations.

WHAT IS FUNDED Christian charitable purposes.

SAMPLE GRANTS Previous beneficiaries have included: Christian Centre (Humberside) Limited (£132,000); Centre for Justice & Liberty (£59,000); Shalom Centre – Grimsby Education (£29,000); Don Summers Evangelistic

Association (£17,400); Caribbean Radio Lighthouse (£8,750); Hull University – Wilberforce Fund Education (£5,000); Kings Christian Bookshop (£4,000); Peace & Hope Trust (£3,000); and Evangelical Library (£500). Other grants totalling £70,000 were made to individuals of which the largest was for Christian broadcasting (£63,520).

FINANCES *Year* 2007–08 *Income* £240,527 *Grants* £441,396 *Assets* £6,277,248

TRUSTEES Christine Ruth Barnett; Doris Dibdin; T P Dibdin; R O Dauncey.

HOW TO APPLY The trust does not accept unsolicited applications. Funds are committed to ongoing projects.

WHO TO APPLY TO I H Davey, Progress House, Progress Park, Cupola Way, Off Normanby Road, Scunthorpe, North Lincolnshire DN15 9YJ *Tel* 01724 863 666

CC NO 1069985   **ESTABLISHED** 1998

■ The Violet Mauray Charitable Trust

WHERE FUNDING CAN BE GIVEN UK.

WHO CAN BENEFIT Registered charities.

WHAT IS FUNDED General charitable purposes, particularly medical charities and Jewish organisations.

WHAT IS NOT FUNDED No grants to individuals.

RANGE OF GRANTS Usually £1,000–£6,000.

SAMPLE GRANTS New North London Synagogue (£6,000); Cherry Lodge Cancer Care, Mango Tree and Opportunities International (£5,000 each); Aqua Box and Shelter Box (£4,000 each); Wells for India (£3,000); Jewish Children (£2,000); Help the Ages and LEPRA (£1,000 each).

FINANCES *Year* 2007–08 *Income* £56,739 *Grants* £65,000 *Assets* £1,756,590

TRUSTEES Mrs A Karlin; John Stephany; Robert Stephany.

HOW TO APPLY In writing to the correspondent.

WHO TO APPLY TO John Stephany, Trustee, HWCA Limited, 3rd Floor, 7–10 Chandos Street, Cavendish Square, London, W1G9DQ

CC NO 1001716   **ESTABLISHED** 1990

■ The Maxell Educational Trust

WHERE FUNDING CAN BE GIVEN Telford and The Wrekin.

WHO CAN BENEFIT Students between the ages of 9 and 25, and teachers.

WHAT IS FUNDED Education, in particular projects with industrial or technological content.

SAMPLE GRANTS Previous beneficiaries have included Shropshire Campus of the University of Wolverhampton to establish an Electronic Design Centre, Southall Special School for computers and software for pupils to produce a school newspaper, Ercall Wood School to establish the Maxell Music Technology Centre and Wrockwardine Wood School to establish the Controlled Technology Centre.

FINANCES *Year* 2007–08 *Income* £12,311 *Grants* £22,771

TRUSTEES Mike Lowe

HOW TO APPLY In writing to the correspondent.

WHO TO APPLY TO Ian Jamieson, MAXELL EUROPE LTD, Apley, Telford TF1 6DA *Tel* 01952 522222

CC NO 702640   **ESTABLISHED** 1990

■ The Maxwell Family Foundation

WHERE FUNDING CAN BE GIVEN UK.

WHO CAN BENEFIT Registered charities in the fields of health, medical research, and the relief of older people and people who are sick or who have disabilities.

WHAT IS FUNDED An established list of charities is supported.

WHAT IS NOT FUNDED The trust states explicitly that there is no support for unsolicited applications. It clearly abides by this policy and we would urge readers who do not know the trustees personally not to write to the trust.

RANGE OF GRANTS Usually £3,500 or under.

SAMPLE GRANTS The largest grant was made to the Martha Trust (£100,000). Smaller grants included those to Deafblind UK (£3,500); Newcastle Society for Blind People (£2,500); St Peter's Hospice, (£1,500 each), the Army Benevolent Fund, British Institute for Brain Injured Children, National Eye Research Centre (£1,000 each); Prostate Cancer Charity (£750); War Memorials Trust (£500); and Young Bristol (£150).

FINANCES *Year* 2007–08 *Income* £147,674 *Grants* £116,650 *Assets* £2,355,642

TRUSTEES E M Maxwell; P M Maxwell.

HOW TO APPLY Applications are neither sought nor acknowledged. There appears little purpose in applying to this trust as no application will be supported unless accompanied by a personal request from someone known by the trustees.

WHO TO APPLY TO E M Maxwell, Trustee, 181 Whiteladies Road, Clifton, Bristol BS8 2RY *Tel* 0117 962 6878

CC NO 291124   **ESTABLISHED** 1965

■ Evelyn May Trust

WHERE FUNDING CAN BE GIVEN UK.

WHO CAN BENEFIT Registered charities, mainly headquarters organisations, especially those benefiting older people, children, medical professionals, research workers, and people disadvantaged by sickness and poverty.

WHAT IS FUNDED Currently the main areas of interest are older people, children, medical projects and natural disaster relief, but support is given to a variety of registered charities.

WHAT IS NOT FUNDED No grants to individuals, including students, or to general appeals or animal welfare charities.

TYPE OF GRANT Often one-off for a specific project, but support for general purposes is also given.

SAMPLE GRANTS Previous beneficiaries include: APT Enterprise Development, British Red Cross in response to the Iraq Crisis Appeal, Listening Books, Respite Association – Essex and Wells for India, Richard House Children's Hospice and Teen Talk Drop-in Centre.

FINANCES *Year* 2007 *Income* £24,244 *Grants* £25,000

TRUSTEES Mrs E Tabersham; Ms K Gray; Ms J Tabersham

HOW TO APPLY In writing to the correspondent.

WHO TO APPLY TO Ms Kim Gray, c/o Messrs Pothecary, Witham, Weld, White Horse Court, North Street, Bishop's Stortford, Hertfordshire CM23 2LD *Tel* 01279 5064210

CC NO 261038   **ESTABLISHED** 1970

■ Mayfair Charities Ltd

WHERE FUNDING CAN BE GIVEN UK and overseas.

WHO CAN BENEFIT Registered charities benefiting Orthodox Jews, particularly children and young adults.

WHAT IS FUNDED Education, religion and medical welfare charities which support Orthodox Judaism.

TYPE OF GRANT Capital and running costs.

RANGE OF GRANTS Typically £500–£2,500.

SAMPLE GRANTS SOFT (£1.18 million); Beth Jacob Grammar School For Girls Ltd (£870,000); Merkaz Lechinuch Torani (£683,000); Ohr Akiva Institute (£251,000); Kollel Chibas Yerushalayim (£248,000); Mesivta Letzeirim (£200,000); Chevras Maoz Ladal (£198,000); Congregation Ichud Chasidim (£159,500); Chaye Olam Institute (£129,000); United Talmudical Association (£110,000); Talmud Torah Zichron Gavriel (£100,000); Friends of Bobov (£75,000); Regent Charities Ltd (£50,000); Comet Charities Ltd (£42,500); Woodstock Sinclair Trust (£24,000); Yesodei Hatorah School (£20,000); Beis Aharon Trust (£15,000); Ezer Mikodesh Foundation (£12,000); Gateshead Jewish Teachers Training College (£8,000); Edgware Foundation (£6,000); Heritage House (£5,000); Kiryat Sanz Jerusalem (£2,500); and PAL Charitable Trust (£1,000).

FINANCES *Year* 2007–08 *Income* £4,504,000 *Grants* £7,796,483 *Assets* £69,221,000

TRUSTEES B S E Freshwater, Chair; D Davis; S I Freshwater.

OTHER INFORMATION The grant total included £4.8 million for the advancement of religion and education and £3 million for the relief of poverty.

HOW TO APPLY In writing to the correspondent.

WHO TO APPLY TO Mark Jenner, Secretary, Freshwater House, 158–162 Shaftesbury Avenue, London WC2H 8HR *Tel* 020 7836 1555 *email* mark.jenner@highdorn.co.uk

CC NO 255281   **ESTABLISHED** 1968

■ The Mayfield Valley Arts Trust

WHERE FUNDING CAN BE GIVEN Unrestricted, but with a special interest in Sheffield and South Yorkshire.

WHO CAN BENEFIT Charities concerned with music and the promotion and presentation of musical events and activities.

WHAT IS FUNDED Support is concentrated on certain beneficiaries, with remaining funds to established chamber music venues.

WHAT IS NOT FUNDED No grants to students.

TYPE OF GRANT Up to three years for core costs.

SAMPLE GRANTS Sheffield Chamber Music in the Round (£30,000); Live Music Now (£28,500); York Early Music Foundation (£27,500); Wigmore Hall (£25,000); and Prussia Cove (£5,000).

FINANCES *Year* 2007–08 *Income* £137,054 *Grants* £116,000 *Assets* £2,328,003

TRUSTEES A Thornton; J R Thornton; Mrs P M Thornton; D Whelton; D Brown; J R Rider.

HOW TO APPLY The trust states that no unsolicited applications are considered.

WHO TO APPLY TO P J Kennan, Administrator, Hawsons, Pegasus House, 463a Glossop Road, Sheffield S10 2QD *Tel* 0114 266 7141

CC NO 327665   **ESTABLISHED** 1988

■ Mazars Charitable Trust

WHERE FUNDING CAN BE GIVEN UK and overseas.

WHO CAN BENEFIT Organisations with charitable purposes.

WHAT IS FUNDED Support is normally only given to projects which are nominated to the management committee by the partners and staff of Mazars (chartered accountants).

WHAT IS NOT FUNDED No grants to individuals, large national charities (rarely), applications from a particular national charity within three years of an earlier grant, or for ongoing funding. Unsolicited appeals are rarely considered.

TYPE OF GRANT Single strategic projects; one-off; research; building; and capital. Funding is for one year or less.

RANGE OF GRANTS £55–£19,000.

SAMPLE GRANTS The Thana Trust (£19,000); Starfish (£17,000); EdUKAid (£12,000); International Needs Network (£11,000); and Allergy UK (£10,000). Other beneficiaries included: British Deaf Sports Council (£5,000); Abigail Project (£3,000); Shelter (£1,500); and Marie Curie Cancer Care (£1,000). 90 other grants of between £55 and £800 each were made totalling £29,000.

FINANCES *Year* 2007 *Income* £239,932 *Grants* £224,267 *Assets* £91,018

TRUSTEES Peter Hyatt; Alan Edwards; David Evans; Bob Neate.

HOW TO APPLY The trustees operate through a management committee which meets annually to consider applications for major grants which fit with the stated criteria. Some monies are allocated to five regional 'pot' holders who approve minor grant applications from within their own region. Applicants for a national grant must be known to the team members of Mazars LLP. National and regional criteria are regularly reviewed but, in general, the trustees consider that the national grant making policy should avoid core funding and other activities that require funding over a number of years. Most national grants are therefore made towards one-off projects.

WHO TO APPLY TO Bryan K Rodgers, Trust Administrator, 1 Cranleigh Gardens, South Croyden CR2 9LD *Tel* 020 8657 3053

CC NO 287735   **ESTABLISHED** 1983

■ The Robert McAlpine Foundation

WHERE FUNDING CAN BE GIVEN UK.

WHO CAN BENEFIT Registered charities and hospitals.

WHAT IS FUNDED Children with disabilities, older people, medical research, social welfare.

WHAT IS NOT FUNDED The trust does not like to fund overheads. No grants to individuals.

RANGE OF GRANTS Up to £90,000.

SAMPLE GRANTS The Ewing Foundation (£90,000); Contact the Elderly (£26,000); Age Concern (£25,000); Merchants Academy – Withywood and Community Self Build Agency (£20,000 each); and National Eye Research Centre (£17,000); Eyeless Trust (£15,000); Greenfingers Appeal and Hi Kent (£10,000 each); Rochdale Special Needs Cycling Club (£5,000); Hillfields Park Baptist Church (£4,000); and Grateful Society (£2,500).

FINANCES *Year* 2007–08 *Income* £599,959 *Grants* £505,000 *Assets* £12,585,178

TRUSTEES Hon. David McAlpine; Malcolm H D McAlpine; Kenneth McAlpine; Cullum McAlpine; Adrian N R McAlpine.

HOW TO APPLY In writing to the correspondent at any time. Considered annually, normally in November.

WHO TO APPLY TO Brian Arter, Eaton Court, Maylands Avenue, Hemel Hempstead, Hertfordshire HP2 7TR *Tel* 01442 233444

CC NO 226646   **ESTABLISHED** 1963

■ The McDougall Trust

WHERE FUNDING CAN BE GIVEN UK and overseas.

WHO CAN BENEFIT Organisations or individuals carrying out charitable work including research in accord with the trust's objects.

WHAT IS FUNDED The knowledge, study and research of: political or economic science and functions of government and the services provided to the community by public and voluntary organisations; methods of election of and the selection and government of representative organisations whether national, civic, commercial, industrial or social; and representative democracy, its forms, functions and development and also its associated institutions. Special priority is given to electoral research projects.

WHAT IS NOT FUNDED No grants to any political party or commercial organisation, for an individual's education, for social welfare matters, or for general appeals, expeditions or scholarships.

TYPE OF GRANT Usually one-off for a specific project or part of a project or work programme. Applications for small 'pump-priming' grants are welcomed. Feasibility studies and research grants are also considered.

RANGE OF GRANTS Minimum grant £250.

SAMPLE GRANTS Previous beneficiaries were Electoral Reform Society and University of Strathclyde.

FINANCES *Year* 2007–08 *Income* £58,892 *Grants* £7,768 *Assets* £930,518

TRUSTEES Elizabeth Bee; David Clover; Elizabeth Collingridge; Ruth Farmer; David Hill; Michael Meadowcroft; Peter Morley; Nigel Siederer; Michael Steed (Chair); Paul Webb.

PUBLICATIONS *Representation: Journal of Representative Democracy*, (quarterly).

OTHER INFORMATION The trustees have established a library called the Lakeman Library for Electoral Studies at the address below. This is available for the use of research workers and the public generally on conditions laid down by the trustees. The trustees also sponsor several prizes in conjunction with the Political Studies Association and the Politics Association.

HOW TO APPLY In writing to the correspondent, including annual accounts. Trustees normally meet quarterly. Brief details of proposal needed. Initial enquiries by telephone accepted. Two deadlines for receipt of applications: 1 May and 1 October. Applications received after a deadline may be held over for consideration at the trustees' discretion.

WHO TO APPLY TO Paul Wilder, Trust Secretary, 6 Chancel Street, London SE1 0UX *Tel* 020 7620 1080 *Fax* 020 7928 1528 *email* admin@ mcdougall.org.uk *Website* www.mcdougall.org. uk

CC NO 212151   **ESTABLISHED** 1959

■ The A M McGreevy No 5 Charitable Settlement

WHERE FUNDING CAN BE GIVEN UK, with a preference for the Bristol and Bath area.

WHO CAN BENEFIT Registered charities.

WHAT IS FUNDED General charitable purposes.

WHAT IS NOT FUNDED No support for individuals.

SAMPLE GRANTS NSPCC (£25,000); London Library (£10,000); Mucopolysaccharide Diseases (£2,000); and Prostate Cancer Charity (£1,000).

FINANCES *Year* 2007–08 *Income* £209,820 *Grants* £38,000 *Assets* £2,311,300

TRUSTEES Avon Executor and Trustee Co. Ltd; Anthony M McGreevy; Elise McGreevy-Harris; Katrina Paterson.

HOW TO APPLY In writing to the correspondent.

WHO TO APPLY TO Karen Ganson, KPMG, 100 Temple Street, Bristol BS1 6AG *Tel* 0117 905 4000

CC NO 280666   **ESTABLISHED** 1979

■ The McKenna Charitable Trust

WHERE FUNDING CAN BE GIVEN England and Wales.

WHO CAN BENEFIT Organisations and individuals.

WHAT IS FUNDED Health, disability, education, children, arts/culture, general.

SAMPLE GRANTS The Young Vic Company (£307,000); SNAP – Special Needs and Parents (£26,000); St Joseph the Worker Primary School (£20,000); Aldeburgh Music (£10,000); BEAT, The Cure Parkinson's Trust and RYL Humane Society (£5,000 each); Little Haven Hospice (£520); and Dumfries and Galloway Museum (£80).

FINANCES *Year* 2007–08 *Income* £108,066 *Grants* £377,968 *Assets* £72,151

TRUSTEES P A McKenna; Mrs M E A McKenna; J L Boyton; H R Jones.

HOW TO APPLY The 2007–08 trustees' report and accounts states: 'The trustees will consider applications for grants from individuals and charitable bodies on their merits but will place particular emphasis on the educational needs and the provision of support for disabled people'.

WHO TO APPLY TO The Trustees, c/o Buzzacoat, 12 New Fetter Lane, London EC4A 1AG *Tel* 020 7319 4000

CC NO 1050672

■ Martin McLaren Memorial Trust

WHERE FUNDING CAN BE GIVEN UK.

WHO CAN BENEFIT Horticulture students.

WHAT IS FUNDED Horticultural scholarships.

RANGE OF GRANTS £50–£12,000.

SAMPLE GRANTS Previous beneficiaries include: Art and Christianity Enquiry Trust, Horticultural Scholarships Fund, European Gardens, St John's Smith Square, Combe PCC, ESU Music Scholarship Fund, Queen Mary's Clothing Guild, Macmillan Cancer Relief, The PCC Busbridge Church and Fairbridge Garden Society.

FINANCES *Year* 2006–07 *Income* £21,886 *Grants* £20,000

TRUSTEES Mrs Nancy Gordon McLaren; Nicholas Durlacher; Michael Robert MacFadyen; Revd Richard Francis McLaren; Sir Kenneth Carlisle; William Francklin.

HOW TO APPLY In writing to the correspondent.

WHO TO APPLY TO Michaiel McFadyen, c/o Charles Russell Solicitors, 8–10 New Fetter Lane, London EC4A 1RS *Tel* 020 7203 5269

CC NO 291609   **ESTABLISHED** 1985

Think carefully about every application. Is it justified?

707

■ The Helen Isabella McMorran Charitable Foundation

WHERE FUNDING CAN BE GIVEN UK.

WHO CAN BENEFIT Registered charities benefiting children, young adults and older people; those in care, fostered and adopted; Christians, Church of England; people with disabilities; people disadvantaged by poverty; homeless and socially isolated people.

WHAT IS FUNDED Older people's welfare, Christian education, churches, the arts, residential facilities and services, social and moral welfare, special schools, cultural and religious teaching, special needs education, health, medical and religious studies, conservation, animal welfare, bird sanctuaries and heritage.

WHAT IS NOT FUNDED No grants to individuals.

TYPE OF GRANT One-off.

RANGE OF GRANTS £500–£2,000.

SAMPLE GRANTS Previous beneficiaries include: Christian Aid, Marine Conservation, Moon Bear Rescue, National Association for Crohn's Disease, National Children's Bureau, React, St Matthews PCC, St Nicholas Church, Sense International and Stoneham Housing Association.

FINANCES *Year* 2007–08 *Income* £21,792 *Grants* £40,000

TRUSTEES NatWest Trust Services

HOW TO APPLY In writing to the correspondent. Brief guidelines are available. The closing date for applications is February each year.

WHO TO APPLY TO NatWest Trust Services, NatWest Trust Services, 5th Floor, Trinity Quay 2, Avon Street, Bristol BS2 0PT *Tel* 0117 940 3283

CC NO 266338   **ESTABLISHED** 1973

■ D D McPhail Charitable Settlement

WHERE FUNDING CAN BE GIVEN UK.

WHO CAN BENEFIT Registered charities, especially those benefiting older people or people with disabilities.

WHAT IS FUNDED Medical research and welfare.

SAMPLE GRANTS Sir William Burrough School (£20,000); Community Links (£7,500); DebRA (£5,000); Spina Bifida & Hydracephalus Association (£3,000); BLISS, I-CAN and RNID (£2,000 each); and The Barbara Bus Fund, International League for the Protection of Horses and The Samaritans – Harrow (£1,000 each).

FINANCES *Year* 2007–08 *Income* £272,928 *Grants* £69,500 *Assets* £8,338,046

TRUSTEES Ian McPhail; Mrs Patricia Cruddas; Mrs Julia Noble; Mrs C Charles-Jones; Tariq Kazi.

HOW TO APPLY In writing to the correspondent.

WHO TO APPLY TO Mrs Sheila Watson, Administrator, PO Box 285, Pinner, Middlesex HA5 3FB

CC NO 267588   **ESTABLISHED** 1974

■ The James Frederick and Ethel Anne Measures Charity

WHERE FUNDING CAN BE GIVEN West Midlands.

WHO CAN BENEFIT All categories within the West Midlands area.

WHAT IS FUNDED General charitable purposes. Applicants must usually originate in the West Midlands and show evidence of self-help in their application. Trustees have a preference for disadvantaged people.

WHAT IS NOT FUNDED Trustees will not consider funding students who have a full local authority grant and want finance for a different course of study. Applications by individuals in cases of hardship will not usually be considered unless sponsored by a local authority, health professional or other welfare agency.

TYPE OF GRANT Recurrent grants are occasionally considered. The trustees favour grants towards the cost of equipment.

RANGE OF GRANTS £100–£1,600.

SAMPLE GRANTS Previous beneficiaries include: Farms for City Children, Royal Wolverhampton School, Bluecoat School, Sight Savers International, National Coastline Institution, Birmingham and Midland Limbless Ex-Service, the Lady Hoare Trust, Shipston Home Nursing, Birmingham Rathbone, Saltley Neighbourhood Pensioners Centre and Birmingham Boys and Girls Union.

FINANCES *Year* 2007–08 *Income* £43,823 *Grants* £20,650 *Assets* £1,107,053

TRUSTEES Dr I Durie-Kerr; M P Green; D A Seccombe; R S Watkins.

HOW TO APPLY In writing to the correspondent. No reply is sent to unsuccessful applicants unless an sae is enclosed. The trustees meet quarterly.

WHO TO APPLY TO Mrs S E Darby, 2nd Floor, 33 Great Charles Street, Birmingham B3 3JN

CC NO 266054   **ESTABLISHED** 1973

■ Medical Research Council

WHERE FUNDING CAN BE GIVEN UK and overseas.

WHO CAN BENEFIT Organisations benefiting medical professionals, research workers and scientists.

WHAT IS FUNDED To promote the development of medical and related biological research and to advance knowledge that will lead to improved health care.

SAMPLE GRANTS Asthma UK, British Heart Foundation, British Red Cross, Leeds University, London School of Hygiene & Tropical Medicine, MRC Clinical Trials Unit, MRC Epidemiology & Medical Care Unit, MRC Gambia Unit, MRC National Institute of Medical Research and Sheffield University.

FINANCES *Year* 2007–08 *Income* £1,818,000 *Grants* £934,000 *Assets* £2,004,000

TRUSTEES Prof. Eve Cordelia Johnstone; Anthony David Smith; Prof. Genevra Mercy Richardson; Charles John Perrin; Michael James Brooks.

HOW TO APPLY **This trust states that it does not respond to unsolicited applications.** Research opportunities are identified by the charity and responded to.

WHO TO APPLY TO Dr Angela Hind, 20 Park Crescent, London W1B 1AL *Tel* 020 7670 5380 *email* angela.hind@headoffice.mrc.ac.uk *Website* www.mrc.ac.uk

CC NO 250696   **ESTABLISHED** 1920

■ The Medlock Charitable Trust

WHERE FUNDING CAN BE GIVEN Overwhelmingly the areas of Bath and Boston in Lincolnshire.

WHO CAN BENEFIT Small local projects and established organisations benefiting children, adults and young people.

WHAT IS FUNDED General charitable purposes, especially education, medicine, research and social services for the benefit of the local community.

WHAT IS NOT FUNDED No grants to individuals or students.

TYPE OF GRANT One-off capital and revenue grants for up to two years.

RANGE OF GRANTS Mainly less than £10,000.

SAMPLE GRANTS Boshier-Hinton Foundation (£312,000); Quartet Community Foundation (£75,000); Butterfly Hospice Trust (£70,000); Covidien UK Ltd (£52,000); Holbourne Museum (£50,000); Beach Cliff School (£30,000); Somerset 500 Club (£25,000); Karnataka Parents Association (£20,000); Wiltshire Music Centre Trust (£10,000); Off the Record (£7,000); Yorkshire Eye Research (£2,000); NSPCC (£1,000); and Banes Credit Union (£500).

FINANCES Year 2007–08 Income £1,297,588 Grants £1,652,163 Assets £26,860,961

TRUSTEES Leonard Medlock; Jacqueline Medlock; David Medlock; Peter Carr.

HOW TO APPLY In writing to the correspondent.

WHO TO APPLY TO Leonard Medlock, Trustee, St George's Lodge, 33 Oldfield Road, Bath BA2 3ND Tel 01225 428221 Fax 01225 789262

CC NO 326927   **ESTABLISHED** 1985

■ The Anthony and Elizabeth Mellows Charitable Settlement

WHERE FUNDING CAN BE GIVEN UK.

WHO CAN BENEFIT UK bodies benefiting: children and young adults; actors and entertainment professionals; musicians; textile workers and designers; and writers and poets.

WHAT IS FUNDED The acquisition of objects to be used or displayed in houses of the National Trust or churches of the Church of England; the encouragement of hospices and medical research; support of the arts; the training and development of children and young people. The trustees can only consider projects recommended to them by those UK institutions with whom they are in close cooperation.

WHAT IS NOT FUNDED Applications from individuals, including students, are ineligible.

TYPE OF GRANT Generally single projects.

SAMPLE GRANTS The Order of St John (£51,000); St John Ambulance Museum (£10,000); the Lambeth Fund and St Martin-in-the Fields (£5,000 each); Royal Academy Trust (£4,500); and Royal Opera House Foundation (£4,000).

FINANCES Year 2007–08 Income £94,280 Grants £86,279 Assets £496,767

TRUSTEES Prof. Anthony R Mellows; Mrs Elizabeth Mellows.

HOW TO APPLY Applications are considered when received, but only from UK institutions. No application forms are used. Grants decisions are made three times a year when the trustees meet to consider applications.

WHO TO APPLY TO Prof. Anthony Mellows, Trustee, 22 Devereux Court, Temple Bar, London WC2R 3JR Tel 020 7583 8813

CC NO 281229   **ESTABLISHED** 1980

■ Melodor Ltd

WHERE FUNDING CAN BE GIVEN UK and overseas.

WHO CAN BENEFIT Organisations benefiting Jewish people.

WHAT IS FUNDED Jewish causes, particularly the advancement of religion in accordance with the orthodox Jewish faith.

RANGE OF GRANTS Up to £30,000.

SAMPLE GRANTS Centre for Torah Education Trust (£30,000); Beis Rochel (£19,000); Chasdei

Yoel (£12,000); Beth Hamedrash Hachodosh (£6,100); Yeshivas Ohel Shimon (£5,300); Beis Minchas Yitzhok (£4,000); Talmud Torah Education Trust (£3,000); Dushinsky Trust (£1,900); and Kollel Chelkas Yakov and Yetev Lev (£1,500 each).

FINANCES Year 2007–08 Income £180,249 Grants £156,062 Assets £854,815

TRUSTEES H Weiss; Mrs Y Weiss; Mrs Z Weiss; Mrs E Henry; Mrs J Bleier; Mrs M Freilander; Mrs M Weiss; Mrs R Rabinowitz; P Weiss; P Neumann; E Neumann; H Neumann; M Neumann; Mrs R Delange; Mrs R Ollech.

HOW TO APPLY In writing to the correspondent.

WHO TO APPLY TO Bernardin Weiss, Secretary, 10 Cubley Road, Salford M7 4GN Tel 0161 720 6188

CC NO 260972   **ESTABLISHED** 1970

■ Melow Charitable Trust

WHERE FUNDING CAN BE GIVEN UK and overseas.

WHO CAN BENEFIT Jewish charities.

WHAT IS FUNDED Jewish charitable purposes.

RANGE OF GRANTS £750–£120,000.

SAMPLE GRANTS Lovlev Charitable Trust (£109,000); Edupoor Ltd (£73,000); Keren Zedokah Foundation (£53,000); Havenpoint Ltd (£50,000); Keren Hachesed Trust (£48,000); and Shalom Torah Centres (£33,000).

FINANCES Year 2006–07 Income £1,136,767 Grants £869,813 Assets £4,288,969

TRUSTEES Miriam Spitz; Esther Weiser.

HOW TO APPLY In writing to the correspondent.

WHO TO APPLY TO J Low, 21 Warwick Grove, London E5 9HX Tel 020 8806 1549

CC NO 275454   **ESTABLISHED** 1978

■ Meningitis Trust

WHERE FUNDING CAN BE GIVEN UK.

WHO CAN BENEFIT Organisations researching meningitis.

WHAT IS FUNDED Research into all aspects of the disease.

FINANCES Year 2007–08 Income £3,462,723 Grants £330,000 Assets £1,639,669

TRUSTEES Lesley Green; Mrs Bernadette Julia McGhie; Mrs Gillian Mae Noble; James William Edward Wilson; Michael Anthony Hall; Peter James Johnson; Robert Johnson; Suzanne Devine; Mike Carroll; James Kilmister; Richard Greenhalgh.

OTHER INFORMATION In 2007–08 a further £193,000 was distributed in grants to individuals.

HOW TO APPLY Application forms are available from the correspondent. Requests for financial support are reviewed regularly by the Financial Grants Review Panel.

WHO TO APPLY TO Tracy Lewendon, Financial Grants & Helpline Administrator, Fern House, Bath Road, Stroud, Gloucestershire GL5 3TJ Tel 01453 768000 Fax 01453 768001 email helpline@meningitis-trust.org Website www.meningitis-trust.org

CC NO 803016   **ESTABLISHED** 1986

■ Menuchar Ltd

WHERE FUNDING CAN BE GIVEN UK.

WHO CAN BENEFIT Jewish organisations.

WHAT IS FUNDED Advancement of religion in accordance with the orthodox Jewish faith, and relief of people in need.

WHAT IS NOT FUNDED No grants to non-registered charities or to individuals.
TYPE OF GRANT Primarily one-off.
SAMPLE GRANTS List of beneficiaries unavailable.
FINANCES *Year* 2007–08 *Income* £281,002 *Grants* £351,668 *Assets* £154,756
TRUSTEES N Bude; Mrs G Bude.
HOW TO APPLY In writing to the correspondent.
WHO TO APPLY TO The Trustees, c/o Barry Flack & Co., Knight House, 27–31 East Barnet Road, Barnet EN4 8RN *Tel* 020 8275 5186
CC NO 262782   **ESTABLISHED** 1971

■ Mercaz Torah Vechesed Limited
WHERE FUNDING CAN BE GIVEN Worldwide.
WHO CAN BENEFIT Charitable organisations and individuals.
WHAT IS FUNDED The advancement of the orthodox Jewish faith, orthodox Jewish religious education, and the relief of poverty and infirmity amongst members of the orthodox Jewish community.
FINANCES *Year* 2007–08 *Income* £1,343,828 *Grants* £1,324,864 *Assets* £41,754
TRUSTEES Jacob Moishe Grosskopf; Joseph Ostreicher; Mordche David Rand.
PUBLICATIONS The trust states that, 'a full list of the material grants made by the charity during the year is available on application in writing to the trustees at the Principal Office'. A request has been sent by this organisation but a reply is yet to be received.
HOW TO APPLY In writing to the correspondent.
WHO TO APPLY TO Joseph Ostreicher, Secretary, 28 Braydon Road, London N16 6QB *Tel* 020 8880 5366
CC NO 1109212   **ESTABLISHED** 2005

■ Brian Mercer Charitable Trust
WHERE FUNDING CAN BE GIVEN UK and overseas.
WHO CAN BENEFIT Charitable organisations.
WHAT IS FUNDED Advancement of education, promotion of medical and scientific research.
TYPE OF GRANT Mainly recurrent.
RANGE OF GRANTS £1,500 to £50,000.
SAMPLE GRANTS Fight for Sight (£50,000); SightSavers International and British Council for the Prevention of Blindness (£20,000 each); Macular Disease Society, Marie Curie Cancer Care and The Living Paintings Trust (£10,000 each); Orbis Charitable Trust and RoRo Sailing Trust (£5,000 each); Royal British Society of Sculptors (£2,700); and Blackburn College (£1,500).
FINANCES *Year* 2007–08 *Income* £604,273 *Grants* £192,973 *Assets* £20,987,480
TRUSTEES Mrs C J Clancy; K J Merrill; A T Rowntree; R P T Duckworth; Mrs A E T Clitheroe.
HOW TO APPLY In writing to the correspondent. Trustees meet at least twice yearly to allocate grants.
WHO TO APPLY TO A T Rowntree, Trustee, c/o Waterworths, Central Buildings, Richmond Terrace, Blackburn BB1 7AP *Tel* 01254 686 600 *email* arowntree@waterworths.co.uk
CC NO 1076925   **ESTABLISHED** 1999

■ The Mercers' Charitable Foundation
WHERE FUNDING CAN BE GIVEN UK; strong preference for London and the West Midlands.
WHO CAN BENEFIT Registered or exempt charities.
WHAT IS FUNDED General welfare, older people, conservation, arts, Christian faith activities, educational institutions.
WHAT IS NOT FUNDED These should be read alongside the specific exclusions for the particular category into which an application falls: animal welfare charities; endowment appeals; work overseas (unless there is a significant relationship with the organisation); projects that are primarily political; activities that are the responsibility of the local, health or education authority or other similar body; activities that have already taken place; other grant making trusts; sponsorship or marketing appeals; fundraising events; loans or business finance; running costs such as rent and service charges. The foundation also states: 'We cannot support capital projects that are submitted by public health or education authorities. Whilst we normally consider a range of capital projects from charities, in the current economic climate we have decided to concentrate our support on maintaining service delivery. Our capital support is restricted to appeals that are within the **last 20% of their target** and for which support in the region of £5,000–£20,000 will make a difference, are **not awaiting an outstanding lottery decision** and include a **realistic business plan** showing how the building will be used and future revenue predictions.'
TYPE OF GRANT Building and other capital grants with certain restrictions; feasibility studies; one-off grants; project and research grants; recurring and start-up costs. Grants given for up to three years.
SAMPLE GRANTS Earl of Northampton's Charity (£880,000); Teach First (£130,000); Federation of London Youth Clubs and Royal Ballet School (£100,000 each); Shelter (£50,000); Thomas Telford School (£38,000); Christianity and Culture (St John's College) (£36,000); Barbican Centre (£33,000); Autism Speaks, Body and Soul, Children's Trust and Treehouse Trust (£25,000 each); Hexham Abbey and Victoria and Albert Museum (£20,000 each); Watts Gallery (£19,000); the Pilgrim Trust (£15,000); and Almshouse Association and Field Lane Foundation (£10,000 each).
FINANCES *Year* 2008–09 *Income* £6,488,000 *Grants* £5,038,540 *Assets* £8,001,000
TRUSTEES First Mercer Trustee Limited; Second Mercer Trustee Limited
HOW TO APPLY Applications can be made online via the foundation's website. Grants officers are happy to give advice by telephone or email.
WHO TO APPLY TO The Clerk, Mercers' Hall, Ironmonger Lane, London EC2V 8HE *Tel* 020 7726 4991 *Fax* 020 7600 1158 *email* mail@mercers.co.uk *Website* www.mercers.co.uk
CC NO 326340   **ESTABLISHED** 1982

■ The Merchant Taylors' Company Charities Fund
WHERE FUNDING CAN BE GIVEN UK, especially inner London.
WHO CAN BENEFIT Organisations benefiting children, older people, actors and entertainment professionals, medical professionals,

musicians, substance misuse, carers, people who are disabled, and homeless people.

WHAT IS FUNDED Areas that may be considered are the arts, social care and community development, disability, older people, poverty, medical studies and research, chemical dependency, homelessness, children, and education, with priority for special needs.

TYPE OF GRANT One-off grants or three-year tapering grants.

RANGE OF GRANTS £1—£10,000.

SAMPLE GRANTS Non-educational awards included those to: Dartford Methodist Mission (£7,500); Deafblind UK and National Youth Orchestra (£5,000 each); St Helen's Church – Bishopgate (£2,000); CREATE – Deptford Churches Centre (£1,700); St Paul's Cathedral of Friends and St Margaret's Church – Lee (£1,000 each); Walk the Walk (£500); and Brandram Road Community Centre (£300).

FINANCES *Year* 2007 *Income* £94,389 *Grants* £98,750 *Assets* £276,190

TRUSTEES Richard Charlton; Peregrine Massey; Christopher Keville; The Earl of Stockton.

HOW TO APPLY Awards are restricted at present to charities nominated by the Livery Committee.

WHO TO APPLY TO Matthew Dear, Charities Officer, 30 Threadneedle Street, London EC2R 8JB *Tel* 020 7450 4440 *email* charities@merchant-taylors.co.uk *Website* www.merchanttaylors.co.uk

CC NO 1069124   **ESTABLISHED** 1941

■ The Merchant Venturers' Charity

WHERE FUNDING CAN BE GIVEN Bristol.

WHO CAN BENEFIT Local and regional organisations and local branches of national organisations particularly those supporting the young, aged and disadvantaged; and some individuals.

WHAT IS FUNDED Any charitable purpose which enhances the quality of life for all, including learning and the acquisition of skills by supporting education; supporting community activity; and assisting in the preservation of open spaces and heritage.

TYPE OF GRANT Some recurrent.

SAMPLE GRANTS Prince's Trust (£19,000); St Mary Redcliffe Organ Appeal (£5,000); and Withywood Community School Leadership Programme (£2,500).

FINANCES *Year* 2008 *Income* £693,956 *Grants* £276,472 *Assets* £4,227,672

TRUSTEES The Standing Committee of the Society of Merchant Venturers of Bristol.

HOW TO APPLY In writing to the correspondent. A sub-committee of the trustees meets bi-annually while the trustees meet monthly and can, if necessary, consider any urgent business at that meeting.

WHO TO APPLY TO Richard Morris, The Society of Merchant Venturers, Merchants' Hall, The Promenade, Clifton, Bristol BS8 3NH *Tel* 0117 973 8058 *Fax* 0117 973 5884 *email* enquiry@merchantventurers.com

CC NO 264302   **ESTABLISHED** 1972

■ The Merchants' House of Glasgow

WHERE FUNDING CAN BE GIVEN Glasgow and the west of Scotland.

WHO CAN BENEFIT Registered charities benefiting seamen, pensioners and young people (aged 10 to 30) in full-time education.

WHAT IS FUNDED Seamen's missions, general charitable purposes, and grants to pensioners and young people in education.

WHAT IS NOT FUNDED The trust will not, unless in exceptional circumstances, make grants to: individuals; churches other than Glasgow Cathedral; organisations that have received support in the two years preceding an application.

TYPE OF GRANT Capital projects.

RANGE OF GRANTS Up to £4,000.

SAMPLE GRANTS Previous grant recipients have included: Erskine Hospital, the National Youth Orchestra of Scotland, Scottish Motor Neurone Disease, the Castle Howard Trust, Delta, the National Burns Memorial Homes, Quarriers Village and Shelter.

FINANCES *Year* 2008 *Income* £825,886 *Grants* £60,000

TRUSTEES The Directors.

HOW TO APPLY In writing to the correspondent at any time, supported by copy of accounts and information about the organisation's principal activities.

WHO TO APPLY TO The Directors, 7 West George Street, Glasgow G2 1BA *Tel* 0141 221 8272 *Fax* 0141 226 2275 *email* theoffice@merchantshouse.org.uk *Website* www.merchantshouse.org.uk

SC NO SC008900   **ESTABLISHED** 1605

■ Mercury Phoenix Trust

WHERE FUNDING CAN BE GIVEN Worldwide.

WHO CAN BENEFIT Registered charities benefiting people with AIDS and the HIV virus.

WHAT IS FUNDED Relief of poverty, sickness and distress of people affected by AIDS and the HIV virus, and to stimulate awareness of the virus throughout the world.

TYPE OF GRANT One-off, capital, project, running costs.

SAMPLE GRANTS Care International – Niger/Ivory Coast, Y Care International – India and Christian Aid – India (£10,000); Mfesane – South Africa (£8,500); Childhope UK – India and GAPA – Brazil (£7,000 each); CAF – Kenya (£6,000); Nepal International, Group 12 – Zamia and Social Welfare – Nepal (£5,000 each).

FINANCES *Year* 2007–08 *Income* £287,280 *Grants* £243,500 *Assets* £1,168,369

TRUSTEES M Austin; H J Beach; B H May; R M Taylor.

HOW TO APPLY In writing to the correspondent.

WHO TO APPLY TO Peter Chant, 22 Cottage Offices, Latimer Park, Latimer, Chesham, Buckinghamshire HP5 1TU *Tel* 01494 766 799 *email* mercuryphoenixtrust@idrec.com *Website* www.mercuryphoenixtrust.com

CC NO 1013768   **ESTABLISHED** 1992

■ The Mersey Docks and Harbour Company Charitable Fund

WHERE FUNDING CAN BE GIVEN Merseyside.

WHO CAN BENEFIT Seafaring, registered charities on Merseyside.

WHAT IS FUNDED The relief of people who are sick, disabled and retired in the dock service or the families of those who were killed in service; and to benefit charities in the town or port of Liverpool.

RANGE OF GRANTS £25–£10,000.

SAMPLE GRANTS The Mersey Mission to Seafarers (£10,000); Apostleship of the Sea, Jubilee

Think carefully about every application. Is it justified?

711

Sailing Trust and Royal Liverpool Seamen's Orphans Institutions (£2,000 each); and Brathay Hall Trust, Brunswick Youth Club, Fairbridge Merseyside, Friends of Old Christ Church, Friends of the Sea, Samaritans and the Salvation Army (£1,000 each).
FINANCES *Year* 2008 *Income* £167,365 *Grants* £89,245 *Assets* £78,769
TRUSTEES S R Baxter; A A Barr.
HOW TO APPLY In writing to the correspondent.
WHO TO APPLY TO C R Marrison Gill, Secretary, The Mersey Docks and Harbour Company, Maritime Centre, Port of Liverpool, Liverpool L21 1LA
CC NO 206913   **ESTABLISHED** 1811

■ Community Foundation for Merseyside

WHERE FUNDING CAN BE GIVEN Merseyside, Halton and Lancashire.
WHO CAN BENEFIT Charitable organisations.
WHAT IS FUNDED General charitable purposes, community, regeneration. The foundation manages funds on behalf of parent donors. Funding priorities will vary considerably depending on the requirements of these donors.
FINANCES *Year* 2008–09 *Income* £4,196,041 *Grants* £3,576,153 *Assets* £2,001,114
TRUSTEES Andrew Kellaway, Chair; Rosemary Hawley; Bob Towers; Mike Eastwood; Sally Yeoman; Andy Wallis.
OTHER INFORMATION The foundation manages funds on behalf of parent donors. Funding priorities will vary considerably depending on the requirements of these donors.
HOW TO APPLY The policy of the foundation is to award grants to organisations that have made a formal application for a grant, that fulfil the requirements of the relevant grant fund and that have the necessary systems to administer a grant. All grant applications are subject to a formal appraisal by the foundation's staff before being presented to the local grant panel for a decision when a scoring system is used to guide decisions.
Full guidelines and application forms for individual funds are available from the foundation's website.
WHO TO APPLY TO Cathy Elliott, Chief Executive, c/o Alliance and Leicester, Bridle Road, Bootle, Merseyside, GIR OAA *Tel* 0151 966 4604 *Fax* 0151 966 3384 *email* info@cfmerseyside.org.uk *Website* www.cfmerseyside.org.uk
CC NO 1068887   **ESTABLISHED** 1998

■ The Zachary Merton and George Woofindin Convalescent Trust

WHERE FUNDING CAN BE GIVEN Preference for Sheffield and Lincoln including the following areas: north Nottinghamshire, north Derbyshire and South Yorkshire.
WHO CAN BENEFIT Organisations benefiting carers, disabled people and people disadvantaged by poverty.
WHAT IS FUNDED Convalescent homes, travelling expenses of convalescent poor people, respite care for carers, people in need through illness, and community medicine.
WHAT IS NOT FUNDED No grants to individuals.
TYPE OF GRANT Recurring costs; up to two years.
RANGE OF GRANTS £500–£3,500.
SAMPLE GRANTS SHARE Psychotherapy Agency (£4,500); British Red Cross Society and Cancer Relief (MacMillan Nurses) (£4,000 each); Trinity

Day Care Trust (£3,500); Marie Curie Cancer Care – Lincoln (£2,000); Age Concern (£1,000); and Sick Children's Hospital Trust (£500).
FINANCES *Year* 2008 *Income* £47,853 *Grants* £42,100 *Assets* £833,861
TRUSTEES G Connell, Chair; M G S Frampton; Mrs T Chattopadhyay; Mrs J Fretwell-Downing; N J A Hutton; C J Jewitt; Mrs P M Perriam; Mrs J Mason; Dr B Sharrack; M P Newton.
HOW TO APPLY In writing to the correspondent, by the middle of March or September.
WHO TO APPLY TO G J Smallman, Secretary, Wrigleys, Fountain Precinct, Balm Green, Sheffield S1 2JA *Tel* 0114 2675 594 *Fax* 0114 2763176
CC NO 221760   **ESTABLISHED** 1956

■ The Tony Metherell Charitable Trust

WHERE FUNDING CAN BE GIVEN UK, especially Hertfordshire and Worcestershire.
WHO CAN BENEFIT Particularly older people and people who have cancer or disabilities.
WHAT IS FUNDED General charitable purposes, including hospices, cancer charities and the care and welfare of older people or people who have disabilities.
WHAT IS NOT FUNDED No grants to overseas causes.
RANGE OF GRANTS Up to £5,000.
SAMPLE GRANTS H Hospice (£2,800).
FINANCES *Year* 2007–08 *Income* £17,803 *Grants* £50,205 *Assets* £663,302
TRUSTEES Barry R M Fox; Ms Carolyn J Good.
HOW TO APPLY In writing to the correspondent.
WHO TO APPLY TO Barry R M Fox, Trustee, Jenningsbury, London Road, Hertford SG13 7NS *Tel* 01992 583978
CC NO 1046899   **ESTABLISHED** 1992

■ The Methodist Relief and Development Fund

WHERE FUNDING CAN BE GIVEN Overseas and UK.
WHO CAN BENEFIT Development – indigenous NGOs in the developing world; humanitarian aid – Action by Churches Together (ACT) and existing partner NGOs/organisations in the developing world; and development education – NGOs implementing development education programmes in the UK.
WHAT IS FUNDED Emergency relief in disasters and long-term refugee assistance; overseas development, including agro forestry (organic farming, permaculture etc.), literacy (particularly non-formal education), water (for drinking and agricultural use), health, disability and community development (skills training, micro-enterprise and capacity building); development education in the UK, including campaigns, publications and support for development education organisations which resource MRDF supporters.
WHAT IS NOT FUNDED No grants to individuals or to organisations without charitable status; UK-based development projects; UK-based organisations for overseas work; scholarships for studies or voluntary work overseas; church-building or evangelism; capital costs, or for individual development education centres affiliated to the development education association; large NGO's or their field offices.
TYPE OF GRANT Project costs. Funding for up to one year in the first instance will be considered.
RANGE OF GRANTS Up to £20,000; average £5,000–£15,000.

712

Does the trust you have chosen match your needs? Haphazard applications waste postage and time

SAMPLE GRANTS Presbyterian Rural Training Centre Fonta (64,000); Samburu Integrated Programme (£42,000); Sense International – Latin America (£25,000); Haritika (£17,000); Labour Behind the Label, Rugmark, World Development Movement and Jubilee Debt Campaign (£15,000 each).

FINANCES *Year* 2007–08 *Income* £1,970,079 *Grants* £1,892,570 *Assets* £569,010

TRUSTEES Clarie Holder; John Cammack; Revd Graham Thompson; Bala Gnanapragasam; Claire Boxall; Prof David Matthews; Max Teare; John Hindson; Revd Kathleen Loughlin; Revd Sonia Hicks; Revd Eric Mustapha.

PUBLICATIONS *Impact* (quarterly publication), development education resources (*Harvest Pack Study Pack*); themed project information sheets; *Lifelines* (monthly e-newsletter).

HOW TO APPLY Applications should be sent to the correspondent. Guidance on funding criteria for development is available on the website or by contacting MRDF. Initial applications should consist of a proposal of no more than ten pages, including a detailed budget. Trustees' meetings are held quarterly, but MRDF may not be able to consider applications for several months and cannot enter into correspondence regarding the status of applications.

WHO TO APPLY TO David Fletcher, 25 Marylebone Road, London NW1 5JR *Tel* 020 7467 5145 *email* mrdf@methodistchurch.org.uk *Website* www.mrdf.org.uk

CC NO 291691   **ESTABLISHED** 1985

■ The Metropolitan Drinking Fountain and Cattle Trough Association

WHERE FUNDING CAN BE GIVEN UK, mainly London; overseas.

WHO CAN BENEFIT Charitable organisations.

WHAT IS FUNDED Projects working to provide clean water supplies in developing countries, the provision of drinking fountains in schools and the restoration of disused drinking fountains. The preservation of the association's archive materials, artefacts, drinking fountains, cattle troughs and other installations.

SAMPLE GRANTS Brooke Animal Hospital, the Busoga Trust, UK Youth and World Vision (£2,000 each); Spana (£1,500); and World horse Welfare (£1,000 each). 25 schools received grants not exceeding £1,000 and totalling £12,000.

FINANCES *Year* 2008 *Income* £37,966 *Grants* £29,389 *Assets* £541,226

TRUSTEES J E Mills, Chair; R P Baber; Mrs S Fuller; Sir J Smith; M W Elliott; M Nation; A King; M Bear; Mrs L Erith.

PUBLICATIONS The Drinking Fountain Association.

HOW TO APPLY In writing to the correspondent. In addition, in considering an application for a grant, trustees also require the following information: A copy of the most recent audited accounts; How has the cost of the project been ascertained, e.g. qualified surveyor?; How many people/animals is it estimated would use the fountain/trough in a day?; Will the charity supervise the project, if not who would?; Where is it anticipated the remainder of the funds to complete the project will come from?

WHO TO APPLY TO R P Baber, Secretary, Oaklands, 5 Queenborough Gardens, Chislehurst, Kent BR7 6NP *Tel* 020 8467 1261 *email* ralph.baber@tesco.net *Website* www.drinkingfountains.org

CC NO 207743   **ESTABLISHED** 1960

■ T and J Meyer Family Foundation Limited

WHERE FUNDING CAN BE GIVEN UK and overseas.

WHO CAN BENEFIT Charitable organisations.

WHAT IS FUNDED The primary focus of the foundation is on education, healthcare and the environment. The criteria for donee charities are: organisations which alleviate the suffering of humanity through health, education and environment; organisations with extremely high correlation between what is gifted and what the beneficiary receives; organisations who struggle to raise funds either because either they are new, their size or their access to funds is constrained; organisations who promote long-term effective sustainable solutions.

SAMPLE GRANTS University of Oregon (£100,000); Sisters of Sacred Heart of J and M (£40,000); Cancer Active (£7,000); Hope and Homes for Children (£5,000); Living Heart – Peru (£4,000); Bowel Cancer UK (£1,500); Dreamscheme Network (£1,000); and Children's Fire and Burns Trust (£750).

FINANCES *Year* 2007 *Income* £239,204 *Grants* £163,724 *Assets* £17,123,507

TRUSTEES A C Meyer; J D Meyer; Q H Meyer; I T Meyer; M M Meyer.

HOW TO APPLY In writing to the correspondent, email info@tjmff.org.

WHO TO APPLY TO The Trustees, 3 Kendrick Mews, London SW7 3HG

CC NO 1087507   **ESTABLISHED** 2001

■ Mickleham Charitable Trust

WHERE FUNDING CAN BE GIVEN UK, with a preference for Norfolk.

WHO CAN BENEFIT Charitable organisations.

WHAT IS FUNDED Relief-in-need, particularly work with young people and people who are blind.

TYPE OF GRANT Mainly recurrent.

RANGE OF GRANTS £500–£10,000.

SAMPLE GRANTS Orbis International (£10,000); Motability – Norfolk (£6,000); Defeating Deafness, East Anglian Children's Hospice, Norfolk & Norwich Association for the Blind and YESU (£5,000 each); SCOPE (£4,000); Age Concern – Norwich (£3,000); Foundation for Conductive Education (£2,000); and British Blind Sport (£1,000).

FINANCES *Year* 2007–08 *Income* £142,708 *Grants* £108,000 *Assets* £3,120,899

TRUSTEES P R Norton; S F Nunney; Mrs J A Richardson.

HOW TO APPLY In writing to the correspondent.

WHO TO APPLY TO Philip Norton, Trustee, c/o Hansells, 13–14 The Close, Norwich NR1 4DS *Tel* 01603 615 731 *email* philipnorton@hansells.co.uk

CC NO 1048337   **ESTABLISHED** 1995

■ Gerald Micklem Charitable Trust

WHERE FUNDING CAN BE GIVEN UK.

WHO CAN BENEFIT Registered charities benefiting at risk groups and people who are disadvantaged by poverty or socially isolated.

WHAT IS FUNDED Medicine and health, welfare and general charitable purposes.

WHAT IS NOT FUNDED The trust does not make grants to individuals, does not enter into sponsorship arrangements with individuals and does not make grants to organisations that are not UK-registered charities. 'The areas of charitable activity that fall outside the trust's current funding priorities are: drug/alcohol misuse and counselling; museums, galleries and heritage; performing arts and cultural organisations; churches; and, overseas aid.'

TYPE OF GRANT One-off and recurrent.

RANGE OF GRANTS £2,000–£4,000.

SAMPLE GRANTS Penny Brohn Cancer Care, Osteopathic Centre for Children and the Rosemary Foundation (£4,000 each); Against Breast Cancer, BRACE, British Schools Exploring Society, Cecily's Fund and Motor Neurone Disease Association (£3,000 each); Hope UK, Open Sight and UK Sports Association for People with Learning Disability (£2,000 each); and Little Ouse Headwaters Project (£1,000).

FINANCES *Year* 2008 *Income* £120,680 *Grants* £96,000 *Assets* £513,783

TRUSTEES Susan J Shone; Joanna L Scott-Dalgleish; Helen Ratcliffe.

HOW TO APPLY In writing to the correspondent. Interested applicants should note that the organisations which have received grants in the past should not be taken as indicative of a geographical or other bias.

WHO TO APPLY TO Mrs S J Shone, Trustee, Bolinge Hill Farm, Buriton, Petersfield, Hampshire GU31 4NN *Tel* 01730 264 207 *email* mail@geraldmicklemct.org.uk *Website* www.geraldmicklemct.org.uk

CC NO 802583   **ESTABLISHED** 1988

■ The Masonic Province of Middlesex Charitable Trust

WHERE FUNDING CAN BE GIVEN Middlesex.

WHO CAN BENEFIT Masons and others.

WHAT IS FUNDED Masonic charities and non-Masonic charities.

RANGE OF GRANTS £100–£5,500.

SAMPLE GRANTS Hillingdon Crossroads Carers, Queen Mary Sailing Club and the Natasha Parket Appeal(£5,000 each); Dreamflight (£3,000); Hillingdon Shopmobility (£2,000); and Mayor's Appeal Brent (£1,000).

FINANCES *Year* 2007–08 *Income* £66,587 *Grants* £31,874 *Assets* £1,405,008

TRUSTEES Peter Richard Alleyne Baker; David Ian Allan; Jonathan Markham Gollow; Adrian John Howorth; Peter Gledhill.

HOW TO APPLY On a form is available from the correspondent or the Provincial Office.

WHO TO APPLY TO Peter Gledhill, Secretary, 85 Fakenham Way, Sandhurst, Berkshire GU47 0YS *email* peter.gledhill@btinternet.com

CC NO 1064406   **ESTABLISHED** 1997

■ Midhurst Pensions Trust

WHERE FUNDING CAN BE GIVEN UK and overseas.

WHO CAN BENEFIT Registered charities and individuals.

WHAT IS FUNDED General charitable purposes and pensions to older people in need in Midhurst – West Sussex.

WHAT IS NOT FUNDED No grants to individuals who do not have a connection to the Cowdray Estate.

SAMPLE GRANTS The Birthday House Trust (£79,000).

FINANCES *Year* 2007–08 *Income* £129,049 *Grants* £78,900 *Assets* £3,984,561

TRUSTEES The Cowdray Trust Limited and Rathbone Trust Company Ltd.

HOW TO APPLY In writing to the correspondent. Acknowledgements will be sent to unsuccessful applicants if a sae is enclosed with the application.

WHO TO APPLY TO Miss Laura Gosling, c/o Millbank Financial Services Ltd, Pollen House, 10–12 Cork Street, London W15 3LW *Tel* 020 7439 9061 *email* charity@mfs.co.uk

CC NO 245230   **ESTABLISHED** 1965

■ The Migraine Trust

WHERE FUNDING CAN BE GIVEN UK and overseas.

WHO CAN BENEFIT Organisations benefiting people suffering from migraines, medical professionals, research workers and scientists.

WHAT IS FUNDED Research grants, fellowships and studentships (studentships are applied for by host institution only) for the study of migraine. Funds provide for research into migraine at recognised institutions, e.g. hospitals and universities.

FINANCES *Year* 2008–09 *Income* £554,925 *Grants* £183,572 *Assets* £372,053

TRUSTEES Andrew Jordan, Chair; J P S Wolff-Ingham; Prof. P J Goadsby; Ms S Hammond; Dr H McGregor; Dr Anne McGregor; Mrs Jennifer Mills; Dr Mark Wetherall; Dr Brendan Davies; Ian Watmore; Mrs Suzanne Marriot.

PUBLICATIONS *Migraine News, Migraine: Understanding and coping with migraine.*

OTHER INFORMATION The trust holds the Migraine Trust International Symposia, funds research into migraine, and has a full sufferer service.

HOW TO APPLY By application form available from trust. Applications will be acknowledged.

WHO TO APPLY TO Adam Speller, 2nd Floor, 55–56 Russel Square, London WC1B 4HP *Tel* 020 7462 6604 *email* info@migrainetrust.org *Website* www.migrainetrust.org

CC NO 1081300   **ESTABLISHED** 1965

■ Miles Trust for the Putney and Roehampton Community

WHERE FUNDING CAN BE GIVEN The borough of Wandsworth.

WHO CAN BENEFIT Organisations benefiting people of all ages, people disadvantaged by poverty and homeless people.

WHAT IS FUNDED Schools, churches, youth organisations, and social welfare organisations caring for older people and people who are poor, homeless or sick.

WHAT IS NOT FUNDED No grants to individuals.

TYPE OF GRANT Some recurring, but new grants may be one-off.

RANGE OF GRANTS £100–£5,000 with occasional larger special grants.

SAMPLE GRANTS 4th Putney Scouts (£6,400); Wandsworth Bereavement Service (£3,000); Putney Poor Relief Committee (£2,500); Wandsworth Mind (£2,000); St Mary's Church of England School (£1,500); and Children's Health Centre Samaritan Fund and Heathside Resource Centre (£1,000 each).

FINANCES *Year* 2008 *Income* £25,916 *Grants* £33,727 *Assets* £451,662

TRUSTEES A R Collender, Chair; Mrs A Raikes; R J G Holman; Revd Dr Giles Fraser; P Kitchen; Dr A Webster; Mrs J Maxwell; Mrs L Moir; Mrs J Walters; Mrs C V M Davey; Mrs Kate Caseley.

HOW TO APPLY In writing to the correspondent. Applications are considered first by a sub-committee of trustees with specialist knowledge of the particular area to which the request for funds relates (church, youth or community); recommendations are then put before full meetings of the Trustees, which are held bi-annually.

WHO TO APPLY TO Mrs Angela Holman, Secretary & Administrator, 11 Genoa Avenue, Putney, London SW15 6DY *email* angelaholman@virgin.net

CC NO 246784   **ESTABLISHED** 1967

··

■ Millennium Stadium Charitable Trust

WHERE FUNDING CAN BE GIVEN Wales.

WHO CAN BENEFIT The trust supports: not-for-profit organisations; properly constituted voluntary organisations; charitable organisations; voluntary groups working with local authorities (applicant cannot be the local authority); applications from groups of any age. Priority is given to organisations serving groups and communities suffering from the greatest disadvantage.

WHAT IS FUNDED Through its grant funding the trust aims to improve the quality of life of people who live and work in Wales. In particular the trust aims to promote education, history, language and culture, particularly for those who face disadvantage or discrimination. The trust makes grants in four programme areas: (1) sport; (2) the arts; (3) the environment; (4) the community. Wales is a country rich in culture, history, language and sporting successes. In today's era of globalisation people often forget what is in their locality. As a result the trust is keen to help young people learn more about their country via exchange programmes and has made provision to support youth exchange programmes which fall in to any of the funding categories of the trust.

WHAT IS NOT FUNDED The trust does not support: projects outside of Wales; day-to-day running costs; projects that seek to redistribute grant funds for the benefit of third party organisations; payments of debts/overdrafts; retrospective requests; requests from individuals; payment to profit-making organisations; applications made solely in the name of a local authority. (N.B. In addition to the above, successful applicants may not reapply to the trust until a three year period from the date of grant offer has elapsed. The grant offer letter will advise applicants of the date when they will be eligible to re-apply.).

RANGE OF GRANTS The trust issues funding according to the size of geographical area that an organisation has a remit to cover.

FINANCES *Year* 2007–08 *Income* £460,343 *Grants* £243,572 *Assets* £448,667

TRUSTEES Peredur Jenkins; Gerallt Hughes; Russell Goodway; Paul Glaze; Wendy Williams; Michael John; Ian Davies; Simon Wakefield; John Lloyd-Jones; Louise Cassella; Gerald Davies.

HOW TO APPLY The trust asks that all applicants call or email the trust office to discuss their application. Deadline dates can be found on the trust's website, along with full guidelines and application forms.

WHO TO APPLY TO The Trust Officer, c/o Fusion, Loft 2, Ocean House, Clarence Road, Cardiff Bay CF10 5FR *Tel* 029 2049 4963 *Fax* 029 2049 4964 *email* msct@fusionuk.org.uk *Website* www.millenniumstadiumtrust.co.uk

CC NO 1086596   **ESTABLISHED** 2001

···

■ The Hugh and Mary Miller Bequest Trust

WHERE FUNDING CAN BE GIVEN Mainly Scotland.

WHO CAN BENEFIT Registered charities. The trust supports disability causes, with the same 18 organisations receiving the majority of funding each year.

WHAT IS FUNDED Healthcare and disability.

WHAT IS NOT FUNDED Only registered charities are supported. No grants to individuals.

TYPE OF GRANT Capital including buildings, core costs, project, research, recurring costs, running costs and salaries. Funding is available for more than three years.

FINANCES *Year* 2007–08 *Grants* £90,000

TRUSTEES G R G Graham; H C Davidson.

OTHER INFORMATION No recent financial information was available, although previous research indicates that grants are made to regular beneficiaries totalling around £90,000 each year.

HOW TO APPLY The trust states that its funds are fully committed.

WHO TO APPLY TO Andrew S Biggart, Secretary, Maclay Murray and Spens, 151 St Vincent Street, Glasgow G2 5NJ *Tel* 0141 248 5011 *Fax* 0141 271 5319 *email* andrew.biggart@mms.co.uk

SC NO SC014950

···

■ The Miller Foundation

WHERE FUNDING CAN BE GIVEN Scotland and other parts of the UK.

WHO CAN BENEFIT Charities benefiting children and young adults; students; at risk groups; disabled groups; those disadvantaged by poverty; and socially isolated people.

WHAT IS FUNDED Grants are given to educational projects, especially at tertiary level. Organisations working for the welfare of humans and animals are also supported, as are schemes working with people who are disabled.

WHAT IS NOT FUNDED No grants to individuals.

RANGE OF GRANTS £1,000–£2,000.

FINANCES *Year* 2007–08 *Income* £195,506 *Grants* £150,000

TRUSTEES C Fleming-Brown; G R G Graham; J Simpson; G F R Fleming-Brown.

HOW TO APPLY The foundation stated in summer 2008 that it was closed to applications.

WHO TO APPLY TO The Secretary, Maclay Murray and Spens, 151 St Vincent Street, Glasgow G2 5NJ

SC NO SC008798   **ESTABLISHED** 1979

Think carefully about every application. Is it justified?

715

■ The Millfield House Foundation

WHERE FUNDING CAN BE GIVEN North east England particularly Tyne and Wear.

WHO CAN BENEFIT Voluntary agencies and other bodies with charitable objectives working with socially and economically disadvantaged people. Bodies undertaking policy research and advocacy should have close links with or voluntary or community organisations in the region. The foundation will support national as well as local bodies, provided that projects are based in the North East of England (includes regional and sub-regional projects; projects which are locally based may be considered so long as they are of wider benefit).

WHAT IS FUNDED Projects supported might for example seek to: give a voice to excluded groups; bring first hand experience of poverty to opinion formers and policy makers; promote social policy discussion in the region; campaign on local social issues. The financial resources of MHF are a tiny fraction of the total available for charitable activity in the North East. The trustees therefore wish to concentrate their resources on projects which most other funding bodies cannot or will not support. As a charity, the foundation must confine its grants to purposes accepted in law as charitable. However, official guidance makes it clear that charities may include a variety of political and campaigning activities to further their purposes. [See 'Speaking Out – Guidance on Political Activity and Campaigning by Charities' published by the Charity Commission].

WHAT IS NOT FUNDED The foundation 'will not fund straightforward service provision, nor mainline university research, nor the wide range of other projects that are eligible for support elsewhere'.

TYPE OF GRANT MHF aims to provide, alone or in partnership with other funders, significant and medium-term support to a small number of carefully selected projects or organisations. It is unlikely to have more than about 6 to 12 grants in payment at the same time and can therefore approve only a small number of new grants in any one year. One-off grants may be between £5,000 and £50,000. Grants for more than one year could be between £20,000 and £30,000 per annum for two or three years.

RANGE OF GRANTS Mostly between £5,000 and £20,000.

SAMPLE GRANTS Institute for Public Policy Research (£60,000); Regional Refugee Forum North East (£30,000); Prison Reform Trust – Smart Justice (£24,000); St Chad's College – Durham University (£19,000); Living Streets (£15,000); Mental Health North East (£5,000); and Church Action on Poverty North East (£3,500).

FINANCES *Year* 2007–08 *Income* £168,312 *Grants* £156,148 *Assets* £6,259,133

TRUSTEES Rosemary Chubb; George Hepburn; Grigor McClelland; Jen McClelland; Stephen McClelland; Sheila Spencer; Jane Streather.

PUBLICATIONS Guidelines for Applicants. Reports on Grant-making: 1984–89 and 1989–96. Report: 'Funding Policy Change for a Better Society in the North East of England', 1996–2004, available in PDF version.

HOW TO APPLY Initial outline proposals should be made in writing to the correspondent. If the application meets the stated guidelines the administrator may request further information or arrange a meeting. Applications unconnected with Tyne and Wear are not acknowledged. The trustees meet twice a year, in May and November so completed applications should arrive by the end of March or end of September.

The administrator is willing to provide guidance for the preparation of final applications, but not without first receiving an outline proposal. Applications should include: (i) Full contact details, including email address if available. A covering letter containing a brief summary of the purpose of the project and the amount sought from MHF, and a substantive paper of no more than four pages. All other information should be provided as Appendices. (ii) A description of the project including its aims and intended outcomes, with specific reference to possible policy implications, an action programme and proposed timescale for delivery. (iii) A budget for the project giving a breakdown of total expenditure and of sources of anticipated income. (iv) A copy of the most recent annual report and audited accounts for the project and/or the sponsoring body. (v) The constitution of the responsible body. (vi) Details of the organisation's policy and procedures for equal opportunities and diversity. (vii) If appropriate, plans for dissemination of the results of the project. (Research reports should be summarised in a format similar to that of the 'Findings' series produced by the Joseph Rowntree Foundation). (viii) Details of arrangements for monitoring and evaluation. (ix) If funding is sought towards the costs of a salaried post, a job description. (x) The names of two independent referees (references may not be taken up in every case). For further information potential applicants are strongly advised to visit the trust's website.

WHO TO APPLY TO Terence Finley, Administrator, 19 The Crescent, Benton Lodge, Newcastle upon Tyne NE7 7ST *Tel* 0191 266 9429 *email* finley@lineone.net *Website* www.mhfdn.org.uk

CC NO 271180   **ESTABLISHED** 1976

■ The Millfield Trust

WHERE FUNDING CAN BE GIVEN UK and worldwide.

WHO CAN BENEFIT Individuals, and organisations benefiting older people, Christians, and people in need.

WHAT IS FUNDED Support of religious or other charitable institutions or work. Advancement of the Protestant and Evangelical tenets of the Christian faith and encouragement of missionary activity. Relief of need. Preference to charities of which the trust has special interest, knowledge or association. Funds fully allocated or committed.

RANGE OF GRANTS £100–£12,500.

SAMPLE GRANTS Gideon's International (£12,500); Mark Gillingham Charitable Trust (£9,200); Ashbury Evangelical Free Church (£3,700); Mission to Europe and Tear Fund – Evangelical Alliance Relief Fund (£3,000 each); and Overseas Council for Theological Education; Swindon Youth for Christ (£1,000); Gospel Printing Mission (£800); Liverpool School of Tropical Medicine (£500); Anglo Peruvian Childcare Mission (£400); Family in Trust (£300); and Spanish Gospel Mission (£100).

FINANCES *Year* 2007–08 *Income* £79,430 *Grants* £69,990 *Assets* £137,865

TRUSTEES D Bunce; P W Bunce; S D Bunce; A C Bunce; Mrs Rita Bunce.

HOW TO APPLY No replies to unsolicited applications.

WHO TO APPLY TO D Bunce, Trustee, Millfield House, Bell Lane, Liddington, Swindon, Wiltshire SN4 0HE *Tel* 01793 790 181

CC NO 262406   **ESTABLISHED** 1971

■ The Millhouses Charitable Trust

WHERE FUNDING CAN BE GIVEN UK and overseas.

WHO CAN BENEFIT Registered charities benefiting Christians, at risk groups, people disadvantaged by poverty, socially isolated people, victims of famine, disasters and war.

WHAT IS FUNDED Overseas aid, social welfare and community services (with a Christian emphasis). A preference is shown for Baptist charities.

WHAT IS NOT FUNDED Grants are made to registered charities only; no grants to individuals.

TYPE OF GRANT Mostly recurrent.

RANGE OF GRANTS £250–£12,000.

SAMPLE GRANTS NSPCC and Christian Solidarity (£5,000 each); Release International and Barnabus Fund (£2,500 each); Children's Society, Crisis and Oasis (£1,000 each); Rehab UK and Medical Foundation (£500 each); and Mercy Ships, Operation Mobilisation and Smile (£250 each).

FINANCES *Year* 2007–08 *Income* £43,773 *Grants* £28,000 *Assets* £844,722

TRUSTEES Revd Jeanetta S Harcus; Dr A W Harcus; Dr J L S Alexander; Ms Penelope A Thornton; Mrs Fiona J van Nieuwkerk.

HOW TO APPLY In writing to the correspondent, but note that most of the grants given by this trust are recurrent. If new grants are made, they are usually to organisations known to the trustees.

WHO TO APPLY TO The Trustees, c/o MacFarlane and Co., Cunard Building, Water Street, Liverpool L3 1DS *Tel* 0151 236 6161

CC NO 327773   **ESTABLISHED** 1988

■ The Millichope Foundation

WHERE FUNDING CAN BE GIVEN UK, especially the West Midlands and Shropshire.

WHO CAN BENEFIT Registered charities, some grants to UK and international organisations; local applications limited to the West Midlands and Shropshire.

WHAT IS FUNDED General charitable purposes. Specific areas of interest are arts and culture, education, conservation, healthcare outside the NHS remit, respite care, environment and local historic buildings (such as churches). It also gives small donations to local community groups, usually in Shropshire, as well as one-off grants for disaster appeals or specific needs.

WHAT IS NOT FUNDED No grants to individuals or non-registered charities.

TYPE OF GRANT Normally an annual commitment for a period of five years.

RANGE OF GRANTS Usually £500–£2,000.

SAMPLE GRANTS Lady Willington Hospital – Manila (£20,000); and Hope & Homes for Children, Shropshire Historic Churches Trust and St Laurence – Special Music Projects (£10,000 each); Animal Health Trust, Brazilian Atlantic Rainforest Trust, Prince's Trust – Shrewsbury and Shropshire Wildlife – Hollies Appeal (£5,000 each); Cambridge Foundation (£4,000); Birmingham City Mission and Sandwell MultiCare (£2,000 each); and Ludlow Music Society (£200).

FINANCES *Year* 2007–08 *Income* £492,574 *Grants* £294,510 *Assets* £6,786,721

TRUSTEES L C N Bury; Mrs S A Bury; Mrs B Marshall.

HOW TO APPLY In writing to the correspondent.

WHO TO APPLY TO Mrs S A Bury, Trustee, Millichope Park, Munslow, Craven Arms, Shropshire SY7 9HA *Tel* 01584 841 234 *email* sarah@ millichope.com

CC NO 282357   **ESTABLISHED** 1981

■ The Mills Charity

WHERE FUNDING CAN BE GIVEN Framlingham and surrounding district.

WHO CAN BENEFIT Charitable organisations and some individuals.

WHAT IS FUNDED General charitable purposes and social welfare.

SAMPLE GRANTS The Mills Educational Foundation (£20,000); St Michaels Parish Church (£10,000); Framlingham Volunteer Centre (£1,200); Disability Advice Service (£1,000); and Kettleborough Village Hall (£800).

FINANCES *Year* 2007–08 *Income* £357,546 *Grants* £34,810 *Assets* £6,661,504

TRUSTEES Mrs P C Booth; K W Musgrove; M J Kellaway; Mrs J E Dewsbury; H Wright; Dr C Wright; Revd M Vipond.

OTHER INFORMATION £1,790 to individuals

HOW TO APPLY In writing to the correspondent.

WHO TO APPLY TO R A Douglas, PO Box 1703, Framlingham, Woodbridge IP13 9WW *Tel* 01728 723188 *Fax* 01728 621321 *email* info@ themillscharity.co.uk *Website* www. themillscharity.co.uk

CC NO 207259   **ESTABLISHED** 1981

■ The Millward Charitable Trust

WHERE FUNDING CAN BE GIVEN UK and overseas.

WHO CAN BENEFIT Charitable organisations.

WHAT IS FUNDED Social welfare, performing arts, medical research and animal welfare.

TYPE OF GRANT One-off grants.

SAMPLE GRANTS Birds Eye View (£36,000 in three grants); Music in the Round (£32,000 in two grants); Interface Uganda and L.I.F.E (£20,0000 each); City of Birmingham Symphony Orchestra (£10,000 in two grants); RSPCA (£8,000 in two grants); St Paul's Church (£6,000 in four grants); Leamington Music (£5,000); and Adoramus and Hillside Animal Sanctuary (£1,000 each).

FINANCES *Year* 2007–08 *Income* £72,449 *Grants* £181,441 *Assets* £2,130,532

TRUSTEES Maurice Millward; Sheila Millward; John Hulse.

HOW TO APPLY In writing to the correspondent.

WHO TO APPLY TO John Hulse, Trustee, c/o Burgis & Bullock, 2 Chapel Court, Holly Walk, Leamington Spa, Warwickshire CV32 4YS *Tel* 01926 451 000

CC NO 328564   **ESTABLISHED** 1989

■ The Clare Milne Trust

WHERE FUNDING CAN BE GIVEN The south west of England, but Devon and Cornwall in practice.

WHO CAN BENEFIT Voluntary and community groups.

WHAT IS FUNDED Disability projects, especially those for adults in the south west of England, mainly in Devon and Cornwall. Preference is given to small and well-run local and regional charities with strong support from volunteers and with only modest expenditure on fundraising and administration.

WHAT IS NOT FUNDED No grants directly to or for individuals or to national charities.

TYPE OF GRANT Generally a partial contribution towards total cost of a project.

RANGE OF GRANTS Typically £1,000–£25,000.

SAMPLE GRANTS CEDA (£36,000); Spectrum (£25,000); Curnow School, Orchard Value Trust, Rainbow Living and Fiveways School (£20,000 each); the Church House Trust (£15,000); Pentreath Limited (£14,000); Crediton and

District Community Transport Co Ltd (£11,000); the Bishops Forum (£10,000); Hayle Day Care Centre Trust and Wolf and Water Arts Company (£6,000 each); Exeter Royal Academy for Deaf Children and Volunteer Centre Crediton (£3,000 each); and Living Options (£2,000).

FINANCES Year 2007–08 Income £891,250 Grants £326,413 Assets £18,702,356

TRUSTEES Michael Brown, Chair; Lesley Milne; Lucie Nottingham; Tim Robinson; Margaret Rogers; Nigel Urwin.

HOW TO APPLY If you think your project meets the trust's criteria, you should write summarising your request on one side of an A4 sheet if possible, with minimal supporting literature; the trust will request a copy of your annual report and accounts later on if necessary. The trustees usually meet four times a year and to save unnecessary administration only applications which fit the trust's criteria will be responded to.

WHO TO APPLY TO Kim Lyons, Secretary, 1 The Sanctuary, Westminster, London SW1P 3JT Tel 020 7960 7173 email milnetrust@hotmail.co.uk Website www.claremilnetrust.com
CC NO 1084733   **ESTABLISHED** 1999

■ Milton Keynes Community Foundation

WHERE FUNDING CAN BE GIVEN Milton Keynes Unitary Authority.

WHO CAN BENEFIT Community groups, community interest companies, social enterprises, sports clubs, parish councils and local registered charities benefiting; people of all ages, at risk groups, carers, disabled people, those disadvantaged by poverty, homeless people, and victims of abuse, crime and domestic violence.

WHAT IS FUNDED The foundation's main priority is to help those in the Milton Keynes Council area who miss out because of poverty, ill health, disability or disadvantage. It also supports important initiatives in the spheres of the arts and leisure.

WHAT IS NOT FUNDED No grants are made to the following types of organisation: statutory organisations – including schools, hospitals and borough councils (applications from parish councils for community projects are accepted); political parties or groups affiliated to a political party; individuals. Grants are normally not given to proposals chiefly focused upon the following: sponsorship and fundraising events; contributions to major appeals; projects outside the beneficial area; political groups; projects connected with promoting a religious message of any kind; work which should be funded by health and local authorities or government grants aid; retrospective grants, nor grants to pay off deficits.

TYPE OF GRANT Small grants of up to £1,500; community grants from £1,500 to £5,000 to cover equipment costs, projects and minor building work, training, publicity and one-off activity costs; arts grants awarded for artistic and cultural activities, particularly of high quality and originality; development grants, up to a maximum, exceptionally, of £25,000 and typically from £9,000 to £20,000 per year, generally for discrete project work (can include salaries, rents and other overheads).

RANGE OF GRANTS £100–£25,000, depending on grant type.

FINANCES Year 2008–09 Income £1,824,643 Grants £733,674 Assets £6,908,314

TRUSTEES Judith Hooper; Fola Komolafe; Francesca Skelton; Jane Matthews; Michael Murray; Peter Kara; Peter Selvey; Richard Brown; Roger Kitchen; Ruth Stone; Stephen Norrish.

PUBLICATIONS What is the Community Trust?, quarterly newsletter, Guide to Grants, annual report.

HOW TO APPLY Application forms and guidelines are available on the website or can be requested by telephoning the office. The grants staff can be contacted to assist with any queries or help with applications.

WHO TO APPLY TO Bart Gamber, Grants Director, Acorn House, 381 Midsummer Boulevard, Central Milton Keynes MK9 3HP Tel 01908 690276 Fax 01908 233635 email information@mkcommunityfoundation.co.uk Website www.mkcommunityfoundation.co.uk
CC NO 295107   **ESTABLISHED** 1987

■ The Edgar Milward Charity

WHERE FUNDING CAN BE GIVEN UK and overseas.

WHO CAN BENEFIT Causes known to the trustees, particularly those supported by the settlor.

WHAT IS FUNDED A limited number of Christian and humanitarian causes. The trustees currently have an established interest in a range of charities. Few new charities will be added to this list.

WHAT IS NOT FUNDED No new applications will be supported.

SAMPLE GRANTS Goal Ministries (£2,500); Bible Society (£2,000); Interserve and REinspired (£1,500 each); Agape Asia, Bibles for Children, Christian Solidarity Worldwide, Eurovision, Kendrick School, Lee Abbey, Reading School Workers Trust, Time for God and Urban Saints (£1,000 each).

FINANCES Year 2007–08 Income £58,702 Grants £56,050 Assets £994,936

TRUSTEES J S Milward, Chair; Mrs M V Roberts; G M Fogwill; S M W Fogwill; A S Fogwill; Mrs F Palethorpe; Mrs J C Austin.

HOW TO APPLY Unsolicited applications cannot be considered.

WHO TO APPLY TO A S Fogwill, Corresponding Secretary, 53 Brook Drive, Corsham, Wiltshire SN13 9AX
CC NO 281018   **ESTABLISHED** 1980

■ The Keith and Joan Mindelsohn Charitable Trust

WHERE FUNDING CAN BE GIVEN Birmingham and West Midlands.

WHO CAN BENEFIT Charitable organisations, with a preference for smaller groups who lack the resources of national organisations and where the grant will make a more noticeable difference.

WHAT IS FUNDED General charitable purposes.

TYPE OF GRANT Project grants.

RANGE OF GRANTS £100–£500.

SAMPLE GRANTS Previous beneficiaries have included KIDS – West Midlands, Motor Neurone Disease, Whizz-Kidz, Heartlands Cystic Fibrosis, Birmingham Rathbone and Lady Hoare Trust.

FINANCES Year 2007–08 Income £20,394 Grants £42,191

TRUSTEES Jane Jaffa; Gillian Amiss.

HOW TO APPLY In writing to the correspondent, preferably via e-mail. The trustees meet three times a year.

■ The Peter Minet Trust

WHERE FUNDING CAN BE GIVEN Mainly south east London boroughs, particularly Lambeth and Southwark.

WHO CAN BENEFIT Registered charities benefiting at risk groups, and people who are disabled, sick or disadvantaged by poverty.

WHAT IS FUNDED Registered charities (not individuals), particularly those working with young people, the sick, people with disabilities, the disadvantaged, older people, the arts and the environment.

WHAT IS NOT FUNDED Grants to registered charities only. No grants are made to individuals. The trust will not give to: local appeals, other than those within or directly affecting the trust's immediate locality; repetitive nationwide appeals by large charities for large sums of money; appeals where all, or most of the beneficiaries live outside the UK; appeals whose sole purpose is to make grants from collected funds; endowment or deficit funding; or medical or other research.

TYPE OF GRANT Usually one-off for a specific project or part of a project.

RANGE OF GRANTS £50–£3,000.

SAMPLE GRANTS Myatt's Field Park Project Group and Studland Village Appeal for Pitwal (£5,000 each); Furniture Aid – South Thames and The Irene Taylor Trust – 'Music in Prisons' (£3,000 each); Big Fish Theatre Company and Waterloo Community Development Group (£2,000 each); the Citizenship Foundation and Sickle Cell and Young Stroke Survivors (£1,000 each).

FINANCES *Year* 2007–08 *Income* £191,514 *Grants* £182,044 *Assets* £3,803,354

TRUSTEES J C B South, Chair; Mrs R L C Rowan; Ms P C Jones; R Luff; Revd Bruce Stokes; Mrs L Cleverly.

PUBLICATIONS Guidelines leaflet available.

HOW TO APPLY Application forms along with guidelines are available either, by post from the correspondent or, by downloading them from the trust's website. The form should be submitted along with your latest audited accounts, details of the project (no more than two sides of A4), a budget breakdown, money raised so far, and a list of other bodies to whom you have applied for funding. Meetings are usually held in February, June and October. Unsuccessful applicants will not be acknowledged unless an sae is enclosed. If you would like to speak to someone about your proposed application then you should telephone 020 8772 3155 between 9 am and 3 pm on Monday or Tuesday each week.

WHO TO APPLY TO The Administrator, 1a Taylors Yard, 67 Alderbrook Road, London SW12 8AD *Tel* 020 8772 3155 *email* info@peterminet.org.uk *Website* www.peterminet.org.uk
CC NO 259963   **ESTABLISHED** 1969

■ Minge's Gift and the Pooled Trusts

WHERE FUNDING CAN BE GIVEN UK.

WHO CAN BENEFIT Registered charities only.

WHAT IS FUNDED General charitable purposes as directed by the Master and Wardens of the Cordwainers Company. The income of Minge's Gift is generally allocated for the long-term support of medical and educational establishments and towards disabled and/or disadvantaged young people. The Polled Trusts mainly support individuals including scholars, the blind, deaf, clergy widows, spinsters of the Church of England, ex-servicemen and their widows and those who served in the merchant services.

WHAT IS NOT FUNDED Grants to individuals are only given through the Pooled Trusts. Generally, only UK-based charitable organisations are supported.

TYPE OF GRANT Grants of up to three years for core costs, projects, research, and recurring costs; start-up costs are considered.

RANGE OF GRANTS £50,000–£10,000.

SAMPLE GRANTS *Standard grants:* University of Northamptonshire (£10,000); London College of Fashion – prizes and scholarships (£7,000); Footwear Friends (£6,500); and Capel Manor College (£5,000); University of Arts (£3,000); Royal London Society for the Blind (£2,500); and Centrepoint, Guildhall School of Music and Drama, Leather Conservation Centre and St Dunstan-in-the-West Church (£1,000 each). *Master's gifts:* Haringey Sea Cadets (£1,000), King's College (£250), City of London Festival (£100) and Keen London (£50). Pooled Trusts – King George's Fund for Sailors, Royal Free Hospital School of Medicine Scholarship and SSAFA (£1,000 each).

FINANCES *Year* 2007–08 *Income* £162,495 *Grants* £50,615 *Assets* £2,465,101

TRUSTEES The Master and Wardens of the Worshipful Company of Cordwainers.

OTHER INFORMATION In 2007–08, £10,379 was given in grants to individuals from the Pooled Trusts.

HOW TO APPLY In writing to the correspondent.

WHO TO APPLY TO John Miller, Clerk, The Worshipful Company of Cordwainers, Clothworkers Hall, Dunster Court, Mincing Lane, London EC3R 7AH *Tel* 020 7929 1121 *Fax* 020 7929 1124 *email* office@cordwain.co.org *Website* www.cordwainers.org
CC NO 266073   **ESTABLISHED** 1972

■ The Minos Trust

WHERE FUNDING CAN BE GIVEN UK and overseas.

WHO CAN BENEFIT Organisations.

WHAT IS FUNDED General charitable purposes, especially Christian causes.

RANGE OF GRANTS £25–£2,000, exceptionally higher.

SAMPLE GRANTS Previous beneficiaries include: Chichester Cathedral Trust, Tigers Club Project, Care Trust, Tearfund, Ashburnham Christian Trust, Bible Society, Friends of the Elderly and Youth with a Mission.

FINANCES *Year* 2007–08 *Income* £22,589 *Grants* £35,000

TRUSTEES Revd K W Habershon; Mrs E M Habershon; Mrs D M Irwin-Clark.

HOW TO APPLY In writing to the correspondent, for consideration on an ongoing basis.

WHO TO APPLY TO The Trustees, Kleinwort Benson Trustees Ltd, 30 Gresham Street, London EC2V 7PG *Tel* 020 8207 7356 *Fax* 020 8207 7665

cc no 265012   ESTABLISHED 1972

■ Minton Charitable Trust

WHERE FUNDING CAN BE GIVEN UK.
WHO CAN BENEFIT Organisations and individuals.
WHAT IS FUNDED General charitable purposes.
FINANCES *Year* 2007–08 *Income* £387,364 *Grants* £200,000 *Assets* £670,900
TRUSTEES Sir Anthony Armitage Greener; Richard J Edmunds; Lady Audrey Greener.
HOW TO APPLY In writing to the correspondent.
WHO TO APPLY TO Sir Anthony Armitage Greener, Trustee, 26 Hamilton House, Vicarage Gate, London W8 4HL
cc no 1112106   ESTABLISHED 2005

■ The Mirfield Educational Charity

WHERE FUNDING CAN BE GIVEN The urban district of Mirfield.
WHO CAN BENEFIT Individuals and organisations.
WHAT IS FUNDED Schools; youth groups; and educational expenses for individuals.
RANGE OF GRANTS £500–£30,000.
SAMPLE GRANTS Batteyford Sports Club (£30,000); Tykes and Trykes Toddler Group (£3,900); Crossley Fields School (£3,400); Old Bank Junior, Inffant & Nursery School (£1,700); and Upper Hopton Cricket Club (£1,600).
FINANCES *Year* 2007–08 *Income* £49,688 *Grants* £48,880 *Assets* £1,349,424
TRUSTEES Dr H G Grason, Chair; D B Brook; B Nicholson; P A Morton; E A Speight; M Bolt; C Oldfield; G Jones.
HOW TO APPLY In writing to the correspondent.
WHO TO APPLY TO Whitfield Hallam Goodall, 7 King Street, Mirfield WF14 8AW
cc no 529334   ESTABLISHED 1961

■ The Mirianog Trust

WHERE FUNDING CAN BE GIVEN UK.
WHO CAN BENEFIT Charitable organisations.
WHAT IS FUNDED General charitable purposes. Currently the trustees give preference to: the relief of poverty; overseas aid and famine relief; accommodation and housing; environment, conservation and heritage.
SAMPLE GRANTS Newcastle University (£22,000); Justice First (£10,000); Sea Change (£5,000); Medical Foundation for the Victims of Torture and Practical Action (£4,000 each); Butterwick Hospice and St Giles (£3,000 each); Fauna and Flora (£1,500); and Cancer Connections (£1,000).
FINANCES *Year* 2007–08 *Income* £68,835 *Grants* £62,734 *Assets* £725,084
TRUSTEES Canon William Broad, Chair; Daphne Broad; Elizabeth Jeary.
HOW TO APPLY In writing to the correspondent. The trustees meet twice each year.
WHO TO APPLY TO Canon W E L Broad, Chair, Moorcote, Thornley, Tow Law, Bishop Auckland DL13 4NU
cc no 1091397   ESTABLISHED 2002

■ The Laurence Misener Charitable Trust

WHERE FUNDING CAN BE GIVEN UK.
WHO CAN BENEFIT There is a tendency to benefit those charities in which the settlor was interested.
WHAT IS FUNDED General charitable purposes, particularly Jewish organisations and medical causes.
RANGE OF GRANTS £4,000–£15,000.
SAMPLE GRANTS Jewish Association for the Physically Handicapped, Jewish Care and Nightingale House (£15,000 each); Robert Owen Foundation (£12,000); Royal College of Surgeons of England (£10,000); Cancer Research UK (£9,000); Jewish Temporary Shelter (£8,000); Great Ormond Street Children's Hospital Fund (£7,000); Age Concern, SSAFA and St George's Church – Dittisham (£6,000 each); and Imperial War Museum Trust (£5,000).
FINANCES *Year* 2007–08 *Income* £137,389 *Grants* £178,200 *Assets* £2,900,976
TRUSTEES Mrs J Legane; Capt. G F Swaine.
HOW TO APPLY In writing to the correspondent.
WHO TO APPLY TO David Lyons, 1 Printing Yard House, London E2 7PR *Tel* 020 7739 8780
cc no 283460   ESTABLISHED 1981

■ The Mishcon Family Charitable Trust

WHERE FUNDING CAN BE GIVEN UK.
WHO CAN BENEFIT Registered charities, particularly Jewish organisations.
WHAT IS FUNDED General charitable purposes. Within the limited funds available each application is considered on its merits with preference given to applications for the relief of poverty from recognised organisations.
TYPE OF GRANT One-off.
RANGE OF GRANTS £20 upwards. Generally £5,000 or less.
SAMPLE GRANTS United Jewish Israel Appeal (£45,000); One Voice Europe (£10,000); MISHOLIM (£4,000); Norwood, Sick Children's Trust and United Synagogue (£2,500 each); Chai Cancer Care, Katherine Domandy Trust and Motivation Charitable Trust (£1,000 each); London Jewish Cultural Centre (£750); Friends of Alyn (£600); Acorn Hospice, The Genesis Appeal and One World Action (£500 each); Dream Holidays (£350); Myeloma UK (£250); Listening Books (£100); Help the Aged (£50); Joely Bear Appeal (£30); and Sports Relief (£20).
FINANCES *Year* 2007–08 *Income* £87,246 *Grants* £96,362 *Assets* £1,904,217
TRUSTEES P A Mishcon; R O Mishcon; Mrs J Landau.
HOW TO APPLY In writing to the correspondent.
WHO TO APPLY TO The Trustees, Summit House, 12 Red Lion Square, London WC1R 4QD
cc no 213165   ESTABLISHED 1961

■ The Misselbrook Trust

WHERE FUNDING CAN BE GIVEN UK with a preference for the Wessex area.
WHO CAN BENEFIT Registered charities.
WHAT IS FUNDED General charitable purposes.
TYPE OF GRANT One-off and recurrent.
RANGE OF GRANTS Up to £3,000.
SAMPLE GRANTS Marwell Preservation Trust (£3,000); AIDS Trust, Blond Mcindoe Centre,

Canine Partner Independence, Fairbridge –
Solent, Hampshire Autistic Society, Honeypot
Charity, Rainbow Centre, Royal Star & Garter
Home, Southampton Churches Rent Bond
Scheme and Southampton Woman's Aid
(£1,000 each). Other grants of £500 or less
were made to 30 institutions and totalled
£15,000.

FINANCES *Year* 2007–08 *Income* £28,920
Grants £30,800 *Assets* £574,657
TRUSTEES M Howson-Green; B M Baxendale;
D A Hoare; Mrs M A Howson-Green.
HOW TO APPLY In writing to the correspondent
WHO TO APPLY TO M Howson-Green, Trustee, Ashton
House, 12 The Central Precinct, Winchester
Road, Chandlers Ford, Eastleigh, Hampshire,
SO53 2GB *Tel* 023 8027 4555
CC NO 327928   **ESTABLISHED** 1988

■ The Brian Mitchell Charitable Settlement

WHERE FUNDING CAN BE GIVEN UK.
WHO CAN BENEFIT Registered charities.
WHAT IS FUNDED General charitable purposes
including education, music and the arts and
also sporting activities.
RANGE OF GRANTS About £500–£200,000.
SAMPLE GRANTS Skinners School (£207,000);
Glyndebourne (£50,000); Canterbury Cathedral
(£15,000); Hospice on the Weald (£11,000); St
Barnabas Project (£10,000); the Temple Church
(£8,000); Sailability (£7,000); British Blind
Sport and Vision Aid Overseas (£5,000 each);
Oasis Trust (£1,500); and Shelter Box (£490).
FINANCES *Year* 2007–08 *Income* £281,175
Grants £344,706 *Assets* £579,484
TRUSTEES Brian Mitchell; Hon. Michael Devonshire;
Duncan Oakley; Andrew Buss; John Andrews.
HOW TO APPLY In writing to the correspondent.
WHO TO APPLY TO The Trustees, Round Oak, Old
Station Road, Wadhurst, East Sussex TN5 6TZ
Tel 01892 782072 *email* mitchell@inweb.co.uk
CC NO 1003817

■ The Mitchell Charitable Trust

WHERE FUNDING CAN BE GIVEN UK and overseas.
WHO CAN BENEFIT Organisations benefiting: people of
all ages; volunteers; Jews; at risk groups;
people disadvantaged by poverty; and victims of
abuse and domestic violence.
WHAT IS FUNDED Jewish organisations, social
welfare, voluntary organisations.
WHAT IS NOT FUNDED No grants to individuals or for
research, education, overseas appeals or non-
Jewish religious appeals. Applicants from small
charities outside London are unlikely to be
considered.
TYPE OF GRANT Some recurring.
RANGE OF GRANTS £50–£38,000.
SAMPLE GRANTS Hammersmith Clinical Research
(£38,000); Ovarian Cancer Care (£33,000);
Prostate Cancer Research Foundation
(£25,000); Jewish Care (£13,000); World
Jewish Relief (£8,000); the National
Organisations for Foetal Alcohol Syndrome
(£8,000); Women to Women International UK
(£1,500); University of Nottingham Karnival
(£900); LSE Students Union (£750); St
Michael's Church Restoration Fund (£500);
Tricycle Theatre (£200); and Spiroark (£50).
FINANCES *Year* 2008–09 *Income* £49,962
Grants £140,977 *Assets* £942,036

TRUSTEES Ashley Mitchell; Elizabeth Mitchell;
Antonia Mitchell; Keren Mitchell.
HOW TO APPLY In writing to the correspondent.
Applications must include financial information.
The trust does not reply to any applications
unless they choose to support them. Trustees
do not meet on a regular basis, thus applicants
may not be advised of a grant for a
considerable period.
WHO TO APPLY TO Ashley Mitchell, Trustee, 28 Heath
Drive, London NW3 7SB *Tel* 020 7794 5668
CC NO 290273   **ESTABLISHED** 1984

■ The Esmé Mitchell Trust

WHERE FUNDING CAN BE GIVEN Ireland, but mainly
Northern Ireland.
WHO CAN BENEFIT Organisations, and individuals who
are involved in the arts and cultural activities.
WHAT IS FUNDED General charitable purposes in
Ireland as a whole but principally in Northern
Ireland with a particular interest in cultural and
artistic objects. Part of the trust fund is only
available to assist certain heritage bodies as
set out in Schedule 3 to the Capital Transfer Act
1984.
WHAT IS NOT FUNDED Grants are not usually given to
individuals wishing to undertake voluntary
service or further education.
TYPE OF GRANT No time limits have generally been
set on grants. The trust has on occasions given
grant assistance over a period of two to three
years but in general tries not to become
involved in commitments of a long-term nature.
FINANCES *Year* 2008–09 *Grants* £120,000
TRUSTEES P J Rankin; Mrs F Jay-O'Boyle;
R P Blakiston-Houston.
OTHER INFORMATION In previous years the trust has
had both an income of, and made grants
totalling, around £120,000. Further information
was not available.
HOW TO APPLY In writing to the correspondent.
Applicants should submit three copies of the
following: a concise description of the proposed
project; a recent statement of accounts and
balance sheet; a copy of the constitution;
details of tax and legal or charitable status; a
list of committee officers; information on other
sources of finance; a contact address and
telephone number.
WHO TO APPLY TO The Trustees, The Northern Bank
Executor and Trustee Co. Ltd, PO Box 183,
Donegall Square West, Belfast BT1 6JS *Tel* 028
9004 8110
IR NO XN48053   **ESTABLISHED** 1965

■ Keren Mitzvah Trust

WHERE FUNDING CAN BE GIVEN UK.
WHO CAN BENEFIT Jewish organisations; registered
charities.
WHAT IS FUNDED General charitable purposes.
TYPE OF GRANT One-off and recurrent.
SAMPLE GRANTS Lezion Berina Institute (£120,000);
CML (£54,000); Wiseheights (£45,000);
Ahaavat Shalom Charity (£43,000); Torah &
Chesed (£34,000); ETC Youth (£18,000);
Gateshead Jewish Academy (£14,000); Project
Seed (£10,000); Jewish Literacy Foundation
(£8,000); and Jewish Learning Exchange
(£5,000).
FINANCES *Year* 2007 *Income* £818,942
Grants £881,315 *Assets* £56,495
TRUSTEES M Weiss; A McCormack; N Bradley.
HOW TO APPLY The trust stated that the trustees
support their own personal charities.

WHO TO APPLY TO The Trustees, 1 Manchester Square, London W1U 3AB *Tel* 020 3219 2600
CC NO 1041948   **ESTABLISHED** 1994

■ The Mizpah Trust

WHERE FUNDING CAN BE GIVEN UK and overseas.
WHO CAN BENEFIT Registered charities.
WHAT IS FUNDED General charitable purposes, especially Christian organisations.
TYPE OF GRANT One-off and recurrent.
RANGE OF GRANTS £50 to £20,000.
SAMPLE GRANTS The Vanessa Grant Trust (£20,000) and CURE International (£15,000); Kenya Outreach Account (£7,000); World Vision (£5,000); the Brentford Trust (£4,000); CARE and Meah Trust (£3,000 each); Lambeth Partnership (£1,000); SOS Children's Villages (£500); and the Treloar Trust (£50).
FINANCES *Year* 2007–08 *Income* £10,618 *Grants* £62,250 *Assets* £199,299
TRUSTEES A C O Bell; Mrs J E Bell.
OTHER INFORMATION £1,500 went in grants to individuals.
HOW TO APPLY The trust has stated that 'no applications will be considered'.
WHO TO APPLY TO A C O Bell, Trustee, Foresters House, Humbly Grove, South Warnborough, Hook, Hampshire RG29 1RY
CC NO 287231   **ESTABLISHED** 1983

■ The Mobbs Memorial Trust Ltd

WHERE FUNDING CAN BE GIVEN Stoke Poges and district within a 35-mile radius of St Giles' Church.
WHO CAN BENEFIT Organisations benefiting: people of all ages; ex-service and service people; volunteers; unemployed; those in care, fostered and adopted; parents and children; at-risk groups; people with disabilities; those disadvantaged by poverty; ex-offenders and those at risk of offending; homeless people; those living in rural areas; socially isolated people; victims of abuse, crime and domestic violence.
WHAT IS FUNDED St Giles' Church and other charitable purposes including: almshouses; sheltered accommodation; community development; support to voluntary and community organisations; combined arts; community arts and recreation; health; conservation and environment; schools and colleges; and community facilities and services.
TYPE OF GRANT Buildings and project. Funding is given for up to three years.
SAMPLE GRANTS Hedgerley Youth Club (£10,000); Pace Centre (£5,000); Chiltern's MS Centre (£4,000); Action for Youth (£3,000); Stoke Poges PCC (£2,500); and Slough Furniture Projects (£1,000).
FINANCES *Year* 2007–08 *Income* £67,828 *Grants* £52,207 *Assets* £2,133,339
TRUSTEES M R Mobbs; Dr C N A Mobbs; C W Mobbs; Mrs S J Greenslade; A N P Mobbs.
OTHER INFORMATION A Further £1,200 was given in grants to individuals.
HOW TO APPLY In writing to the correspondent.
WHO TO APPLY TO N I Hamilton, Secretary to the Trustees, Slough Estates House, 234 Bath Road, Slough, Berkshire SL1 4EE *Tel* 01753 537171
CC NO 202478   **ESTABLISHED** 1963

■ The Modiano Charitable Trust

WHERE FUNDING CAN BE GIVEN UK and overseas.
WHO CAN BENEFIT Charitable organisations, with some preference for Jewish groups.
WHAT IS FUNDED Development work, arts and relief-in-need.
TYPE OF GRANT One-off and recurrent.
RANGE OF GRANTS £50–£20,000.
SAMPLE GRANTS Philharmonia Orchestra (£20,000); Weiznam Institute Foundation (£7,500) UJIA and World Jewish Relief (£5,000 each); Photos of Turkish Synagogues Project (£2,500); the Queen Alexandra Hospital Home (£2,000); Help the Aged (£1,500); European Union Youth Orchestra (£1,000); Inter Act Reading Service (£500); and the Keyboard Charitable Trust (£100).
FINANCES *Year* 2007–08 *Income* £100,000 *Grants* £78,776
TRUSTEES G Modiano; Mrs B Modiano; L S Modiano; M Modiano.
HOW TO APPLY In writing to the correspondent.
WHO TO APPLY TO G Modiano, Trustee, Broad Street House, 55 Old Broad Street, London EC2M 1RX *Tel* 020 7012 0000
CC NO 328372   **ESTABLISHED** 1989

■ The Moette Charitable Trust

WHERE FUNDING CAN BE GIVEN UK and overseas.
WHO CAN BENEFIT People educationally disadvantaged through poverty.
WHAT IS FUNDED 'The principal activity of the trust is the provision of support of the poor and needy for educational purposes.'
SAMPLE GRANTS Finchley Road Synagogue (£15,000); King David Schools (Manchester) and Manchester Charitable Trust (£2,500 each); the Purim Fund (£2,000); Yad Voezer and Yeshivas Lev Aryeh (£1,000 each); Hakalo and London School of Jewish Studies (£500 each); Manchester Jewish Federation (£400); and Manchester Seminary for Girls (£50).
FINANCES *Year* 2006–07 *Income* £30,832 *Grants* £62,675 *Assets* £391,528
TRUSTEES Simon Lopian; Pearl Lopian; David Haffner.
HOW TO APPLY In writing to the correspondent
WHO TO APPLY TO Simon Lopian, Trustee, 1 Holden Road, Salford M7 4NL *Tel* 0161 832 8721
CC NO 1068886   **ESTABLISHED** 1998

■ The Mole Charitable Trust

WHERE FUNDING CAN BE GIVEN UK, with a preference for Manchester.
WHO CAN BENEFIT Individuals, registered charities and institutions benefiting children, young adults, Jews and people disadvantaged by poverty.
WHAT IS FUNDED Jewish causes, educational institutions and organisations to relieve poverty.
RANGE OF GRANTS £1,000–£60,000.
SAMPLE GRANTS Three Pillars Charity (£60,000); Manchester Jewish Grammar School (£26,000); Chasdei Yoel Charitable Trust and United Talmudical Associates Limited (£20,000 each); Binoh of Manchester (£6,000); Beis Ruchel Girls School (£3,000); Manchester Jewish Federation (£2,500); and Our Kids (£1,000).
FINANCES *Year* 2007–08 *Income* £53,368 *Grants* £319,643 *Assets* £2,844,420
TRUSTEES M Gross; Mrs L P Gross.
HOW TO APPLY This trust has stated that it does not accept unsolicited applications.

WHO TO APPLY TO Martin Gross, Trustee, 2 Okeover Road, Salford M7 4JX *Tel* 0161 832 8721 *email* martin.gross@lopiangb.co.uk
CC NO 281452 **ESTABLISHED** 1980

■ The D C Moncrieff Charitable Trust

WHERE FUNDING CAN BE GIVEN UK and worldwide, with a preference for Norfolk and Suffolk.
WHO CAN BENEFIT Registered charities only.
WHAT IS FUNDED General charitable purposes. Trustees already have a list of beneficiaries whose requirements outweigh the trustees' ability to help.
WHAT IS NOT FUNDED No grants for individuals.
RANGE OF GRANTS Usually £400–£2,000. Larger grants for larger one-off projects or certain regularly supported local charities.
SAMPLE GRANTS Previous beneficiaries include: All Hallows Hospital, Henley Church PCC, Lowestoft Girl Guides Association, BREAK, East Anglia Air Ambulance Association and Society for Lincolnshire History and Archaeology.
FINANCES *Year* 2007–08 *Income* £50,127 *Grants* £38,000 *Assets* £1,822,818
TRUSTEES D J Coleman; R E James; M F Dunne.
HOW TO APPLY In writing to the correspondent. The trust has previously stated that demand for funds exceeded available resources; therefore no further requests are currently invited.
WHO TO APPLY TO D J Coleman, Trustee, 8 Quinnell Way, Lowestoft, Suffolk NR32 4WL
CC NO 203919 **ESTABLISHED** 1965

■ Monmouthshire County Council Welsh Church Act Fund

WHERE FUNDING CAN BE GIVEN Blaenau Gwent, Caerphilly, Monmouthshire, Torfaen and Newport.
WHO CAN BENEFIT Students, at risk groups, and people who are disadvantaged by poverty, socially isolated, disaster victims, or sick.
WHAT IS FUNDED Education, relief in sickness and need, people who are blind, older people, medical and social research, probation, social and recreational, libraries, museums and art galleries and protection of historic buildings relating to Wales, places of worship and burial grounds, emergencies and disasters.
TYPE OF GRANT Mostly for provision, upkeep and repair of religious buildings and community halls.
RANGE OF GRANTS Up to £1,000.
SAMPLE GRANTS Previous beneficiaries include: Parish Church Llandogo, Parish Church Llangybi, Bridges Community Centre, St David's Foundation Hospice Care and North Wales Society for the Blind.
FINANCES *Year* 2007–08 *Income* £589,021 *Grants* £140,198 *Assets* £5,040,304
TRUSTEES Monmouthshire County Council.
HOW TO APPLY On a form available from the correspondent, this must be signed by a county councillor. They are considered in March, June, September and December.
WHO TO APPLY TO S K F Greenslade, Treasurer's Department, Monmouthshire County Council, County Hall, Croesyceiliog, Cwmbran NP44 2XH *Tel* 01633 644644 *Fax* 01633 644260
CC NO 507094 **ESTABLISHED** 1996

■ The Montague Thompson Coon Charitable Trust

WHERE FUNDING CAN BE GIVEN UK.
WHO CAN BENEFIT Children with disabilities.
WHAT IS FUNDED Projects involving children with disabilities, particularly those providing opportunities for recreation and access to the countryside.
WHAT IS NOT FUNDED No grants to individuals.
SAMPLE GRANTS Treloar Trust (£8,800 in two grants); Action Medical Research (£7,500); Cultivations, Fairfields School, SCOPE and the Pasque Charity (£5,000 each); the Springhead Trust (£4,000); the PACE Centre (£3,000); and 3H Fund (£2,000).
FINANCES *Year* 2007–08 *Income* £52,200 *Grants* £47,020 *Assets* £1,235,165
TRUSTEES P A Clarke, Chair; J P Lister; Mrs P Blake-Roberts
HOW TO APPLY In writing to the correspondent.
WHO TO APPLY TO Mrs Philippa Blake-Roberts, Trustee, Old Rectory, Church Lane, Colton, Norwich NR9 5DE *Tel* 07766 072592
CC NO 294096 **ESTABLISHED** 1986

■ The Colin Montgomerie Charitable Foundation

WHERE FUNDING CAN BE GIVEN UK.
WHO CAN BENEFIT Charitable organisations.
WHAT IS FUNDED The relief of poverty, the advancement of education and religion, and general charitable purposes.
SAMPLE GRANTS Beneficiaries have included British Lung Foundation, Cancer Vaccine Institute, NSPCC – Full Stop Campaign and University of Glasgow MR Scanner Fund.
FINANCES *Year* 2007 *Income* £12,194 *Grants* £40,000
TRUSTEES Colin Montgomerie; Guy Kinnings; Jonathan Dudman; Miss Donna Cooksley.
HOW TO APPLY In writing to the correspondent.
WHO TO APPLY TO Miss Donna Cooksley, Trustee, c/o Catella, Chiswick Gate, 3rd Floor, 598–608 Chiswick High Road, London W4 5RT
CC NO 1072388 **ESTABLISHED** 1998

■ The Monument Trust

WHERE FUNDING CAN BE GIVEN Unrestricted, but UK in practice.
WHO CAN BENEFIT Registered charities working in the fields outlined below.
WHAT IS FUNDED Health and community care; AIDS; environment; arts; social development; general. Preference is given to new ideas or methods which can be replicated widely or become self-sustaining.
WHAT IS NOT FUNDED Grants are not normally made to individuals.
SAMPLE GRANTS The Art Fund (£9 million) towards the purchase of Dumfries House, its estates and contents and associated costs. Victoria & Albert Museum (£2 million over three years), towards the Medieval and Renaissance Galleries; Lloyds TSB Foundation for Scotland (£1 million over three years) towards Inspiring Scotland, a programme which will provide long-term support for charities using a 'venture philanthropy' model; Help the Hospices (£800,000 over four years), for a national programme to develop modern hospice leadership for up to 150 senior hospice staff; Bowes Museum Trust (£500,000), towards the

Think carefully about every application. Is it justified?

723

renovation of the Bowes Museum; Wells Cathedral (£250,000 over two years), towards the final phases of the redevelopment project; Ulster Museum (£150,000), towards the refurbishment appeal; Ashden Awards for Sustainable Energy (£99,000), towards the costs of commissioning short documentaries; Keystone Development Trust (£40,000), a final grant for Imagine, an initiative based on using local museums and the arts to foster a sense of discovery and imagination in children; Stonewall (£20,000), towards core costs.

FINANCES Year 2007–08 Income £112,206,000 Grants £16,330,000 Assets £215,100,000

TRUSTEES Stewart Grimshaw; Linda Heathcoat-Amory; Sir Anthony Tennant.

OTHER INFORMATION There has been a substantial increase in funds due to the trust being the major beneficiary of the settlor, the late Simon Sainsbury's estate. As a result the trust's grantmaking increased from £2.5 million in 2006/07 to over £16.3 million in 2007/08.

HOW TO APPLY See the guidance for applicants in the entry for the Sainsbury Family Charitable Trusts. A single application will be considered for support by all the trusts in the group. 'Proposals are generally invited by the trustees or initiated at their request. Unsolicited applications are not generally encouraged and are unlikely to succeed, unless they closely match the areas in which the trustees are interested.'

WHO TO APPLY TO Alan Bookbinder, Director, Allington House, 1st Floor, 150 Victoria Street, London SW1E 5AE Tel 020 7410 0330 Fax 020 7410 0332 Website www.sfct.org.uk

CC NO 242575   **ESTABLISHED** 1965

....

■ Moody Charitable Trust

WHERE FUNDING CAN BE GIVEN UK.

WHO CAN BENEFIT Organisations and individuals.

WHAT IS FUNDED General charitable purposes.

RANGE OF GRANTS £50–£10,000.

SAMPLE GRANTS Previous grant recipients have included: Basildon Women's Refuge, Cooksmill Green Congregation Church, St Francis Hospital, Helen Rollanson Cancer Charity, Savillis Teddy Bear Appeal and Breathe Easy.

FINANCES Year 2008 Income £52,321 Grants £19,614

TRUSTEES D A Moody; Mrs S Moody.

HOW TO APPLY In writing to the correspondent.

WHO TO APPLY TO T J Mines, Thomas David Orchard House, 5 The Orchard, Hertford SG14 3HQ Tel 01992 536483

CC NO 326245   **ESTABLISHED** 1982

....

■ George A Moore Foundation

WHERE FUNDING CAN BE GIVEN Principally Yorkshire and the Isle of Man.

WHO CAN BENEFIT Charitable and voluntary organisations.

WHAT IS FUNDED The trustees select causes and projects from the applications received during the year and also independently research and identify specific objectives where they wish to direct assistance. The type of grants made can vary quite widely from one year to another and care is taken to maintain a rough parity among the various fields covered so that one sphere of activity does not benefit unduly at the expense of another. Areas which are not or cannot be covered by official sources are favoured.

WHAT IS NOT FUNDED No assistance will be given to individuals, courses of study, expeditions, overseas travel, holidays, or for purposes outside the UK. Local appeals for UK charities will only be considered if in the area of interest. Because of present long-term commitments, the foundation is not prepared to consider appeals for religious property or institutions.

TYPE OF GRANT Grants are generally non-recurrent and the foundation is reluctant to contribute to revenue appeals.

SAMPLE GRANTS Macmillan Cancer Relief (£140,000); Henshaws College – Living Life Campaign (£27,000); the Ear Trust and Gateway Action (£25,000 each); King James School – Knaresborough and Knaresborough Players – Frazer Theatre (£20,000 each); Teeside Hospice Care Foundation (£10,000); the Woodland Trust (£8,000); British Association for Adoption and Fostering, Harrogate Homeless Project Ltd, Life Education Centres, Ocean Youth Trust – North East and Yorkshire Yoga and Therapy Centre (£5,000 each); Brainwave (£3,000); Ilkley & District CVS (£2,000); Horsforth Live at Home Scheme (£1,000); Blood Pressure Association and Parent Lifeline (£500 each); and Sulby Horticultural Show (£200).

FINANCES Year 2007–08 Income £554,535 Grants £635,135 Assets £7,443,585

TRUSTEES George A Moore; Mrs E Moore; J R Moore; P D Turner

HOW TO APPLY In writing to the correspondent. No guidelines or application forms are issued. The trustees meet approximately four times a year, on variable dates, and an appropriate response is sent out after the relevant meeting.

WHO TO APPLY TO Mrs A L James, Chief Administrator, Mitre House, North Park Road, Harrogate, North Yorkshire HG1 5RX Website www.gamf.org.uk

CC NO 262107   **ESTABLISHED** 1970

....

■ The Henry Moore Foundation

WHERE FUNDING CAN BE GIVEN UK and overseas.

WHO CAN BENEFIT Public visual art and educational bodies.

WHAT IS FUNDED Financial support is given to a broad range of institutions promoting the appreciation of the fine arts and in particular the works of Henry Moore through activities such as exhibitions, acquisitions, research and publishing.

WHAT IS NOT FUNDED The foundation does not give grants to individual applicants, for revenue expenditure. No grant (or any part of grant) may be used to pay any fee or to provide any other benefit to any individual who is a trustee of the foundation.

TYPE OF GRANT One-off.

RANGE OF GRANTS Up to £60,000 depending on grant category.

SAMPLE GRANTS The grant categories are: New projects; Collections; Fellowships for artists and post-doctoral research; Research and development; and Conferences, lectures and publications. Beneficiaries include: Liverpool Biennial, 'Made Up': new commissions by: Annette Messager, David Altmejd, Sarah Sze, U Ram Choe, Tue Greenfort and Ai Wei Wei; Brighton, Fabrica: an exhibition, Thomas Hirschhorn; Guildford, Watts Gallery: towards conservation of the sculpture collection and conservation and display of Physical Energy; Aldeburgh, ArtOffice: Christian Marclay; and Ashmolean Museum, Oxford A 3-volume catalogue of the Ashmolean's holdings of

Medieval and Renaissance sculpture, by Jeremy Warren. For full details and further examples see the foundation's website: www.henry-moore-fdn.co.uk.

FINANCES *Year* 2007–08 *Income* £1,043,640 *Grants* £1,168,102 *Assets* £100,980,978

TRUSTEES Prof. Dawn Ades; David Ansbro; Prof. Malcolm Baker; Marianne Brouwer; Prof. Andrew Causey; James Joll; Simon Keswick; Greville Worthington; Laure Genillard; Duncan Robinson.

PUBLICATIONS *The Henry Moore Foundation Review.*

HOW TO APPLY In writing to the correspondent. The guidelines state that the foundation does not issue application forms but that all applicants should cover the following points: the category under which the application is being made i.e. new projects, collections etc.; the aims and functions of the organisation; the precise purpose for which a grant is sought; the amount required and details of how that figure is arrived at; details of efforts made to find other sources of income, whether any firm commitments have been received, and what others are hoped for; and details of the budget for the scheme and how the scheme will be monitored. Organisations may include supporting material with their application and this will be returned if requested. Applicants should advise the foundation whether it is envisaged that any trustee will have an interest in the project for which a grant is sought. Applications are usually considered at quarterly meetings and should not be made by telephone or in person.

WHO TO APPLY TO Alice O'Connor, Grant Contact, Henry Moore Foundation, Dane Tree House, Perry Green, Much Hadham, Hertfordshire SG10 6EE *Tel* 01279 843 333 *Fax* 01279 843 647 *email* admin@henry-moore-fdn.co.uk *Website* www.henry-moore-fdn.co.uk

CC NO 271370   **ESTABLISHED** 1977

■ The Nigel Moores Family Charitable Trust

WHERE FUNDING CAN BE GIVEN UK, but mostly Wales and Liverpool.

WHO CAN BENEFIT Institutions benefiting children and young adults, actors and entertainment professionals, musicians, students and textile workers and designers.

WHAT IS FUNDED Principal objective should be the raising of the artistic taste of the public whether in relation to music, drama, opera, painting, sculpture or otherwise in connection with the fine arts, the promotion of education in the fine arts and academic education, the promotion of the environment, the provision of recreation and leisure facilities and the advancement of religion.

TYPE OF GRANT One-off and recurrent.

SAMPLE GRANTS A Foundation (£525,000); London Library (£20,000); Mostyn Gallery (£10,000); University of York (£6,750); Art School Palestine (£1,000); and Matts Gallery (£500).

FINANCES *Year* 2007–08 *Income* £375,793 *Grants* £539,464 *Assets* £89,821

TRUSTEES J C S Moores; Mrs P M Kennaway.

HOW TO APPLY In writing to the correspondent.

WHO TO APPLY TO P Kurthausen, Accountant, c/o Macfarlane and Co., 2nd Floor, Cunard Building, Water Street, Liverpool L3 1DS *Tel* 0151 236 6161 *Fax* 0151 236 1095

CC NO 1002366   **ESTABLISHED** 1991

■ John Moores Foundation

WHERE FUNDING CAN BE GIVEN Primarily Merseyside (plus Skelmersdale, Ellesmere Port and Halton); Northern Ireland; and overseas.

WHO CAN BENEFIT Voluntary organisations and community groups in the UK benefiting people who are marginalised as a result of social, educational, physical, economic, cultural, geographical or other disadvantage. International relief organisations are also supported, but only organisations proactively selected by the trustees rather than applicants.

WHAT IS FUNDED Grass roots community groups; black and minority ethnic organisations; women including girls; second chance learning; advice and information to alleviate poverty; support and training for voluntary organisations. And, in Merseyside only: people with disabilities; carers; refugees; homeless people; child care; complementary therapies.

WHAT IS NOT FUNDED Generally the foundation does not fund: individuals; national organisations or groups based outside Merseyside even where some of the service users come from the area; statutory bodies or work previously done by them; mainstream education (schools, colleges, universities); faith-based projects exclusively for members of that faith, or for the promotion of religion; capital building costs – except to improve access for disabled people; festivals, carnivals and fêtes; medicine and health – except under the headings listed above; holidays, expeditions and outings; gifts, parties etc; sport; vehicles; animal charities; arts, crafts, heritage, or local history projects; conservation and environmental projects; employment and enterprise schemes; victims – except rape crisis and domestic violence projects; academic or medical research; uniformed groups (e.g. scouts, cadets, majorettes); sponsorship, advertising or fund-raising events. Applications may be refused where the foundation considers that the organisation concerned is already well funded or has excessive reserves. Unsolicited applications which fall outside the policy criteria are not considered. Unsolicited applications for the categories World Crises and One-off exceptional grants are not responded to.

TYPE OF GRANT One-off, revenue, project, equipment and start-up costs. Funding for up to three years. Volunteers' expenses and help towards education and training costs.

RANGE OF GRANTS £100–£150,000.

SAMPLE GRANTS British Red Cross (£150,000 in two grants); Liverpool 8 Law Centre (£22,000); Newton-le-Willows Family and Community Centre (£11,000); Somali Umbrella Group (£10,000); Sightline Vision North West Ltd (£7,500); Inner City South Belfast Surestart (£5,000); Cloney Rural Development Association (£2,500); Ballymena and District Disability Forum (£1,800); and Brookvale Residents Association (£100).

FINANCES *Year* 2007–08 *Income* £833,952 *Grants* £682,126 *Assets* £22,184,891

TRUSTEES Barnaby Moores; Jane Moores; Kevin Moores.

PUBLICATIONS Applying For A Grant.

HOW TO APPLY Please refer to the foundation's website and make sure your project falls within the criteria. If you are unsure, or if you would like to discuss your application before submitting it, please telephone the foundation staff who will be happy to advise you. Application should be made by letter (no more than four sides of A4) accompanied by a completed application form. Application forms and guidance notes can be obtained by letter, phone or email or from the foundation's website. Decisions about which projects to fund are made by the trustees who meet five to six times a year to consider Merseyside applications and four times a year to consider Northern Ireland applications. As a general rule, Merseyside applicants should allow three to four months for a decision to be made, and applicants from Northern Ireland should allow four to five months. Applicants are welcome to telephone the foundation to find out at which meeting their application will be considered.

WHO TO APPLY TO Phil Godfrey, Grants Director, 7th Floor, Gostins Building, 32–36 Hanover Street, Liverpool L1 4LN *Tel* 0151 707 6077 *Fax* 0151 707 6066 *email* info@johnmooresfoundation.com *Website* www.jmf.org.uk

CC NO 253481   **ESTABLISHED** 1963

■ The Peter Moores Foundation

WHERE FUNDING CAN BE GIVEN UK and Barbados.
WHO CAN BENEFIT Organisations benefiting children and young adults, artists, actors, musicians, textile workers and designers, writers and poets, teachers and sportsmen and women.
WHAT IS FUNDED Projects which come to the attention of the patron or the trustees, that: (a) raise the artistic taste of the public whether in relation to music, drama, opera, painting, sculpture or otherwise, in connection with the fine arts; (b) promote education in the fine arts; (c) promote academic education; (d) promote the Christian religion; or (e) provide facilities for recreation or other leisure-time occupation.
TYPE OF GRANT One-off or recurring, for buildings, revenue costs, capital costs and running costs.
SAMPLE GRANTS Compton Verney House (£1.8 million); 'HIV/AIDS charites' (£126,000); English Pocket Opera (£100,000); Buxton Festival (£90,000); Childline (£72,000); Worshipful Company of Barbers (£50,000); Game and Wildlife Conservation Trust and Welsh National Opera (£40,000 each); Rossini in Wilbad (£35,000); Georgian Theatre Richmond (£23,000); Royal College ofMusic Main Scholarship (£19,000); Woodhouse Grove School (£10,000); and Textile Conservation Foundation (£8,000).
FINANCES *Year* 2007–08 *Income* £5,367,320 *Grants* £3,633,456 *Assets* £1,272,406
TRUSTEES Michael Johnson, Chair; Eileen Ainscough; Ludmilla Andrew; Nicholas Payne; Kirsten Suenson-Taylor; Joanna Laing.
HOW TO APPLY In writing to the correspondent, but applicants should be aware that the foundation has previously stated that it 'will normally support projects which come to the attention of its patron or trustees through their interests or special knowledge. General applications for sponsorship are not encouraged and are unlikely to succeed.'
WHO TO APPLY TO Peter Saunders, Administrator, c/o Wallwork, Nelson and Johnson, Chandler House, 7 Ferry Road, Riversway, Preston PR2 2YH *Tel* 01772 430000 *Fax* 01772 430012 *email* moores@pmf.org.uk *Website* www.pmf.org.uk

CC NO 258224   **ESTABLISHED** 1964

■ The Morel Charitable Trust

WHERE FUNDING CAN BE GIVEN UK and the developing world.
WHO CAN BENEFIT Grants are normally made to projects of which the trustees have personal knowledge. Organisations benefiting people disadvantaged by poverty are prioritised, but those benefiting volunteers, people living in inner city areas, and victims of famine will be considered.
WHAT IS FUNDED The arts, particularly drama; organisations working for improved race relations; inner city projects and developing world projects. Charities working in the fields of arts, culture and recreation; health; conservation and environment; education and training; and social care and development.
WHAT IS NOT FUNDED No grants to individuals.
TYPE OF GRANT Project.
RANGE OF GRANTS £500–£3,000.
SAMPLE GRANTS Child2Child – Ecuador and Oxfam – South Africa (£3,000 each); Planned Parenthood Action – Ghana (£2,500); Harvest Help – Zambia (£2,000); Pecan – UK (£1,000); and Youth Music Theatre (£500).
FINANCES *Year* 2005–06 *Income* £47,648 *Grants* £47,720 *Assets* £1,420,299
TRUSTEES J M Gibbs, Chair; W M Gibbs; S E Gibbs; B M O Gibbs; Dr T Gibbs; Dr Emily Parry; Mrs Susanna Coan.
OTHER INFORMATION No accounts received at the Charity Commission since those for 2005/06.
HOW TO APPLY In writing to the correspondent. The trustees normally meet three times a year to consider applications.
WHO TO APPLY TO S E Gibbs, Trustee, 34 Durand Gardens, London SW9 0PP *Tel* 020 7582 6901

CC NO 268943   **ESTABLISHED** 1972

■ The Morgan Charitable Foundation

WHERE FUNDING CAN BE GIVEN UK.
WHO CAN BENEFIT Registered charities and institutions benefiting at risk groups and people who are disadvantaged by poverty or socially isolated.
WHAT IS FUNDED The trustees are primarily interested in social welfare causes.
WHAT IS NOT FUNDED No grants to individuals.
RANGE OF GRANTS £1,000–£8,000.
SAMPLE GRANTS Magen David Adom and World Jewish Relief (£8,000 each); Chai Cancer Care, JNF Charitable Trust and Mango (£5,000 each); Jewish Care and One to One Children's Fund (£4,000 each); Duke of Edinburgh Award and London Pro Arte Choir (£2,000 each); and In Kind Direct Charity and South East Cancer Help Centre (£1,000 each).
FINANCES *Year* 2008 *Income* £40,977 *Grants* £76,000 *Assets* £3,149,404
TRUSTEES The Morgan Charitable Foundation Trustees Ltd. (A Morgan; L Morgan; Mrs C Morgan).
HOW TO APPLY In writing to the correspondent. Applications will only be considered if accompanied by a copy of the charitable organisation's latest report and accounts. Trustees meet twice a year, usually in April and October. No telephone enquiries please.
WHO TO APPLY TO The Trustees, MCF, PO Box 57749, London Nw11 1FD *Tel* 07968 827709

CC NO 283128   **ESTABLISHED** 1981

■ The Mr and Mrs J T Morgan Foundation

WHERE FUNDING CAN BE GIVEN Mainly Wales.

WHO CAN BENEFIT Churches, and national and local charities benefiting children, young people, students and Christians.

WHAT IS FUNDED Preference is given to the support of charities in Wales and to the promotion of education and religion in Wales.

WHAT IS NOT FUNDED No grants to individuals.

TYPE OF GRANT One-off.

SAMPLE GRANTS Previous beneficiaries have included Cambrian Educational Charity, Morriston Orpheus Choir, St Teilo Church Bishopston and South Gower and Swansea West Fundraisers and Ysgol Gymraeg Lon Las.

FINANCES *Year* 2007–08 *Income* £28,812 *Grants* £27,900 *Assets* £5,494

TRUSTEES Ms E C Phillips; J Aylward; R Morgan.

HOW TO APPLY In writing to the correspondent. All applications are acknowledged, but funds only permit that 1 in 12 applicants receive a grant.

WHO TO APPLY TO J R Morgan, Calvert House, Calvert Terrace, Swansea SA1 6AP *Tel* 01792 655178 *Fax* 01792 467002

CC NO 241835   **ESTABLISHED** 1965

■ The J P Morgan Foundations

WHERE FUNDING CAN BE GIVEN UK, with a special interest in London (south and east), Bournemouth, Edinburgh, Glasgow and Liverpool.

WHO CAN BENEFIT Organisations concerned with education, the arts, young people, women, community.

WHAT IS FUNDED Mainly projects involving community development, youth education and community life.

WHAT IS NOT FUNDED Projects not usually supported include: open appeals from national charities; building appeals; charity gala nights and similar events; or appeals by individuals for study grants, travel scholarships or charity sponsorships.

RANGE OF GRANTS About £1,000–£30,000.

FINANCES *Year* 2006–07 *Income* £292,000 *Grants* £1,208,000 *Assets* £2,653,000

TRUSTEES Carol Lake; Campbell Fleming; Swantje Conrad; Jakob Stott; Eva Lindholm; J P Morgan Asset Management Marketing Limited.

OTHER INFORMATION Please note: the foundation is currently winding up its activities.The following description in the foundation's 2006/07 accounts gives a fuller explanation of it's future plans: 'The increase in grant numbers and donations reflected the trustee policy decision taken in 2006 that all awards would be made by the foundation and no awards would be made from JPMorgan Educational Trust (the connected charity) for 2007. It also reflected the decision to move the foundation towards an orderly closure within a target period of three and a half years (as at 1 January 2007) and to that end to spend out the funds in equal portions. It was further agreed that all new awards would be of a significant amount in order to make a real difference.' The JPMorgan Foundations has previously stated that the JPMorgan Educational Trust will be wound up by 2011. It is not clear whether or not this is still the case in the light of the decision to wind up the JPMorgan Foundation. Despite attempts to contact the foundation, it has not been possible to confirm the future plans for the Educational Trust.

HOW TO APPLY The foundation is due to wind up its activities 2010. The future of the JPMorgan Educational Trust remains unclear (see the 'Other Information' section for details). Please contact the foundation for further information.

WHO TO APPLY TO Ketisha Kinnbrew, Secretary, 10 Aldermanbury, Floor 8, London EC2V 7RF *Tel* 020 7325 1308 *Fax* 020 7325 8195

CC NO 291617   **ESTABLISHED** 1985

■ Diana and Allan Morgenthau Charitable Trust

WHERE FUNDING CAN BE GIVEN Worldwide.

WHO CAN BENEFIT Charitable organisations, with an interest in Jewish groups.

WHAT IS FUNDED Jewish causes, arts, culture, health and education.

RANGE OF GRANTS £150–£20,000.

SAMPLE GRANTS The British Friends of the Jaffa Institute (£20,000); the Central British Fund for World Jewish Relief (£15,000); United Jewish Israel Appeal and JNF Charitable Trust (£10,000 each); Rays of Sunshine (£5,000); the Hope Centre for Cognitive Education (£2,000); Royal National Theatre (£1,000); London Master Class (£500); British WIZO (£250); and Rishon MS Society (£150).

FINANCES *Year* 2007–08 *Income* £125,664 *Grants* £118,900 *Assets* £6,052

TRUSTEES Allan Morgenthau; Diana Morgenthau.

HOW TO APPLY In writing to the correspondent.

WHO TO APPLY TO Allan Morgenthau, Trustee, Flat 27, Berkeley House, 15 Hay Hill, London W1J 8NS *Tel* 020 7493 1904

CC NO 1062180   **ESTABLISHED** 1997

■ The Oliver Morland Charitable Trust

WHERE FUNDING CAN BE GIVEN UK.

WHO CAN BENEFIT Registered charities usually chosen through personal knowledge of the trustees.

WHAT IS FUNDED Most of the funds are given to Quaker projects or Quaker-related projects.

WHAT IS NOT FUNDED No grants to individuals.

TYPE OF GRANT Grants are given for core, capital and project support for up to three years.

RANGE OF GRANTS Up to £30,000.

SAMPLE GRANTS Quaker Peace and Service (£30,000); Quaker Home Service – children and young people (£16,000); Quaker Social Action (£5,000); Ulster Quaker Service (£4,000); Pakistan Environmental Protection Foundation (£3,000); Peter Bedford Trust and the Refugee Council(£2,000 each); Sightsavers International (£1,500); Bristol Mediation, Dorset Wildlife Trust, Glade, Hestercombe Gardens, Medical Aid for Palestine, National Trust, The Leaveners, Somerset Wildlife Trust, and Woodland Trust (£1,000 each); Mendip CAB (£900); SOS Sahel (£750); Bethlehem Link, Community of the Holy Fire and Praxis (£500 each).

FINANCES *Year* 2007–08 *Income* £102,700 *Grants* £114,025 *Assets* £1,543,052

TRUSTEES Priscilla Khan; Stephen Rutter; Joseph Rutter; Jennifer Pittard; Kate Lovell; Charlotte Jones; Simon Pittard.

HOW TO APPLY 'Most of our grants are for continuing support of existing beneficiaries (approx 90%) so there is little left for responding to new appeals. We receive unsolicited applications at the rate of six or seven each week, 99% are not even considered.'

who to apply to J M Rutter, Trustee, Thomas's House, Stower Row, Shaftesbury, Dorset SP7 0QW *Tel* 01747 853524
cc no 1076213   **established** 1999

■ S C and M E Morland's Charitable Trust

where funding can be given UK.
who can benefit Quaker, local and UK charities which have a strong social bias and some UK-based international charities.
what is funded Support to Quaker charities and others which the trustees have special interest in, knowledge of or association with, including religious groups, relief of poverty and ill-health, promotion of peace and development overseas.
what is not funded The trust does not usually give to animal welfare, individuals or medical research.
range of grants Almost all less than £1,000 each.
sample grants £7,000 to Britain Yearly Meeting; £1,000 to Oxfam.
finances *Year* 2007–08 *Income* £42,199 *Grants* £34,350 *Assets* £947,152
trustees J C Morland; Ms J E Morland; Miss E Boyd; H N Boyd.
how to apply In writing to the correspondent. The trustees meet two times a year to make grants, in March and December. Applications should be submitted in the month before each meeting.
who to apply to J C Morland, Trustee, Gable House, Parbrook, Glastonbury, Somerset BA6 8PB *Tel* 01458 850 804
cc no 201645   **established** 1957

■ The Morris Charitable Trust

where funding can be given UK, with a preference for Islington.
who can benefit Small local projects and national organisations.
what is funded General charitable purposes. National, international and local community projects, particularly causes within the community of the London borough of Islington.
what is not funded No grants for individuals. No repeat donations are made within 12 months.
type of grant One-off grants for recurring costs for one year or less are priorities. Building and other capital grants, core costs, research grants, running costs, salaries and start-up costs are considered.
range of grants £1–£7,500; average grant £575.
sample grants Recent grants have been made to: Age Concern – Islington, the Bridge School – Islington and Islington Senior Citizens Fund.
finances *Year* 2007–08 *Income* £105,615 *Grants* £98,370 *Assets* £179,849
trustees J A Morris, chair; P B Morris; A R Stenning.
publications Information pamphlet.
how to apply By application form available from the trust or downloadable from its website. The completed form should be returned complete with any supporting documentation and a copy of your latest report and accounts.
who to apply to Jack A Morris, Trustee, c/o Management Office, Business Design Centre, 52 Upper Street, London N1 0QH *Tel* 020 7359 3535 *Fax* 020 7226 0590 *email* info@morrischaritabletrust.com *Website* www.morrischaritabletrust.com
cc no 802290   **established** 1989

■ The Willie and Mabel Morris Charitable Trust

where funding can be given UK.
who can benefit Registered charities benefiting people who are ill, particularly with cancer, heart trouble, cerebral palsy, arthritis or rheumatism.
what is funded Welfare and disability.
what is not funded No grants for individuals or non-registered charities.
range of grants £100–£15,000.
sample grants Paul Strickland – Mount Vernon Hospital (£15,000); Brickwell and Miller Charity, St John's Hospice and University of Cambridge (£10,000 each); Covent Garden Cancer Research Trust, East Anglian Air Ambulance, The High Blood Pressure Foundation, MS Trust, St Thomas Trust and the Stroke Association (£5,000); The Bedford Hospital Charity (£2,000); Hospices at Home (£1,000); The Dorchester Abbey Preservation Trust (£750); The Royal British Legion (£500); Lowe Syndrome Trust (£250); and The Scleroderma Society (£100).
finances *Year* 2007–08 *Income* £117,230 *Grants* £115,990 *Assets* £3,356,086
trustees Michael Macfadyen; Joyce Tether; Peter Tether; Andrew Tether; Angela Tether; Suzanne Marriott.
how to apply The trustees 'formulate an independent grants policy at regular meetings so that funds are already committed'.
who to apply to Angela Tether, 41 Field Lane, Letchworth Garden City, Hertfordshire SG6 3LD *Tel* 01462 480 583
cc no 280554   **established** 1980

■ The Peter Morrison Charitable Foundation

where funding can be given UK.
who can benefit Registered charities benefiting at risk groups and people who are disadvantaged by poverty and socially isolated.
what is funded A wide range of social welfare causes.
range of grants Up to £10,000.
sample grants World Jewish Relief (£10,000); St Giles Church ((£6,400); St Johns and Highwoods Community Association (£6,300); Project 2005 (£4,800); RNLI (£4,300); and Spinal Injuries Association (£4,200); Donkey Sanctuary (£1,000); Jewish Blind and Disabled (£500); Mind (£300); Prisoners Education Trust (£250); Starlight Children's Foundation (£100); and Tate Friends (£75).
finances *Year* 2007–08 *Income* £27,082 *Grants* £87,470 *Assets* £960,137
trustees M Morrison; I R Morrison; Mrs J Morrison; Mrs L Greenhill.
how to apply In writing to the correspondent.
who to apply to J Payne, Begbies Chettle Agar, Chartered Accountants, Epworth House, 25 City Road, London EC1Y 1AR *Tel* 020 7628 5801
cc no 277202   **established** 1978

■ G M Morrison Charitable Trust

where funding can be given UK.
who can benefit Registered charities only.
what is funded General charitable purposes. The trustees give priority to those charities already supported. Very few charities are added to the list each year.

WHAT IS NOT FUNDED No support for individuals, charities not registered in the UK, schemes or activities which are generally regarded as the responsibility of statutory authorities, short-term projects or one-off capital grants.

TYPE OF GRANT Normally annual.

RANGE OF GRANTS £400–£10,000, average £650.

SAMPLE GRANTS University of Aberdeen Development Trust (£10,000); British. Red Cross and Christian Aid (£3,000 each); The Circulation Foundation (£2,200); Practical Action Bangladesh Emergency Appeal (£2,000); Ninewells Hospital (Dundee) Cancer Campaign (£1,200); Royal Academy of Music (£1,000); Schools Outreach (£950); Corporation for the Sons of the Clergy (£750); Family Welfare Association (£650); British Vascular Foundation (£550); Prisoners Abroad (£450); and Liverpool School of Tropical Medicine (£400).

FINANCES *Year* 2007–08 *Income* £847,138 *Grants* £152,550 *Assets* £7,347,327

TRUSTEES J A Hunt; E H Morrison; N W Smith; A E Cornick.

HOW TO APPLY The trust's annual report states: 'Beneficiaries of grants are normally selected on the basis of trustees' personal knowledge and recommendation. The trust's grant making is however of a long term recurring nature and is restricted by available income. The trustees have decided that for the present, new applications for grants will only be considered in the most exceptional circumstances; any spare income will be allocated to increasing the grants made to charities currently receiving support. In the future this policy will of course be reviewed. Applicants who understanding this policy nevertheless wish to apply for a grant should write to the [correspondent].'

WHO TO APPLY TO A E Cornick, Trustee, Currey and Co, 21 Buckingham Gate, London SW1E 6LS *Tel* 020 7802 2700

CC NO 261380   **ESTABLISHED** 1970

■ The Stanley Morrison Charitable Trust

WHERE FUNDING CAN BE GIVEN The west coast of Scotland, with a preference for Glasgow and Ayrshire.

WHO CAN BENEFIT Organisations benefiting young adults, and sportsmen and women.

WHAT IS FUNDED Sporting activities in Scotland, with particular emphasis on the encouragement of youth involvement; charities which have as their principal base of operation and benefit the west coast of Scotland, in particular the Glasgow and Ayrshire areas; charities whose funds arise from or whose assistance is provided to people having connection with the licensed trades and in particular the whisky industry; Scottish educational establishments.

TYPE OF GRANT Buildings, project and recurring costs. Grants and funding for up to and over three years will be considered.

RANGE OF GRANTS £100–£10,000.

SAMPLE GRANTS Previous beneficiaries include Scottish Cricket Union, Princess Royal Trust for Carers, Riding for the Disabled, Mark Scott Foundation, Glasgow University Sports Sponsorship, Grange Cricket Club – Youth Section, Cancer UK Scotland and Scottish Schools' Badminton Union.

FINANCES *Year* 2007–08 *Income* £51,805 *Grants* £30,000

TRUSTEES S W Morrison; J H McKean; Mrs M E Morrison; T F O'Connell; A S Dudgeon.

HOW TO APPLY In writing to the correspondent. Applicants should include details on the purpose of the grant, what funding has already been secured and the actual sum that they are looking for.

WHO TO APPLY TO The Trustees, c/o French Duncan, 375 West George Street, Glasgow G2 4LW

SC NO SC006610   **ESTABLISHED** 1989

■ Moshal Charitable Trust

WHERE FUNDING CAN BE GIVEN UK.

WHO CAN BENEFIT Jewish causes.

WHAT IS FUNDED General charitable purposes.

SAMPLE GRANTS No sample grants were available for 2007–08.

FINANCES *Year* 2007–08 *Income* £306,594 *Grants* £76,112 *Assets* £525,680

TRUSTEES D Halpern; L Halpern.

HOW TO APPLY In writing to the correspondent.

WHO TO APPLY TO The Trustees, c/o S Yodaiken & Co., 40a Bury New Road, Prestwich, Manchester M25 0LD

CC NO 284448   **ESTABLISHED** 1981

■ Vyoel Moshe Charitable Trust

WHERE FUNDING CAN BE GIVEN UK and overseas.

WHO CAN BENEFIT Registered charities.

WHAT IS FUNDED Education and relief of poverty.

FINANCES *Year* 2007–08 *Income* £1,073,232 *Grants* £1,039,575 *Assets* £55,734

TRUSTEES Y Frankel; B Berger; S Seidenfeld.

HOW TO APPLY In writing to the correspondent.

WHO TO APPLY TO J Weinberger, Secretary, 2–4 Chardmore Road, London N16 6HX

CC NO 327054   **ESTABLISHED** 1986

■ The Moshulu Charitable Trust

WHERE FUNDING CAN BE GIVEN UK.

WHO CAN BENEFIT Charitable organisations.

WHAT IS FUNDED 'Humanitarian' and evangelical causes.

SAMPLE GRANTS Seaway Trust (£40,000); Christ Church (£15,000); SWYM (£12,000); Vineyard (£6,000); Tear Fund (£5,200); Open Door Centre (£2,900); and Care for the Family (£2,500).

FINANCES *Year* 2007–08 *Income* £81,158 *Grants* £95,207 *Assets* £182,614

TRUSTEES H J Fulls; D M Fulls; G N Fulls; S M Fulls; G F Symons.

HOW TO APPLY In writing to the correspondent.

WHO TO APPLY TO H J Fulls, Trustee, Devonshire Road, Heathpark, Honiton, Devon EX14 1SD

CC NO 1071479   **ESTABLISHED** 1998

■ Brian and Jill Moss Charitable Trust

WHERE FUNDING CAN BE GIVEN Worldwide.

WHO CAN BENEFIT Registered charities only.

WHAT IS FUNDED Jewish causes and healthcare.

WHAT IS NOT FUNDED Donations are made to registered charities only.

TYPE OF GRANT Capital projects and towards 'ordinary charity expenditure'.

SAMPLE GRANTS United Jewish Israel Appeal (£43,000); Magen David Adom UK (£31,000); Jewish Care (£16,000); World Jewish Relief (£15,000); Chai Cancer Care (£12,000); United Synagogue-Tribe (£11,000); WIZO UK

Alphabetical register of grant making charitable trusts

(£6,000);National Jewish Chaplaincy Board (£5,500); Prostate Cancer Charitable Trust (£5,000); Myeloma UK (£3,000); Israel Folk Dance Institute (£500); and Jewish Museum and Operation Wheelchairs (£250 each).

FINANCES *Year* 2007–08 *Income* £281,024 *Grants* £177,600 *Assets* £2,986,550

TRUSTEES Brian Peter Moss; Jill Moss; David Paul Moss; Sarah Levy.

HOW TO APPLY In writing to the correspondent. Appeals are considered as they are received and the trustees will make donations throughout the year.

WHO TO APPLY TO The Trustees, c/o Deloitte, Blenheim House, Fitzalan Court, Newport Road, Cardiff CF24 0TS

CC NO 1084664   ESTABLISHED 2000

■ The Moss Charitable Trust

WHERE FUNDING CAN BE GIVEN UK and overseas, with an interest in Dorset, Hampshire and Sussex.

WHO CAN BENEFIT Registered charities, especially Christian.

WHAT IS FUNDED General charitable purposes, specifically for the benefit of the community in the county borough of Bournemouth, and Hampshire, Dorset and Sussex; advancement of religion either UK or overseas; advancement of education; and relief of poverty, disease and sickness.

TYPE OF GRANT Outright grant or interest-free loan.

RANGE OF GRANTS Up to £8,000, but mostly less than £5,000.

SAMPLE GRANTS Tabitha Trust (£8,000); Walking on Water Trust (£6,500); Christ Church – Westbourne (£6,400); Tamil Church (£2,500); Chichester Counselling Service and St James – Poole (£2,000 each); Barnabus Fund (£1,600); European Christian Mission (£1,300); Ebenezer Emergency Fund (£1,200); and Yapton PCC (£1,000).

FINANCES *Year* 2007–08 *Income* £89,823 *Grants* £85,750 *Assets* £59,505

TRUSTEES J H Simmons; A F Simmons; P L Simmons; D S Olby.

OTHER INFORMATION Around £5,000 was given by the trust to individuals.

HOW TO APPLY No funds are available by direct application. Because of the way in which this trust operates it is not open to external applications for grants.

WHO TO APPLY TO P D Malpas, 7 Church Road, Parkstone, Poole, Dorset BH14 8UF *Tel* 01202 730002

CC NO 258031   ESTABLISHED 1969

■ The Robert and Margaret Moss Charitable Trust

WHERE FUNDING CAN BE GIVEN Oxfordshire, with a preference for Oxford.

WHO CAN BENEFIT Charitable organisations.

WHAT IS FUNDED Research into human nutrition, medical research, relief of poverty and education.

SAMPLE GRANTS Oxford Children's Hospital Campaign (£7,500); Blackbird Leys Saturday School, Deafblind UK, Oxfordshire Mind and Pathway Workshop (£2,000 each); Guideposts, Independent Age, Listening Books and The Porch Steppin' Stone Centre (£1,000 each); and The Meningitis Trust (£650).

FINANCES *Year* 2007–08 *Income* £47,539 *Grants* £36,374 *Assets* £1,452,614

TRUSTEES John Cole; Dr Tarrant Stein; Mrs Maggie Perrin.

HOW TO APPLY In writing to the correspondent.

WHO TO APPLY TO Ms Helen Fanyinka, c/o Morgan Cole, Buxton Court, 3 West Way, Oxford OX2 0SZ *Tel* 01865 262 600 *email* info@morgan-cole.com

CC NO 290760   ESTABLISHED 1984

■ Moss Family Charitable Trust

WHERE FUNDING CAN BE GIVEN England.

WHO CAN BENEFIT Jewish organisations.

WHAT IS FUNDED Religious and welfare purposes.

WHAT IS NOT FUNDED Neither music nor the arts is funded.

TYPE OF GRANT One-off.

RANGE OF GRANTS £100–£10,000.

SAMPLE GRANTS Previous beneficiaries include: the Children's Charity, West London Synagogue (WLS), Jewish Child's Day, Norwood, Presidents Club and Hammerson House.

FINANCES *Year* 2007–08 *Income* £85,184 *Grants* £83,466 *Assets* £5,115

TRUSTEES S D Moss; R S Moss; Mrs V J Campus.

HOW TO APPLY In writing to the correspondent. The trust is unlikely to respond to unsolicited applications.

WHO TO APPLY TO K Sage, Administrator, 28 Bolton Street, Mayfair, London W1J 8BP *Tel* 020 7629 9933

CC NO 327529   ESTABLISHED 1987

■ Mothercare Charitable Foundation

WHERE FUNDING CAN BE GIVEN UK and worldwide.

WHO CAN BENEFIT Children and their mothers.

WHAT IS FUNDED Registered charities and research organisations that promote the general well-being of children and their mothers; offering them the very best chance of good health, education, well-being and a secure start in life. Specifically, the foundation welcomes applications from registered charities and research organisations associated with the following criteria: ensuring the good health and well-being of mums-to-be, new mums and their children; special baby-care needs and premature births; other parenting initiatives relating to family well-being.

WHAT IS NOT FUNDED No response to circular appeals. Support is not given to: animal welfare, appeals from individuals, the arts, older people, environment/heritage, religious appeals, political appeals, or sport.

SAMPLE GRANTS Wellbeing of Women (£40,000); the New Children's Hospital Appeal (£20,000); Homestart (£13,000); and the Peace Hospice, Kids, and Whittington Hospital (£5,000 each).

FINANCES *Year* 2007–08 *Income* £129,320 *Grants* £186,431 *Assets* £188,934

TRUSTEES Karren Brady; Ben Gordon; Ian Peacock; Clive Revett.

HOW TO APPLY In writing to the correspondent. Requests for donations will only be considered when made in writing on the application form that can be printed from the company's website. Applications are considered on a quarterly basis. Unsolicited appeals are unlikely to be successful.

Think carefully about every application. Is it justified?

731

WHO TO APPLY TO The Charity Administrator, Cherry Tree Road, Watford, Hertfordshire WD24 6SH *Tel* 01923 241000 *email* simone.spencer-ahmed@mothercare.co.uk *Website* www.mothercare.com
CC NO 1104386   ESTABLISHED 2004

■ Moto in the Community Trust

WHERE FUNDING CAN BE GIVEN Communities local to the 48 Moto service areas around the UK (details of stations can be found on its website).
WHO CAN BENEFIT Supports a wide variety of local charities and community projects.
WHAT IS FUNDED Projects that benefit the local community.
WHAT IS NOT FUNDED The trust does not consider applications that are for the promotion of religion or politics.
SAMPLE GRANTS Wellgate Primary School; Breast Cancer Campaign; Tamworth Sea Cadets; SNAP; Quality Action Group; Marketeers Carnival Club; Wetherby Silver Band; Nixon School of Dance; and the Children's Trust.
FINANCES *Year* 2008 *Income* £223,714 *Grants* £123,168 *Assets* £138,612
TRUSTEES Brian Lotts, Chair; Joanne Mawdsley; Suzanne Hollinshead; Christopher Rogers; Brian Larkin; Helen Budd; IanThomson; Heather Roberts; Sara Davies; Malcolm Plowes; Jack Kidd; Ashleigh Lewis; Ian Kernighan; Jon Shore; Peter Hazzard; Ellis Green.
HOW TO APPLY 'Applications are looked on favourably if the applicant has built a relationship with the local Moto site and discussed opportunities for the Moto site employees to engage with the project/charity. The application should be supported by the General Manager of the Moto service area. Preference will be given to projects which have a long term relationship with Moto, for example schools or community groups which Moto has a relationship with.'
Grants are approved by the Trustees every three months.
Any questions can be directed to the Moto in the Community Trust Administrator (e-mail: motocharity@talking360.com; tel.: 01525 714467 / 717303).
WHO TO APPLY TO Moto in the Community Trust Administrator, Freepost RLYC-BKXA-CJHH, Moto in the Community Trust, 37 Beaumont Road, Flitwick, Bedfordshire MK45 1AL *Tel* 01525 714467 / 717303 *email* motocharity@talking360.com *Website* www.moto-way.com
CC NO 1111147   ESTABLISHED 2005

■ J P Moulton Charitable Foundation

WHERE FUNDING CAN BE GIVEN UK.
WHO CAN BENEFIT Research institutions, disadvantaged people.
WHAT IS FUNDED Medical, education, training and counselling.
TYPE OF GRANT One-off and recurrent.
RANGE OF GRANTS £250–£125,000.
SAMPLE GRANTS Imperial College (£126,000); St Martin-in-the-Fields and The Stoke-on-Trent and North Staffordshire Theatre Trust (£100,000 each); University of Manchester (£76,000); Meningitis Research Foundation (£57,000); University College London and the University of Leicester (£55,000 each); and South Manchester University Hospital (£53,000);

Marlborough Primary School (£50,000); Muir Maxwell Trust (£24,000); St Christopher's Hospice (£5,000); and Action on Addiction (£500).
FINANCES *Year* 2008 *Income* £1,162,156 *Grants* £1,184,342 *Assets* £8,398,009
TRUSTEES J P Moulton; Mrs P M Moulton; Sara Everett.
HOW TO APPLY In writing to the correspondent.
WHO TO APPLY TO J P Moulton, Trustee, The Mount, Church Street Shoreham, Sevenoaks, Kent TN14 7SD *Tel* 01959 524 008
CC NO 1109891   ESTABLISHED 2005

■ The Mount Everest Foundation

WHERE FUNDING CAN BE GIVEN Expeditions from Great Britain and New Zealand.
WHO CAN BENEFIT Organisations, young adults and older people.
WHAT IS FUNDED Support of expeditions for exploration and research in high mountain regions only.
WHAT IS NOT FUNDED Young people, training and commercial expeditions are not eligible.
TYPE OF GRANT Project.
RANGE OF GRANTS £600–£2,500.
FINANCES *Year* 2007–08 *Income* £42,400 *Grants* £24,400 *Assets* £1,017,100
TRUSTEES David Unwin; Paul Rose; Sir John Chapple; Sarah Tyacke; Roy Wood; Dr William Thurston; Martin Scott; Henry Day.
PUBLICATIONS A map of Central Asia has been produced in collaboration with the Royal Geographical Society.
HOW TO APPLY On a form available from the correspondent. Deadlines for receipt of completed application forms are 31 August and 31 December for the following year's expeditions.
WHO TO APPLY TO R F Morgan, 23 Charlwood Road, London W15 1QA *Tel* 020 8788 6251 *Website* www.mef.org.uk
CC NO 208206   ESTABLISHED 1955

■ Mountbatten Festival of Music

WHERE FUNDING CAN BE GIVEN UK.
WHO CAN BENEFIT Registered charities benefiting (ex) servicemen/women.
WHAT IS FUNDED Charities connected with the Royal Marines and Royal Navy.
WHAT IS NOT FUNDED Charities/organisations unknown to the trustees.
TYPE OF GRANT One-off and recurrent.
SAMPLE GRANTS Malcolm Sergeant Cancer Fund (£20,000); Metropolitan Police Benevolent Trust (14,000); RN Benevolent Fund; RNRMC and RM Museum (£10,000 each); Wrens Benevolent Trust, Seafarers UK, Royal British Legion, The 'Not Forgotten' Society, Queen Ann Hospital Home, and Scottish Veterans Residences (£1,000 each).
FINANCES *Year* 2007–08 *Income* £291,885 *Grants* £123,240 *Assets* £158,785
TRUSTEES Commandant General Royal Marines; Director of Royal Marines; Naval Personnel Team (RM) Team Leader
HOW TO APPLY Unsolicited applications are not considered as the trust's income is dependent upon the running and success of various musical events. Any money raised by this means is then disbursed to a set of regular beneficiaries.
WHO TO APPLY TO Lt Col I W Grant, Corps Secretary, The Corps Secretariat, Building 32, HMS

Excellent, Whale Island, Portsmouth PO2 8ER *Tel* 023 9254 7201 *email* royalmarines. charities@charity.vfree.com *Website* www. royalmarinesregimental.co.uk
CC NO 1016088   **ESTABLISHED** 1993

■ The Mountbatten Memorial Trust

WHERE FUNDING CAN BE GIVEN Mainly UK, but some overseas.

WHO CAN BENEFIT Registered charities.

WHAT IS FUNDED Grants restricted to technological research in aid of disabilities.

WHAT IS NOT FUNDED No grants are made towards the purchase of technology to assist people with disabilities.

TYPE OF GRANT Technological research projects.

RANGE OF GRANTS £2,500–£57,000.

SAMPLE GRANTS Atlantic College (£57,000); Soundabout, Soundaround and Seeing Ear (£3,000 each); St Saviour's Youth Club – Nottingham (£4,000); and St Mary's Youth Club – Stratton (£2,500).

FINANCES *Year* 2007–08 *Income* £51,393 *Grants* £72,500 *Assets* £519,881

TRUSTEES Countess Mountbatten of Burma; Lady Pamela Hicks; Ben Moorhead; Ashley Hicks; Hon. Michael John Knatchbull; Hon. Philip Knatchbull.

HOW TO APPLY In writing to the correspondent, at any time.

WHO TO APPLY TO John Moss, Secretary, The Estate Office, Broadlands, Romsey, Hampshire SO51 9ZE *Tel* 01794 529 750

CC NO 278691   **ESTABLISHED** 1979

■ The Edwina Mountbatten Trust

WHERE FUNDING CAN BE GIVEN UK and overseas.

WHO CAN BENEFIT Medical organisations, particularly those benefiting children and nurses.

WHAT IS FUNDED Save the Children Fund (for children who are sick, distressed or in need), the promotion and improvement of the art and practice of nursing, and St John Ambulance.

WHAT IS NOT FUNDED No grants for research or to individual nurses working in the UK for further professional training.

TYPE OF GRANT Project grants.

RANGE OF GRANTS £2,000–£32,000.

SAMPLE GRANTS Save the Children (£32,000); St John Ambulance – Romsey (£21,000); Homestart and St Jerusalem Eye Hospital (£9,000 each); Independent Age UK, Target TB and Whizz Kidz (£5,000 each); Ashram International (£3,000); and Changing Faces and Well Child (£2,000 each).

FINANCES *Year* 2007 *Income* £98,946 *Grants* £97,000 *Assets* £3,367,034

TRUSTEES Countess Mountbatten of Burma, Chair; Hon. Alexandra Knatchbull; Lord Brabourne; Peter H T Mimpriss; Dame Mary Fagan.

HOW TO APPLY In writing to the correspondent. The trustees meet once a year, generally in September/October.

WHO TO APPLY TO John Moss, Secretary, Estate Office, Broadlands, Romsey, Hampshire SO51 9ZE *Tel* 01794 529 750

CC NO 228166   **ESTABLISHED** 1960

■ The Mugdock Children's Trust

WHERE FUNDING CAN BE GIVEN Scotland.

WHO CAN BENEFIT Charities benefiting children up to the age of about 14 who are ill or disabled.

WHAT IS FUNDED 'Poor children from Glasgow or other districts of Scotland who are in need of convalescent treatment for sickness or any other disability; organisations of a charitable nature whose objects either consist of or include the provision in Scotland of rehabilitation, recreation or education for children convalescing or still suffering from the effects of illness, injury or disability; organisations of a charitable nature whose objects either consist of or include the provision in Scotland of accommodation or facilities for children who are in need of care or assistance.'

RANGE OF GRANTS £500–£6,000.

SAMPLE GRANTS Previous beneficiaries have included Abercorn School, Ark Trust, Barnardos, Camphill Foundation, Cancer and Leukaemia in Childhood, Children First, Children's Heart Federation, Glasgow Children's Holiday Playscheme, Hopscotch Holidays Ltd, Sense, Sighthill Youth Centre, Stepping Stones for Families, Wanderers Youth Club and West Scotland Deaf Children's Society.

FINANCES *Year* 2007–08 *Income* £48,676 *Grants* £36,000 *Assets* £1,305,522

TRUSTEES Graham A Philips; Rosamund Blair; Moira Bruce; Dr Anne Cowan; Joyce Duguid; Avril Meighan; Alastair J Struthers; Christine Brown; James Morris.

HOW TO APPLY On a form available from the correspondent. Trustees meet in March and November.

WHO TO APPLY TO Mrs J Simpson, Secretary, Wylie and Bisset Accountants, 168 Bath Street, Glasgow G2 4TP *Tel* 0141 566 7000 *Fax* 0141 566 7001

SC NO SC006001

■ The F H Muirhead Charitable Trust

WHERE FUNDING CAN BE GIVEN UK.

WHO CAN BENEFIT Hospitals/medical research institutes.

WHAT IS FUNDED Specific items of medical equipment for use in research by hospitals and universities. Priority is given to applications from smaller organisations.

WHAT IS NOT FUNDED No grants to non-charitable bodies. No grants for equipment for diagnostic or clinical use.

TYPE OF GRANT Capital grants; research grants considered.

SAMPLE GRANTS Previous beneficiaries include: Defeating Deafness, Cystic Fibrosis Trust, Bath Institute of Medical Engineering, Ehlers-Danlos Support Group, The David Tolkien Trust for Stoke Mandeville NBIC, Covent Garden Cancer Research Trust and High Blood Pressure Foundation.

FINANCES *Year* 2007–08 *Income* £20,387 *Grants* £35,000

TRUSTEES Dr M J Harding; S J Gallico; Dr R C D Staughton; Prof. D Leslie.

HOW TO APPLY On a form available from the correspondent. This should be returned with details of specific items of equipment for which a grant is required. Trustees meet twice a year in March and October. Application forms to be received at least three weeks before the meeting.

WHO TO APPLY TO S J Gallico, Merlin House, 6 Boltro Road, Haywards Heath, West Sussex RH16 1BB *Tel* 01444 411 333
CC NO 327605   **ESTABLISHED** 1987

■ The Mulberry Trust

WHERE FUNDING CAN BE GIVEN UK, with an interest in Harlow, Essex and surrounding areas, including London.
WHO CAN BENEFIT Charitable organisations.
WHAT IS FUNDED General charitable purposes.
RANGE OF GRANTS £1,000–£50,000.
FINANCES *Year* 2007–08 *Income* £186,785 *Grants* £398,925 *Assets* £6,774,282
TRUSTEES John G Marks; Mrs Ann M Marks; Charles F Woodhouse; Timothy J Marks.
HOW TO APPLY The trust has stated that it 'will not, as a matter of policy, consider applications which are unsolicited'.
WHO TO APPLY TO Ms Cheryl Boyce, Farrer and Co, 66 Lincoln's Inn Fields, London WC2A 3LH *Tel* 020 7242 2022
CC NO 263296   **ESTABLISHED** 1971

■ The Edith Murphy Foundation

WHERE FUNDING CAN BE GIVEN UK with some preference for Leicestershire.
WHO CAN BENEFIT Organisations benefiting people in need, animals, children and the disabled.
WHAT IS FUNDED Relief for people suffering hardship/distress due to their age, youth, infirmity, disability, poverty or social and economic circumstances. Relief of suffering of animals and provision for the care of unwanted or sick animals. Other general charitable purposes.
TYPE OF GRANT One-off and recurrent.
RANGE OF GRANTS Up to £80,000.
SAMPLE GRANTS Rainbows Children's Hospice (£80,000); Vitalise (£75,000); The Benjamin Foundation (£70,000); Headway (£65,000); De Montfort University, Help the Aged, The Islamic Foundation and University of East Anglia (£50,000 each); Holy Rosary Parish – Ghana and LOROS Hospice (£35,000 each); All Saints' Church Thurcaston with Cropston, Leicester Cathedral and Teenage Cancer Trust (£25,000 each); the Stroke Association (£20,000); Combat Stress (£15,000); Big C Local Cancer, Changing Faces, Horse's Voice Rescue & Rehabilitation Centre, Konnect 9, Leicester and Leicestershire Animal Aid Association, Motor Neurone Disease Association, PDSA and Southrepps Village Hall (£10,000 each).
FINANCES *Year* 2007–08 *Income* £1,150,422 *Grants* £1,021,084 *Assets* £30,584,685
TRUSTEES David L Tams; Pamela M Breakwell; Christopher P Blakesley; Richard F Adkinson.
HOW TO APPLY In writing to the correspondent.
WHO TO APPLY TO David L Tams, Trustee, C/o Crane and Walton, 113–117 London Road, Leicester LE2 0RG *Tel* 0116 2551901
CC NO 1026062   **ESTABLISHED** 1993

■ Murphy-Newmann Charity Company Limited

WHERE FUNDING CAN BE GIVEN UK, predominantly the south, the south east and the Midlands.
WHO CAN BENEFIT Registered charities only.
WHAT IS FUNDED Financial relief of older people and people who are very young or disabled.

WHAT IS NOT FUNDED No grants to individuals, or non-registered charities.
TYPE OF GRANT Recurrent.
RANGE OF GRANTS £250–£2,000.
SAMPLE GRANTS Contact the Elderly and Evening Argus Christmas Appeal (£1,750 each); Elizabeth Finn Trust, Haemophilia Society, RUKBA, Invalids at Home, Norwood Children's and Families Trust, RNIB Sunshine House Nursery School, South East Cancer Help Centre and North London Hospice (£1,000 each); British Home and Hospital for Incurables and Chicks Camping Holidays (£750 each); REACT and Lowe Syndrome Trust (£500 each); and Dream Makers and 2 Care (£250 each).
FINANCES *Year* 2007–08 *Income* £35,529 *Grants* £28,500 *Assets* £747,113
TRUSTEES M J Lockett; Ms C Sathill; M Richman.
HOW TO APPLY In writing to the correspondent, in a letter outlining the purpose of the required charitable donation. Telephone calls are not welcome. There are no application forms, guidelines or deadlines. No sae required. Grants are usually given in November and December.
WHO TO APPLY TO M J Lockett, Trustee, Hayling Cottage, Upper Street, Stratford-St-Mary, Colchester, Essex CO7 6JW *Tel* 01206 323685 *Fax* 01206 323686 *email* mnccl@keme.co.uk
CC NO 229555   **ESTABLISHED** 1963

■ The John R Murray Charitable Trust

WHERE FUNDING CAN BE GIVEN UK.
WHO CAN BENEFIT Registered charities.
WHAT IS FUNDED 'Arts an literature (although not strictly limited to such areas) and where the award of a grant will have an immediate and tangible benefit to the recipient in question.'
SAMPLE GRANTS National Library of Scotland (£259,000); Strawberry Hill Trust (£80,000); Wordsworth Trust (£70,000); Bodleian Library (£45,000); Koestler Trust (£35,000); the British Library (£32,000); Keats Shelley Memorial Association (£31,000); and British School at Rome, Carmarthenshire Heritage Regeneration Trust and Charles Darwin Trust (£30,000 each).
FINANCES *Year* 2007 *Income* £547,220 *Grants* £783,914 *Assets* £25,419,335
TRUSTEES John R Murray; Virginia G Murray; Hallam J R G Murray; John O G Murray; Charles J G Murray.
OTHER INFORMATION 'In the medium term the trustees' principal aim will be the continued support of the National Library of Scotland.'
HOW TO APPLY The trustees will not consider applications for grants.
WHO TO APPLY TO The Trustees, 50 Albemarle Street, London W1S 4BD
CC NO 1100199   **ESTABLISHED** 2003

■ The Mushroom Fund

WHERE FUNDING CAN BE GIVEN UK and overseas, with a preference for St Helens.
WHO CAN BENEFIT Registered charities. Donations are made only to charities known to the trustees.
WHAT IS FUNDED General charitable purposes.
WHAT IS NOT FUNDED No grants to individuals or to organisations that are not registered charities.
RANGE OF GRANTS Up to £3,000.
SAMPLE GRANTS World Society for the Protection of Animals (£3,000); Hearing Dogs for Deaf People (£2,500); Born Free Foundation and UROLINK

(£2,000 each); and Bicester Intrepid Scout Group, Buckley and Mold Lions Club, Patterdale Mountain Rescue, Rowans Hospice – Purbrook, Topps Training and Walk the Walk Worldwide (£1,000 each).

FINANCES *Year* 2007–08 *Income* £38,988 *Grants* £34,849 *Assets* £977,319

TRUSTEES G Pilkington; Ms H Christian; Mrs R Christian; Mrs J Wailing; J Pilkington; Liverpool Charity and Voluntary Services.

HOW TO APPLY The trust does not consider or respond to unsolicited applications.

WHO TO APPLY TO The Trustees, Liverpool Charity and Voluntary Services, 151 Dale Street, Liverpool L2 2AH *Tel* 0151 227 5177 *email* enquiries@ charitycheques.org.uk

CC NO 259954   **ESTABLISHED** 1969

■ The Music Sales Charitable Trust

WHERE FUNDING CAN BE GIVEN UK, but mostly Bury St Edmunds and London.

WHO CAN BENEFIT Registered charities benefiting children and young adults, musicians, disabled people and people disadvantaged by poverty.

WHAT IS FUNDED The trust supports the education of children attending schools in the UK, relief of need, and other charitable purposes. The trustees are particularly interested in helping to promote music and musical education for young people.

WHAT IS NOT FUNDED No grants to individuals.

RANGE OF GRANTS £1,000–£15,000.

SAMPLE GRANTS Previous beneficiaries include the Purcell School Scholarship, Suffolk County Council – Music Department, Westminster Synagogue and St Edmundsbury Borough Council Festival.

FINANCES *Year* 2007 *Income* £20,000 *Grants* £35,889 *Assets* £6,611

TRUSTEES Robert Wise; T Wise; Ian Morgan; Christopher Butler; A E Latham; David Rockberger; Mrs Mildred Wise.

HOW TO APPLY In writing to the correspondent. The trustees meet quarterly, generally in March, June, September and December.

WHO TO APPLY TO Neville Wignall, Clerk, Music Sales Ltd, Dettingen Way, Bury St Edmunds, Suffolk IP33 3YB *Tel* 01284 702 600 *email* neville. wignall@musicsales.co.uk

CC NO 1014942   **ESTABLISHED** 1992

■ Muslim Hands

WHERE FUNDING CAN BE GIVEN Overseas.

WHO CAN BENEFIT Organisations benefiting people disadvantaged by poverty and victims of man-made or natural disasters and war.

WHAT IS FUNDED The relief of poverty and sickness in the event of natural disasters and areas of war; help to people in need, particularly orphans; advancement of the Islamic faith and distribution of Islamic literature; provision of schools, training colleges, safe water schemes, medical centres, and orphan sponsorship schemes.

FINANCES *Year* 2008 *Income* £8,967,130 *Grants* £6,453,297 *Assets* £5,401,385

TRUSTEES Pir Mohammad Amin-ul Hasanat Shah; Syed Lakhte Hassanain; Dr Musharaf Hussain; Sahibzada Ghulam Jillani

HOW TO APPLY In writing to the correspondent.

WHO TO APPLY TO The Trustees, 148–164 Gregory Boulevard, Nottingham NG7 5JE *Tel* 0115 911 7222 *Fax* 0115 911 7220 *email* contact@ muslimhands.org *Website* www.muslimhands. org

CC NO 1105056   **ESTABLISHED** 1993

■ The Mutual Trust Group

WHERE FUNDING CAN BE GIVEN UK.

WHO CAN BENEFIT Organisations benefiting Jewish people and people disadvantaged by poverty.

WHAT IS FUNDED General charitable purposes. In particular, for the relief of poverty and the advancement of orthodox Jewish religious education.

SAMPLE GRANTS Yeshivat Shar Hashamaym (£168,000); Yeshivat Kesser Hatalmud (£38,000); Congregation Beis Hamedrash (£4,000); and 'other' (£400).

FINANCES *Year* 2008 *Income* £179,994 *Grants* £210,846 *Assets* £142,366

TRUSTEES B Weitz; M Weitz; A Weisz.

HOW TO APPLY In writing to the correspondent.

WHO TO APPLY TO B Weitz, Trustee, 12 Dunstan Road, London NW11 8AA *Tel* 020 8458 7549

CC NO 1039300   **ESTABLISHED** 1994

■ MYA Charitable Trust

WHERE FUNDING CAN BE GIVEN Worldwide.

WHO CAN BENEFIT Children, young adults and Jewish people.

WHAT IS FUNDED Advancement of orthodox Jewish religion and education.

SAMPLE GRANTS Previous beneficiaries include: ZSV Trust, KZF, Beis Rochel, Keren Zedoko Vochesed, London Friends of Kamenitzer Yeshiva, Maos Yesomim Charitable Trust, Bikkur Cholim De Satmar, Keren Mitzva Trust and Wlodowa Charity Rehabilitation Trust.

FINANCES *Year* 2007–08 *Income* £191,112 *Grants* £150,601 *Assets* £893,166

TRUSTEES M Rothfeld; Mrs E Rothfeld; Mrs H Schraiber; J D Pfeffer.

HOW TO APPLY In writing to the correspondent.

WHO TO APPLY TO M Rothfield, Trustee, Medcar House, 149a Stamford Hill, London N16 5LL *Tel* 020 8800 3582

CC NO 299642   **ESTABLISHED** 1987

■ MYR Charitable Trust

WHERE FUNDING CAN BE GIVEN Israel, USA and England.

WHO CAN BENEFIT Members of the Orthodox Jewish faith.

WHAT IS FUNDED Advancement of the Orthodox Jewish religion, relief of sickness and poverty of recognised members of said faith.

SAMPLE GRANTS Previous beneficiaries include: Cong Beth Joseph, HP Charitable Trust, UTA, Gateshead Jewish Boarding School, Keren Eretz Yisorel, SCT Sunderland and GJLC.

FINANCES *Year* 2007 *Income* £103,336 *Grants* £86,349 *Assets* £403,666

TRUSTEES Z M Kaufman; S Kaufman; A A Zonszajn; J Kaufman.

HOW TO APPLY In writing to the correspondent.

WHO TO APPLY TO Z M Kaufman, Trustee, 50 Keswick Street, Gateshead, Tyne and Wear NE8 1TQ

CC NO 1104406   **ESTABLISHED** 2004

The Kitty and Daniel Nabarro Charitable Trust

WHERE FUNDING CAN BE GIVEN UK.
WHO CAN BENEFIT Registered charities.
WHAT IS FUNDED Relief of poverty, advancement of medicine and advancement of education. This trust will consider funding: information technology and computers; support and self-help groups; environmental issues; IT training; literacy; training for work; vocational training; and crime prevention schemes.
WHAT IS NOT FUNDED No grants to individuals.
SAMPLE GRANTS New North London Synagogue – building fund (£50,000); OCD Action (£13,000); Other grants (£19,000).
FINANCES *Year* 2007–08 *Income* £22,588 *Grants* £81,880 *Assets* £790,120
TRUSTEES D J N Nabarro; Katherine Nabarro; Allan Watson.
HOW TO APPLY In writing to the correspondent. However, the trustees allocate grants on an annual basis to an existing list of charities. The trustees do not at this time envisage grants to charities which are not already on the list. **This trust states that it does not respond to unsolicited applications.**
WHO TO APPLY TO D J N Nabarro, Trustee, PO Box 7491, London N20 8LY *email* nabarro.charity@gmail.com
CC NO 1002786   **ESTABLISHED** 1991

The Nadezhda Charitable Trust

WHERE FUNDING CAN BE GIVEN UK and worldwide, particularly Zimbabwe.
WHO CAN BENEFIT Christian organisations.
WHAT IS FUNDED Advancement of Christianity in the UK and overseas. A number of churches, drug rehabilitation centres and street children's projects in Russia and the Ukraine are supported.
WHAT IS NOT FUNDED No grants to individuals.
SAMPLE GRANTS Bible Society – Zimbabwe Ndebele Bibles Project (£17,000); Friends of the Theological College of Zimbabwe in the USA (£12,000); Ebenezer Project (£10,000); Evangelical Fellowship of Zimbabwe (£7,000); Bulawayo Orphanage and CHIPS (£5,000 each); All Saints' Worcester (£2,000); and Friends of George Whitefield College (£1,500).
FINANCES *Year* 2007–08 *Income* £66,395 *Grants* £82,624 *Assets* £35,645
TRUSTEES William M Kingston; Mrs Jill M Kingston; Anthony R Collins; Ian Conolly.
HOW TO APPLY The majority of funds are presently directed to supporting the Christian Church in Zimbabwe. The trust does not, therefore, respond to unsolicited applications.
WHO TO APPLY TO Mrs Jill Kingston, Trustee, C/o Ballard Dale Syree Watson LLP, Oakmore Court, Kingswood Road, Hampton Lovett, Droitwich Spa WR9 0GH
CC NO 1007295   **ESTABLISHED** 1992

The Willie Nagel Charitable Trust

WHERE FUNDING CAN BE GIVEN UK.
WHO CAN BENEFIT Registered charities.
WHAT IS FUNDED Jewish, general charitable purposes.
SAMPLE GRANTS Previously Board of Deputies Charitable Trust, Friends of Wiznitz, Israel Music Foundation, National Children's Home and Victoria and Albert Museum.
FINANCES *Year* 2007–08 *Income* £25,764 *Grants* £16,730 *Assets* £14,217
TRUSTEES W Nagel; A L Sober.
OTHER INFORMATION No grants list has been available at the Charity Commission since that for 1989–90.
HOW TO APPLY In writing to the correspondent.
WHO TO APPLY TO A L Sober, Trustee, Lubbock Fine, Russell Bedford House, City Forum, 250 City Road, London EC1V 2QQ *Tel* 020 7490 7766 *email* anthonysober@lubbockfine.co.uk
CC NO 275938   **ESTABLISHED** 1978

The Naggar Charitable Trust

WHERE FUNDING CAN BE GIVEN UK and overseas.
WHO CAN BENEFIT Jews.
WHAT IS FUNDED Jewish organisations; the arts.
TYPE OF GRANT Some recurrent.
RANGE OF GRANTS £80–£100,000.
SAMPLE GRANTS The Tate Gallery (£100,000); Society of Friends of the Torah (£98,000); British Friends of the Art Museums of Israel (£85,000); the Jerusalem Foundation (£70,000); Office of the Chief Rabbi (£20,000); London Jewish Cultural Centre and United Synagogue Tribe (£10,000 each); Tate Foundation – New York (£5,000); the Prince's Foundation – children (£2,500); Camden Arts Centre and Royal Opera House Foundation (£1,000 each); Cancer Research UK (£500); Jewish Music Institute (£250); and the Conservative Party (£80).
FINANCES *Year* 2007–08 *Income* £527,234 *Grants* £420,543 *Assets* £108,642
TRUSTEES Guy Naggar; Hon. Marion Naggar; Marc Zilkha.
HOW TO APPLY In writing to the correspondent.
WHO TO APPLY TO Mr and Mrs Naggar, Trustees, 61 Avenue Road, London NW8 6HR *Tel* 020 7834 8060
CC NO 265409   **ESTABLISHED** 1973

The Eleni Nakou Foundation

WHERE FUNDING CAN BE GIVEN Worldwide, mostly Continental Europe.
WHO CAN BENEFIT Charitable organisations.
WHAT IS FUNDED Advancement of education of the peoples of Europe in each other's culture, history, literature, language, institutions, art, science, religion, music and folklore, and promotion of the exchange of knowledge about the cultures of northern and southern Europe in order to bridge the divide between these cultures and promote international understanding.
TYPE OF GRANT Recurrent and one-off.
RANGE OF GRANTS £1,000–£45,000.
SAMPLE GRANTS Previous beneficiaries include Danish Institute at Athens, Hellenic Foundation, Eleni Nakou Scholarship Athens and the Scandinavian Society for Modern Greek Studies.
FINANCES *Year* 2007–08 *Income* £649 *Grants* £60,000

TRUSTEES Kleinwort Benson Trustees Ltd.

HOW TO APPLY In writing to the correspondent. Applications are considered periodically. However, the trustees' state: 'It is unusual to respond favourably to unsolicited appeals'.

WHO TO APPLY TO Chris Gilbert, Secretary, c/o Kleinwort Benson Trusteesn Ltd, 30 Gresham Street, London EC2V 7PG *email* chris.gilbert@kbpb.co.uk

CC NO 803753   **ESTABLISHED** 1990

■ The Janet Nash Charitable Settlement

WHERE FUNDING CAN BE GIVEN UK.

WHO CAN BENEFIT Institutions and individuals.

WHAT IS FUNDED General charitable purposes.

TYPE OF GRANT Recurrent.

SAMPLE GRANTS Shirley Medical Centre (£16,000); The Get A-Head Charitable Trust (£15,000); Crimestoppers Trust and Martha Trust – Hereford (£10,000 each); Aide Au Pere Pedro Opeka (£9,000); Dyslexia Institute (£6,000); and London Philharmonic Orchestra and Vision Charity (£4,000 each).

FINANCES *Year* 2007–08 *Income* £451,655 *Grants* £378,355 *Assets* £74,770

TRUSTEES Ronald Gulliver; M S Jacobs; Mrs C E Coyle.

OTHER INFORMATION In 2007–08, grants to individuals totalled £265,000 and were given in two categories: medical (£238,000) and hardship relief (£66,000).

HOW TO APPLY Absolutely no response to unsolicited applications. In 2007, the trustees stated: 'The charity does not, repeat not, ever, consider any applications for benefit from the public'. Furthermore, that: 'Our existing charitable commitments more than use up our potential funds and were found personally by the trustees themselves, never as a result of applications from third parties'.

WHO TO APPLY TO R Gulliver, Trustee, Ron Gulliver and Co. Ltd, The Old Chapel, New Mill Lane, Eversley, Hampshire RG27 0RA *Tel* 01189 733 194

CC NO 326880   **ESTABLISHED** 1985

■ Nathan Charitable Trust

WHERE FUNDING CAN BE GIVEN UK and overseas.

WHO CAN BENEFIT Christian organisations.

WHAT IS FUNDED Evangelical Christian work and mission.

TYPE OF GRANT Mainly recurrent.

SAMPLE GRANTS Operation Mobilisation (£11,000); Carrot Tops, Leprosy Mission and Mission Aviation Fellowship (£10,000); Open Doors (£6,000); African Inland Mission, Bridges for Peace and Open Air Campaigners (£4,000 each); Rhema Theatre Company (£3,000); and Christian Friends of Israel (£1,000).

FINANCES *Year* 2008–09 *Grants* £72,000

TRUSTEES T R Worth; Mrs P J Worth; G A Jones.

HOW TO APPLY Funds are fully committed to current beneficiaries.

WHO TO APPLY TO T R Worth, Trustee, The Copse, Sheviock, Torpoint, Cornwall PL11 3EL *Tel* 01503 230 413

CC NO 251781   **ESTABLISHED** 1967

■ The National Art Collections Fund

WHERE FUNDING CAN BE GIVEN UK.

WHO CAN BENEFIT Any museum, gallery or other institution in the UK with a permanent art collection on public display, providing it is registered with the Museums, Libraries and Archives Council.

WHAT IS FUNDED The purchase of works of art of all kinds. It also: presents works of art, which it has received as gifts or bequests, to museums and galleries; works to promote greater awareness of the visual arts; and campaigns to safeguard public art collections.

WHAT IS NOT FUNDED Grants are restricted to institutions which have a permanent exhibition space, are open to the public and registered with the Museums, Libraries and Archives Council.

TYPE OF GRANT One-off grants.

RANGE OF GRANTS There is no fixed upper or lower limit to the size of grant the committee may offer.

SAMPLE GRANTS London Tate (£1.1 million); National Galleries of Scotland (£625,000); National Portrait Gallery (£445,000); National Trust (£130,000); Mercer Art Gallery (£74,000); Falmouth Art Gallery (£45,500); Captain Cook Memorial Museum (£25,000); Museum of the University of St Andrews and Towner Art Gallery (£16,000 each); British Architectural Library Drawings & Archives Collection (£10,000); Sheffield Galleries and Museums (£7,000); and Bradford National Media Museum, Chepstow Museum and York Museum (£5,000 each).

FINANCES *Year* 2008 *Income* £10,016,000 *Grants* £5,992,000 *Assets* £30,012,000

TRUSTEES David Verey; Paul Zuckerman; David Barrie; Dr Wendy Barron; Prof. Michael Craig-Martin; Christopher Lloyd; Dr David Landau; Prof. Lord Renfrew of Kaimsthorn; Jonathan Marsden; Charles Sebag-Montefiore; Antony Snow; Timothy Stevens; Dr Deborah Swallow; Prof. William Vaughan; The Hon. Felicity Waley-Cohen; Sally Osman; James Lingwood; Richard Calvocoressi.

PUBLICATIONS Review, Art Quarterly, Information notes for grant applicants.

HOW TO APPLY The Art Fund 'actively encourages strong applications from national and designated museums for objects which will enrich their collections and supports their efforts to expand into new collecting areas when appropriate. The Art Fund considers applications for whatever amount is needed. Applicants are expected also to apply for any public funding for which they might be eligible, and to raise funds from other sources if they can'. The Grants Office requires all applications to be made online. To start a Grant Application you will need to register. When you save your form for the first time, your username and password will be confirmed to you by email. Prior beginning the application process please read the instructions on how to complete our form and information we expect you to supply. Before you begin the application process we ask that you contact the Grants Office to discuss your proposed application.

WHO TO APPLY TO Johnathan Guy Cubitt, Millais House, 7 Cromwell Place, London SW7 2JN *Tel* 020 7225 4800 *Fax* 020 7225 4848 *email* grants@artfund.org *Website* www.artfund.org

CC NO 209174   **ESTABLISHED** 1903

■ National Asthma Campaign

WHERE FUNDING CAN BE GIVEN UK.

WHO CAN BENEFIT Organisations benefiting scientists, clinicians, general practitioners, research workers and people with asthma.

WHAT IS FUNDED Research into and the provision of information and education on asthma and allied respiratory disorders.

WHAT IS NOT FUNDED 'Researchers work across a variety of disciplines within hospitals, universities, GP surgeries and clinics throughout the UK. Asthma UK is therefore able to fund researchers who work directly with people with asthma as well as those who are undertaking basic science research in the laboratory.'

TYPE OF GRANT Project grants and fellowships.

FINANCES *Year* 2007–08 *Income* £11,038,000 *Grants* £9,241,000 *Assets* £3,836,000

TRUSTEES Prof. John Price, Chair; Eric Wiles; Prof. John Griffiths; Wendy Npanasurian; June Vanessa Coppel; Barbara Mary Hope Herts; David William Howitt Steeds; John Lelliott; Ayaz Siddiqui; Richard Coombs; Helen Ralston; John Oliver Stanley Belgrave; Ivor Cook.

HOW TO APPLY 'Each year Asthma UK invites proposals for research projects through its website and through the research professional press. All applications for funding are assessed for scientific quality and relevance to asthma by our research committee, which is comprised of an independent panel of scientists, clinicians and lay representatives. Research proposals are also subjected to further scrutiny by international experts through our external review process, who have experience closely related to the subject area. Asthma UK's Council of Trustees then decides how many of the recommended research proposals can be funded, based on the projected income of the charity.'

WHO TO APPLY TO Ian Bucknell, Summit House, 70 Wilson Street, London EC2A 2DB *Tel* 020 7786 4900 *Fax* 020 7256 6075 *email* info@asthma.org.uk *Website* www.asthma.org.uk

CC NO 802364   **ESTABLISHED** 1990

■ The National Churches Trust (formerly the Historic Churches Preservation Trust with the Incorporated Church Building Society)

WHERE FUNDING CAN BE GIVEN UK.

WHO CAN BENEFIT Christian churches of architectural or historical importance that are in need of repair. Churches should meet the following criteria: the building must be open for regular public worship – the trust does not currently have grants available for cathedrals, but any other Christian places of worship can apply if they meet the eligibility criteria; it must be sited in England, Northern Ireland, the Isle of Man, Scotland or Wales; the congregation must belong to a denomination that is a member or associated member of Churches Together in Britain and Ireland; and all projects must be overseen by an architect who is either ARB, RIBA or AABC accredited, or by a chartered surveyor who is RICS accredited.

WHAT IS FUNDED To assist, with grants and loans, the efforts of congregations to carry out of essential repairs to the fabric of historic churches and improve their general facilities e.g. accessible toilets, kitchens and meeting rooms. The trust has also been working with WREN (Waste Recycling Environmental Ltd) to administer grants on their behalf to churches sited within a ten-mile radius of a landfill site operated by Waste Recycling Group. Please contact the trust for further information.

WHAT IS NOT FUNDED Please be aware that the trust cannot make grants for certain purposes including: non-church buildings (such as church halls and vicarages); bell repairs; organ repairs; repairs to internal furnishings; redecoration, other than after structural repairs; clock repairs; monument repairs.

TYPE OF GRANT Capital costs.

RANGE OF GRANTS From £2,500.

SAMPLE GRANTS St Peter – Lenton, Lincolnshire (£40,000); St Peter – Darwen, Lancashire (£20,000); All Saints – Stanton, Suffolk (£7,000); St Michael and All Angels – Brinkworth, Wiltshire (£5,000); St Andrew – Alwington, Devon (£4,500); St Mabli – Llanvapley, Monmouthshire (£2,500); and Holy Trinity – Hartshill, Warwickshire (£1,500).

FINANCES *Year* 2008 *Income* £1,895,400 *Grants* £1,981,325 *Assets* £4,517,502

TRUSTEES Michael Hoare, Chair; Graham Brown; Diana Hunt; Lottie Cole; Revd Dr Nicholas Holtam; Peter Readman; Antony Wedgwood; Jennie Page.

PUBLICATIONS *Keeping Churches Alive – a Brief History of the Trust* available directly from the trust or to download from the website.

OTHER INFORMATION In 2008 the Charity Commission appointed the National Churches Trust (NCT) as the sole trustee of the Historic Churches Preservation Trust (HCPT) and also granted a 'uniting direction'. Consequently, the NCT and HCPT are treated as a single charity for administrative, accounting and regulatory purposes. They will however, remain legally distinct so that the HCPT will operate as restricted funds within the NCT. A similar process is envisaged for the Incorporated Church Building Society (ICBS), which has been managed by the HCPT since 1983.

HOW TO APPLY Application packs can be downloaded from the trust's website. The grants committee meet quarterly to consider applications. **Please note the following statement from the trust:** 'Demand for our grants has risen considerably over recent months and this means that new applicants will not hear from us immediately. You will receive an acknowledgement of receipt as soon as your application arrives, but it is likely that the grants department will not contact you again until at least three months after receipt. We aim to send decisions to applicants within six months where possible. Please ensure that your application is complete when you send it to us. If you are awaiting the outcome of an English Heritage/CADW/Historic Scotland/Heritage Lottery Fund application, please do not apply to us until you know the outcome of any such application.'

WHO TO APPLY TO Alison Pollard, Grants Manager, 31 Newbury Street, London EC1A 7HU *Tel* 020 7600 6090 *Fax* 020 7796 2442 *email* info@nationalchurchestrust.org *Website* www.nationalchurchestrust.org

CC NO 1119845   **ESTABLISHED** 1953

■ The National Manuscripts Conservation Trust

WHERE FUNDING CAN BE GIVEN UK.

WHO CAN BENEFIT Grants are made to record offices, libraries, other similar publicly funded institutions including local authority, university and specialist record repositories, and owners of manuscript material which is conditionally exempt from capital taxation or owned by a charitable trust and where reasonable public access is allowed, suitable storage conditions are available, and there is a commitment to continuing good preservation practice.

WHAT IS FUNDED Conservation of manuscripts and archives.

WHAT IS NOT FUNDED The following are not eligible: public records within the meaning of the Public Records Act; official archives of the institution or authority applying except in the case of some older records; loan collections unless exempt from capital taxation or owned by a charitable trust; and photographic, audio-visual or printed materials.

TYPE OF GRANT The grants cover the cost of repair, binding and other preservation measures including reprography, but not cost of equipment. Funding is for up to three years.

RANGE OF GRANTS To match the applicant's contribution, up to 50% of the total estimated cost. Grants are not normally considered for projects costing less than £1,000 or greater than £50,000.

SAMPLE GRANTS The Fitzwilliam Museum – towards the Founder's Library Conservation Project (£20,000); Cheshire County Council – towards conservation of the Wyatt and associated architectural drawings at Tatton Park (£18,000); Aberystwyth University – towards the conservation of the Library Planning Archive (£11,000); London Metropolitan Archives – towards the conservation of personal record books from Training Ship Exmouth (£10,000); Dean and Chapter, Exeter Cathedral – towards the conservation of the cathedral's archives (£8,000); and The Library and Museum of Freemasonry – towards the conservation of Building Blocks: the Manuscript Old Charges of British Freemasonry (£1,600).

FINANCES *Year* 2008 *Income* £117,954 *Grants* £102,052 *Assets* £1,644,298

TRUSTEES Lord Egremont; B Naylor; C Sebag-Montefiore.

PUBLICATIONS Guide for Applicants.

OTHER INFORMATION Visit the trust's website for full details of how to apply. www.nationalarchives.gov.uk/preservation/trust

HOW TO APPLY Applicants must submit six copies of the application form including six copies of a detailed description of the project. The applicant should also submit one copy of their most recent annual reports and accounts and details of its constitution. Grants are awarded bi-annually, each June and December, for 50% of the cost of conservation of manuscripts held by any record office, library or by an owner of manuscript material that is exempt from capital taxation or owned by a charitable trust. The trustees take into account the significance of the manuscript or archive, the suitability of the storage conditions, the applicants' commitment to continuing good preservation practice, and the requirement for the public to have reasonable access to it.

WHO TO APPLY TO Dr Anna Bulow, Secretary to the Trustees, c/o The National Archives, Ruskin Avenue, Kew, Surrey TW9 4DU *Tel* 020 8392 5218 *email* nmct@nationalarchives.gov.uk *Website* www.nationalarchives.gov.uk/preservation/trust

CC NO 802796   **ESTABLISHED** 1990

■ The Nationwide Foundation

WHERE FUNDING CAN BE GIVEN UK.

WHO CAN BENEFIT Registered UK charities. Note: only those with an income of under £500,000 are eligible for the small grants programme.

WHAT IS FUNDED The foundation makes grants to registered UK charities (including those in Northern Ireland) which offer financial and/or housing related support to survivors of domestic abuse and older people. Beneficiaries in the 'older people' category must be one of the following: aged 70 years and over; aged 50 years and over who have dementia; aged 50 years and over from Black and Minority Ethnic (BME) groups; aged 50 years and over who are carers for family members or partners who are also 50 years or older; aged 50 years and over who have experienced or are experiencing financial abuse; aged 50 years and over who are rurally isolated.

WHAT IS NOT FUNDED The trust will not fund the following: applications which do not fit the funding guidelines or comply with the information on this website; charities which are not registered with either the Charity Commission for England and Wales; the Office of the Scottish Charity Regulator; HM Revenue & Customs (for charities in Northern Ireland); HM Revenue & Customs (for those charities with a turnover of under £5,000); individuals; charities with incomes exceeding £500,000 in respect of the small grants programme; charities with 'unrestricted reserves' which exceed 50% of annual expenditure, as shown their accounts; charities which are in significant debt as shown in their accounts; promotion of religion or politics; overseas travel and work outside of the UK; charities which have received a grant or donation from the Foundation or Nationwide Building Society within the past 12 months; charities which have been declined by the trust under the same grant programme within the past 12 months.

TYPE OF GRANT Project, capital and revenue costs.

RANGE OF GRANTS Mainly up to £5,000 with some larger grants made.

SAMPLE GRANTS Only the recipients of Investor Programme grants were listed in the accounts. Beneficiaries included: Domestic Violence Partnership (£81,000); Refuge (£72,000); Broken Rainbow (£69,000); Public Sector Broadcasting Trust (£60,000); Kurdistan Women's Refugee Organisation (£51,000); Safer Wales (£45,000); Addaction (£42,000); PFFS (£40,000); Storybook Dad (£29,000); Castle Gate Family Trust (£28,000); and Young Offenders Partnership (£6,800).

FINANCES *Year* 2007–08 *Income* €1,170,425 *Grants* €1,749,542 *Assets* €3,928,972

TRUSTEES Richard Davies; Lucy Gampell; John Kingston; Simon Law; Karen McArthur; Dr Michael McCarthy; Jen McKevitt; Tony Prestedge; Benedict Stimson; Maxine Taylor.

OTHER INFORMATION This foundation is funded principally from contributions from Nationwide Building Society

HOW TO APPLY Application forms are only accessible from the foundation's website. Applicants should expect to wait up to three months for a final decision.

WHO TO APPLY TO P Vinall, Secretary, Nationwide House, Pipers Way, Swindon SN38 2SN *Tel* 01793 655113 *Fax* 01793 652409 *email* enquiries@nationwidefoundation.org.uk *Website* www.nationwidefoundation.org.uk
CC NO 1065552   **ESTABLISHED** 1997

■ Nazareth Trust Fund

WHERE FUNDING CAN BE GIVEN UK and developing countries.

WHO CAN BENEFIT Young adults, Christian missionaries and victims of famine, war, and man-made or natural disasters – both individually and through registered institutions.

WHAT IS FUNDED Churches, Christian missionaries, Christian youth work, and overseas aid. Grants are only made to people or causes known personally to the trustees.

WHAT IS NOT FUNDED No support for individuals not known to the trustees.

RANGE OF GRANTS £50–£5,000.

SAMPLE GRANTS Beneficiaries included Bridge Project, Crusaders, Harnham Free Church, Northwood Hills Evangelical Church, Scripture Union and World Vision.

FINANCES *Year* 2007–08 *Income* £42,513 *Grants* £32,407

TRUSTEES Dr Robert W G Hunt; Mrs E M Hunt; Revd David R G Hunt; Mrs Elma R L Hunt; Philip R W Hunt; Mrs Nicola Mhairi Hunt.

OTHER INFORMATION A total of £2,350 was given to individuals.

HOW TO APPLY In writing to the correspondent, although the trust tends to only support organisations it is directly involved with.

WHO TO APPLY TO Dr Robert W G Hunt, Trustee, Barrowmount, 18 Millennium Close, Salisbury, Wiltshire SP2 8TB *Tel* 01722 349 322
CC NO 210503   **ESTABLISHED** 1956

■ The Nchima Trust

WHERE FUNDING CAN BE GIVEN Malawi.

WHO CAN BENEFIT Individuals and established local organisations benefiting children and young adults, at-risk groups, and people who are disadvantaged by poverty or living in rural areas.

WHAT IS FUNDED Initiation and help in schemes aimed at advancing education, health, welfare standards and the provision of clean water, with particular emphasis on self-help schemes and assisting people with disabilities.

FINANCES *Year* 2007–08 *Income* £114,550 *Grants* £50,357 *Assets* £706,911

TRUSTEES Ms M R Richards; Chair; S Gardiner; Mrs K P Legg; Mrs M Lytle; A Scarborough; Mrs J Quinn; Mrs B A Scarborough; Mrs S McAlpine.

OTHER INFORMATION The trust makes fixed grants of approximately £2,500 a year plus other discretionary grants.

HOW TO APPLY In writing to the correspondent.

WHO TO APPLY TO Mrs Josie Quinn, Hon. Secretary and Administrator, 3 Close House Cottages, Knock, Cumbria CA16 6DL *Tel* 017683 62380 *email* admin@nchimatrust.org *Website* www. nchimatrust.org
CC NO 1072974   **ESTABLISHED** 1962

■ Needham Market and Barking Welfare Charities

WHERE FUNDING CAN BE GIVEN The town of Needham Market and the parish of Barking.

WHO CAN BENEFIT Organisations that benefit people in need, hardship or distress.

WHAT IS FUNDED Projects that benefit the local community especially those in need, hardship or distress.

RANGE OF GRANTS Up to £20,000.

SAMPLE GRANTS Grants from the Town Lands Trust included: Needham Market Town Council (£20,000); Barking Village Hall (£12,000); Needham Market Bowls Club and Hurstlea Kerridge Boxing Club (£10,000 each); and Needham Market Community Centre and Needham Market Internet Cafe (£5,000 each).

FINANCES *Year* 2007–08 *Income* £50,230 *Grants* £66,777 *Assets* £1,159,598

TRUSTEES A F Wilcox; J C Dickerson; D M J Page; E J Cross; G C Miller; J Annis; R P Darnell; R D Robertson; Mrs S C Wright; A K Jones; Mrs S Marsh.

OTHER INFORMATION An extra £3,055 was given in grants to individuals.

HOW TO APPLY In writing to the correspondent with audited accounts. Trustees meet every two months. Individuals should apply on the form available from the correspondent.

WHO TO APPLY TO Mrs Louise Gooding, Clerk, 23 School Street, Needham Market, Ipswich IP6 8BB
CC NO 217499   **ESTABLISHED** 1961

■ The Worshipful Company of Needlemakers' Charitable Fund

WHERE FUNDING CAN BE GIVEN City of London.

WHO CAN BENEFIT Organisations associated with the needlemaking industry, the City of London or education, including the Lord Mayor's and the Master's chosen charities.

WHAT IS FUNDED Education, welfare, religion, general charitable purposes.

SAMPLE GRANTS The Royal School of Needlework (£5,000); For a Child Smile (£3,000); Old Palace School (£2,400); Fine Cell Work and the Sheriffs' & Recorder's Fund (£1,000 each); and St James – Garlickhythe (£500).

FINANCES *Year* 2007–08 *Income* £55,428 *Grants* £37,292 *Assets* £1,120,837

TRUSTEES Worshipful Company of Needlemakers.

HOW TO APPLY In writing to the correspondent, but the trust has stated that it tends to support the same charities each year, so unsolicited applications are unlikely to be successful.

WHO TO APPLY TO Philip R Grant, Clerk, Worshipful Company of Needlemakers, PO Box 3682, Windsor SL4 3WR *Tel* 01753 860690 *email* needlemakers.clerk@yahoo.com
CC NO 288646   **ESTABLISHED** 1952

■ The Neighbourly Charitable Trust

WHERE FUNDING CAN BE GIVEN Bedfordshire and Hertfordshire.

WHO CAN BENEFIT Organisations benefiting people with disabilities.

WHAT IS FUNDED General and leisure/adventure trips for people with disabilities.

WHAT IS NOT FUNDED No grants to national charities (except occasionally a local branch) or individuals.

RANGE OF GRANTS £300–£5,000.

Think carefully about every application. Is it justified?

739

SAMPLE GRANTS Reach Out Projects (£5,000); Bedford MENCAP (£2,500); Autism – Bedfordshire (£2,000); Sue Ryder Care (£1,500); Bedfordshire and Northampton MS Therapy Centre and Earthworks St Albans (£1,000 each); and Beds Body Positive (£500).

FINANCES *Year* 2007–08 *Income* £86,559 *Grants* £47,400 *Assets* £2,251,188

TRUSTEES John Sell; Emma Simpson; Jane Wade.

HOW TO APPLY In writing to the correspondent, for consideration at trustees' meetings twice a year.

WHO TO APPLY TO Sharon Long, Secretary, First Floor, Ashbrittle House, 2a Lower Dagnall Street, St Albans, Hertfordshire AL3 4PA *Tel* 01727 843603 *Fax* 01727 843663 *email* admin@iplltd.co.uk

CC NO 258488   ESTABLISHED 1969

■ The James Neill Trust Fund

WHERE FUNDING CAN BE GIVEN Within 20 miles of Sheffield Cathedral.

WHO CAN BENEFIT Voluntary organisations.

WHAT IS FUNDED Voluntary work for the benefit of people in the area specified above.

TYPE OF GRANT Ongoing support for established organisations and one-off grants to meet start-up costs or unexpected expenses.

RANGE OF GRANTS Up to £5,000.

SAMPLE GRANTS SYFC Flood Disaster Relief Fund (£5,000); The Cavendish Centre and South Yorkshire Community Foundation (£2,000 each); South Yorkshire & Hallamshire Clubs for Young People and Voluntary Action Sheffield (£1,000 each); Cruse Bereavement Care – Rotherham Branch (£900); Bluebell Wood Children's Hospice and ENABLE – Sheffield (£750 each); Sheffield Conservation Volunteers and Cathedral Archer Project (£600 each); The Peak Centre, Fare Share South Yorkshire, Dyslexia Action and Music in the Round (£500 each); and Trinity Day Care Trust (£250).

FINANCES *Year* 2007–08 *Income* £42,485 *Grants* £41,462 *Assets* £1,153,174

TRUSTEES Sir Hugh Neill; G H N Peel; Lady Neill; Mrs N R Peel; A M C Staniforth.

OTHER INFORMATION During the year pensioners received Christmas hampers amounting to £13,000 in total.

HOW TO APPLY In writing to the correspondent in July for consideration in August/September.

WHO TO APPLY TO Sir Hugh Neill, Trustee, Barn Cottage, Lindrick Common, Worksop, Nottinghamshire S81 8BA *Tel* 01909 562806

CC NO 503203   ESTABLISHED 1974

■ Nemoral Ltd

WHERE FUNDING CAN BE GIVEN Worldwide.

WHO CAN BENEFIT Orthodox Jewish communities.

WHAT IS FUNDED General charitable purposes, in practice, religious, educational and other charitable institutions serving orthodox Jewish communities.

TYPE OF GRANT One-off, recurring, capital and occasionally loans.

FINANCES *Year* 2007 *Income* £931,166 *Grants* £436,594 *Assets* £3,619,882

TRUSTEES Ellis Moore; Rifka Gross; Michael Saberski.

OTHER INFORMATION A list of grant beneficiaries was not included in the trust's accounts.

HOW TO APPLY In writing to the correspondent.

WHO TO APPLY TO Rifka Gross, Secretary, New Burlington House, 1075 Finchley Road, London NW11 0PU *Tel* 020 8731 0777

CC NO 262270   ESTABLISHED 1971

■ Ner Foundation

WHERE FUNDING CAN BE GIVEN UK and Israel.

WHO CAN BENEFIT People of the Jewish faith.

WHAT IS FUNDED Advancement of the Orthodox Jewish religion.

SAMPLE GRANTS relief of poverty (£104,000); schools (£64,000); yeshivos and seminaries (£23,000); advancement of religion (£14,000); kollel (£10,000); grants under £1,000 each (£7,500).

FINANCES *Year* 2007–08 *Income* £34,372 *Grants* £221,566 *Assets* £431,333

TRUSTEES A Henry; N Neumann; Mrs E Henry.

HOW TO APPLY In writing to the correspondent.

WHO TO APPLY TO A Henry, Trustee, 309 Bury New Road, Salford, Manchester M7 2YN

CC NO 1104866   ESTABLISHED 2004

■ Nesswall Ltd

WHERE FUNDING CAN BE GIVEN UK.

WHO CAN BENEFIT People of the Jewish faith.

WHAT IS FUNDED Jewish organisations, including education.

SAMPLE GRANTS Previous beneficiaries have included Friends of Horim Establishments, Torah Vochesed L'Ezra Vesaad and Emunah Education Centre.

FINANCES *Year* 2007–08 *Income* £154,327 *Grants* £110,245 *Assets* £625,417

TRUSTEES I Teitelbaum, Chair; Mrs R Teitelbaum; I Chersky; Mrs H Wahrhaftig.

HOW TO APPLY In writing to the correspondent, at any time.

WHO TO APPLY TO Mrs R Teitelbaum, Secretary, 28 Overlea Road, London E5 9BG *Tel* 020 8806 2965

CC NO 283600   ESTABLISHED 1981

■ The Nestle Rowntree Employees Community Fund

WHERE FUNDING CAN BE GIVEN The Yorkshire area; mainly York.

WHO CAN BENEFIT Organisations benefiting: people who are disabled; those disadvantaged by poverty; homeless people; victims of abuse and crime; and victims of famine, man-made or natural disasters and war.

WHAT IS FUNDED Health and community services. The fund supports charities in other parts of the UK that are involved in supporting people who are deaf, blind or disabled, disadvantaged children, relief and research organisations and some international relief organisations.

WHAT IS NOT FUNDED No grants to: capital projects; individuals; government-funded organisations; umbrella organisations whose purpose is to collect funds to distribute themselves; or religious or political organisations for overtly or covertly religious or political aims.

TYPE OF GRANT Core costs, one-off, recurring costs, research, running costs and start-up costs are priorities.

RANGE OF GRANTS £3,100–£3,500.

SAMPLE GRANTS Previous beneficiaries included: British Deaf Association; British Polio Fellowship; the Brain Research Trust; Guide

Dogs for the Blind; Listening Books; Lollipop – York & District; Martin House Hospice for Children; the Mental Health Foundation; Motor Neurone Disease Association; Rochdale Special Needs Cycling Club; Royal National Lifeboat Institute; St Leonard's Hospice; York Council for Voluntary Services; and Vitalise.

FINANCES *Year* 2007 *Income* £33,623

TRUSTEES Jackie Johnson; Mike Overhill-Smith; Philip Galloway.

HOW TO APPLY In writing to the correspondent, including financial details. Initial telephone calls are welcomed.

WHO TO APPLY TO Jackie Johnson, Trustee, Nestlé Rowntree, Haxby Road, York YO91 1XY *Tel* 01904 604808

CC NO 516702   **ESTABLISHED** 1985

■ Network for Social Change

WHERE FUNDING CAN BE GIVEN UK and overseas.

WHO CAN BENEFIT Small projects in the UK and overseas which are likely to affect social change, either through research, public education, innovatory services and other charitable activities.

WHAT IS FUNDED The network is a group of givers who actively seek out projects that they want to fund, rather than responding to applications, in the areas of arts and education for change, economic justice, green planet, health and wholeness, human rights and peace.

TYPE OF GRANT Smaller projects.

RANGE OF GRANTS Mainly up to £15,000.

SAMPLE GRANTS Peace Direct (£69,000); Climate Movement (£44,000); Prison Reform Trust (£32,000); MEDACT (£26,000); Poverty and Environment Trust (£21,000); INTERIGHTS – International Centre for The Legal Protection of Human Rights (£14,000); Wilton's Music Hall Trust and Asylum Welcome (£12,000 each); and University of Sussex, Community Arts North West and Project 21 (£10,000 each).

FINANCES *Year* 2007–08 *Income* £789,312 *Grants* £756,008 *Assets* £83,912

TRUSTEES Sue Gillie; Bevis Gillett; Sam Clarke; Monica Marian Sanders; Sara Robin; Tom Bragg; Anthony Stoll.

HOW TO APPLY The network chooses the projects it wishes to support and does not solicit applications. Unsolicited applications cannot expect to receive a reply. However, the network is conscious that the policy of only accepting applications brought by its members could limit the range of worthwhile projects it could fund. To address this, the network has set up a 'Project Noticeboard' (accessed via the network's website) to allow outside organisations to post a summary of a project for which they are seeking funding. Members of the network can then access the noticeboard and, if interested, contact the organisation for further information with a view to future sponsorship. The network states that any posts will be available on the website for six to nine months.

WHO TO APPLY TO Tish McCrory, Administrator, BM 2063, London WC1N 3XX *Tel* 01647 61106 *email* thenetwork@gn.apc.org *Website* thenetworkforsocialchange.org.uk

CC NO 295237   **ESTABLISHED** 1986

■ The New Appeals Organisation for the City and County of Nottingham

WHERE FUNDING CAN BE GIVEN Nottinghamshire.

WHO CAN BENEFIT Individuals and organisations benefiting at-risk groups and people who are disabled, disadvantaged by poverty or socially isolated.

WHAT IS FUNDED Help that is not available from any other source.

WHAT IS NOT FUNDED Appeals to cover debts, arrears, building expenses or educational expenses are not normally considered.

TYPE OF GRANT One-off.

SAMPLE GRANTS Gillies Ward (£6,000); Newstead Primary School (£3,000); Nottingham City Hospital Charity Account (£2,500); Glenbrook P&F School (£1,400); Ravenshead Community Transport and Sherwood United Reform Church (£500 each); and Nottingham Central Womens Aid (£100).

FINANCES *Year* 2007–08 *Income* £50,038 *Grants* £27,448 *Assets* £45,118

TRUSTEES Phillip Everett, Joint Chair; Mrs Carol Wilson, Joint Chair; L S Levin; Mrs E Litman; G Davis.

HOW TO APPLY In writing to the correspondent. An initial telephone call from the applicant is welcome.

WHO TO APPLY TO Philip Everett, The Joint Chair, c/o 4 Rise Court, Hamilton Road, Sherwood Rise, Nottingham NG5 1EU *Tel* 0115 960 9644 (Answerphone)

CC NO 502196   **ESTABLISHED** 1973

■ New Court Charitable Trust

WHERE FUNDING CAN BE GIVEN UK.

WHO CAN BENEFIT Registered charities.

WHAT IS FUNDED General charitable purposes.

SAMPLE GRANTS Previous beneficiaries included: Alone in London, Burma Star Association, Drugscope, Electronic Aids for the Blind, Fight for Sight, Hereford International Summer School, Invalids at Home and Trinity College of Music, New Bridge Motability, Streatham Youth Centre, Universities Settlement in East London, Queen Elizabeth's Foundation for Disabled People and World Jewish Relief.

FINANCES *Year* 2007–08 *Income* £13,965

TRUSTEES Leopold de Rothschild; Bernard Myers; Ms Veronica Kennard.

HOW TO APPLY In writing to the correspondent enclosing annual report and accounts.

WHO TO APPLY TO The Trustees, New Court, St Swithin's Lane, London EC4P 4DU *Tel* 020 7280 5000

CC NO 209790   **ESTABLISHED** 1947

■ Newby Trust Limited

WHERE FUNDING CAN BE GIVEN UK.

WHO CAN BENEFIT Welfare organisations, postgraduates and individuals in need.

WHAT IS FUNDED Within the general objects of the trust (medical welfare, relief of poverty, training and education) one category for special support is selected each year. Recent themes have been: 2008–09 – respite support for carers of older people or those incapacitated and 2009/10 (6 April to 5 April) – project's and/or training that encourage artisan skills e.g. sculpture, printing, thatching, weaving, and so on.

TYPE OF GRANT Usually one-off for part of a project. Buildings, capital, core costs and salaries may be considered.

RANGE OF GRANTS Normally £150–£10,000; the majority for under £1,000.

SAMPLE GRANTS I CAN, InterAct, Liverpool Cathedral, The Martlets Hospice, Rowan Tree Trust and The Social Mobility Foundation (£10,000 each); Echoes of Service (£7,000); Amani Foundation, Blenheim Scout Group, Chance to Shine – the Cricket Foundation, The Hardman Trust, National Literacy Trust and Theatre Royal Bath (£5,000 each); Tall Ships Youth Trust (£4,000); The Michael Palin Centre for stammering Children (£3,600); Citizenship Foundation and Glasgow Social Work (£3,000 each); British Athletic Charitable Trust (£2,500); Bolton Lads and Girls Club and Groundwork – Cheshire (£2,000 each); and No Limits Theatre (£1,000).

FINANCES *Year* 2007–08 *Income* £397,904 *Grants* £414,574 *Assets* £13,306,359

TRUSTEES Mrs S A Charlton; Mrs J M Gooder; Dr R D Gooder; Mrs A S Reed; R B Gooder; Mrs A L Foxell.

OTHER INFORMATION Grants to individuals accounted for around £69,000 of the total.

HOW TO APPLY The application procedure differs between each category as follows: *Annual special category* – unsolicited applications will not be considered; *Education, training and research* – the trust currently has four selected institutions (City University, London, The London School of Economics & Political Science, The University of Edinburgh and The University of Manchester). Grants are awarded at the discretion of these universities subject to guidelines related to the purposes of the trust. *Medical welfare* and *Relief of poverty* – Social Services or similar organisations may apply **only online**on behalf of individuals in need using the pre-application screening form on the trust's website.

WHO TO APPLY TO Miss W Gillam, Secretary, Secretary, Hill Farm, Froxfield, Petersfield, Hampshire GU32 1BQ *Tel* 01730 827 557 *Fax* 01730 827938 *email* info@newby-trust.org. uk *Website* www.newby-trust.org.uk

CC NO 227151   **ESTABLISHED** 1938

··

■ The Newcomen Collett Foundation

WHERE FUNDING CAN BE GIVEN London borough of Southwark.

WHO CAN BENEFIT Individuals and small local projects benefiting children, young adults and students under 25.

WHAT IS FUNDED Education of young people under 25 years of age, including community arts and recreation, with priority for dance and ballet, music and theatre.

WHAT IS NOT FUNDED The trust can only help young people living in the London borough of Southwark. People on courses of further education should have lived in Southwark for at least two years before starting their course.

TYPE OF GRANT One-off.

SAMPLE GRANTS Cathedral Primary School (£5,000); Borough Music School, Highshore School and Royal Opera House (£2,000 each); Fairbridge in London and the Young Vic Theatre (£1,500 each); Collective Artistes, Magic Lantern, Pembroke House Youth Centre, Southwark Heritage Centre, Vounteer Reading Help and Waterloo Sports & Football Club (£1,000 each).

FINANCES *Year* 2007–08 *Income* £224,209 *Grants* £100,147 *Assets* £3,084,782

TRUSTEES Mrs S Hase, Chair; R V Ashdown; E H C Bowman; J Spencer; R Edwards; A G H Stocks; Mrs B S Lane; R Lovell; A Covell; Revd Canon B Saunders.

HOW TO APPLY By application form, available by writing to the clerk. The governors consider requests four times a year.

WHO TO APPLY TO Richard Goatcher, Clerk, Marshall House, 66 Newcomen Street, London Bridge, London SE1 1YT *Tel* 020 7407 2967 *Fax* 020 7403 3969 *email* richard@marshalls.org.uk

CC NO 312804   **ESTABLISHED** 1988

··

■ The Richard Newitt Fund

WHERE FUNDING CAN BE GIVEN UK.

WHO CAN BENEFIT Organisations and institutions benefiting students who are disadvantaged by poverty. The help is for the advancement of a person's further education rather than the financing of a project.

WHAT IS FUNDED The trustees have designated a small number of educational institutions and awards will be made direct to their student hardship funds.

WHAT IS NOT FUNDED No grants to individuals.

TYPE OF GRANT Non-recurring bursaries to students.

RANGE OF GRANTS £5,000–£65,000.

SAMPLE GRANTS Previous beneficiaries include: University of Southampton, Bristol Old Vic Theatre School and Royal Northern College of Music.

FINANCES *Year* 2006–07 *Income* £66,797 *Grants* £75,000 *Assets* £2,350,754

TRUSTEES Kleinwort Benson Trustees Ltd; D A Schofield; Prof. D Holt; Baroness Diana Maddock.

HOW TO APPLY Requests for application forms should be submitted by 1 April in any one-year; applicants will be notified of the results in August. Unsolicited applications are unlikely to be considered, educational institutional applications by invitation only.

WHO TO APPLY TO The Administrator, Kleinwort Benson Trustees Ltd, 30 Gresham Street, London EC2V 7PG *Tel* 020 3207 7356

CC NO 276470   **ESTABLISHED** 1978

··

■ Mr and Mrs F E F Newman Charitable Trust

WHERE FUNDING CAN BE GIVEN UK and overseas.

WHO CAN BENEFIT Charities benefiting children, young adults and older people. At risk groups, people disadvantaged by poverty, socially isolated people, clergy, students, teachers and governesses may also be considered.

WHAT IS FUNDED Primarily local religious purposes; welfare and educational purposes; and other charitable purposes.

WHAT IS NOT FUNDED No grants to individuals.

RANGE OF GRANTS £25–£7,000.

SAMPLE GRANTS 'A' Fund: Christian Aid (£300 in two grants); Prostate Cancer Research (£250); Church urban Fund, Help the Aged and Music as Therapy (£100 each); and Horsell Common Preservation Society (£25). 'B' Fund: Tear Fund (£7,000 in two grants); Resource (£5,500 in two grants); Teso Development (£3,500); Church Missionary Society (£2,000); and Amnesty International and Traidcraft Exchange (£500 each).

FINANCES *Year* 2007–08 *Income* £46,528
Grants £37,450 *Assets* £236,069

TRUSTEES Frederick E F Newman; Margaret C Hayes; Canon Newman; Michael R F Newman; George S Smith.

OTHER INFORMATION Donations from 'A' Fund totalled £1,800 and donations from 'B' Fund totalled £35,650.

HOW TO APPLY In writing to the correspondent.

WHO TO APPLY TO David Quinn, Administrator, c/o David Quinn Associates, Southcroft, Caledon Road, Beaconsfield, Buckinghamshire HP9 2BX *Tel* 01494 674 396

CC NO 263831   **ESTABLISHED** 1972

■ The Frances and Augustus Newman Foundation

WHERE FUNDING CAN BE GIVEN Worldwide, in practice mainly UK.

WHO CAN BENEFIT Mainly professors working in teaching hospitals and academic units.

WHAT IS FUNDED Mainly, but not exclusively, funding for medical research projects and equipment including fellowships of the Royal College of Surgeons.

WHAT IS NOT FUNDED Applications are not normally accepted from overseas. Requests from other charities seeking funds to supplement their own general funds to support medical research in a particular field are seldom supported.

TYPE OF GRANT One-off and recurring. Research and salaries will also be considered. Funding may be given for up to three years.

RANGE OF GRANTS £1,000–£100,000.

SAMPLE GRANTS Peterhouse and Eagle Project – Phase 2 (£100,000 each); University College Cambridge – New Generation Fellowship (£50,000); Meningitis UK (£40,000); Royal College Surgeons – Dupuytrens Disease (£25,000); Age Care – Bradbury Centre (£10,000); and Eastwood Nursery School (£1,000).

FINANCES *Year* 2007–08 *Income* £353,905
Grants £404,368 *Assets* £11,065,924

TRUSTEES Sir Rodney Sweetnam, Chair; Lord Rathcavan; John L Williams.

HOW TO APPLY Applications should include a detailed protocol and costing and be sent to the secretary. They may then be peer-reviewed. The trustees meet in June and December each year and applications must be received at the latest by the end of April or October respectively. The foundation awards for surgical research fellowships should be addressed to the Royal College of Surgeons of England at 35–43 Lincoln's Inn Fields, London WC2A 3PE, which evaluates each application.

WHO TO APPLY TO Hazel Palfreyman, Correspondent, c/o Baker Tilly, Chartered Accountants, Hartwell House, 55–61 Victoria Street, Bristol BS1 6AD *Tel* 0117 945 2000 *Fax* 0117 945 2001 *email* hazel.palfreyman@bakertilly.co.uk

CC NO 277964   **ESTABLISHED** 1978

■ Newpier Charity Ltd

WHERE FUNDING CAN BE GIVEN UK.

WHO CAN BENEFIT Jewish organisations.

WHAT IS FUNDED Advancement of the orthodox Jewish faith and the relief of poverty.

SAMPLE GRANTS Previous beneficiaries have included BML Benityashvut, Friends of Biala, Gateshead Yeshiva, KID, Mesdos Wiznitz and SOFT for redistribution to other charities.

FINANCES *Year* 2007–08 *Income* £915,908
Grants £536,498 *Assets* £4,294,798

TRUSTEES C M Margulies; Mrs H Knopfler; Mrs R Margulies.

OTHER INFORMATION The last available grants list for this charity was from 1997/98.

HOW TO APPLY In writing to the correspondent.

WHO TO APPLY TO Charles Margulies, Trustee, 186 Lordship Road, London N16 5ES

CC NO 293686   **ESTABLISHED** 1985

■ Alderman Newton's Educational Foundation

WHERE FUNDING CAN BE GIVEN Diocese of Leicester.

WHO CAN BENEFIT Individuals and schools.

WHAT IS FUNDED Church of England education.

TYPE OF GRANT One-off and recurrent.

FINANCES *Year* 2007–08 *Income* £118,495
Grants £92,340 *Assets* £2,869,619

TRUSTEES Two ex-officio trustees; eight nominative trustees; three co-optative trustees.

HOW TO APPLY On a form available from the correspondent. Applications may be made at any time.

WHO TO APPLY TO The Clerk, Leicester Charity Link, 20a Millstone Lane, Leicester LE1 5JN *Tel* 0116 222 2200

CC NO 527881   **ESTABLISHED** 1983

■ The NFU Mutual Charitable Trust

WHERE FUNDING CAN BE GIVEN UK.

WHO CAN BENEFIT Organisations.

WHAT IS FUNDED The objects of the trust are the 'promotion and support of charitable purposes in the areas of agriculture, rural development and insurance in the UK – including education, the relief of poverty, social welfare and research – and any other charitable purpose'.

SAMPLE GRANTS Wales Young Farmers Club (£32,500); Faming & Countryside Education (£22,000); Farming Crisis Network (£17,000); Agrifood Charities (£10,000); Shakespeare Hospice at Home Service and Scottish Countryside Alliance Educational Trust (£5,000 each).

FINANCES *Year* 2008 *Income* £165,050
Grants £248,358 *Assets* £248,358

TRUSTEES Sir D Curry; D A S Davies; P A Kendall; J L Lampitt; J C McLaren; J G Furey; I Grant; R Percy.

HOW TO APPLY In writing to the correspondent.

WHO TO APPLY TO J D Creechan, Secretary to the Trustees, Tiddington Road, Stratford-upon-Avon, Warwickshire CV37 7BJ *Website* www.nfumutual.co.uk

CC NO 1073064   **ESTABLISHED** 1998

■ The Chevras Ezras Nitzrochim Trust

WHERE FUNDING CAN BE GIVEN UK, with a preference for London.

WHO CAN BENEFIT Organisations benefiting Jewish people who are disadvantaged by poverty.

WHAT IS FUNDED Orthodox Jewish organisations set up to raise money to help the poor in Jewish communities.

RANGE OF GRANTS £10–£4,000.

SAMPLE GRANTS Previously: Mesifta, Kupas Tzedoko Vochesed, Beis Chinuch Lenonos, Yad Eliezer, Yeshias Hatorah School, Hachzokas Torah Vochesed Trust, Ezras Hakohol Trust,

Woodstock Sinclair Trust, Side by Side, Yeshivas Panim Meiros, Yeahuas Chaim Synagogue, T Y Y Trust, Square Yeshiva, Stanislow and Camp Simcha.

FINANCES *Year* 2008 *Income* £248,740 *Grants* £244,960 *Assets* £1,041

TRUSTEES Joseph Stern; Hertz Kahan.

OTHER INFORMATION £195,000 was distributed to 710 individuals.

HOW TO APPLY In writing to the correspondent.

WHO TO APPLY TO Hertz Kahan, Trustee, 53 Heathland Road, London N16 5PQ *Tel* 020 8800 5187

CC NO 275352   **ESTABLISHED** 1978

■ NJD Charitable Trust

WHERE FUNDING CAN BE GIVEN UK and Israel.

WHO CAN BENEFIT People of the Jewish faith.

WHAT IS FUNDED The relief of poverty and hardship of members of the Jewish faith; the advancement of Jewish religion through Jewish education.

FINANCES *Year* 2007–08 *Income* £103,362 *Grants* £124,921 *Assets* £101,297

TRUSTEES J C Dwek; Mrs N L Dwek; J P Glaskie; J Wolf.

HOW TO APPLY In writing to the correspondent.

WHO TO APPLY TO J C Dwek, Trustee, 35 Frognal, Hampstead, London NW3 6YD *Tel* 020 7435 6883 *email* info@igpinvest.com

CC NO 1109146   **ESTABLISHED** 2005

■ Alice Noakes Memorial Charitable Trust

WHERE FUNDING CAN BE GIVEN Unrestricted.

WHO CAN BENEFIT Organisations and individuals.

WHAT IS FUNDED Animal welfare.

SAMPLE GRANTS University of Cambridge (£20,000); Animal Health Trust and Writtle Agricultural College – Bursary (£15,000 each); RSPCA – Danaher Animal Home for Essex (£10,000); Tikki Hywood Trust (£1,500); Dorset Wildlife Trust, FARM – Africa and Fauna and Flora International (£1,000 each); Greek Cat Welfare Society, Newcastle Dog and Cat Shelter, Portugal Animal Welfare UK and Yorkshire Swan Rescue (£500 each); and Save the Rhino (£100).

FINANCES *Year* 2007–08 *Income* £70,812 *Grants* £74,100 *Assets* £2,165,815

TRUSTEES D W G Whipps; Mrs J H Simpson; S N Bayer; J F Hulme.

HOW TO APPLY 'Applications for grants fitting the trust's objectives should be sent to the trustees at the charity's registered office.' The trustees meet twice a year.

WHO TO APPLY TO The Trustees, Bocking End, Braintree, Essex CM7 9AJ

CC NO 1039663   **ESTABLISHED** 1994

■ The Noel Buxton Trust

WHERE FUNDING CAN BE GIVEN UK, eastern and southern Africa.

WHO CAN BENEFIT Registered charities, although grants are not made to large popular national charities or in response to general appeals. Smaller local bodies and less popular causes are preferred, which benefit: children under 12 in disadvantaged families; prisoners and their families and young people at risk of offending; and education and development in eastern and southern Africa.

WHAT IS FUNDED Welfare of children in disadvantaged families and children in care; prevention of crime, especially among young people; the rehabilitation of prisoners and the welfare of their families; education and development in eastern and southern Africa.

WHAT IS NOT FUNDED The trust does not give to: academic research; advice centres; animals; the arts of any kind; buildings; conferences; counselling; development education; drug and alcohol work; older people; the environment; expeditions, exchanges, study tours, visits, and so on, or anything else involving fares; housing and homelessness; human rights; anything medical or connected with illness or mental or physical disability; anywhere overseas except eastern and southern Africa; peace and disarmament; race relations; young people (except for the prevention of offending); and unemployment. Grants are not made to individuals for any purpose.

TYPE OF GRANT One-off or recurrent. Not for buildings or salaries.

RANGE OF GRANTS £500–£5,000. Most grants are for £1,000 or less.

SAMPLE GRANTS Self Help Africa (£5,000); International Network of Street Papers and Prison Reform Trust (£4,000 each); Tirrim Development Programme (£3,600); Africa Christian Fellowship Reading (£3,000); North Eastern Prison After Care Society (£2,500); Dig Deep, Fair Shares, Footprints Project and Young People taking Action – Bury St Edmunds (£2,000 each); Behind Closed Doors – Leeds, Fun in Action for Children and Halow – Birmingham (£1,500 each); Phapphama Initiatives (£1,100); Campus Children's Holiday – Liverpool and Church Housing Trust (£1,000 each); and Just 42 – Woodbridge (£500).

FINANCES *Year* 2008 *Income* £144,023 *Grants* £117,200 *Assets* £2,007,009

TRUSTEES Richenda Wallace; Joyce Morton; Simon Buxton; Jon Snow; Jo Tunnard; John Littlewood; Brendan Gormley; Miss Emma Ponsonby; Miss Katie Aston.

HOW TO APPLY By letter, setting out the reasons why a grant is being requested. Applications should include the applicant's charity registration number and the name of the organisation to which cheques should be made payable if different from that at the head of the appeal letter. Applications should include: budget for current and following year; details of funding already received, promised or applied for from other sources; latest annual report/accounts in the shortest available form. Applications may be made at any time and are not acknowledged. Successful applicants will normally hear from the trust within six months. The trust will not discuss applications on the telephone or correspond about rejected appeals.

WHO TO APPLY TO Ray Waters, Secretary, PO Box 393, Farnham, Surrey GU9 8WZ *Website* www.noelbuxtontrust.org.uk/index.htm

CC NO 220881   **ESTABLISHED** 1919

■ The Noon Foundation

WHERE FUNDING CAN BE GIVEN UK.

WHO CAN BENEFIT Charitable organisations.

WHAT IS FUNDED General charitable purposes including, education, relief of poverty, community relations and alleviation of racial discrimination.

RANGE OF GRANTS £50–£50,000.

SAMPLE GRANTS Birkbeck University of London (£50,000); Shonia-Stem cell treatment in China (£5,000); University of Coventry (£3,000); London School of Economics (£2,000); and The Calamus Foundation and Well Being of Women (£1,000 each). Other grants made to institutions of less than £1,000 each totalled £50.

FINANCES *Year* 2007 *Income* £194,325 *Grants* £62,050 *Assets* £3,817,420

TRUSTEES Sir Gulam Noon; Akbar Shirazi; Mrs Zeenat Harnal; A M Jepson; A D Robinson; Mrs Zarmin N Sekhon.

HOW TO APPLY All applications and queries should be made by e-mail to: grants@noongroup.co.uk

WHO TO APPLY TO The Trustees, 25 Queen Anne's Gate, St James' Park, London SW1H 9BU *Tel* 020 7654 1600 *email* grants@noongroup.co.uk

CC NO 1053654   **ESTABLISHED** 1995

■ The Norda Trust

WHERE FUNDING CAN BE GIVEN UK.

WHO CAN BENEFIT Registered charities only.

WHAT IS FUNDED The trustees allocate funds principally in support of those working for the rehabilitation of prisoners both before and after release, support for the partners and families of prisoners. Trustees are actively looking into how effective support for those working with asylum seekers can be expanded. As funds permit, the trust can also support small local charities whose primary aim should be to improve the quality of life for the most severely disadvantaged communities or individuals. The trustees have a particular interest in helping to support new initiatives where there is a high level of volunteer involvement. When funds allow applications will be considered from charities and organisations who, by the nature of the work they undertake, do not attract popular support.

WHAT IS NOT FUNDED The following areas are not funded by the trust: medical causes; animal causes; individuals; school fees; proselytising.

TYPE OF GRANT Capital, revenue and full project funding. The majority of awards are made on a one off basis, with very few commitments made over two or more years.

RANGE OF GRANTS Up to £15,000.

SAMPLE GRANTS Christian Care (£10,000); Castle Gate Family Trust (£7,000); Derbyshire Housing Aid (£6,000); 999 Club, Apex Charitable Trust, Burnbake Trust, City Gate Community Project, Dover Detainee Visitor Group, Nehemiah Project, Prisoners Advice Service, Refugee Support Group Devon, Routeways Centre, St Edmund's Society and Wildwood (£5,000 each); London Detainee Support Group, Open Gate and SOFA Project (£4,000 each); Enterprise Education Trust (£3,100); Sudden Productions (£3,000); and Family Medication Scotland and HMP Highpoint (£2,000 each).

FINANCES *Year* 2008 *Income* £189,591 *Grants* £140,100 *Assets* £2,684,325

TRUSTEES J N Macpherson; P Gildener.

HOW TO APPLY Via letter or email, outlining the appeal. The trust will then make contact to request any further information they need.

WHO TO APPLY TO Martin Ward, Administrator, The Shieling, St Agnes, Cornwall TR5 0SS *Tel* 01871 553822 *email* enquiries@thenordatrust.org.uk *Website* www.thenordatrust.org.uk

CC NO 296418   **ESTABLISHED** 1960

■ Norie Charitable Trust

WHERE FUNDING CAN BE GIVEN UK.

WHO CAN BENEFIT Charitable organisations.

WHAT IS FUNDED General charitable purposes.

RANGE OF GRANTS Up to £6,000.

SAMPLE GRANTS Changing Tunes (£5,000), Bath Literary Festival (£3,000); Keynsham Arts and Somerset Crimebeat (£2,000 each); and Bath Film Festival, Pier Art Centre and the Harbour (£1,000 each).

FINANCES *Year* 2007–08 *Income* £26,910 *Grants* £26,390 *Assets* £831,699

TRUSTEES C H W Parish; Miss K Bernstein; Mrs A Wilson.

HOW TO APPLY In writing to the correspondent.

WHO TO APPLY TO The Trustees, Victoria House, 1–3 College Hil, London EC4R 2RA Tel: *Tel* 020 7489 8076

CC NO 1073993   **ESTABLISHED** 1999

■ Normalyn Charitable Trust

WHERE FUNDING CAN BE GIVEN UK.

WHO CAN BENEFIT Jewish people.

WHAT IS FUNDED General charitable purposes.

SAMPLE GRANTS United Jewish Israel Appeal (£7,500); United Synagogue (£6,800); Jewish Women's Aid (£6,100); City of London School Bursary Trust (£4,800); Community Security Trust (£2,700); and World Jewish Relief and UJS Hillel (£1,000 each).

FINANCES *Year* 2007–08 *Income* £44,538 *Grants* £42,567 *Assets* £21,207

TRUSTEES D I Dover; J S Newman; Mrs J Newman.

HOW TO APPLY The trust does not accept unsolicited applications.

WHO TO APPLY TO J S Newman, Trustee, c/o BDO Stoy Hayward LLP, 55 Baker Street, London W1U 7EU *Tel* 020 7486 5888

CC NO 1077985   **ESTABLISHED** 1999

■ The Norman Family Charitable Trust

WHERE FUNDING CAN BE GIVEN Primarily Cornwall, Devon and Somerset.

WHO CAN BENEFIT Registered charities only.

WHAT IS FUNDED Grants are made at the trustees' discretion, mostly in south west England.

WHAT IS NOT FUNDED No grants to individuals. No funding for religious buildings or to assist any organisations using animals for live experimental purposes or generally to fund overseas work.

TYPE OF GRANT One-off, interest-free loans, project, research and start-up costs will be considered. Funding may be given for up to one year.

RANGE OF GRANTS £1,000–£37,000.

SAMPLE GRANTS RNLI (£37,000); Devon Wildlife Trust (£30,000); Resthaven (£25,000); Kenn Parish Hall and Men's Club (£15,000); Sports Ad – South West (£10,000); and Budleigh Youth Project (£7,500); Devon Air Ambulance, Hospicecare – Exeter, Marie Curie Cancer Care and Shelter Box (£5,000 each); Prince's Trust (£4,000); Cats Protection League and Devon Farming and wildlife Advisory (£2,500 each); and Adventure Trust for Girls, Blue Cross, Devon County Association for the Blind and Jubilee Sailing Trust (£2,000 each).

FINANCES *Year* 2008–09 *Income* £433,059 *Grants* £347,460 *Assets* £8,009,482

TRUSTEES R J Dawe, Chair; Mrs M H Evans; M B Saunders; Mrs M J Webb; Mrs C E Houghton.

HOW TO APPLY In writing to the correspondent. A subcommittee of trustees meet regularly to make grants of up to £5,000. Grants in excess of £5,000 are dealt with at one of the quarterly meetings of all the trustees.

WHO TO APPLY TO R J Dawe, Chairman of the Trustees, 14 Fore Street, Budleigh Salterton, Devon EX9 6NG *Tel* 01395 446 699 *Fax* 01395 446698 *email* enquiries@normanfct.plus.com *Website* www.nfct.org

CC NO 277616   **ESTABLISHED** 1979

■ The Duncan Norman Trust Fund

WHERE FUNDING CAN BE GIVEN UK, with a preference for Merseyside.

WHO CAN BENEFIT Registered charities that are known to the trustees.

WHAT IS FUNDED General charitable purposes.

WHAT IS NOT FUNDED No grants to individuals.

SAMPLE GRANTS The Campaign for Drawing (£5,000); PCC of St Gwenfaen Church, Rhoscolyn (£2,000); Army Benevolent Fund, Combat Stress and Royal Star and Garter Home (£1,500 each); Breast Cancer Haven – London, Help for Heroes and PCC of SS Peter & Paul Church – Swalcliffe (£1,000 each).

FINANCES *Year* 2007–08 *Income* £34,733 *Grants* £34,950 *Assets* £799,307

TRUSTEES R K Asser; Mrs C Chapman; Mrs V S Hilton; Mrs C E Lazar; W Stothart.

OTHER INFORMATION Grants of less than £1,000 each totalled £21,500.

HOW TO APPLY The trust states that it only makes grants to charities known to the settlor and unsolicited applications are not considered.

WHO TO APPLY TO The Trustees, Liverpool Charity and Voluntary Services, 151 Dale Street, Liverpool L2 2AH *Tel* 0151 227 5177 *email* enquiries@charitycheques.org.uk *Website* www.merseytrusts.org.uk

CC NO 250434   **ESTABLISHED** 1996

■ The Normanby Charitable Trust

WHERE FUNDING CAN BE GIVEN UK, with a special interest in North Yorkshire and north east England.

WHO CAN BENEFIT Registered charities.

WHAT IS FUNDED General charitable purposes.

WHAT IS NOT FUNDED No grants to individuals, or to non-UK charities.

RANGE OF GRANTS £250–£20,000.

SAMPLE GRANTS The Ashmolean Museum and Ryedale Festival (£20,000 each); Action Trust for the Blind, Child Bereavement Charity, Scarborough Theatre Trust and Trinity Annual Fund (£10,000 each); Scarborough and Ryedale Mountain Rescue (£7,500); Children's Country Holiday Fund (£5,000); Tom Carpenter Centre and Whitby Archive Heritage Centre (£2,000 each); Bognor Fun Buss Co. Ltd (£500); and Esk Moors Active Ltd (£250).

FINANCES *Year* 2007–08 *Income* £339,243 *Grants* £175,053 *Assets* £8,741,909

TRUSTEES The 5th Marquis of Normanby; The Dowager Marchioness of Normanby; Lady Lepel Kornicka; Lady Evelyn Buchan; Lady Peronel Phipps de Cruz; Lady Henrietta Burridge.

HOW TO APPLY In writing to the correspondent. There are no regular dates for trustees' meetings. Please note, only successful applications will be acknowledged.

WHO TO APPLY TO The Trustees, 52 Tite Street, London SW3 4JA

CC NO 252102   **ESTABLISHED** 1966

■ The North British Hotel Trust

WHERE FUNDING CAN BE GIVEN Scotland.

WHO CAN BENEFIT Mainly registered charities.

WHAT IS FUNDED General, mainly welfare, health, older people, people with disabilities.

WHAT IS NOT FUNDED No grants to individuals.

SAMPLE GRANTS Previous beneficiaries include: Dunedin School; Duke of Edinburgh New Start Programme; Hospitality Industry Trust – Scotland; Family Mediation Argyll & Bute; Craigmillar Childline Services; Ark Trust; Arrochar & Tarbet Senior Citizens' Committee; Balloch Over 60's Club; and Westhill Senior Citizens' Club.

FINANCES *Year* 2007–08 *Income* £357,871 *Grants* £532,347 *Assets* £9,606,997

TRUSTEES Ian C Fraser; Dr Ronald L Frew; Jonathan R M MacQueen; Patrick Crerar; Graham Brown; Mrs Jeanette Crerar; Mike Still; James Barrack; John Williams.

OTHER INFORMATION Information on beneficiaries during the year was not available.

HOW TO APPLY Application forms are available from the correspondent.

WHO TO APPLY TO Claire Smith, Clerk, Samuelston Mill House, Haddington, East Lothian EH41 4HG *email* nbht@samuelston.com

CC NO 221335   **ESTABLISHED** 1903

■ The North West Cancer Research Fund

WHERE FUNDING CAN BE GIVEN North West England and North and Mid Wales.

WHO CAN BENEFIT Those undertaking fundamental cancer research approved by and under the direction of the North West Cancer Research Fund Scientific Committee.

WHAT IS FUNDED Fundamental research into the causes of cancer, including the cost of associated equipment.

WHAT IS NOT FUNDED Funding is not given for research whose primary aim is to develop new forms of treatment or evaluate existing ones, such as drug development, nor for clinical trials.

TYPE OF GRANT Project; research; running and start-up costs; and salaries. Usually for three-year periods subject to review.

RANGE OF GRANTS Average grant size is £35,000 per annum, awarded for three years.

FINANCES *Year* 2006–07 *Income* £1,092,379 *Grants* £750,000 *Assets* £4,938,288

TRUSTEES W M Barton; A W Renison; A P Farmer; J C Lewys-Lloyd; Prof. J Caldwell; Mrs W E Hadwin; M S Potts; Mrs A Halewood; Mrs B J Smith; K Jackson; Col. J G Bryson; Mrs P Mann; Mrs S M Renison; Mrs B Lloyd Powell; Mrs H E Dring; Mrs J Pettitt; Mrs S Gill; Mrs O Ley.

HOW TO APPLY Application forms can be downloaded from the fund's website, or obtained from the Scientific Committee Secretary, Tracey Ricketts, on 0151 706 4280 or email: ricketts@liverpool.ac.uk. Applications must be limited to 2,000 words. Relevant papers in print or submitted should be included as an appendix. Applications must be submitted in triplicate to the secretary by 1 April or 1 October. They will be considered approximately eight weeks later. Late applications will be held over to the following meeting.

WHO TO APPLY TO Anne Jackson, 22 Oxford Street, Liverpool L7 7BL *Tel* 0151 709 2919 *email* nwcrf@btclick.com *Website* www.nwcrf.co.uk

CC NO 223598   **ESTABLISHED** 1948

North West London Community Foundation

WHERE FUNDING CAN BE GIVEN London boroughs of Barnet, Brent, Ealing, Enfield, Haringey, Harrow and Hillingdon.

WHO CAN BENEFIT Local community and voluntary organisations.

WHAT IS FUNDED Fields of interest are: children and young people who are disadvantaged or living in poverty; community development; social exclusion and isolation; bringing communities together; health; and learning disabilities.

WHAT IS NOT FUNDED No grants to individuals or to organisations outside the foundation's beneficial area.

TYPE OF GRANT Usually one-off.

FINANCES *Year* 2007–08 *Income* £755,261 *Grants* £550,483 *Assets* £225,117

TRUSTEES Natalie Forbes, Chair; Kanti Nagda; David Wood; Tajinder Nijjar; Howard Bluston; Allan Conway; Malcolm Churchill.

OTHER INFORMATION A grant list was not included in the trust's accounts.

HOW TO APPLY Application forms and further details are available from the correspondent or from the foundation's website.

WHO TO APPLY TO Kath Sullivan, Grants Officer, Room 1, The Wealdstone Centre, 38–40 High Street, Harrow, Middlesex HA3 7AE *Tel* 020 8427 3823 *Fax* 020 8427 2104 *email* info@nwlcommunityfoundation.org.uk *Website* www.nwlcommunityfoundation.org.uk

CC NO 1097648   **ESTABLISHED** 2002

The Northampton Municipal Church Charities

WHERE FUNDING CAN BE GIVEN The borough of Northampton.

WHO CAN BENEFIT Organisations and individuals in need.

WHAT IS FUNDED Social welfare, disability, religion and education.

TYPE OF GRANT One-off and recurrent.

RANGE OF GRANTS Usually £1,000 for individuals and between £1,000 and £30,000 for organisations.

SAMPLE GRANTS Emmanuel Church (£33,000); YMCA (£6,400); CAN, Crime to Christ and Spencer Contact (£2,500 each); Northants Association for the Blind and Northampton Hope Centre (£2,000 each); Listening Books (£1,500); and Salvation Army and Together – Working for Well Being (£1,000 each).

FINANCES *Year* 2007–08 *Income* £233,240 *Grants* £125,325 *Assets* £4,398,429

TRUSTEES Keith Davidson; James Buckby; Mrs Jane Duncan; Ronald Gate; Mrs Ruth Hampson; Mrs Valerie Holmes; Mrs Jean Lineker; Colin Wain; Jonathan Church; Clive Fowler; Mrs Pauline Hoggarth; Brian May; Terrence O'Connor.

OTHER INFORMATION From the grants total £24,000 went to individuals, £35,000 went towards pensioners grants and £5,500 went towards Christmas vouchers.

HOW TO APPLY In writing to the correspondent.

WHO TO APPLY TO Clerk to the Trustees, Wilson Browne Solicitors, 4 Grange Park Court, Roman Way, Grange Park, Northampton NN4 5EA *Tel* 01604 876 697 *email* jforsyth@wilsonbrowne.co.uk

CC NO 259593   **ESTABLISHED** 1969

The Northampton Queen's Institute Relief in Sickness Fund

WHERE FUNDING CAN BE GIVEN The borough of Northampton.

WHO CAN BENEFIT Organisations benefiting children and young adults, at risk groups, and people who are disadvantaged by poverty or socially isolated.

WHAT IS FUNDED Youth groups, welfare organisations, hospitals and health organisations.

TYPE OF GRANT One-off and recurrent.

RANGE OF GRANTS £500–£3,000.

SAMPLE GRANTS Northampton Hope Centre (£3,000); St John Ambulance (£2,000); Home-Start, Life Education Centre Northampton, Northampton PHAB, Northants Association of Youth Clubs and Northants Association for the Blind (£1,500 each); Brittle Bone Society and Combat Stress (£1,000); and Victim Support (£500).

FINANCES *Year* 2007–08 *Income* £36,708 *Grants* £30,000 *Assets* £1,019,263

TRUSTEES D M Orton-Jones, Chair; C F N Pedley; Mrs J Bradshaw; J Mackaness; Dr R Marshall; Dr J McFarlane; David Hammer; Dr J Scrivener Birkhead; Dr Charles Fox.

HOW TO APPLY In writing to the correspondent. There are one or two main meetings where applications are considered during the year, although decisions can be made in between.

WHO TO APPLY TO Mrs Susan Peet, Clerk to the Charity, Shoosmiths, 5 The Lakes, Northampton NN4 7SH *Tel* 01604 543111

CC NO 208583   **ESTABLISHED** 1971

The Earl of Northampton's Charity

WHERE FUNDING CAN BE GIVEN England, with a preference for London and the South East.

WHO CAN BENEFIT Charitable organisations.

WHAT IS FUNDED Welfare causes.

RANGE OF GRANTS £250–£4,000.

SAMPLE GRANTS Trinity Hospital – Clun (£4,000), Trinity Hospital – Castle Rising (£3,000); Jubilee Trust Almshouses (£2,000); and St M Michael's Church Framlington (£250).

FINANCES *Year* 2008–09 *Income* £1,639,000 *Grants* £31,250 *Assets* £18,935,000

TRUSTEES The Mercers Company.

OTHER INFORMATION £22,000 to individuals.

HOW TO APPLY In writing to the correspondent.

WHO TO APPLY TO M McGregor, Clerk to the Mercers' Company, Mercers' Company, Mercers' Hall, Ironmonger Lane, London EC2V 8HE *Tel* 020 7726 4991 *Fax* 020 7600 1158 *email* mail@mercers.co.uk *Website* www.mercers.co.uk

CC NO 210291   **ESTABLISHED** 2003

The Northcott Devon Foundation

WHERE FUNDING CAN BE GIVEN Devon.

WHO CAN BENEFIT 'The principal objects of the charity are to provide support for individuals in Devon and to assist registered charities which seek to improve the living conditions of disabled or disadvantaged persons resident in Devon.'

WHAT IS FUNDED (a) Individuals or families living in Devon who are experiencing distress and hardship deriving from disability, illness, injury, bereavement or exceptional disadvantage, in circumstances where such assistance offers

Think carefully about every application. Is it justified?

747

long-term benefit. (b) Registered charities operating primarily within Devon, whose objects are broadly in sympathy with those of the foundation, and who seek to improve the living conditions or life experiences of people who are disabled or disadvantaged living in Devon.
(c) Young people of limited means undertaking philanthropic activities that are not part of a formal education or training programme, and who live in Devon.

WHAT IS NOT FUNDED The foundation is unable to enter into longer-term financial commitments. Assistance will not be given to statutory agencies, including self-governing National Health Service Trusts, in the performance of their duties. Assistance will not be given to clear any debts owed to statutory agencies or to financial institutions. Other debts will not formally be considered unless agreement has been reached with the creditors for full and final settlement in a substantially reduced sum.

TYPE OF GRANT Usually one-off for a specific purpose or project. Research, capital and buildings will be considered. Core funding is not considered.

RANGE OF GRANTS Normally upwards of £200 to £10,000.

SAMPLE GRANTS Exeter University (£10,000); Northcott Theatre (£2,500); and St Luke's Hospice (£1,000). A further £11,000 was given in small grants to institutions.
Grants to 1,095 individuals totalled £200,000.

FINANCES *Year* 2007–08 *Income* £265,427 *Grants* £225,624 *Assets* £5,456,651

TRUSTEES M Horwood; Maj. Gen. J Grey; M Pentreath.

HOW TO APPLY Organisations should initially apply in writing to the correspondent who will supply an application form and statement of policy. Please enclose a sae.
Applications from individuals are primarily considered through the county social services department or a registered charity.
Assistance will not be given unless applicants or their sponsors have checked thoroughly that assistance or benefit is not available from the Department of Social Security or other public funds.

WHO TO APPLY TO G G Folland, Secretary, 1b Victoria Road, Exmouth, Devon EX8 1DL *Tel* 01395 269204

CC NO 201277   **ESTABLISHED** 1960

....

■ **The Northcott Devon Medical Foundation**

WHERE FUNDING CAN BE GIVEN Devon.

WHO CAN BENEFIT Academics, medical professionals, research workers and postgraduate students.

WHAT IS FUNDED Support of postgraduate, medical research and the improvement of medical practice. Provision of schools, research laboratories, libraries and so on for the promotion of medicine, surgery and other subjects.

WHAT IS NOT FUNDED Tuition fees for medical/nursing undergraduates and living expenses.

RANGE OF GRANTS £1,000 to £7,000.

SAMPLE GRANTS Peninsula Medical School which received funding for ten projects (£33,000); and Plymouth Hospital NHS Trust (£2,200).

FINANCES *Year* 2007–08 *Income* £40,979 *Grants* £35,478 *Assets* £1,148,206

TRUSTEES Dr C Gardner-Thorpe; Prof. D Partridge; Dr A P Warin.

HOW TO APPLY On an application form available from the correspondent.

WHO TO APPLY TO R E T Borton, Secretary, Bishop Fleming, Stratus House, Emperor Way, Exeter Business Park, Exeter EX1 4QS *Tel* 01392 448 800 *email* tborton@bishopfleming.co.uk

CC NO 204660   **ESTABLISHED** 1961

....

■ **The Northern Rock Foundation**

WHERE FUNDING CAN BE GIVEN Cumbria, Northumberland, Tyne and Wear, County Durham and the Tees Valley.

WHO CAN BENEFIT Organisations helping people who are disadvantaged.

WHAT IS FUNDED Grant programmes are: Independence and Choice; Building Positive Lives; and Safety and Justice.

WHAT IS NOT FUNDED 'There are certain organisations, projects and proposals that we will not consider for grants. You should be aware that it costs the equivalent of several small grants to administer ineligible applications each year. If your organisation or your project falls into one of the categories below please do not apply to us for a grant: activities which are not recognised as charitable in law; applications for under £1,000; charities which appear to us to have excessive unrestricted or free reserves (up to 12 months' expenditure is normally acceptable), or are in serious deficit; national charities which do not have a regional office or other representation in North East England or Cumbria; grant-making bodies seeking to distribute grants on our behalf; open-ended funding agreements; general appeals, sponsorship and marketing appeals; corporate applications for founder membership of a charity; retrospective grants; replacement of statutory funding; activities primarily the responsibility of central or local government or health authorities; individuals and organisations that distribute funds to individuals; animal welfare; mainstream educational activity, schools and educational establishments; medical research, hospitals, hospices and medical centres; medical treatments and therapies including art therapy; fabric appeals for places of worship; promotion of religion; expeditions or overseas travel; minibuses, other vehicles and transport schemes except where they are a small and integral part of a larger scheme; holidays and outings; playgrounds and play equipment; private clubs or those with such restricted membership as to make them not charitable; capital bids purely towards compliance with the Disability Discrimination Act; amateur arts organisations; musical instruments; sports kit and equipment.'

TYPE OF GRANT Capital, core or project funding and for up to three or more years (sometimes renewable after that).

RANGE OF GRANTS £1,000–£350,000; typical grant £10,000–£60,000.

SAMPLE GRANTS Contact a Family Incorporated (£233,000 over three years), towards the salaries of two posts to support parent carers of children with disabilities in the North East and Cumbria; Keyfund Federation Limited (£210,000 over three years), to fund a development programme for young people in the North East and Cumbria; Women's Support Network (£148,000 over three years), towards the manager's salary and related costs of this project in Middlesbrough supporting victims of sexual violence; The People's Kitchen (£105,000 over three years), towards volunteer training and recruitment, core costs, and towards work with the Cyrenians to support homeless people in crisis in Newcastle; Newcastle and Gateshead Arts Studio Ltd (£90,000 over three years), towards the core costs of the organisation, which runs an arts studio for people with mental health problems; Durham County Council (£60,000 over three years), to develop an enhanced visual arts programme, which will attract wider audiences, at the DLI Museum and Durham Art Gallery; Open Clasp Theatre Company (£40,000), towards the Herstory Told project which will use drama to look at the impact of sexual exploitation and losing or giving up children on young women in the North East; and Survivors of Domestic Abuse (£5,000, to enable this survivor-led group to support victims of domestic abuse in Redcar.

FINANCES *Year* 2008 *Income* £16,669,000 *Grants* £10,317,428 *Assets* £30,111,000

TRUSTEES Alastair Balls, Chair; David Chapman; David Faulkner; Jackie Fisher; Tony Henfrey; Chris Jobe; Lorna Moran; Frank Nicholson; Mo O'Toole; Julie Shipley.

PUBLICATIONS Grant Programmes – Guidance for Applicants; various reports.

HOW TO APPLY The foundation provides comprehensive advice on making an application (see the publications entitled: Grant Programmes – Guidance for Applicants). The foundation has different grant application processes: one for requests from £1,000 to £20,000; the other for requests over £20,000. Please make sure you complete the correct application form downloadable from the foundation's website. The foundation also has an on-line application form.

WHO TO APPLY TO Penny Wilkinson, Chief Executive, The Old Chapel, Woodbine Road, Gosforth, Newcastle upon Tyne NE3 1DD *Tel* 0191 284 8412 *Fax* 0191 284 8413 *Minicom* 0191 284 5411 *email* generaloffice@nr-foundation.org.uk *Website* www.nr-foundation.org.uk

CC NO 1063906   **ESTABLISHED** 1997

■ The Northmoor Trust

WHERE FUNDING CAN BE GIVEN UK.

WHO CAN BENEFIT Local, regional and UK charitable organisations benefiting people who are disadvantaged.

WHAT IS FUNDED The direct or indirect relief of poverty, hardship or distress.

WHAT IS NOT FUNDED Grants are only made to organisations which one or more of the trustees have direct personal knowledge. No grants to individuals, or organisations concerned with religion, medicine or the arts. Occasionally grants are made to educational charities where the guiding criteria are met. The trust does not respond to general appeals.

TYPE OF GRANT One-off and recurrent.

RANGE OF GRANTS £5,000–£40,000.

SAMPLE GRANTS Zimbabwe Benefit Foundation (£40,000); Release (£25,000); Firebird Trust (£20,000); Education Actional International (£19,000); Family and Friends (£15,000); Blackbird Leys Neighbourhood Support Scheme (£14,000); National AIDS Trust and Prisoners Abroad (£10,000 each); and Lambeth Play Association and Tower Hamlets Friends and Neighbours (£5,000 each).

FINANCES *Year* 2006–07 *Income* £192,225 *Grants* £182,900 *Assets* £4,417,375

TRUSTEES Viscount Runciman; Dame Ruth Runciman; Ms Frances Bennett; Ms Cathy Eastburn.

HOW TO APPLY In writing to the correspondent, including the latest accounts and annual report, a list of the main sources of funding and a budget for the current year including details of other grant applications made. For first time applicants, a general description of aims and achievements to date and an outline of plans for future development. Applications should arrive by 31 January for preliminary consideration in March, decisions are made in May. Applicants may be visited or asked to provide additional information for the May meeting. The trustees may also visit applicants between the two meetings.

WHO TO APPLY TO Mrs Hilary Edwards, Secretary, 44 Clifton Hill, London NW8 0QG *Tel* 020 7372 0698

CC NO 256818   **ESTABLISHED** 1968

■ The Northumberland Village Homes Trust

WHERE FUNDING CAN BE GIVEN Tyne and Wear, Durham, Cleveland and Northumberland.

WHO CAN BENEFIT Individuals and youth organisations benefiting those under 21years of age who are disadvantaged by poverty.

WHAT IS FUNDED The relief of poverty distress and sickness among children and young persons under the age of 21 years, with a preference for those who are resident in Tyne and Wear, Durham, Cleveland and Northumberland.

WHAT IS NOT FUNDED No personal applications will be considered unless supported by a letter from a registered charity or local authority, or unless the applicant is personally known to one of the trustees. No applications will be considered for 'gap year' projects or for work relating to medical research or such matters.

RANGE OF GRANTS £500–£12,000.

SAMPLE GRANTS Children North East (£12,000); NSPCC Newcastle (£5,000); Childline – Yorkshire/Tyne Tees (£4,000); Barnardos North East (£3,000); Turning Point Whitley Bay (£2,500); The Children's Society (£2,000); Cowpen Community Association and the Percy Hedley Trust (£1,000 each); and Respect – Hartlepool and Trinity Youth and Children's Project (£500 each).

FINANCES *Year* 2007–08 *Income* £52,580 *Grants* £46,500 *Assets* £1,229,906

TRUSTEES D Welch, Chair; Lord Gisborough; Mrs E P Savage; Mrs D Barkes.

HOW TO APPLY Applications should be made by 30 September for consideration in November. Applications should be in writing and state: whether the applicant is an individual, private charity or registered charity; the objects (if a charity); the amount required and what it is for; and any other sources of funding.

WHO TO APPLY TO Mrs Savage, Clerk to the Trustees, Savage Solicitors, Robson House, 4 Middle Street, Corbridge NE45 5AT *Tel* 01434 632 505

CC NO 225429   **ESTABLISHED** 1880

■ The Northumbria Historic Churches Trust

WHERE FUNDING CAN BE GIVEN The dioceses of Durham and Newcastle.

WHO CAN BENEFIT Churches that are at least 100 years old.

WHAT IS FUNDED The restoration, preservation, repair, maintenance, reconstruction, improvement and beautification of churches, their contents and their churchyards.

WHAT IS NOT FUNDED 'The trust is unable to help with work on bells, organs, church halls, decoration (unless consequential), notice boards, publications, heating, re-orderings, new facilities or routine maintenance.'

TYPE OF GRANT One-off, feasibility studies and buildings. Funding is for one year or less.

RANGE OF GRANTS £500–£5,000.

SAMPLE GRANTS St Andrew – Stanley and St Michael & All Angels Houghton-le-Spring (£5,000 each); Holy Cross – Ryton and St Michael – Heighington (£4,000 each); Holy Sepulchre – Ashington and St Michael – Ilderton (£3,000 each); Methodist Chapel – Ingleton (£2,000); and Holy Cross – Chatton (£1,000).

FINANCES *Year* 2007–08 *Income* £96,883 *Grants* £44,000 *Assets* £242,023

TRUSTEES G Bell, Chair; Mrs E Conran; C Downs; Ven. P Elliot; M Festing; J B Kendall; Canon J E Ruscoe; Mrs G Walker; Mrs E Norris; Mrs I Ferguson, R C Norris; Revd T Hurst, P Ryder.

OTHER INFORMATION No grants to individuals.

HOW TO APPLY In writing to the correspondent requesting an application form and guidelines. Initial telephone calls to discuss applications are welcomed.

WHO TO APPLY TO Peter De Lange, Secretary, 20 Aykley Vale, Aykley Hands, Durham DH1 5WA *Tel* 0191 383 2704 *email* mailto: northumbriahct@aol.com *Website* www. northumbriahct.org.uk

CC NO 511314   **ESTABLISHED** 1980

··

■ The Northwood Charitable Trust

WHERE FUNDING CAN BE GIVEN Scotland, especially Dundee and Tayside.

WHO CAN BENEFIT Organisations.

WHAT IS FUNDED General charitable purposes. In the past, grants have been given to a university and to medical and educational projects.

TYPE OF GRANT One-off and recurring grants.

SAMPLE GRANTS Previous beneficiaries include: Tenovus Medical Projects, Tayside Orthopaedic and Rehabilitation Technology Centre, Dundee University, Dundee Repertory Theatre, D C Thompson Charitable Trust, Strathmore Hospice, Brittle Bone Society and MacMillan Cancer Relief Scotland.

FINANCES *Year* 2007–08 *Income* £1,800,000 *Grants* £1,500,000 *Assets* £50,000,000

TRUSTEES Brian Harold Thomson; Andrew Francis Thomson; Lewis Murray Thomson.

HOW TO APPLY The trust has previously stated that funds are fully committed and that no applications will be considered or acknowledged.

WHO TO APPLY TO Brian McKernie, Secretary, William Thomson and Sons, 22 Meadowside, Dundee DD1 1LN *Tel* 01382 201534 *Fax* 01382 227654 *email* bmckernie@wtandsons.co.uk

SC NO SC014487   **ESTABLISHED** 1972

··

■ The Norton Foundation

WHERE FUNDING CAN BE GIVEN UK, with a preference for Birmingham, Coventry and the County of Warwick.

WHO CAN BENEFIT Young people under 25 years of age.

WHAT IS FUNDED The trust was created in 1990. Its objects are to help children and young people under 25 who are in 'need of care or rehabilitation or aid of any kind, particularly as a result of delinquency, deprivation, maltreatment or neglect or who are in danger of lapsing or relapsing into delinquency.'

WHAT IS NOT FUNDED No grants for the payment of debts that have already been incurred. Grants are not made for further education (except in very exceptional circumstances).

SAMPLE GRANTS South Birmingham Young Homeless Project (£10,000); Playbox Theatre Company (£4,000); The Wellchild Trust (£3,750); 20th Walsall Scouts Group – St Margaret's (£3,500); Heatlands Church – Stratford (£3,000); Tiny Tim's Children's Centre (£2,500); Birmingham Settlement and The Quizone Centre (£2,000 each); Birmingham Royal Ballet, Rotary Club of Coventry Breakfast, Training Ship – Sutton Coalfield and Warwickshire Clubs for Young People (£1,000 each).

FINANCES *Year* 2007–08 *Income* £145,189 *Grants* £112,751 *Assets* £4,053,124

TRUSTEES R H Graham, Suggett Chair; Peter Adkins; Alan Bailey; Michael R Bailey; Parminder Singh Birdi; Mrs Jane Gaynor; Mrs Sarah V Henderson; Richard G D Hurley; Brian W Lewis; Robert K Meacham; Richard C Perkins; Mrs Louise Sewell.

OTHER INFORMATION A total of £37,310 was given in grants to individuals.

HOW TO APPLY By letter which should contain all the information required as detailed in the guidance notes for applicants. Guidance notes are available from the correspondent or from the foundation's website. Applications from organisations are normally processed by the trustees at their meeting in July each year and should be sent by the end of April.

WHO TO APPLY TO Richard C Perkins, Correspondent, PO Box 10282, Redditch, Worcestershire B97 9ZA *Tel* 01527 544 446 *email* correspondent@nortonfoundation.org *Website* www.nortonfoundation.org

CC NO 702638   **ESTABLISHED** 1990

··

■ The Norton Rose Charitable Foundation

WHERE FUNDING CAN BE GIVEN Worldwide.

WHO CAN BENEFIT Registered charities and organisations conducting charitable activities worldwide.

WHAT IS FUNDED Education, social welfare, medical.

RANGE OF GRANTS Up to £100,000.

SAMPLE GRANTS Barretstown (£100,000).

FINANCES *Year* 2007–08 *Income* £457,813 *Grants* £491,155 *Assets* £91,726

TRUSTEES Simon Cox; Patrick Farrell; Glenn Hall; Campbell Steedman.

HOW TO APPLY 'In many cases, the charities we support are those we have supported in the past, but new charities are considered at all the regular trustee meetings. The trustees also meet on an ad hoc basis to consider specific urgent requests such as the support of major disaster relief appeals.'

WHO TO APPLY TO Susan Neighbour, Secretary, 3 More London Riverside, London SE1 2AQ *Tel* 020 7444 3105 *Website* www.nortonrose. com

CC NO 1102142   **ESTABLISHED** 2004

······································

■ The Norwich Church of England Young Men's Society

WHERE FUNDING CAN BE GIVEN Mainly in the Norfolk area.

WHO CAN BENEFIT Churches and charitable organisations.

WHAT IS FUNDED Local church and young people related activities.

RANGE OF GRANTS £100–£7,500.

SAMPLE GRANTS Beneficiaries included: Swardeston Cricket Club – Youth Section (£7,500); Norwich Cathedral (£2,500); Ashcroft Project and East Norfolk Youth for Christ (£1,000 each); Nancy Oldfield Trust (£750); Norfolk Deaf Association, Hamlet Centre Trust and Nelsons Trust (£500 each); Sewell Community Group (£250); and Norfolk and Norwich Diabetes Trust (£100).

FINANCES *Year* 2007 *Income* £240,391 *Grants* £26,152 *Assets* £1,550,599

TRUSTEES J Pidgen; J Copeman; Canon D Sharp.

HOW TO APPLY In writing to the correspondent. Applications are considered quarterly and only successful ones are acknowledged.

WHO TO APPLY TO C J Free, Secretary, 3 Brigg Street, Norwich NR2 1QN *Tel* 01603 628 572

CC NO 206425   **ESTABLISHED** 1892

······································

■ The Norwich Historic Churches Trust Ltd

WHERE FUNDING CAN BE GIVEN Norwich.

WHO CAN BENEFIT Historic churches.

WHAT IS FUNDED The preservation, repair and maintenance of disused churches of all denominations that have particular architectural or historic value.

FINANCES *Year* 2007–08 *Income* £160,634 *Grants* £234,562 *Assets* £118,786

TRUSTEES R Quinn; S Munro; K Rowe; P Tolley; Mrs R Salt; Ms S Curran; J W Knight; Ms J Lay; N Groves; Dr P Binski; D Bradford; D MacGarry; N Williams; Ms F Hartley.

HOW TO APPLY The trust does not give grants to unsolicited applications, as all their monies are donated to the 17 churches the funds are already committed to.

WHO TO APPLY TO Lucy Tetlow, PO Box 3408, Norwich NR3 3WE *Tel* 01603 611 530 *email* norhistch.trust@btinternet.com *Website* www.norwichchurches.co.uk

CC NO 266686   **ESTABLISHED** 1973

······································

■ The Norwich Town Close Estate Charity

WHERE FUNDING CAN BE GIVEN Within a 20-mile radius of the Guildhall of the city of Norwich.

WHO CAN BENEFIT Only charities based in the area specified and carrying out educational activities will be supported.

WHAT IS FUNDED Primarily Freemen of Norwich, for education, pensions, TV licences, and relief in need. Surplus monies may be used for grants to educational charities.

WHAT IS NOT FUNDED No grants to: individuals who are not Freemen (or dependants of Freemen) of the city of Norwich; charities more than 20 miles from Norwich; or charities which are not educational. Revenue funding for educational charities is not generally given.

TYPE OF GRANT Buildings, capital, one-off and project. Funding for up to one year will be considered.

SAMPLE GRANTS YMCA Norfolk (£50,000); Norfolk and Norwich Association for the Blind (£35,000); Norwich Puppet Theatre Trust (£25,000); Friends of Nightingale School (£15,000); Larkman Primary School (£10,000); University of East Anglia (£8,800); Hethersett Pre-School Playgroup (£5,000); Whitwell Hall Country Centre (£4,000); and Norfolk Country Music Festival (£2,000).

FINANCES *Year* 2007–08 *Income* £815,368 *Grants* £517,403 *Assets* £19,531,090

TRUSTEES David Fullman; John Rushmer; Michael Quinton; Brenda Ferris; Geoffrey Loades; Joyce Hopwood; Philip Blanchflower; Sally Barham; Anthony Hansell; Nigel Black; Peter Colby; Richard Gurney; Jeanette Southgate; Robert Self.

HOW TO APPLY After a preliminary enquiry, in writing to the clerk. When submitting an application the following points should be borne in mind: brevity is a virtue – if too much written material is submitted there is a risk that it may not all be assimilated; the trustees like to have details of any other financial support secured; an indication should be given of the amount that is being sought and also how that figure is arrived at; the trustees will not reimburse expenditure already incurred; nor, generally speaking will the trustees pay running costs, e.g. salaries.

WHO TO APPLY TO David Walker, Clerk, 1 Woolgate Court, St Benedict's Street, Norwich NR2 4AP *email* david.walker@norwichcharitabletrusts.org.uk

CC NO 235678   **ESTABLISHED** 1892

······································

■ Norwood and Newton Settlement

WHERE FUNDING CAN BE GIVEN England and Wales.

WHO CAN BENEFIT Methodist and other mainstream non-conformist churches. Church of England only in exceptional circumstances.

WHAT IS FUNDED New building work in Methodist and other Free Churches. Smaller national charities in which the Settlor expressed a particular interest and other charitable causes that commend themselves to the trustees.

WHAT IS NOT FUNDED Projects will not be considered where an application for National Lottery funding has been made or is contemplated. No grants to individuals, rarely to large UK charities and not for staff/running costs, equipment, repairs or general maintenance.

TYPE OF GRANT Normally one-off.

RANGE OF GRANTS £1,000–£12,500.

SAMPLE GRANTS Holmes Chapel Methodist Church – Cheshire and Maulden Baptist Church – Bedford (£13,000 each); and Bishops Cleave Methodist Church – Cheltenham, Chew Magna Baptist Church – Bristol, Kidlington Baptist Church – Oxon, Southwick Christian Community Church – West Sussex, Tools With a Mission – Ipswich and Youth for Christ HQ – Halesowen (£10,000 each); Etherley Methodist Church – County Durham (£7,500); Worsley Road URC – Manchester (£6,000); Bury St Edmunds Friends Meeting House and Museum of Army Flying (£5,000 each); Wrenthorpe Methodist Church – Wakefield (£3,000); and Wardle Village Church (Meth/CofE) – Rochdale (£1,000).

FINANCES *Year* 2007–08 *Income* £374,488 *Grants* £334,500 *Assets* £7,770,683

TRUSTEES P Clarke; D M Holland; Mrs Stella Holland; W W Leyland; Mrs Susan Newsom.

HOW TO APPLY In writing to the correspondent. In normal circumstances, the trustees' decision is communicated to the applicant within seven days (if a refusal), and if successful, immediately after the trustees' quarterly meetings.

WHO TO APPLY TO David M Holland, Trustee, 126 Beauly Way, Romford, Essex RM1 4XL *Tel* 01708 723 670

CC NO 234964   **ESTABLISHED** 1952

■ The Noswad Charity

WHERE FUNDING CAN BE GIVEN UK.

WHO CAN BENEFIT Emphasis is on charities that benefit the arts and people who are disabled, particularly ex-service people.

WHAT IS FUNDED The trustees continue to support those charitable bodies that they have hitherto supported.

WHAT IS NOT FUNDED No grants to individuals.

RANGE OF GRANTS £600–£2,600.

SAMPLE GRANTS Typically grants are made to Douglas Bader Foundation, Royal Air Force Benevolent Fund, BLESMA, RADAR, Macmillan Cancer Relief and National Arts Collections Fund. It also supports scholarships for postgraduate piano students at London music colleges.

FINANCES *Year* 2007–08 *Income* £24,759 *Grants* £25,000

TRUSTEES J A Mills; C N Bardswell; H E Bromley Davenport.

HOW TO APPLY In writing to the correspondent.

WHO TO APPLY TO C N Bardswell, Trustee, c/o Messrs Belmont and Lowe, Solicitors, Priory House, 18–25 St John's Lane, London EC1M 4HD *Tel* 020 7608 4600 *Fax* 020 7608 4601

CC NO 282080   **ESTABLISHED** 1981

■ The Notgrove Trust

WHERE FUNDING CAN BE GIVEN Generally in the Gloucestershire area.

WHO CAN BENEFIT Local or special interests of the trustees.

WHAT IS FUNDED Any local charities can be considered.

WHAT IS NOT FUNDED No grants available to support individuals or medical research.

TYPE OF GRANT Except in special circumstances, single donations only will be considered.

RANGE OF GRANTS £1,000 to £10,000.

SAMPLE GRANTS Everyman Theatre – Cheltenham and Moreton Green Ltd (£10,000 each); Villager Community Bus Service (£6,500); Dean and Chapter Gloucester Cathedral and West of England School College (£5,000 each); Baden Powell Centre – Chipping Campden (£4,000); Help for Heroes (£3,000); Hunts Service Fund (£2,000); and Canterbury Association Music Trust and Oxford Radcliffe Hospital Charitable Funds (£1,000 each).

FINANCES *Year* 2007–08 *Income* £185,063 *Grants* £124,700 *Assets* £1,878,397

TRUSTEES David Acland; Elizabeth Acland; Harry Acland.

HOW TO APPLY Applications are considered from Gloucestershire charities or from an organisation having an established connection with the trustees. Applicants should include a copy of their latest accounts. Speculative appeals from outside of Gloucestershire are strongly discouraged and unlikely to get a positive response. Past donations to charities outside Gloucestershire should not be taken as an indication of likely future support. The trust

has stated telephone calls are unwelcome and due to a lack of clerical support, unsuccessful appeals will not be acknowledged.

WHO TO APPLY TO David Acland, Trustee, Elmbank Farmhouse, Cold Aston, Cheltenham, Gloucestershire GL54 3BJ *Tel* 01451 810 652

CC NO 278692   **ESTABLISHED** 1979

■ The Nottingham General Dispensary

WHERE FUNDING CAN BE GIVEN Nottingham and Nottinghamshire.

WHO CAN BENEFIT Individuals or other organisations.

WHAT IS FUNDED The alleviation of need or aid in recovery through the provision of items and services not readily available from ordinary channels. Charities working in the fields of: respite; professional bodies; councils for voluntary service; and health will be considered.

TYPE OF GRANT One-off preferred. Capital, project, recurring costs. Funding for up to three years will be considered.

RANGE OF GRANTS £25–£4,000; mostly under £500.

SAMPLE GRANTS Happy Days (£1,500); Vitalise (£1,100); Independent Age (£1,000); Framework Complementary Therapies (£945); Dyslexia Support, Grey Sheets and Indigo Kids (£800 each); Patch (£775); Aphasia (£700); Radford Heart Group (£600); Coping with Anxiety (£575); Sneiton and St Ann's Heart Group (£525); Strongbones Children's Charitable Trust (£400); Two Sides Self Help (£275); South Muskham Carers Group (£250); and Sheffield Hospitals NHS Trust (£130).

FINANCES *Year* 2008–09 *Income* £55,172 *Grants* £26,948 *Assets* £969,781

TRUSTEES R Batterbury, Chair; D Levell; Dr I McLachlan; Mrs P Johnston; Dr S Harris; A Hopwood; Dr Angela Truman.

HOW TO APPLY In writing to the correspondent, supported by medical evidence.

WHO TO APPLY TO C N Cullen, Secretary, Cumberland Court, 80 Mount Street, Nottingham NG1 6HH *Tel* 0115 901 5558

CC NO 228149   **ESTABLISHED** 1963

■ The Nottingham Gordon Memorial Trust for Boys and Girls

WHERE FUNDING CAN BE GIVEN Nottingham and its immediate surrounding area.

WHO CAN BENEFIT Children and young people up to the age of 25.

WHAT IS FUNDED Relief in need, education and educational trips.

TYPE OF GRANT One off preferred.

RANGE OF GRANTS Up to £2,500.

SAMPLE GRANTS Previously: The Nottinghamshire Probation Service (£2,500); the Nottingham Outward Bound Association (£1,500).

FINANCES *Year* 2007 *Income* £49,777 *Grants* £40,837 *Assets* £1,198,830

TRUSTEES C N Cullen, Chair; J Tordoff; D Lowe; P Hill; Revd P Watts; J Foxon.

HOW TO APPLY On a form available from the correspondent.

WHO TO APPLY TO Mrs Colleen Douglas, Clerk to the Trustees, Cumberland Court, 80 Mount Street, Nottingham NG1 6HH *Tel* 0115 901 5558

CC NO 212536   **ESTABLISHED** 1976

■ Nottinghamshire Community Foundation

WHERE FUNDING CAN BE GIVEN Nottinghamshire.

WHO CAN BENEFIT Individuals, community groups and charities.

WHAT IS FUNDED The foundation states: 'We are committed to improving the quality of life of the people of Nottingham and Nottinghamshire by raising and managing funds for distribution in response to local needs.'

'No matter where you live or work, there will be people living close by who suffer disadvantage – it may be through poverty, age, ill-health or disability. If, like us, you believe everyone deserves the chance to contribute and be valued as a member of the community, you can make a difference by helping us to support more local groups. We find, train and fund the smallest most inexperienced grass roots groups as well as working with small charities. Our aim is to find solutions that genuinely help those in need. For some people this can mean learning to read, for others, it is defeating the pervasive influence of drugs and gun crime; and for a few, it is about achieving excellence in a chosen field – sport, music or art.'

WHAT IS NOT FUNDED Please refer to the foundation's website for exclusions specific to each fund.

SAMPLE GRANTS African Initiative Support, Garden of Grace and Harmless (£10,000 each); Integritas Advocacy CIC (£8,000); CHAT (£7,000); Nigerian Community Group, Nottingham Disabled Friendship Club and Russell Youth Club (£5,000 each); West Bridgford Video and Slide Society (£3,000); Vale Liaison Group (£2,000); Bingham Sub Aqua Club (£1,000); and Cotgrave Colts Football Club (£750).

FINANCES *Year* 2007–08 *Income* £4,020,830 *Grants* £3,675,395 *Assets* £1,083,534

TRUSTEES Christopher Hughes; Chris Hughes; Roger Hursthouse; Frances Walker; Philip Marsh; Paul Alfred McDuell; Alan Sutton; Mrs T Winter; Charles Cannon; Alistair McDiarmid.

OTHER INFORMATION The following funds were available at the time of writing: Comic Relief; Fair Share Trust Ashfield; Grassroots Grants Programme; Dave Hartley lFund; Keepmoat Fund; Kynan Eldridge Fund; Nottingham City Primary Care Trust Healthy Hearts Small Grants Scheme; Nottinghamshire Robin Hood Fund; One Nottinghamshire Small Grants Scheme; RTC Fund; and Targeted Support Fund.

HOW TO APPLY Please refer to the foundation's website for full details of how to apply to the various programmes currently being administered.

WHO TO APPLY TO Ms Nina Dauban, Cedar House, Southwell Road West, Rainworth, Mansfield, Nottinghamshire NG21 0HJ *Tel* 01623 636 202 *Fax* 01623 620 204 *email* enquiries@ nottscommunityfoundation.org.uk *Website* www. nottscf.org.uk

CC NO 1069538 **ESTABLISHED** 1998

■ The Nottinghamshire Historic Churches Trust

WHERE FUNDING CAN BE GIVEN Nottinghamshire.

WHO CAN BENEFIT Churches and chapels.

WHAT IS FUNDED The trust gives grants for the preservation and repair of historic churches and chapels in Nottinghamshire and for the monuments, fittings and furniture and so on, of such churches.

WHAT IS NOT FUNDED Works of routine maintenance (such as repainting a door, non-specialist cleaning, etc.), new buildings, extensions, meeting rooms coffee areas, sinks, new furniture, routine decoration (unless needing to use some specialist materials), routine electrical work (new switches, lights, cables for new installations), repair of modern furniture, fixtures, fittings, overhead projector screens, sound systems, new bells and bellframes, any work that has already started or been completed before application made.

RANGE OF GRANTS Up to £13,000.

SAMPLE GRANTS St Mary's – Attenborough (£13,300); St Mary's – East Leake and St Nicholas' – Tuxford (£10,000 each); St Peter's – Farndon (£6,000); St Joseph's – Retford (£5,000); St Michael's – Sutton Bonington (£4,000); St George's – Nottingham, St Helena's – Thoroton and St Mary the Virgin – Lowdham (£2,000 each); St. John the Baptist – Stanford upon Soar (£1,600); Church of the Good Shepherd (£750); St Martha the Housewife – Broxtowe (£300); and All Saints' – Syerston (£200).

FINANCES *Year* 2008–09 *Income* £113,358 *Grants* £115,650 *Assets* £259,423

TRUSTEES R Craven-Smith-Milnes; Mrs J Mellors – Chair; Dr C Brooke; Dr Jenny Alexander; D Atkins; Prof. J V Beckett; G Beaumont; G Renton; Richard Brackenbury; Robert Brackenbury; K Goodman; P Hoare; A Marriott; S Leigh Rix; Revd Canon K Turner.

OTHER INFORMATION The trust administers the Landfill Tax Credit Scheme, which contributed £60,000 to the income, which was also represented in its grant total.

HOW TO APPLY Grant application forms along with guidance notes are available from the trust's website. Alternatively, these can be obtained by ringing or writing to: Mrs L Francis, Grants Administrator, 15 Tattershall Drive, Beeston, Nottingham NG9 2GP. (Tel: 07757 800919; Email: linda.francis15@ntlworld.com).

WHO TO APPLY TO Keith Goodman, 59 Briar Gate, Long Eaton, Nottingham NG10 4BQ *Tel* 0115 972 6590 *email* nhct@keithgoodman.com *Website* www.nottshistoricchurchtrust.org.uk

CC NO 518335 **ESTABLISHED** 1985

■ The Nottinghamshire Miners' Welfare Trust Fund

WHERE FUNDING CAN BE GIVEN Nottinghamshire.

WHO CAN BENEFIT Miners or ex-miners who are retired, redundant or unemployed.

WHAT IS FUNDED The trust supports miners or ex-miners in need living in Nottinghamshire, who are retired or redundant and still unemployed, and their dependants.

RANGE OF GRANTS £150–£9,000.

SAMPLE GRANTS CISWO – social worker funding (£8,800); CISWO – National Schemes of Benefit 2006 (£8,000); Edwinstowe Physiotherapy Clinic (£3,0000); North East Midlands Brass Band Association (£500); and Newstead Youth and Community Centre (£400).

FINANCES *Year* 2007 *Income* £94,694 *Grants* £49,467 *Assets* £2,394,590

TRUSTEES J C H Longden; M F Ball; N Greatrex; M L Stevens.

OTHER INFORMATION Grants to individuals totalled £23,000.

HOW TO APPLY In writing to the correspondent at any time.

WHO TO APPLY TO D A Brooks, Secretary, Coal Industry Social Welfare Organisation, Berry Hill Lane, Mansfield NG18 4JR *Tel* 01623 625 767 *Fax* 01623 626 789
cc no 1001272   ESTABLISHED 1990

....
■ Novi Most International

WHERE FUNDING CAN BE GIVEN Bosnia-Herzegovina.

WHO CAN BENEFIT Bosnians disadvantaged and displaced by war, especially children and young people.

WHAT IS FUNDED Christian youth-based ministry to meet physical, spiritual, emotional and social needs, with particular emphasis on long-term support of children and young people traumatised by war. Reconciliation and community development initiatives are also supported.

WHAT IS NOT FUNDED Grants seldom given to projects not connected with evangelical churches or where the trust's own staff or partners are not involved.

TYPE OF GRANT One-off and recurring.

FINANCES *Year* 2007–08 *Income* £209,304 *Grants* £37,902 *Assets* £121,304

TRUSTEES A Thomas; Revd D Stillman; S Evans; Christine Harris; A Silley; D Turner.

PUBLICATIONS *New Bridge and Bosnia Prayer Briefing.*

HOW TO APPLY Funds fully committed for the foreseeable future. Unsolicited applications are not encouraged or acknowledged.

WHO TO APPLY TO Kathleen J Flory, Bushell House, 118–120 Broad Street, Chesham, Buckinghamshire HP5 3ED *Tel* 01494 793 242 *Fax* 01494 793 771 *email* chesham@novimost. og *Website* www.novimost.org
cc no 1043501   ESTABLISHED 1995

....
■ The Nuffield Foundation

WHERE FUNDING CAN BE GIVEN UK and Commonwealth.

WHO CAN BENEFIT Charitable and voluntary organisations, and universities benefiting children, young adults and older people; research workers; students; legal professionals; those in care, fostered and adopted; parents and children; one-parent families; at risk groups; carers; disabled people; those disadvantaged by poverty; refugees; travellers; and people suffering from arthritis and rheumatism. Grants are not made to individuals except under the fellowship schemes.

WHAT IS FUNDED Research, experiment or practical development in the fields of: child protection; family justice; access to justice; educational provision and children's needs; curriculum innovation; older people and their families; capacity development; miscellaneous.

WHAT IS NOT FUNDED The trustees will not consider the following: general appeals buildings or capital costs; projects which are mainly of local interest; research that is mainly of theoretical interest; day to day running costs or accommodation needs; the provision of health or social services; grants to replace statutory funding; healthcare (outside mental health); the arts; religion; museums, exhibitions, performances; sports and recreation; conservation, heritage or environmental projects; animal rights or welfare; attendance at conferences; expeditions, travel, adventure/ holiday projects; business or job creation projects; academic journals; medical research

(other than in rheumatism and arthritis research). Grants are not made for the following purposes except when the activity is part of a project that is otherwise acceptable: work for degrees or other qualifications; production of films, videos or television programmes; purchase of equipment, including computers.

TYPE OF GRANT One-off grants for projects.

RANGE OF GRANTS £20,000–£250,000.

SAMPLE GRANTS *Access to Justice:* Faculty of Laws, University College London – (£201,000); Release (£15,000); and Fair Trials International (£12,538). *Child Protection and Family Law:* British Association for Adoption and Fostering (£148,000); and One plus One (£14,500). *Education:* Department of Psychology, University of York (£236,000); and Department of Education, University of Oxford (£30,000); and Centre for Studies in Science and Mathematics Education, University of Leeds (£15,000). *Open Door:* Centre for Family Law and Policy, University of Oxford (£299,000); and School of Medicine, Health and Policy Practice, University of East Anglia (£124,000). *Commonwealth:* WHO Collaborating Centre and the Section of Mental Health Policy, King's College, London (£227,000); and Mildmay International (£75,000). *Older People and their Families:* This programme is to be wound up and grant applications for this category will now be handled as a specific theme under the 'Open Door' programme.

FINANCES *Year* 2007–08 *Income* £8,218,000 *Grants* £7,277,645 *Assets* £191,810,000

TRUSTEES Baroness O'Neill, Chair; Sir Tony Atkinson; Prof. Genevra Richardson; Prof. Lord Krebs (from March 2008); Prof. Sir Michael Rutter; Prof. Sir David Watson; Dr Peter Doyle; Prof. David Rhind.

OTHER INFORMATION Grants to individuals – £391,000. Grants to organisations – £6,887,000.

HOW TO APPLY 'If you are thinking of making an application, you must first send a written outline proposal. A member of staff will then advise you whether the proposal comes within the trustees' terms of reference and whether there are any particular questions or issues you should consider. The outline should describe: the issue or problem you wish to address; the expected outcome(s); what will happen in the course of the project; (for research projects) an outline of the methods to be employed; an outline of the budget and the timetable. The outline must not exceed three sides of A4, but you are welcome to include additional supporting information about yourself and your organisation. If you are advised to proceed with a full application, the staff member dealing with your proposal may suggest a meeting or, if matters are straightforward, may advise you to proceed straight to a full application.' .... 'If your work straddles more than one area of interest, or if you are unsure within which area it might lie, you do not need to enquire about who to send it to or how you should label it. Simply send it to one or other of the appropriate staff and they will ensure that it is handled appropriately.' Extensive guidance on the preparation of full applications, too long to be summarised here, is available from the foundation and is published on its excellent website where you will also find application timetables for project grants.

WHO TO APPLY TO Clerk to the Trustees, 28 Bedford Square, London WC1B 3JS *Tel* 020 7631 0566 *Fax* 020 7232 4877 *email* info@nuffieldfoundation.org *Website* www.nuffieldfoundation.org
CC NO 206601   **ESTABLISHED** 1943

Think carefully about every application. Is it justified?

755

■ The Father O'Mahoney Memorial Trust

WHERE FUNDING CAN BE GIVEN Developing countries.

WHO CAN BENEFIT Organisations benefiting 'impotent people and those disadvantaged by poverty'.

WHAT IS FUNDED The relief of 'impotent and poor' people in all parts of the world except the UK.

WHAT IS NOT FUNDED UK organisations; individual requests.

RANGE OF GRANTS Depends on finances; maximum usually £5,000.

SAMPLE GRANTS Grants were made mainly to missionaries or organisations in South America, Africa and Asia.

FINANCES *Year* 2007–08 *Income* £51,891 *Grants* £105,115 *Assets* £166,600

TRUSTEES C Carney-Smith; Ms C A Hearn; D M Maclean; M A Moran; Fr G Murray; A H Sanford; Mrs M Jennings; Mrs B Carney; H Smith.

HOW TO APPLY In writing to the correspondent. The trustees meet every two months to consider applications.

WHO TO APPLY TO Revd Gerry Murray, Our Lady of the Wayside Church, 566 Stratford Road, Shirley, Solihull, West Midlands B90 4AY *Tel* 0121 744 1967 *email* trust@olwayside.fsnet.co.uk

CC NO 1039288   **ESTABLISHED** 1993

■ The Sir Peter O'Sullevan Charitable Trust

WHERE FUNDING CAN BE GIVEN Worldwide.

WHO CAN BENEFIT Charitable organisations.

WHAT IS FUNDED Animal welfare.

TYPE OF GRANT Recurrent.

SAMPLE GRANTS Blue Cross, Brooke Hospital for Animals, Compassion in World Farming, International League for the Protection of Horses, the Racing Welfare Charities and the Thoroughbred Rehabilitation Centre (£50,000 each).

FINANCES *Year* 2007–08 *Income* £372,231 *Grants* £300,000 *Assets* £106,863

TRUSTEES Christopher Spence; Lord Oaksey; Sir Peter O'Sullevan; Nigel Payne; Geoffrey Hughes; Bob McCreery; Michael Dillon.

HOW TO APPLY In writing to the correspondent.

WHO TO APPLY TO Nigel Payne, Trustee, The Old School, Bolventor, Launceston PL15 7TS *Tel* 01566 880 292 *email* nigel@earthsummit. demon.co.uk *Website* www.thevoiceofracing. com

CC NO 1078889   **ESTABLISHED** 2000

■ The Oak Trust

WHERE FUNDING CAN BE GIVEN UK.

WHO CAN BENEFIT Registered charities. Preference to charities that the trust has special interest in, knowledge of or association with and with a turnover of below £1 million.

WHAT IS FUNDED General charitable purposes.

WHAT IS NOT FUNDED No support to individuals.

TYPE OF GRANT One-off and recurrent.

RANGE OF GRANTS £250–£4,000.

SAMPLE GRANTS The Cirdan Sailing Trust (£3,000); Christian Aid and Prader-Willi Syndrome

Association UK (£2,000 each); Children's Overseas Relief Fund and Voice (£1,000 each); Cambridge Society for the Blind and Partially-sighted, Detention Advice Service, Practical Action – Darfor Appeal, The Swiften Charitable Trust and Westcott House (£500 each); Grace of God Church – Malawi and Maranatho Orphanage Ministries – Malawi (£250 each).

FINANCES *Year* 2007–08 *Income* £27,976 *Grants* £27,550 *Assets* £517,471

TRUSTEES Revd A C C Courtauld; J Courtauld; Dr Elizabeth Courtauld; Miss C M Courtauld.

HOW TO APPLY Written applications will no longer be accepted. Applications must be submitted via the online form on the trust's website. Details of the next submission date are included on the application form. Applicants will receive an acknowledgement of their application and notification of the outcome within ten days of the Review Meeting by email.

WHO TO APPLY TO Bruce Ballard, Clerk, Essex House, 42 Crouch Street, Colchester CO3 3HH *email* bruce.ballard@birkettlong.co.uk *Website* www.oaktrust.org.uk

CC NO 231456   **ESTABLISHED** 1963

■ The Oakdale Trust

WHERE FUNDING CAN BE GIVEN UK, especially Wales and overseas.

WHO CAN BENEFIT Organisations doing social and medical work benefiting at risk groups, carers, disabled people, those disadvantaged by poverty, ex-offenders and those at risk of offending, homeless people, refugees, and victims of crime, famine and war.

WHAT IS FUNDED The trust gives preference to Welsh charities engaged in social work, medical support groups and medical research. Some support is given to UK charities working overseas and to conservation projects at home and abroad. Some arts and community arts activities, infrastructure support and development, community facilities and services, mediation, peace and disarmament will also be considered. The trust also supports Quaker activities.

WHAT IS NOT FUNDED No grants to individuals, holiday schemes, sport activities or expeditions.

TYPE OF GRANT Single outright grants. Buildings, capital, core costs, feasibility studies, one-off, project, research, recurring costs, salaries and start-up costs will be considered. Funding may be given for up to one year.

RANGE OF GRANTS Typical grant around £750.

SAMPLE GRANTS The Brandon Centre (£15,000) and Concern Universal (£10,000); Medical Foundation for Care of Victims of Torture (£5,000); Radnorshire Wildlife Trust (£3,000); Cambridge Female Education Trust (£2,000); Howard League for Penal Reform (£1,500); The Penllergare Trust, Shakespeare Link, Simon Community and Y Care International (£1,000 each); Prisoners Abroad and Sherman Cymru (£500 each); and Adel Quaker Appeal and SOS Africa (£250 each).

FINANCES *Year* 2007–08 *Income* £225,755 *Grants* £166,300 *Assets* £5,617,119

TRUSTEES Brandon Cadbury; Mrs Flavia Cadbury; Rupert Cadbury; Bruce Cadbury; Mrs Olivia Tatton-Brown; Dr Rebecca Cadbury.

HOW TO APPLY An official application form is available on request. However applicants are free to submit requests in any format so long as applications are clear and concise, covering aims, achievements, plans and needs supported by a budget. Applicants applying for grants in excess of £750 are asked to submit a copy of a recent set of audited annual accounts (which can be returned on request). The trustees meet twice a year in April and October to consider applications and to award grants. No grants are awarded between meetings. The deadline for the April meeting is 1 March and for the October meeting 1 September. The trust is administered by the trustees at no cost, and owing to a lack of secretarial help and in view of the numerous requests received, no applications are acknowledged even when accompanied by a stamped addressed envelope.

WHO TO APPLY TO Rupert Cadbury, Tansor House, Tansor, Oundle, Peterborough PE8 5HS *email* oakdale@tanh.demon.co.uk

CC NO 218827   **ESTABLISHED** 1950

■ The Oakley Charitable Trust

WHERE FUNDING CAN BE GIVEN UK, but with a strong preference for the Midlands and Channel Isles.
WHO CAN BENEFIT Registered charities.
WHAT IS FUNDED Predominantly welfare; health; education; arts; and conservation.
WHAT IS NOT FUNDED No grants to individuals can be considered. Grants are only made to registered charities.
TYPE OF GRANT One-off, core costs, project, research, recurring costs and buildings. Funding is available for one year or less.
RANGE OF GRANTS £50–£3,000.
SAMPLE GRANTS Historic Churches Trust and Prostate Cancer Charity (£3,000 each); Blue Cross Animal Welfare and Jersey Hospice (£2,000 each); Birmingham Centre for Arts Therapies and Terrence Higgins Trust (£1,000 each); RNLI – St Helier Lifeboat Appeal and Juvenile Diabetes Research Fund (£500 each); Warley Woods Community Trust (£200); and British Heart Foundation (£50).
FINANCES *Year* 2007–08 *Income* £137,279 *Grants* £62,634 *Assets* £2,051,186
TRUSTEES Mrs C M Airey; G M W Oakley; S M Sharp.
HOW TO APPLY In writing to the correspondent. Trustees usually meet in March, July and November.
WHO TO APPLY TO G M W Oakley, Trustee, 10 St Mary's Road, Harborne, Birmingham B17 0HA *Tel* 0121 427 7150
CC NO 233041   **ESTABLISHED** 1963

■ The Oakmoor Charitable Trust

WHERE FUNDING CAN BE GIVEN UK.
WHO CAN BENEFIT Registered charities.
WHAT IS FUNDED General charitable purposes.
WHAT IS NOT FUNDED No grants to individuals.
RANGE OF GRANTS Up to £10,000.
SAMPLE GRANTS The London Library and Mary Rose Trust (£10,000 each); Save Britain's Heritage (£7,500); CAFOD (£5,000); Institute of Economic Affairs (£3,000); Downe House Trust (£2,000); Armed Forces Memorial, Elias Ashmole Group and Hampshire Country Learning (£1,000 each); Bembridge Harbour Trust and Convent of St Lucy – Chichester (£500 each); Cancer Research (£250); and Friends of the Royal Opera House Foundation (£100).
FINANCES *Year* 2007–08 *Income* £32,475 *Grants* £48,925 *Assets* £1,333,581
TRUSTEES Rathbone Trust Company Ltd; P M H Andreae; Mrs R J Andreae.

HOW TO APPLY The trust states that it does not respond to unsolicited applications.
WHO TO APPLY TO The Administrator, Rathbone Trust Company Limited, Rathbone Trust Company Limited, 159 New Bond Street, London W1S 2UD *Tel* 020 7399 0811
CC NO 258516   **ESTABLISHED** 1969

■ The Odin Charitable Trust

WHERE FUNDING CAN BE GIVEN UK.
WHO CAN BENEFIT Registered charities.
WHAT IS FUNDED General charitable purposes with preference for: the arts; care for people who are disabled and disadvantaged people; hospices, homeless people, prisoners' families, refugees, gypsies and 'tribal groups' research into false memories and dyslexia.
WHAT IS NOT FUNDED Applications from individuals are not considered.
RANGE OF GRANTS £1,000–£3,000.
SAMPLE GRANTS Action for Prisoners' Families and Hartlepool and District Hospice (£3,000 each for three years); Interact Reading Scheme (£2,500 a year for three years); Asylum Link Merseyside (£2,000 a year for three years); Blaen Wern Farm Trust and Survival (£3,000 each); Clothing Solutions for Disabled People and Space Trust (£2,500 each); Ellenor Foundation, Jessie's Fund, Prison Fellowship and Willow Wood Hospice (£2,000 each); Lewisham Churches for Asylum Seekers and 9 Lives Furniture Scheme (£1,500 each); and Cherished Memories and Knowsley Carers Centre (£1,000 each).
FINANCES *Year* 2007–08 *Income* £479,667 *Grants* £157,000 *Assets* £5,207,805
TRUSTEES Mrs S G P Scotford; Mrs A H Palmer; Mrs D L Kelly; Mrs P C Cherry.
HOW TO APPLY In writing to the correspondent.
WHO TO APPLY TO Mrs S G P Scotford, Trustee, PO Box 1898, Bradford-on-Avon, Wiltshire BA15 1YS
CC NO 1027521   **ESTABLISHED** 1993

■ Ogilvie Charities Deed No.2 (including the Charity of Mary Catherine Ford Smith)

WHERE FUNDING CAN BE GIVEN England and Wales, mainly, Suffolk, Essex and all London boroughs.
WHO CAN BENEFIT Organisations and individuals.
WHAT IS FUNDED Specific philanthropic work. Assistance to present or former governesses or female teachers in straitened circumstances. Country holidays for London children. Support of the charity's own homes and almshouses and residents living in them. Aid to other charitable institutions in the London boroughs, Essex and Suffolk or, if situated beyond, serving the needs of people living in those areas. Support may also be given to infrastructure and technical support and religious ancillary buildings.
WHAT IS NOT FUNDED No payment of debts.
TYPE OF GRANT One-off usually. Grants for individuals must be made through medical and other social workers. Funding may be given for up to one year.
SAMPLE GRANTS £250,000 to Ogilvie Charities Deed No.1. Grants totalling £8,800 were made to other charitable organisations and for charitable purposes as follows: 'Various other grants (£7,640); Children's Country Holidays (£1,000); Governesses (£200); and Bedford Institute Association (£100).

FINANCES *Year* 2007 *Income* £87,766
Grants £258,326 *Assets* £1,743,364
TRUSTEES Felicity Lowe, Chair; Jean Goyder; Jolyon Hall; Margaret Smith; Dick Aynsley-Smith; Roger Brayshaw; Patrick Grieve; D Allan Howell; Simon Gibbs.
OTHER INFORMATION Ogilvie Charities Deed No. 2 is primarily to benefit the Ogilvie Charities Deed No. 1. Any remaining income is applied to making grants to any charity for the benefit of people in Essex, Suffolk or London which are for specific fund raising projects. Charity of Mary Catherine Ford – Grants are given from this fund to other charities to help them with a specific project. £1,500 was paid from the trust in grants to individuals.
HOW TO APPLY In writing to the correspondent. Preliminary telephone enquiries are acceptable. Applicant organisations must send details of their project and copies of annual accounts. Grants are awarded for specific fund raising projects, not running costs and are allocated in October or November. Grants for individuals must be made through medical and other social workers.
WHO TO APPLY TO Mrs Gillian Galvan, General Manager, The Gate House, 9 Burkitt Road, Woodbridge, Suffolk IP12 4JJ *Tel* 01394 388746 *Fax* 01394 388746 *email* ogilviecharities@btconnect.com *Website* www.theogilvietrust.org.uk
CC NO 211778 **ESTABLISHED** 1890

....

■ The Ogle Christian Trust

WHERE FUNDING CAN BE GIVEN Worldwide.
WHO CAN BENEFIT Registered charities benefiting Bible students, pastors, Christians, evangelists and victims of famine.
WHAT IS FUNDED The trust's main concern is the promotion of Biblical Christianity. Currently it includes: new initiatives in evangelism; support for the publishing and distribution of scriptures and Christian literature; training of Bible students and pastors; and Christian social enterprise and famine relief.
WHAT IS NOT FUNDED Applications from individuals are discouraged; those granted require accreditation by a sponsoring organisation. Grants are rarely made for building projects. Funding will not be offered in response to general appeals from large national organisations.
TYPE OF GRANT Normally one-off or short-term commitments only. Salaries will not be funded.
RANGE OF GRANTS Up to £22,000.
SAMPLE GRANTS Operation Mobilisation (£18,000); Tear Fund (£6,000); Translation Trust (£4,000); Chessington Evangelical Church, Elm Foundation School – Nigeria, Global Care, The Lighthouse Group and The Source – China (£3,000 each); France Mission Trust, Middle East Concern, PECAN, Stepping Stones Trust and The Thana Trust (£2,000 each); and CARE, caring for Life, Make Jesus Known and Rhema Theatre Company (£1,000).
FINANCES *Year* 2008 *Income* £131,842
Grants £124,800 *Assets* £2,179,098
TRUSTEES D J Harris, Chair; R J Goodenough; S Proctor; Mrs F J Putley; Mrs L M Quanrud.
HOW TO APPLY In writing to the correspondent, accompanied by documentary support and an sae. Trustees meet in May and November, but applications can be made at any time.

WHO TO APPLY TO Mrs F J Putley, Trustee, 43 Woolstone Road, Forest Hill, London SE23 2TR *Tel* 020 8699 1036
CC NO 1061458 **ESTABLISHED** 1938

....

■ Oglesby Charitable Trust

WHERE FUNDING CAN BE GIVEN The North West of England.
WHO CAN BENEFIT Charitable organisations.
WHAT IS FUNDED Educational grants and building projects; environmental improvement projects; improving the life and welfare of the underprivileged, where possible, the encouragement of self-help; and medical aid and research.
WHAT IS NOT FUNDED The trust will not support: non registered charities; those whose activities are for the purpose of collecting funds for redistribution to other charities; animal charities; charities whose principal operation area is outside the UK; church and all building fabric appeals; conferences; continuing running costs of an organisation; costs of employing fundraisers; expeditions; general sports, unless strongly associated with a disadvantaged group; holidays; individuals; loans or business finance; religion; routine staff training; sectarian religions; sponsorship and marketing appeals.
RANGE OF GRANTS Usually between £5,000–£20,000. Small grants of less than £1,000 are available.
SAMPLE GRANTS Previous beneficiaries include: Action for Kids, Alcohol Drug Abstinence Service, Centre for Alternative Technology, Cheadle Hulme School, Cheetham's School, Fairbridge – Family Contact Line, Halle Youth Orchestra, Manchester City Art Gallery, Manchester University Arts and Drama, Motor Neurone Disease, National Asthma Campaign, National Library for the Blind, Stroke Research and Whitworth Art Gallery.
FINANCES *Year* 2007–08 *Income* £818,767
Grants £693,367 *Assets* £596,130
TRUSTEES Jean Oglesby; Michael Oglesby; Robert Kitson; Kate Vokes; Jane Oglesby; Chris Oglesby; Peter Renshaw.
OTHER INFORMATION The trust also has a small grants programme, the Seed Fund, which is administered by the Community Foundation for Greater Manchester, Beswick House, Beswick Row, Manchester M4 4LA; Tel: 0161 214 0940; website: www.communityfoundation.co.uk
HOW TO APPLY 'To enable the trustees to assess all applications from a similar basis, they ask that every applicant complete the Stage 1 Application Form. The trustees undertake to respond to this in six weeks. If this response is positive, then applicants will be required to complete a more detailed form under Stage 2. By Stage 2, wherever possible, the trustees will require a proper Financial Plan prepared by the applicant. This should contain clear and measurable goals, which will be reviewed at regular intervals by the parties. In cases where the applicant does not possess either the skills or the resources to prepare such a Plan, the trust may be prepared to assist.
Finally, the trustees will want to interview the applicant(s) at their place of operation or project site, both prior to the granting of funds and during the lifetime of the project, to monitor its progress. In addition the trustees will expect regular communication from the applicant, either verbal or by letter, to keep them informed of how the project is moving forward.'

WHO TO APPLY TO PO Box 336, Altrincham, Cheshire WA14 3XD *email* oglesbycharitabletrust@bruntwood.co.uk *Website* www.oglesbycharitabletrust.co.uk
CC NO 1026669   ESTABLISHED 1992

....

■ The Oikonomia Trust

WHERE FUNDING CAN BE GIVEN UK and overseas.

WHO CAN BENEFIT Organisations benefiting evangelists.

WHAT IS FUNDED Evangelical work, famine and other relief through Christian agencies, particularly when accompanied with the offer of the Gospel. The trust is not looking for new outlets as those it has knowledge of are sufficient to absorb its available funds.

WHAT IS NOT FUNDED No grants made in response to general appeals from large national organisations.

RANGE OF GRANTS £500–£5,000.

SAMPLE GRANTS Barnabus Trust (£5,500); Slavic Gospel Association (£5,000); Bethel Church (£4,000); Asia Link, Association of Evangelists and Caring for Life (£3,000 each); Japan Mission (£2,500); Starbeck Mission (£2,000); People International (£1,000); and Carey Outreach Ministries (£500).

FINANCES *Year* 2007–08 *Income* £31,664 *Grants* £47,500 *Assets* £395,590

TRUSTEES D H Metcalfe; R H Metcalfe; S D Metcalfe; C Mountain; Revd R O Owens.

HOW TO APPLY In writing to the correspondent, although the trust has stated that most grants are made to the same organisations each year and as such new applications are unlikely to be successful. If an applicant desires an answer, an sae should be enclosed. Applications should arrive in January.

WHO TO APPLY TO Colin Mountain, Trustee, 98 White Lee Road, Batley, West Yorkshire WF17 8AF *Tel* 01924 502 616 *email* c.mountain@ntlworld.com

CC NO 273481   ESTABLISHED 1977

....

■ The Oizer Charitable Trust

WHERE FUNDING CAN BE GIVEN UK with a preference for Greater Manchester.

WHO CAN BENEFIT Registered charities.

WHAT IS FUNDED Education and welfare.

SAMPLE GRANTS Jewish High School for Girls (£15,000); Chasdei Yoel (£3,360); Bnos Yisroel Schools (£2,500).

FINANCES *Year* 2007–08 *Income* £5,280,626 *Grants* £633,815 *Assets* £2,943,262

TRUSTEES J Halpern; Mrs C Halpern.

HOW TO APPLY In writing to the correspondent.

WHO TO APPLY TO Joshua Halpern, Trustee, 35 Waterpark Road, Salford M7 0FT *Tel* 0161 798 6000

CC NO 1014399   ESTABLISHED 1992

....

■ The Old Broad Street Charity Trust

WHERE FUNDING CAN BE GIVEN UK and overseas.

WHO CAN BENEFIT Registered charities benefiting children, young adults, students, people working in a bank or financial institution, actors and entertainment professionals, musicians, textile workers and designers, and writers and poets.

WHAT IS FUNDED General charitable purposes with an emphasis on arts and education. Funding

scholarships for people serving in a bank or financial institution in the UK to spend time in any seat of learning (principally INSEAD) to attain the highest level of executive management.

WHAT IS NOT FUNDED The trustees only support organisations of which they personally have some knowledge.

TYPE OF GRANT One-off and project grants for one year or less.

SAMPLE GRANTS Foundation Henri Cartier-Bresson (£49,000), Grant Life – Moscow (£15,000), Societe Francaise le Lutte contre la Cecite et contre le Tranchome (£10,700), Bezirksfursorge – Saanen (£8,600), Camphill Village Trust (£5,0000, International Menuhin Music Academy (£4,300), Royal Academy of Arts (£2,500), The National Gallery Trust (£2,000), Tate Gallery Foundation (£1,000); and Artangel (£400).

FINANCES *Year* 2007–08 *Income* £79,451 *Grants* £133,436 *Assets* £1,916,638

TRUSTEES Mrs Evelyn J Franck; Mrs Martine Cartier-Bresson; Adrian T J Stanford; Peter A Hetherington; Christopher J Sheridan; Clare Gough.

OTHER INFORMATION This charity includes the Louis Franck Scholarship Fund, which gave six grants totalling £35,000 in 2007–08

HOW TO APPLY In writing to the correspondent. Unsolicited applications are not considered.

WHO TO APPLY TO Simon Jennings, Secretary to the Trustees, Rawlinson and Hunter, Eighth Floor, 6 New Street Square, London EC4A 3AQ *Tel* 020 7482 2000

CC NO 231382   ESTABLISHED 1964

....

■ The Old Enfield Charitable Trust

WHERE FUNDING CAN BE GIVEN The ancient parish of Enfield (old borough of Enfield).

WHO CAN BENEFIT Charities and individuals in need.

WHAT IS FUNDED Community projects and relief-in-need and educational grants to individuals.

SAMPLE GRANTS Nightingale Community Hospice Trust (£6,200); DAZU (£5,400); Durants School (£4,000); Vitalise (£3,200); Age Concern (£2,100); 11th Enfield Boys Brigade, Eastern Enfield Good Neighbours and Mind in Enfield (£2,000 each); and Enfield Association for the Blind and Enfield Visually Impaired Bowls Club (£1,000 each).

FINANCES *Year* 2007–08 *Income* £584,582 *Grants* £373,195 *Assets* £6,090,082

TRUSTEES Gordon Smith; Colin Griffiths; Audrey Thacker; Clive Parker; Horace Brown; Jim Eustance; Michael Braithwaite; Nicholas Taylor; Dr Patrick O'Mahony; Phyllis Oborn; Richard Cross; Susan Attwood; Chris Bond; Sam Bell; Bob Sander.

OTHER INFORMATION The 2007–08 grant total includes £164,836 donated to individuals in relief-in-need and educational grants.

HOW TO APPLY In writing to the correspondent. Application forms and guidelines are available. Initial telephone calls are welcome. There is no deadline for applications.

WHO TO APPLY TO The Trust Administrator, The Old Vestry Office, 22 The Town, Enfield, Middlesex EN2 6LT *Tel* 020 8367 8941 *email* enquiries@toect.org.uk *Website* www.toect.org.uk

CC NO 207840   ESTABLISHED 1962

■ Old Possum's Practical Trust

WHERE FUNDING CAN BE GIVEN UK.

WHO CAN BENEFIT Registered charities and individuals of all ages.

WHAT IS FUNDED The increase of knowledge and appreciation of any matters of historic, artistic, architectural, aesthetic, literary, musical, theatrical or scientific interest; human and animal welfare.

WHAT IS NOT FUNDED The trust does not support the following: activities or projects already completed, capital building projects, personal training and education e.g. tuition or living costs for college or university, projects outside the UK, medical care or resources, feasibility studies, national charities having substantial amounts of potential funding likely from other sources.

RANGE OF GRANTS £250–£25,000.

SAMPLE GRANTS High Tide Festival (£25,000); Dogs for the Disabled, First Story and Shakespeare School Festival (£20,000 each); Poetry Book Society – T S Eliot Poetry Prize costs (£17,500); Arete and Victoria & Albert Museum (£15,000 each); Poetry Book Society – Children's Competition (£12,000); MK City Orchestra, St Bride Foundation, The Book Trade Benevolent Society and Wordsworth Trust (£10,000 each); Little Angel Theatre and London Film School (£7,500 each); Farms for City Children, The Mousetrap Foundation and Queens University Belfast Festival (£5,000 each); Snowflake School (£4,000); Finchley Children's Music Group, Octopus and Strongbones Children's Charitable Trust (£3,000 each); Classworks Theatre and Felixstowe Youth Group (£2,000 each); Hospice in the Weald (£1,500); Listening Books, Manzini Youth Centre and Welsh Youth Classical Music Foundation (£1,000 each); Leeds Metropolitan University – The Big Draw (£500); and St Mary's Woburn Flower Festival (£250).

FINANCES *Year* 2007–08 *Income* £513,819 *Grants* £287,389 *Assets* £7,944,964

TRUSTEES Mrs Esme Eliot; Mrs Judith Hooper; Mrs D Simpson; Clare Reihill.

HOW TO APPLY Online submission is the preferred method of application. Faxed or emailed applications will be rejected but you may post your application if you have a good reason why you cannot submit your request online at: www.old-possums-practical-trust.org.uk. To download the printable version you require which you can complete and send by post, click either 'Individual' or 'Charity' on the 'Apply for Funding' page. In so doing you will be required to explain why you cannot use the on-line application process.

WHO TO APPLY TO The Trustees, PO Box 5701, Milton Keynes MK9 2WZ *email* generalenquiry@old-possums-practical-trust.org.uk *Website* www.old-possums-practical-trust.org.uk

CC NO 328558   **ESTABLISHED** 1990

■ The John Oldacre Foundation

WHERE FUNDING CAN BE GIVEN UK.

WHO CAN BENEFIT Universities, agricultural colleges and innovative projects benefiting students and research workers.

WHAT IS FUNDED Research and education in agricultural sciences.

WHAT IS NOT FUNDED No grants towards tuition fees.

TYPE OF GRANT One-off, recurrent, feasibility, project, research and funding of up to three years will be considered.

RANGE OF GRANTS Up to £30,000.

SAMPLE GRANTS Royal Agricultural College (£40,000 in two grants), University of Bristol (£30,000), Harper Adams University College (£16,500), Nuffield Fanning Trust (£15,000), TAG Arable Group (£14,000); and NIAB (£7,500).

FINANCES *Year* 2007–08 *Income* £122,373 *Grants* £125,500 *Assets* £7,364,735

TRUSTEES H B Shouler; S J Charnock; D G Stevens.

OTHER INFORMATION A grant to an individual was made for £2,500.

HOW TO APPLY In writing to the correspondent.

WHO TO APPLY TO Henry Shouler, Trustee, Hazleton House, Hazleton, Cheltenham, Gloucestershire GL54 4EB *Tel* 01451 860 752

CC NO 284960   **ESTABLISHED** 1981

■ The Oldham Foundation

WHERE FUNDING CAN BE GIVEN The north west and south west of England.

WHO CAN BENEFIT Organisations benefiting children, young adults, ex-service and service people, Church of England and former employees of Oldham Batteries (employed before 1971). Funding is considered for people disadvantaged by poverty, victims of man-made or natural disasters, and people with cancer, HIV and AIDS and mental illness.

WHAT IS FUNDED Donations to former employees of Oldham Batteries (employed before 1971) and charitable activities where trustees give personal service or where they know people who do so. Charities working in the fields of arts, culture and recreation; conservation and environment; and churches will be considered. Support may also be given to hospices, nursing services, cancer research, libraries and museums, day centres, holidays and outings.

WHAT IS NOT FUNDED No grants for UK appeals or individuals.

TYPE OF GRANT Annual grant to former employees. Grants usually one-off. Does not provide core funding. General charitable grants with bias towards active participation by trustees.

RANGE OF GRANTS £250–£20,000; typical grant £250–£1,000.

SAMPLE GRANTS Cheltenham Arts Festival (£20,000); Electric Palace (£3,000); East Cheshire Hospice and Pettypool Trust (£2,500 each); Brookes – Relief for Animals Abroad and Teachers House (£2,000 each); Ghurkha Welfare Trust and St Peter's Church – Winchcombe (£1,000 each); and Dorothy House Hospice and Vale Wildlife Hospital (£500 each).

FINANCES *Year* 2007–08 *Income* £72,169 *Grants* £74,995 *Assets* £1,207,357

TRUSTEES John Wetherherd Sharpe.

HOW TO APPLY In writing to the correspondent. Applications should include clear details of projects, budgets and/or accounts where appropriate. Telephone calls are not welcomed. The trustees meet annually but applications can be considered between meetings. Inappropriate appeals are not acknowledged.

WHO TO APPLY TO John Wetherherd Sharpe, c/o Osborne Clarke Solicitors, 2 Temple Back East, Temple Quay, Bristol BS1 6EG *Tel* 0117 917 3022 *Fax* 0117 917 3033

CC NO 269263   **ESTABLISHED** 1974

■ The Olga Charitable Trust

WHERE FUNDING CAN BE GIVEN UK and overseas.

WHO CAN BENEFIT National organisations benefiting children, young adults, at risk groups, people disadvantaged by poverty, socially isolated people, and carers.

WHAT IS FUNDED Health and welfare, youth organisations, children's welfare, carers' organisations. All must be known to the trustees.

RANGE OF GRANTS £500–£12,000.

SAMPLE GRANTS Columba 1400 (£12,000); Holy Trinity Church (£8,250); Kingston Hospital and St Andrew's Church – Ham (£5,000 each); Maggie's (£2,000); Arundel Castle Cricket Club, Foundation Recal and Piggy Bank Kids (£1,000 each); and Castle of Mey Trust and Walsingham Appeal (£500 each).

FINANCES *Year* 2007–08 *Income* £185,595 *Grants* £51,196 *Assets* £1,042,891

TRUSTEES HRH Princess Alexandra; James Robert Bruce Ogilvy.

HOW TO APPLY In writing to the correspondent, although the trust states that its funds are fully committed and applications made cannot be acknowledged.

WHO TO APPLY TO Adam Broke, Accountant, Mercer & Hole, London International Press Centre, 76 Shoe Lane, London EC4A 3JB *Tel* 020 7353 1597

CC NO 277925　　　**ESTABLISHED** 1979

■ Onaway Trust

WHERE FUNDING CAN BE GIVEN UK, USA and worldwide.

WHO CAN BENEFIT Registered charities benefiting indigenous peoples, in the main, Native Americans, and animal welfare.

WHAT IS FUNDED Trustees like to provide seed funds for self-generating, self-sufficiency projects based upon indigenous traditional beliefs and practices. The trustees concentrate mainly on Native Americans. The Onaway Trust's wide remit is to relieve poverty and suffering. This is expressed in many areas: the environment, child and animal welfare, world refugees and human rights.

WHAT IS NOT FUNDED No grants for administration costs, travel expenses or projects considered unethical or detrimental to the struggle of indigenous people.

TYPE OF GRANT Small, start-up costs.

RANGE OF GRANTS £300–£9,000.

SAMPLE GRANTS Plenty USA (£20,000 towards six projects); Institute for Development Exchange – India and Jeel Al Amal – Middle East (£9,000 each); Fundacion Redes De Santas (£8,000); Rainforest Foundation UK (£5,000); Lotus Children's Centre Charitable Trust (£4,500); Opera North (£4,000); The Gorilla Organisation and WaterAid (£3,000 each); Magic of Life Butterfly House – UK and Vetaid Africa (£2,000 each); and Greenpeace, Sea Shepherd and Yellow House – China (£1,000 each); and Deafway – Nepal and The Simon Community (£500 each).

FINANCES *Year* 2008 *Income* £176,604 *Grants* £95,426 *Assets* £3,801,631

TRUSTEES J Morris; A Breslin; C Howles; Ms Annie Smith; Ms V A Worwood; Ms Elaine Bradley; D Watters.

HOW TO APPLY In writing to the correspondent, enclosing an sae.

WHO TO APPLY TO David Watters, Trust Administrator, 275 Main Street, Shadwell, Leeds LS17 8LH *Tel* 0113 265 9611 *email* david@onaway.org *Website* www.onaway.org

CC NO 268448　　　**ESTABLISHED** 1974

■ Open Gate

WHERE FUNDING CAN BE GIVEN Derbyshire and surrounding areas; also developing countries.

WHO CAN BENEFIT Charitable organisations.

WHAT IS FUNDED Small-scale environmental, technological and educational projects in Derbyshire and the surrounding conurbations as well as in developing countries.

WHAT IS NOT FUNDED No grants to individuals.

TYPE OF GRANT Project grants for up to three years.

RANGE OF GRANTS £500–£5,000.

SAMPLE GRANTS Fauna and Flora International – Flower Valley Education Centre (£5,200); Christian Aid, Harvest Help and Tools for Self Reliance (£5,000 each); Tree Aid and VETAID (£4,000 each); Children of the Andes and Farm Africa (£3,000 each); Oasis (£2,000); Appropriate Technology Asia (£1,500); The Nepalese Children's Trust (£1,000); and Pump Aid (£500).

FINANCES *Year* 2007–08 *Income* £69,725 *Grants* £190,019 *Assets* £1,838,114

TRUSTEES Tom Wiltshire, chair; Mary Wiltshire; John Wiltshire; Jane Methuen; Ned Wiltshire; Alice Wiltshire; Mrs Lesley Williamson.

HOW TO APPLY In writing to the correspondent. Quarterly meetings are held in the middle of January, April, July and October.

WHO TO APPLY TO Mary Wiltshire, Trustee, Brownhouse Cottage, Ashleyhay, Wirksworth, Matlock, Derbyshire DE4 4AH *Tel* 01629 822 018 *Website* www.opengatetrust.org.uk

CC NO 1081701　　　**ESTABLISHED** 2000

■ The Ormsby Charitable Trust

WHERE FUNDING CAN BE GIVEN UK, London and the South East.

WHO CAN BENEFIT Registered charities.

WHAT IS FUNDED Mainly organisations concerned with people who are sick, older people and young people.

WHAT IS NOT FUNDED No grants to individuals, animals or religious causes.

SAMPLE GRANTS The Royal Marsden Hospital Charity (£6,000); Honey Pot House and In Kind Direct (£4,000 each); Breast Cancer Haven, Seeability – Royal Society for the Blind and Wessex Children's Hospice Trust (£3,200 each); Newbury Community Resource Centre, the Stroke Association and the Woodland Trust (£2,000 each); RSPB (£1,000); and the Living Paintings Trust and Thrive (£500 each).

FINANCES *Year* 2007–08 *Income* £57,130 *Grants* £61,500 *Assets* £1,591,257

TRUSTEES Rosemary Ormsby David; Angela Ormsby Chiswell; Katrina Ormsby McCrossan.

HOW TO APPLY In writing to the correspondent.

WHO TO APPLY TO Mrs K McCrossan, Trustee, Wasing Old Rectory, Shalford Hill, Aldermaston, Reading RG7 4NB *Tel* 0118 981 9663

CC NO 1000599　　　**ESTABLISHED** 1990

■ Orrin Charitable Trust

WHERE FUNDING CAN BE GIVEN UK with a strong preference for Scotland.

WHO CAN BENEFIT Registered charities.

WHAT IS FUNDED General charitable purposes including conservation, disability and galleries.

WHAT IS NOT FUNDED Grants are not given to individuals.

RANGE OF GRANTS Up to £10,000.

SAMPLE GRANTS Help for Heroes (£10,000); National Army Museum (£5,000); Art Academy, Atlantic Salmon Conservation Trust and Wheeley Boat Trust (£3,000 each); National Gallery of Scotland (£2,000); and St Mary & All Souls (£500).

FINANCES *Year* 2007–08 *Income* £45,381 *Grants* £26,500 *Assets* £649,726

TRUSTEES Mrs E Y MacDonald-Buchanan; H J MacDonald-Buchanan; A J MacDonald-Buchanan.

HOW TO APPLY The trust will not accept any unsolicited appeals.

WHO TO APPLY TO Stephen Tuck, c/o Hedley Foundation, Victoria House, 1–3 Collrge Hill, London EC4R 2RA *Tel* 020 7489 8076

CC NO 274599 **ESTABLISHED** 1977

■ The Ouseley Trust

WHERE FUNDING CAN BE GIVEN England, Wales and Ireland.

WHO CAN BENEFIT Cathedrals, choirs, parish churches, and choir schools. Children who are members of choirs of recognised choral foundations. Funding is only given to individuals through institutions.

WHAT IS FUNDED Projects that promote and maintain to a high standard the choral services of the Church of England, the Church in Wales or the Church of Ireland. These may include contributions to endowment funds, courses, fees, repairs of organs, and the purchase of music.

WHAT IS NOT FUNDED Grants will not be awarded to help with the cost of fees for ex-choristers, for chant books, hymnals or psalters. Grants will not be made for the purchase of new instruments or for the installation of an instrument from another place of worship where this involves extensive reconstruction. Under normal circumstances, grants will not be awarded for buildings, cassettes, commissions, compact discs, furniture, pianos, robes, tours or visits. No grants are made towards new organs or the installation of one which involves extensive reconstruction.

RANGE OF GRANTS Up to £50,000.

SAMPLE GRANTS Previously: Hereford Cathedral (£25,000); Carlisle Cathedral (£15,000); two separate grants to Abbey School – Tewkesbury (£18,000); two grants to York Minster (£6,000); St Thomas the Apostle – Wigston (£5,000); St James's School – Grimsby and Well Cathedral School (£4,000 each); Bradford Cathedral Salisbury Cathedral School and Oundle International Organ Festival (£3,000 each); and Christ Church Cathedral School, St Mary the Virgin, Thomas Attwood Project and Wells Cathedral School (£2,000 each).

FINANCES *Year* 2008 *Income* £160,748 *Grants* £94,474 *Assets* £2,967,335

TRUSTEES Dr Christopher Robinson, Chair; Dr J A Birch; Rev Canon Mark Boyling; Dr S M Darlington; Prof B W Harvey; Mrs Gillian Perkins; Martin Pickering; Adam Ridley; Dr John Rutter; Revd A F Walters; Richard White; Sir David Willcocks.

HOW TO APPLY Applicants are strongly advised to obtain a copy of the trust's guidelines (either from the correspondent or their website, currently under construction at the time of writing) before drafting an application. Applications must be submitted by an institution on a form available from the correspondent. Closing dates for applications are 31 January for the March meeting and 30 June for the October meeting.

WHO TO APPLY TO Martin Williams, Clerk, PO Box 281, Stamford, Lincolnshire PE9 9BU *Tel* 01780 752 266 *email* ouseleytrust@btinternet.com *Website* www.ouseleytrust.org.uk

CC NO 527519 **ESTABLISHED** 1989

■ The Owen Family Trust

WHERE FUNDING CAN BE GIVEN UK, with a preference for West Midlands.

WHO CAN BENEFIT Schools (independent and church), Christian youth centres, churches, community associations, national organisations benefiting people of all ages, and people with Alzheimer's disease, cancer and strokes.

WHAT IS FUNDED Mainly support for projects known personally by the trustees. Christian outreach projects are supported, with consideration also given to the arts, conservation, cancer research, Christian education, church and related community buildings.

WHAT IS NOT FUNDED The trust states 'No grants to individuals unless part of a charitable organisation'.

TYPE OF GRANT Buildings, capital, and recurring costs will be considered. Funding may be given for more than three years.

RANGE OF GRANTS £100–£15,000.

SAMPLE GRANTS Oundle School Foundation (£15,000); Black Country Museum Development Trust, Lichfield Cathedral and NAYC – Pioneer Centre (£5,000 each); Acorns, Birmingham Federation of Clubs for Young People and Lozells Project Trust (£3,000 each); Chaplaincy Plus, The Public Catalogue Foundation, St Giles Hospice (£1,000); The Army Benevolent Fund – Birmingham and Ben Uri Gallery (£500 each); and Dorothy Parkes Centre and St Peter's Little Aston PCC (£250 each).

FINANCES *Year* 2008–09 *Income* £67,933 *Grants* £87,077 *Assets* £1,150,147

TRUSTEES Mrs H G Jenkins; A D Owen.

HOW TO APPLY In writing to the correspondent including annual report, budget for project and general information regarding the application. Organisations need to be a registered charity; however an 'umbrella' body which would hold funds would be acceptable. Only a small number of grants can be given each year and unsuccessful applications are not acknowledged unless an sae is enclosed. The trustees meet quarterly.

WHO TO APPLY TO A D Owen, Trustee, C/o Rubery Owen Holdings Limited, PO Box 10, Wednesbury WS10 8JD *Tel* 0121 526 3131

CC NO 251975 **ESTABLISHED** 1967

■ Oxfam (GB)

WHERE FUNDING CAN BE GIVEN Africa, Asia, Caribbean, Central America, Eastern Europe, countries of the former Soviet Union, Great Britain, Middle East, South America.

WHO CAN BENEFIT Organisations which benefit people of all ages who are disadvantaged by poverty, disabled or victims of famine, disasters or war.

WHAT IS FUNDED Organisations worldwide working for the relief of hunger, disease, exploitation and poverty. Organisations working in public education in the UK and Ireland.

WHAT IS NOT FUNDED Applications for individuals are not considered.

SAMPLE GRANTS CHF International (£1.1 million in two grants); Australia Indonesia Partnership for Reconstruction and Development (£860,000 in two grants); Horn of Africa Voluntary Youth Committee (£600,000 in four grants); Scottish Youth Parliament (£440,000 in two grants); Tearfund (£260,000); and Welfare Foundation (£175,000).

FINANCES *Year* 2007–08 *Income* £266,700,000 *Grants* £53,400,000 *Assets* £70,700,000

TRUSTEES Prof. John Gaventa; Gareth Davies; Maureen Connelly; Sandra Dawson; Andrew Friend; Prof. Adebayo Olukoshi; Ms Patricia Zipfel; Miss Vanessa Godfrey; Rajiv Joshi; Matthew Martin; Ms Maja Daruwala.

HOW TO APPLY Applications should be made to the Regional Management Centre in the region concerned.

WHO TO APPLY TO Joss Saunders, 2700 John Smith Drive, Oxford Business Park South, Oxford OX4 2JY *Tel* 0870 333 2444 *email* enquiries@oxfam.org.uk *Website* www.oxfam.org.uk

CC NO 202918 **ESTABLISHED** 1958

....

■ City of Oxford Charity

WHERE FUNDING CAN BE GIVEN The city of Oxford only.

WHO CAN BENEFIT Charitable organisations, schools and individuals.

WHAT IS FUNDED Educational needs, such as help with school uniforms, attending school trips and books and materials.

FINANCES *Year* 2008 *Income* £261,727 *Grants* £77,155 *Assets* £3,926,408

TRUSTEES 11 co-opted trustees; six nominated by the City Council; two nominated by the University of Oxford; one representing Oxfordshire Area Health Authority.

OTHER INFORMATION The charity also runs almshouses situated in St Clements – Oxford. The sum of £89,000 was spent on its upkeep in 2008.

HOW TO APPLY Application forms can be downloaded form the charity's website. Trustees meet to consider applications four times a year in March, June, September and December.

WHO TO APPLY TO David Wright, Clerk, 11 Davenant Road, Oxford OX2 8BT *Tel* 01865 247161 *email* enquiries@oxfordcitycharities.fsnet.co.uk *Website* www.oxfordcitycharities.org

CC NO 239151 **ESTABLISHED** 2004

....

■ The Oxfordshire Community Foundation

WHERE FUNDING CAN BE GIVEN Oxfordshire.

WHO CAN BENEFIT Community-based non-profit organisations constituted in Oxfordshire. Beneficiaries of all ages, social circumstances, family situations and medical conditions will be considered, although the following are prioritised: parents and children; at risk groups; carers; disabled people; people disadvantaged by poverty; homeless people; immigrants; those living in rural areas; socially isolated people; victims of domestic violence; those with hearing loss, mental illness, and sight loss; and substance misusers.

WHAT IS FUNDED Specific projects up to one year with outputs related to poverty, unemployment, education and health promotion, including charities working in the fields of infrastructure and technical support, infrastructure development, charity or voluntary umbrella bodies, residential facilities and services, self-help groups, campaigning for health issues, health related volunteer schemes, equal opportunities and various community facilities and services.

WHAT IS NOT FUNDED Please refer to the foundation's website for exclusions specific to each fund.

TYPE OF GRANT One-off; capital. One-year start-up for projects, training and equipment.

RANGE OF GRANTS Up to £7,000.

SAMPLE GRANTS Abingdon Bridge, Chabad, Goring on Thames Sailing Club, Steeple Aston Youth Club, Sunflower Toddler Group, and UK Dads and the Potential Project (£7,000 each); Azad Hill FC (£6,900); Parasol Project (£6,800); Oxford Concert Party (£6,600); and Fusion (£6,200).

FINANCES *Year* 2007–08 *Income* £547,645 *Grants* £333,776 *Assets* £1,462,372

TRUSTEES John Briggs; Colin Alexander; Mrs Glyn Benson; Malcolm Cochrane; Ian Workman; Anna Moon; Lady North; Ms Jane Mactaggert; Nigel Talbot-Rice; Nigel Williams; Ian Lenagan; John Hemingway; Mrs Jane Wates; Prof. Ann Buchanan; Ms Shree Hindocha.

PUBLICATIONS *The Other Oxfordshire.*

HOW TO APPLY Please refer to the foundation's website for full details of how to apply to the various programmes currently being administered.

WHO TO APPLY TO Grants Manager, 3 Woodin's Way, Oxford OX1 1HD *Tel* 01865 798 666 *Fax* 01865 245 385 *email* grants@oxfordshire.org *Website* www.oxfordshire.org

CC NO 1046432 **ESTABLISHED** 1995

■ The P F Charitable Trust

WHERE FUNDING CAN BE GIVEN Unrestricted. In practice UK with local interests in Oxfordshire and Scotland.

WHO CAN BENEFIT Voluntary organisations and charitable groups.

WHAT IS FUNDED General charitable purposes.

WHAT IS NOT FUNDED No grants to individuals or non-registered charities.

TYPE OF GRANT One-off and recurring, buildings, core costs, project, research and running costs. Funding may be given for up to three years.

RANGE OF GRANTS Mainly up to £50,000.

SAMPLE GRANTS National Star Centre for Disabled Youth (£250,000), towards a development providing new facilities for the students; Great Ormond Street Hospital Children's Charity, towards building a new heart and lung centre and Royal Marsden Cancer Campaign, towards the continuing costs of medical research (£100,000 each); British Heart Foundation, towards the continuing costs of medical research, the Institute of Cancer Research, towards the continuing costs of medical research and Liverpool Cathedral, towards the integrated visitor centre project (£50,000); Neuropathy Trust (£29,000); St Dunstan's (£27,000); Bloxham School Development Trust (£25,000); Seven Springs Foundation (£20,000); Oxford Brookes University (£18,000); City and Guilds of London Art School (£15,000); Citizens Advice – Banbury (£12,000); Friends of Chelsea (£10,000).

FINANCES *Year* 2007–08 *Income* £1,812,817 *Grants* £2,661,400 *Assets* £100,034,199

TRUSTEES Robert Fleming; Philip Fleming; Rory D Fleming.

HOW TO APPLY Applications to the correspondent in writing. Trustees usually meet monthly to consider applications and approve grants.

WHO TO APPLY TO The Secretary to the Trustees, 15 Suffolk Street, London SW1Y 4HG *Tel* 020 7036 5685

CC NO 220124   **ESTABLISHED** 1951

■ The Doris Pacey Charitable Foundation

WHERE FUNDING CAN BE GIVEN UK and Israel.

WHO CAN BENEFIT Charitable organisations.

WHAT IS FUNDED Jewish, medical, educational and social.

TYPE OF GRANT One-off and recurrent.

RANGE OF GRANTS £500–£138,000.

SAMPLE GRANTS British Friends of Bar Ulan University (£138,000); Magen David Adom (£60,000); Jewish Chaplaincy (£36,000); UJIA – Palmach Club (£19,000); Courtaulds Institute of Art and World Jewish Relief (£15,000 each); Simon Marks School (£10,000); and One Family UK and St Christopher's Hospice (£1,000 each).

FINANCES *Year* 2007–08 *Income* £204,246 *Grants* £297,567 *Assets* £6,176,265

TRUSTEES J D Cohen; R Locke; L Powell.

HOW TO APPLY Unsolicited applications are not considered.

WHO TO APPLY TO J D Cohen, Trustee, 30 Old Burlington Street, London W1S 3NL *Tel* 020 7468 2600

CC NO 1101724   **ESTABLISHED** 2004

■ Padwa Charitable Foundation

WHERE FUNDING CAN BE GIVEN UK.

WHO CAN BENEFIT Organisations and individuals.

WHAT IS FUNDED The trust has the following aims: the relief of poverty; education; and charitable purposes beneficial to the community. Donations are given to both individuals and organisations.

RANGE OF GRANTS Up to £5,000.

SAMPLE GRANTS Headway – Tunbridge Wells; Richard House Trust; Fair Havens Hospice; Little Havens Children's Hospice; Starlight Children's Foundation; Universal Benevolent Society and Cancerkin (£5,000 each) Sense West (£4,250); Look (£3,500); Leonard Cheshire Disability (£3,300); Buckingham Emergency Food Appeal (£1,000); and three other grants of less than £1,000 each (amounting to £1,850).

FINANCES *Year* 2007–08 *Income* £15,581,637 *Grants* £48,891 *Assets* £15,480,374

TRUSTEES Neville R Evenden; Jeremy Randall; Terrence Chandler; Alan C Goreham; Neil A Fulton.

HOW TO APPLY In writing to the correspondent.

WHO TO APPLY TO Stephen Bailey, Secretary, Walpole Group Plc, 3 Northington Street, London WC1N 2JE *Tel* 020 7831 1872

CC NO 1019274   **ESTABLISHED** 1992

■ The Pallant Charitable Trust

WHERE FUNDING CAN BE GIVEN UK, with a preference for areas within 50 miles of Chichester.

WHO CAN BENEFIT Church musicians and choristers.

WHAT IS FUNDED Chorister's scholarships and musician's salaries.

WHAT IS NOT FUNDED No grants to individuals, or for computer equipment or sponsorship for concerts.

SAMPLE GRANTS Chichester Cathedral Choristers Scholarships – Prebendal School Fees (£33,000 for four individuals); Friends of St Mary's Church – Stoughton (£7,000); Bosham PCC (£1,000); and RSCM Sussex area (£750).

FINANCES *Year* 2006–07 *Income* £43,880 *Grants* £41,774 *Assets* £1,243,959

TRUSTEES A J Thurlow; S A E Macfarlane; C Smyth; C J Henville.

HOW TO APPLY In writing to the correspondent. Applications should be submitted by recognised organisations such as churches, schools, colleges or charities working in the field of church music.

WHO TO APPLY TO Simon Macfarlane, Trustee, c/o Thomas Eggar, The Corn Exchange, Baffins Lane, Chichester, West Sussex PO19 1GE *Tel* 01243 786 111 *Fax* 01243 532 001

CC NO 265120   **ESTABLISHED** 1972

■ The Palmer Foundation

WHERE FUNDING CAN BE GIVEN Tower Hamlets.

WHO CAN BENEFIT Selected registered charities chosen by the trustees. Children and young adults at Coopers' Company and Coborn School and Strode's College will be considered.

WHAT IS FUNDED Grants and donations to charitable organisations and payments for educational scholarships, bursaries and prizes at Coopers'

Company and Coborn School and Strode's College.

TYPE OF GRANT Recurrent grants for up to three years will be considered.

SAMPLE GRANTS Welfare (£14,400); educational (£9,200); City of London (£7,700); children (£4,000); and 'other' (£500).

FINANCES *Year* 2007–08 *Income* £44,041 *Grants* £35,787 *Assets* £615,968

TRUSTEES The Coopers' Company.

HOW TO APPLY The trust conducts its own research and does not respond to unsolicited applications.

WHO TO APPLY TO Adrian Carroll, Clerk to the Trustees, Coopers' Hall, 13 Devonshire Square, London EC2M 4TH *Tel* 020 7247 9577 *email* clerk@coopers-hall.co.uk *Website* www.coopers-hall.co.uk

CC NO 278666   **ESTABLISHED** 1979

■ Eleanor Palmer Trust

WHERE FUNDING CAN BE GIVEN Former urban districts of Chipping Barnet and East Barnet.

WHO CAN BENEFIT Charities benefiting people disadvantaged by poverty, hardship or distress.

WHAT IS FUNDED Relief in need.

WHAT IS NOT FUNDED Anything other than relief-in-need is not considered.

TYPE OF GRANT One-off, project and capital. Funding for one year or less will be considered.

RANGE OF GRANTS £100–£5,000.

SAMPLE GRANTS Grants are broken down as follows: amenities for and grants for residents (£6,000); grants for relief in need (£17,000); lunch club for residents (£5,600).

FINANCES *Year* 2007–08 *Income* £1,124,058 *Grants* £29,001 *Assets* £3,885,025

TRUSTEES Anthony Grimwade, Chair; Anthony Alderman; Helena Davis; Stephen G Lane; Peter J Mellows; Catherine Older; Stephen Payne; Wendy Prentice; Samuel Hall Speers.

HOW TO APPLY In writing to the correspondent, providing details of your organisation's circumstances, the purpose of the grant and a copy of your latest accounts.

WHO TO APPLY TO Fred Park, Clerk to the Trustees, 106b Wood Street, Barnet, Hertfordshire EN5 4BY *Tel* 020 8441 3222 *email* info@eleanorpalmertrust.org.uk *Website* www.eleanorpalmertrust.org.uk

CC NO 220857   **ESTABLISHED** 1558

■ The Panacea Society

WHERE FUNDING CAN BE GIVEN UK, with a strong preference for Bedford and its immediate region.

WHO CAN BENEFIT Christian organisations that promote the religious aims of the Panacea Society.

WHAT IS FUNDED Advancement and promotion of the religious beliefs of the Society and the Christian religion generally; relief of sickness for the benefit of people living within the town of Bedford and its immediate region; and advancement of education generally and in the production, publication and dissemination of religious works. Grants awarded must be for charitable purposes and are made to UK-based organisations only. Priority will usually be given to grants that: will promote the religious aims of the Panacea Society; can benefit large numbers of people; will have a lasting impact; are of a capital nature; are to organisations rather than individuals; operate in Bedfordshire.

WHAT IS NOT FUNDED The society will not make grants: to political parties or political lobbying; to pressure groups; which support commercial ventures; or which could be paid out of central or local government funds.

SAMPLE GRANTS Pasque Charity – Keech Children's Hospice (£30,000 over three years); CHUMS (£10,000); Road Victims Trust (£4,600); Retirement Education Centre Bedford Ltd (£3,500); Friendship Link Action Group (£2,000); Bedford Cerebral Palsy (£1,500); and Yarls Wood Befrienders Group (£1,000).

FINANCES *Year* 2008 *Income* £653,685 *Grants* £284,367 *Assets* £20,301,899

TRUSTEES G Allan; L Aston; Revd Dr Jane Shaw; Prof. C Rowland; Dr J Meggitt.

HOW TO APPLY The trust has previously stated that it receives many applications that they are unable or unwilling to support. Please read the grant criteria carefully before submitting an application. Unsolicited applications are not responded to. Any organisation considering applying for funding support should make a formal application in writing to the correspondent. The application should set out the purpose for which the funding is required, and explain how it falls within the funding criteria and complies with their requirements. Full information on the work of the applicant body together with details of how the proposed funding will be applied should be given. The correspondent will acknowledge receipt of an application, and indicate if the application falls within their parameters. At this point the society may call for additional information, or indicate that it is unable to consider the application further. Most applications fail because they fall outside the criteria, however the society does not provide additional reasons why it is unable to support a particular application. When all relevant information has been received the application will be discussed at the next meeting of the society's trustees together with other valid applications. The trustees may at that meeting refuse or defer any application or request further information without giving reasons. Applicants will be advised in writing of the trustees' decision.

WHO TO APPLY TO David McLynn, Business Administrator, 14 Albany Road, Bedford MK40 3PH *Tel* 01234 359 737 *email* admin@panacea-society.org *Website* www.panacea-society.org

CC NO 227530   **ESTABLISHED** 1926

■ Panahpur Charitable Trust

WHERE FUNDING CAN BE GIVEN UK, overseas.

WHO CAN BENEFIT Christian charities and individuals, especially Christian missionary organisations.

WHAT IS FUNDED Scripture distribution/reading encouragement, relief work, missionary work, education and retreats.

RANGE OF GRANTS £500–£38,000.

SAMPLE GRANTS Oasis International (£38,000); Operation Agape (£25,000); 180 Degrees – Viva Network (£23,000); Ambassadors in Sport and European Christian Mission (£15,000 each); EMMS International (£10,000); World Radio (£8,0000; Retrack (£7,000); Global Connection (£4,000); St Stephen's Society (£2,000); SOMA UK (£1,000); Redcliffe College (£500); and Cloud Trust (£475).

FINANCES *Year* 2007–08 *Income* £275,414 *Grants* £344,507 *Assets* £6,560,118

TRUSTEES P East; Miss D Haile; D Harland; A Matheson; A E Perry; J Perry.

HOW TO APPLY The trustees do their own research and do not respond to unsolicited applications.

WHO TO APPLY TO The Trust Department, Jacob Cavenagh and Skeet, 5 Robin Hood Lane, Sutton, Surrey SM1 2SW *Tel* 020 8643 1166 *email* bob.moffett@panhpur.org

CC NO 214299   **ESTABLISHED** 1911

······································

■ Panton Trust

WHERE FUNDING CAN BE GIVEN UK and overseas.

WHO CAN BENEFIT Worldwide organisations concerned with animal wildlife; UK: the environment.

WHAT IS FUNDED The trust states that it is 'concerned with any animal or animals or with wildlife in any part of the world, or with the environment of the UK or any part thereof. The trustees consider applications from a wide variety of sources and favour smaller charities which do not have the same capacity for large-scale fundraising as major charities in this field'.

TYPE OF GRANT Grants are made for strategic planning and project funding and can be for up to three years.

SAMPLE GRANTS Gonville and Caius (£6,000); St. Tiggywinkles Wildlife Hospital, Whales and Dolphin Conservation Society and Wroxton Abbey Charitable Trust (£5,000 each); Royal Botanic Garden Kew and Zoological Society (£3,000 each); and Arrow Riding Centre and Association for Protection of Animals – Algone (£2,500 each).

FINANCES *Year* 2007–08 *Income* £66,448 *Grants* £53,150 *Assets* £216,328

TRUSTEES L M Slavin; R Craig.

OTHER INFORMATION Other grants of less than £1,000 totalled £5,250

HOW TO APPLY In writing to the correspondent.

WHO TO APPLY TO Laurence Slavin, Trustee, Ramsay House, 18 Vera Avenue, Grange Park, London N21 1RB *Tel* 020 8370 7700

CC NO 292910   **ESTABLISHED** 1983

······································

■ The James Pantyfedwen Foundation

WHERE FUNDING CAN BE GIVEN Wales.

WHO CAN BENEFIT Welsh people; and organisations in Wales benefiting children, young adults, clergy, musicians, students, Christians, at risk groups, people disadvantaged by poverty and homeless people.

WHAT IS FUNDED Church buildings; religious purposes; students (mainly for postgraduate study); registered charities; local Eisteddfodau; and Sunday Schools. Charities working in the field of Christian education; religious umbrella bodies; infrastructure, support and development; cultural activity; academic research; and various community services and facilities will be considered.

WHAT IS NOT FUNDED No grants are made for revenue funding of any kind.

TYPE OF GRANT One-off.

RANGE OF GRANTS Up to a maximum of £15,000 in special cases; lower maximum in other cases.

SAMPLE GRANTS Grants were broken down as follows: Educational purposes (students) – £101,500; Religious buildings – £94,500; Eisteddfodau – £62,500; Registered charities – £26,000; Religious purposes – £12,600; Urdd Gobaith Cymru – £10,000; Special Projects – £6,500.

FINANCES *Year* 2008–09 *Income* £484,763 *Grants* £315,022 *Assets* £8,997,347

TRUSTEES E W Jones, Chair; Revd Dr R A Evans; Dr G T Hughes; I M Hughes; G E Humphries; G R Jones; Miss G Pierce Jones; Revd J E Jones; D G Lewis; Most Revd Dr B C Morgan; Prof D L Morgan; W J Phillips; K Richards; Revd I Roberts; R F Sharp; Revd P M Thomas; Prof Marc Clement; Dr P Elfed-Owens; Dr R Griffiths; Revd Canon E Morgan; Revd Dr G Tudur.

OTHER INFORMATION Organisations and individuals

HOW TO APPLY Applications should be made on a form available from the correspondent. Applications from churches and registered charities can be submitted at any time (trustees meet about five times a year in March, May, July, September and December); student applications should be submitted before 31 July in the academic year for which the application is being made. Applications to the special projects funds are considered twice a year and should be received by 15 June or 15 November for consideration in July or December respectively. All unsuccessful applicants receive a reply.

WHO TO APPLY TO Richard H Morgan, Executive Secretary, Pantyfedwen, 9 Market Street, Aberystwyth SY23 1DL *Tel* 01970 612806 *Fax* 01970 612806 *email* pantyfedwen@ btinternet.com *Website* www. jamespantyfedwenfoundation.org.uk

CC NO 1069598   **ESTABLISHED** 1998

······································

■ The Paphitis Charitable Trust

WHERE FUNDING CAN BE GIVEN UK and overseas.

WHO CAN BENEFIT Charitable organisations.

WHAT IS FUNDED General charitable purposes, particularly children's charities.

SAMPLE GRANTS Milwall Community Scheme (£5,000); the Child Care Trust and DebRA (£2,000 each); Chipstead C and W Cricket Club, Forgotten Children and Police Community Clubs (£1,500 each); British Blind Sport (£1,400); Access to Employment, Children's' Hospice South West, Lions Club of Sunderland, NSPCC and Whirlon Hall Farm Trust (£1,000 each); Race For Life (£500); Brooklands College and Princess Alice Hospice (£250 each).

FINANCES *Year* 2007–08 *Income* £99,519 *Grants* £23,758 *Assets* £127,929

TRUSTEES Malcolm Cooke; Richard Towner; Kypros Kyprianou; Ann Mantz.

OTHER INFORMATION This trust was set up by entrepreneur Theo Paphitis.

HOW TO APPLY In writing to the correspondent.

WHO TO APPLY TO The Trustees, 2nd Floor, 22–24 Worple Road, London SW19 4DD

CC NO 1112721   **ESTABLISHED** 2005

······································

■ The Paragon Trust

WHERE FUNDING CAN BE GIVEN UK and overseas.

WHO CAN BENEFIT Charities and occasionally certain individuals but only those known to the trustees.

WHAT IS FUNDED A wide range of charitable bodies.

TYPE OF GRANT The majority of donations are standing orders.

RANGE OF GRANTS £500–£5,000.

SAMPLE GRANTS Compassion in World Farming (£5,000); Army Benevolent Fund (£4,000); British Red Cross (£3,000); Holy Cross Centre Trust and Demelza House Children's Hospice (£2,000 each); Mary Fielding Guild (£1,500); The Art Fund, Buildings at Risk, National Autistic Society and Mines Advisory Group (£1,000 each); Whizz-Kidz, Church Housing Trust and Cystic Fibrosis (£750 each); and The Canon Collins Educational Trust for Southern Africa, South London Industrial Mission and St Dunstan's (£500 each).

FINANCES *Year* 2007–08 *Income* £103,898 *Grants* £97,715 *Assets* £1,870,581

TRUSTEES The Lord Wrenbury; Revd Canon R Coppin; Miss L J Whistler; P Cunningham; Dr Fiona Cornish.

HOW TO APPLY The trust states that it does not respond to unsolicited applications; all beneficiaries 'are known personally to the trustees and no attention is paid to appeal literature, which is discarded on receipt. Fundraisers are therefore urged to save resources by not sending literature.'

WHO TO APPLY TO Mrs Kathy Larter, c/o Thomson Snell and Passmore Solicitors (ref: 1211), 3 Lonsdale Gardens, Tunbridge Wells, Kent TN1 1NX *Tel* 01892 701 211

CC NO 278348   **ESTABLISHED** 1979

■ The Park Charitable Trust

WHERE FUNDING CAN BE GIVEN UK.

WHO CAN BENEFIT Charitable organisations.

WHAT IS FUNDED 'The objects of the charity are the advancement of the Jewish Faith; the advancement of Jewish education; the relief of poverty amongst the Jewish community; the relief of patients suffering from cancer and heart conditions; giving financial support to hospitals and furthering such other charitable purposes as the trustees may from time to time determine in support of their charitable activities.'

FINANCES *Year* 2007–08 *Income* £1,117,503 *Grants* £990,998 *Assets* £3,782,989

TRUSTEES D Hammelburger; Mrs M Hammelburger; E Pine.

HOW TO APPLY In writing to the correspondent.

WHO TO APPLY TO E Pine, Trustee, 69 Singleton Road, Salford M7 4LX

CC NO 1095541

■ The Park House Charitable Trust

WHERE FUNDING CAN BE GIVEN UK and overseas, with a preference for the Midlands, particularly Coventry and Warwickshire.

WHO CAN BENEFIT Charitable organisations.

WHAT IS FUNDED General charitable purposes, with preference towards social welfare and Christian causes.

WHAT IS NOT FUNDED No grants to individuals.

TYPE OF GRANT Normally one-off for general funds.

RANGE OF GRANTS £2,000–£60,000.

SAMPLE GRANTS Mary's Meals (£60,000); Krizevac Project (£50,000); St Joseph and the Helper's Charity (£35,000); Life (£30,000); Maryvale Institute and Society for the Protection of Unborn Children (£15,000 each); CAFOD and Serenity (£10,000 each); Ear Foundation (£5,000); Armonico Consort, Coventry Jesus Centre, International Rescue Committee UK, Malawi Link Trust, Operation Smile and Tiny Tim's Children's Centre (£2,000 each).

FINANCES *Year* 2008 *Income* £269,735 *Grants* £278,000 *Assets* £1,087,571

TRUSTEES N P Bailey; Mrs M M Bailey; P Bailey; Dr M F Whelan.

HOW TO APPLY In writing to the correspondent. The trust has stated that it does not expect to have surplus funds available to meet the majority of applications.

WHO TO APPLY TO Paul Varney, Dafferns, Queen's House, Queen's Road, Coventry CV1 3DR *Tel* 024 7622 1046

CC NO 1077677   **ESTABLISHED** 1999

■ The Frank Parkinson Agricultural Trust

WHERE FUNDING CAN BE GIVEN UK.

WHO CAN BENEFIT Mainly corporate entities benefiting the improvement of agriculture and horticulture.

WHAT IS FUNDED The improvement and welfare of British agriculture, primarily to agricultural colleges and affiliated institutions.

WHAT IS NOT FUNDED Grants are given to corporate bodies and the trust is not able to assist with financial help to any individuals undertaking postgraduate studies or degree courses.

TYPE OF GRANT Short-term: two to four years preferred. One-off will also be considered.

RANGE OF GRANTS One-off at Chair's discretion: smallest £200; largest over three years £100,000; typical grants (over two years) £40,000.

SAMPLE GRANTS Nuffield Farming Scholarships Trust (£15,000 in four payments); Institute of Agricultural Management Leadership Development Programme (£8,000); St George's House – Windsor Castle (£5,000); and AgriFood Charities Partnership (£500).

FINANCES *Year* 2008 *Income* £58,817 *Grants* £28,660 *Assets* £1,051,372

TRUSTEES Prof. J D Leaver; C Bourchier; J S Sclanders; Prof. Paul Webster.

PUBLICATIONS A history of the trust since its inception in 1943, including an outline of projects previously funded, is available in a book entitled *Tale of Two Trusts*, which is available from the correspondent.

HOW TO APPLY In writing to the correspondent. The trustees meet annually in April and applicants are expected to make an oral presentation. Further details of the whole application process can be found in the useful 'Guidelines for Grant Applications' which is available from the trust. Please note, however: 'The chairman has the authority to approve small grants between annual meetings, but these are only for minor sums and minor projects.'

WHO TO APPLY TO Miss Janet Smith, Secretary to the Trustees, 11 Alder Drive, Pudsey LS28 8RD *Tel* 0113 257 8613 *email* janet.oudsey@live.co.uk

CC NO 209407   **ESTABLISHED** 1943

■ The Samuel and Freda Parkinson Charitable Trust

WHERE FUNDING CAN BE GIVEN UK.

WHO CAN BENEFIT Registered charities specified by the founder of the trust.

WHAT IS FUNDED General charitable purposes.

RANGE OF GRANTS £5,000–£25,000.

SAMPLE GRANTS Salvation Army (£25,000); Leonard Cheshire Foundation (£24,000); Church Army (£20,000); RNLI (£10,000); RSPCA (£6,000); and Animal Concern, Animal Rescue and Animal Welfare (£5,000 each).

FINANCES *Year* 2007–08 *Income* £126,234 *Grants* £100,000 *Assets* £2,483,752

TRUSTEES D E G Roberts; Miss J A Todd; M J Fletcher.

HOW TO APPLY The founder of this charity restricted the list of potential beneficiaries to named charities of his choice and accordingly the trustees do not have discretion to include further beneficiaries, although they do have complete discretion within the stated beneficiary list.

WHO TO APPLY TO Trust Administrator, Thomson Wilson Pattinson, Trustees' Solicitors, Stonecliffe, Lake Road, Windermere, Cumbria LA23 3AR *Tel* 01539 442 233 *Fax* 01539 488 810

CC NO 327749   **ESTABLISHED** 1987

■ The Parthenon Trust

WHERE FUNDING CAN BE GIVEN Unrestricted.

WHO CAN BENEFIT Charitable organisations.

WHAT IS FUNDED International aid, medical research, assistance to the disadvantaged including people with disabilities, culture and heritage, medical treatment and care, education, promotion of civil society and research on current affairs.

WHAT IS NOT FUNDED No grants for individuals, scientific/geographical expeditions or projects which promote religious beliefs.

TYPE OF GRANT Normally one-off grants for general purposes.

SAMPLE GRANTS Cancer Research UK (£775,000 over four years); International Committee of the Red Cross (£600,000); José Carreras International Leukaemia Foundation (£275,000); Friends of Diva Opera, SMA Trust, St George's Chapel – Windsor Castle and Youth Business International (£250,000 each); Mont Blanc Foundation (£200,000); Ungureni Trust (£160,000); Royal Ballet School (£150,000); Society for the Relief of Disabled Children (£100,000); Bath University (£75,000); Winds of Hope Foundation (£50,000); Action Against Hunger UK (£25,000); Haven of Hope Christian Service (£20,000); West London Churches Homeless Concern (£19,000); Civitas: Institute for the Study of Civil Society (£15,000); Learning Challenge Foundation (£12,000); and United Aid for Azerbaijan (£10,000).

FINANCES *Year* 2007 *Income* £5,317,290 *Grants* £4,044,442 *Assets* £1,611,569

TRUSTEES Dr J M Darmady; J E E Whittaker; Mrs Y G Whittaker.

HOW TO APPLY In writing to the correspondent. Anyone proposing to submit an application should telephone the secretary beforehand. Unsolicited written applications are not normally acknowledged. Most grants are awarded at a trustees' meeting held early in the new year, although grants can be awarded at any time.

WHO TO APPLY TO J E E Whittaker, The Secretary, Saint-Nicolas 9 2000 Neuchatel *Tel* 00 41 32 724 8130

CC NO 1051467   **ESTABLISHED** 1995

■ Arthur James Paterson Charitable Trust

WHERE FUNDING CAN BE GIVEN UK.

WHO CAN BENEFIT Organisations benefiting children, older people, retired people, at risk groups, socially isolated people and those disadvantaged by poverty.

WHAT IS FUNDED Medical research, welfare of older people and children.

TYPE OF GRANT One-off.

SAMPLE GRANTS Glenalmond College and Worcester College (£4,700 each); The Children's Trust, Elderly Accommodation Counsel, MDF The

Bipolar Organisation, Demand, London Air Ambulance and Tommy's (£3,415 each); and Children First, Dance Umbrella, Jubilee Sailing Trust, Leukaemia and Polka Children's Theatre (£1,175 each).

FINANCES *Year* 2007–08 *Income* £58,250 *Grants* £35,765 *Assets* £1,686,247

TRUSTEES Royal Bank of Canada Trust Corporation Ltd.

HOW TO APPLY There are no application forms. Send your application with a covering letter and include the latest set of report and accounts. Deadlines are February and August.

WHO TO APPLY TO Anita Carter, Royal Bank of Canada Trust Corporation Limited, 71 Queen Victoria Street, London EC4V 4DE *Tel* 020 7653 4756 *email* anita.carter@rbc.com

CC NO 278569   **ESTABLISHED** 1979

■ The Constance Paterson Charitable Trust

WHERE FUNDING CAN BE GIVEN UK.

WHO CAN BENEFIT Organisations benefiting children, older people, retired people, ex-service and service people, at risk groups, socially isolated people and those disadvantaged by poverty. Carers, disabled people, homeless people, victims of abuse, crime or domestic violence and people with dyslexia are also considered.

WHAT IS FUNDED Medical research, health care, welfare of older people and children (including accommodation and housing) and service people's welfare.

WHAT IS NOT FUNDED No grants to individuals.

TYPE OF GRANT One-off grants, which can be for capital costs (including buildings), core or running costs, project or research funding, or salaries.

RANGE OF GRANTS Up to £2,000.

SAMPLE GRANTS Ataxia – Telangiectasia Society, Changing Faces, Havens Hospices, Theodora Children's Trust and Orchid (£2,220 each); Children 1st, CLAPA, The Jennifer Trust, Charity Search and Medical Engineering Resource Unit (£1,550 each).

FINANCES *Year* 2008–09 *Income* £39,652 *Grants* £18,730 *Assets* £1,176,959

TRUSTEES Royal Bank of Canada Trust Corporation Ltd.

HOW TO APPLY In writing to the correspondent, including covering letter and latest set of annual report and accounts. The trust does not have an application form. Deadlines for applications are June and December.

WHO TO APPLY TO Miss Anita Carter, Administrator, Royal Bank of Canada Trust Corporation Limited, 71 Queen Victoria Street, London EC4V 4DE *Tel* 020 7653 4756 *email* anita.carter@rbc.com

CC NO 249556   **ESTABLISHED** 1966

■ Miss M E Swinton Paterson's Charitable Trust

WHERE FUNDING CAN BE GIVEN Scotland.

WHO CAN BENEFIT Organisations benefiting Christians and young people.

WHAT IS FUNDED Support to the Church of Scotland and other Christian groups in the maintenance of church buildings and in their work with young people.

WHAT IS NOT FUNDED No grants to individuals or students.

TYPE OF GRANT Average about £1,000.

SAMPLE GRANTS Previous beneficiaries included: L'Arche Edinburgh Community (£2,000).; Livingstone Baptist Church, Lloyd Morris Congregational Church, Haddington West Parish Church, Acorn Christian Centre, Stranraer YMCA, Care for the Family, Boys' and Girls' Clubs of Scotland, Fresh Start, Friends of the Elms, Iona Community, Edinburgh Young Carers' Project and Epilepsy Scotland (£1,000 each); and Stoneykirk Parish Church, Scotland Yard Adventure Centre, Atholl Centre, Scottish Crusaders, Disablement Income Group Scotland and Artlink (£500 each).

FINANCES *Year* 2008–09 *Income* £55,792 *Grants* £40,000

TRUSTEES Michael A Noble; J A W Somerville; C S Kennedy; R J Steel.

HOW TO APPLY In writing to the correspondent. Trustees meet once a year in July to consider grants.

WHO TO APPLY TO The Trustees, Lindsays' Solicitors, Calendonian Exchange, 19a Canning Street, Edinburgh EH3 8HE

SC NO SC004835　　　**ESTABLISHED** 1989

■ The Patrick Charitable Trust

WHERE FUNDING CAN BE GIVEN UK, with a special interest in Cornwall and the West Midlands.

WHO CAN BENEFIT Registered charities.

WHAT IS FUNDED General charitable purposes.

WHAT IS NOT FUNDED No grants to individuals.

TYPE OF GRANT One-off or recurrent.

SAMPLE GRANTS Royal Shakespeare Company (£40,000); Oundle School Foundation (£25,000); Birmingham Royal Ballet (£21,000); the Princess Royal Trust for Carers (£6,000); Cornwall Community Foundation (£5,100); Birmingham Hippodrome Theatre (£5,000); the Peckwood Centre (£3,000); Earth Restoration Service, Friends of Brandwood End Cemetery, Oundle International Festival and Queen Alexandra College (£1,000 each); Wells Cathedral (£500); and Oesophageal Patients Association (£200).

FINANCES *Year* 2008–09 *Income* £163,982 *Grants* £138,218 *Assets* £5,796,403

TRUSTEES J A Patrick, Chair; M V Patrick; Mrs H P Cole; W Bond-Williams; N C Duckitt; G Wem.

HOW TO APPLY In writing to the correspondent at any time. The trust endeavours to reply to all applications with a decision.

WHO TO APPLY TO J A Patrick, Chair, The Lakeside Centre, 180 Lifford Lane, Birmingham B30 3NU *Tel* 0121 486 3399

CC NO 213849　　　**ESTABLISHED** 1962

■ The Jack Patston Charitable Trust

WHERE FUNDING CAN BE GIVEN Preferably Leicestershire and Cambridgeshire.

WHO CAN BENEFIT Charitable organisations, including rural churches.

WHAT IS FUNDED Preservation of wildlife and the environment, advancement of religion and preservation of rural church fabric.

WHAT IS NOT FUNDED No grants to individuals.

TYPE OF GRANT Single payments.

RANGE OF GRANTS Up to £6,000.

SAMPLE GRANTS Peterborough Cathedral Development and Preservation Trust (£6,000); Sue Ryder Care – Peterborough, Train a Priest Fund and St Peter's Church – Ashby Parva (£5,000 each); the Countryside Restoration

Trust and Wildfowl and Wetlands Trust (£4,000 each); RSPB and Woodland Trust (£3,000 each); the Fenland Archaeological Trust and East Anglia Children's Hospices (£2,500 each); the Bat Conservation Trust and the Barn Owl Trust (£2,000 each); the Carers Centre – CLASP (£1,500); Christ in the Centre – Leicester (£1,000); and St Andrew's Church – Foxton (£500).

FINANCES *Year* 2007–08 *Income* £98,344 *Grants* £123,500 *Assets* £2,520,436

TRUSTEES Allan A Veasey; Charles J U Applegate.

HOW TO APPLY In writing to the correspondent.

WHO TO APPLY TO Charles J U Applegate, Trustee, Buckles Solicitors LLP, Grant House, 101 Bourges Boulevard, Peterborough PE1 1NG *Tel* 01733 888888 *Fax* 01733 888800

CC NO 701658　　　**ESTABLISHED** 1989

■ Paycare Charity Trust (previously known as Patients' Aid Association Hospital and Medical Charities Trust)

WHERE FUNDING CAN BE GIVEN Generally in the East and West Midlands, Staffordshire and Shropshire and other areas where the association operates.

WHO CAN BENEFIT Mainly NHS hospitals and registered, medically related charities benefiting: children; young adults; older people; ex-service and service people; medical professionals; nurses and doctors; research workers; volunteers; people in care; at risk groups; carers; disabled people; those disadvantaged by poverty; homeless people; victims of abuse and domestic violence.

WHAT IS FUNDED Provision of equipment and patient amenities to NHS hospitals, hospices, convalescent homes and other medically related charities in the area where the parent association operates. These include: support to volunteers; health professional bodies; councils for voluntary service; advancement of respite; sheltered accommodation; health; special schools; speech therapy; special needs education; scholarships; medical research; specialist research; and community services.

WHAT IS NOT FUNDED Appeals must be from officials of the appealing body and submitted on official stationery. Appeals are not accepted from, or on behalf of, individuals or for provision of vehicles or general running costs.

TYPE OF GRANT Mainly medical equipment. Grants are not made towards running costs or administration.

RANGE OF GRANTS £100–£1,000.

SAMPLE GRANTS Action Medical Research, British Red Cross, The Children's Aid Team and Well Being of Women (£1,000 each); St Richard's Hospice (£950); Headway – North Staffordshire (£880); Opportunities Through Technology (£600); For Children in Hospital (£500); British Sin Foundation (£450); and High Blood Pressure Foundation (£320).

FINANCES *Year* 2008 *Income* £36,813 *Grants* £23,199 *Assets* £41,757

TRUSTEES E P Booth; D Bradley; G F Lewis; Mrs H Lisle; D Clegg; Patricia Stokes.

HOW TO APPLY Application forms are available from the correspondent. Any hospital or registered charity may apply for a grant and all such applications are considered by the trustees who meet four times a year. '[The] reason for the rejection of appeals is due usually to an excessive amount involved.' Each application is considered on merit.

WHO TO APPLY TO Janet Wrighton, Secretary, Paycare House, George Street, Wolverhampton WV2 4DX *Tel* 01902 371000 *Fax* 01902 371030 *email* enquiries@paycare.org

CC NO 240378　　　　　**ESTABLISHED** 1964

■ The Payne Charitable Trust

WHERE FUNDING CAN BE GIVEN Christian in Wales, West Midlands, Cumbria and India.

WHO CAN BENEFIT Missionaries, churches, and people engaged in the propagation of the Christian gospel.

WHAT IS FUNDED To support religious and charitable objects. The main area of interest is the support of evangelical Christians in the promotion and proclamation of the Christian gospel.

WHAT IS NOT FUNDED No grants for repairs to church buildings or towards education.

TYPE OF GRANT One-off grants and loans; capital support.

RANGE OF GRANTS Up to £30,000.

SAMPLE GRANTS Dayspring Trust for India (£30,000); Andrew League Trust (£28,500); Crusaders (£6,000); SASRA (£2,250); Nate & Ali Ussery – missionaries (£1,500); Armed Forces Christian Union and Heart Cry for Wales (£1,000 each); OAC West Midlands (£500); and Keith & Dorothy Ward – missionaries (£100).

FINANCES *Year* 2007–08 *Income* £39,078 *Grants* £70,850 *Assets* £628,777

TRUSTEES John Payne; Eric Payne.

OTHER INFORMATION Due to the large number of applications, some considerable time can elapse before communication can be sent.

HOW TO APPLY In writing to the correspondent. Applications should be submitted between 1 January and 21 March only, for grants made from the following 1 May. The trustees regret that they cannot support many of the deserving organisations that apply for a grant. Due to the large number of applications, some considerable time can elapse before communication can be sent.

WHO TO APPLY TO John Payne, Trustee, Fourwinds, Copthorn Road, Colwyn Bay LL28 5YP *Tel* 01492 532 393 *email* paynecharitable@aol.com

CC NO 241816　　　　　**ESTABLISHED** 1965

■ The Harry Payne Trust

WHERE FUNDING CAN BE GIVEN Birmingham and the immediately surrounding areas of the West Midlands.

WHO CAN BENEFIT Voluntary organisations and charitable groups only. Support will be considered for a wide variety of medical conditions, but particularly where there is evidence of social disadvantage. The trust operates a non-discriminatory policy as regards religion.

WHAT IS FUNDED Priority is given to charitable work in Birmingham, where the trust was founded. Funding may be given to churches and religious ancillary buildings; family planning and Well Women clinics; hospices and hospitals; pre-school and special needs education; advice centres and community services and other charitable organisations.

WHAT IS NOT FUNDED No grants to individuals or organisations outside the beneficial area.

TYPE OF GRANT Capital (including buildings), one-off, research, running costs (including salaries),

recurring costs and start-up costs will be considered. Funding may be given for up to three years.

RANGE OF GRANTS £100–£6,000, typical grant £250.

SAMPLE GRANTS £4,000 to Balsall Heath Church Centre; £2,000 to the Birmingham Settlement; £1,000 to the Dorothy Parkes Central; £500 each to RSPB, Safeline and Weoley Castle Community Church; and £250 each to Happy Days Children's Charity, Bromsgrove Bereavement Counselling Service and Birmingham Mental Health Leisure Forum.

FINANCES *Year* 2007–08 *Income* £57,214 *Grants* £53,200 *Assets* £1,376,326

TRUSTEES D J Cadbury; R C King; Mrs F M Adams; Mrs V C Dub; S S King; Mrs B J Major; D A Payne; R I Payne.

HOW TO APPLY On a form available from the trust's website (or from the correspondent). Applications should include the organisation's most recent set of audited accounts and must be submitted by the end of May for the summer meeting and the end of November for the winter meeting. Successful applications will be acknowledged as soon as possible after the meeting at which they are considered.

WHO TO APPLY TO Robert C King, Secretary, 1 Matthews Close, Rushton, Kettering, Northamptonshire NN14 1QJ *Tel* 01536 418905 *email* robcking@aol.com *Website* www.harrypaynetrust.org.uk

CC NO 231063　　　　　**ESTABLISHED** 1939

■ The Peacock Charitable Trust

WHERE FUNDING CAN BE GIVEN UK with a possible preference for London and the south of England

WHO CAN BENEFIT Registered charities benefiting children and young adults, ex-service and service people, disabled people, ex-offenders, at risk groups and carers. Also people with Alzheimer's disease, arthritis and rheumatism, cancer, hearing loss, heart disease, mental illness, multiple sclerosis, and substance abuse.

WHAT IS FUNDED Charities which the trustees have special knowledge of, interest in, or association with, in the fields of medical research, disability, and some youth work.

WHAT IS NOT FUNDED No donations are made to individuals and only in rare cases are additions made to the list of charities already being supported.

TYPE OF GRANT Capital, project and some recurring.

RANGE OF GRANTS £1,000–£105,000.

SAMPLE GRANTS Cancer Research UK (£105,000); Fairbridge (£100,000); Marie Curie Cancer Care (£82,000); Neuro Disability Research Trust (£70,000) Chichester Harbour Trust (£50,000); British Heart Foundation (£40,000); Epsom Medical Research (£30,000); Action for ME (£25,000); Woodland Trust (£8,000); REACH Volunteering (£6,000); League of Ventures – Search and Rescue (£5,000); and Trinity College Centre (£1,200).

FINANCES *Year* 2007–08 *Income* £1,959,816 *Grants* £1,725,000 *Assets* £39,070,965

TRUSTEES Susan Peacock; Charles Peacock; Kenneth Burgin; Bettine Bond; Dr Clare Sellors.

HOW TO APPLY In writing to the correspondent.

WHO TO APPLY TO The Administrator, c/o Charities Aid Foundation, Kings Hill, West Malling, Kent ME19 4TA *Tel* 01732 520081 *Fax* 01732 520001

CC NO 257655　　　　　**ESTABLISHED** 1968

■ The Susanna Peake Charitable Trust

WHERE FUNDING CAN BE GIVEN UK, with a preference for the south west of England, particularly Gloucestershire.

WHO CAN BENEFIT Registered charities.

WHAT IS FUNDED General charitable purposes.

WHAT IS NOT FUNDED No grants to individuals.

TYPE OF GRANT Usually one-off grants.

RANGE OF GRANTS Usually £500–£5,000.

SAMPLE GRANTS Chipping Norton Theatre and Friends Group and The Nelson Trust (£10,000 each); Fine Cell Work, Gurkha Welfare Trust and The Museum of London (£5,000 each); Interact Reading Service and Pain Relief Foundation (£3,000 each); Gloucestershire Historic Churches and Tax Aid (£2,000 each); The Gloucestershire Society (£1,000); Charity Aid Fund (£750); and Canine Partners (£500).

FINANCES *Year* 2007–08 *Income* £188,068 *Grants* £164,750 *Assets* £5,191,241

TRUSTEES Susanna Peake; David Peake.

HOW TO APPLY In writing to the correspondent. 'The trustees meet on an ad hoc basis to review applications for funding, and a full review is undertaken annually when the financial statements are available. Only successful applications are notified of the trustees' decision.'

WHO TO APPLY TO The Administrator, Rathbone Trust Company Limited, 159 New Bond Street, London W1S 2UD *Tel* 020 7399 0820

CC NO 283462   **ESTABLISHED** 1981

■ The David Pearlman Charitable Foundation

WHERE FUNDING CAN BE GIVEN UK.

WHO CAN BENEFIT Jewish people.

WHAT IS FUNDED General charitable purposes.

SAMPLE GRANTS British Friends of Igud Hakolelim B'Yerushalayim (£60,000); Lolev Charitable Trust (£30,000); Jewish Care (£16,000); Chevras Mo'oz Ladol (£15,000); Norwood (£12,000); the Duke of Edinburgh Trust (£7,000); Community Security Trust (£6,000); Life's 4 Living Trust Ltd (£6,400); Children Number One Foundation (£3,750); the Variety Club Children's Charity (£2,750); London Academy of Jewish Studies (£1,500); Jewish Music Institute and United Jewish Israel Appeal (£1,000).

FINANCES *Year* 2007–08 *Income* £72,384 *Grants* £160,108 *Assets* £1,298,107

TRUSTEES D A Pearlman; M R Goldberger; S Appleman; J Hager.

HOW TO APPLY In writing to the correspondent.

WHO TO APPLY TO M R Goldberger, Trustee, New Burlington House, 1075 Finchley Road, London NW11 0PU *Tel* 020 8731 0777

CC NO 287009   **ESTABLISHED** 1983

■ The Pears Foundation

WHERE FUNDING CAN BE GIVEN Worldwide.

WHO CAN BENEFIT Charitable organisations.

WHAT IS FUNDED 'The Pears Foundation invests in five main areas – (1) Community and young people: Shared Society – we aim to promote respect and understanding between people of different backgrounds and to enable individuals to participate in society based on a strong sense of personal identity and responsibility. Faith and Social Justice – we aim to support faith communities to take a more central role in building a society based around the values of social justice. Empowering Vulnerable Groups – we aim to support vulnerable groups in society and enable them to campaign effectively on their own behalf. (2) Genocide prevention: Holocaust Education – we aim to improve the quality and geographic reach of education about the Holocaust, including its causes, its effects, its place in history and its role in our understanding about ideas of citizenship. Genocide Education and Campaigns – we aim to promote education about the causes and consequences of genocide and also support campaigns to prevent genocide today. (3) International development: Rights-based Development – we aim to make a contribution to a rights-based approach to international development. Faith-based Development – we aim to support Jewish engagement in international development and research about the contribution that faith communities can make. (4) Israel: Promoting Israel's Academic Expertise – we aim to support the application of Israel's academic expertise to the challenges of the world. Civil Society – we aim to support universal rights for all of Israel's citizens. Israeli Arabs – we aim to increase engagement and understanding about the issues facing Israel's Arab citizens. (5) Philanthropy: we aim to work with other philanthropic organisations committed to thinking about and advancing the role of philanthropy in society.'

TYPE OF GRANT Core, project and capital.

FINANCES *Year* 2008–09 *Income* £4,861,627 *Grants* £5,850,841 *Assets* £15,129,454

TRUSTEES Trevor S Pears, Chair; Mark Pears; David Pears; Michael Keidan.

HOW TO APPLY 'Please note that we do not accept unsolicited applications. The foundation has a full time staff, and specialist consultants, who proactively research areas of interest, creating strategic plans and partnerships with organisations seeking to effect sustainable change. The trustees meet quarterly to review the strategic direction of the foundation and to consider major proposals.'

WHO TO APPLY TO The Trustees, 2 Old Brewery Mews, Hampstead, London NW3 1PZ *Website* www.pearsfoundation.org.uk

CC NO 1009195   **ESTABLISHED** 1991

■ Pearson's Holiday Fund

WHERE FUNDING CAN BE GIVEN UK.

WHO CAN BENEFIT Children and young people aged between 4 and 16 who: have learning difficulties, physical disabilities or other heath related problems; have experienced abuse or violence in the home or are regarded as being at risk; have to care for older parents or parents who have disabilities; or have other problems, such as being refugees or homeless.

WHAT IS FUNDED Helping disadvantaged children and young people living in the United Kingdom to have holidays, outings in the United Kingdom that take them away for a little while from their otherwise mundane or restricted environment which would not be possible without some external financial support.

RANGE OF GRANTS Up to £75 per individual.

FINANCES *Year* 2008 *Income* £60,586 *Grants* £36,423 *Assets* £117,061

TRUSTEES A John Bale, Chair; John S Bradley; David P Golder; John F Gore; Mark A Hutchings; Ms Jan Elbourn.

Think carefully about every application. Is it justified?

771

HOW TO APPLY In writing to the correspondent. However due to the trust's low income in recent years, the trust may not be able to provide some activities. Potential applicants are strongly advised to visit the trust's website where full details of the trust's position are posted. Full guidelines are available from the correspondent (upon receipt of an sae) or downloadable from the website. Completed forms must be returned with a sae. Applications will not be accepted by e-mail. Applications must include evidence the criteria and conditions of the fund are being met, the number of children/young people expected to benefit from the activity, the amount requested and details of who the cheque should be made payable to. Applications for individuals must be supported by a referring agency, such as social workers, health visitors, teachers, doctors, ministers of religion and so on.

WHO TO APPLY TO The General Secretary, PO Box 3017, South Croydon CR2 9PN *Tel* 020 8657 3053 *Website* www.pearsonsholidayfund.org

CC NO 217024   **ESTABLISHED** 1910

■ The Pedmore Sporting Club Trust Fund

WHERE FUNDING CAN BE GIVEN West Midlands.

WHO CAN BENEFIT Registered charities and individuals.

WHAT IS FUNDED General charitable purposes.

WHAT IS NOT FUNDED No grants towards running costs or salaries.

TYPE OF GRANT Recurrent.

RANGE OF GRANTS £250 to £40,000.

SAMPLE GRANTS Three Roses Homes (£15,000); Primrose Hospice and Kemp Hospice (£2,500 each); Phoenix Centre (£2,000); Four Wheels Travel and Stourbridge Cricket Club (£1,000 each); West Midlands Disability Swim Squad (£650); LARA (£500); Black Country Talking News (£280); and Norton Sunshine (£250).

FINANCES *Year* 2008 *Income* £50,662 *Grants* £56,014 *Assets* £267,847

TRUSTEES N A Hickman; R Herman-Smith; R Williams; T J Hickman; J M Price.

OTHER INFORMATION In 2007/08, 33 grants were made to organisations.

HOW TO APPLY In writing to the correspondent. The trustees meet to consider grants in January, May, September and November.

WHO TO APPLY TO Alan Nicklin, Secretary, Sims Lane, Netherton, Dudley, West Midlands DY2 9BL *Tel* 07791 500449 *email* psclub@ pedmorehouse.co.uk

CC NO 263907   **ESTABLISHED** 1973

■ The Dowager Countess Eleanor Peel Trust

WHERE FUNDING CAN BE GIVEN Worldwide in practice UK, with a preference for Lancashire (especially Lancaster and District), Cumbria, Greater Manchester, Cheshire and Merseyside.

WHO CAN BENEFIT Registered charities.

WHAT IS FUNDED General charitable purposes, particularly medical charities, charities for older people and socially disadvantaged people.

WHAT IS NOT FUNDED Grants are not made to charities substantially under the control of central or local government or charities primarily devoted to children. Due to the number of applications received, the trust is usually unable to support small local charities with a gross

annual income of less than £50,000, or those with substantial surpluses. Applications from individuals are not considered.

TYPE OF GRANT The trust prefers to support projects rather than running costs.

RANGE OF GRANTS Mostly between £1,000 and £5,000.

SAMPLE GRANTS University of Liverpool (£150,000); Peel Medical Research Trust (£85,000); Nottingham Trent University (£75,000); Peel Studentship Trust (£40,000); Cancer Care North Lancs and South Lakeland (£20,000); British Red Cross (£10,000); Age Concern England (£12,000); Deafway (£6,000); Hospital of the Blessed Trinity and Karen Hilltribes Trust (£5,000 each); Touchstones 12 (£3,000); and West Cumbria Society for the Blind (£2,500).

FINANCES *Year* 2007–08 *Income* £630,482 *Grants* £598,844 *Assets* £14,577,791

TRUSTEES Sir Robert Boyd; Richard L Rothwell Jackson; John W Parkinson; Michael Parkinson.

HOW TO APPLY The trustees apply the following criteria in making grants: there is no geographical limitation on applications, however applications from charities in the 'preferred Locations' of Lancashire (especially Lancaster and District), Cumbria, Greater Manchester, Cheshire and Merseyside will receive preference over applications from other geographical areas; the trustees focus on small to medium sized charities where grants will make a difference. Applications from large well-funded charities (with income in excess of £2.5 million per annum) will normally be rejected, unless the project is a capital project; the trustees aim to support fewer charities with larger average grants (£5,000 or more); the trustees' preference is to support capital projects or project driven applications and not running costs, although the trustees are flexible to take account of the needs of smaller charities; the trustees do make grants to disaster appeals which are considered on a case by case basis. The trustees feel it is important to know the charities to which grants are or may be awarded. They will therefore from time to time arrange to visit the charity and/or arrange for the charity to make a presentation to a trustees meeting. The following information is required in an application: a general outline of the reasons for the application; the amount of grant applied for; the latest annual report and audited accounts; if the application is for a major capital project, details of the cost of the project together with information regarding funds already in hand or pledged. A grant application form can be downloaded from the trust's website – print it out before filling it in and enclosing it with any other information that you may feel is relevant. *Applications for Medical Research Grants* – Applications for medical research grants will be categorised as appropriate for a 'minor grant' (£10,000 or less) or a 'major grant' (greater than £10,000 per annum for a defined research project for one to three years). Applications to be considered for a major grant will be assessed en-block annually at the trustee's March meeting. Applications will be competitive and will be met from funds set aside for this purpose. The following additional information is required: aims, objectives and direction of the research project; the institution where the research will be carried out and by whom (principal researchers); an outline of costs and of funding required for the project and details of any funds already in hand. A brief (but not too technical) annual report on the progress of projects receiving major grants will be requested from the research team.

WHO TO APPLY TO Allan J Twitchett, Secretary, Trowers & Hamlins LLP, Sceptre Court, 40 Tower Hill, London EC3N 4DX *Tel* 020 7423 8000 *Fax* 020 7423 8001 *email* secretary@ peeltrust.com *Website* www.peeltrust.com
CC NO 214684　　**ESTABLISHED** 1951

■ Pegasus (Stanley) Trust

WHERE FUNDING CAN BE GIVEN Mainly Shropshire.
WHO CAN BENEFIT Organisations and individuals.
WHAT IS FUNDED The main object of the trust is relief in need for people who have had cancer and/or strokes, grants are also given to other charities.
SAMPLE GRANTS The Prince's Trust (£20,000); St John Ambulance (£4,000); Breakthrough Breast Cancer, County Air Ambulance, Hope House, Macmillan Cancer Support and Severn Hospice (£3,000 each); Golden Years Appeal (£2,000); and Global Witness Trust (£1,000).
FINANCES *Year* 2007–08 *Income* £332,140 *Grants* £46,000 *Assets* £191
TRUSTEES H R Gabb; H Carpenter; F Bury; C Gabb.
OTHER INFORMATION The trust organises an annual event in May at Stanley Hall, in Shropshire, to raise funds.
HOW TO APPLY In writing to the correspondent.
WHO TO APPLY TO The Trustees, Underhill Langley & Wright Solicitors, St Leonard's House, St Leonard's Close, Bridgnorth, Shropshire WV16 4EJ
CC NO 1108684　　**ESTABLISHED** 2005

■ Peltz Trust

WHERE FUNDING CAN BE GIVEN UK and Israel.
WHO CAN BENEFIT Charitable organisations.
WHAT IS FUNDED Arts, cultural and educational initiatives; health and welfare projects; religion.
WHAT IS NOT FUNDED No grants to individuals for research or educational awards.
RANGE OF GRANTS £1,000–£20,000.
SAMPLE GRANTS Norwood Ravenswood and St Stephen's Trust (£20,000 each); Hampstead Theatre (£18,000); Jewish Care (£12,500); CLIC Sargent (£11,000); Central Synagogue General Charities, City of London School Bursary Trust, Lubavitch Foundation and Oxford Centre for Hebrew and Jewish Studies (£10,000 each); Community Security Trust (£7,000); INF Charitable Trust (£6,250); Levka 2000 (£6,000); Beth Shalom Ltd, Facing History and Ourselves Ltd, Nightingale House, One Family and Willow Foundation (£5,000 each); Wellbeing of Woman (£4,500); Greenhouse Schools Project (£4,000); War Memorials Trust (£2,500); Tikun (£2,000); and Shakespeare Globe Trust and Westminster Synagogue Memorial Scrolls (£1,000 each).
FINANCES *Year* 2007–08 *Income* £89,840 *Grants* £233,734 *Assets* £306,123
TRUSTEES Martin D Paisner; Daniel Peltz; Hon. Elizabeth Wolfson Peltz.
HOW TO APPLY In writing to the correspondent. The trustees meet at irregular intervals during the year to consider appeals from appropriate organisations.
WHO TO APPLY TO Martin D Paisner, Trustee, Berwin Leighton Paisner, Adelaide House, London Bridge, London EC4R 9HA *Tel* 020 7760 1000
CC NO 1002302　　**ESTABLISHED** 1991

■ The Pennycress Trust

WHERE FUNDING CAN BE GIVEN UK and worldwide, with a preference for Cheshire and Norfolk.
WHO CAN BENEFIT Voluntary organisations and charitable groups only.
WHAT IS FUNDED General charitable purposes. Support is given to a restricted list of registered charities only, principally in Cheshire and Norfolk, in the fields of: arts and cultural heritage; education; infrastructure, support and development; science and technology; community facilities; campaigning on health and social issues; health care and advocacy; medical studies and research; and animal welfare.
WHAT IS NOT FUNDED No support for individuals.
TYPE OF GRANT Recurrent and one-off.
RANGE OF GRANTS Usually £100–£500.
SAMPLE GRANTS Previous beneficiaries have included All Saints' Church – Beeston Regis, Brain Research Trust, Brighton and Hove Parents' and Children's Group, British Red Cross, Crusaid, Depaul Trust, Elimination of Leukaemia Fund, Eyeless Trust, Genesis Appeal, Help the Aged, Matthew Project, RUKBA, St Peter's – Eaton Square Appeal, Salvation Army, Tibet Relief Fund, West Suffolk Headway, Women's Link and Youth Federation.
FINANCES *Year* 2007–08 *Income* £90,979 *Grants* £53,900 *Assets* £2,041,579
TRUSTEES Lady Aline Cholmondeley; Anthony J M Baker; C G Cholmondeley; Miss Sybil Sassoon.
HOW TO APPLY In writing to the correspondent. 'No telephone applications please.' Trustees meet regularly. They do not have an application form as a simple letter will be sufficient.
WHO TO APPLY TO Mrs Doreen Howells, Secretary to the Trustees, Flat D, 15 Millman Street, London WC1N 3EP *Tel* 020 7404 0145
CC NO 261536　　**ESTABLISHED** 1970

■ The Performing Right Society Foundation

WHERE FUNDING CAN BE GIVEN UK.
WHO CAN BENEFIT Music creators, performers and promoters who are involved in creatively adventurous or pioneering musical activity.
WHAT IS FUNDED A huge range of new music activity, for example, unsigned band showcases, festivals, residencies for composers, ground breaking commissions, live electronica, training of music producers, cross art form commissioning and special projects.
WHAT IS NOT FUNDED The foundation will not offer funding for: individuals; recordings/demos; college fees; musical equipment or instruments; activity taking place outside of the UK.
TYPE OF GRANT Usually one year funding for revenue costs.
SAMPLE GRANTS Supersonic Festival; Punch Records; Birmingham Jazz; Music Theatre Wales; Cambria Arts Association; Bruised Fruit; Paragon Ensemble; Cambridge Folk Festival; and Drake Music Project Scotland.
FINANCES *Year* 2008 *Income* £1,694,145 *Grants* £1,378,581 *Assets* £276,187
TRUSTEES Sally Taylor; Nigel Elderton; Mick Leeson; Paulette Long; Anthony Mackintosh; Estelle Morris; Michael Noonan; Stephen McNeff; Edward Gregson.
OTHER INFORMATION A list of grant recipients was not included in the accounts. However, details of previously funded projects are available on the foundation's website, though without information on the individual grant awards.

HOW TO APPLY On an application form available to download from the foundation's website, or by telephoning the foundation. The application forms for each programme also include full guidelines for applicants. Only one scheme per calendar year can be applied for. Deadlines for applications vary from programme to programme. Contact the foundation or go to the website for further information. The foundation stresses that it funds NEW music. Note: the foundation will be rolling out an online application system across all its programmes during 2010.

WHO TO APPLY TO James Hannam, Applications Manager, 29–33 Berners Street, London W1T 3AB *Tel* 020 7306 4044 *Fax* 020 7306 4814 *email* info@prsfoundation.co.uk *Website* www.prsfoundation.co.uk

CC NO 1080837   **ESTABLISHED** 2000

■ B E Perl Charitable Trust

WHERE FUNDING CAN BE GIVEN UK.

WHO CAN BENEFIT Orthodox Jewish organisations.

WHAT IS FUNDED General charitable purposes.

SAMPLE GRANTS Previously: The Huntingdon Foundation Limited (£1.6 million); Kisharon, Gateshead Yeshiva, Talmud Torah School, Hertsmere Jewish High School, the Harav Lord Jacobovits Torah Institute of Contemporary Issues, Gateshead Jewish Academy for Girls, Or Chadash Children's Town, the British Friends of Shuvu and the Before Trust (£1,000 or more each).

FINANCES *Year* 2007–08 *Income* £1,268,754 *Grants* £99,882 *Assets* £11,658,985

TRUSTEES B Perl, Chair; Dr S Perl; Jonathan Perl; Joseph Perl; Naomi Sorotzkin; Mrs R Jeidal.

HOW TO APPLY In writing to the correspondent.

WHO TO APPLY TO B Perl, Chair, Foframe House, 35–37 Brent Street, Hendon, London NW4 2EF

CC NO 282847   **ESTABLISHED** 1981

■ The Persson Charitable Trust (formerly Highmoore Hall Charitable Trust)

WHERE FUNDING CAN BE GIVEN UK and overseas.

WHO CAN BENEFIT Registered charities benefiting: Christians; at risk groups; and victims of famine, man-made and natural disasters and war.

WHAT IS FUNDED Christian mission societies and relief agencies.

WHAT IS NOT FUNDED No grants to non-registered charities.

TYPE OF GRANT Mainly recurrent.

SAMPLE GRANTS Bible Reading Fellowship – Foundations 21 course and Tearfund – Christian relief (£50,000 each), Alpha International (£40,000), Christian Solidarity Worldwide (£21,000) and Reaching the Unchurched (£20,000). Other listed grants included those to Integral Alliance – networking Christian relief (£12,500) and Jubilee Centre Trust – encouraging and resourcing Christians (£10,000). Smaller grants totalled almost £50,000.

FINANCES *Year* 2007–08 *Income* £343,866 *Grants* £254,486 *Assets* £449,225

TRUSTEES P D Persson; Mrs A D Persson; J P G Persson; A S J Persson.

HOW TO APPLY The trust states that it does not respond to unsolicited applications. Telephone calls are not welcome.

WHO TO APPLY TO P D Persson, Trustee, Long Meadow, Dark Lane, Chearsley, Aylesbury, Buckinghamshire HP18 0DA

CC NO 289027   **ESTABLISHED** 1984

■ The Persula Foundation

WHERE FUNDING CAN BE GIVEN Predominantly UK; overseas grants are given, but this is rare.

WHO CAN BENEFIT Mainly small registered charities benefiting at risk groups, people who are socially isolated, disadvantaged by poverty or homeless, people with cancer or disabilities, including visual impairment, deafness, spinal injuries and multiple sclerosis, and animals.

WHAT IS FUNDED Original and unique projects of national benefit in the areas of homelessness, disability, and human and animal welfare.

WHAT IS NOT FUNDED No grants to individuals, including sponsorship, for core costs, buildings/ building work or to statutory bodies.

TYPE OF GRANT Up to two years.

SAMPLE GRANTS Tapesense (£47,000).

FINANCES *Year* 2007–08 *Income* £469,377 *Grants* £622,260 *Assets* £9,306

TRUSTEES Julian Richer; David Robinson; David Highton; Mrs R Richer; Mrs H Oppenheim.

PUBLICATIONS Guidelines are available from the foundations website.

HOW TO APPLY In writing to the correspondent.

WHO TO APPLY TO Fiona Brown, Chief Executive, Unit 3/4, Gallery Court, Hankey Place, London SE1 4BB *Tel* 020 7357 9298 *Fax* 020 7357 8685 *email* fiona@persula.org *Website* www.persula.org

CC NO 1044174   **ESTABLISHED** 1994

■ The Pestalozzi Overseas Children's Trust

WHERE FUNDING CAN BE GIVEN Worldwide, especially Asia and Africa.

WHO CAN BENEFIT Schools in the developing world with which the trustees have a connection.

WHAT IS FUNDED Bursary funds towards the education of individuals identified by the schools who could not otherwise attend. The schools receive an amount for distribution as they see fit rather than a decision about ultimate beneficiaries being made by the trustees.

WHAT IS NOT FUNDED The trust emphasised that funding is not available to individuals, including students.

SAMPLE GRANTS Charitable expenditure totalled £803,988 of which £524,703 was on capital projects and £279,285 was given towards school fees.

FINANCES *Year* 2008 *Income* £915,177 *Grants* £803,988 *Assets* £2,346,332

TRUSTEES Lady Butler; J J Dilger; S P Pahlson-Moller; F Von Hurter.

HOW TO APPLY Applications cannot be made to this trust. It works in partnerships with schools it identifies through its own research and networks and are given proactively by the trust. The trust will contact organisations it wants to support proactively.

WHO TO APPLY TO Simon Wakely, Charity Correspondent, 15 Ebner Street, Wandsworth, London SW18 1BT *Tel* 020 8704 4455 *email* info@pestalozziworld.com *Website* www.pestalozziworld.com

CC NO 1046599   **ESTABLISHED** 1995

■ The Jack Petchey Foundation

WHERE FUNDING CAN BE GIVEN London boroughs, Essex and the Algarve, Portugal.

WHO CAN BENEFIT Registered charities and organisations supporting young people aged between 11 and 25.

WHAT IS FUNDED Support for young people through different programmes including: Achievement Award Scheme, Leader Award Scheme, Projects Grants and Sponsorship. Project grants and achievement awards are designed to give young people the opportunity to help themselves. Project grants are available to: promote community involvement and personal responsibility within society; provide financial assistance to clubs, youth groups, schools, etc., that demonstrate that they are enabling individuals to achieve their potential, take control of their lives and contribute to society as a whole; support the training of youth leaders; support other youth projects. Achievement awards are given to young people who make a 'wholehearted contribution' to their club, group or community. The grant must be spent on a community project chosen by the winner. Organisations may select award candidates each month. For other, smaller programmes, (including sponsorship of up to £300 for young people on gap year programmes or undertaking fundraising initiatives for other people or charities), please see the foundation's website.

WHAT IS NOT FUNDED The foundation does not support: organisations who have applied within the last 12 months; the replacement of statutory funding; individuals; except through the sponsorship programme; work that has already taken place; work that does not directly benefit people in the UK; medical research; animal welfare; endowment funds; general appeals or circulars. The foundation is also unlikely to support: building or major refurbishment projects; conferences or seminars; religious projects. Applications from outside the foundation's catchment area will not be supported.

SAMPLE GRANTS SpeakersBank Limited (£550,000); Royal Academy of Dance (£298,000); Young Enterprise London (£270,000); Mercy ships (£250,000); CBM (£223,000); Summer Uni London (£200,000); Newham Out of School Hours Learning (£193,000); Essex Association of Boys Clubs (£80,000); Sightsavers International (£50,000); YMCA George Williams College (£35,000); City Gateway, Knights Youth Centre and Newham Music Trust (£30,000 each); New Horizon Youth Centre (£25,000); Barbara Melunsky Refugee Youth Agency Limited (£22,000); and Alford House Club, Common Purpose, In-Volve, Kith & Kids, London International Festival of Theatre and Thames Gateway Youth Football Project (£20,000 each).

FINANCES *Year* 2008 *Income* £8,234,156 *Grants* £14,563,818 *Assets* £0

TRUSTEES Jack Petchey Foundation Company

HOW TO APPLY Application forms for each of the grant schemes can be downloaded from the foundation's website. There are no deadlines for applications but they should be made in 'good time' before the money is needed. The foundation holds monthly management meetings and aims to give a decision within six weeks.

WHO TO APPLY TO Andrew Billington, Director, Exchange House, 13–14 Clements Court, Clements Lane, Ilford, Essex IG1 2QY *Tel* 020 8252 8000 *Fax* 020 8477 1088 *email* mail@jackpetcheyfoundation.org.uk *Website* www.jackpetcheyfoundation.org.uk

CC NO 1076886   **ESTABLISHED** 1999

■ The Petplan Charitable Trust

WHERE FUNDING CAN BE GIVEN UK.

WHO CAN BENEFIT Animal charities and organisations benefiting students, research workers and veterinarians.

WHAT IS FUNDED Veterinary research, animal welfare, education in animal welfare, and other charitable purposes. Help is limited to dogs, cats and horses only, those being the animals insured by Pet Plan. Rabbits will be considered.

WHAT IS NOT FUNDED No grants to individuals or non-registered charities. The trust does not support or condone invasive procedures, vivisection or experimentation of any kind.

RANGE OF GRANTS Scientific grants: £3,000–£200,000. Welfare and education: Grants £500–£10,000.

SAMPLE GRANTS University of Glasgow (£200,000); Hampshire Fire and Rescue (£65,000); Cats Protection and Mayhew Animal Home (£10,000 each); Stokenchurch Dog Rescue (£7,500); Cat Chat (£6,000); Assisi Animal Sanctuary (£5,000); Royal Veterinary College (£3,100); Exmoor Search and Rescue (£3,000); and Cotton Tails – rabbit and guinea pig rescue (£2,000).

FINANCES *Year* 2008 *Income* £529,908 *Grants* £517,271 *Assets* £179,144

TRUSTEES David Simpson, Chair; Clarissa Baldwin; Patsy Bloom; John Bower; Ted Chandler; George Stratford.

HOW TO APPLY Closing dates for scientific and welfare applications vary so please check the trust's website first. Grant guidelines and application forms can also be downloaded from the trust's website.

WHO TO APPLY TO Catherine Bourg, Administrator, Great West House GW2, Great West Road, Brentford, Middlesex TW8 9EG *Tel* 020 8580 8013 *Fax* 020 8580 8186 *email* catherine.bourg@allianz.co.uk *Website* www.petplantrust.org

CC NO 1032907   **ESTABLISHED** 1994

■ The Phillips and Rubens Charitable Trust

WHERE FUNDING CAN BE GIVEN UK.

WHO CAN BENEFIT Registered charities, especially Jewish causes.

WHAT IS FUNDED Jewish organisations, especially those in the fields of education, children's charities, the arts, and medical groups.

WHAT IS NOT FUNDED No grants are made to individuals.

TYPE OF GRANT Recurrent and one-off.

SAMPLE GRANTS Phillips Family Charitable Trust (£110,000); United Jewish Israel Appeal (£41,000); Charities Aid Foundation and Jewish Community Secondary School (£25,000 each); Royal Opera House Foundation (£11,000); Holocaust Educational Trust (£10,000); British ORT (£7,500); Nightingale House (£5,000); Wizo Charitable Foundation (£2,000); and City of London School (£1,000).

FINANCES *Year* 2007–08 *Income* £142,168 *Grants* £339,822 *Assets* £9,783,678

TRUSTEES Michael L Philips; Mrs Ruth Philips; Martin D Paisner; Paul Philips; Gary Philips; Carolyn Mishon.

OTHER INFORMATION Grants to organisations of less than £1,000 each totalled £5,400.

HOW TO APPLY In writing to the correspondent at any time.

WHO TO APPLY TO M L Phillips, Trustee, Fifth Floor, Berkeley Square House, Berkeley Square, London W1J 6BY *Tel* 020 7491 3763 *Fax* 020 7491 0818

CC NO 260378   **ESTABLISHED** 1970

■ The Phillips Charitable Trust

WHERE FUNDING CAN BE GIVEN UK, with a preference for the Midlands, particularly Northamptonshire.

WHO CAN BENEFIT Seafarer organisations, animal welfare organisations, the National Trust and English Heritage, and smaller one-off grants for national or local projects.

WHAT IS FUNDED Seafaring and animal welfare.

TYPE OF GRANT Recurrent.

RANGE OF GRANTS £500–£14,000.

SAMPLE GRANTS St John's Home (£14,000); Peterborough Cathedral Development & Preservation Trust and The National Trust (£10,000 each); SportsAid East (£7,500); Naseby Battlefield Project (£5,000); Animals in Need (£4,000); Warwickshire & Northamptonshire Air Ambulance (£2,500); Ro-Ro Sailing Project and Northampton Sea Cadets (£2,000 each); and 11th Company of Boys Brigade (£500).

FINANCES *Year* 2007–08 *Income* £95,673 *Grants* £61,300 *Assets* £2,098,547

TRUSTEES M J Ford; M J Percival; Mrs A M Marrum; P R Saunderson; S G Schanschieff.

HOW TO APPLY In writing to the correspondent.

WHO TO APPLY TO M J Percival, Trustee, Oxford House, Cliftonville, Northampton NN1 5PN *Tel* 01604 230 400 *Fax* 01604 604 164

CC NO 1057019   **ESTABLISHED** 1995

■ The Phillips Family Charitable Trust

WHERE FUNDING CAN BE GIVEN UK.

WHO CAN BENEFIT Registered charities only.

WHAT IS FUNDED General charitable purposes, mainly Jewish organisations, and those concerned with older people, children, refugees and education.

WHAT IS NOT FUNDED No grants to individuals.

TYPE OF GRANT Grants are given for core, capital and project support.

RANGE OF GRANTS Up to £15,000, but mostly £5,000 or less.

SAMPLE GRANTS UJIA (£15,000); Holocaust Educational Trust (£10,000 in two grants); Jewish Leadership Council (£7,000 in two grants); Chief Rabbinate Trust and Community Security Trust (£5,000 each); elephant family (£3,500); Lubavitch Foundation (£3,000); Maccabi GB (£2,000); President's Club Charitable Trust (£1,500); and Royal National Institute for the Blind and Windsor Jewish Cultural Centre (£1,000 each).

FINANCES *Year* 2008–09 *Income* £90,244 *Grants* £93,819 *Assets* £26,060

TRUSTEES Michael L Phillips; Mrs Ruth Phillips; Martin D Paisner; Paul S Phillips; Gary M Phillips.

HOW TO APPLY In writing to the correspondent. Please note, the trust informed us that there is not much scope for new beneficiaries.

WHO TO APPLY TO Paul S Phillips, Trustee, Berkeley Square House, Berkeley Square, London W1J 6BY *Tel* 020 7491 3763

CC NO 279120   **ESTABLISHED** 1979

■ Philological Foundation

WHERE FUNDING CAN BE GIVEN City of Westminster and London borough of Camden.

WHO CAN BENEFIT Schools in the City of Westminster and the London borough of Camden, and their pupils and ex-pupils under 25 years of age.

WHAT IS FUNDED Individuals may receive grants for educational expenses and tuition fees; schools in the area may benefit over a wide range of purposes.

WHAT IS NOT FUNDED No support for schools not in Westminster or Camden and individuals who did not attend school in the City of Westminster or London borough of Camden. The foundation does not give bursaries, scholarships or loans.

RANGE OF GRANTS £200–£2,000.

FINANCES *Year* 2007–08 *Income* £46,520 *Grants* £42,409 *Assets* £838,369

TRUSTEES P E Sayers; Mrs S Standing; Cllr Mrs G Hampson; Mrs M Hall; Mrs J Keen; D Jones; G Margolis; R P Rea.

HOW TO APPLY There is an application form available for schools which may be obtained from the foundation. Individuals should apply in writing to the clerk. Trustees meet typically in January, March, June, September and December. Applications should be submitted several weeks before the relevant meeting. Successful applicants may reapply after one year.

WHO TO APPLY TO Mrs Audrey Millar, Clerk, Apartment 15, Fitzwarren House, Hornsey Lane, Highgate, London N6 5LX *Tel* 020 7281 7439 *email* audreymillar@btinternet.com

CC NO 312692   **ESTABLISHED** 1982

■ The David Pickford Charitable Foundation

WHERE FUNDING CAN BE GIVEN UK (with a preference for Kent and London) and overseas.

WHO CAN BENEFIT Mainly, but not solely, young people and Christian evangelism.

WHAT IS FUNDED Support of a residential Christian youth centre in Kent for those in the 15 to 25 age group and other similar activities, mainly Christian youth work.

WHAT IS NOT FUNDED No grants to individuals. No building projects.

TYPE OF GRANT One-off and recurrent.

SAMPLE GRANTS CARE (£5,000); Chaucer Trust (£4,000); Oasis Trust (£2,500); Brighter Future and Pastor Training International (£1,000 each); Toybox (£750); Alpha International, Flow Romania and Mersham Parish Church (£500 each); Compassion (£300); Samaritans (£250); and Lionhart (£15).

FINANCES *Year* 2006–07 *Income* £23,712 *Grants* £34,065 *Assets* £833,324

TRUSTEES D M Pickford; C J Pickford; Mrs E J Pettersen.

HOW TO APPLY In writing to the correspondent. Trustees meet every other month from January. Applications will not be acknowledged. The correspondent states: 'It is our general policy only to give to charities to whom we are personally known'. Those falling outside the criteria mentioned above will be ignored.

WHO TO APPLY TO D M Pickford, Trustee, Elm Tree Farm, Mersham, Ashford, Kent TN25 7HS
Tel 01233 720 200 *Fax* 01233 720 522
CC NO 243437   **ESTABLISHED** 1965

....

■ The Bernard Piggott Trust

WHERE FUNDING CAN BE GIVEN North Wales and Birmingham.

WHO CAN BENEFIT Organisations benefiting children, young adults, medical, actors and entertainment professionals, and Church of England and Wales.

WHAT IS FUNDED Church of England; Church of Wales; education; medical charities, both care and research; drama and the theatre; young people and children.

WHAT IS NOT FUNDED No grants to individuals.

TYPE OF GRANT Usually one-off capital. No further grants within two years.

RANGE OF GRANTS £250–£5,000. Average about £1,000.

SAMPLE GRANTS The Black Country Living Museum (£4,000); Cynllun Efe (£3,000); St Tanwg Church – Llandanwg (£2,500); Acorns, Cure Leukaemia, Parkinson's Disease Society and Sunfield (£2,000 each); Conway County District Scouts, DebRA and Listening Books (£1,500); and Birmingham Focus on Blindness and British Stammering (£1,000 each).

FINANCES *Year* 2007–08 *Income* £101,708 *Grants* £68,630 *Assets* £1,318,877

TRUSTEES D M P Lea; N J L Lea; R J Easton; Archdeacon of Bangor.

HOW TO APPLY The trustees meet in May/June and November. Applications should be in writing to the secretary including annual accounts and details of the specific project including running costs and so on. General policy is not to consider any further grant to the same institution within the next two years.

WHO TO APPLY TO Miss J P Whitworth, 4 Streetsbrook Road, Shirley, Solihull, West Midlands B90 3PL
Tel 0121 744 1695 *Fax* 0121 744 1695
CC NO 260347   **ESTABLISHED** 1970

....

■ The Claude and Margaret Pike Charity

WHERE FUNDING CAN BE GIVEN Mainly Devon.

WHO CAN BENEFIT Individuals and organisations.

WHAT IS FUNDED Projects that benefit people living in Devon.

WHAT IS NOT FUNDED No appeals from outside of Devon will be considered.

TYPE OF GRANT One-off grants.

SAMPLE GRANTS Dean and Chapter of Exeter Cathedral (£5,000); Teign Heritage – Teignmouth and Shaldon Museum (£2,500 each); Belstone Village Hall and Hospiscare – Exeter (£2,000 each); Dartington International Summer School – bursaries (£1,200); Wolborough PCC – Newton Abbot (£1,000); Sir Francis Chichester Trust (£750); and 1st Newton Abbot Scout Group – Kingsteignton, Bidwell Brook Foundation, Kingsteignton Athletic Football Club, Positive Lifestyle in Devon, Stallcombe House and Torquay Museum Society (£500 each).

FINANCES *Year* 2007–08 *Income* £79,891 *Grants* £40,634 *Assets* £227,423

TRUSTEES J D Pike; Dr P A D Holland; Mrs S S Pike.

OTHER INFORMATION The 2007–08 grant total included £10,075 donated in 71 grants to individuals. Grants are made to young people to

encourage and advance their leadership qualities and gain experience through organisations such as the Projects Trust, Operation Raleigh, British Schools Exploration Society and the Duke of Edinburgh Gold Award Scheme.

HOW TO APPLY In writing to the correspondent.

WHO TO APPLY TO John D Pike, Trustee, Dunderdale Lawn, Penshurst Road, Newton Abbey, Devon TQ12 1EN
CC NO 247657   **ESTABLISHED** 1965

....

■ The Pilgrim Trust

WHERE FUNDING CAN BE GIVEN UK, but not the Channel Islands and the Isle of Man.

WHO CAN BENEFIT Local and UK charities and recognised public bodies.

WHAT IS FUNDED Preservation (covering ecclesiastical buildings, secular buildings), learning and social welfare.

WHAT IS NOT FUNDED Grants are not made to: 'individuals; non UK registered charities or charities registered in the Channel Islands or the Isle of Man; projects based outside the United Kingdom; projects where the work has already been completed or where contracts have already been awarded; organisations that have had a grant awarded by us within the past two years. Note: this does not refer to payments made within that timeframe; projects with a capital cost of over £1 million pounds where partnership funding is required; projects where the activities are considered to be primarily the responsibility of central or local government; general appeals or circulars; projects for the commissioning of new works of art; organisations seeking publishing production costs; projects seeking to develop new facilities within a church or the re-ordering of churches or places of worship for wider community use; any social welfare project that falls outside the trustees' current priorities; arts and drama projects – unless they can demonstrate that they are linked to clear educational goals for prisoners or those with drug or alcohol problems; drop in centres – unless the specific work within the centre falls within one of the trustees' current priority areas; youth or sports clubs, travel or adventure projects, community centres or children's play groups; organisations seeking funding for trips abroad; organisations seeking educational funding, e.g. assistance to individuals for degree or post-degree work or school, university or college development programmes; one-off events such as exhibitions, festivals, seminars, conferences or theatrical and musical productions.'

TYPE OF GRANT Infrastructure costs for specific projects (salary and running costs up to a maximum of three years), capital grants. Also buildings, one-off, research and start-up costs.

SAMPLE GRANTS National Churches Trust (£140,000); Bowes Museum (£80,000); Shelter (£67,000); Revolving Doors Agency (£60,000); Coultard Institute of Art (£40,200); Westminster Abbey (£40,000); Caledonian Youth Limited (£38,000); North East Scotland Preservation Trust (£30,000); East Potential (£20,000); Salford Unemployed and Community Resource Centre (£15,000); and Children's Link (£4,500).

FINANCES *Year* 2008 *Income* £1,587,979 *Grants* £1,996,230 *Assets* £47,456,366

TRUSTEES Lady Jay of Ewelme, Chair; Lord David Cobbold; Dame Ruth Runciman; Tim Knox; Paul Richards; Mark Jones; Sir Alan Moses; John

Podmore; James Fergusson; David Verey; Lord Crisp.

HOW TO APPLY 'Main Grant Fund: as our primary grant outlet, this fund distributes approximately 90% of our annual grant budget. If the project fits our programme criteria, organisations can apply under this scheme for sums above £5,000. Small Grant Fund: this fund is reserved for requests of £5,000 or less. Applications to this fund normally require less detailed assessment (though a visit or meeting may be required) but applicants should include the names of two referees from organisations with whom they work.' Full funding guidelines are available from the trust's website. Applications can also be made online or a form can be requested from the correspondent. The trustees meet quarterly.

WHO TO APPLY TO Miss Georgina Nayler, Director, Clutha House, 10 Storeys Gate, London SW1P 3AY *Tel* 020 7222 4723 *Fax* 020 7976 0461 *email* georgina.nayler@thepilgrimtrust.org. uk *Website* www.thepilgrimtrust.org.uk

CC NO 206602   **ESTABLISHED** 1930

....

■ The Cecil Pilkington Charitable Trust

WHERE FUNDING CAN BE GIVEN UK, particularly Sunningwell in Oxfordshire and St Helens.

WHO CAN BENEFIT Registered charities only.

WHAT IS FUNDED This trust supports conservation and medical research causes across the UK. It also has general charitable purposes.

WHAT IS NOT FUNDED No grants to individuals or non-registered charities.

RANGE OF GRANTS £500–£60,000.

SAMPLE GRANTS Peninsular Medical School Foundation (£12,000); St Leonard's Church Restoration (£10,000); Alzheimer's Research Trust (£6,000); SANE (£5,000); RABI and Willowbrooke Hospice (£3,000 each); Compassion in World Farming, Global Canopy Foundation and Lepus UK (£2,000 each); Barn Owl Trust, Diabetes UK, PEACH and Rare Breeds Survival Trust (£1,000 each); and Agro Forestry Research Trust (£500).

FINANCES *Year* 2007–08 *Income* £256,623 *Grants* £92,500 *Assets* £6,804,177

TRUSTEES A P Pilkington; R F Carter Jonas; M R Feeny.

HOW TO APPLY The trust does not respond to unsolicited appeals.

WHO TO APPLY TO The Administrator, Duncan Sheard Glass, Castle Chambers, 43 Castle Street, Liverpool L2 9TL

CC NO 249997   **ESTABLISHED** 1966

....

■ The Pilkington Charities Fund

WHERE FUNDING CAN BE GIVEN Worldwide, in practice mainly UK with a preference for Merseyside.

WHO CAN BENEFIT Registered charities.

WHAT IS FUNDED Health, social welfare, people with disabilities, older people and victims of natural disaster or war.

WHAT IS NOT FUNDED Applications from unregistered organisations and individuals are not considered.

TYPE OF GRANT Capital (including buildings), core costs, one-off, project, research, recurring costs. Funding for more than three years will be considered.

RANGE OF GRANTS Up to £10,000, although exceptional large grants are made.

SAMPLE GRANTS C & A Pilkington Trust Fund (£77,000); Arthritis Research Campaign, Cancer Research UK, Help the Aged, Willowbrook Hospice – St Helens and YWCA (£10,000 each); BiPolar Organisation (£8,000); Cystic Fibrosis Trust, Children at Risk Foundation and the Samaritans (£5,000 each); Leukaemia Research and St Cleopas 468 Community Centre (£4,000 each); Autism Initiative, St Michael's and Lark Lane Community Association and the Salvation Army – Liverpool Walton Corps (£3,000 each); Riverside Credit Union and Women Supporting Women (£2,000 each); and Listening Books and Warrington Wolves Foundation (£1,000 each).

FINANCES *Year* 2007–08 *Income* £590,046 *Grants* £385,912 *Assets* £17,599,658

TRUSTEES Neil Pilkington Jones; Mrs Jennifer Jones; Arnold Philip Pilkington.

HOW TO APPLY In writing to the correspondent. Applications should include charity registration number, a copy of the latest accounts and details of the project for which support is sought.

WHO TO APPLY TO Sarah Nicklin, Trust Administrator, Rathbones, Port of Liverpool Building, Pier Head, Liverpool L3 1NW *Tel* 0151 236 6666 *Fax* 0151 243 7003 *email* sarah.nicklin@ rathbones.com

CC NO 225911   **ESTABLISHED** 1964

....

■ The Austin and Hope Pilkington Trust

WHERE FUNDING CAN BE GIVEN Unrestricted, but see Exclusions field.

WHO CAN BENEFIT Registered charities only. National projects are preferred to those with a local remit.

WHAT IS FUNDED The trust has a three-year cycle of funding. (2009 – community and disability; 2010 – children, young people, older people and medical; and 2011 – music and the arts and overseas.) These categories are then repeated in a three-year rotation.

WHAT IS NOT FUNDED Grants only to registered charities. No grants to individuals, including individuals embarking on a trip overseas with an umbrella organisation. Overseas projects can only be supported in the stated year. National organisations are more likely to be supported than purely local organisations. Charities working in the following areas are not supported: religion (including repair of Church fabric), animals (welfare and conservation).

TYPE OF GRANT Grants are usually awarded for one year only.

RANGE OF GRANTS Grants are usually between £1,000 and £10,000, with the majority being £5,000 or less. Exceptionally, grants of up to £20,000 are made, but these are usually for medical research projects.

SAMPLE GRANTS *Arts and music:* Centre Point, Great Ormond Street Hospital and Sir John Soane Museum (£5,000 each); Academy of St Martin-in-the-Fields, Bournemouth Symphony Orchestra, Derby Playhouse, Live Arts in Pembrokeshire, Tate Modern and Youth at Risk (£3,000 each); Buxton Opera House, Deep Impact Theatre Company, Handel House Museum, Opera North, Orcadia Creative Learning Centre, Opheus Centre and Reach Inclusive Arts (£1,000 each). *Overseas:* Learning for Life (£9,000); Interact Worldwide and Oxfam (£5,000 each); Care International, Farm Africa, Plan and St Dunstan's (£3,000 each); Harvesthelp, Target

Tuberculosis, Tools for Self Reliance, Tree Aid, War Child, Water Aid and Wells for India (£1,000 each).

FINANCES *Year* 2007 *Income* £282,979 *Grants* £313,304 *Assets* £9,468,512

TRUSTEES Jennifer Jones; Deborah Nelson; Penny Shankar.

HOW TO APPLY Applicants are strongly advised to visit the trust's website as projects supported and eligibility criteria change from year to year. Grants are made twice a year, with deadlines for applications being 1 June and 1 November. Applications should be made in writing to the correspondent. To apply for a grant, please submit the following: a letter summarising the application, including acknowledgement of any previous grants awarded from the trust; a maximum of two sides of A4 (including photographs) summarising the project; a detailed budget for the project; a maximum of two sides of A4 (including photographs) summarising the charity's general activities; the most recent accounts and annual report. 'Please do not send CDs, DVDs, or any other additional information. If we require further details, we will contact the charity directly. Charities are therefore advised to send in applications with sufficient time before the June or November deadlines to allow for such enquiries.'

WHO TO APPLY TO Karen Frank, Administrator, PO Box 124, Stroud, Gloucestershire GL6 7YN *email* admin@austin-hope-pilkington.org.uk *Website* www.austin-hope-pilkington.org.uk

CC NO 255274   **ESTABLISHED** 1967

....

■ The Sir Harry Pilkington Trust

WHERE FUNDING CAN BE GIVEN UK, with a preference for Merseyside.

WHO CAN BENEFIT Charitable organisations.

WHAT IS FUNDED General charitable purposes.

SAMPLE GRANTS Liverpool Council for Voluntary Service (£50,000); Shopmobility St Helens (£3,200); Black and Equality Merseyside Network, Dingle Community Theatre, Everton Red Triangle ABC, Merseyside Dance Initiative and Youth Communications Network (£3,000 each); St John's Youth and Community Centre (£2,500); Henshaws Society for the Blind, Toxteth Learning and Unity Theatre – Homotopia (£2,000 each); the Activate Project (£1,600); Kuumba Imani Millennium Centre and Southport Flower Show (£1,500 each); and Coast International Artists Limited and Listening Ear – Merseyside (£1,000 each).

FINANCES *Year* 2007–08 *Income* £207,064 *Grants* £176,590 *Assets* £5,066,274

TRUSTEES Liverpool Charity and Voluntary Services.

HOW TO APPLY In writing to the correspondent.

WHO TO APPLY TO The Trustees, Liverpool Charity And Voluntary Services, 151 Dale Street, Liverpool L2 2AH

CC NO 206740   **ESTABLISHED** 1962

....

■ The Col W W Pilkington Will Trusts – The General Charity Fund

WHERE FUNDING CAN BE GIVEN UK, with a preference for Merseyside.

WHO CAN BENEFIT Registered charities only.

WHAT IS FUNDED Medical, arts, social welfare, drugs misuse, international and environmental charities.

WHAT IS NOT FUNDED No support for non-registered charities, building projects, animal charities or individuals.

TYPE OF GRANT Generally annual.

SAMPLE GRANTS Exeter University Postgraduate Medical School (£8,000); No Panic, Marie Stopes International and Windows Project (£2,000 each); and British Friends of Neve Shalom, Farm Africa, Lupus UK, Marine Conservation Society, Merseyside Dance Initiative, Royal British Legion, Soil Association and WISH (£1,000 each).

FINANCES *Year* 2007–08 *Income* £56,736 *Grants* £41,000 *Assets* £1,685,377

TRUSTEES Arnold Pilkington; Hon. Mrs Jennifer Jones; Neil Pilkington Jones.

HOW TO APPLY In writing to the correspondent.

WHO TO APPLY TO The Clerk, PO Box 8162, London W2 1GF

CC NO 234710   **ESTABLISHED** 1964

....

■ Miss A M Pilkington's Charitable Trust

WHERE FUNDING CAN BE GIVEN UK, with a preference for Scotland.

WHO CAN BENEFIT Registered charities.

WHAT IS FUNDED General charitable purposes, including conservation/environment, health and social welfare.

WHAT IS NOT FUNDED Grants are not given to overseas projects or political appeals.

FINANCES *Year* 2008–09 *Income* £151,715

HOW TO APPLY The trustees state that, regrettably, they are unable to make grants to new applicants since they already have 'more than enough causes to support'.

WHO TO APPLY TO The Clerk, Carters Chartered Accountants, Pentland House, Saltire Centre, Glenrothes, Fife KY6 2AH

SC NO SC000282

....

■ Mrs Pilkington's Charitable Trust

WHERE FUNDING CAN BE GIVEN UK.

WHO CAN BENEFIT Organisations benefiting older people and people who are infirm or poor, or horses.

WHAT IS FUNDED Welfare and relief work as well as prevention of cruelty.

SAMPLE GRANTS £115,000 to provide help for aged infirm or poor and £85,000 to prevent cruelty to equine animals.

FINANCES *Year* 2006–07 *Income* £97,106 *Grants* £199,350 *Assets* £3,473,608

TRUSTEES Mrs Caroline Doulton, Chair; Mrs Tara Economakis; Revd Rob Merchant; Mrs Helen Timpany.

OTHER INFORMATION There were 25 grants made during the year.

HOW TO APPLY In writing to the correspondent.

WHO TO APPLY TO Lord Brentford, Taylor Wessing, Carmelite, 50 Victoria Embankment, London EC4Y 0DX *Tel* 020 300 7000

CC NO 278332   **ESTABLISHED** 1979

■ The Platinum Trust

WHERE FUNDING CAN BE GIVEN UK.

WHO CAN BENEFIT Charities benefiting people with disabilities.

WHAT IS FUNDED The relief of children with special needs and adults with mental or physical disabilities 'requiring special attention'.

WHAT IS NOT FUNDED No grants for services run by statutory or public bodies, or from mental-health organisations. No grants for: medical research/treatment or equipment; mobility aids/wheelchairs; community transport/disabled transport schemes; holidays/exchanges/holiday playschemes; special-needs playgroups; toy and leisure libraries; special Olympic and Paralympics groups; sports and recreation clubs for people with disabilities; residential care/sheltered housing/respite care; carers; conservation schemes/city farms/horticultural therapy; sheltered or supported employment/community business/social firms; purchase/construction/repair of buildings; and conductive education/other special educational programmes.

RANGE OF GRANTS Usually £5,000–£40,000.

SAMPLE GRANTS UKDPC (£45,000); Disability, Pregnancy and Parenthood International (£40,000); Centre for Studies on Inclusive Education (£32,000); Disability Equality in Education (£25,000); Alliance for Inclusive Education (£22,000); Parents for Inclusion (£20,000); Independent Panel for Special Education Advice (£15,000); Vassal Centre Trust (£10,000); Multiple Sclerosis Trust and VSO (£5,000 each); SENSE (£3,000); the Snowdon Award Scheme (£2,500); and the Simon Pauk Foundation (£1,200).

FINANCES *Year* 2007–08 *Income* £491,709 *Grants* £516,069 *Assets* £150,631

TRUSTEES G K Panayiotou; S Marks; C D Organ.

HOW TO APPLY The trust does not accept unsolicited applications; all future grants will be allocated by the trustees to groups they have already made links with.

WHO TO APPLY TO The Secretary, Sedley Ricchard Laurence Voulters, Kendal House, 1 Conduit Street, London W1S 2XA

CC NO 328570   **ESTABLISHED** 1990

■ G S Plaut Charitable Trust Limited

WHERE FUNDING CAN BE GIVEN Predominantly UK.

WHO CAN BENEFIT Voluntary organisations and charitable groups only.

WHAT IS FUNDED Sickness, disability, Jewish, older people, Christian and general charitable purposes.

WHAT IS NOT FUNDED No grants to individuals or for repeat applications.

SAMPLE GRANTS Previous beneficiaries have included Book Aid International, British Deaf Association, Down's Syndrome Association, Friends of Meals on Wheels Service – Liverpool, Gurkha Welfare Trust, Hull Jewish Community Care, Liverpool School of Tropical Medicine, Nightingale Home for Aged Jews, Rehearsal Orchestra, RNIB Talking Book Services, St George's Crypt – Leeds, Southend Riding Club for the Disabled, TOC H and VSO.

FINANCES *Year* 2007–08 *Income* £227,107 *Grants* £24,620 *Assets* £1,108,031

TRUSTEES W E Murfett; Miss T A Warburg; Dr A M S Shaw; Mrs B A Sprinz.

HOW TO APPLY In writing to the correspondent. Applications are reviewed twice a year. An sae

should be enclosed. Applications will not be acknowledged.

WHO TO APPLY TO Dr R A Speirs, Secretary, 39 Bay Road, Wormit, Newport-on-Tay, Fife DD6 8LW

CC NO 261469   **ESTABLISHED** 1970

■ Polden-Puckham Charitable Foundation

WHERE FUNDING CAN BE GIVEN UK and overseas.

WHO CAN BENEFIT Registered charities only.

WHAT IS FUNDED Peace and conflict resolution, ecological issues, and corporate responsibility, ethical investment, trade, human rights and women's issues, especially where it involves policy change work related to peace and ecological issues.

WHAT IS NOT FUNDED The foundation does not support: individuals; travel bursaries (including overseas placements and expeditions); study; academic research; capital projects (e.g. building projects or purchase of nature reserves); community or local projects (except innovative prototypes for widespread application); general appeals; or organisations based overseas (unless they have a well established relationship with a UK charitable organisation).

TYPE OF GRANT Core costs and project funding for up to three years.

RANGE OF GRANTS Normally £5,000 to £15,000.

SAMPLE GRANTS Quaker Peace and Social Witness (£20,000); Oxford Research Group (£18,000); New Economics Foundation and Responding to Conflict (£15,000 each); British American Security Information Council (£12,000); Climate Action Groups – Climate Outreach Information Network (£11,000); Campaign for Better Transport and Anti-Apathy (£10,000 each); Platform (£9,000); Corporate Watch Cooperative – Climate Outreach Information Network (£8,000); Living Witness Project (£6,000); Ecological Land Cooperative (£5,000); Mines and Communities Network – Missionary Society of St Columban (£4,000); Women's International League for Peace and Freedom – WOMANKIND Worldwide (£3,000); and Cooperation for Peace and Unity – Peace Direct (£2,000).

FINANCES *Year* 2007–08 *Income* £465,313 *Grants* £476,096 *Assets* £13,215,256

TRUSTEES Harriet Gillett; Jenepher Gordon; Linda Patten; Daniel Barlow; Bevis Gillett; Val Ferguson; Gerardo Fragoso; Ben Gillett; Suzy Gillett.

HOW TO APPLY The trustees meet twice a year in spring and autumn. Application forms and guidance notes can be downloaded from the foundation's website and must be submitted via email. Applicants are also asked to submit their latest set of audited accounts and an annual report, preferably via email. Application deadlines are usually in February/March and September but exact dates can be found on the website. Trustee meetings are generally held in April and October/November. Please note: the foundation is happy to provide brief feedback on applications one week after the trustees have made a decision.

WHO TO APPLY TO Bryn Higgs, Secretary, BM PPCF, London WC1N 3XX *email* ppcf@polden-puckham.org.uk *Website* www.polden-puckham.org.uk

CC NO 1003024   **ESTABLISHED** 1970

■ The Polehanger Trust

WHERE FUNDING CAN BE GIVEN Worldwide.
WHO CAN BENEFIT Christian organisations.
WHAT IS FUNDED Christian causes.
SAMPLE GRANTS Stopsley Baptist Church – Global Sunday Appeal and Tear Fund (£5,000 each); Luton Christian Educational Trust (£2,000); Oasis Charitable Trust (£1,500); and Bedfordshire Festival of Music, Speech and Drama (£100 each).
FINANCES *Year* 2007–08 *Income* £71,443 *Grants* £50,351 *Assets* £215,001
TRUSTEES C S Foster; Mrs C J Foster.
HOW TO APPLY No grants to unsolicited applications.
WHO TO APPLY TO C S Foster, Trustee, Polehanger Farm, Shefford Road, Meppershall, Shefford, Bedfordshire SG17 5LH
CC NO 1076447   **ESTABLISHED** 1999

■ The Poling Charitable Trust

WHERE FUNDING CAN BE GIVEN Mainly Sussex.
WHO CAN BENEFIT Organisations.
WHAT IS FUNDED General charitable purposes.
WHAT IS NOT FUNDED No support for individuals or medical causes. No new proposals.
RANGE OF GRANTS £25–£5,600.
SAMPLE GRANTS Previous beneficiaries have included Arundel Festival, Chichester Cathedral Development Trust, City Music Society, Friends of Covent Garden, Parochial Church Council of St Nicholas, RAF Escapers, Royal Academy of Music, Sherborne Abbey, Sussex Association for Rehabilitation of Offenders, Sussex Association for the Deaf, Sussex Trust for Nature Conservation, Wave Heritage Trust, Pallant House Gallery and West Dean Foundation.
FINANCES *Year* 2007–08 *Income* £59,899 *Grants* £59,102
TRUSTEES A Hopkinson; Mrs P Hopkinson.
HOW TO APPLY In writing to the correspondent, however the trust stated that it has no spare income, as it is all fully committed.
WHO TO APPLY TO D H L Hopkinson, St John's Priory, Poling Street, Poling, Arundel, West Sussex BN18 9PS *Tel* 01903 882 393
CC NO 240066   **ESTABLISHED** 1964

■ The George and Esme Pollitzer Charitable Settlement

WHERE FUNDING CAN BE GIVEN UK.
WHO CAN BENEFIT Registered charities, particularly Jewish organisations.
WHAT IS FUNDED General charitable purposes and Jewish causes.
SAMPLE GRANTS Royal School for Needlework (£15,000); Royal Hospital for Neuro Disability (£5,000); Deafblind UK (£3,000); Jewish Children's Holidays Fund, London Youth Support Trust and the Weiner Library (£2,000 each); Apex Trust, Atlantic College, the Foundation for Conductive Education, Independent Age, Mencap, Pestalozzi International Village Trust and the Prostate Cancer Charity (£1,500 each); Contact the Elderly (£1,000); and Crimestoppers Trust (£500).
FINANCES *Year* 2007–08 *Income* £116,365 *Grants* £109,500 *Assets* £2,959,196
TRUSTEES J Barnes; B G Levy; R F C Pollitzer.
HOW TO APPLY In writing to the correspondent.
WHO TO APPLY TO J Barnes, Trustee, Saffery Champness, Beaufort House, 2 Beaufort Road, Clifton, Bristol B58 2AE
CC NO 212631   **ESTABLISHED** 1960

■ The J S F Pollitzer Charitable Settlement

WHERE FUNDING CAN BE GIVEN UK and overseas.
WHO CAN BENEFIT Registered charities only.
WHAT IS FUNDED General charitable purposes.
WHAT IS NOT FUNDED No grants to individuals or students, i.e. those without charitable status.
TYPE OF GRANT One-off.
RANGE OF GRANTS Typically £1,000 each.
SAMPLE GRANTS Casa Allianza, Children's Hospice South West, Comex, the Community Furniture Project, Disability Snowsport UK, the Eyeless Trust, Foundation for the Relief of Disabled Orphans, Free the Way, Headway, Help for Heroes, Mercy Corps, the Spiro Ark, Spinal Injuries Association, Steps, the Theatres Trust Charitable Fund, Tolerance International and Youth Net (£1,000 each).
FINANCES *Year* 2007–08 *Income* £40,813 *Grants* £21,000 *Assets* £676,087
TRUSTEES R F C Pollitzer, Chair; Mrs J F A Davis; Mrs S C O'Farrell
HOW TO APPLY In writing to the correspondent. Grants are distributed twice a year, usually around April/May and November/December.
WHO TO APPLY TO P Samuel, Accountant, Mary Street House, Mary Street, Tounton, Somerset TA1 3NW *Tel* 020 7388 7000
CC NO 210680   **ESTABLISHED** 1960

■ The Pollywally Charitable Trust

WHERE FUNDING CAN BE GIVEN UK.
WHO CAN BENEFIT Jewish institutions of primary, secondary and further education and those caring for the poor and sick.
WHAT IS FUNDED Jewish causes, education, and welfare.
SAMPLE GRANTS Edgware Foundation (£15,200); Bridge Lane Beth Hamedrash (£4,000); Kehillas Machzikei Hadass Edgware (£3,200); Baer Hatorah Limited (£1,300); and London Jewish Girls School Education and The Clubhouse (£1,000 each). Grants of less than £1,000 each were made to 47 organisations.
FINANCES *Year* 2007–08 *Income* £35,603 *Grants* £41,575 *Assets* £4,271
TRUSTEES J H Pollins; Mrs S L Pollins; J Waller; Mrs S Waller.
HOW TO APPLY In writing to the correspondent.
WHO TO APPLY TO Jeremy Waller, Trustee, c/o Waller Pollins, 8th Floor, Premier House, 112 Station Road, Edgware, Middlesex HA8 7BJ *Tel* 020 8238 5858
CC NO 1107513   **ESTABLISHED** 2005

■ The Ponton House Trust

WHERE FUNDING CAN BE GIVEN The Lothians.
WHO CAN BENEFIT Organisations benefiting disadvantaged groups, principally young and older people.
WHAT IS FUNDED Grants are given mainly to support small charities working with young people, older people and disadvantaged groups.
WHAT IS NOT FUNDED No grants to individuals or non-charitable organisations.
TYPE OF GRANT One-off.
RANGE OF GRANTS Up to £6,300.
SAMPLE GRANTS Edinburgh Voluntary Organisations Trust (£9,000), for onward distribution to individuals; Bethany Christian Trust and Lothian Autistic Society (£1,500 each); Garvald Traning Centre, Venture Scotland, Circle, Children 1st and Partners for Advocacy (£1,000 each); Rock Trust

(£900); and Maggies Cancer Caring Centres (£750).

FINANCES *Year* 2007–08

TRUSTEES Revd John Munro, Chair; Shulah Allen; Patrick Edwardson; Julie Matthews; Ian Boardman; James Verth.

HOW TO APPLY In writing to the correspondent, there are no specific application forms. Trustees usually meet in January, April, July and October. Applications should include a full explanation of the project for which funding is sought plus annual reports and accounts.

WHO TO APPLY TO David S Reith, Secretary, Lindsays WS, Caledonian Exchange, 19A Canning Street, Edinburgh EH3 8HE *Tel* 0131 229 1212 *Fax* 0131 229 5611 *email* dsr@lindsays.co.uk

SC NO SC021716   ESTABLISHED 1993

■ **The Mayor of Poole's Appeal Fund**

WHERE FUNDING CAN BE GIVEN Dorset, Poole.

WHO CAN BENEFIT Charitable organisations.

WHAT IS FUNDED Work of particular interest to the Mayor.

SAMPLE GRANTS Poole Forum (£28,000); Citizens Advice (£20,000); Help & Care (£10,000); Harbour Challenge (£1,000); and Rotary District 1110 (£300).

FINANCES *Year* 2007–08 *Income* £28,569 *Grants* £65,100 *Assets* £7,991

TRUSTEES Joyce Lavender; J A McBride; Jeffrey Allen; Judith Butt.

HOW TO APPLY In writing to the correspondent, but note the comments in the general section. Applications should be made before February each year, but preferably several months before February.

WHO TO APPLY TO Josephine Clements, Mayor's Secretary, Mayor's Office, Borough of Poole, Civic Centre, Poole, Dorset BH15 2RU *Tel* 01202 633 200 *Fax* 01202 633 094 *email* j.clements@poole.gov.uk *Website* www.boroughofpoole.com

CC NO 1027462   ESTABLISHED 1993

■ **Edith and Ferdinand Porjes Charitable Trust**

WHERE FUNDING CAN BE GIVEN UK and overseas.

WHO CAN BENEFIT Jewish organisations; registered charities.

WHAT IS FUNDED General charitable purposes, particularly Jewish causes.

SAMPLE GRANTS London School of Jewish Studies (£30,000); the Jewish Museum (£25,000); Queen Mary University of London (£15,000); the Cancer Treatment and Research Trust and European Jewish Publication Society (£5,000 each); British Friends of the Art Museums of Israel (£3,000); and British Friends of OHEL Sarah (£2,000).

FINANCES *Year* 2007–08 *Income* £63,690 *Grants* £85,000 *Assets* £1,484,264

TRUSTEES M D Paisner; A S Rosenfelder; H Stanton.

HOW TO APPLY In writing to the correspondent.

WHO TO APPLY TO M D Paisner, Trustee, Adelaide House, London Bridge, London EC4R 9HA

CC NO 274012   ESTABLISHED 1973

■ **The John Porter Charitable Trust**

WHERE FUNDING CAN BE GIVEN Worldwide, but mainly UK and Israel.

WHO CAN BENEFIT Registered and exempt charities.

WHAT IS FUNDED Education, culture, environment, health and welfare.

WHAT IS NOT FUNDED No grants to individuals.

RANGE OF GRANTS Up to £25,000.

SAMPLE GRANTS Sapling Foundation Limited (£25,000); Friends of the Verbier Festival (£21,000); University of Oxford and Maccabi GB (£5,000 each); Bet Safer Limited (£2,500); the Next Century Foundation (£1,500); Brown Family Trust and Israel Diaspora Trust (£1,000 each).

FINANCES *Year* 2007–08 *Income* £340,276 *Grants* £61,202 *Assets* £10,707,343

TRUSTEES John Porter; Peter Green; Robert Glatter.

HOW TO APPLY In writing to the correspondent.

WHO TO APPLY TO The Trustees, c/o Blink Rothenberg, 12 York Gate, London NW1 4QS *Tel* 020 7544 8863

CC NO 267170   ESTABLISHED 1974

■ **The Porter Foundation**

WHERE FUNDING CAN BE GIVEN Israel and the UK.

WHO CAN BENEFIT Registered charities and community organisations.

WHAT IS FUNDED Practical projects to enhance the quality of people's lives and environment. Priorities are health, education, the environment and culture.

WHAT IS NOT FUNDED The foundation makes grants only to registered charitable organisations or to organisations with charitable objects that are exempt from the requirement for charitable registration. Grants will not be made to: individuals; general appeals such as direct mail circulars; charities which redistribute funds to other charities; third-party organisations raising money on behalf of other charities; or cover general running costs.

TYPE OF GRANT Usually project-based and capital.

SAMPLE GRANTS Friends of Daniel for Rowing Association (£49,000); Tel Aviv Foundation (£27,000); New Israel Fund (£25,000); British Friends of the Verbier Festival and Academy (£12,000); Imperial War Museum (£10,000); Royal Opera House Foundation (£8,000); Trinity Laban (£6,000); Norwood Ravenswood (£5,000); ESRA Community Fund (£2,900); and Wigmore Hall Trust (£1,000).

FINANCES *Year* 2007–08 *Income* £1,341,248 *Grants* £225,450 *Assets* £48,233,389

TRUSTEES David Brecher; Albert Castle; Dame Shirley Porter; Steven Porter; Sir Walter Bodmer; John Porter; Linda Streit.

OTHER INFORMATION During recent years the foundation has cut back on the number of beneficiaries supported and is making fewer, larger grants, mainly to the connected Porter School of Environmental Studies at Tel Aviv University, or the university itself, and to other causes in Israel. This has led to a temporary reduction in UK-based activity. A limited number of community awards continue to be given, though usually to organisations already known to the foundation.

HOW TO APPLY An initial letter summarising your application, together with basic costings and background details on your organisation, such as the annual report and accounts, should be sent to the director. Speculative approaches containing expensive publicity material are not encouraged. If your proposal falls within the foundation's current funding criteria you may be contacted for further information, including perhaps a visit from the foundation staff. There is no need to fill out an application form. Applications fulfilling the criteria will be considered by the trustees, who meet three times a year, usually in March, July and November. You will hear shortly after the meeting whether your application has been successful. Unfortunately, it is not possible to acknowledge all unsolicited applications (unless a stamped, addressed envelope is enclosed). If you do not hear from the foundation, you can assume that your application has been unsuccessful. Due to limits on funds available, some excellent projects may have to be refused a grant. In such a case the trustees may invite the applicant to re-apply in a future financial year, without giving a commitment to fund.

WHO TO APPLY TO Paul Williams, Executive Director, 5a Jewry St, Winchester SO23 8RZ *Tel* 01962 849684 *email* theporterfoundation@btinternet.com

CC NO 261194   **ESTABLISHED** 1970

....

■ Porticus UK

WHERE FUNDING CAN BE GIVEN UK.
WHO CAN BENEFIT Registered charities.
WHAT IS FUNDED The charity's four areas of interest are: strengthening family relationships; enriching education; transformation through faith; and ethics in practice.
WHAT IS NOT FUNDED No grants to non-registered charities. Applications for the following will not be considered: high profile appeals; major capital projects or restoration of buildings; grants to individuals; endowment appeals; overseas projects (including travel).
RANGE OF GRANTS £10,000 to £25,000.
FINANCES *Year* 2009
TRUSTEES L A Adams; M C L Brenninkmeyer; S R M Brenninkmeyer.
OTHER INFORMATION Porticus UK is not in itself a grantmaker – it advises and assesses grants on behalf of several foundations in the Netherlands, including Stichting Porticus. It recommends in the region of 170 grants each year.
HOW TO APPLY On an application form available from the charity's website. Applications can be submitted at any time. The charity also says that: 'if you are unsure whether your project/organisation fits in with our guidelines, you are welcome to submit an initial brief outline of your organisation and funding requirements'.
WHO TO APPLY TO Nathan Koblintz, 4th Floor, Eagle House, 108–110 Jermyn Street, London SW1Y 6EE *Tel* 020 7024 3503 *Fax* 020 7024 3501 *email* porticusuk@porticus.com *Website* www.porticusuk.com
CC NO 1069245

....

■ The Portishead Nautical Trust

WHERE FUNDING CAN BE GIVEN Bristol and North Somerset.
WHO CAN BENEFIT People under 25 years of age who are disadvantaged or at risk; voluntary and charitable groups working with such people, with young offenders and with people with addictions.
WHAT IS FUNDED Projects with young people who are disadvantaged; educational support for such people; counselling services; and youth groups.
WHAT IS NOT FUNDED No grants for further education costs of non-disadvantaged people.

TYPE OF GRANT One-off, project, recurring costs and running costs will be considered. Funding may be given for up to three years.
RANGE OF GRANTS Usually £100–£5,000.
SAMPLE GRANTS Dyslexia Action in Portishead (£17,500); St Johns Family Resource Unit (£5,000); Whizz Kidz (£2,000); Leonard Cheshire Disability (£1,750); Avonmouth Sea Cadets, Bridge Foundation and Happy Days Children's Charity (£1,500 each); Avon Outward Bound and Bristol Music Space (£1,000 each); and Portishead Primary School (£660).
FINANCES *Year* 2007–08 *Income* £88,434 *Grants* £47,627 *Assets* £1,639,576
TRUSTEES Miss S Belk; G Russ; Revd T J White; Mrs M Hoskins; Mrs I Perry; Mrs T J F Kirby; Mrs A F Kay; S P Gillingham; M R Cruse; C Crossman.
OTHER INFORMATION In 2007–08 the trust gave £2,500 in grants to individuals.
HOW TO APPLY In writing to the correspondent.
WHO TO APPLY TO Brian Ruse, Secretary, c/o Dingley-Brown, 108 High Street, Portishead, Bristol BS20 6AJ *Tel* 01275 847 463 *Fax* 01275 818 871
CC NO 228876   **ESTABLISHED** 1964

....

■ The Portrack Charitable Trust

WHERE FUNDING CAN BE GIVEN Some preference for Scotland.
WHO CAN BENEFIT Charitable organisations.
WHAT IS FUNDED General charitable organisations.
WHAT IS NOT FUNDED Grants are not given to individuals.
FINANCES *Year* 2007–08 *Income* £46,157 *Grants* £46,700 *Assets* £2,140,237
TRUSTEES Charles Jencks; Keith Galloway; John Jencks.
HOW TO APPLY In writing to the correspondent.
WHO TO APPLY TO The Trustees, Butterfield Bank, 99 Gresham Street, London EC2V 7NG
CC NO 266120   **ESTABLISHED** 1973

....

■ The J E Posnansky Charitable Trust

WHERE FUNDING CAN BE GIVEN Worldwide, in practice mainly UK.
WHO CAN BENEFIT Charitable organisations.
WHAT IS FUNDED Jewish charities, health, social welfare, humanitarian.
WHAT IS NOT FUNDED No grants to individuals.
TYPE OF GRANT One-off.
RANGE OF GRANTS Typically £500–£30,000.
SAMPLE GRANTS Magen David Adom UK and UKIA (£20,000 each); British WIZO and Friends of Alyn (£15,000 each); the Jewish Aid Committee and Jewish Care (£7,500 each); Ben Gurion University Foundation (£5,000); Nightingale House (£3,000); Sight Savers International and Water Aid (£2,500 each); Amnesty International (£1,000); British Limbless Ex-Servicemen (£1,000); and Kisharon Day School Charity Trust and St Luke's Hospice (£500 each).
FINANCES *Year* 2007–08 *Income* £153,385 *Grants* £144,750 *Assets* £3,730,863
TRUSTEES Mrs G Raffles; A Posnansky; P A Mishcon; Mrs E J Feather; N S Posnansky.
HOW TO APPLY Unsolicited applications will not be considered.
WHO TO APPLY TO Mr N S Posnansky, Trustee, Sobell Rhodes, Monument House, 215 Marsh Road, Pinner, London WA5 5NE *Tel* 020 7431 0909 *Fax* 020 7435 1516
CC NO 210416   **ESTABLISHED** 1962

■ The Mary Potter Convent Hospital Trust

WHERE FUNDING CAN BE GIVEN Nottinghamshire.

WHO CAN BENEFIT Organisations and individuals.

WHAT IS FUNDED Relief of medical and health problems.

WHAT IS NOT FUNDED No grants to non-registered charities, or for capital/building costs.

TYPE OF GRANT Mainly one-off grants, but payments over two or three years may be considered.

SAMPLE GRANTS Grants included those made to Macmillan Cancer Relief (£10,000); Friary Drop In and Motor Neuron Association (£5,000 each); and New Life and Nottingham Hospice (£4,000 each).

FINANCES *Year* 2007–08 *Income* £97,656 *Grants* £89,480 *Assets* £2,574,860

TRUSTEES Rupert A L Roberts, Chair; C N Bain; Sister Ann Haugh; Dr J P Curran; Mrs Jennifer M Farr; Christopher J Howell; Michael F Mason; Frederick T C Pell; Ms Jo Stevenson; Sister Margaret Watson.

HOW TO APPLY In writing to the correspondent. Unsuccessful applicants will not be notified.

WHO TO APPLY TO Michael F Mason, Administrator, Massers Solicitors, 15 Victoria Street, Nottingham NG1 2JZ *Tel* 0115 851 1666 *Fax* 0115 851 1673 *email* michaelm@massers. co.uk

CC NO 1078525   **ESTABLISHED** 1999

■ The David and Elaine Potter Foundation

WHERE FUNDING CAN BE GIVEN UK and other countries with particular emphasis on the developing world.

WHO CAN BENEFIT Charitable organisations working in the areas of education, science, human rights, and the general strengthening of civil society.

WHAT IS FUNDED Advancement of education and scientific research. Most grants are made for scholarships and other related activities that will improve understanding, governance and the promotion of a civil society; research through the creation of institutions and other means; human rights activism; initiatives that support democratic governance; and agencies and charities carrying out development, research and educational projects.

RANGE OF GRANTS £500–£58,000.

SAMPLE GRANTS Open Trust – China Dialogue (£58,000); Centre of Investigative Journalism (£51,000); Performa (£50,000); International Alert (£45,000); Royal Society Edinburgh and Canon Collins Trust (£30,000 each); the Howard League (£20,000); Reform Research (£15,000); HemiHelp (£7,500); Donmar Warehouse Projects (£3,000); Variety Club Children's Charity and Almeida Theatre (£1,000 each); and Wellbeing for Women (£500).

FINANCES *Year* 2007 *Income* £1,188,369 *Grants* £211,763 *Assets* £18,167,513

TRUSTEES M S Polonsky; M Langley; D Potter; E Potter.

HOW TO APPLY 'The trustees' policy is to consider all applications received, but they prefer to seek projects that they wish to support rather than to receive unsolicited applications.'

WHO TO APPLY TO Mrs Angela Seay, Director, 10 Park Crescent, London W1B 1PQ *Tel* 020 7291 3993 *Website* www.potterfoundation.com

CC NO 1078217   **ESTABLISHED** 1999

■ The Powell Foundation

WHERE FUNDING CAN BE GIVEN Within the Milton Keynes Unitary Council area.

WHO CAN BENEFIT Individuals and local organisations benefiting older people and people of any age with disabilities.

WHAT IS FUNDED Grants for the benefit of older people and mentally and physically disabled people. Localised charities working in the fields of community development including supporting voluntary organisations, community arts and recreation, community facilities and services for people with disabilities, healthcare and special needs education.

SAMPLE GRANTS Milton Keynes Community Foundation (£80,000).

FINANCES *Year* 2007–08 *Income* £144,667 *Grants* £95,592 *Assets* £3,656,696

TRUSTEES R W Norman; R Hill; P Smith.

HOW TO APPLY Please visit the trust's website for full guidelines and details of how to apply. Application forms are available on request from the grants team who can either post or e-mail the forms.

WHO TO APPLY TO Julia Upton, Chief Executive, c/o Milton Keynes Community Foundation, Acorn House, 381 Midsummer Boulevard, Central Milton Keynes MK9 3HP *Tel* 01908 690276 *Fax* 01908 233635 *email* information@ mkcommunityfoundation.co.uk *Website* www. mkcommunityfoundation.co.uk

CC NO 1012786   **ESTABLISHED** 1992

■ Prairie Trust

WHERE FUNDING CAN BE GIVEN Worldwide.

WHO CAN BENEFIT Charitable organisations.

WHAT IS FUNDED A small number of organisations working on issues of third world development, the environment and conflict prevention, and particularly to support policy and advocacy work in these areas. The trustees are also interested in supporting innovative and entrepreneurial approaches to traditional problems.

WHAT IS NOT FUNDED No grants to individuals, for expeditions or for capital projects.

SAMPLE GRANTS The Funding Network London (£31,000); Oxford Research Group (£10,000); Global Democratic Citizens Union and Women in Dialogue (£5,000 each); Bedouin Wool Project (£4,700); the Funding Network Leeds (£3,000); the Funding Network Toronto (£2,800); Women in Need – India leprosy project (£2,500); Pegasus Theatre (£1,000); British Institute Florence (£500); CIVA and Peace Direct (£250 each); and Merseyside Community Federation for Adult Dyslexia, Stroke Association and Willow Foundation (£100 each).

FINANCES *Year* 2007–08 *Income* £1,437,846 *Grants* £70,011 *Assets* £1,614,591

TRUSTEES Dr Frederick Mulder; Hannah Mulder.

HOW TO APPLY The trust states: 'As we are a proactive trust with limited funds and administrative help, we are unable to consider unsolicited applications'.

WHO TO APPLY TO The Administrator, 83 Belsize Park Gardens, London NW3 4NJ

CC NO 296019   **ESTABLISHED** 1987

■ The W L Pratt Charitable Trust

WHERE FUNDING CAN BE GIVEN UK, particularly York, and overseas.

WHO CAN BENEFIT Charitable organisations.

WHAT IS FUNDED In the UK: to support religious and social objectives with priority for York and district, including health and community services. Overseas: to help the developing world by assisting in food production and relief of famine and disease.

WHAT IS NOT FUNDED No grants to individuals. No grants for buildings or for upkeep and preservation of places of worship.

SAMPLE GRANTS York Diocesan Board of Finance (£4,300); St Leonard's Hospice (£2,300); Christian Aid and Sight Savers International (£2,200 each); Wilberforce Trust (£2,200); Save the Children and York Minster Fund (£1,800 each); the Army Benevolent Fund North Region (£1,300); Barnados and Salvation Army (£1,100 each); Guide Dogs for the Blind, RNLI and St Johns Ambulance (£1,000 each); and Abbeyfield York Society, British Red Cross – North Yorkshire Branch, Camphill Village Trust – Croft Community, Sue Ryder Foundation, WRVS and York Sea Cadets (£500 each).

FINANCES *Year* 2007–08 *Income* £60,455 *Grants* £61,150 *Assets* £1,715,256

TRUSTEES J L C Pratt; C M Tetley; C C Goodway.

HOW TO APPLY In writing to the correspondent. Applications will not be acknowledged unless an sae is supplied. Telephone applications are not accepted.

WHO TO APPLY TO C C Goodway, Trustee, Messrs Grays, Duncombe Place, York YO1 7DY *Tel* 01904 634771 *email* christophergoodway@ grayssolicitors.co.uk

CC NO 256907   **ESTABLISHED** 1968

■ Premierquote Ltd

WHERE FUNDING CAN BE GIVEN Worldwide.

WHO CAN BENEFIT People of the Jewish faith.

WHAT IS FUNDED Jewish charitable purposes, relief of poverty, general charitable purposes.

SAMPLE GRANTS Previous beneficiaries have included Achisomoch, Belz Yeshiva Trust, Beth Jacob Grammar School for Girls Ltd, British Friends of Shuvu, Friends of Ohel Moshe, Friends of Senet Wiznitz, Friends of the United Institutions of Arad, Kehal Chasidel Bobov, Meadowgold Limited, Menorah Primary School, North West London Communal Mikvah and Torah Vedaas Primary School.

FINANCES *Year* 2007–08 *Income* £1,145,803 *Grants* £650,261 *Assets* £7,290,411

TRUSTEES D Last; Mrs L Last; H Last; M Weisenfeld.

HOW TO APPLY In writing to the correspondent.

WHO TO APPLY TO D Last, Trustee, 18 Green Walk, London NW4 2AJ

CC NO 801957   **ESTABLISHED** 1985

■ Premishlaner Charitable Trust

WHERE FUNDING CAN BE GIVEN UK and worldwide.

WHO CAN BENEFIT Jewish people and people disadvantaged by poverty.

WHAT IS FUNDED To advance orthodox Jewish education; to advance the religion of the Jewish faith in accordance with the orthodox practice; to relieve poverty; other general charitable purposes.

SAMPLE GRANTS Gateshead Jewish Primary School, Shaat Ratzon, TTBA and Zichron Yechezkel Trust

(£10,000 each); J and R Charitable Trust (£8,000); and Hadras Kodesh and Kehal Yisroel (£5,000 each).

FINANCES *Year* 2007–08 *Income* £101,140 *Grants* £99,056 *Assets* £425,033

TRUSTEES H C Freudenberger; C M Margulies.

HOW TO APPLY In writing to the correspondent.

WHO TO APPLY TO C M Margulies, Trustee, 186 Lordship Road, London N16 5ES

CC NO 1046945   **ESTABLISHED** 1995

■ The Douglas Prestwich Charitable Trust

WHERE FUNDING CAN BE GIVEN UK, with a possible preference for the south of England.

WHO CAN BENEFIT Hospices and other organisations benefiting older people and people with disabilities.

WHAT IS FUNDED Help to older people, especially through hospices, and help for people with disabilities, especially through mechanical and other aids.

RANGE OF GRANTS Income grants usually £5,0000; capital grants up to £50,000.

SAMPLE GRANTS Previous beneficiaries include: Douglas Prestwich Award, Compaid, Disabled Living Foundation, Motability and the Mobility Trust.

FINANCES *Year* 2007–08 *Income* £9,357 *Grants* £30,000

TRUSTEES Margaret Prestwich; Peter Duthie; David Monro.

HOW TO APPLY In writing to the correspondent; however, please note the trust stated that its 'present policy [] is only to consider grants to institutions which it has already assisted and where the need continues to be shown'.

WHO TO APPLY TO David Monro, 8 Great James Street, London WC1N 3DF *Tel* 020 8332 2310 *email* ddcm@monro-fisher.com

CC NO 1017597   **ESTABLISHED** 1993

■ The William Price Charitable Trust

WHERE FUNDING CAN BE GIVEN Fareham's town parishes of St Peter and St Paul, Holy Trinity with St Columba and St John the Evangelist. Please note this area is that of the Fareham town parishes and not the borough of Fareham.

WHO CAN BENEFIT Schools and individuals under the age of 25 in the parishes.

WHAT IS FUNDED Schools for educational benefits not normally provided by the local education authority, and individuals for help with fees, travel, outfits, clothing, books and so on. Also promoting education in the doctrines of the Church of England.

WHAT IS NOT FUNDED Grants cannot be given to persons who live outside the area of the Fareham town parishes or to any organisation or establishment other than those outlined in this entry.

TYPE OF GRANT One-off.

FINANCES *Year* 2008–09 *Income* £211,897 *Grants* £163,649 *Assets* £5,115,157

TRUSTEES William Price Trust Company.

HOW TO APPLY On a form available from the correspondent. 'Whenever possible applications should be made through the establishment concerned. Application forms are available on request. Larger grants are considered by trustees on a six-monthly basis with closing dates for applications of 1 March and 1

September. Smaller grants for individuals are considered quickly and normally in less than one month.'

WHO TO APPLY TO Dr C D Thomas, Clerk, 24 Cuckoo Lane, Stubbington, Fareham, Hampshire PO14 3PF *Tel* 01329 663685

cc no 307319   **ESTABLISHED** 1989

■ The Lucy Price Relief-in-Need Charity

WHERE FUNDING CAN BE GIVEN The parish of Baginton in Warwickshire only.

WHO CAN BENEFIT Individuals up to the age of 25 and organisations benefiting such people.

WHAT IS FUNDED Education, sports and youth work.

SAMPLE GRANTS No grants list available.

FINANCES *Year* 2008 *Income* £6,779 *Grants* £55,773 *Assets* £1,278,414

TRUSTEES Mrs J E Fawcett; G R Yates; A J Brown; Nigel Thomas; S Williams; Mrs L Given.

HOW TO APPLY On a form available from the correspondent, or any of the trustees.

WHO TO APPLY TO G Meredith, Clerk, 39 Westbrook Court, Sutherland Avenue, Coventry CV5 7RB *Tel* 024 7646 1845

cc no 516967   **ESTABLISHED** 1982

■ Sir John Priestman Charity Trust

WHERE FUNDING CAN BE GIVEN County borough of Sunderland and historic counties of Durham and York.

WHO CAN BENEFIT Local organisations benefiting children and older people, clergy, people of the Church of England and people disadvantaged by poverty.

WHAT IS FUNDED The trust includes a clothing fund to provide clothing for poor children resident in Sunderland who attend churches and Sunday school; and a general fund to provide for the relief of older people and people who are poor or infirm. Also the establishment of hospitals and convalescent homes; the advancement of education of candidates for Holy Orders who after ordination will work in Durham for not less than six years; the benefit of the Church of England.

RANGE OF GRANTS £400–£10,000.

SAMPLE GRANTS Outward Bound Trust (£12,000); Friends of Barbara Priestman School, Sunderland (£10,000); Selby Abbey Appeal (£6,000); Durham Association of Clubs for Young People (£5,000); Royal Blind Society County Durham (£3,000); and North East Disabilities Resource Centre (£1,000).

FINANCES *Year* 2008 *Income* £368,909 *Grants* £296,801 *Assets* £7,485,715

TRUSTEES J R Heslop; R W Farr; T R P S Norton; P W Taylor; R S Heslop.

HOW TO APPLY In writing to the correspondent. The trustees meet in January, April, July and October. Applications should include clear details of the need the project is designed to meet plus estimates, where appropriate, and details of amounts subscribed to date.

WHO TO APPLY TO The Trustees, McKenzie Bell, 19 John Street, Sunderland SR1 1JG *Tel* 0191 567 4857

cc no 209397   **ESTABLISHED** 1931

■ The Primrose Trust

WHERE FUNDING CAN BE GIVEN UK.

WHO CAN BENEFIT Registered charities.

WHAT IS FUNDED General charitable purposes.

WHAT IS NOT FUNDED Grants are given to registered charities only.

SAMPLE GRANTS Murry Foundation (£210,000); Bill Jordan Foundation for Wildlife (£15,000); and Langford Trust (£10,000).

FINANCES *Year* 2007–08 *Income* £142,728 *Grants* £235,000 *Assets* £3,582,170

TRUSTEES M G Clark; Susan Boyes-Korkis.

HOW TO APPLY In writing to the correspondent, including a copy of the most recent accounts. The trust does not wish to receive telephone calls.

WHO TO APPLY TO M G Clark, Trustee, Blenheim House, Fitzalan Court, Newport Road, Cardiff CF24 0TS

cc no 800049   **ESTABLISHED** 1986

■ The Prince's Charities Foundation

WHERE FUNDING CAN BE GIVEN Unrestricted.

WHO CAN BENEFIT Registered charities mainly in which the Prince of Wales has a particular interest.

WHAT IS FUNDED Culture, the environment, medical welfare, education, children and young people and overseas aid.

WHAT IS NOT FUNDED No grants to individuals.

TYPE OF GRANT One-off grants for capital or core expenditure.

RANGE OF GRANTS Usually £100–£15,000, typical grant £500.

SAMPLE GRANTS The National Art Collections Fund (£13.8 million in connection with the purchase of Dumfries House); The Great Steward of Scotland's Dumfries House Trust (£5 million); The Prince of Wales's Foundation for Integrated Health (£400,000); The Prince's Foundation for the Built Environment (£277,000); The Rainforest Project (£228,000); Northumberland Wildlife Trust (£87,000); Turquoise Mountain Foundation (£71,000); North Highlands Initiative (£65,000); The Soil Association (£35,000); Music in Country Churches (£30,000); Arts Council of Wales (£20,000); and The National Trust (£13,000).

FINANCES *Year* 2007–08 *Income* £23,347,203 *Grants* £21,937,398 *Assets* £2,125,811

TRUSTEES Sir Michael Peat; Philip Reid; Hon. Lord Rothschild; Leslie Jane Ferrar.

HOW TO APPLY In writing to the correspondent, with full details of the project including financial data. The Prince's Charities Foundation receives an ever-increasing number of requests for assistance, which are considered on a regular basis by The Prince of Wales and the trustees

WHO TO APPLY TO David Hutson, The Prince of Wales's Office, Clarence House, St James's, London SW1A 1BA *Tel* 020 7930 4832 ext 4788 *Fax* 020 7930 0119 *Website* princeofwales.gov.uk

cc no 1127255   **ESTABLISHED** 1979

■ Princess Anne's Charities

WHERE FUNDING CAN BE GIVEN UK.

WHO CAN BENEFIT Registered charities, especially charities in which Princess Anne has a particular interest.

WHAT IS FUNDED Social welfare; medical research; children and young people; environment and wildlife; armed forces; religion; and general charitable purposes.

WHAT IS NOT FUNDED No grants to individuals.

SAMPLE GRANTS Butler Trust, the Canal Museum Trust Cranfield Trust, Dogs Trust, Dorothy House Foundation, Durrell Wildlife Conservation Trust, the Evelina Children's Hospital Appeal, Farms for City Children, Farrer and Co Charitable Trust, Fire Services National Benevolent Fund, the Home Farm Trust, Intensive Care Society, International League for the Protection of Horses, King Edward VIII Hospital-Sister Agnes, National Autistic Society, Minchinhampton Centre for the Elderly, Mission to Seafarers, Princess Royal Trust for Carers, REDR, RYA Sailability, Save the Children Fund, Scottish Field Studies Association, Scottish Motor Neurone Disease Association, SENSE, Spinal Injuries Association, Strathcarron Hospice, Transaid, London Bombing Relief Charitable Fund, Victim Support, VSO and Women's Royal Navy Benevolent Trust.

FINANCES *Year* 2007–08 *Income* £161,770 *Grants* £128,025 *Assets* £4,844,973

TRUSTEES Hon. M T Bridges; Rear Admiral T J H Laurence; B Hammond.

HOW TO APPLY 'The trustees are not anxious to receive unsolicited general applications as these are unlikely to be successful and only increase the cost of administration of the charity.'

WHO TO APPLY TO Capt. N Wright, Buckingham Palace, London SW1A 1AA

CC NO 277814   **ESTABLISHED** 1979

■ The Priory Foundation

WHERE FUNDING CAN BE GIVEN UK.

WHO CAN BENEFIT Registered charities, especially those benefiting children.

WHAT IS FUNDED General charitable purposes.

SAMPLE GRANTS Saracens Foundation (£34,000); Infer Trust and Ovarian Cancer Action (£30,000 each); London Borough of Barnet (£29,000); Wellbeing (£25,000); Arundel Castle Cricket Foundation (£24,000); Watford Palace Theatre (£21,000); Get-A-Head Appeal (£19,000); Barnet CAB (£6,500); Barnet Primary Care NHS Trust (£3,400); Children for Peace (£2,500); Disability Aid Fund (£1,000); Tim Parry Jonathan Ball Foundation for Peace and Dame Vera Lynn Trust (£2,500 each); and Mill Hill School (£1,000).

FINANCES *Year* 2007 *Income* £142,943 *Grants* £741,082 *Assets* £1,921,189

TRUSTEES N W Wray; L E Wray; T W Bunyard; D Poutney.

HOW TO APPLY In writing to the correspondent.

WHO TO APPLY TO The Trustees, c/o Cavendish House, 18 Cavendish Square, London W1G 0PJ

CC NO 295919   **ESTABLISHED** 1986

■ Prison Service Charity Fund

WHERE FUNDING CAN BE GIVEN UK.

WHO CAN BENEFIT Charitable organisations.

WHAT IS FUNDED The trust does not accept outside applications – the person making the application has got to be a member of staff.

SAMPLE GRANTS The Robbie James Trust and Women for Women Fund (£3,000 each); Michael Charlton Appeal (£2,600); Breast cancer Care (£2,500); Teenage Cancer Trust and Phyllis Tuckwell Hospice (£2,400); Cancer Research UK and Motor Neurone Disease Association (£2,300 each); Riding for the

Disabled Association and Yorkshire Disabled Powerlifting (£2,000 each); Friends of Abbey Hill and Walton Hall School (£1,500 each); Earl Mountbatten Hospice, Children with Leukaemia, Great North Air Ambulance and Prison Service Special Games (£1,000 each); Neuroblastoma Society (£800); St Anne's Hospice (£600); Cystic Fibrosis Trust and National Autistic Society (£500 each); Great North Air Ambulance (£400); Dysphasia Society (£200); and Breast Care Awareness (£80).

FINANCES *Year* 2009 *Income* £150,805 *Grants* £145,123 *Assets* £489,339

TRUSTEES A N Joseph, Chair; P Ashes; J Goldsworthy; R Howard; P McFall; Ms C F Smith; K Wingfield.

HOW TO APPLY The trust does not accept outside applications – the person making the application has to be a member of staff.

WHO TO APPLY TO The Trustees, The Lodge, 8 Derby Road, Garstang, Preston PR3 1EU

CC NO 801678   **ESTABLISHED** 1989

■ Private Equity Foundation

WHERE FUNDING CAN BE GIVEN UK.

WHO CAN BENEFIT Children and young people, particularly those classed as NEET (Not in education, employment or training).

WHAT IS FUNDED Education and training.

TYPE OF GRANT One-off and recurrent.

SAMPLE GRANTS In 2008: Every Child a Chance Trust, Fairbridge, School-Home Support, Skill Force and Tomorrow's People.

FINANCES *Year* 2006–07 *Income* £4,614,917 *Grants* £2,448,393 *Assets* £1,297,775

TRUSTEES David Blitzer; Scott Collins; Todd Fisher; Charlie Green; Carl Parker; Stephen Peel; Dwight Poler; Ramez Sousou; David Barker.

HOW TO APPLY Private Equity Foundation has its own charity selection process. It makes information available on its website when it is seeking new charities to join its portfolio.

WHO TO APPLY TO Shaks Ghosh, Chief Executive Officer, 2 Bath Place, Rivington Street, London EC2A 3DB *Tel* 0845 838 7330 *email* info@privateequityfoundation.org *Website* www.privateequityfoundation.org

CC NO 1116139   **ESTABLISHED** 2006

■ The Privy Purse Charitable Trust

WHERE FUNDING CAN BE GIVEN UK.

WHO CAN BENEFIT Registered charities.

WHAT IS FUNDED General charitable purposes. 'The main aims of the trustees are to make grants to charities of which The Queen is patron and to support ecclesiastical establishments associated with The Queen.'

RANGE OF GRANTS Usually up to £1,000.

SAMPLE GRANTS The chapels at Hampton Court Palace (£83,000); St James's Palace (£49,000); and Windsor Great Park (£12,000). 'Sandringham Group of Parishes' also received £51,000.

FINANCES *Year* 2007–08 *Income* £431,761 *Grants* £328,000 *Assets* £2,201,103

TRUSTEES Ian McGregor; Sir Alan Reid; Christopher Geidt.

HOW TO APPLY The trust makes donations to a wide variety of charities, but does not respond to unsolicited applications.

Think carefully about every application. Is it justified?

787

WHO TO APPLY TO Ian McGregor, Trustee, Buckingham Palace, London SW1A 1AA *Tel* 020 7930 4832 *email* ian.mcgregor@royal.gsx.gov.uk
CC NO 296079   **ESTABLISHED** 1987

....

■ The Proven Family Trust

WHERE FUNDING CAN BE GIVEN Cumbria, Halton, Knowsley, Liverpool, St Helens, Sefton, Warrington and Wirral.

WHO CAN BENEFIT Organisations benefiting children and older people; those in care, fostered and adopted; and animals. Support may be given to at risk groups and people who are disabled, disadvantaged by poverty, homeless, victims of abuse or domestic violence or who have Alzheimer's disease, arthritis and rheumatism, asthma, cancer, motor neurone disease, multiple sclerosis, Parkinson's disease or sight loss.

WHAT IS FUNDED Charities working in the fields of holiday and respite accommodation; volunteer bureaux; religious and historic buildings; health; community facilities and services; and animal welfare. Other charitable purposes will be considered.

WHAT IS NOT FUNDED No grants to individuals.

TYPE OF GRANT One-off grants for up to three years. Research grants will be considered.

RANGE OF GRANTS Up to £1,000.

SAMPLE GRANTS Previously: Claire House Children's Home (£1,000); Winged Fellowship Trust (£620); Watermillock First Responders, Cockermouth School, Kirkgate Pre-School and Listening Books (£500 each); WBS Birkenhead, Vickerstown School and Roundabout Centre (£400 each); Camblesby Youth Community Centre and Wigan and District Community Transport (£300 each); and Penrith Methodist Church, Cockermouth Youth Action Limited and Cerebral Palsy (£250 each).

FINANCES *Year* 2007–08 *Income* £114,725 *Grants* £32,350 *Assets* £736,891

TRUSTEES G R Quigley; M C Taxman; C J Worthington; S Griffiths.

HOW TO APPLY In writing to the correspondent for consideration twice a year.

WHO TO APPLY TO Colin Worthington, Trustee, 35 The Mount, Papcastle, Cockermouth, Cumbria CA13 0JY *Tel* 01900 823 324
CC NO 1050877   **ESTABLISHED** 1995

....

■ The Provincial Grand Charity of the Province of Derbyshire

WHERE FUNDING CAN BE GIVEN Derbyshire.

WHO CAN BENEFIT Masons and dependants; other charitable organisations.

WHAT IS FUNDED Masonic charities and general charitable purposes.

SAMPLE GRANTS Blythe House Hospice (£1,000); WORK, Derby Kids' Camp and Ryder-Cheshire Volunteers (£500 each); Brin's Cottage, Lennox Children's Cancer Fund and Ian Appeal (£300 each); and Guide Association Chesterfield HQ and 3rd Wingerworth Scout Group, Muscular Dystrophy Campaign and Nicholson Court Social Club (£250 each).

FINANCES *Year* 2007–08 *Income* £126,955 *Grants* £22,850 *Assets* £1,291,001

TRUSTEES J G R Rudd; G M Sissons; Dr B Quartermain.

OTHER INFORMATION Grants were broken down as follows: Non-Masonic Charities £17,000; TLC

Appeal – £3,250; Seasonal Relief – £1,500; and Albert Wilson Trust – £1,100

HOW TO APPLY In writing to the correspondent.

WHO TO APPLY TO Graham Sisson, Secretary, 21 Netherfield Road, Chapel-en-le-Frith, High Peak SK23 0PN *Tel* 01298 812801 *email* graham.sisson@redboxinternet.net *Website* www.derbyshiremason.org
CC NO 701963   **ESTABLISHED** 1989

....

■ PSA Peugeot Citroen Charity Trust

WHERE FUNDING CAN BE GIVEN Coventry and Warwickshire.

WHO CAN BENEFIT Local voluntary organisations and small charitable groups only.

WHAT IS FUNDED General charitable purposes. Causes are often associated with the motor industry.

WHAT IS NOT FUNDED No grants are given to individuals or outside the beneficial area. Sponsorships and charitable advertising are not considered.

TYPE OF GRANT One-off grants.

RANGE OF GRANTS £50–£1,500; average £200–£300.

SAMPLE GRANTS Previously: PT Charitable Fund for Employees (£1,500); Peugeot Seven (£400); Allesley Park Community Centre, Mercia MS Therapy Centre, Cancer Research UK and the Sycamore Tree Counselling Service (£300 each); Coventry Sphinx FC and GA Sports FC (£250 each); Tiny Tim's Children's Centre and Rugby CVS (£200 each); Warwickshire & Northamptonshire Air Ambulance and Bell House Rugby (£100 each); and Walsgrave Amateur Riding Club (£50).

FINANCES *Year* 2007–08 *Income* £43,714 *Grants* £31,883 *Assets* £85,831

TRUSTEES M Barnes; R Lewis; M J Lynch; C Lees.

HOW TO APPLY In writing to the correspondent.

WHO TO APPLY TO Glenda Gilkes, Secretary, Pinley House, 2 Sunbeam Way, Coventry CV3 1ND *Tel* 024 7688 4386 *Fax* 024 7688 4640 *email* glenda@heartofenglandcf.co.uk
CC NO 266182   **ESTABLISHED** 1970

....

■ The Puebla Charitable Trust

WHERE FUNDING CAN BE GIVEN Worldwide.

WHO CAN BENEFIT Organisations benefiting people disadvantaged by poverty living in both urban and rural areas.

WHAT IS FUNDED 'At present, the council limits its support to charities which assist the poorest sections of the population and community development work – either of these may be in urban or rural areas, both in the UK and overseas.'

WHAT IS NOT FUNDED No grants for capital projects, religious institutions, research or institutions for people who are disabled. Individuals are not supported and no scholarships are given.

TYPE OF GRANT Up to three years.

SAMPLE GRANTS Recent beneficiaries have included: Action on Disability and Development, the Cambodia Trust, Child Poverty Action Group, Family Welfare Association, Mines Advisory Group, Shelter, South West London Law Centres, Immigrants Aid and Zimbabwe Benefit Foundation.

FINANCES *Year* 2007–08 *Income* £115,472 *Grants* £0 *Assets* £2,488,274

TRUSTEES J Phipps; M A Strutt.

OTHER INFORMATION During 2006–07 the trust committed to pay grants of £450,000 over a three year period, and this commitment was recognised in the accounts for that year. No grants were paid during the year.

HOW TO APPLY In writing to the correspondent. The trustees meet in July. The trust is unable to acknowledge applications.

WHO TO APPLY TO The Clerk, Ensors, Cardinal House, 46 St Nicholas Street, Ipswich IP1 1TT *Tel* 01473 220 022

CC NO 290055   **ESTABLISHED** 1984

■ The Richard and Christine Purchas Charitable Trust

WHERE FUNDING CAN BE GIVEN UK.

WHO CAN BENEFIT Medical organisations.

WHAT IS FUNDED Medical research, medical education and patient care.

FINANCES *Year* 2007–08 *Income* £139,062 *Grants* £140,000 *Assets* £2,507,536

TRUSTEES Daniel Auerbach; Mrs Pauline Auerbach; Dr Douglas Rossdale; Robert Auerbach.

OTHER INFORMATION No list of grants was included with the accounts filed at the Charity Commission. Previously the trust has part-funded the post of Consultant Speech Therapist at the Charing Cross Hospital in association with Macmillan Cancer Relief.

HOW TO APPLY In writing to the correspondent.

WHO TO APPLY TO Daniel Auerbach, Trustee, 46 Hyde Park Gardens Mews, London W2 2NX

CC NO 1083126   **ESTABLISHED** 2000

■ The Puri Foundation

WHERE FUNDING CAN BE GIVEN Nottinghamshire, India (particularly the towns of Mullan Pur near Chandigarh and Ambala).

WHO CAN BENEFIT Organisations benefiting: children; young adults; students; older people; Hindus; the disabled; at risk groups; those disadvantaged by poverty; and socially isolated people.

WHAT IS FUNDED Welfare and community centres. The trust aims to: relieve those in conditions of need, hardship or distress; advance education; provide facilities for recreation; and relieve and rehabilitate young unemployed people in the Nottinghamshire area.

WHAT IS NOT FUNDED No grants are given for holidays.

RANGE OF GRANTS Minimum of £50.

SAMPLE GRANTS The Puri Foundation for Education in India (£550,000); National Hindu Student Forum (£12,500); Dinesh Bhakta (£2,500); Mandeep Singh (£1,950); and Mornington School (£1,000).

FINANCES *Year* 2007–08 *Income* £789,299 *Grants* £578,330 *Assets* £3,185,143

TRUSTEES N R Puri; A Puri; Miss M K McGowan.

HOW TO APPLY In writing to the correspondent.

WHO TO APPLY TO N R Puri, Trustee, Environment House, 6 Union Road, Nottingham NG3 1FH *Tel* 0115 901 3000 *Fax* 0115 901 3100

CC NO 327854   **ESTABLISHED** 1988

■ Mr and Mrs J A Pye's Charitable Settlement

WHERE FUNDING CAN BE GIVEN UK, with a special interest in the Oxford area and, to a lesser extent, in Reading, Cheltenham and Bristol.

WHO CAN BENEFIT Organisations benefiting children and young adults are given priority, although those benefiting older people will also be funded.

WHAT IS FUNDED General charitable purposes at the trustees' discretion. Of particular interest are: environmental – this subject particularly deals with organic farming matters, conservation generally and health related matters such as pollution research and some wildlife protection; adult health and care – especially causes supporting: post natal depression, schizophrenia, mental health generally and research into the main causes of early death; children's health and care – for physical, mental and learning disabilities, respite breaks and so on; youth organisations – particularly projects encouraging self reliance or dealing with social deprivation; education – nursery, primary, secondary or higher/institutions (not individuals); regional causes around Oxford, Reading, Cheltenham and Bristol – under this category the trustees will consider academic and arts projects.

WHAT IS NOT FUNDED No grants for: organisations that are not recognised charities; activities which are primarily the responsibility of government or some other responsible body; activities which collect funds for subsequent re-distribution to other charities; corporate affiliation or membership of charities; endowment funds; expeditions or overseas charities; fabric appeals for places of worship, other than in geographical locations indicated above; fundraising events or activities; hospitals or medical centres (except for projects that are clearly additional to statutory responsibilities); individual, including students; overseas appeals; promotion of religion.

TYPE OF GRANT One-off, core costs, projects, research, recurring, running and start-up costs, and salaries. Capital costs may be considered. Funding may be given for up to or more than three years. Also interest-free loans.

RANGE OF GRANTS £250–£135,000.

SAMPLE GRANTS Organic Research Centre (£135,000); Music@Oxford (£77,000); University College Oxford (£50,000); Harris Manchester College (£30,000); British Trust for Conservation Volunteers (£15,000); Oxford Literary and Debating Union Trust (£10,000); Mansfield College (£6,000); Oxfordshire Community Foundation (£5,000); Marie Curie Cancer Care (£3,000); Children with AIDS Charity and the Reading Foundation for Art Charity (£2,000 each); and Bristol & District Tranquilliser Project, Dyslexia Institute and the Wildfowl & Wetlands Trust (£1,000 each).

FINANCES *Year* 2008 *Income* £659,803 *Grants* £587,932 *Assets* £9,515,599

TRUSTEES Simon Stubbings; David S Tallon.

PUBLICATIONS Guidelines for applicants.

HOW TO APPLY There are no application forms but the following information is essential: registered charity number or evidence of an organisation's tax exempt status; brief description of the activities of the charity; the names of the trustees and chief officers (NB: more important than patrons); details of the purpose of the application and where funds will be put to use; details of the funds already raised and the proposals for how remaining funds are to be raised; the latest trustees' report and full audited or independently examined accounts (which must comply with Charity Commission guidelines and requirements). Applications can be made at any time, with the trustees meeting quarterly to take decisions. Any decision can therefore take up to four months before it is finally taken. However, all applicants are informed of the outcome of their applications and all applications are acknowledged. Telephone contact will usually be counterproductive, as the trust only wishes to respond to written applications.

WHO TO APPLY TO David S Tallon, Trustee, c/o Mercer and Hole Chartered Accountants, Gloucester House, 72 London Road, St Albans, Hertfordshire AL1 1NS *Tel* 01727 869141 *Fax* 01727 869149

CC NO 242677   **ESTABLISHED** 1965

....

■ The Pyne Charitable Trust

WHERE FUNDING CAN BE GIVEN UK and overseas, particularly Malawi, Moldova, Slovakia and Ukraine.

WHO CAN BENEFIT Organisations and individuals.

WHAT IS FUNDED Christian and health causes.

SAMPLE GRANTS Good Shepherd Mission (£60,000); Amersham Christian Housing Association (£34,000); Teen Challenge London and Wings Eagles Trust (£2,400 each); Crossroads Christian Counselling (£1,200); Release International (£600); Serpentine Gallery (£500); and Cancer Research UK and Lawrence's Roundabout Well Appeal (£100 each).

FINANCES *Year* 2008 *Income* £89,770 *Grants* £101,300 *Assets* £19,482

TRUSTEES Michael Brennan; Pauline Brennan; Mike Mitchell.

HOW TO APPLY Ongoing support appears to be given to projects selected by the trustees.

WHO TO APPLY TO Pauline Brennan, Secretary, 26 Tredegar square, London E3 5AG

CC NO 1105357   **ESTABLISHED** 2004

■ Quartet Community Foundation (formerly the Greater Bristol Foundation)

WHERE FUNDING CAN BE GIVEN West England – Bristol, North Somerset, South Gloucestershire, Bath and North East Somerset.

WHO CAN BENEFIT Any charity aimed at increasing opportunities and enhancing the quality of life in the area; particularly smaller, low-profile community groups and people at a particular disadvantage through discrimination.

WHAT IS FUNDED There are a number of specific schemes which support the four geographical beneficial areas, aiming to help local communities. Grants are made for a wide range of charitable purposes including: education, the protection of good health, relief of poverty and sickness, social welfare and the environment. For further information on types of grants and guidance towards the most appropriate fund(s) for your organisation contact the foundation or visit their website.

WHAT IS NOT FUNDED The foundation does not give grants to: individuals; general appeals; statutory organisations or the direct replacement of statutory funding; political groups or activities promoting political beliefs; religious groups promoting religious beliefs; arts projects with no community or charitable element; sports projects with no community or charitable element; medical research, equipment or treatment; animal welfare; or projects that take place before an application can be processed.

SAMPLE GRANTS Voluntary Action North Somerset (£59,000); Converging World (£40,000); Second Step Housing Association (£20,000); Re: Work (£15,000); Armstrong Hall (£12,000); Community Action (£10,000); Bradford Environmental Action Trust (£8,000); Awaz Utaoh and NESA (£7,000 each).

FINANCES *Year* 2007–08 *Income* £2,912,923 *Grants* £2,835,806 *Assets* £13,971,358

TRUSTEES John Kane; Alexander Hore-Ruthven; Mary Prior; Peter Rilett; Alison Reed; Tim Ross; Anna Schiff; Gail Bragg; Prof. Murray Stewart; Cedric Clapp; William Lee; Gill Stobart; Richard Hall; Lin Whitfield.

HOW TO APPLY Before you apply to the community foundation check that your group or project meets the following requirements: you must be a small charity, community group or local voluntary organisation operating in the West of England i.e. Bath and North East Somerset, Bristol, North Somerset or South Gloucestershire; you do not need to be a registered charity but you must be able to provide a copy of your group's constitution or set of rules; your group must be managed by a board of trustees or management committee; and you must be able to provide the foundation with up-to-date financial information for your group.

Help and advice on making an application is always available from the foundation's grant team, members of which can be contacted at the following local offices: **Bristol and South Gloucestershire:** Royal Oak House, Royal Oak Avenue, Bristol BS1 4GB. Tel: 0117 989 7700; Email: info@quartetcf.org.uk; **Bath & North East Somerset:** 12 Pierrepoint Street, Bath BA1 1LA. Tel: 01225 420 300; Email: banes@quartetcf.org.uk; **North Somerset:** Badger Centre 3–6 Wadham Street, Weston-Super-Mare BS23 1JY. Tel: 01934 641 965; Email: northsomerset@quartetcf.org.uk. Applications can be made using the online form available on the foundation's website. Alternatively you can download an application form from the website or request one to be sent by post by contacting your local office.

WHO TO APPLY TO Helen Moss, Director, Royal Oak House, Royal Oak Avenue, Bristol BS1 4GB *Tel* 0117 989 7700 *Fax* 0117 989 7701 *email* info@quartetcf.org.uk *Website* www.quartetcf.org.uk

CC NO 1080418   **ESTABLISHED** 1987

■ The Queen Anne's Gate Foundation

WHERE FUNDING CAN BE GIVEN UK and overseas.

WHO CAN BENEFIT Charitable organisations.

WHAT IS FUNDED 'The foundation seeks to support projects and charities within the following broad criteria. It seeks to make a contribution that is meaningful in the context of the project/charity with which it is working. It tries to focus in particular on projects which might be said to make potentially unproductive lives productive. This tends to mean a bias towards educational, medical and rehabilitative charities and those that work with underprivileged areas of society. There is an attempt to focus a significant proportion of donations on Asia, Malawi and the UK.'

SAMPLE GRANTS Previous beneficiaries included Hackney Music Development Trust, Merlin, Udavum Karangal and World Medical Fund.

FINANCES *Year* 2007–08 *Income* £4,064,000 *Grants* £398,000 *Assets* £4,624,868

TRUSTEES N T Allan; J M E Boyer; I G Lewis.

HOW TO APPLY In writing to the correspondent.

WHO TO APPLY TO The Trustees, WillcoxLewis LLP, The Old Coach House, Bergh Apton, Norwich, Norfolk NR15 1DD

CC NO 1108903   **ESTABLISHED** 2005

■ Queen Mary's Roehampton Trust

WHERE FUNDING CAN BE GIVEN UK.

WHO CAN BENEFIT Ex-servicemen or women who were disabled in service and their dependants.

WHAT IS FUNDED Grants are made to charities supporting ex-service personnel who suffered disability while in service that provide welfare services, residential or nursing homes and their widows/widowers and dependants.

WHAT IS NOT FUNDED Individual grants.

TYPE OF GRANT Annual recurring, one-off. Also capital and project. Funding may be given for up to two years.

RANGE OF GRANTS Usually £1,000–£50,000.

SAMPLE GRANTS Army Benevolent Fund (£45,000); SSAFA Forces Help (£35,000); Broughton House (£32,000); Chelsea Pensioners Appeal (£25,000); Royal Commonwealth Ex-Services League (£20,000); Gurkha Welfare Trust (£12,000); Chaseley Trust (£10,000); Vitalise (£6,000); Royal Homes and Royal Cambridge Home for Soldiers' Widows (£5,000); and Spinal Injuries Association (£1,000).

FINANCES *Year* 2007–08 *Income* £532,909 *Grants* £497,000 *Assets* £11,388,644

TRUSTEES Col. S D Brewis, Chair; Maj. Gen. R P Craig; J J McNamara; Brig. A K Dixon; R R Holland; Dr J G Paterson; Mrs C M Walker; Mrs S Freeth; C Green; Col. K George; Col. P Cummings; Ms P Melville-Brown.

HOW TO APPLY On a standard application form available from the correspondent. Representatives of the trust may visit beneficiary organisations.

WHO TO APPLY TO Alan Baker, Clerk to the Trustees, 13 St George's Road, Wallington, Surrey SM6 0AS *Tel* 020 8395 9980 *Fax* 020 8255 1457 *email* alanbaker13@hotmail.com

CC NO 211715   ESTABLISHED 1928

....

■ The Queen's Silver Jubilee Trust

WHERE FUNDING CAN BE GIVEN UK, the Channel Islands, Isle of Man and the Commonwealth.

WHO CAN BENEFIT Registered charities.

WHAT IS FUNDED Organisations working with young people, aged 14–30, across the UK, Commonwealth, Channel Islands and the Isle of Man, particularly those that support disadvantaged young people or those that enable young people to volunteer in their local community, broadly defined.

WHAT IS NOT FUNDED Grants are only made to registered charities. No grants to individuals.

TYPE OF GRANT One-off and recurring.

RANGE OF GRANTS Up to £10,000.

SAMPLE GRANTS The Prince's Trust (£1.2 million); Youth Business International (£10,000); Campus Children's Holiday, Cirdan Sailing Trust, Tommy's The Baby Charity, Coaching Highland, The Arkwright Society, Florance Home Foundation, Project Trust and Liverpool Community Spirit (£5,000 each); The Malt Cross Trust (£4,000); ProjectScotland (£2,000); and the 2nd Sanquhar Boys Brigade (£1,000).

FINANCES *Year* 2007–08 *Income* £1,112,000 *Grants* £1,256,000 *Assets* £34,640,000

TRUSTEES Rt Hon Christopher Geidt; Sir Fred Goodwin; Stephen Hall; Sir Alan Reid; Peter Mimpriss; Sir John Riddell.

HOW TO APPLY Potential applicants are advised to email the contact before making a formal application. Applicants must ensure that: their organisation is eligible; they have read the Terms and Conditions and other guidance notes; they enclose their most recent annual report and accounts, or financial projections and previous income expenditure charts if the organisation is less that two years old; they enclose their most recent annual review or a brief summary of what their organisation does; retain a photocopy of all submitted materials. An application form is available to download from the trust's website. Deadlines for applications are also published on the trust's website.

WHO TO APPLY TO Nicola Brentnall, The Prince's Trust, 17–18 Park Square East, London NW1 4LH *Tel* 020 7543 1234 *Fax* 020 7543 1200 *email* nicola.brentnall@princes-trust.org.uk *Website* www.queenssilverjubileetrust.org.uk

CC NO 272373   ESTABLISHED 1976

....

■ Quercus Trust

WHERE FUNDING CAN BE GIVEN UK.

WHO CAN BENEFIT Established organisations and registered charities.

WHAT IS FUNDED Mainly the arts, and other purposes which seek to further public knowledge, understanding and appreciation of any matters of artistic, aesthetic, scientific or historical interest.

WHAT IS NOT FUNDED No grants to individuals.

SAMPLE GRANTS Recent beneficiaries have included: Almedia Theatre Company, British Friends of the Art Museums of Israel, Central School of Ballet, English Stage Company, George Piper Dances, Kangyur Rinpoche Foundation, Random Dance Company, Sadler's Wells Trust, Siobahn Davies' Dance Company, Tate Foundation and Wigmore Hall Trust.

FINANCES *Year* 2007–08 *Grants* £100,000

TRUSTEES Lord Bernstein; Lady Bernstein; Kate E Bernstein.

HOW TO APPLY In writing to the correspondent, but please note, the trust states: 'All of the trust's funds are currently earmarked for existing projects. The trust has a policy of not making donations to individuals and the trustees regret that, in order to keep administrative costs to a minimum, they are unable to reply to any unsuccessful applicants.'

WHO TO APPLY TO The Trustees, Chantrey Vellacott, Russell Square House, 10–12 Russell Square, London WC1B 5LF

CC NO 1039205   ESTABLISHED 1993

....

■ Quothquan Trust

WHERE FUNDING CAN BE GIVEN Birmingham and the West Midlands.

WHO CAN BENEFIT Projects known to the trustees, usually Christian organisations benefiting the community.

WHAT IS FUNDED Usually local Christian projects. Any project outside the West Midlands must be known to the trustees, whether in the UK or abroad.

WHAT IS NOT FUNDED No grants are given towards: anything that does not have the promotion of Christianity as part of its ethos; activities that are the primary responsibility of central or local government; animal welfare; church buildings for restorations, improvements, renovations or new building; environmental projects such as conservation and protection of wildlife and landscape; expeditions and overseas trips; hospitals and health centres; individuals are not normally supported; large national charities are not normally supported, even for local projects; loans and business finance; medical research projects; overseas appeals, unless there is a recommendation from someone known personally to the trustees; promotion of any non-Christian religion; schools, universities and colleges.

SAMPLE GRANTS Churches and Christian centres (£201,300); Second Quothquan Charitable Trust (£200,000); evangelism, bibles and education (£98,400); overseas missions and workers (£81,200); full-time Christian worker (£60,100); promotion of prayer (£19,000); low income or lone parent families (£6,000); family, young people and children (£3,500); students (£2,400); and volunteers (£1,000).

FINANCES *Year* 2007 *Income* £240,427 *Grants* £673,014 *Assets* £2,043,985

TRUSTEES Archie Gilmour; Mrs J A Gilmour.

OTHER INFORMATION Grants totalling £84,000 were made to 48 individuals.

HOW TO APPLY In writing to the correspondent.

WHO TO APPLY TO Archie Gilmour, Trustee, Dale Farm, Worcester Lane, Four Oaks, Sutton Coldfield, West Midlands B75 5PR *Tel* 0121 323 3236 *Fax* 0121 323 3237 *email* appeals@quothquan.org

CC NO 1110647   ESTABLISHED 2005

R

■ The R D Crusaders Foundation

WHERE FUNDING CAN BE GIVEN Worldwide.
WHO CAN BENEFIT Charitable organisations.
WHAT IS FUNDED The relief of poverty and sickness, particularly among children.
TYPE OF GRANT Core, capital and project funding in one-off and recurrent grants.
SAMPLE GRANTS Marie Curie Cancer Care (£1 million); Moorfields Eye Hospital Development Fund (£500,000); Jewish Care (£435,000); Fight for Sight (£100,000); Maggie's – Joy of Living Campaign (£25,000); Variety Club Children's Charity (£20,000); Zoe's Place Hospice (£15,000); COSMIC and the Healing Foundation (£10,000 each); Ovarian Cancer Action and UK Jewish Film Festival (£5,000 each); World Jewish Affairs Fund (£3,000); and Cued Speech Association Centre, Magen David Adom and RISE Foundation (£1,000 each).
FINANCES *Year* 2008 *Income* £336,532 *Grants* £3,824,631 *Assets* £817,974
TRUSTEES R C Desmond; Mrs J Desmond.
HOW TO APPLY In writing to the correspondent.
WHO TO APPLY TO The Trustees, The Northern and Shell Building, No. 10 Lower Thames Street, London EC3R 6EN
CC NO 1014352   **ESTABLISHED** 1992

■ R S Charitable Trust

WHERE FUNDING CAN BE GIVEN UK.
WHO CAN BENEFIT Registered charities.
WHAT IS FUNDED Jewish causes and the relief of poverty.
SAMPLE GRANTS Previous beneficiaries have included British Friends of Tshernobil, Forty Ltd, NRST, Society of Friends of the Torah, Talmud Hochschule, Viznitz, Yeshiva Horomo and Yeshivas Luzern.
FINANCES *Year* 2006–07 *Income* £668,178 *Grants* £485,130 *Assets* £2,004,363
TRUSTEES Harvey Freudenberger; Max Reudenberger; Michelle Freudenberger; Stuart Freudenberger; Max Freudenberger.
HOW TO APPLY In writing to the correspondent.
WHO TO APPLY TO Max Freudenberger, Trustee, 138 Stamford Hill, London N16 6QT
CC NO 1053660   **ESTABLISHED** 1996

■ The R V W Trust

WHERE FUNDING CAN BE GIVEN UK.
WHO CAN BENEFIT Organisations and individuals, particularly composers, musicians and music students.
WHAT IS FUNDED The trust's current grant-making policies are as follows: (1) To give assistance to British composers who have not yet achieved a national reputation. (2) To give assistance towards the performance and recording of music by neglected or currently unfashionable 20th century British composers, including performances by societies and at festivals which include works by such composers in their programmes. (3) To assist UK organisations that promote public knowledge and appreciation of 20th and 21st century British music. (4) To assist education projects in the field of music. (5) To support post-graduate students of composition taking first masters degrees at British universities and conservatoires.
WHAT IS NOT FUNDED No grants for local authority or other government-funded bodies, nor degree courses, except first Masters' degrees in musical composition. No support for dance or drama courses. No grants for workshops without public performance, private vocal or instrumental tuition or the purchase or repair of musical instruments. No grants for concerts that do not include music by 20th and 21st century composers or for musicals, rock, pop, ethnic, jazz or dance music. No grants for the construction or restoration of buildings. The trust is not able to make grants towards the music of Ralph Vaughan Williams.
SAMPLE GRANTS British Music Information Centre, Society for the Promotion of New Music and Vaughan Williams Memorial Library (£25,000 each); Huddersfield Contemporary Music Festival and Park Lane Group (£15,000 each); Royal Philharmonic Society Composition Prize (£7,000); Birmingham Contemporary Music Group, Corsham Festival, Opera Circus, Opera Group, Orchestra of the Swan, Presteigne Festival, Royal Northern College of Music, Frederic Cox Award, Scottish Opera, Spitalfields Festival, University of York and Worcester Three Choirs Festival (£5,000 each); Hampstead and Highgate Festival and London Sinfonietta (£4,000 each); English Music Festival, Brighton Festival and London Festival of Contemporary Church Music (£3,000 each); and Cheltenham Music Society, Deal Festival and Music Theatre Wales (£2,000 each).
FINANCES *Year* 2008 *Income* £431,285 *Grants* £281,384 *Assets* £1,112,570
TRUSTEES Hugh Cobbe, Chair; Dr Michael Kennedy; The Lord Armstrong of Ilminster; Andrew Hunter Johnston; Sir John Manduell; Jeremy Dale Roberts; Musicians Benevolent Fund.
HOW TO APPLY All potential applicants should contact the trust for further details of current grant-making policy and details of how to apply by emailing the secretary. The trust holds three main grant-making meetings a year. Closing dates for applications are 2 January, 1 May and 1 September. Applicants are notified of the results approximately eight weeks after these dates.
WHO TO APPLY TO Ms Helen Faulkner, Administrator, 7–11 Britannia Street, London WC1X 9JS *email* helen@rvwtrust.org.uk *Website* www.rvwtrust.org.uk
CC NO 1066977   **ESTABLISHED** 1958

■ The Monica Rabagliati Charitable Trust

WHERE FUNDING CAN BE GIVEN UK.
WHO CAN BENEFIT Charitable organisations. 'The trustees have decided to prioritise small/medium sized organisations where possible.'
WHAT IS FUNDED Mostly support for 'organisations that focus on the alleviation of child suffering and deprivation'. The trust also supports humanitarian and medical causes.
SAMPLE GRANTS St Joseph Priestly Scholarships (£10,000); Children in Distress (£4,000); International Childcare Trust (£3,500); Centrepoint, DebRA and U-Turn (£2,500 each); RNLI (£2,000); and Children's Hope Foundation, the Children's Voice, CHICKS, Kid Connect,

Place2be, Refuge and Surrey Care Trust
(£1,000 each).
FINANCES *Year* 2007–08 *Income* £49,408
Grants £60,000 *Assets* £1,943,813
TRUSTEES S G Hambros Trust Company Limited;
R L McLean
HOW TO APPLY In writing to the correspondent. 'The
trustees assess grant applications and make
appropriate grants twice yearly.'
WHO TO APPLY TO The Administrator, S G Hambros
Trust Company Limited, S G House, 41 Tower
Hill, London EC3N 4SG *Website* www.rabagliati.
org.uk
CC NO 1086368   **ESTABLISHED** 2001

....

■ Rachel Charitable Trust

WHERE FUNDING CAN BE GIVEN Unrestricted.
WHO CAN BENEFIT Charitable organisations, mostly
Jewish groups.
WHAT IS FUNDED General charitable purposes, in
practice, mainly Jewish organisations.
SAMPLE GRANTS Previous beneficiaries include:
British Friends of Shuut Ami, Children's Hospital
Trust Fund, Cometville Limited, Encounter –
Jewish Outreach Network, Chosen Mishpat
Centre, Gertner Charitable Trust, Hertsmere
Jewish Primary School, Jewish Learning
Exchange, London Millennium Bikeathon,
Manchester Jewish Grammar School, Project
Seed, Shaarei Zedek Hospital, Shomrei
Hachomot Jerusalem, Yeshiva Ohel Shimon
Trust, Yeshiva Shaarei Torah Manchester.
FINANCES *Year* 2007–08 *Income* £7,666,692
Grants £3,151,817 *Assets* £11,421,809
TRUSTEES Leopold Noe; Susan Noe; Simon Kanter.
HOW TO APPLY In writing to the correspondent.
WHO TO APPLY TO Robert Chalk, Secretary, c/o 5
Wigmore Street, London W1U 1PB
CC NO 276441

....

■ The Mr and Mrs Philip Rackham Charitable Trust

WHERE FUNDING CAN BE GIVEN Norfolk.
WHO CAN BENEFIT Registered charities.
WHAT IS FUNDED General charitable purposes,
although there is some preference for asthma
charities and Samaritans.
WHAT IS NOT FUNDED No grants to individuals.
RANGE OF GRANTS Up to £5,750.
SAMPLE GRANTS NNAB and RABI (£5,000 each);
Bowthorpe Community Trust (£2,500); the
Derma Trust and the Magdalene Group (£1,000
each); and ADAPT and Norfolk Scouts (£500
each).
FINANCES *Year* 2007–08 *Income* £41,424
Grants £25,500 *Assets* £878,686
TRUSTEES Neil G Sparrow; C W L Barratt; Ann
E S Rush.
HOW TO APPLY In writing to the correspondent.
WHO TO APPLY TO Neil G Sparrow, Clerk, Birketts, 16
Queen Street, Norwich, Norfolk NR2 4SQ
Tel 01603 232300 *Fax* 01603 230533
CC NO 1013844   **ESTABLISHED** 1992

....

■ Richard Radcliffe Charitable Trust

WHERE FUNDING CAN BE GIVEN UK.
WHO CAN BENEFIT Charitable organisations.
WHAT IS FUNDED The trust stated its policy as being
to support, through making grants to other
organisations, the following charitable activities:

to assist physically disabled people; to provide
technical training to give young people a start in
life; to support hospice care for people who are
terminally ill; to provide help for people who are
severely deaf and/or blind.
TYPE OF GRANT Mainly recurrent.
RANGE OF GRANTS Up to £4,000.
SAMPLE GRANTS Martlets Hospice (£4,000); St
Barnabas Hospice, and RNIB (£2,000 each);
Orbis, 4 Sight and Sight Savers (£1,500 each);
and St Peters and St James Hospice, Mcmillan
Cancer Relief, Independent Age and Harvest
Trust (£1,000 each).
FINANCES *Year* 2007–08 *Income* £37,718
Grants £26,500 *Assets* £1,065,220
TRUSTEES Miss I M R Radcliffe; Miss P Radcliffe;
A M Bell.
HOW TO APPLY In writing to the correspondent.
WHO TO APPLY TO Adrian Bell, Senior Partner, Griffith
Smith Solicitors, 32 Keymer Road, Hassocks,
West Sussex BN6 8AL *Tel* 01273 843 405
CC NO 1068930   **ESTABLISHED** 1998

....

■ The Radcliffe Trust

WHERE FUNDING CAN BE GIVEN UK.
WHO CAN BENEFIT Registered or exempt charities.
Organisations and schemes benefiting
musicians and those involved in the crafts.
WHAT IS FUNDED (1) Music: 'The Radcliffe Trust
supports classical music performance and
training especially chamber music, composition
and music education. Particular interests within
music education are music for children and
adults with special needs, youth orchestras and
projects at secondary and higher levels,
including academic research. (2) Craft: The
Radcliffe Trust supports craft training among
young people both at the level of apprenticeship
and also at the post-graduate and post-
experience levels. Crafts are broadly defined,
including building conservation skills, rural skills
and traditional creative craft skills. The trustees
are also concerned to promote a standard of
excellence through support for conservation and
craft projects involving traditional or innovative
craft skills. Direct applications for the
restoration or conservation of old or otherwise
interesting buildings are accepted only in
exceptional circumstances.
WHAT IS NOT FUNDED No grants to individual
applicants. No retrospective grants are made,
nor for deficit funding, core costs, general
appeals or endowment funds. No new building
appeals.
RANGE OF GRANTS Mostly £1,000–£5,000.
SAMPLE GRANTS The Allegri String Quartet
(£20,000); National Library of Scotland
(£15,000); Royal Academy of Music and Trinity
College of Music (£12,000 each); Edward
Barnsley Education Trust (£11,000); Scottish
Lime Centre (£10,000); Meridian Trust
Association (£7,000); Aldeburgh Productions,
Chamber Music at the Purcell School, Handel
House Museum, Kettles Yard University and
London Philharmonic Orchestra (£5,000 each);
Orton Trust (£3,500); Dartington International
Summer School (£3,000); Salisbury Cathedral
and Wells Cathedral (£2,000 each); Worcester
Cathedral Development and Restoration Trust
(£1,500); Edinburgh and Lothians Greenspace
Trust (£1,000).
FINANCES *Year* 2007–08 *Income* £375,919
Grants £282,355 *Assets* £13,683,971
TRUSTEES Felix Warnock, Chair; Sir Henry Aubrey-
Fletcher; Lord Balfour of Burleigh; Christopher
Butcher; Dr Ivor Guest; Mary Ann Sieghart.

HOW TO APPLY Trustees meet twice yearly to administer the charity. There is a music panel of advisers who also meet twice a year to consider music applications. The deadlines for music applications are 31 January for the spring panel and 31 August for the autumn panel. The deadlines for craft applications are 30 April for the June meeting and 31 August for the November meeting. Please note that it is advisable to submit an application well in advance of the deadline. An application should include: (i) A cover letter, which should include official address, telephone number, email address and charity registration number. The applicant should make clear their position in the charity. (ii) No more than two pages outlining the proposal and the specific request to the Trust. Please note that it is important to give an indication of the timing of the project, as the trustees do not make retrospective grants. (iii) Other relevant supporting information, but applicants should be aware that additional information may not be circulated to Trustees. (iv) A budget, which must include the total cost of the project; the amount requested, and other income secured or requested. (v) An indication of past grants from the trust.

WHO TO APPLY TO The Secretary to the Trustees, 6 Trull Farm Buildings, Tetbury, Gloucestershire GL8 8SQ *Tel* 01285 841900 *email* radcliffe@thetrustpartnership.com *Website* www.theradcliffetrust.org

CC NO 209212   **ESTABLISHED** 1714

··
■ The Bishop Radford Trust

WHERE FUNDING CAN BE GIVEN UK.

WHO CAN BENEFIT Christian organisations, including churches.

WHAT IS FUNDED The promotion of 'the work of the Christian church in a manner consistent with the doctrines and principles of the Church of England'. This includes the renovation, construction and maintenance of churches, the education of church workers and church ministry.

SAMPLE GRANTS Anglican Investment Agency Trust (£154,000); Tearfund (£56,000); St Luke's Hospital for the Clergy and World Vision (£50,000 each); Diocese of Liverpool (£45,000); Bible Reading Fellowship (£40,000); St Barnabas PCC (£20,000); and Bible Reading Fellowship and the Quiet Garden Trust (£10,000 each).

FINANCES *Year* 2007–08 *Income* £3,430,457 *Grants* £199,000 *Assets* £3,563,914

TRUSTEES Stephen Green; Janian Green; Suzannah O'Brien; Ruth Dare.

HOW TO APPLY In writing to the correspondent.

WHO TO APPLY TO The Secretary, Devonshire House, 1 Devonshire Street, London W1W 5DR

CC NO 1113562   **ESTABLISHED** 2006

··
■ Radio City Charity Foundation

WHERE FUNDING CAN BE GIVEN The Radio City broadcast area (Merseyside and North Wales).

WHO CAN BENEFIT Local children who are in need. Consideration is given to projects aiming to help children from the following categories: children with mental, physical or sensory disabilities; children with behavioural or psychological disorders; children living in poverty or situations of deprivation; children experiencing distress, abuse or neglect.

WHAT IS FUNDED Relief of poverty, sickness or disability amongst children under 18 years of age, or to assist in the promotion of the physical, mental or general welfare of children.

TYPE OF GRANT One-off.

RANGE OF GRANTS Grants do not normally exceed £2,000.

FINANCES *Year* 2007–08 *Income* £145,741 *Grants* £196,859 *Assets* £114,750

TRUSTEES Jonathan Mounsey; Pauline Marsden; Susan Newton; David Mathieson; Stephen Hawkins; Michelle Surrell; Richard Maddock.

HOW TO APPLY Applications must be made before 31 March or 30 September each year on a form available from the correspondent. All applications must be accompanied by the most recently completed annual accounts. Successful applicants will be notified within a month of the allocation committee's meetings in May and November.

WHO TO APPLY TO Collette Lowe, Radio City, St John's Beacon, 1 Houghton Street, Liverpool L1 1RL *Tel* 0151 472 6827 *Fax* 0151 472 6821 *email* collette.lowe@radiocity.co.uk *Website* www.radiocity.co.uk/charity

CC NO 1038060   **ESTABLISHED** 1994

··
■ The Ragdoll Foundation

WHERE FUNDING CAN BE GIVEN UK and worldwide.

WHO CAN BENEFIT Projects that involve children during their early years, although appropriate projects for older children will be considered.

WHAT IS FUNDED Arts projects with children which: promote the development of children through children's imaginative thinking; encourage innovation and innovative thinking and influence good practice elsewhere; offer creative solutions that deal with the causes of problems in childhood; ensures effective evaluation of projects to promote sharing and learning; or above all demonstrate how the voices of children can be heard.

WHAT IS NOT FUNDED Grants are not given for: replacement of statutory funding; work that has already started or will have been completed whilst the application is being considered; promotion of religion; animal welfare charities; vehicles, emergency relief work; general fundraising or marketing appeals; open ended funding arrangements; loans or business advice; charities which are in serious deficit; holidays; any large capital; endowment or widely distributed appeal; specialist schools; school fees for people over 17 years of age; and gap year funds.

RANGE OF GRANTS Typically £500–£20,000, although large-scale grants will be considered.

FINANCES *Year* 2007–08 *Income* £147,650 *Grants* £24,800 *Assets* £105,702

TRUSTEES Katherine Wood; Peter Hollingsworth; Peter Thornton; Anne Wood; Carole Thomson.

OTHER INFORMATION 'The Ragdoll Foundation is dedicated to developing the power of imaginative responses in children through the arts. It owns 15% of its parent company and springs from the same philosophical roots. This can be summed up by the quotation from Sylvia Ashton-Warner in her book *Teacher*, which has greatly influenced Anne's work: *I see the mind of a five year old as a volcano with two vents; destructiveness and creativeness. And I can see that to the extent that we widen the creative channel, we atrophy the destructive one.*'

HOW TO APPLY To register interest in future funding schemes please email the foundation. The email should contain the following details – your name, organisation, title of the proposed project and indicative project timescale.

WHO TO APPLY TO Karen Newell, Development Co-ordinator, Timothy's Bridge Road, Stratford upon Avon, Warwickshire CV37 9NQ *Tel* 01789 404100 *email* info@ragdollfoundation.org.uk *Website* www.ragdollfoundation.org.uk
CC NO 1078998   **ESTABLISHED** 2000

■ The Rainford Trust

WHERE FUNDING CAN BE GIVEN Worldwide, with a preference for areas in which Pilkington plc have works and offices, especially St Helens and Merseyside.

WHO CAN BENEFIT Individuals and charitable and voluntary organisations.

WHAT IS FUNDED The trust's accounts stated that its objectives are to: 'apply money for charitable purposes and to charitable institutions within the St Helens MBC area, and other places in the UK or overseas where Pilkington has employees. This does not prejudice the trustees' discretion to help charities that operate outside those areas.' Further to this the trust's charitable purposes are to support: 'the relief of poverty, the aged, the sick, helpless and disabled, and the unemployed' and 'the advancement of education including the arts, and other purposes with wide benefit for the community such as environmental and conservation projects'.

WHAT IS NOT FUNDED Funding for the arts is restricted to St Helens only. Applications from individuals for grants for educational purposes will be considered only from applicants who are normally resident in St Helens.

SAMPLE GRANTS The Citadel Arts Centre (£49,000 in two grants); Clonter Opera (£15,000); Alzheimer's Research Trust, British Association for Performing Arts Medicine, British Institute for Brain Injured Children and Eccleston Mere Primary School (£2,000 each); Skill Force (£1,500); Book Aid International, National Talking Newspapers and Magazines, St Helens CVS and Voluntary Service Overseas (£1,000 each); War Memorials Trust (£750); the Cricket Foundation (£600); and Action Transport Theatre Company Limited, Landlife and Volunteer Reading Help (£500 each).

FINANCES *Year* 2007–08 *Income* £198,463 *Grants* £191,389 *Assets* £6,802,671

TRUSTEES Dr F Graham; Mrs A J Moseley; H Pilkington; Lady Pilkington; D C Pilkington; R G Pilkington; S D Pilkington; Mrs I Ratiu; Mrs L F Walker.

HOW TO APPLY On a form available from the correspondent. Applications should be accompanied by a copy of the latest accounts and cost data on projects for which funding is sought. Applicants may apply at any time. Only successful applications will be acknowledged.

WHO TO APPLY TO W H Simm, Secretary, c/o Pilkington plc, Prescot Road, St Helens, Merseyside WA10 3TT *Tel* 01744 20574 *email* rainfordtrust@btconnect.com
CC NO 266157   **ESTABLISHED** 1973

■ The Peggy Ramsay Foundation

WHERE FUNDING CAN BE GIVEN British Isles.

WHO CAN BENEFIT Writers who have some writing experience who need time to write and cannot otherwise afford to do so; companies which might not otherwise be able to find, develop or use new work; and projects which may facilitate new writing for the stage.

WHAT IS FUNDED The advancement of education by the encouragement of the art of writing and the relief of poverty amongst stage writers and their families.

WHAT IS NOT FUNDED No grants are made for productions or writing not for the theatre. Commissioning costs are often considered as part of production costs. Course fees are not considered. Aspiring writers without some production record are not usually considered.

TYPE OF GRANT Grants awarded for projects, recurring costs and salaries, for up to three years.

SAMPLE GRANTS Pearson Playwrights (£7,000); Polka Theatre (£6,000); High Tide Festival Limited and Talawa (£5,000 each); Society of Authors (£3,000); and the New Works (£1,500).

FINANCES *Year* 2008 *Income* £270,133 *Grants* £217,407 *Assets* £4,117,890

TRUSTEES G Laurence Harbottle; Simon P H Callow; Michael Codron; Sir David Hare; John Tydeman; Harriet Walter; Tamara C Harvey; Dominic L Cavendish.

OTHER INFORMATION The grants total in 2008 included £189,000 given in grants to individuals.

HOW TO APPLY Applications should be made by writing a short letter, when there is a promising purpose not otherwise likely to be funded and which will help writers or writing for the stage. Grants are considered at four or five meetings during the year, although urgent appeals can be considered at other times. All appeals are usually acknowledged.

WHO TO APPLY TO G Laurence Harbottle, Trustee, Harbottle and Lewis Solicitors, Hanover House, 14 Hanover Square, London W1S 1HP *Tel* 020 7667 5000 *Fax* 020 7667 5100 *email* laurence.harbottle@harbottle.com *Website* www.peggyramsayfoundation.org
CC NO 1015427   **ESTABLISHED** 1992

■ The Joseph and Lena Randall Charitable Trust

WHERE FUNDING CAN BE GIVEN Worldwide.

WHO CAN BENEFIT Registered charities (mainly headquarters organisations) benefiting at risk groups and people who are disadvantaged by poverty or socially isolated.

WHAT IS FUNDED Regular support to a selection of charities, providing medical, educational and cultural facilities. The following is taken from the Report of Trustees: 'As always most of our awards went to organisations committed to the relief of hardship, suffering and poverty, particularly of minorities. The balance was directed to supporting initiatives dedicated to providing medical, educational and cultural facilities.'

WHAT IS NOT FUNDED No grants to individuals.

SAMPLE GRANTS Previous beneficiaries have included: Cancer Research UK, Community Security Trust, Diabetes UK, Downe House 21st Century Appeal, Holocaust Educational Trust, Jewish Care, Jewish Deaf Association, LPO, LSE Foundation, Motor Neurone Disease Association, ROH Foundation and Transplant Trust.

FINANCES *Year* 2007–08 *Income* £97,492 *Grants* £100,044 *Assets* £893,065

TRUSTEES Rofrano Trustee Services Ltd.

HOW TO APPLY The trust has stated that funds are fully committed and that it was 'unable to respond to the many worthy appeals'.

WHO TO APPLY TO The Secretary, Europa Residence, Place des Moulins, Monte-Carlo MC98 000

CC NO 255035   **ESTABLISHED** 1967

■ The Rank Foundation

WHERE FUNDING CAN BE GIVEN UK.

WHO CAN BENEFIT Organisations working in the areas of promoting Christianity, promoting education and general charitable purposes.

WHAT IS FUNDED (a) Youth programmes: projects in this area are mainly identified by staff who have considerable experience and contacts within the field. The four main programmes are Youth or Adult?, Skills Apprenticeship Scheme, Investing in Success and Key Workers, and Rank Volunteer (Gap) Awards. (b) Community service: especially those concerned with support for older people and people who are sick or have disabilities and their carers. (c) Promotion of Christianity, substantial and continuing support to CTVC for television, radio and new media, which means that the funds available for this purpose are effectively committed.

WHAT IS NOT FUNDED Grants to registered charities only. Appeals from individuals or appeals from registered charities on behalf of named individuals will not be considered; neither will appeals from overseas or from UK-based organisations where the object of the appeal is overseas. In an endeavour to contain the calls made upon the foundation to a realistic level, the directors have continued with their policy of not, in general, making grants to projects involved with: agriculture and farming; cathedrals and churches (except where community facilities form an integral part); culture; university/school building and bursary funds; medical research.

TYPE OF GRANT One-off, recurrent, capital, research, salaries, buildings.

RANGE OF GRANTS Mostly small grants up to £7,500.

SAMPLE GRANTS CTVC Limited (£1.3 million); Help the Hospices (£100,000); Belfast Community Sports Development Network (£60,000); Senior Citizens Consortium (£48,000); Ellesmere Port Project (£34,000); Children's Society (£20,000); Counselling and Prayer Trust (£15,000); Jubilee Sailing Trust (£11,000); and Interest Link Borders (£9,000).

FINANCES *Year* 2008 *Income* £11,591,000 *Grants* £7,412,000 *Assets* £181,334,000

TRUSTEES Earl St Aldwyn; James A Cave; Andrew E Cowan; Mark E T Davies; Lindsay G Fox; Joey R Newton; Lucinda C Onslow; Valentine A L Powell; Lord Shuttleworth; Hon. Caroline Twiston-Davies; Johanna Ropner; Rose Fitzpatrick; Daniel Simon.

OTHER INFORMATION In general, the directors are active in identifying initiatives where they provide substantial support and the vast majority of unsolicited appeals, particularly for major grants, do not receive funding.

HOW TO APPLY '(i) Major grants: if you are interested in a major grant (over £7,500) you should contact the respective executive director. If you would like to submit an application for a major grant, in either the Special Project or Community Care category, then you should email a one page outline to the respective executive: Caroline Broadhurst for Community Care and David Sanderson for Special Projects. This should contain the following information: organisation objectives, location and structure

(staff numbers); outline of what you do and where; what you are seeking support for – details of the specific programme including costs; any evidence of partnership working or summary of existing evaluation. Organisations interested in making an application for any of the youth programmes, should first contact the relevant youth office for further advice and information. (Charles Harris, Director of Youth Projects, England and Wales, The Rank Foundation Ltd, 28 Bridgegate, Hebden Bridge, West Yorkshire HX7 8EX. E-mail: charles.harris@rankfoundation.com; Chris Dunning, Director of Youth Projects, Scotland, The Rank Foundation Ltd, 9/10 Redhills House, Redhills Lane, Penrith CA11 0DT. E-mail: chris.dunning@rankfoundation.com; Steve Cheal, Assistant Director of Youth Projects, England, N. Ireland, Isle of Man. The Rank Foundation Ltd, PO Box 2536, Woodford Green, Essex, IG8 1JE. Tel: 020 8500 2782. Email: steve.cheal@rankfoundation.com)

(ii) Small Grants: There is no formal application form. For administrative purposes, the foundation asks that the appeal letter be kept to one or two sides of A4 paper, which may be supported by background information. However, videos, tapes or bulky reports are not welcome and are unlikely to be returned. The following information is required: charity name and registration number; brief details about the project and the sum to be raised – please ensure you include a clear aim or list of objectives; details of the amount raised so far towards the target and if relevant, briefly mention how you intend to raise the rest; a copy of the last audited accounts and annual report. The directors meet quarterly and applicants will be notified when their appeal is to be considered. Please note: due to the overwhelming number of appeals, we can only fund about 25% of current applications. If you are unsure whether your appeal is likely to succeed then please contact us for further advice. Regrettably, due to overwhelming demand, unsolicited appeals are extremely unlikely to attract a grant in connection with salaries, general running costs or major capital projects. We also do not support overseas schemes or appeals on behalf of individuals.'

WHO TO APPLY TO Jan Carter, Grants Administrator, 12 Warwick Square, London SW1V 2AA *Tel* 020 7834 7731 *email* jan.carter@rankfoundation.co.uk *Website* www.rankfoundation.com

CC NO 276976   **ESTABLISHED** 1953

■ The Joseph Rank Trust

WHERE FUNDING CAN BE GIVEN Unrestricted. In practice, UK.

WHO CAN BENEFIT Registered charities benefiting Methodists, children, young adults, older people, and people with disabilities.

WHAT IS FUNDED The building, maintenance or adaptation of Methodist church properties; support for Christian-based social work, categorised under youth projects, community service, religious education, people with disabilities, older people, health.

WHAT IS NOT FUNDED No grants to individuals, for charities on behalf of individuals, or for unregistered organisations.

TYPE OF GRANT One-off and recurring.

RANGE OF GRANTS £10,000–£50,000.

SAMPLE GRANTS Ambassadors in Sport (£94,500 over five years), part-funding the staff costs of the London Director of Sport; PSALMS – 2nd Project (£90,000 over five years), towards costs of a Sports Minister to help to develop sports ministry with young adults in Gloucestershire; North East Help Link Trust – Seaham (£51,500), a one-off grant to replace a vehicle and part-funding, over three years, for salaries to enable the operation of a daily soup kitchen; Good News Family Care – Buxton (£45,000 over three years), towards costs of a Recovery Support Coordinator, working to empower individuals to overcome dependencies; Cornerstone Church Project, Cwmbach (£30,000 over three years), part-funding the Centre Manager of a community project in a socially deprived ex-mining community in Wales; Yellow Wales (£30,000 over three years), towards the salary costs of a Training Officer to help young homeless people of Bridgend; Methodist Ministers' Pension Scheme (£25,000), towards Christmas gifts for widows and widowers of Methodist Ministers; and Gatwick Detainees Welfare Group (£15,000 over three years), part-funding staff costs at project working with asylum seekers and other immigrants held in detention.

FINANCES *Year* 2008 *Income* £2,966,000 *Grants* £2,247,333 *Assets* £61,944,000

TRUSTEES Colin Rank, Chair; Revd David Cruise; Revd Paul Hulme; Gay Moon; Sue Warner; James Rank; Michael Shortt; Tony Reddall.

HOW TO APPLY Ongoing commitments, combined with the fact that the trustees are taking an increasingly active role in identifying projects to support, means that uncommitted funds are limited and it is seldom possible to make grants in response to unsolicited appeals. If applicants consider that their work might fall within the areas of interest of the trust the following basic information is required: charity name and charity registration number; an outline of the project for which funding is sought; details of the total amount required to fund the project in its entirety; details of the amount already raised, or irrevocably committed, towards the target; a copy of the most recent annual report and audited accounts. Applicants should endeavour to set out the essential details of a project on no more than two sides of A4 paper, with more detailed information being presented in the form of appendices. In normal circumstances, papers received before the middle of February, May, August and November may be considered in March, June, September and December respectively. Visits to appeals may be made by the secretary and trustees. All appeals are acknowledged and the applicants advised that if they do not receive a reply by a specified date it has not been possible for the trustees to make a grant.

WHO TO APPLY TO Dr John Higgs, Secretary, Worth Corner, Turners Hill Road, Crawley RH10 7SL *Tel* 01293 873947 *email* secretary@ranktrust. org *Website* www.ranktrust.org

CC NO 1093844   **ESTABLISHED** 1929

....

■ Ranworth Trust

WHERE FUNDING CAN BE GIVEN UK and developing countries, with a preference for Norfolk.

WHO CAN BENEFIT Registered charities.

WHAT IS FUNDED General charitable purposes.

WHAT IS NOT FUNDED No grants to non-registered charities.

FINANCES *Year* 2006–07 *Income* £250,003 *Grants* £272,105 *Assets* £5,470,373

TRUSTEES Hon. Mrs J Cator; F Cator; C F Cator; M Cator.

OTHER INFORMATION In 2006–07 a further donation was made from capital funds to the Limbourne

Trust, a registered charity in which Mrs E A Thistlethwayte, a former trustee of the Ranworth Trust and a daughter of the Hon. Mrs J Cator and Mr F Cator, is both Settlor and trustee.

HOW TO APPLY The trust does not respond to unsolicited applications.

WHO TO APPLY TO Hon. Mrs J Cator, Trustee, The Old House, Ranworth, Norwich NR13 6HS

CC NO 292633   **ESTABLISHED** 1985

....

■ The Fanny Rapaport Charitable Settlement

WHERE FUNDING CAN BE GIVEN North west England.

WHO CAN BENEFIT Registered charities only.

WHAT IS FUNDED The trust supports mainly, but not exclusively, Jewish charities and health and welfare organisations.

WHAT IS NOT FUNDED No grants to individuals.

SAMPLE GRANTS Previous beneficiaries included Brookvale, Christie Hospital NHS Trust, Community Security Trust, Delamere Forest School, the Heathlands Village, King David Schools, Manchester Jewish Federation, South Manchester Synagogue, United Jewish Israel Appeal and World Jewish Relief.

FINANCES *Year* 2007–08 *Income* £27,668 *Grants* £20,950 *Assets* £787,090

TRUSTEES J S Fidler; N Marks.

HOW TO APPLY Trustees hold meetings twice a year in March/April and September/October with cheques for donations issued shortly thereafter. If the applicant does not receive a cheque by the end of April or October, the application will have been unsuccessful. No applications are acknowledged.

WHO TO APPLY TO J S Fidler, Trustee, Kuit Steinart Levy, 3 St Mary's Parsonage, Manchester M3 2RD

CC NO 229406   **ESTABLISHED** 1963

....

■ The Ratcliff Foundation

WHERE FUNDING CAN BE GIVEN UK, with a preference for local charities in the Midlands, North Wales and Gloucestershire.

WHO CAN BENEFIT Any organisation that has charitable status for tax purposes.

WHAT IS FUNDED General charitable purposes.

WHAT IS NOT FUNDED No grants to individuals.

RANGE OF GRANTS £2,000–£12,000; most are for £5,000 or less.

SAMPLE GRANTS Organic Research Centre (£12,000); Warwickshire and Northamptonshire Air Ambulance (£7,000); Avoncroft Museum of Historic Buildings, Myton Hospices and SSAFA Forces Help (£5,000 each); Harbury Village Hall (£4,000); Meningitis Trust and Music for Youth (£3,000 each); Motability (£2,800); and Cruse Bereavement Carem Foundation for Conductive Education, Lighthorne PCC, Multiple Births Foundation, Wildfowl and Wetlands Trust (£2,000 each).

FINANCES *Year* 2007–08 *Income* £243,602 *Grants* £217,500 *Assets* £3,584,734

TRUSTEES David M Ratcliff, Chair; Edward H Ratcliff; Carolyn M Ratcliff; Gillian Mary Thorpe; James M G Fea; Christopher J Gupwell.

HOW TO APPLY In writing to the correspondent.

WHO TO APPLY TO Christopher J Gupwell, Secretary and Trustee, Clement Keys, 39–40 Calthorpe Road, Edgbaston, Birmingham B15 1TS *Tel* 0121 456 4456 *email* chris.gupwell@ btinternet.com

CC NO 222441   **ESTABLISHED** 1959

■ The Ratcliff Pension Charity

WHERE FUNDING CAN BE GIVEN The borough of Tower Hamlets, with a preference for the Stepney area.

WHO CAN BENEFIT Individuals and organisations benefiting older people, young people, at-risk groups, and people who are disadvantaged by poverty, socially isolated or in need.

WHAT IS FUNDED The welfare of older people, general welfare and community organisations.

SAMPLE GRANTS Individuals in need (£10,000); Community centres and churches (£5,250); young people charities (£4,500); elderly, disabled and welfare charities (£3,400); contingency fund payments (£3,100); and shelters for the homeless (£1,750).

FINANCES *Year* 2007–08 *Income* £48,998 *Grants* £28,098 *Assets* £261,845

TRUSTEES The Coopers' Company.

OTHER INFORMATION The grants total includes payments to twenty-two elderly individuals and grants to thirty-four welfare and community organisations. In addition Contingency Fund payments were made through social services (Tower Hamlets) and Age Concern amounting to £4,000.

HOW TO APPLY In writing to the correspondent.

WHO TO APPLY TO A Carroll, Clerk, Coopers' Hall, 13 Devonshire Square, London EC2M 4TH *Tel* 020 7247 9577 *email* clerk@coopers-hall.co.uk *Website* coopers-hall.co.uk

CC NO 234613   **ESTABLISHED** 1967

■ The Ratcliffe Charitable Trust

WHERE FUNDING CAN BE GIVEN UK.

WHO CAN BENEFIT Registered charities.

WHAT IS FUNDED General charitable purposes.

SAMPLE GRANTS Previous beneficiaries included Barnardos, Family Holiday Association, New Martin Community Youth Trust, Motor Neurone Disease Association, Orchdale Vale Trust Limited, VSO, Cancer Care Dorset, GUTS, British Council for the Prevention of Blindness, British Laser Appeal, Save the Children, Brainwave, Compaid Trust, Chicks (camping for inner city kids) and South West Thames Kidney Fund.

FINANCES *Year* 2007–08 *Income* £39,180 *Grants* £37,000 *Assets* £1,189,386

TRUSTEES Timothy Christopher James Adams; David Robbins; George Vellam.

HOW TO APPLY In writing to the correspondent.

WHO TO APPLY TO The Trustees, c/o Barlow Robbins LLP, 55 Quarry Street, Guildford, Surrey GU1 3UE *Tel* 01483 543 200

CC NO 802320   **ESTABLISHED** 1989

■ The E L Rathbone Charitable Trust

WHERE FUNDING CAN BE GIVEN UK, with a strong preference for Merseyside.

WHO CAN BENEFIT Registered charities.

WHAT IS FUNDED General charitable purposes, especially social work charities. Preference to charities that the trust has special interest in, knowledge of, or association with.

WHAT IS NOT FUNDED No grants to individuals seeking support for second degrees.

RANGE OF GRANTS £250–£5,000.

SAMPLE GRANTS Shaftesbury Youth Club, Tranmere Alliance and Wirral Community Narrowboat Trust (£3,000 each); Huntingdon's Disease Association, Liverpool Cathedral, Merseyside Holiday Service, RASA and RNCM (£2,000 each); No Panic (£1,500); PSS (£1,000); and Sprowston High School (£150).

FINANCES *Year* 2007–08 *Income* £85,153 *Grants* £46,650 *Assets* £2,087,283

TRUSTEES J B Rathbone; Mrs S K Rathbone; Mrs V P Rathbone; R S Rathbone.

HOW TO APPLY In writing to the correspondent.

WHO TO APPLY TO The Secretary, Rathbone Investment Management Ltd, Port of Liverpool Building, Pier Head, Liverpool L3 1NW *Tel* 0151 236 6666

CC NO 233240   **ESTABLISHED** 1921

■ The Eleanor Rathbone Charitable Trust

WHERE FUNDING CAN BE GIVEN UK, with the major allocation for Merseyside; also international projects (Africa, the Indian Sub Continent, plus exceptionally Iraq and Palestine).

WHO CAN BENEFIT Organisations benefiting general charitable projects in Merseyside; women; and unpopular and neglected causes.

WHAT IS FUNDED The trust concentrates its support largely on the following: (1) charities and charitable projects focused on Merseyside; (2) charities benefiting women and unpopular and neglected causes but avoiding those with a sectarian interest; (3) charities with which any of the trustees have a particular knowledge or association or in which it is thought Eleanor Rathbone or her father William Rathbone VI would have had a special interest; (4) charities providing holidays for disadvantaged people from Merseyside. The trust also makes international grants which are governed by the following criteria: (1) The trust will only consider projects from Africa, the Indian Sub Continent, plus exceptionally Iraq and Palestine; (2) Applications will be considered only from small or medium sized charities; (3) Projects must be sponsored and monitored by a UK based charity. In addition, projects must meet one or more of the following criteria: (i) they will benefit women or orphan children; (ii) they will demonstrate local involvement in scoping and delivery, except where skills required are not currently available e.g. eye surgeons in remote rural areas; (iii) they will aim to repair the damage in countries recently ravaged by international or civil war; (iv) they will deliver clean water.

WHAT IS NOT FUNDED Grants are not made in support of: any activity which relieves a statutory authority of its obligations; individuals, unless (and only exceptionally) it is made through a charity and it also fulfils at least one of the other positive objects mentioned above; overseas organisations without a sponsoring charity based in the UK. The trust does not generally favour grants for running costs, but prefers to support specific projects, services or to contribute to specific developments.

TYPE OF GRANT Most donations are on a one-off basis, although requests for commitments over two or more years are considered.

RANGE OF GRANTS £100–£3,000 and exceptionally higher.

FINANCES *Year* 2007–08 *Income* £289,013 *Grants* £252,535 *Assets* £7,611,043

TRUSTEES William Rathbone; Jenny Rathbone; Andrew Rathbone; Lady Morgan; Mark Rathbone.

HOW TO APPLY There is no application form. The trust asks for a brief proposal for funding including costings, accompanied by the latest

Think carefully about every application. Is it justified?

799

available accounts and any relevant supporting material. It is useful to know who else is supporting the project. To keep administration costs to a minimum, receipt of applications is not usually acknowledged. Applicants requiring acknowledgement should enclose an sae. Trustees currently meet three times a year on varying dates (contact the Administrator for information on the latest deadlines).

WHO TO APPLY TO Mrs Liese Astbury, Administrator, 546 Warrington Road, Rainhill, Merseyside L45 4LZ *email* eleanor.rathbone.trust@ tinyworld.co.uk
CC NO 233241   **ESTABLISHED** 1947

■ **The Sigrid Rausing Trust**

WHERE FUNDING CAN BE GIVEN Unrestricted.
WHO CAN BENEFIT Charitable or voluntary organisations.
WHAT IS FUNDED Human, women's and minority rights and social and environmental justice.
WHAT IS NOT FUNDED Individuals and faith based groups.
SAMPLE GRANTS Fahamu (£405,000); Global Witness (£395,000); International Crisis Group (£300,000); Friends of the Earth International – Netherlands (£250,000); Urgent Action Fund – Kenya (£240,000); Asylum Aid UK (£193,000); Council for Assisting Refugee Academics (£160,000); Article 19 (£95,000); International Gay and Lesbian Human Rights Commission (£75,000); Abdorrahman Boroumand Foundation – USA (£50,000); and Center for Egyptian Women's Legal Assistance – Egypt (£33,000).
FINANCES *Year* 2007 *Income* £4,990,742 *Grants* £17,152,177 *Assets* £60,281,083
TRUSTEES Dr Sigrid Rausing; Joshua Mailman; Susan Hitch; Andrew Puddephatt; Geoff Budlender.
HOW TO APPLY Applications are considered only from organisations that have been invited to apply. There is, however, an open pre-application process. Applicants should check the guidelines detailed on the trust's website. If you are confident that your work falls clearly within them, and you wish to be considered for an invitation, you should complete the short two page enquiry form (for Main or Small grants, as appropriate) available on the trust's website. Completed forms should be submitted by email. As trustees consider grant applications under each sub-programme once a year, organisations should register an enquiry as early as possible, if possible at least six months before the intended start of the project. The trust does not give grants to individuals and only funds projects or groups that are charitable under the law of England and Wales. The vast majority of the work it funds is internationally based. It is interested in rights based advocacy and not the delivery of services. Based on the information provided in the enquiry form, the trustees will decide which groups to invite to apply for funding. Applications pass through a careful vetting process. Even if your organisation falls within the guidelines this is not a guarantee that you will be invited to apply. The trust considers grants to cover core costs, and project work. It also considers advancement grants to help groups extend their reach and operating abilities, but only for those organisations with which it has an established relationship. All those who receive an invitation to apply for a grant, are assessed by the relevant programme officer. Applicants should be aware that the trustees take the application process and the

meeting of their deadlines seriously. Sending an incomplete application can count against a group. Failing to submit reports on how the grant was spent by the requested deadline will also be taken into account.
WHO TO APPLY TO Sheetal Patel, Administrator, Eardley House, 4 Uxbridge House, London W8 7SY *Tel* 020 7908 9870 *Fax* 020 7908 9879 *email* info@srtrust.org *Website* www.sigrid-rausing-trust.org
CC NO 1046769   **ESTABLISHED** 1995

■ **The Ravensdale Trust**

WHERE FUNDING CAN BE GIVEN Merseyside, particularly St Helens.
WHO CAN BENEFIT Registered charities.
WHAT IS FUNDED General, health, welfare, children, young people, conservation, heritage and Christian causes.
WHAT IS NOT FUNDED No grants to individuals.
TYPE OF GRANT One-off and recurrent.
RANGE OF GRANTS Usually £100–£3,000.
SAMPLE GRANTS Willowbrook Hospice (£50,000); Liverpool Cathedral Centenary Fund (£25,000); URC St Helens (£3,000); Liverpool Hope University – Music Department and The Hope Centre (£2,500 each); Arena and St David's – Carr Mill (£2,000 each); Victim Support (£1,500); Alder Hey Imagine Appeal and Derbyshire Hill Family and Community Association (£1,000 each); and Family Welfare Association and World Friendship Trust (£500 each).
FINANCES *Year* 2007–08 *Income* £61,828 *Grants* £152,500 *Assets* £1,816,002
TRUSTEES Mrs J L Fagan; M R Feeny; Mrs C B Cudmore.
HOW TO APPLY In writing to the correspondent. No application form. No acknowledgement of applications are made. Grants are paid in May and October.
WHO TO APPLY TO Mrs J Fagan, Trustee, Brabners Chaffe Street, Horton House, Exchange Flags, Liverpool L2 3YL *Tel* 0151 600 3000 *Fax* 0151 600 3300
CC NO 265165   **ESTABLISHED** 1973

■ **The Rayden Charitable Trust**

WHERE FUNDING CAN BE GIVEN UK.
WHO CAN BENEFIT Jewish organisations.
WHAT IS FUNDED General charitable purposes.
SAMPLE GRANTS Or Chadash (£7,500); Western Marble Arch (£3,800); Yesodey Hatorah (£2,600); Carl Bach Shul Trust and City of London School (£2,500 each); AISH, Hampstead Theatre and London School of Economics (£2,000 each); UK Friends Awis (£1,500); Lolev Trust (£1,200); and British Technion Society, St John's Wood Synagogue (£1,000 each).
FINANCES *Year* 2008–09 *Income* £66,684 *Grants* £64,002 *Assets* £12,490
TRUSTEES S Rayden; C Rayden; P Rayden.
HOW TO APPLY In writing to the correspondent.
WHO TO APPLY TO The Trustees, c/o Vantis Group Ltd, 82 St John Street, London EC1M 4JN
CC NO 294446   **ESTABLISHED** 1985

■ The Roger Raymond Charitable Trust

WHERE FUNDING CAN BE GIVEN UK (and very occasionally large, well-known overseas organisations).

WHO CAN BENEFIT Mainly headquarters organisations. Overseas grants are only made to large, well-known organisations (such as Sight Savers International and UNICEF).

WHAT IS FUNDED Older people, education and medical causes.

WHAT IS NOT FUNDED Grants are rarely given to individuals.

TYPE OF GRANT One-off and recurrent.

SAMPLE GRANTS Bloxham School (£172,000); Nanyuki Children's Home (£3,500); and the Brain Research Trust, Great Ormond Street Hospital Children's Charity, NSPCC, MacMillan Cancer Nurses Foundation, Project Trust and Sight Savers International (£2,000 each).

FINANCES *Year* 2007–08 *Income* £263,652 *Grants* £225,956 *Assets* £12,629,408

TRUSTEES R W Pullen; P F Raymond; M G Raymond.

OTHER INFORMATION Bloxham School is the principal beneficiary each year.

HOW TO APPLY The trust stated that applications are considered throughout the year, although funds are not always available.

WHO TO APPLY TO R W Pullen, Trustee, Suttondene, 17 South Border, Purley, Surrey CR8 3LL *Tel* 020 8660 9133 *email* russell@pullen.cix. co.uk

CC NO 262217   **ESTABLISHED** 1971

■ The Rayne Foundation

WHERE FUNDING CAN BE GIVEN UK.

WHO CAN BENEFIT Registered charities.

WHAT IS FUNDED Medicine, education, social welfare and the arts. Under these four headings the foundation encourages applications which apply to its evolving list of areas of special interest: achieving learning outcomes through the work of artists and arts organisations; developing numeracy skills; and improved quality of life for older people. Excellent applications outside these areas are also welcomed. In the last 12 months over 50% of awards have been outside these areas.

WHAT IS NOT FUNDED Grants are not made: to individuals; to organisations working outside the UK; for work that has already taken place; for repayment of debts; for endowments; to those who have applied in the last twelve months. Please do not send 'round robin' or general appeals.

TYPE OF GRANT Salaries and all types of project costs plus a reasonable contribution to overheads (there is no fixed percentage); general running or core costs (normally for a maximum of three years); capital costs of buildings and equipment (unless specifically stated in certain sectors).

RANGE OF GRANTS £250–£250,000.

SAMPLE GRANTS Praxis (£250,000); the Place to Be (£200,000); Catch 22 (£50,000); Dance UK (£40,000); Cheltenham School of Music (£25,000); Sense About Science (£20,000); Refugee New Arrivals Project – Sheffield (£16,000); Missing People and Naz Project – London (£15,000 each); and Innovations in Dementia CIC and Independent Photography (£10,000 each).

FINANCES *Year* 2007–08 *Income* £2,392,816 *Grants* £1,959,708 *Assets* £39,150,631

TRUSTEES The Hon Robert Rayne, Chair; Lord Claus Moser; Lady Jane Rayne; Lord Bridges; Lady Hilary Browne-Wilkinson; Prof. Dame Margaret Turner-Warwick; Prof. Anthony Newman Taylor; The Hon Natasha Rayne; The Hon Nicholas Rayne.

HOW TO APPLY Applying for a grant is a two-stage process. First you must fill in the Stage One Application Form available from the foundation's website, which you can complete and email to applications@raynefoundation.org.uk or print out and post. Stage One applications are accepted at any time. The foundation aims to reply with a decision within one month. If you make it through to the second stage, the foundation will ask for a more detailed application. At this point the foundation will notify you of the date you can expect to receive a final decision. This will normally be within four months but it also depends on how long you take to complete your Stage Two application. Trustee meetings take place approximately every three months but these dates are not publicised. Continuation funding – if you have previously received a grant from the foundation, you must complete a satisfactory monitoring report before reapplying. Organisations can only hold one grant at a time. Please use the two-stage process for all applications, even if you are asking the foundation to continue funding the same project. Please check the website for full details and up-to-date information. Note: the foundation states that it is 'not in a position to talk through Rayne Grants applications in detail before submission. We believe that this website contains all the information you need in order to decide whether to apply.'

WHO TO APPLY TO Morin Carew, Grants Administrator, Carlton House, 33 Robert Adam Street, London W1U 3HR *Tel* 020 7487 9650 *email* info@ raynefoundation.org.uk *Website* www. raynefoundation.org.uk

CC NO 216291   **ESTABLISHED** 1962

■ The Rayne Trust

WHERE FUNDING CAN BE GIVEN UK and Israel.

WHO CAN BENEFIT Registered charities.

WHAT IS FUNDED Jewish organisations and charities benefiting children, older and young people, at risk groups and people disadvantaged by poverty or socially isolated.

WHAT IS NOT FUNDED No grants to individuals or non-registered charities.

TYPE OF GRANT Capital expenditure and recurrent expenses.

SAMPLE GRANTS The Jewish Joint Distribution Committee (£60,000); Chicken Shed Theatre Trust, Jerusalem Cinematheque and Topolski Memoir (£25,000 each); North London Hospice and Schonfeld Square Home for the Elderly (£20,000 each); Forward Thinking and Windows for Peace (£15,000); Jewish Care (£12,500); and Jerusalem Foundation, the Jewish-Arab Community Association, Marianne's Early Childhood and Family Centre, Shluvim, the St John of Jerusalem Eye Hospital and Workers Advice Centre (£10,000 each).

FINANCES *Year* 2007–08 *Income* £385,325 *Grants* £554,120 *Assets* £20,600,378

TRUSTEES Lady Jane Rayne; the Hon Robert A Rayne.

HOW TO APPLY If you are considering applying to the trust you should first discuss your proposal with the Grants Manager, Susan O'Sullivan (tel. 020 7487 9630 or e-mail: sosullivan@raynefoundation.org.uk).

WHO TO APPLY TO Tim Joss, Director, Carlton House, 33 Robert Adam Street, London W1U 3HR
Website www.raynefoundation.org.uk
CC NO 207392   **ESTABLISHED** 1958

■ The John Rayner Charitable Trust

WHERE FUNDING CAN BE GIVEN England, with a preference for Merseyside and Wiltshire.
WHO CAN BENEFIT Registered charities. There is a preference for small charities in the UK to receive the largest donations.
WHAT IS FUNDED General charitable purposes.
WHAT IS NOT FUNDED No grants to individuals or non-registered charities.
TYPE OF GRANT One-off and recurrent grants. Funding may be given for up to three years.
RANGE OF GRANTS Up to £5,000.
SAMPLE GRANTS Breast Cancer Haven and Help for Heroes (£5,000 each); BIME, Carers UK and Music in Hospitals (£4,000 each); the Country Trust and Jubilee Sailing Trust (£3,000 each); Bootle YMCA (£2,000); and Dressability, Kennet Furniture Recycling, the Sand Rose Project and University of Liverpool – The Reader (£1,000 each).
FINANCES *Year* 2007–08 *Income* £34,582 *Grants* £34,000 *Assets* £837,563
TRUSTEES Mrs J Wilkinson; Dr J M H Rayner; Mrs A L McNeilage.
HOW TO APPLY In writing to the correspondent by 31 January each year. Trustees meet to allocate donations in February/March. Only successful applicants will be contacted. There are no application forms or guidelines.
WHO TO APPLY TO Mrs J Wilkinson, Trustee, Manor Farmhouse, Church Street, Great Bedwyn, Marlborough, Wiltshire SN8 3PE
CC NO 802363   **ESTABLISHED** 1989

■ The Albert Reckitt Charitable Trust

WHERE FUNDING CAN BE GIVEN UK.
WHO CAN BENEFIT UK registered charities including those which benefit the Society of Friends.
WHAT IS FUNDED General charitable purposes (excluding political or sectarian) including charities connected with the Society of Friends.
WHAT IS NOT FUNDED No support to individuals. No grants for political or sectarian charities, except for non-political charities connected with the Society of Friends.
TYPE OF GRANT One-off donations or yearly subscriptions.
RANGE OF GRANTS £250–£750.
FINANCES *Year* 2007–08 *Income* £96,485 *Grants* £73,600 *Assets* £2,792,779
TRUSTEES J Hughes-Reckitt, Chair; Mrs S C Bradley, Chair; Mrs G M Atherton; P C Knee; Dr A Joy; W Russell.
HOW TO APPLY In writing to the correspondent. Trustees meet in June/July and applications need to be received by the end of March.
WHO TO APPLY TO John Barrett, Secretary, 7 Derrymore Road, Willerby, Hull Hu10 6ES
CC NO 209974   **ESTABLISHED** 1946

■ The Sir James Reckitt Charity

WHERE FUNDING CAN BE GIVEN Hull and the East Riding of Yorkshire, UK and occasional support of Red Cross or Quaker work overseas.
WHO CAN BENEFIT Registered charities covering a wide range of causes, including Quaker causes and occasional relief for victims of overseas disasters.
WHAT IS FUNDED Charitable organisations submitting applications within the framework of the following priorities. General charitable purposes, with priority in descending order: the Society of Friends (Quakers) in all localities; Hull and the East Riding of Yorkshire, which excludes York; national and regional charities, particularly those concerned with current social issues and whose work extends to the Hull and East Yorkshire areas; local non-registered organisations in Hull provided they are known to the local Council for Voluntary Service through whom grants may be channelled; and international in special circumstances only, e.g. major disasters.
WHAT IS NOT FUNDED Grants are normally made only to registered charities. Local organisations outside the Hull area are not supported, unless their work has regional implications. Grants are not normally made to individuals other than Quakers and residents of Hull and the East Riding of Yorkshire. Support is not given to causes of a warlike or political nature.
TYPE OF GRANT One-off towards projects or running costs.
RANGE OF GRANTS Up to £64,000.
SAMPLE GRANTS Bootham School Trust (£64,000); Britain Yearly Meeting (£59,000); Dove House Hospice (£30,000); Zimbabwe A National Emergency – ZANE (£20,000); Foundation Training Company Limited (£10,000); Hull Boys Club (£7,200); Hull Afro-Caribbean Association (£3,700); Humberside Scout Council (£2,900); Age Concern – East Riding (£2,200); and South Holderness Countryside Society (£650).
FINANCES *Year* 2008 *Income* £937,745 *Grants* £813,968 *Assets* £19,942,228
TRUSTEES William Upton; James Harrison Holt; Caroline Jennings; Philip James Harrison Holt; Robin James Upton; Sarah Helen Craven; Martin Dickinson; Charles Maxsted; Simon J Upton; Simon E Upton; James Marshall; Sara Fenander; Edward Upton; Becky Holt; Dr Karina Mary Upton.
PUBLICATIONS *A History of the Sir James Reckitt Charity 1921–1979* by B N Reckitt; *A History of the Sir James Reckitt Charity 1921–1999* by G M Atherton. A leaflet detailing the charity's grant guidelines.
OTHER INFORMATION £43,577 was distributed in grants to individuals.
HOW TO APPLY In writing to the correspondent. The charity provides a checklist of information which should be included in any letter of application: the nature of your organisation, its structure and its relationship with other agencies and networks; the aims of your organisation and its mission statement; the purpose of the project, the need which has been identified and evidence of the need; exactly what the grant will be used for; the total cost of the project and how you intend to raise any balance; who will benefit from the project, the outcomes and how you will know if the project is successful; whether your organisation is a registered charity or, if a small local group, is it known to a local CVS; your bank account payee name to whom the cheque can be made payable; a set of the latest accounts or a record of income and

expenditure which has been subject to independent scrutiny; your contact details, i.e. address, telephone number and email. Applications are measured against the charity's guidelines and decisions are taken at a twice-yearly meeting of trustees in May and October. Applications should be submitted by mid-April and mid-September respectively.

WHO TO APPLY TO James McGlashan, Administrator, 7 Derrymore Road, Willerby, East Yorkshire HU10 6ES *Tel* 01482 655861 *Fax* 01482 655861 *email* jim@derrymore.karoo.co.uk *Website* www.thesirjamesreckittcharity.org.uk
CC NO 225356   **ESTABLISHED** 1921

■ Eva Reckitt Trust Fund

WHERE FUNDING CAN BE GIVEN UK and overseas.
WHO CAN BENEFIT Charitable organisations.
WHAT IS FUNDED Welfare and relief-in-need; organisations supporting the extension and development of education and victims of war.
SAMPLE GRANTS Medical Foundation for the Care of Victims of Torture (£4,000); Water and Sanitation for the Urban Poor (£3,000); Prisoners of Conscience Appeal Fund (£2,000); Children of the Andes, One World Action, St John of Jerusalem Eye Hospital, St Mungo's and World Development Movement (£1,000 each); and Christian Engineers in Development, Computer Aid International, Crisis, Stephen Lawrence Charitable Trust, Orbis, Send a Cow and Traidcraft (£500 each).
FINANCES *Year* 2008 *Income* £33,137 *Grants* £53,488 *Assets* £651,273
TRUSTEES Anna Bunney; Chris Whittaker; David Birch; Diana Holliday.
HOW TO APPLY In writing to the correspondent.
WHO TO APPLY TO David Birch, Trustee, 1 Somerford Road, Cirencester, Gloucestershire GL7 1TP *email* davidbirch50@googlemail.com
CC NO 210563   **ESTABLISHED** 1940

■ The Red Arrows Trust

WHERE FUNDING CAN BE GIVEN UK.
WHO CAN BENEFIT Royal Air Force and general charities.
WHAT IS FUNDED General charitable purposes.
SAMPLE GRANTS No information on beneficiaries was available.
FINANCES *Year* 2007–08 *Income* £5,485 *Grants* £20,000
TRUSTEES Roger Bowder; Keith Harkness; Mark Dunkley
HOW TO APPLY The trustees meet to consider grants in March and September and applications need to be received by February and August.
WHO TO APPLY TO K R Harkness, Trustee, Orchard House, 67 Ankle Road, Melton Mowbray LE1 7LT *Tel* 01664 566 844
CC NO 283461

■ Red Hill Charitable Trust

WHERE FUNDING CAN BE GIVEN South east England.
WHO CAN BENEFIT Charitable organisations.
WHAT IS FUNDED The promotion of education, including social and physical training, of individuals under the age of 25 who have emotional and/or behavioural difficulties and disorders.
WHAT IS NOT FUNDED No grants to individuals. Research projects are not normally considered.

TYPE OF GRANT The trustees prefer to make grants for a year at a time, and are reluctant to take on any open-ended commitments.
RANGE OF GRANTS Generally £1,000–£5,000.
SAMPLE GRANTS Dandelion Club (£20,000 in two grants); Ormiston Trust, Redhill and Reigate YMCA (£10,000 each); Caldecott Foundation (£8,000); Releasing Potential (£6,100); Dover Counselling Service and Surrey Care Trust (£6,000 each); Relate (£4,700); Dermatrust (£2,000); Purbrook Infant School (£1,900); Golwyn Special School (£1,500); and Challenger Centre (£500).
FINANCES *Year* 2007–08 *Income* £131,980 *Grants* £139,145 *Assets* £2,639,986
TRUSTEES D E Wilson, Chair; A Bunting; J Hay; K Hall; W Mather; B Clifford; R Barton; B Head.
HOW TO APPLY On a form available from the correspondent by written request or e-mail.
WHO TO APPLY TO The Clerk, 2 Fulbert Drive, Bearsted, Maidstone ME14 4PU *Website* www.redhilltrust.org
CC NO 307891   **ESTABLISHED** 1997

■ The Red Rose Charitable Trust

WHERE FUNDING CAN BE GIVEN UK with a preference for Lancashire and Merseyside.
WHO CAN BENEFIT Charities working with older people who or people who have physical or mental disabilities.
WHAT IS FUNDED Welfare causes.
SAMPLE GRANTS Liverpool Cathedral Centenary Fund (£5,000); the Barnstondale Centre (£2,000); Help the Aged, the National Autistic Society, Sense and Wirral Autistic Society (£1,000 each); and Local Solutions, McIntyre Housing Association and Neuromuscular Centre (£500 each).
FINANCES *Year* 2007–08 *Income* £53,494 *Grants* £44,850 *Assets* £1,111,084
TRUSTEES James N L Packer; Jane L Fagan.
HOW TO APPLY In writing to the correspondent.
WHO TO APPLY TO J N L Packer, Trustee, c/o Rathbones, Port of Liverpool Building, Pier Head, Liverpool L3 1NW
CC NO 1038358   **ESTABLISHED** 1994

■ The C A Redfern Charitable Foundation

WHERE FUNDING CAN BE GIVEN UK.
WHO CAN BENEFIT Registered UK charities.
WHAT IS FUNDED General charitable purposes, with some preference for those concerned with health and welfare.
WHAT IS NOT FUNDED No grants for building works or individuals.
TYPE OF GRANT Core costs, one-off, project and research. Funding is available for one year or less.
RANGE OF GRANTS £250–£50,000. The majority were between £250–£5,000.
SAMPLE GRANTS South Buckinghamshire Riding for the Disabled (£50,000); Saints and Sinners (£30,000); Ghurkha Welfare Trust (£7,000); Live Music Now! and St Botolph without Bishopsgate (£5,000 each); St Christopher's Hospice (£4,000); BEN (£3,000); Breast Cancer Haven and Fight for Sight (£1,000 each); Cancer Resource Centre and St Mary's of Paddington Charitable Trust (£5,000 each); CRUSE (£3,000); NSPCC (£500); and Hope House Hospice (£250).

FINANCES *Year* 2007–08 *Income* £230,416 *Grants* £225,500 *Assets* £5,335,650

TRUSTEES Cecil Redfern, Chair; Sir Robert Clark; William Maclaren; David Redfern; Terence Thornton; Simon Ward.

HOW TO APPLY The trust does not accept unsolicited applications.

WHO TO APPLY TO The Trustees, PricewaterhouseCoopers, 9 Greyfriars Road, Reading, Berkshire RG1 1JG

CC NO 299918   ESTABLISHED 1989

....

■ Redfern Charitable Trust

WHERE FUNDING CAN BE GIVEN UK.

WHO CAN BENEFIT Charitable organisations.

WHAT IS FUNDED General charitable purposes.

SAMPLE GRANTS Age Concern, Arthritis Rheumatism Council, British Red Cross, NSPCC, Stroke Association, RNIB, RNID and World Wildlife Fund (£7,500 each); CLIC (£2,500); and Crisis and DES – Bangladesh Flood (£500 each).

FINANCES *Year* 2008–09 *Income* £78,500 *Grants* £48,063 *Assets* £901,255

TRUSTEES Miss M D Roe; M St Clair Thomas; A S Hatt.

HOW TO APPLY In writing to the correspondent.

WHO TO APPLY TO The Trustees, Hedges Solicitors, The Glass Tower, 6 Station Road, Dichot, Oxfordshire OX11 7LL

CC NO 1090647

....

■ The Reed Foundation

WHERE FUNDING CAN BE GIVEN UK and overseas.

WHO CAN BENEFIT Charitable organisations.

WHAT IS FUNDED General charitable purposes, with an interest in the arts, education and women's causes.

SAMPLE GRANTS Academy of Enterprise (£121,000); The Royal Opera House and WOMANKIND (£100,000 each); West London Academy (£75,000); The Big Give and Ethiopiaid – Australia (£50,000 each); Chipping Norton Theatre (£34,000); British Humanist Association (£15,000); Haven Breast Cancer (£5,000); and Get Kids Going (£1,000).

FINANCES *Year* 2007 *Income* £1,079,831 *Grants* £650,140 *Assets* £15,580,132

TRUSTEES A E Reed; J A Reed; R A Reed; A M Chapman.

HOW TO APPLY In writing to the correspondent. The trust states that it does not respond to unsolicited applications.

WHO TO APPLY TO The Secretary, 6 Sloane Street, London SW1X 9LE *Tel* 020 7201 9980 *email* reed.foundation@reed.co.uk

CC NO 264728   ESTABLISHED 1972

....

■ Richard Reeve's Foundation

WHERE FUNDING CAN BE GIVEN Camden, City of London and Islington.

WHO CAN BENEFIT Individuals up to the age of 25 (in certain circumstances up to the age of 40).

WHAT IS FUNDED Educational costs, uniforms, books, travel expenses, living costs, equipment and organisation projects that benefit a significant number of children at a time.

WHAT IS NOT FUNDED No grants for building costs, independent school fees, furniture/household goods, school meals, holidays, school outings or to replace statutory funding.

TYPE OF GRANT Normally cash – but uniforms bought from a recognised supplier.

RANGE OF GRANTS £350–£50,000.

SAMPLE GRANTS School Home Support (£58,000); Christ's Hospital (£20,000); Centrepoint (£8,500); The Little Angel Theatre (£6,000); Central and Cecil Housing Trust, City University and Drake Music Project (£5,000 each); Until the Violence Stops (£4,500); Groove Your Arts and The Film and Video Workshop (£4,000 each); UCanDoIt (£3,000); and Camden Arts Centre (£2,500).

FINANCES *Year* 2007–08 *Income* £413,945 *Grants* £333,818 *Assets* £16,151,982

TRUSTEES Ms Angela Brook; Ian L Rodgers; Billy Dove; Miss Eleanor Stanier; Walter P Wright; Sylvan Dewing; John Tickle; Sarah Reed; Cllr Ruth Polling; Milena Renshaw.

OTHER INFORMATION Grants are mainly made to individuals for educational purposes. In 2007–08 grants were paid to, or on behalf of 52 individuals totalling £207,865

HOW TO APPLY Initially in writing to the correspondent outlining the request. An application form, or rejection letter, is then sent back, as appropriate. Applications from organisations must be accompanied by a set of the latest accounts, the constitution, details of need the work will address and a detailed budget. A visit and/or interview is usually arranged before a final decision is made. Completed proposals should be returned by the middle of February, May, August or November for consideration by the end of the next calendar month.

WHO TO APPLY TO Shirley Scott, Clerk to the Govenors, 2 Cloth Court, London EC1A 7LS *Tel* 020 7726 4230 *email* enquiries@ richardreevesfoundation.org.uk *Website* richardreevesfoundation.org.uk

CC NO 312504   ESTABLISHED 1928

....

■ The Rehoboth Trust

WHERE FUNDING CAN BE GIVEN UK and Israel.

WHO CAN BENEFIT Christians.

WHAT IS FUNDED Christian churches and ministers.

SAMPLE GRANTS Elm Church Kensington Temple (£20,000); St Paul's Howell Hill (£10,000); Macmillan Nurses £4,000); Valley Life Ministries (£2,500); 'Others' (£6,000).

FINANCES *Year* 2007 *Income* £97,744 *Grants* £123,171 *Assets* £5,064

TRUSTEES Shakti Sisodia; Andrea Sisodia; Lyndon Bowring.

HOW TO APPLY In writing to the correspondent.

WHO TO APPLY TO Shakti Sisodia, Trustee, 71 Rydal Gardens, Hounslow TW3 2JJ *Tel* 020 8643 3386

CC NO 1114454   ESTABLISHED 2006

....

■ The Max Reinhardt Charitable Trust

WHERE FUNDING CAN BE GIVEN UK.

WHO CAN BENEFIT Charitable organisations.

WHAT IS FUNDED The trust supports organisations benefiting people who are deaf and fine arts promotion.

WHAT IS NOT FUNDED No grants to individuals.

SAMPLE GRANTS Previous beneficiaries have included: the Art Fund, Art in Healthcare, Concern Worldwide, Delta, St George's Medical School, NDCS, Paintings in Hospitals, RNID, Salvation Army, Sound Seekers and Top Banana.

FINANCES *Year* 2007–08 *Income* £44,724 *Grants* £28,158 *Assets* £519,942

TRUSTEES Joan Reinhardt; Veronica Reinhardt.

HOW TO APPLY In writing to the correspondent.

WHO TO APPLY TO The Secretary, c/o BSG Valentine, Lynton House, 7–12 Tavistock Square, London WC1H 9BQ

CC NO 264741   **ESTABLISHED** 1973

■ Relief Fund for Romania Limited

WHERE FUNDING CAN BE GIVEN Romania.

WHO CAN BENEFIT Romanian charities.

WHAT IS FUNDED Street children; work with older people and people who are infirm or have disabilities; children in hospital; medical programmes to isolated rural areas; 'begging children' and the Roma community; children and adults with special needs in institutions; families at risk; people with tuberculosis; medical disability and the mental health arena; and children and adolescents with physical disabilities.

SAMPLE GRANTS Beneficiaries included: M.S.Curie Hospital Bucharest / aka The Budimex; FAST; Estuar; and Fundatia de Sprijin Comunitar.

FINANCES *Year* 2007–08 *Income* £653,792 *Grants* £131,925

TRUSTEES A Adams; N Ratiu; S Cucos.

HOW TO APPLY A brief, two-page proposal should be sent by post or e-mail to the correspondent. Applicants who interest the trustees will then be asked to complete a second, more detailed proposal.

WHO TO APPLY TO E Parry, Secretary, 18 Fitzharding Street, London W1H 6EQ *Tel* 020 8761 2277 *Fax* 020 8761 0020 *email* mail@relieffundforromania.co.uk *Website* www.relieffundforromania.co.uk

CC NO 1046737   **ESTABLISHED** 1989

■ REMEDI

WHERE FUNDING CAN BE GIVEN UK.

WHO CAN BENEFIT Hospitals and universities.

WHAT IS FUNDED The support of pioneering research into all aspects of disability in the widest sense of the word, with special emphasis on disability and the way in which it limits the activities and lifestyle of all ages. Preference for applicants who wish to carry out innovative and original research and experience difficulty in attracting funding from the larger and better-known organisations. Collaboration with other charities working in the same field is encouraged.

WHAT IS NOT FUNDED Cancer and cancer-related diseases are not supported.

TYPE OF GRANT Grants are usually given for one year, occasionally for two and exceptionally for three years. Projects, equipment and therapy research are supported.

FINANCES *Year* 2007–08 *Income* £325,665 *Grants* £113,140 *Assets* £251,583

TRUSTEES Dr Anthony K Clarke, Chair; James Mosley; Brian Winterflood; Dr Adrian H M Heagerty; Colin Maynard; Mrs Karin Russell; Dr I T Stuttaford; Dr Anthony B Ward; Michael Hines.

HOW TO APPLY By e-mail to the correspondent. Applications are received throughout the year. They should initially include a summary of the project on one side of A4 with costings. The Chair normally considers applications on the third Tuesday of each month with a view to inviting applicants to complete an application form by e-mail.

WHO TO APPLY TO Rosie Wait, Director, Elysium House, 126–128 New Kings Road, London SW6 4LZ *Tel* 020 7384 2929 *email* research@remedi.org.uk *Website* www.remedi.org.uk

CC NO 1063359   **ESTABLISHED** 1973

■ The Rest Harrow Trust

WHERE FUNDING CAN BE GIVEN UK.

WHO CAN BENEFIT Registered charities benefiting people who are in poor health, disabled, disadvantaged by poverty or homeless.

WHAT IS FUNDED Main areas of interest are older people, education, disability, housing, poverty, and youth. Particularly Jewish organisations.

WHAT IS NOT FUNDED No grants to non-registered charities or to individuals.

TYPE OF GRANT Occasionally one-off for part or all of a particular project.

RANGE OF GRANTS £100–£5,500. The majority were under £500 each.

SAMPLE GRANTS Nightingale House (£5,500); Jewish Care (£2,500); World Jewish Relief (£2,000); British Friends of the Hebrew University (£1,500); JNF Charitable Trust and Weizmann Institute Foundation (£1,000 each); British Friends of Neve Shalom, Cheltenham Ladies College (for Bursaries Fund), Jewish Deaf Association and St Christopher's Hospice (£500 each); Action for Kids, Age Concern, Appropriate Technology Asia and Breast Cancer Care (£200 each); and Back to Work for the Over 40s, Canine Partners for Independence, Heartline and Princess Royal Trust for Carers (£100 each).

FINANCES *Year* 2007–08 *Income* £75,413 *Grants* £52,800 *Assets* £896,262

TRUSTEES Mrs J B Bloch; Miss J S Portrait; HON and V Trustee Limited; D B Flynn.

OTHER INFORMATION Grants are usually made to national bodies rather than local branches, or local groups.

HOW TO APPLY In writing to the correspondent. Applications are considered quarterly. Only submissions from eligible bodies are acknowledged.

WHO TO APPLY TO Miss Judith S Portrait, c/o Portrait Solicitors, 1 Chancery Lane, London WC2A 1LF *Tel* 020 7320 3890

CC NO 238042   **ESTABLISHED** 1964

■ Reuben Brothers Foundation

WHERE FUNDING CAN BE GIVEN UK and overseas.

WHO CAN BENEFIT Charitable organisations, with a possible preference for those operating in the UK, Israel, India and Iraq.

WHAT IS FUNDED Healthcare, education and general charitable purposes.

SAMPLE GRANTS Israel Cancer Association (£143,000); Community Security Trust (£50,000); Norwood (£11,000); and Nancy Reuben Primary School, Jewish Care and Princess Royal Trust Carers (£10,000).

FINANCES *Year* 2008 *Income* £2,272,116 *Grants* £449,179 *Assets* £58,204,251

TRUSTEES Richard Stone, Chair; Simon Reuben; David Stone; Robin Turner; Michael Gubbay; Annie Benjamin; Patrick O'Driscoll.

OTHER INFORMATION This relatively new trust was established in 2002 as an outlet for the charitable giving of billionaire property investors David and Simon Reuben. The foundation was endowed by the brothers with a donation of $100 million (£54.1 million), with the income generated to be donated to a range of charitable causes, particularly healthcare organisations and educational purposes.

HOW TO APPLY In writing to the correspondent, although the trust has stated that applications are by invitation only. Grant applications are processed with all requests for funds being put before the trustee meetings and the merits of each application being considered. Unsuccessful applicants are notified by post. Donations are sent out to the successful applicants having regard to the current reserves and the long-term policy of the foundation. Trustees meetings are held every month.

WHO TO APPLY TO Patrick O'Driscoll, Trustee, Millbank Tower, 21–24 Millbank, London SW1P 4PQ *Tel* 020 7802 5000 *Fax* 020 7802 5002 *email* contact@reubenfoundation.com *Website* www.reubenfoundation.com

CC NO 1094130   **ESTABLISHED** 2002

....

■ The Joan K Reynell Charitable Trust

WHERE FUNDING CAN BE GIVEN UK.
WHO CAN BENEFIT Registered charities.
WHAT IS FUNDED General charitable purposes.
RANGE OF GRANTS Up to £3,000.
SAMPLE GRANTS Cambridge University Vetinary School Trust, Compassion in World Farming, Hearing Dogs for Deaf People, Oxfam, RSPCA, the Cinnamon Trust, the Soil Association, the Woodland Trust, Tibet Foundation and Voluntary Services Overseas (£3,000 each).
FINANCES *Year* 2007–08 *Income* £49,525 *Grants* £54,000 *Assets* £1,561,660
TRUSTEES Anthony Reynell; Michael Reynell.
HOW TO APPLY In writing to the correspondent.
WHO TO APPLY TO The Trustees, c/o HSBC Trust Co. Ltd, Norwich House, Nelson Gate, Southampton SO15 1GX *Tel* 023 8072 2226
CC NO 1069397   **ESTABLISHED** 1997

....

■ The Nathaniel Reyner Trust Fund

WHERE FUNDING CAN BE GIVEN Merseyside area.
WHO CAN BENEFIT Registered charities and Christian organisations helping children, young adults, older people, clergy, Baptists, Church of England, Christians, evangelists and Methodists.
WHAT IS FUNDED The promotion of evangelical Christianity and also general charitable purposes, particularly the advancement of Christian religion and Christian religious buildings.
WHAT IS NOT FUNDED No grants to individuals, medical research, the arts or denominations other than URC or Baptist unless there is a clear and overriding ecumenical or community objective.
RANGE OF GRANTS Up to £5,000.
SAMPLE GRANTS Baptist Missionary Society Merseyside Auxiliary and North West Baptist Association (£3,500 each); Heswall United Reformed Church, Parkgate & Neston United Reformed Church and The United Reformed Church Caradoc Mission (£2,500 each); Council for World Mission and Laird Street Baptist Church Family Support Centre (£1,000 each); Adelaide House, After Adoption, the Aspire Trust Ltd, BIRD, Contact the Elderly, Listening Ear, Shaftesbury Youth Club and Weston Spirit (£500 each).
FINANCES *Year* 2007–08 *Income* £41,763 *Grants* £36,375 *Assets* £805,751

TRUSTEES D E G Faragher, Chair; J R Watson; W B Howarth; Miss M Proven; F N Ward; D Craig; Miss J Hope.
HOW TO APPLY In writing to the correspondent. Trustees meet in April and November.
WHO TO APPLY TO Lawrence Downey, Secretary, Drury House, 19 Water Street, Liverpool L2 0RP *Tel* 0151 236 8989 *email* lawrence.downey@ maceandjones.co.uk
CC NO 223619   **ESTABLISHED** 1965

....

■ The Rhododendron Trust

WHERE FUNDING CAN BE GIVEN UK and overseas.
WHO CAN BENEFIT Registered charities.
WHAT IS FUNDED Overseas charities, UK social welfare charities and UK cultural charities.
WHAT IS NOT FUNDED The trust does not support medical research, individual projects, or local community projects in the UK.
TYPE OF GRANT Preferably project-based.
RANGE OF GRANTS £500 or £1,000 each.
SAMPLE GRANTS Find Your Feet, Sound Seekers, MAG, Health Unlimited and C.A.S.A. Alianzia (£1,000 each) and Cambodia Trust, Survival International, Young Actors Theatre, Africa Equipment for Schools and Children in Crisis (£500 each).
FINANCES *Year* 2007–08 *Income* £79,017 *Grants* £44,000 *Assets* £1,428,335
TRUSTEES Peter Edward Healey; Dr Ralph Walker; Mrs Sarah Ray; Mrs Sarah Oliver.
HOW TO APPLY In writing to the correspondent at any time. The majority of donations are made in March. Applications are not acknowledged.
WHO TO APPLY TO P E Healey, Trustee, Lewis House, 12 Smith Street, Rochdale OL16 1TX
CC NO 267192   **ESTABLISHED** 1974

....

■ The Rhondda Cynon Taff Welsh Church Acts Fund

WHERE FUNDING CAN BE GIVEN Rhondda-Cynon-Taff, Bridgend and Merthyr Tydfil County Borough Councils, i.e. the former county of Mid Glamorgan, with the exception of Rhymney Valley which is now outside the area of benefit.
WHO CAN BENEFIT Churches, youth organisations and musical groups benefiting children, young adults, Christians, at risk groups, and people who are disadvantaged by poverty or socially isolated.
WHAT IS FUNDED Churches; youth activities; and welfare.
WHAT IS NOT FUNDED No grants to students, individuals, or projects of other local authorities. Grants are not given for running costs.
SAMPLE GRANTS Cancer Support RCT, Christ Church – Pant, Cynon Best Community Arts Ltd, EcoDysgu-EcoLearn – Aberkenfig, and Gospel Hall – Bridgend (£10,000 each); St Luke's Evangelist Church – Cilfynydd (£7,000); Christian Youth Outreach – Bridgend and Mountain Ash YMCA (£4,000 each); Trinity Presbyterian Church – Tonypandy (£3,000); and Wesley Church Dowlais (£2,000).
FINANCES *Year* 2007–08 *Income* £463,000 *Grants* £241,805 *Assets* £9,854,000
TRUSTEES Rhondda Cynon Taff County Borough Council.
HOW TO APPLY The charity invites applications for funding of projects through advertising in the local press.
WHO TO APPLY TO George Sheldrick, Rhondda Cyon Taff Council, Accounts Section, Bronwydd

House, Porth CF39 9DL *Tel* 01443 680 573
Fax 01443 680 592
cc no 506658   established 1977

■ Daisie Rich Trust

WHERE FUNDING CAN BE GIVEN UK, with a priority for
the Isle of Wight.
WHO CAN BENEFIT Organisations and individuals.
WHAT IS FUNDED General charitable purposes.
RANGE OF GRANTS From £150 to £30,000.
SAMPLE GRANTS Earl Mountbatten Hospice
(£30,000); Macmillan Cancer Relief, Marie
Curie Nurses and SSAFA Isle of White (£3,000
each); Isle of White RCC 'Helping Hands', Isle of
White Youth Trust and St Vincent's Residential
Home (£2,000 each); Haig Homes and Island
Women's Refuge (£1,500 each); Carisbrooke
Priory Trust and Semi-Colon Group (£1,000
each); Challenge and Adventure and Isle of
White Hospital Broadcasting Association (£500
each); Isle of White Gateway Club and RNID –
Isle of White Sound Advice (£250 each); and
Rope Walk Social Club (£150).
FINANCES *Year* 2007–08 *Income* £169,358
Grants £119,735 *Assets* £3,215,179
TRUSTEES A H Medley (Chair); Mrs A C Medley;
M J Flux; D J Longford.
OTHER INFORMATION In 2007–08 grants to ex-
employees of Upward and Rich Ltd and their
dependants totalled £36,410.
HOW TO APPLY In writing to the correspondent. The
trustees hold regular meetings to decide on
grant applications and are assisted by
information gathered by the administrator.
WHO TO APPLY TO Mrs L Mitchell, Administrator, The
Hawthorns, School Lane, Arreton, Newport, Isle
of Wight PO30 3AD *Tel* 07866 449 855
email daisierich@yahoo.co.uk
cc no 236706   established 1964

■ The Sir Cliff Richard Charitable Trust

WHERE FUNDING CAN BE GIVEN UK.
WHO CAN BENEFIT Registered charities only,
benefiting a broad spectrum, including: children,
adults and young people; Baptists, Methodists,
Anglicans and Evangelists; people who are
disabled or have a medical condition.
WHAT IS FUNDED Smaller, grass-roots projects are
often preferred, for general charitable purposes
that reflect the support, Christian commitment
and interest of Sir Cliff Richard, including:
special schools, special needs education and
vocational training; community centres, village
halls, playgrounds and playschemes; care in the
community and community transport; respite
care and care for carers; cancer, MS and
neurological research; Christian education and
outreach; missionaries and evangelicals; and
animal homes and welfare.
WHAT IS NOT FUNDED Capital building projects, church
repairs and renovations are all excluded. No
support for individuals.
TYPE OF GRANT Usually small one-off sums for
operational needs.
RANGE OF GRANTS Around £2,000 to £50,000.
SAMPLE GRANTS Major beneficiaries included:
Banardo's (£50,000); New Israel Fund
(£12,500); Genesis Trust (£7,000); and the
Arts Centre Group (£5,000).
FINANCES *Year* 2006–07 *Income* £179,660
Grants £143,902 *Assets* £168,986

TRUSTEES William Latham; Malcolm Smith; Sir Cliff
Richard.
OTHER INFORMATION Smaller grants of less than
£5,000 were made totalling £82,000.
HOW TO APPLY Applications should be from
registered charities only, in writing, and for one-
off needs. All applications are acknowledged.
Grants are made quarterly in January, April, July
and October.
WHO TO APPLY TO William Latham, Trustee, Harley
House, 94 Hare Lane, Claygate, Esher, Surrey
KT10 0RB *Tel* 01372 467 752 *Fax* 01372 462
352 *email* general@cliffrichard.org
cc no 1096412   established 1969

■ C B Richard Ellis Charitable Trust

WHERE FUNDING CAN BE GIVEN Unrestricted.
WHO CAN BENEFIT Registered charities or recognised
charitable causes.
WHAT IS FUNDED General charitable causes.
WHAT IS NOT FUNDED No grants to third parties, such
as fundraising organisations or publication
companies producing charity awareness
materials.
RANGE OF GRANTS £50–£10,000.
SAMPLE GRANTS Riders for Health (£11,000); The
Story of Christmas (£3,300); Cancer Research
UK (£2,400); British Heart Foundation (£1,200);
Child Rights and You UK and Wellbeing of
Women (£1,000 each); and Walk the Walk
Worldwide (£600).
FINANCES *Year* 2007–08 *Income* £76,624
Grants £62,398 *Assets* £27,981
TRUSTEES M D A Black; F G Morris; K Bramley;
L Patel; M J Prentice; N R Martel.
HOW TO APPLY In writing to the correspondent.
The trust stated that in recent years they have
received as many as two hundred unsolicited
requests for support that do not meet with the
above donations criteria. Given the size of the
trust, a response to such requests is not always
possible.
WHO TO APPLY TO A C Naftis, Secretary to the
Trustees, St Martin's Court, 10 Paternoster
Row, London EC4M 7HP *Tel* 020 7182 3452
Fax 020 718 22001 *email* anaftis@
cbhillierparker.com
cc no 299026   established 1987

■ The Clive Richards Charity

WHERE FUNDING CAN BE GIVEN UK, with a preference
for Herefordshire.
WHO CAN BENEFIT Individuals and registered charities
benefiting children and older people, musicians,
Roman Catholics, people who are disabled or
disadvantaged by poverty and victims of crime.
WHAT IS FUNDED The assistance of education,
people with disabilities, the arts, conservation
and religion, mostly in the county of
Herefordshire, especially in church schools.
TYPE OF GRANT One-off, project and buildings.
Interest-free loans are considered. Grants may
be for up to two years.
RANGE OF GRANTS From £1,000.
SAMPLE GRANTS Vesey Foundation (£250,000); John
Kyrle School (£100,000); Queen Elizabeth High
School (£50,000); Luctonians Youth
Development (£35,000); Chance to Shine
Appeal (£20,000); Worshipful Company of
Gunmakers (£10,000); Royal Shakespeare
Company (£5,000); Hereford Police Choir
(£3,000); Royal Naval Museum (£2,500); and

Think carefully about every application. Is it justified?

807

Deafblind UK (£1,000). Grants of less than £1,000 each totalled £19,000.

FINANCES *Year* 2007–08 *Income* £54,506 *Grants* £730,251 *Assets* £199,319

TRUSTEES Anna Lewis; Clive Richards; Sylvia Richards.

HOW TO APPLY In writing to the correspondent. The trustees meet monthly to consider applications. Please note, the trust has previously stated that due to its resources being almost fully committed it is extremely selective in accepting any requests for funding.

WHO TO APPLY TO Anna Lewis, Trustee, Lower Hope, Ullingswick, Herefordshire HR1 3JF *Tel* 01432 820557 *Fax* 01432 820772 *email* anna@crco. co.uk

CC NO 327155   **ESTABLISHED** 1986

■ The Violet M Richards Charity

WHERE FUNDING CAN BE GIVEN UK, with a preference for East Sussex, particularly Crowborough.

WHO CAN BENEFIT Organisations benefiting: older people; medical professionals; researchers; medical students; and people with a medical condition.

WHAT IS FUNDED The trust's objects are the relief of age and ill health, through the advancement of medical research (particularly into geriatric problems), medical education, homes and other facilities for older people and those who are sick. The trustees are happy to commit themselves to funding a research project over a number of years, including 'seedcorn' projects. However, the trust has stated that for the next two to three years it will be focusing on a small number of medical research projects and is unlikely to have any surplus funds to support external applications.

WHAT IS NOT FUNDED No support for individuals.

TYPE OF GRANT Applications for grants of all types will be considered.

RANGE OF GRANTS £5,000–£50,000.

SAMPLE GRANTS British Liver Trust (£51,000); Stroke Association (£32,000); and Lee Smith Foundation (£5,000).

FINANCES *Year* 2007–08 *Income* £79,293 *Grants* £88,178 *Assets* £2,153,810

TRUSTEES Mrs E H Hill; G R Andersen; C A Hicks; Miss M K Davies; Mrs M Burt; Dr J Clements.

HOW TO APPLY In writing to the correspondent, however the trust states in its accounts that the trustees 'prefer to be proactive with charities of their own choice, rather than reactive to external applications.' The trustees generally meet to consider grants twice a year in the spring and the autumn. There is no set format for applying and only successful applications are acknowledged. Due to the change of grant policy to focus on a smaller number of projects, external applications are unlikely to be successful and are therefore discouraged.

WHO TO APPLY TO Charles Hicks, Secretary, c/o Wedlake Bell, 52 Bedford Row, London WC1R 4LR *Tel* 020 7395 3155 *Fax* 020 7395 3100 *email* chicks@wedlakebell.com

CC NO 273928   **ESTABLISHED** 1977

■ The Richmond Parish Lands Charity

WHERE FUNDING CAN BE GIVEN Richmond, Kew, North Sheen, East Sheen, Ham, Petersham and Mortlake.

WHO CAN BENEFIT Charitable organisations and individuals. Children, young adults and older people; musicians; sportsmen and women; artists; people with disabilities, disadvantaged by poverty or with mental illness.

WHAT IS FUNDED Current activities are: general grants to charitable organisations and individuals in need within the benefit area; grants to support the education and training of individuals and education projects within the benefit area; winter 'Warm Campaign' of heating grants to older people in need in the benefit area; provision of social housing to those in need from the benefit area; hiring of the Vestry Hall as a public meeting room; renting of the craft workshops or studios to local artists and crafts people.

WHAT IS NOT FUNDED Projects and organisations located outside the benefit area, unless it can be demonstrated that a substantial number of residents from the benefit area will gain from their work. UK charities (even if based in the benefit area), except for that part of their work which caters specifically for the area.

TYPE OF GRANT One-off and recurring.

RANGE OF GRANTS £100–£48,000.

SAMPLE GRANTS Richmond Mind (£48,000); Richmond CAB (£39,000); Crossroads Care (£25,500); SPEAR (£21,000); Integrated Neurological Services (£17,500); Richmond Music Trust (£15,000); Handyperson Scheme (£11,500); Care Leavers Support (£10,000); Kew Community Trust (£8,500); Central and Cecil Community Trust (£7,000); Latchmere House (£6,000); Brentford Community Football Sports (£5,000); Meadlands School Friends (£2,500); and Bold Balladiers (£1,000).

FINANCES *Year* 2008–09 *Income* £1,640,247 *Grants* £604,500 *Assets* £56,680,377

TRUSTEES 15 trustees all of whom live within the borough. Three of them are nominated by the borough council, five are nominated by local voluntary organisations and the remainder are co-opted from the community. The Mayor is an ex-officio member of the board of trustees.

OTHER INFORMATION Grants are also made to individuals.

HOW TO APPLY 'Organisations receiving core grants from the RPLC must apply by the deadlines set out in the documents [available from the charity's website] and use the new application form. Our Strategic Priority for 2009/10 is Support for organisations working with people affected by family breakdown. A specific application form for applications in this category [is available from the charity's website]. If you are applying for a grant that is new or a one-off application, and it does not fall within our recent Strategic Priorities your application will not be considered until January – June 2010. [Check the charity's website for information on current priorities.]

How to Apply: if you would like some clarification on whether your organisation would qualify for a grant, please contact the charity on 020 8948 5701 for guidance. [There are separate application forms for larger and small grants, both available from the charity's website.]

How the charity will deal with your application: when your application is received, it will be evaluated and any queries arising from it will be followed up. You may be assured that all eligible applications will be put before the trustees. There are currently 15 trustees, all of whom live within the benefit area. Three of them are nominated by the Borough Council, five are nominated by local voluntary organisations and the remainder are co-opted from the community. The Mayor is an ex officio member of the Board of Trustees. Eligible applications must be received at least ten working days before the meeting at which they will be considered. All organisations receiving core grants on an annual basis now have a specified date for submission of their applications. [Deadlines are published on the charity's website.] You will be advised by letter within fourteen days of the meeting whether or not your application has been successful. Following agreement for a grant you will be sent a Conditions of Grant form setting out the terms and conditions of the grant. Payment will be arranged on receipt of a signed agreement. A Monitoring and Evaluation Form will also be required on completion of your next application form.'

WHO TO APPLY TO Jonathan Monckton, Director, The Vestry House, 21 Paradise Road, Richmond, Surrey TW9 1SA *Tel* 020 8948 5701 *Fax* 020 8332 6792 *Website* www.rplc.org.uk
CC NO 200069   **ESTABLISHED** 1786

....

■ The Muriel Edith Rickman Trust

WHERE FUNDING CAN BE GIVEN UK.
WHO CAN BENEFIT Hospitals and research organisations benefiting people with cancer or sight loss.
WHAT IS FUNDED Emphasis on cancer and blindness but other areas are not excluded. Normally research and research equipment is funded.
WHAT IS NOT FUNDED The trustees will not respond to individual students, clubs, community projects or expeditions.
TYPE OF GRANT One-off payments on research and specified equipment.
RANGE OF GRANTS £250–£30,000.
SAMPLE GRANTS The major beneficiary was University of Manchester (£1 million) and others included: Cancer Research (£40,000); Leukaemia Busters and Kings College (£10,000); Neuro-disability Research Trust (£3,000); and Great Ormond Street (£100).
FINANCES *Year* 2006–07 *Income* £1,067,920 *Grants* £1,106,728 *Assets* £118,117
TRUSTEES H P Rickman, Chair; A S Purcell; Prof J Waxman; R Tallis.
HOW TO APPLY There are no guidelines for applications and the trust only replies if it is interested at first glance; it will then ask for further details. Trustees meet as required.
WHO TO APPLY TO H P Rickman, Trustee, 12 Fitzroy Court, 57 Shepherds Hill, London N6 5RD
CC NO 326143   **ESTABLISHED** 1982

....

■ Ridgesave Limited

WHERE FUNDING CAN BE GIVEN UK and overseas.
WHO CAN BENEFIT Individuals and organisations benefiting Jews and people disadvantaged by poverty.
WHAT IS FUNDED The advancement of religion in accordance with the orthodox Jewish faith; the relief of poverty; education and other charitable purposes.
RANGE OF GRANTS Previously £40–£170,000.
SAMPLE GRANTS Previous beneficiaries were: Keren Associates Ltd, BAT, UTA, CM L, TYY, Square Foundation Ltd, Ateres Yeshua Charitable Trust,

Side by Side, My Dream Time, British Friends of Rinat Aharon, Chanoch Lenaar, and All in Together Girls.
FINANCES *Year* 2007–08 *Income* £1,551,909 *Grants* £1,727,787 *Assets* £3,375,307
TRUSTEES Joseph Weiss; Zelda Weiss; E Englander.
OTHER INFORMATION No grants list was available.
HOW TO APPLY In writing to the correspondent.
WHO TO APPLY TO Zelda Weiss, Trustee, 141b Upper Clapton Road, London E5 9DB
CC NO 288020   **ESTABLISHED** 1983

....

■ The Ripple Effect Foundation

WHERE FUNDING CAN BE GIVEN UK.
WHO CAN BENEFIT Registered charities.
WHAT IS FUNDED General charitable purposes, particularly the broad fields of environmental work, empowering young people in the UK and third world development.
WHAT IS NOT FUNDED No grants made to individuals.
TYPE OF GRANT Multiple year funding available.
SAMPLE GRANTS Devon Community Foundation (£50,000); Network for Social Change (£11,000); and Homestart UK (£5,000).
FINANCES *Year* 2007–08 *Income* £42,594 *Grants* £65,800 *Assets* £1,627,314
TRUSTEES Miss Caroline D Marks; I R Marks; I S Wesley.
HOW TO APPLY The trust states that it does not respond to unsolicited applications.
WHO TO APPLY TO Caroline D Marks, Trustee, Marlborough Investment Consultants Ltd, Wessex House, Oxford Road, Newbury, Berkshire RG14 1PA *Tel* 01635 814 470
CC NO 802327   **ESTABLISHED** 1989

....

■ The Sir John Ritblat Family Foundation

WHERE FUNDING CAN BE GIVEN UK.
WHO CAN BENEFIT Charitable organisations, with a preference for Jewish groups.
WHAT IS FUNDED General charitable purposes.
WHAT IS NOT FUNDED No grants to individuals.
SAMPLE GRANTS South Bank Centre (£175,000); Imperial College (£100,000); Weizman UK (£42,000); Jewish Care and Norwood (£11,000 each); Tate Foundation (£5,000); St Richards Hospital and Tennis and Racquets Association (£1,000 each); UK Jewish Film Festival (£500); and Barnardos (£300).
FINANCES *Year* 2007–08 *Income* £60,812 *Grants* £384,422 *Assets* £1,165,275
TRUSTEES J H Ritblat; N S J Ritblat; C B Wagman; J W J Ritblat.
HOW TO APPLY The trust has previously stated that its funds are fully committed.
WHO TO APPLY TO The Clerk, Baker Tilly, 1st Floor, 46 Clarendon Road, Watford WD17 1JJ *Tel* 01923 816400
CC NO 262463   **ESTABLISHED** 1971

....

■ The River Farm Foundation

WHERE FUNDING CAN BE GIVEN UK and overseas.
WHO CAN BENEFIT Charitable organisations working in the UK and overseas.
WHAT IS FUNDED General charitable purposes.
SAMPLE GRANTS Busoga Trust (£10,500); and Noah's Ark Children's Hospice and Building for Babies (£2,500 each).
FINANCES *Year* 2007–08 *Income* £466,860 *Grants* £15,500 *Assets* £1,852,575

TRUSTEES M Haworth; Mrs E Haworth; M D Willcox.

HOW TO APPLY 'The trust is very selective in the grant making process and applications are reviewed by the trustees personally.'

WHO TO APPLY TO M D Willcox, Trustee, The Old Coach House, Bergh Apton, Norwich NR15 1DD *Tel* 01508 480100 *email* info@willcoxlewis.co.uk

CC NO 1113109 ESTABLISHED 2006

■ The River Trust

WHERE FUNDING CAN BE GIVEN UK, with a preference for Sussex.

WHO CAN BENEFIT Organisations benefiting Christians.

WHAT IS FUNDED Evangelical Christian charities.

WHAT IS NOT FUNDED No grants to individuals. The trust does not support 'repairs of the fabric of the church' nor does it give grants for capital expenditure.

TYPE OF GRANT Certain charities are supported for more than one year.

RANGE OF GRANTS £500–£13,000.

SAMPLE GRANTS Youth with a Mission (£13,000); Barcombe Parochial Church (£7,000); Harrow Development Trust, Ironmongers Foundation, Chasah Trust and St Mary's Church PCC Barcombe (£5,000 each); Youth with a Mission Scotland and Interhealth (£3,000); Tear Fund (£2,700); The R Foundation and Scriptural Knowledge Institute (£1,500); St Barnabus Church and St Barnabas Hospices (£1,000 each); Stewards Trust (£750); St Stephen's Society, African Enterprise, ICCOWE and Mitchell Ministries (£500 each).

FINANCES *Year* 2006–07 *Income* £91,929 *Grants* £77,540 *Assets* £655,579

TRUSTEES Kleinwort Benson Trustees Ltd.

HOW TO APPLY In writing to the correspondent. It is unusual for unsolicited appeals to be successful. Only successful applicants are notified of the trustees' decision. Some charities are supported for more than one year, although no commitment is usually given to the recipients.

WHO TO APPLY TO The Trustees, c/o Kleinwort Benson Trustees Ltd, PO Box 57005, 30 Gresham Street, London EC2V 7PG *Tel* 020 3207 7337 *Fax* 020 3207 7665

CC NO 275843 ESTABLISHED 1977

■ The Rivers Charitable Trust

WHERE FUNDING CAN BE GIVEN UK.

WHO CAN BENEFIT Charitable organisations.

WHAT IS FUNDED General charitable purposes.

RANGE OF GRANTS £200–£20,000.

SAMPLE GRANTS Christina Noble Foundation (£20,000); African Equipment for Schools (£8,000); Kids Cookery School and Mathari Children's Foundation (£5,000 each); South Bank Foundation (£4,000); Prospex (£2,300); Scientific Exploration Society (£1,400); Cedars Project (£1,000); CNCF Sponsor a Child (£240); and Harrodian School (£200).

FINANCES *Year* 2007–08 *Income* £98,594 *Grants* £47,347 *Assets* £738,441

TRUSTEES A J Rivers; K Constable; Mrs C J Bolton.

HOW TO APPLY In writing to the correspondent.

WHO TO APPLY TO The Trustees, 110 Ledbury Road, London W11 2AH *Tel* 020 7792 1234 *email* ajrultra@btopenworld.com

CC NO 1078545 ESTABLISHED 1999

■ Riverside Charitable Trust Limited

WHERE FUNDING CAN BE GIVEN Mainly Lancashire.

WHO CAN BENEFIT Individuals and organisations benefiting people disadvantaged by poverty and illness, older people, and people employed or formerly employed in the shoe trade.

WHAT IS FUNDED Relief of need, education, healthcare, and other charitable purposes.

WHAT IS NOT FUNDED No grants for political causes.

TYPE OF GRANT Recurring costs.

SAMPLE GRANTS Grants were made to the following causes: Relief for sickness, infirmity and for the older people – 26 grants totalling £34,000; General charitable public benefits – 72 grants totalling £57,000; Relief of poverty – 71 grants totalling £40,000; Death grants – 15 grants totalling £3,400; Educational support – 1 grant totalling £1,000.

FINANCES *Year* 2007–08 *Income* £111,124 *Grants* £135,725 *Assets* £2,371,056

TRUSTEES B J Lynch; I B Dearing; J A Davidson; F Drew; H Francis; A Higginson; G Maden; L Clegg; B Terry.

HOW TO APPLY In writing to the correspondent.

WHO TO APPLY TO F Drew, Trustee, Riverside, Bacup, Lancashire OL13 0DT *Tel* 01706 874 961

CC NO 264015 ESTABLISHED 1972

■ The Daniel Rivlin Charitable Trust

WHERE FUNDING CAN BE GIVEN UK.

WHO CAN BENEFIT Mainly Jewish organisations.

WHAT IS FUNDED Mainly Jewish charitable purposes.

SAMPLE GRANTS Previous beneficiaries include: Donisthorpe Hall; Friends of Israel; Hay on Wye Festival of Literature; Makor Charitable Trust; Make a Dream; Pockilington and Market Weighton Rotary Club; UJIA; Yad Vashem.

FINANCES *Year* 2007–08 *Income* £5,820 *Grants* £20,000 *Assets* £65,428

TRUSTEES D R Rivlin; N S Butler; M Miller.

HOW TO APPLY The trust states that funds are fully committed and does not welcome unsolicited applications.

WHO TO APPLY TO D R Rivlin, Trustee, Manor House, Northgate Lane, Linton, Wetherby, West Yorkshire LS22 4HN *Tel* 01937 589645

CC NO 328341 ESTABLISHED 1989

■ Rix-Thompson-Rothenburg Foundation

WHERE FUNDING CAN BE GIVEN UK.

WHO CAN BENEFIT People with a learning disability.

WHAT IS FUNDED Projects connected with the care, education, training, development and leisure activities of people with a learning disability, particularly those that will enhance opportunity and lifestyle.

SAMPLE GRANTS Beneficiaries included: Centre 404, and Dundee Independent Advocacy Service (£5,000); Accessible Arts and Media, Artslink Central Limited, Colchester Gateway Clubs, Enable Ability and Half Moon Young People's Theatre Limited (£4,000 each); and Oswestry and District Mencap (£1,000).

FINANCES *Year* 2008 *Income* £141,296 *Grants* £97,510 *Assets* £1,215,804

TRUSTEES Lord Rix; Sir Anthony S Jolliffe; Joss Nangle; Walter Rothenberg; Loretto Lambe; Fred Heddell; Barrie Davis; Jonathan Rix; Brian Baldock.

■ RJM Charitable Trust

WHERE FUNDING CAN BE GIVEN UK and worldwide.
WHO CAN BENEFIT Jewish organisations.
WHAT IS FUNDED Jewish charitable purposes.
SAMPLE GRANTS UJIA (£55,000); Aish Hatorah Rabbi
Schiff (£16,000); KD AD Min (£11,000); CRT
and CST (£10,000 each); Friends of Brei Akiva
(£6,000); Jewish Hum Foundation and
Manchester Eruv (£5,000 each); the Fed
(£3,000); MJS (£2,000); Our Kids and
Gateshead Tal College Rabbi Z Cohen (£1,000
each); Jew Chap (£500); BFIWD (£200); and
Child Resettlement (£100).
FINANCES *Year* 2007–08 *Income* £159,909
Grants £165,312 *Assets* £223,402
TRUSTEES J Rowe; Mrs M B Rowe.
HOW TO APPLY In writing to the correspondent.
WHO TO APPLY TO J Rowe, Trustee, 84 Upper Park
Road, Salford M7 4JA *Tel* 0161 720 8787
email joshua@broomwell.com
CC NO 288336   **ESTABLISHED** 1983

■ The Alex Roberts-Miller Foundation

WHERE FUNDING CAN BE GIVEN UK.
WHO CAN BENEFIT Charitable organisations working
with young people.
WHAT IS FUNDED Its main goal is to help provide
educational, sporting and social opportunities
for disadvantaged young people. It aims to
target funds where they will have a direct and
significant impact on the lives of the people they
are trying to help. The foundation also promotes
road safety and its education.
WHAT IS NOT FUNDED No grants to individuals.
SAMPLE GRANTS Back-up Trust (£25,000); SeeAbility
(£9,000); Red Balloon (£8,000); Capital Kids
Cricket (£5,500); Sutton Trust (£4,000); CCB&H
Young Carers (£3,000); and RoadPeace
(£2,000).
FINANCES *Year* 2006–07 *Income* £117,260
Grants £56,500 *Assets* £160,381
TRUSTEES Will Armitage; David Avery-Gee; Emma
Temple; Richard Roberts-Miller; Fiona Roberts-
Miller; Jo Roberts-Miller; Beth Roberts-Miller.
HOW TO APPLY The foundation researches its own
beneficiaries. The trust states: 'if you represent
a registered charity with goals consistent with
ours, you are welcome to write or e-mail, but
please understand that our resources are
limited and we already receive many
applications – far more than we are able even to
acknowledge'.
WHO TO APPLY TO The Trustees, PO Box 104,
Dorking, Surrey RH5 6YN *Tel* 01306 741 368
email alexrmfoundation@mac.com
Website www.alexrmfoundation.org.uk
CC NO 1093912   **ESTABLISHED** 2002

■ Thomas Roberts Trust

WHERE FUNDING CAN BE GIVEN UK.
WHO CAN BENEFIT Organisations benefiting people
with a disability or illness.
WHAT IS FUNDED The trust mainly makes grants to
medical (particularly cancer support and
research), disability and welfare organisations. It
also considers applications from employees and
former employees of the Thomas Roberts Group
Companies.
RANGE OF GRANTS From £100 to £6,000.
SAMPLE GRANTS Cancer Research UK (£6,000);
Macmillan Cancer Relief and Marie Curie Cancer
Care (£3,000 each); Age Concern (£2,100);
Winchester Churches Nightshelter (£750);
Diabetes UK and Riding for the Disabled (£500
each); Parkinson's Disease Society (£250); and
Breast Cancer Campaign (£100).
FINANCES *Year* 2007–08 *Income* £24,499
Grants £45,290 *Assets* £1,028,580
TRUSTEES R E Gammage; J Roberts; Mrs
G Hemmings.
HOW TO APPLY In writing to the correspondent.
Applicants are required to provide a summary of
their proposals to the trustees, explaining how
the funds would be used and what would be
achieved.
WHO TO APPLY TO James Roberts, Trustee, 5–6 The
Square, Winchester, Hampshire SO23 9WE
Tel 01962 843 211 *Fax* 01962 843 223
email trtrust@thomasroberts.co.uk
CC NO 1067235   **ESTABLISHED** 1997

■ The Robertson Trust

WHERE FUNDING CAN BE GIVEN Scotland.
WHO CAN BENEFIT Registered charities only.
WHAT IS FUNDED Priority areas: health, care,
education and training and community arts and
sport. Other areas supported: work with
children, young people and families;
preservation of the environment; the
strengthening of local communities; the
development of culture, heritage and science;
animal welfare; and the saving of lives.
WHAT IS NOT FUNDED The trust does not support:
individuals or organisations which are not
recognised as charities by the Office of the
Scottish Charity Regulator (OSCR); general
appeals or circulars, including contributions to
endowment funds; local charities whose work
takes place outside Scotland; generic
employment or training projects; community
projects where the applicant is a housing
association; core revenue costs for playgroups,
nurseries, after school groups etc; projects
which are exclusively or primarily intended to
promote political beliefs; students or
organisations for personal study, travel or for
expeditions whether in the United Kingdom or
abroad; medical research; organisations and
projects whose primary object is to provide a
counselling, advocacy, advice and/or
information service. The trust is unlikely to
support: charities which collect funds for onward
distribution to others; umbrella groups which do
not provide a direct service to individuals e.g.
CVS; feasibility studies and other research;
charities already in receipt of a current donation
from the trust.
TYPE OF GRANT One-off, annual, pledges (to give
grants if a target figure is raised), and recurring.
SAMPLE GRANTS Robertson Scholarship Trust
(£600,000); University of Strathclyde
(£500,000); University of Edinburgh
Development Trust (£300,000); Youth Scotland
(£100,000); Jeely Piece Club (£70,000); East
Lothian Women's Aid (£20,000); Broomhouse
Centre (£10,000); Scotland's Churches Scheme
(£3,500); Bobath Scotland (£740); and Lanton
Village Hall (£500).
FINANCES *Year* 2008–09 *Income* £9,747,866
Grants £9,900,000 *Assets* £340,433,499

TRUSTEES Sir Ian Good, Chair; Richard J A Hunter; Dame Barbara M Kelly; Shonaig Macpherson; David D Stevenson; Ian B Curle.

HOW TO APPLY Applicants are advised to read the recently revised guidelines before making any application. These are available to download on the trust's website. The trust does not have an application form. Applications are invited by letter to enable applicants to express themselves in their own words without the restrictions of set questions. However, there are certain details you should include and questions you will need to answer to enable the trust to make an informed decision on whether or not to fund your organisation. A brief description of the organisation, including past developments and successes; a description of the project – what do you want to do, who will be involved, where will it take place and how will it be managed; how you have identified the need for this work; what you hope will be the outputs and outcomes of this work and the key targets have you set; how you intend to monitor and evaluate the work so that you know whether or not you have been successful; the income and expenditure budget for this piece of work; how you propose to fund the work, including details of funds already raised or applied for; the proposed timetable?. In addition the trust will also require three supporting documents. These are: a completed copy of the Organisation Information Sheet, which is available from the trust's website or the trust office; a copy of your most recent annual report and accounts. These should have been independently examined or audited; a job description, if you are applying for salary costs for a specified worker. The trust requests that applicants do not send a constitution or memorandum and articles. If there is any other bulky information which you feel may be relevant, such as a feasibility study, business plan or evaluation, then you should refer to it in your application, so that the assessment team can request it if required. Small and main donations form the bulk of the donations made by the trust and are assessed on a rolling programme with recommendations made to the trustees six times a year. Applications for major capital donations are considered three times a year in January, May and September.

WHO TO APPLY TO Christine Scullion, Assessment Manager, 85 Berkeley Street, Glasgow G3 7DX *Tel* 0141 221 3151 *Fax* 0141 221 0744 *email* christine@therobertsontrust.org.uk *Website* www.therobertsontrust.org.uk
SC NO SC002970   **ESTABLISHED** 1961 and 1963

■ Edwin George Robinson Charitable Trust

WHERE FUNDING CAN BE GIVEN UK.
WHO CAN BENEFIT Medical research organisations.
WHAT IS FUNDED The trustees favour applications from smaller organisations for specific research projects.
WHAT IS NOT FUNDED No grants to individuals or for general running costs for small local organisations.
RANGE OF GRANTS Mostly £500–£6,500.
SAMPLE GRANTS Marie Curie Cancer Care (£6,500); Diabetes UK (£5,000); Bath Institute of Medical Engineering (£4,000); Deafness Research (£2,000); Brainwave, Action for Medical Research and Ness Foundation (£1,000 each);

and Cure Parkinsons and Holly Lodge Centre (£500 each).
FINANCES *Year* 2007–08 *Income* £14,894 *Grants* £47,095 *Assets* £302,602
TRUSTEES E C Robinson; Mrs S C Robinson.
HOW TO APPLY In writing to the correspondent.
WHO TO APPLY TO E C Robinson, Trustee, 71 Manor Road South, Hinchley Wood, Surrey KT10 0QB *Tel* 020 8398 6845
CC NO 1068763   **ESTABLISHED** 1998

■ Robyn Charitable Trust

WHERE FUNDING CAN BE GIVEN UK and Overseas.
WHO CAN BENEFIT Organisations benefiting children and young people.
WHAT IS FUNDED Education and social welfare for children in any part of the world.
WHAT IS NOT FUNDED No grants to individuals.
SAMPLE GRANTS Previous beneficiaries have included: One to One Children's Fund, The Purcell School, Variety Club, The Honeypot Charity, Malawi Against AIDS and Teenage Cancer Trust.
FINANCES *Year* 2007–08 *Income* £38,003 *Grants* £17,101 *Assets* £286,112
TRUSTEES Malcolm Webber; Mark Knopfler; Ronnie Harris.
HOW TO APPLY In writing to the correspondent.
WHO TO APPLY TO The Trustees, c/o Harris and Trotter, 65 New Cavendish Street, London W1G 7LS *Tel* 020 7467 6300
CC NO 327745

■ The Rochester Bridge Trust

WHERE FUNDING CAN BE GIVEN Kent.
WHO CAN BENEFIT Charitable bodies.
WHAT IS FUNDED The maintenance and reconstruction of the Rochester bridges, Medway tunnel and any other crossings of the River Medway. After this has been achieved, grants can be made for other general charitable purposes. Around £100,000 is available for charities each year.
WHAT IS NOT FUNDED No grants to individuals. No funding for revenue.
TYPE OF GRANT Capital including equipment, buildings and one-off.
RANGE OF GRANTS Up to £100,000.
SAMPLE GRANTS University of Greenwich (£73,000); Rochester Cathedral (£50,000); Royal Engineers Museum Foundation and St. Margaret's Church – Rainham (£10,000 each).
FINANCES *Year* 2007–08 *Income* £2,766,144 *Grants* £261,700 *Assets* £65,717,284
TRUSTEES Rodney B Chambers; Frank Gibson; Paul E J Harriot; Dr Anne F H Logan; Paul E Oldham; Russel J Race; Russell G Cooper; John A Spence; Richard G Thornby; Cllr Anthony R Goulden; Alan L Jarrett; Michael V Snelling.
HOW TO APPLY In writing to the correspondent, with the latest accounts. Applications should be submitted by 30 June each year and grants are decided by August.
WHO TO APPLY TO Mrs Threader, Bridge Clerk, The Bridge Chamber, 5 Esplanade, Rochester, Kent ME1 1QE *Tel* 01634 846 706 *Fax* 01634 840125 *email* bridgeclerk@rbt.org.uk *Website* www.rbt.org.uk
CC NO 207100   **ESTABLISHED** 1399

■ The Rock Foundation

WHERE FUNDING CAN BE GIVEN Worldwide.

WHO CAN BENEFIT Charitable organisations, especially those which are built upon a clear biblical basis and which, in most instances, receive little or no publicity.

WHAT IS FUNDED Christian ministries and other charitable work.

SAMPLE GRANTS Beneficiaries included: Cranleigh Baptist Church (£21,000); Proclamation Task (£15,000); Proclamation Trust (£11,000); Crosslinks (£6,000); Simon Trust (£4,900); Friends International (£4,700); City Partnership (£4,500); Harare Central Baptist Church (£4,000); Lahore Evangelical Ministries (£3,700); British Urological Foundation (£2,500); Agape (£1,500); and Truth Mission (£1,100).

FINANCES *Year* 2007–08 *Income* £207,168 *Grants* £166,955 *Assets* £84,660

TRUSTEES Richard Borgonon; Andrew Green; Kevin Locock; Jane Borgonon; Colin Spreckley.

OTHER INFORMATION The sum of £71,000 was distributed to 18 individuals.

HOW TO APPLY The trust has previously stated: 'the trust identifies its beneficiaries through its own networks, choosing to support organisations it has a working relationship with. This allows the trust to verify that the organisation is doing excellent work in a sensible manner in a way which cannot be conveyed from a written application. As such, all appeals from charities the foundation do not find through their own research are simply thrown in the bin. If a sae is included in an application, it will merely end up in the foundation's waste-paper bin rather than a post box.'

WHO TO APPLY TO The Trustees, Park Green Cottage, Barhatch Road, Cranleigh, Surrey GU6 7DJ

CC NO 294775   **ESTABLISHED** 1986

■ The Rock Solid Trust

WHERE FUNDING CAN BE GIVEN Worldwide.

WHO CAN BENEFIT Christian charities and Christian projects.

WHAT IS FUNDED The advancement of the Christian religion; the maintenance, restoration and repair of the fabric of Christian church; the education and training of individuals; relief of need.

RANGE OF GRANTS £100–£20,000.

SAMPLE GRANTS Beneficiaries included: Christchurch Clifton and Sherborne School Foundation (£20,000 each); Bristol University (£5,000); Chain of Hope and London School of Theology (£500 each); and RNLI (£100).

FINANCES *Year* 2007–08 *Income* £25,539 *Grants* £59,489 *Assets* £626,015

TRUSTEES J D W Pocock; T P Wicks; T G Bretell.

OTHER INFORMATION Grants to individuals totalled £12,000

HOW TO APPLY In writing to the correspondent.

WHO TO APPLY TO J D W Pocock, Trustee, 7 Belgrave Place, Clifton, Bristol BS8 3DD

CC NO 1077669   **ESTABLISHED** 1999

■ The Roddick Foundation

WHERE FUNDING CAN BE GIVEN Worldwide.

WHO CAN BENEFIT Charitable organisations.

WHAT IS FUNDED Arts, education, environmental, human rights, humanitarian, medical, poverty, social justice.

WHAT IS NOT FUNDED The trust states that it is 'particularly not interested in the following:

funding anything related to sport; funding fundraising events or conferences; and sponsorship of any kind'.

RANGE OF GRANTS Up to £350,000.

SAMPLE GRANTS The Hepatitis C Trust (£328,000); Soil Action and The Helen Bamber Foundation (£300,000 each); Climate Justice Programme (£286,000); Children & Woman Abuse Studies Unit (£230,000); Platform (£150,000); New Economic Foundation (£100,000); the Prisons Video Trust and Amnesty International (£50,000 each); Chichester Festival Theatre (£40,000); Burma UK (£35,000); Hetrich-Martin Institute (£25,000); The Missing Foundation (£20,000); Arun Children and Families Trust (£10,000); Peepal Enterprises Ltd (£3,000); and The Body Shop Foundation (£200).

FINANCES *Year* 2007–08 *Income* £733,786 *Grants* £3,026,483 *Assets* £25,571,073

TRUSTEES J Roddick; S Roddick; T G Roddick; S C A Schlieske.

HOW TO APPLY The foundation does not accept or respond to unsolicited applications. 'Grants made by the foundation are at the discretion of the board of trustees. The board considers making a grant and, if approved, notifies the intended recipient.'

WHO TO APPLY TO J Roddick, Secretary, Emerald House, East Street, Epsom, Surrey KT17 1 HS *Website* www.theroddickfoundation.org

CC NO 1061372   **ESTABLISHED** 1997

■ The Rofeh Trust

WHERE FUNDING CAN BE GIVEN UK.

WHO CAN BENEFIT Charitable organisations.

WHAT IS FUNDED General charitable purposes, with a possible preference for Jewish causes.

FINANCES *Year* 2007–08 *Income* £75,583 *Grants* £45,660 *Assets* £865,767

TRUSTEES Martin Dunitz; Ruth Dunitz; Vivian Wineman; Henry Eder.

HOW TO APPLY In writing to the correspondent.

WHO TO APPLY TO The Trustees, 44 Southway, London NW11 6SA *Tel* 020 8458 7382

CC NO 1077682   **ESTABLISHED** 1999

■ Richard Rogers Charitable Settlement

WHERE FUNDING CAN BE GIVEN UK.

WHO CAN BENEFIT Charitable organisations.

WHAT IS FUNDED General purposes.

SAMPLE GRANTS National Communities Research Centre (£50,000); the Constant Gardener Trust and the National Community Resource Ltd (£13,000 each); Serpentine Gallery (£11,000); Refuge (£10,000); Tree House (£6,400); Crisis (£1,000); Trafford Hall (£900); British Heart Foundation (£500); Scientists for Global Responsibility (£330); Walk the Walk Worldwide (£300); and The RSA (£95).

FINANCES *Year* 2007–08 *Income* £80,331 *Grants* £127,410 *Assets* £992,305

TRUSTEES Lord R G Rogers; Lady R Rogers.

HOW TO APPLY In writing to the correspondent.

WHO TO APPLY TO K A Hawkins, Lee Associates, 5 Southampton Place, London WC1A 2DA *Tel* 020 7025 4600

CC NO 283252   **ESTABLISHED** 1981

■ Rokach Family Charitable Trust

WHERE FUNDING CAN BE GIVEN UK.

WHO CAN BENEFIT Jewish organisations; registered charities.

WHAT IS FUNDED Advancement of the Jewish religion; general charitable purposes.

SAMPLE GRANTS Previous beneficiaries have included: Before Trust, Kisharon Charitable Trust, Cosmon Limited; Moreshet Hatorah Ltd, Belz Synagogue and Friends of Wiznitz.

FINANCES *Year* 2005–06 *Income* £507,789 *Grants* £500,000

TRUSTEES N Rokach; Mrs H Rokach; Mrs E Hoffman; Mrs M Feingold; Mrs A Gefilhaus; Mrs N Brenig.

OTHER INFORMATION No accounts received at the Charity Commission since those for 2005/06.

HOW TO APPLY In writing to the correspondent.

WHO TO APPLY TO Norman Rokach, Trustee, 20 Middleton Road, London NW11 7NS *Tel* 020 8455 6359

CC NO 284007   **ESTABLISHED** 1981

■ The Helen Roll Charitable Trust

WHERE FUNDING CAN BE GIVEN UK.

WHO CAN BENEFIT Registered charities only, including universities, schools, colleges, research institutions, groups helping disadvantaged people, theatres, animal welfare charities, and environmental and wildlife organisations.

WHAT IS FUNDED General charitable purposes, particularly: education, especially higher education; libraries and museums; the arts; health and animal welfare.

WHAT IS NOT FUNDED No support for individuals or non-registered charities.

TYPE OF GRANT Generally one-off for specific projects, but within a framework of charities whose work is known to the trustees.

RANGE OF GRANTS £600–£13,000.

SAMPLE GRANTS Home Farm Trust (£13,500); Pembroke College Oxford (£10,000); Oxford University Ashmolean Museum (£7,500); Sick Children's Trust (£6,000); Purcell School (£5,000); Canine Partners for Independence (£4,000); Alzheimer's Research Trust (£3,000); SeeSaw (£2,000); and Gerald Moore Award, Carers UK and Barn Owl Trust (£1,000 each).

FINANCES *Year* 2007–08 *Income* £62,702 *Grants* £128,400 *Assets* £1,633,446

TRUSTEES Christine Chapman; Paul Strang; Christine Reid; Jennifer Williamson; Dick Williamson; Stephen G Williamson; Patrick Stopford.

HOW TO APPLY In writing to the correspondent during the first fortnight in February. Applications should be kept short, ideally on one sheet of A4. Further material will then be requested from those who are short-listed. The trustees normally make their distributions in March.

WHO TO APPLY TO F R Williamson, Trustee, 30 St Giles, Oxford OX1 3LE *Tel* 01865 559 900

CC NO 299108   **ESTABLISHED** 1988

■ The Sir James Roll Charitable Trust

WHERE FUNDING CAN BE GIVEN UK.

WHO CAN BENEFIT Registered charities.

WHAT IS FUNDED Mainly the promotion of mutual tolerance, commonality and cordiality in major world religions; promotion of improved access to computer technology in community-based projects other than political parties or local government; funding of projects aimed at early

identification of specific learning disorders; and any other charitable projects as the trustees see fit.

RANGE OF GRANTS £1,000–£10,000, although mostly £1,000.

SAMPLE GRANTS DEC Bangladesh Cyclone Appeal and DEC Darfur and Chad Crisis Appeal (£10,000 each); and CRISIS at Christmas (£5,000). Grants of £1,000 went to Cricket Foundation, Computer Aid International, Family Holiday Association, Help the Hospices, Howard League for Penal Reform, Kent Association for the Blind, Jubilee Sailing Trust, SSAFA, Support Dogs Ltd, Whizz-Kidz, and Shelter.

FINANCES *Year* 2007–08 *Income* £233,724 *Grants* £185,000 *Assets* £4,231,882

TRUSTEES N T Wharton; B W Elvy; J M Liddiard.

HOW TO APPLY In writing to the correspondent.

WHO TO APPLY TO N T Wharton, Trustee, 5 New Road Avenue, Chatham, Kent ME4 6AR *Tel* 01634 830 111

CC NO 1064963   **ESTABLISHED** 1997

■ The Roman Research Trust

WHERE FUNDING CAN BE GIVEN UK, but preference given to Wiltshire and neighbouring counties to the west.

WHO CAN BENEFIT Individuals and organisations benefiting postgraduate students, professional archaeologists and non-professionals of equivalent standing.

WHAT IS FUNDED Excavation, recording, analysis and publication of Romano-British archaeological research not otherwise funded or for which existing funds are insufficient. Romano-British archaeological exhibitions in museums and other places accessible to the public; educational programmes related to Roman Britain.

WHAT IS NOT FUNDED Undergraduate or postgraduate courses.

TYPE OF GRANT Project and research. Funding is for one year or less.

RANGE OF GRANTS £200–£10,000. Typical grant £2,000.

SAMPLE GRANTS Previously: University of Oxford for excavation of the amphitheatre at Frilford, and Wiltshire Archaeology and Natural History Society for work on the Littlecoat excavation archive (£5,000 each); University of Sheffield for excavation and geophysical survey at Chedworth Villa (£2,000); Primary Latin Project for illustrations for 'Minimus 2' (£1,500); Liverpool Museum for analysis of Roman artefacts from the Wirral (£1,000); Yorkshire Archaeological Society for publication of excavations at Newton Kyme (£500).

FINANCES *Year* 2007–08 *Income* £70,773 *Grants* £43,051 *Assets* £1,260,840

TRUSTEES Prof. Alan K Bowman, Chair; Dr Janet Delaine; Robin Birch; Dr Ralph Jackson; Hamish Orr-Ewing; Ms Amanda Claridge; Prof. Mike Fulford; Paul Boot; Mrs Jenny Hall.

OTHER INFORMATION No organisations were granted awards during 2007–08. The grant total was dispersed between nine individual applicants as follows: £40,000 for general archaeological purposes and £3,000 in bursary awards.

HOW TO APPLY By 15 November and 15 April annually. Application forms and guidelines available from the correspondent.

WHO TO APPLY TO Dr John Pearce, General Secretary, Department of Classics, Kings College London, Strand, London WC2R 2LS *Tel* 020 7848 2252 *email* john.pearce@kcl.ac.uk *Website* rrt. classics.ox.ac.uk
CC NO 800983 **ESTABLISHED** 1990

■ Romeera Foundation

WHERE FUNDING CAN BE GIVEN Worldwide.
WHO CAN BENEFIT Charitable organisations.
WHAT IS FUNDED General charitable purposes.
SAMPLE GRANTS British Heart Foundation (£1,650); Shri Kathiawar Nirashrit Balashram (£1,170); John Grooms (£330); and Breakthrough Breast Cancer (£250).
FINANCES *Year* 2007–08 *Income* £117,824 *Grants* £3,401 *Assets* £2,086,505
TRUSTEES Madoo Mehta; Meenal Mehta.
HOW TO APPLY In writing to the correspondent.
WHO TO APPLY TO The Trustees, 16 Heathgate, London NW11 7AN *Tel* 020 8458 5864
CC NO 1076325 **ESTABLISHED** 1999

■ The Gerald Ronson Foundation

WHERE FUNDING CAN BE GIVEN UK and overseas.
WHO CAN BENEFIT Registered charities.
WHAT IS FUNDED General charitable activities with a preference for Jewish causes.
RANGE OF GRANTS Up to £400,000.
SAMPLE GRANTS Jewish Care (£401,000); Community Security Trust (£103,000); Lubavitch Foundation (£50,000); Roundhouse Trust (£35,000); Royal Opera House (£30,000); and Jewish Leadership Council and Traditional Alternatives Foundation (£25,000 each). Other grants of less than £20,000 totalled £327,000..
FINANCES *Year* 2008–09 *Income* £497,201 *Grants* £930,410 *Assets* £12,159,285
TRUSTEES Gerald Maurice Ronson, Chair; Dame Gail Ronson; Alan Irving Goldman; Jonathan Simon Goldstein; Lisa Debra Ronson; Nicole Julia Ronson Allalouf; Hayley Victoria Goldenberg.
HOW TO APPLY In writing to the correspondent. 'The trust generally makes donations on a quarterly basis in June, September, December and March. In the interim periods, the Chairman's Action Committee deals with urgent requests for donations which are approved by the trustees at the quarterly meetings.'
WHO TO APPLY TO Jeremy Trent, Secretary, Acre House, 11–15 William Road, London NW1 3ER *Tel* 020 7388 7000
CC NO 1111728 **ESTABLISHED** 2005

■ The C A Rookes Charitable Trust

WHERE FUNDING CAN BE GIVEN South Warwickshire, especially Stratford-upon-Avon.
WHO CAN BENEFIT Small local projects, innovative projects and UK organisations benefiting older people in particular.
WHAT IS FUNDED Older people, general charitable purposes.
WHAT IS NOT FUNDED No grants to individuals for educational purposes.
TYPE OF GRANT One-off and recurrent.
RANGE OF GRANTS Up to £3,000.
SAMPLE GRANTS Bigwood's Christmas Gifts the Elderly (£2,000); the Good Companions Club (£1,500); Orchestra of the Swan, South Warwickshire Haematology Trust Fund, Stratford Music Festival and Warwick Hospital Cancer

Ward Appeal (£1,000 each); Armonico Consort Limited and Mayday Trust (£750 each); and Myton Hamlet Hospital and Stratford Sea Cadets (£500 each).
FINANCES *Year* 2007–08 *Income* £49,106 *Grants* £11,000 *Assets* £1,206,464
TRUSTEES Christopher Ironmonger.
HOW TO APPLY In writing to the correspondent at any time including an sae.
WHO TO APPLY TO C James Bragg Flint, Trustee, Bigwood, 3 Union Street, Stratford Upon Avon, Warwickshire CV37 6QT *Tel* 0178 948 8401
CC NO 512437 **ESTABLISHED** 1980

■ Mrs L D Rope Third Charitable Settlement

WHERE FUNDING CAN BE GIVEN UK and overseas, with a particular interest in Suffolk.
WHO CAN BENEFIT For unsolicited applications, charities who work at grassroots level within their community, generally small in size, that are little catered for from other sources, or those that are based in particularly deprived areas. Charities with a large and committed volunteer base and those that have relatively low administration costs, in terms of staff salaries.
WHAT IS FUNDED Relief of poverty, advancement of education, advancement of religion and other charitable purposes.
WHAT IS NOT FUNDED The following categories of unsolicited applications will not be successful: overseas projects; national charities; requests for core funding; buildings; medical research/ health care (outside of the beneficial area); students (a very limited amount is available for foreign students); schools (outside of the beneficial area); environmental charities and animal welfare; the arts; matched funding; repayment of debts for individuals.
TYPE OF GRANT For unsolicited requests, grants are usually one-off and small scale. Funding is given for one year or less.
RANGE OF GRANTS Generally £100–£1,000.
SAMPLE GRANTS Science Human Dimension Project (£50,000); East Anglian Children's Hospice (£30,000); Traidcraft – project in Bangladesh (£20,000); Shelter (£15,000); Downing College – Cambridge (£10,000); Ipswich Furniture Project (£8,000); Cafod – work in Gaza (£7,000); Norfolk Venda Project (£6,500); and Mencap – Ipswich and Jacobs Hospice Homes – India (£5,000 each).
FINANCES *Year* 2008–09 *Income* £1,660,439 *Grants* £566,976 *Assets* £38,656,973
TRUSTEES Crispin Rope; Jeremy Heal; Anne Walker; Ellen Jolly; John Wilkins; Catherine Scott; Paul Jolly.
OTHER INFORMATION Grants to organisations totalled £381306; grants to individuals totalled £185,669.
HOW TO APPLY Please send a concise letter (preferably one side of A4) explaining the main details of your request. Please always send your most recent accounts and a budgeted breakdown of the sum you are looking to raise. The trust will also need to know whether you have applied to other funding sources and whether you have been successful elsewhere. Your application should say who your trustees are and include a daytime telephone number.
WHO TO APPLY TO Crispin Rope, Trustee, Crag Farm, Boyton, Near Woodbridge, Suffolk IP12 3LH *Tel* 01473 333288
CC NO 290533 **ESTABLISHED** 1984

Think carefully about every application. Is it justified?

815

■ Rosa – the UK fund for women and girls

WHERE FUNDING CAN BE GIVEN UK.

WHO CAN BENEFIT Charitable organisations.

WHAT IS FUNDED Women's organisations and projects supporting women.

RANGE OF GRANTS £2,000–£20,000.

SAMPLE GRANTS June 2009: ICA: UK / Feminist Webs, The Powerhouse and Mimbre.

FINANCES *Year* 2009 *Grants* £25,000

TRUSTEES Mrs Marilyn List; Ms Maggie Baxter; Ms Vivienne Hayes.

HOW TO APPLY Full guidelines can be downloaded at the Rosa website.

WHO TO APPLY TO Ann-Sophie Morrissette, c/o Women's Resource Centre, Ground Floor East, 33–41 Dallington Street, London EC1V 0BB *Tel* 020 7324 3044 *email* info@rosauk.org *Website* www.rosauk.org

CC NO 1124856   **ESTABLISHED** 2008

■ The Rosca Trust

WHERE FUNDING CAN BE GIVEN The boroughs of Southend-on-Sea, Castle Point and Rochford District Council only.

WHO CAN BENEFIT Registered charities.

WHAT IS FUNDED The trust supports registered health and welfare charities particularly those working with young and older people in its beneficial area.

WHAT IS NOT FUNDED Grants are not given outside the beneficial area or to individuals.

RANGE OF GRANTS Usually £250–£5,000.

SAMPLE GRANTS St Edmunds Community Centre and SOS Bus Southend (£5,000 each); Milton Community Partnership (£3,500); Citizens' Advice Bureau – Southend and South East Essex Advocacy for Older People (£3,000 each); Aspire, Essex Association of Boys Clubs, Sadlers Farm Riding for the Disabled and Southend Boys Choir Trust (£2,500); Benfleet Methodist Church and Headway – Essex (£2,000 each); Brentwood Catholic Children's Society, Canvey Island Senior Citizens Association and Our Lady of Lourdes Playschool (£1,500 each); Royal Association in Aid of Deaf People and Space Resource Information Service (£1,000 each); Friends of Winter Garden Canvey Island (£500); and Happy Days (£300).

FINANCES *Year* 2007–08 *Income* £108,968 *Grants* £90,320 *Assets* £581,424

TRUSTEES K J Crowe; T T Ray; Mrs D A Powell; Mrs M Frewin.

HOW TO APPLY In writing to the correspondent. Applications are reviewed in January, April and September. An sae is appreciated. Preliminary telephone calls are considered unnecessary.

WHO TO APPLY TO K J Crowe, Trustee, 19 Avenue Terrace, Westcliff-on-Sea, Essex SS0 7PL *Tel* 01702 307840 *email* kenbarcrowe@ blueyonder.co.uk

CC NO 259907   **ESTABLISHED** 1966

■ The Rose Foundation

WHERE FUNDING CAN BE GIVEN In and around London.

WHO CAN BENEFIT Registered charities.

WHAT IS FUNDED The main emphasis is on financing building projects for other charities, where the cost is less than £200,000. A policy of seeking small self-contained projects usually in London or the Home Counties has been adopted. The trustees' policy is to offer assistance where needed with the design and construction

process, ensuring wherever possible that costs are minimised and the participation of other contributing bodies can be utilised to maximum benefit.

WHAT IS NOT FUNDED The foundation can support any type of building project (decoration, construction, repairs, extensions, adaptations) but not the provision of equipment (such as computers, transportation and so on). Items connected with the finishes, such as carpets, curtains, wallpaper and so on, should ideally comprise a part of the project not financed by the foundation. Funding will not be given for the purchase of a building or a site or for the seed money needed to draw up plans.

TYPE OF GRANT Part-funding building projects.

RANGE OF GRANTS Typically £5,000–£10,000.

SAMPLE GRANTS St John Ambulance (£680,000); New Amsterdam Charitable Foundation (£97,000); Fred Hollows Foundation (£32,000); Jewish Care (£20,000); Central Synagogue General Charities Fund (£12,000); Zoological Society of London (£10,000); Royal Academy of Arts (£8,000); Langdon Foundation (£4,000); Speech Language and Hearing Centre (£2,000); and Weizmann Institute Foundation (£1,000).

FINANCES *Year* 2007–08 *Income* £570,304 *Grants* £1,147,675 *Assets* £18,187,059

TRUSTEES Martin Rose; Alan Rose; John Rose; Paul Rose.

HOW TO APPLY In writing to the correspondent including details of the organisation and the registered charity number, together with the nature and probable approximate cost of the scheme and its anticipated start and completion dates. Applications can be submitted anytime between 1 July and 31 March (the following year). The foundation hopes to inform applicants of its decision by the second week in July. For more information on the foundation's grant making policies and application process, go to the website.

WHO TO APPLY TO Martin Rose, Trustee, 28 Crawford Street, London W1H 1LN *Tel* 020 7262 1155 *Website* www.rosefoundation.co.uk

CC NO 274875   **ESTABLISHED** 1977

■ The Cecil Rosen Foundation

WHERE FUNDING CAN BE GIVEN UK.

WHO CAN BENEFIT Organisations benefiting people who are disabled or have diabetes, hearing and sight loss, heart disease or mental illness. Medical professionals and research workers are also considered.

WHAT IS FUNDED General charitable purposes especially to assist people who are blind, deaf, physically or mentally disabled; also for research into causes of heart disease, diabetes and mental illness.

WHAT IS NOT FUNDED No grants to individuals.

TYPE OF GRANT Research is considered.

SAMPLE GRANTS Previous beneficiaries included: Jewish Blind and Disabled and the Cecil Rosen Charitable Trust.

FINANCES *Year* 2007–08 *Income* £643,360 *Grants* £326,620 *Assets* £5,418,885

TRUSTEES M J Ozin; J A Hart; P H Silverman.

HOW TO APPLY The correspondent has previously stated that 'no new applications can be considered'. Unsuccessful applications are not acknowledged.

WHO TO APPLY TO M J Ozin, Trustee, 22 Lisson Grove, London NW1 6TT

CC NO 247425   **ESTABLISHED** 1966

■ Rosetrees Trust

WHERE FUNDING CAN BE GIVEN Worldwide, in practice, UK.

WHO CAN BENEFIT Independent vetted medical research projects, especially if departmentally backed and peer reviewed.

WHAT IS FUNDED Medical research only.

WHAT IS NOT FUNDED No support for individuals, or for non-medical research.

TYPE OF GRANT Project and research funding for up to three years will be considered. Seed corn funding for a preliminary or pilot report is also available.

RANGE OF GRANTS About £200–£300,000.

SAMPLE GRANTS University College London and Royal Free (£306,000); Hebrew University (£97,000); Kings College (£91,000); Imperial College London (£87,000); Institute of Cancer Research (£45,000); Oxford University (£27,000); Cardiff University (£26,000); Southampton University (£22,000); Manchester University (£18,000); and Newcastle University (£16,000).

FINANCES *Year* 2008–09 *Income* £877,128 *Grants* £894,890 *Assets* £448,447

TRUSTEES R A Ross; Lee Portnoi; Clive Winkler.

PUBLICATIONS A brochure, which outlines the trust's approach to the 100 projects it helps fund and its future plans, is available.

OTHER INFORMATION Note: the trust is very keen to share the expertise it has developed over 20 years, which is available to co-donors at no cost. Organisations interested in sharing this knowledge should contact the trust directly. Six-monthly progress reports in layman's terms are a condition of any grant made. These should give the trustees a clear and concise picture of whether anticipated targets have been achieved. Peer review and endorsement are required.

HOW TO APPLY In writing to the correspondent. Applicants must complete a simple pro forma which sets out briefly in clear layman's terms the reason for the project, the nature of the research, its cost, its anticipated benefit and how and when people will be able to benefit. Proper reports in this form will be required at least six-monthly and continuing funding will be conditional on these being satisfactory. The trust has previously stated: 'The trustees are not medical experts and require short clear statements in plain English setting out the particular subject to be researched, the objects and likely benefits, the cost and the timescale. Unless a charity will undertake to provide two concise progress reports each year, they should not apply as this is a vital requirement. It is essential that the trustees are able to follow the progress and effectiveness of the research they support.'

WHO TO APPLY TO R Ross, Chief Executive, 140 High Street, Edgware, Middlesex HA8 7LW *Tel* 020 8952 1414 *email* richard@rosetreestrust.co.uk *Website* www.rosetreestrust.co.uk

CC NO 298582 **ESTABLISHED** 1987

■ The Rothera Charitable Settlement

WHERE FUNDING CAN BE GIVEN UK.

WHO CAN BENEFIT Registered charities.

WHAT IS FUNDED Welfare, animals, overseas aid, medical.

RANGE OF GRANTS £250–£650.

SAMPLE GRANTS Parkinson's Disease Society (£650); NSPCC (£600); Children's Brain Tumor Research (£550); Christian Aid (£500); The Big Issue Foundation (£450); The Brace Appeal

Office (£400); Psychiatry Research Trust (£350); The Army Benevolent Fund (£300); The Cinnamon Trust and Wheel Power (£250 each).

FINANCES *Year* 2008 *Income* £40,226 *Grants* £39,550 *Assets* £11,414

TRUSTEES Mrs C A Rothera; Mrs S E Rothera.

HOW TO APPLY Charities are selected at the discretion of the trustees.

WHO TO APPLY TO Mrs C A Rothera, Trustee, The Dumbles, Lowdham Road, Epperstone, Nottingham NG14 6BB *Tel* 0115 966 3005 *email* crothera@aol.com

CC NO 283950 **ESTABLISHED** 1982

■ The Rothermere Foundation

WHERE FUNDING CAN BE GIVEN UK.

WHO CAN BENEFIT Registered charities and individual graduates of the Memorial University of Newfoundland.

WHAT IS FUNDED Establishment and maintenance of 'Rothermere Scholarships' to be awarded to graduates of the Memorial University of Newfoundland to enable them to undertake further periods of study in the UK; and general charitable causes.

TYPE OF GRANT Fellowship grants, scholarships, other educational grants.

SAMPLE GRANTS Sandroyd School (£90,000); Tick Tock Club (£75,000); Kings Rifles & East African Forces Association and Museum of Garden History (£10,000 each); Help for Heroes (£5,000); and Southbank Centre (£1,000).

FINANCES *Year* 2007–08 *Income* £764,966 *Grants* £476,388 *Assets* £16,668,703

TRUSTEES Rt Hon. Viscount Rothermere; Viscountess Rothermere; V P W Harmsworth; J G Hemingway; Hon. Esme Countess of Cromer.

OTHER INFORMATION Three fellowship grants were awarded totalling £128,000.

HOW TO APPLY In writing to the correspondent.

WHO TO APPLY TO V P W Harmsworth, Secretary, Beech Court, Canterbury Road, Challock, Ashford, Kent TN25 4DJ

CC NO 314125 **ESTABLISHED** 1964

■ The Rotherwick Foundation

WHERE FUNDING CAN BE GIVEN Within a 20-mile radius of either Ashdown Park Hotel, Wych Cross, East Sussex; Grand Hotel, Eastbourne, East Sussex; or Tylney Hall Hotel, Rotherwick, Hampshire.

WHO CAN BENEFIT Individuals and organisations benefiting students and Protestant Christians.

WHAT IS FUNDED The provision of scholarships, bursaries and maintenance allowances and educational grants tenable at any school, university or other educational establishment to people under 25 who, or whose parents or guardians, are resident in the specified localities or have for not less than five years attended a school or other educational establishment within those localities; the provision of financial assistance, equipment, books and clothing to such people on leaving school, university or other educational establishment for entry into a trade or profession; the provision of amenities and facilities including public recreation and sports grounds for public benefit; the advancement of religion and other charitable works of, and the maintenance of, Protestant churches; the provision, maintenance, improvement and equipment of hospitals, nursing homes, hospices and clinics; and such other charitable purposes as the trustees in their absolute discretion think fit to support or establish.

TYPE OF GRANT Funding is available for over to two years.

SAMPLE GRANTS Brighton & Sussex Medical School, Lord Wandsworth College and Plumpton College (£20,000 each); St Peter and St James Hospice – Lewes and University of Sussex (£16,000 each); Beacon Community College – Crowborough and Marie Curie Cancer Care (£15,000); Hospice in the Weald, and Eastbourne Multiple Sclerosis Society (£10,000 each).

FINANCES *Year* 2008–09 *Income* £275,022 *Grants* £142,563 *Assets* £5,435,566

TRUSTEES T E Mugleston; G C Bateman; A H W Dixon; Miss R T Mooney.

HOW TO APPLY In writing to the correspondent.

WHO TO APPLY TO G C Bateman, Trustee and General Manager, Ashdown Park, Wych Cross, Forest Row, East Sussex RH18 5JR *Tel* 01342 820 227 *Fax* 01342 820222 *email* rotherwickfoundation@ashdownpark.com *Website* www.rotherwickfoundation.org

CC NO 1058900   **ESTABLISHED** 1996

....

■ The Rothley Trust

WHERE FUNDING CAN BE GIVEN Northumberland, North and South Tyneside, Newcastle upon Tyne, Gateshead and the former counties of Cleveland and Durham (including Darlington) and Cleveland.

WHO CAN BENEFIT Registered charities only.

WHAT IS FUNDED Children, community, education, disability, medical, developing world and young people. Apart from a few charities with which the trust has been associated for many years, its activities are now directed exclusively towards north east England (Northumberland to Cleveland inclusive). Developing world appeals, arising from this area only, will be considered.

WHAT IS NOT FUNDED No grants for further education, the repair of buildings used solely for worship, the advancement of religion, advancement in the arts, heritage or science, advancement of amateur sport (unless it has the means of alleviating the problems within the trust's approved categories above), advancement of human rights, conflict resolution or reconciliation (except family mediation), advancement of environmental protection or improvement, advancement of animal welfare and organisations focused on older people.

TYPE OF GRANT Mainly one-off donations towards specific projects and not running costs. Start-up costs, buildings, equipment, resources and capital grants will be considered.

RANGE OF GRANTS Typical grant £300.

SAMPLE GRANTS The MEA Trust (£10,000); Citizens' Advice Bureau – Newcastle and Greggs Hardship Fund (£1,800 each). Grants of less than £1,500 each to organisations totalled £99,000.

FINANCES *Year* 2008–09 *Income* £4,159,738 *Grants* £122,608 *Assets* £5,030,529

TRUSTEES Dr H A Armstrong, Chair; Mrs R V Barkes; Mrs J Brown; C Bucknall; Mrs A Galbraith; M Bridgeman; G Salvin; H Hargreave; D Holborn.

OTHER INFORMATION Grants to individuals totalled £10,000.

HOW TO APPLY Write to the correspondent including a copy of latest accounts/annual reports. An SAE is appreciated.

WHO TO APPLY TO Diane Lennon, Secretary, Mea House, Ellison Place, Newcastle upon Tyne NE1 8XS *Tel* 0191 232 7783 *Fax* 0191 232 7783

CC NO 219849   **ESTABLISHED** 1959

....

■ The Rothschild Foundation

WHERE FUNDING CAN BE GIVEN Unrestricted, with a special interest in Buckinghamshire.

WHO CAN BENEFIT Registered charities.

WHAT IS FUNDED General charitable purposes. The current policy set by the trustees is to support charitable projects originated by the Rothschild family, in particular, and to make grants to other organisations at their discretion.

TYPE OF GRANT Generally one-off, some recurrent.

RANGE OF GRANTS Up to £760,000, but mostly under £10,000.

SAMPLE GRANTS Eton College (£760,000); the Butrint Foundation and Stoke Mandeville Hospital (£100,000 each); the Royal Society and the British Association for Adopting and Fostering (£25,000 each); Watts Gallery (£20,000); Louisa Cottages Charity (£10,000); Refuge (£6,000); Lifeline Humanitarian (£2,000); and Irish Georgian Trust and Soil Association (£1,000 each).

FINANCES *Year* 2007–08 *Income* £198,193 *Grants* £1,307,702 *Assets* £48,397,839

TRUSTEES Sir Edward Cazalet; Lord Rothschild; Lady Rothschild; Hannah Rothschild; Peter Troughton.

HOW TO APPLY In writing to the correspondent. Applications are considered at half-yearly meetings.

WHO TO APPLY TO Fiona Sinclair, The Dairy, Queen Street, Waddesdon, Aylesbury, Buckinghamshire HP18 0JW *Tel* 01296 653235 *Fax* 01296 651142 *email* f_sinclair@ritcap.co.uk

CC NO 230159   **ESTABLISHED** 1956

....

■ The Roughley Charitable Trust

WHERE FUNDING CAN BE GIVEN Birmingham area (excluding Wolverhampton, Coventry, Worcester and the Black Country towns).

WHO CAN BENEFIT Registered charities; some UK and international projects supported but only where the trustees have a special interest.

WHAT IS FUNDED General charitable purposes. Funds are mostly committed to projects known to the trustees.

WHAT IS NOT FUNDED No support for animal charities, for individuals, for unsolicited projects outside of the Birmingham area or for Birmingham branches of national charities.

RANGE OF GRANTS Mostly £500 to £1,000. Larger grants to projects where trustees have special knowledge.

SAMPLE GRANTS Birmingham Settlement (£35,000), MAC Building Project (£30,000), Birmingham Law Centre and RAPt (£20,000 each); Christian Aid and Emmaus (£10,000 each); Appropriate Technology Asia (£6,000); Medical Foundation for the Care of Victims of Torture (£5,000); Birmingham Centre for Art Therapies and Practical Action (£3,000 each); Birmingham Printmakers, Ernest Mason Foundation, Prison Reform Trust and West Midlands Quaker Peace Education Project (£2,000 each); Birmingham Clubs for Young People, Birmingham Royal Ballet and Thames Rivers Restoration Trust (£1,000 each); and Time Out Saturday Club and Yemeni Elderly in Small Heath and the Black Country (£500 each).

FINANCES *Year* 2007–08 *Income* £211,069
Grants £191,000 *Assets* £4,023,937
TRUSTEES Mrs D M Newton; J R L Smith;
M C G Smith; V A Thomas.
HOW TO APPLY The trust has an annual meeting in
September to consider written applications with
report and accounts from Birmingham charities
only for grants of up to £1,000. Larger grants
are only made to Birmingham area projects in
which trustees have a special interest.
WHO TO APPLY TO J R L Smith, Trustee, 90 Somerset
Road, Edgbaston, Birmingham B15 2PP
Tel 0121 454 4508 *email* correspondent@
roughleytrust.org.uk *Website* www.roughleytrust.
org.uk
CC NO 264037   **ESTABLISHED** 1972

....

■ Mrs Gladys Row Fogo Charitable Trust

WHERE FUNDING CAN BE GIVEN Edinburgh, Lothians
and Dunblane.
WHO CAN BENEFIT Research workers and people with
neurological diseases, but other medical
research and charitable purposes are
considered.
WHAT IS FUNDED Medical research, particularly in the
field of neuroscience; also to local charity
projects and to small charities mostly in Central
Scotland.
WHAT IS NOT FUNDED No grants to individuals.
SAMPLE GRANTS Previous beneficiaries: SHEFC Brain
Imaging Research Centre (£187,000);
Macmillan Cancer Relief (£8,000); RNLI
(£6,000); Alzheimer Scotland Action on
Dementia, Age Concern and Salvation Army
(£5,000 each); Multiple Sclerosis Society,
Muscular Dystrophy Campaign and The
Wishbone Trust (£4,500 each); Drum Riding for
the Disabled, Invalids at Home and Stobhill
Kidney Patient's Association (£4,000 each); The
Sandpiper Trust (£3,500); and Erskine Hospital
and Tak Tent (£3,000 each).
FINANCES *Year* 2008–09 *Income* £168,151
Grants £150,000
TRUSTEES E J Cuthbertson; A W Waddell; Dr
C Brough.
HOW TO APPLY In writing to the trustees.
WHO TO APPLY TO The Trustees, Brodies LLP
Solicitors, 15 Atholl Crescent, Edinburgh
EH3 8HA *Tel* 0131 228 3777 *Fax* 0131 228
3878
SC NO SC009685   **ESTABLISHED** 1970

....

■ The Rowan Charitable Trust

WHERE FUNDING CAN BE GIVEN UK, especially
Merseyside, and overseas.
WHO CAN BENEFIT Registered charities benefiting
children and young adults, medical
professionals, students, teachers, and
unemployed people. Also carers, and people
who are disabled, homeless, living in rural areas
or blind.
WHAT IS FUNDED Overseas: agriculture (especially
crop and livestock production and settlement
schemes); community development (especially
appropriate technology and village industries);
health (especially preventative medicine, water
supplies, blindness); education (especially adult
education and materials); environment
(especially protecting and sustaining ecological
systems at risk); human rights (especially of
women, children and people with disabilities);
and fair trade (especially relating to primary

producers and workers). UK: housing and
homelessness; social and community care;
education; employment/unemployment; aftercare; welfare rights; community development;
and environmental improvement.
WHAT IS NOT FUNDED The trust does not give grants
for individuals, buildings, building work or office
equipment (including IT hardware), academic
research and medical research or equipment,
expeditions, bursaries or scholarships, vehicle
purchases, or animal welfare charities.
TYPE OF GRANT One-off, recurring.
RANGE OF GRANTS £1,000–£50,000.
SAMPLE GRANTS UK grants: 9 Lives Furniture, Duke
of Edinburgh Award (for Merseyside, one year)
and Whizz-Kidz (£10,000 each); Housing Justice
(£8,000); Combat Stress (£7,000); Wirral
Autistic Society (£5,000); Where Next
Association (£2,000); and Bibic (£1,000).
Overseas grants: Christian Aid and Practical
Action (£50,000 each); CMS – Samaritans,
Rurcon and Wateraid (£20,000 each); Find Your
Feet (£15,000); Sense International (£10,000);
Quakers (£5,000); the Rainforest Foundation
(£3,000); and Children of the Andes (£1,000).
FINANCES *Year* 2007–08 *Income* £1,317,418
Grants £636,688 *Assets* £5,108,315
TRUSTEES C R Jones; Revd J R Pilkington; Mrs
M C Pilkington.
PUBLICATIONS Guidelines for applicants.
OTHER INFORMATION The trust generally allocates two
thirds of its grant funds to overseas projects
and one third to United Kingdom based projects.
In 2007 £199,000 was given to UK
organisations and £437,000 to overseas
organisations.
HOW TO APPLY In writing to the correspondent. No
application forms are issued but applicant
guidelines are available on request. Applications
should include a brief description (two sides of
A4 paper) of, and a budget for, the work for
which the grant is sought and the organisation's
annual report and accounts (this is essential).
The applications need to provide the trustees
with information about: the aims and objectives
of the organisation; its structure and
organisational capacity; what the funds are
being requested for and how much is being
requested; and how progress of the work will be
monitored and evaluated. Trustees meet twice a
year. The closing dates for applications are
usually in June and December. The trust has
previously stated that: 'unfortunately the volume
of applications received precludes
acknowledgement on receipt or notifying
unsuccessful applicants. The trust emphasises
that it is unable to make donations to
applicants who are not, or do not have links
with, a UK-registered charity.'
WHO TO APPLY TO Mr Jonathan C M Tippett, Mr
Jonathan C M Tippett, c/o Morley Tippett, White
Park Barn, Loseley Park, Guildford GU3 1HS
Tel 01483 575193
CC NO 242678   **ESTABLISHED** 1964

....

■ Rowanville Ltd

WHERE FUNDING CAN BE GIVEN UK and Israel.
WHO CAN BENEFIT Jewish organisations.
WHAT IS FUNDED Established organisations for the
advancement of religion in accordance with the
orthodox Jewish faith.
RANGE OF GRANTS About £200–£50,000.
SAMPLE GRANTS Chevras Mo'oz Ladol (£44,000);
Yesodey HaTorah Schools (£40,000);
Gateshead Talmudical College (£28,000);
Tchabe Kolel (£25,000); Atereth Yehoshua

Charity (£20,000); Beis Yaacov Institutions (£15,000); Jewish Teachers Training College (£11,000); Yad Eliezer Trust (£6,000); Kisharon (£3,200); Noam Primary School (£1,800); and Keren HaTorah (£500).

FINANCES *Year* 2007–08 *Income* £1,172,946 *Grants* £679,917 *Assets* £3,992,631

TRUSTEES Joseph Pearlman; Ruth Pearlman; Michael Neuberger; M D Frankel.

HOW TO APPLY The trust has previously stated that applications are unlikely to be successful unless one of the trustees has prior personal knowledge of the cause, as this charity's funds are already very heavily committed.

WHO TO APPLY TO Ruth Pearlman, Secretary, 8 Highfield Gardens, London NW11 9HB *Tel* 020 8458 9266

CC NO 267278   **ESTABLISHED** 1973

······································

■ The Christopher Rowbotham Charitable Trust

WHERE FUNDING CAN BE GIVEN Bolton, Cheshire, Gateshead, Lancashire, Newcastle upon Tyne, North Tyneside and Northumberland.

WHO CAN BENEFIT Registered charities.

WHAT IS FUNDED 'The trustees prefer to give regular grants and are especially interested in: (i) People with physical or mental handicaps – improving their quality of life through equipment, activities and holidays. (ii) The young – with particular emphasis on improving prospects of employment by education and meaningful activities. (iii) Health – improving the quality of life of the ill, their carers and the old either at home or in hospital.' There is a preference for small local groups with low overheads.

WHAT IS NOT FUNDED Grants are only given to registered charities. No grants to individuals or overseas charities and no grants for capital building costs. The trust prefers to give regular grants but does not fund salaries.

RANGE OF GRANTS Up to £3,500.

SAMPLE GRANTS Shiplake College (£3,500); Vitalise (£2,000); and Calvert Trust – Keilder, Calvert Trust – Keswick, Coombe Trust Fund and Lionheart (£1,000 each).

FINANCES *Year* 2007–08 *Income* £39,329 *Grants* £26,000 *Assets* £967,409

TRUSTEES Mrs C A Jackson, Chair; Mrs E J Wilkinson; R M Jackson.

HOW TO APPLY In writing to the correspondent. There are no application forms, guidelines or deadlines. Telephone calls are not welcome. No sae is required; applications are not acknowledged. Trustees meet annually in the autumn. Applications can be sent at any time.

WHO TO APPLY TO Mrs C A Jackson, Chair, 18 Northumberland Square, North Shields, Tyne and Wear NE30 1PX

CC NO 261991   **ESTABLISHED** 1970

······································

■ The Rowing Foundation

WHERE FUNDING CAN BE GIVEN UK.

WHO CAN BENEFIT Organisations and clubs whose requirements may be too small or who may be otherwise ineligible for an approach to the National Lottery or other similar sources of funds.

WHAT IS FUNDED The aid and support of young people (those under 18 or 23 if still in full-time education) and people who are disabled of all ages, through their participation in water sports, particularly rowing. Grants have also been made

towards the purchase of buoyancy aids, splash suits, canoes and the promotion of taster rowing courses for youth clubs, sailing and other water sports clubs.

WHAT IS NOT FUNDED The foundation does not give grants to individuals, only to clubs and organisations, and for a specific purpose, not as a contribution to general funds.

TYPE OF GRANT Pump-priming.

RANGE OF GRANTS £500–£2,000.

SAMPLE GRANTS Headway (£4,800); London Youth (£3,000); Cranmore School RC (£2,000); University of Derby and Oarsport-Sculls (£1,200 each); and Back Up Trust (£900).

FINANCES *Year* 2007 *Income* £36,160 *Grants* £25,845 *Assets* £295,064

TRUSTEES Iain Reid, chair; John Buchan; Simon Goodey; Philip J Phillips; Roger S Smith; John Chick.

HOW TO APPLY Applications should be made on a form, available to download from the Amateur Rowing Association website.

WHO TO APPLY TO Pauline Churcher, Secretary, The Priory, 6 Lower Mall, Hammersmith, London W6 9DJ *Tel* 020 8878 3723 *Fax* 020 8878 6298 *email* p.churcher@sky.com *Website* www.ara-rowing.org/rowing-foundation

CC NO 281688   **ESTABLISHED** 1981

······································

■ The Rowland Family Foundation

WHERE FUNDING CAN BE GIVEN UK and overseas.

WHO CAN BENEFIT Charitable organisations.

WHAT IS FUNDED Principal objectives include the relief of poverty, the advancement of education and religion and other purposes beneficial for the community.

RANGE OF GRANTS From £2,000.

SAMPLE GRANTS Hope and Homes for Children (£212,000); Balikpapan Orangutan Survival Foundation and Child Welfare Scheme (£25,000 each); and Light from Africa (£2,000).

FINANCES *Year* 2007–08 *Income* £154,433 *Grants* £263,971 *Assets* £5,433,371

TRUSTEES Mrs A M Rowland; N G Rowland.

HOW TO APPLY In writing to the correspondent.

WHO TO APPLY TO Lucy Gibson, Harcus Sinclair, 3 Lincoln's Inn Fields, London WC2A 3AA *Tel* 020 7242 9700 *email* lucy.gibson@harcus-sinclair.co.uk

CC NO 1111177   **ESTABLISHED** 2005

······································

■ The Rowlands Trust

WHERE FUNDING CAN BE GIVEN West and South Midlands, including Hereford and Worcester, Gloucester, South Shropshire and Birmingham.

WHO CAN BENEFIT Organisations benefiting people of all ages, research workers, disabled people and those disadvantaged by poverty.

WHAT IS FUNDED Medical and scientific research; the welfare of elderly, infirm, poor and disabled people; support for music and the arts; the environment; the encouragement of education and training for individuals to better themselves.

WHAT IS NOT FUNDED No support for individuals or to animal charities. No support is given for revenue funding.

TYPE OF GRANT One-off, capital including buildings, project and research.

RANGE OF GRANTS £500–£25,000.

SAMPLE GRANTS Worcestershire Wildlife Trust (25,000); Hereford and Worcester Gardens Trust (£20,000); Worcester Acute Hospitals NHS Trust – Islet Research Laboratory (£15,000); City Technology College (£14,000);

Royal Star and Garter Homes (£10,000); Myton Hospices (£5,000); Cerebal Palsy, West Midlands (£3,000); Plantlife International (£1,000); and Langley Band (£750).

FINANCES *Year* 2007 *Income* £230,236 *Grants* £362,528 *Assets* £6,677,172

TRUSTEES A C S Hordern, Chair; Mrs F J Burman; Mrs A M I Harris; G B G Hingley; K G Mason.

HOW TO APPLY Applications forms are available from the correspondent and are the preferred means by which to apply. Completed forms should be returned with a copy of the most recent accounts. The trustees meet to consider grants four times a year.

WHO TO APPLY TO Ms N Fenn, Clerk to the Trustees, c/o Mills and Reeve, 78–84 Colmore Row, Birmingham B3 2AB *Tel* 0121 456 8341 *Fax* 0121 200 3028 *email* nicola.fenn@ mills-reeve.com

CC NO 1062148 **ESTABLISHED** 1997

······································

■ The Joseph Rowntree Charitable Trust

WHERE FUNDING CAN BE GIVEN Unrestricted, in practice mainly UK, Republic of Ireland and Europe.

WHO CAN BENEFIT Registered charities, voluntary organisations and charitable groups.

WHAT IS FUNDED The trust generally funds work under one of the following five programmes: peace, racial justice, power and responsibility, Quaker issues and Ireland and Northern Ireland (promoting a peaceful society).

WHAT IS NOT FUNDED Generally, the trust does not make grants for: 'the personal support of individuals in need; educational bursaries; travel or adventure projects; medical research; building, buying or repairing buildings; business development or job creation; general appeals; providing care for elderly people, children, people with learning difficulties, people with physical disabilities, or people using mental health services; work which has already been done; work in larger, older national charities which have an established constituency of supporters; work in mainstream education; academic research, except as an integral part of policy and campaigning work that is central to our areas of interest; work on housing and homelessness; the arts, except where a project is specifically concerned with issues of interest to the trust; work which we believe should be funded from statutory sources, or which has been in the recent past; work which tries to make a problem easier to live with, rather than getting to the root of it; local work in Britain (except racial justice work in West Yorkshire); work outside the UK, Ireland and South Africa (except for groups working elsewhere within Europe at a European level). Further specific exclusions are included for individual programmes and information on these can be found on the trust's website. Within its areas of interest, the trust makes grants to a range of organisations and to individuals. It is not necessary to be a registered charity to apply to the trust.' However, it can only support work which is legally charitable.

TYPE OF GRANT Single and multi-year funding for core and project costs.

RANGE OF GRANTS A few hundred pounds to over £100,000.

SAMPLE GRANTS Responding to Conflict – for core costs (£140,000); Public Interest Research Centre Ltd – core costs for programme on climate change (£139,000); Immigration Law Practitioners' Association – for a simplification project (£99,000); Civil Liberties Trust – 'Common Values' campaign (£75,000); Equality and Rights Alliance – core costs for a campaign to build an effective and resilient equality and human rights infrastructure in Ireland (€60,000); Westmeath Employment Pact – dialogue programme to explore underlying causes of intra- and inter-community conflicts affecting the Traveller community (€50,000); British American Security Information Council – for the facilitation of the All-Party Parliamentary Group on Global Security and Non-Proliferation (£47,000); East Leeds Health for All – a part-time co-ordinator to establish the peer support group and community advocates (£40,000); Christian Peacemaker Teams – for UK Christian Peacemakers Corps training (£9,500); Edge Hill University – symposium to compare Irish and Muslim experiences of counter-insurgency law and policies (£6,200); and Institute of Race Relations – work on preventing violent extremism policies and practice (£2,800).

FINANCES *Year* 2008 *Income* £5,745,000 *Grants* £5,921,000 *Assets* £116,997,000

TRUSTEES David Shutt; Beverley Meeson; Christine Davis; Emily Miles; Margaret Bryan; Marion McNaughton; Peter Coltman; Susan Seymour; Helen Carmichael; Imran Tyabi; Paul Henderson.

OTHER INFORMATION The Joseph Rowntree Charitable Trust is a Quaker trust and the value base of the trustees, as of the founder Joseph Rowntree (1836–1925), reflects the religious convictions of the Society of Friends.

HOW TO APPLY The trust expects all applicants to have made themselves familiar with the relevant funding programmes, summarised here but set out in full on the website and available in leaflet form. They then require an application letter (including budget, accounts and equal opportunities policy) and a completed registration form. The details expected in the letter are set out in detail on the website and in the leaflet. Applications can be submitted either online or by post. Organisations submitting an application by post can download a registration form from the website to complete. For those submitting their applications online, the registration details are included in the initial steps. There is a deadline for receipt of applications of around ten weeks before the meeting of trustees. It is very helpful if applications arrive well before the deadline. The period immediately after the deadline is the trust's busiest time, so it cannot normally consider applications that arrive late until the following funding round. The trust has three grant-making rounds each year. Contact the trust or go to the website for the latest information on deadlines.

WHO TO APPLY TO Stephen Pittam, Trust Secretary, The Garden House, Water End, York YO30 6WQ *Tel* 01904 627810 *Fax* 01904 651990 *email* jrct@jrct.org.uk *Website* www.jrct.org.uk

CC NO 210037 **ESTABLISHED** 1904

······································

■ The Joseph Rowntree Foundation

WHERE FUNDING CAN BE GIVEN UK, with some preference for York and Bradford.

WHO CAN BENEFIT Organisations carrying out social science research.

WHAT IS FUNDED This is not a conventional grant-making foundation. It supports research, of a rigorous kind, usually carried out in universities or research institutes, but also has a wide range of other activities not necessarily involving grants of any kind. The foundation initiates, manages and pays for an extensive social research programme. It does not normally respond to unsolicited applications and many of its programmes issue formal and detailed requests for proposals. However modest proposals for minor gap-filling pieces of work in the foundation's fields of interest may sometimes be handled less formally and more rapidly. For 2009–2011 the foundation's strategic objectives are research into 'Poverty', 'Place' and 'Empowerment'.

WHAT IS NOT FUNDED With the exception of funds for particular projects in York and the surrounding area, the foundation does not generally support: projects outside the topics within its current priorities; development projects which are not innovative; development projects from which no general lessons can be drawn; general appeals, for example from national charities; conferences and other events, websites or publications, unless they are linked with work which the foundation is already supporting; grants to replace withdrawn or expired statutory funding, or to make up deficits already incurred; educational bursaries or sponsorship for individuals for research or further education and training courses; grants or sponsorship for individuals in need.

TYPE OF GRANT Project and research. Funding can be given for up to two years.

FINANCES *Year* 2008 *Income* £9,680,000 *Grants* £3,519,000 *Assets* £201,711,000

TRUSTEES Don Brand; Debby Ounsted; Dame Dr Ann Bowtell; Susan Hartshorne; Ashok Jashapara; Bharat Mehta; Nigel Naish; Tony Stoller; Dame Mavis McDonald; Steven Burkeman.

PUBLICATIONS Findings – short briefing papers summarising the main findings of projects in the Research and Development Programme; Special Reports designed to present research results with clarity and impact.

HOW TO APPLY The foundation does not respond to unsolicited applications. Instead, it issues 'calls for proposals' and invites submissions to them. Detailed information, including guidance and a proposal registration form, is available from the foundation's website. The foundation also operates a grant funding stream called 'New Insights and Innovations' to consider proposals which reflect's its core strategic priorities but may not fall within specific programmes.

WHO TO APPLY TO Julia Unwin, Chief Executive, The Homestead, 40 Water End, York YO30 6WP *Tel* 01904 629241 *Fax* 01904 620072 *email* info@jrf.org.uk *Website* www.jrf.org.uk **CC NO** 210169   **ESTABLISHED** 1904

....

■ Joseph Rowntree Reform Trust Limited

WHERE FUNDING CAN BE GIVEN Mainly UK.

WHO CAN BENEFIT Campaigning organisations and individuals who have reform as their objective and are ineligible for charitable support.

WHAT IS FUNDED The promotion of political and democratic reform and the defence of civil liberties. The trust's main aims are to: correct imbalances of power; strengthen the hand of individuals, groups and organisations who are striving for reform; foster democratic reform, civil liberties and social justice.

WHAT IS NOT FUNDED The trust is not a registered charity and provides grants for non-charitable political and campaigning activities. Examples of work for which the trust does not make grants are: the personal support of individuals in need; educational bursaries; travel and adventure projects; building, buying or repairing properties; business development or job creation; general appeals; academic research; work which the trust believes should be funded from statutory sources, or which has been in the recent past; administrative or other core costs of party organisations.

SAMPLE GRANTS Compass – to assist the campaign (£45,000); Privacy International – towards their work on privacy issues in the lead up to the General Election (£40,000); NO2ID – Stopping the Database State – towards their 'grassroots' local groups campaign (£26,000); Index on Censorship – towards their campaign against the rise of self-censorship in Britain's arts (£12,000); Camp for Climate Action Legal Team – additional funding to assist the team to effectively protect the civil liberties of those who exercise their right to protest, responding to the media interest following the G20 protests (£5,000); and Lord Tyler – towards the preparation of a Private Member's Bill on Constitutional Renewal (£3,000).

FINANCES *Year* 2009 *Grants* £1,000,000 *Assets* £30,000,000

TRUSTEES Danny Alexander; Christine Day; Dr Christopher Greenfield; Lord (David) Shutt; Paedar Cremin; Mandy Cormack; Andrew Neal.

OTHER INFORMATION The trust is not a charity and therefore pays tax on its income. Very little financial information was available; the trust budgets £1 million each year for grants.

HOW TO APPLY Applicants should email a one page outline to the correspondent before making a formal application. If accepted, a full application can then be made. The trust does not have a standard form, but any application should include: an Application Registration Form (available to download from the website); up to four pages setting out the proposal; a full budget for the project; the most recent audited accounts; a CV, if applying as an individual. Trust staff make an initial assessment of applications and are authorised to reject those that are clearly inappropriate. All staff rejections are reported to the directors at their next meeting, when they consider all remaining applications. The meetings take place at quarterly intervals in March, July, October and December and the deadline for applications is approximately four or five weeks prior to the trust meeting. Applications for small grants of up to £5,000 can, however, be considered at any time and applicants should hear of the decision within two weeks.

WHO TO APPLY TO Tina Walker, Trust Secretary, The Garden House, Water End, York YO30 6WQ *Tel* 01904 625744 *Fax* 01904 651502 *email* info@jrrt.org.uk *Website* www.jrrt.org.uk   **ESTABLISHED** 1904

....

■ Royal Artillery Charitable Fund

WHERE FUNDING CAN BE GIVEN UK and overseas.

WHO CAN BENEFIT Service charities.

WHAT IS FUNDED Welfare of service and ex-service personnel.

RANGE OF GRANTS £1,000–£55,000.

SAMPLE GRANTS Royal Artillery Institution (£55,000); Army Benevolent Fund (£50,000); Regiment and Batteries (£22,000); Gunner Magazine

(£20,000); RAA Grants (£7,000); Ex Service Fellow Centre (£3,500); Not Forgotten Association (£3,000); King Edward VII Hospital (£2,800); and Independent Age (£1,000).

FINANCES *Year* 2007 *Income* £1,442,381 *Grants* £904,159 *Assets* £13,812,093

TRUSTEES Brig. A Gordon; Col. G Gilchrist; Col. A Jolley; Col. C Fletcher-Wood; Lieut. Col. M J Darmody; Maj. ATG Richards; Maj. AJ Dines; Brig. RPM Weighill; Brig. ND Ashmore; Col. PRL Lane; Col. CJ Nicholls; Lieut. Col. IA Vere Nicoll.

OTHER INFORMATION Included in the grants total were grants to individuals amounting to £740,759.

HOW TO APPLY In writing to the correspondent.

WHO TO APPLY TO The Welfare Secretary, Artillery House, Artillery Centre, Larkhill, Wiltshire SP4 8QT *Tel* 01980 845698 *email* AC-RHQRA-RACF-WelfareClk2@mod.uk *Website* www.forums.theraa.co.uk

CC NO 210202

■ Royal British Legion

WHERE FUNDING CAN BE GIVEN UK, excluding Scotland.

WHO CAN BENEFIT People who have served in the Armed Forces, their widow(er) s and dependants, and those organisations which help them. Beneficiaries include those who have served in a hostile area with bodies such as the Mercantile Marines, the Allied Civil Police forces, the Home Guard, the Voluntary Aid Society and the Polish Resettlement Corps.

WHAT IS FUNDED The welfare of men and women who have served in the armed forces.

WHAT IS NOT FUNDED Memorials, commercial ventures, or any potential commercial ventures, for example clubs. Grants are not normally given for core costs, for example, administration or running costs of an organisation that is supporting ex-Service personnel. However, there may be exceptions to this, and the Royal British Legion aims to respond flexibly to applications, and is prepared to negotiate if there are special circumstances, for example, if the withholding of grant would harm the interests of ex-Service personnel.

TYPE OF GRANT One-off and recurring costs.

RANGE OF GRANTS £10–£1,000,000.

SAMPLE GRANTS Officers' Association (£1.6 million); Sir Oswald Stoll Foundation (£357,000); Royal British Legion Industries Ltd (£275,000); Skill Force (£186,000); E Hayes Dashwood Foundation (£120,000); Alcohol Recovery Project (£62,000); Sailors Family Centre (£50,000); Earl Haig Fund Scotland (£43,000); and Prisoners Education Trust (£25,000). Smaller grants of £25,000 or less totalled £107,000.

FINANCES *Year* 2007–08 *Income* £104,081,000 *Grants* £3,436,000 *Assets* £199,218,000

TRUSTEES Col R R St J Barkshire; C W Carson; R E Clark; P D Cleminson; E Dixon; Brig J R Drew; J Farmer; E W Hefferman; Dr D M Henderson; G Lewis; W J H Lodge; M T McCaw; W Parkin; K F Pritchard; Ms J Rowe; D A Walker; T W Whittles; Rev M D A Williams; A Burn; J Crisford; K Draper.

PUBLICATIONS *The Legion* magazine.

OTHER INFORMATION A further £25,724,000 was given to individuals. For further information, see *A Guide to Grants for Individuals in Need* also published by the Directory of Social Change.

HOW TO APPLY In the first instance you should contact Scarlet Harris, External Grants Officer (Tel. 020 3207 2138 or Email: externalgrants@britishlegion.org.uk) in order to explore whether you may be eligible for a grant, and at what level, so that you can be advised further on the detailed requirements. Following this, you will be sent an application form which will explain on it the information you need to send in depending on the size of grant you are asking for. Successful applicants, depending on the level of grant applied for, can expect to receive an award in between two and six months of sending in a correctly completed application form.

WHO TO APPLY TO Scarlet Harris, External Grants Officer, Haig House, 199 Borough High Street, London SE1 1AA *Tel* 08457 725 725 *Fax* 020 3207 2218 *email* info@britishlegion.org.uk *Website* www.britishlegion.org.uk

CC NO 219279 **ESTABLISHED** 1921

■ Royal Docks Trust (London)

WHERE FUNDING CAN BE GIVEN Part of the London Borough of Newham.

WHO CAN BENEFIT The trust supports the community in that part of the London borough of Newham that lies to the south of the London – Tilbury Trunk Road (A13) known as Newham Way.

WHAT IS FUNDED General charitable purposes. Areas of specific interest are: educational and vocational training; recreational and leisure-time pursuits; advancement of public education in the arts; general improvement of the physical and social environment; relief of poverty and sickness; housing for people with disabilities or are otherwise in need; and preservation of buildings of historical or architectural significance.

WHAT IS NOT FUNDED No grants to individuals. It does not give revenue, top-up or retrospective funding.

SAMPLE GRANTS Ascension Eagles Cheerleaders and St Johns Community Centre (£30,000 each); Community Links – Britannia Village (£20,000); Ascension Community Trust and Groundwork East London – Future Footprints (£16,500 each); Community Links – ASTA Centre (£15,000); West Silvertown Village Community Foundation (£13,000); Newham Music Trust – Learning Through Music and Seeds 4 Life (£12,000 each); and Iroko Theatre Company (£10,000).

FINANCES *Year* 2009–10 *Grants* £190,000

TRUSTEES Eric Sorenson, Chair; Steve Nicholas; Sid Keys; Richard Gooding; Cllr Patrick Murphy; Cllr Paul Schafer; Michael Grier; Alan Taylor.

OTHER INFORMATION Minor Community Grants amounted to £15,000.

HOW TO APPLY The trust operates an annual joint grants programme with the London Borough of Newham and applications are invited in the autumn for grants from the following year's programme. For an application form or for more information please contact Stephen Collins at: Community Support Unit, Culture and Community Department, London Borough of Newham, 292 Barking Road, East Ham, London, E6 3BA; Tel: 020 8430 2433; e-mail: Stephen.Collins@newham.gov.uk. Further information and application forms for minor grants can also be obtained from the trust's website.

WHO TO APPLY TO Stephen Collins, Administrator, Community Support Unit, London Borough of Newham, Building 1000, Dockside Road, London E16 2QU *Tel* 020 8430 2433 *email* stephen.collins@newham.gov.uk *Website* www.royaldockstrust.org.uk

CC NO 1045057 **ESTABLISHED** 1995

Think carefully about every application. Is it justified?

823

■ Royal Masonic Trust for Girls and Boys

WHERE FUNDING CAN BE GIVEN UK.

WHO CAN BENEFIT Charities and individual children of Freemasons.

WHAT IS FUNDED This trust predominantly makes grants to individual children of Freemasons who are in need. However grants are also made to UK organisations working with children and young people; it also supports bursaries at cathedrals and collegiate chapels.

SAMPLE GRANTS Non-Masonic grants went to Choral Bursaries (£204,000) and Ripon Cathedral Development (£14,000). The trust stated in its annual accounts that it 'continued to limit its non-Masonic activities to its existing Choral Bursary project, as there were insufficient funds available to make donations to other charities'.

FINANCES *Year* 2007 *Income* £6,638,000 *Grants* £218,000 *Assets* £126,715,000

TRUSTEES Rt Hon. Earl Cadogan; P A Marsh; O N N Hart; C F Harris.

OTHER INFORMATION The grant total shown in this entry only refers to the funds distributed to non-Masonic charities. A further £5.4 million went to other beneficiaries.

HOW TO APPLY In writing to the correspondent. Please note: the trust states on its website that, 'at present, the trust's resources are sufficient only to support its primary beneficiaries and its existing projects. It is not able to consider applications for new non-Masonic grants at this time'. Any change to this policy will also be noted on the trust's website.

WHO TO APPLY TO W Bro Les Hutchinson, Chief Executive, Freemasons' Hall, 60 Great Queen Street, London WC2B 5AZ *Tel* 020 7405 2644 *Fax* 020 7831 4094 *email* info@rmtgb.org *Website* www.rmtgb.org

CC NO 285836   **ESTABLISHED** 1982

■ The Royal Scots Benevolent Society

WHERE FUNDING CAN BE GIVEN UK.

WHO CAN BENEFIT Soldiers and former soldiers, and their dependants, of the Royal Scots (The Royal Regiment) who are in need.

WHAT IS FUNDED Service welfare causes.

FINANCES *Year* 2009 *Grants* £50,000

TRUSTEES D J C Meehan, Chair; C B S Richardson; G S Richardson; Henderson Loggie.

HOW TO APPLY Applications should be made via SSAFA Forces Help or British Legion.

WHO TO APPLY TO Trust Administrator, Henderson Loggie, 34 Melville Street, Edinburgh EH3 7HA

SC NO SC011397   **ESTABLISHED** 1960

■ The RRAF Charitable Trust

WHERE FUNDING CAN BE GIVEN UK and the developing world.

WHO CAN BENEFIT Charitable organisations.

WHAT IS FUNDED General, medical research, children who are disadvantaged, religious organisations, aid for the developing world and support for older people.

RANGE OF GRANTS £500–£50,000.

SAMPLE GRANTS The Extra Care Charitable Trust and Southwell Cathedral Chapter (£50,000 each); Ethiopiaid, Mums for Mums – c/o FECIN and Trinity Church (£25,000 each); Methodist Homes for the Aged (£2,000); and Sightsavers International (£500).

FINANCES *Year* 2007–08 *Income* £25,275 *Grants* £177,500 *Assets* £700,077

TRUSTEES Rathbone Trust Company Limited; Claire Tufnell; Emilie Astley-Arlington; Joanne Mcarthy; Rosemary Mcarthy; Elizabeth Astley-Arlington.

HOW TO APPLY In writing to the correspondent. Only successful applicants are notified of the trustees' decision.

WHO TO APPLY TO The Administrator, Rathbone Trust Company Limited, 159 New Bond Street, London W1S 2UD *Tel* 020 7399 0807

CC NO 1103662   **ESTABLISHED** 2004

■ The Alfred and Frances Rubens Charitable Trust

WHERE FUNDING CAN BE GIVEN UK.

WHO CAN BENEFIT Registered charities only.

WHAT IS FUNDED General charitable purposes and Jewish causes.

TYPE OF GRANT Recurrent.

RANGE OF GRANTS £25–£2,000.

SAMPLE GRANTS Friends of the Jewish Museum, Jewish Care and Norwood Ravenswood (£2,000 each); Beth Shalom (£1,000); Chai Lifeline, Delamere Forest School, Wiener Library Endowment Trust and World Jewish Relief (£500 each); Friends of the Victoria and Albert Museum (£250); Institute of Jewish Affairs and Samaritans (£100 each); World Wildlife Fund (£50); and Society of Jewish Study (£25).

FINANCES *Year* 2007–08 *Income* £26,650 *Grants* £16,704 *Assets* £567,749

TRUSTEES Mrs J F Millan; Mrs A E Gutwin; Mrs W C Lambros.

HOW TO APPLY The trust states that it does not respond to unsolicited applications.

WHO TO APPLY TO Mrs J F Millan, Trustee, 4 Court Close, St John's Wood Park, London NW8 6NN

CC NO 264430   **ESTABLISHED** 1972

■ The Rubin Foundation

WHERE FUNDING CAN BE GIVEN UK and overseas.

WHO CAN BENEFIT Organisations benefiting Jewish people, students and people who are sick.

WHAT IS FUNDED Primarily, but not exclusively, Jewish charities. Also, medical charities, arts organisations and universities.

RANGE OF GRANTS Mostly up to £25,000; exceptionally up to £400,000.

SAMPLE GRANTS ULIA (£405,000); Jewish Community Secondary School Trust (£250,000); Jewish Museum (£50,000); Civitas (£25,000); Peace and Sport (£14,000); Weidenfeld Institute for Strategic Dialogue (£10,000); South Bank Centre (£8,000); Board of Deputies of British Jews (£6,000); Royal Opera House Foundation (£4,200); the Roundhouse (£3,000); Cancer Backup (£1,300); and Maccabiah Football Bursaries (£1,000).

FINANCES *Year* 2007–08 *Income* £143,296 *Grants* £984,025 *Assets* £1,142,366

TRUSTEES Alison Mosheim; Angela Rubin; R Stephen Rubin; Andrew Rubin; Carolyn Rubin.

OTHER INFORMATION Smaller grants of less than £1,000 were made totalling £12,000.

HOW TO APPLY The foundation has previously stated that 'grants are only given to people related to our business', such as charities known to members of the Rubin family and those associated with Pentland Group Ltd. Unsolicited applications are very unlikely to succeed.

WHO TO APPLY TO Allison McMillan, Secretary, The Pentland Centre, Lakeside House, Squires Lane,

Finchley, London N3 2QL *Tel* 020 8346 2600
email amcmillan@pentland.com
cc no 327062   established 1986

■ William Arthur Rudd Memorial Trust

where funding can be given In practice UK and Spain.
who can benefit UK and certain Spanish charities.
what is funded General charitable purposes.
finances *Year* 2007 *Income* £39,622
  Grants £41,000 *Assets* £902,555
trustees Miss A A Sarkis; D H Smyth; R G Maples.
other information The trust's accounts state that donations were made to registered charities in the UK and to certain Spanish charities; however, no grants list was provided.
how to apply As the trust's resources are fully committed, the trustees do not consider unsolicited applications.
who to apply to Miss A A Sarkis, Trustee, 12 South Square, Gray's Inn, London WC1R 5HH *Tel* 020 7405 8932 *email* mail@mmandm.co.uk
cc no 326495   established 1983

■ The Rufford Maurice Laing Foundation

where funding can be given Developing countries, UK.
who can benefit UK registered charities only, mainly in developing countries.
what is funded The focus is on conservation, environmental and sustainable development projects in developing countries. UK organisations supporting social welfare may also receive support.
what is not funded The foundation will not generally fund the following: building or construction projects; donations to individuals or projects that directly benefit one individual; UK projects with a local or regional focus; loans; endowment funds; student/gap year conservation expeditions; general appeals or circulars.
range of grants Up to £350,000 but mainly £15,000 or less.
sample grants Natural History Museum (£350,000); EIA Charitable Trust (£300,000); Peace Parks Foundation (£150,000); University of Southampton (£101,000); Institute of Zoology (£92,000); Impact Foundation (£60,000); Crime Concern and Wildscreen Trust (£50,000 each); Earthwatch Institute and Ecology Trust (£30,000 each); Anti-Slavery International (£28,000); Oxford Brookes University (£25,000); British Institute for Brain Injured Children and Topsy Foundation UK (£20,000 each); St Albans High School for Girls (£16,000); Marine Conservation Society (£13,000); Changing Faces (£10,000); Children in Distress (£6,000); Woman's Trust (£3,000); and Centrepoint Soho (£1,500).
finances *Year* 2007–08 *Income* £3,388,083
  Grants £5,095,363 *Assets* £64,787,444
trustees Charles Barbour; Anthony Johnson; John Laing; Col. Iain Smailes; Robert Reilly.
other information Due to the success of the Rufford Small Grants facility the foundation decided to establish a new grant-making trust, The Rufford Small Grants Foundation – RSGF (CC no. 1117270) to award the Rufford Small Grants in perpetuity. Sufficient assets

(£27 million) were transferred from the foundation to generate approximately £1.2 million in income. The new foundation started operations on 6th April 2007. More information on RSGF can be found on its website: www.ruffordsmallgrants.org/rsg.
how to apply The trust considers all applications which meet its criteria but states that 'with limited funds available it is neither possible to give detailed reasons why applications are not successful nor to enter into any dialogue or correspondence regarding projects which have been refused funding. In all cases, organisations are only able to make a single application for funding from the foundation during any one-year period.' All applications must be received by post [addressed to the correspondent]. All new applicants must be charities registered in the UK.
There is no set form but applications must include: a covering letter with contact details; a comprehensive plan outlining the project for which funding is being sought, including measurable objectives (four to six pages maximum); a full budget – with details of funding secured to date, other funding applications being made and the amount being requested from the foundation; a copy of the charity's most recent accounts; a copy of the latest annual report (if available). Please note, the foundation does not accept applications for funding by email and is unable to discuss the suitability of an application by telephone. Applications are accepted throughout the year. The foundation strives to respond to all applications within four weeks of receipt and asks that applicants do not telephone to check on their application, as they will be contacted in due course.
who to apply to Simon Mickleburgh, Grants Manager, 6th Floor, 248 Tottenham Court Road, London W1T 7QZ *Tel* 020 7436 8604 *Website* www.rufford.org
cc no 326163   established 1982

■ The Rufford Small Grants Foundation

where funding can be given Worldwide.
who can benefit Individuals and small groups outside of the developed world.
what is funded Conservation of threatened animals, habitats and organisms.
what is not funded The following is generally not eligible for funding: projects in first world countries; pure research; expeditions; a conference or seminar.
sample grants Recent beneficiaries include: Aaranyak – India, Roehampton University, Karina Tavera – Mexico, Passanan Cutter – Thailand, Nguyen Vinh Thanh – Vietnam and Gonwouo Nono Legrand – Cameroon.
finances *Year* 2007–08 *Income* £28,126,631
  Grants £1,212,562 *Assets* £26,140,694
trustees John H Laing; Col. M.I.T Smailes; Sarah Brunwin; Ben Edwards.
other information A detailed breakdown, including project summaries, of recent grant recipients is available on the trust's website: www.ruffordsmallgrants.org/rsg/projects/recent.
how to apply Application forms can be downloaded from the foundation's website. They must be submitted as an email attachment and sent to the Rufford Small Grants Director care of: jane@rufford.org. Applications are considered on a rolling basis, there is no deadline.

WHO TO APPLY TO Josh Cole, Grants Director, 6th Floor, 248 Tottenham Court Road, London W1T 7QZ *Tel* 020 7436 8604 *email* josh@rufford.org *Website* www.ruffordsmallgrants.org/rsg
CC NO 1117270

■ The Rugby Group Benevolent Fund Limited

WHERE FUNDING CAN BE GIVEN The Midlands.
WHO CAN BENEFIT Employees and ex-employees of the Rugby Group Limited; young people; older people; charitable organisations.
WHAT IS FUNDED Relief-in-need; general charitable purposes.
SAMPLE GRANTS Chinnor Village Hall (£100,000); Lions Hospice – Gravesend (£70,000); Stepping Stones Nursery – Stockton (£60,000); Winteringham Village Hall (£40,000); Rugby CVS – volunteer coordinator (£12,500); Rugby Cruse Bereavement Care (£8,000); and Long Itchington School PTA and The Square Methodist Church – Dunstable (£5,000 each).
FINANCES *Year* 2008 *Income* £118,272 *Grants* £505,452 *Assets* £2,594,279
TRUSTEES G T Fuller; R J Millard; I M Southcott; C J Coates; C N Jones; J P Whyatt; J D Wootten; G D L Thomas.
OTHER INFORMATION Around £40,000 was donated to individuals in the form of cash, fuel and Christmas hampers.
HOW TO APPLY In writing to the correspondent.
WHO TO APPLY TO Daphne Murray, Cemex House, Coldharbour Lane, Thorpe, Egham, Surrey TW20 8TD *Tel* 01932 583 181
CC NO 265669 **ESTABLISHED** 1973

■ The Russell Trust

WHERE FUNDING CAN BE GIVEN UK, especially Scotland.
WHO CAN BENEFIT Registered charities.
WHAT IS FUNDED General charitable purposes.
WHAT IS NOT FUNDED Only registered charities or organisations with charitable status are supported.
TYPE OF GRANT Pump-priming for new projects rather than annual grants.
RANGE OF GRANTS Usually in the range of £250–£2,000. Three or four larger grants of £20,000 may be awarded annually.
SAMPLE GRANTS No grants list was available, but previously donations have been broken down as follows: music and the Arts (£36,000); education (£26,000); St Andrew's University (£24,000); archaeology (£21,000); health and welfare (£19,000); National Trust for Scotland (£15,000); youth work (£15,000); preservation work (£12,000); local (£9,000); church (£7,000); general (£5,500); and The Iona Community (£5,000).
FINANCES *Year* 2007–08 *Income* £272,940 *Grants* £200,000
TRUSTEES Fred Bowden; Mrs Cecilia Croal; Graeme Crombie; David Erdal; Don Munro; Ms Iona Russell; Alan Scott.
HOW TO APPLY On a form available from the correspondent. A statement of accounts must be supplied. Trustees meet quarterly, although decisions on the allocation of grants are made more regularly.

WHO TO APPLY TO Iona Russell, Administrator and Trustee, Markinch, Glenrothes, Fife KY7 6PB *Tel* 01592 753311 *email* russelltrust@trg.co.uk
SC NO SC004424 **ESTABLISHED** 1985

■ Ryklow Charitable Trust 1992

(also known as A B Williamson Charitable Trust)
WHERE FUNDING CAN BE GIVEN Worldwide.
WHO CAN BENEFIT Organisations, generally to small or start up charities, and individuals.
WHAT IS FUNDED Medical research, especially that which benefits children; assistance to students from overseas wishing to study in the UK or for UK students volunteering for unpaid work overseas; projects in the developing world – especially those which are intended to be self-sustaining or concerned with education; help for vulnerable families, minorities and the prevention of abuse or exploitation of children; and conservation of natural species, landscape and resources.
RANGE OF GRANTS £500 to £3,000.
SAMPLE GRANTS No grants list was available but previous beneficiaries have included: Ark Trust, BLISS, Books Abroad, Care International UK, Children in Crisis, Interact Worldwide, International Otter Survival Fund, Motor Neurone Research, Nepal Trust, Soil Association, Sun Seed (Tanzania) Trust, Water Aid, Wildlife Conservation Research Unit, Wolf Trust and Young Minds.
FINANCES *Year* 2007–08 *Income* £694,172 *Grants* £35,306 *Assets* £1,564,741
TRUSTEES J V Woodward; A Williamson; E J S Cannings: P W Hanson; Mrs S Taylor.
HOW TO APPLY On a form available from the correspondent or to download from the trust's website. Applications should be brief and include an audited financial report (or at least a statement of finances). Forms should be submitted between 1 September and 31 December. The trustees usually make a decision once a year in March, with grants being award by the end of the month. Only in cases of real emergency will applications be considered at other times. Only successful applicants will be notified.
WHO TO APPLY TO Stephen F Marshall, c/o Robinsons Solicitors, 10–11 St James Court, Friar Gate, Derby DE1 1BT *Tel* 01332 291 431 *Fax* 01332 254 141 *email* stephen.marshall@robinsons-solicitors.co.uk *Website* ryklowcharitabletrust.org
CC NO 1010122 **ESTABLISHED** 1992

■ The J S and E C Rymer Charitable Trust

WHERE FUNDING CAN BE GIVEN East Yorkshire.
WHO CAN BENEFIT People who have retired from rural industry or agriculture.
WHAT IS FUNDED Housing for retired people who have spent the major part of their working lives in rural industry or agriculture; general charitable purposes in the specified area.
WHAT IS NOT FUNDED No grants to charities outside East Yorkshire.
RANGE OF GRANTS £10–£1,000.
SAMPLE GRANTS Recipients included local churches, community healthcare and NSPCC (regional branch).
FINANCES *Year* 2007–08 *Income* £65,687 *Grants* £94,407
TRUSTEES Mrs E C Rymer; T S Rymer; G H Brand.

HOW TO APPLY In writing to the correspondent.
WHO TO APPLY TO D Milburn, Southburn Offices,
Southburn, Driffield, East Yorkshire YO25 9ED
Tel 01377 227764 *Fax* 01377 227802
email charitable.trust@jsr.co.uk
CC NO 267493   **ESTABLISHED** 1974

■ S F Foundation

WHERE FUNDING CAN BE GIVEN Worldwide.

WHO CAN BENEFIT Jewish organisations.

WHAT IS FUNDED The trust gives grants towards the 'advancement and furtherance of the Jewish religion and Jewish religious education and the alleviation of poverty amongst the Jewish community throughout the world.'

FINANCES *Year* 2007–08 *Income* £6,485,430 *Grants* £2,835,962 *Assets* £8,784,441

TRUSTEES Hannah Jacob; Rivka Niederman; Miriam Schrieber.

HOW TO APPLY 'The charity accepts applications for grants from representatives of various charities, which are reviewed by the trustees on a regular basis.'

WHO TO APPLY TO Rivka Niederman, Secretary, 143 Upper Clapton road, London E5 9DB

CC NO 1105843   **ESTABLISHED** 2004

■ S O Charitable Trust

WHERE FUNDING CAN BE GIVEN Gateshead.

WHO CAN BENEFIT Jewish people.

WHAT IS FUNDED Jewish causes.

SAMPLE GRANTS Ber Er Hatorah (£18,000); Beis Soroh Schneirer and Beis Hamdrash (£9,000 each); 'Unknown' (£8,000); Letora Ve Horda (£6,000); and Gateshead Foundation for Torah (£5,000).

FINANCES *Year* 2007–08 *Income* £62,876 *Grants* £69,750 *Assets* £631,623

TRUSTEES Rabbi Simon Ohayon; N Ohayon; Mrs S Ohayon; A Ohayon.

HOW TO APPLY In writing to the correspondent.

WHO TO APPLY TO Rabbi Simon Ohayon, Trustee, 19 Oxford Terrace, Gateshead, Tyne and Wear NE8 1RQ *Tel* 0191 477 0408

CC NO 326314   **ESTABLISHED** 1982

■ The Michael Sacher Charitable Trust

WHERE FUNDING CAN BE GIVEN UK and Israel.

WHO CAN BENEFIT Charitable organisations, with a preference for Jewish organisations.

WHAT IS FUNDED General, including arts, culture and heritage; medical and disability; community and welfare; education, science and technology; children and young people; and religion.

RANGE OF GRANTS £100–£30,000.

SAMPLE GRANTS Royal College of Music (£31,000); Anna Freud Centre (£22,000); Kings College London, the National Gallery and Jerusalem Foundation (£10,000 each); Friends of the Hebrew University (£8,600); FEROP (£6,600); British Friends of Kishorit (£1,000); Motor Neurone Disease Association and Childrens Neurosurgery Ward, Southampton Hospital (£500 each); St Johns Smith Square (£360); and New Israel Fund (£120).

FINANCES *Year* 2007–08 *Income* £153,363 *Grants* £125,973 *Assets* £1,468,168

TRUSTEES Simon John Sacher; Jeremy Michael Sacher; Hon. Mrs Rosalind E C Sacher; Mrs Elisabeth J Sacher.

HOW TO APPLY In writing to the correspondent at any time.

WHO TO APPLY TO John Sacher, 16 Clifton Villas, London W9 2PH *Tel* 020 7289 5873

CC NO 206321   **ESTABLISHED** 1957

■ The Michael Harry Sacher Trust

WHERE FUNDING CAN BE GIVEN UK and overseas.

WHO CAN BENEFIT Registered charities.

WHAT IS FUNDED General charitable purposes with a preference for arts, education, animal welfare, Jewish organisations and health. Requests are generally only considered if they are from organisations that are personally known to the trustees.

WHAT IS NOT FUNDED No grants to individuals or organisations which are not registered charities.

RANGE OF GRANTS £250–£30,000.

SAMPLE GRANTS Royal Opera House Foundation (£11,000); National Gallery Trust (£10,000); Goldsmith College (£9,300); Singapore Zoo (£8,500); Friends of the Hebrew University (£4,500); Jeremy and John Sacher Charitable Trust (£3,100); Norwood Ltd and Friends of Alyn (£2,000 each); New West End Synagogue and Nightingale House (£1,000 each); and Crusaid and Donkeys in the Holy Land (£500).

FINANCES *Year* 2007–08 *Income* £70,566 *Grants* £100,802 *Assets* £2,315,320

TRUSTEES Nicola Shelley Sacher; Michael Harry Sacher.

HOW TO APPLY In writing to the correspondent.

WHO TO APPLY TO The Trustees, c/o H W Fisher and Co, 11–15 William Road, London NW1 3ER *Tel* 020 7388 7000

CC NO 288973   **ESTABLISHED** 1984

■ Dr Mortimer and Theresa Sackler Foundation

WHERE FUNDING CAN BE GIVEN UK.

WHO CAN BENEFIT Large institutions benefiting, arts and culture or medical research or actors and entertainment professionals, musicians, textile workers and designers, and writers and poets.

WHAT IS FUNDED Arts and culture, science and medical research generally.

TYPE OF GRANT Some recurring; others one-off.

RANGE OF GRANTS Up to £500,000.

SAMPLE GRANTS Edinburgh and Glasgow Universities (joint grant of £500,000); Museum of London (£333,000); Watermill Theatre (£160,000); National History Museum (£125,000); Dulwich Picture Gallery Centre for Arts Education (£70,000); Chiswick House and Gardens Trust (£50,000); Capital City Academy (£25,000); and Charity Global (£12,000). Donations under £10,000 each totalled £92,000.

FINANCES *Year* 2007 *Income* £3,117,804 *Grants* £1,770,601 *Assets* £4,989,133

TRUSTEES Dr Mortimer Sackler; Theresa Sackler; Christopher Mitchell; Raymond Smith; Ilene Lefcourt Sackler; Marissa Sackler; Peter Stormonth Darling.

HOW TO APPLY In writing to the correspondent.

WHO TO APPLY TO Christopher B Mitchell, Trustee, 9th Floor, New Zealand House, 80 Haymarket, London SW1Y 4TQ *Tel* 020 7930 4944

CC NO 327863   **ESTABLISHED** 1988

■ The Raymond and Beverley Sackler Foundation

WHERE FUNDING CAN BE GIVEN UK.

WHO CAN BENEFIT The trust has a list of regular beneficiaries.

WHAT IS FUNDED Grants are given to the arts, sciences and medical research.

TYPE OF GRANT Annual grants.

FINANCES *Year* 2007 *Income* £3,048,834 *Grants* £641,409 *Assets* £4,413,646

TRUSTEES C B Mitchell; Dr R R Sackler; J D Sackler; R M Smith; Dr R S Sackler; A Wikstrom; A Mattessich.

HOW TO APPLY Grants are not open to application.

WHO TO APPLY TO C B Mitchell, Trustee, New Zealand House, 9th Floor, 80 Haymarket, London SW1Y 4TQ *Tel* 020 793 4944

CC NO 327864   **ESTABLISHED** 1988

■ The Ruzin Sadagora Trust

WHERE FUNDING CAN BE GIVEN UK and Israel.

WHO CAN BENEFIT Charities benefiting Jewish people.

WHAT IS FUNDED Preference for Jewish charities.

SAMPLE GRANTS Beth Israel Ruzin Sadagora (£196,000); Friends of Ruzin Sadagora (£180,000); Beth Kaknesset Ohr Yisroel (£91,600); Mosdos Sadigur (£40,000); Yeshivas Torah Temimah (£9,000); Chevras Moaz Lodol (£6,500); Pardes House (£2,000).

FINANCES *Year* 2007–08 *Income* £635,834 *Grants* £527,746 *Assets* £529,202

TRUSTEES Rabbi I M Friedman; Mrs S Friedman.

HOW TO APPLY In writing to the correspondent.

WHO TO APPLY TO Rabbi I M Friedman, Trustee, 269 Golders Green Road, London NW11 9JJ

CC NO 285475   **ESTABLISHED** 1982

■ The Saddlers' Company Charitable Fund

WHERE FUNDING CAN BE GIVEN UK.

WHO CAN BENEFIT Registered charities and institutions.

WHAT IS FUNDED Grants are made by the company in the following categories: City of London; saddlery trade; equestrian; education; disability charities, service charities and general charitable purposes.

WHAT IS NOT FUNDED No grants to individuals.

TYPE OF GRANT Usually one-off for one year.

SAMPLE GRANTS Alleyn's School (£130,000); British Horse Society (£37,000); Riding for the Disabled Association (£27,500); City & Guilds of London Institute (£9,000); Help for Heroes and Rochester Cathedral Trust (£5,000 each); Leather Conservation Centre (£4,000); Salisbury Cathedral (£3,000); The Warehouse (£2,000); St Luke's Hospital for the Clergy (£1,500); and the Samaritans and Tower Hamlets Mission (£1,000 each).

FINANCES *Year* 2008–09 *Income* £436,843 *Grants* £424,472 *Assets* £7,079,229

TRUSTEES The Saddlers' Company. The company is directed by the court of assistants consisting of the master, three wardens, a number of past masters and up to four junior assistants. There shall be a minimum of 12 and a maximum of 24.

HOW TO APPLY In writing to the correspondent. Grants are made in January and July, following trustees' meetings. Charities are asked to submit reports at the end of the following year on their continuing activities and the use of any grant received.

WHO TO APPLY TO Nigel Lithgow, Clerk to the Company, Saddlers' Hall, 40 Gutter Lane, London EC2V 6BR *Tel* 020 7726 8661/6 *Fax* 020 7600 0386 *email* clerk@saddlersco. co.uk *Website* www.saddlersco.co.uk

CC NO 261962   **ESTABLISHED** 1970

■ Erach and Roshan Sadri Foundation

WHERE FUNDING CAN BE GIVEN Worldwide.

WHO CAN BENEFIT Registered charities, community groups and religious institutions.

WHAT IS FUNDED The main objects of the foundation are: providing financial assistance for education and welfare purposes; relieving poverty by alleviating homelessness; and assisting members of the Zoroastrian religious faith.

WHAT IS NOT FUNDED Applications are unlikely to be successful if they: involve animal welfare or heritage; are a general appeal from large UK organisations.

TYPE OF GRANT One-off grants for project costs.

RANGE OF GRANTS Up to around £20,000.

SAMPLE GRANTS In 2008/09: Parsi Anjuman (£48,000), towards the Indore Temple; Tyneside Cyrenians (£25,000), towards specialist equipment for the homeless hostel; Honeypot (£21,000), for the respite holiday programme; Afghan Appeal Fund (£20,000), Little Sisters of the Poor – Ireland (£15,000), towards rebuilding a nursing home; Halcrow (£10,000), for a deposit scheme for the homeless; and All Cannings (£2,000), for specialist computer equipment.

FINANCES *Year* 2007–08 *Income* £45,467 *Grants* £482,973 *Assets* £5,551,705

TRUSTEES Margaret Lynch; Shabbir Merali; Darius Sarosh; Jehangir Sarosh; Donald Wratten.

HOW TO APPLY On a form which can be downloaded from the foundation's website, along with full and detailed guidelines. Forms can be returned by post or email. Meetings are held four times a year. Please note: 'Unsolicited material sent in addition to the clear and concise requirements of the application form is very likely to prove detrimental to your application. The trustees insist that additional items such as annual reports, glossy brochures, Christmas cards and accounts are not sent unless specifically requested.'

WHO TO APPLY TO Mark Cann, Administrator, 10a High Street, Pewsey, Wiltshire SN9 5AQ *email* markcann@ersf.org.uk *Website* www.ersf. org.uk

CC NO 1110736   **ESTABLISHED** 2005

■ Saga Charitable Trust

WHERE FUNDING CAN BE GIVEN Developing countries.

WHO CAN BENEFIT Charitable organisations and projects.

WHAT IS FUNDED The prime objective is to benefit under-privileged communities at destinations in developing countries that host Saga Holidaymakers. It aims not just to donate money, but to invest in projects that will 'empower and support' local communities, provide practical help to those in need, and offer increased opportunities for disadvantaged groups to benefit from tourism.

WHAT IS NOT FUNDED No grants to individuals.

FINANCES *Year* 2007–08 *Income* £207,000 *Grants* £136,410 *Assets* £183,121

TRUSTEES Peter Carr; The Hon. Emma Soames; Chris Simmonds; Mrs Makala Thomas; John Goodsell; Toby Hughes; Miss Aynsley Jardin; James Duguid.

HOW TO APPLY In writing to the correspondent at any time. 'Project funding is agreed by our Board of Trustees, who take care to ensure there is a reliable local sponsor to account for all expenditure.'

WHO TO APPLY TO Janice Lee, Director, The Saga Building, Enbrook Park, Folkestone, Kent CT20 3SE *Tel* 01303 771 766 *Fax* 01303 776358 *email* contact@sagacharitabletrust.org *Website* www.sagacharitabletrust.org
CC NO 291991 ESTABLISHED 1985

....

■ The Jean Sainsbury Animal Welfare Trust

WHERE FUNDING CAN BE GIVEN UK and overseas.

WHO CAN BENEFIT UK registered national and international animal welfare charities.

WHAT IS FUNDED Projects concerned with animal welfare and wildlife.

WHAT IS NOT FUNDED No grants are given to charities which: are mainly engaged with the preservation of specific species of wild animals; have available reserves equal to more than one year's running costs (unless it can be demonstrated that reserves are being held for a designated project); are offering sanctuary to animals, with no effort to re-home, foster or rehabilitate; do not have a realistic policy for animals that cannot be given a reasonable quality of life; are involved with assistance animals e.g. Hearing Dogs for the Deaf, Riding for the Disabled etc; spend more than a reasonable proportion of their income on administration or cannot justify their costs per animal helped; are registered outside the UK. No support is given to veterinary schools (unless the money can be seen to be directly benefiting the type of animals the Trust would want to support). No individuals are supported.

TYPE OF GRANT Capital, buildings, campaigning, core costs, project, running costs and recurring costs. Funding for up to one year is available.

RANGE OF GRANTS £100–£12,000.

SAMPLE GRANTS Gambia Horse and Pony Trust and Danaher Animal Home (£12,000 each); North Clwyd Animal Rescue and Greyhound Rescue West of England (£10,000 each); Lluest Horse and Pony Trust (£7,000); Shropshire Cat Rescue and Three Owls (£5,000 each); Exotic Pet Refuge (£3,000); Bunny Burrows (£2,000); Maggies Pet Rescue (£1,000); Safe Haven for Donkeys in the Holy Land (£750); Greek Cat Welfare Society and Mountains Animal Sanctuary (£500 each); Hollyfield Wild Bird Hospital and Withington Hedgehog Care – Manchester (£300 each); and Trinity Hospice (£100).

FINANCES *Year* 2007 *Income* £4,957,876 *Grants* £317,800 *Assets* £13,740,950

TRUSTEES Colin Russell; Gillian Tarlington; James Keliher; Mark Spurdens; Evelyn Jane Winship; Valerie Pike; Michelle F O'Brien.

HOW TO APPLY On a form available from the correspondent or to download from the trust's website. Applicants should complete and return seven copies of the form, their latest set of audited accounts and any other information which may be relevant to the application. Please note: the trust requests that you do not send originals as these cannot be returned. There are three trustees' meetings every year, usually in March, July and November and applications should be submitted by 1 February, 1 June and 1 October respectively. Further application information and policy guidelines are available by visiting the website.

WHO TO APPLY TO Madeleine Orchard, Administrator, PO Box 50793, London NW6 9DE *Tel* 020 7602 7948 *Website* jeansainsburyanimalwelfare.org.uk
CC NO 326358 ESTABLISHED 1982

....

■ The Alan and Babette Sainsbury Charitable Fund

WHERE FUNDING CAN BE GIVEN Worldwide.

WHO CAN BENEFIT Registered charities.

WHAT IS FUNDED Projects in the following fields: support for ethnic minority and refugee groups, civil liberties, overseas, youth work, scientific and medical research, the arts and general.

WHAT IS NOT FUNDED Grants are not normally made to individuals.

TYPE OF GRANT One-off and ongoing, core costs, capital, project and running costs.

RANGE OF GRANTS £1,000–£80,000.

SAMPLE GRANTS Kinder Children's Choirs of the High Peak (£35,000); Jewish Association for Business Ethics and Theatre Royal, Bury St Edmunds (£30,000 each); British Friends of Neve Shalom and Canon Collins Educational Trust For South Africa (£28,000 each); Southwark Playhouse and Refugees into Jobs (£25,000 each); Holocaust Educational Trust and Female Prisoners' Welfare Project Hibiscus (£20,000 each); Cooltan Arts (£12,000); Kampala Music School and Anglo-Israel Association (£10,000 each); and Lindsay Rural Players and Anne Frank Trust (£5,000 each).

FINANCES *Year* 2007–08 *Income* £480,781 *Grants* £477,391 *Assets* £13,375,687

TRUSTEES The Hon. Sir Timothy Sainsbury; Miss Judith Portrait.

HOW TO APPLY The trust states that: 'proposals are likely to be invited by the trustees or initiated at their request. Unsolicited applications will only be successful if they fall precisely within an area in which the trustees are interested'. A single application will be considered for support by all the trusts in the Sainsbury family group.

WHO TO APPLY TO Alan Bookbinder, Director, Allington House, 1st Floor, 150 Victoria Street, London SW1E 5AE *Tel* 020 7410 0330 *Fax* 020 7410 0332 *Website* www.sfct.org.uk
CC NO 292930 ESTABLISHED 1953

....

■ St Andrew Animal Fund

WHERE FUNDING CAN BE GIVEN UK and overseas, with a preference for Scotland.

WHO CAN BENEFIT Registered charities and individuals concerned with animal welfare.

WHAT IS FUNDED Priorities are: support for the development of non-animal research techniques; funding farm animal, companion animal and wildlife studies to improve welfare; supporting projects which will enhance the welfare of animals.

WHAT IS NOT FUNDED No support for routine day-to-day expenses.

TYPE OF GRANT The trust will consider grants for buildings and other capital, projects, research and start-up costs, for up to three years.

SAMPLE GRANTS Previously: Lawrence and Beavan Website Project (£11,000); Tinto Kennels (£3,000); InterNICHE and Uist Hedgehog Rescue (£2,000 each); and Captive Animals Protection Society and Norwegian School of Veterinary Science (£1,200 each).

FINANCES *Year* 2007–08 *Income* £33,876
　Grants £25,000

TRUSTEES Murray McGrath, Chair; David Martin; Dr Jane Goodall; Heather Petrie; Rebecca Ford; Shona McManus; Stephen Blakeway; Emma Law, Audrey Fearn; Duchess of Hamilton; Virginia Hay; Les Ward; Sheelagh Graham.

HOW TO APPLY In writing to the correspondent. The trustees meet in April and applications must reach the fund by 28 February for consideration at the next meeting. Applications should include a copy of the latest accounts, the name and address of a referee (e.g. veterinary surgeon or an animal welfare organisation), the purpose for which any grant will be used and, where relevant, two estimates. Receipts for work carried out may be requested and the fund states that visits by representatives of the fund to those organisations receiving grants will be made at random.

WHO TO APPLY TO Secretary to the Trustees, 10 Queensferry Street, Edinburgh EH2 4PG *Tel* 0131 225 2116 *Fax* 0131 220 6377 *email* info@advocatesforanimals.org *Website* www.advocatesforanimals.org

SC NO SC005337　　　**ESTABLISHED** 1969

■ St Andrew's Conservation Trust

WHERE FUNDING CAN BE GIVEN Preference for the south west of England.

WHO CAN BENEFIT Charitable organisations.

WHAT IS FUNDED The conservation, restoration and preservation of monuments, sculptures and artefacts of historic or public interest which are upon or attached to property owned by any charitable organisation.

WHAT IS NOT FUNDED No support is given for conservation or restoration of churchyard table tombs except in very restricted circumstances.

RANGE OF GRANTS £100–£10,000.

SAMPLE GRANTS South Somerset District Council – churchyard monuments (£10,000); Grinling Gibbons Angels (£5,000); Cruwys Morchard, Devon – chancel and parclose screens (£3,000); Tyntesfield, North Somerset – stained glass in chapel (£2,000); and Cattistock, Dorset – wall paintings (£1,000).

FINANCES *Year* 2008 *Income* £29,350
　Grants £39,770 *Assets* £406,069

TRUSTEES Gerard M Leighton; Hugh G L Playfair; Simon R V Pomeroy; Alan W G Thomas; Mrs Elsa van der Zee; John Reed; S J C Tudway Quilter; John Bucknall.

OTHER INFORMATION In previous years the trust has stated: 'The trustees continue to have concern about the paucity and lack of quality of applications for grants; they are of the opinion that there is no lack of small projects which they would be willing to assist if only the applicant were prepared to do some administration work'.

HOW TO APPLY On a form available from the correspondent.

WHO TO APPLY TO Simon R V Pomeroy, Trustee, Duddle Farm, Nr Bockhampton, Dorchester, Dorset DT2 8QL *Tel* 01305 264516 *Fax* 01305 257159

CC NO 282157　　　**ESTABLISHED** 1980

■ St Christopher's College Educational Trust

WHERE FUNDING CAN BE GIVEN UK.

WHO CAN BENEFIT Organisations and individuals connected to the Church of England.

WHAT IS FUNDED Education and the support of children and youth organisations.

TYPE OF GRANT Small grants, usually one-off; some part-funded projects.

RANGE OF GRANTS Up to £5,000.

SAMPLE GRANTS The Cathedral Church of St Nicholas (£5,000); Wakefield Cathedral Project (£4,000); The Queens Foundation- Aigofie David Marino (£3,000); Bradford Ripon & Leeds Diocesan Board of Education (£2,500); Sheffield Diocesan Board of Education and Adventure Plus (£2,000 each); Derby Diocesan Board of Education (£1,000); DDE Association Grant (£800); and St Lukes Church (£400).

FINANCES *Year* 2008 *Income* £151,922
　Grants £21,175

TRUSTEES Dr D Sellick; Revd Prof. Le Francis; Mrs B Harvey; Revd Canon D Isaac; J Swallow; Miss M Braithwaite; Miss M Code; Ven. P Wheatley; Revd J Ainsworth; M Hawes; P Bissell; Revd Canon Dr K Denison.

HOW TO APPLY In writing to the correspondent.

WHO TO APPLY TO The Trustees, c/o The National Society, Church House, Great Smith Street, Westminster, London SW1P 3NZ

CC NO 313864　　　**ESTABLISHED** 1971

■ St Francis's Leprosy Guild

WHERE FUNDING CAN BE GIVEN Developing countries.

WHO CAN BENEFIT People with leprosy or affected by leprosy, leprosy workers and medical staff.

WHAT IS FUNDED Leprosy treatment and care programmes, social, economic and physical rehabilitation, leprosy training and education, medical elective projects related to leprosy.

WHAT IS NOT FUNDED Centres not run by Catholic missionaries or not approved by the local bishop.

TYPE OF GRANT Money for running costs or for specific projects. Capital grants.

RANGE OF GRANTS Average grant: £3,000.

SAMPLE GRANTS £327,000 in maintenance grants; £90,000 in special projects; and £42,000 in educational grants.

FINANCES *Year* 2008 *Income* £310,432
　Grants £458,776 *Assets* £477,756

TRUSTEES Dr Gosia Brykczynska; Ms Margaret Hood; Ms Veronica Melia; Revd Francis Wahle; Very Revd Fr Michael Copps; Mrs Gwen Sankey; Timothy Lawrence.

HOW TO APPLY In writing for an application form to Honorary Secretary. Applications must be supported by expenditure details, the total cost and anticipated start date. In all cases charity registration title and number must be given. The committee regrets that applications cannot be acknowledged.

WHO TO APPLY TO Eric Williams, trust administrator, 73 St Charles Square, London W10 6EJ *Tel* 020 8969 1345 *Fax* 020 8969 3272 *email* enquiries@stfrancisleprosy.org *Website* www.stfrancisleprosy.org

CC NO 208741　　　**ESTABLISHED** 1895

■ St Gabriel's Trust

WHERE FUNDING CAN BE GIVEN Mainly in the UK.

WHO CAN BENEFIT Institutions engaged in higher or further religious education, with a view to training school RE teachers. Young adults and members of the Church of England may benefit.

WHAT IS FUNDED Higher and further religious education with the purpose of training RE teachers and encouraging good practice in RE.

WHAT IS NOT FUNDED Grants are not normally available for: any project for which local authority money is available, or which ought primarily to be funded by the church – theological study, parish or missionary work – unless school RE is involved; and research projects where it will be a long time before any benefit can filter down into RE teaching. No grants are made to schools as such; higher and further education must be involved.

TYPE OF GRANT Recurring, one-off, project, research and start-up will be considered.

SAMPLE GRANTS ACCT Virtual RE Centre (£23,000); ACCT – Teach RE (£7,500); Lambeth Palace Library (£5,500); and St Paul's Cathedral Foundation (£1,600).

FINANCES *Year* 2007 *Income* £269,046 *Grants* £212,883 *Assets* £7,459,042

TRUSTEES Dr Priscilla Chadwick, Chair; Arthur Pendlebury-Green; Susanna Ainsworth; Prof Andrew Wright; James Cowen; Linda Borthwick; Jan Ainsworth; Colin Alves; John Keast; Jessica Giles; Barbara Lane; Mary Halvorson; David Stephenson.

OTHER INFORMATION The trust spent £141,900 on the St Gabriel's programme, an ongoing venture that has been run jointly with the Culham Institute. Grants were also made to 21 individuals totalling £24,603.

HOW TO APPLY In writing to the correspondent with an sae. Applicants are asked to describe their religious allegiance and to provide a reference from their minister of religion. Applications need to be received by the beginning of January, April or September as trustees meet in February, May and October.

WHO TO APPLY TO Peter Duffell, Clerk, Ladykirk, 32 The Ridgeway, Enfield, Middlesex EN2 8QH *Tel* 020 8363 6474

CC NO 312933   **ESTABLISHED** 1977

■ St Hilda's Trust

WHERE FUNDING CAN BE GIVEN The diocese of Newcastle (Newcastle upon Tyne, North Tyneside and Northumberland).

WHO CAN BENEFIT Young people, generally and in particular today's equivalent of the original clientele of St Hilda's School (an approved school and community home); and people whose needs are not met by state social welfare provisions.

WHAT IS FUNDED Organisations working with young people and people in need (as specified above). Also considered are community businesses and development, support to voluntary and community groups, training for work, community centres and village halls, and community services.

TYPE OF GRANT Wide-ranging; sometimes recurring. The trustees prefer to support projects involving the employment of staff qualified to provide care and support to those in need rather than to provide buildings, equipment or motor vehicles.

RANGE OF GRANTS £100–£5,000.

FINANCES *Year* 2008 *Income* £41,423 *Grants* £29,500 *Assets* £1,202,604

TRUSTEES Revd Canon A S Craig; Mrs R Nicholson; Rt Revd M Wharton; Dr M Wilkinson; N Brockbank; D Welsh.

HOW TO APPLY Application forms will be sent on request. Completed forms should be returned by the last day of March, June, September and December.

WHO TO APPLY TO Vanessa Ward, Church House, St John's Terrace, North Shields NE29 6HS *Tel* 0191 270 4100 *Fax* 0191 270 4101 *email* v.ward@newcastle.anglican.org

CC NO 500962   **ESTABLISHED** 1904

■ St James' Trust Settlement

WHERE FUNDING CAN BE GIVEN Worldwide, with a preference for the UK and USA.

WHO CAN BENEFIT Registered charities.

WHAT IS FUNDED Projects in the areas of health, education and social justice.

WHAT IS NOT FUNDED No grants to individuals.

TYPE OF GRANT Core costs, one-off, project, research, recurring costs, salaries and start-up costs. Funding is for up to three years.

SAMPLE GRANTS Blackstock Trust (£12,000); Prisoners Abroad and Yakar Educational Foundation (£10,000 each); Trevor Day School (£9,600); Joshua Foundation and Global Grassroots (£7,300 each); CARIS, South East Cancer Centre and Enfant du Monde (£5,000 each); VH1 Save the Music (£4,000); Friends of Israel Trust (£2,500); Dramatists Guild Fund for Kitty Hart (£1,200); AIDS Walk New York (£490); and Naked Mind Productions (£250).

FINANCES *Year* 2007–08 *Income* £113,460 *Grants* £81,725 *Assets* £3,620,945

TRUSTEES Jane Wells; Cathy Ingram; Simon Taffler.

HOW TO APPLY The trust states that it 'does not seek unsolicited applications for grants and, without paid staff, are unable to respond to such applications'.

WHO TO APPLY TO The Trustees, Epworth House, 25 City Road, London EC1Y 1AR *Tel* 020 7628 5801

CC NO 280455   **ESTABLISHED** 1980

■ St James's Place Foundation

WHERE FUNDING CAN BE GIVEN In practice mainly UK.

WHO CAN BENEFIT Registered charities supporting children and young people (up to the age of 25) with mental or physical conditions, life threatening or degenerative illnesses. Hospices are also supported, regardless of the ages of their clients.

WHAT IS FUNDED The small grants programme gives grants of up to £10,000 to organisations with a turnover of less than £200,000 a year. The major grants programme gives up to £25,000 for a maximum of two years to organisations with a turnover of less than £2 million. These turnover limitations do not apply to hospices.

WHAT IS NOT FUNDED The foundation has a policy of not considering an application from any charity within two years of receiving a previous application. The trust does not provide support for: charities with reserves of over 50% of income; administrative costs; activities primarily the responsibility of statutory agencies; replacement of lost statutory funding; research; events; advertising; holidays; sponsorship; contributions to large capital appeals; single faith charities; social and economic deprivation; charities that are raising funds on behalf of another charity.

TYPE OF GRANT One-off.

RANGE OF GRANTS Mainly between £500–£10,000.
SAMPLE GRANTS The Children's Trust – Tadworth (£900,000), for the first and second tranches of a grant for a hydrotherapy pool; Hope & Homes for Children (£190,000), to support their work in Romania and Bosnia & Herzegovinia; Teenage Cancer Trust (£120,000), to fund patient technology at the Teenage Cancer Trust Unit at the Royal Marsden Hospital; and Help for Heroes (£10,000), towards the Headley Court Appeal; St Peter's Hospice (£9,600), for specialist equipment; The Bren Project (£8,800), towards the costs of the 'Moving On' project; Court Meadow School Association (£8,000), for equipment, refurbishments and maintenance; Cued Speech Association UK (£6,800), towards a Summer school based around communication; Nordoff-Robbins Music Therapy in Scotland (£5,400), towards a project at the Berryknows Centre working with young people with special needs; St John's Hospice – Wirral (£4,000), to fund the Nurse Call System at the new Out Patient Services Unit; and Brittle Bone Society – Dundee (£2,100), to fund a youth worker at a special two day event.
FINANCES *Year* 2008 *Income* £2,626,958 *Grants* £2,730,888 *Assets* £1,710,222
TRUSTEES Malcolm Cooper-Smith, Chair; David Bellamy; Ian Gascoigne; Mike Wilson; Andrew Croft; Hugh Gladman; David Lamb.
HOW TO APPLY Application forms are available from the foundation office and must be returned by post. Applications will only be considered if accompanied by a signed copy of the most recent audited accounts and annual report. An initial enquiry should be made before applying for a major grant. Applications will be assessed against a number of criteria, including user involvement, sustainability, maximum benefit and volunteer involvement. Assessment visits may be made. Small grant applications will normally be processed within two months from date of application. Major grant applications will be considered between July and December and successful applicants will be notified at the end of the following January.
WHO TO APPLY TO Mark Longbottom, 1 Tetbury Road, Cirencester, Gloucestershire GL7 1FP *Tel* 01285 878 562 *email* mark.longbottom@ sjp.co.uk *Website* www.sjp.co.uk/foundation
CC NO 1031456   **ESTABLISHED** 1994

■ Sir Walter St John's Educational Charity

WHERE FUNDING CAN BE GIVEN The boroughs of Wandsworth and Lambeth, with a preference for Battersea.
WHO CAN BENEFIT Young people under 25 who are resident in Wandsworth and Lambeth and who are in financial need. Grants are awarded both to individuals and local schools, colleges, youth clubs, and voluntary and community organisations. Special consideration is given to meeting the educational needs of young people who are disabled.
WHAT IS FUNDED The education of young people under 25 who are resident in Wandsworth and Lambeth. The charity has a special interest in the education of young people excluded from school, in early years education, and in young refugees and asylum seekers. The charity also supports the development of new educational initiatives and projects, curriculum enrichment programmes, and playscheme holiday projects.

Student grants are made only to individuals on approved or recognised courses.
WHAT IS NOT FUNDED The charity does not normally fund expenditure involving ongoing salary or premises costs or donations to general fund-raising appeals. School pupils under 16, full-time students on postgraduate courses or gap-year travel are not normally supported.
TYPE OF GRANT One-off, buildings, capital, projects and start-up costs. Funding is for up to three years. Student grants are normally awarded yearly to meet the cost of books and equipment, travel to college, and childcare.
RANGE OF GRANTS £200–£50,000; typically less than £5,000. Most student grants are in the range £350–£600.
SAMPLE GRANTS Katherine Low Settlement – refugees and asylum seekers' Home School Support Project (£101,000); OASIS Children's Venture (£10,000); South London Botanical Institute (£8,000); Lilford Estate Women's Action (£5,000); Young and Creative (£3,000); and Pumphouse Gallery (£1,000).
FINANCES *Year* 2007–08 *Income* £140,377 *Grants* £244,068 *Assets* £3,530,001
TRUSTEES A Tuck, chair; C Blackwood; Ms D Daytes; P Dyson; Revd. P Kennington; J O Malley; Ms S Rackham; J Radcliffe; Ms J Scribbins; Cllr S Wilkie; Cllr K Abrams; B Fairbank; G Allen; Cllr P Dawson.
OTHER INFORMATION In 2007–08, £8,600 was given in grants to individuals.
HOW TO APPLY *Organisations:* Applicants will be asked to complete an application form and submit a two-page supporting letter. Organisations and individuals who wish to apply for grants are welcome to contact the charity's office by letter, e-mail or telephone for further information and advice.
WHO TO APPLY TO Melanie Griffiths, Manager, Unit 11, Culvert House, Culvert Road, London SW11 5DH *Tel* 020 7498 8878 *email* manager@swsjcharity.org.uk
CC NO 312690   **ESTABLISHED** 1992

■ St Katharine and Shadwell Trust

WHERE FUNDING CAN BE GIVEN The London boroughs of Tower Hamlets, Hackney and City of London.
WHO CAN BENEFIT Grants are available to voluntary and community organisations. Some grants may be made to statutory organisations such as schools.
WHAT IS FUNDED 'We give grants and run projects to improve the quality of life in the local area. We work in the London Boroughs of Tower Hamlets Hackney and the City of London.'
WHAT IS NOT FUNDED The trust is unable to make grants either to or for individuals.
TYPE OF GRANT Capital, revenue and full project funding.
FINANCES *Year* 2008 *Income* £1,008,710 *Grants* £583,120 *Assets* £7,673,184
TRUSTEES Sir Robin Mountfield; Sir David Hardy; Eric Sorensen; Lindsay Driscoll; Dan Jones; Mary Nepstad; Maj. Gen. Keith Cima; Mark Gibson; Cllr Shafiqul Haque; Cllr Denise Jones.
OTHER INFORMATION 'We are a Community Foundation, raising funds and awarding grants to run and support a wide range of projects in East London. We have been actively working in Tower Hamlets for 18 years and in 2006 extended our work into Hackney, Newham and the City of London. Our knowledge of the area and the relationships we have developed enable us to support and sustain positive change. Our aim is to ensure that the ideas and aspirations

of local people for improving their area can be realised.'

HOW TO APPLY Please see the trust's website for details of up-to-date schemes.

WHO TO APPLY TO The Director, PO Box 1779, London E1W 2BY *Tel* 020 7782 6962 *email* enquiries@skst.org *Website* www.skst.org

CC NO 1001047   **ESTABLISHED** 1990

■ The St Laurence Relief In Need Trust

WHERE FUNDING CAN BE GIVEN The ancient parish of St Laurence, then the borough of Reading.

WHO CAN BENEFIT Persons resident generally, or individually, in the area of the ancient parish of St Laurence in Reading and, thereafter, persons resident generally, or individually, in the county borough of Reading.

WHAT IS FUNDED Persons, generally or individually, who are in conditions of need, hardship or distress.

WHAT IS NOT FUNDED No grants to individuals outside the ancient parish of St Laurence, Reading or the county borough of Reading, even when supported by social services or similar agencies.

TYPE OF GRANT One-off or annual.

RANGE OF GRANTS £1,000 annual to £10,000 one-off.

FINANCES *Year* 2008 *Income* £70,927 *Grants* £45,300 *Assets* £158,700

TRUSTEES Ian Hammond; Patricia Thomas; Rev. Canon Brian Shenton; Cllr. Rosemary Williams; Rev. Christopher Russell; M G Burges; S Hotston; L C Joslin.

HOW TO APPLY In writing to the correspondent, supplying latest accounts or details of bank balances and so on, together with reason for application. The trustees meet twice a year in April and November.

WHO TO APPLY TO John M James, Vale and West, Victoria House, 26 Queen Victoria Street, Reading RG1 1TG *Tel* 0118 957 3238

CC NO 205043   **ESTABLISHED** 1962

■ Saint Luke's College Foundation

WHERE FUNDING CAN BE GIVEN UK and overseas, with some preference for Exeter and Truro.

WHO CAN BENEFIT Individual or corporate applications for studies or research in theology or religious education, including the provision of these subjects for colleges and universities.

WHAT IS FUNDED Encouraging original work and imaginative new projects by educational and training bodies. Postgraduate education and various study costs are also supported.

WHAT IS NOT FUNDED Grants are not made for studies or research in fields other than religious studies, or for buildings or schools (except indirectly through courses or research projects undertaken by RE teachers). Block grants to support schemes or organisations are not made. Grants are not normally made for periods in excess of three years.

TYPE OF GRANT Normally for a specific project or part of a project, or for a specific course or research. Grants can be made for periods of up to three years.

SAMPLE GRANTS Grants were broken down into following categories: Chapel and chaplaincy: £41,000; Personal and corporate grants: £40,000; University of Exeter – Chair of Theology: £31,000.

FINANCES *Year* 2007–08 *Income* £164,325 *Grants* £143,675 *Assets* £3,928,674

TRUSTEES The Bishop of Exeter; The Dean of Exeter; Diocesan Director of Education; Chairman of Diocesan Board of Finance; Revd David Moss; Prof Grace Davie; Dr Michael Wykes; Prof Mark Overton; Revd Canon Bruce Duncan; Prof Dame Margaret Turner Warwick; Dr Barbara Wintersgill.

OTHER INFORMATION The trust's scheme requires that the first charge on the foundation's income is the maintenance of a chapel and a chaplaincy: grants can be made from the residue. The trust stated that about £50,000 is given in grants each year.

HOW TO APPLY Requests for application packs, and all other correspondence, should be sent to the correspondent. Applications are considered once a year and should be received by 1st May.

WHO TO APPLY TO Professor Michael Bond, Director, Heathayne, Colyton, Devon EX24 6RS *Tel* 01297 552281 *Fax* 01297 552281

CC NO 306606   **ESTABLISHED** 1977

■ St Mark's Overseas Aid Trust (SMOAT)

WHERE FUNDING CAN BE GIVEN Developing countries.

WHO CAN BENEFIT Charitable organisations.

WHAT IS FUNDED International development projects, largely self-help projects where a little money can go a long way.

FINANCES *Year* 2008 *Income* £22,290 *Grants* £20,000

TRUSTEES R Salmon, Chair; Mrs C Ingram; A Preston; B Perkins; I Stratford.

HOW TO APPLY Unsolicited applications are unlikely to be funded as grants are usually made through personal contact with a trustee.

WHO TO APPLY TO R Salmon, Chair, 49 Redstone Hill, Redhill RH1 4BG *Tel* 01737 772811 *Website* www.smoat.org.uk

CC NO 280091   **ESTABLISHED** 1980

■ St Michael's and All Saints' Charities

WHERE FUNDING CAN BE GIVEN City of Oxford.

WHO CAN BENEFIT Charitable organisations, with an interest in Christian groups.

WHAT IS FUNDED Health and welfare.

WHAT IS NOT FUNDED Individuals are very rarely supported.

SAMPLE GRANTS Leys Youth Programme (£7,500); Cowley Child Contact Centre (£5,700); Oxford Christian Institute for Counselling (£4,000); Elmore Community Services and Abbeyfield Society (£3,000 each); Asylum Welcome (£2,500); and Archway and Oxford Young Cruse (£2,000 each).

FINANCES *Year* 2007 *Income* £53,843 *Grants* £51,759 *Assets* £1,053,871

TRUSTEES P Beavis; C Burton; Rev H Lee; P Eldridge; Prof. P Langford; M Lear; Sir John Krebs; The Ven J Morrison; A Paine.

HOW TO APPLY In writing to the correspondent.

WHO TO APPLY TO Robert J Spencer Hawes, St Michael's Church Centre, St Michael at the North Gate, Cornmarket Street, Oxford OX1 3EY *Tel* 01865 240940 *email* robert.hawes@smng.org.uk

CC NO 202750   **ESTABLISHED** 1980

■ St Monica Trust Community Fund

WHERE FUNDING CAN BE GIVEN Preference for the south west of England, particularly Bristol and the surrounding area.

WHO CAN BENEFIT People with a physical or long-term physical health problem.

WHAT IS FUNDED To be considered, organisations must meet all of the following criteria: (i) Benefit people (over 16 years old) who have a physical disability or long-term physical health problem, including those with infirmities due to old age. (ii) Benefit people living in Bristol or the surrounding area (North Somerset, Somerset, South Gloucestershire, Gloucestershire, Bath and North East Somerset and Wiltshire). (iii) Make a real difference to people's daily lives. (iv) Be both properly constituted and a not-for-profit organisation. (v) Fit in with the fund's current theme. Each year has a different theme – the 2009 grants scheme was open to organisations working with older people living with a long-term physical disability, impairment or physical health problem where substance misuse has been a contributing factor. Please see www.communityfund.stmonicatrust.org.uk for up-to-date information.

WHAT IS NOT FUNDED No grants to fund buildings, adaptations to buildings or minibus purchases.

TYPE OF GRANT Capital items, running costs.

RANGE OF GRANTS Grants of up to £10,000 each are available to organisations.

SAMPLE GRANTS Citizen's Advice (£9,800); St Peter's Hospice, Headway Bristol and Motor Neurone Disease Association (£7,500 each); IT Help@Home (£5,000); the New Place (£3,900); Bristol and Avon Chinese Women's Group (£2,000); Bath Institute of Medical Engineering (£1,500); and Western Active Stroke Group (£1,000).

FINANCES *Year* 2007 *Income* £14,841,000 *Grants* £139,374 *Assets* £189,926,000

TRUSTEES Revd Robert Grimley Dean Of Bristol; Timothy Thom; Robert Bernays; Revd Ian Gobey; Jane Edwards Cork; Peter Sherwood; Trevor Smallwood; Mary Prior Lord Lieutenant of Bristol; John Laycock; Gillian Camm; Charles Hunter; Judith Pearce; Prof. Patricia Broadfoot; Dr. Pippa Marsh.

OTHER INFORMATION This trust has provided accommodation, care and support for older and disabled people for over 85 years. Grants are also made to individuals.

HOW TO APPLY On a form available from the correspondent, or to download from the fund's website. All applicants must submit a form together with additional information that is requested, for example, an annual report. Applications are considered once a year; please see the fund's website for deadline dates. All applications will be considered by the Community Fund Committee of the trust. Notification of the outcome will be made in writing. The fund states: 'we receive many more requests than we have funds available. For example, in 2009 we received 35 applications with requests totalling over £318,000: well above the £110,000 we had available. In practice this means that we do not give grants to organisations which do not fully meet our criteria'.

WHO TO APPLY TO Kate Stobie, Community Fund Manager, Cote Lane, Westbury-on-Trym, Bristol BS9 3UN *Tel* 0117 949 4003 *Fax* 0117 949 4044 *email* kate.stobie@stmonicatrust.org.uk *Website* www.communityfund.stmonicatrust.org. uk

CC NO 202151   **ESTABLISHED** 1962

■ The Late St Patrick White Charitable Trust

WHERE FUNDING CAN BE GIVEN UK, with a possible preference for Hampshire.

WHO CAN BENEFIT Registered charities.

WHAT IS FUNDED Large UK charities catering for older people, people with disabilities, and local groups in Hampshire. The trust has a list of regular beneficiaries, although grants are available to other organisations.

RANGE OF GRANTS Between £1,000 and £5,000.

SAMPLE GRANTS Age Concern, Arthritis Concern, Barnardo's, Guide Dogs for the Blind Association and The Salvation Army (£5,000 each); Prostate Cancer and Tuberous Sclerosis Association (£2,500 each); and Braille Chess Association, National Blind Children's Society and The Seeing Ear (£1,000 each).

FINANCES *Year* 2007–08 *Income* £52,771 *Grants* £35,000 *Assets* £2,108,354

TRUSTEES HSBC Trusts Co. (UK) Ltd.

HOW TO APPLY In writing to the correspondent. Applications are considered in February, May, August and November.

WHO TO APPLY TO Lee Topp, Trust Manager, HSBC Trust Co UK Ltd, Norwich House, Nelson Gate, Commercial Road, Southampton SO15 1GX *Tel* 023 8072 2240

CC NO 1056520   **ESTABLISHED** 1995

■ Saint Sarkis Charity Trust

WHERE FUNDING CAN BE GIVEN UK and overseas.

WHO CAN BENEFIT Smaller registered charities benefiting Armenians and offenders.

WHAT IS FUNDED Primarily charitable objectives with an Armenian connection including Armenian religious buildings; and other small charities developing innovative projects to support prisoners in the UK.

WHAT IS NOT FUNDED The trust does not give grants to: individual applicants; organisations that are not registered charities; and registered charities outside the UK, unless the project benefits the Armenian community in the UK and/or overseas. The trust does not fund: general appeals; core costs or salaries (as opposed to project costs); projects concerning substance misuse; or medical research.

TYPE OF GRANT Mainly confined to one-off grants for capital projects or operational expenses.

RANGE OF GRANTS £400–£125,000.

SAMPLE GRANTS Armenian Church of Saint Sarkis (£123,000); Friends of Armenia (£48,000); Fonds Armenia de France (£25,000); Centre for Armenian Information and Advice (£15,000); Revolving Doors Agency and Action for Prisoners (£10,000 each); London Armenian Poor Relief (£8,000); Armenian Patriarchate – Jerusalem Library (£6,600); Howard League for Penal Reform (£5,000); Send Family Link (£1,000); Armenian Institute (£800); and SPODA (£500).

FINANCES *Year* 2007–08 *Income* £356,386 *Grants* £289,093 *Assets* £7,082,409

TRUSTEES Martin Sarkis Essayan; Boghos Parsegh Gulbenkian; Rita Alice Vartoukian; Robert Brian Todd.

Think carefully about every application. Is it justified?

835

HOW TO APPLY In writing to the correspondent. There is no standard application form so applicants should write a covering letter including: an explanation of the exact purpose of the grant; how much is needed, with details of how the budget has been arrived at; details of any other sources of income (firm commitments and those still being explored); the charity registration number; the latest annual report and audited accounts; and any plans for monitoring and evaluating the work.

WHO TO APPLY TO Louisa Hooper, Secretary, 98 Portland Place, London W1B 1ET *Tel* 020 7908 7604 *Fax* 020 7908 7582 *email* info@ saintsarkis.org.uk *Website* www.saintsarkis.org. uk

CC NO 215352   **ESTABLISHED** 1954

....

■ St Teilo's Trust

WHERE FUNDING CAN BE GIVEN Wales.

WHO CAN BENEFIT Christian organisations.

WHAT IS FUNDED Evangelistic initiatives in parishes, for example, Alpha courses, evangelistic events and literature distribution.

SAMPLE GRANTS Previous beneficiaries include: Llandeilo PC, Gobaith Gymru, St Michael's Aberyswyth, Cilcoed Christian Centre, Parish of Bargoed, Postal Bible School and St David's Diocesan Council.

FINANCES *Year* 2007–08 *Income* £13,024 *Grants* £40,000

TRUSTEES P C A Mansel Lewis, Chair; Mrs C Mansel Lewis; Revd Canon S R Bell; Revd Dr W A Strange; Revd P A Bement; Revd Bob Capper.

OTHER INFORMATION No grants list was available.

HOW TO APPLY In writing to the correspondent. Trustees meet in February, May and September. Applications should be sent by January, April and August. Guidelines are available from the trust.

WHO TO APPLY TO Rev P Mansel Lewis, Capel Isaf, Manordeilo, Llandeilo, Carmarthenshire SA19 7BS *Tel* 01558 822273

CC NO 1032405   **ESTABLISHED** 1993

....

■ The Saintbury Trust

WHERE FUNDING CAN BE GIVEN West Midlands and Warwickshire (which the trust considers to be post code areas B, CV, DY, WS and WV), Worcestershire, Herefordshire and Gloucestershire (post code areas WR, HR and GL).

WHO CAN BENEFIT Registered charities.

WHAT IS FUNDED General charitable purposes with a preference for, addiction, arts and leisure, care of the dying, childhood and young people, community work, disability, education, environment, health, heritage, homelessness, old age, other special needs and prisons.

WHAT IS NOT FUNDED No grants to animal charities, individuals (including individuals seeking sponsorship for challenges in support of charities), 'cold-calling' national charities or local branches of national charities. The trust only gives grants to charities outside of its beneficial area if the charity is personally known to one or more of the trustees.

SAMPLE GRANTS Midlands Arts Centre (£90,000); Birmingham Children's Hospitals Charities (£20,000); RAPt and Royal Surgical Aid Society (£15,000 each); Trinity Winchester (£10,000); UCE Birmingham Conservatoire, Pimlico Opera and St Richard's Hospice Foundation (£5,000 each); Freshwinds, St Basil's and Kings Norton

PCC Restoration (£2,000 each); Adoption Support and McMillan Cancer Support (£1,000 each); and Gloucester Choral Society (£500).

FINANCES *Year* 2007 *Income* £281,829 *Grants* £269,000 *Assets* £7,203,939

TRUSTEES Victoria K Houghton; Anne R Thomas; Jane P Lewis; Amanda E Atkinson-Willes; Harry O Forrester.

HOW TO APPLY In writing to the correspondent. Applications are considered in twice a year, usually in April and November.

WHO TO APPLY TO Mrs J P Lewis, Trustee, P O Box 464, Abinger Hammer, Dorking, Surrey RH4 9AF *Tel* 01306 730119

CC NO 326790   **ESTABLISHED** 1985

....

■ The Saints and Sinners Trust

WHERE FUNDING CAN BE GIVEN Mostly UK.

WHO CAN BENEFIT Registered charities.

WHAT IS FUNDED General charitable purposes, mainly welfare and medical. Priority is given to requests for grants sponsored by members of Saints and Sinners.

WHAT IS NOT FUNDED No grants to individuals or non-registered charities.

RANGE OF GRANTS £500–£10,000 but generally in the range of £1,000–£3,000.

SAMPLE GRANTS Royal Opera House (£10,000); South Bucks Riding for the Disabled and White Ensign Association Limited (£5,000 each); Marine Conversation Society and AJET (£3,000 each); Police Rehabilitation Trust and Sandy Gall's Afghanistan Appeal (£2,000 each); and British Limbless Ex-service Men's Association, Spina! Injuries Association and Foundation for the Study of Infant Deaths (£1,000 each).

FINANCES *Year* 2007–08 *Income* £152,476 *Grants* £74,500 *Assets* £328,168

TRUSTEES N W Benson; Sir Donald Gosling; N C Royds; I A N Irvine.

HOW TO APPLY Applications are not considered unless nominated by members of the club.

WHO TO APPLY TO N W Benson, Trustee, Lewis Golden and Co., 40 Queen Anne Street, London W1G 9EL *Tel* 020 7580 7313

CC NO 200536   **ESTABLISHED** 1961

....

■ The Salamander Charitable Trust

WHERE FUNDING CAN BE GIVEN Worldwide.

WHO CAN BENEFIT Registered charities benefiting children, young adults, people disadvantaged by poverty and people who are disabled.

WHAT IS FUNDED The trust has a list of charities, in the fields of advancement of education and religion, and relief of poverty or physical disability, to which it gives on an annual basis. No other charities are funded.

WHAT IS NOT FUNDED No grants to individuals. Only registered charities are supported.

RANGE OF GRANTS £250–£3,000, generally £1,000 or less.

SAMPLE GRANTS Previous beneficiaries included: SAT- 7 Trust, All Nations Christian College, All Saints in Branksome Park, Birmingham Christian College, Christian Aid, Churches Commission on Overseas Students, FEBA Radio, International Christian College, London Bible College, Middle East Media, Moorland College, St James PCC in Poole, SAMS, Trinity College and Wycliffe Bible Translators.

FINANCES *Year* 2007–08 *Income* £64,766 *Grants* £80,750 *Assets* £2,075,951

TRUSTEES J R T Douglas; Sheila M Douglas; Mrs A M Hardwick; R P Douglas.

836

Does the trust you have chosen match your needs? Haphazard applications waste postage and time

HOW TO APPLY The trust's income is fully allocated each year, mainly to regular beneficiaries. The trustees do not wish to receive any further new requests.

WHO TO APPLY TO John R T Douglas, Trustee, Threave, 2 Brudenell Avenue, Canford Cliffs, Poole, Dorset BH13 7NW *Tel* 01202 706661

CC NO 273657 **ESTABLISHED** 1977

■ The Salt Foundation

WHERE FUNDING CAN BE GIVEN Saltaire and Shipley.

WHO CAN BENEFIT Individuals and schools benefiting children, young adults, older people and students. During the year the foundation concentrated on its commitment to maintain one of its properties, Victoria Hall, but hopes to resume normal grantmaking in the near future.

WHAT IS FUNDED Education.

WHAT IS NOT FUNDED No grants to replace statutory funding.

TYPE OF GRANT One-off grants (although applicants may reapply), capital, project and recurring costs for funding of one year or less.

FINANCES *Year* 2007–08 *Income* £276,195 *Grants* £5,500 *Assets* £298,293

TRUSTEES Alex McClelland; Geraldine Whelan; James Flood; Robert Sowman; Ted Watson; Norman Roper; John Briggs; John Carroll; Alec Law.

OTHER INFORMATION The foundation stated in 2009 that it has not made grant awards for the past three years because of the need to repair property for which it has responsibility.

HOW TO APPLY In writing to the correspondent.

WHO TO APPLY TO Mrs M Davies, Clerk, 17 Springfield Road, Baildon, Shipley, Yorkshire BD17 5NA *Tel* 01274 591 508 *email* marjoriedavies@tiscali.co.uk

CC NO 511978 **ESTABLISHED** 1981

■ The Salt Trust

WHERE FUNDING CAN BE GIVEN UK.

WHO CAN BENEFIT Charitable organisations.

WHAT IS FUNDED General charitable purposes.

SAMPLE GRANTS The trust stated that it 'supported a crisis debt counselling centre, schools and community workers, a church, youth organisations, a young person undertaking training, a school building project in Burkino Faso and other works in keeping with the purpose of the charity.'

FINANCES *Year* 2007–08 *Income* £62,001 *Grants* £36,852 *Assets* £24,779

TRUSTEES Norman Adams; Dianne Parsons; Robert Parsons; Stephen Williams; Mark Molden.

HOW TO APPLY The trust does not accept unsolicited applications.

WHO TO APPLY TO Jill Jameson, 10 Tarragon Way, Pontprennau, Cardiff CF23 8SN *Tel* 029 2073 3422

CC NO 1062133 **ESTABLISHED** 1977

■ The Salters' Charities

WHERE FUNDING CAN BE GIVEN Greater London or UK.

WHO CAN BENEFIT Priority is given to funding small nationwide charities and organisations connected with the City of London, where the trusts contribution would make a 'real difference'. As a matter of general policy, the company supports those charities where Salters are involved.

WHAT IS FUNDED The trust makes donations for a wide range of charitable purposes including, children and young people, health, homelessness, Christian aid, the developing world, the environment and members of the armed forces.

WHAT IS NOT FUNDED Grants are not normally made to charities working with people who are homeless unless there is some connection with a liveryman of the company or with the Salters' City Foyer and the charities involved.

RANGE OF GRANTS Around £2,000.

SAMPLE GRANTS UNEP – WCMC (£9,000); Arkwright Schools Scholarships (£5,400); The Lord Todd Memorial Bursary (£3,200); Wheelpower, Lord Mayor Treloar Trust and TEAR Fund (£3,000 each); Rainbow Trust, the Passage, Sheriffs' and Recorders' Fund and Blind in Business (£2,000 each); and the National Deaf Children's Society, Thames Hospice Care and Chelsea Pensioners Appeal (£1,000 each).

FINANCES *Year* 2007–08 *Income* £162,045 *Grants* £147,700 *Assets* £845

TRUSTEES The Salters' Company.

HOW TO APPLY In writing to the correspondent. Please note: the trust states that email requests for funding will not be considered.

WHO TO APPLY TO Diane Bundock, Administrator, The Salters' Company, Salters' Hall, 4 Fore Street, London EC2Y 5DE *Tel* 020 7588 5216 *Fax* 020 7638 3679 *email* diane@salters.co.uk *Website* www.salters.co.uk

CC NO 328258 **ESTABLISHED** 1989

■ The Andrew Salvesen Charitable Trust

WHERE FUNDING CAN BE GIVEN UK, with a preference for Scotland.

WHO CAN BENEFIT Organisations benefiting children who are ill and people who are disabled or homeless.

WHAT IS FUNDED Grants are made to a variety of charitable organisations who work for sick children, people who are disabled, homeless people and a range of other causes.

WHAT IS NOT FUNDED No grants to individuals.

SAMPLE GRANTS Previous beneficiaries have included Bield Housing Trust, William Higgins Marathon Account, Multiple Sclerosis Society in Scotland, Royal Zoological Society of Scotland, Sail Training Association, Scottish Down's Syndrome Association and Sick Kids Appeal.

FINANCES *Year* 2007–08 *Income* £110,388 *Grants* £100,000

TRUSTEES A C Salvesen; Ms K Turner; V Lall.

HOW TO APPLY The trustees only support organisations known to them through their personal contacts. The trust has previously stated that all applications sent to them are 'thrown in the bin'.

WHO TO APPLY TO The Trustees, c/o Meston Reid and Co., 12 Carden Place, Aberdeen AB10 1UR *Tel* 01224 625554

SC NO SC008000 **ESTABLISHED** 1989

■ The Sammermar Trust

WHERE FUNDING CAN BE GIVEN UK and overseas.

WHO CAN BENEFIT Charitable organisations.

WHAT IS FUNDED General charitable purposes.

RANGE OF GRANTS £1,000–£125,000.

SAMPLE GRANTS Wantage Nursing Home Charitable Trust (£125,000); Mango Tree (£12,000); Book Aid International, Sparsholt PCC and Vulcan to the Sky Trust (£10,000 each); Oxford Nature Conservation Forum (£5,000 each); Griffin Hall (£4,000); Warwickshire Firefighters Families Fund (£3,000); Headington School (£2,500); Myton Hospice (£2,000); and Head and Neck Cancer Research Trust and Guild of Air Pilots and Air Navigators (£1,000 each).

FINANCES *Year* 2007 *Income* £244,150 *Grants* £248,007 *Assets* £7,581,857

TRUSTEES Lady Judith Swire; M Dunne; M B Swire; Mrs M V Allfrey.

OTHER INFORMATION Grants of less than £1,000 each totalled £7,800.

HOW TO APPLY In writing to the correspondent. The trust states that: 'although the trustees make some grants with no formal applications, they normally require organisations to submit a request saying how the funds could be used and what would be achieved'. The trustees usually meet monthly.

WHO TO APPLY TO Mrs Yvonne Barnes, Swire House, 59 Buckingham Gate, London SW1E 6AJ *Tel* 020 7834 7717

CC NO 800493   **ESTABLISHED** 1988

·········

■ Basil Samuel Charitable Trust

WHERE FUNDING CAN BE GIVEN UK and worldwide.

WHO CAN BENEFIT Registered charities.

WHAT IS FUNDED General charitable purposes but mainly, medical, socially supportive, educational and cultural charities.

WHAT IS NOT FUNDED Only applications from registered charities are considered.

TYPE OF GRANT 'One-off' and recurring.

RANGE OF GRANTS £1,000–£100,000.

SAMPLE GRANTS Royal National Theatre (£100,000); Macmillan Cancer Support (£60,000); Mary Rose Trust (£40,000); Great Ormond Street Hospital (£25,000); RNIB (£15,000); British Museum and Thomas Coram Foundation for Children (£10,000 each); Attingham Trust, Hampstead Theatre and the Police Rehabilitation Trust (£5,000 each); Commonwealth Jewish Trust (£2,000); and Countryside Foundation for Education (£1,000).

FINANCES *Year* 2007–08 *Income* £477,583 *Grants* £498,000 *Assets* £9,766,447

TRUSTEES Coral Samuel; Richard M Peskin.

HOW TO APPLY In writing to the correspondent. The trustees meet on a formal basis annually and regularly on an informal basis to discuss proposals for individual donations.

WHO TO APPLY TO Mrs Coral Samuel, Trustee, Smith & Williamson, 25 Moorgate, London EC2R 6AY *Tel* 020 7131 4376

CC NO 206579   **ESTABLISHED** 1959

·········

■ Coral Samuel Charitable Trust

WHERE FUNDING CAN BE GIVEN UK.

WHO CAN BENEFIT Registered charities only.

WHAT IS FUNDED General charitable purposes, including educational, cultural and socially supportive charities.

WHAT IS NOT FUNDED Grants are only made to registered charities.

RANGE OF GRANTS £500–£50,000.

SAMPLE GRANTS South Bank Foundation (£50,000); Victoria and Albert Museum (£25,000); Natural History Museum Development Trust, Royal Opera House Foundation and SAVE (£10,000 each); Chelsea Physic Garden (£5,000); Maccabi GB (£2,000); Royal British Legion and Mercers' Charitable Foundation (£1,000 each); and European Union Youth Orchestra (£500).

FINANCES *Year* 2007–08 *Income* £244,374 *Grants* £137,500 *Assets* £4,945,490

TRUSTEES Coral Samuel; P Fineman.

HOW TO APPLY In writing to the correspondent.

WHO TO APPLY TO Mrs Coral Samuel, Trustee, c/o Smith and Williamson, 25 Moorgate, London EC2R 6AY

CC NO 239677   **ESTABLISHED** 1962

·········

■ The Hon. M J Samuel Charitable Trust

WHERE FUNDING CAN BE GIVEN UK and overseas.

WHO CAN BENEFIT Charitable organisations.

WHAT IS FUNDED The trust supports a wide range of causes, many of them Jewish, environmental or to do with mental health.

WHAT IS NOT FUNDED No grants to individuals.

TYPE OF GRANT Core costs, project and research. Funding of up to two years will be considered.

SAMPLE GRANTS Anna Freud Centre (£250,000); Institute Trust Fund (£5,000); Liver Research Trust (£4,000); Atlantic Salmon Trust (£3,500); the Children's Hospice (£3,000); BAAF, Brogdale Horticultural Trust and the Wheelyboat Trust (£2,500 each); Chicken Shed Theatre Company (£2,000); the Tyne Rivers Trust (£1,500); and TATE Foundation, Valid Nutrition and the Henry van Straubenzee Memorial Fund (£1,000 each).

FINANCES *Year* 2007–08 *Income* £101,514 *Grants* £287,372 *Assets* £2,960,083

TRUSTEES Hon. Michael Samuel; Hon. Mrs Julia A Samuel; Viscount Bearsted.

HOW TO APPLY In writing to the correspondent.

WHO TO APPLY TO The Secretary, 35 Connaught Square, London W2 2HL

CC NO 327013   **ESTABLISHED** 1985

·········

■ The Peter Samuel Charitable Trust

WHERE FUNDING CAN BE GIVEN UK, with some preference for local organisations in South Berkshire, Highlands of Scotland and East Somerset.

WHO CAN BENEFIT Registered charities benefiting medical professionals, scientists, at-risk groups and people disadvantaged by poverty.

WHAT IS FUNDED Medical sciences, the quality of life in local areas, heritage and land/forestry restoration.

WHAT IS NOT FUNDED No grants to purely local charities outside Berkshire or to individuals.

TYPE OF GRANT Single and annual donations.

RANGE OF GRANTS £200–£20,000.

SAMPLE GRANTS Game Conservancy (£25,000); Marie Curie, Outreach and Anna Freud Centre (£5,000 each); Cancer Research (£3,000); St Mary's Paddington Charitable Trust (£2,500); NSPCC, Highland Hospice and I Can (£2,000 each); London String Quartet and Chicken Shed Theatre (£1,000 each); National Talking Newspapers & Magazines and Oxford University Jewish Society (£500 each); and BBONT (£200).

FINANCES *Year* 2007–08 *Income* £102,589 *Grants* £95,085 *Assets* £3,433,485

TRUSTEES Hon. Viscount Bearsted; Hon. Michael Samuel.

HOW TO APPLY In writing to the correspondent. Trustees meet twice-yearly.

·········

WHO TO APPLY TO Miss Emma Chapman, Trust Administrator, The Estate Office, Farley Hall, Castle Road, Farley Hill, Berkshire RG7 1UL *Tel* 0118 973 0047 *Fax* 0118 973 0385 *email* emma@farleyfarms.co.uk
CC NO 269065   **ESTABLISHED** 1975

....

■ The Camilla Samuel Fund

WHERE FUNDING CAN BE GIVEN UK.
WHO CAN BENEFIT Medical research projects in a discipline agreed by the trustees at their annual meetings. Funding may be given to medical professionals and research workers.
WHAT IS FUNDED The promotion, encouragement, assistance, support, conduct and accomplishment of any research or inquiry into any matters relating to the causes, prevention, diagnosis, incidence, treatment, cure or effects of any form of illness, injury or disability requiring medical or dental treatment.
WHAT IS NOT FUNDED No grants to individuals, general appeals or any other charitable institution.
TYPE OF GRANT Agreed expenses of research only. Maximum period three years, subject to satisfactory annual report and review by trustees.
SAMPLE GRANTS Previous beneficiaries have included Imperial Cancer Research Fund and EORTC.
FINANCES *Year* 2007–08 *Income* £17,372 *Grants* £25,000
TRUSTEES Sir Ronald Grierson; Hon. Mrs Waley-Cohen; Dr Hon. J P H Hunt.
HOW TO APPLY The trustees will request written applications following the recommendation of a suitable project by the medical trustees. However, please note as all the money available, together with the fund's future income, has been earmarked for four years for an important research project, the fund will not be in a position to consider any applications for grants during this period.
WHO TO APPLY TO The Secretary to the Trustees, 40 Berkerly Square, London W1J 5AL
CC NO 235424   **ESTABLISHED** 1964

....

■ The Samworth Foundation

WHERE FUNDING CAN BE GIVEN Derby, Leicestershire and Nottinghamshire.
WHO CAN BENEFIT Registered charities only.
WHAT IS FUNDED General charitable purposes.
WHAT IS NOT FUNDED No grants to individuals.
RANGE OF GRANTS Between £10 and £100,000.
SAMPLE GRANTS Thorpe Satchville Village Hall (£107,000); Mango Tree (£60,000); Cancer Research UK (£8,000); Royal Agricultural Society of England (£6,300); EM Radiation Research Trust (£5,000); and Melton Young Singles Trust (£1,000).
FINANCES *Year* 2007–08 *Income* £3,905,842 *Grants* £242,113 *Assets* £5,083,841
TRUSTEES Bob Dowson; Mrs Clare Price; Mrs Viccy Stott.
OTHER INFORMATION Donations of less than £1,000 each totalled £3,255.
HOW TO APPLY In writing to the correspondent. The foundation's grant-making policy is to support a limited number of causes known to the trustees. Unsolicited applications are not normally considered.

WHO TO APPLY TO Miss W A Bateman, c/o Samworth Brothers (Holdings) Ltd, Chetwode House, 1 Samworth Way, Melton Mowbray, Leicestershire LE13 1GA *Tel* 01664 414500 *Fax* 01664 414501
CC NO 265647   **ESTABLISHED** 1973

....

■ The Sandhu Charitable Foundation

WHERE FUNDING CAN BE GIVEN Worldwide.
WHO CAN BENEFIT Charities and charitable causes.
WHAT IS FUNDED General charitable purposes.
SAMPLE GRANTS £25,000 between Grand Bahama Children's Home, Emmaus Hampshire and Young Enterprise.
FINANCES *Year* 2007–08 *Income* £397,123 *Grants* £25,000 *Assets* £1,021,661
TRUSTEES B S Sandhu, Chair; S Carey.
HOW TO APPLY 'The charity is to support individual charities or charitable causes, mainly on a single donation basis, which they themselves identify.'
WHO TO APPLY TO The Trustees, First Floor, 21 Knightsbridge, London SW1X 7LY
CC NO 1114236   **ESTABLISHED** 2006

....

■ The Sandra Charitable Trust

WHERE FUNDING CAN BE GIVEN Not defined, in practice UK with slight preference for south east England.
WHO CAN BENEFIT Organisations benefiting children and young people, hospices, education, people with disabilities, people disadvantaged by poverty, the arts, and individual grants for nurses.
WHAT IS FUNDED Animal welfare and research, environmental protection, social welfare, health and youth development.
WHAT IS NOT FUNDED No grants to individuals other than nurses.
TYPE OF GRANT One-off and recurring.
RANGE OF GRANTS Typically £5,000 or less.
SAMPLE GRANTS Barnardo's (£75,000); Arundle Castle Cricket Foundation and the Florence Nightingale Foundation (£25,000 each); Dorchester Abbey Preservation Trust (£12,000); and Leukaemia Research and RNIB (£10,000); British Trust for Ornithology and Sightsavers (£5,000 each); Alone in London, Joint Educational Trust and the Woodland Trust (£3,000 each); Cure Parkinson's Trust and Music in Hospitals (£2,000 each); and Ability Net, Fine Cell Block and the Imperial War Museum (£1,000 each).
FINANCES *Year* 2007–08 *Income* £529,289 *Grants* £596,003 *Assets* £14,864,990
TRUSTEES Richard Moore; Michael Macfadyen.
OTHER INFORMATION The grant total included £81,000 made to 143 individuals
HOW TO APPLY The trust states that 'unsolicited applications are not requested, as the trustees prefer to support charities whose work they have researched … the trustees receives a very high number of grant applications which are mostly unsuccessful'.
WHO TO APPLY TO Keith Lawrence, Secretary, Moore Stephens, St Paul's House, Warwick Lane, London EC4P 4BN *Tel* 020 7334 9191 *Fax* 020 7651 1953 *email* keith.lawrence@ moorestephens.com
CC NO 327492   **ESTABLISHED** 1987

Think carefully about every application. Is it justified?

839

■ Santander UK Foundation Limited

WHERE FUNDING CAN BE GIVEN UK. 'In areas where Santander has a significant presence we have established Community Partnership Groups. These are made up of existing staff, pensioners and a local infrastructure charity such as a community foundation or Council for Voluntary Services. Grants of up to £30,000 are available in the following nine areas: London Borough of Camden; Milton Keynes covering Buckinghamshire, Northamptonshire and Bedfordshire; Leicestershire and Rutland; Sheffield covering South Yorkshire; Bradford covering West Yorkshire; Teesside covering the area from Redcar to Darlington and Sunderland; Merseyside; Greater Glasgow; Northern Ireland.'

WHO CAN BENEFIT Registered, excepted or exempt charities. Industrial and Provident societies can only be supported if they are founded under charitable, not membership, rules.

WHAT IS FUNDED 'All of our funding must directly help disadvantaged people through one or both of these charitable priorities – education and training, or financial capability. Education and training: this could be any activity disadvantaged people undertake where they improve their confidence in a skill or their understanding of a subject This does not have to be formal training or lead to a qualification, although those activities would be eligible too. It could be any activity disadvantaged people undertake where they improve their confidence in a skill or their understanding of a subject. Examples could include independent living skills, anger management, or improving self esteem. Other examples could include reminiscence projects for older people, art and craft sessions as well as IT classes. These are just a few examples and should not be regarded as a definitive list. Financial capability: this priority covers activities which help disadvantaged people understand how to manage their money. It could include budgeting skills, accessing affordable credit as well as managing the challenges that arise from being a carer, unemployment, disability or relationship break up. Examples could be the costs of running a credit union, projects delivering financial advice and helping people to understand their benefit entitlement. Successful applications under this priority have included equipping a training kitchen for homeless people who learnt how to budget effectively for their food and then went on to apply these principals to other parts of their lives.'

WHAT IS NOT FUNDED Donations are not made for: statutory duties; part of a major capital appeal; a specific individual (this includes gap year funding, overseas travel, medical treatment or holidays); lobbying or political parties; the benefit of a single religious or single ethnic group; causes outside the UK; gaining specialist school status; commercial sponsorship or for fundraising events, conferences or advertising.

TYPE OF GRANT All funding is for one off donations. Grants are available to buy tangible items such as equipment or training materials. Grants are also available to fund project costs such as sessional worker fees, salaries, room hire or other costs incurred in the delivery of the charitable priorities.

RANGE OF GRANTS Up to £30,000.

FINANCES *Year* 2008 *Grants* £2,528,747

TRUSTEES Lord Burns; M Young; S Williams.

OTHER INFORMATION The foundation changed its name from the Abbey Charitable Trust in early 2010. In 2010, the foundation will be making £3.3 million available to UK charities.

HOW TO APPLY The following guidance on making an application is given on the foundation's website. 'We have made applying to us as straightforward as possible and do not use an application form. We operate a rolling programme, with no deadlines for applications. Download and print off the grant application cover sheet which you can use as a checklist as you put together your application [available from the foundation's website]. You need to write us a letter on the headed notepaper of your charity which should include your registered charity number or whatever is appropriate for your charitable status. The letter should include the following: how much you are asking for?; what will this pay for? Include a simple budget detailing the main costs; how will disadvantaged people directly benefit? Include an estimate of the long term difference this grant will make; how does this meet one or both of our charitable priorities?; if the funding is for an existing project, tell us how our funding fits your funding strategy and what the project has achieved so far; if the funding is for a new project, tell us how you identified the need for this piece of work; if applicable, which other funders are you applying to? Make sure the letter is signed by two people, one of whom must be a trustee of the charity. If it helps explain what your project will do, you may want to include a flyer, newsletter or other sample training material that is produced for the beneficiaries. Please do not include: annual reports and accounts; DVDs or CDs; business plan or constitution; any other bulky items, plastic binders or covers. If you want confirmation that we have received your application, please enclose a self-addressed postcard or envelop with your application letter. We will post this to you when we open your application. If you do not receive any other correspondence from us within six weeks then you should assume that your application has been unsuccessful. We regret that due to the very high volume of requests received, we do not notify unsuccessful applicants or offer feedback on why your application has not been successful. We regret that we cannot accept online or emailed applications.'

WHO TO APPLY TO Alan Eagle, Foundation Manager, 201 Grafton Gate East, Milton Keynes MK9 1AN *Tel* 01908 343224 *email* alan. eagle@santander.co.uk *Website* www. santanderfoundation.org.uk

CC NO 803655   **ESTABLISHED** 1990

■ Jimmy Savile Charitable Trust

WHERE FUNDING CAN BE GIVEN UK.

WHO CAN BENEFIT Registered charities, hospitals and educational institutions.

WHAT IS FUNDED General charitable purposes.

TYPE OF GRANT One-off grants.

SAMPLE GRANTS University of Leeds for the Lure Scholarships (£48,000); Laniado Hospital (£5,000); Across, Royal Marines Atlantic Challenge, RMA Jubilee Fund, Scope and William Merritt Disabled Living Centre (£1,000 each); Music in Hospitals, Walk the Walk Worldwide, Kidney Research UK and Dame Vera Lynn Trust (£500 each); Hops and Sick Children's Trust (£250); and University of Bradford – IK Mitchal Fund (£100).

FINANCES *Year* 2007–08 *Income* £176,088 *Grants* £77,300 *Assets* £3,549,629

TRUSTEES Sir James Savile; James Collier; Luke Lucas; Dr Roger Bodley.

840

Does the trust you have chosen match your needs? Haphazard applications waste postage and time

How to apply The trust does not respond to unsolicited applications.

Who to apply to The Trustees, Stoke Mandeville Hospital, Mandeville Road, Aylesbury, Buckinghamshire HP21 8DL

cc no 326970   **Established** 1984

■ The Scarfe Charitable Trust

Where funding can be given UK, with an emphasis on Suffolk.

Who can benefit Individuals and organisations working in the fields of arts, music, medical research and the environment.

What is funded This trust will consider funding: conservation; environmental interests; medical research; hospices; arts and arts facilities; churches; religious ancillary buildings; art galleries and cultural centres; libraries and museums; and theatres and opera houses.

Type of grant Capital, core costs, one-off, project, research, recurring costs and running costs. Funding is normally for one year or less.

Range of grants £150–£19,000.

Sample grants Aldeburgh Music (£19,000); St Peters PCC Bruisyard (£2,500); Shadingfield PCC, MacMillan Cancer Support and Mahogany Opera (£2,000 each); Red Rose Chain (£1,250); Poetry Trust, City of London Sinfonia, RSPB, Dunwich PCC and Ickworth Church Conservation Trust (£1,000 each); St John Campsea Ashe Bells project (£700); Terrence Higgins Trust (£600); St Peter and St Paul PCC Clare (£500); Blyth Valley Chamber Music (£200); and Friends of Kirton Church (£150).

Finances *Year* 2007–08 *Income* £75,183 *Grants* £64,583 *Assets* £1,261,590

Trustees N Scarfe; E Maule; John McCarthy.

Other information Two grants were also made to individuals totalling £1,800.

How to apply In writing to the correspondent by post or email. The trustees meet quarterly to consider applications.

Who to apply to Eric Maule, Trustee, Salix House, Falkenham, Ipswich, Suffolk IP10 0QY *Tel* 01394 448 339 *Fax* 01394 448 339 *email* ericmaule@hotmail.com

cc no 275535   **Established** 1978

■ The Schapira Charitable Trust

Where funding can be given UK.

Who can benefit Organisations benefiting Jewish people.

What is funded Jewish charitable purposes.

Range of grants £500–£136,000.

Sample grants Friends of Tashbar Chazon Ish (£136,000); Emuno Education Centre (£48,000); KSH (£38,000); SOFT (£33,000); the New Rachmistrivke Synagogue (£9,000); Trustees of Bais Rizhin Trust and Friends of Horim (£7,700 each); T & S Trust (£5,000); Mercaz Hatorah (£2,000); Stanislow (£1,000); and Kiryat Sanz Jerusalem (£500).

Finances *Year* 2007 *Income* £443,263 *Grants* £378,950 *Assets* £6,953,702

Trustees Issac Y Schapira; Michael Neuberger; Suzanne L Schapira.

How to apply In writing to the correspondent.

Who to apply to The Trustees, 2 Dancastle Court, 14 Arcadia Avenue, Finchley, London N3 2JU *Tel* 020 8371 0381 *email* londonoffice@istrad.com

cc no 328435   **Established** 1989

■ The Annie Schiff Charitable Trust

Where funding can be given UK, overseas.

Who can benefit Orthodox Jewish institutions supporting religious, educational and relief of poverty aims.

What is funded The relief of poverty generally and payment to needy individuals of the Jewish faith, for the advancement of education and religion.

What is not funded No support for individuals and non-recognised institutions.

Range of grants £600–£20,000.

Sample grants Friends of Beis Yisrael Trust (£20,000); Friends of 'Seret Wiznitz' (£7,500); Yeshivo Horomo Talmudical College and Tiferes High School (£5,000 each); Jewish Learning Exchange (£4,000); Menorah Grammar School Trust (£2,000); and Sassoon Memorial (£600).

Finances *Year* 2007–08 *Income* £68,542 *Grants* £69,020 *Assets* £244,027

Trustees J Pearlman; Mrs R Pearlman.

How to apply In writing to the correspondent, but grants are generally made only to registered charities.

Who to apply to J Pearlman, Trustee, 8 Highfield Gardens, London NW11 9HB *Tel* 020 8458 9266

cc no 265401   **Established** 1973

■ The Schmidt-Bodner Charitable Trust

Where funding can be given UK and overseas.

Who can benefit Jewish organisations and other registered charities.

What is funded Health, education and welfare.

Range of grants £250–£35,000.

Sample grants Lubavitch Foundation (£35,000); Nightingale House and Jewish Care (£15,000 each); World Jewish Relief (£11,000); Community Security Trust and UJIA (£10,000 each); Yesodey Hatorah School (£5,000); HGSS Friends of Lvov (£4,000); British Friends of Or Chadash (£3,000); British Emunah (Child Resettlement Fund) (£2,000); Holocaust Educational Trust (£1,000); and United Synagogue (£250).

Finances *Year* 2007–08 *Income* £39,215 *Grants* £111,700 *Assets* £925,456

Trustees Daniel Dover; Martin Paisner.

How to apply In writing to the correspondent.

Who to apply to Daniel Dover, 55 Baker Street, London W1U 7EU *Tel* 020 7486 5888

cc no 283014   **Established** 1981

■ The R H Scholes Charitable Trust

Where funding can be given England.

Who can benefit Registered charities, particularly those benefiting children and young adults, the Church of England, and people who are disabled or disadvantaged by poverty.

What is funded Preference is given to charities that the trustees have a special interest in, knowledge of, or association with. If any new charities are to be supported it will be in the fields helping children and young people who are disadvantaged or disabled. Particularly charities working in the fields of: residential facilities; respite and sheltered accommodation; Anglican bodies; music and opera; special schools and special needs education; training for community development; care in the community; day centres; holidays and outings; playschemes; and research into medicine.

WHAT IS NOT FUNDED Grants only to registered charities. No grants to individuals, animal charities, expeditions or scholarships. The trust tries not to make grants to more than one charity operating in a particular field, and does not make grants to charities outside England.

TYPE OF GRANT Both recurrent and one-off grants are made depending upon the needs of the beneficiary. Core costs, project and research. Funding for more than three years will be considered.

RANGE OF GRANTS £100–£1,000.

SAMPLE GRANTS £1,000 each went to the Church of England Pensions Board, the Friends of Lancing Chapel, Historic Churches Preservation Trust, St Catherine's Hospice, St Luke's Hospital for the Clergy and the Children's Country Holidays Fund.

FINANCES *Year* 2006–07 *Income* £224,951 *Grants* £31,950 *Assets* £794,799

TRUSTEES R H C Pattison; Mrs A J Pattison.

OTHER INFORMATION All other grants were between £100 and £800.

HOW TO APPLY Due to a lack of funds the trust is not currently accepting unsolicited applications from organisations it is not already supporting.

WHO TO APPLY TO R H C Pattison, Trustee, Fairacre, Bonfire Hill, Southwater, Horsham, West Sussex RH13 9BU *email* roger@rogpat.plus.com

CC NO 267023   **ESTABLISHED** 1974

■ The Schreib Trust

WHERE FUNDING CAN BE GIVEN UK.

WHO CAN BENEFIT Jewish people, especially those disadvantaged by poverty.

WHAT IS FUNDED Relief of poverty and advancement of religion and religious education.

RANGE OF GRANTS Around £500–£80,000.

SAMPLE GRANTS Previous beneficiaries have included: Lolev, Yad Eliezer, Ponovitz, Craven Walk Charity Trust, Shaar Hatalmud, Beis Rochel, Beth Jacob Building Fund, Toiras Chesed and Oneg Shabbos.

FINANCES *Year* 2007–08 *Income* £312,857 *Grants* £947,217 *Assets* £416,795

TRUSTEES A Green; Mrs R Niederman; D Schreiber; Mrs I Schreiber.

OTHER INFORMATION No grants list was available.

HOW TO APPLY In writing to the correspondent.

WHO TO APPLY TO Mrs R Niederman, Trustee, 147 Stamford Hill, London N16 5LG *Tel* 020 8802 5492

CC NO 275240   **ESTABLISHED** 1977

■ The Schreiber Charitable Trust

WHERE FUNDING CAN BE GIVEN UK.

WHO CAN BENEFIT Registered charities benefiting Jewish people.

WHAT IS FUNDED Jewish with a preference for education, social welfare and medical causes.

RANGE OF GRANTS £100–£50,000.

SAMPLE GRANTS Friends of Rabbinical College Kol Tora Jerusalem (£50,000); SOFT (£12,000); Gateshead Talmudical College (£11,000); British Friends of Gesher (£10,000); Ner Israel Educational Trust (£9,000); and Aish Hatorah UK Limited, Seed and Menorah High School for Girls (£5,000 each).

FINANCES *Year* 2007–08 *Income* £697,987 *Grants* £175,255 *Assets* £3,594,965

TRUSTEES Graham S Morris; David A Schreiber; Sara Schreiber.

OTHER INFORMATION Other grants of less than £5,000 totalled £68,000.

HOW TO APPLY The trust states that the trustees 'regularly appraise new opportunities for direct charitable expenditure and actively seek suitable causes to reduce the unrestricted fund to the appropriate level'.

WHO TO APPLY TO G S Morris, Trustee, PO Box 35547, The Exchange, 4 Brent Cross Gardens, London NW4 3WH *email* graham@schreibers.com

CC NO 264735   **ESTABLISHED** 1972

■ Schroder Charity Trust

WHERE FUNDING CAN BE GIVEN Worldwide.

WHO CAN BENEFIT Preference for UK-registered charities.

WHAT IS FUNDED Medicine and health; older people; social welfare; education; humanities; arts; environment; international causes; and general charitable purposes.

WHAT IS NOT FUNDED No grants to individuals.

TYPE OF GRANT One-off and recurring.

RANGE OF GRANTS Mainly small grants from £200–£5,000.

SAMPLE GRANTS Royal Chapel – Windsor and Prostate Cancer Research Centre (£25,000 each); Cirencester Parish Church (£15,000); Muscular Dystrophy Campaign (£5,000); Place 2Be (£4,000); Tearfund (£3,000); Almshouse Association (£2,000); HemiHelp (£1,500); Children in Crisis (£1,000); and Farms for City Children (£600).

FINANCES *Year* 2008–09 *Income* £182,160 *Grants* £231,788 *Assets* £4,323,920

TRUSTEES Claire Fitzalan Howard; Charmaine Mallinckrodt; Bruno Schroder; T B Schroder; Leonie Fane; Jessica Schroder.

HOW TO APPLY In writing to the correspondent. Applicants should briefly state their case and enclose a copy of their latest accounts or annual review. Requests will be acknowledged in writing. The trust does not have the capacity to correspond with organisations on the progress of their application. Therefore, if you have not heard from the trust after six months, you can assume that the application has not been successful.

WHO TO APPLY TO Sally Yates, Secretary, 31 Gresham Street, London EC2V 7QA

CC NO 214050   **ESTABLISHED** 1944

■ The Schroder Foundation

WHERE FUNDING CAN BE GIVEN Worldwide, in practice mainly UK.

WHO CAN BENEFIT Charitable causes with a previous track record and organisations in which the foundation has a special interest.

WHAT IS FUNDED General mainly within the areas of the environment, education, arts, culture and heritage, social welfare, the community and international relief and development.

SAMPLE GRANTS Eton College (£117,000); Merlin (£80,000); Royal Geographical Society (£73,000); University College Oxford and Campaign for Female Education – CAFED (£50,000 each); Historic Palaces Kensington (£25,000); CSV Volunteers in Child Protection (£20,000); Islay and Jura Community Enterprise Trust (£15,000); Argyllshire Gathering (£7,700); and Smaull Song (£500).

FINANCES *Year* 2008–09 *Income* £5,281,708 *Grants* £1,378,095 *Assets* £10,608,799

TRUSTEES Bruno Schroder, Chair; Edward Mallinckrodt; Nicholas Ferguson; Charmaine Mallinckrodt; Leonie Fane.

HOW TO APPLY 'The trustees identify projects and organisations they wish to support and the foundation does not make grants to people or organisations who apply speculatively.' This trust **does not** respond to unsolicited applications.

WHO TO APPLY TO Sally Yates, Secretary, 31 Gresham Street, London EC2V 7QA

CC NO 1107479   **ESTABLISHED** 2005

■ The Scotshill Trust

WHERE FUNDING CAN BE GIVEN UK and overseas.

WHO CAN BENEFIT Registered charities.

WHAT IS FUNDED General, particularly health, arts, conservation, education, social needs, animal welfare and conservation.

WHAT IS NOT FUNDED No grants to individuals.

RANGE OF GRANTS £250-.

SAMPLE GRANTS Oxfam (£50,000); UJIA (£30,000); Samaritans (£25,000); Crisis (£20,000); Amnesty International, Medical Foundation, Big Issue, Richmond Fellowship and Salvation Army (£10,000 each); CARE International, Demand and SNAP (£5,000 each); Nightstop (£2,500); Amber Trust (£1,500); the Horse Trust and Redwings Horse (£1,000); and ILPH and Pace Centre (£500).

FINANCES *Year* 2007–08 *Income* £448,659 *Grants* £276,750 *Assets* £4,999,040

TRUSTEES Amanda Claire Burton; Paul Howard Burton; Deborah Maureen Hazan; Jeremy John Burton.

HOW TO APPLY Appeals should be in writing only to the trust managers. Unsuccessful appeals will not necessarily be acknowledged.

WHO TO APPLY TO The Trust Manager, Trustee Management Limited, 19 Cookridge Street, Leeds LS2 3AG *Tel* 0113 243 6466

CC NO 1113071   **ESTABLISHED** 2006

■ Scott (Eredine) Charitable Trust

WHERE FUNDING CAN BE GIVEN Not defined.

WHO CAN BENEFIT Charitable organisations.

WHAT IS FUNDED Service and ex-service charities; and medical and welfare causes.

SAMPLE GRANTS Scots Guards Charitable Funds (£28,000); Hampshire Youth Options (£7,000); Combat Stress (£5,100); Army Benevolent Fund, BLESMA and SSAFA (£4,600 each); the Tall Ships Trust (£3,000); Age Concern and Starlight Children's Foundation (£1,800 each); and the Born Free Foundation, EIA Charitable Trust, Send a Cow and Wheely Boat Trust (£500 each).

FINANCES *Year* 2008 *Income* £169,169 *Grants* £155,200 *Assets* £211,617

TRUSTEES M B Scott; K J Bruce-Smith; A J Scott.

HOW TO APPLY In writing to the correspondent.

WHO TO APPLY TO The Trustees, 40 Victoria Embankment, London EC4Y 0BA

CC NO 1002267   **ESTABLISHED** 1990

■ The Scott Bader Commonwealth Ltd

WHERE FUNDING CAN BE GIVEN UK, France, South Africa, Croatia, Dubai, USA, Czech Republic, Sweden, Spain.

WHO CAN BENEFIT Projects, activities or charities which: find difficulty raising funds; are innovative, imaginative and pioneering; or are initiated and/or supported by local people. Each year there is a particular area of focus, so applicants should check current focus before applying.

WHAT IS FUNDED Assistance of distressed and needy people of all nationalities. The commonwealth looks for projects, activities or charities which respond to the needs of those who are most underprivileged, disadvantaged, poor or excluded e.g. poor, homeless, vulnerable children, women and minority communities and people affected by poverty, hunger and disease. Also those who encourage the careful use and protection of the earth's resources (those which assist poor rural people to become self-reliant are particularly encouraged); or promote peace-building and democratic participation. The commonwealth also supports the research, development and advancement of education and advancement of education in industrial participation of a nature beneficial to the community.

WHAT IS NOT FUNDED No support for charities concerned with the well-being of animals, individuals in need or organisations sending volunteers abroad. It does not respond to general appeals or support the larger well-established national charities. It does not provide grants for medical research. It does not make up deficits already incurred, or support the arts, museums, travel/adventure, sports clubs or the construction, renovation or maintenance of buildings.

TYPE OF GRANT One-off and funding over a period (three to five years).

RANGE OF GRANTS Central Fund: Up to £25,000.

SAMPLE GRANTS Grants were given in two categories. Local funds – UK: Play Therapy (£5,000); Ro-Ro Sailing Project (£2,000); and June and Brian Cox Educational Trust (£1,000). France: continued supporting Kuborroto School, Guinea Bissau and gave aid to the flood victims in Ethopia (£7,000). Croatia: Firefly and SNAGA (£2,000 each); and Association of Parents of Children with Special Needs and Croatian Association of the Blind (£1,000). Sweden: Handikappidrott Falkenberg who provide sport programmes for the disabled (£400). Czech Republic: School of Hearing for Handicapped Children in Liberec (£500). Spain: Casa Dels Infants Del Raval (£300). South Africa: Fulton School for the Deaf (£3,000); Thusang HIV/AIDS Project for Orphans and Open Door Crisis Centre (£1,000 each); and VEMA (£350). USA: donations to Children's Museum of Cleveland, Stewart's Caring Place, Big Brothers Big Sister of Greater Cleveland, the Gathering Place totalling £600. Dubai: Dubai Cares Campaign (£5,000). Tools for Self Reliance and Children in Crisis, DRC received grants from the Central Fund.

FINANCES *Year* 2007 *Income* £159,351 *Grants* £111,500 *Assets* £36,242

TRUSTEES The Board of Management: Angela Miller, Jon Wiles, Celia Clayson, Kevin Hendrikse, Richard Stillwell, Heather Puddephatt, Paul Palmer, Sylvia Brown.

OTHER INFORMATION There are two categories of grants as follows: Local Funds and Central

Funds. Currently the Central Fund supports two large community based environmental/ educational projects to the value of £25,000 each.

HOW TO APPLY In writing or by e-mail to the correspondent. Trustees meet quarterly in February, May, September and November.

WHO TO APPLY TO Sue Carter, Secretary, Wollaston Hall, Wellingborough, Northamptonshire NN29 7RL *Tel* 01933 666755 *Fax* 01933 666608 *email* commonwealth_office@ scottbader.com *Website* www.scottbader.com

CC NO 206391   **ESTABLISHED** 1951

■ The Francis C Scott Charitable Trust

WHERE FUNDING CAN BE GIVEN Cumbria and north Lancashire (comprising the towns of Lancaster, Morecambe, Heysham and Carnforth).

WHO CAN BENEFIT Mostly registered charities addressing the needs of 0–19 year olds in the most deprived communities in Cumbria and north Lancashire. Organisations who are pursuing charitable objectives and have not-for-profit aims/constitution may be considered. Applications from national organisations will only be considered if the beneficiaries and project workers are based within the beneficial area.

WHAT IS FUNDED There is an emphasis on community services, support and development for youth organisations, family support services and community development projects.

WHAT IS NOT FUNDED The trust does not consider appeals: from individuals; from statutory organisations; from national charities without a local base/project; from charities with substantial unrestricted reserves; from medical/ health establishments; from schools/ educational establishments; from infrastructure organisations/second-tier bodies; for projects principally benefiting people outside Cumbria/ north Lancashire; for retrospective funding; for expeditions or overseas travel; for the promotion of religion; for animal welfare.

TYPE OF GRANT Most grants are multi-year revenue grants (i.e. salaries and running costs); capital projects that make a tangible difference to a local community are also supported. Funding for up to three years may be given.

RANGE OF GRANTS Up to £275,000.

SAMPLE GRANTS Brathay Hall Trust (£275,000); Cumbria Community Foundation (£75,000); Brathay Group Sponsorship Fund (£35,000); Living Well Trust (£30,000); Cumbria Federation of Young Farmers (£22,000); Safety Net Advice and Support Centre (£20,000); Eden (Young) Carers (£15,000); Low Luckens Organic Resource Centre (£8,000); More Music in Morecambe (£5,000); Lords House Farm (£2,500); and West Cumberland Choral Society Junior Choirs (£250).

FINANCES *Year* 2008 *Income* £932,242 *Grants* £1,217,646 *Assets* £21,993,130

TRUSTEES Susan Bagot, Chair; Richard Boddy; Ian Pirnie; Joanna Plumptre; Alexander Scott; Madeleine Scott; Don Shore; Clare Spedding.

OTHER INFORMATION Please note: the trust stated in its 2008 accounts that it envisaged conducting a major review of its grant-giving policies towards the end of 2009. This was re-scheduled to take place in March 2010. The above guidelines were correct at the time of writing and are not expected to change significantly but organisations are advised to check the trust's website or contact the trust directly for the

latest information before making any application.

HOW TO APPLY The trust is always pleased to hear from charities that need help. If an organisation thinks that it may come within the trust's criteria it is encouraged to contact the director for an informal discussion before making an application. Application forms are available to download from the trust's website or can be requested by phone, email or post. Initial applications should be made on the trust's standard form which should be completed and returned with the latest set of accounts. Grants below £5,000 are decided on a monthly basis with larger appeals going to the full trustees' meetings in March, July and November. Applications for over £5,000 should arrive at least four weeks before the meeting. Details of upcoming deadlines can be found on the trust's website.

WHO TO APPLY TO Chris Batten, Director, Suite 3, Sand Aire House, New Road, Kendal, Cumbria LA9 4UJ *Tel* 01539 741610 *Fax* 01539 741611 *email* info@fcsct.org.uk *Website* www. fcsct.org.uk

CC NO 232131   **ESTABLISHED** 1963

■ The Frieda Scott Charitable Trust

WHERE FUNDING CAN BE GIVEN Old county of Westmorland and the area covered by South Lakeland District Council.

WHO CAN BENEFIT Small local charities, parish halls, youth groups and occasionally locally based work of larger charities.

WHAT IS FUNDED A very wide range of registered charities concerned with social welfare, community projects, the upkeep of village halls and voluntary sector infrastructure support and development.

WHAT IS NOT FUNDED Applications are not considered if they are from outside the beneficial area. No grants to individuals. No grants for parish councils, hospitals, schools, church restoration, environmental causes, wildlife or animal charities, heritage sites, national charities, property buying, direct sporting activities or retrospective grants.

TYPE OF GRANT Capital including building costs, core costs, one-off, project, research, recurring costs, running costs, salaries and start-up costs. Funding of up to three years may be considered.

RANGE OF GRANTS £200–£10,000 with some larger grants.

SAMPLE GRANTS Young Cumbria – South Lakeland (£15,000); Young Cumbria – Eden (£13,000); Ryan Smith Rising Sun Trust (£10,000); Home-start – Copeland (£8,000); North Stainmore Nursery (£1,500); Storth Village Hall (£3,000); Sunbeams Trust (£2,500); Lower Holker Village Hall (£1,000); and Dent Folk Festival (£500).

FINANCES *Year* 2007–08 *Income* £308,103 *Grants* £344,107 *Assets* £6,606,746

TRUSTEES Sally J H Barker; Richard Brownson; Stuart Fairclough; Claire Hensman; Philip V Hoyle; Margaret G Wilson.

OTHER INFORMATION Please note: the trust asks that charities do not apply to both the Frieda Scott and Francis C Scott Charitable Trusts at the same time. If unsure, contact the trust for further guidance.

HOW TO APPLY An application form is available from the correspondent, or from the trust's website, which should be returned by email or post with the latest set of audited accounts. Potential applicants are welcome to ring for an informal discussion before submitting an application. Applications are considered at meetings in March, June, September and December and should be sent to the Grants Coordinator at least a month beforehand. Grants of less than £3,500 are considered by the small grants committee in between main trustee meetings.

WHO TO APPLY TO Debra Jessett, Grants Coordinator, Suite 3, Sand Aire House, New Road, Kendal, Cumbria LA9 4UJ *Tel* 01539 741610 *Fax* 01539 741611 *email* info@fcsct.org.uk *Website* www.friedascott.org.uk

CC NO 221593   **ESTABLISHED** 1962

■ Sir Samuel Scott of Yews Trust

WHERE FUNDING CAN BE GIVEN UK.

WHO CAN BENEFIT Medical research bodies benefiting medical professionals and research workers.

WHAT IS FUNDED Medical research.

WHAT IS NOT FUNDED No grants for: core funding; purely clinical work; individuals (although research by an individual may be funded if sponsored by a registered charity through which the application is made); research leading to higher degrees (unless the departmental head concerned certifies that the work is of real scientific importance); medical students' elective periods; or expeditions (unless involving an element of genuine medical research).

TYPE OF GRANT One-off, project.

RANGE OF GRANTS £1,000–£15,000.

SAMPLE GRANTS Prostate Cancer Charity (£15,000); Meningitis UK, Royal United Hospital – Bath Cancer Research, BIME – Bath Institute of Medical Engineering and Breast Cancer Campaign (£10,000 each); British Orthopaedic Association, Islet Research Laboratory NHS Trust, Research into Ageing and RNID (£5,000 each); DebRA (£3,000); Fight for Sight, FSID, Kings College London – Professor Paul Ciclitira (£2,000 each); and Tommy's the Baby Charity, Research Institute for the Care of the Elderly and Foundation for Conductive Education (£1,000 each).

FINANCES *Year* 2007–08 *Income* £144,750 *Grants* £107,000 *Assets* £5,352,538

TRUSTEES Lady Phoebe Scott; Hermione Stanford; Edward Perks.

HOW TO APPLY In writing to the correspondent. Trustees hold their half-yearly meetings in April and October and applications have to be submitted two months before. There are no special forms, but applicants should give the following information: the nature and purpose of the research project or programme; the names, qualifications and present posts of the scientists involved; reference to any published results of their previous research; details of present funding; and if possible, the budget for the next 12 months or other convenient period. All applications are acknowledged and both successful and unsuccessful applicants are notified after each meeting of the trustees. No telephone calls.

WHO TO APPLY TO The Secretary, c/o Currey and Co, 21 Buckingham Gate, London SW1E 6LS *Tel* 020 7802 2700 *Fax* 020 7828 5049

CC NO 220878   **ESTABLISHED** 1951

■ The Sir James and Lady Scott Trust

WHERE FUNDING CAN BE GIVEN The borough and district of Bolton.

WHO CAN BENEFIT Organisations that are clearly pursuing charitable objectives.

WHAT IS FUNDED The trustees give priority to projects which help disadvantaged people or communities in Bolton. These have included projects which help older people, people with disabilities, young people, children and ethnic minority groups.

WHAT IS NOT FUNDED The trust does not consider applications from individuals or for church restoration, medical causes, expeditions and scholarships.

TYPE OF GRANT Recurring costs; one-off; capital costs including buildings; core costs; endowment; feasibility studies; project research; running costs; salaries; and start-up costs. Funding is available for one year or less.

SAMPLE GRANTS Sycamore Project – Zac's Youth Bar (£15,000); Bolton Lads & Girls Club and Mental Health Independent Support Team (£4,000 each); Birtenshaw Hall – Children's Charitable Trust (£3,000); St Vincent de Paul Society (£2,000); and Diversity in Barrier-Breaking Communications (£1,000).

FINANCES *Year* 2007–08 *Income* £62,189 *Grants* £53,505 *Assets* £2,246,322

TRUSTEES Christopher J Scott, Chair; Madeleine M Scott; William L G Swan.

OTHER INFORMATION Grants of £15,100 were made to individuals.

HOW TO APPLY On a form available from the correspondent, or from the trust's website, together with a latest set of audited accounts. An initial telephone call is welcomed.

WHO TO APPLY TO Chris Batten, Secretary, Suite 3, Sand Aire House, New Road, Kendal, Cumbria LA9 4UJ *Tel* 01539 741 610 *Fax* 01539 741611 *email* info@fcsct.org.uk *Website* www. sjlst.org.uk

CC NO 231324   **ESTABLISHED** 1907

■ The Scott Trust Foundation

WHERE FUNDING CAN BE GIVEN UK and overseas.

WHO CAN BENEFIT Children, young adults, students and journalists.

WHAT IS FUNDED 'The Scott Trust Charitable Fund was established in March 2005 by the Scott Trust Foundation. Its purpose is to foster, promote and support one of the key objectives of the Scott Trust, namely 'promoting the causes of freedom of the press and liberal journalism both in Britain and elsewhere'. Proposals which answer the following criteria will be considered for support: independent journalism; media literacy; journalistic training; journalistic ethics.

WHAT IS NOT FUNDED As a rule the charitable trust will not fund: building projects; fellowships, internships, bursaries other than their own unless there are exceptional circumstances; new lecture series other than those planned at Kings Place.

TYPE OF GRANT One-off.

FINANCES *Year* 2008–09 *Income* £250,771 *Grants* £100,000

TRUSTEES Larry Elliott; Alan Rusbridger; Geraldine Proudler; Jonathan Scott; Carolyn McCall; Liz Forgan; Will Hutton; Andrew Graham; Anthony Salz; Ms Maleiha Malik.

HOW TO APPLY All proposals should include: brief outline of what your organisation does, its constitution, articles, etc. (if appropriate) and a list of the key individuals involved; specifics of the project and who will benefit; how the money would be spent; timescales. Proposals should be emailed to kate.o'toole@guardian.co.uk or by post to Kate O'Toole, Scott Trust Co-ordinator, Kings Place, 90 York Way, London, N1 9GU. Please kindly note that any offers of funding should be taken up within three months of notification.

WHO TO APPLY TO Kate O'Toole, Scott Trust Co-ordinator, Kings Place, 90 York Way, London N1 9GU. *email* kate.o'toole@guardian.co.uk
CC NO 1027893   **ESTABLISHED** 1993

■ The Storrow Scott Will Trust

WHERE FUNDING CAN BE GIVEN Preference for the north east of England.
WHO CAN BENEFIT Charitable organisations.
WHAT IS FUNDED General charitable purposes.
WHAT IS NOT FUNDED Grants for individuals and for the purchase of depreciating assets such as mini-buses will not be considered.
RANGE OF GRANTS Up to £10,000.
SAMPLE GRANTS Newcastle Theatre Royal Trust (£10,000); Great North Air Ambulance Service (£8,000); The Anaphylaxis Campaign and Camphill Village Trust (£5,000 each); Chance to Shine (£3,000); National Rheumatoid Arthritis Society and Songs Bird Survival (£1,000 each); Dame Allan's Schools and Wallsend Sea Cadet Corps – Unit 345 (£500 each); and Rift Valley Newcastle Justice Project (£250).
FINANCES *Year* 2007–08 *Income* £47,024 *Grants* £40,250 *Assets* £761,295
TRUSTEES G W Meikle; J S North Lewis.
HOW TO APPLY In writing to the correspondent. There are no formal application forms.
WHO TO APPLY TO G W Meikle, c/o Dickinson Dees, One Trinity Gardens, Broad Chare, Newcastle upon Tyne NE1 2HF *Tel* 0191 279 9000 *Fax* 0191 279 9100
CC NO 328391   **ESTABLISHED** 1989

■ The Scottish Arts Council

WHERE FUNDING CAN BE GIVEN Scotland.
WHO CAN BENEFIT Individuals and arts organisations.
WHAT IS FUNDED A range of arts including Scotland's indigenous arts, the encouragement of international links and artistic innovation, the creation of greater access to the arts and the improvement of arts marketing.
WHAT IS NOT FUNDED No grants for people in full-time or part-time education or for individual children.
TYPE OF GRANT Revenue and project grants; one-off and recurring grants; and capital grants.
RANGE OF GRANTS Generally £75–£5,000.
FINANCES *Year* 2009–10 *Income* £65,954,000 *Grants* £57,650,000
TRUSTEES Richard Holloway, Chair; Steven Grimmond; John Mulgrew; Ben Twist; Dinah Caine; Donald Emslie; Charles Lovatt; Ray Macfarlane; Barbara McKissack; Jim McSharry; Rab Noakes; Iain Smith.
PUBLICATIONS A wide range of publications is available. See the website or contact the help desk for further information.
HOW TO APPLY Applicants can download application forms and guidelines from the council's website. Alternatively telephone or e-mail the help desk for advice.

WHO TO APPLY TO The Help Desk, 12 Manor Place, Edinburgh EH3 7DD *Tel* 0845 603 6000 *Fax* 0131 225 9833 *Minicom* 18001 603 6000 (Typetalk) *email* help.desk@scottisharts.org.uk *Website* www.scottisharts.org.uk
SC NO SC002835   **ESTABLISHED** 1967

■ Scottish Churches' Community Trust

WHERE FUNDING CAN BE GIVEN Scotland.
WHO CAN BENEFIT People living in areas of greatest disadvantage.
WHAT IS FUNDED Work developed by churches and community groups meeting real and identified needs in either a local community or among groups of people who are disadvantaged.
WHAT IS NOT FUNDED No funding for: work developed by organisations working in isolation from others; building work being done solely in compliance with legislation or not in direct support of a project for community benefit; one-off short-term activities such as trips or excursions, holiday clubs, mission events and festivals; work developed by organisations whose primary purpose is the promotion of abortion, euthanasia or artificial contraception; or work not carried out by recognised charities or properly constituted groups.
TYPE OF GRANT One-off or for a period of between one and four years.
RANGE OF GRANTS Normally in the range £3,000 to £5,000. Maximum normally available will be £20,000 over four years; or up to one third of the total costs.
SAMPLE GRANTS Previously: Starter Packs Angus for starter packs for the homeless (Angus), Pollock Village for storytelling work with children (Glasgow), Whitechurch Youth Mentoring for a mentoring programme with local young people (Glasgow), Grangemouth Enterprises for a furniture initiative (Grangemouth), The Ripple Project for various activities in their work across the generations (Edinburgh) (£20,000 each); Bethany Christian Trust for their winter night shelter for the homeless (£18,000); Caithness Rural Transport for the running of a transport scheme (£2,500); ALLIES for work to benefit people who are homeless (£2,000).
FINANCES *Year* 2008 *Income* £127,141,000 *Grants* £100,000
TRUSTEES Gordon Armour; Sandra Carter; Nena Dinnes; Irene Hudson; Frank Maxwell; Robert Owens; Hilary Davis; Ruth Angove; Desmond Maguire; Ewan Aitken; Graham Bell.
HOW TO APPLY In writing to the correspondent. The trust produces helpful step-by-step guidelines to assist applicants which are available to download on its website. Applications are considered in May and November.
WHO TO APPLY TO The Administrator, 759a, Argyle Street, Glasgow G3 8DS *Tel* 0141 336 3766 *Fax* 0141 336 3771 *email* admin@scct.org.uk *Website* www.scct.org.uk
SC NO SC030315   **ESTABLISHED** 2000

■ Scottish Coal Industry Special Welfare Fund

WHERE FUNDING CAN BE GIVEN Scotland.
WHO CAN BENEFIT Miners.
WHAT IS FUNDED The fund was set up to improve the conditions of people employed in the mining industry and their families. It supports

individuals in need and also the provision of recreational facilities, youth clubs and courses.

FINANCES *Year* 2007–08 *Income* £70,666 *Grants* £60,000

TRUSTEES Keith Jones, Chair; William Menzies; Robert McGill.

OTHER INFORMATION In November 2005 we reported that the fund's website contained only basic information, and that potential applicants should check it for further details on recent beneficiaries and other information as it develops. Over four years later there have been no developments.

HOW TO APPLY 'If you feel you, your group or organisation would qualify for some financial assistance from the fund, please write to us to request a grant. Please include as much information as possible in your letter to avoid any delay caused by questions raised by the trustees prior to grant issue. It is also extremely important to highlight your link to the coal mining industry in your grant request. The trustees meet quarterly to consider grant requests.' In November 2005 the trust stated that it intended to have an application form available to download from its website – in December 2009 this had still not happened.

WHO TO APPLY TO Ian McAlpine, Secretary, c/o CISWO, Second Floor, 50 Hopetoun Street, Bathgate, West Lothian EH48 4EU *Tel* 01506 635550 *Fax* 01506 631555 *email* ian.mcalpine@ciswo.org.uk *Website* www.sciswf.org.uk

SC NO SC001200

■ The Scottish Community Foundation

WHERE FUNDING CAN BE GIVEN Scotland.

WHO CAN BENEFIT Small organisations helping to build and sustain local communities.

WHAT IS FUNDED There are two broad programmes, under which there are a range of different funds. *Scotland-wide programmes* – provide awards of £250 to £5,000 for a wide range of projects. Subject to eligibility, not-for-profit groups working to benefit people in Scotland can apply to these programmes at any time, although please note that some programmes have annual deadlines. Further information can be found on the website. *Local grants programmes* – there are a variety of programmes which benefit people in specific areas of Scotland. Each has different grant levels, deadline dates and decision making practices. A list of local programmes is available on the foundation's website.

WHAT IS NOT FUNDED The foundation does not usually fund: individuals or groups which do not have a constitution; groups other than not-for-profit groups; groups whose grant request is for the advancement of religion or a political party (this means the foundation won't fund grant requests to support the core activities of religious or political groups); the purchase of second hand vehicles; trips abroad; the repayment of loans, payment of debts, or other retrospective funding; payments towards areas generally understood to be the responsibility of statutory authorities; groups who will then distribute the funds as grants or bursaries; applications that are for the sole benefit to flora and fauna. Applicants are invited to demonstrate the direct benefit to the local community and/or service users in cases where the grant application is concerned with flora and fauna; projects which do not benefit people in Scotland. Please note

different grant programmes may have additional restrictions.

TYPE OF GRANT Capital, revenue and full project funding.

RANGE OF GRANTS Usually between £250 and £5,000 – occasionally larger grants are made.

FINANCES *Year* 2007–08 *Income* £6,629,000 *Grants* £2,718,000 *Assets* £1,895,000

TRUSTEES Anne Boyd, Chair; Hamish Buchan; Helen Mackie; Robert Anderson; Beth Edberg; Alan Harden; Colin Liddell; Lady Emily Stair; Bob Benson; Gillian Donald; Ian McAteer.

PUBLICATIONS *2009 Yearbook* is available to download from the foundation's website.

OTHER INFORMATION Please note that grant schemes change frequently and potential applicants should consult the foundation's website for details of current programmes and their deadlines.

HOW TO APPLY The foundation's website has details of the grant schemes currently being administered. Organisations are welcome to contact the grants team to discuss their funding needs before making any application (Tel: 0141 341 4960).

WHO TO APPLY TO Giles Ruck, Chief Executive, 22 Calton Road, Edinburgh EH8 8DP *Tel* 0131 524 0300 *Fax* 0131 524 0329 *Website* www.scottishcommunityfoundation.com

SC NO SC022910   **ESTABLISHED** 1995

■ The Scottish International Education Trust

WHERE FUNDING CAN BE GIVEN Scotland.

WHO CAN BENEFIT Scots (by birth or upbringing) taking advanced studies for which support from public funds is not available.

WHAT IS FUNDED Grants are given to organisations and individuals whose concerns lie in education, the arts or the areas of economic or social welfare.

WHAT IS NOT FUNDED No grants to commercial organisations, for capital work, general maintenance, or for courses (e.g. undergraduate study) for which there is support from statutory bodies/public funds.

TYPE OF GRANT Normally one-off.

RANGE OF GRANTS Usually £1,000 to £3,000.

SAMPLE GRANTS Previous beneficiaries included Royal Scottish Academy of Music and Drama, Scottish International Piano Competition, Scottish Schools Debating Council and Scotland Yard Adventure Centre.

FINANCES *Year* 2007–08 *Income* £75,453 *Grants* £65,000

TRUSTEES Andy Irvine, Chair; Joseph Campbell; Sir Menzies Campbell; Sir Sean Connery; Tom Fleming; Lady Gibson; Prof. Sir Alistair Macfarlane; Sir Jackie Stewart; John F McClellan; Gerda Stevenson; Alex Salmond; David Michie.

HOW TO APPLY In writing to the correspondent. Guidelines for applicants are also available from the correspondent.

WHO TO APPLY TO The Director, 22 Manor Place, Edinburgh EH3 7DS *Tel* 0131 225 1113 *email* siet@ukonline.co.uk *Website* www.scotinted.org.uk

SC NO SC009207   **ESTABLISHED** 1970

■ The Scouloudi Foundation

WHERE FUNDING CAN BE GIVEN UK charities working domestically or overseas.

WHO CAN BENEFIT (a) The Institute of Historical Research, University of London, for publications, research and fellowships ('Historical Awards'), (b) registered charities in the fields of older people; children and young people; environment; famine relief and overseas aid; disability; the humanities (archaeology, art, history, libraries, museums, records); medicine, health and hospices; social welfare; and welfare of armed forces and sailors.

WHAT IS FUNDED Candidates fulfilling the Institute of Historical Research's criteria may apply to the Institute for their research and publication costs to be funded. 'Special Donations' are made for extraordinary appeals and capital projects, and not day-to-day expenditure or staff costs. No applications for 'Regular Donations' are invited as these are normally specially selected.

WHAT IS NOT FUNDED Donations are not made to individuals, and are not normally made for welfare activities of a purely local nature. The trustees do not make loans or enter into deeds of covenant.

TYPE OF GRANT There are three categories of grant: an annual donation for historical research and fellowships to the Institute of Historical Research at the University of London; recurring grants to a regular list of charities; and 'special donations' which are one-off grants, usually in connection with capital projects.

RANGE OF GRANTS Typically £1,000–£2,000.

SAMPLE GRANTS University of London – Institute of Historical Research (£81,000); British Red Cross Disaster Fund (£10,000); Action for Prisoners' Families, Barnardo's, Christina Noble Children's Foundation, Friends of the National Libraries, Gurkha Welfare Trust and Great Ormond Street Hospital (£2,300 each); and Art Fund – National Art Collections Fund, British and International Sailor's Society, British Records Association, Landmark Trust, Shooting Star Children's Hospice and Sightsavers International – Royal Commonwealth Society for the Blind (£1,300 each).

FINANCES *Year* 2007–08 *Income* £284,000 *Grants* £212,000 *Assets* £5,900,000

TRUSTEES Sarah Stowell; David Marnham; James Sewell.

PUBLICATIONS Notes for the guidance of applicants for 'Special Donations' and 'Historical Awards'.

HOW TO APPLY Only Historical grants are open to application. Copies of the regulations and application forms for 'Historical Awards' can be obtained from: The Secretary, The Scouloudi Foundation Historical Awards Committee, c/o Institute of Historical Research, University of London, Senate House, Malet Street, London WC1E 7HU.

WHO TO APPLY TO The Administrators, c/o Haysmacintyre, Fairfax House, 15 Fulwood Place, London WC1V 6AY *Tel* 020 7969 5500 *Fax* 020 7969 5600

CC NO 205685   **ESTABLISHED** 1962

■ Seafarers UK (formerly King George's Fund for Sailors)

WHERE FUNDING CAN BE GIVEN UK and Commonwealth.

WHO CAN BENEFIT Organisations caring for seafarers whether these are officers or ratings, men or women, past or present of the Royal Navy, the Merchant Navy, the Fishing Fleets and their dependants.

WHAT IS FUNDED Registered nautical charities and other registered charities which assist seafarers and their dependants in distress, provide training for young people to become sailors, provide training for sailors and support for other institutions which promote safety at sea.

WHAT IS NOT FUNDED The fund does not make any grants directly to individuals but rather helps other organisations which do this. However, the fund may be able to advise in particular cases about a suitable organisation to approach. Full details of such organisations are to be found in *The Guide to Grants for Individuals in Need*, published by DSC.

TYPE OF GRANT Annual grants for general purposes; capital grants for specific projects such as new buildings, modernisations, conversions, etc.; and interim grants may be considered at any time. Core costs, feasibility studies, recurring and running costs will also be considered.

SAMPLE GRANTS Shipwrecked Fishermen & Mariners' Royal Benevolent Society (£277,000); Royal Navy and Royal Marines Charity (£158,000); Marine Society and Sea Cadets (£100,000); Grimsby Sailors & Fishing Charity (£66,000); KIDS – South East (£55,000); Merchant Navy Welfare Board (£40,000); Royal Alfred Seafarers' Society (£30,000); Scottish Veterans' Residences (£21,000); Merchant Seamen's War Memorial Society (£15,000); and Lord Kitchener Memorial Holiday Centre (£2,500).

FINANCES *Year* 2008 *Income* £4,714,000 *Grants* £2,576,000 *Assets* £34,423,000

TRUSTEES Peter McEwen; Charles Maisey; Frank Welsh; Barry Miller; Sir John Ritblat; Capt. Duncan Glass; Rodney Hazlit; Mark Brownrigg; Anthony Lydekker; Capt. David Parsons; James Watson; Jonathan Baker; Michael Acland; Capt. Paul Du Vivier; Peter Mamelok; Timothy Warren; John Thompson; Christine Gould; Christian Marr; Commander James McClurg; Simon Rivett-Carnac.

PUBLICATIONS *Flagship* and the *Nautical Welfare Guide*.

HOW TO APPLY On an application form available from the correspondent or the charity's website. The fund also has plans to introduce an online application form – check its website for up-to-date information on any developments in this area. Trustees meet in July and November.

WHO TO APPLY TO Dennis Treleaven, Head of Grants, 8 Hatherley Street, London SW1P 2YY *Tel* 020 7932 0000 *Fax* 020 7932 0095 *email* seafarers@seafarers-uk.org *Website* www.seafarers-uk.org

CC NO 226446   **ESTABLISHED** 1917

■ Seamen's Hospital Society

WHERE FUNDING CAN BE GIVEN UK.

WHO CAN BENEFIT Medical, care and welfare organisations working with seafarers and to individual seafarers and their dependants.

WHAT IS FUNDED Welfare causes.

RANGE OF GRANTS £4,000–£128,000.

SAMPLE GRANTS Seafarers' Benefits Advice Line (£128,000); NUMAST Welfare Fund – Mariners' Park (£45,000); Merchant Seamen's War Memorial Society and Royal Alfred Seafarers' Society (£25,000 each); Royal National Mission to Deep Sea Fishermen (£13,000); Queen Victoria Seamen's Rest (£10,000); and Mission to Seafarers – Dreadnought Visitor and Scottish Nautical Welfare Society (£4,000 each).

FINANCES *Year* 2007 *Income* £495,262
Grants £253,200 *Assets* £9,453,177
TRUSTEES J Guthrie, Chair; Capt. D Glass; Capt.
P M Hambling; J C Jenkinson; Dr J F Leonard;
P McEwan; R Chichester; A R Nairne; Capt.
A J Speed; S Todd; Capt. C Stewart; G Ellis;
J Newton; Dr C Mendes.
OTHER INFORMATION The society also operates the
Seafarers' Benefits Advice Line, which provides
free confidential advice and information on
welfare benefits, housing, consumer problems,
legal matters, credit and debt, matrimonial and
tax. In 2007 assistance to individual seafarers
and their dependants totalled £100,588.
HOW TO APPLY On a form available from the
correspondent. Grants are awarded in November
of each year.
WHO TO APPLY TO Peter Coulson, General Secretary,
29 King William Walk, Greenwich, London
SE10 9HX *Tel* 020 8858 3696 *Fax* 020 8293
9630 *email* admin@seahospital.org.uk
Website www.seahospital.org.uk
CC NO 231724 **ESTABLISHED** 1999

....

■ The Searchlight Electric Charitable Trust

WHERE FUNDING CAN BE GIVEN UK, with a preference
for Manchester.
WHO CAN BENEFIT Registered charities. In the past
the trustees have stated that it is their policy to
only support charities already on their existing
list of beneficiaries, or those already known to
them.
WHAT IS FUNDED General charitable purposes.
WHAT IS NOT FUNDED No grants for individuals.
SAMPLE GRANTS UJIA (£45,000); CST (£6,000); Bnei
a Kivah Sefer Torah (£5,000); Guide Dogs for
the Blind (£4,000); Young Israel Synagogue
(£2,600); the Federation (£2,000); Langdon
College (£1,500); Heathlands, Lubavitch
Manchester and Manchester Eruv Committee
(£1,000 each); Reshet and the Purim Fund
(£750 each); and Sense, Nightingales and
Chabad Vilna (£500 each).
FINANCES *Year* 2007–08 *Income* £176,226
Grants £98,873 *Assets* £1,305,880
TRUSTEES D M Hamburger, Chair; H E Hamburger;
M E Hamburger.
OTHER INFORMATION Grants of less than £500
totalled £15,000.
HOW TO APPLY In writing to the correspondent, but
please note that in the past the trustees have
stated that it is their policy to only support
charities already on their existing list of
beneficiaries or those already known to them.
WHO TO APPLY TO H E Hamburger, Trustee,
Searchlight Electric Ltd, 900 Oldham Road,
Manchester M40 2BS *email* heh@slightdemon.
co.uk
CC NO 801644 **ESTABLISHED** 1988

....

■ The Searle Charitable Trust

WHERE FUNDING CAN BE GIVEN UK.
WHO CAN BENEFIT Established youth organisations
benefiting those disadvantaged by poverty.
WHAT IS FUNDED Projects/organisations connected
with sailing for youth development.
WHAT IS NOT FUNDED No grants for individuals or for
appeals not related to sailing.
TYPE OF GRANT One-off, recurring costs, project and
core costs. Funding is available for up to three
years.

SAMPLE GRANTS RONA Trust (£53,000); and Royal
National Institute for the Deaf (£1,000).
FINANCES *Year* 2007–08 *Income* £117,925
Grants £54,198 *Assets* £3,574,416
TRUSTEES Andrew D Searle; Victoria C Searle.
OTHER INFORMATION The trust funds the 'Donald
Searle' sail training yacht which is part of a fleet
of vessels run and operated by the London
Sailing Project based at Southampton. The main
aim of the trust is youth development within a
nautical environment.
HOW TO APPLY In writing to the correspondent.
WHO TO APPLY TO Sarah Sharkey, 30 Watling Street,
St Albans AL1 2QB
CC NO 288541 **ESTABLISHED** 1982

....

■ The Helene Sebba Charitable Trust

WHERE FUNDING CAN BE GIVEN UK, Canada and Israel.
WHO CAN BENEFIT Organisations involved in welfare
and health, including medical research, and
those benefiting people with disabilities or
people of the Jewish faith.
WHAT IS FUNDED Support for: welfare, health and
medical research; people who are disabled; and
people of the Jewish faith.
RANGE OF GRANTS £500–£40,000.
SAMPLE GRANTS Menorah Primary School (£40,000);
Friends of Israel Sports Centre for the Disabled
(£25,000); Ehlers-Danlos and Connective Tissue
Disorders Research Fund (£15,000);
CAREducation Trust (£10,000); SAS Success
After Stroke (£7,000); Ferring Country Centre,
Jersey Heritage Trust and AKIM- Wings of Love
(£5,000 each); Prostate Cancer Charity
(£3,500); Friends of Morris Fienmann Homes
and Brainstrust (£3,000 each); Scope and Beth
Hayeled (£2,000 each); Royal Geographical
Society (£1,500); Breakthrough Breast Cancer
and Age Concern (£1,000 each); and AKIM and
National Jewish Chaplaincy (£500 each).
FINANCES *Year* 2007–08 *Income* £65,256
Grants £172,500 *Assets* £2,633,434
TRUSTEES Mrs N C Klein; Mrs J C Sebba; L Sebba.
HOW TO APPLY In writing to the correspondent.
WHO TO APPLY TO David L Hull, PO Box 326, Bedford
MK40 3XU *Tel* 01234 266657
CC NO 277245 **ESTABLISHED** 1978

....

■ The Samuel Sebba Charitable Trust

WHERE FUNDING CAN BE GIVEN UK and Israel.
WHO CAN BENEFIT Charitable bodies with a
preference for Jewish organisations.
WHAT IS FUNDED The trust focuses on the areas of
education, community, children and young
people, medical, hospice and older people, arts,
interfaith, medical, people with disabilities,
mental health, health, asylum seekers and
preventative medicine. The trust hopes to
expand on its present grant giving and from time
to time respond to environmental concerns and
international aid.
WHAT IS NOT FUNDED No grants to individuals.
SAMPLE GRANTS Jewish Learning Exchange
(£75,000); Tel Aviv University Trust (£60,000);
Eden Association (£53,000); Hebrew University
of Jerusalem (£50,000); Friends of Neve
Menashe (£40,000); Kisharon (£30,000);
Relatives and Residents Association (£20,000);
and the American Jewish Committee (£15,000).
FINANCES *Year* 2007–08 *Income* £1,980,595
Grants £2,394,432 *Assets* £56,343,916

......

TRUSTEES Leigh Sebba; Stanley Sebba; Prof. Leslie Sebba; Victor Klein; Clive M Marks; Lady Winston; Sallie Tangir.

HOW TO APPLY Organisations applying must provide proof of need, they must forward the most recent audited accounts, a registered charity number, and most importantly a cash flow statement for the next 12 months. All applications should have a stamped addressed envelope enclosed. It is also important that the actual request for funds must be concise and preferably summarised on one side of A4. The trustees meet quarterly. However, because of ongoing support to so many organisations already known to the trust, it is likely that unsolicited applications will, for the foreseeable future, be unsuccessful.

WHO TO APPLY TO David Lerner, Chief Executive, 25–26 Enford Street, London W1H 1DW *Tel* 020 7723 6028 *Fax* 020 7724 7412

CC NO 253351   **ESTABLISHED** 1967

....

■ The Seedfield Trust

WHERE FUNDING CAN BE GIVEN Worldwide.

WHO CAN BENEFIT Registered charities benefiting: Christians; evangelists; victims of famine, man-made and natural disasters, and war; people disadvantaged by poverty; retired clergy; and missionaries.

WHAT IS FUNDED To support the preaching and teaching of the Christian faith throughout the world, including publication and distribution of Scripture, Christian literature and audio-visual aids. To assist in the relief of hardship and poverty, including retired ministers and missionaries.

WHAT IS NOT FUNDED No grants to individuals.

TYPE OF GRANT The trust rarely makes grants towards core funding or for activities that may require funding over a number of years, preferring to make one-off project grants.

RANGE OF GRANTS Up to £15,000.

SAMPLE GRANTS Dorothea Trust (£11,000); European Christian Mission, International and Overseas Missionary Fellowship (£10,000 each); Gideons International (£8,000); Mullers (£6,000); Mercy Ships (£5,000); Churches Child Protection Advisory Service (£3,000); Anglo-Peruvian Childcare Mission, Hope 2008 and St Mary's PCC – for Vision Ignition (£2,000 each); Interhealth and Care for the Family (£1,000 each); OMS International (£800); and Christians Against Poverty (£500).

FINANCES *Year* 2007 *Income* £106,099 *Grants* £82,000 *Assets* £2,730,302

TRUSTEES Paul Vipond; Keith Buckler; David Ryan; Revd Lionel Osborn; Janet Buckler; Valerie James.

HOW TO APPLY In writing to the correspondent, for consideration by the trustees who meet twice each year. Please enclose a sae for acknowledgement.

WHO TO APPLY TO The Trustees, 3 Woodland Vale, Lakeside, Ulverston, Cumbria LA12 8DR *Tel* 01768 777 377

CC NO 283463   **ESTABLISHED** 1981

....

■ Leslie Sell Charitable Trust

WHERE FUNDING CAN BE GIVEN UK and worldwide.

WHO CAN BENEFIT Scout and Guide Associations.

WHAT IS FUNDED Assistance for Scout and Guide Associations, mainly but not exclusively in Bedfordshire, Hertfordshire, and Buckinghamshire area.

TYPE OF GRANT Usually one-off payments for a small project, such as building repair works, transport or equipment.

SAMPLE GRANTS No grants list was available.

FINANCES *Year* 2007–08 *Income* £178,891 *Grants* £168,176 *Assets* £3,001,765

TRUSTEES Mrs M R Wiltshire; A H Sell; J Byrnes.

OTHER INFORMATION Grants are also available to individuals making trips in the UK and overseas.

HOW TO APPLY In writing to the correspondent. Applications should include clear details of the project or purpose for which funds are required, together with an estimate of total costs and details of any funds raised by the group or individual for the project. The trust states that: 'Applications are usually treated sympathetically provided they are connected to the Scouting or Guide movement'.

WHO TO APPLY TO Sharon Long, Secretary, Ashbrittle House, 2a Lower Dagnall Street, St Albans, Hertfordshire AL3 4PA *Tel* 01727 843 603 *Fax* 01727 843 663 *email* admin@iplltd.co.uk *Website* www.lesliesellct.org.uk

CC NO 258699   **ESTABLISHED** 1969

....

■ Sellata Ltd

WHERE FUNDING CAN BE GIVEN UK.

WHO CAN BENEFIT Charitable organisations.

WHAT IS FUNDED The advancement of religion and the relief of poverty.

FINANCES *Year* 2007–08 *Income* £190,402 *Grants* £6,544 *Assets* £436,303

TRUSTEES E S Benedikt; N Benedikt; P Benedikt; J Stern.

HOW TO APPLY In writing to the correspondent.

WHO TO APPLY TO E S Benedikt, Trustee, 29 Fontayne Road, London N16 7EA

CC NO 285429   **ESTABLISHED** 1980

....

■ SEM Charitable Trust

WHERE FUNDING CAN BE GIVEN Mainly South Africa, Israel and UK.

WHO CAN BENEFIT Mainly educational institutions benefiting disabled people, children and young adults.

WHAT IS FUNDED Mainly recommendations of the settlor, particularly charities working in the fields of the education of disadvantaged and disabled people; and the empowerment of grassroots people in developing countries.

WHAT IS NOT FUNDED No grants to individuals.

TYPE OF GRANT Recurring and one-off.

SAMPLE GRANTS Natal Society for Arts (£46,000); Play Action Ltd (£8,000); the Valley Trust (£3,000); Ezrath Nasiim Herzog Hospital (£2,000); Art & Power Community, Council of Kwazulu Natal Jewry and Ipswich Community (£1,000 each); and Local Solutions and Ilan Israel Foundation for Handicapped Children (£500 each).

FINANCES *Year* 2007–08 *Income* £176,904 *Grants* £76,951 *Assets* £1,238,494

TRUSTEES Sarah Radomir; Michael Radomir.

HOW TO APPLY In writing to the correspondent.

WHO TO APPLY TO The Trustees, Reeves and Neylan, 37 St Margaret's Street, Canterbury, Kent CT1 2TU *Tel* 01227 768231

CC NO 265831   **ESTABLISHED** 1973

■ The Ayrton Senna Foundation

WHERE FUNDING CAN BE GIVEN Worldwide.

WHO CAN BENEFIT Children's health and education charities.

WHAT IS FUNDED The relief of poverty and the advancement of education, religion and health, particularly the provision of education, healthcare and medical support for children.

WHAT IS NOT FUNDED No grants to individuals.

SAMPLE GRANTS Instituto Ayrton Senna (£146,000).

FINANCES *Year* 2007 *Income* £303,275 *Grants* £145,898 *Assets* £2,740,551

TRUSTEES Viviane Lalli; Milton Guerado Theodoro da Silva; Neyde Joanna Senna da Silva; Leonardo Senna da Silva; Christopher Bliss; Stephen Howard Ravenscroft.

HOW TO APPLY In writing to the correspondent.

WHO TO APPLY TO Christopher Bliss, Trustee, 8th Floor, 6 New Street Square, London EC4A 3AQ *Tel* 020 7842 2000

CC NO 1041759   **ESTABLISHED** 1994

■ The Seven Fifty Trust

WHERE FUNDING CAN BE GIVEN UK and worldwide.

WHO CAN BENEFIT Registered charities benefiting Christians.

WHAT IS FUNDED Trustees mainly give to causes they have supported for many years.

WHAT IS NOT FUNDED No support for unsolicited requests.

RANGE OF GRANTS Up to £15,000.

SAMPLE GRANTS All Saints Church – Crowborough (£15,000); St Matthew's – Fulham (£4,700); the Langham Partnership (£4,200); Christian Fellowship (£3,400); Church Mission Society (£2,700); Overseas Missionary Fellowship (£2,600); Care for the Family (£1,700); and Church Resources Ministries (£530).

FINANCES *Year* 2007–08 *Income* £60,438 *Grants* £53,724 *Assets* £1,874,656

TRUSTEES Rev Andrew C J Cornes; Katherine E Cornes; Peter N Collier; Rev Susan M Collier.

OTHER INFORMATION Grants are also made to individuals.

HOW TO APPLY Unsolicited applications will not be considered.

WHO TO APPLY TO Revd Andrew C J Cornes, Trustee, All Saints Vicarage, Church Road, Crowborough, East Sussex TN6 1ED *Tel* 01892 667384

CC NO 298886   **ESTABLISHED** 1988

■ The Severn Trent Water Charitable Trust Fund

WHERE FUNDING CAN BE GIVEN The area covered by Severn Trent Water Ltd, which stretches from Wales to east Leicestershire and from the Humber estuary down to the Bristol Channel.

WHO CAN BENEFIT Charitable organisations helping people in financial need. Organisations must be able to demonstrate that their project is likely to benefit customers of Severn Trent Water Ltd.

WHAT IS FUNDED Relief of poverty, money advice and debt counselling.

TYPE OF GRANT Revenue grants, capital grants of up to £1,500. Continuation funding is available.

SAMPLE GRANTS In 2007 beneficiaries of revenue funding included: Bassetlaw Citizens Advice Bureau (CAB), Blakenhall Community Advice Centre, Bridging the Gap, Derbyshire Housing Aid, Forest of Dean CAB, Free@last, Nottingham Unemployed Workers Centre. ARC Addington Fund, South Leicester CAB, Melton Mowbray

CAB and North West Leicestershire CAB all received capital funding.

FINANCES *Year* 2007–08 *Income* £4,582,533 *Grants* £248,646 *Assets* £966,629

TRUSTEES Dr Derek Harris, Chair; Elizabeth Pusey; Mary Milton; Kim Kupfer; Sue Hayman; David Vaughan.

OTHER INFORMATION Grants to individuals totalled £3.7 million.

HOW TO APPLY If you would like to apply for a grant on behalf of your organisation you can email the trust at: office@sttf.org.uk. A reply within 48 hours can be expected. Alternatively, initial interest can be lodged by posting no more that two A4 sheets outlining your proposed project to the following address: Severn Trent Trust Fund, PO Box 8778, Sutton Coldfield, B72 1TP. Only applications from organisations within the Severn Trent Trust Fund area will be considered. A map of this area can be found on the trust's website.

WHO TO APPLY TO Gay Hammett, Operations Manager, Auriga Services Limited, FREEPOST RLZE-EABT-SHSA, Sutton Coldfield B72 1TJ *Tel* 0121 355 7766 or 0121 321 1324 *email* office@sttf.org.uk *Website* www.sttf.org.uk

CC NO 1108278   **ESTABLISHED** 1997

■ sfgroup Charitable Fund for Disabled People

WHERE FUNDING CAN BE GIVEN Primarily the Midlands, the north west of England and Yorkshire.

WHO CAN BENEFIT Individuals, organisations and national and local charities.

WHAT IS FUNDED Disabled individuals and organisations that provide care for those with physical or mental disabilities.

TYPE OF GRANT Small, one-off grants.

RANGE OF GRANTS Up to a maximum of £5,000.

SAMPLE GRANTS Previously: £5,000 to Acorns Children's Hospice for part-funding for a specialist nurse; £4,100 to Green Acres Day Centre for a walking frame; £2,900 to Willow Wood Day Centre for a combined hoist.

FINANCES *Year* 2008 *Income* £147,057 *Grants* £63,957 *Assets* £257,563

TRUSTEES Mrs Warwick; R Yong; M Taylor.

HOW TO APPLY Initial applications can be made by filling in a short application form. This can be done online at the sfgroup website, or by completing the form attached to its information leaflet which can be request by phone or email. The Fund Manager will contact potential recipients within two weeks of receiving applications to discuss requests in more detail.

WHO TO APPLY TO Brenda Yong, Fund Manager, FREEPOST NAT13205, Nottingham NG8 6ZZ *Tel* 0115 942 5646 *email* brenda.yong@ sfcharity.co.uk *Website* www.sfgroup.com

CC NO 1104927   **ESTABLISHED** 2004

■ SFIA Educational Trust Limited

WHERE FUNDING CAN BE GIVEN UK.

WHO CAN BENEFIT Schools and educational organisations.

WHAT IS FUNDED Bursaries to cover part fees for pupils with special learning difficulties, who are disadvantaged, have emotional/behavioural difficulties or physical disabilities, are gifted in a specialist area or have a specific boarding need. Grants are also given towards educational projects, books, equipment and school trips to promote the advancement of learning. Grants will only be considered for specific projects.

WHAT IS NOT FUNDED No applications will be considered from individuals or from schools/organisations in respect of pupils/students over the age of 18.

TYPE OF GRANT Specific projects and bursary funds.

RANGE OF GRANTS £500–£30,000.

SAMPLE GRANTS Emmott Foundation (£30,000); King Edward's School Witley (£15,000); Frank Buttle Trust (£12,000); Rubella Association and Shebbear College (£10,000 each); Choir Schools' Association (£8,000); Awards for Young Musicians and Royal Welsh College of Music and Drama (£5,000 each); Jessie's Fund and Puzzle Pre-School (£2,000 each); Royal London Society for Blind and Etwall Primary School (£1,000 each); and Talley County Primary School and Butterflies (£500 each).

FINANCES *Year* 2007–08 *Income* £164,175 *Grants* £281,900 *Assets* £5,627,475

TRUSTEES Beatrice Roberts; Anthony Hastings; David Prince; John Rees; Hugh Monro.

HOW TO APPLY Application forms are available on the trust's website. All applications should be received by 31 January accompanied by the most recent set of audited accounts. Applications are considered in March/April each year. After the meeting, all applicants will be informed of the outcome as soon as possible.

WHO TO APPLY TO Anne Feek, Chief Executive, Tectonic Place, Holyport Road, Maidenhead, Berkshire SL6 2YE *Tel* 01628 502040 *Fax* 01628 502049 *email* admin@plans-ltd.co.uk *Website* www.plans-ltd.co.uk/trusts

CC NO 270272   **ESTABLISHED** 1959

■ The Cyril Shack Trust

WHERE FUNDING CAN BE GIVEN UK.

WHO CAN BENEFIT Voluntary organisations and charitable groups only.

WHAT IS FUNDED General charitable purposes, with a preference for Jewish organisations.

WHAT IS NOT FUNDED No grants for expeditions, travel bursaries, scholarships or to individuals.

TYPE OF GRANT Capital; recurring.

SAMPLE GRANTS No grants list was available. Previous beneficiaries have included Finchley Road Synagogue, Nightingale House and St John's Wood Synagogue.

FINANCES *Year* 2007–08 *Income* £73,681 *Grants* £84,559 *Assets* £682,122

TRUSTEES J Shack; C C Shack.

HOW TO APPLY In writing to the correspondent.

WHO TO APPLY TO The Clerk, Queensmead, St Johns Wood Park, London NW8 6RE *Tel* 020 7490 7766

CC NO 264270   **ESTABLISHED** 1972

■ Peter Shalson Family Charitable Trust

WHERE FUNDING CAN BE GIVEN UK.

WHO CAN BENEFIT Charitable organisations.

WHAT IS FUNDED 'In general the trustees seek to support clients operating in the areas of community relations, young people and medicine.'

SAMPLE GRANTS Elton John's AIDS Foundation (£100,000); Hasassah UK (£25,000); RD Crusaders (£24,000); Community Security Trust (£20,000); Norwood (£11,000); ARK, Hunter Foundation and Treehouse Trust (£10,000 each); President's Club Charitable Trust

(£6,250); Game Conservancy Trust and Scottish Countryside Alliance (£4,000); After Adoption, Drugsline and Ordinary 2 Extraordinary (£1,000 each); Alzheimer's Society (£500); and Wings of Hope (£250).

FINANCES *Year* 2007–08 *Income* £254,279 *Grants* £228,545 *Assets* £101,627

TRUSTEES Peter Shalson; Mary Theresa Gater; Daniel Isaac Dover.

HOW TO APPLY In writing to the correspondent. 'All applications received are considered by the trustees on their own merit for suitability of funding.'

WHO TO APPLY TO Daniel Dover, Trustee, 55 Baker Street, London W1U 7EU

CC NO 1073322   **ESTABLISHED** 1999

■ The Jean Shanks Foundation

WHERE FUNDING CAN BE GIVEN UK.

WHO CAN BENEFIT People involved in medical research, i.e. medical schools, medical Royal Colleges and similar bodies.

WHAT IS FUNDED Medical research and education, with a preference for the area of pathology.

WHAT IS NOT FUNDED No grants for capital items. No grants for research which is already supported by another grant giving body or for projects of the type normally dealt with by bodies such as the MRC or Wellcome Trust.

TYPE OF GRANT Scholarships, research – up to three years.

RANGE OF GRANTS £7,500–£50,000.

SAMPLE GRANTS Royal London Hospital (£50,000); Royal College of Pathologists (£42,000); University of Oxford (£30,000); University of Cambridge (£20,000); University of Leeds and University of Leicester (£15,000 each); and Keele University, St George's, University of London, Queen's University Belfast, Brighton and Sussex Medical School and University of Manchester (£7,500 each).

FINANCES *Year* 2007–08 *Income* £724,541 *Grants* £307,310 *Assets* £16,268,703

TRUSTEES Prof. Sir Dillwyn Williams; Dr Julian Axe; Alistair Jones; Eric Rothbarth; Prof. Dame Lesley Rees; Prof. Andrew Carr; Prof. Sir James Underwood; Prof. Sir Nicholas Wright.

HOW TO APPLY In writing to the correspondent. Please note: full grant guidelines are available on the foundation's website.

WHO TO APPLY TO Mrs B Sears, Peppard Cottage, Peppard Common, Henley on Thames, Oxon RG9 5LB *email* barbara.sears@ukgateway.net *Website* jeanshanksfoundation.org/index.html

CC NO 293108   **ESTABLISHED** 1985

■ The Shanley Charitable Trust

WHERE FUNDING CAN BE GIVEN Worldwide.

WHO CAN BENEFIT Charitable organisations.

WHAT IS FUNDED The relief of poverty.

FINANCES *Year* 2007–08 *Income* £69,835 *Grants* £55,000 *Assets* £1,431,892

TRUSTEES C A Shanley; R F Lander; S J Atkins.

HOW TO APPLY In writing to the correspondent.

WHO TO APPLY TO S J Atkins, Trustee, Knowles Benning Solicitors, 32 High Street, Shefford, Bedfordshire SG17 5DG

CC NO 1103323   **ESTABLISHED** 2003

■ The Shanti Charitable Trust

WHERE FUNDING CAN BE GIVEN UK, with preference for West Yorkshire, and developing countries (especially Nepal).
WHO CAN BENEFIT Charitable organisations.
WHAT IS FUNDED General, Christian, international development.
WHAT IS NOT FUNDED No grants to gap year students, or political or animal welfare causes.
RANGE OF GRANTS £100–£100,000.
SAMPLE GRANTS St. John's Church – Aiden Project (£100,000); Missionaries of Charity (£40,000); International Nepal Fellowship (£12,000); Protac/Theotac, Nepal (£8,000); Development Associates International and CBRS (£5,000 each); Tear Fund (£3,000); Urban Vision (£2,500); Sue Ryder – Manorlands (£1,000); and Kidz Klub Bradford and Nepal Leprosy Trust (£500 each).
FINANCES *Year* 2007–08 *Income* £151,187 *Grants* £184,800 *Assets* £220,306
TRUSTEES Barbara Gill; Timothy Parr; Ross Hyett.
OTHER INFORMATION International Nepal Fellowship is a large beneficiary each year.
HOW TO APPLY In writing to the correspondent. Please note most beneficiaries are those the trustees already have contact with.
WHO TO APPLY TO Timothy Parr, Trustee, Baker Tilly, The Waterfront, Salts Mill Road, Saltaire, Shipley BD17 7EZ *Tel* 01274 536 400
CC NO 1064813   **ESTABLISHED** 1997

■ ShareGift (The Orr Mackintosh Foundation)

WHERE FUNDING CAN BE GIVEN UK.
WHO CAN BENEFIT UK registered charities.
WHAT IS FUNDED General charitable purposes, guided by the wishes of the donors of shares, from where its income derives.
WHAT IS NOT FUNDED No grants to non-UK registered charities.
SAMPLE GRANTS Oxfam – two grants (£60,000); Impetus Trust and British Red Cross (£50,000 each); Firefly Trust (£25,000); Mission Aviation Fellowship UK (£20,000); WaterAid – two grants (£15,000); Trees for Cities (£10,000); Art Fund – two grants (£7,500); PiggyBankKids (£5,000); Christian Blind Mission UK, Garden Organic and Donkey Sanctuary (£1,000 each); Scoo-B-Doo (£500); and York Pregnancy Crisis Centre Service Trust (£250).
FINANCES *Year* 2007–08 *Income* £1,486,912 *Grants* £1,059,243 *Assets* £554,591
TRUSTEES Viscount Mackintosh of Halifax; Matthew Orr; Stephen Scott; Baroness Goudie.
HOW TO APPLY Applications for funding are not accepted and no response will be made to charities that send inappropriate applications. ShareGift's trustees choose to support UK registered charities which reflect the broad range of charities which are of interest to the people and organisations that help to create the charity's income by donating their unwanted shares, or by supporting the charity's operation in other practical ways.
However, charities wishing to receive a donation from ShareGift's trustees can increase their chances of doing so by encouraging their supporters to donate unwanted shares to ShareGift and to make a note of their charitable interests when so doing, using the regular donation form provided by ShareGift. In addition, ShareGift is willing to use its extensive experience of share giving philanthropically to help charities which wish to start receiving gifts of

shares themselves. Charities are, therefore, welcome to contact ShareGift to discuss this further. ShareGift advises that, as basic training on share giving is now available elsewhere, charities wishing to benefit from their advice should ensure that they have first researched share giving generally and put some thought into how their charity intends to initiate and run a share giving appeal or strategy. Further information on this and other issues is available on the charity's website.
WHO TO APPLY TO Rachel Addison, 17 Carlton House Terrace, London SW1Y 5AH *Tel* 020 7930 3737 *Fax* 020 7839 2214 *email* help@sharegift.org.uk *Website* www.sharegift.org
CC NO 1052686   **ESTABLISHED** 1995

■ The Linley Shaw Foundation

WHERE FUNDING CAN BE GIVEN UK.
WHO CAN BENEFIT Registered charities in rural locations.
WHAT IS FUNDED The conservation, preservation and restoration of the natural beauty of the countryside of the UK for the public benefit. In particular, charities that organise voluntary workers to achieve these objectives.
WHAT IS NOT FUNDED No grants to non-charitable organisations, or to organisations whose aims or objects do not include conservation, preservation or restoration of the natural beauty of the UK countryside, even if the purpose of the grant would be eligible. No grants to individuals.
RANGE OF GRANTS £500–£8,000.
SAMPLE GRANTS Beneficiaries included: Durham Wildlife; Gazen Salts Nature Reserve; Little Ouse Project; and Wales Wildlife Trust.
FINANCES *Year* 2007–08 *Income* £62,157 *Grants* £79,500 *Assets* £1,559,700
TRUSTEES National Westminster Bank plc.
HOW TO APPLY In writing to the correspondent. All material will be photocopied by the trust so please avoid sending 'bound' copies of reports and so on. Evidence of aims and objectives are needed, usually in the forms of accounts, annual reports or leaflets, which cannot be returned. Applications are considered in February/early March and should be received by December/early January.
WHO TO APPLY TO The Trust Section, Natwest Trust Services, 5th Floor, Trinity Quay 2, Avon Street, Bristol BS2 0PT *Tel* 0117 940 3283 *Fax* 0117 940 3275
CC NO 1034051   **ESTABLISHED** 1993

■ The Sheepdrove Trust

WHERE FUNDING CAN BE GIVEN UK, but especially north Lambeth, London, where applicable.
WHO CAN BENEFIT Registered charities only.
WHAT IS FUNDED General charitable purposes, particularly sustainability, biodiversity, organic farming, educational research and spiritual care.
TYPE OF GRANT One-off and recurrent.
SAMPLE GRANTS Watermill Theatre (£300,000); Friends of the Earth (£100,000); University of the Arts Consortium (£60,000); African Water Filters – Peter Tamaloe (£50,000); Kids Company (£30,000); Pesticide Action Network and Human Rights Watch (£25,000 each); Roots and Shoots (£20,000); Vauxhall City Farm (£15,000); Amics de la Terra Balears (£10,000); Mother Meera Symposium (£7,600); CLIC Sargent and Corporate Watch Co-operative (£5,000 each); Newbury Fringe Food Festival

(£2,000); and Wetlands Advisory Service
(£510).
FINANCES *Year* 2007 *Income* £1,263,352
Grants £831,258 *Assets* £20,725,060
TRUSTEES Juliet E Kindersley; Peter D Kindersley;
Harriet R Treuille; Barnabas G Kindersley.
HOW TO APPLY In writing to the correspondent.
WHO TO APPLY TO Juliet E Kindersley, Trustee,
Sheepdrove Organic Farm, Lambourn, Berkshire
RG17 7UN *Tel* 01488 674726
CC NO 328369   ESTABLISHED 1989

....

■ The Sheffield and District Hospital Services Charitable Fund

WHERE FUNDING CAN BE GIVEN Mostly South
Yorkshire, also UK.
WHO CAN BENEFIT NHS hospitals and trusts;
registered charities.
WHAT IS FUNDED Medical equipment and general
charitable purposes.
SAMPLE GRANTS Sheffield Teaching Hospitals NHS
Foundation trust (£200,000); Age Concern
(£45,000); British Transplant Games (£30,000);
Yorkshire Air Ambulance (£25,000); PACT
(£20,000); Medtronic (£12,000); and SeeAbility
(£10,000).
FINANCES *Year* 2007–08 *Income* £827,178
Grants £594,169 *Assets* £741,907
TRUSTEES G Moore, Chair; D J Whitney;
J D S Hammond.
HOW TO APPLY In writing to the correspondent.
WHO TO APPLY TO The Secretary, Westfield House,
87 Division Street, Sheffield S1 1HT *Tel* 0114
272 9521 *email* kmiller@westfieldhealth.com
Website www.westfieldhealth.com
CC NO 246057   ESTABLISHED 1965

....

■ The Sheldon Trust

WHERE FUNDING CAN BE GIVEN West Midlands.
WHO CAN BENEFIT Registered charities.
WHAT IS FUNDED The relief of poverty and distress in
society, concentrating on community projects.
Aftercare, hospice at home, respite care, self-
help and support groups, and rehabilitation
centres are also considered. Facilities for
people who are disadvantaged or disabled.
Encouragement of local voluntary groups;
recreational facilities; young people; community;
rehabilitation for drugs, alcohol, and solvent
misuse; religion; older people; mental health;
and learning difficulties.
WHAT IS NOT FUNDED The trust does not consider
general appeals from national organisations and
does not usually consider appeals in respect of
the cost of buildings.
SAMPLE GRANTS St Basils, Nuneaton and Bedworth
Doorway and Sutton Coldfield YMCA (£15,000
each); Wolverhampton Asylum Seeker and
Refugee Services (£9,000); St James
Community Support and Advice Centre (£6,000);
Birmingham Centre for Arts Therapies,
Birmingham Rathbone Society, Edenbridge
Music and Arts and Birmingham Focus on
Blindness (£5,000 each); Sound It Out
Community Music, African Caribbean Community
Initiative, Barton Training Trust and the Living
Paintings Trust (£4,000 each); Acorn Trust,
Warwickshire Clubs for Young People and Age
Concern Dudley (£3,000 each); the Friendship
Project for Children (£2,000); and Dystonia
Society (£1,300).

FINANCES *Year* 2007–08 *Income* £193,535
Grants £171,275 *Assets* £3,826,459
TRUSTEES Mrs R M Bagshaw; A Bidnell; Revd
R S Bidnell; J K R England; R V Wiglesworth;
Mrs R Beatton; Mrs R Gibbins.
HOW TO APPLY Application forms are available from
the correspondent but the trust prefers
applicants to complete and submit their
application online. The trustees meet three
times a year, in April, August and November.
Application forms, including the most recent
signed accounts, a project budget and a job
description (if applying for a salary) should be
received at least six weeks before the date of
the next meeting. Successful organisations will
be sent a grant offer and any conditions.
Unsuccessful applicants will have to wait two
years before re-applying. Please note: a
designated sum is set aside for the holiday
grants programme and applications are
considered in April each year. Applications
should be submitted by the end of February.
WHO TO APPLY TO The Trust Administrator, White
Horse Court, 25c North Street, Bishop's
Stortford, Hertfordshire CM23 2LD *Tel* 01279
506 421 *email* charities@pwwsolicitors.co.uk
Website www.pwwsolicitors.co.
uk/charitable-applications/the-sheldon-trust
CC NO 242328   ESTABLISHED 1965

....

■ P and D Shepherd Charitable Trust

WHERE FUNDING CAN BE GIVEN Worldwide but
particularly the north of England and Scotland.
WHO CAN BENEFIT Mainly local organisations –
particularly those in the north of England.
WHAT IS FUNDED General charitable purposes. Local
charities or charities with which the trustees
have personal knowledge of, interest in or
association with.
TYPE OF GRANT Mainly one-off.
SAMPLE GRANTS St Peter's School Foundation
(£100,000); St Edward the Confessor Church
(£25,000); Henshaw's College (£10,000); Army
Cadet Fund, York Minster Fund and Yorkshire
Cadet Trust (£5,000 each); and Hearing Dogs
for the Deaf (£1,000).
FINANCES *Year* 2007–08 *Income* £146,115
Grants £198,956 *Assets* £520,795
TRUSTEES Mrs P Shepherd; Mrs J L Robertson;
Patrick M Shepherd; D R Reaston;
I O Robertson; Mrs C M Shepherd; Michael
James Shepherd; J O Shepherd; R O Robertson.
OTHER INFORMATION In 2007–08 the trust gave £70
in one grant to an individual.
HOW TO APPLY In writing to the correspondent.
WHO TO APPLY TO The Trustees, 5 Cherry Lane,
Dringhouses, York YO24 1QH
CC NO 272948   ESTABLISHED 1973

....

■ The Sylvia and Colin Shepherd Charitable Trust

WHERE FUNDING CAN BE GIVEN North east England,
but mostly within a 25-mile radius of York.
WHO CAN BENEFIT Registered charities only,
benefiting children and older people, retired
people and people who are disabled.
WHAT IS FUNDED In the medium-term the policy is to
build up the trust's capital base. Currently the
main areas of interest are community initiatives,
care of older people, childcare, people who are
mentally or physically disabled, conservation,
and medical support and equipment.

WHAT IS NOT FUNDED Applications from individuals will not be considered and support does not extend to organisations working outside the areas defined above and excludes overseas activities.

TYPE OF GRANT Usually for specific projects on an enabling basis. Core funding or ongoing support will not normally be provided.

RANGE OF GRANTS £100–£7,000, typically £100–£500.

SAMPLE GRANTS Midsummer Minster Merriments (£7,000); Carr Junior School Fund and York Merchant Adventurers Minster Appeal (£5,000 each); St Peter's Schools Foundations (£4,000); University of Your – Jack Birch Unit (£3,600); and Action Aid (£2,000); Yorkshire Air Ambulance (£1,000); York Arc Light Project (£750); Friends of Beverley School (£500); British Blind Sport (£300); Seafarers UK (£200); and Blind Jack Statue Project (£100).

FINANCES *Year* 2007–08 *Income* £150,108 *Grants* £112,972 *Assets* £2,825,860

TRUSTEES Mrs Sara C Dickson; David Dickson; Mrs Sylvia Shepherd.

HOW TO APPLY In writing to the correspondent. The trustees meet frequently. Applications should include details of the need to be met, achievements and a copy of the latest accounts.

WHO TO APPLY TO Mrs Sara C Dickson, Trustee, 15 St Edward's Close, York YO24 1QB *Tel* 01904 702 762

CC NO 272788   **ESTABLISHED** 1973

....

■ The Archie Sherman Cardiff Foundation

WHERE FUNDING CAN BE GIVEN UK, Canada, Australia, New Zealand, Pakistan, Sri Lanka, South Africa, India, Israel, USA and other parts of the British Commonwealth.

WHO CAN BENEFIT Charitable organisations.

WHAT IS FUNDED Health, education, training, overseas aid, community and Jewish causes.

WHAT IS NOT FUNDED No grants to individuals.

SAMPLE GRANTS JNF Charitable Trust (£48,000); Friends of the Hebrew University of Jerusalem (£35,000); Tel Aviv Foundation (£20,000); WIZO (£12,000); and Central British Fund for World Jewish Relief (£10,000).

FINANCES *Year* 2007–08 *Income* £164,700 *Grants* £125,402 *Assets* £2,479,727

TRUSTEES Rothschild Trust Corporation Ltd.

HOW TO APPLY In writing to the correspondent.

WHO TO APPLY TO The Trustees, 27 Berkeley House, 15 Hay Hill, London W1J 8NS *Tel* 020 7280 5000

CC NO 272225   **ESTABLISHED** 1976

....

■ The Archie Sherman Charitable Trust

WHERE FUNDING CAN BE GIVEN UK and overseas.

WHO CAN BENEFIT Charitable organisations.

WHAT IS FUNDED Most grants are to Jewish organisations. Other causes supported are the arts, education, health, welfare and overseas aid.

TYPE OF GRANT Capital, buildings and project. Funding may be given for more than three years.

SAMPLE GRANTS Diana and Allan Morgenthau Charitable Trust and Rosalyn and Nicholas Springer Charitable Trust (£125,000 each); Jacqueline and Michael Gee Charitable Trust (£101,000); British WIZO (£71,000); Jewish

Care (£38,000); Therapeutic Riding School – Israel (£31,000); Norwood Ravenswood (£25,000); Royal National Theatre (£20,000); Yad Vashem UK Foundation (£17,000); Magen David Adorn UK (£13,000); and United Jewish Israel Appeal (£6,000).

FINANCES *Year* 2007–08 *Income* £1,481,635 *Grants* £854,032 *Assets* £21,766,755

TRUSTEES Michael J Gee; Allan H S Morgenthau; Eric A Charles.

HOW TO APPLY In writing to the correspondent. Trustees meet every month except August and December.

WHO TO APPLY TO Michael Gee, Trustee, 27 Berkeley House, Hay Hill, London W1J 8NS *Tel* 020 7493 1904 *email* trust@sherman.co.uk

CC NO 256893   **ESTABLISHED** 1967

....

■ The R C Sherriff Trust

WHERE FUNDING CAN BE GIVEN The borough of Elmbridge.

WHO CAN BENEFIT Local individuals for art training bursaries (short courses only) and local amateur and professional organisations planning arts activities of a developmental nature.

WHAT IS FUNDED The trust is primarily concerned with arts development projects and funds charities, schools and constituted organisations working with one or more art form for the benefit of members of the local community, especially where a professional artist is involved. The trust has funded projects concerned with music, dance, drama, visual arts, crafts, literature, film and new media.

WHAT IS NOT FUNDED Any project taking place outside the borough cannot be supported unless the principal beneficiaries are Elmbridge residents. The trust does not give retrospective grants; it does not fund higher education courses or long-term vocational training; and it rarely agrees to be the sole funder of a project, applicants are expected to raise funds from a variety of sources.

TYPE OF GRANT Capital, one-off, event underwriting, project and school funds. Funding of up to three years will be considered.

RANGE OF GRANTS £180–£11,000; typical grant £1,000.

FINANCES *Year* 2007 *Income* £172,775 *Grants* £101,576 *Assets* £3,881,189

TRUSTEES Ms H Chadwick; Cllr Nigel Cooper; Cllr Claire Gibbens; Mrs Penny Harris; Cllr S Kapadia; Mrs Ruth Lyon; Cllr Mrs Tannia Shipley – chair; Cllr Mrs Janet Turner; Cllr James Vickers.

OTHER INFORMATION Grants to individuals and schools are unlikely to exceed £500 and grants to organisations and venues are unlikely to exceed £2,500.

HOW TO APPLY On a form which can be downloaded from the website or obtained from the trust office. Application deadlines, grant decision dates and full grant guidelines are also available. Trustees meet four times a year to consider applications. Applicants are advised to discuss their proposals and check their eligibility, with the Director, in advance. The website will also give information on past and current projects and successful applications.

WHO TO APPLY TO Loretta Howells, Director, Case House, 85–89 High Street, Walton on Thames, Surrey KT12 1DZ *Tel* 01932 229 996 *email* arts@rcsherrifftrust.org.uk *Website* www.rcsherrifftrust.org.uk

CC NO 272527   **ESTABLISHED** 1976

....
■ The Shetland Charitable Trust

WHERE FUNDING CAN BE GIVEN Shetland only.

WHO CAN BENEFIT Self-help and voluntary organisations benefiting the inhabitants of Shetland.

WHAT IS FUNDED Social welfare; art and recreation; environment and amenity.

WHAT IS NOT FUNDED Funds can only be used to benefit the inhabitants of Shetland.

TYPE OF GRANT Project, one-off, capital, running and recurring costs, agricultural ten-year loan scheme.

SAMPLE GRANTS Shetland Recreational Trust (£2.8 million); Shetland Amenity Trust (£1 million); Shetland Arts Development Agency (£806,000); Shetland Youth Information Service (£170,000); Shetland Alcohol Advice Services (£150,000); Voluntary Services Resource Centre (£140,000); The Swan Trust (£40,000).

FINANCES *Year* 2007–08 *Income* £13,816,000 *Grants* £11,675,000 *Assets* £219,506,000

TRUSTEES Bill Manson, Chair; James Henry; Leslie Angus; Laura Baisley; James Budge; Alexander Cluness; Alastair Cooper; Adam Doull; Allison Duncan; Elizabeth Fullerton; Florence Grains; Iris Hawkins; Robert Henderson; Andrew Hughson; Caroline Miller; Richard Nickerson; Valerie Nicolson; Frank Robertson; Gary Robinson; Joseph Simpson; John Scott; Cecil Smith; Jonathon Wills; Allan Wishart.

HOW TO APPLY Applications are only accepted from Shetland-based charities. The trustees meet every two months.

WHO TO APPLY TO Jeff Goddard, Acting General Manager, 22–24 North Road, Lerwick, Shetland ZE1 0NQ *Tel* 01595 744994 *Fax* 01595 744999 *email* mail@shetlandcharitabletrust.co. uk *Website* www.shetlandcharitabletrust.co.uk

SC NO SC027025   **ESTABLISHED** 1976

....
■ SHINE (Support and Help in Education)

WHERE FUNDING CAN BE GIVEN Greater London and Manchester.

WHO CAN BENEFIT Organisations working with underachieving 7 to 18 year olds living in disadvantaged areas.

WHAT IS FUNDED Educational programmes which give young people the extra support and attention they need to learn the basic but essential tools for life. SHINE also supports projects that help talented children from poor neighbourhoods to recognise and then realise their full potential. Projects include intensive one-to-one literacy and numeracy support, Saturday learning programmes, homework clubs and computer-assisted study projects.

WHAT IS NOT FUNDED SHINE will not fund: individuals; the direct replacement of statutory funding; schools or other educational establishments, except where funding is for activities which are clearly additional; short term programmes; programmes targeted at specific subject or beneficiary groups; parenting programmes, where the primary focus is the parent rather than the child; activities promoting particular political or religious beliefs; projects taking place outside Greater London, except projects that are part of SHINE's replication programme.

TYPE OF GRANT Start ups, pilots, core costs and development or replication of projects.

RANGE OF GRANTS Up to £458,000.

SAMPLE GRANTS Lift for Learning (£458,000); SHINE @ Rotherfield (£210,000); SHINE @ St Aloysius (£135,000); the Lyric (£90,000); BAAF (£58,000); Baytree Centre (£50,000); SHINE @ Preston Manner (£30,000); and SHINE @ Archbishop Sumner (£8,600).

FINANCES *Year* 2007–08 *Income* £3,014,673 *Grants* £2,008,836 *Assets* £4,960,831

TRUSTEES Jim O'Neill, Chair; David Blood; Gavin Boyle; Mark Heffernan; John Phizackerley; Richard Rothwell; Dr Caroline Whalley; Anthony Salz; Krutika Pau; Mark Ferguson.

HOW TO APPLY All potential applicants must initially speak to a member of the grants team by telephoning 020 8393 1880. The trustees meet about three times a year, but not at fixed intervals.

WHO TO APPLY TO Stephen Shields, Chief Executive, 1 Cheam Road, Ewell Village, Surrey KT17 1SP *Tel* 020 8393 1880 *email* info@shinetrust.org. uk *Website* www.shinetrust.org.uk

CC NO 1082777   **ESTABLISHED** 1999

....
■ The Barnett and Sylvia Shine No 2 Charitable Trust

WHERE FUNDING CAN BE GIVEN UK and overseas.

WHO CAN BENEFIT Registered charities.

WHAT IS FUNDED General charitable purposes.

WHAT IS NOT FUNDED No grants to individuals.

TYPE OF GRANT Usually one-off.

SAMPLE GRANTS One grant was made to the One-to-One Children's Fund – Vygrond Community Development Trust totalling £45,000.

FINANCES *Year* 2007–08 *Income* £58,914 *Grants* £45,070 *Assets* £1,353,806

TRUSTEES M D Paisner; Barbara J Grahame; Prof R Grahame.

HOW TO APPLY In writing to the correspondent.

WHO TO APPLY TO M D Paisner, Trustee, Berwin Leiton Paisner, Adelaide House, London Bridge, London EC4R 9HA *Tel* 020 7760 1000 *Fax* 020 7760 1111

CC NO 281821   **ESTABLISHED** 1980

....
■ The Bassil Shippam and Alsford Trust

WHERE FUNDING CAN BE GIVEN UK, with a preference for West Sussex.

WHO CAN BENEFIT Organisations benefiting young and older people, people with learning disabilities, Christians and health and educational purposes.

WHAT IS FUNDED General charitable purposes. Support is concentrated on local charities located in West Sussex rather than on UK appeals, with emphasis on Christian objects and youth.

RANGE OF GRANTS £100–£40,000.

SAMPLE GRANTS Chichester Boys Club (£38,000); Donnington House Care Home Ltd. (£12,000); Friends of Cobnor (£9,000); Outset Youth Action South West Sussex (£7,200); St Wilfrid's Hospice (£5,000); Christian Care Association (£4,000); West Sussex Learning Links (£2,000); Life Education Centre (£1,000); Chichester Art Trust, Careforce and Bognor Regis Youth Wing (£500 each); Scripture Union (£300); Bognor Can, Dreams Come True and Bikeability (£250 each); and Wellspring West Sussex (£100).

FINANCES *Year* 2007–08 *Income* £136,000 *Grants* £158,000 *Assets* £3,800,000

TRUSTEES J H S Shippam; C W Doman; S A E MacFarlane; S W Young; Mrs M Hanwell; R Tayler; Mrs S Trayler.

HOW TO APPLY In writing to the correspondent, including a copy of the latest set of reports, accounts and forecasts. The trustees meet three times a year to consider applications.

WHO TO APPLY TO Simon MacFarlane, Clerk to the Trustees, Thomas Eggar, The Corn Exchange, Baffins Lane, Chichester, West Sussex PO19 1GE *Tel* 01243 786111 *Fax* 01243 775640

CC NO 256996   **ESTABLISHED** 1967

■ The Shipwrights' Company Charitable Fund

WHERE FUNDING CAN BE GIVEN UK.

WHO CAN BENEFIT Individuals and organisations with a maritime connection. Emphasis is given to those benefiting young people, church work and the City.

WHAT IS FUNDED Maritime training, sailors' welfare and maritime heritage. Churches and Anglican bodies are also supported.

WHAT IS NOT FUNDED Any application without a clear maritime connection.

TYPE OF GRANT Annual donations, general donations and outdoor activity bursaries. Buildings, capital, core costs, one-off, project and start-up costs. Funding for one year or less will be considered.

RANGE OF GRANTS Mainly £500–£5,000. Larger grants can be made from unspent surpluses from previous years.

SAMPLE GRANTS Grant recipients included: Sea Cadets, Sea Scout Association, Cutty Sark Trust, Fairbridge Volunteer Bosun Traineeship, Royal Society of Marine Artists, Westminster Boating Base, Meridian Trust Association, British Maritime Federation and Ahoy Centre.

FINANCES *Year* 2007–08 *Income* £391,784 *Grants* £107,131 *Assets* £2,783,218

TRUSTEES The Worshipful Company of Shipwrights

HOW TO APPLY In writing to the correspondent. Applications and guidelines are available from the trust's website. Applications are considered in February, June and November.

WHO TO APPLY TO The Clerk, Ironmongers' Hall, Shaftesbury Place, Barbican, London EC2Y 8AA *Tel* 020 7606 2376 *Fax* 020 7600 8117 *email* clerk@shipwrights.co.uk *Website* www.shipwrights.co.uk

CC NO 262043   **ESTABLISHED** 1971

■ The Shirley Foundation

WHERE FUNDING CAN BE GIVEN Unrestricted, in practice, mainly UK.

WHO CAN BENEFIT Registered charities.

WHAT IS FUNDED Future focus will be mainly on Autism Spectrum Disorders and, within that, on larger projects that can clearly have strategic impact on the sector as a whole. Particularly collaborative medical research to explore the causes of autism and to lever extra resources for this area. Most of the annual grant total goes to organisations with which the foundation has close connections or at least an established relationship.

WHAT IS NOT FUNDED No grants to individuals, or for non autism-specific work. The foundation does not make political donations.

SAMPLE GRANTS Autism Speaks (£1.5 million); Mental Health Foundation (£7,700); Balliol College – Oxford (£5,000); and Autism Cymru (£300).

FINANCES *Year* 2007–08 *Income* £1,177,808 *Grants* £1,517,439 *Assets* £4,285,789

TRUSTEES Dame Stephanie Shirley, Chair; Prof. Eve Johnstone; Michael Robert Macfadyen; Anne McCartney Menzies.

HOW TO APPLY In writing to the correspondent, although it should be noted that the foundation has committed to making significant donations to Autism Speaks until 2012, so it is likely that funds are fully committed until then.

WHO TO APPLY TO Anne McCartney Menzies, Trustee, North Lea House, 66 Northfield End, Henley-on-Thames, Oxfordshire RG9 2BE *Tel* 01491 579004 *Fax* 01491 574995 *email* steve@steveshirley.com *Website* www.steveshirley.com/tsf

CC NO 1097135   **ESTABLISHED** 1996

■ Shlomo Memorial Fund Limited

WHERE FUNDING CAN BE GIVEN Unrestricted.

WHO CAN BENEFIT Individuals and organisations, particularly those benefiting Jewish people.

WHAT IS FUNDED Jewish charitable purposes.

SAMPLE GRANTS Previous beneficiaries include: Amud Haolam, Nachlat Haleviim, Torah Umesorah, Beit Hillel, ZSV Charities, Layesharim Tehilla, British Friends of Tashbar Chazon Ish, Chazon Ish, Mei Menuchos, Mor Uketsio, Shoshanat Hoamakim, Millenium Trust, and Talmud Torah Zichron Meir.

FINANCES *Year* 2007–08 *Income* £3,927,262 *Grants* £3,078,013 *Assets* £35,410,257

TRUSTEES E Kleineman; I D Lopian; H Toporowitz; A Toporowitz; C Y Kaufman.

HOW TO APPLY In writing to the correspondent.

WHO TO APPLY TO I Lopian, Secretary, Cohen Arnold and Co., New Burlington House, 1075 Finchley Road, London NW11 0PU *Tel* 020 8731 0777 *Fax* 020 8731 0778

CC NO 278973   **ESTABLISHED** 1980

■ The Shoe Zone Trust

WHERE FUNDING CAN BE GIVEN Preference for Leicestershire and Rutland and for certain charities operating in the Philippines and other countries.

WHO CAN BENEFIT Children and young people.

WHAT IS FUNDED Welfare, education and young people.

SAMPLE GRANTS Shepherd of the Hills – Philippines (£38,000); Ministries without Borders – Philippines (£16,000); 500 Miles (£5,000); Wishes 4 Kids (£4,000); Cystic Fibrosis, Leicester Charity Link and Rhema Youth Works (£2,000 each); and Rainbow Trust – Africa (£1,600).

FINANCES *Year* 2008 *Income* £105,232 *Grants* £76,840 *Assets* £71,343

TRUSTEES Michael Smith, Chair, Charles Smith; Anthony Smith.

OTHER INFORMATION Donations of £500 and under totalled £4,200.

HOW TO APPLY In writing to the correspondent.

WHO TO APPLY TO The Trustees, Haramead Business Centre, Humberstone Road, Leicester LE1 2LH *Tel* 0116 222 3000 *Website* www.shoezone.net/sztrust.html

CC NO 1112972   **ESTABLISHED** 2005

■ The J A Shone Memorial Trust

WHERE FUNDING CAN BE GIVEN Merseyside and overseas.

WHO CAN BENEFIT Registered charities known to the trustees.

WHAT IS FUNDED Christian and local causes in Merseyside and mission work overseas.

RANGE OF GRANTS Usually up to £10,000.

SAMPLE GRANTS Toxteth Tabernacle (£12,000); Misison Aviation Fellowship (£10,000); RNLI Appeal (£5,000); St Luke's Development Fund – Hoylake (£2,500); Kids Alive. Tear Fund, Titus Trust and Royal Liverpool Philharmonic Society (£2,000 each); Youth for Christ and Shaftesbury Society (£1,500 each); and Wirral Ark, Bible Lands and Methodist Homes for the Aged (£1,000 each).

FINANCES *Year* 2007–08 *Income* £40,384 *Grants* £48,000 *Assets* £779,738

TRUSTEES Anthony W Shone; Susan J Gilchrist; P Shone; Liverpool Charity and Voluntary Services

HOW TO APPLY The trust has previously stated that it does not respond to unsolicited applications.

WHO TO APPLY TO Anthony W Shone, Trustee, Liverpool Charity and Voluntary Services, 151 Dale Street, Liverpool L2 2AH *Tel* 0151 236 2226

CC NO 270104   **ESTABLISHED** 1974

■ The Charles Shorto Charitable Trust

WHERE FUNDING CAN BE GIVEN UK.

WHO CAN BENEFIT Schools, churches, hospitals, medical centres and other organisations, especially those working in communities in which Charles Shorto lived.

WHAT IS FUNDED General charitable purposes, with a preference for projects benefiting people who are disadvantaged or disabled and their carers.

SAMPLE GRANTS Arnold Foundation for Rugby School (£53,000); Oxford Youth Works (£35,000); Cumnor PCC (£29,000); Exmouth & District Community Transport Group (£10,000); All Saints Church East Budleigh (£5,200); Brecon Cathedral Choir Endowment Fund (£5,000); St Basils (£2,000); and Extra Care Charitable Trust – Coventry, Warwickshire & Northamptonshire Air Ambulance and Grassland Trust (£1,000 each).

FINANCES *Year* 2007–08 *Income* £210,976 *Grants* £163,400 *Assets* £4,451,669

TRUSTEES Joseph A V Blackham; Brian M Dent.

HOW TO APPLY In writing to the correspondent at any time. The trustees meet four times a year.

WHO TO APPLY TO T J J Baxter, c/o Taylors, Mercury House, 1 Mason Road, Redditch, Worcestershire B97 5DA *Tel* 01527 544 221 *email* tom@taylorssolicitors.com

CC NO 1069995   **ESTABLISHED** 1998

■ The Barbara A Shuttleworth Memorial Trust

WHERE FUNDING CAN BE GIVEN UK, with a preference for West Yorkshire.

WHO CAN BENEFIT Organisations benefiting people with disabilities, particularly children.

WHAT IS FUNDED Charities working with children who are disabled and associated causes. Grants are given especially for equipment and premises, but holidays and outings, training courses, and other needs are also considered.

TYPE OF GRANT Capital grants.

SAMPLE GRANTS National Deaf Children's Society (£2,300); Chapel Grange Special School and Children's Liver Disease Foundation (£2,000 each); Aidis Trust (£1,500); United Response – York and Sunny Days Children's Charity (£1,000 each); St James's Hospital for 'Chemo Ducks' (£900); Muscular Dystrophy Group (£600); Symbol Trust (£500); Rutland House School for Parents (£350); and British Diabetic Association (£250).

FINANCES *Year* 2007–08 *Income* £25,310 *Grants* £42,409 *Assets* £526,189

TRUSTEES John Alistair Baty, Chair; Barbara Anne Shuttleworth; John Christopher Joseph Eaton; William Fenton.

HOW TO APPLY In writing to the correspondent.

WHO TO APPLY TO John Baty, Chair, Baty Casson Long, Shear's Yard, 21 Wharf Street, The Calls, Leeds LS2 7EQ *Tel* 0113 242 5848 *Fax* 0013 247 0342 *email* baty@btinternet.com

CC NO 1016117   **ESTABLISHED** 1992

■ The Mary Elizabeth Siebel Charity

WHERE FUNDING CAN BE GIVEN Within a 12-mile radius of Newark Town Hall.

WHO CAN BENEFIT Individuals and organisations benefiting older people who are ill, have disabilities or who are disadvantaged by poverty, and their carers.

WHAT IS FUNDED Hospice at home, respite care for carers and care in the community. Preference is given to assisting people who wish to live independently in their own homes.

TYPE OF GRANT Flexible, but one-off grants preferred for buildings, capital and core costs.

SAMPLE GRANTS Crossroads Care (£16,000).

FINANCES *Year* 2007–08 *Income* £133,874 *Grants* £103,375 *Assets* £2,268,646

TRUSTEES P Blatherwick; D McKenny; Mrs R White; Mrs A Austin; Mrs S Watson; Miss J Moore.

OTHER INFORMATION The grant total includes £85,825 given to individuals.

HOW TO APPLY In writing to the correspondent, requesting an application form. The trustees meet every couple of months to discuss applications.

WHO TO APPLY TO Mrs Frances C Kelly, Administrator, Tallents, 3 Middlegate, Newark, Nottinghamshire NG24 1AQ *Tel* 01636 671881 *Fax* 01636 700148 *email* fck@tallents.co.uk

CC NO 1001255   **ESTABLISHED** 1990

■ David and Jennifer Sieff Charitable Trust

WHERE FUNDING CAN BE GIVEN UK.

WHO CAN BENEFIT Registered charities.

WHAT IS FUNDED General charitable purposes.

WHAT IS NOT FUNDED No grants to individuals.

RANGE OF GRANTS £100 to £34,000.

SAMPLE GRANTS Mentor Foundation UK (£34,000); Community Security Trust (£13,000); the Southbank Centre (£12,000); British ORT (£7,600); Westminster Synagogue (£5,800); Festival De Valloires (£2,500); Anglo-Israel Association and Imperial Society of Knights Bachelors (£1,000 each); Union of Jewish Women (£500); and Toy Trust (£250).

FINANCES *Year* 2007–08 *Income* £46,673 *Grants* £105,070 *Assets* £609,863

TRUSTEES Hon. Sir David Daniel Sieff; Lady Jennifer Riat Sieff; Lord Wolfson of Sunningdale.

HOW TO APPLY In writing to the correspondent.
WHO TO APPLY TO The Trustees, H W Fisher and Company, Acre House, 11–15 William Road, London NW1 3ER *Tel* 020 7388 7000
CC NO 206329   **ESTABLISHED** 1970

■ The Julius Silman Charitable Trust

WHERE FUNDING CAN BE GIVEN UK.
WHO CAN BENEFIT Charitable organisations.
WHAT IS FUNDED Support of at risk groups and humanitarian causes.
WHAT IS NOT FUNDED No grants to individuals.
TYPE OF GRANT One-off and recurrent.
RANGE OF GRANTS Up to £3,000.
SAMPLE GRANTS Kids for Kids (£2,600); Neve Michael and New Israel Fund (£1,000 each); Anti-Slavery, Norwood, Motability and Heads Up (£500 each); World Jewish Relief, Friendship Way and Jewish Childs Day (£250 each); and Samaritans of Bath, Wiltshire Splash and Cancer Research (£100 each).
FINANCES *Year* 2007–08 *Income* £32,060 *Grants* £15,812 *Assets* £961,141
TRUSTEES S A Silman; Mrs C Smith; Mrs W Silman.
HOW TO APPLY In writing to the correspondent. The trustees meet about four times a year.
WHO TO APPLY TO S A Silman, Trustee, Roselands, 2 High Street, Steeple Ashton BA14 6EL *Tel* 01380 870 421
CC NO 263830   **ESTABLISHED** 1971

■ The Leslie Silver Charitable Trust

WHERE FUNDING CAN BE GIVEN UK, but mostly West Yorkshire.
WHO CAN BENEFIT Small local projects, new organisations and established organisations primarily benefiting children, young adults and Jewish causes.
WHAT IS FUNDED Medicine and health; welfare; sciences and humanities; the advancement of the Jewish religion, synagogues, Jewish religious umbrella bodies; arts, culture and recreation; community facilities; and other charitable purposes.
WHAT IS NOT FUNDED No grants to individuals or students.
TYPE OF GRANT One-off grants.
RANGE OF GRANTS £500–£55,000.
SAMPLE GRANTS Donisthorpe Hall (£55,000); Leeds Centre for Deaf and Blind People (£16,000); Holocaust Centre and Variety Club Children's Charity (£10,000 each); UJIA and Jewish National Fund (£5,000 each); the Zone (£4,000); Children in Crisis and Lord Mayor's Charity Appeal (£2,000 each); Second World War Experience (£1,000); and Holocaust Educational Trust (£500).
FINANCES *Year* 2007–08 *Income* £26,806 *Grants* £129,000 *Assets* £546,985
TRUSTEES Leslie H Silver; Mark S Silver; Ian J Fraser.
HOW TO APPLY In writing to the correspondent following a specific format. Please note the trust has previously stated that, 'the recipients of donations are restricted almost exclusively to the concerns in which the trustees take a personal interest and that unsolicited requests from other sources, although considered by the trustees, are rejected almost invariably'.

WHO TO APPLY TO Ian J Fraser, Trustee, Bentley Jennison, 2 Wellington Place, Leeds LS1 4AP *Tel* 0113 244 5451 *Fax* 0113 242 6308
CC NO 1007599   **ESTABLISHED** 1991

■ The Simpson Education and Conservation Trust

WHERE FUNDING CAN BE GIVEN UK and overseas, with a preference for the neotropics (South America).
WHO CAN BENEFIT Charitable organisations.
WHAT IS FUNDED Advancement of education, including medical and scientific research; the conservation and protection of the natural environment and endangered species of plants and animals with special emphasis on the protection of forests and endangered avifauna in the neotropics (South America).
WHAT IS NOT FUNDED No grants to individuals.
TYPE OF GRANT One-off or up to three years, for development or project funding.
RANGE OF GRANTS £1,000–£60,000.
SAMPLE GRANTS Jocotoco Foundation (£62,000); and Lord Trealor Trust and Friends of RBG Kew – for Tanzania (£1,000 each).
FINANCES *Year* 2007–08 *Income* £79,394 *Grants* £63,519 *Assets* £67,367
TRUSTEES Dr R N F Simpson, Chair; Prof. D M Broom; Dr J M Lock; Prof. S Chang; Dr K A Simpson.
HOW TO APPLY In writing to the correspondent. The day-to-day activities of this trust are carried out by e-mail, telephone and circulation of documents, since the trustees do not all live in the UK.
WHO TO APPLY TO N Simpson, Chair, Honeysuckle Cottage, Tidenham Chase, Chepstow, Gwent NP16 7JW *Tel* 01291 689423 *Fax* 01291 689803
CC NO 1069695   **ESTABLISHED** 1998

■ The Simpson Foundation

WHERE FUNDING CAN BE GIVEN UK.
WHO CAN BENEFIT Registered charities only, particularly those benefiting Roman Catholics.
WHAT IS FUNDED The support of charities favoured by the founder in his lifetime and others with similar objects; mainly Catholic charities.
WHAT IS NOT FUNDED No grants to non-registered charities or individuals.
SAMPLE GRANTS Venerable Collegio Inglese, St Benedict's Abbey, Sisters of Charity of Jesus and Mary, The Access Partnership, Congregation of the Blessed Sacrament and Providence Row Night Refuge and Home.
FINANCES *Year* 2007–08 *Income* £17,658 *Grants* £25,000
TRUSTEES C E T Bellord; P J M Hawthorne; P J O Herschan.
HOW TO APPLY In writing to the correspondent, at any time. No telephone applications will be considered.
WHO TO APPLY TO P J O Herschan, Trustee, 70 St George's Square, London SW1V 3RD *Tel* 020 7821 8211 *Fax* 020 7630 6484
CC NO 231030   **ESTABLISHED** 1961

Think carefully about every application. Is it justified?

859

■ The Huntly and Margery Sinclair Charitable Trust

WHERE FUNDING CAN BE GIVEN UK.

WHO CAN BENEFIT Generally to registered charities.

WHAT IS FUNDED Well-established charities in particular.

RANGE OF GRANTS Up to £10,000.

SAMPLE GRANTS Priors Court School (£6,000); Starlight CHildren's Fund and St Patrick's Catholic Church (£3,000 each); Old Etonian Masonic Lodge (£2,000); Eddies, PDSA and County Air Ambulance (£1,000 each); Army Benevolent Fund and NSPCC (£500 each); Elkstone Church PCC (£400); Coeliac (£350); and Breast Cancer Haven (£200).

FINANCES *Year* 2007–08 *Income* £48,142 *Grants* £39,000 *Assets* £1,349,811

TRUSTEES Mrs A M H Gibbs; Mrs M A H Windsor; Mrs J Floyd.

HOW TO APPLY Unsolicited applications are rarely successful and due to the high number such requests the trust is not able to respond to them or return any printed materials supplied.

WHO TO APPLY TO Wilfrid Vernor-Miles, Administrator, c/o Vernor-Miles and Noble Solicitors, 5 Raymond Buildings, Gray's Inn, London WC1R 5DD *Tel* 020 7242 8688 *Fax* 020 7242 3192 *email* wilfridvm@vmn.org.uk

CC NO 235939   **ESTABLISHED** 1964

■ Sino-British Fellowship Trust

WHERE FUNDING CAN BE GIVEN UK and China.

WHO CAN BENEFIT Institutions benefiting individual postgraduate students.

WHAT IS FUNDED Scholarships to Chinese citizens to enable them to pursue their studies in Britain. Grants to British citizens in China to educate/train Chinese citizens in any art, science or profession.

TYPE OF GRANT Fees; fares; and allowances.

RANGE OF GRANTS £6,000–£82,000.

SAMPLE GRANTS Royal Society (£82,000); British Library (£23,000); China Scholarship Council (£21,000); British Academy and Universities China Committee (£20,000 each); Chinese University of Hong Kong and Open University of Hong Kong (£16,500 each); Great Britain China Educational Trust, Hong Kong University and School of Oriental & African Studies (£15,000 each); Lingnan University (£7,500) Needham Research Institute (£6,800); Institute of Archaeology (£6,000).

FINANCES *Year* 2007 *Income* £553,125 *Grants* £263,390 *Assets* £13,244,281

TRUSTEES Prof. H D R Baker; Mrs A E Ely; P J Ely; Prof. Sir B Heap; Dr J A Langton; Mrs L Thompson; Prof. Sir D Todd; Lady P Youde.

OTHER INFORMATION Grants totalling £38,000 were also made to individuals.

HOW TO APPLY On a form available by writing to the address below.

WHO TO APPLY TO Mrs Anne Ely, Flat 23 Bede House, Manor Fields, London SW15 3LT *Tel* 020 8788 6252

CC NO 313669   **ESTABLISHED** 1948

■ The Skelton Bounty

WHERE FUNDING CAN BE GIVEN Lancashire (as it existed in 1934).

WHO CAN BENEFIT Registered charities benefiting young, older and infirm people.

WHAT IS FUNDED Restricted to Lancashire charities (not national ones unless operating in Lancashire from a permanent establishment within the county predominantly for the benefit of residents from that county) assisting young, older and infirm people.

WHAT IS NOT FUNDED No grants to individuals, religious charities or medical or scientific research.

TYPE OF GRANT Capital expenditure preferred.

RANGE OF GRANTS £50–£8,500.

SAMPLE GRANTS Action Force Africa – Liverpool and Bowland Pennine Mountain Rescue Team – Clitheroe (£5,000 each); Lancashire Partnership Against Crime – Preston and Our Lady Star of the Sea Parish Centre – Lytham St Annes (£4,000 each); Music Space North West – Liverpool (£3,300); Autism Initiatives UK – Liverpool (£2,500); Deafway – Preston (£2,000); Citizens Advice – South Lakeland (£1,700); Royal Liverpool Philharmonic (£1,000); and The Eyeless Trust (£600).

FINANCES *Year* 2007–08 *Income* £114,098 *Grants* £90,857 *Assets* £2,393,559

TRUSTEES Sidney R Fisher; William D Fulton; Lord Shuttleworth; Sir Alan Waterworth; David G Wilson; Patricia Wilson; Margo Crighton Pitt

HOW TO APPLY On a form available from the correspondent. Requests for application forms should be made as soon as possible after 1 January each year. The completed form should be returned before 31 March immediately following. Applications received after this date will not be considered. The trustees meet annually in July, with successful applicants receiving their grant cheques in late July/early August. Applications should include the charitable registration number of the organisation, or, where appropriate, a letter confirming charitable status.

WHO TO APPLY TO The Trustees, Cockshott Peck Lewis, 24 Hoghton Street, Southport, Merseyside PR9 0PA *Tel* 01704 534 034

CC NO 219370   **ESTABLISHED** 1934

■ The Charles Skey Charitable Trust

WHERE FUNDING CAN BE GIVEN UK.

WHO CAN BENEFIT Organisations which the trustees have come across from their own research.

WHAT IS FUNDED General charitable purposes.

TYPE OF GRANT Grants are given on a one-off and recurring basis for core and capital support.

RANGE OF GRANTS £500–£10,000.

SAMPLE GRANTS Lloyds Patriotic Fund (£60,000); Trinity Hospice (£7,500); Children's Trust (£5,000); Stepping Stones Trust (£4,500); Roses Charitable Trust (£4,000); Camphill Village Trust (£3,000); St Dunstans, Water Aid, Christian Care Association and the Royal British Legion (£2,000 each); Poole Hospital NHS Trust, Heritage of London Trust, the Dagenham Gospel Trust and Institute of Cancer Research (£1,000 each); and Salisbury Spinal Injuries Trust (£500).

FINANCES *Year* 2007–08 *Income* £233,869 *Grants* £114,000 *Assets* £3,195,489

TRUSTEES C H A Skey, Chair; J M Leggett; C B Berkeley; Revd J H A Leggett.

HOW TO APPLY The trust has previously stated that no written or telephoned requests for support will be entertained.

WHO TO APPLY TO J M Leggett, Trustee, Flint House, Park Homer Road, Colehill, Wimborne, Dorset BH21 2SP

CC NO 277697   **ESTABLISHED** 1979

■ Skipton Building Society Charitable Foundation

WHERE FUNDING CAN BE GIVEN England and Wales.
WHO CAN BENEFIT Charitable organisations, schools and other organisations.
WHAT IS FUNDED General charitable organisations.
WHAT IS NOT FUNDED The foundation will not consider donations: to non-registered charities or individuals; to activities which are primarily the responsibility of central or local government or other responsible bodies; towards running costs including rent or staff wages; towards restoration or upkeep of buildings; towards expeditions or overseas travel; towards fundraising events, sponsorship or marketing appeals; towards the cost or maintenance of vehicles; to large national charities; or from charities which have applied to the foundation within the previous 12 months.
RANGE OF GRANTS Up to £5,000.
SAMPLE GRANTS 1 Voice Communicating Together (£5,000); The Joshua Foundation (£4,000); Central & Cecil Housing Trust and Disability Snowsport UK (£3,000 each); Child Action Northwest and Live Music Now (£2,000 each); Caring Together in Woodhouse and Little London and Lytham St Anne's and Flyde Sea Cadets (£1,000 each); Deafway (£600); and Lakelands Day Care Hospice (£400).
FINANCES *Year* 2008–09 *Income* £153,730 *Grants* £128,072 *Assets* £105,479
TRUSTEES Diana Chambers; Richard Twigg; Bishop Hope; Richard Robinson; Mrs Ethne Bannister.
HOW TO APPLY In writing to the correspondent enclosing the application form available on the trust's website. 'Your completed form must be returned enclosing your latest 2 years' Annual Accounts and any supporting literature you feel will strengthen your chances of receiving a grant.'
WHO TO APPLY TO Gill Davidson, Secretary, The Bailey, Skipton, North Yorkshire BD23 1DN *Tel* 01756 705 000 *Fax* 01756 705743 *email* gill.davidson@skipton.co.uk *Website* www.skiptoncharitablefoundation.co.uk
CC NO 1079538   **ESTABLISHED** 2000

■ The John Slater Foundation

WHERE FUNDING CAN BE GIVEN UK, with a strong preference for the north west of England especially West Lancashire.
WHO CAN BENEFIT Registered charities.
WHAT IS FUNDED Welfare, including animal welfare, and general charitable purposes.
WHAT IS NOT FUNDED No grants to individuals.
RANGE OF GRANTS £500–£10,000.
SAMPLE GRANTS Blackpool Ladies Sick Poor Association (£9,100); Grand Theatre Blackpool (£7,300); Adlington Community Centre (£7,200); Bury Grammar School for Girls (£5,500); Fleetwood and Wyre Mencap (£3,700); Redwings Horse Sanctuary, Cancer Care – Lancaster, Liverpool School for Tropical Medicine and Christ's Church – Thornton (£1,800 each); and Mersey Inshore Rescue (£1,000).
FINANCES *Year* 2007–08 *Income* £152,620 *Grants* £176,560 *Assets* £3,882,315
TRUSTEES HSBC Trust Co. Ltd.
HOW TO APPLY In writing to the correspondent, including accounts. Applications are considered twice a year, in May and November.

WHO TO APPLY TO Colin Bould, HSBC Trust Services, 10th Floor, Norwich House, Nelson Gate, Commercial Road, Southampton SO15 1GX *Tel* 023 8072 2231 *Fax* 023 8072 2250
CC NO 231145   **ESTABLISHED** 1963

■ Sloane Robinson Foundation

WHERE FUNDING CAN BE GIVEN UK.
WHO CAN BENEFIT Educational establishments.
WHAT IS FUNDED 'The foundation's principal charitable purpose is the advancement of the education of the public [...] The foundation is developing long term relationships with a number of academic institutions, with the ultimate goal of establishing scholarships and bursary schemes for overseas students to study in the UK.'
SAMPLE GRANTS Lincoln College – Oxford (£158,000); Oxford University (£155,000); Science for Humanity (£45,000); Keble College – Oxford (£31,000); Policy Exchange Limited (£30,000); Rugby School (£28,000); and Christian Friends of Korea (£15,000).
FINANCES *Year* 2007–08 *Income* £1,349,571 *Grants* £513,846 *Assets* £21,905,599
TRUSTEES G E S Robinson; H P Sloane; M D Willcox.
OTHER INFORMATION The grant total in 2007/08 included £52,000 donated to individuals.
HOW TO APPLY In writing to the correspondent. 'The trustees are pleased to receive updates from successful applicants to keep the trustees updated on the effective use of those funds – usually this is done by receiving a newsletter or similar.'
WHO TO APPLY TO M D Willcox, Trustee, The Old Coach House, Bergh Apton, Norwich NR15 1DD
CC NO 1068286   **ESTABLISHED** 1998

■ Rita and David Slowe Charitable Trust

WHERE FUNDING CAN BE GIVEN UK and overseas.
WHO CAN BENEFIT Registered charities.
WHAT IS FUNDED General charitable purposes.
WHAT IS NOT FUNDED No grants are made to individuals (including gap year students) or religious bodies.
RANGE OF GRANTS £5,000–£13,000.
SAMPLE GRANTS Shelter (£13,000); Computer Aid International, David Baum Foundation and Big Issue Foundation (£10,000 each); and Wells for India, Action Aid, Books Abroad, Excellent Development and Send a Cow (£5,000 each).
FINANCES *Year* 2007–08 *Income* £64,167 *Grants* £67,500 *Assets* £652,470
TRUSTEES R L Slowe; Mrs E H Douglas; J L Slowe; G Weinberg.
HOW TO APPLY In writing to the correspondent.
WHO TO APPLY TO R L Slowe, Trustee, 32 Hampstead High Street, London NW3 1JQ *Tel* 020 7435 7800
CC NO 1048209   **ESTABLISHED** 1995

■ Ruth Smart Foundation

WHERE FUNDING CAN BE GIVEN Worldwide.
WHO CAN BENEFIT Registered charities and charitable organisations.
WHAT IS FUNDED Relief of animal suffering.
TYPE OF GRANT One-off.
RANGE OF GRANTS £250–£12,000.
SAMPLE GRANTS Fauna & Flora International Africa Programmes (£12,000); Mauritian Wildlife

Foundation (£8,000); Durrell Wildlife Conservation (£5,000); Save the Elephants (£4,000); David Sheldrick Wildlife Foundation (£3,000); University of Southampton – Biological Sciences Ecology Group (£1,000); Animal Rescue Charity and Canine Concern Scotland Trust (£500 each); RSPB (£300); and World Society for the Protection of Animals (£250).

FINANCES *Year* 2008 *Income* £116,467 *Grants* £79,218 *Assets* £3,607,685

TRUSTEES Wilfrid Edward Vernor-Miles; John Crosfield Vernor-Miles; Paul Williams.

HOW TO APPLY 'The trustees support a number of charities on a regular basis and in practice finds that their income is fully committed and there is little, if any, surplus income available for distribution in response to unsolicited appeals.'

WHO TO APPLY TO The Trustees, c/o Vernor-Miles and Noble, 5 Raymond Buildings, Gray's Inn, London WC1R 5DD *Tel* 020 7242 8688

CC NO 1080021   **ESTABLISHED** 2000

....

■ The SMB Charitable Trust

WHERE FUNDING CAN BE GIVEN UK and overseas.

WHO CAN BENEFIT Organisations for the advancement of the Christian religion and the relief of need, hardship or distress.

WHAT IS FUNDED Christian and welfare organisations. Accommodation and housing, various community services, healthcare, health facilities and buildings, famine/emergency aid, medical studies and research, and environmental and wildlife projects and campaigning will also be considered.

WHAT IS NOT FUNDED Grants to individuals are not normally considered, unless the application is made through a registered charity which can receive the cheque.

TYPE OF GRANT One-off grants, project grants and grants for recurring costs are prioritised. Also considered are building and other capital grants, funding for core and running costs, funding for salaries and start-up costs.

RANGE OF GRANTS Up to £4,000.

SAMPLE GRANTS London City Mission and Pilgrim Homes (£4,000 each); Salvation Army and Hope Now (£3,000 each); Baptist Missionary Society and British Red Cross (£2,500 each); All Nations Christian College, Dentaid and Scripture Union (£2,000 each); Shaftesbury Society (£1,500); People International (£1,000); and St Andrews Leyland (£500).

FINANCES *Year* 2007–08 *Income* £334,551 *Grants* £201,150 *Assets* £8,803,299

TRUSTEES E D Anstead; P J Stanford; Barbara O'Driscoll; J A Anstead; Claire Swarbrick.

HOW TO APPLY In writing to the correspondent, including the aims and principal activities of the applicant, the current financial position and details of any special projects for which funding is sought. Application forms are not used. Trustees normally meet in March, June, September and December and applications should be received before the beginning of the month in which meetings are held. Because of the volume of appeals received, unsuccessful applicants will only receive a reply if they enclose an sae. However, unsuccessful applicants are welcome to reapply.

WHO TO APPLY TO Mrs B M O'Driscoll, Trustee, 15 Wilman Rd, Tunbridge Wells, Kent TN4 9AJ *Tel* 01892 537 301 *Fax* 01892 618 202

CC NO 263814   **ESTABLISHED** 1962

....

■ The Mrs Smith and Mount Trust

WHERE FUNDING CAN BE GIVEN London and south east England, i.e. Norfolk, Suffolk, Cambridgeshire, Hertfordshire, Essex, Kent and Surrey.

WHO CAN BENEFIT Organisations benefiting people with mental illness or learning disability, homelessness and family support. Counselling is also supported with these categories.

WHAT IS FUNDED The trust has three main areas of interest mental illness/learning difficulties, family support within other two areas and homelessness.

WHAT IS NOT FUNDED The trustees do not consider building costs, only refurbishment or alterations necessary to bring them up to health and safety/fire regulations. No grants to individuals.

TYPE OF GRANT One-off and continuing revenue grants are considered.

RANGE OF GRANTS £1,000 to £7,500.

SAMPLE GRANTS Emmaus Colchester (£10,000); Bromely Mencap, HOPE Worldwide, Post Adoption, Prisoners Abroad, Shepherd's Bush Families Project, Woman's Trust and Sutton Counselling (£5,000 each); St Edmunds Society (£4,000); and Cambridge Family Mediation Service and Quaker Social Action (£3,000 each).

FINANCES *Year* 2008–09 *Income* £232,622 *Grants* £238,560 *Assets* £4,695,209

TRUSTEES Mrs Gillian M Gorell Barnes; Richard S Fowler; Douglas J Mobsby; Lisa Weaks.

HOW TO APPLY 'The trustees meet three times per year in March, July and November and application forms and supporting documentation must reach our offices by the end of January, May and September respectively. We prefer all applicants to submit their application online. Applicants may download the application questions and prepare their answers in advance. You will be able to begin your application and then save and return to it later if required.'

WHO TO APPLY TO Mrs Jayne Day, Administrator, PWW Solicitors, White Horse Court, 25c North Street, Bishop's Stortford, Hertfordshire CM23 2LD *Tel* 01279 506421 *email* charities@pwwsolicitors.co.uk *Website* www.pwwsolicitors.co.uk

CC NO 1009718   **ESTABLISHED** 1992

....

■ The N Smith Charitable Settlement

WHERE FUNDING CAN BE GIVEN Worldwide.

WHO CAN BENEFIT Registered charities.

WHAT IS FUNDED General charitable purposes but mainly social work, medical research, education, environment/animals, arts and overseas aid.

WHAT IS NOT FUNDED Grants are only made to registered charities and not to individuals.

TYPE OF GRANT Appeals for capital equipment are preferred over salary costs.

RANGE OF GRANTS £500–£5,000.

SAMPLE GRANTS Oxfam GB (£5,000); Alzheimer's Research Trust (£2,000); Books Abroad, British Dyslexics, ChildHope and Tree Aid (£1,000 each); Contact a Family and Y Care International (£750 each); Derby Playhouse and Rehearsal Orchestra (£600 each); and Royal Botanic Gardens Kew and Fauna and Flora International (£500 each).

FINANCES *Year* 2007–08 *Income* £167,934 *Grants* £162,050 *Assets* £4,207,572

TRUSTEES T R Kendal; Miss A E Merricks; J H Williams-Rigby; G Wardle.

HOW TO APPLY In writing to the correspondent. The trustees meet twice a year.

WHO TO APPLY TO Anne E Merricks, Linder Myers, Phoenix House, 45 Cross Street, Manchester M2 4JF *Tel* 0161 832 6972 *Fax* 0161 834 0718

CC NO 276660   **ESTABLISHED** 1978

■ The Smith Charitable Trust

WHERE FUNDING CAN BE GIVEN UK and overseas.

WHO CAN BENEFIT Registered charities, usually large, well-known UK organisations, which are on a list of regular beneficiaries.

WHAT IS FUNDED General charitable purposes.

WHAT IS NOT FUNDED No grants to animal charities or to individuals.

RANGE OF GRANTS £4,000–£12,000.

SAMPLE GRANTS Sue Ryder Care (£12,000); Research Institute for the Care of the Elderly and Macmillan Cancer Relief (£8,000 each); St Nicholas' Hospice and NCH (£6,000 each); and the Marine Society and Sea Cadets, Mind, Royal British Legion and SCOPE (£4,000 each).

FINANCES *Year* 2007–08 *Income* £89,018 *Grants* £124,000 *Assets* £5,062,010

TRUSTEES A G F Fuller; P A Sheils; R I Turner; R J Weetch.

HOW TO APPLY Unsolicited applications are not considered.

WHO TO APPLY TO Paul Shiels, Trustee, c/o Moon Beever, Solicitors, 24 Bloomsbury Square, London WC1A 2PL *Tel* 020 7637 0661

CC NO 288570   **ESTABLISHED** 1983

■ The Amanda Smith Charitable Trust

WHERE FUNDING CAN BE GIVEN UK.

WHO CAN BENEFIT Registered charities.

WHAT IS FUNDED General charitable purposes.

SAMPLE GRANTS Previous beneficiaries included Cedar School and Nordoff Robbins Music Therapy.

FINANCES *Year* 2008 *Income* £19 *Grants* £25,000

TRUSTEES C Smith, Chair; Ms A Smith.

HOW TO APPLY In writing to the correspondent.

WHO TO APPLY TO Neil Bradley, 1 Manchester Square, London W1U 3AB *Tel* 020 3219 2600

CC NO 1052975   **ESTABLISHED** 1996

■ The E H Smith Charitable Trust

WHERE FUNDING CAN BE GIVEN UK, some preference for the Midlands.

WHO CAN BENEFIT Local and national organisations.

WHAT IS FUNDED General charitable purposes.

WHAT IS NOT FUNDED No grants to political parties. Grants are not normally given to individuals.

RANGE OF GRANTS Up to around £5,000 each; average about £750.

SAMPLE GRANTS Severn Valley Railway (£5,000); Romania Challenge (£4,900); Betel (£2,500); Solihull Hall (£1,500); Cancer Research UK (£900); County Air Ambulance (£700); Smile Train UK (£600); and Crash Christmas Cards, NSPCC and Junior Heybridge Swifts FC (£500 each).

FINANCES *Year* 2007–08 *Income* £86,704 *Grants* £67,811 *Assets* £227,975

TRUSTEES K H A Smith; Mrs B M Hodgskin-Brown; D P Ensell.

HOW TO APPLY In writing to the correspondent at any time.

WHO TO APPLY TO K H A Smith, Trustee, Westhaven House, Arleston Way, Shipley, West Midlands B90 4LH *Tel* 0121 706 6100

CC NO 328313   **ESTABLISHED** 1989

■ The Henry Smith Charity

WHERE FUNDING CAN BE GIVEN UK. Specific local programmes in East and West Sussex, Hampshire, Kent, Gloucestershire, Leicestershire, Suffolk and Surrey.

WHO CAN BENEFIT Charitable organisations.

WHAT IS FUNDED The trustees use the following programme areas to classify their grants: Black, Asian and Minority Ethnic (BAME); Carers; Community Service; Disability; Domestic and Sexual Violence; Drugs, Alcohol and Substance Misuse; Ex-Service Men and Women; Family Services; Healthcare; Homelessness; Lesbian, Gay, Bisexual and Transgender; Mental Health; Older People; Prisoners and Ex-offenders; Prostitution and Trafficking; Refugees and Asylum Seekers; and Young People.

WHAT IS NOT FUNDED Grants are not made towards the following: local authorities and areas of work usually considered a statutory responsibility; state maintained schools, colleges, universities and friend/parent-teacher associations, or independent schools not exclusively for students with special educational needs; organisations not providing direct services to clients such as umbrella, second tier or grant-making organisations; youth clubs, except those in areas of high deprivation; uniformed groups such as Scouts and Guides, except those in areas of high deprivation; community centres, except those in areas of high deprivation; community transport organisations or services; professional associations or projects for the training of professionals; start up costs or organisations unable to demonstrate a track record; individuals, or organisations and charities applying on their behalf; projects that promote a particular religion, or capital appeals for places of worship; arts projects, except those which can clearly demonstrate a therapeutic or rehabilitative benefit to disabled people, prisoners or young people who experience educational, social and economic disadvantage, including young people in, or leaving, care; education projects except those which can clearly demonstrate a rehabilitative benefit to disabled people, prisoners or young people who experience educational, social and economic disadvantage, including young people in, or leaving, care; leisure, recreation or play activities, except those exclusively for disabled people or those which can clearly demonstrate a significant rehabilitative benefit to people with mental health problems or that significantly improve opportunities and maximise the potential of young people who experience educational, social and economic disadvantage; overseas trips; projects taking place or benefiting people outside the UK; residential holidays for young people (except those that qualify under the Holiday Grants scheme); counselling projects, except those in areas of high deprivation and with a clearly defined client group; environmental projects where the primary purpose is conservation of the environment; Citizens Advice Bureau or projects solely providing legal advice; core running costs of hospices; feasibility studies; social research; campaigning or lobbying projects; projects where website development or maintenance is the focus of the bid; IT equipment (unless as direct

Think carefully about every application. Is it justified?

863

support costs for a funded staff member); capital projects to meet the requirements of the Disability Discrimination Act; applicants declined within the previous six months.

TYPE OF GRANT Capital and revenue; one-off grants and recurrent grants for up to 3 years.

RANGE OF GRANTS Small grants: £500–£10,000; Large grants: over £10,000.

SAMPLE GRANTS In 2009: Impetus Trust (£325,000), towards four years' support for the Reducing Re-Offending Fund, a joint venture between Impetus Trust, Indigo Trust, Esmée Fairbairn and Henry Smith Charity that will fund third sector organisations working to make a significant impact on reducing re-offending; Furzedown Project (£108,000), towards three years' running costs of a home visiting service for older people in London Borough of Wandsworth; Amber Foundation (£90,000), towards three years' salary and on costs of a Recruitment Manager and costs associated with their work in prisons across the South West; Age Concern Warwickshire (£60,000), towards two years' salary and on costs of a part-time Counselling Co-ordinator at a support project for older people who care for grown up children with mental health problems; Chooselife Cymru (£50,000), towards two years' core costs of a centre for people with drug and alcohol dependency and their families in Cardiff; Woodhouse Close Church Community Centre (£45,000), towards three years' running costs of a lunch club for older people on an estate in a deprived part of Bishop Auckland; Skye and Lochalsh Community Care Forum (£40,000), towards three years' salary and on costs of a Deputy Manager at a community care project on the Isle of Skye; YMCA Lurgan (£35,500), towards two years' running costs of a cross sectarian youth work programme in Co. Armagh for young people at risk; Speaking Up (£32,400), towards three years' salary and on costs of the Head of Active Voices at a mentoring project in Cambridgeshire for young people with learning disabilities; Blackbird Leys Neighbourhood Support Scheme (£30,000), towards two years' core costs of the Advice Centre; University of Cambridge – Wolfson Brain Imaging Centre (£17,600), towards the development of a Brain Computer Interface to improve the quality of life of people with impaired consciousness following brain injury; Centre for African Resources Research and Development (£10,000), towards one year's running costs of the Healthittude project for people from BAME communities in Leicestershire; Relate – Brighton, Hove, Worthing & Districts (£4,000), towards running costs of a project in East Sussex that offers counselling at a reduced costs to couples experiencing financial disadvantage; Sefton Children's Trust (£2,000), towards a trip to Manor Adventure in Shropshire for a group of 72 disadvantaged young people from Liverpool; and Haverhill and District Volunteer Centre (£1,000), towards one year's running costs of a volunteering project for people in Suffolk experiencing or recovering from mental health problems.

FINANCES *Year* 2008 *Income* £21,307,000 *Grants* £26,754,000 *Assets* £582,137,000

TRUSTEES Rt Hon Max Egremont; Ronnie Norman; Carola Godman-Law; James Hambro; Anna McNair Scott; Merlyn Lowther; Gordon Steere; Noel Manns; Anne Allen; Rt Hon Claire Countes; Diana Barran; Marilyn Gallyer; Mark Newton; Peter Smallridge; Tristan Millington Drake; Nicholas Acland; Miko Geidroyc.

HOW TO APPLY 'Each of our grant programmes has a slightly different application and assessment process. You will find information about how to make your application in the guidelines for each type of grant. Some of our grants require you to fill in an application form. For others there is no application form; instead we provide guidance about to structure your application and what supporting documents you need to send us. Please ensure you send us all the supporting documents we ask you to include with your application. Incomplete applications will be returned unread. We strongly recommend that you download and read the guidelines of the relevant grant programme carefully before you start your application. It is important that you follow our guidance on how to apply. Guidelines for each programme can be downloaded from the Grant Programmes section of the website.'

WHO TO APPLY TO Richard Hopgood, Director, 6th Floor, 65 Leadenhall Street, London EC3A 2AD *Tel* 020 7264 4970 *Fax* 020 7488 9097 *Website* www.henrysmithcharity.org.uk

CC NO 230102   **ESTABLISHED** 1628

....

■ The Leslie Smith Foundation

WHERE FUNDING CAN BE GIVEN UK with a preference for Wiltshire, Norfolk, Middlesex, London and Dorset.

WHO CAN BENEFIT Registered charities, with a preference for those benefiting children with illnesses, both terminal and non-terminal, in the UK (excluding respite care and research); orphans; and schools, specifically special needs schools based in the UK.

WHAT IS FUNDED Preference is given to charities which the trust has special interest in, knowledge of, or association with, but with an emphasis on: counselling services; children's and young persons' welfare; health and allied services; ex-servicemen's welfare; and other causes the trustees deem appropriate.

WHAT IS NOT FUNDED Grants are given to registered charities only. No grants for individuals.

TYPE OF GRANT Buildings, capital, one-off, research and recurring costs. Funding is available for up to one year.

RANGE OF GRANTS £500–£14,000.

SAMPLE GRANTS Gaddum Centre, Joseph Weld Hospice and Royal British Legion (£10,000 each); Manna House Counselling Services, Shooting Star Children's Hospice and London Youth (£5,000 each); Community Fund Wiltshire and Swindon (£2,500); Norfolk Accident Rescue Service and Wooden Spoon Society (£2,000 each); Bingham Chapel Project (£1,100); and St Peter and St Paul – Bergh Apton (£500).

FINANCES *Year* 2007–08 *Income* £304,766 *Grants* £110,110 *Assets* £4,080,880

TRUSTEES M D Willcox; H L Young Jones.

HOW TO APPLY In writing to the correspondent, including a summary of the project and a copy of the latest accounts. Only successful applications are acknowledged.

WHO TO APPLY TO The Directors, c/o Willcox & Lewis, The Old Coach House, Sunnyside, Bergh Apton, Norwich NR15 1DD *Tel* 01508 480100 *Fax* 01508 480001 *email* info@willcoxlewis.co. uk

CC NO 250030   **ESTABLISHED** 1964

■ The Martin Smith Foundation

WHERE FUNDING CAN BE GIVEN UK.

WHO CAN BENEFIT Organisations and individuals.

WHAT IS FUNDED Projects supporting art, music, sports and education.

TYPE OF GRANT One-off and recurrent.

RANGE OF GRANTS £50–£750,000.

SAMPLE GRANTS National Museum of Science and Industry (£750,000); Orchestra of the Age of Enlightenment – Smith Challenge (£165,000); Royal Academy of Music (£106,000); Bath Mozartfest (£15,000); Tetbury Music Festival (£7,500); Royal Philharmonic Society (£5,900); International Musicians Seminar Prussia Cove (£2,800); Ashmolean Museum (£1,000); and Wellbeing of Women (£250).

FINANCES *Year* 2007–08 *Income* £4,162,078 *Grants* £1,071,422 *Assets* £3,223,508

TRUSTEES Martin G Smith, Chair; Elise Smith; Jeremy J G Smith; Katherine Wake; Elizabeth F C Buchanan; B Peerless.

OTHER INFORMATION Grants totalling £31,000 were also made to individuals.

HOW TO APPLY This trust does not consider unsolicited applications.

WHO TO APPLY TO Martin Smith, 4 Essex Villas, London W8 7BN *Tel* 020 7937 0027

CC NO 1072607

■ Stanley Smith General Charitable Trust

WHERE FUNDING CAN BE GIVEN UK.

WHO CAN BENEFIT Any organisations or people who are in need.

WHAT IS FUNDED General charitable purposes.

SAMPLE GRANTS Sutton Veny CE Primary School (£10,300); Royal College of Art (£10,000); Aviation for Paraplegics and Tetraplegics Charitable Trust and the Living Paintings Trust (£3,000 each); Special Yoga Centre (£2,000); Pony Club (£1,0000; and Beating Bowel Cancer (£500).

FINANCES *Year* 2007–08 *Income* £77,623 *Grants* £29,810 *Assets* £2,345,297

HOW TO APPLY In writing to the correspondent.

WHO TO APPLY TO George Georghiou, Mercer and Hole Trustees Ltd, 72 London Road, St Albans, Hertfordshire AL1 1NS *Tel* 01727 869 141

CC NO 326226 **ESTABLISHED** 1982

■ The Stanley Smith UK Horticultural Trust

WHERE FUNDING CAN BE GIVEN UK and overseas.

WHO CAN BENEFIT Grants are made to individuals or to institutions benefiting botany and horticulture.

WHAT IS FUNDED Grants are made to individual projects which involve the advancement of amenity horticulture and horticultural education. In the past, assistance has been given to: the creation, preservation and development of gardens to which the public is admitted; the cultivation and wider distribution of plants derived by breeding or by collection from the wild, to research; and to the publication of books with a direct bearing on horticulture.

WHAT IS NOT FUNDED Grants are not made for projects in commercial horticulture (crop production) or agriculture, nor are they made to support students taking academic or diploma courses of any kind, although educational institutions are supported.

TYPE OF GRANT Capital (including buildings), core costs, feasibility studies, interest-free loans, one-off, research and start-up costs. Grants are normally made as a contribution to cover the costs of identified projects. In exceptional cases grants are made over a three-year period.

SAMPLE GRANTS Anglo-Greek Collaboration (£8,000); Dundee University Botanic Garden and Grounds (£6,000); Botanic Gardens Conservation International; Friends of Urchfront Gardens – Wiltshire and Galapagos Conservation Trust (£2,500 each); and Plants for Life – Kenya and Cambridgeshire Gardens Trust (£1,000 each).

FINANCES *Year* 2007–08 *Income* £135,529 *Grants* £92,600 *Assets* £3,204,094

TRUSTEES C D Brickell; Lady Renfrew; J B E Simmons; A De Brye; P R Sykes; Dr D A H Rae; E Reed.

HOW TO APPLY In writing to the correspondent. *Guidelines for Applicants* are available from the trust. The director is willing to give advice on how applications should be presented. Grants are awarded twice a year, in spring and autumn. To be considered in the spring allocation, applications should reach the director before 15 February of each year; for the autumn allocation the equivalent date is 15 August. Potential recipients are advised to get their applications in early.

WHO TO APPLY TO James Cullen, Director, Cory Lodge, PO Box 365, Cambridge CB2 1HR *Tel* 01223 336 299 *Fax* 01223 336 278

CC NO 261925 **ESTABLISHED** 1970

■ Philip Smith's Charitable Trust

WHERE FUNDING CAN BE GIVEN UK with a preference for Gloucestershire.

WHO CAN BENEFIT Local and national registered charities.

WHAT IS FUNDED The trust makes grants mainly in the fields of welfare, older people and children.

RANGE OF GRANTS £100–£20,000.

SAMPLE GRANTS NSPCC (£20,000); Star Appeal, Gloucester Community Foundation and Gloucestershire Flood Relief Fund (£5,000 each); Salvation Army (£2,500); Wester Ross Fisheries Trust (£2,000); Merlin (£1,000); Pied Piper Appeal (£500); St Richards Hospice (£350); and Royal Green Jackets (£100).

FINANCES *Year* 2007–08 *Income* £48,331 *Grants* £80,650 *Assets* £1,197,251

TRUSTEES Hon. Philip R Smith; Mary Smith.

HOW TO APPLY In writing to the correspondent. The trustees meet regularly to consider grants. A lack of response can be taken to indicate that the trust does not wish to contribute to an appeal.

WHO TO APPLY TO Helen D'Monte, Bircham Dyson Bell, 50 Broadway, London SW1H 0BL *Tel* 020 7783 3685 *Fax* 020 7222 3480 *email* helendmonte@bdb-law.co.uk

CC NO 1003751 **ESTABLISHED** 1991

■ The R C Snelling Charitable Trust

WHERE FUNDING CAN BE GIVEN Within a 30-mile radius of the village of Blofield in Norfolk.

WHO CAN BENEFIT UK registered charities, children, young and older people.

WHAT IS FUNDED Medical, educational, religious, welfare or environmental resources.

WHAT IS NOT FUNDED The trust gave the following list of ineligible expenditures: salaries; sponsorship for less than one year; general appeals where the need could be met several times over by grantors; national appeals; continued assistance with running costs.

TYPE OF GRANT One-off.

RANGE OF GRANTS £100–£5,000.

SAMPLE GRANTS Royal Air Force Air Defence Radar Museum (£6,800); East Anglia's Children's Hospice and YMCA Norfolk (£5,000); North East Norfolk 1st Rural Scouts (£4,000); East Norfolk Youth for Christ (£3,000); Norfolk and Norwich Scope Association (£2,000); Blofield Heath Bowls Club (£1,000); Benjamin Foundation and Nelson's Journey (£500 each); the Clare School (£250); and St Margaret's Church Drayton (£100).

FINANCES *Year* 2007–08 *Income* £499,886 *Grants* £37,866 *Assets* £1,241,648

TRUSTEES R C Snelling; P Buttinger; R A Cogman; T Wise; P Minns; J Drake; R Nash.

HOW TO APPLY An online application form can be completed from the company's website. The trust is happy to receive queries via email.

WHO TO APPLY TO The Trustees, R C Snelling Ltd, Lijas Field, Laundry Lane, Blofield Heath, Norwich NR13 4SQ *Tel* 01603 712 202 *email* trust@snellings.co.uk *Website* www.snellings.co.uk/charitable-trust.aspx

CC NO 1074776   **ESTABLISHED** 1999

■ The Snowball Trust

WHERE FUNDING CAN BE GIVEN Coventry and Warwickshire.

WHO CAN BENEFIT Individuals or institutions for the benefit of children up to 21 years of age who are disabled.

WHAT IS FUNDED The provision of moveable equipment for sick and disabled children.

WHAT IS NOT FUNDED Applications for administration and maintenance costs, salaries, fees, short-term respite care and holidays are rejected.

TYPE OF GRANT Capital and one-off.

RANGE OF GRANTS Generally £500–£5,000, although there are no upper or lower limits.

FINANCES *Year* 2008–09 *Income* £53,718 *Grants* £56,195 *Assets* £121,255

TRUSTEES Shaun Flaherty; Elaine Hancox; David Fisher; Dr Alan Rhodes; David Brookes.

OTHER INFORMATION £41,522 to organisations and £14,673 to individuals.

HOW TO APPLY On a form available from the correspondent.

WHO TO APPLY TO Shaun Flaherty, Trustee, 80 Howes Lane, Coventry CV3 6PJ *Tel* 024 7641 5733

CC NO 702860   **ESTABLISHED** 1989

■ The Sobell Foundation

WHERE FUNDING CAN BE GIVEN Unrestricted, in practice, UK, Israel and the Commonwealth of Independent States.

WHO CAN BENEFIT Small national or local registered charities or organisations registered with the Inland Revenue.

WHAT IS FUNDED Jewish charities; medical care and treatment; care and education for children and adults with physical and/or mental disabilities; homelessness; care and support for older people; care and support for children from disadvantaged backgrounds.

WHAT IS NOT FUNDED Individuals.

TYPE OF GRANT One-off, capital, project, running costs, buildings, core costs and recurring costs. Funding may be given for up to and over three years.

RANGE OF GRANTS £250–£50,000.

SAMPLE GRANTS Major donations were made to 25 organisations and ranged from £20,000 to £50,000. The foundation renewed its support for the Royal Brompton and Harefield Trust, committing to a five year grant of £250,000. A grant of £50,000 was also given to the Jewish Museum London and the first instalment of a three year grant worth £150,000 was paid to the Rainbow Centre for Conductive Research. A further 391 smaller grants were also made.

FINANCES *Year* 2007–08 *Income* £2,949,155 *Grants* £2,738,838 *Assets* £59,410,524

TRUSTEES Susan Lacroix; Roger Lewis; Andrea Scouller.

HOW TO APPLY Applications should be made in writing to the administrator using the application form obtainable from the foundation or printable from its website. The application form should be accompanied by: current year's summary income and expenditure budget; most recent annual report; most recent full accounts; and Inland Revenue certificate of exemption (if required).

It will generally be two to three months before applicants are notified of the trustees' decision. The trustees receive a large number of applications for funding from registered charities during the year and support as many as possible of those which fall within the foundation's objectives. They aim to deal with requests within three months of receipt and to respond to each application received, whether or not a grant is made. Trustees meet every three to four months and major grants are considered at these meetings. Requests for smaller amounts may be dealt with on a more frequent basis. Most applications are dealt with on an ongoing basis, and there are no deadlines for the receipt of applications. Organisations should wait 12 months before reapplying.

WHO TO APPLY TO Penny Newton, Administrator, PO Box 2137, Shepton Mallet, Somerset BA4 6YA *Tel* 01749 813 135 *Fax* 01749 813 136 *email* enquiries@sobellfoundation.org.uk *Website* www.sobellfoundation.org.uk

CC NO 274369   **ESTABLISHED** 1977

■ Solev Co Ltd

WHERE FUNDING CAN BE GIVEN UK.

WHO CAN BENEFIT Individuals and organisations benefiting Jewish people.

WHAT IS FUNDED Principally Jewish causes.

SAMPLE GRANTS Previous beneficiaries include: Dina Perelman Trust Ltd (£100,000); Songdale Ltd (£40,000); Society of Friends of the Torah (£3,900); Finchley Road Synagogue (£2,300); NW London Talmudical College (£1,500); Yesodey Hatorah School (£700); and Gateshead Talmudical College (£400).

FINANCES *Year* 2007–08 *Income* £1,630,856 *Grants* £826,782 *Assets* £4,123,357

TRUSTEES R Tager; S Tager; J Tager; C M Frommer.

OTHER INFORMATION No information on grant beneficiaries has been included in the charity's accounts in recent years.

HOW TO APPLY In writing to the correspondent.

WHO TO APPLY TO R Tager, Trustee, Romeo House, 160 Bridport Road, London N18 1SY

CC NO 254623   **ESTABLISHED** 1967

■ Solihull Community Foundation

WHERE FUNDING CAN BE GIVEN Borough of Solihull and the surrounding area.

WHO CAN BENEFIT Registered charities, community and voluntary groups working to help local people across Solihull.

WHAT IS FUNDED General charitable purposes. The foundation is currently managing the following funds: Grassroots Grants, Sport Relief and the European Social Fund Community Grants. Please note: grant schemes can change frequently and potential applicants are advised to consult the foundation's website for details of open programmes and their deadlines.

FINANCES *Year* 2007–08 *Income* £285,471 *Grants* £243,030 *Assets* £131,912

TRUSTEES Eric Baptiste; John Powell; Maggie Throup; Denis Ellis; George Lester.

HOW TO APPLY The foundation's website has details of the grant schemes currently being administered.

WHO TO APPLY TO Sharon Pinnock, Manager, Block 80, Land Rover, Lode Lane, Solihull B92 8NW *Tel* 0121 700 3934 *Fax* 0121 700 9158 *email* director@solihullcf.org *Website* www.solihullcf.org

CC NO 1063014   **ESTABLISHED** 1997

■ The Solo Charitable Settlement

WHERE FUNDING CAN BE GIVEN UK and Israel.

WHO CAN BENEFIT Organisations benefiting Jewish people, disabled people, research workers and medical professionals.

WHAT IS FUNDED Jewish organisations, medical research, arts and disability.

RANGE OF GRANTS Between £100–£30,000.

SAMPLE GRANTS Jewish Care (£30,000); Community Security Trust (£11,000); Norwood Ravenswood (£10,000); Nightingale House (£5,500); Holocaust Education Trust (£2,500); Royal Opera House Campaign (£2,400); Eve Appeal (£2,000); Cancer Research (£1,000); English Stage Company (£500); Chai Cancer Care (£300); One Family UK (£250); and Walk the Walk (£100).

FINANCES *Year* 2007–08 *Income* £256,326 *Grants* £81,375 *Assets* £5,227,300

TRUSTEES Peter D Goldstein; Edna A Goldstein; Paul Goldstein; Dean Goldstein; Jamie Goldstein; Tammy Ward.

HOW TO APPLY In writing to the correspondent.

WHO TO APPLY TO The Trustees, c/o Randall Greene, 32–34 London Road, Guildford, Surrey GU1 2AB *Tel* 01483 230440

CC NO 326444   **ESTABLISHED** 1983

■ Dr Richard Solomon's Charitable Trust

WHERE FUNDING CAN BE GIVEN Overseas.

WHO CAN BENEFIT Voluntary groups and charitable organisations only.

WHAT IS FUNDED General, international development. The trust has previously stated that it prefers to support 'ecologically sound democratic projects'.

WHAT IS NOT FUNDED Individuals are not supported.

RANGE OF GRANTS Up to £21,000.

SAMPLE GRANTS INDEPO – Institute for Rural Development – Bolivia (£21,000); Tools for Self Reliance and Appropriate Technology Asia (£3,500 each); Tree Aid and Forest Peoples Project (£2,500 each); Civil Liberties Trust and Refugee Council (£1,500 each); and Computer

Aid International and Microloan Foundation (£1,000 each).

FINANCES *Year* 2007 *Income* £34,059 *Grants* £40,167 *Assets* £387,988

TRUSTEES Richard Edgar Bethel Solomon; Stella Natasha Solomon; Diana Jean Huntingford; Alison Margaret Sepping.

HOW TO APPLY In writing to the correspondent.

WHO TO APPLY TO Dr Richard Solomons, Trustee, Fell Edge Farm, Straight Lane, Addingham, Moorside, West Yorkshire LS29 9JY *Tel* 01943 830841

CC NO 277309   **ESTABLISHED** 1978

■ David Solomons Charitable Trust

WHERE FUNDING CAN BE GIVEN UK.

WHO CAN BENEFIT UK and local charitable organisations benefiting people who have learning difficulties and their carers.

WHAT IS FUNDED Mostly capital projects for disability groups.

WHAT IS NOT FUNDED No grants to individuals.

TYPE OF GRANT Capital (including buildings), feasibility studies, one-off, project, research and start-up costs. Funding for up to or more than three years will be considered.

RANGE OF GRANTS Mostly £1,000–£2,000.

SAMPLE GRANTS Down's Syndrome Association (£11,000); Kids Care (£2,500); Birmingham Royal Ballet, Camphill Communities and Mencap (£2,000 each); TACT and Play Matters (£1,500 each); Royal School for Deaf & Communications Disorder and Sleep Scotland (£1,000 each); and Our Choice (£750). Smaller donations of £500 or £250 each included those to Edenbridge & District Mencap, Friends of Beverley School, Grosby & District Out of School Club, Medical Engineering Resource Unit, Parents United and Grosby & District Out of School Club.

FINANCES *Year* 2007–08 *Income* £102,358 *Grants* £147,850 *Assets* £2,226,802

TRUSTEES J L Drewitt; J J Rutter; W H McBryde; Dr R E B Solomons; M T Chamberlayne; Dr L B Cooke; D J Huntingford.

HOW TO APPLY In writing to the correspondent. The trustees meet three times a year to consider applications.

WHO TO APPLY TO Graeme Crosby, Administrator, Jasmine Cottage, 11 Lower Road, Breachwood Green, Hitchin, Hertfordshire SG4 8NS *Tel* 01438 833254 *email* g.crosby@waitrose.com

CC NO 297275   **ESTABLISHED** 1986

■ Friends of Somerset Churches and Chapels

WHERE FUNDING CAN BE GIVEN The historic county of Somerset.

WHO CAN BENEFIT Churches and chapels.

WHAT IS FUNDED The repair of churches and chapels, which are open for worship in Somerset.

WHAT IS NOT FUNDED No grants to individuals. No support for new work, reordering or repairs to moveable items.

RANGE OF GRANTS Up to £10,000.

SAMPLE GRANTS Church beneficiaries include: Goathurst, Wells St Cuthbert, Seavington St Michael, High Ham, Blackford and Clatworthy.

FINANCES *Year* 2007–08 *Income* £40,541 *Grants* £22,600 *Assets* £105,142

TRUSTEES Hugh Playfair; Gerard Leighton; John Wood; David Sisson; Dr Robert Dunning;

Think carefully about every application. Is it justified?

867

Jennifer Beazley; Rear Admiral Roger Morris; Jane Venner-Pack; The Very Revd Abbot of Downside.

PUBLICATIONS *Somerset Churches – Building, Repair and Restoration* was published by the trust in June 2007.

HOW TO APPLY Application forms and guidelines are available from the correspondent or to download from the website. Trustees meet four times a year.

WHO TO APPLY TO Angela Dudley, Grants Secretary, Whynot Cottage, Wellow, Bath, Somerset BA2 8QA *Tel* 01225 837134 *email* chedburn@chedburn.com *Website* www.fscandc.org.uk

CC NO 1055840   **ESTABLISHED** 1996

■ Songdale Ltd

WHERE FUNDING CAN BE GIVEN UK and Israel.

WHO CAN BENEFIT People of the Orthodox Jewish faith.

WHAT IS FUNDED All of which is in accordance with the Orthodox Jewish faith. Jewish general charitable purposes.

RANGE OF GRANTS £1,000–£53,000.

SAMPLE GRANTS Previous beneficiaries included: Cosmon Belz Ltd (£53,000); Kollel Belz (£50,000); BFOT (£27,000); Ezras Yisroel (£20,000); Forty Limited (£17,000); Darkei Ovois (£10,400); Germach Veholachto and Keren Nedunnia Lchasanim (£10,000 each); Belz Nursery (£9,500); and Bais Chinuch (£9,000).

FINANCES *Year* 2007–08 *Income* £518,842 *Grants* £234,202 *Assets* £2,909,181

TRUSTEES M Grosskopf; Mrs M Grosskopf; Y Grosskopf.

OTHER INFORMATION No grants list was available.

HOW TO APPLY In writing to the correspondent.

WHO TO APPLY TO M Grosskopf, 6 Spring Hill, London E5 9BE *Tel* 020 8806 5010

CC NO 286075   **ESTABLISHED** 1961

■ The E C Sosnow Charitable Trust

WHERE FUNDING CAN BE GIVEN UK and overseas.

WHO CAN BENEFIT Cultural institutions; UK and international organisations benefiting children, young people, students, older people and people who are disadvantaged.

WHAT IS FUNDED Education; medical organisations; emergency overseas aid; disability; the arts; and people who are underprivileged.

WHAT IS NOT FUNDED No grants are made to individuals.

TYPE OF GRANT One-off.

RANGE OF GRANTS £200–£5,500.

SAMPLE GRANTS HET (£5,500); London Youth and Nightingale House (£3,000 each); Griffins Society, Place to Be, Worldwide Volunteering and Chicken Shed Theatre (£2,000 each); NSPCC and Brent Adolescent Centre (£1,000 each); Woodstock Sinclair Trust (£500); and Ohel Sarah (£200).

FINANCES *Year* 2007–08 *Income* £78,655 *Grants* £41,000 *Assets* £1,862,895

TRUSTEES E R Fattal; Mrs F J M Fattal.

HOW TO APPLY In writing to the correspondent.

WHO TO APPLY TO The Trustees, PO Box 13398, London SW3 6ZL

CC NO 273578   **ESTABLISHED** 1977

■ The Souter Charitable Trust

WHERE FUNDING CAN BE GIVEN UK, but with a preference for Scotland; overseas.

WHO CAN BENEFIT Grants are given to a variety of organisations supporting people of all ages; people who are in care, fostered or adopted; Christians; evangelists; carers; people disadvantaged by poverty; refugees; or victims of famine, man-made or natural disasters or war.

WHAT IS FUNDED Relief of human suffering, particularly projects with a Christian emphasis.

WHAT IS NOT FUNDED Building projects, individuals, personal education grants and expeditions are not supported.

TYPE OF GRANT One-off and recurring grants.

RANGE OF GRANTS Mostly £1,000 or less.

SAMPLE GRANTS Previous beneficiaries include: Alpha International (an Anglican evangelical movement based in London), Highland Theological College, Operation Mobilisation, Prince's Trust – Scotland, Sargent Cancer Care, Scripture Union and Turning Point Scotland.

FINANCES *Year* 2007–08 *Income* £12,025,695

TRUSTEES Brian Souter; Betty Souter; Ann Allen.

OTHER INFORMATION Despite making a written request for the accounts of this trust (including an sae) these were not provided. The following entry is based on information filed with the Office of the Scottish Charity Regulator.

HOW TO APPLY In writing to the correspondent. Please keep applications brief and no more than two sides of A4 paper: if appropriate, please send audited accounts, but do not send brochures, business plans, dvds and so on. The trust states that it will request more information if necessary. The trustees meet every two months or so, and all applications will be acknowledged in due course, whether successful or not. A stamped addressed envelope would be appreciated. Subsequent applications should not be made within a year of the initial submission.

WHO TO APPLY TO Andy Macfie, Secretary, PO Box 7412, Perth PH1 5YX *Tel* 01738 634745

SC NO SC029998   **ESTABLISHED** 1991

■ The South Square Trust

WHERE FUNDING CAN BE GIVEN UK, with a preference for London and the Home Counties.

WHO CAN BENEFIT The trust assists in two areas with general donations to registered charities, and support of individual students undertaking full-time undergraduate or postgraduate courses connected with the fine and applied arts within the UK. Individuals are considered especially for courses related to goldsmithing, silversmithing, and metalwork but also for music, drama and dance. Preference is given to students commencing undergraduate studies – students must be at least 18 years old. The trust has established scholarships and bursaries with schools connected with the fine and applied arts and a full list of these schools can be obtained from the clerk to the trustees. Where a school is in receipt of a bursary, no further assistance will be given to individuals as the school will select candidates themselves.

WHAT IS FUNDED Annual income is allocated in awards to individuals for educational purposes, specifically help with tuition fees but living expenses will be considered for courses as specified above. Donations are also considered to registered charities working in fields of the elderly, medical research and equipment, support groups, community groups, horticulture, green issues and other projects connected with the fine and applied arts.

WHAT IS NOT FUNDED No support for building projects, salaries or individuals wishing to start up a business. No grants given to individuals under 18 or those seeking funding for expeditions, travel, courses outside UK, short courses or courses not connected with fine and applied arts.

TYPE OF GRANT Registered charities: single donations to assist with specific projects, one-off expenses, core costs and research. Individual students: funding may be given for the duration of a course, for up to three years, payable in three term instalments to help with tuition fees or living expenses.

RANGE OF GRANTS Individuals: £500–£1,500; charities: £300–£2,000.

SAMPLE GRANTS St Paul's School (£23,000); Royal Academy of Music (£15,000); Royal College of Art (£12,000); Royal Northern College of Music (£8,000); London Contemporary Dance School (£3,000); Hertfordshire Community Foundation (£2,000); and Gordonstoun School Ltd and Monkton Combe School (£1,500 each).

FINANCES *Year* 2007–08 *Income* £186,502 *Grants* £150,300 *Assets* £3,390,836

TRUSTEES A E Woodall; W P Harriman; C P Grimwade; D B Inglis; R S Baldock.

OTHER INFORMATION In 2007–08 grants were broken down as follows: annual donations to charities – £19,000; general charitable donations – £38,000; bursaries and scholarships to schools/colleges – £94,000; directly aided students and single payment grants – £14,000.

HOW TO APPLY Registered charities: In writing to the correspondent with details about your charity and the reason for requesting funding. Applications are considered three times a year, in November, March and June, and should be submitted at least one month before the next meeting. It is advisable to telephone the correspondent for up-to-date information about the criteria for funding.Individuals: Standard application forms are available from the correspondent. Forms are sent out between January and April only, to be returned by the end of April for consideration for the following academic year.

WHO TO APPLY TO Mrs Nicola Chrimes, Clerk to the Trustees, PO Box 169, Lewes, East Sussex BN7 9FB *Tel* 01825 872264 *Website* www.southsquaretrust.org.uk

CC NO 278960   **ESTABLISHED** 1979

■ The Stephen R and Philippa H Southall Charitable Trust

WHERE FUNDING CAN BE GIVEN UK, but mostly Herefordshire.

WHO CAN BENEFIT Registered charities.

WHAT IS FUNDED General charitable purposes, with a preference for promoting education and conservation of the natural environment and cultural heritage.

RANGE OF GRANTS Up to about £20,000.

SAMPLE GRANTS Hereford Waterworks Museum Trust (£23,000); National Museum and Galleries for Wales and Tobacco Factory Arts Trust (£5,000 each); National Trust (£500); Dogs for the Disabled and Home Start Herefordshire (£250 each); Herefordshire Historical Churches Trust (£200); British Legion (£100); and RNLI (£20).

FINANCES *Year* 2007–08 *Income* £59,037 *Grants* £38,290 *Assets* £2,154,940

TRUSTEES Stephen Readhead Southall; Philippa Helen Southall; Anna Catherine Southall; Candia Helen Compton.

OTHER INFORMATION The trust has previously stated that it uses its surplus income for world emergencies and the development of Hereford Waterwork Museum.

HOW TO APPLY The trust makes several repeat donations and has previously stated that: 'no applications can be considered or replied to'.

WHO TO APPLY TO Philippa Southall, Trustee, Porking Barn, Clifford, Hereford HR3 5HE *Tel* 01497 831243

CC NO 223190   **ESTABLISHED** 1947

■ The W F Southall Trust

WHERE FUNDING CAN BE GIVEN UK and overseas.

WHO CAN BENEFIT Registered charities, especially imaginative new grassroots initiatives and smaller charities where funding will make a significant difference.

WHAT IS FUNDED Work of the Society of Friends; peace-making and conflict resolution; alcohol, drug misuse and penal affairs; environmental action; homelessness; community action; and overseas development.

WHAT IS NOT FUNDED No grants to individuals or large national charities.

TYPE OF GRANT Normally one-off payments.

RANGE OF GRANTS Up to £55,000; usually £100–£5,000.

SAMPLE GRANTS Yearly Meeting – Society of Friends (£55,000); St Giles Trust (£46,000); Counselling in Prison (£25,000); Friends World Committee for Consultation and Woodbrooke Quaker Study Centre (£10,000 each); Responding to Conflict (£7,600); International Voluntary Services and Oxfam (£6,500 each); Quaker Social Action (£5,000); Refugee Council (£4,000); and West Midlands Quaker Peace Education Project, John Muir Trust and Asylum Welcome (£3,000 each).

FINANCES *Year* 2007–08 *Income* £326,148 *Grants* £324,032 *Assets* £7,955,088

TRUSTEES Donald Southall, Chair; Joanna Engelkamp; Claire Greaves; Mark Holtom; Daphne Maw; Annette Wallis.

OTHER INFORMATION Grants of less than £3,000 each were made to 49 organisations totalling nearly £100,000.

HOW TO APPLY In writing to the correspondent (via post or email), requesting an application form. Applications are usually considered in February/March and November. Applications received between meetings are considered at the next meeting.

WHO TO APPLY TO The Secretary, c/o Rutters Solicitors, 2 Bimport, Shaftesbury, Dorset SP7 8AY *Tel* 01747 852377 *Fax* 01747 851989 *email* southall@rutterslaw.co.uk

CC NO 218371   **ESTABLISHED** 1937

■ The Southdown Trust

WHERE FUNDING CAN BE GIVEN UK.

WHO CAN BENEFIT Young people aged 17 to 26 years.

WHAT IS FUNDED Grants towards the education of the specified age group.

WHAT IS NOT FUNDED No grants towards courses in the following subjects: law, journalism, women's studies, counselling, veterinary studies, computer/IT studies and media studies.

SAMPLE GRANTS Christ Church Oxford and Joint Educational Trust (£6,000 each); Silcock Trust (£3,000); Hope UK (£275).

FINANCES *Year* 2007–08 *Income* £49,448 *Grants* £35,340 *Assets* £932,070

TRUSTEES John Geoffrey Wyatt; Hugh Rowland Wyatt; Andrew Cartwright Pugh; John Rowland Blades McBeath.

HOW TO APPLY The trust does not respond to unsolicited applications.

WHO TO APPLY TO John Geoffrey Wyatt, Trustee, Holmbush, 64 High Street, Findon, Worthing, West Sussex BN14 0SY *Tel* 01903 872 618

CC NO 235583   **ESTABLISHED** 1963

■ R H Southern Trust

WHERE FUNDING CAN BE GIVEN Worldwide.

WHO CAN BENEFIT Charitable organisations.

WHAT IS FUNDED Advancement of education (including medical and scientific research); relief of poverty; disability; and preservation, conservation and protection of the environment (especially climate change).

TYPE OF GRANT Mainly long term core funding and special projects.

RANGE OF GRANTS £3,000–£30,000.

SAMPLE GRANTS Feasta (£30,000); Equal Adventure (£23,000); New Economics Foundation (£20,000); Soil Association (£15,000); Oxford Research Group and Friends of the Earth (£10,000 each); Action Village India and Just Change – Oxfam (£10,000 each); E I Rural Links – Tam Wed (£8,500); and Corporate Europe Observatory (£5,000).

FINANCES *Year* 2007–08 *Income* £155,574 *Grants* £194,500 *Assets* £3,403,656

TRUSTEES Marion Valiant Wells; Charles Sebastian Rivett Wells; Charles James Long Bruges; Colkin Trustee Company Limited.

HOW TO APPLY In writing to the correspondent.

WHO TO APPLY TO The Trustees, 23 Sydenham Road, Cotham, Bristol BS6 5SJ *Tel* 0117 942 5834

CC NO 1077509   **ESTABLISHED** 1999

■ The Southover Manor General Education Trust

WHERE FUNDING CAN BE GIVEN Sussex.

WHO CAN BENEFIT Schools, colleges and individuals under the age of 25.

WHAT IS FUNDED The trustees support the 'education of boys and girls under 25 by providing books and equipment, supporting provision of recreational and educational facilities, scholarships and awards'.

WHAT IS NOT FUNDED No grants for people over 25 years of age. Organisations and individuals outside Sussex are not supported.

TYPE OF GRANT Capital and projects.

SAMPLE GRANTS Holy Cross CE Primary School (£10,000); Horsted Keynes CE School and West Hove Junior School (£8,000 each); Downsview School and St. Wilfred's CE Primary School (£5,000 each); and Christ's Hospital Foundation (£2,000).

FINANCES *Year* 2008–09 *Income* £111,120 *Grants* £58,500 *Assets* £2,070,555

TRUSTEES B J Hanbury, Chair; Mrs R C Teacher; P E Cooper; Mrs J S Gordon-Lennox; Mrs C M Duffield; Mrs J A Hall; J W Wakely; J Farmer; Mrs W Bradley; Mrs J Peel.

OTHER INFORMATION In 2008–09 a grant of £500 was made to an individual.

HOW TO APPLY In writing to the correspondent.

WHO TO APPLY TO The Secretary to the Trustees, PO Box 159, Lewes, East Sussex BN7 9ER *Tel* 01273 472 882 *email* southovermanor@ btinternet.com

CC NO 299593   **ESTABLISHED** 1988

■ The Southwold Trust

WHERE FUNDING CAN BE GIVEN Southwold and Reydon.

WHO CAN BENEFIT Registered charities.

WHAT IS FUNDED General charitable purposes.

RANGE OF GRANTS Up to £50,000.

SAMPLE GRANTS Southwold Millennium Foundation (£50,000); Southwold and Reydon Recreation and Development Council (£41,000); 1st Southwold Scout Group and Southwold Museum (£4,000 each); Southwold Methodist Church (£2,000); Southwold Parochial Charity (£1,500); Southwold Day Centre and Southwold and Aldeburgh Theatre Trust (£1,000 each); Crick Court Social Club (£500); and Reydon Village Hall (£350).

FINANCES *Year* 2007–08 *Income* £46,394 *Grants* £33,837 *Assets* £65,902

TRUSTEES B T Segrave-Daly; Mrs E Utting; G J Filby; J W Denny; R Lee; J French; H Fuller; Sir Richard Dales; Michael Mayhew.

HOW TO APPLY In writing to the correspondent.

WHO TO APPLY TO David Gaffney, Treasurer, Margary and Miller, 73 High Street, Southwold, Suffolk IP18 6DS *Tel* 01502 723 308

CC NO 206480   **ESTABLISHED** 1962

■ The Sovereign Health Care Charitable Trust

WHERE FUNDING CAN BE GIVEN UK with a preference for Bradford.

WHO CAN BENEFIT Generally local organisations benefiting older people, at risk groups, and people with disabilities, disadvantaged by poverty or socially isolated.

WHAT IS FUNDED The provision of amenities for hospital patients and to make grants to charitable organisations 'for the relief and assistance of needy, sick and elderly persons'.

WHAT IS NOT FUNDED No grants to individuals.

TYPE OF GRANT Buildings, core costs, one-off or recurrent, project, research, running costs.

RANGE OF GRANTS Up to £35,000.

SAMPLE GRANTS Yorkshire Air Ambulance (£35,000); Manorlands and Bradford Soup Run (£25,000 each); Airedale NHS Trust (£16,000); National Heart Research (£15,000); Bradford Teaching Hospitals (£13,000); Macmillan Cancer Relief (£11,000); AFCO (£10,000); Deafblind UK (£7,500); Heartbeat Appeal (£6,200); Christians Against Poverty (£5,000); British Red Cross (£2,500); Bradford Toy Library (£1,500); and St Georges Crypt and Help the Heroes Ball (£1,000 each).

FINANCES *Year* 2008 *Income* £504,466 *Grants* £524,699 *Assets* £62,631

TRUSTEES Mark Hudson, chair; Michael Austin; Dennis Child; Michael Bower; Russ Piper; Kate Robb-Webb; Robert Dugdale.

HOW TO APPLY In writing to the correspondent.

WHO TO APPLY TO The Secretary, Royal Standard House, 26 Manningham Lane, Bradford, West Yorkshire BD1 3DN *Tel* 01274 729472 *Fax* 01274 722252 *email* charities@ sovereignhealthcare.co.uk *Website* www. sovereignhealthcare.co.uk

CC NO 1079024   **ESTABLISHED** 1955

■ Spar Charitable Fund

WHERE FUNDING CAN BE GIVEN UK.

WHO CAN BENEFIT Registered charities, mostly well-known national organisations.

WHAT IS FUNDED General charitable purposes, with some preference for projects benefiting young people.

SAMPLE GRANTS NSPCC (£344,000); the Woodland Trust (£12,000); and Business in the Community (£8,800).

FINANCES *Year* 2007–08 *Income* £373,823 *Grants* £364,398 *Assets* £975,076

TRUSTEES The National Guild of Spar Ltd.

OTHER INFORMATION This trust tends to choose one main beneficiary, which receives most of its funds, with smaller grants being made to similar beneficiaries each year.

HOW TO APPLY In writing to the correspondent.

WHO TO APPLY TO P W Marchant, Director and Company Secretary, Mezzanine Floor, Hygeia Building, 66 – 68 College Road, Harrow, Middlesex HA1 1BE *Tel* 020 8426 3700 *email* philip.marchant@spar.co.uk

CC NO 236252　　　**ESTABLISHED** 1964

■ Sparks Charity (Sport Aiding Medical Research For Kids)

WHERE FUNDING CAN BE GIVEN UK.

WHO CAN BENEFIT Research units at UK hospitals and universities.

WHAT IS FUNDED Medical research to enable children to be born healthy and to stay healthy.

WHAT IS NOT FUNDED The charity is unable to consider: applications which are concurrently submitted to other funding bodies; grants for further education, for example, MSc/PhD course fees; grants towards service provision or audit studies; grants for work undertaken outside the UK; grants towards 'top up' funding for work supported by other funding bodies; or grants to other charities.

TYPE OF GRANT project grants up to the value of £200,000, Research Training Fellowships and Programme grants.

RANGE OF GRANTS £50,000–£150,000. Applications outside this range will be considered.

SAMPLE GRANTS The Institute of Child Health, Programme Grant (£631,000); University of Manchester (£196,000); University of Newcastle (£149,500 in two grants); University of Glasgow (£143,000); University of Liverpool (£137,000); and University College London (£132,000).

FINANCES *Year* 2008–09 *Income* £3,500,000 *Grants* £2,356,974 *Assets* £777,000

TRUSTEES T Brooke-Taylor; Sir T Brooking; H Emeades; M Higgins; D Mills; R Uttley; S Waugh; J Wilkinson; F Benjamin; J Britton; V Glaysher; G Gregory; G Logan; D Orr; F van den Bosch.

HOW TO APPLY Sparks funds project grants up to the value of £200,000, Research Training Fellowships and Programme grants. Prior to submitting a full application, all applicants are required to complete an outline proposal form which is available for download from the charity's website in Word format. Completed outlines and any queries should be sent to: Dr Kirti Patel, Medical Research Manager, email: kirti@sparks.org.uk, direct Tel/Fax 020 7799 2111/020 7222 2701. Please refer to the Sparks website for outline closing dates. Applicants with suitable research projects will be sent an application form (by email in Word format) and a copy of the relating terms and conditions. Closing dates for full applications are generally March and October; please refer to the Sparks website.

WHO TO APPLY TO Dr Kirti Patel, Medical Research Manager, Heron House, 10 Dean Farrer Street, London SW1H 0DX *Tel* 020 7799 2111 *Fax* 020 7222 2701 *email* kirti@sparks.org.uk *Website* www.sparks.org.uk

CC NO 1003825　　　**ESTABLISHED** 1991

■ Sparquote Limited

WHERE FUNDING CAN BE GIVEN A preference for north and west London, including Edgware in Middlesex.

WHO CAN BENEFIT Jewish charities.

WHAT IS FUNDED Education and welfare.

RANGE OF GRANTS Up to £40,000.

SAMPLE GRANTS The Wlodowa Charity and Rehabilitation Trust (£41,000); The Telz Academy Trust (£30,000); British Friends of Mosdos Tchernobyl (£20,000); The Society of Friends of the Torah (£19,000); Gevurath Ari Torah Trust (£15,000); Beis Nadvorna Charitable Trust (£10,000); The Edgware Foundation and Penshurst Corporation Limited (£5,000 each); Gateshead Institute for Rabbinical Studies (£3,500 each); Dina Perelman Trust Limited (£1,800); and American Friends (£1,000).

FINANCES *Year* 2007–08 *Income* £640,446 *Grants* £243,981 *Assets* £3,752,645

TRUSTEES David Reichmann; Dov Reichmann; Mrs A M Reichmann.

HOW TO APPLY In writing to the correspondent.

WHO TO APPLY TO Anne-Mette Reichmann, Secretary, Grovesnor House, 1 High Street, Edgware, Middlesex, HA87TA *Tel* 020 8731 0777 *Fax* 020 8731 0778

CC NO 286232　　　**ESTABLISHED** 1982

■ The Spear Charitable Trust

WHERE FUNDING CAN BE GIVEN UK.

WHO CAN BENEFIT Individuals and organisations, particularly employees and former employees of J W Spear and Sons plc, their families and dependants.

WHAT IS FUNDED Welfare of employees and former employees of J W Spear and Sons plc, their families and dependants; also general charitable purposes, with some preference for animal welfare, the environment and health.

WHAT IS NOT FUNDED Appeals from individuals are not considered.

SAMPLE GRANTS RSPCA – Enfield (£8,000); Fuerth Jewish Cemetery (£7,000); Imagine – Mozambique (£6,000); Friends of the Earth (£5,000); British Philatelic Trust and East-Side Educational Trust (£2,500 each); Devon Wildlife Trust and Trees for Life (£2,000 each); and Greyhounds Compassion, Bowel Disease Research Foundation and Greater Shankhill Youth Initiative (£1,000 each).

FINANCES *Year* 2007 *Income* £145,100 *Grants* £109,448 *Assets* £4,883,244

TRUSTEES P N Harris; F A Spear; H E Spear; N Gooch.

OTHER INFORMATION In 2007 individuals connected with J W Spear and Sons plc received £25,842.

HOW TO APPLY In writing to the correspondent.

WHO TO APPLY TO Hazel E Spear, Secretary, Roughground House, Old Hall Green, Ware, Hertfordshire SG11 1HB *Tel* 01920 823071 *Fax* 01920 823071

CC NO 1041568　　　**ESTABLISHED** 1962

Think carefully about every application. Is it justified?

871

■ Spears-Stutz Charitable Trust

WHERE FUNDING CAN BE GIVEN Worldwide.
WHO CAN BENEFIT Registered charities.
WHAT IS FUNDED General charitable purposes, relief of poverty, Jewish causes, museums and arts organisations.
SAMPLE GRANTS Previous beneficiaries included Cancer Macmillan Fund, Royal Academy Trust, Royal Academy of Arts, Wellbeing, King Edward Hospital, Help the Aged and Westminster Synagogue.
FINANCES *Year* 2007–08 *Income* £23,646 *Grants* £35,000
TRUSTEES Mrs R L Spears.
OTHER INFORMATION This trust was previously known as the Roama Spears Charitable Settlement.
HOW TO APPLY In writing to the correspondent.
WHO TO APPLY TO The Trustees, 4 More London Riverside, London SE1 2AU *Tel* 020 7759 6734
CC NO 225491   **ESTABLISHED** 1964

■ The Worshipful Company of Spectacle Makers' Charity

WHERE FUNDING CAN BE GIVEN Worldwide.
WHO CAN BENEFIT Registered charities.
WHAT IS FUNDED Work concerned with visual impairments, with a preference for national rather than local causes.
WHAT IS NOT FUNDED No grants are made to individuals.
TYPE OF GRANT Specific projects, not general funds.
SAMPLE GRANTS Action for Blind People, Blind in Business, Childhood Eye Cancer Trust, Eyeless Trust, St John's Eye Hospital in Jerusalem, Prison Fellowship, Optical Workers' Benevolent Fund, British Council for the Prevention of Blindness, Vision 2020UK, Livings Paintings Trust, Vision Aid Overseas, Macular Disease Society, British Blind Sport and the Talking Newspaper Association.
FINANCES *Year* 2007–08 *Income* £63,326 *Grants* £53,102 *Assets* £657,172
TRUSTEES Michael Barton; David Burt; John Marshall; Brian Mitchell; Christine Tomkins.
HOW TO APPLY In writing to the correspondent including details of how the grant will be used and a copy of the latest audited accounts. Please note: the trustees meet in early spring to decide on grants, meaning that applications received between June and March are unlikely to be addressed quickly.
WHO TO APPLY TO John Salmon, Clerk, Apothecaries Hall, Blackfriars Lane, London EC4V 6EL *Tel* 020 7236 2932 *email* clerk@ spectaclemakers.com *Website* www. spectaclemakers.com
CC NO 1072172   **ESTABLISHED** 1998

■ The Jessie Spencer Trust

WHERE FUNDING CAN BE GIVEN UK, with a preference for Nottinghamshire.
WHO CAN BENEFIT Registered charities, with a preference for those in Nottinghamshire.
WHAT IS FUNDED General charitable purposes.
WHAT IS NOT FUNDED Grants are rarely made for the repair of parish churches outside Nottinghamshire.
TYPE OF GRANT Grants are made towards both capital and revenue expenditure. They can be recurrent for up to ten years.
RANGE OF GRANTS £100–£10,000.
SAMPLE GRANTS Nottinghamshire Historic Churches Trust (£10,000); Rutland House School

(£6,000); Nottingham University Hospitals Charity, Charis Life Church and Core – Digestive Disorders Foundation (£5,000 each); Nottinghamshire Hospice (£2,000); Vitalise (£1,500); Bromley House Library, Shelter – Nottinghamshire, Deafness Research UK and Shakespeare Youth Festival (£1,000 each); Open Minds, SSAFA, Nottinghamshire Wildlife Trust and Think Children (£500 each); People's Dispensary for Sick Animals (£250); and Linby and Papplewick PCC (£100).
FINANCES *Year* 2007–08 *Income* £147,239 *Grants* £117,000 *Assets* £3,498,313
TRUSTEES V W Semmens; R S Hursthouse; Jennifer Galloway; Bethan Mitchell.
OTHER INFORMATION There were also grants made to individuals totalling £1,600.
HOW TO APPLY In writing to the correspondent, including the latest set of audited accounts, at least three weeks before the trustees' meetings in March, June, September and December. Unsuccessful applications will not be notified.
WHO TO APPLY TO The Trustees, Berryman Shacklock LLP, Park House, Friar Lane, Nottingham NG1 6DN *Tel* 0115 945 3700 *Fax* 0115 948 0234
CC NO 219289   **ESTABLISHED** 1962

■ The Ralph and Irma Sperring Charity

WHERE FUNDING CAN BE GIVEN The parishes situated within a five-mile radius of the church of St John the Baptist, Midsomer Norton.
WHO CAN BENEFIT Organisations and individuals in the beneficial area.
WHAT IS FUNDED Grants are given to: provide or assist with the provision of residential accommodation; for the relief of older people and people who have disabilities or are in need; assist with the establishment of village halls, recreation grounds, charitable sports grounds and playing fields; further the religious or other charitable work of the Anglican churches in the parishes; support hospitals and their leagues of friends; and further education of children and young people at educational institutions.
FINANCES *Year* 2007–08 *Income* £221,878 *Grants* £131,296 *Assets* £5,248,116
TRUSTEES Revd C G Chiplin; E W L Hallam; Miss S Blanning; K G W Saunders; Mrs N E Busby.
HOW TO APPLY In writing to the correspondent.
WHO TO APPLY TO E W L Hallam, Trustee, Thatcher and Hallam Solicitors, Island House, Midsomer Norton, Radstock BA3 2HJ *Tel* 01761 414 646
CC NO 1048101   **ESTABLISHED** 1995

■ The Moss Spiro Will Charitable Foundation

WHERE FUNDING CAN BE GIVEN UK.
WHO CAN BENEFIT Jewish people.
WHAT IS FUNDED Grants are made towards Jewish welfare.
SAMPLE GRANTS Previous beneficiaries have included American Friends of Yershivas Birchas Ha Torah, Lubavitch Foundation, J T Tannenbaum Jewish Cultural Centre, Friends of Neve Shalom, Jewish Care and HGS Emunah.
FINANCES *Year* 2008–09 *Income* £2,311 *Grants* £25,000
TRUSTEES Trevor David Spiro; Melvin Clifford Kay; David Jeremy Goodman.
HOW TO APPLY In writing to the correspondent.

WHO TO APPLY TO Trevor Spiro, Trustee, Crowndean House, 26 Bruton Lane, London W1J 6JH *Tel* 020 7491 9817 *Fax* 020 7499 6850 *email* trevor@assassin.co.uk
CC NO 1064249   **ESTABLISHED** 1997

··

■ Split Infinitive Trust

WHERE FUNDING CAN BE GIVEN UK, with a preference for Yorkshire.

WHO CAN BENEFIT Individuals and companies and organisations with charitable status.

WHAT IS FUNDED Arts, education and the alleviation of sickness, poverty, hardship and distress.

RANGE OF GRANTS Grants are generally made between £500 and £5,000.

SAMPLE GRANTS The National Student Drama Festival Limited and Paddington Arts (£5,000 each); NDCS (£2,500); and Clothing Solutions and Buckle for Dust Limited (£1,000 each).

FINANCES *Year* 2008–09 *Income* £53,265 *Grants* £26,040 *Assets* £131,938

TRUSTEES Sir Alan Ayckbourn, Chair; Heather Stoney; Paul Allen; Neil Adleman; Elizabeth Bell.

HOW TO APPLY 'Applicants are asked to supply a letter describing the project with budget and, if relevant, an indication of where other funds are coming from. In the case of a performing arts production, a basic but precise production budget is requested. As support given for a production is not considered an investment seeking a return, no box office figures are requested although feedback as to how a production has been received is helpful but not a requisite.'

WHO TO APPLY TO Heather Stoney, Trustee, PO Box 409, Scarborough YO11 9AJ *Tel* 01723 365742 *email* splitinfin@pendon.eclipse.co.uk
CC NO 1110380   **ESTABLISHED** 2005

··

■ W W Spooner Charitable Trust

WHERE FUNDING CAN BE GIVEN UK, with a preference for Yorkshire especially West Yorkshire.

WHO CAN BENEFIT Specific causes reflecting the founder's interests; projects and welfare within the community; young people; education; assistance in the purchase of works of art for the benefit of the public. The trust responds to appeals from individuals, institutions, voluntary organisations and charitable groups. Preference given to Yorkshire-based appeals.

WHAT IS FUNDED The trustees invite appeals which broadly fall within the following selected fields: Youth – welfare, sport and education including school appeals and initiatives, clubs, scouting, guiding and adventure training; individual voluntary service overseas and approved expeditions. The community – including churches, associations, welfare and support groups. Healing – care of sick, disabled and underprivileged people; welfare organisations, victim support, hospitals, hospices and selected medical charities and research. The countryside – protection and preservation of the environment including rescue and similar services; preservation and maintenance of historic buildings. The arts – including museums, teaching, performing, musical and literary festivals; selective support for the purchase of works of art for public benefit.

WHAT IS NOT FUNDED 'No grants for high-profile appeals seeking large sums.' Most donations are for less than £500.

TYPE OF GRANT Recurring annual donations to a set list of charities. One-off to 50–60 single appeals a year.

RANGE OF GRANTS £200–£3,500; average £250–£350.

SAMPLE GRANTS Previous beneficiaries have included Wordsworth Trust – Grasmere, Parish of Tong and Holme Wood, Guide Dogs for the Blind, St Margaret's PCC – Ilkley, Abbeyfield Society, All Saints' Church – Ilkley, Ardenlea, Hawksworth Church of England School, Leith School of Art, Martin House Hospice, North of England Christian Healing Trust, St Gemma's Hospice, St George's Crypt, Wheatfield House and Yorkshire Ballet Seminar.

FINANCES *Year* 2006–07 *Income* £82,510 *Grants* £99,993 *Assets* £1,942,475

TRUSTEES M H Broughton; Sir James F Hill; J C Priestley; T J P Ramsden; Mrs J M McKiddie; J H Wright.

HOW TO APPLY In writing to the correspondent.

WHO TO APPLY TO M H Broughton, Chair and Trustee, Tree Tops, Main Street, Hawksworth, Leeds LS20 8NX
CC NO 313653   **ESTABLISHED** 1961

··

■ Stanley Spooner Deceased Charitable Trust

WHERE FUNDING CAN BE GIVEN UK.

WHO CAN BENEFIT Organisations, particularly those benefiting children and people who are disadvantaged by poverty.

WHAT IS FUNDED General charitable purposes, in particular the Metropolitan Police Courts Poor Boxes (Drinan Bequest), the Docklands Settlements, and the Church of England Children's Society.

SAMPLE GRANTS In previous years the three regular beneficiaries have been the Children's Society, Docklands Settlement and Metropolitan Police Courts Poor Boxes (Drinan Bequest).

FINANCES *Year* 2007–08 *Income* £94,230 *Grants* £52,470 *Assets* £1,377,193

OTHER INFORMATION Included in the trust's objectives are percentages of the trust's income to go to the Drinan Bequest, the Dockland Settlements and the Church of England Children's Society.

HOW TO APPLY In writing to the correspondent.

WHO TO APPLY TO Miss Suzanne Marks, Trust Officer, The Public Trustee (Ref. G5361), Official Solicitor and Public Trustee, 81 Chancery Lane, London WC2A 1DD *Tel* 020 7911 7073 *email* suzanne.marks@offsol.gsi.gov.uk
CC NO 1044737   **ESTABLISHED** 1995

··

■ The Spoore, Merry and Rixman Foundation

WHERE FUNDING CAN BE GIVEN The (pre-1974) borough of Maidenhead and the ancient parish of Bray, not the whole of Royal Borough of Windsor and Maidenhead.

WHO CAN BENEFIT People under the age of 25 living in the beneficial area.

WHAT IS FUNDED The trust was set up to benefit people 'who need financial assistance in way of scholarships, bursaries, maintenance allowances or other benefits' to further their education.

SAMPLE GRANTS A list of beneficiaries was unavailable.

FINANCES *Year* 2008 *Income* £319,551 *Grants* £322,444 *Assets* £8,477,017

TRUSTEES Miss S Beedell; Mrs D Kemp; J Powell; Mrs P Proctor; Mrs A Redgrave; I Thomas; L Walters; G Fisher; E Richards; S Dudley; The Mayor – Royal Borough of Windsor & Maidenhead.

OTHER INFORMATION Grants to organisations totalled £135,000, with a further £188,000 given in grants to individuals.

HOW TO APPLY On a form available from the correspondent. Applications are considered in January, April, July and October.

WHO TO APPLY TO M J Tanner, Secretary, Abbot Lloyd Howorth, 22–30 York Road, Maidenhead, Berkshire SL6 1SF *Tel* 01628 798800 *Fax* 08712 100041 *Website* www. smrfmaidenhead.org.uk

CC NO 309040   **ESTABLISHED** 1958

■ The Spring Harvest Charitable Trust

WHERE FUNDING CAN BE GIVEN UK and overseas.
WHO CAN BENEFIT Organisations and individuals.
WHAT IS FUNDED Christian evangelism and welfare.
WHAT IS NOT FUNDED Grants are not made for salaries.
RANGE OF GRANTS £1,000 to £25,000, although almost half were for £1,000.
SAMPLE GRANTS Bible Society (£214,000); Oasis India (£110,000); The Salvation Army (£60,000); Wycliffe UK Ltd (£39,000); Clarendon Trust Ltd (£17,000); Youth for Christ (£17,000); Active Media Publishing Ltd (£5,000); Barnabus Fund (£4,000); Kingscare (£3,000); Mission Aviation Fellowship (£2,500); and the France Mission Trust (£2,000).
FINANCES *Year* 2007–08 *Income* £546,049 *Grants* £693,000 *Assets* £389,058
TRUSTEES Revd Stephen Gaukroger; Marion White; Revd Ian Coffey; Very Revd John Richardson; Mark Smith.
HOW TO APPLY There is one round of funding applications per year, usually at the end of November/early December, for distribution the following year. An application form is made available on the trust's website from October. 'Spring Harvest welcomes applications on behalf of projects for the advancement of the Christian religion (such as pastoral and evangelistic work) and for educational work in the UK or elsewhere giving priority where the organisation has a Christian basis and where there is a link with the Spring Harvest theme of that year. Applications will only be considered if presented on our application form. Spring Harvest is not able to commit to ongoing funding so do not usually support salary costs. Spring Harvest always receives many more applications for funding than they are able to meet and reluctantly have to turn down many good applications.'
WHO TO APPLY TO C I Macdowell, Secretary, 14 Horsted Square, Bellbrook Industrial Estate, Uckfield, East Sussex TN22 1QG *Tel* 01825 769111 *Fax* 01825 769141 *email* theclerk@ shct.springharvest.org *Website* www. springharvest.org

CC NO 1042041   **ESTABLISHED** 1994

■ Rosalyn and Nicholas Springer Charitable Trust

WHERE FUNDING CAN BE GIVEN UK.
WHO CAN BENEFIT Organisations, particularly those supporting Jewish people, and individuals.
WHAT IS FUNDED The promotion of welfare, education and personal development, particularly amongst the Jewish community.
RANGE OF GRANTS £100–£35,000, but mostly £1,000 or less.
SAMPLE GRANTS UJIA (£35,000); North London Collegiate (£22,000); MDA UK (£13,000); Community Security Trust (£4,000); Maccabi GB and Cancerkin (£2,500 each); West London Synagogue (£2,400); Ovarian Cancer Action (£1,300); Royal Opera House Foundation (£1,100); British Wizo (£1,000); Coram Family (£750); and Resources for Autism (£350).
FINANCES *Year* 2007–08 *Income* £125,489 *Grants* £136,436 *Assets* £36,036
TRUSTEES Rosalyn Springer; N S Springer; Judith Joseph.
HOW TO APPLY The trust has previously stated that it only supports organisations it is already in contact with. Therefore, 99% of unsolicited applications are unsuccessful and because of the volume it receives, the trust is unable to reply to such letters. It would therefore not seem appropriate to apply to this trust.
WHO TO APPLY TO Nicholas Springer, Trustee, Flat 27, Berkeley House, 15 Hay Hill, London W1J 8NS *Tel* 020 7493 1904

CC NO 1062239   **ESTABLISHED** 1997

■ The Springfields Employees' Medical Research and Charity Trust Fund

WHERE FUNDING CAN BE GIVEN Preston and South Ribble, Blackpool, Wyre and Fylde Areas.
WHO CAN BENEFIT Organisations benefiting disabled people.
WHAT IS FUNDED Grants to hospitals and local medical and welfare charities for medical equipment.
WHAT IS NOT FUNDED Support is only provided for specific pieces of equipment therefore funding is not available for items such as projects and salaries.
TYPE OF GRANT One-off grants.
RANGE OF GRANTS Up to £4,000.
SAMPLE GRANTS The Legacy Rainbow House (£1,7000); Foundation for the Study of Infant Deaths (£1,600); Preston Samaritans, Addiction Dependency Solutions and Little Sisters of the Poor (£1,300 each); Children's Heart Foundation (£1,200); Lifelites (£1,100); Genesis Appeal (£1,000); St John Ambulance (£800); and Preston Council for Voluntary Service (£500).
FINANCES *Year* 2008 *Income* £50,577 *Grants* £13,846
TRUSTEES D J Craig; I R Driver; Miss J A Humphreys.
HOW TO APPLY In writing to the correspondent.
WHO TO APPLY TO Ian R Driver, Welfare Officer and Trustee, Westing House, Springfields Fuels Limited, Springfields, Salwick, Preston PR4 0XJ *Tel* 01772 764578 *Fax* 01772 762929 *email* ian.r.driver@springfieldsfuels.com

CC NO 518005   **ESTABLISHED** 1985

■ Springrule Ltd

WHERE FUNDING CAN BE GIVEN UK.
WHO CAN BENEFIT Jewish organisations.
WHAT IS FUNDED Advancement of the Jewish faith and the relief of poverty.
SAMPLE GRANTS Beis Yaakov Institutions, Friends of Horim and Torah Vechesed (£25,000 each); Yad Eliezer (£5,000).
FINANCES *Year* 2007–08 *Income* £340,319 *Grants* £350,800 *Assets* £505,221
TRUSTEES M Jacober; R Nevies; J Monderer; H R Monderer; Mrs R L Nevies.
HOW TO APPLY In writing to the correspondent.
WHO TO APPLY TO Mrs M Jacober, Secretary, 5 North End Road, London NW11 7RJ
CC NO 802561   **ESTABLISHED** 1992

■ The Spurrell Charitable Trust

WHERE FUNDING CAN BE GIVEN UK, with some preference for Norfolk.
WHO CAN BENEFIT Charities known personally to the trustees.
WHAT IS FUNDED General charitable purposes.
RANGE OF GRANTS Up to £7,500.
SAMPLE GRANTS East Anglian Air Ambulance (£7,500); Merlin (£5,000); Donna's Dream House (£4,500); Royal Agricultural Benevolent Institution (£4,000); Rowans Hospice (£2,000); Break (£1,500); Alzheimer's Research Trust, Brooke Hospital for Animals and Camphill Village Trust (£1,000 each); Caister Volunteer Rescue Service (£750); Dream Makers and Church Urban Fund (£500); and North Norfolk District 1st Rural Scout Group (£250).
FINANCES *Year* 2007–08 *Income* £91,684 *Grants* £82,950 *Assets* £2,237,392
TRUSTEES Alan T How; Richard J K Spurrell; Mrs Inge H Spurrell; Martyn R Spurrell.
HOW TO APPLY Unsolicited applications are not considered.
WHO TO APPLY TO A T How, Trustee, 16 Harescroft, Moat Farm, Tunbridge Wells, Kent TN2 5XE *Tel* 01892 541565
CC NO 267287   **ESTABLISHED** 1960

■ The Geoff and Fiona Squire Foundation

WHERE FUNDING CAN BE GIVEN UK.
WHO CAN BENEFIT Charitable organisations.
WHAT IS FUNDED General charitable purposes.
RANGE OF GRANTS £500–£230,000.
SAMPLE GRANTS Friends of Hursley School (£230,000); Naomi House – Wessex Children's Hospice Trust (£194,000); Changing Faces (£114,000); Hillier Arboreteum (£80,000); Grange Park Opera (£60,000); Lord's Taverners (£29,000); Animal Health Trust, Sportability and Cancer Research UK (£5,000 each); RNIB (£4,800); Strong Bones Children's Charitable Trust (£2,000); St Johns Ambulance (£750); and Brendencare Club (£500).
FINANCES *Year* 2007–08 *Income* £345,059 *Grants* £1,077,542 *Assets* £12,807,128
TRUSTEES G W Squire; Fiona Squire; B P Peerless.
HOW TO APPLY The trust has previously stated: 'the trustees have in place a well-established donations policy and we do not therefore encourage unsolicited grant applications, not least because they take time and expense to deal with properly'.

WHO TO APPLY TO Fiona Squire, Trustee, Home Farm House, Hursley, Winchester, Hampshire SO21 2JL
CC NO 1085553   **ESTABLISHED** 2001

■ The Stafford Trust

WHERE FUNDING CAN BE GIVEN UK, with a preference for Scotland.
WHO CAN BENEFIT Charities registered in the UK.
WHAT IS FUNDED Animal welfare, medical research, local community projects, relief in need, HM Services personnel, overseas appeals, environment and sea rescue.
WHAT IS NOT FUNDED The trust does not support: religious organisations; political organisations; retrospective grants; student travel or expeditions.
RANGE OF GRANTS Mostly £500–£10,000. Occasionally recurring grants of up to three years. (Please note: Some of the grants detailed in this entry are payable over more than one year.).
SAMPLE GRANTS University of Glasgow Small Animal Hospital (£250,000); Scottish Community Foundation (£150,000); Animal Health Trust, Braveheart and Carers Forum Stirling (£30,000 each); Aberloar Childcare Trust, Community Housing Alloa, CLIC Sargent and Headway Edinburgh (£10,000 each); Central Scotland Forest Trust (£8,000); Battersea Dogs Home, Rock Trust and SSPCA (£5,000 each); Crossroads Stirling (£2,500); and Riding for the Disabled (£1,500).
FINANCES *Year* 2007–08 *Income* £573,946 *Grants* £695,500
TRUSTEES A Peter M Walls; Hamish N Buchan; Gordon M Wyllie; Angus Morgan.
OTHER INFORMATION The Stafford Trust was set up in 1991 by the late Mrs Gay Stafford of Sauchie Estate near Stirling. During her lifetime, Mrs Stafford made substantial gifts to the Trust and on her death in 2005, the residue of her estate was bequeathed to the trust. Over £10 million was received in the financial year 2006–07.
HOW TO APPLY The trust has a short application form which can be downloaded from its website. Applicants are invited to complete the form using their own words without the restrictions of completing set questions. Please also supply the following, where appropriate: a brief description of your charity; a copy of your most recent annual report and accounts; a description of the project/funding requirement – what do you want to achieve and how will it be managed (the trustees look for clear, realistic and attainable aims); what is the expenditure budget for the project and the anticipated timescale; what funds have already been raised and what other sources are being approached; the need for funding must be clearly demonstrated; what will be the benefits of the project and how do you propose to monitor and evaluate whether the project has been successful; if applicable, what plans do you have to fund the future running costs of the project?
WHO TO APPLY TO Margaret Kane or Hugh Biggans, c/o Dickson Middleton CA, PO Box 14, 20 Barnton St, Stirling FK8 1NE *Tel* 01786 474718 *email* staffordtrust@dicksonmiddleton. co.uk *Website* www.staffordtrust.org.uk
SC NO SC018079   **ESTABLISHED** 1991

■ Miss Doreen Stanford Trust

WHERE FUNDING CAN BE GIVEN UK.

WHO CAN BENEFIT Registered charities.

WHAT IS FUNDED General charitable purposes.

WHAT IS NOT FUNDED No grants are given towards building repairs, alterations to property, electrical goods, floor coverings, holidays for individuals or towards household furniture or equipment.

RANGE OF GRANTS Up to about £2,500.

SAMPLE GRANTS Happy Days (£2,700); Deafblind (£2,000); Harvest Trust (£1,500); British Wireless for the Blind (£1,300); Fulham Good Neighbours (£1,000); Sense (£650); Sailors Families Society (£300); and Access to Arts (£210).

FINANCES *Year* 2007 *Income* £42,229 *Grants* £20,115 *Assets* £780,600

TRUSTEES T Carter; R S Borner; T Butler; D Valder; Miss M Winter.

OTHER INFORMATION The trust also awarded two bursaries for tuitions fees with the Cheltenham Ladies College totalling £2,000.

HOW TO APPLY In writing to the correspondent, enclosing a sae. Allocations of grants are made once a year in March at the trustees' meeting.

WHO TO APPLY TO Mrs G M B Borner, Secretary, 26 The Mead, Beckenham, Kent BR3 5PE *Tel* 020 8650 3368

CC NO 1049934   **ESTABLISHED** 1995

■ The Stanley Foundation Ltd

WHERE FUNDING CAN BE GIVEN UK.

WHO CAN BENEFIT Charitable organisations.

WHAT IS FUNDED Older people, medical care and research, education and social welfare.

WHAT IS NOT FUNDED No grants to individuals.

RANGE OF GRANTS £1,000–£10,000.

SAMPLE GRANTS Share Community, Friends of the Fitzwilliam Museum and King's College Cambridge (£10,000 each); Penny Brohn Cancer Care (£7,000); Homes for Heroes (£5,000); Royal Hospital for Neuro Disability (£3,000); Tusk (£2,500); Killing Cancer (£2,000); and PSP Association, Museum of Garden History and Wells Cathedral Girls Chorister Trust (£1,000 each).

FINANCES *Year* 2007–08 *Income* £98,017 *Grants* £141,429 *Assets* £3,662,907

TRUSTEES N Stanley, Chair; S R Stanley; Mrs E Stanley; S H Hall.

OTHER INFORMATION Donations of less than £1,000 each totalled £3,500 (seven charities).

HOW TO APPLY In writing to the correspondent.

WHO TO APPLY TO N Stanley, Secretary, Flat 3, 19 Holland Park, London W11 3TD *Tel* 020 7792 3854 *email* nick@meristan.com

CC NO 206866   **ESTABLISHED** 1962

■ The Stanton Ballard Charitable Trust

WHERE FUNDING CAN BE GIVEN City of Oxford and the immediate neighbourhood.

WHO CAN BENEFIT Individuals, charities, institutions and organisations.

WHAT IS FUNDED Residents of the City of Oxford who are in conditions of need, hardship or stress; voluntary organisations providing services and facilities for such people; provision of leisure services; and the promotion of education.

WHAT IS NOT FUNDED No grants towards buildings or salaries.

RANGE OF GRANTS £100–£6,000.

SAMPLE GRANTS Rose Hill & Donnington Advice Centre (£6,000); Oxfordshire County Council (£5,600); Connection (£5,000); Oxford Citizens Housing Association (£3,000); St Bartholomew's Health Centre (£2,000); Barton Information Centre (£1,000); Listening Books (£500); Oxford Family Mediation (£450); Universal Benefit Society (£250); and First Wednesday Lunch Club (£100).

FINANCES *Year* 2007–08 *Income* £105,517 *Grants* £52,755 *Assets* £2,636,878

TRUSTEES Mrs M J Tate; Mrs J Kimberley; Mrs R Nicholson; J Martin; K Pawson; A Woodward; M Slade; H Minns.

HOW TO APPLY On an application form available from the correspondent on receipt of an sae. The trustees meet about every nine weeks to consider applications.

WHO TO APPLY TO The Secretary, PO Box 81, Oxfordshire OX4 4ZA *Tel* 0870 760 5032

CC NO 294688   **ESTABLISHED** 1986

■ The Staples Trust

WHERE FUNDING CAN BE GIVEN Overseas, UK.

WHO CAN BENEFIT Charities working in the fields of international development, environment and women's issues organisations benefiting victims of abuse and domestic violence.

WHAT IS FUNDED *Overseas development*: projects which contribute to the empowerment of women, the rights of indigenous people, improved shelter and housing, income-generation in disadvantaged communities and sustainable agriculture and forestry. There is a particular interest in development projects which take account of environmental sustainability and, in many cases, the environmental and developments benefits of the project are of equal importance. *Environment*: support for projects in developing countries, Central and Eastern Europe and the UK. Grants for renewable energy technology, training and skills upgrading and, occasionally, research. In Central and Eastern Europe, particular interest is given to providing training opportunities for community/business leaders and policy makers, and in contributing to the process of skill-sharing and information exchange. In the UK, there is an interest in helping communities protect, maintain and improve areas of land and to support work aimed at informing rural conservation policy. *Women's issues*: the interest is in domestic violence issues. The priority is for innovative or strategic programmes of support with a national focus (particularly work to tackle domestic violence from the male perpetrator perspective), also smaller grants to assist local refuge services and women's self-help groups. *General*: Frankopan Scholarship Fund, established to assist exceptionally talented students from Croatia to further or complete their studies (in any discipline) in the UK.

WHAT IS NOT FUNDED Normally, no grants to individuals.

TYPE OF GRANT One off and recurring for up to three years.

SAMPLE GRANTS University of Cambridge to fund the post of the Frankopan Director of Gender Studies (£290,500); The Ashmolean Museum (£50,000), towards its redevelopment; Womenkind Worldwide (£30,000), towards the costs of an anti-sex trafficking animated film to be broadcast in source countries in continental Europe; Business & Human Rights Resource Centre (£15,000), towards the recruitment and salary costs of a new regional researcher to cover Eastern Europe and Central Asia; and INCREASE (International Centre for Reproductive Health and Sexual Rights) (£5,000), towards core costs to advocate for sexual health and the rights of Nigeria's most marginalised groups.

FINANCES *Year* 2007–08 *Income* £609,893 *Grants* £596,523 *Assets* £12,650,850

TRUSTEES Jessica Frankopan; Peter Frankopan; James Sainsbury; Alex Sainsbury; Judith Portrait.

OTHER INFORMATION The trust is one of the Sainsbury Family Charitable Trusts which share a common administration. Grants approved during the year totalled just under £1.3 million.

HOW TO APPLY See the guidance for applicants section in the entry for the Sainsbury Family Charitable Trusts. A single application will be considered for support by all the trusts in the group. However, for this, as for many of the family trusts, 'proposals are generally invited by the trustees or initiated at their request. Unsolicited applications are discouraged and are unlikely to be successful, even if they fall within an area in which the trustees are interested'.

WHO TO APPLY TO Alan Bookbinder, Director, Allington House, 1st Floor, 150 Victoria Street, London SW1E 5AE *Tel* 020 7410 0330 *Fax* 020 7410 0332 *Website* www.sfct.org.uk

CC NO 1010656   **ESTABLISHED** 1992

■ The Star Charitable Trust

WHERE FUNDING CAN BE GIVEN UK.

WHO CAN BENEFIT Charitable organisations.

WHAT IS FUNDED General charitable purposes.

SAMPLE GRANTS A list of grants was not available.

FINANCES *Year* 2007–08 *Income* £11,846 *Grants* £20,000

TRUSTEES D D Fiszman; P I Propper; D A Rosen.

HOW TO APPLY In writing to the correspondent.

WHO TO APPLY TO The Trustees, 2nd Floor, 16–18 Hatton Garden, London EC1N 8AT *Tel* 020 7404 2222 *Fax* 020 7404 3333

CC NO 266695   **ESTABLISHED** 1974

■ The Starfish Trust

WHERE FUNDING CAN BE GIVEN Within a 25-mile radius of Bristol.

WHO CAN BENEFIT Individuals and charitable organisations in the Bristol area.

WHAT IS FUNDED Direct assistance is given to people who are disabled and people who have an illness or disease. Medical research and welfare are also supported.

WHAT IS NOT FUNDED Individuals and charitable organisations outside a 25-mile radius of Bristol or not working in the areas defined above.

TYPE OF GRANT Buildings, individual projects, research and recurring costs will be considered.

RANGE OF GRANTS £250–£48,000.

SAMPLE GRANTS Meningitis UK (£48,000); Hop, Skip and a Jump, the Seven Springs Foundation (£45,000); SWALLOW (£15,000); Cirencester Opportunity Group (£10,000); Ridgeway Care and Repair (£2,000); Bristol Music Space (£1,600); Swansea University (£1,500); Mobility Trust (£1,000); Carousel Community Base (£500); and Penpole Residents Association (£250).

FINANCES *Year* 2007–08 *Income* £81,262 *Grants* £119,911 *Assets* £1,311,778

TRUSTEES Charles E Dobson; Mary Dobson.

OTHER INFORMATION Grants were also made to 23 individuals totalling £25,384.

HOW TO APPLY In writing to the correspondent.

WHO TO APPLY TO Robert Woodward, PO Box 213, Patchway, Bristol BS32 4YY *Tel* 0117 970 1756 *Fax* 0117 970 1756

CC NO 800203   **ESTABLISHED** 1988

■ The Peter Stebbings Memorial Charity

WHERE FUNDING CAN BE GIVEN UK and developing countries.

WHO CAN BENEFIT Registered charities.

WHAT IS FUNDED The objects of the trust are to fund, in particular, medical research and education, and the welfare of those who are poor, old or sick.

WHAT IS NOT FUNDED No grants to individuals, non-registered charities or for salaries.

TYPE OF GRANT One-off grants only, for capital other than buildings, core costs, projects and start-up costs.

RANGE OF GRANTS Up to £100,000.

SAMPLE GRANTS Westminster Patrol Found (£100,000); Maya Centre (£30,000); Berkeley Reafforestation Trust (£20,000); Koestler Trust (£10,000); Tools for Self Reliance and CanSupport (£5,000 each); TB Alert (£1,500); and Multiple Birth Foundation (£1,000).

FINANCES *Year* 2007–08 *Income* £240,699 *Grants* £177,500 *Assets* £7,218,689

TRUSTEES A J F Stebbings; N F Cosin; Mrs J A Clifford.

HOW TO APPLY It is the trustee's policy to make more substantial grants to a limited number of charities. Please note: the trust has previously stated that it does not respond to unsolicited applications and that its funds are fully committed.

WHO TO APPLY TO Andrew Stebbings, Trustee, 45 Pont Street, London SW1X 0BX *Tel* 020 7591 3333

CC NO 274862   **ESTABLISHED** 1977

■ The Steel Charitable Trust

WHERE FUNDING CAN BE GIVEN Mainly UK with 30% of all grants made to organisations in the Luton and Bedfordshire areas.

WHO CAN BENEFIT Registered charities.

WHAT IS FUNDED General, including social welfare; culture; recreation; health; medical research; environment; and overseas aid.

WHAT IS NOT FUNDED Individuals, students and expeditions are not supported.

TYPE OF GRANT 'One-off' and recurring.

RANGE OF GRANTS £1,000–£50,000.

SAMPLE GRANTS Pasque Hospice (£50,000); Cancer Research UK, Asthma UK, British Eye Research Foundation, National Deaf Children's Society, St. Albans Cathedral Music Trust and Salvation Army (£25,000 each); The Donkey Sanctuary, International League for the Protection of Horses, PDSA and Royal Ballet School (£20,000 each); Anthony Nolan Trust, Friends of Michael Sobell House and St Luke's Hospital for the Clergy (£5,000 each); Special Care Baby Unit and Red Squirrels in Scotland (£3,000 each); Soil Association (£2,000); and Alternative Animal Sanctuary, Conservation Foundation, Friends of Cardigan Bay, Green Light Trust and VETAID (£1,000 each).

FINANCES *Year* 2008–09 *Income* £1,290,639 *Grants* £1,491,500 *Assets* £17,701,765

TRUSTEES Nicholas E W Wright; John A Childs, Chair; John A Maddox; Anthony W Hawkins; Paul

Stevenson; Wendy Bailey; Mary Briggs; Philip Lawford.

HOW TO APPLY All applicants must complete the online application form. Applications submitted by post will not be considered. There is no deadline for applications and all will be acknowledged. Trustees meet regularly during the year, usually in February, May, August and November. All successful applicants will be notified by email and will be required to provide written confirmation of the details of the project or work for which they are seeking a grant. Payment is then made in the following month. To comply with the Data Protection Act 1998, applicants are required to consent to the use of personal data supplied by them in the processing and review of their application. This includes transfer to and use by such individuals and organisations as the trust deems appropriate. The trust requires the assurance of the applicant that personal data about any other individual is supplied to the trust with his/her consent. At the point of submitting an online application, applicants are asked to confirm this consent and assurance.

WHO TO APPLY TO Carol Langston, Administrator, Holme Farm, Fore Street, Bradford, Holsworthy, Devon EX22 7AJ *Tel* 01409 281403 *email* administrator@steelcharitabletrust.org.uk *Website* www.steelcharitabletrust.org.uk
CC NO 272384   **ESTABLISHED** 1976

··

■ The Cyril and Betty Stein Charitable Trust

WHERE FUNDING CAN BE GIVEN UK and Israel.
WHO CAN BENEFIT Jewish organisations.
WHAT IS FUNDED Predominantly Jewish causes, including education, advancement of the Jewish religion and welfare.
TYPE OF GRANT One-off and recurring.
RANGE OF GRANTS £1,000–£111,000.
SAMPLE GRANTS The Institute for the Advancement of Education in Jaffa (£111,000); Jewish National Fund (£55,000); Bar Amana (£25,000); Mizrahi Charitable Trust (£13,000); Friends of Bnei David (£12,000); New Heritage Foundation (£10,000); British Friends of Tikva Odessa (£4,900); Western Marble Arch Synagogue (£2,700); and Chief Rabbinate Charitable Trust (£1,000).
FINANCES *Year* 2007–08 *Income* £225,062 *Grants* £293,872
TRUSTEES Mrs B Stein; C Stein; D Stein; L Curry.
HOW TO APPLY In writing to the correspondent.
WHO TO APPLY TO The Trustees, c/o Clayton Stark and Co., 5th Floor, Charles House, 108–110 Finchley Road, London NW3 5JJ *Tel* 020 7431 4200
CC NO 292235   **ESTABLISHED** 1985

··

■ The Steinberg Family Charitable Trust

WHERE FUNDING CAN BE GIVEN UK, with a preference for Greater Manchester.
WHO CAN BENEFIT Charitable organisations, with a preference for Jewish groups.
WHAT IS FUNDED General charitable purposes.
WHAT IS NOT FUNDED Registered charities only.
RANGE OF GRANTS £150–£10,000; average grant £2,300.
SAMPLE GRANTS Netanya Supporters of Laniado Hospital and Women's UJIA (£20,000 each); Community Security Trust, Imperial War Museum

and North West Cancer (£10,000 each); and Hale Adult Hebrew Education Trust (£8,000). Other beneficiaries included: National Library for the Blind (£6,000 in two grants); Alzheimer's Society, RNIB and World Jewish Relief (£5,000 each); Auditory Verbal UK, Studley Royal Cricket Club and Zichron Manachem (£2,000 each); Dreams Come True Charity (£1,500); Manchester YMCA (£1,000); and Rochdale Special Needs Cycling Club (£500).
FINANCES *Year* 2005–06 *Income* £3,609,027 *Grants* £225,587 *Assets* £9,732,280
TRUSTEES D Burke, Chair; Lady Steinberg; J Steinberg; D K Johnston; Mrs L Rochelle Attias.
OTHER INFORMATION Accounts for 2006–07 and 2007–08 were overdue at the Charity Commission.
HOW TO APPLY In writing to the correspondent, including evidence of charitable status, the purpose to which the funds are to be put, evidence of other action taken to fund the project concerned, and the outcome of that action.
WHO TO APPLY TO The Trustees, Lime Tree Cottage, Bollingway, Hale, Altrincham WA15 0NZ *Tel* 016 903 8851 *email* admin@steinberg-trust.co.uk
CC NO 1045231   **ESTABLISHED** 1995

··

■ The Hugh Stenhouse Foundation

WHERE FUNDING CAN BE GIVEN Mainly Scotland, with an emphasis on the west coast.
WHO CAN BENEFIT Charities benefiting children; young adults; those in care, fostered and adopted; and people disadvantaged by poverty. The foundation had stated that it tends to support smaller charities.
WHAT IS FUNDED General charitable purposes, including welfare, young people, and nature reserves, woodlands and bird sanctuaries.
WHAT IS NOT FUNDED Grants are not given for political appeals or to individuals.
TYPE OF GRANT Recurring, one-off and core costs. Funding is available for more than three years.
SAMPLE GRANTS Maxwelton Chapel Trust (£24,000); Glasgow City Mission and Hopscotch (£2,000 each); Salvation Army (£1,700); REACT and the Safety Zone (£1,600 each); Lilias Graham Trust (£1,000); Visibility (£800); and Erskine Hospital (£650).
FINANCES *Year* 2007–08 *Income* £56,589 *Grants* £42,800 *Assets* £1,396,757
TRUSTEES Mrs A D Irvine Robertson; M R L Stenhouse; R G T Stenhouse; Mrs R C L Stewart.
HOW TO APPLY In writing to the correspondent. Trustees meet in March and September. Applications should be received by February and August respectively.
WHO TO APPLY TO The Secretary, c/o Bell Ingram Ltd, Durn, Isla Road, Perth PH2 7HF
SC NO SC015074   **ESTABLISHED** 1968

··

■ C E K Stern Charitable Trust

WHERE FUNDING CAN BE GIVEN UK and overseas.
WHO CAN BENEFIT Orthodox Jewish charities.
WHAT IS FUNDED Orthodox Jewish causes.
FINANCES *Year* 2007–08 *Income* £130,325 *Grants* £23,950 *Assets* £725,525
TRUSTEES Z M Kaufman; Mrs C E Stern; S Kaufman; Z Stern.
HOW TO APPLY In writing to the correspondent.
WHO TO APPLY TO Z M Kaufman, Trustee, 50 Keswick Street, Gateshead NE8 1TQ
CC NO 1049157   **ESTABLISHED** 1992

■ The Sigmund Sternberg Charitable Foundation

WHERE FUNDING CAN BE GIVEN Worldwide.

WHO CAN BENEFIT Registered charities.

WHAT IS FUNDED Interfaith activities to promote racial and religious harmony, in particular between Christian, Jewish and Muslim faiths, and the education in, and understanding of, their fundamental tenets and beliefs.

WHAT IS NOT FUNDED No grants to individuals.

TYPE OF GRANT One-off or recurring.

RANGE OF GRANTS Up to £50,000, although most grants are of £1,000 or less.

SAMPLE GRANTS Three Faiths Forum (£86,000); the Reform Synagogues of Great Britain (£70,000); the Board of Deputies Charitable Foundation (£18,000); National Portrait Gallery (£10,000); the Interreligious Coordinating Council in Israel (£6,800); Brighton Islamic Mission (£2,300); World Jewish Aid (£2,000); Institute of Business Ethics (£1,000); and Age Exchange Theatre Trust (£430).

FINANCES *Year* 2007–08 *Income* £244,339 *Grants* £251,540 *Assets* £4,727,184

TRUSTEES Sir S Sternberg; V M Sternberg; Lady Sternberg; Rev M C Rossi Braybrooke; M A M Slowe; R Tamir; M D Paisner.

OTHER INFORMATION There were 74 grants of less than £1,000 each, totalling £9,688.

HOW TO APPLY In writing to the correspondent.

WHO TO APPLY TO Sir S Sternberg, Trustee, Star House, 104/108 Grafton Road, London NW5 4BA *Tel* 020 7431 4200

CC NO 257950   **ESTABLISHED** 1968

■ Stervon Ltd

WHERE FUNDING CAN BE GIVEN UK.

WHO CAN BENEFIT Jewish people.

WHAT IS FUNDED Jewish causes and general charitable purposes.

SAMPLE GRANTS Previous beneficiaries include: Eitz Chaim, Rehabilitation Trust, Chasdei Yoel, Beis Yoel, Friends of Horeinu, Beis Hamedrash Hachadash, Tashbar, Tov V' Chessed, Beth Sorah Schneirer and Asser Bishvil.

FINANCES *Year* 2007 *Income* £347,843 *Grants* £316,693 *Assets* £75,410

TRUSTEES A Reich; G Rothbart.

OTHER INFORMATION No grants list was available.

HOW TO APPLY In writing to the correspondent.

WHO TO APPLY TO A Reich, Secretary, c/o Stervon House, 1 Seaford Road, Salford, Greater Manchester M6 6AS *Tel* 0161 737 5000

CC NO 280958   **ESTABLISHED** 1980

■ The Stevenage Community Trust

WHERE FUNDING CAN BE GIVEN The borough of Stevenage and the surrounding villages of Aston, Benington, Cromer, Datchworth, Graveley, Knebworth, Little Wymondley, Old Knebworth, Walkern, Watton-at-Stone, Weston, and Woolmer Green.

WHO CAN BENEFIT Organisations and individuals in need who are recommended by a third party agency.

WHAT IS FUNDED General charitable purposes including community projects, disability, older people, children and young people.

WHAT IS NOT FUNDED Religious, education and political appeals are not supported.

TYPE OF GRANT Maximum £2,000 through the grant committee, larger grant requests go the full Board of Trustees.

RANGE OF GRANTS Generally for up to £2,000.

FINANCES *Year* 2007–08 *Income* £99,511 *Grants* £49,104 *Assets* £511,464

TRUSTEES K Follet, chair; M Addrison; R Ball; S Hollingsworth; D Wall; M Hurle; A Fuller; M Hennessey; A Juggins; A Lang; R Stewart; I D Campbell; I Morton; Dr R Gomm; M Phoenix; Mrs B Vincent.

HOW TO APPLY On a form available from the trust by post, e-mail, telephone or from the website. Grants applications are considered quarterly.

WHO TO APPLY TO June Oldroyd, Stevenage Community Trust, c/o EADS Astrium, Gunnels Wood Road, Stevenage, Hertfordshire SG1 2AS *Tel* 01438 773 368 *Fax* 01438 773 341 *email* info@sct.uk.net *Website* www. stevenagecommunitytrust.org

CC NO 1000762   **ESTABLISHED** 1990

■ The June Stevens Foundation

WHERE FUNDING CAN BE GIVEN UK, but mostly Gloucestershire.

WHO CAN BENEFIT Charitable organisations mainly for older and young people and animals.

WHAT IS FUNDED General charitable purposes.

WHAT IS NOT FUNDED No grants to individuals.

RANGE OF GRANTS £200–£1,000.

SAMPLE GRANTS Previous beneficiaries have included: Greek Animal Welfare Fund (£2,000); Brooke Hospital for Animals and the Royal British Legion (£1,500 each); Gloucestershire Historic Churches Trust (£1,000); Cirencester House for Young People and Gloucestershire Playing Fields Association (£750 each); and Cotswold Care Hospice and Women's Holiday Fund (£500 each).

FINANCES *Year* 2007–08 *Income* £19,715 *Grants* £40,241

TRUSTEES Miss J D Stevens; A J Quinton; A R St C Tahourdin.

HOW TO APPLY In writing to the correspondent.

WHO TO APPLY TO A R St C Tahourdin, Trustee, Herrington and Carmichael, 4 Station Rd, Aldershot GU11 1HU *Tel* 01252 322451

CC NO 327829   **ESTABLISHED** 1988

■ Stevenson Family's Charitable Trust

WHERE FUNDING CAN BE GIVEN Worldwide, in practice mainly UK.

WHO CAN BENEFIT Registered charities.

WHAT IS FUNDED Culture and arts, conservation and heritage, education, health and general charitable purposes.

WHAT IS NOT FUNDED No grants to individuals.

TYPE OF GRANT One-off and recurring.

RANGE OF GRANTS £250–£50,000.

SAMPLE GRANTS Holbourne Museum Limited (£50,000); National Trust for Scotland (£25,000); St Michael and All Angels – Sunninghill (£15,000); Royal Opera House Foundation (£6,500); Changing Faces (£5,000); Sense (£2,000); Ross Goobey Charitable Trust (£1,000 each); National Gardens Scheme (£820); Haven House Foundation (£500); and Reed's School Foundation Appeal (£250).

FINANCES *Year* 2007–08 *Income* £109,608 *Grants* £178,766 *Assets* £2,732,170

TRUSTEES Hugh Stevenson; Catherine Stevenson; Sir Jeremy Lever.

HOW TO APPLY 'No unsolicited applications can be considered as the charity's funds are required to support purposes chosen by the trustees.'

WHO TO APPLY TO Hugh Stevenson, Old Waterfield, Winkfield Road, Ascot SL5 7LJ
CC NO 327148   **ESTABLISHED** 1986

■ The Steventon Allotments and Relief-in-Need Charity

WHERE FUNDING CAN BE GIVEN Parish of Steventon only.
WHO CAN BENEFIT Residents and groups in the parish of Steventon.
WHAT IS FUNDED Projects benefiting the local community, churches, schools, older people and the maintenance of the allotments.
SAMPLE GRANTS St Michael's School (£20,000 in two grants); Abingdon Alzheimer's Society (£2,500); Steventon Friendly Association (£2,000); Steventon Parish Council (£1,500); Steventon Cricket Club (£750); and Steventon Mother and Toddler Group (£500).
FINANCES *Year* 2008 *Income* £134,662 *Grants* £51,131 *Assets* £2,409,772
TRUSTEES Diana Ruth Bowder; Anne Veronica Shrimpton; Philip Michael Brew; William Temple; Robin Wilkinson; Steven Arthur Frederick Ward.
OTHER INFORMATION Grants totalling £18,687 were donated to 48 individuals.
HOW TO APPLY In writing to the correspondent. The trustees meet monthly.
WHO TO APPLY TO Mrs Patrina Effer, 19 Lime Grove, Southmoor, Abingdon, Oxfordshire OX13 5DN *Tel* 01865 821 055 *email* sarinc@patrina.co.uk
CC NO 203331   **ESTABLISHED** 1987

■ The Stewards' Charitable Trust

WHERE FUNDING CAN BE GIVEN Principally the UK.
WHO CAN BENEFIT Organisations and clubs benefiting young sportsmen and women.
WHAT IS FUNDED Support of rowing at all levels, from grassroots upwards. Beneficiaries should be in full-time education or training.
WHAT IS NOT FUNDED No grants to individuals or for building or capital costs.
TYPE OF GRANT Preferably one-off and especially where there are matched funds raised elsewhere.
RANGE OF GRANTS £3,000–£194,000.
SAMPLE GRANTS ARA Scholarships (£194,000); ARA London Youth Rowing (£25,000); River and Rowing Museum and Project Oarsome – Boat Refurbishment (£20,000 each); Rowing Foundation (£15,000); ARA Regional Sculling Camps (£12,000); Upper Thames Rowing Club – Junior Development (£10,000); Mark Lees Foundation (£5,000); and Ball Cup Regatta (£3,500).
FINANCES *Year* 2007–08 *Income* £419,533 *Grants* £304,750 *Assets* £4,356,153
TRUSTEES M A Sweeney; C G V Davidge; C L Baillieu; R C Lester; Sir S Redgrave.
HOW TO APPLY In writing to the correspondent. Applications are usually first vetted by Amateur Rowing Association.
WHO TO APPLY TO Daniel Grist, Secretary, Regatta Headquarters, Henley-on-Thames, Oxfordshire RG9 2LY *Tel* 01491 572153 *Fax* 01491 575509 *Website* www.hrr.co.uk
CC NO 299597   **ESTABLISHED** 1988

■ The Stewards' Company Limited (incorporating the J W Laing Trust and the J W Laing Biblical Scholarship Trust)

WHERE FUNDING CAN BE GIVEN Unrestricted.
WHO CAN BENEFIT Organisations involved with training people in religious education. About half the trust's funds are given for work overseas.
WHAT IS FUNDED Christian evangelism, especially but not exclusively that of Christian Brethren assemblies (different to those of the 'Exclusive' or 'Plymouth' Brethren). Grants given overseas are made under the following categories: church buildings; scriptures and literature; education and orphanages; education of missionaries' children; national evangelists and missionaries' vehicles. Grants given in the UK are categorised under: church buildings; evangelistic associations; scriptures and literature; teachers and evangelists; and young people and children. Substantial funds are also transferred to the Beatrice Laing Trust (see separate entry).
TYPE OF GRANT Usually one-off.
RANGE OF GRANTS About £15,000–£1 million.
SAMPLE GRANTS Echoes of Service (£1 million); UCCF (£852,000); Beatrice Laing Trust (£587,000); Kharis Productions (£500,000); Retired Missionary Aid Fund (£200,000); International Fellowship of Evangelical Students (£125,000); Lapido Media (£70,000); Ethiopian Graduate School of Theology (£43,000); Bible Society (£30,000); and Interhealth (£15,000).
FINANCES *Year* 2007–08 *Income* £5,452,330 *Grants* £6,124,745 *Assets* £121,119,512
TRUSTEES Brian Chapman; Alexander McIlhinney; Dr Alexander Scott; David Restall; Douglas Spence; James Hopewell; John McEwen; Paul Young; Robin Boles; William Brian Adams; William Wood; Andrew Street; William Rutherford Rabey; Prof Arthur Williamson; Philip Page; Denis Cooper; Alan Paterson; Philip Collett Dalling; Glyn Davies; Dr John Burness; Andrew Griffiths; Ian Childs; James Crookes; John Gamble; Philip Symons.
HOW TO APPLY In writing to the correspondent.
WHO TO APPLY TO Brian Chapman, Secretary, 124 Wells Road, Bath BA2 3AH *Tel* 01225 427236 *Fax* 01225 427278 *email* stewardsco@stewards.co.uk
CC NO 234558   **ESTABLISHED** 1947

■ The Andy Stewart Charitable Foundation

WHERE FUNDING CAN BE GIVEN Worldwide.
WHO CAN BENEFIT Charitable organisations.
WHAT IS FUNDED General charitable purposes.
SAMPLE GRANTS Healthcare related (59%); children (20%); animals (14%); other (7%).
FINANCES *Year* 2008 *Income* £102,121 *Grants* £40,000 *Assets* £629,313
TRUSTEES Andy Stewart; Ivonne Cantu; Nicholas Weston Wells.
HOW TO APPLY In writing to the correspondent.
WHO TO APPLY TO The Trustees, c/o Cenkos Securities plc, 6–8 Tokenhouse Yard, London EC2R 7AS *Tel* 020 7397 8900
CC NO 1114802   **ESTABLISHED** 2006

■ The Sir Halley Stewart Trust

WHERE FUNDING CAN BE GIVEN Unrestricted, but mainly UK in practice with an interest in South and West Africa.

WHO CAN BENEFIT Charitable organisations and researchers.

WHAT IS FUNDED Research, innovative projects, feasibility and pilot studies and development projects in medical, social, educational and religious fields.

WHAT IS NOT FUNDED The trust will be unable to help with funding for any of the following: general appeals of any kind; the purchase, erection or conversion of buildings; capital costs; university overhead charges; the completion of a project initiated by other bodies. The trust does not normally fund: projects put forward indirectly through other umbrella or large charities; educational or 'gap' year travel projects; running costs of established organisations; climate change issues; personal education fees or fees for taught courses-unless connected with research which falls within current priority areas. Applications for such research work are normally made by a senior researcher seeking support for a student, or if coming directly from the student it should have project supervisor's written support; the trust does not favour grantmaking to enable the completion of a project or PhD.

TYPE OF GRANT One-off and project grants. Feasibility studies, research and salaries will also be considered. Funding may be given for up to three years.

RANGE OF GRANTS Up to £65,000.

SAMPLE GRANTS Oxford University (£65,000); Kings College (£56,000); Abraham Path Initiative (£50,000); Southampton University Hospitals (£40,000); Trinity Foundation and Coalition for Removal of Pimping (£32,000 each); Christianity and Culture (£30,000); British Orthopaedic Foundation (£24,000); the Stammering Association (£18,000); and St Paul's Centre – London (£17,000).

FINANCES *Year* 2007–08 *Income* £1,160,000 *Grants* £1,003,000 *Assets* £24,056,000

TRUSTEES Lord Stewartby, President; Prof. Philip Whitfield, Chair; Prof. John Lennard Jones; Dr Duncan Stewart; William P Kirkman; George Russell; Prof. Phyllida Parsloe; Barbara Clapham; Prof. John Wyatt; Michael Ross Collins; Joanna Womack; Revd Lord Griffiths; Dr Caroline Berry; Prof. Gordon Willcock; Caroline Thomas.

PUBLICATIONS The trust has a helpful website with clear guidelines for applicants.

HOW TO APPLY The following guidelines for applicants is taken from the trust's website: applications will not be accepted by fax or e-mail; applicants should make sure that their project fits the trust's objects and falls within its current priority areas; telephone enquiries to the trust's office are welcomed to discuss the suitability of an application. Please note there is only one member of staff so please be patient and try again if there is no one in the office when you telephone. The trust does not have an application form. Applicants should write to the administrator always including a one-page lay 'executive' summary of the proposed work. The proposal should state clearly: what the aims of the project are and why it is believed to be innovative; what the overall budgeted cost of the project is and how much is being requested from the trust; what the grant will be used for and how long the project will take to have practical benefits; how the project/research

results will be disseminated; personal medical applications should be accompanied by a letter of support from a senior colleague or research supervisor; development projects should indicate where they would hope to obtain future funding from; where appropriate it is helpful to include a CV; job description, set of audited signed accounts and annual report. There are no set application deadlines. When the trust has received your application they will make contact (normally within two weeks) either to ask for further information; to tell you the application will be going forward to the next stage of assessment and what the timetable for a final decision will be; or to tell you that they are unable to help. The trust imposes terms and conditions on each award. Please note that the trust receives many applications for support, and although an application may fit the objects of the trust, it may not necessarily be able to help.

WHO TO APPLY TO Sue West, Administrator, 22 Earith Rd, Willingham, Cambridge, Cambridgeshire CB24 5LS *Tel* 01954 260707 *Fax* 01954 260707 *email* email@sirhalleystewart.org.uk *Website* www.sirhalleystewart.org.uk

CC NO 208491   **ESTABLISHED** 1924

■ The Leonard Laity Stoate Charitable Trust

WHERE FUNDING CAN BE GIVEN England and Wales with a preference for the southwest of England, Bristol, Cornwall, Devon, Dorset and Somerset (especially West Somerset).

WHO CAN BENEFIT Methodist organisations benefiting children and young adults, people who are disabled and people disadvantaged by poverty. Community organisation projects and small local innovatory projects with a strong emphasis on self-help are preferred.

WHAT IS FUNDED The broad categories the trust supported are: medical and disability; churches; young people and children; community projects; disadvantage; and environment.

WHAT IS NOT FUNDED No grants to: individuals unless supported by a registered charity; large projects (over £500,000 and/or with more than £250,000 still to raise); general appeals by national charities; the running expenses of a charity.

TYPE OF GRANT Usually one-off for a specific project or part of a project.

RANGE OF GRANTS £100–£2,000, typically £500– £1,000.

SAMPLE GRANTS Harry's Hydro Appeal and Training for Life (£2,000 each); and Cornwall Disability Arts Group (£1,500). Other beneficiaries included: North Devon Community Transport Association; Vranch House; NCH Action for Children; Plymouth Foodbank; Exford Parish Memorial Hall; Stroud Valley Project; Marine Conservation Society; and Sherborne Museum Association.

FINANCES *Year* 2008–09 *Income* £76,735 *Grants* £51,000 *Assets* £1,375,794

TRUSTEES Mrs Sarah J Boughton; Stephen R Duckworth; Mrs Susan Harnden; Dr Christopher Stoate; Philip J Stoate; Rev. Ward Jones; Dr Pam Stoate.

OTHER INFORMATION Although the trust does not want to rule out anywhere in England and Wales, it is a comparatively small trust and is forced to be very selective. Therefore, the further an applicant is from the trust's core area the less likely they are to be successful.

HOW TO APPLY 'There is no special application form, but applications should be in writing; neither telephone nor e-mail applications will be entertained. Please supply clear details of: the need the intended project is designed to meet; the amount raised so far, with a breakdown of how much has been raised from within the local community and how much from other grant making bodies or other sources. Please also supply where possible: your registered charity number or, for unregistered organisations, a copy of your constitution; accounts or budgets; an e-mail address for follow-up correspondence or application acknowledgement. Whilst applications can be considered at any time, the bulk are decided at our half-yearly meetings in mid-March and September of each year. Thus December to February and June to August are probably the best times to submit applications.'
WHO TO APPLY TO Philip J Stoate, Secretary, 7 Sherwood Close, Bracknell, Berkshire RG12 2SB *email* charity@erminea.org.uk *Website* www.stoate-charity.org.uk
CC NO 221325   **ESTABLISHED** 1950

■ The Stobart Newlands Charitable Trust

WHERE FUNDING CAN BE GIVEN UK.
WHO CAN BENEFIT Registered charities.
WHAT IS FUNDED General charitable purposes at the discretion of the trustees; mainly Christian organisations and missionary societies.
WHAT IS NOT FUNDED No grants for individuals.
TYPE OF GRANT Mainly recurrent.
SAMPLE GRANTS World Vision and Mission Aviation Fellowship (£200,000 each); Operation Mobilisation (£170,000); Tear Fund and Every Home Crusade (£35,000 each); London City Mission and Open Air Mission (£25,000 each); Way to Life (£20,000); Faith Mission (£13,000); Trans World Radio (£10,000); Seamen's Christian Friends (£8,000); Trinitarian Bible Society (£6,500); Templar Trust (£4,000); and Bible Lands (£2,500).
FINANCES *Year* 2007 *Income* £960,285 *Grants* £935,800 *Assets* £217,659
TRUSTEES Richard Stobart; Margaret Stobart; Ronnie Stobart; Peter Stobart; Linda Rigg.
OTHER INFORMATION Grants of £1,000 or less totalled £4,100.
HOW TO APPLY Unsolicited applications are most unlikely to be successful.
WHO TO APPLY TO Margaret Stobart, Trustee, Mill Croft, Hesket Newmarket, Wigton, Cumbria CA7 8HP
CC NO 328464   **ESTABLISHED** 1989

■ The Edward Stocks-Massey Bequest Fund

WHERE FUNDING CAN BE GIVEN Burnley.
WHO CAN BENEFIT Charitable organisations.
WHAT IS FUNDED Education, music, arts, culture and recreation.
SAMPLE GRANTS Lancashire County Council – seven grants (£20,000); Burnley Borough Council – seven grants (£18,000); Burnley Mechanics Institute Trust (£6,000); Prince's Trust (£3,000); Brunshaw Action Group (£2,000); Burnley Municipal Choir (£1,200); Burnley Youth Theatre (£1,000); and Burnley Junior Alliance Band (£330).
FINANCES *Year* 2007–08 *Income* £54,430 *Grants* £65,000 *Assets* £1,019,645

TRUSTEES A David Knagg; Neil Beecham.
OTHER INFORMATION £54,000 to organisations and £9,000 in scholarships to individuals.
HOW TO APPLY On a form available from the correspondent.
WHO TO APPLY TO Saima Afzaal, Burnley Borough Council, Town Hall, Manchester Road, Burnley BB11 1JA *Tel* 01282 425011 *Fax* 01282 438772
CC NO 526516   **ESTABLISHED** 1910

■ The Stokenchurch Educational Charity

WHERE FUNDING CAN BE GIVEN The parish of Stokenchurch.
WHO CAN BENEFIT Local nursery, primary and middle schools; children, young adults and students under the age of 25 residing in the Parish of Stokenchurch.
WHAT IS FUNDED Grants are given for educational purposes.
WHAT IS NOT FUNDED No grants to applicants from outside the Parish of Stokenchurch.
SAMPLE GRANTS Stokenchurch Primary School (£9,000); The Mary Towerton School (£450); Radnage C of E Infant School (£440); Ibstone C of E Infant School (£405); Stokenchurch Medical Centre (£300); Living Springs (£150); Studley Green Youth Club (£130); and Stokenchurch Village Fete (£100).
FINANCES *Year* 2007–08 *Income* £85,015 *Grants* £42,765 *Assets* £1,546,803
TRUSTEES Mrs M Shurrock, Chair; A Palmer; A Saunders; F Downes; Revd A France; Mrs C Baker.
OTHER INFORMATION Grants to individuals totalled about £32,000.
HOW TO APPLY On a form available from the correspondent. The trustees place an annual advertisement in the local press and two public places in Stokenchurch inviting applications. Educational applications must be received by 30 November of each academic year, community grants by 30 September each year.
WHO TO APPLY TO P H Cannon, c/o Cannon Moorcroft Ltd, 3 Manor Courtyard, Hughenden Avenue, High Wycombe, Bucks HP13 5RE *Tel* 01494 450 123 *Fax* 01494 510 190 *email* canmoor@cannonmoorcroft.co.uk
CC NO 297846   **ESTABLISHED** 1987

■ The Stoller Charitable Trust

WHERE FUNDING CAN BE GIVEN UK, with a preference for the Greater Manchester area.
WHO CAN BENEFIT Established UK charities and local causes benefiting children and young adults.
WHAT IS FUNDED Preference for medically related causes, though other charitable purposes will be considered.
WHAT IS NOT FUNDED No grants to individuals.
TYPE OF GRANT Buildings, capital, one-off, project, research, recurring costs and start-up costs will be considered. Funding may be given for up to three years.
SAMPLE GRANTS Broughton House and Farmers Help Farmers (£20,000 each); Brathay Hall Trust and Live Music Now (£10,000 each); Life Education Centres North West (£6,000); Christie Hospital (£5,000); Duke of Edinburgh Golf Society (£3,000); Diggle & Uppermill Ecumenical Youth Project, Ambassadors in Sport and Opera North (£1,000 each); St Ann's Hospice (£500); and

Rotary Club of Windermere and Sight Savers (£250).

FINANCES *Year* 2007–08 *Income* £130,917 *Grants* £353,100 *Assets* £6,692,224

TRUSTEES Norman K Stoller, Chair; Roger Gould; Jan Fidler; Sheila M Stoller.

HOW TO APPLY In writing to the correspondent. Applications need to be received by February, May, August or November. The trustees usually meet in March, June, September and December.

WHO TO APPLY TO Alison M Ford, Secretary, PO Box 164, Middleton, Manchester M24 1XA *Tel* 0161 653 3849

CC NO 285415   **ESTABLISHED** 1982

■ The M J C Stone Charitable Trust

WHERE FUNDING CAN BE GIVEN UK.

WHO CAN BENEFIT UK charities and smaller scale local organisations.

WHAT IS FUNDED General with a preference for education, medicine and health, conservation and religion.

RANGE OF GRANTS Up to £50,000.

SAMPLE GRANTS Westonbirt School (£50,000); Bradfield Foundation (£26,000); Wotton Under Edge Community Sports Fund (£20,000); Civitas (£15,000); Countryside Foundation for Education (£12,000); African Parks Foundation, Maggie Keswick Jencks Cancer and Gloucestershire Community Foundation (£10,000 each); National Trust (£5,000); Dean Forest Hospital (£1,300); Tyndale Choral Society (£500); Game Conservancy Trust (£250); and Song Bird Survival (£20).

FINANCES *Year* 2007 *Income* £38,553 *Grants* £258,907 *Assets* £693,480

TRUSTEES Michael Stone; Louisa Stone; Charles Stone; Andrew Stone; Nicola Farquhar.

HOW TO APPLY The trust does not accept unsolicited applications.

WHO TO APPLY TO Michael Stone, Trustee, Estate Office, Ozleworth Park, Wotton-under-Edge, Gloucestershire GL12 7QA *Tel* 01453 845591

CC NO 283920   **ESTABLISHED** 1981

■ The Stone Family Foundation

WHERE FUNDING CAN BE GIVEN Worldwide.

WHO CAN BENEFIT Charities and international aid organisations.

WHAT IS FUNDED Relief of need or hardship.

WHAT IS NOT FUNDED No grants to individuals.

SAMPLE GRANTS Previous beneficiaries included: Hope and Homes for Children; Opportunity International; Save the Children; WaterAid; Pratham UK Ltd; Pump Aid; Rainforest Saver Foundation; Children's Fire and Burn Trust; and LSCDPA – Laos.

FINANCES *Year* 2008 *Income* £7,529,211 *Grants* £422,000

TRUSTEES Coutts & Co; John Kyle Stone; Vanessa Jane Stone.

HOW TO APPLY 'Applicants for grants and loans must be in writing, and trustees seek the completion of formal terms and conditions.'

WHO TO APPLY TO The Clerk, Coutts & Co, 440 Strand, London WC2R 0QS

CC NO 1108207   **ESTABLISHED** 2005

■ The Stone-Mallabar Charitable Foundation

WHERE FUNDING CAN BE GIVEN UK.

WHO CAN BENEFIT Registered charities.

WHAT IS FUNDED Particularly medical charities but will occasionally give to the arts, religion, overseas appeals, welfare and education.

WHAT IS NOT FUNDED No grants to individuals.

SAMPLE GRANTS Sheffield Institute Foundation for Motor Neurone Disease (£53,000); Brain Research Trust (£25,000); Trinity Laban (£4,000); Bolshoy Ballet School (£3,800); Zimbabwe Benefit Foundation and Thalidomide at 50 (£2,500 each); R Ziegler – Thalidomide Research (£2,000); National Trust (£1,100); Beating Bowel Cancer Awareness Education & Support, Dermatrust and West London Mission (£1,000 each).

FINANCES *Year* 2007–08 *Income* £77,738 *Grants* £102,645 *Assets* £892,327

TRUSTEES Jonathan Stone; Thalia Stone; Robin Paul; Graham Hutton.

OTHER INFORMATION Unlisted grants of less than £1,000 each totalled £5,600.

HOW TO APPLY In writing to the correspondent.

WHO TO APPLY TO Jonathan Stone, Trustee, 41 Orchard Court, Portman Square, London W1H 6LF *email* jmls@ymail.com

CC NO 1013678   **ESTABLISHED** 1992

■ The Samuel Storey Family Charitable Trust

WHERE FUNDING CAN BE GIVEN UK, with a preference for Yorkshire.

WHO CAN BENEFIT Registered charities.

WHAT IS FUNDED General charitable purposes.

WHAT IS NOT FUNDED The trust does not support non-registered charities or individuals.

RANGE OF GRANTS Generally £2–£5,000.

SAMPLE GRANTS Hope and Homes for Children (£27,000); Cancer Vaccine Institute (£10,000); Giles Worsley Travel Fellowship (£5,000); Paint a Smile (£3,300); Pebbles Project and Rhino Rescue Trust (£2,000 each); Ryedale Festival Friends (£1,300); Tadcaster Community Swimming and Woodland Trust (£1,000 each); WSPA (£500); World Monument Fund in Britain (£350); Yorkshire Historic Churches Trust (£250); and Horse Trust (£25).

FINANCES *Year* 2007–08 *Income* £156,291 *Grants* £115,542 *Assets* £4,841,361

TRUSTEES Hon. Sir Richard Storey; Wren Hoskyns Abrahall; Kenelm Storey.

HOW TO APPLY In writing to the correspondent.

WHO TO APPLY TO Hon. Sir Richard Storey, Trustee, 21 Buckingham Gate, London SW1E 6LS *Tel* 020 7802 2700

CC NO 267684   **ESTABLISHED** 1974

■ Peter Stormonth Darling Charitable Trust

WHERE FUNDING CAN BE GIVEN UK.

WHO CAN BENEFIT Organisations benefiting children, young adults, and sportsmen and women.

WHAT IS FUNDED Preference for heritage, education, healthcare and sports facilities.

WHAT IS NOT FUNDED No grants to individuals.

RANGE OF GRANTS Up to £12,000.

SAMPLE GRANTS Black Watch Heritage Appeal (£12,000); Friends of East Sussex Hospices (£10,000); Reed's School (£4,000); Rainbow Trust and Chelsea Physic Garden (£3,000

each); Wintershall Charitable Trust and Perth College Development Trust (£2,500 each); and National Gallery, Christ Church Chelsea and Leonard Cheshire Disability (£2,000 each).

FINANCES *Year* 2008 *Income* £173,938 *Grants* £54,000 *Assets* £2,081,053

TRUSTEES Tom Colville; John Rodwell; Peter Stormonth Darling; Elizabeth Cobb; Arabella Johannes; Christa Taylor.

HOW TO APPLY This trust states that it does not respond to unsolicited applications.

WHO TO APPLY TO Peter Stormonth Darling, Soditic Ltd, Wellington House, 125–130 Strand, London WC2R 0AP

CC NO 1049946   **ESTABLISHED** 1995

■ Peter Storrs Trust

WHERE FUNDING CAN BE GIVEN UK.

WHO CAN BENEFIT Registered charities.

WHAT IS FUNDED The advancement of education.

FINANCES *Year* 2007–08 *Income* £105,563 *Grants* £70,350 *Assets* £2,490,770

TRUSTEES G V Adams; A R E Curtis; J A Fordyce.

HOW TO APPLY In writing to the correspondent. Applications are considered every three to six months. Please note, the trust receives far more applications than it is able to support, many of which do not meet the criteria outlined above. This results in a heavy waste of time and expense for both applicants and the trust itself.

WHO TO APPLY TO J A Fordyce, Trustee, Smithfield Accountants, 117 Charterhouse Street, London EC1M 6AA *Tel* 020 7253 3757

CC NO 313804   **ESTABLISHED** 1970

■ The Strangward Trust

WHERE FUNDING CAN BE GIVEN Eastern England and the East Midlands.

WHO CAN BENEFIT Small local organisations concerned with people with disabilities.

WHAT IS FUNDED Funding for care and treatment of people who are physically or mentally disabled, particularly charities working in the field of the nursing service, hospice in the home, special schools, and holidays and outings.

TYPE OF GRANT One-off, capital, core costs. Funding is for one year or less.

RANGE OF GRANTS Up to £2,000.

SAMPLE GRANTS ASBAH – Peterborough, Bag Books, The Children's Adventure Farm Trust, Happy Days, Red 2 Green and Seeing Ear (£2,000 each); and The Camphill Family, The Nancy Oldfield Trust and UK Sports Association for people with learning disability (£1,000 each).

FINANCES *Year* 2007–08 *Income* £113,392 *Grants* £45,500 *Assets* £3,141,690

TRUSTEES Mrs T A Strangward; R Jones; J Higham Mrs E Conroy.

HOW TO APPLY In writing to the correspondent.

WHO TO APPLY TO Mrs L Davies, Administrator, Vincent Sykes and Higham, Montague House, Chancery Lane, Thrapston, Northamptonshire NN14 4LN *Tel* 01832 732 161 *Fax* 01832 733 701 *email* louise.davies@vshlaw.co.uk *Website* www.vshlaw.co.uk

CC NO 1036494   **ESTABLISHED** 1993

■ The Strasser Foundation

WHERE FUNDING CAN BE GIVEN Staffordshire.

WHO CAN BENEFIT Organisations and individuals.

WHAT IS FUNDED General charitable purposes.

RANGE OF GRANTS Up to £1,000.

SAMPLE GRANTS Previous beneficiaries have included ARCH, Action Medical Research, British Blind Sport, Dystonia Society, Happy Days, Listening Books, Douglas Macmillan Hospice, No Panic, Starlight Children's Foundation, Vitalise and Westbury and Clayton Youth Club.

FINANCES *Year* 2007–08 *Income* £30,929

TRUSTEES A F Booth; A P Bell.

HOW TO APPLY In writing to the correspondent. The trustees meet quarterly. Applications are only acknowledged if an sae is sent.

WHO TO APPLY TO F Hayes, c/o Knight and Sons, The Brampton, Newcastle-under-Lyme, Staffordshire ST5 0QW

CC NO 511703   **ESTABLISHED** 1978

■ Stratford upon Avon Town Trust

WHERE FUNDING CAN BE GIVEN Stratford upon Avon.

WHO CAN BENEFIT Organisations benefiting people living in the Stratford-upon-Avon council area.

WHAT IS FUNDED Relief of need, hardship and distress; relief of sickness, disability, old age and infirmity; support of facilities for education, including the advancement of learning and knowledge; support for recreations and other leisure-time facilities; advancement of the Christian religion.

WHAT IS NOT FUNDED No grants to organisations outside Stratford upon Avon.

TYPE OF GRANT Capital and revenue grants for up to three years.

RANGE OF GRANTS Up to £100,000.

SAMPLE GRANTS RSC (£100,000); Citizen's Advice Bureau (£70,000); Shakespeare's Hospice (£65,000); Stratford Upon Avon Christmas Lights Co Ltd (£50,000); World Class Stratford (£42,000); Friends' of Shakespeare Church (£30,000); Stratford in Bloom (£28,000); and Stratford High School (£25,000).

FINANCES *Year* 2008 *Income* £2,117,104 *Grants* £1,209,551 *Assets* £3,352,497

TRUSTEES Jean Holder; Donna Barker; Jenny Fradgley; Rosemary Hyde; Juliet Short; Carole Taylor; Dr Nick Woodward; Tim Wightman; John Lancaster; Charles Michaelis; Paul Stanton.

OTHER INFORMATION This trust was created in May 2001 after an investigation by the Charity Commission into the workings of two long-standing trusts in the town, The College Estate Charity and The Guild Estate Charity. During 2008 the trust changed its financial year-end from 30 September to 31 December. Consequently all 2008 figures are for a fifteen month period.
Under the trust's constitution there are two beneficiaries who have a specified entitlement to financial support: King Edward VI Grammar School (received £706,000 in 2008) and the Vicar of the Holy Trinity Church (£8,800). The trust also contributes to the maintenance of 24 almshouses in the town (£37,000).

HOW TO APPLY Application forms can be completed online (www.stratfordtowntrust.co.uk). Please note: there are two forms, one for those applying for less than £2,500 and one for those requesting larger grants. Awards are made on a quarterly basis. The latest application deadlines are listed on the trust's website.

WHO TO APPLY TO Richard Eggington, Chief Executive, 14 Rother Street, Stratford-upon-Avon,

Warwickshire CV32 6LU *Tel* 01789 207111 *Fax* 01789 207119 *email* admin@ stratfordtowntrust.co.uk *Website* www. stratfordtowntrust.co.uk

cc no 1088521   established 2001

■ Strathclyde Police Benevolent Fund

where funding can be given Strathclyde.

who can benefit Organisations and members of Strathclyde police, retired members, and widows or other dependants who may be in need.

what is funded General charitable purposes.

finances *Year* 2008 *Income* £146,346 *Grants* £130,000

trustees G Carmichael, chair; A Gillies; Linda McCartney; J Foster; R Watterson.

how to apply In writing to the correspondent. Applications to be received by the end of March for consideration in the annual meeting held in April.

who to apply to The Trustees, Strathclyde Police Federation, 151 Merrylee Road, Glasgow G44 3DL *Tel* 0141 633 2020 *Fax* 0141 633 0276

sc no SC009899   established 1975

■ The Strawberry Charitable Trust

where funding can be given Not defined but with a preference for Manchester.

who can benefit Registered charities.

what is funded The relief of poverty and hardship amongst Jewish persons and the advancement of the Jewish religion.

range of grants Up to £32,000.

sample grants Community Security Trust (£32,000); United Jewish Israel Appeal (£30,000); Christies (£20,000); Manchester Jewish Federation (£11,000); Philip Green Memorial Trust (£6,300); Manchester Jewish Community Care (£5,100); World Jewish Relief (£5,000); Belz (£3,000); and Jewish Care and Heathlands Animal Sanctuary (£2,500 each).

finances *Year* 2007–08 *Income* £289,810 *Grants* £138,182

trustees Emma Myers; Laura Avigdori; Anthony Leon.

other information Smaller grants of less than £1,000 were not listed separately, but totalled £11,000.

how to apply In writing to the correspondent.

who to apply to Anthony Leon, Trustee, 4 Westfields, Hale, Altrincham WA15 0LL *email* anthonysula@hotmail.com

cc no 1090173   established 2000

■ The W O Street Charitable Foundation

where funding can be given Worldwide. In practice there is a preference for the north west of England and Jersey.

who can benefit Registered charities.

what is funded Support is given for education, relief of poverty, helping people in financial difficulties (particularly older people and people who are blind or who have disabilities), the relief of sickness and social welfare generally.

what is not funded No grants towards: schools, colleges or universities; running or core costs; religion or church buildings; medical research; animal welfare; hospices; overseas projects or charities; NHS trusts. Applications directly from individuals are not considered.

type of grant One-off and recurring grants.

range of grants Generally £1,000 to £15,000.

sample grants DEG educational bursaries (£48,000); W O Street Jersey Charitable Trust (£42,000); Combined Trusts Scholarship (35,000); and Community Foundation for Greater Manchester (£22,000).

finances *Year* 2007 *Income* £492,131 *Grants* £410,497 *Assets* £17,655,926

trustees Barclays Bank Trust Co. Ltd; Mr C D Cutbill.

how to apply In writing to the correspondent. Applications are considered on a quarterly basis, at the end of January, April, July and October.

who to apply to The Trust Officer, c/o Barclays Bank Trust Company Ltd, PO Box 15, Osborne Court, Gadbrook Park, Northwich CW9 7UR *Tel* 01606 313 173

cc no 267127   established 1973

■ The A B Strom and R Strom Charitable Trust

where funding can be given UK.

who can benefit Registered charities.

what is funded A set list of charities working with older people, schools/colleges, hospitals and Christian causes.

sample grants Yeshivas Hanegev (£10,000); Redcroft and Russian Immigrants (£5,000 each).

finances *Year* 2007–08 *Income* £113,409 *Grants* £33,836 *Assets* £548,725

trustees Mrs R Strom; Mrs D Weissbraun.

how to apply In writing to the correspondent. Please note that the same organisations are supported each year.

who to apply to Mrs R Strom, Trustee, c/o 11 Gloucester Gardens, London NW11 9AB *Tel* 020 8455 5949 *email* m@michaelpasha. worldonline.co.uk

cc no 268916   established 1971

■ The Sudborough Foundation

where funding can be given UK, with a preference for Northamptonshire.

who can benefit Educational establishments and other charities.

what is funded Students in need or for scholarships; general charitable purposes.

what is not funded No grants for expeditions or drama and dance courses.

range of grants Up to £5,000.

sample grants Home-Start Northampton (£5,000); Parkinson's Disease Society and NSPCC (£2,500 each); Annie Holt and Vera Ashton Music Scholarship Service (£2,000); Guilsborough Playing Fields Association (£1,000); Northampton Door to Door Service and The Volunteer Centre (£500 each); Northampton Sailability (£200); and St Matthew's Scout Group and Jewish Child's Day (£100 each).

finances *Year* 2007–08 *Income* £58,429 *Grants* £33,891 *Assets* £446,676

trustees Sir J Lowther; Mrs E A Engel; W M Reason; Mrs S E Leatham; Simon J A Powis; Julian Woolfson; R Engel; Miss R Engel.

how to apply The foundation does not respond to unsolicited applications.

WHO TO APPLY TO Richard Engel, Trustee, 8 Hazelwood Road, Northampton NN1 1LP
CC NO 272323   ESTABLISHED 1976

■ Sueberry Ltd

WHERE FUNDING CAN BE GIVEN UK and overseas.
WHO CAN BENEFIT Jewish organisations; UK welfare and medical organisations benefiting children and young adults; at risk groups; people who are disadvantaged by poverty, or socially isolated people.
WHAT IS FUNDED Jewish organisations, medical, educational and welfare charities.
TYPE OF GRANT Mostly recurrent.
SAMPLE GRANTS In previous years the trust has supported educational, religious and other charitable organisations.
FINANCES *Year* 2007–08 *Income* £246,238 *Grants* £163,435 *Assets* £61,515
TRUSTEES J Davis, Chair; Mrs H Davis; Mrs M Davis; D S Davis; C Davis; A D Davis; S M Davis; Y Davis.
HOW TO APPLY In writing to the correspondent.
WHO TO APPLY TO Mrs M Davis, Trustee, 18 Clifton Gardens, London N15 6AP
CC NO 256566   ESTABLISHED 1968

■ The Suffolk Foundation

WHERE FUNDING CAN BE GIVEN Suffolk.
WHO CAN BENEFIT Registered charities and community groups.
WHAT IS FUNDED The foundation has a range of different funds designed for small community and voluntary groups working to help local people across Suffolk. Each scheme tends to have a different application procedure and size of award. The foundation is currently managing the following grant programmes: grassroots grants; Suffolk single gateway fund; Suffolk voluntary sector training programme fund; somebody's daughter grant; healthy ambitions grant; comic relief; high sheriff grants and award. Please note: grant schemes can change frequently. Potential applicants are advised to consult the foundation's website for details of current programmes and their deadlines.
WHAT IS NOT FUNDED No funding for: projects not benefiting people living in Suffolk; individuals for their personal needs; direct replacement of statutory obligation and public funding; general large appeals; medical research and equipment; statutory work in educational institutions; promotion of religious or political causes; sponsored events; fundraising events; retrospective grants; animal welfare; overseas travel or expeditions for individuals and groups. Please note: different programmes may have further exclusions. Organisations are advised to read the guidelines carefully before making an application.
TYPE OF GRANT One-off grants for capital and revenue costs and full project funding.
RANGE OF GRANTS Small grants averaging around £2,000.
FINANCES *Year* 2008–09 *Income* £1,764,602 *Grants* £1,080,659 *Assets* £994,865
TRUSTEES David Sheepshanks; David Barclay; Deborah Cadman; James Dinwiddy; The Countess of Euston; Stephen Fletcher; Revd Canon Graham Hedger; Claire Horsley; Lady Howes; Graeme Kalbraier; Fiona Mahony; Sir David Rowland.

HOW TO APPLY The foundation's website has details of the grant schemes currently being administered.
WHO TO APPLY TO Enid Kimes, Grants Officer, Old Reading Rooms, The Green, Grundisburgh, Woodbridge, Suffolk IP13 6TA *Tel* 01473 734120 *Fax* 01473 734121 *email* info@suffolkfoundation.org.uk *Website* www.suffolkfoundation.org.uk
CC NO 1109453   ESTABLISHED 2005

■ The Suffolk Historic Churches Trust

WHERE FUNDING CAN BE GIVEN Suffolk.
WHO CAN BENEFIT Churches and chapels over 100 years old of all denominations.
WHAT IS FUNDED The preservation, repair, maintenance, restoration and improvement of churches in Suffolk.
WHAT IS NOT FUNDED The trust does normally make grants for: electrical work; furnishings and fittings; churchyard walls; brasses and bells; monuments; redecoration, unless needed as part of an eligible project; new buildings or extensions to existing buildings.
RANGE OF GRANTS £300–£10,000. Higher than the maximum is only given in exceptional circumstances.
FINANCES *Year* 2007–08 *Income* £379,143 *Grants* £159,550 *Assets* £798,715
TRUSTEES Robert Rous, Chair; the Ven Geoffrey Arrand; Alan Barker; Martin Favell; Mrs Diana Hunt; Christopher Spicer; Robert Williams; Simon Tennent; Mrs Celia Stephens; Clive Paine; Patrick Grieve.
HOW TO APPLY Application forms can be downloaded from the trust's website. 'The Grants Committee normally meets in the second week of January, April, July and October. Applications received by the end of the month prior to the meeting are considered at the meeting.'
WHO TO APPLY TO The Secretary, Brinkleys, Hall Street, Long Melford, Suffolk CO10 9JR *Tel* 01787 883 884 *Website* www.shct.org.uk
CC NO 267047   ESTABLISHED 1973

■ The Alan Sugar Foundation

WHERE FUNDING CAN BE GIVEN UK.
WHO CAN BENEFIT Registered charities.
WHAT IS FUNDED Grants are made to causes of current and ongoing interest to the trustees.
WHAT IS NOT FUNDED No grants for individuals or to non-registered charities.
TYPE OF GRANT One-off and recurring, capital and project.
SAMPLE GRANTS Great Ormond Street Hospital (£500,000); Jewish Community Secondary School Trust and Cancer Research UK (£250,000 each); Jewish Care (£200,000); LIV – Cystic Fibrosis (£75,000); Myeloma (£10,000); Second Space (£5,200); the Drugs Line (£5,000); Prostate Cancer Charitable Fund (£2,000); and Cancerbackup (£1,000).
FINANCES *Year* 2007–08 *Income* £1,141,954 *Grants* £1,298,200 *Assets* £235,236
TRUSTEES Sir Alan Sugar; Colin Sandy; Simon Sugar; Daniel Sugar; Louise Baron.
HOW TO APPLY This trust states that it does not respond to unsolicited applications. All projects are initiated by the trustees.

WHO TO APPLY TO Colin Sandy, Trustee, Sterling House, Langston Road, Loughton, Essex IG10 3TS *Tel* 020 3225 5560 *email* colin@amsprop.com

CC NO 294880 **ESTABLISHED** 1986

....
■ The Summerfield Charitable Trust

WHERE FUNDING CAN BE GIVEN Gloucestershire.

WHO CAN BENEFIT Registered charities local to Gloucestershire.

WHAT IS FUNDED The trustees are interested in hearing from those involved in helping older people, people in need and the arts. Viewed especially favourably are: the needs of people living in rural areas; ventures which make a point of using volunteers (and which train volunteers); applicants who show clear indications that they have assessed the impact of their project upon the environment; and joint appeals from groups working in similar areas, who wish to develop a partnership. The trustees particularly welcome innovative ideas from: small, voluntary groups; schemes that indicate planning for long-term self-sufficiency; and projects that demonstrate active involvement with the beneficiaries.

WHAT IS NOT FUNDED Donations are not given towards medical research, private education or animal welfare appeals. Applications from individuals are no longer accepted. Should an individual resident of Gloucestershire require financial support for educational needs, they are recommended to contact the Lumb's Education Trust. SCT awards an annual grant to Lumb's to enable it to support local residents on SCT's behalf. Write to: Mrs Margaret Wanless, Lumb's Education Trust, 4 Manor View, Cold Pool Lane, Up Hatherley, Cheltenham, GL51 6HZ. Appeals from churches for renovation and repair will not be accepted in 2010. You are advised to contact Gloucestershire Historic Churches Trust.

TYPE OF GRANT Usually one-off. The trustees prefer to award one-off grants to help fund specific projects rather than to make payments for revenue items. The trustees will occasionally consider start-up costs and grants for up to three years.

RANGE OF GRANTS £500–£29,000.

SAMPLE GRANTS Previously: Cheltenham Arts Festivals Ltd (£29,000); Art Shape Limited and Brewery Arts (£20,000 each); Forest of Dean Music Makers (£15,000); Abbey Schools (£12,000); Cotswold Players, Global Dimension Trust, Gloucester Emergency Accommodation Resource, Thomas Morley Trust and Uplands Care Service (£10,000 each).

FINANCES *Year* 2008 *Income* £395,703 *Grants* £365,297 *Assets* £7,854,956

TRUSTEES Charles Fisher, Chair; Mrs Jamila Gavin; Dr The Hon. Gilbert Greenall; Mrs Jan Urban-Smith; Richard Wakeford.

OTHER INFORMATION For 2008, grants were broken down as follows: Disadvantaged and vulnerable sectors (£129,000 in 24 grants); Arts, museums and built heritage (£84,000 in 16 grants); Community work (£78,000 in 13 grants); Education, sport and recreation (£53,000 in 12 grants); Environment and natural heritage (£22,000 in four grants). Note: these figures include support costs.

HOW TO APPLY The trustees meet quarterly; usually in March, June, September and December (see the trust's website for deadline dates). 'You should write to Mrs Lavinia Sidgwick, Administrator, stating in your own words what is required and why, and enclose your completed grant application cover sheet with supporting information. It helps if you advise us which other trusts you are applying to as we may consult them, unless you specifically ask us not to.' Applicants must download a grant application cover sheet. When compiling their application, applicants are welcome to telephone the trust and discuss queries. One of the trust's independent advisors is often asked to visit organisations who apply.

WHO TO APPLY TO Mrs Lavinia Sidgwick, Administrator, PO Box 4, Winchcombe, Cheltenham, Gloucestershire GL54 5ZD *Tel* 01242 676 774 *Fax* 01242 677120 *email* admin@summerfield.org.uk *Website* www.summerfield.org.uk

CC NO 802493 **ESTABLISHED** 1989

....
■ The Bernard Sunley Charitable Foundation

WHERE FUNDING CAN BE GIVEN Unrestricted, but mainly southern England.

WHO CAN BENEFIT Registered charities.

WHAT IS FUNDED General charitable purposes; with grants categorised under: education; arts; religion; community; children and young people; older people; health; social welfare; environment; animal welfare; amateur sport; emergency and armed services; and overseas.

WHAT IS NOT FUNDED 'We would reiterate that we do not make grants to individuals; we still receive several such applications each week. This bar on individuals applies equally to those people taking part in a project sponsored by a charity such as VSO, Duke of Edinburgh Award Scheme, Trekforce, Scouts and Girl Guides, and so on, or in the case of the latter two to specific units of these youth movements.'

TYPE OF GRANT One-off, capital and recurring, for up to a maximum of three years.

RANGE OF GRANTS £100–£100,000; typical grant £5,000–£10,000.

SAMPLE GRANTS London Youth (£250,000); Royal Institution of Great Britain and Royal Marines Museum (£100,000 each); White Ensign Association (£40,000); Royal Marsden Hospital Cancer Campaign (£30,000); St Paul's Church – Mill Hill (£20,000); Cricket Foundation and Merlin (£10,000 each); Crimestoppers Trust – Kent and Almshouse Association (£5,000 each); Deal Festival of Music and the Arts (£4,000); YMCA – Reading and Royal Hospital for Neuro-disability – Putney (£2,000 each); Dogs for the Disabled (£1,200); and Tramps Fund – Gibraltar (£1,000).

FINANCES *Year* 2007–08 *Income* £3,106,000 *Grants* £2,276,000 *Assets* £76,010,000

TRUSTEES John B Sunley; Joan M Tice; Bella Sunley; Sir Donald Gosling; Brian W Martin; Anabel Knight; William Tice.

HOW TO APPLY 'Appeals are considered regularly, but we would emphasise that we are only able to make grants to registered charities and not to individuals. There is no application form, but the covering letter to the director should give details as to the points below, and should be accompanied by the latest approved report and accounts. The details requested are as follows: a description of what the charity does and what its objectives are; an explanation of the need and purpose of the project for which the grant is required; how much will the project cost? The costing should be itemised and supported with

Think carefully about every application. Is it justified?

887

quotations etc. as necessary; the size of grant requested; how much has already been raised and from whom. How is it planned to raise the shortfall; if applicable, how the running costs of the project will be met, once the project is established; any other documentation that the applicant feels will help to support or explain the appeal.'

WHO TO APPLY TO John Rimmington, Director, 20 Berkeley Square, London W1J 6LH *Tel* 020 7408 2198 *Fax* 020 7499 5859 *email* office@ sunleyfoundation.com

CC NO 1109099   **ESTABLISHED** 1960

....

■ Surrey Community Foundation

WHERE FUNDING CAN BE GIVEN Surrey.

WHO CAN BENEFIT Organisations and individuals.

WHAT IS FUNDED Strengthening communities in Surrey.

TYPE OF GRANT Surrey Community Foundation has an ongoing grant programme consisting of a number of funds established by individuals, families, trusts and companies. The foundation also administers *Grassroots Grants*, a national programme (2008–11) to support small, voluntary led community groups to build stronger more active communities. Grants for running costs or capital items of between £250 and £5,000 are available for small groups with an average annual income of less than £20,000.

FINANCES *Year* 2007–08 *Grants* £155,366

TRUSTEES Prof. Patrick Dowling, Chair; Steve Blunt; Matthew Bowcock; David Charlesworth; Richard Edmondson; Bishop Christopher Hill (Bishop of Guildford); Sir Stephen Lamport; Gordon Lee-Steere; Jim McAllister; Lavinia Sealy; Nick Skellett; Andrew Wates; Peter Hampson; John Lavers.

OTHER INFORMATION Surrey Community Foundation is part of a national network of community foundations.

HOW TO APPLY To discuss your project, or apply for funding, please contact Liz Westwood – Grants Manager (tel.: 01483 555641 or e-mail: liz@surreycommunityfoundation.org.uk).

WHO TO APPLY TO Wendy Varcoe, Director, Beaufort House, Chertsey Street, Guildford, Surrey GU1 4HA *Tel* 01483 409230 *email* info@ surreycommunityfoundation.org.uk *Website* www.surreycommunityfoundation.org.uk

CC NO 1111600   **ESTABLISHED** 2005

....

■ The Surrey Historic Buildings Trust Ltd

WHERE FUNDING CAN BE GIVEN Surrey.

WHO CAN BENEFIT Individuals or groups.

WHAT IS FUNDED Preservation of the historical, architectural and constructional heritage existing in Surrey.

WHAT IS NOT FUNDED No support for local authority-owned buildings or the general upkeep of places of worship (although specific artefacts or architectural features may attract a grant).

RANGE OF GRANTS Up to £6,000; usually £1,000 to £3,000.

SAMPLE GRANTS Abbotts Hospital – Guildford (£6,000); Monks House – Gomshall and Lovelace Mausoleum – East Horsley (£3,000 each); Tenchley's Manor – Limpsfield and Waverley Abbey House – Farnham (£2,000 each); Manor Cottage – Betchworth and Church of St Nicholas – Lychgate (£1,500 each); and Wray Common Windmill – Reigate (£1,000).

FINANCES *Year* 2007–08 *Income* £61,604 *Grants* £45,593 *Assets* £470,109

TRUSTEES Timothy Ashton; Alan Black; John Davey; David Davis; Angela Fraser; Dr Lynne Hack; Jean Smith; Jennifer Powell; Mrs P Adamson; Dennis Turner; Mrs N Westbury; Mrs Celia Savage; J H Jessup; John Garrett.

OTHER INFORMATION Grants of less than £1,000 each were made to nine individuals and totalled £4,900.

HOW TO APPLY On an application form available from the correspondent or the website. Applicants should, where possible, produce two detailed estimates. In the case of highly specialised work, a single estimate may be acceptable. The application cannot be considered unless photographs of the building accompany it and, where available, plans should also be submitted.

WHO TO APPLY TO Nicola Morris, Assistant Honarary Secretary, Room 122, County Hall, Kingston-upon-Thames, Surrey KT1 2DN *Tel* 020 8541 7198 *email* nicola.morris@ surreycc.gov.uk *Website* surreycc.gov.uk

CC NO 279240   **ESTABLISHED** 1979

....

■ Sussex Community Foundation

WHERE FUNDING CAN BE GIVEN East Sussex, West Sussex or Brighton and Hove.

WHO CAN BENEFIT Charities and community groups whose work benefits people in East Sussex, West Sussex or Brighton and Hove. The foundation welcomes applications from established organisations as well as new groups and projects.

WHAT IS FUNDED The foundation is particularly interested in supporting smaller community based groups where a small grant can make a difference.

WHAT IS NOT FUNDED No support for: individuals; organisations that are part of central, local or regional government; major capital appeals; fundraising events; sponsorship.

RANGE OF GRANTS Mostly £1,000–£5,000.

FINANCES *Year* 2008–09 *Income* £1,747,524 *Grants* £859,860 *Assets* £934,505

TRUSTEES Trevor James; John Peel; Kathy Gore; Neil Hart; Jeremy Leggett; Steve Manwaring; Caroline Nicholls; Sharon Phillips; Lesley Wake; Mike Simpkin; Humphrey Price; Richard Pearson; Margaret Johnson; Michael Martin.

HOW TO APPLY The foundation manages a range of funds on behalf of donors, each of which has its own priorities and criteria. Application forms and guidelines can be downloaded from the foundation's website. Applicants must have a constitution or set of rules, and be able to show that they are not-for-profit, but do not always have to be a charity.

WHO TO APPLY TO Kevin Richmond, Administrator, Suite B, Falcon Wharf, Railway Lane, Lewes BN7 2AQ *Tel* 01273 409 440 *email* info@ sussxgiving.org.uk *Website* www.sussexgiving. org.uk

CC NO 1113226   **ESTABLISHED** 2006

■ The Sussex Historic Churches Trust

WHERE FUNDING CAN BE GIVEN Sussex.

WHO CAN BENEFIT Churches of any denomination over 100 years old and of some architectural or historical significance.

WHAT IS FUNDED Preservation, repair, maintenance and restoration of churches in Sussex.

WHAT IS NOT FUNDED No grants for bells.

TYPE OF GRANT Interest-free loans and buildings will be considered.

RANGE OF GRANTS £1,000–£10,000, typical grant £5,000.

SAMPLE GRANTS Previously: Saint John the Baptist – Kirdford (£15,000); Saint Peter – Westhampnett (£10,000); Saint Mary – Salehurst (£6,000); Saint Mary – Bepton and Southwick, C.C.C. (£5,000 each); Saint Mary – Broadwater, Saint John the Baptist – Crawley, Saint Peter ad Vincula – Folkington and Saint Dunstan – Mayfield (£3,000 each).

FINANCES *Year* 2008 *Income* £107,231 *Grants* £58,000 *Assets* £739,345

TRUSTEES Countess De La Warr; the Archdeacon of Chichester; the Archdeacon of Horsham; Christopher Whittick; Ven. Douglas McKittrick; Philip Jones; Lady Pamela Wedgwood; Ven. Roger Combes; John Barkshire.

HOW TO APPLY In writing to the correspondent giving an outline of the work to be done and some indication of the financial state of the parish or congregation. An application form will then be sent to you, if what you propose qualifies for help. Applications must be made before work is started.

WHO TO APPLY TO The Secretary, Diocesan Church House, 211 New Church Road, Hove, East Sussex BN3 4ED *Tel* 01273 421 021 *Website* www.sussexhistoricchurches.org.uk

CC NO 282159   **ESTABLISHED** 1981

■ The Adrienne and Leslie Sussman Charitable Trust

WHERE FUNDING CAN BE GIVEN UK, in practice Greater London, particularly Barnet.

WHO CAN BENEFIT Registered charities.

WHAT IS FUNDED General, Jewish.

WHAT IS NOT FUNDED No grants to branches of UK charities outside Barnet, non-registered charities and individuals.

SAMPLE GRANTS Previous beneficiaries have included BF Shvut Ami, Chai – Lifeline and B'nai B'rith Hillel Fund, Child Resettlement, Children and Youth Aliyah, Finchley Synagogue, Jewish Care, Nightingale House, Norwood Ravenswood and Sidney Sussex CLL.

FINANCES *Year* 2007–08 *Income* £194,089 *Grants* £71,460 *Assets* £1,715,395

TRUSTEES Adrienne Sussman; Leslie Sussman; Martin Paisner.

HOW TO APPLY In writing to the correspondent.

WHO TO APPLY TO Adrienne Sussman, 25 Tillingbourne Gardens, London N3 3JJ

CC NO 274955   **ESTABLISHED** 1977

■ The Sutasoma Trust

WHERE FUNDING CAN BE GIVEN UK and overseas.

WHO CAN BENEFIT Individuals and organisations.

WHAT IS FUNDED Bursaries and support to institutions in the field of social sciences, humanities and humanitarian activities. General grants may also be made.

TYPE OF GRANT Mainly recurrent.

SAMPLE GRANTS Lucy Cavendish College Fellowship (£16,000); University of Bergen (£12,000); LACP Zambia (£7,000); Practical Action Disappearing Lands (£6,000); Emslie Horniman Fund and School of Oriental and African Studies (£5,000 each); Merlin Medical Relief (£3,000); Corporation of Haverford and Link Literacy Training (£2,000 each); Harmony House Kerala (£1,000); and Anti-Slavery International (£500).

FINANCES *Year* 2007–08 *Income* £122,569 *Grants* £104,664 *Assets* £2,335,451

TRUSTEES Dr Angela R Hobart; Marcel A Burgauer; Jane M Lichtenstein; Prof. Bruce Kapferer; Dr Sally Wolfe; Dr Piers Vitebsky.

HOW TO APPLY In writing to the correspondent.

WHO TO APPLY TO Jane M Lichtenstein, PO Box 1118, Cottenham, Cambridge CB24 8WQ *Tel* 07768 245384 *email* sutasoma.trust@ ntlworld.com

CC NO 803301   **ESTABLISHED** 1990

■ Sutton Coldfield Municipal Charities

WHERE FUNDING CAN BE GIVEN The former borough of Sutton Coldfield, comprising three electoral wards: New Hall, Vesey and Four Oaks.

WHO CAN BENEFIT Individuals in need and organisations, without restriction, in Sutton Coldfield.

WHAT IS FUNDED The aims are: to help people who are aged, sick, have disabilities or living in poverty; to support facilities for recreational and leisure activities; to promote the arts and advance religion; the repair of historic buildings; and advancement of education through grants to schools for maintenance and equipment.

WHAT IS NOT FUNDED No awards are given to individuals or organisations outside the area of benefit, unless the organisations are providing essential services in the area.

TYPE OF GRANT The trustees will consider making grants for buildings, projects, research, start-up costs, and capital and running costs for up to three years or as one-off payments. No cash payments are made; payments are made via invoices or vouchers.

RANGE OF GRANTS Up to £75,000.

SAMPLE GRANTS Previous beneficiaries include: St Giles Hospice; John Willmott School; Boldmere Swimming Club; New Hall Ward Advisory Board; New Hall Primary School; Holy Trinity (CE) Parish Church; Boldmere Methodist Church; Victim Support; Walmley Women's Institute; and Sutton Coldfield Asian Society.

FINANCES *Year* 2007–08 *Income* £2,073,423 *Grants* £1,152,327 *Assets* £39,444,704

TRUSTEES Rodney Kettel, Chair; Sue Bailey; Dr Freddie Gick; John Gray; Donald Grove; Cllr Susanna McCorry; Alfred David Owen; Jane Rothwell; Cllr David Roy; Michael Waltho; Cllr James Whorwood; Carole Hancox; Cllr Margaret Waddington; Dr S C Martin; Cllr Malcolm Cornish; Neil Andrews.

OTHER INFORMATION As well as providing grants, the charities maintain 46 almshouses and provide school clothing grants to individuals.

HOW TO APPLY Contact the charity, either by letter, or by telephoning: 0121 351 2262; outline your needs and request a copy of the charity's guidelines for applicants; if appropriate, seek a meeting with a member of staff in making your application; ensure that all relevant documents, including estimates and accounts, reach the charity by the requested dates. Receipt of applications is not normally acknowledged unless a stamped addressed envelope is sent with the application. Applications may be submitted at any time. The grants committee meets at least eight times a year. The board of trustees must approve requests for grants over £30,000. At all stages, staff at the charities will give assistance to those making applications. For example, projects and applications can be discussed, either at the charity's office or on site. Advice about deadlines for submitting applications can also be given. There are application forms for individuals, who must obtain them from the charity.

WHO TO APPLY TO Andrew MacFarlane, Clerk to the Trustees, Lingard House, Fox Hollies Road, Sutton Coldfield, West Midlands B76 2RJ *Tel* 0121 351 2262 *Fax* 0121 313 0651 *Website* www.suttoncoldfieldmunicipalcharities. com

CC NO 218627   **ESTABLISHED** 1898

....

■ The Sutton Nursing Association

WHERE FUNDING CAN BE GIVEN Sutton.

WHO CAN BENEFIT Individuals and organisations.

WHAT IS FUNDED Grants to alleviate hardship and the effects of sickness.

WHAT IS NOT FUNDED Ongoing liabilities and anything that does not help people who are sick or otherwise in need.

TYPE OF GRANT Usually grant by cheque through social worker or similar professional, according to requirement, but usually not more than £500 unless there are exceptional circumstances.

SAMPLE GRANTS Sutton Staying Put (£6,000); Citizens' Advice Bureau – Sutton Borough (£4,000); Medical Engineering Research Unit (£1,500); Mayor's Charity and SSAFA (£1,000 each); and Age Concern (£100). 'Sundry' grants totalled £3,900.

FINANCES *Year* 2008 *Income* £25,578 *Grants* £21,794 *Assets* £617,245

TRUSTEES Dr Frank Assinder; Reginald Baldwin Whellock; Mrs Marilyn Gordon-Jones; Dr Peter Heywood; R Hobbs; David N Skingle; Tony Stacey; Pamela Norton; Mrs F Owen; Mrs J Alexander; Mrs J Herrington; Mrs Betsy Graham.

HOW TO APPLY In writing to the correspondent.

WHO TO APPLY TO David N Skingle, Secretary and Treasurer, 8 Glengarry Way, Friars Cliff, Christchurch, Dorset BH23 4EQ *Tel* 01425 278 485 *Fax* 01425 272 118 *email* sna@skingle. co.uk

CC NO 203686   **ESTABLISHED** 1955

....

■ The Sutton Trust

WHERE FUNDING CAN BE GIVEN UK only.

WHO CAN BENEFIT Educational institutions, and other groups that organise formal education projects or undertake educational research.

WHAT IS FUNDED Providing educational opportunities for children and young people from non-privileged backgrounds. Funding is now focused primarily on research and policy work, as well as a small number of innovative pilot initiatives.

TYPE OF GRANT Core costs, feasibility studies, interest-free loans, one-off, project, research, recurring costs, running costs, salaries and start-up costs. Capital and equipment grants are not considered. Grants are usually provided for one to two years only, but can be extended up to a maximum of three years, and further in exceptional circumstances.

SAMPLE GRANTS Beneficiaries included: Bristol University Summer School, Oxford Access Scheme, LEAPS, Industrial Trust Schools Project, INTO University, Parents as First Teachers, University of York, Social Mobility Summit and Durham University.

FINANCES *Year* 2008 *Income* £4,786,271 *Grants* £3,301,463 *Assets* £1,350,481

TRUSTEES Sir Peter Lampl; David Backinsell; Glyn Morris.

HOW TO APPLY The trust states that it, 'is now focusing on research and policy work, and will only be funding a select handful of small scale pilot projects. We envisage that most of these projects will be developed through existing contacts and partnerships'. As such, unsolicited applications are unlikely to be successful.

WHO TO APPLY TO The Trust Administrator, 111 Upper Richmond Road, Putney, London SW15 2TJ *Tel* 020 8788 3223 *Fax* 020 8788 3993 *Website* www.suttontrust.com

CC NO 1067197   **ESTABLISHED** 1998

....

■ The Suva Foundation Limited

WHERE FUNDING CAN BE GIVEN Unrestricted with a preference for Henley-on-Thames.

WHO CAN BENEFIT Charitable organisations.

WHAT IS FUNDED General charitable purposes. The following was taken from the foundation's 2007/08 annual report: 'The charity's principal activity during the year was the support of charities through the payments of donations. The objects of the charity are to promote any charitable purpose or support any charity selected by the directors. It is expressly contemplated that the Arbib Foundation (Charity Commission no. 296358) may be the beneficiary of the application of some or all funds or other benefits by the charity.'

SAMPLE GRANTS The Arbib Foundation (£255,000); Pangbourne College, Thames Valley and Cheltenham Ambulance Fund (£1,000 each); Langalanga Scholarship Fund and Remenham PCC (£500 each); and Friends of Henley Festival Society (£250).

FINANCES *Year* 2007–08 *Income* £245,704 *Grants* £258,250 *Assets* £8,953,708

TRUSTEES Mrs A Nicoll; P Nicoll.

HOW TO APPLY This trust does not accept unsolicited applications.

WHO TO APPLY TO The Trustees, c/o 89 New Bond Street, London W1S 1DA

CC NO 1077057   **ESTABLISHED** 1999

....

■ Swan Mountain Trust

WHERE FUNDING CAN BE GIVEN UK.

WHO CAN BENEFIT Organisations benefiting mental health patients and prisoners, ex-offenders and potential offenders.

WHAT IS FUNDED Projects and activities.

WHAT IS NOT FUNDED No grants for annual holidays, debt repayment, large appeals or for causes outside the trust's two main areas of work.

TYPE OF GRANT One-off.

RANGE OF GRANTS £250–£1,500.

SAMPLE GRANTS AVID – Association of Visitors to Immigrant Detainees (£2,000); Sheffield Mind (£1,600); Prision Advice and Care Trust – London (£1,500); HMP Morton Hall (£1,200); Community Action Halfway Home (£1,000); Foundation for the Arts and Mental Health (£940); Lifecraft – Cambridge and Corner House Resource Centre (£750 each); and Wigan and

Leigh CVS – Freebirds Mental Health Group (£450).

FINANCES *Year* 2007–08 *Income* £105,881 *Grants* £31,630 *Assets* £994,192

TRUSTEES Dodie Carter; Janet Hargreaves; Peter Kilgarriff; Calton Younger.

HOW TO APPLY In writing to the correspondent, enclosing an up-to-date report on your fundraising, and a copy of your most recent annual report and accounts (or any financial information you have). The trustees meet in February, June and October each year, but can occasionally reach decisions quickly in an emergency. Applications should be made at least four weeks before the trustees' next meeting. The trust tries to be as responsive as it can be to appropriate applicants.

WHO TO APPLY TO Janet Hargreaves, Trustee, 7 Mount Vernon, London NW3 6QS *Tel* 020 7794 2486

CC NO 275594   **ESTABLISHED** 1977

··

■ **The Swan Trust**

WHERE FUNDING CAN BE GIVEN Overseas and the UK, with a preference for East Sussex, Kent, Surrey and West Sussex.

WHO CAN BENEFIT Registered charities.

WHAT IS FUNDED General charitable purposes, including arts, culture and recreation.

WHAT IS NOT FUNDED No grants to individuals or non-registered charities.

TYPE OF GRANT One-off capital grants; funding for up to two years are considered.

RANGE OF GRANTS £20–£11,000.

SAMPLE GRANTS Withyham Parochial Church Council (£11,000); Royal National Theatre (£1,500); Royal Academy Trust (£1,300); Blond McIndoe Centre (£1,000); Bowles (£500); Chichester Cathedral Restoration and Development Trust (£350); Combat Stress (£250); London Philharmonic Orchestra (£120); Southbank Centre (£45); and Friends of Friendless Churches (£20).

FINANCES *Year* 2007–08 *Income* £26,672 *Grants* £30,467 *Assets* £1,113,386

TRUSTEES The Cowdray Trust Limited.

OTHER INFORMATION Applications for grants will only be acknowledged if a donation is to be sent.

HOW TO APPLY In writing to the correspondent. Acknowledgements will only be sent if a grant is being made.

WHO TO APPLY TO Laura Gosling, Pollen House, 10–12 Cork Street, London W1S 3LW *Tel* 020 7439 9061 *email* charity@mfs.co.uk

CC NO 261442   **ESTABLISHED** 1970

··

■ **Swansea and Brecon Diocesan Board of Finance Limited**

WHERE FUNDING CAN BE GIVEN Diocese of Swansea and Brecon (Neath Port Talbot, Powys and Swansea).

WHO CAN BENEFIT Clergy and organisations.

WHAT IS FUNDED The majority portion of the board's expenditure is on clergy stipends, emoluments and housing, with the balance being spent on Diocesan activities, grants and administration.

WHAT IS NOT FUNDED 'Applications from organisations outside the diocese will not be considered.'

FINANCES *Year* 2008 *Income* £3,267,667 *Grants* £177,000

TRUSTEES Archdeacon Randolf Thomas; Gwyn Lewis; Rt Rev. John Davies; Ven. Robert Williams; Clive Rees; Revd Canon Peter Williams; Mrs Gillian

Knight; David Davies; Nicolas Paravicini; John Lloyd.

HOW TO APPLY The charity does not respond to unsolicited applications.

WHO TO APPLY TO Mrs Heather Price, Diocesan Centre, Cathedral Close, Brecon, Powys LD3 9DP *Tel* 01874 623 716 *email* heatherprice@churchinwales.org.uk *Website* www.churchinwales.org.uk/swanbrec

CC NO 249810   **ESTABLISHED** 1968

··

■ **The John Swire (1989) Charitable Trust**

WHERE FUNDING CAN BE GIVEN UK.

WHO CAN BENEFIT Charitable organisations.

WHAT IS FUNDED General charitable purposes, especially arts, welfare, education, medicine and research.

RANGE OF GRANTS £1,000–£80,000.

SAMPLE GRANTS Canterbury Cathedral Developments Ltd (£80,000); Rod Kesson Benefit Fund (£50,000); The Sir John Swire St Nicholas School and Educational Trust (£30,000); DISCS (£15,000); St John of Jerusalem Eye Hospital (£12,000); Inge Wakehurst Trust (£11,000); and Demelza – Hospice Care for Children and Prior's Court Foundation (£10,000 each); Bird Atlas (£5,000); Action for ME (£4,000); Edenbridge Hospital (£3,000); Order of St John of Kent (£2,000); and Atlantic Salmon Trust, Downs Syndrome Association, Irish Guards Benevolent Fund, National Back Pain Association, Royal Association for Deaf and Dumb and Sustrans – National Cycle Network (£1,000 each).

FINANCES *Year* 2007 *Income* £721,007 *Grants* £425,136 *Assets* £13,957,610

TRUSTEES Sir John Swire; J S Swire; B N Swire; M C Robinson; Lady Swire.

HOW TO APPLY In writing to the correspondent.

WHO TO APPLY TO Michael Todhunter, Charities Administrator, John Swire and Sons Ltd, Swire House, 59 Buckingham Gate, London SW1E 6AJ *Tel* 020 7834 7717

CC NO 802142   **ESTABLISHED** 1989

··

■ **The Swire Charitable Trust**

WHERE FUNDING CAN BE GIVEN UK.

WHO CAN BENEFIT Regional and UK organisations.

WHAT IS FUNDED Children, the arts and heritage, medical research, welfare, the environment and general charitable purposes.

SAMPLE GRANTS Marine Society & Sea Cadets and Wantage Nursing Home Charitable Trust (£50,000 each); Neck & Head Cancer Research Trust (£25,000); Air League Educational Trust (£23,000); and Children in Crisis and Prior's Court Foundation (£20,000 each); Breast Cancer Haven (£15,000); Head First (£10,00); Brooklands Museum Trust Limited (£5,000); Chelsea & Westminster Health Charity (£3,000); Warwickshire Firefighters Families Fund (£2,000); and The Cardinal Hume Centre (£1,000).

FINANCES *Year* 2007 *Income* £478,903 *Grants* £476,950 *Assets* £66,640

TRUSTEES Sir J Swire; Sir Adrian Swire; B N Swire; M J B Todhunter; P A Johansen; J S Swine.

HOW TO APPLY In writing to the correspondent. Applications are considered throughout the year.

WHO TO APPLY TO Michael Todhunter, Charities Administrator, John Swire and Sons Ltd, Swire

Think carefully about every application. Is it justified?

891

House, 59 Buckingham Gate, London
SW1E 6AJ *Tel* 020 7834 7717
cc no 270726   **established** 1976

....

■ The Hugh and Ruby Sykes Charitable Trust

where funding can be given Principally South Yorkshire, also Derbyshire.

who can benefit Registered charities.

what is funded Principally local charities but some major UK charities are supported. The trust has major commitments with several medical charities. It is the policy of the trust to distribute income and preserve capital.

what is not funded No grants are made to individuals. Most grants are made to organisations which have a connection to one of the trustees.

finances *Year* 2007–08 *Income* £136,469 *Grants* £103,975 *Assets* £2,278,535

trustees Sir Hugh Sykes; Lady Ruby Sykes.

other information A list of beneficiaries was not included in the accounts.

how to apply Applications can only be accepted from registered charities and should be in writing to the correspondent. In order to save administration costs, replies are not sent to unsuccessful applicants. If the trustees are able to consider a request for support, they aim to express interest within one month.

who to apply to Brian Evans, Administrator, The Coach House, Brookfield Manor, Hathersage, Hope Valley, Derbyshire S32 1BR *Tel* 01433 651190 *email* info@brookfieldmanor.com

cc no 327648   **established** 1987

....

■ The Charles and Elsie Sykes Trust

where funding can be given In practice, anywhere in the UK with a preference for Yorkshire.

who can benefit Registered charities only.

what is funded Animals and birds; people who are blind or partially sighted; children and young people; cultural and environmental heritage; people who are deaf, hard of hearing or speech impaired; people with disabilities; education; hospices and hospitals; medical research; medical welfare; mental health and mental disability; welfare of older people; overseas aid; services and ex-services; social and moral welfare; trades and professions; and sundry.

what is not funded Unregistered and overseas charities are not considered. Individuals, local organisations not in the north of England, and recently-established charities are unlikely to be successful.

type of grant One off and recurring.

range of grants £500–£25,000.

sample grants Cancer Research UK (£26,000); Harrogate & District NHS Foundation Trust (£13,000); Royal Northern College of Music (£10,000); Scargill House (£7,000); and British Heart Foundation, Bowel Disease Research Foundation, Swaledale Festival, Richmond YMCA – Yorkshire and the Lighthouse Group (£5,000 each).

finances *Year* 2007 *Income* £805,941 *Grants* £404,000 *Assets* £12,931,680

trustees John Ward, Chair; Mrs Anne E Brownlie; Martin P Coultas; Michael G H Garnett; R Barry Kay; Dr Michael D Moore; Dr Michael W McEvoy; Peter G Rous.

how to apply Only applications from registered charities are considered, with a preference for those in, or benefiting people in, Yorkshire. Application forms can be requested from the trust or downloaded from the trust's website. The form should then be sent to the trust along with a copy of the organisation's latest accounts, annual report and any other relevant information. It is more favourable for the application if the accounts are current. If a grant is required for a particular project, full details and costings should be provided. Applications from schools, playgroups, cadet forces, scouts, guides, and churches must be for outreach programmes, and not for maintenance projects. Successful applications will receive a donation which may or may not be subject to conditions.

who to apply to Mrs Judith M Long, Secretary, 6 North Park Road, Harrogate, Yorkshire HG1 5PA *Tel* 01423 817238 *Fax* 01423 851112 *Website* www.charlesandelsiesykestrust.co.uk

cc no 206926   **established** 1954

....

■ The Sylvanus Charitable Trust

where funding can be given Europe and North America.

who can benefit Organisations benefiting Roman Catholics and animals.

what is funded The traditional Catholic Church and animal welfare, including wildlife sanctuaries.

what is not funded No grants for expeditions, scholarships or individuals.

type of grant One-off and recurring.

range of grants £1,000–£5,000.

sample grants Mauritian Wildlife Foundation and Save the Elephants (£5,000 each); Durrell Wildlife Conservation Trust and Fauna & Flora International (£2,000 each); Mayhew Animal Home and Prevent Unwanted Pets (£1,500 each); and Blue Cross, Help in Suffering, Newcastle Dog and Cat Shelter and Society for Abandoned Animals (£1,000 each).

finances *Year* 2007 *Income* £75,317 *Grants* £32,500 *Assets* £1,676,666

trustees John C Vernor Miles; Alexander D Gemmill; Wilfred E Vernor Miles; Gloria Taviner.

other information This trust has a sterling section for European grants and a dollar section for USA grants. The financial information in this entry relates to the Sterling section. In the dollar section grants totalled $70,500 (US).

how to apply In writing to the correspondent. The trustees meet once a year.

who to apply to John C Vernor Miles, Trustee, Vernor Miles and Noble, 5 Raymond Buildings, Gray's Inn, London WC1R 5DD *Tel* 020 7242 8688

cc no 259520   **established** 1968

....

■ The Stella Symons Charitable Trust

where funding can be given UK.

who can benefit Registered charities.

what is funded Residential facilities and services; infrastructure, support and development; the advancement of religion; arts, culture and recreation; health; conservation and environment; education and training; and social care and development will be considered.

what is not funded The trustees do not normally favour projects which provide a substitute for the statutory obligations of the state or projects which in their opinion should be commercially viable operations. No grants to individuals or to politically biased organisations.

TYPE OF GRANT Outright gifts and larger sums on loan on beneficial terms. Buildings, capital, core costs, one-off, project, research, recurring and running costs, salaries, and start-up costs. Funding for up to and over three years will be considered.

RANGE OF GRANTS Most grants were for £250.

SAMPLE GRANTS British Consultancy Charitable Trust, Combat Stress Ex-Services Mental Welfare Society, Dreams Come True, The John Fawcett Foundation UK, The Institute for Cancer Research, International Childcare Trust, National Playing Fields Association, Princess Royal Trust, and Tiny Tim's Children's Centre, YMCA (£250 each); Cuba Night, The Eve Appeal, Gurkha Welfare Trust and Shipston League of Hospital Friends (£200 each); and Barnardo's (£100).

FINANCES *Year* 2007–08 *Income* £64,036 *Grants* £32,600 *Assets* £1,401,579

TRUSTEES Jonathan S S Bosley; Mrs Mervyne E Mitchell; Mrs Katherine A Willis.

HOW TO APPLY In writing to the correspondent.

WHO TO APPLY TO Jonathan S S Bosley, 20 Mill Street, Shipston-on-Stour, Warwickshire CV36 4AW

CC NO 259638   **ESTABLISHED** 1968

■ T and S Trust Fund

WHERE FUNDING CAN BE GIVEN UK.

WHO CAN BENEFIT Jewish organisations and the Jewish community.

WHAT IS FUNDED 'The advancement of education according to the tenets of the Orthodox Jewish Faith, the advancement of the Orthodox Jewish Religion and the relief of poverty amongst the elderly or persons in need, hardship and distress in the Jewish Community.'

TYPE OF GRANT One-off and recurrent.

SAMPLE GRANTS Stervon Ltd and Tomchei Yotzei Anglia (£23,000 each); VHLT (£16,000); Y Y Gemach (£2,000); Bnos Yisroel School (£1,500); Gateshead Hebrew Congregation, Manchester Talmudical College and Sameach (£1,000 each).

FINANCES *Year* 2007–08 *Income* £43,224 *Grants* £92,380 *Assets* £621,911

TRUSTEES A T Sandler; Mrs S Sandler; E Salomon.

OTHER INFORMATION In addition to the listed beneficiaries there were 'relief of poverty grants' (£15,000) and 'educational grants' (£5,600). Donations of under £1,000 each totalled £3,350.

HOW TO APPLY In writing to the correspondent.

WHO TO APPLY TO A Sandier, Trustee, 96 Whitehall Road, Gateshead, Tyne And Wear NE8 4ET *Tel* 0191 482 5050

CC NO 1095939   **ESTABLISHED** 2002

■ The Tabeel Trust

WHERE FUNDING CAN BE GIVEN Worldwide with a preference for Clacton.

WHO CAN BENEFIT Evangelical Christian organisations.

WHAT IS FUNDED Christian charitable purposes, where the trustees have an existing interest.

RANGE OF GRANTS Up to £30,000.

SAMPLE GRANTS St George's Crypt – Leeds (£30,000); Essex County Evangelists' – Accommodation Trust (£10,000); ZACS (£6,000); Radio Worldwide (£5,000); Barnabas Fund (£4,000); Viz a Viz (£3,000); Tabernacle Baptist Church – Penarth (£2,000); Christian Institute (£1,000); and Upesi (£500).

FINANCES *Year* 2007–08 *Income* £46,399 *Grants* £112,700 *Assets* £870,347

TRUSTEES Douglas K Brown; Pauline M Brown; Barbara J Carter; Dr Mary P Clark; Jean A Richardson; James Davey; Sarah Taylor; Nigel Davey.

HOW TO APPLY Only charities with which a trustee already has contact should apply. Grants are considered at trustees' meetings in May and November.

WHO TO APPLY TO Douglas K Brown, Secretary, Dairy House Farm, Little Clacton Road, Great Holland, Frinton-on-Sea, Essex CO13 0EX *Tel* 01255 812130

CC NO 266645   **ESTABLISHED** 1974

■ Tadlus Limited

WHERE FUNDING CAN BE GIVEN UK and Israel.

WHO CAN BENEFIT Institutions, organisations and individuals involved in the orthodox Jewish faith.

WHAT IS FUNDED The promotion of religious education and worship.

TYPE OF GRANT One off and recurrent.

FINANCES *Year* 2007–08 *Income* £76,050 *Grants* £0 *Assets* £1,017,957

TRUSTEES J M Grosskopf; M Grosskopf; C S Grosskopf.

OTHER INFORMATION No grants were made during the year, for which no explanation was given in the accounts.

HOW TO APPLY In writing to the correspondent.

WHO TO APPLY TO J Grosskopf, 6 Spring Hill, London E5 9BE

CC NO 1109982   **ESTABLISHED** 2005

■ The Tajtelbaum Charitable Trust

WHERE FUNDING CAN BE GIVEN Mainly UK and Israel.

WHO CAN BENEFIT Jewish organisations benefiting children, young adults and students will be considered. Support may be given to older and sick people.

WHAT IS FUNDED Orthodox synagogues, education establishments, hospitals and homes for older people.

RANGE OF GRANTS £500–£150,000.

SAMPLE GRANTS Previous beneficiaries include: United Institutions Arad, Emuno Educational Centre, Ruzin Sadiger Trust, Gur Foundation, Before Trust, Beth Hassidei Gur, Comet Charities Limited, Delharville, Kupat Gemach Trust, Centre for Torah and Chesed, Friends of Nachlat David and Friends of Sanz Institute.

FINANCES *Year* 2007–08 *Income* £691,760 *Grants* £759,201 *Assets* £3,745,146

TRUSTEES Ilsa Tajtelbaum; Jacob Tajtelbaum; Emanuel Tajtelbaum.

HOW TO APPLY In writing to the correspondent.

WHO TO APPLY TO Ilsa Tajtelbaum, 17 Western Avenue, London NW11 9HE *Tel* 020 8202 3464

CC NO 273184   **ESTABLISHED** 1974

■ The Gay and Keith Talbot Trust

WHERE FUNDING CAN BE GIVEN Worldwide.

WHO CAN BENEFIT Charities working in developing countries.

WHAT IS FUNDED General charitable purposes including research and development of Cystic Fibrosis, Fistula work and overseas aid.

TYPE OF GRANT One off and recurring. Capital costs, revenue costs and full project funding.

SAMPLE GRANTS Medical Missionaries of Mary – Uganda and Nigeria (£12,000); Cystic Fibrosis Trust (£10,000); SVP – Sudan, Impact Foundation – Bangladesh and Uganda Childbirth Injury Fund (£5,000 each); Rwanda Group Trust (£1,500); CAFOD – Sudan and Door of Hope (£1,000 each); and Our Lady of Windermere and St Herbert (£500).

FINANCES *Year* 2007–08 *Income* £147,560 *Grants* £41,000 *Assets* £131,422

TRUSTEES Gay Talbot; Keith Talbot.

HOW TO APPLY In writing to the correspondent.

WHO TO APPLY TO Keith Talbot, Fold Howe, Kentmere, Kendal, Cumbria LA8 9JW

CC NO 1102192   **ESTABLISHED** 2004

■ The Talbot Trusts

WHERE FUNDING CAN BE GIVEN Sheffield and immediate surrounding areas.

WHO CAN BENEFIT Organisations directly benefiting people who are sick, convalescent, disabled or infirm.

WHAT IS FUNDED Items, services or facilities which are calculated to relieve suffering or assist recovery.

WHAT IS NOT FUNDED No grants are given towards the direct relief of rates, taxes or other public funds and no commitment can be made to repeat or renew grants. Grants are not normally given to: non-registered charities or other organisations; individuals; appeal requests, research or educational costs; or to finance fundraising initiatives.

TYPE OF GRANT One-off, capital, core costs, running costs, salaries and start-up costs. Funding may be given for up to one year.

SAMPLE GRANTS Sheffield Area Health Authority (£11,000); Sheffield Motability (£4,500); Family Welfare Association, Trinity Day Care Trust and Age Concern Sheffield (£3,000 each); the Brainwave Centre, Care in Crosspool and Transport 17 (£2,000 each); St Luke's Hospice and Listening Books (£1,500 each); Happy Outings (£1,000); and Sheffield Disabled Fishing Group (£500).

FINANCES *Year* 2007–08 *Income* £89,767 *Grants* £89,708 *Assets* £2,020,669

TRUSTEES Dr Brenda P Jackson; Dr Lawrence C Kershaw; Godfrey Smallman; Rev. Can. Paul Shackerley; Ronald Jones; Jo Frisby.

HOW TO APPLY On a form available from the correspondent, for consideration in July and December.

WHO TO APPLY TO Neil Charlesworth, Clerk, 11 Russett Court, Maltby, Rotherham S66 8SP *Tel* 01709 769022

CC NO 221356   **ESTABLISHED** 1928

■ The Talbot Village Trust

WHERE FUNDING CAN BE GIVEN The boroughs of Bournemouth, Christchurch and Poole; the districts of east Dorset and Purbeck.

WHO CAN BENEFIT Community organisations (such as schools, churches, youth clubs, playgroups and so on).

WHAT IS FUNDED Young people, older people and church-related charities.

WHAT IS NOT FUNDED No grants for individuals.

TYPE OF GRANT Grants and loans. Mainly for capital costs.

RANGE OF GRANTS Up to £38,000.

SAMPLE GRANTS Bournemouth War Memorial Homes (£38,000); Butterfly Appeal (£35,000); Kinson Community Centre (£25,000); Lighthouse Family Church (£20,000); Deanery Youth Worker Project (£16,000); International Care Network (£10,000); Purbeck Strings (£6,000); St. Luke's Church Hall (£4,000); Children's Heart Foundation (£2,500); and Embassy Youth Centre (£1,300).

FINANCES *Year* 2008 *Income* £1,850,420 *Grants* £592,965 *Assets* £27,939,671

TRUSTEES Christopher Lees, Chair; James Fleming; Sir George Meyrick; Sir Thomas Salt; Russell Rowe; Earl of Shaftesbury.

HOW TO APPLY In writing to the correspondent.

WHO TO APPLY TO Gary S Cox, Clerk, Dickinson Manser, 5 Parkstone Road, Poole, Dorset BH15 2NL *Tel* 01202 673071 *email* garycox@dickinsonmanser.co.uk

CC NO 249349   **ESTABLISHED** 1867

■ Tallow Chandlers Benevolent Fund

WHERE FUNDING CAN BE GIVEN London, mostly City of London.

WHO CAN BENEFIT Charitable organisations, schools and universities.

WHAT IS FUNDED Medical research, care of people with disabilities and the encouragement of excellence at schools and universities. It also helps City of London-based charities and charities where a liveryman or freeman is actively involved. Youth clubs are particularly supported.

RANGE OF GRANTS Up to £20,000.

SAMPLE GRANTS London Youth (£20,000); Bart's & Royal London School of Medicine (£15,000); Treloar Trust (£10,000); Bridge School (£7,500); Centrepoint (£5,000); Army Benevolent Fund (£3,000); Prince's Youth Business Trust (£2,500); and Coram Family Trust, Family Welfare Association, International Spinal Research and St Luke's Hospice for the Clergy (£1,000 each).

FINANCES *Year* 2007–08 *Income* £437,492 *Grants* £164,877 *Assets* £3,822,579

TRUSTEES C P Tootal; D Kirby Johnson; R A B Nicolle; D R Newnham.

HOW TO APPLY In writing to the correspondent. 'Every request for assistance will be considered first by the clerk and the chairman and then shortlisted for consideration by the education and charity committee.'

WHO TO APPLY TO Brig. R M Wilde, Clerk to the Trustees, Tallow Chandlers Hall, 4 Dowgate Hill, London EC4R 2SH *Tel* 020 7248 4726 *Fax* 020 7236 0844 *email* clerk@tallowchandlers.org *Website* www.tallowchandlers.org

CC NO 246255   **ESTABLISHED** 1966

■ Talteg Ltd

WHERE FUNDING CAN BE GIVEN UK, with a preference for Scotland.

WHO CAN BENEFIT Registered charities benefiting Jewish people, children, young adults and people disadvantaged by poverty.

WHAT IS FUNDED To support the advancement of religion, especially Jewish, and the relief of poverty. Educational and other charitable purposes are also supported.

SAMPLE GRANTS Previous beneficiaries: British Friends of Laniado Hospital, Centre for Jewish Studies, Society of Friends of the Torah, Glasgow Jewish Community Trust, National Trust for Scotland, Friends of Hebrew University of Jerusalem, Ayrshire Hospice, Earl Haig Fund – Scotland, RSSPCC.

FINANCES *Year* 2008 *Income* £511,877 *Grants* £361,110 *Assets* £3,426,164

TRUSTEES F S Berkeley, Chair; M Berkeley; A N Berkeley; M Berkeley; Miss D L Berkeley.

HOW TO APPLY In writing to the correspondent.

WHO TO APPLY TO F S Berkeley, Trustee, 90 Mitchell Street, Glasgow G1 3NQ *Tel* 0141 221 3353

CC NO 283253   **ESTABLISHED** 1981

■ The Tangent Charitable Trust

WHERE FUNDING CAN BE GIVEN UK.

WHO CAN BENEFIT Registered charities and voluntary organisations.

WHAT IS FUNDED General charitable purposes.

SAMPLE GRANTS Previous beneficiaries included Westminster Synagogue, Imperial College,

Think carefully about every application. Is it justified?

895

London, Central Synagogue General Charities Fund and Community Security Trust, Institute for Jewish Policy Research and Maccabi G B, Eastern Grey Parochial Church Council and Adelburgh Productions.

FINANCES *Year* 2007–08 *Income* £3,151 *Grants* £50,000

TRUSTEES Information was obtained from the Charity Commission.

HOW TO APPLY In writing to the correspondent.

WHO TO APPLY TO Beverley Matthews, 21 South Street, London W1 2XB *Tel* 020 7663 6402

CC NO 289729   **ESTABLISHED** 1984

■ The Lady Tangye Charitable Trust

WHERE FUNDING CAN BE GIVEN UK and worldwide, with some preference for the Midlands.

WHO CAN BENEFIT Charitable organisations, with a preference for work in the Midlands or developing world.

WHAT IS FUNDED General charitable purposes, with Christian and environmental causes are well-represented in the grants list.

SAMPLE GRANTS West Midland Urban Wildlife Trust (£3,000); Spana, Childline – Midlands and Aid to the Church in Need (£2,000 each); Amnesty International, Priest Training Fund and Crew Trust (£1,500 each); St Saviours Church, Walsall and District Samaritans, Life and European Childrens Trust (£1,000 each); and Charity Ignite – Big Ideal (£500).

FINANCES *Year* 2007–08 *Income* £29,907 *Grants* £28,500 *Assets* £583,475

TRUSTEES Gitta Clarisse Gilzean Tangye; Colin Ferguson Smith.

HOW TO APPLY In writing to the correspondent.

WHO TO APPLY TO Colin Ferguson Smith, Trustee, 55 Warwick Crest, Arthur Road, Birmingham B15 2LH

CC NO 1044220   **ESTABLISHED** 1995

■ The David Tannen Charitable Trust

WHERE FUNDING CAN BE GIVEN UK.

WHO CAN BENEFIT Jewish organisations.

WHAT IS FUNDED Advancement of the Jewish religion.

RANGE OF GRANTS About £1,000–£100,000.

SAMPLE GRANTS Previous beneficiaries include: Cosmon Beiz Academy, Gevurath Ari Trust, Telz Academy Trust, Friends of Ohr Elchonon, Beis Ahron Trust, Wlodowa Charity, Chai Cancer Care, Kollel Skver Trust, Centre for Torah Trust, Gateshead Talmudical College, Jewish Women's Aid Trust, Torah 5759 Ltd and YTAF.

FINANCES *Year* 2007–08 *Income* £2,799,158 *Grants* £645,374 *Assets* £25,155,788

TRUSTEES Jonathon Miller; Alan Rose; David Tannen.

HOW TO APPLY In writing to the correspondent.

WHO TO APPLY TO Jonathon Miller, Sutherland House, 70–78 West Hendon Broadway, London NW9 7BT *Tel* 020 8202 1066

CC NO 280392   **ESTABLISHED** 1974

■ The Tanner Trust

WHERE FUNDING CAN BE GIVEN UK, with a slight preference for the south of England, and overseas.

WHO CAN BENEFIT Foundations, schools, societies, charities and projects.

WHAT IS FUNDED General charitable purposes.

WHAT IS NOT FUNDED No grants to individuals.

RANGE OF GRANTS £300–£5,000; exceptionally higher.

SAMPLE GRANTS Help for Heroes (£7,000); Foresta 2000 – Din L-Art Helwa and National Trust (£6,000 each); Yorkshire Dales Millenium Trust and Truro Cathedral Music (£5,000 each); Holton Lee (£4,500); Practical Action (£4,000); Homeopaths without Borders (£3,000); Cooltan Arts (£2,800); Book Power (£2,000); and Elliot Foundation (£500).

FINANCES *Year* 2007–08 *Income* £430,695 *Grants* £381,984 *Assets* £5,227,711

TRUSTEES Alice P Williams; Lucie Nottingham.

HOW TO APPLY The trust states that unsolicited applications are, without exception, not considered. Support is only given to charities personally known to the trustees.

WHO TO APPLY TO Celine Lecomte, Trust Administrator, c/o Blake Lapthorn Tarlo Lyons, Harbour Court, Compass Road, Portsmouth PO6 4ST *Tel* 023 9222 1122 *Fax* 023 9222 1123

CC NO 1021175   **ESTABLISHED** 1993

■ The Lili Tapper Charitable Foundation

WHERE FUNDING CAN BE GIVEN UK.

WHO CAN BENEFIT Organisations benefiting Jewish people.

WHAT IS FUNDED Preference to charitable purposes or institutions which are for the benefit of Jewish people.

WHAT IS NOT FUNDED No grants to individuals.

SAMPLE GRANTS Previous beneficiaries include: UJIA, CST, Manchester Jewish Foundation, Teenage Cancer Trust, Keshet Eilon, Israel Educational Foundation, Chicken Shed Theatre Company and Jewish Representation Council.

FINANCES *Year* 2007–08 *Income* £156,306 *Grants* £38,700 *Assets* £2,914,870

TRUSTEES Michael Webber; Dr Jonathan Webber.

OTHER INFORMATION No details of grant beneficiaries were available.

HOW TO APPLY The trust states that it does not respond to any unsolicited applications.

WHO TO APPLY TO Michael Webber, Yew Tree Cottage, Artists Lane, Nether Alderley, Macclesfield SK10 4UA

CC NO 268523   **ESTABLISHED** 1974

■ The Mrs A Lacy Tate Trust

WHERE FUNDING CAN BE GIVEN East Sussex.

WHO CAN BENEFIT Individuals and organisations benefiting at risk groups and people who are disabled, disadvantaged by poverty or socially isolated.

WHAT IS FUNDED Welfare, disability and medical charities.

TYPE OF GRANT Often recurrent.

RANGE OF GRANTS £250–£5,000.

SAMPLE GRANTS Queen Alexandra Cottage Homes (£5,000); Surviving Christmas and Sedlescombe Pavilion Fund (£2,000 each); South Downs Community Special School (£800); Brighton Women's Centre, Sussex Air Ambulance, Disability Aid Fund and Farley Bank Estate Action (£500 each); Eastbourne Lions Club and Carousel (£250 each); and Extratime (£100).

FINANCES *Year* 2007–08 *Grants* £42,113

TRUSTEES Linda A Bursess; Lesley A Macey; Ian M A Stewart; June M Roberts.

OTHER INFORMATION Grants to 138 individuals totalled £18,000.

HOW TO APPLY In writing to the correspondent.

WHO TO APPLY TO Ian M A Stewart, Heringtons Solicitors, 39 Gildredge Road, Eastbourne, East Sussex BN21 4RY *Tel* 01323 411020 *Fax* 01323 411040

CC NO 803596 **ESTABLISHED** 1990

....

■ The Tay Charitable Trust

WHERE FUNDING CAN BE GIVEN UK, with a preference for Scotland, particularly Dundee.

WHO CAN BENEFIT Registered charities.

WHAT IS FUNDED General charitable purposes.

WHAT IS NOT FUNDED Grants are only given to charities recognised by the Inland Revenue. No grants to individuals.

TYPE OF GRANT One-off and recurring.

RANGE OF GRANTS £250–£5,000.

SAMPLE GRANTS Dundee Heritage Trust and RNLI (£5,000 each); Boarders Forest Trust, DermaTrust, Edinburgh World Heritage Trust, Maritime Volunteer Service and Univeristy of St Andrews – Low Scholarship (£3,000 each); Bowel Cancer UK, High Blood Pressure Foundation, John Muir Trust and National Trust for Scotland (£2,000 each); Princess Royal Trust for Carers (£1,500); and Army Benevolent Fund, Changing Faces, Dundee Symphony Orchestra, Guide Dogs for the Blind, Lincoln Cathedral, Samaritans, Scottish Countryside Alliance Trust, Skillforce Development and Tayside Council on Alcohol (£1,000 each).

FINANCES *Year* 2008–09 *Income* £231,421 *Grants* £215,350 *Assets* £4,148,506

TRUSTEES Mrs E A Mussen; Mrs Z C Martin; G C Bonar.

HOW TO APPLY No standard form; applications in writing to the correspondent, including a financial statement. An sae is appreciated.

WHO TO APPLY TO Mrs E A Mussen, Trustee, 6 Douglas Terrace, Broughty Ferry, Dundee DD5 1EA

SC NO SC001004 **ESTABLISHED** 1951

....

■ C B and H H Taylor 1984 Trust

WHERE FUNDING CAN BE GIVEN West Midlands, Ireland and overseas.

WHO CAN BENEFIT Approximately 60% of funds available are currently given to the work and concerns of the Religious Society of Friends. The remaining funds are allocated to those charities in which the trustees have a special interest, particularly in the West Midlands. Applications are encouraged from minority groups and woman-led initiatives.

WHAT IS FUNDED The general areas of benefit are: (i) The Religious Society of Friends (Quakers) and other religious denominations. (ii) Healthcare projects. (iii) Social welfare: community groups; children and young people; older people; disadvantaged people; people with disabilities; homeless people; housing initiatives; counselling and mediation agencies. (iv) Education: adult literacy schemes; employment training; youth work. (v) Penal affairs: work with offenders and ex-offenders; police projects. (vi) The environment and conservation work. (vii) The arts: museums and art galleries; music and drama. (viii) Ireland: cross-community health and social welfare projects. (ix) UK charities working overseas on long-term development projects.

WHAT IS NOT FUNDED The trust does not fund: individuals (whether for research, expeditions, educational purposes and so on); local projects or groups outside the West Midlands; or projects concerned with travel or adventure.

TYPE OF GRANT Regular annual donations and some single donations to special appeals.

RANGE OF GRANTS £500–£5,000. Larger grants are seldom awarded.

SAMPLE GRANTS Britain Yearly Meeting (£27,000); Bournville Almshouses (£25,000); Warwickshire Monthly Meeting (£9,500); Friends of Swanirvar (£6,000); Tiny Tim's Children's Centre (£5,000); Fry Housing Trust (£4,000); Community Initiative Programme (£3,000); Medical Aid for Palestinians (£1,500); Bees Abroad (£1,000); Christ's Church Selly Park (£850); Circul-8 Credit Union (£200); and Dudley Association of Community Networks (£100).

FINANCES *Year* 2007–08 *Income* £260,272 *Grants* £260,500 *Assets* £7,590,136

TRUSTEES Clare H Norton; Elizabeth J Birmingham; John A B Taylor; William James Taylor; Constance M Penny; Thomas W Penny; Robert J Birmingham; Simon B Taylor.

HOW TO APPLY There is no formal application form. Applicants should write to the correspondent giving the charity's registration number, a brief description of the charity's activities, and details of the specific project for which the grant is being sought. Applicants should also include a budget of the proposed work, together with a copy of the charity's most recent accounts. Trustees will also wish to know what funds have already been raised for the project and how the shortfall will be met. The trust states that it receives more applications than it can support. Therefore, even if work falls within its policy it may not be able to help, particularly if the project is outside the West Midlands. Trustees meet twice each year, in May and November. Applications will be acknowledged if a sae is provided.

WHO TO APPLY TO William James Taylor, Trustee, c/o Home Farm, Abberton, Pershore, Worcestershire WR10 2NR

CC NO 291363 **ESTABLISHED** 1946

....

■ Humphrey Richardson Taylor Charitable Trust

WHERE FUNDING CAN BE GIVEN Surrey and South London Boroughs.

WHO CAN BENEFIT Schools, choirs, amateur orchestras and individuals.

WHAT IS FUNDED Tuition fees, purchasing of instruments, music building-projects and grants to musical societies.

WHAT IS NOT FUNDED Projects or causes that are not associated with music.

RANGE OF GRANTS £250–£22,000.

SAMPLE GRANTS Sutton Youth Music Service (£22,000); Warden Park (£20,000); Royal College of Music (£19,000); Lenthorne School (£17,000); Glenthorne High School (£12,000); Southbank Sinfonia (£7,000); Royal Russet School (£5,000); Banstead Arts Festival, Croydon Symphony Orchestra and Epsom Light Opera (£3,000 each); Wimbledon Chamber Choir (£2,000); Dorking Lunchtime Concerts (Melisma) (£1,500); and Woking Musical Theatre (£250).

FINANCES *Year* 2008 *Income* £244,092 *Grants* £201,783 *Assets* £6,329,061

TRUSTEES W J F Malings; M J Palmer; J B Sharp; Mrs R M Cox; R K Bryce.

OTHER INFORMATION Grants were made to individuals totalling £9,750.

HOW TO APPLY In writing to the correspondent.

WHO TO APPLY TO The Administrator, c/o Messrs Palmers, 28 Chipstead Station Parade, Chipstead, Coulsdon, Surrey CR5 3TF *Tel* 01737 557 546 *email* administrator@ hrtaylortrust.co.uk

CC NO 1062836   ESTABLISHED 1997

■ The A R Taylor Charitable Trust

WHERE FUNDING CAN BE GIVEN UK, but with some emphasis on Hampshire.

WHO CAN BENEFIT Registered charities.

WHAT IS FUNDED General charitable purposes, there is a preference for charities with which the trustees have special interest in, knowledge of or association with, particularly ex-service charities, independent schools, social welfare charities, churches and hospices.

WHAT IS NOT FUNDED No grants to individuals.

TYPE OF GRANT Both one-off and recurrent grants. There is no formal limit to the length of time for recurrent grants.

SAMPLE GRANTS Previous beneficiaries have included: British Red Cross – S E Asia Disaster Fund, Ex-Services Mental Welfare Society, Winchester College, Regimental HQ 1st Grenadier Regimental Foot Guards' Charity and the Lawrence Barham Memorial Trust.

FINANCES *Year* 2007–08 *Income* £35,997 *Grants* £24,975

TRUSTEES A R Taylor; Mrs E J Taylor.

HOW TO APPLY Applications may be made at any time but will only be considered periodically. The trust does not use an application form. Unsuccessful applications will generally not be acknowledged.

WHO TO APPLY TO The Trustees, c/o Birketts Solicitors, 24–26 Museum Street, Ipswich IP1 1HZ

CC NO 275560   ESTABLISHED 1978

■ The Connie and Albert Taylor Charitable Trust

WHERE FUNDING CAN BE GIVEN West Midlands.

WHO CAN BENEFIT Organisations concerned with medical research, hospices, education and recreation, and preservation.

WHAT IS FUNDED The trust was established by the will of Mrs Constance Iris Taylor in 1998 for the benefit of the West Midlands with the following object: research into the cure and causes of cancer, blindness and heart disease provision and maintenance of nursing homes for older people and people who are unable to look after themselves provision of maintenance of hospices for people with terminal illnesses facilities for the education and recreation of children and young people the preservation, protection and improvements of any amenity or land of beauty, scientific or of horticultural interest and any building of historical, architectural or artistic or scientific interest.

SAMPLE GRANTS Birmingham Children's Hospital – Burns Centre, Katherine House Hospice – Stafford and National Star College – Cheltenham (£50,000 each); the Donna Louise Trust (£30,000); St Giles Hospice – Litchfield and Well Being of Women – ovarian cancer research (£25,000 each); KING Edward VI School – Litchfield (£15,000); the Albrighton Trust, Birmingham Institute for the Deaf,

Foundation for Conductive Education and Sense (£5,000 each); and RSPB (£1,000).

FINANCES *Year* 2007 *Income* £257,268 *Grants* £360,500 *Assets* £5,849,783

TRUSTEES Alan Foster; Harry Grundy; Richard D Long.

HOW TO APPLY In writing to the correspondent. The trust may visit applicants/beneficiaries.

WHO TO APPLY TO Harry Grundy, Trustee, The Farmhouse, Darwin Park, Abnalls Lane, Lichfield, Staffordshire WS13 8BJ *email* applications@ taylortrust.co.uk *Website* www.taylortrust.co.uk

CC NO 1074785   ESTABLISHED 1998

■ The Cyril Taylor Charitable Trust

WHERE FUNDING CAN BE GIVEN Generally in Greater London.

WHO CAN BENEFIT Organisations benefiting students.

WHAT IS FUNDED General charitable purposes; to advance the education of the students of Richmond College and the American International University in London.

RANGE OF GRANTS Usually between £500–£3,000.

SAMPLE GRANTS Richmond Foundation (£25,000); Institute of Economic Affairs and the British Friends of Harvard Business School (£3,000 each); and Trinity Hall, Cambridge (£1,000).

FINANCES *Year* 2007–08 *Income* £64,103 *Grants* £32,000 *Assets* £39,212

TRUSTEES Sir Cyril Taylor, Chair; Clifford D Joseph; Robert W Maas; Peter A Tchereprine; Stephen Rasch; Christopher Lintott; Lady June Taylor; Jonathan Berry; William Gertz; Marcie Schneider.

HOW TO APPLY In writing to the correspondent.

WHO TO APPLY TO Christopher Lintott, Trustee, Penningtons, Abacus House, 33 Gutter Lane, London EC2V 8AR *Tel* 020 7457 3000 *Fax* 020 7457 3240 *email* chris.lintott@ penningtons.co.uk

CC NO 1040179   ESTABLISHED 1994

■ The Taylor Family Foundation

WHERE FUNDING CAN BE GIVEN UK and overseas, with a preference for London and the south east.

WHO CAN BENEFIT Children and young people. 'The objectives of the Taylor Family Foundation are to help and support children and young people, particularly those from disadvantaged backgrounds, in the areas of education, health, recreation and the performing arts.'

WHAT IS FUNDED Registered charities and statutory bodies.

WHAT IS NOT FUNDED No grants to individuals.

SAMPLE GRANTS Beatbullying and Volunteer Reading Help (£50,000 each); Central School of Ballet (£30,000); Jigsaw4u and NSPCC (£25,000 each); Wimbledon Civic Theatre (£20,000); Lucy Faithful Foundation, Prison Radio Foundation and World Land Trust – Venezuela (£15,000 each); Prostate Cancer Research Centre (£10,000); St. Raphael's Hospice (£5,000); and the Princess Royal Trust for Carers (£500).

FINANCES *Year* 2007–08 *Income* £1,319,655 *Grants* £497,000 *Assets* £776,544

TRUSTEES Ian R Taylor; Cristina A Taylor; Neville P Shepherd.

HOW TO APPLY In writing to the correspondent.

WHO TO APPLY TO Neville Shepherd, Trustee, 55a High Street, Wimbledon, London SW19 5BA *Tel* 020 8605 2629 *email* cathy@ thetaylorfamilyfoundation.co.uk *Website* www. thetaylorfamilyfoundation.co.uk

CC NO 1118032   ESTABLISHED 2007

■ A P Taylor Trust

WHERE FUNDING CAN BE GIVEN The parishes of Hayes and Harlington (as they existed on 9 January 1953).

WHO CAN BENEFIT Charitable organisations.

WHAT IS FUNDED The provision of recreational and leisure activities.

RANGE OF GRANTS The majority of grants are for £500 or less.

SAMPLE GRANTS Previous beneficiaries have included: Harlington Locomotive Society, Hillingdon Table Tennis Club, Station Road Allotment Society, Broughton Pensioners, Immaculate Heart of Mary Senior Citizens' Club, Westcombe Lodge Club, Hayes Town Women's Institute and Royal British Legion Women's Section.

FINANCES *Year* 2007–08 *Income* £92,973 *Grants* £32,460 *Assets* £1,164,802

TRUSTEES A J Tyrrell, Chair; T McCarthy; M J Fitzpatrick; A Woodhouse; K Tyrrell.

HOW TO APPLY In writing to the correspondent.

WHO TO APPLY TO Sean Fitzpatrick, Homeleigh, 68 Vine Lane, Hillingdon, Middlesex UB10 0BD *email* enquiries@aptaylortrust.org.uk *Website* www.aptaylortrust.org.uk

CC NO 260741   **ESTABLISHED** 1969

■ Rosanna Taylor's 1987 Charity Trust

WHERE FUNDING CAN BE GIVEN UK and overseas, with a preference for Oxfordshire and West Sussex.

WHO CAN BENEFIT Registered charities only.

WHAT IS FUNDED General charitable purposes, including support for medical, cancer, children's development and environmental charities.

WHAT IS NOT FUNDED No grants to individuals or non-registered charities.

SAMPLE GRANTS Charities Aid Foundation (£28,000); and Pearson Taylor Trust (£26,000).

FINANCES *Year* 2007–08 *Income* £34,306 *Grants* £53,500 *Assets* £1,151,460

TRUSTEES The Cowdray Trust Limited.

HOW TO APPLY In writing to the correspondent. Acknowledgements are not sent to unsuccessful applicants.

WHO TO APPLY TO Laura Gosling, The Cowdray Trust Ltd, Pollen House, 10–12 Cork Street, London W1S 3LW *Tel* 020 7439 9061 *email* charity@mfs.co.uk

CC NO 297210   **ESTABLISHED** 1987

■ Tearfund

WHERE FUNDING CAN BE GIVEN Worldwide, but mainly in poorer countries.

WHO CAN BENEFIT Evangelical Christian organisations which benefit at risk groups; people who are disabled, disadvantaged by poverty or socially isolated; and victims of famine, man-made or natural disasters, and war.

WHAT IS FUNDED Evangelical Christian ministry to meet all needs – physical, mental, social and spiritual. Funding is given to partner organisations only.

WHAT IS NOT FUNDED Applications for individuals will not be considered.

TYPE OF GRANT Project/partner.

RANGE OF GRANTS Smallest £1,000; typical £15,000.

FINANCES *Year* 2007–08 *Income* £63,189,000 *Grants* £25,114,000 *Assets* £19,291,000

TRUSTEES Ms Anne de Leyser; Prof. Julian Evans; Kim Hurst; Revd John Smith; Revd Sarah Tillett;

Prof. Andrew Tomkins; David Todd; Andy Hickford; Simon Laver; Robert Camp; Clive Mather.

PUBLICATIONS *Tear Times.*

HOW TO APPLY Initial approaches by potential partner organisations should be made in writing.

WHO TO APPLY TO Graham Fairbairn, Secretary, 100 Church Road, Teddington, Middlesex TW11 8QE *Tel* 0845 355 8355 *email* enquiry@tearfund.org *Website* www.tearfund.org

CC NO 265464   **ESTABLISHED** 1968

■ The Tedworth Charitable Trust

WHERE FUNDING CAN BE GIVEN Unrestricted, but UK in practice.

WHO CAN BENEFIT Registered charities.

WHAT IS FUNDED Parenting, family welfare and child development; environment and the arts; general.

WHAT IS NOT FUNDED Grants are not normally made to individuals.

TYPE OF GRANT One-off and core costs.

RANGE OF GRANTS Up to £35,000.

SAMPLE GRANTS Best Beginnings (£35,000), towards the production of an educational video for expectant and nursing mothers about breast-feeding and development of the charity's website; Ashden Awards for Sustainable Energy (£30,000), towards the cost of the 2007 awards; Worcester College, Oxford (£25,000), towards the endowment appeal; Home Start (£13,500), towards core costs; Women's Environmental Network (£10,000), towards a photographic and food growing project for community groups in east London; Margate Rocks (£5,000), towards the art festivals' education programme; and the British Friends Of The Sengwer Tribe of Kenya (£1,000), to fund the connection of the community cultural centre in Kaplolet to the mains electricity supply.

FINANCES *Year* 2007–08 *Income* £527,090 *Grants* £301,307 *Assets* £11,302,195

TRUSTEES Alex J Sainsbury; Margaret Sainsbury; Jessica M Sainsbury; Timothy J Sainsbury; Judith S Portrait.

OTHER INFORMATION The trust is one of the Sainsbury Family Charitable Trusts which share a common administration. An application to one is taken as an application to all.

HOW TO APPLY 'Proposals are likely to be invited by the trustees or initiated at their request. Unsolicited applications are unlikely to be successful, even if they fall within an area in which the trustees are interested.' A single application will be considered for support by all the trusts in the Sainsbury family group.

WHO TO APPLY TO Alan Bookbinder, Director, Allington House, 1st Floor, 150 Victoria Street, London SW1E 5AE *Tel* 020 7410 0330 *Fax* 020 7410 0332 *Website* www.sfct.org.uk

CC NO 328524   **ESTABLISHED** 1990

■ Tees Valley Community Foundation

WHERE FUNDING CAN BE GIVEN The former county of Cleveland, being the local authority areas of Hartlepool, Middlesbrough, Redcar and Cleveland and Stockton-on-Tees.

WHO CAN BENEFIT Registered charities and constituted community groups.

WHAT IS FUNDED General charitable purposes. The foundation makes grants from various different funds, each with its own criteria.

WHAT IS NOT FUNDED No grants for major fundraising appeals, sponsored events, promotion of religion, holidays or social outings. Each fund has separate exclusions; contact the foundation for further details.

TYPE OF GRANT Capital or revenue.

RANGE OF GRANTS Mostly under £10,000.

FINANCES *Year* 2007–08 *Income* £2,363,804 *Grants* £1,804,294 *Assets* £8,684,711

TRUSTEES Alan Kitching; John Sparke; Keith Bayley; Christopher Hope; Jack Ord; John Bennett; Pamela Ann Taylor; Mr McDougall; Craig Monty; Neil Etherington; Rosemary Young; John Irwin; Jacqueline Taylor; Marjory Houseman; Keith Robinson; Brian Beaumont; Neil Kenley.

PUBLICATIONS Periodic newsletter.

HOW TO APPLY Contact the correspondent to discuss your project and request an application form.

WHO TO APPLY TO Hugh McGouran, Southlands Business Centre, Ormesby Road, Middlesbrough TS3 0HB *Tel* 01642 314200 *Fax* 01642 313700 *email* info@teesvalleyfoundation.org *Website* www.teesvalleyfoundation.org
CC NO 1111222   **ESTABLISHED** 1988

....

■ Tegham Limited

WHERE FUNDING CAN BE GIVEN UK.

WHO CAN BENEFIT Registered charities.

WHAT IS FUNDED Jewish Orthodox faith and the relief of poverty.

FINANCES *Year* 2007–08 *Income* £278,520 *Grants* £372,096 *Assets* £1,584,370

TRUSTEES Mrs S Fluss; Miss N Fluss.

HOW TO APPLY The trust has stated that it has enough causes to support and does not welcome other applications.

WHO TO APPLY TO Mrs S Fluss, Trustee, 1 Hallswelle Road, London NW11 0DH
CC NO 283066   **ESTABLISHED** 1981

....

■ The Templeton Goodwill Trust

WHERE FUNDING CAN BE GIVEN Glasgow and the West of Scotland (the Glasgow postal area).

WHO CAN BENEFIT Scottish registered charities.

WHAT IS FUNDED General charitable purposes. It is interested in supporting organisations which help others. Types of beneficiaries include: youth organisations, medical research charities, churches, ex-services' organisations and other organisations concerned with social work and providing caring services for all age groups.

WHAT IS NOT FUNDED Support is given to Scottish registered charities only. Individuals are not supported and grants are generally not given to arts or cultural organisations.

TYPE OF GRANT Discretionary, both continuing annual sums and 'one-off', support grants.

RANGE OF GRANTS £450–£4,600.

SAMPLE GRANTS Girl Guides Association (£6,500); SSAFA (£4,200); Salvation Army, Scout Association (£4,000 each); Scottish Furniture Trades Benevolent Association (£3,300); Cancer Research UK and Marie Curie Memorial Foundation (£2,800 each); Tenovus Scotland (£2,500); Scottish Bible Society (£1,900); Dyslexia Scotwest (£1,000); The Fishermen's Mission (£700); and Diabetes UK Scotland (£500).

FINANCES *Year* 2008–09 *Income* £180,168 *Grants* £151,450 *Assets* £2,667,670

TRUSTEES J H Millar, Chair; B Bannerman; W T P Barnstaple; C Barrowman.

HOW TO APPLY In writing to the correspondent, preferably including a copy of accounts. Applications should be received by April as the trustees meet once a year, at the end of April or in May. Initial telephone calls are welcome. An sae is required from applicants to receive a reply.

WHO TO APPLY TO W T P Barnstaple, Trustee and Administrator, 12 Doon Street, Motherwell ML1 2BN *Tel* 01698 262202
SC NO SC004177

....

■ Tesco Charity Trust

WHERE FUNDING CAN BE GIVEN UK.

WHO CAN BENEFIT National and local charity appeals benefiting children's welfare and education, older people and people with disabilities.

WHAT IS FUNDED Main areas of interest are: local charities promoting welfare and education of children, older people and people with disabilities.

WHAT IS NOT FUNDED No grants to political organisations, individuals or towards new buildings. The trust will not make donations to other trusts or charities for onward transmission to other charitable organisations.

TYPE OF GRANT Generally one-off, or for one year or less.

RANGE OF GRANTS Up to £20,000.

SAMPLE GRANTS British Red Cross Nation Floods Appeal (£100,000); Trinity Hospice (£20,000); Chickenshed Theatre Group (£18,000); UK Career Academy (£15,000); Crimestoppers Trust (£11,000); Barking Badgers (£10,000); Groundwork Hertfordshire (£8,000); Falmouth Youth Club, Happy Days Children's Charity and Chelmsford Women's Aid (£5,000 each); and Culdrose Youth Football Club and Ace Centre Advisory Trust (£4,000 each).

FINANCES *Year* 2007–08 *Income* £4,643,178 *Grants* £5,523,343 *Assets* £1,175,933

TRUSTEES David Reid; Lucy Neville-Rolfe; Paul Smythe; Paul Dickens; Juliet Crisp; Christophe Roussel.

HOW TO APPLY 'Community Awards Scheme: Applications should be made via the charity's website. There are two categories of Community Awards: 1. Grants to support children's welfare and/or children's educations (including special needs schools); 2. Grants to support older people and/or adults and children with disabilities. There are two rounds of funding every year for each category, please see the timescales below. Applications made outside the timescales for your category cannot be accepted. Decisions will not be finalised for approximately three months after the closing date of each round. Please consider this when completing your application. *Grants for children's education and children's welfare:* applications should be made between 1 December and 31 January or 1 May and 30 June. *Grants for older people and adults and children with disabilities: applications should be made between:* 1 February and 31 March or 1 August and 30 September. NB: charities can only make one application per year. **Larger Grants (Trust Meeting Grant):** A certain amount of budget is available at each Tesco Charity Trust meeting. However the number of donation requests we receive always exceeds the funds available. Therefore some good applications, while meeting our criteria, may have to be refused. To apply for a trust meeting grant and for information on deadlines for applying, please email michelina.filocco@uk.tesco.com with details of your project. If your project fits within our criteria we will send you an application form.'

WHO TO APPLY TO Michelina Filocco, Secretary, Tesco House, Delamare Road, Cheshunt, Hertfordshire EN8 9SL *Tel* 01992 644 143 *Fax* 01992 646 794 *email* michelina.filocco@uk.tesco.com *Website* www.tescoplc.com/plc/corporate_responsibility/local_communities/community_investment/charitable_giving/tesco_charity_trust

CC NO 297126   **ESTABLISHED** 1987

■ Thackray Medical Research Trust

WHERE FUNDING CAN BE GIVEN Worldwide.

WHO CAN BENEFIT Charities, university departments and individual researchers.

WHAT IS FUNDED Provision of medical supplies to the developing world and research into, or organising conferences concerning, the history of medicine.

TYPE OF GRANT The 2005/06 annual report states that: 'The trust wishes to encourage grant applications from international medical supply charities for pump-priming funds or project launch funds.'

SAMPLE GRANTS The Thackray Museum (£150,000); and the Liverpool School of Tropical Medicine (£3,000).

FINANCES *Year* 2007–08 *Income* £234,451 *Grants* £156,653 *Assets* £5,998,493

TRUSTEES S Warren, Chair; J Campbell; W Mathie; M S Schweiger; C Thackray; W M Wrigley.

OTHER INFORMATION The trust initiated and supported the establishment of the award-winning Thackray Museum in Leeds, one of the largest medical museums in the world, and continues to support the research resource there.

HOW TO APPLY In writing to the correspondent. The trustees usually meet twice a year.

WHO TO APPLY TO The Chair of the Trustees, c/o Thackray Museum, Beckett Street, Leeds LS9 7LN *Website* www.tmrt.co.uk

CC NO 702896   **ESTABLISHED** 1990

■ Thames Community Foundation

WHERE FUNDING CAN BE GIVEN London boroughs of Hounslow, Kingston, Richmond, Sutton, Merton and Wandsworth.

WHO CAN BENEFIT Local charitable and voluntary organisations providing welfare, working with young people, helping adults with disabilities or with all problems of addiction.

WHAT IS FUNDED Encouraging links between the local communities of the area and the business sector.

WHAT IS NOT FUNDED Grants will not be made to: capital building projects, political or religious causes, although faith based groups that are open to the wider community and who engage in social welfare projects may apply, individuals or national charities, who will only be considered, in exceptional circumstances, for truly local projects.

RANGE OF GRANTS Up to £7,000 a year.

FINANCES *Year* 2007–08 *Income* £473,859 *Grants* £387,473 *Assets* £694,937

TRUSTEES Monica Unwin, Chair; Edward Bentall; Nigel Carey; Grant Gordon; Deborah James;

Mukesh Malhotra; Martin Richards; Andrew Lane; Davina Judelson.

HOW TO APPLY 'Thames Community Foundation currently holds 20 individual Named Funds on behalf of donors. These are used to support the Foundation's general grant funding programmes and other specific projects (which may be time limited). All are based in the local area. All funds are open to applications by local community and voluntary groups. Applicants do not need to be registered charities but must have a charitable purpose and possess as a minimum a constitution or set of rules, at least two officers and a separate bank account. If you have seen a grant that you would like to apply for, and consider that you fulfil the requirements, then download the application form and guidelines from the foundation's website and send the completed form to our team at Thames Community Foundation. Each fund has different guidelines and instructions but we are more than happy to help you, just call our grants team on 0208 943 6030 or email us at grantstcf@btconnect.com. Simply submit your application form ensuring that you have all the requested supporting information and leave the rest to us. Grant applications are considered every two months so the maximum wait from receipt of a completed application form to decision should never exceed ten weeks.'

WHO TO APPLY TO Nigel Hay, Director, NPL Building 5, Room 112, Hampton Road, Teddington, Middlesex TW11 0LW *Tel* 020 8943 5525 *Fax* 020 8943 2319 *email* tcf@btconnect.com *Website* www.thamescommunityfoundation.org.uk

CC NO 1001994   **ESTABLISHED** 1990

■ The Thames Wharf Charity

WHERE FUNDING CAN BE GIVEN UK.

WHO CAN BENEFIT Charitable organisations.

WHAT IS FUNDED General charitable purposes.

WHAT IS NOT FUNDED No grants for the purchase of property, motor vehicles or holidays.

SAMPLE GRANTS Ellenor Foundation Ltd (£6,800); Amnesty International (£6,600); Clinical Science Foundation and Mossbourne Academy (£5,000 each); Medical Aid for Palestinians (£3,000); British Heart Foundation (£2,800); BUKKA Education and Research Trust (£2,500); SCOPE and Willow Foundation (£1,500 each); Zoological Society (£1,300); Art Academy, Bedford Pentecostal Church and Foresight (£1,000 each); National Gallery (£600); Cornwall Hospice, Human Rights Watch Charitable Trust and Tibet Relief Fund (£500 each); Hope Hospice (£450); Greenpeace Environmental Trust and Royal Marsden Hospital Charity (£400 each); and Macintyre Charitable Trust (£100).

FINANCES *Year* 2007–08 *Income* £548,206 *Grants* £260,339 *Assets* £838,493

TRUSTEES Avtar Lotay; Patrick Burgess; Graham Stirk.

HOW TO APPLY In writing to the correspondent.

WHO TO APPLY TO The Trustees, Thames Wharf Studios, Rainville Road, London W6 9HA

CC NO 1000796   **ESTABLISHED** 1990

■ The Thistle Trust

WHERE FUNDING CAN BE GIVEN UK.

WHO CAN BENEFIT Charitable institutions or projects in the UK.

WHAT IS FUNDED The promotion of study and research in the arts; and furthering public knowledge and education of art.

WHAT IS NOT FUNDED No grants to individuals.

RANGE OF GRANTS £200–£8,000.

SAMPLE GRANTS Juventus Lyrica Asociación (£8,000); Prix de Lausanne (£6,000); the Opera Group, the Place, Wells Cathedral School and Whitechapel Art Gallery (£5,000 each); Yvonne Arnaud Theatre (£3,500); Welsh Youth Classical Music (£3,000); Royal Liverpool Philharmonic (£2,500); Blindart, Grid Iron Theatre Co Ltd, Making Music and Somerset House Trust (£2,000 each); Bampton Classical, Conquest Art Centre, Late Music Festival, Polka Children Theatre Ltd, Scottish Opera and Sheffield Mencap and Gateway (£1,000 each); Heather Music Festival (£500); and Deep Impact Theatre Co. (£200).

FINANCES *Year* 2007–08 *Income* £49,058 *Grants* £64,866 *Assets* £1,294,491

TRUSTEES Madeleine, Lady Kleinwort; Nigel Porteous; Neil Morris; Donald McGilvray; Nicholas Kerr-Sheppard.

HOW TO APPLY In writing to the correspondent including most recent report and financial accounts. The trustees meet at least once a year with only successful applicants notified of the trustees' decision.

WHO TO APPLY TO Nicholas Kerr-Sheppard, Secretary, PO Box 57005, 30 Gresham Street, London EC2P 2US

CC NO 1091327   **ESTABLISHED** 2002

■ The Loke Wan Tho Memorial Foundation

WHERE FUNDING CAN BE GIVEN Worldwide.

WHO CAN BENEFIT Registered charities only.

WHAT IS FUNDED Medical studies and research; conservation and environment; and overseas aid.

TYPE OF GRANT One-off project and research grants.

SAMPLE GRANTS Opportunity International (£5,000); Alzheimer's Disease International, Brooke Hospital for Animals, Plantlife, Rainforest Concern, SPANA, Tree Aid and University of Bristol – Animal Welfare Group (£4,000 each); Cancer Research UK (£3,000); and THRIVE (£2,000).

FINANCES *Year* 2007–08 *Income* £152,746 *Grants* £63,000 *Assets* £5,453,627

TRUSTEES Lady Y P McNeice; Mrs T S Tonkyn; A P Tonkyn.

HOW TO APPLY In writing to the correspondent.

WHO TO APPLY TO The Secretary, Abacus Financial Services Ltd, La Motte Chambers, St Helier, Jersey, Channel Islands JE1 1BJ

CC NO 264273   **ESTABLISHED** 1972

■ The David Thomas Charitable Trust

WHERE FUNDING CAN BE GIVEN UK, in particular Gloucester and surrounding districts.

WHO CAN BENEFIT Institutions and registered charities.

WHAT IS FUNDED Social welfare and general charitable purposes.

RANGE OF GRANTS Up to £10,000.

SAMPLE GRANTS Oxfam (£9,000); UNICEF UK (£8,000); Save the Children UK (£5,000); Cancer Research UK (£4,000); British Red Cross, Elizabeth Finn Care, Help the Aged, Marie Curie Cancer Care, Multiple Sclerosis Society, NSPCC, the Salvation Army and SENSE (£3,000 each); the Eve Appeal, Museum of Garden History, Royal British Legion, the Sandpiper Trust, Scots Guards Charitable Fund and St Mungo's Community Housing Association (£2,000 each); the Prostate Cancer Charity (£1,500); All Saints Church – Selsey, Cotswold Care Hospice, Gloucestershire Dance and James Hopkins Trust (£1,000 each); and Gloucestershire County Cricket Club (£500).

FINANCES *Year* 2007–08 *Income* £278,000 *Grants* £94,000 *Assets* £1,700,000

TRUSTEES David Thomas; Charles Clark; James Davidson; R F Trustee Co. Limited.

HOW TO APPLY In writing to the correspondent.

WHO TO APPLY TO The Trustees, c/o R F Trustee Co. Limited, Ely House, 37 Dover Street, London W1S 4NJ

CC NO 1083257   **ESTABLISHED** 2000

■ The Thomas Wall Trust

WHERE FUNDING CAN BE GIVEN UK.

WHO CAN BENEFIT Individuals and registered charities. Small charities and small schemes are preferred to large national ones.

WHAT IS FUNDED 'The object must be in a broad sense educational and/or concerned with social service.'

WHAT IS NOT FUNDED Grants are not made: towards the erection, upkeep or renovation of buildings; to hospitals, almshouses or similar institutions; for objects which are purely medical; for projects outside of the UK.

TYPE OF GRANT 'The application should preferably be for some specific scheme or objective, but in some cases single grants will be considered towards general running costs.' Successful applicants will normally not receive recurrent funding and can only reapply after five years.

SAMPLE GRANTS Konnect9 Worldwide, Octobus Project and Seafood Training Centre (£2,000 each); Back to Work (£1,500); the Asha Centre (£1,200); and Acorn Christian Ministries, Barton Training Trust, Cleveland Housing Advice Centre, Derby Toc H Children's Camp, Dressability, the Dystonia Society, Federation of Artistic and Creative Therapy, Island Advice Centre, Volunteer Centre North Warwickshire, Where Next Association and Wildwood Trust (£1,000 each).

FINANCES *Year* 2007–08 *Income* £122,758 *Grants* £69,042 *Assets* £2,699,800

TRUSTEES Dr G.M. Copland, Chair; Mrs M A Barrie; P Bellamy; C R Broomfield; Miss A S Kennedy; Miss A-M. Martin; Mrs A Mullins; J Porteous; Revd Dr R Waller.

OTHER INFORMATION The grant total in 2007–08 included £37,000 donated to individuals.

HOW TO APPLY There is no application form for charitable organisations to use except that all applicants must complete a cover sheet which can be downloaded from the trust's website. A copy of the latest available set of accounts for their charity should be included along with an sae, which will be used to acknowledge receipt of application. The trustees meet twice a year, in July and November. Applications for the July meeting must be received by mid-May and for the November meeting by end of September.

WHO TO APPLY TO Prof. G Holt, Director, PO Box 52781, London EC2P 2UT *email* information@

thomaswalltrust.org.uk *Website* www.
thomaswalltrust.org.uk
cc no 206121   established 1920

....

■ The Arthur and Margaret Thompson Charitable Trust

where funding can be given The towns or burghs of Kinross and Milnathort.

who can benefit Registered charities in the beneficial area.

what is funded General charitable purposes.

finances *Year* 2008–09 *Income* £156,552

trustees Dr D P Anderson; Revd Dr J P L Munro; J Greig; D L Sands; A G Dorward; I D Donaldson.

how to apply The trustees meet to consider applications about every four months.

who to apply to The Trustees, Miller Hendry, 10 Blackfriars Street, Perth PH1 5NS

sc no SC012103   established 1973

....

■ The Maurice and Vivien Thompson Charitable Trust

where funding can be given UK.

who can benefit UK registered charities.

what is funded General charitable purposes.

sample grants Beacon Fellowship Charitable Trust (£15,000); Martin Johnson Development Scholarship (£7,500); Pelican Cancer Foundation (£3,000); Leicester and Rutland Crimebeat (£1,800); Shackleton Foundation and Sight for Africa (£1,000 each); RIED (£200); and Bridge2Aid (£100).

finances *Year* 2007–08 *Income* £239,112 *Grants* £29,288 *Assets* £1,311,488

trustees M N B Thompson; Mrs V Thompson; P Rhodes.

how to apply In writing to the correspondent.

who to apply to M N B Thompson, Trustee, 2 The Orchard, London W4 1JX

cc no 1085041   established 2000

....

■ The Thompson Family Charitable Trust

where funding can be given UK.

who can benefit Registered charities only.

what is funded General charitable purposes, although the trustees are particularly interested in educational, medical and veterinary charities.

what is not funded No grants to individuals.

type of grant The trust makes one-off grants, recurring grants and pledges.

range of grants Generally £200–£5,000, occasionally larger.

sample grants Racing Welfare Charities (£25,000 in two grants); North London Hospice (£11,000 in two grants); Cambridge Women's Aid, East Anglian Children's Hospices, Multiple Sclerosis Society and St Nicholas Hospice (£10,000 each); Score (£5,000); Childline and Juvenile Diabetes Research Foundation (£2,000 each); Cancer Research UK, Marie Curie Cancer Care and University of Cambridge Veterinary School Trust (£1,000 each); and Special Olympics Appeal (£500).

finances *Year* 2007–08 *Income* £2,575,533 *Grants* £105,350 *Assets* £51,257,612

trustees D B Thompson; Mrs P Thompson; Mrs K P Woodward.

other information This trust regularly builds up its reserves to enable it to make large donations in the future, for example towards the construction

of new medical or educational facilities. 'The trustees intend to continue to reserve a proportion of the annual investment income until an appropriate project has been identified and approved'. In view of the trustees' reserves policy, it is likely that the trust's grantmaking will increase substantially in the future.

how to apply In writing to the trustees.

who to apply to The Trustees, Hillsdown Court, 15 Totteridge Common, London N20 8LR

cc no 326801   established 1985

....

■ The Len Thomson Charitable Trust

where funding can be given Scotland, with a preference for Midlothian, particularly Dalkeith.

who can benefit Charitable organisations.

what is funded The trust supports young people, local community organisations and medical research.

range of grants £1,000–£5,000.

sample grants The Edinburgh Sick Kids Friends Foundation (£5,000); Brass in the Park (£3,000); CHAS, Maggie's Centre and Mercy Ships (£2,000 each); and British Red Cross, Lothian Special Olympics, Newtongrange Children's Gala Day, the Princess Royal Trust for Carers and Save the Children Fund (£1,000 each).

finances *Year* 2008 *Income* £25,886 *Grants* £20,000 *Assets* £708,053

trustees Douglas A Connell; Mrs Elizabeth Thomson.

how to apply The trust does not reply to unsolicited applications.

who to apply to Douglas A Connell, Trustee, Turcan Connell WS, Princes Exchange, 1 Earl Grey Street, Edinburgh EH3 9EE *Tel* 0131 228 8111 *email* dac@turcanconnell.com

sc no SC000981   established 1989

....

■ The Sue Thomson Foundation

where funding can be given UK, Sussex, London or Surrey.

who can benefit Organisations.

what is funded (i) Major grants – The majority of the funds went to Christ's Hospital, which received £82,000. The foundation nominates one new entrant each year from a needy background to the school, subject to the child meeting Christ's Hospital's own admissions criteria academically, socially and in terms of need. The foundation commits to contributing to the child's costs at a level agreed with Christ's Hospital for as long as each of them remains in the school. (ii) Regular grants – It is the policy of the trustees to provide up to 10% of the foundation's available income each year for grants in this category, subject to the foundation's commitments to Christ's Hospital having been satisfied. Charities eligible for consideration for grants at this level include: Charities related to Christ's Hospital including the sister school, King Edward's – Witley; UK booktrade charities, including the charities of the Worshipful Company of Stationers and Newspaper Makers; Suitable grant-making charities selected in recognition of pro-bono professional work done for the foundation by its trustees or others; Special situations or other applications at the trustees' discretion. Grants in this category may be spread over a period of years. (iii) Special grants – It is the policy of the trustees to set aside a further 10% of available income each year for this programme, subject to its commitments in the major and medium categories and other financial needs having been met. Special grants are awarded to up to four small charities at any one time. They are confined to charities that support young and older people in need through no fault of their own, often via well run small self-help organisations. They are confined to charities in Sussex, Surrey or London.

WHAT IS NOT FUNDED No grants to large, national charities (except Christ's Hospital) or individuals, except as part of a specific scheme. No research projects, charities concerned with animals, birds, the environment, gardens or historic buildings.

TYPE OF GRANT Major grants which are above £5,000; regular grants which can be from £500 to £5,000; special grants which can be up to £3,000 per year.

RANGE OF GRANTS Major grants which can be above £3,000 in any one year; Medium grants which can be from £500 to £3,000 in any one year; Special grants which can be up to £3,000 per year for periods of one to three years.

SAMPLE GRANTS Christ's Hospital (£82,000); Leonard Sainer Legal Education Foundation and the Sussex Snowdrop – Chichester (£3,000 each); Book Trade Benevolent Society – Kings Langley, Brighton and Hove Parents and Children Group, King Edward's School – Witley and Streets Alive Theatre Company – Lambeth (£2,000 each); the National Literacy Trust – London (£1,400); and the Publishing Training Centre – London, Society for Editors and Proofreaders and the St Bride Foundation – London (£500 each).

FINANCES *Year* 2007–08 *Income* £433,867 *Grants* £106,167 *Assets* £2,638,951

TRUSTEES Susan M Mitchell, Chair; Timothy J Binnington; Charles L Corman; Kathleen Duncan; Susannah Holliman.

OTHER INFORMATION The grant total includes £1,599 paid to individual students.

HOW TO APPLY In writing to the correspondent, or preliminary telephone enquiry. Unsolicited applications are not acknowledged, unless accompanied by an sae.

WHO TO APPLY TO Jane Akers, Administrator, Furners Keep, Furners Lane, Henfield, West Sussex BN5 9HS *Tel* 01273 493461 *email* thesuethomsonfoundation@macdream.net

CC NO 298808   **ESTABLISHED** 1988

■ The Sir Jules Thorn Charitable Trust

WHERE FUNDING CAN BE GIVEN Unrestricted.

WHO CAN BENEFIT Registered charities engaged in medical research (universities/hospitals only); medically related work; and humanitarian work.

WHAT IS FUNDED Medical research with strong clinical relevance, medicine generally, and small grants for humanitarian appeals.

WHAT IS NOT FUNDED The trust does not fund: research which is considered unlikely to provide clinical benefit within five years; research which could reasonably be expected to be supported by a disease specific funder, unless there is a convincing reason why the trust has been approached; research into cancer or AIDS, for the sole reason that they are relatively well funded elsewhere; grants for ongoing projects; research which will also involve other funders, apart from the institution itself; individuals –

except in the context of a project undertaken by an approved institution which is in receipt of a grant from the trust; research or data collection overseas; research institutions which are not registered charities; third parties raising resources to fund research themselves.

TYPE OF GRANT Medical research projects usually covering a period of up to three years, plus one-off donations to other charities.

SAMPLE GRANTS Moorfields Eye Hospital Development Fund (£526,000), to fund the development of a new stem cell therapy unit to help make stem cell regeneration of the eye, and restoration of vision, a reality; Prior's Court Foundation (£250,000), to fund a training and development centre at Prior's Court School in Thatcham for children with severe autism; and the National Hospital for Neurology and Neurosurgery Development Foundation (£105,000), towards the brain tumour unit at the hospital. Small grants of £1,000 each included those to: Anthony Nolan Trust, Changing Faces, Deafblind UK, London's Air Ambulance, SSAFA Forces Help, The Butler Trust, and West Suffolk Voluntary Association for the Blind.

FINANCES *Year* 2008 *Income* £4,047,193 *Grants* £2,925,556 *Assets* £83,126,916

TRUSTEES Mrs Elizabeth S Charal; Prof Sir Ravinder N Maini; Sir Bruce McPhail; Nancy V Pearcey; Christopher Sporborg; William Sporborg; John Rhodes; Prof David Russell-Jones.

HOW TO APPLY *Medically-related grants*: appeals are considered annually by the trustees, usually in November. There is no specific application form. Proposals should be submitted to the trust's director and should cover: the background to the appeal, including any brochures and feasibility assessment; information about the applicant, which must be an institution having charitable status. Applications from individuals cannot be considered; details of the appeal, including the total sum being raised, donations or pledges already received, and the plans for securing the remainder. Timescales for implementation should be given; the latest trustees' report and audited financial statements should be provided. Potential applicants who wish to establish whether their appeal would fit the criteria should contact the trust.

Small grants: on an application form available from the trust's website or by contacting the office. There are no specific dates for submitting applications. Appeals may be made at any time and will be considered by the trustees as soon as possible, depending on volumes.

WHO TO APPLY TO David H Richings, Director, 24 Manchester Square, London W1U 3TH *Tel* 020 7487 5851 *Fax* 020 7224 3976 *email* info@julesthorntrust.org.uk *Website* www.julesthorntrust.org.uk

CC NO 233838   **ESTABLISHED** 1964

■ The Thornton Foundation

WHERE FUNDING CAN BE GIVEN UK.

WHO CAN BENEFIT Charities which are personally known to the trustees.

WHAT IS FUNDED General charitable purposes.

SAMPLE GRANTS The Marine Society and Sea Cadets (£130,000); St Dunstan-in-the-West (£50,000); the Tick Tock Club (£32,000); Stowe School Foundation (£10,000); the Cirdan Sailing Trust (£7,500); Helen House (£6,000); Action for Blind People, Books Abroad, Keble College – Oxford and Reed's School Foundation (£5,000 each); the Tait Memorial Trust (£3,000); BREAK Prisoners of Conscience and St Paul's Church Knightsbridge (£2,000 each); and Bishop's Castle Hospital Patient's Fund and the Handel Society (£1,000 each).

FINANCES *Year* 2007–08 *Income* £74,064 *Grants* £274,800 *Assets* £4,145,177

TRUSTEES R C Thornton, Chair; A H Isaacs; H D C Thornton; Mrs S J Thornton.

HOW TO APPLY The trust strongly emphasises that it does not accept unsolicited applications, and, as it states above, only organisations that are known to one of the trustees will be considered for support. Any unsolicited applications will not receive a reply.

WHO TO APPLY TO A H Isaacs, Stephenson Harwood, 1 St Paul's Churchyard, London EC4M 8SH

CC NO 326383   **ESTABLISHED** 1983

■ The Thornton Trust

WHERE FUNDING CAN BE GIVEN UK and overseas.
WHO CAN BENEFIT Charitable organisations.
WHAT IS FUNDED 'Promoting and furthering education and the evangelical Christian faith and assisting in the relief of sickness, suffering and poverty.'
SAMPLE GRANTS Christian Action Research and Education (£53,000); Africa Inland Mission (£23,000); Saffron Walden Baptist Church (£11,000); London School of Theology (£7,000); Tyndale House (£6,000); Bible Society, Keswick Convention (£5,000); Mildmay Mission Hospital (£4,500); Send a Cow (£3,000); Stort Valley Schools Trust (£2,500); Criccieth HC Evangelism Trust, International Fellowship of Evangelical Students and Salvation Army (£2,000 each); National Library for the Blind (£1,000); Childline (£200); Hertford Museum (£150); and CIOB Benevolent Fund (£50).
FINANCES *Year* 2007–08 *Income* £79,708 *Grants* £217,878 *Assets* £1,211,624
TRUSTEES D H Thornton; Mrs B Y Thornton; J D Thornton.
HOW TO APPLY The trust states: 'Our funds are fully committed and we regret that we are unable to respond to the many unsolicited calls for assistance we are now receiving'.
WHO TO APPLY TO D H Thornton, Trustee, Hunters Cottage, Hunters Yard, Debden Road, Saffron Walden, Essex CB11 4AA
CC NO 205357   **ESTABLISHED** 1962

■ The Three Guineas Trust

WHERE FUNDING CAN BE GIVEN Worldwide, in practice mainly UK.
WHO CAN BENEFIT Currently, registered charities working with people suffering from autism and Asperger's Syndrome.
WHAT IS FUNDED Initiatives related to autism and Asperger's Syndrome.
WHAT IS NOT FUNDED No grants for individuals or for research (except where it has an immediate benefit).
TYPE OF GRANT One off and recurrent.
RANGE OF GRANTS Up to £94,000.
SAMPLE GRANTS National Autistic Society (£94,000); Brighton and Hove Community Initiatives (£85,000); University of Cambridge – Asperger Resource Centre (£64,000); Asperger East Anglia (£50,000); Assert (£33,000); Wirral Autistic Society (£14,000); Human Appeal International (£6,200); Project Ability (£4,900); and the Sainsbury Archive (£650).

FINANCES *Year* 2007–08 *Income* £421,135 *Grants* £468,552 *Assets* £14,417,026
TRUSTEES Clare Sainsbury; B Willis; Judith Portrait.
OTHER INFORMATION The trust is one of the Sainsbury Family Charitable Trusts which share a common administration. An application to one is taken as an application to all.
HOW TO APPLY See the guidance for applicants in the entry for the Sainsbury Family Charitable Trusts. A single application will be considered for support by all the trusts in the group. The following statement is taken from the trust's 2007/08 accounts and explains it's current application policy: 'The trustees do not at present wish to invite applications, except in the field of autism and Asperger's syndrome, where they will examine unsolicited proposals alongside those that result from their own research and contacts with expert individuals and organisations working in this field. The trustees prefer to support innovative schemes that can be successfully replicated or become self-sustaining. They are also keen that, wherever possible, schemes supporting adults and teenagers on the autistic spectrum should include clients/service users in decision-making.'
WHO TO APPLY TO Alan Bookbinder, Director, Allington House, 1st Floor, 150 Victoria Street, London SW1E 5AE *Tel* 020 7410 0330 *Fax* 020 7410 0332 *Website* www.sfct.org.uk
CC NO 1059652   **ESTABLISHED** 1996

■ The Three Oaks Trust

WHERE FUNDING CAN BE GIVEN UK and overseas, with a preference for West Sussex.
WHO CAN BENEFIT Organisations that promote the welfare of individuals and families. Grants are also made to individuals via statutory authorities or voluntary agencies.
WHAT IS FUNDED The trust regularly supports the same welfare organisations in the UK and overseas each year.
WHAT IS NOT FUNDED No direct applications from individuals. Applications from students for gap year activities are not a priority and will not be funded.
SAMPLE GRANTS Crawley Open House and Mind (£10,000 each); Dalesdown and Raynauds Association (£7,500 each); Abilitynet, Adoption Support UK, British Yemeni Society, CECO, Coventry Cyrenians Janeve Foundation and Kaloko Trust UK (£5,000); Adur Information Shop (£2,500); and CFDP (£1,000).
FINANCES *Year* 2007–08 *Income* £226,911 *Grants* £212,178 *Assets* £5,915,724
TRUSTEES Mrs M E Griffin; Mrs C A Johnson; Mrs P A Wilkinson; Dr P Kane; Mrs S A Kane.
OTHER INFORMATION The grant total in 2007–08 included £63,000 donated to individuals.
HOW TO APPLY 'The trustees intend to continue supporting the organisations that they have supported in the past and are not planning to fund any new projects in the near future. To save administrative costs, the trustees do not respond to requests, unless they are considering making a donation.'
WHO TO APPLY TO The Trustees, PO Box 243, Crawley, West Sussex RH10 6YB *email* contact@thethreeoakstrust.co.uk *Website* www.thethreeoakstrust.co.uk
CC NO 297079   **ESTABLISHED** 1987

■ The Thriplow Charitable Trust

WHERE FUNDING CAN BE GIVEN Preference for British institutions.

WHO CAN BENEFIT Universities, university colleges and other places of learning benefiting young adults and older people, academics, research workers and students.

WHAT IS FUNDED Advancement of higher and further education, the promotion of research and the dissemination of the results of such research.

WHAT IS NOT FUNDED Grants can only be made to charitable bodies or component parts of charitable bodies. In no circumstances can grants be made to individuals.

TYPE OF GRANT Research study funds, research fellowships, certain academic training schemes, computer facilities and building projects related to research.

RANGE OF GRANTS £2,000–£8,000.

SAMPLE GRANTS Previous beneficiaries have included Cambridge University Library, Centre of South Asian Studies, Computer Aid International, Fight for Sight, Fitzwilliam Museum, Foundation for Prevention of Blindness, Foundation of Research Students, Hearing Research Trust, Inspire Foundation, Loughborough University, Marie Curie Cancer Care, Royal Botanic Gardens, Royal College of Music, Transplant Trust and University of Reading.

FINANCES *Year* 2007–08 *Income* £93,806 *Grants* £83,080

TRUSTEES Sir Peter Swinnerton-Dyer, Chair; Dr Harriet Crawford; Prof. Christopher Bayly; Sir David Wallace; Dame Jean Thomas.

HOW TO APPLY There is no application form. A letter of application should specify the purpose for which funds are sought and the costings of the project. It should be indicated whether other applications for funds are pending and, if the funds are to be channelled to an individual or a small group, what degree of supervision over the quality of the work would be exercised by the institution. Trustee meetings are held twice a year – in spring and in autumn.

WHO TO APPLY TO Mrs C Walston, PO Box 225, Royston SG8 1BG

CC NO 1025531 **ESTABLISHED** 1993

■ The Tillett Trust

WHERE FUNDING CAN BE GIVEN UK.

WHO CAN BENEFIT Young musicians of outstanding talent residing in the UK.

WHAT IS FUNDED Funds are directed towards assisting outstanding young classical musicians at the start of their professional solo careers and in the main to help them obtain performing experience. It is not available for those at student level, either undergraduate or postgraduate.

WHAT IS NOT FUNDED Funding for the purchase of musical instruments, for study courses, for commercial recordings or for the commissioning of new works. Applications for ordinary subsistence costs are also not considered.

TYPE OF GRANT Non-recurrent.

FINANCES *Year* 2006–07 *Income* £33,098 *Grants* £47,023 *Assets* £685,537

TRUSTEES Paul Strang, Chair; Fiona Grant; Yvonne Minton; David Stiff; Clara Taylor; Howard Davis; Paul Harris.

HOW TO APPLY In writing to the correspondent. No application form is used and there are no deadlines. Enclose a CV or biography and references, also a performance cassette and budget for the project.

WHO TO APPLY TO Miss K Avey, The Administrator, PO Box 667, Dunsford, Exeter EX6 7WW *Tel* 0845 0704969 *email* info@TheTillettTrust. org.uk *Website* www.thetilletttrust.org.uk

CC NO 257329 **ESTABLISHED** 1963

■ Mrs R P Tindall's Charitable Trust

WHERE FUNDING CAN BE GIVEN Africa, Wiltshire, Dorset.

WHO CAN BENEFIT Charitable organisations, churches, students in need and members of the clergy.

WHAT IS FUNDED Relief of poverty, furtherance of the work of the Christian church and advancement of education. Grants are also made to students in need and for the welfare of the clergy and their dependants.

FINANCES *Year* 2008 *Income* £87,000 *Grants* £61,000 *Assets* £2,000,000

TRUSTEES D P Herbert; M R F Newman; G Fletcher; Revd Canon A C Philp.

OTHER INFORMATION Grants to individuals totalled £3,706, and included £2,750 given in book tokens to 55 post-ordinands.

HOW TO APPLY In writing to the correspondent enclosing an sae.

WHO TO APPLY TO Mrs I Rider, Secretary, Appletree House, Wishford Road, Middle Woodford, Salisbury SP4 6NG *Tel* 01722 782329

CC NO 250558 **ESTABLISHED** 1966

■ The Tinsley Foundation

WHERE FUNDING CAN BE GIVEN UK and overseas.

WHO CAN BENEFIT Charitable organisations.

WHAT IS FUNDED The foundation will support: charities which promote human rights and democratisation and/or which educate against racism, discrimination and oppression; charities which promote self-help in fighting poverty and homelessness; and charities which provide reproductive health education in underdeveloped countries, but specifically excluding charities whose policy is against abortion or birth control.

SAMPLE GRANTS Jubilee Action (£42,000); Human Rights Watch Charitable Trust (£22,000); Network for Africa (£20,000); the Carter Centre UK Foundation (£13,000); Peace Brigades International UK (£11,000); Business Solutions to Poverty (£10,000); Reprieve (£8,500); Conciliation Resources (£4,200); Learning for Life, Marie Stopes International, Prisoners of Conscience, Refugee Council and World Vision (£2,500 each); Fairtrade Foundation (£1,500); and English National Opera and Royal Star and Garter Home (£1,000 each).

FINANCES *Year* 2007–08 *Income* £207,201 *Grants* £153,010 *Assets* £2,640,581

TRUSTEES H C Tinsley; Mrs R C Tinsley; T A Jones.

HOW TO APPLY 'While the charity welcomes applications from eligible potential grantees, the trustees seek out organisations that will effectively fulfil our objectives.'

WHO TO APPLY TO Henry C Tinsley, Trustee, 14 St Mary's Street, Stamford, Lincolnshire PE9 2DF *Tel* 01780 762056 *Fax* 01780 767594 *email* hctinsley@aol.com

CC NO 1076537 **ESTABLISHED** 1999

■ The Tisbury Telegraph Trust

WHERE FUNDING CAN BE GIVEN UK and overseas.
WHO CAN BENEFIT Registered charities only.
WHAT IS FUNDED Christian, overseas aid and general charitable purposes. Most distributions are to charities of which the trustees have personal knowledge. Other applications are unlikely to be successful.
WHAT IS NOT FUNDED Grants are only made to registered charities. No applications from individuals for expeditions or courses can be considered.
TYPE OF GRANT Core costs, one-off, project, research and running costs will be considered.
SAMPLE GRANTS World Vision (£160,000); Romania Care (£54,000); Friends of Kiwoko Hospital (£50,000); Practical Action (£49,000); St Mary's Building Fund (£15,000); Tear Fund (£12,000); All Saints Church (£9,000); Church Mission Society (£3,000); Bible Society (£2,500); Crisis and Salvation Army (£1,000 each); and Lee Abbey and Shelter (£500 each).
FINANCES *Year* 2007–08 *Income* £342,679 *Grants* £398,000 *Assets* £114,388
TRUSTEES Alison Davidson; John Davidson; Eleanor Orr; Roger Orr; Sonia Phippard.
HOW TO APPLY In writing to the correspondent. However, it is extremely rare that unsolicited applications are successful and the trust does not respond to applicants unless an sae is included. No telephone applications please.
WHO TO APPLY TO Mrs E Orr, Trustee, 35 Kitto Road, Telegraph Hill, London SE14 5TW
CC NO 328595   **ESTABLISHED** 1990

■ TJH Foundation

WHERE FUNDING CAN BE GIVEN England and Wales with some preference for organisations based in the north west of England.
WHO CAN BENEFIT Charitable organisations.
WHAT IS FUNDED Social welfare, medical causes and racing welfare.
TYPE OF GRANT Mostly one-off.
SAMPLE GRANTS The Princess Royal Trust for Carers (£1 million in six grants); Maggie's Centres (£25,000); Leyland Methodist Church (£10,000); Macmillan Cancer Relief (four grants totalling £7,000); Royal Lancashire Agricultural Society (£4,300); the Marina Dalglish Appeal (£3,000); Cancer Vaccine Institution (£2,500); British Red Cross (£1,500); Little Sisters of the Poor (£1,000); Injured Jockeys Fund (£500 in two grants); St David's Care in the Community (£250); and the Lambourn Valley Housing Trust and Moorcroft Racehorse Welfare Centre (£100 each).
FINANCES *Year* 2007–08 *Income* £1,098,690 *Grants* £1,073,400 *Assets* £1,942,137
TRUSTEES T J Hemmings, Chair; Mrs M Catherall; J C Kay; Ms K Revitt.
HOW TO APPLY In writing to the correspondent.
WHO TO APPLY TO J C Kay, Trustee, Gleadhill House, Dawbers Lane, Euxton, Chorley, Lancashire PR7 6EA
CC NO 1077311   **ESTABLISHED** 1999

■ The Tolkien Trust

WHERE FUNDING CAN BE GIVEN Worldwide.
WHO CAN BENEFIT Mainly registered charities.
WHAT IS FUNDED General charitable purposes including charities and charitable causes supporting children, young people, families, older people, homeless people, socially disadvantaged people, organisations supporting overseas aid and development, refugees, medical aid, research, education, the arts and religion.
RANGE OF GRANTS £1,000–£220,000.
SAMPLE GRANTS Oxfam International (£220,000); Rebuilding Sri Lanka (£100,000); St Int Graalbeweging Best (£50,000); Bodleian Library – Archiving (£31,000); St Peter's Church – Eynsham (£30,000); Find Your Feet Limited (£25,000); Medecins Sans Frontieres (£20,000); Botley Alzheimer's Home (£15,000); Emmaus Oxford (£14,000); Ty Hafan Children's Hospice (£13,000); Medical Foundation for the Care of the Victims of Torture (£10,000); Climate Outreach Information Network (£9,000); World Cancer Research Fund (£6,000); WWF – Canada (£5,000); Horse's Voice (£3,000); and United Christian Broadcasters Ltd (£2,000).
FINANCES *Year* 2007–08 *Income* £577,760 *Grants* £1,325,425 *Assets* £6,784,682
TRUSTEES Christopher Reuel Tolkien; Priscilla Mary Anne Reuel Tolkien; Joanna Reuel Tolkien; Baillie Tolkien.
HOW TO APPLY In writing to the correspondent. The majority of donations are made to charities or causes selected by the trustees. There are no guidelines for applicants and the trust does not enter into correspondence with applicants in the interests of controlling administrative costs. Grant awards are usually made in the spring.
WHO TO APPLY TO Cathleen Blackburn, 9400 Garsington Road, Oxford Business Park North, Oxford OX4 2HN *Tel* 01865 722106 *Fax* 01865 201012 *email* cathleen.blacburn@manches.com
CC NO 273615   **ESTABLISHED** 1977

■ Tollemache (Buckminster) Charitable Trust

WHERE FUNDING CAN BE GIVEN UK.
WHO CAN BENEFIT Voluntary organisations and charitable groups only.
WHAT IS FUNDED General charitable purposes.
WHAT IS NOT FUNDED No grants to individuals.
SAMPLE GRANTS Previous beneficiaries have included Alzheimer's Society, Bassingthorpe PCC, Brooke Hospital for Animals, Buckminster Primary School, Buckminster United Football Club, Cancer Research, Cats Protection League, Coldstream Guards Association, Coston PCC, Ex Services Mental Welfare, NSPCC, Oxfam, Parkinson's Disease Society, Rainbows, Royal Hospital for Neuro-Disability, Royal Star & Garter Home, Rutland House School for Parents, Sight Savers, Society for the Protection of Animals Abroad, South Witham PCC, Springfield Rifle Club, St Peter's Church and WSPA.
FINANCES *Year* 2007–08 *Income* £23,500 *Grants* £20,000 *Assets* £713,000
TRUSTEES Richard Tollemache; William H G Wilks.
HOW TO APPLY In writing to the secretary. No acknowledgements sent.
WHO TO APPLY TO Roger Stafford, Estate Office, Buckminster, Grantham, Lincolnshire NG33 5SD *Tel* 01476 860471 *Fax* 01476 861235
CC NO 271795   **ESTABLISHED** 1976

■ Tomchei Torah Charitable Trust

WHERE FUNDING CAN BE GIVEN UK.
WHO CAN BENEFIT Jewish people and organisations.
WHAT IS FUNDED Jewish causes.
RANGE OF GRANTS Average £5,000.
SAMPLE GRANTS Friends of Mir (£122,000); MST College (£35,000); Friends of Sanz Institutions (£25,000); United Talmudical Associates (£15,000); Ezer North West and Menorah Grammar School (£10,000 each); Friends of Torah Ohr (£5,000); Ruzin Sadagora Trust (£4,000); Achisomoch Aid Co (£3,600); and Chesed Charity Trust (£2,600).
FINANCES *Year* 2007–08 *Income* £1,545,690 *Grants* £288,327
TRUSTEES I J Kohn; S M Kohn; A Frei.
HOW TO APPLY In writing to the correspondent at any time.
WHO TO APPLY TO The Trustees, 36 Cranbourne Gardens, London NW11 0HP
CC NO 802125   **ESTABLISHED** 1989

■ The Tompkins Foundation

WHERE FUNDING CAN BE GIVEN UK, with a stated preference for the parishes of Hampstead Norreys, Berkshire and West Grinstead, West Sussex.
WHO CAN BENEFIT Registered charities.
WHAT IS FUNDED Health, education, religion and community purposes.
WHAT IS NOT FUNDED Grants are not given to individuals.
TYPE OF GRANT One-off and recurring.
RANGE OF GRANTS £500–£50,000.
SAMPLE GRANTS Royal National Orthopaedic NHS Trust and the Foundation of Nursing Studies (£50,000 each); Chicken Shed Theatre (£25,000); International Centre for Children Studies, Toynbee Hall and the Leonard Cheshire Foundation (£20,000 each); St Edmunds School Fund (£10,000); Isabel Hospice Ball and Gayfields Home of Rest (£5,000 each); Help the Aged and St Mary's Performing Arts (£1,000 each).
FINANCES *Year* 2007–08 *Income* £484,355 *Grants* £343,500 *Assets* £11,484,850
TRUSTEES Elizabeth Tompkins; Peter Vaines.
HOW TO APPLY In writing to the correspondent. 'The trustees aim to respond to need and therefore consider that more specific plans [for the future] would be too restrictive.'
WHO TO APPLY TO Richard Geoffrey Morris, 7 Belgrave Square, London SW1X 8PH *Tel* 020 7235 9322 *Fax* 020 7259 5129
CC NO 281405   **ESTABLISHED** 1980

■ Toni and Guy Charitable Foundation Limited

WHERE FUNDING CAN BE GIVEN England and Wales.
WHO CAN BENEFIT Registered charities and hospitals.
WHAT IS FUNDED General charitable purposes.
SAMPLE GRANTS Variety Club Children's Charity (£30,000); and Italian Church Charity (£3,500).
FINANCES *Year* 2006–07 *Income* £218,763 *Grants* £33,439 *Assets* £128,269
TRUSTEES Richard A M Freeman; Pauline R Mascolo; Rupert Berrow; James McDonnell; Toni Mascolo; Sister Julia Lanagham; Angela James.
HOW TO APPLY In writing to the correspondent. The trustees meet regularly throughout the year to consider grants to be made.

WHO TO APPLY TO Sarah Oakes, 19 Doughty Street, London WC1N 2PL *Tel* 020 7440 6660 *email* charitablefoundation@toniandguy.co.uk
CC NO 1095285   **ESTABLISHED** 2002

■ The Torah Temimah Trust

WHERE FUNDING CAN BE GIVEN UK.
WHO CAN BENEFIT Orthodox Jewish organisations.
WHAT IS FUNDED Orthodox Jewish religious education and religion.
FINANCES *Year* 2007–08 *Income* £62,721 *Grants* £77,650 *Assets* £38,522
TRUSTEES Mrs E Bernath; M Bernath; A Grunfeld.
HOW TO APPLY In writing to the correspondent.
WHO TO APPLY TO Mrs E Bernath, Trustee, 16 Reizel Close, Stamford Hill, London N16 5GY
CC NO 802390

■ Toras Chesed (London) Trust

WHERE FUNDING CAN BE GIVEN Worldwide.
WHO CAN BENEFIT Jewish organisations.
WHAT IS FUNDED the objects of the charity are: the advancement of the Orthodox Jewish faith; the advancement of Orthodox Jewish religious education; the relief of poverty and infirmity among persons of the Jewish faith; to provide a safe and user friendly environment to share mutual problems and experiences; to encourage active parental participation in their children's education.
FINANCES *Year* 2007–08 *Income* £198,173 *Grants* £208,273 *Assets* £10,399
TRUSTEES A Stenn; S Stern; A Langberg.
HOW TO APPLY 'Applications for grants are considered by the trustees and reviewed in depth for final approval.'
WHO TO APPLY TO A Langberg, Trustee, 14 Lampard Grove, London N16 6UZ
CC NO 1110653   **ESTABLISHED** 2005

■ The Tory Family Foundation

WHERE FUNDING CAN BE GIVEN Worldwide, but principally Folkestone.
WHO CAN BENEFIT Charitable organisations.
WHAT IS FUNDED 'The charity was formed to provide financial help to a wide range of charitable needs. It is currently supporting causes principally in the locality of Folkestone. These causes include education, religious, social and medical subjects and the donees themselves are often registered charities.'
WHAT IS NOT FUNDED Grants are given to registered charities only. Applications outside Kent are unlikely to be considered. No grants are given for further education.
TYPE OF GRANT The charity does not normally aim to fund the whole of any given project, and thus applicants are expected to demonstrate a degree of existing and regular support.
RANGE OF GRANTS Up to £10,000, mostly £1,000 or less.
SAMPLE GRANTS Previous beneficiaries have included: Ashford YMCA, Bletchley Park, Canterbury Cathedral, Concern Worldwide, Deal Festival, Disability Law Service, Folk Rainbow Club, Foresight, Friends of Birzett, Gurkha Welfare, Kent Cancer Trust, Royal British Legion, Uppingham Foundation and Youth Action Wiltshire.
FINANCES *Year* 2007–08 *Income* £120,868 *Grants* £74,494 *Assets* £3,241,190
TRUSTEES P N Tory; J N Tory; Mrs S A Rice.

OTHER INFORMATION Some beneficiaries receive more than one grant during the year and many have been supported in previous years.

HOW TO APPLY In writing to the correspondent. Applications are considered throughout the year. To keep costs down, unsuccessful applicants will not be notified.

WHO TO APPLY TO Paul N Tory, Trustee, The Estate Office, Etchinghill Golf Club, Folkestone, Kent CT18 8FA

CC NO 326584 **ESTABLISHED** 1984

······································

■ Tottenham Grammar School Foundation

WHERE FUNDING CAN BE GIVEN The borough of Haringey.

WHO CAN BENEFIT Individuals under 25 who are in education in the borough, schools and voluntary organisations.

WHAT IS FUNDED Equipment and activities not provided by local authorities. Activities supported include youth clubs, Saturday schools and sports promotion. Grants are also made to individuals under 25 who, or whose parents, normally live in the borough, or who have attended school in the borough.

WHAT IS NOT FUNDED The foundation cannot fund: the direct delivery of the National Curriculum; the employment of staff; the construction, adaptation, repair and maintenance of buildings; the repair and maintenance of equipment.

SAMPLE GRANTS Haringey Council (£59,000 in 13 grants); Haringey Sports Development Trust (£42,600 in 13 grants); Park View Academy School (£19,600 in three grants); Chaverim Youth Organisation (£17,000 in three grants); Lubavich Youth Groups (£11,000 in three grants); North London Cricket Club (£7,500); Youth Action (£5,000); and Hornsey YMCA (£3,000).

FINANCES *Year* 2006–07 *Income* £981,265 *Grants* £611,389 *Assets* £21,803,976

TRUSTEES Keith V Brown; Terry J R Clarke; Paul Compton; Anthony G Fogg; Frederick Gruncell; Peter Jones; Michael J McLellan; Keith McGuinness; Ms Victoria Phillips; Andrew Krokou.

OTHER INFORMATION The foundation halted all grant making in 2009 due to a drop in investment income. Please refer to the foundation's website for up-to-date information on the current situation.

HOW TO APPLY On a form available from the correspondent, however, please see 'other information'.

WHO TO APPLY TO Graham Chappell, Clerk, PO Box 34098, London N13 5XU *Tel* 020 8882 2999 *Fax* 020 8882 9724 *email* trustees@tgsf.org.uk *Website* www.tgsf.org.uk

CC NO 312634 **ESTABLISHED** 1989

······································

■ The Tower Hill Trust

WHERE FUNDING CAN BE GIVEN Tower Hill and St Katherine's ward in Tower Hamlets.

WHO CAN BENEFIT Community-based organisations and appeals benefiting children and young adults, at risk groups, people disadvantaged by poverty and socially isolated people.

WHAT IS FUNDED Organisations working for the relief of need or sickness, the provision of leisure and recreation facilities for social welfare and in support of education, and to provide and maintain gardens and open spaces.

WHAT IS NOT FUNDED No grants to individuals.

TYPE OF GRANT General and capital projects involving building renovation will be considered.

RANGE OF GRANTS Generally £300–£25,000.

SAMPLE GRANTS City of London Girls (£43,500); Historic Royal Palaces (£20,500); City of London CAB (£16,000); Wapping Bangladesh Association (£12,500); Attlee Foundation (£6,600); Whizz Kids (£5,000); Newark Youth London (£4,000); Common Ground East (£2,000); and Alternative Arts (£1,000).

FINANCES *Year* 2007–08 *Income* £212,727 *Grants* £212,049 *Assets* £4,784,758

TRUSTEES Mrs Davina Walter, Chair; Maj. Gen. Christopher Tyler; John Polk; Comm. John Burton-Hall; Hamish Ritchie; Mrs Susan Wood.

HOW TO APPLY 'We have a two-stage application process. Stage One – Initial Proposal: Initially we ask you to send in a proposal (up to three pages) that covers the points below. We also ask for certain additional documents (see below). When we receive your proposal we will send you an acknowledgement and may ask you for further clarification. You may submit your proposal at any time. Every three months (February, May, August and November), Trustees will look at all of the initial proposals we have received and draw up a shortlist. All proposals that are not on the shortlist will be rejected. Stage Two – Further Information:If your proposal is successfully shortlisted, you move on to stage two of the process and will be asked for further information. You may also receive a visit from our Grant Officer. Your proposal will then be presented to a Trustees' meeting, which will make the final decision about your request. Not all shortlisted organisations will receive funding, as the Trust considers more proposals than we are able to support. Please note that the whole process (stage one and stage two) is likely to take up to four months.'

WHO TO APPLY TO Elaine Crush, Grants Officer, Attlee House, 28 Commercial Street, London E1 6LR *Tel* 020 7377 6614 *Fax* 020 7377 9822 *email* enquiries@towerhilltrust.org.uk *Website* www.towerhilltrust.org.uk

CC NO 206225 **ESTABLISHED** 1938

······································

■ The Towry Law Charitable Trust

(also known as the Castle Educational Trust)

WHERE FUNDING CAN BE GIVEN UK, with a slight preference for the south of England.

WHO CAN BENEFIT Organisations benefiting people of all ages and disabled people.

WHAT IS FUNDED Education, medical research and social welfare.

WHAT IS NOT FUNDED No grants to individuals, bodies which are not UK-registered charities, local branches or associates of UK charities.

RANGE OF GRANTS Up to £10,000.

SAMPLE GRANTS RNIB (£10,000); Berkshire Community Foundation (£7,000); Campden Area Nursing Home Trust (£5,000); Skeletal Cancer Action Trust (£3,000); Thames Valley & Chiltern Air Ambulance Trust (£2,000); and Spinal Research (£1,000).

FINANCES *Year* 2007–08 *Income* £88,151 *Grants* £63,265 *Assets* £1,794,908

TRUSTEES Andrew Fisher; David Middleton; Ms Alex Rickard.

HOW TO APPLY The trust has previously stated that unsolicited applications are not considered. The trust currently states that 'grants are agreed by the trustees at their half yearly meetings, to a mixture of national and local charities which come to their attention as operating in their respective local communities. These are usually for specific projects where it is believed that the relatively small grants feasible within our budget "will make a difference"'.

WHO TO APPLY TO Jacqueline Gregory, Towry Law Group, 6 New Street Square, London EC4A 3BF *Tel* 020 7936 7236 *email* jacqui.gregory@ towrylaw.com

CC NO 278880   **ESTABLISHED** 1979

■ The Toy Trust

WHERE FUNDING CAN BE GIVEN UK.
WHO CAN BENEFIT Children's charities.
WHAT IS FUNDED Projects benefiting children.
SAMPLE GRANTS Great Ormond Street Hospital (£47,000); the National Autistic Society (£30,000); the Friends of Baale Mane Gopalapura (£28,000); Action Force for Africa (£5,900); Cerebra, Cystic Fibrosis Dream Holidays, Lennox Children's Cancer Fund and Whizz Kids (£5,000 each); Rays of Sunshine Children's Charity (£4,800); and PACE, South Tyneside Football Trust and YWCA England and Wales (£4,000 each).
FINANCES *Year* 2008 *Income* £228,493 *Grants* £184,274 *Assets* £145,088
TRUSTEES The British Toy and Hobby Association; Roger Dyson, Chair; Nick Austin; Clive Jones; Christine Nicholls.
OTHER INFORMATION This trust was registered in 1991 to centralise the giving of the British Toy and Hobby Association.
HOW TO APPLY In writing to the correspondent.
WHO TO APPLY TO The Secretary, c/o British Toy and Hobby Association, 80 Camberwell Road, London SE5 0EG *Website* www.btha.co.uk
CC NO 1001634   **ESTABLISHED** 1991

■ The Mayor of Trafford's Charity Fund

WHERE FUNDING CAN BE GIVEN The borough of Trafford.
WHO CAN BENEFIT Voluntary organisations and charitable groups only.
WHAT IS FUNDED The mayor/mayoress chooses a single charity (occasionally two) to support the year before he/she takes office; the charity must benefit the inhabitants of the borough of Trafford.
TYPE OF GRANT Capital; one-off; one year or less.
SAMPLE GRANTS Previous beneficiaries include: Victim Support (£18,000); Intergen (£1,000); and 'Earthquake Appeal' (£500).
FINANCES *Year* 2007–08 *Income* £19,145 *Grants* £19,145
TRUSTEES Ian Duncan; Beverley Dunn; David Higgins.
HOW TO APPLY As the recipient charity is selected before the mayor takes office, there is little point applying to this fund.
WHO TO APPLY TO The Mayor's Office, Mayor's Office, Trafford Town Hall, Talbot Road, Stretford, Trafford, Manchester M32 0YT *Tel* 0161 912 4106 *Fax* 0161 912 1251 *email* mayors. office@trafford.gov.uk
CC NO 512299   **ESTABLISHED** 1982

■ Annie Tranmer Charitable Trust

WHERE FUNDING CAN BE GIVEN UK, particularly Suffolk and adjacent counties.
WHO CAN BENEFIT Organisations and individuals.
WHAT IS FUNDED The objectives of the trust are to: make grants in the county of Suffolk and adjacent counties; make grants to national charities according to the wished of Mrs Tranmer during her lifetime; advance education and historical research relating to the national monument known as Sutton Hoo burial site and Sutton Hoo estate; protect and preserve the Sutton Hoo burial site; to further the education of children and young people in Suffolk; make grants for general charitable purposes.
SAMPLE GRANTS East Anglian Air Ambulance and the Suffolk Punch Trust (£10,000 each); Hope House Suffolk (£6,400); Great Ormond Street Hospital (£6,000); the Seckford Foundation (£5,000); Independent Age and Motor Neurone Disease (£3,000 each); Children with Leukaemia (£2,500); Bowel Cancer UK (£2,250); St Elizabeth Hospice (£2,000); Ipswich Furniture Project, the National Autistic Society and RNIB (£1,000 each); Listening Books (£600); Suffolk Family Carers and Wellchild (£500 each); and Bredfield Youth Project (£250).
FINANCES *Year* 2007–08 *Income* £116,787 *Grants* £132,229 *Assets* £3,719,460
TRUSTEES J F F Miller; V A Lewis; N J Bonham-Carter.
OTHER INFORMATION The grant total in 2007–08 included £12,000 donated to 28 individuals.
HOW TO APPLY This trust does not accept unsolicited applications.
WHO TO APPLY TO Mrs M R Kirby, Clerk to the Trustees, 51 Bennett Road, Ipswich IP1 5HX
CC NO 1044231   **ESTABLISHED** 1989

■ Anthony Travis Charitable Trust

WHERE FUNDING CAN BE GIVEN UK.
WHO CAN BENEFIT Charitable organisations.
WHAT IS FUNDED General charitable purposes.
SAMPLE GRANTS Chetham's School of Music, Maggie's Cancer Caring Centres, the Three Miracles Fund and Volunteer Reading Help (£5,000 each); St Mary's School Ascot Development Fund (£3,000); Dyslexia Teaching Centre (£2,500); the Berkley Reforestation Trust, Derry Hill Trust (£2,000); Compassion in World Farming (£1,000); Children's Hospital Trust Fund (£500); Cancer Research UK (£200); and Filipino Club at Westminster Cathedral (£100).
FINANCES *Year* 2008–09 *Income* £94,763 *Grants* £53,250 *Assets* £1,614,544
TRUSTEES E R A Travis; M J Travis; P J Travis.
HOW TO APPLY In writing to the correspondent. The trustees meet on a regular basis to consider what grants they will make.
WHO TO APPLY TO Anthony Travis, 86 Drayton Gardens, London SW10 9SB
CC NO 1095198   **ESTABLISHED** 2003

■ The Constance Travis Charitable Trust

WHERE FUNDING CAN BE GIVEN UK (national charities only); Northamptonshire (all sectors).
WHO CAN BENEFIT UK-wide organisations and local groups in Northamptonshire.
WHAT IS FUNDED General charitable purposes.

WHAT IS NOT FUNDED No grants to individuals or non-registered charities.

TYPE OF GRANT One-off grants for core, capital and project support.

RANGE OF GRANTS Up to £30,000.

SAMPLE GRANTS Museum of Leathercraft (£100,000); Northamptonshire Community Foundation (£35,000); Cynthia Spencer Hospice Appeal (£30,000); Age Concern Northamptonshire (£20,000); Three Little Miracles Fund (£15,000); Royal Academy of Music (£10,000); Deafness Research UK (£7,000); Action for ME, Grange Park Church, Northampton Hope Centre and RNIB (£5,000 each); Crimestoppers Trust and Prisoners Abroad (£4,000 each); Cancerbackup and St Francis' Children's Society (£3,000 each); British Liver Trust and Volunteer Action Northamptonshire (£2,000 each); and Battersea Dogs & Cats Home and Weston Favell Ceva Primary School (£1,000 each).

FINANCES *Year* 2008 *Income* £3,938,884 *Grants* £902,500 *Assets* £27,148,747

TRUSTEES Mrs Constance M Travis; Earnest R A Travis; Peta J Travis; Matthew Travis.

HOW TO APPLY In writing to the correspondent.

WHO TO APPLY TO Earnest R A Travis, Trustee, Quinton Rising, Quinton, Northampton NN7 2EF *Tel* 01604 862296

CC NO 294540   **ESTABLISHED** 1986

■ The Treeside Trust

WHERE FUNDING CAN BE GIVEN UK, but mainly in Oldham.

WHO CAN BENEFIT Mainly small local charities, as well as a few UK-wide charities which are supported on a regular basis.

WHAT IS FUNDED General charitable purposes.

TYPE OF GRANT One-off.

RANGE OF GRANTS The trust states: 'In the main the trustees intend to make a limited number of substantial grants each year, rather than a larger number of smaller ones, in order to make significant contributions to some of the causes supported.'

SAMPLE GRANTS A list of beneficiaries was unavailable.

FINANCES *Year* 2007–08 *Income* £157,813 *Grants* £108,000 *Assets* £1,201,386

TRUSTEES C C Gould; J R B Gould; J R W Gould; D M Ives; R J Ives; B Washbrook.

HOW TO APPLY The trust has stated that they 'do not welcome unsolicited applications'.

WHO TO APPLY TO John Gould, Trustee, 4 The Park, Grasscroft, Oldham OL4 4ES *Tel* 01457 876422

CC NO 1061586   **ESTABLISHED** 1997

■ The Tresillian Trust

WHERE FUNDING CAN BE GIVEN Worldwide.

WHO CAN BENEFIT Charitable organisations.

WHAT IS FUNDED Overseas aid and welfare causes.

SAMPLE GRANTS International Rescue Committee (£20,000); Sightsavers International, the Bishop Simeon Trust and Street Child Africa (£5,000 each); Avert, Families of Spinal Muscular Atrophy, One Ummah Foundation and Saigon Children's Charity (£2,000 each); and the Condor Trust for Education and Contact the Elderly (£1,000 each).

FINANCES *Year* 2007–08 *Income* £1,282,051 *Grants* £56,102 *Assets* £2,897,438

TRUSTEES G E S Robinson; P W Bate; M D Willcox.

HOW TO APPLY In writing to the correspondent. 'The trust is very selective in the grant making process and applications are reviewed by the trustees personally.'

WHO TO APPLY TO M D Willcox, Trustee, Old Coach House, Sunnyside, Bergh Apton, Norwich NR15 1DD

CC NO 1105826   **ESTABLISHED** 2004

■ The Triangle Trust (1949) Fund

WHERE FUNDING CAN BE GIVEN Worldwide, but in practice, the UK.

WHO CAN BENEFIT Individuals and organisations, mainly registered charities.

WHAT IS FUNDED Organisations supporting carers, people with disabilities, older people, disadvantaged people, integration and rehabilitation and community arts and education. Also individuals in need who are employed or who have been employed in the pharmaceutical industry, and their dependants.

WHAT IS NOT FUNDED Direct applications from individuals; overseas charities or projects outside the UK; charities for the promotion of religion; medical research; environmental, wildlife or heritage appeals; applications funded in the last two years, unless at the trustees invitation.

TYPE OF GRANT One-off, recurring, salaries and running costs.

RANGE OF GRANTS £1,000–£55,000.

SAMPLE GRANTS Family Welcome Association (£55,000); Leicester Charity Link (£17,000); Dundee City Council (£16,000); Somerset Community Foundation (£15,000); Seesaw (£13,000); Mobility Trust (£12,000); Fine Cell Work (£10,000); Aidis Trust (£5,000); 999 Club (£4,000); the Seeing Ear (£3,000); Kennett Furniture Recycling (£2,800); Winchester Young Carers (£2,000); and Beacon of Hope (£1,000).

FINANCES *Year* 2007–08 *Income* £527,235 *Grants* £573,794 *Assets* £16,268,271

TRUSTEES Melanie Burfitt, Chair; Dr Robert Hale; Mark Powell; Bruce Newbigging; Philip Davies; Kate Purcell; Helen Evans; Jamie Dicks.

OTHER INFORMATION In addition to the figure given above, £43,000 was given in grants to 56 individuals in need.

HOW TO APPLY Organisations should apply using the trust's application form, available from its website. Guidelines are also provided by the trust. Application hardcopies should be typed, and applicants should include their latest report and accounts with the application form (if submitting an online application, applicants should send their latest report and accounts separately as soon possible). The trustees meet quarterly in February, June, October and December to award grants. Applications should be submitted in the preceding month (January, May, September and November). Please note: applicants may be asked to present their project(s) to the trustees.

WHO TO APPLY TO Lesley Lilley, Secretary to the Trust, 32 Bloomsbury Street, London WC1B 3QJ *Tel* 020 7299 4245 *email* lesleylilley@triangletrust.org *Website* www.thetriangletrust1949fund.org.uk

CC NO 222860   **ESTABLISHED** 1949

Think carefully about every application. Is it justified?

911

■ The True Colours Trust

WHERE FUNDING CAN BE GIVEN Mostly UK and Africa.
WHO CAN BENEFIT Registered charities.
WHAT IS FUNDED Grant-making is focused in three areas: children and young people with complex disabilities in the UK; palliative care for children and young people in the UK; and palliative care in sub-Saharan Africa. The trust also makes small grants to local charities supporting disabled children, children with life-limiting conditions, their siblings and their families.
WHAT IS NOT FUNDED No grants to individuals.
TYPE OF GRANT One-off and recurring. Local grants tend to be one-off and for capital expenditure.
RANGE OF GRANTS Up to £436,000.
SAMPLE GRANTS Association for Children's Palliative Care (£436,000); African Palliative Care Association (£150,000); National Deaf Children's Society (£148,000); Maua Methodist Hospital (£90,000); Tower Hamlets Toyhouse Library (£57,000); Back-Up Trust (£25,000); Parity for Disability (£15,000); Children's Adventure Farm Trust (£10,000); and Princess Royal Trust (£6,000).
FINANCES *Year* 2007–08 *Income* £2,915,986 *Grants* £2,538,903 *Assets* £8,266,236
TRUSTEES Lucy A Sainsbury; Dominic B Flynn; Bernard J C Willis.
HOW TO APPLY The trust states that projects for the three strategic programmes are usually invited by the trustees or initiated at their request, and while they are keen to learn more about organisations whose work fits into these categories, unsolicited applications are not encouraged and are unlikely to be successful. Please note: unsolicited applications for the 'Local Causes for Disadvantaged Children' programme are welcomed.
See the guidance for applicants in the entry for the Sainsbury Family Charitable Trusts. A single application will be considered for support by all the trusts in the group. However, please see comments regarding the selection of beneficiaries.
WHO TO APPLY TO Alan Bookbinder, Director, Allington House, 1st Floor, 150 Victoria Street, London SW1E 5AE *Tel* 020 7410 0330 *Fax* 020 7410 0332 *email* truecolours@sfct.org.uk *Website* www.truecolourstrust.org.uk
CC NO 1089893   **ESTABLISHED** 2001

■ Truedene Co. Ltd

WHERE FUNDING CAN BE GIVEN UK and overseas.
WHO CAN BENEFIT Organisations benefiting children, young adults, students and Jewish people.
WHAT IS FUNDED Educational, religious and other charitable institutions, principally Jewish.
RANGE OF GRANTS £1,000–£150,000.
SAMPLE GRANTS Previous beneficiaries have included: Beis Ruchel D'Satmar Girls School Ltd, British Friends of Tchernobyl, Congregation Paile Yoetz, Cosmon Belz Limited, Friends of Mir, Kolel Shomrei Hachomoth, Mesifta Talmudical College, Mosdos Ramou, Orthodox Council of Jerusalem, Tevini Limited, United Talmudical Associates Limited, VMCT and Yeshivo Horomo Talmudical College.
FINANCES *Year* 2007–08 *Income* £1,018,024 *Grants* £1,125,616 *Assets* £4,077,004
TRUSTEES Sarah Klein, Chair; Samuel Berger; Solomon Laufer; Sije Berger; Zelda Sternlicht.
HOW TO APPLY In writing to the correspondent

WHO TO APPLY TO The Trustees, c/o Cohen Arnold and Co., 1075 Finchley Road, London NW11 0PU
CC NO 248268   **ESTABLISHED** 1966

■ The Truemark Trust

WHERE FUNDING CAN BE GIVEN UK.
WHO CAN BENEFIT Registered charities with preference for small local charities, neighbourhood-based community projects and innovative work with less popular groups.
WHAT IS FUNDED 'The relief of all kinds of social distress and disadvantage.'
WHAT IS NOT FUNDED Grants are made to registered charities only. Applications from individuals, including students, are ineligible. No grants are made in response to general appeals from large national charities. Grants are seldom available for churches or church buildings or for scientific or medical research projects.
TYPE OF GRANT Usually one-off for a specific project or part of a project. Core funding and/or salaries rarely considered.
RANGE OF GRANTS Average grant £1,000.
SAMPLE GRANTS Inner Yoga Trust, Petersfield (£5,000); Jumbulance (£4,000); Acorn to Oak Children's Trust and Winchester Youth Counselling (£3,000 each); Children's Chronic Arthritis Association (£2,500); Access to Art, Clothing Solutions, Norfolk Association for the Disabled, Norris Green Youth Centre Ltd and Sussex Autistic Society (£2,000 each); Different Strokes, East Didsbury Methodist Church and Hertfordshire Gardens Trust (£1,500 each); and Brighton Unemployed Centre Families Project, Citylife, Olive Branch Counselling and Wishing Well Waters (£1,000 each).
FINANCES *Year* 2007–08 *Income* £479,925 *Grants* £283,500 *Assets* £10,446,119
TRUSTEES Sir T Lucas; S Neil; Mrs W Collett; D Hawkins; Mrs J Hayward; R Wolfe.
HOW TO APPLY In writing to the correspondent, including the most recent set of accounts, clear details of the need the project is designed to meet and an outline budget. Trustees meet four times a year. Only successful applicants receive a reply.
WHO TO APPLY TO The Trustees, PO Box 2, Liss, Hampshire GU33 6YP
CC NO 265855   **ESTABLISHED** 1973

■ Truemart Limited

WHERE FUNDING CAN BE GIVEN UK-wide and overseas, with a preference for Greater London.
WHO CAN BENEFIT Charitable organisations.
WHAT IS FUNDED The advancement of religion in accordance with the Orthodox Jewish faith, the relief of poverty and general charitable purposes.
FINANCES *Year* 2006–07 *Income* £56,636 *Grants* £71,610
TRUSTEES I Heitner; I M Cymerman; B Hoffman.
HOW TO APPLY In writing to the correspondent.
WHO TO APPLY TO Mrs S Heitner, Secretary, 34 The Ridgeway, London NW11 8QS
CC NO 1090586   **ESTABLISHED** 1984

■ Trumros Limited

WHERE FUNDING CAN BE GIVEN UK.

WHO CAN BENEFIT Jewish institutions.

WHAT IS FUNDED Jewish religious and educational institutions.

RANGE OF GRANTS £100–£20,000; typical grant under £1,000.

SAMPLE GRANTS Chevras Mo'oslodol (£34,000); Beis Joseph Zvi Jerusalem (£29,000); Menorah Primary School (£25,000); BEFORE Trust (£20,000); Yeshiva Orah Yehoshua (£18,000); Shomrei Emunim (£12,000); Chevras Ezros Nizrochim (£10,000); London Academy of Jewish Studies (£9,600); Toldos Aharon (£9,000); and Jewish Learning Exchange (£8,500).

FINANCES *Year* 2008 *Income* £983,417 *Grants* £518,670 *Assets* £6,626,778

TRUSTEES R S Hofbauer; Mrs H Hofbauer.

HOW TO APPLY In writing to the correspondent, but note that the trust states it is already inundated with applications.

WHO TO APPLY TO Mrs H Hofbauer, Trustee, 282 Finchley Road, London NW3 7AD

CC NO 285533   **ESTABLISHED** 1982

■ The Trust for Education

WHERE FUNDING CAN BE GIVEN UK and Africa with a preference for West Yorkshire.

WHO CAN BENEFIT Educational institutions and charities.

WHAT IS FUNDED 'The charity's objects are to advance education of the public, in particular, by the development of people's abilities to enter into post-compulsory education and the promotion and development of pubic knowledge and understanding about the institutions engaged in post-compulsory education and the range and diversity of their provision.'

WHAT IS NOT FUNDED 'The charity does not make grants to individuals for educational purposes, but only works through charities advancing education directly or indirectly.'

SAMPLE GRANTS Barnardo's (£268,000); The Prince's Trust (£178,000); CAMFED International (£50,000); Impetus Trust (£25,000); Caring for Life (£20,000); Careers Bradford and L'Ouverlure (£10,000 each); Leeds Common Purpose (£7,000); Leeds Rugby Foundation (£4,000); and Bradford Nightstop and York Travellers Trust (£1,000 each).

FINANCES *Year* 2006–07 *Income* £149,546 *Grants* £668,192 *Assets* £2,437,204

TRUSTEES Francis J Griffiths, Chair; Derek J Betts; Richard Mansell; Thomas Riordan.

HOW TO APPLY In writing to the correspondent.

WHO TO APPLY TO Malcolm J Lynch, Secretary, Wrigleys Solicitors, 19 Cookridge Street, Leeds LS2 3AG

CC NO 1000408   **ESTABLISHED** 1990

■ Trust for London

WHERE FUNDING CAN BE GIVEN Greater London.

WHO CAN BENEFIT Organisations that: benefit local people and communities in London; are open to all members of the community; help local communities to identify and tackle local problems; do work that might be used to teach others; local people and communities have set up to help themselves; are open to all members of their community; and are set up to tackle a specific issue. Funding is mainly given to refugee and migrant groups; self-help groups, educational activities for children and young people, black, Asian and minority ethnic groups, organisations for people with disabilities, estate-based organisations, lesbian and gay groups, older people's groups, organisations set up to tackle a specific issue, women's groups and youth groups; and supplementary and mother-tongue schools.

WHAT IS FUNDED The trust aims to develop supportive relationships with the community and voluntary organisations that it funds and to provide a 'funding-plus' approach. 'Funding-plus' includes providing advice, guidance, and where appropriate, consultancy support and training to help organisations grow and develop. Current aims are: to challenge discrimination faced by disabled people; to promote the inclusion and integration of recently established communities; to strengthen mother-tongue and supplementary schools to provide creative educational opportunities; to address new and emerging needs.

WHAT IS NOT FUNDED The following applications are not considered: from organisations which have paid staff who between them work more than 35 hours per week; for work that is the responsibility of statutory funders such as local and central government and health authorities; that directly replace or subsidise statutory funding; from individuals or which are for the benefit of an individual; for medical purposes including hospitals and hospices; for distribution by umbrella bodies; for general appeals; for holiday playschemes or playgroups; for major expenses for buying or building premises; for research; for trips abroad; for the promotion of religion; for work that has already taken place; for animal welfare; from applicants who have been rejected by the trust within the last six months; and from organisations which have received funding from the trust's sister fund, City Parochial Foundation. The trust is unlikely to support proposals: from organisations based outside London; for work that takes place in schools during school hours; from organisations with significant unrestricted reserves (including those that are designated). Generally up to six months expenditure is normally acceptable; and from organisations in serious financial deficit.

TYPE OF GRANT Core costs, part-time or sessional salaries (not full-time), equipment, capital purchases.

RANGE OF GRANTS Maximum grant available is £10,000 a year.

SAMPLE GRANTS Kanlungan Filipino Consortium (£49,000); Ocean Women's Association (£30,000); Food4Thought (£22,000); Islington Borough User Group (£19,000); Kongolese Children's Association (£16,000); South East Russian Language Society (£14,000); Bromley Somali Community Association (£12,000); Clapham and Stockwell Faith Forum (£8,000); and True Heart Theatre (£5,000).

FINANCES *Year* 2008 *Income* £644,908 *Grants* £778,919 *Assets* £14,767,303

TRUSTEES Nigel Pantling, Chair; Miles Barber; Maggie Baxter; Tzeggai Yohannes Deres; Revd Dr Martin Dudley; The Archdeacon of London, The Ven. Peter Delaney; Archie Galloway; Roger Evans; Deborah Finkler; Cllr Lynne Hillan; Robert Hughes-Penney; Robert Laurence; Elahe Panahi; Ingrid Posen; Wilfred Weeks; Peter Williams.

OTHER INFORMATION The trust also works with other funding organisations and funded groups to identify emerging needs and to develop and make appropriate responses.

HOW TO APPLY The trust's funding guidelines for 2007–11 are available to download from its website. Alternatively contact the trust's office for hard copies. It is strongly recommended that potential applicants read the guidelines before making an application. There is a two-stage application process – *Stage one:* an initial proposal to be submitted by post. There are three closing dates for proposals to be submitted by – you may submit your proposal at any time but it will only be assessed once the next closing date has passed. Closing dates are: 7 February for the June Grants Committee; 30 May for the October Grants Committee; 25 October for the March Grants Committee. *Stage two:* all organisations whose initial proposals are shortlisted will be visited by the foundation to assess their suitability for funding.

WHO TO APPLY TO Bharat Mehta, Clerk to the Trustees, 6 Middle Street, London EC1A 7PH *Tel* 020 7606 6145 *Fax* 020 7600 1866 *email* trustforlondon@cityparochial.org.uk *Website* www.trustforlondon.org.uk
CC NO 294710   **ESTABLISHED** 1986

....
■ Trust Sixty Three

WHERE FUNDING CAN BE GIVEN UK and overseas, with a preference for Bedfordshire and Hertfordshire.
WHO CAN BENEFIT Mostly disability causes, overseas aid and famine relief.
WHAT IS FUNDED General charitable purposes.
WHAT IS NOT FUNDED No grants to individuals.
SAMPLE GRANTS Previous beneficiaries include Brandles School, Bedfordshire County Council, Pasque Hospice, St Mary's Church, Home Start Hitchin, Mobility Trust, SCOPE, Clophill Churches Aid Appeal, Botton Village, North Hertfordshire Sanctuary, Bedfordshire Cargen Carers and Hertfordshire Community Foundation.
FINANCES *Year* 2007–08 *Income* £5,162 *Grants* £50,000
TRUSTEES Joanne Hobbs; Clive G Nott; Deborah Staines.
HOW TO APPLY The trust has previously stated that in the future it will be focussing solely on its existing grantees.
WHO TO APPLY TO Joanne Hobbs, Trustee, Notts Ltd, 38B Rothesay Road, Luton LU1 1QZ *Tel* 01525 860777 *Fax* 01525 545090
CC NO 1049136   **ESTABLISHED** 1995

....
■ The Trusthouse Charitable Foundation

WHERE FUNDING CAN BE GIVEN Unrestricted, but mainly UK.
WHO CAN BENEFIT Registered charities and other not-for-profit organisations.
WHAT IS FUNDED Within the trust's overarching themes, there are three broad areas of funding: community support; disability and healthcare; arts, education and heritage.
WHAT IS NOT FUNDED The foundation will not normally consider supporting the following: animal welfare; applications for revenue funding for more than one year; capital appeals for places of worship; grant making organisations or umbrella groups; grants for individuals; feasibility studies and evaluations; local authorities; local education authority schools or their PTA's, except if those schools are for students with special needs; medical research projects; organisations that have received a grant for three consecutive years from the foundation; projects involving the start-up or piloting of new services; projects where the

primary objective is environmental or conservation; projects where the primary objective is the promotion of a particular religion; revenue funding for organisations with an income of over £300,000 a year; services operated by the NHS; social research; training of professionals within the UK; renovation or alteration projects to make a building compliant with the Disability & Discrimination Act; office IT equipment.

TYPE OF GRANT One-off for specific purposes.
SAMPLE GRANTS Age Concern – Montgomeryshire (£39,000); Arch – North Staffordshire (£23,000); Linden Lodge Charitable Trust (£20,000); Bluecoat Arts Centre Ltd (£15,000); Ravensthorpe Community Centre and LEPRA (£10,000 each); Storybook Dads (£9,500); Mentoring Plus Ltd (£8,000); Wings – Wombourne Special Needs Support Group (£7,000); Autism Networks and Leeds Black Elders Association (£6,000 each); Home-Start Isle of Wight and Northampton Hope Centre (£4,000 each); King's Outreach (£3,000); Musical Arc (£1,500); Thorpland United Football Club (£1,100); and Merthyr Women's Aid (£800).
FINANCES *Year* 2007–08 *Income* £2,412,000 *Grants* £2,070,675 *Assets* £67,136,000
TRUSTEES Sir Richard Carew Pole, Chair; Sir Jeremy Beecham; Lord Bernstein of Craigwell; The Baroness Cox of Queensbury; The Earl of Gainsborough; The Duke of Marlborough; The Hon. Mrs Olga Polizzi; Sir Hugh Rossi; The Lady Stevenson; Baroness Hogg; Anthony Peel; Lady Janet Balfour of Burleigh.
HOW TO APPLY The following application guidelines are taken from the trust's website: 'The trustees require all applicants to complete a one page application form which summarises their appeal [...] All sections of the form must be completed fully, it is not sufficient to refer to 'see attached documents'. Applicants are also required to provide supporting information on approximately two A4 sheets in accordance with guidelines available from the foundation by post or its website.
WHO TO APPLY TO Judith Leigh, Grants Manager, 6th Floor, 65 Leadenhall Street, London EC3A 2AD *Tel* 020 7264 4990 *Website* www. trusthousecharitablefoundation.org.uk
CC NO 1063945   **ESTABLISHED** 1997

....
■ The Tubney Charitable Trust

WHERE FUNDING CAN BE GIVEN Unrestricted.
WHO CAN BENEFIT UK registered, exempt and excepted charities which undertake charitable activities where there is a demonstrable element of outward provision and benefit to the community at large, to ensure that as many people benefit as possible.
WHAT IS FUNDED Conservation of the natural environment of the UK and farmed animal welfare.
Please note: the trust plans to allocate its remaining funds by 2011. For this reason it has closed its open programmes in order to focus on funding proactive work on an invitation-to-bid basis only.
TYPE OF GRANT Capital and revenue.
SAMPLE GRANTS Farm Animal Welfare Trust (£1.5 million); RSPCA (£1.2 million); University of Bristol – two grants (£965,000); Woodland Trust (£750,000); Devon Wildlife Trust (£500,000); National Trust (£222,000); World Society for the Protection of Animals (£100,000); Vale Landscape Heritage Trust

(£70,000); Tweed Forum Ltd. (£69,000); Yorkshire Dales Millennium Trust (£60,000); Little Ouse Headwaters Charity (£55,000); and Argyll Green Woodworkers Association (£46,000).

FINANCES *Year* 2007–08 *Income* £2,056,000 *Grants* £7,354,000 *Assets* £29,412,000

TRUSTEES Jonathan Burchfield, Chair; Terry Collins; Jim Kennedy; René Olivieri.

HOW TO APPLY As of June 2008 the trust no longer accepts unsolicited applications. Applications will be on an invitation-to-bid basis only.

WHO TO APPLY TO Sarah Ridley, Executive Director, First Floor, Front Wing, 30–31 Friar Street, Reading RG1 1DX *Tel* 0118 958 6100 *Fax* 0118 959 4400 *email* info@tubney.org.uk *Website* www.tubney.org.uk

CC NO 1061480 **ESTABLISHED** 1997

■ The James Tudor Foundation

WHERE FUNDING CAN BE GIVEN UK and overseas.

WHO CAN BENEFIT Institutions and registered charities.

WHAT IS FUNDED The foundation's six programme areas are: palliative care; medical research; health education, awards and scholarship; the direct relief of sickness; the UK independent healthcare sector; the fulfilment of the foundation's charitable objects by other means.

WHAT IS NOT FUNDED Grants are not made: 'that directly replace, or negatively affect, statutory funding; for work that has already taken place; for endowment funds; for economic, community development or employment use; for adventure or residential courses, expeditions or overseas travel; for sport or recreation uses, including festivals; for environmental, conservation or heritage causes; for animal welfare; from applicants who have applied to us within the last 12 months.'

TYPE OF GRANT Project funding, awards and scholarships, capital projects and equipment and staffing costs.

RANGE OF GRANTS Mostly up to £10,000.

SAMPLE GRANTS Tommy's, the Baby Charity (£75,000 in total); Children's Hospice South West (£45,000); St Peter's Hospice – Bristol (£35,000); Tim Reeve Foundation/University College London (£30,000); CLIC (£16,000); National Rheumatoid Arthritis Association (£15,000); Braveheart – Falkirk and Clackmannanshire (£10,000); Locharber Centre for Deaf People in Scotland (£4,800); National Tremor Association (£4,000); and Community Relief North London (£1,000).

FINANCES *Year* 2007–08 *Income* £792,376 *Grants* £607,500 *Assets* £23,047,575

TRUSTEES Martin G Wren, Chair; Richard R G Esler; Malcolm R Field; Roger K Jones; Cedric B Nash.

HOW TO APPLY On an application form available from the foundation's website. Comprehensive guidelines for applicant are also available from there.

WHO TO APPLY TO The Secretary, WestPoint, 78 Queens Road, Clifton, Bristol BS8 1QU *Tel* 0117 985 8715 *Fax* 0117 985 8716 *email* admin@jamestudor.org.uk *Website* www.jamestudor.org.uk

CC NO 1105916 **ESTABLISHED** 2004

■ Tudor Rose Ltd

WHERE FUNDING CAN BE GIVEN UK.

WHO CAN BENEFIT Registered charities benefiting Jewish people and people disadvantaged by poverty.

WHAT IS FUNDED Advancement of religion (orthodox Jewish), relief of poverty and other charitable purposes.

SAMPLE GRANTS Lolev Charitable Trust (£58,000); Woodlands Charity (£32,000); KTV (£14,000); Bell Synagogue (£11,000); Hatzola (£10,000); Lubavitch Centre (£5,000); and TCT (£4,000).

FINANCES *Year* 2006–07 *Income* £359,748 *Grants* £219,000 *Assets* £2,787,091

TRUSTEES M Lehrfield; M Taub; A Taub; S Taub; S L Taub.

HOW TO APPLY In writing to the correspondent.

WHO TO APPLY TO Samuel Taub, Secretary, c/o Martin and Heller, 5 North End Road, London NW11 7RJ

CC NO 800576 **ESTABLISHED** 1987

■ The Tudor Trust

WHERE FUNDING CAN BE GIVEN UK and sub-Saharan Africa.

WHO CAN BENEFIT Registered charities and other charitable organisations.

WHAT IS FUNDED 'The Tudor Trust is an independent grant-making charitable trust which supports organisations working across the UK. We do not focus our funding on specific themes or programmes. Instead we want to fund a wide range of people and organisations working to achieve lasting change in their communities. Our role is to support and enable their visions, trusting the groups we fund to do the work that is needed. Tudor aims to support work which addresses the social, emotional and financial needs of people at the margins of our society. We are interested in how organisations tackle these needs, and their root causes. We want to encourage growth, progression and development, not just keeping things as they are. Although we still make grants across our established funding areas (youth, older people, community, relationships, housing, mental health, substance misuse, learning, financial security and criminal justice) we are also open to hearing about work in areas we have not funded before. We receive many more applications than we will ever be able to fund, so we have introduced a two-stage application process. This is designed to reduce the time, effort and resources organisations spend on their first approach to us. All applicants are therefore asked to complete a brief first-stage proposal for initial assessment. There are some types of organisation and work which we will not consider for funding [see *What is not funded*].'

WHAT IS NOT FUNDED 'We want to be clear about areas in which we will not make grants, so we list here the types of proposal we will not consider for funding. Some are self-explanatory while others derive from the Trust's history and experience. To save yourself time and effort please check this section carefully before starting work on your proposal. We do not make grants to individuals. We will not consider proposals from these types of organisations: statutory bodies; hospitals, health authorities and hospices (or towards any sort of medical care, medical equipment or medical research); universities, colleges and schools (or towards academic research, bursaries or scholarships); organisations working primarily with children under five; organisations working primarily in the field of physical disability, learning disability, autistic spectrum disorder, physical illness or sensory impairment; organisations focusing primarily on: adult learning, skills training or employment training; the restoration or conservation of buildings or habitats; animal charities; scouts, guides and other uniformed youth groups; voluntary rescue or first aid societies; museums, places of entertainment, leisure centres and clubs, social clubs or sports clubs; larger charities (both national and local) enjoying widespread support. We will not consider funding the core work of: advice and information-giving bodies; community foundations; volunteer bureaux and centres; Councils for Voluntary Service; infrastructure organisations/second-tier bodies (i.e. organisations fulfilling a supporting, co-ordinating or development role within the voluntary sector). Finally, we will not consider funding: the promotion of religion; overseas projects (we run a targeted grants programme promoting sustainable agriculture in sub-Saharan Africa so we don't consider speculative proposals from overseas groups); one-off holidays, residentials, trips, exhibitions; arts and sports-based projects unless there is a particularly strong focus on developing marginalised groups; endowment appeals; work that has already taken place.'

TYPE OF GRANT Capital and revenue grants.

RANGE OF GRANTS From £5,000 upwards. Average grant in 2009 was £54,808.

SAMPLE GRANTS Family Centre Trust (£1.3 million), towards the capital costs of building a new family and visitors' centre at HMP Wormwood Scrubs; Transition Network (£240,000), over two years towards core costs, including salaries, for a national organisation which leads on the transition model working to help communities change how they will use energy in the future; Music in Detention (£108,000), over three years towards the salary of a programme manager for an organisation running music workshops with detainees in immigration removal centres; Beat (£100,000), over three years to fund a network support officer to support and develop eating disorder self-help groups throughout England; Longbenton Community Action Team (£80,000), over three years towards the salary of a community animator to continue the 'Listening Matters' process and support residents of Longbenton, Newcastle-upon-Tyne to make changes to benefit their community; Open Door – St Albans (£50,000), towards the refurbishment of a hostel for homeless people; North Glasgow Community Food Initiative (£45,000), over three years as continuation core funding for this healthy eating and local food growing project for marginalised communities, including refugees and asylum seekers; Mankind UK (£30,000), over three years towards the running costs of an organisation supporting adult male victims of rape and sexual abuse in the South East; Holbeck Elderly Aid (£20,000), towards core funding for this older people's resource centre in Leeds; and East Howden Community Association (£15,000), as continuation funding towards the salary of a development worker at a community centre on an isolated estate in North Shields.

FINANCES *Year* 2008–09 *Income* £13,493,000 *Grants* £17,812,000 *Assets* £204,821,000

TRUSTEES Mary Graves; Helen Dunwell; Desmond Graves; Nell Buckler; Christopher Graves; Catherine Antcliff; Louise Collins; Elizabeth

Crawshaw; Matt Dunwell; James Long; Ben Dunwell; Francis Runacres; Monica Barlow; Vanessa James.

PUBLICATIONS *Guidelines for Applicants.*

HOW TO APPLY There is a two-stage application process. Forms are available to download from the trust's website.

WHO TO APPLY TO The Trustees, 7 Ladbroke Grove, London W11 3BD *Tel* 020 7727 8522 *Fax* 020 7221 8522 *Website* www.tudortrust.org.uk

CC NO 1105580   **ESTABLISHED** 1955

■ The Tufton Charitable Trust

WHERE FUNDING CAN BE GIVEN UK.

WHO CAN BENEFIT Individuals and organisations.

WHAT IS FUNDED Christian activity supporting evangelism.

WHAT IS NOT FUNDED No grants for repair or maintenance of buildings.

TYPE OF GRANT One-off and project-related.

SAMPLE GRANTS The Church of England (£137,000); Nuffield Hospitals (£37,000); Martha Trust (£30,000); the Dorothy Kerin Trust (£25,000); Alpha International and London Institute of Christianity (£10,000 each); Bible by the Beach, Relationships Foundation and Right to Life (£7,500 each); and Catholic Foundation and St John Ambulance (£5,000 each).

FINANCES *Year* 2008 *Income* £612,182 *Grants* £333,848 *Assets* £422,730

TRUSTEES Sir Christopher Wates; Lady Wates; J R F Lulham.

HOW TO APPLY In writing to the correspondent, including an sae.

WHO TO APPLY TO The Trustees, c/o Baker Tilly, 4th Floor, 65 Kingsway, London WC2B 6TD

CC NO 801479   **ESTABLISHED** 1989

■ The R D Turner Charitable Trust

WHERE FUNDING CAN BE GIVEN UK, with a preference for the Worcestershire area.

WHO CAN BENEFIT Registered charities only.

WHAT IS FUNDED General charitable purposes.

WHAT IS NOT FUNDED No grants to non-registered charities or to individuals.

TYPE OF GRANT One-off and recurrent.

RANGE OF GRANTS £500–£15,000.

SAMPLE GRANTS St Richard's Hospice (£15,000); Worcestershire and Dudley Historic Churches Trust (£12,000); British Red Cross Hereford and Worcester (£10,000); Kemp Hospice (£6,000); Cookley Playing Fields Association and Ombersley Memorial Hall (£5,000 each): St Peter's Church Upper Arley (£4,000); County Air Ambulance Trust and Relate Worcestershire (£3,000); Kidderminster Disabled Club (£2,500); Listening Books (£1,000); and Talking Newspapers of the UK (£500).

FINANCES *Year* 2008–09 *Income* £707,997 *Grants* £163,600 *Assets* £25,369,850

TRUSTEES J M Del Mar, Chair; D P Pearson; S L Preedy; P J Millward; J M G Fea.

HOW TO APPLY In writing to the correspondent with a copy of your latest annual report and accounts. There are no application forms. The trustees meet in February, May, August and December to consider applications, which should be submitted in the month prior to each meeting. Telephone enquiries may be made before submitting an appeal.

WHO TO APPLY TO Timothy J Patrickson, Administrator, 3 Poplar Piece, Inkberrow, Worcester WR7 4JD *Tel* 01386 792014 *email* timpatrickson@hotmail.co.uk
CC NO 263556 **ESTABLISHED** 1971

■ The Douglas Turner Trust

WHERE FUNDING CAN BE GIVEN Not defined, but in practice there is a preference for Birmingham and the West Midlands.
WHO CAN BENEFIT Registered charities.
WHAT IS FUNDED Mainly local charities including charities supporting: young people and children; work in the community; health and people with disabilities; hospices; older people; international aid; environment and heritage; social support; the arts; and medical research.
WHAT IS NOT FUNDED No grants to individuals or unregistered charities.
TYPE OF GRANT Recurring and one-off donations, capital and core costs.
RANGE OF GRANTS £500–£20,000.
SAMPLE GRANTS Acorns Children's Hospice (£20,000); St. Mary's Hospice (£15,000); Birmingham Council for Old People (£12,000); Birmingham Settlement (£10,000); Friends of TAFO (£7,000); Age Concern Birmingham (£6,000); Midlands Art Centre (£5,000); Birmingham Botanical Gardens (£4,000); Juvenile Diabetes Research Fund (£3,000); ER Mason Youth Centre and British Forces Foundation (£2,000 each); Karis Neighbour Scheme and Dial Walsall (£1,000 each); and Gingerbread (£500).
FINANCES *Year* 2007–08 *Income* £526,397 *Grants* £426,073 *Assets* £14,772,889
TRUSTEES J M Del Mar, Chair; J M G Fea; P J Millward; D P Pearson; S L Preedy.
HOW TO APPLY In writing to the correspondent with a copy of the latest annual report and accounts. There are no application forms. The trustees meet in February, May, August and December to consider applications, which should be submitted in the month prior to each meeting. Telephone enquiries may be made before submitting an appeal.
WHO TO APPLY TO Tim J Patrickson, Trust Administrator, 3 Poplar Piece, Inkberrow, Worcester WR7 4JD *Tel* 01386 792014 *email* timpatrickson@hotmail.co.uk
CC NO 227892 **ESTABLISHED** 1964

■ The Florence Turner Trust

WHERE FUNDING CAN BE GIVEN UK, but with a strong preference for Leicestershire.
WHO CAN BENEFIT Smaller projects are favoured where donations will make a 'quantifiable difference to the recipients rather than favouring large national charities whose income is measured in millions rather than thousands.' Grants are made for the benefit of individuals through a referring agency such as social services, NHS trusts or similar responsible bodies.
WHAT IS FUNDED 'It is usual practice to make grants for the benefit of individuals through a referring agency such as Social Services, NHS Trusts or similar responsible bodies, and rather.
WHAT IS NOT FUNDED The trust does not support individuals for educational purposes.
SAMPLE GRANTS Leicester Charity Organisation Society (£12,000); Leicester Grammar School – Bursary (£8,800); Age Concern – Leicestershire, Leicestershire Scout Council, MOSAIC and

VISTA (£2,300 each); Shelter Housing Aid and Research Project (£2,000 each); Guide Dogs for the Blind Association – Leicester (£1,800); Elizabeth Finn Care (£1,500); Barnardos (£1,300); and the Carers Centre – Leicestershire and Rutland and Vitalise (£1,000 each).
FINANCES *Year* 2007–08 *Income* £198,982 *Grants* £160,890 *Assets* £5,213,778
TRUSTEES Roger Bowder; Allan A Veasey; Caroline A Macpherson.
HOW TO APPLY In writing to the correspondent. Trustees meet every eight or nine weeks.
WHO TO APPLY TO The Trustees, c/o Harvey Ingram Owston, 20 New Walk, Leicester LE1 6TX
CC NO 502721 **ESTABLISHED** 1973

■ Miss S M Tutton Charitable Trust

WHERE FUNDING CAN BE GIVEN UK.
WHO CAN BENEFIT The trust provides financial support to young singers through the Sybil Tutton Awards. In addition it makes grants to selected music colleges and training opera companies.
WHAT IS FUNDED Awards and grants for postgraduate opera studies and grants to music colleges, charities and opera companies. The trust has some funds available for occasional discretionary grants, but they are very limited.
SAMPLE GRANTS National Opera Studio (£11,000); British Youth Opera (£10,000); Clonter Farm Music Trust (£3,300); Young Concert Artists Trust (£2,200); and Britten-Pears School (£1,700).
FINANCES *Year* 2007–08 *Income* £84,774 *Grants* £28,150 *Assets* £2,702,664
TRUSTEES Rosemary Pickering; Richard Van Allan; Susan Dolton; Susan Bullock.
OTHER INFORMATION In 2007–08 a further £34,000 was given via the Sybil Tutton Awards.
HOW TO APPLY Individuals seeking grants for opera studies should consider applying directly to the Musicians' Benevolent Fund (charity no: 228089) which administers the Sybil Tutton Awards. Organisations should submit full details of projects to the address below. The trust has some funds available for occasional discretionary grants, but they are very limited. Assistance is generally provided only where students are recommended by organisations with which the trust has a close working relationship.
WHO TO APPLY TO The Trustees, BDO Stoy Hayward LLP, 55 Baker Street, London W1U 7EU
CC NO 298774 **ESTABLISHED** 1988

■ The TUUT Charitable Trust

WHERE FUNDING CAN BE GIVEN Worldwide.
WHO CAN BENEFIT Small to medium-sized organisations, particularly those having close associations with trade unions.
WHAT IS FUNDED General at trustees' discretion, with an overriding priority to charities with strong trade union connections or interests.
WHAT IS NOT FUNDED No grants to individuals or to charities based overseas.
SAMPLE GRANTS NACRO (£40,000); Alma Hospital and PFA Centenary Fund (£5,000 each); Macmillan Cancer Relief (£3,000); Evelina Children's Hospital Appeal (£2,300); CCA, Concern Worldwide and Scrap Poverty in Africa (£2,000 each); UK Sports Association and

Woking Hospice (£1,000 each); and World Development Movement Trust, Hope and Homes for Children, Cruse Bereavement Care and the Respite Association (£500 each).

FINANCES *Year* 2007–08 *Income* £114,072 *Grants* £80,549 *Assets* £2,293,489

TRUSTEES Lord Christopher; A Tuffin; M Walsh; M Bradley; B Barber; Lord Brookman; E Sweeney.

OTHER INFORMATION The grant total in 2007–08 included a Fellowship Award of £7,000.

HOW TO APPLY 'To apply for a grant, charitable organisations should apply for a Form of Request and submit this, duly completed. The Trustees meet three times a year to consider requests received.'

WHO TO APPLY TO Ann Smith, Secretary, Congress House, Great Russell Street, London WC1B 3LQ *Tel* 020 7637 7116 *Fax* 020 7637 7087 *email* info@tufm.co.uk *Website* www.tufm.co.uk

CC NO 258665   ESTABLISHED 1969

·········

■ Community Foundation Serving Tyne and Wear and Northumberland

WHERE FUNDING CAN BE GIVEN Tyne and Wear and Northumberland.

WHO CAN BENEFIT Voluntary organisations benefiting the local community.

WHAT IS FUNDED The help of those in greatest need. The funds generally have a specific cause as their individual funding priority, but overall the foundation has social welfare as its predominant cause to support. Projects that help communities and individuals who are disadvantaged because of poverty, poor health or disability are of particular interest. Some arts and environment work is funded, but only when it is of direct benefit to those in social need.

WHAT IS NOT FUNDED The foundation does not normally make grants for the following purposes: sponsorship and fundraising events; small contributions to major appeals; large capital projects; endowments; political or religious groups; work which should be funded by health and local authorities; projects outside it's area (unless funding is made available by a supporter from funds they have contributed to the foundation).

TYPE OF GRANT Mostly single grants, but some grants recurrent for up to three years. Will consider capital, core costs, recurring, running and start-up costs, as well as one-off, feasibility studies and salaries.

RANGE OF GRANTS Usually up to £5,000, exceptionally up to £100,000.

SAMPLE GRANTS Previous beneficiaries include: St Martin's Centre Partnership Development of Children's Centre; Monkchester Family Centre (salary costs for manager); Sunderland Carers' Centre (development workers salary); Age Concern Newcastle (Active Citizenship Project); Shelter; Northumberland Toy Library (Saturday play sessions for parents and toddlers); BRF Project worker for Barnabas in the North East; St Mary's Parish Church (towards a stair lift); Newcastle Disability Forum (ICT outreach project); Wallsend Sea Cadets (running costs); George Stephenson High School (garden project); Tyne & Wear Museums, City; Lynemouth Childrens Gala and Morpeth Music Society; Eversley Primary School (water cooler); Alnwick Garden Trust; and Springwell Over 50's Group (bingo machine and cooker).

FINANCES *Year* 2007–08 *Income* £10,145,677 *Grants* £7,610,511 *Assets* £43,999,391

TRUSTEES Hugh Welch, Chair; Jan Worters; Richard Maudslay; John Josephs; Trevor Shears; Sue Winfield; Jamie Martin; Shobha Srivastava; Lisa Charlton; Andrew Kerr; Jill Dixon; John Sands; Jo Curry; Charles Harvey; Dean T Huggins; Liz Prudhoe; Ashley Winter.

PUBLICATIONS Guidance notes for applicants.

OTHER INFORMATION The grant total includes £985,000 administered on behalf of the Henry Smith Charity.

HOW TO APPLY 'Applications are accepted at anytime. All you need to do is to complete the application form [available by calling the foundation or downloadable from its website] and send it to the foundation with the items listed at the end of the form. A decision is normally made within three months. Only one application need be made as the foundation will match it with an appropriate fund or funds. Applications can also be made online.'

WHO TO APPLY TO The Grants Team, 9th Floor, Cale Cross House, 156 Pilgrim Street, Newcastle upon Tyne NE1 6SU *Tel* 0191 222 0945 *Fax* 0191 230 0689 *email* grants@communityfoundation.org.uk *Website* www.communityfoundation.org.uk

CC NO 700510   ESTABLISHED 1988

·········

■ Trustees of Tzedakah

WHERE FUNDING CAN BE GIVEN Worldwide, in practice UK and Israel.

WHO CAN BENEFIT Mainly Jewish religious institutions and people disadvantaged by poverty.

WHAT IS FUNDED The relief of poverty; advancement of education; advancement of religion; and general charitable purposes.

WHAT IS NOT FUNDED Grants only to registered charities. No grants to individuals.

RANGE OF GRANTS £25–£35,000.

SAMPLE GRANTS Hasmonean High School Charitable Trust (£35,000); Gertner Charitable Trust (£27,000); Society of Friends of the Torah (£20,000); Hendon Adath Yisroel Synagogue (£17,000); Medrash Shmuel Theological College (£13,000); Torah Temimoh (£6,400); Willow Foundation (£4,500); Tifferes Girls School (£3,200); Sage Home for the Aged (£2,000); Wizo (£450); and Torah Movement of Great Britain (£25).

FINANCES *Year* 2006–07 *Income* £477,847 *Grants* £425,887 *Assets* £326,545

TRUSTEES Trustees of Tzedakah Ltd.

HOW TO APPLY **This trust states that it does not respond to unsolicited applications.**

WHO TO APPLY TO Colin Hollander, Correspondent, Brentmead House, Britannia Road, London N12 9RU *Tel* 020 8446 6767

CC NO 251897   ESTABLISHED 1966

■ UKI Charitable Foundation

WHERE FUNDING CAN BE GIVEN UK.

WHO CAN BENEFIT Registered charities and individuals.

WHAT IS FUNDED General charitable purposes, education training, medical/health/sickness, disability, the relief of poverty and religious activities.

SAMPLE GRANTS The accounts stated that a list of donations paid could be obtained from the correspondent. Despite a request being made in writing, including an SAE, no list was received.

FINANCES *Year* 2007–08 *Income* £2,161,235 *Grants* £675,537 *Assets* £5,405,701

TRUSTEES Jacob Schimmel; Vered Schimmel; Abraham Schimmel; Eliane Schimmel.

HOW TO APPLY In writing to the correspondent.

WHO TO APPLY TO Abraham Schimmel, Trustee, UKI International, 54–56 Euston Street, London NW1 2ES *Tel* 020 7387 0155

CC NO 1071978   **ESTABLISHED** 1998

■ Ulster Garden Villages Ltd

WHERE FUNDING CAN BE GIVEN Northern Ireland.

WHO CAN BENEFIT Organisations and individuals.

WHAT IS FUNDED Financial assistance is given to aid housing for people who are disadvantaged, older people or people who have disabilities as well as donations to assist improvements in quality of life for such people. There are also interests in helping youth organisations and movements, preservation of heritage and organisations seeking to improve health in the community.

WHAT IS NOT FUNDED Grants are not made to: individuals; organisations whose application is not charitable and with public benefit; activities which are primarily the responsibility of central and local government; sponsorship or marketing appeals; promotion of religion; expeditions or overseas travel; charities who collect funds for distribution to other charities.

RANGE OF GRANTS Usually £1,000 to £5,000; up to £250,000 is considered.

SAMPLE GRANTS Beneficiaries have included Royal Victoria Hospital – Institute of Vision Science, Belfast City Hospital – the Garden Village Suite, the Northern Ireland Children's Hospice, QUB Foundation Great Hall, Belmont Tower, the Lyric Theatre, Camphill Communities in Northern Ireland, Croft Community, Clifton Nursing Home, Habitat for Humanity Northern Ireland, the Scout Association, Ulster Waterways Group and Rams Island.

FINANCES *Year* 2007–08 *Grants* £1,000,000

TRUSTEES Tony Hopkins; Kevin Baird; Mrs Martie Boyd; Drew Crawford; Susan Crowe; Brian Garrett; Erskine Holmes; Sir Desmond Lorimer; William J Webb.

OTHER INFORMATION Grants have been made in the following areas: health; culture and heritage; people with disabilities; older people and disadvantaged; environment; and community and young people.

HOW TO APPLY On an application form available from the charity's website.

WHO TO APPLY TO Mrs Martie Boyd, Executive Director, Forestview, Purdy's Lane,

Newtonbreda, Belfast BT8 7AR *Tel* 028 9049 1111 *Fax* 028 9049 1007 *email* admin@ulstergardenvillages.co.uk *Website* www.ulstergardenvillages.co.uk

ESTABLISHED 1946

■ Ultach Trust

WHERE FUNDING CAN BE GIVEN Northern Ireland only.

WHO CAN BENEFIT Generally voluntary Irish-language or cross-community groups based in Northern Ireland. Irish medium schools benefiting children and young adults.

WHAT IS FUNDED The trust normally funds new or established groups based in Northern Ireland involved in the promotion of the Irish language. Grants are normally aimed at specific projects and schemes rather than ongoing costs. Particular consideration is given to groups developing inter-community Irish-language activities. The trustees also, in exceptional cases, support projects aimed at improving the position of Irish people in the community and promoting knowledge of the language.

WHAT IS NOT FUNDED Generally the following are not supported: individuals, ongoing running costs, major capital programmes, to substitute cutbacks in statutory funding, travel expenses, publications or videos.

TYPE OF GRANT Except with regard to Irish-medium education, funding is generally restricted to starter finances and single projects.

FINANCES *Year* 2007–08 *Grants* £50,000

TRUSTEES Ruairí Ó Bléine; Bill Boyd; Réamonn Ó Ciaráin; Seán Ó Coinn; Déaglán Ó Doibhlín; Risteard Mac Gabhann; Joyce Gibson; Sue Pentel; Robin Glendinning; Barry Kinghan.

PUBLICATIONS Titles of publications and Irish courses available on request.

HOW TO APPLY An application form and condition's of funding are available from the trust's website.

WHO TO APPLY TO Róise Ní-Bhaoill, Deputy Director, 6/10 William Street, Cathedral Quarter, Belfast BT1 1PR *Tel* 028 9023 0749 *Fax* 028 9023 0749 *email* info@ultach.org *Website* www.ultach.org

IR NO XN83581   **ESTABLISHED** 1989

■ Ulting Overseas Trust

WHERE FUNDING CAN BE GIVEN The developing world (mostly, but not exclusively, Asia, Africa and South and Central America).

WHO CAN BENEFIT Christian workers in the developing world undergoing further training for Christian service.

WHAT IS FUNDED Bursaries, normally via grants to Christian theological training institutions or organisations with a training focus, for those in the developing world who wish to train for the Christian ministry, or for those who wish to improve their ministry skills. It gives priority to the training of students in their home countries or continents.

WHAT IS NOT FUNDED No grants are given for capital projects such as buildings or library stock, nor for training in subjects other than Biblical, theological and missionary studies. Grants are only made to institutions to pass on to their students; direct grants to individuals cannot be made.

RANGE OF GRANTS Up to £14,000.

SAMPLE GRANTS IFES (£16,000); Scripture Union international (£14,000); Langham Trust (£13,000); Oxford Centre for Mission Studies (£7,500 in two grants); Pan African Christian

Think carefully about every application. Is it justified?

919

College (£6,300 in two grants); Asian Theological Seminary and Discipleship Training College – Singapore (£4,800 each); Cornerstone Christian College (£2,000); Buenos Aires Bible Institute (£1,000); and Bangladesh Bible School Sim UK (£700).

FINANCES *Year* 2007–08 *Income* £141,444 *Grants* £106,700 *Assets* £3,695,035

TRUSTEES A J Bale, Chair; Mrs M Brinkley; D Ford; J C Heyward; J Kapolyo; Dr J B A Kessler; N Sylvester; T B Warren.

OTHER INFORMATION In 2007–08 a further grant of £1,000 was made to an individual.

HOW TO APPLY The funds of the trust are already committed. Unsolicited applications cannot be supported.

WHO TO APPLY TO T B Warren, Trustee, Pothecary Witham Weld, 70 St George's Square, London SW1V 3RD

CC NO 294397   **ESTABLISHED** 1986

....

■ The Ulverscroft Foundation

WHERE FUNDING CAN BE GIVEN Worldwide.

WHO CAN BENEFIT Projects which will have a positive effect on the quality of life of visually impaired people (blind and partially sighted). Funding is channelled via recognised organisations which help the visually impaired, for example, libraries, hospitals, clinics, schools and colleges, and social and welfare organisations.

WHAT IS FUNDED To support sick and disabled people, particularly those with defective eyesight, and to promote or conduct medical research. Grants are given to hospitals for research, and to libraries and groups of visually impaired people for items such as computer equipment.

WHAT IS NOT FUNDED Applications from individuals are not encouraged. Generally, assistance towards salaries and general running costs are not given.

TYPE OF GRANT Annual for up to and more than three years. Buildings; capital; project and research; one-off and recurring grants.

SAMPLE GRANTS Vision Research Group – Great Ormond Street Hospital (£107,000); Ulverscroft IFLA Award 2007 (£20,000); Calibre (£4,200); Kenya Albino Child Support (£3,300); National Blind Children's Society (£3,000); Force Foundation UK and Look Essex (£2,000 each); and Computer Aid international, East Sussex Association for the Blind, Queen Alexandra Hospital Home and St John of Jerusalem Eye Hospital (£1,000 each).

FINANCES *Year* 2007–08 *Income* £13,494,462 *Grants* £242,900

TRUSTEES A W Leach, Chair; P H F Carr; M K Down; D Owen; R Crooks.

OTHER INFORMATION The foundation controls a trading subsidiary which republishes books in a form accessible by people with failing sight.

HOW TO APPLY In writing to the correspondent including latest annual report and accounts. Applicants are advised to make their proposal as detailed as possible, to include details of the current service to people who are visually impaired, if any, and how the proposed project will be integrated or enhanced. If possible the trust asks for an estimate of how many people who are visually impaired use/will use the service, the amount of funding obtained to date, if any, and the names of other organisations to whom they have applied. The success of any appeal is dependent on the level of funding at the time of consideration. The trustees meet four times a year to consider applications.

WHO TO APPLY TO Joyce Sumner, Secretary, 1 The Green, Bradgate Road, Anstey, Leicester LE7 7FU *Tel* 0116 236 1595 *Fax* 0116 236 1594 *email* foundation@ulverscroft.co.uk *Website* www.foundation.ulverscroft.com

CC NO 264873   **ESTABLISHED** 1972

....

■ Ulverston Town Lands Charity

WHERE FUNDING CAN BE GIVEN The urban district of Ulverston.

WHO CAN BENEFIT Local organisations and schools.

WHAT IS FUNDED Young people, health, welfare, disability.

WHAT IS NOT FUNDED No grants outside the beneficial area. Grants are generally given to organisations and not to individuals.

TYPE OF GRANT One-off grants for specific items or equipment.

RANGE OF GRANTS Up to £2,500.

SAMPLE GRANTS Alzheimer's Society – Furness (£3,300 in total); St Mary's Hospice (£3,000); Heart of Oaks Boat Trust (£1,000); Ford Park Community Group (£950 in total); Ulverston Disabled Club (£500); and Ulverston Church Walk School (£250).

FINANCES *Year* 2007–08 *Income* £41,588 *Grants* £30,040 *Assets* £95,378

TRUSTEES Edwin Twentyman, Chair; Colin Hodgeson; Cllr J W Prosser; Cllr Janette Jenkinson; Anthony Edmondson; Colin Williams; Cynthia Earnshaw; Anthony Bryson; Janet Hancock.

HOW TO APPLY In writing to the correspondent. Trustees meet four or five times a year.

WHO TO APPLY TO J Going, Secretary to the Trustees, Messrs Hart Jackson and Sons, PO Box 2, 8 and 10 New Market Street, Ulverston, Cumbria LA12 7LW *Tel* 01229 583291 *Fax* 01229 581136

CC NO 215779   **ESTABLISHED** 1963

....

■ The Underwood Trust

WHERE FUNDING CAN BE GIVEN Worldwide. In practice UK with a preference for Scotland and Wiltshire.

WHO CAN BENEFIT Registered charities only, or bodies with equivalent status such as universities or churches.

WHAT IS FUNDED General charitable purposes, in particular, medicine and health, social welfare, education arts, environment and wildlife.

WHAT IS NOT FUNDED Individuals directly; political activities; commercial ventures or publications; the purchase of vehicles including minibuses; overseas travel or holidays; retrospective grants or loans; direct replacement of statutory funding or activities that are primarily the responsibility of central or local government; large capital, endowment or widely distributed appeals.

RANGE OF GRANTS Up to £100,000.

SAMPLE GRANTS Friends of the Earth and National Eye Research Centre (£100,000 each); Restorative Solutions (£80,000); Shooting Star Children's Hospice (£70,000); Thames Rivers Restoration Trust (£60,000); London Library (£50,000); Speech Therapy Research Centre – Frenchay Hospital (£39,000); the Aigis Trust (£25,000); National Youth Orchestra (£15,000); British Red Cross – National Floods Appeal (£10,000); and Highland Hospice (£5,000).

FINANCES *Year* 2007–08 *Income* £1,442,114 *Grants* £1,236,257 *Assets* £34,762,263

TRUSTEES Robin Clark, Chair; Jack C Taylor; Briony Wilson.

HOW TO APPLY Please do not apply to the trust unless invited to do so. The trust's website clearly states that: 'There has recently been a change of policy by the trustees. Recently the trust has made a number of large donations and commitments. As such there are currently no free funds in the trust and therefore the trust is unable to accept unsolicited applications. This position is expected to continue for the foreseeable future, but any changes to this will be posted on this website at the time.' 'Please note the trust is unable to deal with telephone or email enquiries about an application.

WHO TO APPLY TO Antony P Cox, Trust Manager, Fourth Floor South, 35 Portman Square, London W1H 6LR *Tel* 020 7486 0100 *Website* www. theunderwoodtrust.org.uk
CC NO 266164   **ESTABLISHED** 1973

■ The Union of Orthodox Hebrew Congregation

WHERE FUNDING CAN BE GIVEN UK.
WHO CAN BENEFIT Jewish organisations.
WHAT IS FUNDED To protect and to further in every way the interests of traditional Judaism in Great Britain and to establish and support such institutions as will serve this object.
SAMPLE GRANTS Previous beneficiaries have included: Addas Yisoroel Mikva Foundation, Achieve Trust, Atereth Shau, Beis Malka, Beis Shmuel, Belz Nursery, Bnos Yerushaim, Chesed Charity Trust, London Board of Schechita, Mutual Trust, Maoz Ladol, North West London Mikvah, Needy Families and Poor Families Pesach, Society of Friends of the Torah, Talmud Centre Trust and VMCT.
FINANCES *Year* 2007 *Income* £1,307,261 *Grants* £288,067 *Assets* £1,649,359
TRUSTEES B S F Freshwater; I Cymerman; C Konig; Rabbi A Pinter.
HOW TO APPLY In writing to the correspondent.
WHO TO APPLY TO The Administrator, 140 Stamford Hill, London N16 6QT
CC NO 249892   **ESTABLISHED** 1966

■ The Unite Foundation (The Amicus Foundation)

WHERE FUNDING CAN BE GIVEN Worldwide.
WHO CAN BENEFIT Charitable organisations.
WHAT IS FUNDED The aim of the charity is to provide support worldwide to organisations in the following areas: disasters; education; health; the developing world; trade unions; and trade union development. It works together with other charities to fund activities 'where it is assessed that there is a potential for change and betterment'.
WHAT IS NOT FUNDED No grants to individuals.
SAMPLE GRANTS Disability Sport Events and Siglio XX National University (£25,000 each); Transplant Sport UK (£10,000); the Jericho Foundation (£2,500); Noah's Ark Trust (£2,000); Love Hoops Foundation (£500); and Deafblind UK (£400).
FINANCES *Year* 2008 *Income* £90,263 *Grants* £67,400 *Assets* £433,549
TRUSTEES Jack Harrison, Chair; Simon Dubbins; Janet Moir; Richard O'Brien; Stephen Skinner; Derek Simpson; Bill Weale.
OTHER INFORMATION The foundation (registered with the Charity Commission as the AEEU Learning Fund) is connected to Unite, the trade union.
HOW TO APPLY 'All applicants for funding must apply on a standard, detailed form which is available from the fund's website. Applications are

considered at the trustees' meetings and successful applicants are required to provide feedback at half-yearly intervals.'
WHO TO APPLY TO Stephen Skinner, Secretary, AEEU Learning Fund, Hayes Court, West Common Road, Hayes, Bromley, Kent BR2 7AU *email* charity@unitetheunion.com *Website* www. unitetheunion.com
CC NO 1085736   **ESTABLISHED** 2001

■ The United Society for the Propagation of the Gospel

WHERE FUNDING CAN BE GIVEN Mainly churches in Africa, West Indies, South Pacific, South America, Pakistan, India, Indian Ocean, Myanmar (Burma), Bangladesh, East Asia.
WHO CAN BENEFIT Overseas Anglican provinces and dioceses and churches in communion with the Anglican Church which benefit Christians and other disadvantaged groups.
WHAT IS FUNDED The promotion of the Christian religion and related charitable works.
WHAT IS NOT FUNDED Direct applications from individuals are not considered.
TYPE OF GRANT One-off grants; bursaries; loans.
FINANCES *Year* 2007 *Income* £5,785,528 *Grants* £1,966,772 *Assets* £43,170,957
TRUSTEES The Revd Alan Moses, Chair; The Revd Roger Antell; Richard Barrett; Mrs Monica Bolley; The Rt Revd Purely Lyngdoh; Most Revd Mauricio Andrade; Revd Canon Christopher Atkinson; Revd Canon Christopher Chivers; Roger Eastman; Mrs Yoshimi Gregory; Revd Canon Huw Mosford; Delbert Sandiford; Rt Revd Royden Screech; Rt Revd Joseph Seoka; Canon Linda Ali.
HOW TO APPLY Applications must be submitted by Anglican Archbishops or Bishops to the Finance in Mission Officer.
WHO TO APPLY TO Finance in Mission Officer, 200 Great Dover Street, London SE1 4YB *Tel* 020 7378 5678 *Fax* 020 7378 5650 *email* enquiries@uspg.org.uk *Website* www. uspg.org.uk
CC NO 234518   **ESTABLISHED** 1701

■ United Trusts

WHERE FUNDING CAN BE GIVEN Unrestricted but in practice mainly organisations operating in North West England and North Wales.
WHO CAN BENEFIT Charitable organisations.
WHAT IS FUNDED General charitable purposes.
WHAT IS NOT FUNDED Individuals. Grants to individuals, called 'people for people funds' are made through umbrella charities.
FINANCES *Year* 2007–08 *Income* £400,247 *Grants* £364,610 *Assets* £291,618
TRUSTEES Liverpool Charity and Voluntary Services, Susan Newton; Harry Williams.
OTHER INFORMATION 'United Trust's main objective is to promote tax-free payroll giving to workplace charity funds, where gift distributions can be made by a workplace charity fund committee. We operate nationwide, but our main area of activity is North West England and North Wales. In addition we operate the Give As You Earn elective payroll giving service that enables individual donors, at the time the payroll deductions are authorised, to nominate which charities are to receive their gifts.'
HOW TO APPLY It is requested that applications should be made to the secretary of the local United Trust Fund or Workplace Charity Fund

concerned. If the address is not know, applicants are advised to telephone the correspondent of the trust.

WHO TO APPLY TO The Secretary, Liverpool Charity and Voluntary Services, 151 Dale Street, Liverpool L2 2AH *Tel* 0151 227 5177 *email* information@unitedtrusts.org.uk *Website* www.unitedtrusts.org.uk
CC NO 327579   **ESTABLISHED** 1987

....

■ United Utilities Trust Fund

WHERE FUNDING CAN BE GIVEN The area supplied by United Utilities Water Plc (predominantly the north west of England).
WHO CAN BENEFIT Mainly individuals, but also organisations.
WHAT IS FUNDED Social welfare and debt advice.
WHAT IS NOT FUNDED The trust will not fund: 'existing projects; charities which appear to us to have sufficient unrestricted or free reserves, or are in serious deficit; projects outside the geographical area; national charities that do not have the facility to accept the funding on a regional basis; grant making bodies seeking to distribute grants on UUTF's behalf; general appeals, sponsorship and marketing appeals; replacement of existing programmes or statutory funding.'
TYPE OF GRANT Small one-off donations and larger grants for up to two years.
RANGE OF GRANTS Up to £1,500; up to £30,000.
SAMPLE GRANTS Wythenshawe Law Centre (£30,000); Manchester Refugee Support Network (£29,000); Broad African Representative Council (£28,000); North Liverpool CAB (£27,000); MHIST (£21,000); Age Concern Blackburn and Darwen (£20,000); and Middleton/Brentwood Day Centre (£1,000).
FINANCES *Year* 2007–08 *Income* £3,036,705 *Grants* £156,000 *Assets* £529,531
TRUSTEES Michael Shields, Chair; Gabrielle Cox; Alan Manning; Deborah Moreton; Alastair Richards; Nick Pearson.
OTHER INFORMATION During the year a further £2.6 million was given on behalf of individuals.
HOW TO APPLY On an application form available from the correspondent or the trust's website.
WHO TO APPLY TO The Secretary (Auriga Services Limited), FREEPOST RLYY-JHEJ-XCXS, Sutton Coldfield B72 1TJ *Tel* 0845 179 1791 *email* contact@uutf.org.uk *Website* www.uutf. org.uk
CC NO 1108296   **ESTABLISHED** 2005

....

■ The Michael Uren Foundation

WHERE FUNDING CAN BE GIVEN UK.
WHO CAN BENEFIT Registered charities.
WHAT IS FUNDED General charitable purposes. 'The trustees are particularly keen on making grants for specific large projects. This could mean that, to satisfy this objective, no significant grants are paid in one year. With the resultant reserves retained a large grant could be made in the following year.'
TYPE OF GRANT Mainly large project grants.
RANGE OF GRANTS £500–£500,000.
SAMPLE GRANTS Combat Stress, the Gurkha Welfare Trust, Royal Hospital Chelsea and SSAFA Forces Help (£500,000 each); King Edward VII Hospital (£115,000); Rycote Chapel (£74,000); Parochial Church Council (£13,000); Royal London Society for the Blind (£10,000); Canterbury Cathedral (£3,000); Project Trust (£2,500); and Territorial Army (£500).

FINANCES *Year* 2007–08 *Income* £122,940 *Grants* £2,217,600 *Assets* £56,273,905
TRUSTEES John Uren; Christopher Hill; Janis Bennett; Alastair McDonald.
HOW TO APPLY In writing to the correspondent.
WHO TO APPLY TO Anne Gregory-Jones, Haysmacintyre, Fairfax House, 15 Fulwood Place, London WC1V 6AY *email* agregory-jones@ haysmacintyre.com
CC NO 1094102   **ESTABLISHED** 2002

....

■ The David Uri Memorial Trust

WHERE FUNDING CAN BE GIVEN Worldwide.
WHO CAN BENEFIT Registered charities benefiting Jewish people, at risk groups and people who are disadvantaged by poverty or socially isolated.
WHAT IS FUNDED Mainly Jewish organisations; also welfare and education charities.
WHAT IS NOT FUNDED No grants to individuals.
SAMPLE GRANTS Previous beneficiaries have included: National Jewish Chaplaincy Board, Age Concern, Crisis at Christmas, Jefferies Research Wing Trust, NSPCC and Yakar Education Foundation.
FINANCES *Year* 2007–08 *Income* £375,363 *Grants* £102,950 *Assets* £2,531,121
TRUSTEES Mrs S Blackman; Mrs B Roden; B Blackman.
HOW TO APPLY In writing to the correspondent.
WHO TO APPLY TO The Trustees, Suite 511, 19–21 Crawford Street, London W1H 1PJ
CC NO 327810   **ESTABLISHED** 1988

....

■ Uxbridge United Welfare Trust

WHERE FUNDING CAN BE GIVEN Former urban district of Uxbridge, includes Uxbridge, Hillingdon, Ickenham, Harefield and Cowley.
WHO CAN BENEFIT Local organisations benefiting children, young adults and people disadvantaged by poverty.
WHAT IS FUNDED Education, relief of poverty, including the provision of almshouses.
WHAT IS NOT FUNDED No grants are made outside the beneficial area.
FINANCES *Year* 2007 *Income* £517,805 *Grants* £62,379 *Assets* £6,780,092
TRUSTEES Mrs Susan M Pritchard, Chair; John Childs; Mrs Pauline Crawley; David Driver; Lewis R Pond; Mrs Betty O'Rourke; David Routledge; Peter Ryerson; Gerda Driver; Betty Jones.
HOW TO APPLY In writing to the correspondent.
WHO TO APPLY TO Pauline Crawley, Trustee, Trustees' Room, Woodbridge House, New Windsor Street, Uxbridge UB8 2TY *Tel* 01895 232976 *email* uuwt.mail@tiscali.co.uk
CC NO 217066   **ESTABLISHED** 1991

■ 'v'

WHERE FUNDING CAN BE GIVEN England.
WHO CAN BENEFIT Young people aged between 16 and 25.
WHAT IS FUNDED 'v' is an independent charity set in 2006 up to inspire a new generation of young volunteers and enable lasting change in the quality, quantity and diversity of volunteering opportunities for 16 to 25 year olds in England. It aim is to implement the recommendations of the Russell Commission, looking to 'revolutionise youth volunteering in England and create a culture where it is natural for young people to volunteer and natural for organisations to support them in doing so, because the benefits of volunteering are widely understood and celebrated'. Its Advisory Board of young people – 'v20' – play a fundamental role in guiding the work of the charity. 'v' aims to inspire more investment in youth volunteering and supports cutting edge partnerships between the private and third sector. Through the 'V'Match Fund, 'V'can match up to 100% of new investment from private companies, individuals, foundations or charitable trusts. This could make you more attractive to a sponsor, as with double the budget, you could double the impact of their investment.
WHAT IS NOT FUNDED 'v'cannot match funds from public sector organisations, (for example: national and local government, EU funding or lottery funders).
TYPE OF GRANT Match funding.
FINANCES *Year* 2007–08 *Income* £48,470,994 *Grants* £36,784,397 *Assets* £6,512,214
TRUSTEES Rod Aldridge; Tanni Grey Thomson; Manni Amadi; Justin Davis Smith; Tim Smart; Joan Watson; Tricia Killen; Lorraine O'Reilly; Natalie Campbell; Sasha Kasthuriarachchi; Amanda Duggan; Jared Nessa.
HOW TO APPLY Go to: www.vgrantfunding.com/matchfunding and complete the online eligibility questionnaire. An application form and guidance notes will then be emailed to you.
WHO TO APPLY TO Jayne Colquhoun, Secretary, Dean Bradley House, 52 Horseferry Road, London SW1P 2AF *Tel* 020 7960 7019 *Fax* 020 7960 7099 *Minicom* illion *email* info@wearev.com *Website* www.vinspired.com
CC NO 1113255   **ESTABLISHED** 2006

■ The Vail Foundation

WHERE FUNDING CAN BE GIVEN UK and overseas.
WHO CAN BENEFIT Registered charities.
WHAT IS FUNDED Jewish causes.
RANGE OF GRANTS Up to £400,000.
SAMPLE GRANTS Project Seed (£75,000); Friends of Swiss Cottage and Swiss Cottage Specialist SEN School (£50,000 each); University Jewish Chaplaincy Board (£45,000); Community Security Trust (£40,000); Jewish Learning Exchange (£35,000); Central British Fund of Jewish World Relief (£25,000); United Synagogue (£20,000); Roundabout Trust (£15,000); Yakar Educational Foundation and Simon Marks Jewish Primary School (£10,000 each); London Jewish Family Centre (£7,000);

Camp Simcha, Chai Lifeline Cancer Care and Nightingale House (£5,000 each); UK Friends of the Association for the Wellbeing of Israel's Soldiers (£2,500); and Israeli Dance Institute (£1,000).
FINANCES *Year* 2007–08 *Income* £417,759 *Grants* £1,352,912 *Assets* £10,675,925
TRUSTEES M S Bradfield; P Brett; M H Goldstein.
HOW TO APPLY 'The trustees consider all requests which they receive and make such donations as they feel appropriate.
WHO TO APPLY TO The Trustees, c/o Blick Rothenberg, 12 York Gate, Regent's Park, London NW1 4QS
CC NO 1089579   **ESTABLISHED** 2001

■ Vale of Glamorgan – Welsh Church Fund

WHERE FUNDING CAN BE GIVEN Vale of Glamorgan and City of Cardiff council areas.
WHO CAN BENEFIT Organisations benefiting children, young adults, students and local communities may all be considered.
WHAT IS FUNDED Restoration of churches and memorials; education and training, particularly vocational or religious; health; social welfare; arts and culture; recreation and sport; environment and animals; faith activities; science and technology; social sciences, policy and research; and philanthropy and the voluntary sector.
WHAT IS NOT FUNDED No grants to individuals.
TYPE OF GRANT One-off.
RANGE OF GRANTS 'Whilst no maximum/minimum grant levels are stipulated, awards are usually in the region of £1,500.'
SAMPLE GRANTS St Augustine's Parish Community Hall – Penarth (£10,000); Bonvilston Parochial Church Council (£3,000); Coastlands Family Church – Barry (£2,500); St Cadoc's Church – Pendoylan and St Paul's Church – Grangetown (£2,000 each); St Paul's Community Church – Butetown (£1,500); Bethel Evangelical Chapel – Rhoose and St Illtud's Church – Llantwit Major (£1,000 each); and Ararat Baptist Church – Whitchurch, Llandaff Cathedral and St Canna's Church, Llangan (£500 each).
FINANCES *Year* 2007–08 *Income* £59,000 *Grants* £42,000 *Assets* £2,917,000
TRUSTEES The Vale of Glamorgan County Borough Council.
HOW TO APPLY For organisations based in the Vale of Glamorgan, further information can be obtained from A D Williams via the contact details given in this entry. For organisations based in Cardiff, please contact R Anthony at Cardiff County Council (tel. 029 2087 2395). Applications are accepted throughout the year and meetings of the trustees convened to consider applications as and when required.
WHO TO APPLY TO A D Williams, Director of Finance, ICT and Property, The Vale of Glamorgan Council, Civic Offices, Holton Rd, Barry CF63 4RU *Tel* 01446 709250 *email* adwilliams@valeofglamorgan.gov.uk
CC NO 506628   **ESTABLISHED** 1996

■ The Valentine Charitable Trust

WHERE FUNDING CAN BE GIVEN Unrestricted, but mainly Dorset. Developing countries.
WHO CAN BENEFIT Registered charities.
WHAT IS FUNDED Welfare, the environment and overseas aid.

WHAT IS NOT FUNDED No grants to individuals. The trust would not normally fund appeals for village halls or the fabric of church buildings.

TYPE OF GRANT Core, capital and project support is given as well as loan finance. One-off grants are preferred, but funding can be for longer periods.

SAMPLE GRANTS Priest's House Museum and Wessex Autistic Society (£25,000 each); Help for Heroes and Lewis-Manning Cancer Trust (£20,000 each); The Prince's Trust and Bournemouth Symphony Orchestra (£15,000 each); Bournemouth Nightclub Outreach (£12,000); Canine Partners for Independence, Fine Cell Work and Tregonwell Alms House Trust (£10,000 each); St Phillip's Church Project (£8,000); Rainbow Trust (£6,000); Christians Against Poverty, Dorset Blind Association, Fernheath Play Association and Tree Aid (£5,000 each); Bournemouth Town Centre Detached Youth (£3,000); Cruse Bereavement Care and the Margaret Green Foundation (£2,000 each); and the Salvation Army and Traffic of the Stage (£1,000 each).

FINANCES *Year* 2007–08 *Income* £1,012,038 *Grants* £814,090 *Assets* £22,684,689

TRUSTEES Douglas J E Neville-Jones; Roger A Gregory; Mrs Shiela F Cox; Mrs Susan Patterson; Mrs Patricia B N Walker; Peter Leatherdale; Mrs Diana Tory.

HOW TO APPLY In writing to the correspondent. The trust provides the following insight into its application process in its annual report: 'All applications will be acknowledged with standard letters, even those that are not appropriate for receiving a grant. This responsibility is delegated to Douglas J E Neville-Jones who then provides a report to the next trustees' meeting. The following general comments summarise some of the considerations the trustees seek to apply when considering applications for funding. The trustees look for value for money. While this concept is difficult to apply in a voluntary sector it can certainly be used on a comparative basis and subjectively. If the trustees have competing applications they will usually decide to support just one of them as they believe that to concentrate the charity's donations is more beneficial than to dilute them. Regular contact with the charities to which donations are made is considered essential. Reports and accounts are also requested from charities which are supported and the trustees consider those at their meetings. The trustees take great comfort from the fact that they employ the policy of only making donations to other charities or similar bodies. However they are not complacent about the need to review all donations made and the objects to which those have been given. The trustees are conscious that, particularly with the smaller and local charities, the community of those working for and with the charity is an important consideration. The trustees regularly review the classifications to which donations have been made so that they can obtain an overview of the charity's donations and assess whether their policies are being implemented in practice. They are conscious that when dealing with individual donations it is easy to lose sight of the overall picture.'

WHO TO APPLY TO Douglas J E Neville-Jones, Trustee, Preston Redman LLP, Hinton House, Hinton Road, Bournemouth, Dorset BH1 2EN *Tel* 01202 292424 *Fax* 01202 552758 *email* valentine@prestonredman.co.uk

CC NO 1001782   **ESTABLISHED** 1990

■ The Albert Van Den Bergh Charitable Trust

WHERE FUNDING CAN BE GIVEN UK and overseas.

WHO CAN BENEFIT Charitable organisations.

WHAT IS FUNDED Medical research, disability, community and general charitable purposes.

SAMPLE GRANTS Previous beneficiaries have included BLISS, Bishop of Guildford's Charity, British Heart Foundation, Counsel and Care for the Elderly, Leukaemia Research Trust, Multiple Sclerosis Society, Parentline Surrey, National Osteoporosis Society, RNID, Riding for the Disabled – Cranleigh Age Concern, SSAFA, St John Ambulance and United Charities Fund – Liberal Jewish Synagogue.

FINANCES *Year* 2008–09 *Income* £103,237 *Grants* £94,800 *Assets* £2,527,297

TRUSTEES Mrs J M Hartley; Mrs N Glover; B Hopkins.

HOW TO APPLY In writing to the correspondent, including accounts and budgets.

WHO TO APPLY TO Mrs J Hartley, Trustee, Trevornick Farmhouse, Holywell Bay, Newquay, Cornwall TR8 5PW

CC NO 296885   **ESTABLISHED** 1987

■ John and Lucille van Geest Foundation

WHERE FUNDING CAN BE GIVEN UK, with some interest in south Lincolnshire and adjoining areas; occasionally overseas.

WHO CAN BENEFIT Registered charities.

WHAT IS FUNDED Medical research in the following areas: brain damage e.g. Alzheimer's Disease, Huntington's Disease, Parkinson's Disease and strokes; cancer; heart disease; lung disease; sight and/or hearing loss. Healthcare for people in need through illness, infirmity or social circumstances and in particular the welfare of older people and of children resident in South Lincolnshire.

WHAT IS NOT FUNDED No grants to individuals.

TYPE OF GRANT Capital, revenue and full project funding. Primarily one-off, although any type of grant is considered.

RANGE OF GRANTS £1,500–£340,000.

SAMPLE GRANTS University of Leicester (£340,000); Foundation for the Prevention of Blindness (£130,000); University of Cambridge Brain Repair Centre (£110,000); Deafness Research UK (£40,000); Kidney Research UK (£34,000); Lincolnshire and Nottinghamshire Air Ambulance (£24,000); East Anglia Children's Hospices (£20,000); British Heart Foundation (£15,000); Cancer Research (£10,000); Tapping House Hospice (£10,000); Blind Outdoor Leisure (£3,000); and the Dystonia Society (£1,500).

FINANCES *Year* 2008–09 *Income* £1,061,202 *Grants* £872,051 *Assets* £29,201,133

TRUSTEES Hilary P Marlowe; Stuart R Coltman; Tonie Gibson.

HOW TO APPLY In writing to the correspondent. Please note that only charities engaged in areas of work to which the trust's policy extends are considered (and in the case of healthcare grants, only charities providing services in South Lincolnshire and adjoining area). Telephone calls are welcome. The trustees meet two to three times a year to consider applications, but there are no set dates. Every applicant will receive a reply.

WHO TO APPLY TO Brenda Ruysen, Clerk to the Trustees, 108 Pinchbeck Road, Spalding,

Lincolnshire PE11 1QL *Tel* 01775 769501
email trustees@
johnandlucillevangeestfoundation.org
Website johnandlucillevangeestfoundation.org
cc no 1001279   **established** 1990

■ The Van Neste Foundation

where funding can be given UK (especially the
Bristol area) and overseas.
who can benefit Registered charities.
what is funded Currently the main areas of interest
are: developing world; older people or people
with disabilities; advancement of religion;
community and 'Christian family life' and
'respect for the sanctity and dignity of life'.
what is not funded No grants to individuals or to
large, well-known charities. Applications are only
considered from registered charities.
type of grant Usually one-off for a specific project
or part of a project. Core funding is rarely
considered.
sample grants St James Priory Project (£75,000);
CHAS Bristol (£30,000); CAFOD (£29,000);
Avon and Bristol Law Centre (£15,000);
Families for Children, Housing Justice and the
Withywood Centre (£10,000 each); Emmaus
House Bristol and St Peter's Hospice and
Spadework (£5,000 each); St Angela's Home
for the Elderly and Salvation Army (£1,000
each); and St Mary's RC Church Cardiff (£250).
finances *Year* 2007–08 *Income* £248,171
Grants £265,400 *Assets* £6,746,050
trustees M T M Appleby, Chair; F J F Lyons;
G J Walker; J F Lyons; B M Appleby.
how to apply Applications should be in the form of
a concise letter setting out the clear objectives
to be obtained, which must be charitable.
Information must be supplied concerning agreed
funding from other sources together with a
timetable for achieving the objectives of the
appeal and a copy of the latest accounts. The
foundation does not normally make grants on a
continuing basis. To keep overheads to a
minimum, only successful applications are
acknowledged. Appeals are considered by the
trustees at their meetings in January, June and
October.
who to apply to Fergus Lyons, Secretary, 15
Alexandra Road, Clifton, Bristol BS8 2DD
cc no 201951   **established** 1959

■ Mrs Maud Van Norden's Charitable Foundation

where funding can be given UK.
who can benefit Registered UK charities only.
what is funded General charitable purposes,
particularly aid to younger or older people. Also
preservation of the environment and heritage,
disability and animal welfare.
what is not funded No grants to individuals,
expeditions or scholarships. The trustees make
donations to registered UK charities only.
type of grant One-off and research.
range of grants All but one of grants made were
for £1,500 each.
sample grants Royal Hospital for Neuro-Disability
(£2,500); and Changing Faces, Church Urban
Fund, Cured Speech Association UK, the Daisy
Trust, Help for Heroes, Humane Slaughter
Association, National Rheumatoid Arthritis
Society, Police Community Clubs of Great
Britain, Royal British Legion, the Samaritans,

Victim Support and Women's Link (£1,500
each).
finances *Year* 2008 *Income* £43,558
Grants £43,000 *Assets* £823,009
trustees Ena Dukler; John Gordon; Elizabeth
Humphryes; Neil Wingerath.
how to apply All appeals should be by letter
containing the following: aims and objectives of
the charity; nature of the appeal; total target, if
for a specific project; contributions received
against target; registered charity number; any
other factors. Letters should be accompanied by
a copy of the applicant's latest reports and
accounts.
who to apply to The Trustees, BM Box 2367,
London WC1N 3XX
cc no 210844   **established** 1962

■ The Vandervell Foundation

where funding can be given UK.
who can benefit Individuals and organisations.
what is funded General charitable purposes.
range of grants £1,000–£20,000.
sample grants Royal College of Surgeons and
Prisoners Educational Trust (£20,000 each);
Oxford Medical School (£18,000); Arts
Education School Tring Park (£15,000);
Guildhall School Trust, King's College London
School of Medicine, PMS Foundation and
University of Leeds School of Medicine
(£10,000 each); Fareshare, Royal National
Theatre and St George's Youth Club (£5,000
each).
finances *Year* 2008 *Income* £372,450
Grants £307,608 *Assets* £5,990,239
trustees The Vandervell Foundation Limited
Trustee Company.
other information The 2008 grant total included
£17,000 distributed in 55 educational grants to
individuals.
how to apply In writing to the correspondent.
Trustees meet every two months to consider
major grant applications; smaller grants are
considered more frequently.
who to apply to Valerie Kaye, Administrator,
Hampstead Town Hall Centre, 213 Haverstock
Hill, London NW3 4QP
cc no 255651   **established** 1968

■ The Vardy Foundation

where funding can be given UK with a preference
for North East England, overseas.
who can benefit Charitable organisations and
individuals.
what is funded General charitable purposes,
education in North East England, young people
and social welfare.
type of grant One-off and recurrent.
range of grants Up to £250,000.
sample grants Angel Foundation (£1 million);
Caring for Life (£250,000); Youth for Christ
(£220,000); Christians Against Poverty
(£175,000); and the Message Trust
(£150,000).
finances *Year* 2007–08 *Income* £1,708,995
Grants £2,926,104 *Assets* £20,585,994
trustees Sir Peter Vardy; Lady Margaret Barr Vardy;
Peter D D Vardy; Richard Vardy.
other information Individual grants totalled
£137,500.
how to apply In writing to the correspondent.

WHO TO APPLY TO Jo Lavender, Foundation Executive, Venture House, Aykley Heads, Durham DH1 5TS *Tel* 0191 374 4727 *email* foundation@regvardy. com *Website* vardyfoundation.com
CC NO 328415 **ESTABLISHED** 1987

■ The Variety Club Children's Charity

WHERE FUNDING CAN BE GIVEN UK.
WHO CAN BENEFIT Hospitals, schools, charities and other organisations.
WHAT IS FUNDED The welfare of children up to the age of 19 who are disadvantaged or have disabilities.
WHAT IS NOT FUNDED For grants to organisations: trips abroad; medical treatment or research; administrative or salary costs; maintenance or ongoing costs; repayment of loans; distribution to other organisations; computers for mainstream schools or non-disabled children; basic cost of a family vehicle; non-specific appeals.
TYPE OF GRANT One-off and recurring. Money and equipment, including coaches, to organisations. Individual children have received money, electric wheelchairs, toys and holidays.
RANGE OF GRANTS Up to £35,000.
FINANCES *Year* 2008 *Income* £10,376,935 *Grants* £2,300,000
TRUSTEES Kenneth R Mustoe; Paul Lawrence; Keith Andrews; Philip Austin; John E Barnett; Gary Beckwith; Anthony Blackburn; Malcolm Brenner; Laurence Davis; Alan Fraser; Anthony Henry-Lyons; Lionel Rosenblatt; John Sachs; Jonathan Shalit; Anthony Simmonds; Pamela Sinclair; Anne Wadsworth; Norman Kaphan; Russ Kane; Ronnie Nathan; Anthony Harris; Stephen Crown; Jarvis Astaire; Tony Hatch; John Ratcliff.
HOW TO APPLY There are application forms for each programme, available from the charity or through its website.
WHO TO APPLY TO Anthony Simmonds, Variety Club House, 93 Bayham Street, London NW1 0AG *Tel* 020 7428 8100 *email* info@varietyclub.org. uk *Website* www.varietyclub.org.uk
CC NO 209259 **ESTABLISHED** 1949

■ Veneziana Fund

WHERE FUNDING CAN BE GIVEN Venice and the UK.
WHO CAN BENEFIT Charitable organisations working with old buildings or art.
WHAT IS FUNDED This trust gives half its grant total to the Venice in Peril Fund (amounting to £30,900 in 2006–07), and in the UK or the preservation, restoration, repair and maintenance of: buildings originally constructed before 1750; the fixtures and fittings of such buildings; and works of art made before 1750 (including the purchase of such items).
WHAT IS NOT FUNDED No grants are made towards heating systems or toilets.
RANGE OF GRANTS Up to £1,500.
SAMPLE GRANTS 28 grants to churches, with the exception of a grant of £1,500 to the Norfolk and Norwich Film Theatre.
FINANCES *Year* 2006–07 *Income* £66,577 *Grants* £61,800 *Assets* £7,522
TRUSTEES Peter J Boizot; Richard S Fowler; Jackie Freeman; Jane Botros.
HOW TO APPLY In writing to the correspondent to request an application form.
WHO TO APPLY TO Jayne Day, The Trust Administrator, c/o White Horse Court, 25c North

Street, Bishops Stortford, Hertfordshire CM23 2LD *Tel* 01279 506421 *email* charities@pwwsolicitors.co.uk *Website* www.pwwsolicitors.co.uk
CC NO 1061760 **ESTABLISHED** 1997

■ The William and Patricia Venton Charitable Trust

WHERE FUNDING CAN BE GIVEN UK.
WHO CAN BENEFIT Older people, day centres, animal welfare.
WHAT IS FUNDED Relief in need for older people, particularly day centre provision and the prevention of cruelty and suffering among animals.
SAMPLE GRANTS Beneficiaries were: Plymouth Age Concern (£55,000); Age Concern Northamptonshire (£25,000); Queen Alexandra Cottage Homes Eastbourne (£16,000); Barn Owl Trust (£6,000); Owton Fens Community Association (£5,000); and Extra Care Charitable Trust (£3,000).
FINANCES *Year* 2008–09 *Income* £373,424 *Grants* £109,866 *Assets* £1,998,878
TRUSTEES G B Hillman-Liggett; C C Saunby; G J Cudlipp
HOW TO APPLY In writing to the correspondent.
WHO TO APPLY TO The Trustees, Laytons Solicitors, Carmelite, 50 Victoria Embankment, Blackfriars, London EC4Y 0LS
CC NO 1103884 **ESTABLISHED** 2004

■ The Verdon-Smith Family Charitable Settlement

WHERE FUNDING CAN BE GIVEN South-West England, and especially Somerset, Bristol, Wiltshire, South Gloucestershire and North Dorset.
WHO CAN BENEFIT Registered charities with emphasis on local activity and needs benefiting: people of all ages; ex-service and service people; seafarers and fishermen; musicians; widows and widowers; Church of England; disabled people; disaster victims; and homeless people.
WHAT IS FUNDED This trust will consider funding: almshouses and respite accommodation; architecture; music; visual arts; arts education; orchestras; cultural activities; religious buildings; acute health care; hospices and hospice at home; respite care for carers; cancer and MS research; conservation; animal welfare; church schools; independent schools; care in the community and day centres. There is a quarterly review of regular donations with occasional addition of new donations.
WHAT IS NOT FUNDED No grants to individuals, or for salaries or running costs. Grants to organisations with recognised charitable status only.
TYPE OF GRANT Recurrent, occasional one-off, buildings, capital, core costs, project and research. Funding is available for one year or less.
RANGE OF GRANTS £100–£250.
SAMPLE GRANTS Average grant of £150. Beneficiaries included: Corsham Festival; Devon Wildlife Trust; Gloucestershire Society; Salisbury Trust for the Homeless; Shaw Trust; Royal Hospital for Children – Bristol; Jubilee Sailing Trust; West Lavington Youth Club; Canine Partners for Independence; Motability for Somerset; Arthritis Research Campaign; Royal British Legion; Building of Bath Museum Appeal;

Salisbury Cathedral Choral Foundation; Grateful Society; Genesis Trust; and Avon Outward Bound Association.

FINANCES *Year* 2007–08 *Income* £37,187 *Grants* £28,682 *Assets* £657,656

TRUSTEES William G Verdon-Smith, Chair; Mrs Elizabeth J White; Mrs Diana N Verdon-Smith.

HOW TO APPLY In writing to the correspondent. The trustees meet quarterly and applications will not be acknowledged unless successful.

WHO TO APPLY TO Mrs Elizabeth J White, Trustee, 5 Sydney Buildings, Bath, Somerset BA2 6BZ *Tel* 0122 542 6458

CC NO 284919   **ESTABLISHED** 1983

■ Roger Vere Foundation

WHERE FUNDING CAN BE GIVEN UK and worldwide, with a special interest in High Wycombe.

WHO CAN BENEFIT Charitable organisations.

WHAT IS FUNDED The relief of financial hardship; advancement of education; advancement of religion; advancement of scientific and medical research; conservation and protection of the natural environment and endangered plants and animals; relief of natural and civil disasters; and general charitable purposes.

RANGE OF GRANTS In 2005–06 no single grant exceeded £500.

SAMPLE GRANTS Previous beneficiaries have included Cord Blood Charity, the Leprosy Mission, Claire House Children's Hospice, Angels International, Signalong Group, Changing Faces, Women's Aid, St John Water Wing, UK Youth and Jubilee Plus.

FINANCES *Year* 2007–08 *Income* £297,958

TRUSTEES Mrs Rosemary Vere, Chair; Mrs Marion Lyon; Peter Allen.

OTHER INFORMATION In 2005–06 the sum of £3,450 went to individuals.

HOW TO APPLY In writing to the correspondent.

WHO TO APPLY TO Peter Allen, Trustee, 19 Berwick Road, Marlow, Buckinghamshire SL7 3AR

CC NO 1077559   **ESTABLISHED** 1999

■ Victoria Homes Trust

WHERE FUNDING CAN BE GIVEN Northern Ireland.

WHO CAN BENEFIT Registered charities benefiting children and young people.

WHAT IS FUNDED Voluntary projects in the fields of homelessness, alcohol and drug misuse and counselling.

WHAT IS NOT FUNDED Grants are not normally given to individuals.

FINANCES *Year* 2008–09 *Grants* £50,000

HOW TO APPLY On a form available from the correspondent or from the charity's website. A copy of the most recent audited accounts should be included. Applications should be typed or written in block capital letters using black ink. If the project requires work which involves planning permission, evidence that the permission has been granted should be enclosed. The trust asks that pamphlets or other printed matter should not be sent. Trustees meet in June and January. Applications should be submitted before 30 April and 30 November respectively.

WHO TO APPLY TO Derek H Catney, Secretary, 2 Tudor Court, Rochester Road, Belfast BT6 9LB *Tel* 028 9079 4306 *email* derek.catney1@ btinternet.com *Website* www.victoriahomestrust. org.uk

IR NO XN45474

■ Viking Cares (previously For the Kids)

WHERE FUNDING CAN BE GIVEN East Yorkshire and northern Lincolnshire.

WHO CAN BENEFIT Children who have experienced abuse or neglect, are sick, disabled, have special needs or who require extra care or attention, and organisations caring for such people.

WHAT IS FUNDED Welfare and other needs.

SAMPLE GRANTS Previous beneficiaries include: Home Learning Service, Riverside Special School – Goole, Hull Women's Aid, Handicapped Children's Action Group, Thorpe's Community Centre and Pooh Bear Reading Society.

FINANCES *Year* 2007–08 *Income* £119,433 *Grants* £39,867 *Assets* £35,830

TRUSTEES Irene Heffernan; Stephen Allbones; Sidonie Myers; Jonathan Symonds; Mark Lonsdale; Alex Knaggs.

HOW TO APPLY On a form available from the trust's website. They are considered quarterly.

WHO TO APPLY TO Rebecca Poppleton, Administrator, c/o Viking FM, Commercial Road, Hull HU1 2SG *Tel* 01482 325141 *email* rebecca.poppleton@ vikingfm.co.uk *Website* www.vikingfm.co. uk/sectional.asp?id=23669

CC NO 1102289   **ESTABLISHED** 2003

■ The Nigel Vinson Charitable Trust

WHERE FUNDING CAN BE GIVEN UK, with a preference for north east England.

WHO CAN BENEFIT Individuals and organisations.

WHAT IS FUNDED Economic/community development and employment; and general charitable purposes.

TYPE OF GRANT Capital (including buildings), one-off, project and research. Funding is for one year or less.

SAMPLE GRANTS Institute for Policy Research (£73,000); Renewable Energy Foundation (£47,000); Civitas (£30,000); Institute of Economic Affairs (£11,000); Electoral Reform Society (£10,000); Foundation for Social and Economic Thinking (£8,000); the Almshouse Association, Hampden Trust and Hart Charity (£5,000 each); Christian Institute and Reform Research Trust (£4,000 each); International Policy Network (£2,000); and Christian Fellowship (£1,000).

FINANCES *Year* 2007–08 *Income* £272,152 *Grants* £224,925 *Assets* £4,142,775

TRUSTEES Mrs Rowena A Cowan; Rt Hon. Lord Vinson of Roddam Dene; Thomas O C Harris; Hon. Miss Bettina C Witheridge; Hon. Mrs Antonia C Bennett.

HOW TO APPLY In writing to the correspondent. The trustees meet periodically to consider applications for grants of £1,000 and above. All grants below £1,000 are decided by The Rt. Hon. Nigel Lord Vinson on behalf of the trustees.

WHO TO APPLY TO The Trustees, Hoare Trustees, 37 Fleet Street, London EC4P 4DQ

CC NO 265077   **ESTABLISHED** 1973

Think carefully about every application. Is it justified?

927

■ The William and Ellen Vinten Trust

WHERE FUNDING CAN BE GIVEN UK, but mostly Bury St Edmunds.

WHO CAN BENEFIT Individuals, schools and colleges; and industrial firms and companies. There is a strong preference for Bury St Edmunds.

WHAT IS FUNDED The 2007/08 trustees' report stated that: 'The principal activity of the trust during the year was continuing to pursue initiatives to increase the interest of schools and college students in the Bury St Edmunds' area in science and technology subjects, with a view to increasing the numbers who might consider careers related to the subjects and improving their attainment.'

FINANCES *Year* 2007–08 *Income* £70,910 *Grants* £65,375 *Assets* £1,385,720

HOW TO APPLY The trust stated that as a proactive charity it does not seek unsolicited applications. Such applications are now so significant in number that the trust has decided not to respond to them, however discourteous this may seem.

WHO TO APPLY TO The Chair of the Trustees, 80 Guildhall Street, Bury St Edmunds, Suffolk IP33 1QB

CC NO 285758   **ESTABLISHED** 1982

■ The Vintners' Company Charitable Foundation

WHERE FUNDING CAN BE GIVEN Greater London only.

WHO CAN BENEFIT Schools and charitable organisations.

WHAT IS FUNDED Prevention of drug and alcohol misuse. Funding for schools can be for general purposes.

WHAT IS NOT FUNDED No grants to UK-wide or research charities.

TYPE OF GRANT One-off.

SAMPLE GRANTS National Association of Children of Alcoholics (£30,000). Also, £12,000 to general charities and £5,000 in educational grants.

FINANCES *Year* 2007–08 *Income* £126,832 *Grants* £47,425 *Assets* £534,284

TRUSTEES Michael Davies; Sam Dow; Anthony Edwards; Martin Mason; Michael Turner.

HOW TO APPLY In writing to the correspondent.

WHO TO APPLY TO Kate Marshall, Charities Secretary, Vintners' Company, Vintners' Hall, Upper Thames Street, London EC4V 3BG *Tel* 020 7236 1863 *Fax* 020 7236 8177 *email* catherine@vintnershall.co.uk *Website* www.vintnershall.co.uk

CC NO 1015212   **ESTABLISHED** 1992

■ Vintners' Gifts Charity

WHERE FUNDING CAN BE GIVEN Greater London.

WHO CAN BENEFIT Hospices, hospitals and organisations benefiting older people, people with disabilities, those who have experienced abuse or addiction, young people, the homeless and the disadvantaged.

WHAT IS FUNDED The Vintners' Company concentrates on different sections of charitable giving every six months. They will only respond to applications from charities in these sections during each period. The sections will be: May 2010 – older people; November 2010 – hospices/hospitals; May 2011 – youth/youth projects.

WHAT IS NOT FUNDED No grants to national charities, research organisations or charities that help buildings (as opposed to people).

TYPE OF GRANT One-off.

RANGE OF GRANTS Up to £12,000.

SAMPLE GRANTS Noah's Ark Children's Charity (£6,500); Breast Cancer Haven, Newham Music Trust and Vauxhall City Farm (£5,000 each); Trinity Hospital (£4,000); St Joseph's Hospice (£3,500); Friends Chelsea and Westminster (£1,000); Action for Kids, Islington Somali Community and Step by Step (£750 each); and Carers UK, Refresh and the Peaceful Place (£500 each).

FINANCES *Year* 2007–08 *Income* £175,186 *Grants* £149,000 *Assets* £2,059,901

TRUSTEES The Master and Wardens of the Vintners' Company.

HOW TO APPLY In writing to the correspondent, giving details of the charity and a brief description of the project, if applicable, together with a copy of the latest audited accounts. Applicants must be prepared to be visited by a member of The Vintners' Company. The Charities Committee Meetings are in May and November. Applications should be received by 14 February for May Meetings and 14 August for November Meetings.

WHO TO APPLY TO Mrs Kate Marshall, Charities Secretary, Vintners' Company, Vintners' Hall, Upper Thames Street, London EC4V 3BG *Tel* 020 7236 1863 *Fax* 020 7236 8177 *email* catherine@vintnershall.co.uk *Website* www.vintnershall.co.uk

CC NO 1091238   **ESTABLISHED** 1992

■ Vision Charity

WHERE FUNDING CAN BE GIVEN UK and overseas.

WHO CAN BENEFIT 'Registered institutional charities and other organisations and individuals involved in helping blind, dyslexic or visually impaired children.'

WHAT IS FUNDED Welfare of children with dyslexia or visual difficulties.

TYPE OF GRANT 'The monies raised are used expressly to purchase equipment, goods or specialist services. The Vision Charity will make cash donations only in very exceptional circumstances, as approved by its Board of Trustees.'

SAMPLE GRANTS London Society for the Blind – Dorton House School (£45,000); Dyslexia Action (£24,000); New College – Worcester (£14,000); the Eyeless Trust (£10,000); Milton Margai School (£9,000); SENSE (£8,000); Joseph Clark School (£5,000); and See Ability (£3,600).

FINANCES *Year* 2007–08 *Income* £476,912 *Grants* £130,037 *Assets* £238,995

TRUSTEES Herbert Brenninkmeijer, Chair; Bill Bohanna; Larry Davis; David Pacy.

PUBLICATIONS *Vision Charity News* (published twice yearly).

OTHER INFORMATION 'Vision is keen to emphasize its increasing international focus, both it terms of its fundraising activities and in directing its donations.'

HOW TO APPLY A brief summary of the request should be sent to the correspondent. If the request is of interest to the trustees, further details will be requested. If the request has not been acknowledged within three months of submission, the applicant should assume that it has not been successful. The charity is interested to receive such applications but regrets that it is not able to acknowledge every unsuccessful submission.

WHO TO APPLY TO The Trustees, PO Box 553, Chatham ME4 9AN *Website* www.visioncharity. co.uk

CC NO 1075630 　　　　**ESTABLISHED** 1976

....

■ Vivdale Ltd

WHERE FUNDING CAN BE GIVEN UK.

WHO CAN BENEFIT Jewish people.

WHAT IS FUNDED To advance religion in accordance with the orthodox Jewish faith and general charitable purposes.

SAMPLE GRANTS Previous beneficiaries have included: Achisomach Aid Company Ltd, Beis Soroh Schneirer, Beis Yaakov Town, Beis Yisroel Tel Aviv, Comet Charities Ltd, Friends of Harim Bnei Brak, Jewish Teachers Training College Gateshead, Mosdos Bnei Brak, Torah Vechesed Ashdod and Woodstock Sinclair Trust.

FINANCES *Year* 2007–08 *Income* £122,722 *Grants* £126,541 *Assets* £2,378,797

TRUSTEES D H Marks; L Marks; F Z Sinclair.

HOW TO APPLY In writing to the correspondent.

WHO TO APPLY TO D H Marks, Trustee, 17 Cheyne Walk, London NW4 3QH

CC NO 268505 　　　　**ESTABLISHED** 1974

....

■ The Viznitz Foundation

WHERE FUNDING CAN BE GIVEN UK and abroad.

WHO CAN BENEFIT Organisations, including schools and registered charities.

WHAT IS FUNDED 'The objects of the charity are to pay and apply and appropriate the whole of the trust fund to those purposes both in the UK and abroad recognised as charitable by English Law and in accordance with the trust deed and the wishes of the Grand Rabbi of Viznitz.'

FINANCES *Year* 2007–08 *Income* £199,035 *Grants* £73,658 *Assets* £1,634,816

TRUSTEES H Feldman; E Kahan.

HOW TO APPLY In writing to the correspondent.

WHO TO APPLY TO H Feldman, Trustee, 23 Overlea Road, London E5 9BG

CC NO 326581 　　　　**ESTABLISHED** 1984

....

■ The Vodafone (Group) Foundation

WHERE FUNDING CAN BE GIVEN Worldwide. In the UK: Banbury, Newark, Northern Ireland, Stoke, Trowbridge, Warrington, West Berkshire and where Vodafone stores are located.

WHO CAN BENEFIT Registered charities and community groups.

WHAT IS FUNDED Organisations working with young people aged between 16 and 25. 'In the UK the Vodafone Foundation focuses on helping 16–25 year-olds facing exclusion from society, whether reaching a cross road in their lives, struggling with emotional well-being or having difficulty accessing the information that they need. It is committed to creating sustainable change and working collaboratively with its charity partners providing a range of resources in addition to financial support wherever possible. It also supports young people in local communities where Vodafone has significant physical presence, and Vodafone employees who are involved in community activities.'

WHAT IS NOT FUNDED No grant to individuals.

FINANCES *Year* 2007–08 *Income* £25,000,000 *Grants* £2,900,000 *Assets* £15,600,000

TRUSTEES Nick Land, Chair; Margherita Della Valle; Elizabeth Filkin; Ian Gray; Lord Hastings of Scarisbrick; Matthew Kirk; Guy Laurence; Frank Rovekamp; Ronald Schellekens; Tina Southall.

OTHER INFORMATION Almost all of the foundation's income comes from Vodafone Group Plc. This global foundation has taken over the function of the Vodafone UK Foundation, which ceased to exist in early 2009. Grants worldwide totalled £22.9 million.

HOW TO APPLY On a form available to download from the foundation's website.

WHO TO APPLY TO Andrew Dunnett, Director, Vodafone Group PLC, Vodafone House, The Connection, Newbury, Berkshire RG14 2FN *email* groupfoundation@vodafone.com

CC NO 1089625 　　　　**ESTABLISHED** 2002

....

■ The Volant Charitable Trust

WHERE FUNDING CAN BE GIVEN UK, with a preference for Scotland, and overseas.

WHO CAN BENEFIT Organisations benefiting women, children, the relief of poverty, the alleviation of social deprivation and the provision of social benefit to the community.

WHAT IS FUNDED Social welfare, the protection of women and children, medical research, particularly into multiple sclerosis, and international aid.

WHAT IS NOT FUNDED No grants to individuals.

TYPE OF GRANT One-off and recurrent grants; core costs and project grants.

SAMPLE GRANTS Disasters Emergency Committee (£2 million); UNICEF (£500,000); and Motherwell and Wishaw Citizens Advice Bureau, Multi-Cultural Family Base, Pallion Action Group, Altrusa Careers Trust and Bringing East End Together (£75,000 each).

FINANCES *Year* 2008–09 *Income* £4,592,556 *Grants* £3,739,074 *Assets* £38,403,823

TRUSTEES J K Rowling; Dr N S Murray; G C Smith; R D Fulton.

HOW TO APPLY Applications for funding requests of £10,000 or less, for those projects based in **Scotland** only, are dealt with by the trust's appointed agents, the Scottish Community Foundation. All other requests for funding are dealt with via an application form available from the trust's website. Complete and return the application form, plus any supporting materials by post. Applications should not be hand delivered. If an application is hand delivered, management at Mail Boxes are not in a position to discuss applications and will not be expected to provide any form of receipt.

WHO TO APPLY TO Christine Collingwood, Administrator, PO Box 8, 196 Rose Street, Edinburgh EH2 4AT *Website* www.volanttrust. com

SC NO SC030790 　　　　**ESTABLISHED** 2000

....

■ Voluntary Action Fund

WHERE FUNDING CAN BE GIVEN Scotland.

WHO CAN BENEFIT Registered charities and organisations with a constitution and activities that could be considered charitable.

WHAT IS FUNDED The fund currently runs three grant-making programmes: Volunteering Scotland Grant Scheme; Equality Grants Programme; and Community Grants. All are linked by the common threads of social inclusion and support for organisations to become stronger. See the fund's website for up-to-date programme information.

WHAT IS NOT FUNDED Each programme has its own set of eligibility criteria. Please contact the fund directly or go to the website for full details.

TYPE OF GRANT Small Grants Scheme: starter grants for up to one year, which are not renewable. Main Grants Programme: three-year project grants. Feasibility studies, core costs, running costs and salaries will also be considered.

RANGE OF GRANTS Up to about £40,000 but mostly under £5,000.

SAMPLE GRANTS Previous beneficiaries include: Glasgow Braendam Link, Calman Trust Ltd, Jeely Piece Club, Street League Scotland, Chinese Community Development Partnership – Glasgow, Duncholgan Playgroup, Gorbals Initiative, Sikh Sanjog, British Red Cross, Legal Services Agency and Umoja.

FINANCES *Year* 2007–08 *Income* £2,648,978

TRUSTEES Dave Milliken, Chair; Farkhanda Chaudhry, Michael Cunningham, Julie Hogg, Caron Hughes, Pam Judson, Stuart McGregor, Dorothy MacLauchlan, Abi Mordin, Helen Munro, Laurie Naumann, Jonathan Squire.

PUBLICATIONS Annual accounts for 2006/07 were available to download from the fund's website.

HOW TO APPLY Application forms and guidance notes for open programmes are available on the fund's website. The fund recommends that interested parties contact them to discuss the project before making any application.

WHO TO APPLY TO Keith Wimbles, Chief Executive, Dunfermline Business Centre, Unit 14, Izatt Avenue, Dunfermline KY11 3BZ *Tel* 01383 620780 *Fax* 01383 626314 *email* info@voluntaryactionfund.org.uk *Website* www.voluntaryactionfund.org.uk

SC NO SC035037   **ESTABLISHED** 1982

■ Wade's Charity

WHERE FUNDING CAN BE GIVEN Leeds, within the pre-1974 boundary of the city (approximately LS1 to LS17 postcodes).

WHO CAN BENEFIT Charities benefiting people of all ages and those living in urban areas. Mainly youth organisations and community centres. (Grants are only a part of the charity's activities.)

WHAT IS FUNDED 'The provision of facilities for recreation, amusement, entertainment and general social intercourse for citizens of every age of areas of population in the City of Leeds occupied in the main by the working classes including in any such objects the establishment of what are commonly known as community centres and youth centres.' Please see the charity's website for full guidelines.

WHAT IS NOT FUNDED No grants given to: applications from outside the beneficial area, i.e. from outside the pre-1974 boundary of the city of Leeds covered roughly by postcodes LS1 to LS17; applications from non-charitable organisations; applications from individuals; applications for church repairs (unless there is proven significant community use); circulars or general appeals from high profile national charities; applications which do not offer benefit within the terms of the trust; applications for activities which are the responsibility of statutory or local authority funding, particularly within health or education; applications to fund salaries.

TYPE OF GRANT The majority of grants are given on a one-off basis.

RANGE OF GRANTS Average grant around £2,000.

SAMPLE GRANTS Hawksworth Wood YMCA (£7,000); Belle Isle Family Centre (£5,000); No Way Trust (£4,800); Central Yorkshire County Scout Council (£4,000); the Hunslet Initiative (£3,000); Lifeforce Productions (£2,500); Friends of PHAB, Girl Guiding Leeds, Kidz Klub Leeds, Leeds Holiday Fund and St Richard's Church Holiday Club (£2,000 each); Meeting Point (£1,500); Breast Cancer Haven (£1,000); and Live Music Now (£750).

FINANCES *Year* 2008 *Income* £182,203 *Grants* £140,640 *Assets* £4,279,275

TRUSTEES Cllr Bernard Atha; Peter Marshall; Martin Arnold; Susan Reddington; John Tinker; Ann Chadwick; Revd Canon Anthony Bundock; Cllr Ann Blackburn; John Roberts; John Stoddart-Scott; John Thorpe; Martin Dodgson; Martin Scurrah Wainwright.

OTHER INFORMATION A small grants programme has been operating through Voluntary Action Leeds for many years. This programme enables small community groups (with an annual income of less than £10,000) who may not be a registered charity to apply for funds of up to £100 to contribute towards their administrative costs.

HOW TO APPLY Main grants – In writing to the correspondent, include the following information: the name, address and telephone number of both the applicant and the organisations they are applying on behalf of; registered charity number; an outline of what the organisation does; an outline of the purpose for which the grant is being sought; a copy of the latest signed accounts. If an application potentially fulfils at least one of the primary charitable objectives of the charity, an appointment will then be made for the Grants Adviser to visit the organisation to establish further relevant information about the application. The application will then be considered by the board of trustees at one of their grants meetings, these are usually held in April, July and November. The deadline for inclusion at any meeting is four weeks prior to the meeting date. The charity is happy to discuss ideas before a formal application is made. Applicants may only submit an application once per calendar year. Voluntary Action Leeds advertises the small grants programme in their newsletter at the start of each year.

WHO TO APPLY TO Kathryn Hodges, 12 Mill Lane, Stutton, Tadcaster, North Yorkshire LS24 9BT *Tel* 01937 830295 *email* wadescharity@btinernet.com *Website* www.wadescharity.org

CC NO 224939　　　　**ESTABLISHED** 1530

■ The Scurrah Wainwright Charity

WHERE FUNDING CAN BE GIVEN Preference for Yorkshire, South Africa and Zimbabwe.

WHO CAN BENEFIT Charitable organisations.

WHAT IS FUNDED The charity 'looks for innovative work in the field of social reform, with a preference for "root-cause" rather than palliative projects. It favours causes that are outside the mainstream, and unlikely to be funded by other charities.'

WHAT IS NOT FUNDED No support is given to: individuals; animal welfare; buildings; medical research or support for individual medical conditions; substitution for Government funding (e.g. in education and health); charities who send unsolicited general appeal letters.

TYPE OF GRANT Contributions to core costs.

RANGE OF GRANTS Typically £1,000–£5,000, but in 'cases of exceptional merit' larger grants may be awarded.

SAMPLE GRANTS Asylum Support Housing Advice, Fairshare Education Foundation and Refugee Action (£5,000 each); Domestic Violence Service (£4,500); Actionaid and War on Want (£3,000 each); Mustard Seed Communities (£3,000); International Children's Trust (£2,500); Bradford Nightstop, Next Steps Ryedale and St Wilfred's Centre (£2,000 each); and Ravenscliffe Community Development (£1,000 each).

FINANCES *Year* 2007–08 *Income* £57,596 *Grants* £86,233 *Assets* £1,768,043

TRUSTEES M S Wainwright, Chair; R R Bhaskar; H P I Scott; H A Wainwright; J M Wainwright; P Wainwright; T M Wainwright.

OTHER INFORMATION 'The Wainwright family runs two trusts, one charitable [The Scurrah Wainwright Charity], one non-charitable [The Andrew Wainwright Reform Trust Ltd]. The trusts are based on the family's traditions of liberal values and support for the socially disempowered. The trustees are all family members, based in West Yorkshire.'

HOW TO APPLY In writing to the correspondent, covering the following: 'background information about you and/or your organisation; the nature of the project you wish to pursue and what it seeks to achieve; your plans for practical implementation of the work and a budget; your most recent accounts and details of any additional sources of funding already secured or to be sought; whether you will accept a contribution to the amount requested; where you heard about the charity; a summary on no more than two sides of A4, using a font no smaller than 12-point.' Trustees meet in March, July and November. Applications should be received by the first day of the preceding month. For further information please visit the trust's website. Applicants may contact the administrator by email, for any clarification.

WHO TO APPLY TO Kerry McQuade, Administrator, 16 Blenheim Street, Hebden Bridge, West Yorkshire HX7 8BU *email* admin@wainwrighttrusts.org.uk *Website* www.wainwrighttrusts.org.uk

CC NO 1002755   **ESTABLISHED** 1991

■ The Wakefield and Tetley Trust

WHERE FUNDING CAN BE GIVEN London boroughs of Tower Hamlets, Southwark and the City of London.

WHO CAN BENEFIT Community groups and charities.

WHAT IS FUNDED Social welfare and general charitable purposes.

WHAT IS NOT FUNDED The trust will not support: grants to individuals; work that has already taken place; applicants who have been rejected by the trust within the last six months; organisations with significant unrestricted reserves; organisations in serious financial deficit; the promotion of religion; animal charities; statutory bodies and work that is primarily the responsibility of central or local government; health trusts, health authorities and hospices (or any sort of medical equipment or medical research). The trust is unlikely to support: building restoration or conservation; uniformed youth groups; schools, supplementary schools or vocational training; environmental improvements.

TYPE OF GRANT Up to three years for project costs and core costs.

RANGE OF GRANTS Grants range from £500 to £45,000 over one year; the average grant awarded in 2008 was £6,000.

SAMPLE GRANTS All Hallows by the Tower (£58,500), to support five new community projects, including Beyond Boyle catering and educational projects; Quaker Social Action (£20,000), to support the 'Knees Up' community development programme; FareShare (£10,000), to support a free food delivery service to 13 community groups and a new Employability Training programme; Blackfriars Settlement (£9,000), to establish a weekly activities centre for older people in north Southwark; Women's Environmental Network (£5,000), to support a food-growing advisory project for community groups; Horn Afrik Integration Project (£4,000), to support a community safety programme for Somali women; Bijoy Youth Group (£2,000), to support a supplementary education project for Bangladeshi children; and Arts for All (£1,000), towards trips and arts activities for children and young people.

FINANCES *Year* 2008 *Income* £393,523 *Grants* £392,214 *Assets* £5,549,759

TRUSTEES The Venerable Peter Delaney, Chair; Bill Almond; Jean Harris; Ronke Kokoruwe; Patrick Kelly; Lady Judy Moody-Stuart; Stuart Morganstein; Ken Prideaux-Brune; Helal Rahman.

HOW TO APPLY 'You will need to demonstrate that your organisation: benefits people resident or working in Tower Hamlets and/or Southwark and/or the City of London; undertakes charitable work (however you do not have to be a registered charity); has a constitution or a set of rules which governs its activities; has its own bank or building society account where two or more named people (including one trustee or management committee member) have to sign all the cheques; can provide annual accounts for the previous year (if your organisation is new, copies of your most recent bank or building society statements will suffice).

The trust is likely to receive many more proposals than we are able to fund so the following funding priorities have been agreed. The trust particularly welcomes applications for: cross-cultural and intergenerational projects that help to bring people together, reduce barriers and support community cohesion; new initiatives that address emerging needs new methods of tackling existing problems.

The trust will prioritise: projects with local support and beneficiary involvement; projects that have a well-considered plan and demonstrate the difference that will be made; organisations with an annual turnover of less than £500,000; organisations with a relevant track record and experience. These priorities will be subject to regular review. We are happy to consider requests to fund project costs, relevant core costs and associated training. However the trust is unlikely to support equipment or capital costs. We usually make grants over one, two or three years, however, funding cannot continue indefinitely as we are keen to support a range of projects and organisations, including those which are new to us.'

WHO TO APPLY TO Elaine Crush, Grant Officer, Attlee House, 28 Commercial Street, London E1 6LR *Tel* 020 7377 6614 *email* enquiries@ wakefieldtrust.org.uk *Website* www. wakefieldtrust.org.uk

CC NO 1121779   **ESTABLISHED** 2008

■ Wakeham Trust

WHERE FUNDING CAN BE GIVEN UK.

WHO CAN BENEFIT Registered charities.

WHAT IS FUNDED 'We provide grants to help people rebuild their communities. We are particularly interested in neighbourhood projects, community arts projects, projects involving community service by young people, or projects set up by those who are socially excluded. 'We also support innovative projects to promote excellence in teaching (at any level, from primary schools to universities), though we never support individuals.'

WHAT IS NOT FUNDED No grants to individuals or large, well-established charities, or towards buildings and transport.

RANGE OF GRANTS Normally £75–£750.

SAMPLE GRANTS Den Montford University (£8,000); Sharana – India (£5,000); Unite (£1,500); Bristol Cathedral Trust, Streatham Youth and Community Centre (£600 each); BUGS and the Initiative (£500 each); Bexley Trust for Adult Students (£400); Darlington Boys Club (£300); Brighton and Hove Unemployed Centre (£250); Dyslexia Action, Rising Brook Writers and South Tyneside Football Trust (£200 each); Springtime Lunch Club, Tree the Way and Waterloo Housing Society (£150 each); and Bridestone Village Hall (£100).

FINANCES *Year* 2007–08 *Income* £48,805 *Grants* £85,355 *Assets* £1,591,965

TRUSTEES Harold Carter; Barnaby Newbolt; Tess Silkstone.

HOW TO APPLY By letter or by filling in the online form on the trust's website. The trust prefers online applications. Full guidelines are also available on the trust's website.

WHO TO APPLY TO The Trustees, Wakeham Lodge, Rogate, Petersfield, Hampshire GU31 5EJ *Tel* 01730 821748 *email* wakehamtrust@mac. com *Website* www.wakehamtrust.org

CC NO 267495   **ESTABLISHED** 1974

. . . .

■ The Community Foundation in Wales

WHERE FUNDING CAN BE GIVEN Wales.

WHO CAN BENEFIT Local charities, community groups and voluntary organisations that are engaged in tackling social need and economic disadvantage at a grass-roots level.

WHAT IS FUNDED The promotion of any charitable purposes for the benefit of communities within Wales. Projects providing worthwhile service to the community. The foundation manages a number of funds, many with their own individual criteria and some which relate to specific geographical areas of Wales. Although not exhaustive, the following list offers a flavour of the themes that the foundation's donors like to address: community cohesion; the environment; older people; minority groups; young people; economic disadvantage; social exclusion; rural isolation; crime reduction; substance misuse and addiction; skills development and confidence-building; education and lifelong learning; and sport as a vehicle for social inclusion.

WHAT IS NOT FUNDED 'The current focus of our clients is broad, however, we are unlikely to support: political organisations and pressure groups; religious organisations, where the primary aim of the project is the promotion of faith; individuals, unless the specific focus of a fund; general appeals; sports organisations where no obvious charitable element exists; medical research; statutory bodies e.g. schools, local authorities and councils, although we will consider applications from school PTAs if the intended project is non- statutory in nature; animal welfare; arts and heritage projects unless there exists a clear, demonstrable community benefit; large capital projects; retrospective applications for projects that have taken place.'

RANGE OF GRANTS Most of the grants awarded are under £5,000.

SAMPLE GRANTS Grants were made in the following categories: community cohesion – £227,000; improving health – £152,000; enabling youth - £75,000; empowering the disadvantaged – £132,000; small voluntary organisations £80,000; environment and heritage £15,000.

FINANCES *Year* 2007–08 *Income* £1,175,144 *Grants* £1,059,772 *Assets* £1,278,399

TRUSTEES Antony Lewis; Kim Brook; David Dudley; Prof. Mohan John Pathy; Gen. Christopher Last; Duncan Brydges; Michael Westerman; Julian Smith; Frank Learner; Ilene Hoyle; Drewe Lacey; Dr Caryl Cresswell.

OTHER INFORMATION 'The Community Foundation in Wales promotes the cause of philanthropy in Wales by creating and managing relationships between donors and those who are running life-enhancing initiatives. We are dedicated to strengthening local communities by providing a permanent source of funding, building endowment and *immediate impact* funds to link donors to local needs.'

HOW TO APPLY Please visit the 'current grants' page of its website. If an organisation is uncertain

about whether it meets the criteria for any of its named funds a general application may be completed at any time during the year. The foundation aims to match proposals to available funding and make contact if further information is required.

WHO TO APPLY TO The Company Secretary, 14–16 Merthyr Road, Whitchurch, Cardiff CF14 1DG *Tel* 029 2052 0250 *email* mail@cfiw.org.uk *Website* www.cfiw.org.uk

CC NO 1074655   **ESTABLISHED** 1999

. . . .

■ Wales Council for Voluntary Action

WHERE FUNDING CAN BE GIVEN Wales.

WHO CAN BENEFIT Registered charities and voluntary organisations only.

WHAT IS FUNDED Grants schemes include the Communities First Trust Fund.

WHAT IS NOT FUNDED Grants are made to constituted voluntary organisations only.

TYPE OF GRANT Capital, core costs, one-off, project, recurring costs, running costs, start-up costs.

FINANCES *Year* 2007–08 *Income* £29,000,160 *Grants* £21,073,766 *Assets* £10,412,794

TRUSTEES Louise Bennett; Nerys Haf Biddulph; Jacquy Box; Ian Charlesworth; Maureen Davies; Walter Dickie; Eurwen E Edwards; Catrin Fletcher; Win Griffiths; Simon Harris; Margaret Jervis; John R Jones; Harri Jones; Mike Lewis; Cath Lindley; James Maiden; Marcella Maxwell; Liz Neal; Jane Pagler; Chad Patel.

PUBLICATIONS Guidance notes for applicants available on request. Visit www.wcva.org.uk or call the Helpdesk on 0870 607 1666.

OTHER INFORMATION Contact WCVA directly for up-to-date information on open schemes.

HOW TO APPLY There are separate application forms for each scheme. Contact WCVA on 0870 607 1666, or visit its website, for further information.

WHO TO APPLY TO Graham Benfield, Chief Executive, Baltic House, Mount Stuart Square, Cardiff CF10 5FH *Tel* 0870 607 1666 *Fax* 029 2043 1701 *Minicom* 029 2043 1702 *email* help@ wcva.org.uk *Website* www.wcva.org.uk

CC NO 218093   **ESTABLISHED** 1963

. . . .

■ Robert and Felicity Waley-Cohen Charitable Trust

WHERE FUNDING CAN BE GIVEN Warwickshire and Oxfordshire.

WHO CAN BENEFIT Charitable organisations, schools and those of the Jewish faith.

WHAT IS FUNDED Jewish, children, education, fine arts, health.

WHAT IS NOT FUNDED No grants to individuals.

RANGE OF GRANTS £20–£50,000.

SAMPLE GRANTS The National Trust (£50,000); Oxford Radcliffe Hospitals Charitable Funds (£24,000); The Serpentine Trust (£9,000); Spinal Injuries Association (£8,000); Policy Exchange, Royal Shakespeare Company and Tate Foundation (£5,000 each); Tour de France (£3,000); Jewish Care (£1,000); Pace Centre (£500); CLIC Sargent (£350); Ashmolean Museum and Racing Welfare (£250 each); and Canine Partners, The Eve Appeal and The Moorecroft Racehorse Welfare Fund (£100 each).

FINANCES *Year* 2007–08 *Income* £123,619 *Grants* £131,546 *Assets* £1,689,928

TRUSTEES R Waley-Cohen; Hon F Waley-Cohen.

HOW TO APPLY In writing to the Correspondent.
WHO TO APPLY TO R Waley-Cohen, Trustee, 18 Gilston Road, London SW10 9SR *Tel* 020 7244 6022 *email* ccopeman@alliance.co.uk
CC NO 272126   **ESTABLISHED** 1976

■ The Walker Trust

WHERE FUNDING CAN BE GIVEN Shropshire.
WHO CAN BENEFIT Individuals and organisations benefiting children and young adults who are in care, fostered and adopted.
WHAT IS FUNDED The establishment or towards maintenance of any hospital, infirmary, convalescent home or other institution having for its object the relief of sickness or promoting convalescence; the provision of medical or surgical aid or appliance; any institution for the maintenance and education of orphans.
WHAT IS NOT FUNDED No grants to individuals for second degrees or postgraduate courses. Appeals from outside Shropshire will not be considered or replied to.
RANGE OF GRANTS Up to £25,000.
SAMPLE GRANTS Maurice Chandler Sports Centre (£25,000); Pioneer Centre (£15,000); Derwen College (£10,000); Albrighton Trust and RNIB (£5,000 each); Bridges Development Centre (£3,000); Shropshire Youth Adventure Trust (£2,000); and the Wilfred Owen Association (£1,500).
FINANCES *Year* 2007–08 *Income* £205,216 *Grants* £154,983 *Assets* £5,994,554
TRUSTEES A E H Herber-Percy, Chair; Nicholas Bishop; Brian Gillow; Mrs Caroline Paton-Smith; Joy Francis; Brian Williams.
OTHER INFORMATION The grant total in 2007–08 included: £92,649 to organisations and £62,334 to individuals.
HOW TO APPLY In writing to the correspondent. Details of other assistance applied for must be given and, in the case of organisations, the latest annual report and accounts. The trustees meet in January, April, July and October each year, but arrangements can be made for urgent applications to receive consideration between meetings. Applications must reach the clerk not less than one month before a decision is required.
WHO TO APPLY TO Edward Hewitt, Clerk, 2 Breidden Way, Bayston Hill, Shrewsbury SY3 0LN *Tel* 01743 873866
CC NO 215479   **ESTABLISHED** 1897

■ Wallace and Gromit's Children's Foundation

WHERE FUNDING CAN BE GIVEN UK.
WHO CAN BENEFIT Children's hospitals, hospices and healthcare organisations.
WHAT IS FUNDED Wallace & Gromit's Children's Foundation is a national charity raising funds to improve the quality of life for children in hospitals and hospices throughout the UK. The foundation provides funding to support projects such as: (i) Arts, music play and entertainment programmes to stimulate young minds and divert attention away from illness. (ii) Providing welcoming and accessible environments and surroundings, designed specifically for children in a fun and engaging way. (iii) Funding Education and Information Programmes to educate young people and recognising the importance of self help and health related issues. (iv) Helping to fund the acquisition of medical facilities, which can help to improve diagnosis and treatment of a wide range of conditions and illnesses in children. (v) Sustaining family relationships helping to keep families together during emotionally difficult times. (vi) Helping to meet the cost of care in a children's hospice where children and their families are cared for during good days, difficult days and last days. (vii) Supporting children with physical and emotional difficulties empowering and increasing confidence.
WHAT IS NOT FUNDED No support for; charities not supporting children's healthcare; organisations that do not have charitable status; animal, religious or international charities; retrospective funding; organisations that do not work within a hospital or hospice environment; organisations that provide excursions, holidays or away days; no grants will be made to individuals.
SAMPLE GRANTS Aberdeen Children's Hospital, Acorn's Children's Hospice Birmingham, Alder Hey Children's Hospital, Belfast Children's Hospital, Bristol Children's Hospital, Butterwick Children's Hospice – Stockton on Tees, Edinburgh Children's Hospital, Glasgow Children's Hospital, Naomi House Children's Hospice – Winchester, Oxford Children's Hospital, St Oswald's Children's Hospice – Newcastle and the Whittington Hospital (£10,000 each); Addenbrooke's Hospital – Cambridge and SeeSaw (£7,000 each); MedEquip4Kids (£2,100); Rainbows Children's Hospice (£2,000); and Hope House Children's Hospice and Shooting Star Hospice (£1,000 each).
FINANCES *Year* 2007–08 *Income* £190,625 *Grants* £182,800 *Assets* £9,990
TRUSTEES I Hannah, Chair; S Cooper; P Lord; J Moule; N Park; D Sproxton.
OTHER INFORMATION Wallace and Gromit's Wrong Trousers Day is the Foundations primary fundraising event which encourages the general public to wear the wrong trousers for the day and donate funds raised to the foundation.
HOW TO APPLY Grants are distributed on an annual basis. Application forms and guidelines are posted on the foundation's website from October and the closing date for applications is usually in December. All awards are made by the end of March.
WHO TO APPLY TO The Company Secretary, PO Box 2186, Bristol BS99 7NT *email* info@ wrongtrousersday.org *Website* www. wallaceandgromitfoundation.org
CC NO 1096483   **ESTABLISHED** 2003

■ Wallington Missionary Mart and Auctions

WHERE FUNDING CAN BE GIVEN Overseas.
WHO CAN BENEFIT Missionary societies working overseas benefiting Christians.
WHAT IS FUNDED Christian education and outreach.
WHAT IS NOT FUNDED Only registered Christian charities may receive support. Applications from individuals are only considered if funds will go to a Christian missionary society or Christian charity.
TYPE OF GRANT Usually one-off grants for core costs. Fully committed for charities selected by the trustees.
SAMPLE GRANTS Lamuru Children's Centre – Kenya (£40,000); Wycliffe Bible Translators (£9,000); OMF International UK (£5,000); Operation Mobilisation (£3,000); Crosslinks (£2,000);

Axminster Task Centre (£1,500); and the Oasis Trust (£1,000).

FINANCES *Year* 2008 *Income* £204,036 *Grants* £97,135 *Assets* £185,957

TRUSTEES Stephen J Crawley; Brian E Chapman; Harry F Curwood; Geoffrey C Willey; Derek C Lewin; Mrs Sylvia M Symes; Pat Collett.

OTHER INFORMATION This trust receives its income through receiving donated goods from the public, which are sold at the auctions it stages four to six times a year. For further information on these auctions, please see its website.

HOW TO APPLY In writing to the correspondent, with an sae. The trustees meet to consider grants throughout the year.

WHO TO APPLY TO Brian E Chapman, Trustee, 99 Woodmansterne Road, Carshalton Beeches, Surrey SM5 4EG *Tel* 020 8643 3616 *Website* www.wallingtonmissionary.org.uk

CC NO 289030   **ESTABLISHED** 1965

■ The F J Wallis Charitable Settlement

WHERE FUNDING CAN BE GIVEN UK, with some interest in Hampshire and Surrey.

WHO CAN BENEFIT Charitable organisations, including both headquarters and branches of large UK charities.

WHAT IS FUNDED General charitable purposes. In 2005/06 the settlement introduced a criteria-based approach to grantmaking. The trustees intend to alternate the areas of charitable activity that will receive grants between disability, children charities and medical research/health and sickness in one year and animal charities, community charities and hospices in the next.

WHAT IS NOT FUNDED No grants to individuals or to local charities except those in Surrey or in Hampshire. The same organisation is not supported twice within a 24-month period.

TYPE OF GRANT Mostly one-off but there are some recurring grants.

RANGE OF GRANTS £500–£1,000.

SAMPLE GRANTS Naomi House Children's Hospice and Princess Alice Hospice (£2,000 each); and Association of Children's Hospices, British Association for Adopting and Fostering, Chase Hospice Care for Children, Crisis, Down's Syndrome Association, GASP, Great Ormond Street Hospital Children's Charity, Headway, Hope House Children's Hospice, Independent Age, National Talking Newspapers, St John's Hospice, Trinity Hospice and Winchester Youth Counselling (£1,000 each); Cystic Fibrosis Trust (£500); and Forget Me Not and Leukaemia Research (£250 each).

FINANCES *Year* 2007–08 *Income* £60,474 *Grants* £41,000 *Assets* £1,222,241

TRUSTEES F H Hughes; A J Hills; Revd J J A Archer.

HOW TO APPLY In writing to the correspondent. No telephone calls. Applications are not acknowledged and unsuccessful applicants will only be contacted if an sae is provided. Trustees meet in March and September and applications need to be received the month prior to the trustees' meeting.

WHO TO APPLY TO F H Hughes, Trustee, c/o Bridge House, 11 Creek Road, Hampton Court, East Molesey, Surrey KT8 9BE

CC NO 279273   **ESTABLISHED** 1979

■ Walton on Thames Charity

WHERE FUNDING CAN BE GIVEN Ancient parish of Walton on Thames, Surrey.

WHO CAN BENEFIT Charitable and other community organisations, including schools and sports clubs.

WHAT IS FUNDED Social welfare.

SAMPLE GRANTS Previous beneficiaries included Ashley School, Bell Farm School, Cardinal Newman RC School, Cleeves School, Citizens Advice, Painshill Park and Scout Groups.

FINANCES *Year* 2007–08 *Income* £1,330,459 *Grants* £86,984 *Assets* £19,574,203

TRUSTEES Chris Sadler; David Nash; Tony Pollington; Clare Warne; Barry Cheyne; Robert Freeman; Mary Trimble; Duncan Parkes; Valerie Saint; Mary Sheldon; Canon Charles Stewart; Ben White; Christine Cross; Rosemary Dane; Christine Elmer.

HOW TO APPLY Application forms are available by telephone.

WHO TO APPLY TO Victor Cass, Mayfield, 74 Hersham Road, Walton on Thames KT12 5NU *Tel* 01932 220242 *Fax* 01932 252603 *email* vcass@waltoncharity.org.uk *Website* www.waltoncharity.org.uk

CC NO 230652   **ESTABLISHED** 1984

■ War on Want

WHERE FUNDING CAN BE GIVEN Developing countries only.

WHO CAN BENEFIT Typically, War on Want directly funds the work of labour organisations and NGOs in developing countries, usually trade unions or similar workers' organisations, and women's organisations.

WHAT IS FUNDED Overseas development projects that address the root causes of poverty, oppression and injustice in developing countries.

WHAT IS NOT FUNDED War on Want is an overseas development agency and does not make grants to organisations in the UK.

TYPE OF GRANT Continuous project funding.

SAMPLE GRANTS Sweatshops and plantations (£428,000); Informal economies (£294,000); Food justice (£217,500); Economic justice (£177,400); Global justice (£176,000); Conflict zones (£97,000).

FINANCES *Year* 2007–08 *Income* £2,010,202 *Grants* £1,389,520 *Assets* £1,583,841

TRUSTEES Alex Boyle; Martin Hughes; Sue Branford; James O'Nions; Nicholas Dearden; David Spooner; Polly Jones; David Hillman; Paul Moon; Mark Luetchford; Guillermo Rogel; Steve Preston.

PUBLICATIONS *Upfront* (a regular newsletter); publications list – covering subjects such as health, women, trade, aid, Asia, Latin America and Africa.

HOW TO APPLY Unsolicited applications are not accepted and will not be acknowledged.

WHO TO APPLY TO The Director, 56–64 Leonard Street, London EC2A 4LT *Tel* 020 7549 0563 *Fax* 0207 549 0556 *email* mailroom@waronwant.org *Website* www.waronwant.org

CC NO 208724   **ESTABLISHED** 1959

■ Sir Siegmund Warburg's Voluntary Settlement

WHERE FUNDING CAN BE GIVEN UK, especially London.
WHO CAN BENEFIT Charitable organisations.
WHAT IS FUNDED The arts.
WHAT IS NOT FUNDED No grants to individuals.
TYPE OF GRANT Recurring.
SAMPLE GRANTS Charleston Trust and National Gallery (£250,000 each); Ashmolean Museum (£200,000); Wordsworth Trust (£120,000); Garsington Opera (£105,000); Wallace Collection (£100,000); London Handel Festival (£10,000); and St Paul's Girl's School (£2,000).
FINANCES *Year* 2008–09 *Income* £488,215 *Grants* £1,037,000 *Assets* £10,180,750
TRUSTEES Hugh A Stevenson, Chair; Doris E Wasserman; Dr Michael J Harding; Christopher Purvis.
HOW TO APPLY In writing to the correspondent.
WHO TO APPLY TO The Secretary, c/o 33 St Mary Axe, London EC3A 8LL
CC NO 286719   **ESTABLISHED** 1983

■ The Ward Blenkinsop Trust

WHERE FUNDING CAN BE GIVEN UK, with a special interest in Merseyside and surrounding counties.
WHO CAN BENEFIT Charitable organisations.
WHAT IS FUNDED General charitable purposes with emphasis on support for medical research, social welfare, arts and education.
WHAT IS NOT FUNDED No grants to individuals.
SAMPLE GRANTS Previous beneficiaries have included Action on Addiction, BID, Chase Children's Hospice, Clatterbridge Cancer Research, Clod Ensemble, Comic Relief, Depaul Trust, Fairley House, Give Youth a Break, Halton Autistic Family Support Group, Hope HIV, Infertility Network, George Martin Music Foundation, Royal Academy of Dance, St Joseph's Family Centre, Strongbones Children's Charitable Trust, Walk the Walk, Winchester Visitors Group and Wirral Holistic Care Services.
FINANCES *Year* 2007–08 *Income* £477,205 *Grants* £367,270
TRUSTEES A M Blenkinsop; Ms S J Blenkinsop; Ms C A Blenkinsop; Mrs F A Stormer; Mrs H E Millin.
HOW TO APPLY In writing to the correspondent.
WHO TO APPLY TO Charlotte Blenkinsop, Trustee, PO Box 28840, London SW13 0WZ
CC NO 265449   **ESTABLISHED** 1972

■ The George Ward Charitable Trust

WHERE FUNDING CAN BE GIVEN The area covered by Hinckley and Bosworth Borough Council.
WHO CAN BENEFIT Organisations and former employees of George Ward (Barwell) Ltd and George Geary and Son Ltd, and their dependants.
WHAT IS FUNDED General charitable purposes.
RANGE OF GRANTS Usually up to £2,000.
SAMPLE GRANTS £2,000 to John Cleveland College; £1,000 each to County Air Ambulance and St Mary's Church, Barwell; £750 each to Rainbows Children Hospice, LOROS and Starlight Children's Foundation; £500 each to William Bradford Community College, ProstAid and Hinckley and District Mencap Society; £350 each to Adapt and Voluntary Action Hinckley and Bosworth; and £200 to Hinckley Civic Society.
FINANCES *Year* 2008–09 *Income* £47,598 *Grants* £21,646 *Assets* £765,778
TRUSTEES D M Radford; J A Calow.
HOW TO APPLY In writing to the correspondent at any time.
WHO TO APPLY TO Mrs S Hiom, Secretary, Thomas May and Co., Allen House, Newarke Street, Leicester LE1 5SG *Tel* 0116 233 5959 *Fax* 0116 233 5958 *email* stephaniehiom@thomasmay.co.uk
CC NO 516954   **ESTABLISHED** 1985

■ The Barbara Ward Children's Foundation

WHERE FUNDING CAN BE GIVEN England and Wales.
WHO CAN BENEFIT Registered charities and other institutions.
WHAT IS FUNDED Mostly work with children who are seriously or terminally ill, disadvantaged or otherwise.
TYPE OF GRANT Grants given range from one-off donations to project-related grants that run for two or three years.
SAMPLE GRANTS the Rainbow Centre (£37,000); MERU (£35,000); Tree House (£33,000); Richard House Children's Hospice (£28,000); WellChild (£23,000); Dame Vera Lynn Trust (£22,000); New College Worcester (£20,000); the Ellenor Foundation (£14,000); the Bobath Centre (£13,000); National Blind Children's Society (£10,000); Dogs for the Disabled (£8,500); React (£8,000); the Ear Foundation (£6,700); Hop, Skip and Jump – South West (£6,000); Army Cadet Force Association (£5,000); Ipswich Community Playbus (£4,000); Deafway (£3,000); the Rose Road Association (£2,500); and the Asha Centre (£500).
FINANCES *Year* 2008 *Income* £484,554 *Grants* £505,552 *Assets* £6,509,181
TRUSTEES Mrs B I Ward, Chair; D C Bailey; J C Banks; A M Gardner; K R Parker; B M Walters.
HOW TO APPLY In writing to the correspondent including latest set of audited financial statements. The trustees usually meet quarterly.
WHO TO APPLY TO The Trustees, 5 Great College Street, London SW1P 3SJ *Website* www.bwcf.org.uk
CC NO 1089783   **ESTABLISHED** 2001

■ The John Warren Foundation

WHERE FUNDING CAN BE GIVEN Lincolnshire, then Bedfordshire, Northamptonshire and Nottinghamshire.
WHO CAN BENEFIT Churches.
WHAT IS FUNDED Church fabric repairs.
WHAT IS NOT FUNDED No support for major cathedral appeals.
TYPE OF GRANT One-off grants.
SAMPLE GRANTS 29 charitable donations principally relating to the upkeep, repair and improvement of churches and church buildings.
FINANCES *Year* 2007–08 *Income* £29,280 *Grants* £23,150 *Assets* £731,122
TRUSTEES J E Lamb; R H Lamb; B H Marshall.
HOW TO APPLY In writing to the correspondent.

WHO TO APPLY TO J E Lamb, Trustee, Lamb and Holmes Solicitors, West Street, Kettering, Northamptonshire NN16 0AZ *Tel* 01536 513195 *Fax* 01536 410191 *email* enquiries@lamb-holmes.co.uk

CC NO 201522   **ESTABLISHED** 1949

■ The Waterloo Foundation

WHERE FUNDING CAN BE GIVEN UK, with a preference for Wales, and overseas.

WHO CAN BENEFIT Organisations working with children, in the developing world, the environment, and projects in Wales.

WHAT IS FUNDED 'We welcome applications from registered charities and organisations with projects that have a recognisable charitable purpose. Your project has to be allowed within the terms of your constitution or rules and, if you are not a registered charity, you will need to send us a copy of your constitution or set of rules. We make grants for all types of projects; start-up, initial stages and valuable ongoing funding. This can include running costs and overheads as well as posts; particularly under the World Development and Projects in Wales. We do not have any upper or lower limit on the amount of grant we offer but it is unlikely that we would offer a grant of more that £100,000.'

WHAT IS NOT FUNDED 'The foundation will not support: applications for grants for work that has already taken place; applications for grants that replace or subsidise statutory funding. We will not consider applications for grants in the following areas: the arts and heritage, except in Wales; animal welfare; the promotion of religious or political causes; general appeals or circulars. We are unlikely to support projects in the following areas: from individuals; for the benefit of an individual; medical charities (except under certain aspects of our "Child Development" programme, particularly mental health); festivals, sports and leisure activities; websites, publications, conferences or seminars, except under our "Child Development" programme.'

TYPE OF GRANT Project and core costs; one-off and recurrent grants.

RANGE OF GRANTS Up to £100,000.

FINANCES *Year* 2008 *Income* £4,556,471 *Grants* £4,354,496 *Assets* £92,112,545

TRUSTEES Heather Stevens; David Stevens; Janet Alexander; Caroline Oakes.

HOW TO APPLY 'We hope to make applying for a grant fairly painless and fairly quick. However it will help us a great deal if you could follow the simple rules below when sending in an application (there are no application forms). Email applications to applications@waterloofoundation.org.uk (nowhere else please!). Include a BRIEF description (equivalent to two sides of A4) within your e-mail, but NOT as an attachment, of your project or the purpose for which you want the funding, detailing: your charity's name, address and charity number; email, phone and name of a person to reply to; a link to your website; what it's for; who it benefits; how much you want and when; what happens if you don't get our help; the programme under which you are applying. Don't write long flowery sentences – we won't read them. Do be brief, honest, clear and direct. Use abbrevns if you like! Don't send attachments to your email – your website will give us an introduction to you so you don't need to cover that.

Who can apply?
We welcome applications from registered charities and organisations with projects that have a recognisable charitable purpose. Your project has to be allowed within the terms of your constitution or rules and, if you are not a registered charity, you will need to send us a copy of your constitution or set of rules. We make grants for all types of projects; start-up, initial stages and valuable ongoing funding. This can include running costs and overheads as well as posts; particularly under the World Development and Projects in Wales. We do not have any upper or lower limit on the amount of grant we offer but it is unlikely that we would offer a grant of more that £100,000.'

WHO TO APPLY TO Janice Matthews, Finance Manager, c/o 46–48 Cardiff Road, Llandaff, Cardiff CF5 2DT *Tel* 029 2083 8980 *email* info@waterloofoundation.org.uk *Website* www.waterloofoundation.org.uk

CC NO 1117535   **ESTABLISHED** 2007

■ G R Waters Charitable Trust 2000

WHERE FUNDING CAN BE GIVEN UK, also North and Central America.

WHO CAN BENEFIT Registered charities.

WHAT IS FUNDED General charitable purposes.

SAMPLE GRANTS Dream Holidays and React (£5,000 each); British Volunteer Fireman (£2,600); and Lance Armstrong Foundation (£1,700).

FINANCES *Year* 2007–08 *Income* £124,454 *Grants* £14,283 *Assets* £1,468,342

TRUSTEES M Fenwick; A Russell.

OTHER INFORMATION This trust was registered with the Charity Commission in 2002, replacing Roger Waters 1989 Charitable Trust (Charity Commission number 328574), which transferred its assets to this new trust. (The 2000 in the title refers to when the declaration of trust was made.) Like the former trust, it receives a share of the Pink Floyd's royalties as part of its annual income. It has general charitable purposes throughout the UK, as well as North and Central America.

HOW TO APPLY In writing to the correspondent.

WHO TO APPLY TO Michael Lewis, Finers Stephens Innocent, 179–185 Great Portland Street, London W1W 5LS

CC NO 1091525   **ESTABLISHED** 2000

■ The Waterways Trust

WHERE FUNDING CAN BE GIVEN England and Wales.

WHO CAN BENEFIT Organisations, community groups or schools.

WHAT IS FUNDED Waterway related projects; projects providing lasting environmental enhancement; projects encouraging involvement in the waterways; and projects involving and benefiting the community.

TYPE OF GRANT Project funding.

RANGE OF GRANTS Up to £5,000.

FINANCES *Year* 2007–08 *Income* £2,770,369 *Grants* £4,990 *Assets* £3,545,154

TRUSTEES Francis Done; Helen Carey; Ian Valder; John Hume; Christopher Mitchell; Richard Combes; Laurence Newman; Chris Coburn; Judy Niner.

HOW TO APPLY The Small Grants Scheme application form is available from the trust's website.

WHO TO APPLY TO A F Lutman, Secretary, LLanthony Warehouse, The Docks, Gloucester GL1 2EH *Tel* 01452 318 220 *email* enquiries@ thewaterwaystrust.org.uk *Website* www. thewaterwaystrust.org.uk

CC NO 1074541 **ESTABLISHED** 1999

....

■ The Wates Foundation

WHERE FUNDING CAN BE GIVEN Berkshire; Bristol, Avon & Somerset; Buckinghamshire; Dorset; Gloucestershire; Middlesex; Nottinghamshire; Oxfordshire; Surrey; Sussex and the Greater London Metropolitan Area as defined by the M25 motorway.

WHO CAN BENEFIT Projects with charitable status. Practical projects involving people are preferred especially those benefiting young and disadvantaged people.

WHAT IS FUNDED The foundation aims to alleviate distress and improve the quality of life by promoting a broad range of social priorities that include the physical, mental and spiritual welfare of the young and disadvantaged aged 5–25; the rehabilitation of offenders; community integration and cohesion; and addressing substance misuse. Programmes are: Building Family Values; Community Health; Safer Communities; Sustaining the Environment; Strengthening the Charitable & Voluntary Sectors; Strategic Programme.

WHAT IS NOT FUNDED 'As a general rule we expect that applicants will have considered the Guidance for Applications on the foundation's website. Our preferred format for initial approaches for funding is laid down in the section How to Apply [see 'Applications']. Applications that make no effort to meet this simple requirement will be rejected automatically. We cannot fund: organisations that are not registered or recognised as charities unless in the process of registering. Applications by regulated not-for-profit social enterprises may be considered; work that is not legally charitable; political parties, political lobbying or campaigning; churches or other religious organisations where an award will be used for religious purposes. We do not fund: individuals for any purpose; large, well-established or national charities; organisations whose income in the year preceding an application exceeded £700,000; statutory bodies including local authorities and their agencies; grant-making bodies except through partnerships; heritage, conservation or archival projects unless relevant to the urban or rural built environment; capital projects; conferences; appeals of any kind including for disaster relief, sporting, social or other fund-raising events; animal welfare organisations; activity taking place overseas; work delivered outside of the counties of Berkshire; Bristol, Avon & Somerset; Buckinghamshire; Dorset; Gloucestershire; Middlesex; Nottinghamshire; Oxfordshire; Surrey; Sussex and the Greater London Metropolitan Area as defined by the M25 motorway. Grants will not be made to: work that is a public funding or statutory responsibility whether fulfilled or not; replace cuts in funding by statutory bodies where the foundation becomes the largest single provider; top up funding on under-priced contracts or other commissioned work; organisations where we become the largest single income provider.'

TYPE OF GRANT Grants may be one-off and for salaries, although buildings, capital, project,

research, start-up, core, running and recurring costs will also be considered.

RANGE OF GRANTS Normally up to £50,000.

SAMPLE GRANTS Cool2Care – Surrey (£50,000), towards an expansion of the service throughout Surrey to support more families with disabled children; Jessie May Trust – Bristol (£45,000), towards the core costs of a qualified nurse home-visiting service for terminally-ill children; Apex Charitable Trust (£40,000), towards core costs of a London programme working with offenders on release; Small Charities Coalition (£36,000), towards start-up funding; FAME – Nottingham (£35,000), towards core costs of running a mediation service for low income families; SuperKidz – South London (£29,000), towards a Volunteer Coordinator's post in a parenting and youth project; Friends of Baale Mane – Gopalapura, India (£23,500), towards a building project at a girls' school; Gardening Leave (£20,000), towards repairing and conserving the Stovehouse; STOP Trafficking UK (£10,000), towards core costs; Art for Youth (£5,000), towards an annual award for new artists.

FINANCES *Year* 2008–09 *Income* £425,000 *Grants* £3,000,000 *Assets* £20,100,000

TRUSTEES Revd John Wates; Jane Wates; Annabelle Elliott; James Wates; Nick Edwards; Christopher Agace.

HOW TO APPLY 'Applications to the foundation are accepted at any time on a rolling basis. An acknowledgement can normally be expected within 14 working days. We operate a two stage application process that should reduce the time that applicants may spend preparing material and allow us to give a response to the application in a reasonable time. On average, 90% or more of requests are rejected before the second stage.

First Stage: we do not use an application form so that applicants are not constrained in promoting their case for an award. However, we do expect that you comply with our format. Applications that make no effort to meet this simple requirement will be rejected automatically. The basics: initial applications should be of no more than four A4 pages (minimum font size Arial 11 point) addressing the questions below. These are designed to elicit sufficient information to explain your application without having to contact you; a budgetary breakdown may be attached additional to the four-page limit. Budgets covering more than one year should include elements for inflation. Salaries should identify NI costs and pensions where appropriate; your application must be accompanied by a signed copy of your latest Annual Report and Accounts which comply with Charity Commission requirements; additional publicity material including pamphlets, newspaper cuttings, Annual Reviews and DVDs will not be read. *Tell us:* who you are and what you do; about the work you want funded including beneficiaries, location and timescales; how much you need from us and over what period – one year, two years or three; where any balance of funding is coming from and how you intend to fund the work when our award ends how this work will make a difference to those people you seek to benefit; how you intend to monitor the work, measure its success and ensure its quality; how your work benefits the public in accordance with the requirements of the Charities Act 2006. Your application MUST contain the following statement:

''We are aware that supplying any deliberately false information or making any deliberately false statement may result in prosecution. To the best

of our knowledge and belief, all statements made in this application and its associated documentation are true and accurate. I am authorised to sign on behalf of the organisation. Name .... Position ...."

What Happens Next

All requests for support are rigorously filtered. The assessment process includes financial and other due diligence checks to establish the authenticity of your application; this may involve a preliminary visit. Application to the second stage will only be invited after this process. We send out a letter outlining the broad elements identified in the initial application together with the second stage application questions. You will have assembled much of the information to answer these as part of your initial approach to the Foundation. Where appropriate, the completed application questionnaire will be supported by a business or work plan and future funding strategy. The process of preparing an application that goes to a Grants Committee including arranging a visit to you by a member of the Committee can take three months or more. There is no time limit before unsuccessful applicants at any stage might re-apply. If requested we can provide feedback on why an application was unsuccessful. Before re-applying, however, a telephone call to the foundation is always advisable. Although we have a small staff, we are happy for potential applicants to ring us up and discuss funding opportunities or seek clarification if you are in doubt about whether you are eligible under our guidelines: this often saves on needless correspondence.'

WHO TO APPLY TO Brian Wheelwright, Director, Wates House, Station Approach, Leatherhead, Surrey KT22 7SW *Tel* 01372 861000 *Fax* 01372 861252 *email* director@watesfoundation.org.uk *Website* www.watesfoundation.org.uk
CC NO 247941   **ESTABLISHED** 1966

....

■ Blyth Watson Charitable Trust

WHERE FUNDING CAN BE GIVEN UK.
WHO CAN BENEFIT Charitable organisations.
WHAT IS FUNDED The trust dedicates its grant-giving policy in the area of humanitarian causes based in the UK. A number of hospices are supported each year.
SAMPLE GRANTS Previous beneficiaries have included: Army Benevolent Fund, Breast Cancer Haven, Children's Fire and Burns Trust, King Edward VII Hospital, Over the Wall Gang Camp, Pace Centre, Regalia Aid, Society for the Relief of Distress, St John's Hospice, St John of Jerusalem Eye Hospital, St Leonard's Hospice, St Luke's Hospital, St Martin-in-the-Fields Christmas Appeal, Vision Aid Overseas, Waterways Trust and Wavemakers.
FINANCES *Year* 2007–08 *Income* £98,427 *Grants* £71,500 *Assets* £2,780,598
TRUSTEES Edward Brown; Ian McCulloch.
HOW TO APPLY In writing to the correspondent. Trustees usually meet twice during the year.
WHO TO APPLY TO The Trustees, 50 Broadway, Westminster, London SW1H 0BL
CC NO 1071390   **ESTABLISHED** 1997

....

■ The Howard Watson Symington Memorial Charity

WHERE FUNDING CAN BE GIVEN The former urban district of Market Harborough.
WHO CAN BENEFIT Residents of Market Harborough.
WHAT IS FUNDED The trust has a particular interest towards relief of need, welfare, recreation, leisure and education.
RANGE OF GRANTS Up to £10,000.
SAMPLE GRANTS £5,000 to St Nicholas Church; £3,000 to Marshall Court; £1,500 to Arts Fresco; £500 to Global Young Leaders Conference; and £100 to Robert Smyth Cricket Festival.
FINANCES *Year* 2007–08 *Income* £67,509 *Grants* £25,009
TRUSTEES Harborough District Council.
HOW TO APPLY In writing to the correspondent. Applications are considered in early autumn.
WHO TO APPLY TO Anne Cowan, Events Co-ordinator, Harborough District Council, Council Offices, Adam and Eve Street, Market Harborough, Leicestershire LE16 7AG *Tel* 01838 821 291
CC NO 512708   **ESTABLISHED** 1946

....

■ John Watson's Trust

WHERE FUNDING CAN BE GIVEN Scotland, with a strong preference for Lothian.
WHO CAN BENEFIT Individuals, charitable organisations, ad hoc groups, research bodies or individuals. Beneficiaries must be under 21 years of age. People in care, fostered or adopted; children of one-parent families; people with disabilities; and people disadvantaged by poverty will be considered.
WHAT IS FUNDED (a) Grants to children and young people under 21, physically or mentally disabled or socially disadvantaged, for education and training, equipment, travel, and educational, social, recreational and cultural activities. Grants can be made to charitable organisations and ad hoc groups in this field and to bodies and individuals for educational research. (b) Grants for boarding education to orphans and children subject to some other special family difficulty.
WHAT IS NOT FUNDED No general appeals. Grants are not given for running or capital costs.
TYPE OF GRANT Equipment, small capital expenditure, tuition, student support, personal equipment (such as special wheelchairs, special typewriters), projects and activities including travel. One year only, but can be extended.
SAMPLE GRANTS Dunedin School (£5,000); Lothian Special Olympics (£3,500); Craigroyston High School, Nancy Ovens Trust and Scouts Scotland (£2,000 each); Gracemount Primary School and Multicultural Family Base (£1,500 each); and Cosgrove Care, Ferryhill Primary School and Sleep Scotland (£1,000 each).
FINANCES *Year* 2008 *Income* £239,712 *Grants* £148,406 *Assets* £2,854,170
TRUSTEES Six representatives of the Society of Writers to Her Majesty's Signet; two nominated by the City of Edinburgh Council; one nominated by the Lothian Association of Youth Clubs; one nominated by the Merchant Company Education Board; one co-opted trustee.
PUBLICATIONS Background notes and application forms available.
OTHER INFORMATION The 2008 grant total includes £58,582 distributed to individuals.
HOW TO APPLY On a form, available from the correspondent, or downloadable from the trust's website.

WHO TO APPLY TO Iola Wilson, Administrator, The Merchants Hall, 22 Hanover Street, Edinburgh EH2 2EP *Tel* 0131 220 1640 *Fax* 0130 220 1640 *email* johnwatsons@onetel.com *Website* www.johnwatsons.com
SC NO SC014004   **ESTABLISHED** 1984

■ Weatherley Charitable Trust

WHERE FUNDING CAN BE GIVEN Unrestricted.
WHO CAN BENEFIT Grants to individuals and organisations.
WHAT IS FUNDED General charitable purposes.
FINANCES *Year* 2007–08 *Income* £37,187 *Grants* £57,700 *Assets* £744,000
TRUSTEES Christine Weatherley; Richard Weatherley; Steven Chambers.
HOW TO APPLY This trust does not accept unsolicited applications.
WHO TO APPLY TO Christine Weatherley, Trustee, Northampton Science Park Ltd, Newton House, Kings Park Road Moulton Park, Northampton NN3 6LG
CC NO 1079267   **ESTABLISHED** 1999

■ The Weavers' Company Benevolent Fund

WHERE FUNDING CAN BE GIVEN UK.
WHO CAN BENEFIT Registered charities; preference to small, community-based groups, rather than larger, established charities. 'To be eligible for funding, local organisations such as those working in a village, estate or small town should normally have an income of less than about £100,000. Those working across the UK should normally have an income of not more than about £250,000.'
WHAT IS FUNDED Supporting work with: disadvantaged young people; and offenders and ex-offenders, particularly those under 30 years of age. 'We like to encourage new ideas and to fund projects that could inspire similar work in other areas of the country.'
WHAT IS NOT FUNDED 'Funding is not given for the following: (i) Long-term support – We will not normally provide long-term support. (ii) General appeals – We will not support sponsorship, marketing or other fundraising activities. (iii) Endowment funds – We will not support endowment funds, nor bursaries or long-term capital projects. (iv) Grant-giving charities. (v) Retrospective funding – We will not make grants for work that has been completed or will be completed while the application is being considered. (vi) Replacement funding – We will not provide grants for work that should be covered by statutory funding. (vii) Building projects – We will not fund building work but may help with the cost of equipment or furnishings. (viii) Disability Discrimination Act – We will not fund capital projects to provide access in compliance with the DDA (ix) Personal appeals – We will not make grants to individuals. Applicants must be registered charities, in the process of registering, or qualified as charitable. (x) Umbrella bodies or large, established organisations – We will not normally support projects in which the charity is collaborating or working in partnership with umbrella bodies or large, established organisations. (xi) Overseas – We will not support organisations outside the UK, nor overseas expeditions or travel. Funding is not usually given for the following: (i) Work with children under five years of age. (ii) Universities or colleges. (iii) Medical charities or those involved in medical care. (iv) Organisations of and for disabled people. (v) Environmental projects. (vi) Work in promotion of religious or political causes.'
TYPE OF GRANT Grants may be awarded for up to three years. The trust particularly welcome applications for pump-priming grants from small community-based organisations where a grant would form a major element of the funding. It prefers to support projects where the grant will be used for an identified purpose. Applications for core funding will be considered, such as general administration and training that enable an organisation to develop and maintain expertise. The trust appreciates the importance of providing ongoing funding for successful projects, which have 'proved their worth'. Salaries are normally funded for up to three years but payment of the second and third year grants are subject to satisfactory progress reports. In exceptional circumstances, the trust may provide emergency or deficit funding for an established organisation. Applicants most likely to be granted emergency funding are charities which the company knows or has previously supported.
RANGE OF GRANTS Usually up to £15,000, but applications for smaller amounts from small or new organisations are welcomed.
SAMPLE GRANTS Weavers Company Education Fund (£70,000); Weavers' Company Millennial Fund (£35,000); Emmanuel Youth Club, Straight Talking Peer Education – Surrey, Synergy Theatre and Project Voice UK (£15,000 each); Upper Room (£12,000); Northumbria Coalition Against Crime, Strood Community Project and Zone Youth Project (£10,000 each); People and Drugs – Northumberland (£5,200); Safety Zone – Glasgow (£5,000); Guildhall School of Music and Drama (£3,000); Jim Bareham Minibus Trust (£1,000); the Prison Phoenix Trust (£500); and City of London Freemen's School and St Luke's Hospital for the Clergy (£250 each).
FINANCES *Year* 2008 *Income* £257,505 *Grants* £333,278 *Assets* £6,423,770
TRUSTEES The Worshipful Company of Weavers.
HOW TO APPLY Detailed *Guidelines for Applicants* are available from the the Weaver's Company website. Application forms can be downloaded from the fund's website, or by post or e-mail. The grants committee meets in February, June and October of each year, it may take up to four months for applications to be processed.
WHO TO APPLY TO John Snowdon, Clerk, The Worshipful Company of Weavers', Saddlers' House, Gutter Lane, London EC2V 6BR *Tel* 020 7606 1155 *Fax* 020 7606 1119 *email* charity@weaversco.co.uk *Website* www. weavers.org.uk
CC NO 266189   **ESTABLISHED** 1973

■ Webb Memorial Trust

WHERE FUNDING CAN BE GIVEN UK and Eastern Europe.
WHO CAN BENEFIT Individuals, universities and other organisations.
WHAT IS FUNDED The trust is set up with the aims of the advancement of education and learning with respect to the history and problem of government and social policy (including socialism, trade unionism and co-operation) in Great Britain and elsewhere by: research; lectures, scholarships and educational grants;

such other educational means as the trustees may from time to time approve.

WHAT IS NOT FUNDED No grants in support of any political party.

FINANCES *Year* 2008–09 *Grants* £70,000

TRUSTEES Richard Rawes, Chair; Mike Parker; Robert Lloyd-Davies; Dianne Hayter; Mike Gapes; Barry Knight.

OTHER INFORMATION The Webb Memorial Trust was established as a memorial to the socialist pioneer Beatrice Webb.

HOW TO APPLY See the trust's website for details of availability.

WHO TO APPLY TO Mike Parker, The Hon. Secretary, Mount Royal, Allendale Road, Hexham, Northumberland NE46 2NJ *Website* www. webbmemorialtrust.org.uk

CC NO 313760   **ESTABLISHED** 1944

....

■ The David Webster Charitable Trust

WHERE FUNDING CAN BE GIVEN UK.

WHO CAN BENEFIT Charitable organisations.

WHAT IS FUNDED 'Ecological and broadly environmental projects.'

SAMPLE GRANTS Bird Life International (£100,000); Wells Cathedral (£25,000); Hertfordshire and Middlesex Wildlife Trust (£15,000); St George's Church (£13,000); National Trust, Nottingham Wildlife Trust and Oxford Arboretum (£5,000 each); Bat Conservation Trust and Norfolk Wherry Trust (£2,000 each); and Bettisfield Church (£1,000).

FINANCES *Year* 2007–08 *Income* £236,443 *Grants* £173,500 *Assets* £2,837,697

TRUSTEES T W D Webster; Mrs N Thompson.

HOW TO APPLY In writing to the correspondent.

WHO TO APPLY TO The Trustees, Marshalls, Marshalls Lane, High Cross, Ware, Hertfordshire SG11 1AJ

CC NO 1055111   **ESTABLISHED** 1995

....

■ The William Webster Charitable Trust

WHERE FUNDING CAN BE GIVEN North East England.

WHO CAN BENEFIT Registered charitable organisations in the north east of England, or for the benefit of branches in the north east of England.

WHAT IS FUNDED General charitable purposes.

WHAT IS NOT FUNDED No grants to individuals or to non-charitable organisations. Core/running costs are not funded.

TYPE OF GRANT One-off only, for capital projects.

SAMPLE GRANTS Bubble Foundation and the Derwentside Hospice Car Foundation (£4,000 each); the National Rheumatoid Arthritis Society Richmond (£2,500); YMCA, St Columbus United Reformed Church (£2,000 each); Teesdale Disability Access Forum (£1,500); Different Strokes and Longframlington Memorial Hall (£1,000 each); and Aidis Trust (£500).

FINANCES *Year* 2007–08 *Income* £105,375 *Grants* £89,200 *Assets* £2,389,139

TRUSTEES Barclays Estates and Trusts.

HOW TO APPLY Applications should be submitted by the end of May for consideration in July; by the end of September for consideration in November; and by January for consideration in March. They should include details of the costings of capital projects, of funding already raised, a set of the latest annual accounts and details of the current charity registration.

WHO TO APPLY TO Robin Taylor, Trust Adminstrator, Barclays Bank Trust Company Ltd, Osborne Court, Gadbrook Park, Rudheath, Northwich, Cheshire CW9 7UE *Tel* 01606 313188 *Fax* 01606 313005

CC NO 259848   **ESTABLISHED** 1969

....

■ The Weinberg Foundation

WHERE FUNDING CAN BE GIVEN UK and overseas.

WHO CAN BENEFIT Registered charities.

WHAT IS FUNDED General charitable purposes.

SAMPLE GRANTS Natan Foundation (£23,000); Friends of EORTC (£20,000); Amnesty International (£15,000); Community Security trust (£12,500); Ability Net, Philharmonia Orchestra, the Royal Shakespeare Theatre and St James's Palace Foundation (£10,000 each); University of Cambridge (£5,000); UJIA Campaign (£4,000); South Bank Foundation (£2,000); and Elton John AIDS Foundation (£1,000).

FINANCES *Year* 2007–08 *Income* £33,504 *Grants* £165,961 *Assets* £819,000

TRUSTEES N H Ablitt; C L Simon.

HOW TO APPLY In writing to the correspondent.

WHO TO APPLY TO The Trustees, 2nd Floor, Manfield House, 1 Southampton Street, London WC2R 0LR

CC NO 273308   **ESTABLISHED** 1971

....

■ The Weinstein Foundation

WHERE FUNDING CAN BE GIVEN Worldwide.

WHO CAN BENEFIT Registered charities.

WHAT IS FUNDED Jewish, medical and welfare causes.

WHAT IS NOT FUNDED No grants to individuals.

TYPE OF GRANT Recurrent.

RANGE OF GRANTS Up to £20,000.

SAMPLE GRANTS Chevras Evas Nitzrochim Trust (£8,000); Friends of Mir (£6,000); SOFT UK (£2,200); Chesed Charitable Trust and Hachnosas Torah Vechesed Charity (£1,500 each); and Youth Aliyah (£1,000).

FINANCES *Year* 2007–08 *Income* £53,353 *Grants* £52,431 *Assets* £1,592,466

TRUSTEES Stella Weinstein; Michael Weinstein; Philip Weinstein; Lennne Newman.

HOW TO APPLY In writing to the correspondent.

WHO TO APPLY TO M L Weinstein, Trustee, 32 Fairholme Gardens, Finchley, London N3 3EB

CC NO 277779   **ESTABLISHED** 1979

....

■ The Weinstock Fund

WHERE FUNDING CAN BE GIVEN Unrestricted, but with some local interest in the Wiltshire and Newbury area.

WHO CAN BENEFIT Registered charities.

WHAT IS FUNDED 'The trustees support a wide range of charitable causes, particularly in the field of welfare, children, education, medicine and arts.'

WHAT IS NOT FUNDED No grants to individuals or unregistered organisations.

RANGE OF GRANTS Usually £500–£5,000.

SAMPLE GRANTS Previous beneficiaries have included: Army Benevolent Fund, Ashmolean Museum, British Friends of Hatzolah Israel, British ORT, Chicken Shed Theatre Company, CLIC Sargent, Community Security Trust, Delamere Forest School, Donmar Warehouse, Dorothy House Foundation, Home Warmth for the Aged, Garsington Opera, Hampstead Theatre, Jewish Care Oxford Synagogue, Jewish

....

Centre, Multiple Sclerosis Society, NICHS, National Gallery Trust, Holocaust Educational Trust, London Symphony Orchestra, Rainbow Trust, St Hilda's College, St Paul's Girls School Development Trust, Save the Children Fund, Royal Opera House Foundation, UK Youth, Winchester College Development Fund and Yetev Lev Youth Club.

FINANCES *Year* 2007–08 *Income* £453,661 *Grants* £250,000

TRUSTEES Susan G Lacroix; Michael Lester; Laura H Weinstock.

HOW TO APPLY In writing to the correspondent. There are no printed details or applications forms. Previous information received stated 'Where nationwide charities are concerned, the trustees prefer to make donations centrally.' Donations can only be made to registered charities, and details of the registration number are required before any payment can be made.

WHO TO APPLY TO Miss Jacqueline Elstone, Trust Administrator, PO Box 17734, London SW18 3ZQ

CC NO 222376   **ESTABLISHED** 1962

■ The James Weir Foundation

WHERE FUNDING CAN BE GIVEN UK, with a preference for Ayrshire and Glasgow.

WHO CAN BENEFIT Recognised charities in the UK, mainly Scottish charities benefiting people who are sick.

WHAT IS FUNDED The foundation has general charitable purposes, giving priority to schools and educational institutions; Scottish organisations, especially local charities in Ayrshire and Glasgow; and charities with which either James Weir or the trustees are particularly associated.

WHAT IS NOT FUNDED Grants are given to recognised charities only. No grants to individuals.

TYPE OF GRANT One-off and recurrent.

RANGE OF GRANTS Mostly £1,000–£3,000.

SAMPLE GRANTS University of Strathclyde (£8,500); British Association for the Advancement of Science, National Trust for Scotland, RAF Benevolent Fund, Royal College of Surgeons and Royal College of Physicians (£5,000 each); Action for Blind People, Bowel Cancer UK, Jubilee Sailing Trust, National Autistic Society, SSAFA Forces Help and ZANE (£3,000 each); and American Museum in Bath and Prostate UK (£1,000 each).

FINANCES *Year* 2008 *Income* £267,581 *Grants* £253,500 *Assets* £5,439,596

TRUSTEES Simon Bonham; William Ducas; Elizabeth Bonham.

OTHER INFORMATION The following six charities are listed in the trust deed as potential beneficiaries: the Royal Society; the British Association for Advancement of Science; the RAF Benevolent Fund; the Royal College of Surgeons; the Royal College of Physicians; and the University of Strathclyde.

HOW TO APPLY In writing to the correspondent. Distributions are made twice-yearly in June and November when the trustees meet. Applications should be received by May or October.

WHO TO APPLY TO The Secretary, 84 Cicada Road, London SW18 2NZ

CC NO 251764   **ESTABLISHED** 1967

■ The Barbara Welby Trust

WHERE FUNDING CAN BE GIVEN UK, with a small preference for Lincolnshire.

WHO CAN BENEFIT Normally limited to established charitable foundations and institutions.

WHAT IS FUNDED General charitable purposes. Preference is given to charities of which the founder had special knowledge or those with objects with which she was specially associated.

WHAT IS NOT FUNDED Applications for individual assistance are not normally considered unless made through an established charitable organisation.

RANGE OF GRANTS £500–£7,500.

SAMPLE GRANTS Lincolnshire Agricultural Society (£7,500); Lincoln Cathedral (£5,000); Braceby Church (£1,500); Be Your Best Foundation, CAFOD, the Connection at St Martins, Hearing Dogs for Deaf People, the Lincolnshire Foundation, St John Ambulance, St Luke's Hospital for the Clergy, Stroxton Church and Usher Junior School (£1,000 each); and British Heart Foundation, and University of Nottingham – scanner appeal (£500 each).

FINANCES *Year* 2007–08 *Income* £42,370 *Grants* £40,000 *Assets* £1,044,988

TRUSTEES N J Barker; C W H Welby; C N Robertson.

HOW TO APPLY In writing at any time to the above address, although the trustees meet to consider grants in March and October.

WHO TO APPLY TO The Trustees, Hunters, 9 New Square, Lincoln's Inn, London WC2A 3QN

CC NO 252973   **ESTABLISHED** 1967

■ The Weldon UK Charitable Trust

WHERE FUNDING CAN BE GIVEN UK and overseas.

WHO CAN BENEFIT Registered charities.

WHAT IS FUNDED The trust has previously had an interest in arts institutions, although this emphasis is decreasing in favour of social welfare and educational projects.

WHAT IS NOT FUNDED No grants to individuals.

TYPE OF GRANT Capital grants.

SAMPLE GRANTS Connection at St Martins (£32,000); and Red Balloon (£10,000). Four other organisations received grants of less than £10,000 each totalling £16,700.

FINANCES *Year* 2007–08 *Income* £48,376 *Grants* £58,719 *Assets* £589,694

TRUSTEES Nabil Fattal; Anthony Weldon.

HOW TO APPLY In writing to the correspondent, although the trust has previously stated that it is fully committed with existing projects.

WHO TO APPLY TO Howard Long, 4 Grosvenor Place, London SW1X 7HJ *Tel* 020 7235 6146 *Fax* 020 7235 3081

CC NO 327497   **ESTABLISHED** 1987

■ The Wellcome Trust

WHERE FUNDING CAN BE GIVEN UK and overseas.

WHO CAN BENEFIT Academic researchers working in the fields of human and veterinary medicine, bio-ethics, public understanding of science and the history of medicine.

WHAT IS FUNDED The support of clinical and basic scientific research into human and veterinary medicine; support of research in tropical medicine; the social and ethical implications of medical advances; and the history of medicine. Grants to individuals are usually given via a university, although small grants for travel or developing public understanding of science may be given directly.

WHAT IS NOT FUNDED The trust does not normally consider support for the extension of professional education or experience, the care of patients or clinical trials. Contributions are not made towards overheads and not normally towards office expenses. The trust does not supplement support provided by other funding bodies, nor does it donate funds for other charities to use, nor does it respond to general appeals.

TYPE OF GRANT All types of grant including project grants, programme grants, fellowships, research expenses, travel grants, equipment and occasionally laboratory equipment for research in human and veterinary medicine and the history of medicine. Grants may last for more than three years.

SAMPLE GRANTS University of Oxford (£78.2 million); University of Cambridge (£46.9 million); King's College London (£25.6 million); University of Dundee (£17.5 million); Kenya Medical Research Institute, Kenya (£15.9 million); Liverpool School of Tropical Medicine (£13.3 million); University of Manchester (£10 million); University College Dublin (£7.8 million); International Development Research Council, Canada (£5.1 million); and University of Liverpool (£3.8 million).

FINANCES *Year* 2007–08 *Income* £258,100,000 *Grants* £598,500,000 *Assets* £12,031,700,000

TRUSTEES Prof. Adrian Bird; Sir William Castell; Prof. Dame Kay Davies; Prof. Christopher Fairburn; Prof. Richard Hynes; Roderick Kent; Baroness Eliza Manningham-Buller; Prof. Peter Rigby; Prof. Peter Smith; Edward Walker-Arnott.

PUBLICATIONS The trust produces various reports and publications, all of which are available from its website.

OTHER INFORMATION The Wellcome Trust is one of the world's leading biomedical research charities and is the UK's largest non-governmental source of funds for biomedical research. It is also the UK's largest charity.

HOW TO APPLY *eGrants – online application*: 'The eGrants system enables applicants to apply for grants online. The system provides workflow to steer the application through head of department and university administration approval steps until final submission to the Wellcome Trust. Most applicants for Science Funding and Medical Humanities grants are required to submit their applications via our eGrants system. However, Word forms are still available for: preliminary applications; Public Engagement grants; Technology Transfer grants; and applicants who have limited/unreliable access to the internet – please email the eGrants helpdesk – ga-formsupport@wellcome. ac.uk – if this is the case.

If you haven't applied using eGrants before, here is what you need to do: make sure your institution (or the institution that would be administering the grant, if you are not already based there) is registered with the trust; access the eGrants page of the trust's website and fill in a home page for yourself (this will include your personal details that can be downloaded onto future application forms). Other people – such as coapplicants – will need to fill in details too.

The benefits of the eGrants system include: better functionality; clear sign off process through the host institution; reduced administration at the trust; helping us to capture management information (useful for the trust and the applicant).'

How to register: You can register with eGrants through the log-in page on the trust's website. Further information on the registration process, help and guidance notes are available by accessing this page.

Registration status of institutions: If you wish to register with eGrants but are not sure whether your institution is registered, you can check the list of registered institutions on the trust's website. If your institution is not on this list you should contact your administration office directly for further information.

Frequently asked questions: A list of frequently asked questions for eGrants is available from the trust's website.

WHO TO APPLY TO Grants Information Officer, Gibbs Building, 215 Euston Road, London NW1 2BE *Tel* 020 7611 8888 *Fax* 020 7611 8545 *email* grantenquiries@wellcome.ac.uk *Website* www.wellcome.ac.uk
CC NO 210183   **ESTABLISHED** 1936

....

■ Welsh Church Fund – Dyfed area (Carmarthenshire, Ceredigion and Pembrokeshire)

WHERE FUNDING CAN BE GIVEN Carmarthenshire, Ceredigion and Pembrokeshire.

WHO CAN BENEFIT Individuals, churches, chapels, and registered charities, particularly those concerned with health and welfare.

WHAT IS FUNDED General charitable purposes, particularly religious work, health and welfare.

TYPE OF GRANT One-off and recurrent.

RANGE OF GRANTS To a maximum of £8,000.

SAMPLE GRANTS St David's Church – Llanarthne and Mentro Luest (£10,000 each); Small World Theatre (£6,000); Capel Newydd Independent Chapel (£3,000); Tabernacle Chapel Uandovery (£2,000); St Martin's Church – Clarbesten (£1,500); and Musicfest (£1,000).

FINANCES *Year* 2008–09 *Income* £89,918 *Grants* £121,159 *Assets* £4,553,186

TRUSTEES Selected members of Carmarthenshire, Ceredigion and Pembrokeshire County Councils.

HOW TO APPLY In writing to the correspondent.

WHO TO APPLY TO Anthony Parnell, Resources Department, Carmarthenshire County Council, County Hall, Carmarthen, Dyfed SA31 1JP *Tel* 01267 224180 *Fax* 01267 228638 *Website* www.carmarthenshire.gov.uk
CC NO 506583   **ESTABLISHED** 1977

....

■ The Welton Foundation

WHERE FUNDING CAN BE GIVEN UK.

WHO CAN BENEFIT Registered charities and voluntary organisations.

WHAT IS FUNDED Principally supports projects in the health and medical fields. Other charitable purposes considered include education, welfare and arts organisations.

WHAT IS NOT FUNDED Grants only to registered charities, and not in response to general appeals.

TYPE OF GRANT Some recurrent funding and several small and large donations.

SAMPLE GRANTS The Healing Foundation (£250,000); National Centre for Young People with Epilepsy (£100,000); Raynaud's and Scleroderma Association (£89,500); Priors Court Foundation (£10,000); Joint Educational Trust (£5,300); Worshipful Company of Musicians, Sheffield Institution for Motor Neurone Disease, Aidis Trust, British

Association for Adoption and Fostering and the Public Catalogue Foundation (£5,000 each); Kidscape and Academy of St Mary's – Wimbledon (£3,000 each); and the Stroke Association and Wednesday's Child (£1,000 each).

FINANCES *Year* 2007–08 *Income* £381,072 *Grants* £487,729 *Assets* £8,253,785

TRUSTEES D B Vaughan; H A Stevenson; Dr Michael Harding.

HOW TO APPLY The foundation has previously stated that 'due to the number of appeals received, the foundation only replies to those that are successful'. However the foundation now also states that grants are not made to unsolicited applicants.

WHO TO APPLY TO The Trustees, 33 St Mary Axe, London EC3A 8LL *Tel* 020 7342 2630

CC NO 245319   **ESTABLISHED** 1965

....

■ Wessex Cancer Trust

WHERE FUNDING CAN BE GIVEN Dorset, Hampshire, Wiltshire, the Isle of Wight and the Channel Islands.

WHO CAN BENEFIT Primary care trusts, cancer patients, families and carers.

WHAT IS FUNDED Improvement of cancer care, by promoting cancer prevention; supporting patients, families and carers; providing education and information for patients, families and professionals; and funding early detection and research.

FINANCES *Year* 2007–08 *Income* £916,381 *Grants* £456,709 *Assets* £319,093

TRUSTEES David A Hoare; R Starr; T J Titheridge; Malcolm Le Bas; Asha Senapati; Dr C James; Dr C Wood; Dr Jennifer Stutley; J E Beschi; P Robertson; Dr C Baughan; S Wood; Dr Geoffrey Sharpe; John Mansell; Dr Lara Alloway; Helena Bridgman; Prof. Christian Ottensmeier.

OTHER INFORMATION The 2007–08 grant total includes £112,500 given to individuals.

HOW TO APPLY In writing to the correspondent.

WHO TO APPLY TO Sally Hall, Bellis House, 11 Westwood Road, Southampton SO17 1DL *Tel* 023 8067 2200 *Fax* 023 8067 2266 *email* wct@wessexcancer.org *Website* www.wessexcancer.org

CC NO 1110216   **ESTABLISHED** 1980

....

■ The Wessex Youth Trust

WHERE FUNDING CAN BE GIVEN Worldwide.

WHO CAN BENEFIT Registered charities with which the Earl and Countess have a personal interest.

WHAT IS FUNDED General charitable purposes. 'The charity is particularly, although not exclusively, interested in supporting projects which provide opportunities to help, support and advance young people.'

WHAT IS NOT FUNDED No grants are made to: non-registered charities or causes; individuals, including to people who are undertaking fundraising activities on behalf of a charity; organisations whose main objects are to fund or support other causes; organisations whose accounts disclose substantial financial resources and that have well-established and ample fundraising capabilities; fund research that can be supported by government funding or that is popular among trusts.

TYPE OF GRANT Mostly one-off grants. Substantial recurrent grants are also made.

SAMPLE GRANTS Beneficiaries included: Blind in Business, the Brainwave Centre, Cardboard

Citizens, Caring for Life, Children's Adventure Farm Trust, Classworks Theatre, the Country Trust, Demelza Hospice Care for Children, East Reading Explorer Scouts, Happy Days Children's Charity, Kidscape, Project Scotland, Tolerance International UK and the Wessex Autistic Society.

FINANCES *Year* 2007–08 *Income* £211,713 *Grants* £75,691 *Assets* £411,359

TRUSTEES Mark Foster-Brown; Malcolm Cockren; Denise Poulton; Robert Clinton; Kate Cavelle.

HOW TO APPLY In writing to the correspondent in the first instance. A response will be made within two weeks in the form of an application form and guidelines to eligible applicants or a letter of rejection if more appropriate. Completed forms, which are not acknowledged upon receipt, need to be submitted by 1 May or 1 November, for consideration by the end of the month. Clarity of presentation and provision of financial details are among the qualities which impress the trustees. Successful applicants will receive a letter stating that the acceptance of the funding is conditional on an update being received before the next meeting. The trust's criteria state other correspondence cannot be entered into, and organisations cannot reveal the size of any grants they receive.

WHO TO APPLY TO Jenny Cannon, c/o Farrer and Co, 66 Lincoln's Inn Fields, London WC2A 3LH

CC NO 1076003   **ESTABLISHED** 1999

....

■ The West Derby Wastelands Charity

WHERE FUNDING CAN BE GIVEN The ancient township of West Derby in Liverpool.

WHO CAN BENEFIT Local organisations and local branches of national organisations benefiting volunteers; at-risk groups; carers; people disadvantaged by poverty; socially isolated people; and victims of abuse, crime or domestic violence.

WHAT IS FUNDED Health and welfare; carers organisations; victim support and volunteer organisations.

WHAT IS NOT FUNDED The trust has stated that 'education or maintenance during education is not funded'.

RANGE OF GRANTS £150–£6,500.

SAMPLE GRANTS Greenbank Project (£6,500); Corinthian Community Primary School (£3,500); Lister Steps (£2,000); Sandfield Park School, Fire Fighters Charity and Clubmoor Youth Centre (£1,000 each); Friends of Renew (£750); and 445 St Paul's Guides (£500).

FINANCES *Year* 2008 *Income* £66,421 *Grants* £43,250 *Assets* £1,324,382

TRUSTEES Mrs Joan Driscoll; Barry Flynn; Mrs Dorothy Gavin; Mrs Jean Holmes; John F Kerr; Mrs Barbara Kerr; Sydney D Lunt; Peter H North; John Ruddock; Barbara A Shacklady.

OTHER INFORMATION The grant total includes £2,500 given to individuals.

HOW TO APPLY In writing to the correspondent.

WHO TO APPLY TO Lawrence Downey, Secretary, c/o Mace and Jones, Drury House, 19 Water Street, Liverpool L2 ORP *Tel* 0151 236 8989 *Fax* 0151 227 5010 *email* lawrence.downey@maceandjones.co.uk

CC NO 223623   **ESTABLISHED** 1964

■ West London Synagogue Charitable Fund

WHERE FUNDING CAN BE GIVEN UK.

WHO CAN BENEFIT Registered charities only.

WHAT IS FUNDED Grants are made to Jewish, Israeli, inter-faith and non-Jewish charities for general charitable purposes, at a national level and a local level within Westminster and Marylebone.

WHAT IS NOT FUNDED No grants to individuals.

RANGE OF GRANTS Up to £8,000.

SAMPLE GRANTS Motor Neurone Disease (£6,000); Hammerson House (£5,000); Karen Morris Memorial Trust (£4,000); Berkley Street Club and West London Synagogue (£2,000 each); Rabbi Freeman's Discretionary Fund (£800); Jewish Child's Day, Psoriasis Society and World Jewish Relief (£500 each); and Centrepoint Soho, City Escape, Dystonia Society, Headway, Oasis of Peace, Strongbones and World Union of Progressive Judaism (£250 each).

FINANCES *Year* 2008 *Income* £41,402 *Grants* £42,100 *Assets* £4,147

TRUSTEES Elizabeth Shrager, Chair; Simon Raperport; Alan Bradley; Jane Cutter; Michael Cutter; Francine Epstein; Vivien Feather; Jacqui Green; Ruth Jacobs; Hermy Jankel; Monica Jankel; Phyllis Levy; Elaine Parry; Jean Regen; and four ex-officio trustees.

OTHER INFORMATION The fund prefers to be involved with charities which synagogue members are involved with or helped by.

HOW TO APPLY In writing to the correspondent.

WHO TO APPLY TO The Fund Coordinator, 33 Seymour Place, London W1H 5AU

CC NO 209778   **ESTABLISHED** 1959

■ The West Yorkshire Police Community Fund

WHERE FUNDING CAN BE GIVEN West Yorkshire.

WHO CAN BENEFIT Charitable organisations and serving and former members of the West Yorkshire Police Force.

WHAT IS FUNDED Awareness of crime prevention, promotion of road safety and education in all matters relating to drug, alcohol and other substance misuse.

RANGE OF GRANTS Up to £2,500.

SAMPLE GRANTS Previous beneficiaries include: Pitstop (£2,200); Bradford Street Angels (£2,000); Action for Black Community Development (£1,500); Big Swing Adventure Playground (£1,000); SAFE (£680); South Leeds Saints Football Club (£490); and Rothwell Town AFC (£360).

FINANCES *Year* 2008–09 *Income* £45,983 *Grants* £39,464 *Assets* £384,624

TRUSTEES Martin A Stubbs; Frank Willans; Barry Thorn; Peter Scott; Mark Aspin; Jessica Wainwright; Andy Mitchell; Andrew Mitchell; Mick Murgatroyd; Alan Lees; Kerry Holden; Michael Downes; Chief Constable of West Yorkshire.

HOW TO APPLY Application forms, guidelines and grant round information is available on the fund's website.

WHO TO APPLY TO Martin A Stubbs, Trustee, Finance Department, West Yorkshire Police HQ, PO Box 9, Wakefield, West Yorkshire WF1 3QP *Tel* 01924 292229 *Fax* 01924 292229 *Website* www.westyorkshire.police.uk

CC NO 505514   **ESTABLISHED** 1996

■ Mrs S K West's Charitable Trust

WHERE FUNDING CAN BE GIVEN UK.

WHO CAN BENEFIT Registered charities.

WHAT IS FUNDED Charities are selected by the trustees. General charitable purposes.

SAMPLE GRANTS Previous beneficiaries have included Bible Society, BLESMA, Cancer Help – Preston, Christians Against Poverty, Go Africa, Holme Christian Care Centre, OMF International, Otley Meeting Room, Salvation Army, Shaftesbury Society, Spen Valley Faith In Schools Trust, Tear Fund and Turning Point.

FINANCES *Year* 2007–08 *Income* £35,218 *Grants* £0 *Assets* £467,186

TRUSTEES P Schoon; Chris Blakeborough; J Grandage.

HOW TO APPLY The trust states that it does not respond to unsolicited applications and would prefer not to receive any such applications asking for support.

WHO TO APPLY TO P J Schoon, Trustee, 20 Beech Road, Garstang, Preston PR3 1FS

CC NO 294755   **ESTABLISHED** 1986

■ The Westcroft Trust

WHERE FUNDING CAN BE GIVEN Unrestricted, but with a special interest in Shropshire – causes of local interest outside Shropshire are rarely supported.

WHO CAN BENEFIT Registered charities only.

WHAT IS FUNDED Currently the trustees have five main areas of interest: international understanding, including conflict resolution and the material needs of the developing world; religious causes, particularly of social outreach, usually of the Society of Friends (Quakers) but also for those originating in Shropshire; development of the voluntary sector in Shropshire; special needs of people with disabilities, primarily in Shropshire; development of community groups and reconciliation between different cultures in Northern Ireland. Woodlands and medical research into orthopaedics will be considered. Medical education is only helped by support for expeditions abroad which include pre-clinical students. Medical aid, education and relief work in developing countries are helped but mainly through UK agencies; international disasters may be helped in response to public appeals.

WHAT IS NOT FUNDED Grants are given to charities only. No grants to individuals or for medical electives, sport, the arts (unless specifically for people with disabilities in Shropshire) or armed forces charities. Requests for sponsorship are not supported. Annual grants are withheld if recent accounts are not available or do not satisfy the trustees as to continuing need.

TYPE OF GRANT Single or annual with or without specified time limit. Few grants for capital or endowment. One-off, research, recurring costs, running costs and start-up costs. Funding for up to and over three years will be considered.

SAMPLE GRANTS Previous beneficiaries included Action Village Trust Tsunami Appeal, Britain Yearly Meeting, Bradford University, British Epilepsy Association, Budiriro Trust, Canon Collins Trust, HOAP, Northern Friends Peace Board and Oxfam.

FINANCES *Year* 2007–08 *Income* £106,384 *Grants* £88,639 *Assets* £2,153,721

TRUSTEES Mary C Cadbury; Richard G Cadbury; James E Cadbury; Erica R Cadbury.

HOW TO APPLY In writing to the correspondent. There is no application form or set format but applications should be restricted to a maximum of three sheets of paper, stating purpose, overall financial needs and resources together with previous years' accounts if appropriate. Printed letters signed by 'the great and good' and glossy literature do not impress the trustees, who prefer lower-cost applications. Applications are dealt with about every two months. No acknowledgement will be given. Replies to relevant but unsuccessful applicants will be sent only if a stamped-addressed envelope is enclosed. As some annual grants are made by Bank Telepay, details of bank name, branch, sort code, and account name and number should be sent in order to save time and correspondence.

WHO TO APPLY TO Mary Cadbury, Managing Trustee, 32 Hampton Road, Oswestry, Shropshire SY11 1SJ

CC NO 212931   **ESTABLISHED** 1947

■ The Westminster Foundation

WHERE FUNDING CAN BE GIVEN Unrestricted, mainly UK.

WHO CAN BENEFIT Registered charities.

WHAT IS FUNDED Social welfare, military charities, education, environment and conservation.

WHAT IS NOT FUNDED No grants to individuals, 'holiday' charities, student expeditions, or research projects.

TYPE OF GRANT Usually one-off, but any type is considered.

FINANCES *Year* 2008 *Income* £2,431,211 *Grants* £1,506,411 *Assets* £30,937,887

TRUSTEES The Duke of Westminster, Chair; Jeremy H M Newsum; Mark Loveday; Lady Edwina Grosvenor.

OTHER INFORMATION In 2009 the foundation reduced and clarified its funding categories into social welfare, military charities, education, environment and conservation.

HOW TO APPLY In writing to the secretary, enclosing an up-to-date set of accounts, together with a brief history of the project to date, and the current need. The trustees meet four times a year.

WHO TO APPLY TO Mrs J Sandars, Administrator, 70 Grosvenor Street, London W1K 3JP *Tel* 020 7408 0988 *Fax* 020 7312 6244 *email* westminster.foundation@grosvenor.com *Website* www.grosvenorestate.com/charity

CC NO 267618   **ESTABLISHED** 1974

■ The Garfield Weston Foundation

WHERE FUNDING CAN BE GIVEN UK.

WHO CAN BENEFIT UK registered charities, independent schools, housing corporations and churches.

WHAT IS FUNDED A broad range of activities in the fields of education, the arts, health (including research), welfare, environment, young people, religion and other areas of general benefit to the community.

WHAT IS NOT FUNDED The foundation cannot consider any funding request made within 12 months of the outcome of a previous application, whether a grant was received or not. It will only considers applications from UK registered charities and your registration number is required (unless you have exempt status as a church, educational establishment, hospital or housing corporation). Projects outside the UK, even if the organisation is a registered charity within Britain, are not typically funded. The foundation is not able to accept applications

from individuals or for individual research or study. It does not support animal welfare charities. Typically the foundation does not fund one-off events, galas or festivals, even if for fundraising purposes. It does not fund specific salaries and positions (though we will consider contributing to the core operating costs of charitable organisations). Funding commitments over several years are not made – grants made are typically for a single year. It is unusual for the foundation to consider making a grant to organisations who cannot demonstrate significant progress with fundraising, so please bear this in mind when considering the timing of your application. In general, the trustees look for organisations to have raised the majority of funding through local or statutory sources before an approach is made. The foundation does not place limits on information sent, however we ask that applications are concise and include only the most relevant details relating to the application.

TYPE OF GRANT Usually small contributions to a specific project or part of a project. Capital (including buildings), core costs, endowments, one-off, research, recurring costs, running costs and start-up costs. Salaries are rarely considered. Funding is given by means of a single cash donation.

RANGE OF GRANTS £100–£2,000,000.

SAMPLE GRANTS Oxford University (£10 million); Victoria and Albert Museum (£1.5 million); Royal College of Art (£1 million); Kingsgate Community Centre – Peterborough (£250,000); Sadlers Wells (£150,000); London Philharmonic Orchestra and Changing Faces (£100,000 each); Pembroke House, Father Thames Trust and Parchment Trust (£50,000 each); Hansel Foundation (£30,000); Kids' City (£15,000); and St Mary's Church – Chiddingfold and Friends of Anne of Cleves House – Sussex (£5,000 each).

FINANCES *Year* 2007–08 *Income* £42,728,000 *Grants* £54,796,500 *Assets* £3,720,613,000

TRUSTEES Guy H Weston, Chair; R Nancy Baron; Miriam L Burnett; Camilla H W Dalglish; Catrina A Hobhouse; Jana R Khayat; Sophia M Mason; Eliza L Mitchell; W Galen Weston; George G Weston.

HOW TO APPLY All applications are considered on an individual basis by a committee of trustees. From time to time, more information about a charity or a visit to the project might be requested. Trustees meet monthly and there is no deadline for applications, which are considered in order of receipt. It normally takes three or four months for an application to be processed. All applicants are notified of the outcome by letter. Grants are normally made by means of a single payment and the foundation does not normally commit to forward funding. In writing to the correspondent. A basic details form is available to download from the foundation's website and must be included with a letter of application. All applications are considered on an individual basis by a committee of trustees. From time to time, more information about a charity or a visit to the project might be requested. Trustees meet monthly and there is no deadline for applications, which are considered in order of receipt. It normally takes three or four months for an application to be processed. All applicants are notified of the outcome by letter. Grants are normally made by means of a single payment and the foundation does not normally commit to forward funding. All applications are asked to include the following information: the charity's registration number; a copy of the most recent report and audited accounts; an outline description of the charity's activities; a synopsis of the project requiring funding, with details of who will benefit; a financial plan; and details of current and proposed fundraising.

WHO TO APPLY TO Philippa Charles, Administrator, Weston Centre, 10 Grosvenor Street, London W1K 4QY *Tel* 020 7399 6565 *Website* www.garfieldweston.org

CC NO 230260   **ESTABLISHED** 1958

■ The Barbara Whatmore Charitable Trust

WHERE FUNDING CAN BE GIVEN UK.

WHO CAN BENEFIT Charitable organisations.

WHAT IS FUNDED The arts and music and the relief of poverty.

RANGE OF GRANTS Up to £3,500.

SAMPLE GRANTS Campaign for Drawing (£6,500); Foundation for Young Musicians (£6,000); Diocese of Norwich (£4,300); Pro Corda (£4,000); Kew Gardens – Marianne North Gallery and Orange Tree Theatre (£3,000 each); National Youth Orchestra (£2,400); Aldeburgh Music and Watts Gallery – Compton (£2,000 each); Aldeburgh Museum, Flag Fen, Ilketshall – St Andrews, St Botolph's – Cambridge, St Mary's – Troston and Wonderful Beast Theatre Company (£1,500 each); National Youth Strings Academy (£1,000); Southwell Minster (£800); Ashmolean Museum and St Paul's Cathedral (£500 each); and New Lanark Conservation (£250).

FINANCES *Year* 2007–08 *Income* £112,406 *Grants* £74,750 *Assets* £1,308,531

TRUSTEES Patricia Marion Cooke-Yarborough, Chair; David Eldridge; Denis Borrow; Gillian Lewis; Luke Alec Gardiner; Sally Carter; Stephen James Bate.

HOW TO APPLY In writing to the correspondent.

WHO TO APPLY TO Mrs P M Cooke-Yarborough, Chair, Spring House, Priors Way, Aldeburgh, Suffolk IP15 5EW

CC NO 283336   **ESTABLISHED** 1981

■ The Whitaker Charitable Trust

WHERE FUNDING CAN BE GIVEN UK, but mostly east Midlands and Scotland.

WHO CAN BENEFIT UK-wide organisations and local organisations (registered charities only).

WHAT IS FUNDED The trust has general charitable objects, although with stated preferences in the following fields: local charities in Nottinghamshire and the east Midlands; music; agriculture and silviculture; countryside conservation; Scottish charities.

WHAT IS NOT FUNDED Support is given to registered charities only. No grants are given to individuals or for the repair or maintenance of individual churches.

SAMPLE GRANTS Atlantic College (£36,000); Nottingham University – Faculty of Medicine and Royal Forestry Society (£10,000 each); Leith School of Art (£8,000); Opera North (£7,500); Bassetlaw Hospice and Game Conservancy Scottish Research Trust (£3,000 each); Lincoln Cathedral Fabric Fund (£2,500); Arkwright Scholarships (£2,000); VSO (£1,500); Drake Music Project, Music in Hospitals, Portland College and Tree Aid (£1,000 each); and Cambridge Arthritis Research Endeavour (£500).

FINANCES *Year* 2007–08 *Income* £213,154 *Grants* £122,461 *Assets* £7,475,747

TRUSTEES E R H Perks; D W J Price; Lady Elizabeth Whitaker.

HOW TO APPLY In writing to the correspondent. Applications should include clear details of the need the intended project is designed to meet plus a copy of the latest accounts available and an outline budget. If an acknowledgement of the application, or notification in the event of the application not being accepted, is required, an sae should be enclosed. Trustees meet on a regular basis.

WHO TO APPLY TO The Trustees, c/o Currey and Co., 21 Buckingham Gate, London SW1E 6LS

CC NO 234491   **ESTABLISHED** 1964

■ The Colonel W H Whitbread Charitable Trust

WHERE FUNDING CAN BE GIVEN UK, with an interest in Gloucestershire.

WHO CAN BENEFIT Charitable organisations.

WHAT IS FUNDED The promotion of education and in particular: (a) the provision of financial assistance towards the maintenance and development of Aldenham School, and (b) the creation of Colonel W H Whitbread scholarships or bursaries or prizes to be awarded to pupils at Aldenham School; charitable organisations within Gloucestershire; the preservation, protection and improvement for the public benefit of places of historic interest and natural beauty. The trustees make charitable distributions on an arbitrary basis, having reviewed all applications and considered other charities that they wish to benefit.

RANGE OF GRANTS £1,000–£5,000; occasionally larger amounts are given. The trustees will only in exceptional circumstances consider grant applications for purposes which fall outside its stated areas of support. In these cases, the trustees will distribute a minimum of £500 per distribution.

SAMPLE GRANTS Previous beneficiaries have included: 1st Queen's Dragon Guards Regimental Trust, Abbey School Tewkesbury, Army Benevolent Fund, CLIC Sargent, DEC Tsunami Earthquake Appeal, Friends of Alderman Knights School, Gloucestershire Historic Churches Trust, Great Ormond Street Hospital Children's Charity, Household Cavalry Museum Appeal, Hunt Servants' Fund, Queen Mary's Clothing Guild, Royal Hospital Chelsea and St Richard's Hospice.

FINANCES *Year* 2008 *Income* £161,215 *Grants* £67,000 *Assets* £5,589,286

TRUSTEES H F Whitbread; J R Barkes; R T Foley.

HOW TO APPLY A brief summary (no more than one side of A4) in writing (by e-mail if possible) to the correspondent. It is not necessary to send any accompanying paperwork at this stage. Should the trustees wish to consider any application further, then an application form would be sent out.

WHO TO APPLY TO Mrs Susan M Smith, Fir Tree Cottage, World's End, Sinton Green, Worcestershire WR2 6NN *Tel* 07812 454321 *email* whwhitbread.trust@googlemail.com

CC NO 210496   **ESTABLISHED** 1953

Think carefully about every application. Is it justified?

947

■ The Simon Whitbread Charitable Trust

WHERE FUNDING CAN BE GIVEN UK, with a preference for Bedfordshire.

WHO CAN BENEFIT Registered charities, or bodies with similar status.

WHAT IS FUNDED The trust supports general causes in Bedfordshire, and education, family welfare, medicine, medical research and preservation UK-wide. Preference is given to charities which the trustees have special interest in, knowledge of, or association with.

WHAT IS NOT FUNDED Generally no support for local projects outside Bedfordshire.

TYPE OF GRANT Usually one-off, but dependent on circumstances.

SAMPLE GRANTS Previous beneficiaries have included All Saints Church, Army Benevolent Fund, Arthritis Care, Bedfordshire Historical Records Society, Bedfordshire Music Trust, Chillingham Wild Cattle, Countryside Foundation for Education, Gravenhurst Parish Council, Mencap, National Association of Widows, St Luke's Hospital for the Clergy, Spurgeons Child Care, Royal Green Jackets, Retirement Education Centre Bedfordshire, RSPB, St Mungo's and SCOPE.

FINANCES *Year* 2008–09 *Income* £135,521

TRUSTEES Mrs H Whitbread; S C Whitbread; E C A Martineau; Mrs E A Bennett.

HOW TO APPLY In writing to the correspondent. Acknowledgements are not given. Please do not telephone.

WHO TO APPLY TO E C A Martineau, Hunters, 9 New Square, Lincoln's Inn, London WC2A 3QN

CC NO 200412   **ESTABLISHED** 1961

■ The Melanie White Foundation Limited

WHERE FUNDING CAN BE GIVEN Unrestricted.

WHO CAN BENEFIT Charitable organisations.

WHAT IS FUNDED General charitable purposes. 'The charity's principal activity during the year was the support of charities through the payments of donations. The objects of the charity are to promote any charitable purpose or support any charity selected by the directors. It is expressly contemplated that the Arbib Foundation [Charity Commission no. 296358] may be a beneficiary of the application of some or all funds or other benefits by the charity.'

SAMPLE GRANTS The Arbib Foundation (£245,000); Will Greenwood Testimonial Year (£25,000); and CLIC Sargent (£500).

FINANCES *Year* 2007–08 *Income* £257,661 *Grants* £270,500 *Assets* £9,554,337

TRUSTEES Mrs M White; A White.

HOW TO APPLY This trust does not accept unsolicited applications.

WHO TO APPLY TO The Trustees, c/o 89 New Bond Street, London W1S 1DA

CC NO 1077150   **ESTABLISHED** 1999

■ White Rose Children's Aid International Charity

WHERE FUNDING CAN BE GIVEN UK and overseas.

WHO CAN BENEFIT Organisations and institutions benefiting children with special needs.

WHAT IS FUNDED Hospitals, respite homes, special needs schools and youth groups.

RANGE OF GRANTS Mainly £1,000 or less.

SAMPLE GRANTS Bents Green School (£8,100); and Bassetlaw Hospital (£4,500); Heritage Park School and Rowan School (£1,000 each); Langold Dyscarr School (£820); Norfolk Park School (£700); Hilltop School (£500); and Sandon School (£100).

FINANCES *Year* 2007–08 *Income* £23,034 *Grants* £18,420 *Assets* £94,942

TRUSTEES Darryl Dawson; Eric Hewlett; Richard Rosser; Joan Sirrett; Eric Straw; Bob Urie; Audrey Wright; John Vessey; Gordon Mayo.

HOW TO APPLY In writing to the correspondent.

WHO TO APPLY TO Audrey Wright, Trustee, 23 Teesdale Road, Ridgeway, Sheffield S12 3XH

CC NO 1036377   **ESTABLISHED** 1994

■ The Whitecourt Charitable Trust

WHERE FUNDING CAN BE GIVEN UK and overseas, with a preference for Sheffield.

WHO CAN BENEFIT Organisations benefiting Christians.

WHAT IS FUNDED General charitable purposes. Trustees prefer to support Christian projects, especially near Sheffield.

WHAT IS NOT FUNDED No support for animal or conservation organisations or for campaigning on social issues.

RANGE OF GRANTS £25–£5,000.

SAMPLE GRANTS Christ Church Fulwood – General Fund (£5,500), Missionary Fund (£4,000) and the Vicar's Discretionary Fund (£1,000); Monkton Combe School Bursary Fund (£3,000); SRSB Appeal (£2,000); Church Mission Society and South Yorkshire Community Foundation (£1,100 each); Children's Homes in India (£1,000); Careforce (£750); Frontier Youth Trust (£700); Extra Care Charitable Trust and London Institute for Contemporary Christianity (£300); Barnabas Fund, Daylight Christian Prison Trust, Leprosy Mission, Off the Fence and Yorkshire Cadet Trust (£100 each); Sheffield Botanical Gardens Trust (£50); and Muscular Disease Society and Royal Hallamshire Hospital (£25 each).

FINANCES *Year* 2007–08 *Grants* £48,655

TRUSTEES P W Lee; Mrs G W Lee; M P W Lee.

HOW TO APPLY In writing to the correspondent, at any time. However, the trust states very little money is available for unsolicited applications, due to advance commitments.

WHO TO APPLY TO Mrs G W Lee, Trustee, 48 Canterbury Avenue, Fulwood, Sheffield S10 3RU

CC NO 1000012   **ESTABLISHED** 1990

■ A H and B C Whiteley Charitable Trust

WHERE FUNDING CAN BE GIVEN England, Scotland and Wales, with a special interest in Nottinghamshire.

WHO CAN BENEFIT Registered charities.

WHAT IS FUNDED General charitable purposes, particularly the arts and environment.

RANGE OF GRANTS Up to £10,000.

SAMPLE GRANTS National Trust (£15,000); Southwell Minister (£12,000); St Peters Ravenshead PCC (£7,000); Lincolnshire and Nottinghamshire Air Ambulance, Macmillan Cancer Relief, Portland College and Queens Court Hospice (£5,000 each); and Friends of St Peter's and Paul's (£3,000).

FINANCES *Year* 2007–08 *Income* £50,703 *Grants* £56,500 *Assets* £1,277,508

TRUSTEES E G Aspley; K E B Clayton.

HOW TO APPLY The trust does not seek applications.
WHO TO APPLY TO E G Aspley, Trustee, Marchants, Regent Chambers, Regent Street, Mansfield, Nottinghamshire NG18 1SW
CC NO 1002220   **ESTABLISHED** 1990

■ The Norman Whiteley Trust

WHERE FUNDING CAN BE GIVEN Worldwide, although in practice mainly Cumbria.
WHO CAN BENEFIT Organisations benefiting Christians and evangelists.
WHAT IS FUNDED To help evangelical Christian causes primarily.
WHAT IS NOT FUNDED Whilst certain overseas organisations are supported, applications from outside of Cumbria are not accepted.
TYPE OF GRANT One-off, recurrent, capital, running costs.
SAMPLE GRANTS Lakes Gospel Choir – All Who Thirst (£11,000); Osterreichische Evangelische Allianz (£10,000); Agape Osterreich and Alpha Osterreich (£6,900 each); Greenstones Christian Trust and Sports Reach (£5,000 each); Bibellesbund (£4,100); Before the Throne Ministries (£3,000); United Christian Broadcasters (£2,200); Lakes Christian Centre (£2,000); Christians Against Poverty (£1,000); and Bootle Evangelical Church and Millom Methodist Church (£500).
FINANCES *Year* 2007–08 *Income* £143,806 *Grants* £104,288 *Assets* £2,521,700
TRUSTEES Mrs B M Whiteley; P Whiteley; D Dickson; J Ratcliff.
HOW TO APPLY In writing to the correspondent. Trustees meet to consider applications twice a year.
WHO TO APPLY TO The Trustees, Lane Cove, Grassgarth Lane, Ings, Cumbria LA8 9QF
CC NO 226445   **ESTABLISHED** 1963

■ The Whitley Animal Protection Trust

WHERE FUNDING CAN BE GIVEN UK and overseas, with a preference for Scotland.
WHO CAN BENEFIT Registered charities only.
WHAT IS FUNDED Prevention of cruelty to animals and promoting their conservation and environment.
WHAT IS NOT FUNDED No grants to non-registered charities.
TYPE OF GRANT Core and project grants, one-off or for several years.
RANGE OF GRANTS Generally £1,000–£5,000, although larger amounts are often given.
SAMPLE GRANTS Whitley Fund for Nature (£162,000); Hawk and Owl Trust (£75,000); Rivers and Fisheries Trust of Scotland (£30,000); Wildlife Conservation Research Unit University of Oxford (£15,000); the Dee Fishery Association, Fauna and Flora International and Shropshire Wildlife Trust (£10,000 each); Murton Wildlife Trust (£7,500); RSPB Scotland (£5,000); the Wye and Usk Foundation (£3,000); Shropshire Wildlife Trust (£1,000); and Petsavers (£500).
FINANCES *Year* 2008 *Income* £411,721 *Grants* £341,202 *Assets* £7,593,918
TRUSTEES E Whitley, Chair; Mrs P A Whitley; E J Whitley; J Whitley.
HOW TO APPLY The trust has previously stated that: 'The trust honours existing commitments and initiates new ones through its own contacts rather than responding to unsolicited applications.'

WHO TO APPLY TO M T Gwynne, Secretary, Padmore House, Hall Court, Hall Park Way, Telford TF3 4LX
CC NO 236746   **ESTABLISHED** 1964

■ The Whittlesey Charity

WHERE FUNDING CAN BE GIVEN The parishes of Whittlesey Urban and Whittlesey Rural.
WHO CAN BENEFIT Charitable organisations within the beneficial area.
WHAT IS FUNDED General charitable purposes.
RANGE OF GRANTS Mostly less than £1,000.
SAMPLE GRANTS St Andrew's Church and Holy Trinity Church Friends (£5,000 each); St Mary's PCC (£2,000); Hospital at Home (£1,000); First Whittlesey Scouts (£500); Whittlesey Contact Group (£300); and FAC Transport (£250).
FINANCES *Year* 2008 *Income* £55,071 *Grants* £29,651 *Assets* £1,637,928
TRUSTEES Mrs Pearl Beeby; Ralph Butcher; David W Green; Geoffrey Oldfield; Gordon Ryall; Revd Nigel A Whitehouse; David Wright; Philip Oldfield; Roger Brown; Gill Lawrence.
HOW TO APPLY Charities in the parishes of Whittlesey Urban and Whittlesey Rural should apply in writing for consideration in February, May or September (although urgent requests can be dealt with more quickly). Charities from outside these parishes should not apply as they will not receive any response.
WHO TO APPLY TO P S Gray, Secretary, 33 Bellamy Road, Oundle, Peterborough PE8 4NE
Tel 01832 273085 *Fax* 01832 273085
CC NO 1005069   **ESTABLISHED** 1990

■ The Lionel Wigram Memorial Trust

WHERE FUNDING CAN BE GIVEN UK, with a preference for Greater London.
WHO CAN BENEFIT Registered charities and voluntary organisations.
WHAT IS FUNDED General charitable purposes. The trustees 'have particular regard to projects which will commemorate the life of Major Lionel Wigram who was killed in action in Italy in 1944'. The trust makes grants to a wide range of organisations, especially in the illness and disabilities sector.
TYPE OF GRANT One-off and recurrent.
SAMPLE GRANTS Beneficiaries included: U Can Do IT (£32,000 in four grants); Newbury Spring Festival Society Ltd (£3,000); Bath Institute of Medical Engineering, Braille Chess Association, Compaid Trust, the Eyeless Trust, Happy Days Children's Charity, Hotham Arts Centre, Music Alive, Spadework, Summer Adventure for Inner Londoners, UK Youth, the Vine Project, Vitalise and the War Memorials Trust (£500 each); and Community Links Trust Limited (£250).
FINANCES *Year* 2007–08 *Income* £91,343 *Grants* £53,400 *Assets* £680,824
TRUSTEES A F Wigram, Chair; Mrs S A Wigram.
HOW TO APPLY In writing to the correspondent.
WHO TO APPLY TO A F Wigram, Chair, Highfield House, 4 Woodfall Street, London SW3 4DJ
CC NO 800533   **ESTABLISHED** 1988

■ The Richard Wilcox Welfare Charity

WHERE FUNDING CAN BE GIVEN UK.

WHO CAN BENEFIT Registered charities.

WHAT IS FUNDED Prevention of cruelty and relief of suffering and distress of animals of any species who are in need of care, attention and protection; relief of sickness and protection and preservation of good health; promoting the research and advancement of the causes and treatment of diseases; relief of patients receiving treatment in hospital or on discharge; providing, maintaining and improving hospitals and other institutions providing medical treatment; assisting or promoting any charitable organisation or charitable purpose.

SAMPLE GRANTS Ian Rennie Hospice (£210,000); DNA (£100,000); Chiltern Air Ambulance (£48,000); Nyumbarni (£41,000); Tiggywinkles (£20,000); Fairbridge Tyne and Wear (£5,000); Vision Aid Overseas (£3,000); and Hike for Hope (£500).

FINANCES *Year* 2007–08 *Income* £154,024 *Grants* £431,250 *Assets* £2,116,674

TRUSTEES John Ingram; Nick Sargent; Roger Danks.

OTHER INFORMATION The charity stated in 2007–08 that it 'plans to increase its grant giving over the next twelve months by continuing to support, where appropriate, those charities it has supported in the past, and to look for further organisations that would benefit from the charity's financial support through one off or regular grants'.

HOW TO APPLY In writing to the correspondent. The trustees meet quarterly to assess grant applications.

WHO TO APPLY TO Richard Oury, Administrator, Herschel House, 58 Herschel Street, Slough SL1 1PG

CC NO 1082586   **ESTABLISHED** 2000

■ The Felicity Wilde Charitable Trust

WHERE FUNDING CAN BE GIVEN UK.

WHO CAN BENEFIT Registered charities only.

WHAT IS FUNDED Children's charities and medical research, particularly into asthma.

WHAT IS NOT FUNDED No grants to individuals or non-registered charities.

SAMPLE GRANTS Previous beneficiaries have included Action on Addiction, Asthma UK, Bobath – Glasgow, Breakthrough Breast Cancer, British Epilepsy Association, British Lung Foundation, ChildLine, Children's Liver Disease Foundation, Darlington Association on Disability, East Anglia Children's Hospices, Home-Start Leicester, Honeypot Charity, Kids Out, Meningitis Research Foundation, National Back Pain Association, National Eczema Society, Shooting Star Trust Children's Hospice, Southampton University Development Trust, Sparks, Starlight Children's Foundation, West Midlands Post Adoption Service and Who Cares? Trust.

FINANCES *Year* 2007–08 *Income* £82,225 *Grants* £99,000 *Assets* £1,842,806

TRUSTEES Barclays Bank Trust Co Ltd.

HOW TO APPLY In writing to the correspondent at any time. Applications are usually considered quarterly.

WHO TO APPLY TO The Clerk, Barclays Bank Trust Company Ltd, Estates and Trusts, Osborne Court, Gadbrook Park, Northwich, Cheshire CW9 7UE

CC NO 264404   **ESTABLISHED** 1972

■ The Wilkinson Charitable Foundation

WHERE FUNDING CAN BE GIVEN UK.

WHO CAN BENEFIT Academic institutions.

WHAT IS FUNDED The trust was set up for the advancement of scientific knowledge and education at Imperial College – University of London. The trustees have continued their policy of supporting research and initiatives commenced in the founder's lifetime and encouraging work in similar fields to those he was interested in.

WHAT IS NOT FUNDED No grants to individuals.

SAMPLE GRANTS Wolfson College – Oxford (£31,000); Imperial College of Science, Technology and Medicine (£20,000); University College – London (£5,000); Lady Margaret Hall Development Fund (£2,500); British Heart Foundation (£2,000); and Foundation for the Prevention of Blindness, St Peter Trust, Vassall Centre Trust and Wellbeing of Women (£500 each).

FINANCES *Year* 2007–08 *Income* £61,907 *Grants* £62,500 *Assets* £1,508,701

TRUSTEES B D S Lock; G C Hurstfield.

HOW TO APPLY In writing to the correspondent.

WHO TO APPLY TO B D S Lock, Trustee, c/o Lawrence Graham LLP, 4 More London Riverside, London SE1 2AU

CC NO 276214   **ESTABLISHED** 1978

■ The Will Charitable Trust

WHERE FUNDING CAN BE GIVEN Worldwide, in practice UK.

WHO CAN BENEFIT Registered or exempt charities with a proven record.

WHAT IS FUNDED Care of and services for blind people, and the prevention and cure of blindness; care of people with learning disabilities in a way that provides lifelong commitment, a family environment and the maximum choice of activities and lifestyle; care of and services for people suffering from cancer, and their families; conservation of the countryside in Britain, including its flora and fauna.

WHAT IS NOT FUNDED Grants are only given to registered or exempt charities. 'It is unlikely that applications relating to academic or research projects will be successful. The trustees recognise the importance of research, but lack the resources and expertise required to judge its relevance and value.'

TYPE OF GRANT One-off or recurring.

RANGE OF GRANTS £4,000–£25,000.

SAMPLE GRANTS Beacon (£100,000); Bradford Cancer Support Daisy Bank and SeeAbility (£25,000 each); Home Farm Trust and Sightsavers (£20,000 each); Canterbury Oast Trust (£16,000); Cornerstone and Breast Cancer Care (£15,000 each); Nottingham Wildlife Trust, MPS Society and County Durham Society (£10,000 each); and York Blind and Partially Sighted Society (£5,000).

FINANCES *Year* 2007–08 *Income* £665,410 *Grants* £714,000 *Assets* £17,129,385

TRUSTEES Mrs Vanessa A Reburn; Alastair J McDonald; Ian C McIntosh; Rodney Luff.

HOW TO APPLY Applications in writing to the correspondent. There are no application forms – the trust offers the following advice on its website on how applications should be presented: 'We are not necessarily looking for glossy professional bids and understand that your application to us will vary according to the size of organisation you are, and the size of the proposed project. It can be a professionally prepared presentation pack, but can equally be a short letter with supporting information. Both will receive equal consideration. Whatever the presentation, the following is a guide to the main areas that we like to see covered. This is however intended only as a guide to assist you in preparing an application, it should *not* be seen as a prerequisite for applying for a grant – we understand that some small organisations will not have the sort of project(s) that need detailed treatment. Generally, we expect most applications will contain the following: an overview of your organisation. Please tell us in a nutshell who you are and what you do; tell us what you want a grant for/towards. Give us a full description of your project. For instance, what do you hope to achieve/who will benefit from the project and how? Costs: Tell us what your project is going to cost, giving details of the main items of expenditure. Tell us how you intend to fund it, and how much you have raised so far; a contingency plan. What will you do if you do not raise the funds you need? A timetable: Tell us your timescale for raising funds and when you aim to have the project up and running; a copy of your latest audited Annual Accounts must be included. A copy of your Annual Review is also useful if you have one. Other information: Please include any other information which you feel will assist us in judging your application. This could include for example a copy of any newsletter you produce, or short promotional/advertising leaflets. Such publications often help give a flavour of an organisation.'

Deadlines: *Blind people and Learning disabilities* – applications should be submitted from November and by 31 January at the latest. Decisions are made in the following March and successful applicants will be notified by the end of the month; *Cancer care and Conservation* – applications should be submitted from June and by 31 August at the latest. Decisions are made in the following November and successful applicants will be notified by the end of the month.

WHO TO APPLY TO Christine Dix, Grants Administrator, Grants Office, Sunbury International Business Centre, Brooklands Close, Windmill Road, Sunbury on Thames, Middlesex TW16 9DX *Tel* 01932 724148 *email* admin@willcharitabletrust.org.uk *Website* willcharitabletrust.org.uk
CC NO 801682   **ESTABLISHED** 1989

....

■ The Kay Williams Charitable Foundation

WHERE FUNDING CAN BE GIVEN UK.
WHO CAN BENEFIT Registered charities.
WHAT IS FUNDED General charitable purposes including medical research and disability causes.
SAMPLE GRANTS Royal Opera House Trust (£4,400); Cancer Research Campaign (£3,200); Mind, NSPCC, RSPCA and VSO (£2,000 each); URCDT (£1,500); BACUP, Richmond Concert Society and Shooting Star Children's Hospice (£1,000 each); the Genesis Appeal (£750); and English National Opera and the Mission to Seafarers (£500 each).
FINANCES *Year* 2007–08 *Income* £28,332 *Grants* £41,400 *Assets* £813,549
TRUSTEES R M Cantor; Mrs M C Williams.

HOW TO APPLY In writing to the correspondent.
WHO TO APPLY TO R M Cantor, Trustee, BDO Stoy Hayward, Kings Wharf, 20–30 Kings Road, Reading, Berkshire RG1 3EX
CC NO 1047947   **ESTABLISHED** 1995

....

■ The Williams Charitable Trust

WHERE FUNDING CAN BE GIVEN UK.
WHO CAN BENEFIT Charitable organisations.
WHAT IS FUNDED 'The objects of the trust are to support education and training, the advancement of medicine and general charitable purposes.' The 2007/08 trustees' report stated that: 'During the year, the trustees have allocated funds to financially support the theatre, medical research and various local community initiatives.'
SAMPLE GRANTS Donmar Warehouse (£107,000); Asthma UK (£28,000); Unicorn Theatre (£11,000); Prostate Scotland (£10,000); Almeida Theatre (£6,200); Gate Theatre and Theatre 503 Limited (£5,000 each); Mercury Music Developments (£2,000); Mousetrap Theatre Project (£1,000); Bliss (£500); and Kidbrooke Primary School (£300).
FINANCES *Year* 2007–08 *Income* £215,712 *Grants* £177,570 *Assets* £2,806,269
TRUSTEES S K M Williams; Mrs H A Williams; J Riddick; A M Williams; M T M Williams.
HOW TO APPLY In writing to the correspondent.
WHO TO APPLY TO Stuart Williams, Trustee, 85 Capital Wharf, 50 Wapping High Street, London E1W 1LY
CC NO 1086668   **ESTABLISHED** 2001

....

■ The Williams Family Charitable Trust

WHERE FUNDING CAN BE GIVEN Worldwide.
WHO CAN BENEFIT Jewish people.
WHAT IS FUNDED Organisations benefiting Jewish people.
RANGE OF GRANTS Generally less than £1,000.
SAMPLE GRANTS Previous beneficiaries have included But Chabad, Friends of Mifalhtorah for Shiloh, Holon Association for Absorption of Immigrants, Ingun Yedidut, Israel Concern Society, Karen Denny Pincus, Mogdal Un, Yedidut Maabeh Eliahu and Yesodrey Hetorah Schools.
FINANCES *Year* 2007–08 *Income* £52,411 *Grants* £48,150
TRUSTEES Shimon Benison; Arnon Levy; Barry Landy.
HOW TO APPLY In writing to the correspondent.
WHO TO APPLY TO Barry Landy, Trustee, 192 Gilbert Road, Cambridge CB4 3PB
CC NO 255452   **ESTABLISHED** 1959

....

■ Williams Serendipity Trust

WHERE FUNDING CAN BE GIVEN UK, with a preference for Greater London.
WHO CAN BENEFIT Children, education, medical, general.
SAMPLE GRANTS Donations were made to 23 different charities including a range of children's charities, medical charities and educational organisations. Beneficiaries included: YMCA (£70,000); Pembroke College Cambridge (£50,000); Care for Children (£25,000); Y Care International (£11,000); Ecologia Youth Trust, GBM, Gorilla Organisation, Kingfishers Bridge Wetland Trust, Peterborough Cathedral Trust, RNLI Clovelly and Westmonasterium Trust

Think carefully about every application. Is it justified?

951

(£10,000 each); Kids (£2,500); Alzheimer's Society, Cancer Research UK, Harrow Development Trust, International Centre for Child Studies and Two Tim Two Trust (£1,000 each); Uppingham School Rugby Tour (£500); and Breast Cancer Research (£100).

FINANCES *Year* 2007 *Income* £49,746 *Grants* £234,600 *Assets* £1,099,166

TRUSTEES C C Williams; Mrs G B Williams; R M Walkden.

HOW TO APPLY In writing to the correspondent. Trustees' meetings are held at least twice each year.

WHO TO APPLY TO Colin Williams, Trustee, R M Walkden & Co Ltd, 14 Pensioner's Court, Charterhouse Square, London EC1M 6AU

CC NO 1114631   **ESTABLISHED** 2006

■ The H D H Wills 1965 Charitable Trust

WHERE FUNDING CAN BE GIVEN Mainly UK.

WHO CAN BENEFIT Registered or recognised charities only.

WHAT IS FUNDED General charitable purposes. The Martin Wills Fund gives particular favour to wildlife conservation projects in years three and four of its seven year funding priority cycle.

WHAT IS NOT FUNDED No grants to individuals or national charities.

TYPE OF GRANT One-off grants.

RANGE OF GRANTS The vast majority of grants from the General Fund total £1,000 or less.

SAMPLE GRANTS General Fund – there were 177 grants made in 2007/08 totalling £93,000. The vast majority of grants (175) were for less than £1,000 each. Grants of more than £1,000 went to United World College of the Atlantic (£25,000) and Sandford St Martin PCC (£10,000). No further information was available. Previous information has indicated that grants are well spread around the country, with Scotland, perhaps, coming nearest to being over represented. A small proportion of the grants have been given to charities working overseas. Knockando Church Fund – A grant of £3,000 was made towards the upkeep and repair of the church. Martin Wills Fund – 2007/08, being the 2nd year of the cycle, saw a grant totalling £894,000 being made to Rendcombe College – Gloucestershire.

FINANCES *Year* 2007–08 *Income* £2,384,561 *Grants* £990,180 *Assets* £47,006,376

TRUSTEES John Carson; The Lord Killearn; Lady E H Wills; Dr Catherine Wills; Liell Francklin; Martin Fiennes.

OTHER INFORMATION The trust runs three separate funds: the General Fund, the Knockando Church Fund and the Martin Wills Fund. The three funds operate in different areas of grantmaking and, in the case of the Martin Wills Fund, on a seven-year cycle.

HOW TO APPLY In writing to the correspondent. The trust considers small appeals monthly and large ones bi-annually from the Martin Wills Fund. Only one application from a given charity will be considered in any 18-month period.

WHO TO APPLY TO Wendy Cooper, Trust Secretary, Henley Knapp Barn, Fulwell, Chipping Norton, Oxfordshire OX7 4EN *Tel* 01608 678051 *email* hdhwills@btconnect.com

CC NO 1117747   **ESTABLISHED** 1965

■ Dame Violet Wills Charitable Trust

WHERE FUNDING CAN BE GIVEN UK and overseas, but there may be a preference for Bristol.

WHO CAN BENEFIT Registered evangelical Christian charities.

WHAT IS FUNDED Evangelical Christian activities.

WHAT IS NOT FUNDED Grants are not given to individuals.

SAMPLE GRANTS WC and SWET – Evangelists Fund (£13,000); Echoes of Service – Bristol Missionaries (£2,400); Bristol International Student Centre (£2,000); FEBA Radio, International Fellowship of Evangelical Students and SAT-7 Trust (£1,500 each); Brass Tacks (£800); Medical Missionary News (£750); Cutting Edge Ministries (£500); SU Int Ukraine (£300); Open Air Mission and True Freedom Trust (£250 each); and Prison Fellowship – England and Wales (£200).

FINANCES *Year* 2008 *Income* £96,637 *Grants* £70,190 *Assets* £1,409,009

TRUSTEES D G Cleave, Chair; S Burton; H E Cooper; Miss R Daws; J R Dean; G J T Landreth; Mrs M J Lewis; Revd Dr E C Lucas; Mrs J Persson; Mrs R E Peskett; Revd A J G Cooper; D R Caporn; Revd R W Lockhart; J P Marsh; Mrs E Street.

HOW TO APPLY In writing to the correspondent. Trustees meet in March and in September.

WHO TO APPLY TO The Secretary, Ricketts Cooper & Co., 1 Deerhurst, Kingswood, Bristol BS15 1XH

CC NO 219485   **ESTABLISHED** 1955

■ The Dame Violet Wills Will Trust

WHERE FUNDING CAN BE GIVEN Bristol and south Devon areas.

WHO CAN BENEFIT Registered charities.

WHAT IS FUNDED The support of homes established privately by the late Dame Violet Wills and charities active in Bristol and south Devon.

TYPE OF GRANT Single donations.

SAMPLE GRANTS Previous beneficiaries have included Amos Vale, Bristol and the Colston Society, Bristol Cathedral Trust, Church of the Good Shepherd, Clifton Gateway Club, Guide Dogs for the Blind, Lord Mamhead Homes, RNLI, Rainbow Centre, Rowcroft Hospice, Samaritans, St Loye's Foundation and WRVS.

FINANCES *Year* 2007–08 *Income* £100,070 *Grants* £83,300 *Assets* £2,498,463

TRUSTEES H J Page; D P L Howe; T J Baines.

HOW TO APPLY In writing to the correspondent. The trustees meet four times per year to consider applications.

WHO TO APPLY TO D P L Howe, Trustee, 7 Christchurch Road, Clifton, Bristol BS8 4EE

CC NO 262251   **ESTABLISHED** 1965

■ The Wilmcote Charitrust

WHERE FUNDING CAN BE GIVEN Birmingham and Midlands.

WHO CAN BENEFIT Registered charities and voluntary organisations.

WHAT IS FUNDED General charitable purposes.

TYPE OF GRANT Mainly recurrent.

RANGE OF GRANTS £70–£3,600; mainly around £250.

SAMPLE GRANTS Douglas House (£1,500); Alzheimers Research Trust and Stonehouse Gang (£1,000 each); Action for Blind, British Stammering Association, Community Holy Fire, Coventry Boys' Club, Gurkha Trust, Home from Hospital Care, Noah's Ark Trust and Warwick

Arts Centre (£500 each); Coundon Care Centre and National patients Support Trust (£300 each); and Royal Regiment of Fusiliers and NSPCC (£100).

FINANCES *Year* 2008–09 *Income* £93,476 *Grants* £79,893 *Assets* £1,357,127

TRUSTEES G C Allman; B W Frost; Mrs A L M Murphy; Mrs R J S Whiteside.

HOW TO APPLY In writing to the correspondent.

WHO TO APPLY TO Carol Worrall, Trust Administrator, Warren Chase, Wilmcote, Stratford-upon-Avon CV37 9XG *Tel* 01789 298472 *Fax* 01789 298472

CC NO 503837   **ESTABLISHED** 1974

....

■ The John Wilson Bequest Fund

WHERE FUNDING CAN BE GIVEN Edinburgh.

WHO CAN BENEFIT Charities which are concerned with people who are poor or unwell living in Edinburgh, especially those which make special provision for women. It also supports individuals in need in Edinburgh and foreign missionaries of any protestant church in Scotland while they are at home.

WHAT IS FUNDED Welfare needs and missionary work.

SAMPLE GRANTS A list of beneficiaries was not available.

FINANCES *Year* 2008 *Income* £88,333

HOW TO APPLY In writing to the correspondent.

WHO TO APPLY TO The Administrator, J and R A Robertson, 15 Great Stuart Street, Edinburgh EH3 7TS

SC NO SC010651

....

■ Sumner Wilson Charitable Trust

WHERE FUNDING CAN BE GIVEN UK.

WHO CAN BENEFIT Registered charities.

WHAT IS FUNDED General charitable purposes.

SAMPLE GRANTS St James's Place Foundation (£20,000); Prostate Cancer Charitable Trust and Wheelpower (£5,000 each); Langalanga Scholarship Fund (£3,000); and Army Benevolent Fund, the Born Free Foundation, Breast Cancer Haven, Head and Neck Cancer Research Trust, Mission for Vision, Prospect Hospice, RAFT, Relate Winchester and Special Boat Service Association (£1,000 each).

FINANCES *Year* 2007–08 *Income* £107,233 *Grants* £51,750 *Assets* £2,646,076

TRUSTEES Lord Joffe; Mrs A W S Christie; M S Wilson.

HOW TO APPLY In writing to the correspondent, or to the trustees.

WHO TO APPLY TO N A Steinberg, Munslows, Mansfield House, 2nd Floor, 1 Southampton Street, London WC2R 0LR *Tel* 020 7845 7500

CC NO 1018852   **ESTABLISHED** 1992

....

■ David Wilson Foundation

WHERE FUNDING CAN BE GIVEN UK with a strong preference for the Leicestershire and Rutland area.

WHO CAN BENEFIT Primarily organisations which benefit the Leicestershire and Rutland area.

WHAT IS FUNDED General charitable purposes.

RANGE OF GRANTS Up to £66,000.

SAMPLE GRANTS Ibstock United Football Club (£66,000); University of Reading and Leicestershire Young Cricketers Educational Trust (£50,000 each); Leicestershire County Cricket Club (£6,000); Parish of Tilton (£5,000);

Army Benevolent Fund (£2,500); Rainbows Children's Hospice and Childhood Eye Cancer Trust (£1,000 each); Mercury Action Trust (£500); and Cantamici Choir (£250).

FINANCES *Year* 2007–08 *Income* £10,584,593 *Grants* £198,647 *Assets* £8,940,484

TRUSTEES James Wilson; Thomas Neiland; Laura Wilson; Richard Wilson.

OTHER INFORMATION Three donations were made to individuals totalling £4,000.

HOW TO APPLY In writing to the correspondent.

WHO TO APPLY TO John Gillions, Administrator, Fisher Solicitors, 4–8 Kilwardby Street, Ashby de la Zouch, Leicestershire LE65 2FU *Tel* 01530 412167 *email* john.gillions@fisherslaw.co.uk

CC NO 1049047   **ESTABLISHED** 1995

....

■ The Wilson Foundation

WHERE FUNDING CAN BE GIVEN Northamptonshire.

WHO CAN BENEFIT Organisations working with people aged 14 to 21.

WHAT IS FUNDED Educational purposes, including activity-based courses/centres.

SAMPLE GRANTS Previous beneficiaries have included: Oakham School; Longtown Busary; Bunbury ESCA Festival; Heads Up; Farming and Countryside Education and Rutland Kids Are Us; Meeting Point Youth Group; and Wilby Primary School.

FINANCES *Year* 2007–08 *Income* £3,011,519

TRUSTEES A Hewitt; G Wilson; N Connolly Wilson; Mrs F Wilson; A Welch; Mrs P S Wilson.

HOW TO APPLY In writing to the correspondent.

WHO TO APPLY TO Clare Elizabeth Vivienne Colacicchi, Trustee, The Maltings, Tithe Farm, Moulton Road, Holcot, Northamptonshire NN6 9SH *Tel* 01604 782240 *Fax* 01604 782241 *email* info@thewilsonfoundation.co.uk *Website* www.thewilsonfoundation.co.uk

CC NO 1074414   **ESTABLISHED** 1999

....

■ J and J R Wilson Trust

WHERE FUNDING CAN BE GIVEN Mainly Scotland, particularly Glasgow and the west coast of Scotland.

WHO CAN BENEFIT Organisations benefiting older people and animals and birds.

WHAT IS FUNDED Grants are given to charitable bodies which are concerned with older people, or the care of both domestic and wild animals and birds.

WHAT IS NOT FUNDED No grants to individuals.

SAMPLE GRANTS Royal Society for the Protection of Birds (£4,500); Cancer Bacup (£4,000); St Margaret's Hospice – Clydebank and SSPCA (£3,000 each); Maggie's Cancer Care – Glasgow and Marine Connection (£2,000 each); and Accord Hospice – Paisley, Ardgowan Hospice – Greenock, British Red Cross, Princess Royal Trust for Carers, Royal National Institute of Blind People, Royal Zoological Society Scotland and Trees for Life (£1,000 each).

FINANCES *Year* 2007–08 *Income* £147,206 *Grants* £84,000 *Assets* £2,804,350

TRUSTEES H M K Hopkins; J G L Robinson; K H Mackenzie; R N C Douglas; G I M Chapman.

HOW TO APPLY In writing to the correspondent. The trustees meet at least once a year.

WHO TO APPLY TO Hugh Hopkins, Secretary and Trustee, BMK Wilson Solicitors, 90 St Vincent Street, Glasgow G2 5UB

SC NO SC007411

■ The Community Foundation for Wiltshire and Swindon

WHERE FUNDING CAN BE GIVEN Wiltshire and Swindon only.

WHO CAN BENEFIT Local voluntary and community groups.

WHAT IS FUNDED The primary focus is on disadvantage including, supporting community care, tackling isolation and investing in young people. There are other funds, please see www.wscf.org.uk for details of up-to-date schemes.

TYPE OF GRANT Project, core costs and capital grants.

RANGE OF GRANTS Main grants: £500–£3,000 per year for three years. Small grants: £50–£500 on a one-off basis.

FINANCES *Year* 2007–08 *Income* £4,391,364 *Grants* £724,583 *Assets* £7,525,435

TRUSTEES Richard Handover, Chair; David Holder; Clare Evans; Tim Odoire; John Rendell; Sarah Troughton; Simon Wright; Nicky Alberry; Ray Fisher; Angus Macpherson; Dr Fiona Richards; Ram Thaigarajah; Elizabeth Webbe; Geraldine Wimble; John Woodget.

HOW TO APPLY The foundation's website has details of the grant schemes currently being administered. All applicants must have: a constitution or set of rules (if you are applying for a Small Grant it may be possible to receive funding before you have a constitution, but only if you are working towards adopting one); a bank account in the group's name, or another eligible organisation that is happy to receive the grant on your behalf. Applicants should first complete an 'expression of interest' form on the foundation's website. If the project is eligible for funding the foundation will send out an application pack.

WHO TO APPLY TO Chan Chitroda, Grants Officer, 48 New Park Street, Devizes, Wiltshire SN10 1DS *Tel* 01380 729284 *Fax* 01380 729772 *email* info@wscf.org.uk *Website* www.wscf.org. uk

CC NO 298936   **ESTABLISHED** 1991

■ The Benjamin Winegarten Charitable Trust

WHERE FUNDING CAN BE GIVEN UK.

WHO CAN BENEFIT Individuals and organisations benefiting Jewish people and people disadvantaged by poverty.

WHAT IS FUNDED Relief of poverty and the advancement of Jewish religion and religious education.

RANGE OF GRANTS £200–£5,000.

SAMPLE GRANTS Previous beneficiaries have included Hechal Hatovah Institute, the Jewish Educational Trust, the Mechinah School, Merkaz Lechinuch Torani Zichron Ya'akov, Ohr Someach Friends, Or Akiva Community Centre, Yeshiva Hovomo Talmudical College and ZSVT.

FINANCES *Year* 2007–08 *Income* £153,008 *Grants* £59,100 *Assets* £687,711

TRUSTEES B A Winegarten; Mrs E Winegarten.

OTHER INFORMATION The grant total in 2007–08 includes £4,000 donated to individuals.

HOW TO APPLY In writing to the correspondent.

WHO TO APPLY TO B A Winegarten, Trustee, 25 St Andrew's Grove, Stoke Newington, London N16 5NF

CC NO 271442   **ESTABLISHED** 1976

■ The Harold Hyam Wingate Foundation

WHERE FUNDING CAN BE GIVEN UK and developing world.

WHO CAN BENEFIT Registered charities and organisations working in developing countries.

WHAT IS FUNDED Jewish life and learning, performing arts, music, education and social exclusion, overseas development and medical research (travel costs).

WHAT IS NOT FUNDED No grants to individuals (the scholarship fund is administered separately). The foundation will not normally make grants to the general funds of large charitable bodies, wishing instead to focus support on specific projects.

TYPE OF GRANT Either one-off or recurrent for a limited period. Also capital projects on a highly selective basis.

RANGE OF GRANTS £150–£173,000; generally £10,000 or less.

SAMPLE GRANTS Centre of the Cell (£173,000); Queen Mary and Westfield College (£155,000); Bradford Media Museum (£75,000); Queen Mary University London (£60,000); Foundation for Conductive Education (£56,000); Oxford Centre for Hebrew and Jewish Studies (£25,000); English National Opera (£10,000); Little Angel Theatre (£8,500); Jerusalem Foundation (£7,800); Live Music Now (£6,000); One World Broadcasting Trust (£5,000); Young Concert Artists Trust (£2,500); Keele University (£1,000); and Anglo Israel Association (£150).

FINANCES *Year* 2007–08 *Income* £417,795 *Grants* £1,033,799 *Assets* £11,799,250

TRUSTEES Roger Wingate; Tony Wingate; Prof. Robert Cassen; Prof. David Wingate; Prof. Jonathon Drori.

OTHER INFORMATION The foundation also operates a scholarship scheme, under the name of Wingate Scholarships. Further details can be found on the website or by emailing Sarah Mitchell at sarah.mitchell@wingate.org.uk. In 2007/08 £417,373 was awarded in scholarship funds.

HOW TO APPLY Applicants are advised to write to the trust administrator with full details, including the most recent financial accounts. Applications are only acknowledged if a stamped addressed envelope is enclosed or if the application is successful. The administrator of the foundation only deals with enquiries by post and it is hoped that the guidelines and examples of previous support for successful applicants, given on the foundation's website, provides sufficient information. There is no email address for the foundation. Trustee meetings are held quarterly and further information on upcoming deadlines can also be found on the website.

WHO TO APPLY TO Karen Marshall, Trust Administrator, 2nd Floor, 20–22 Stukeley Street, London WC2B 5LR *Website* www. wingatefoundation.org.uk

CC NO 264114   **ESTABLISHED** 1960

■ The Francis Winham Foundation

WHERE FUNDING CAN BE GIVEN England.

WHO CAN BENEFIT Older people.

WHAT IS FUNDED Organisations, institutions and foundations benefiting older people.

SAMPLE GRANTS Cotswold Care Hospice (£100,000); Royal British Legion (£83,000 in 122 grants); SSAFA (£74,000 in 159 donations); Ashgate Hospice, East Cheshire Hospice, Eden Valley Hospice and St Michael's Hospice (£50,000 each); Ellenor Lions Hospice (£45,000);

Rotherham Hospice (£32,000); Heart of Kent Hospice (£29,000); Care and Repair – Rhondda Cynon Taf (£27,000 in 35 donations); Prospect Hospice and Universal Beneficent Society (£20,000 each); Independence at Home (£10,000); Brendon Care Foundation (£6,000); Abbeyfield Bromley Society, the Ghurkha Welfare Trust, Henshaws Society for Blind People and Luton Community Housing (£5,000 each); Brighton and Hove Jewish Centre (£3,000); Age Concern – Solihull (£2,500); Chiltern MS Centre (£2,000); Newcastle Society for Blind People (£1,500); and Community Relief Project and Wilshire Blind Association (£1,000 each).

FINANCES *Year* 2007–08 *Income* £1,113,250 *Grants* £1,493,069 *Assets* £3,208,072

TRUSTEES Francine Winham; Dr John Norcliffe Roberts; Josephine Winham; Elsa Peters.

HOW TO APPLY In writing to the correspondent. The trust regrets it cannot send replies to applications outside its specific field of help for older people. Applications should be made through registered charities or social services departments only.

WHO TO APPLY TO Mrs J Winham, Trustee, 41 Langton Street, London SW10 0JL *Tel* 020 7795 1261 *email* francinetrust@btopenworld.com

CC NO 278092   **ESTABLISHED** 1979

■ Anona Winn Charitable Trust

WHERE FUNDING CAN BE GIVEN UK.

WHO CAN BENEFIT Charitable organisations.

WHAT IS FUNDED Health, medical and welfare.

WHAT IS NOT FUNDED No applications are considered from individuals.

SAMPLE GRANTS CAF (£40,000); British Heart Foundation (£10,000); RNLI (£5,000); Help for Heroes (£4,000); the Playhouse – Cheltenham and the Smile Train (£3,000 each); St John of Jerusalem Eye Hospital (£2,000); St Wilfrid's Hospice (£2,000); the Sustainable Trust (£1,500); Motor Neurone Disease Association (£1,000); and Eyeless Trust, Rainbow Centre for Children and Trinity Hospice (£500 each).

FINANCES *Year* 2008 *Income* £54,730 *Grants* £100,000 *Assets* £867,059

TRUSTEES Trefoil Trustees Ltd.

HOW TO APPLY Applications will only be considered if received in writing and accompanied by the organisation's latest report and full accounts.

WHO TO APPLY TO The Trustees, New Inn Cottage, Croft Lane, Winstone, Cirencester GL7 7LN

CC NO 1044101   **ESTABLISHED** 1995

■ The Winton Charitable Foundation

WHERE FUNDING CAN BE GIVEN National and overseas.

WHO CAN BENEFIT Academic institutions and other organisations.

WHAT IS FUNDED Academic, recreation.

SAMPLE GRANTS Previous beneficiaries include: Absolute Return for Kids (£201,000); and the University of Cambridge for the Winton Professorship of the Public Understanding of Risk (£110,000).

FINANCES *Year* 2008 *Income* £254,639 *Grants* £192,662 *Assets* £154,850

TRUSTEES M J Hunt; D W Harding

HOW TO APPLY In writing to the correspondent.

WHO TO APPLY TO M J Hunt, Trustee, 1–5 St Mary Abbot's Place, London W8 6LS

CC NO 1110131   **ESTABLISHED** 2005

■ Wirral Mayor's Charity

WHERE FUNDING CAN BE GIVEN Wirral.

WHO CAN BENEFIT Local organisations, and local branches of UK organisations.

WHAT IS FUNDED A large variety of causes including welfare and medical charities, children and youth organisations, and disability groups. Many are community-based or local branches of UK charities.

SAMPLE GRANTS Previous beneficiaries include: Birkenhead Youth Club, Bromborough Youth Club, Chernobyl Children Life Line, Friends of Wallasey Central Park, Heygarth United Junior FC, North Birkenhead Neighbourhood Forum, Pet Aid Society, Roundabout Centre, Sports Aid NW – Merseyside Division, Wirral Heart Beat and Woodchurch Community Centre.

FINANCES *Year* 2007–08 *Income* £62,263 *Grants* £29,004

TRUSTEES Stephen Maddox; Ian Coleman; the present and previous Mayor of Wirral.

HOW TO APPLY In writing to the correspondent.

WHO TO APPLY TO The Mayor's Secretary, Wirral Borough Council, Town Hall, Brighton Street, Wallasey, Wirral CH44 8ED *Tel* 0151 691 8527 *Fax* 0151 691 8468 *email* mayor@wirral.gov.uk

CC NO 518288   **ESTABLISHED** 1986

■ WISCM

WHERE FUNDING CAN BE GIVEN UK.

WHO CAN BENEFIT Voluntary and community groups, or any non-profit-making organisation working for the benefit of young people living within the UK.

WHAT IS FUNDED Youth-based activity/alternative education. Funding is given via three funds:
(i) Major grants: Each year the trust supports two projects with a substantial grant. These will be projects working specifically with young people, providing alternative education.
(ii) Small grants: Of particular interest are projects that demonstrate an enthusiasm and determination to meet immediate and emerging needs and which have captured the imagination and commitment of local communities. The trust is particularly interested in giving support to local voluntary and community groups who may seek funds between £250 and £20,000 approximately. (iii) David Bellew Memorial Fund: The money is used to help young people (aged 16 to 25) take part in expeditions to broaden their horizons.

WHAT IS NOT FUNDED No grants to: projects operating outside of the trust's objectives; animal welfare; general appeals; political promotion; large capital appeals; statutory agencies in the discharge of their statutory obligations. The trust will not look to support organisations that do not have a permanent presence in the UK.

FINANCES *Year* 2007–08 *Income* £603,080 *Grants* £494,335

TRUSTEES Matthew Nicholas; Simon Bossons.

OTHER INFORMATION The trust primarily funds the work of the Welsh Independent School of Climbing and Mountaineering who work with young people aged between 12 and 25 by providing programs which develop alternative education through the outdoors.

HOW TO APPLY For applications contact the trust via email.

WHO TO APPLY TO E1, Trentham Business Quarter, Trentham Lakes South, Trentham, Stoke-on-Trent ST4 8GB *email* applications@wiscm.org.uk

CC NO 1116459   **ESTABLISHED** 2006

■ The Witzenfeld Foundation

WHERE FUNDING CAN BE GIVEN UK and Israel.
WHO CAN BENEFIT Charitable organisations.
WHAT IS FUNDED General charitable purposes.
FINANCES *Year* 2007–08 *Income* £79,333
Grants £75,850 *Assets* £3,793
TRUSTEES Alan Witzenfeld; Lyetta Witzenfeld; Emma Witzenfeld; Mark Witzenfeld.
HOW TO APPLY In writing to the correspondent.
WHO TO APPLY TO Alan Witzenfeld, Trustee, 9 Chadwick Road, Westcliff on Sea, Essex SSO 8LS
CC NO 1115034   **ESTABLISHED** 2006

■ The Michael and Anna Wix Charitable Trust

WHERE FUNDING CAN BE GIVEN UK.
WHO CAN BENEFIT Registered charities (mainly UK) benefiting students, at risk groups, and people who are disabled, disadvantaged by poverty or socially isolated.
WHAT IS FUNDED Main areas of interest are older people, disability, education, medicine and health, poverty and welfare and Jewish.
WHAT IS NOT FUNDED Applications from individuals are not considered. Grants are to national bodies rather than local branches or local groups.
TYPE OF GRANT 'Modest semi-regular' donations. Also one-off for part or all of a specific project.
RANGE OF GRANTS Mostly for smaller amounts in the range of £100 and £500 each.
SAMPLE GRANTS Nightingale House (£5,000); British Technion Society, Jewish Care and Weizmann Institute Foundation (£2,000 each); British Friends of the Hebrew University (£1,500); British ORT, Norwood and World Jewish Relief (£1,000 each); Jewish Museum (£500); Action on Addiction, British Fiends of Ohel Sarah, Carers UK, Cosgrove Care, Eyeless Trust, Lupus UK, Motability, Queen Elizabeth's Foundation, Shelter and Whizz Kidz (£200 each); and British Blind Sport, Centrepoint, Daneford Trust, Elizabeth Finn Care, Gurkha Welfare Trust, Jewish Marriage Council, Migraine Trust, Rehab UK, Strongbones Children's Charitable Trust and Vitalise (£100 each).
FINANCES *Year* 2007–08 *Income* £82,243
Grants £55,700 *Assets* £1,801,819
TRUSTEES Mrs J B Bloch; D B Flynn; Miss Judith Portrait.
HOW TO APPLY In writing to the trustees. Applications are considered half-yearly. Only applications from registered charities are acknowledged. Frequent applications by a single charity are not appreciated.
WHO TO APPLY TO The Trustees, Portrait Solicitors, 1 Chancery Lane, London WC2A 1LF
CC NO 207863   **ESTABLISHED** 1955

■ The Wixamtree Trust

WHERE FUNDING CAN BE GIVEN UK, in practice mainly Bedfordshire.
WHO CAN BENEFIT Local charities and a small number of national charities with a focus on family social issues. Applicants must be a registered charity or considered to be charitable in nature by the Inland Revenue.
WHAT IS FUNDED General. In particular, social welfare, environment and conservation, medicine and health, the arts, education, sports and leisure, international and training and employment.

WHAT IS NOT FUNDED No grants to non-registered charities or individuals.
TYPE OF GRANT One-off projects, capital, core costs and research. Single grants are usually given but successful applicants may reapply on an annual basis.
RANGE OF GRANTS On average £1,000–£5,000, although larger grants can be made.
SAMPLE GRANTS Beneficiaries were not listed in the accounts but could be viewed on the website: though individual grant awards were not included. Beneficiaries included: Bedfordshire Body Positive, Hospice at Home Volunteers – Bedford, Hope UK, Guinness Place and Kimble Drive Residents Association, Family Welfare Association, Youth Music Theatre UK, European Squirrel Initiative, National Youth Orchestra of Great Britain, St Gregory's Foundation and Sharnbrook Playing Field Association.
FINANCES *Year* 2007–08 *Income* £1,065,334
Grants £726,937 *Assets* £23,351,543
TRUSTEES Sam C Whitbread; Mrs J M Whitbread; H F Whitbread; Charles E S Whitbread; Geoff McMullen; I A D Pilkington.
HOW TO APPLY Application forms can be downloaded from the website or requested via email or post. The trust prefers completed forms to be returned by e-mail so that any amendments can be made before they are presented to the trustees for consideration at their quarterly meetings. Future meeting dates and application deadlines are listed on the website. All requests for support should be accompanied by a current report and accounts.
WHO TO APPLY TO Paul Patten, Administrator, 148 The Grove, West Wickham, Kent BR4 9JZ *Tel* 020 8777 4140 *email* wixamtree@thetrustpartnership.com *Website* www.wixamtree.org/index.asp?ID=5
CC NO 210089   **ESTABLISHED** 1949

■ The Woburn 1986 Charitable Trust

WHERE FUNDING CAN BE GIVEN Primarily Woburn.
WHO CAN BENEFIT Primarily older people; also welfare and medical charities.
WHAT IS FUNDED The provision and maintenance of housing for Woburn estate pensioners in need; research into, and the provision of facilities for, the welfare of elephants.
TYPE OF GRANT Recurrent and single donations.
RANGE OF GRANTS Up to £10,000.
SAMPLE GRANTS The David and Jennifer Sieff Charitable Trust (£13,000); Emmaus Village Carlton (£3,500); Bedfordshire and Luton Community Foundation (£3,000); East Anglia Air Ambulance Appeal (£2,000); Deafblind UK, Lowe Syndrome Trust and M S Therapy Trust (£1,000 each); Windmill Pre School (£500); and Thoroughbreds Breeders Association (£250).
FINANCES *Year* 2007–08 *Income* £91,807
Grants £29,400 *Assets* £1,517,024
TRUSTEES The Duke of Bedford; D H Fox; P R W Pemberton.
HOW TO APPLY In writing to the correspondent.
WHO TO APPLY TO K Shurrock, Administrator, The Bedford Office, Woburn, Milton Keynes, Bedfordshire MK17 9WA *Tel* 01525 290333 *Fax* 01525 290731 *email* kshurrock@woburnabbey.co.uk
CC NO 295525   **ESTABLISHED** 1986

■ The Maurice Wohl Charitable Foundation

WHERE FUNDING CAN BE GIVEN UK and Israel.

WHO CAN BENEFIT In practice, Jewish groups and health, welfare and medical organisations.

WHAT IS FUNDED Support is given to organisations in the UK with particular emphasis on the following areas: the care, welfare and support of children (including education); the promotion of health, welfare and the advancement of medical services; the relief of poverty, indigence and distress; the care, welfare and support of the aged, inform, handicapped and disabled; the support of the arts.

WHAT IS NOT FUNDED The trustees do not in general entertain applications for grants for ongoing maintenance projects. The trustees do not administer any schemes for individual awards or scholarships and they do not, therefore, entertain any individual applications for grants.

SAMPLE GRANTS Jewish Care (£6 million); Shaare Zedek UK (£2 million); Nightingale House (£1.8 million); Ovarian Cancer Action (£1 million); Jewish Care, Medical Aid Trust and Yeshiva Ohel Torah Beth David (£10,000 each); Community Security Trust (£5,000); and Emunah (£3,000).

FINANCES *Year* 2007–08 *Income* £56,258,182 *Grants* £9,860,275 *Assets* £63,845,787

TRUSTEES Mrs Ella Latchman; Prof. David Latchman; Martin D Paisner; Daniel Dover; Sir Ian Gainsford.

HOW TO APPLY In writing to the correspondent. The trustees meet regularly throughout the year.

WHO TO APPLY TO J Houri, Secretary, 7–8 Conduit Street, London W1S 2XF

CC NO 244519   **ESTABLISHED** 1965

■ The Charles Wolfson Charitable Trust

WHERE FUNDING CAN BE GIVEN Unrestricted, mainly UK.

WHO CAN BENEFIT Registered charities, hospitals and schools. Particular, but not exclusive regard is given to the Jewish community.

WHAT IS FUNDED Medical and scientific research and facilities, education and welfare.

WHAT IS NOT FUNDED No grants to individuals.

TYPE OF GRANT Mostly capital or fixed term projects and the provision of rent-free premises. Grants may be made for up to three years.

RANGE OF GRANTS Up to £500,000.

SAMPLE GRANTS Addenbrookes Charitable Trust and Yavneh College Trust (£500,000 each); Jewish Care (£350,000); Cure Parkinsons Trust (£200,000); Huntingdon Foundation (£125,000); Royal Marsden Cancer Campaign (£50,000); Sir George Pinker Appeal (£30,000); Zoological Society of London (£25,000); Priors Court Foundation (£10,000); Tavistock Trust for Aphasia (£5,000); and the Roundhouse Trust (£1,000).

FINANCES *Year* 2007–08 *Income* £6,841,959 *Grants* £6,769,106 *Assets* £5,369,117

TRUSTEES Lord David Wolfson of Sunningdale; Hon. Simon Wolfson; Dr Sara Levene; Hon. Andrew Wolfson.

HOW TO APPLY In writing to the correspondent. Grants are made in response to applications, and while all applications will be considered, the trustees cannot undertake to notify all unsuccessful applicants because of the volume of appeals received.

WHO TO APPLY TO Ricky Cohen, Administrator, c/o 129 Battenhall Road, Worcester WR5 2BU *Tel* 020 7636 0604

CC NO 238043   **ESTABLISHED** 1960

■ The Wolfson Family Charitable Trust

WHERE FUNDING CAN BE GIVEN Israel and UK.

WHO CAN BENEFIT Particularly Jewish groups and Israeli institutions.

WHAT IS FUNDED Science, technology and medicine; education; medical research and care and welfare; arts and humanities.

WHAT IS NOT FUNDED Grants are not made to individuals.

TYPE OF GRANT One-off for capital costs and equipment.

RANGE OF GRANTS Up to £750,000.

SAMPLE GRANTS Hebrew University of Jerusalem, Tel Aviv University and Weizmann Institute (£750,000 each), for equipment for microRMA research; Soroka Medical Centre – Beer Sheva (£630,000), for a PET CT scanner; Rambam Health Care Centre – Haffa (£615,000), for MRI equipment; Hadassah University Hospital – Jerusalem (£525,000); Edith Wolfson Medical Centre – Holon (£470,000), towards a cardiac catheterisation laboratory and medical camera equipment; Sourasky Medical Centre – Tel Aviv (£420,000), towards a linear accelerator; Chaim Sheba Medical Centre – Tel Hashomer (£350,000), for breast MRI equipment; Negev Hospice (£150,000), towards the building of a new hospice; Technion – Israel Institute of Technology (£100,000), towards the renovation of the Churchill Auditorium; Youth Aliyah (£75,000), towards the renovation of the Edith Wolfson dormitory; Yad Sarah – Jerusalem (£50,000), towards equipment for people with disabilities; St Mary's Hospital – London (£45,000), towards equipment for the baThe Israel Philharmonic Orchestra (£20,000), towards instruments; Bevis Marks Synagogue – London (£15,000), for conservation costsby unit; World ORT (£25,000), for science equipment for eight schools in Israel; Northern Israel (£12,000), towards IT equipment for children in hospital; Beit Moriah – Beer Sheva (£11,000), towards refurbishment work to accomodate people with disabilities; Nalaga'at – Jerusalem (£10,000), for specialist equipment in a theatre for people with sensory impairments; Shema Kolenu – Jerusalem (£10,000), towards equipment for children with disabilities; Tel Aviv (£6,000) and Centre for the Blind in Israel – Tel Aviv (£6,000), towards IT equipment; Or Simcha – Kfar Chabad (£5,000), for refurbishment of a residential home; Shalheveth – Jerusalem (£5,000), towards a mini-bus; and Al-Taj – Arraba (£1,000), towards IT equipment.

FINANCES *Year* 2007–08 *Income* £2,012,000 *Grants* £10,466,000 *Assets* £28,599,000

TRUSTEES Sir Eric Ash; The Hon. Janet Wolfson de Botton; Lord Turnberg; Lord Wolfson of Marylebone; Martin D Paisner; Sir Bernard Rix; Lady Wolfson; Sir Ian Gainsford; The Hon. Laura Wolfson Townsley.

HOW TO APPLY The trust shares its application procedure with the Wolfson Foundation. A brief explanatory letter, with organisation and project details, including costs and current shortfalls, will elicit an up-to-date set of guidelines in return, if the charity is able to consider the project concerned.

The Wolfson Foundation

WHERE FUNDING CAN BE GIVEN Mainly UK, but also Israel.

WHO CAN BENEFIT Registered charities and exempt charities (such as universities), benefiting people of all ages, especially academics, scientists and terminally ill people.

WHAT IS FUNDED Renovation of historic buildings; libraries; support for preventative medicine; science and technology; programmes for people with special needs, and education. Grants for university research are awarded through competitive programmes.

WHAT IS NOT FUNDED No grants for: overheads, running or administrative costs, VAT or professional fees; non-specific appeals (including circulars), endowment funds or conduit organisations; costs of meetings, exhibitions, concerts, expeditions, etc.; the purchase of land; research involving live animals; or film or video production.

TYPE OF GRANT Capital, equipment.

RANGE OF GRANTS £2,000–£3,000,000.

SAMPLE GRANTS University College London (£2 million), for the renovation and restructuring of research facilities at the Royal Free Campus; University of Glasgow (£1.75 million), for the Beatson Translational Research Centre; University of Southampton (£500,000), for a specific area within new Life Sciences Building; Academy of Medical Sciences (£350,000), for a conference suite in refurbished 41 Portland Place; Royal Horticultural Society (£100,000), for a teaching space in new Learning Centre at Harlow Carr, Yorkshire; Whittington Hospital (£82,500), towards equipment for neonatal intensive care incubator suite; National Library of Scotland (£75,000), for a new visitor centre; Countryside Education Trust, Hampshire (£25,000), for new buildings to replace the existing New Forest Study Centre.

FINANCES *Year* 2008–09 *Income* £32,482,000 *Grants* £39,192,000 *Assets* £647,000,000

TRUSTEES Lord Wolfson of Marylebone, Chair; Lord Quirk; Hon Mrs Laura Wolfson Townsley; Lord Quinton; Lord McColl; Sir Eric Ash; Lord Turnberg; Lady Wolfson of Marylebone; Sir Derek Roberts; Hon Mrs Janet Wolfson de Botton; Sir David Weatherall.

OTHER INFORMATION Eligible applications from registered charities will normally be considered only when at least 50% of the appeal has been raised.

HOW TO APPLY Before submitting an application please write to enquire whether your project is eligible, enclosing a copy of the organisation's audited accounts for the previous two years. If a project is eligible, further details of the application process will be provided.

WHO TO APPLY TO Paul Ramsbottom, Executive Secretary, 8 Queen Anne Street, London W1G 9LD *Tel* 020 7323 5730 *Fax* 020 7323 3241 *Website* www.wolfson.org.uk

CC NO 206495   ESTABLISHED 1955

The Wolseley Charitable Trust

WHERE FUNDING CAN BE GIVEN UK.

WHO CAN BENEFIT Grants are made to organisations and individuals situated locally to the businesses of Wolseley plc and its subsidiary companies, or for causes recommended by employees of such subsidiary companies.

WHAT IS FUNDED General charitable purposes that benefit the communities in which the business of Wolseley plc and its subsidiary companies operate.

RANGE OF GRANTS Up to £28,000.

SAMPLE GRANTS Jamestown UK Foundation Limited (£25,000); Jamestown 2007 Inc (£16,000); Jamestown-Yorktown Foundation Inc (£13,000); Helen and Douglas House and Ripon International Festival (£5,000); Acorns Children's Hospice (£3,000); the Berkshire Community Foundation (£2,500); St Christopher's Hospice (£1,000); and Against Breast Cancer, Birmingham Children's Hospital Charity, Chase, Clover House Therapy, Meningitis Research Foundation and Rainbow Family Trust (£500 each).

FINANCES *Year* 2006–07 *Income* €213,740 *Grants* €142,313 *Assets* €288,182

TRUSTEES R Smith; S P Webster; M J White.

HOW TO APPLY In writing to the correspondent.

WHO TO APPLY TO The Trustees, Parkview 1220, Arlington Business Park, Theale, Reading RG7 4GA

CC NO 326607

Women Caring Trust

WHERE FUNDING CAN BE GIVEN Northern Ireland.

WHO CAN BENEFIT Integrated schools; community playgroups; play buses; youth clubs; women's groups; cross-community holiday schemes benefiting children and young adults.

WHAT IS FUNDED To give practical help to innocent families in the troubled areas of Northern Ireland; to promote integrated education and the support of groups and organisations working for peace and reconciliation among young people. 'A leg-up, not a hand-out.' Trustees are keen to encourage new projects, particularly cross-community, wherever possible.

WHAT IS NOT FUNDED No grants for individuals, large capital expenditure or salaries, organisations solely for the welfare of physically or mentally disabled people, or drug or alcohol related projects. No grants for holidays outside the island of Ireland.

TYPE OF GRANT Recurring costs funded for up to one year.

RANGE OF GRANTS £200–£2,000.

SAMPLE GRANTS Previous beneficiaries have included Voluntary Service Bureau, Glen Ward Community Development Association, NI Community Holidays, Dove House, Corrymeela Community, 123 House Belfast, Living Hope Charity, Old Museum Arts Centre, Croosgar Community Association and Young Belfast Singers.

FINANCES *Year* 2007 *Income* £12,797

TRUSTEES Johnny Scott Barber; Miss Jane Charley; Miss Julia Corkey; Mrs Hett Day; Mrs Rose Foyle; The Viscount Gough; Mrs Judy Lindsay; Mrs Visbe Lunn; Mrs Judy Moriaty; Mrs Rosalind Mulholland; Miss Hilary Redmond; Anthony Watson.

HOW TO APPLY In writing to the correspondent, providing full details of the project, with copies of accounts showing simple details of income and expenditure, and a daytime telephone number. The trustees meet four or five times a year and receive many more applications than can be accepted.

WHO TO APPLY TO The Secretary, c/o Voluntary Service Bureau, 24 Shaftesbury Square, Belfast BT2 7DB *Tel* 020 9020 0850 *Fax* 020 7720 9890

CC NO 264843   **ESTABLISHED** 1972

■ Women's World Day of Prayer

WHERE FUNDING CAN BE GIVEN UK and worldwide.
WHO CAN BENEFIT Christian literature societies.
WHAT IS FUNDED Promotion of the Christian faith through education, literature and audio-visual material.
WHAT IS NOT FUNDED No grants to individuals.
TYPE OF GRANT Annual, regular or one-off.
RANGE OF GRANTS £200–£21,000.
SAMPLE GRANTS World Day of Prayer International Committee (£21,000); World Day of Prayer National Committee of Guyana (£10,0000; Bible Society, Feed the Minds and United Society for Christian Literature (£15,000 each); Lifewords and Wycliffe UK Ltd (£8,000 each); Bible Reading Fellowship and International Reading Association (£6,000 each); Operation Mobilisation and The Salvation Army – Missionary Literature Fund (£3,000 each); Connections Trust and Fellowship of Women Christians (£2,500 each); St John's Guild for the Blind, the Leprosy Mission and United Christian Broadcasters (£1,700 each); Sat 7 Trust (£1,500); and Kafforwoda (£1,200); Mission to Deep Sea Fishermen (£850); Bible Times – Wales, The Word Publications and Wales Sunday Schools Council (£500 each); Christians Against Torture – Wales and Society for the Blind – Wales (£400 each); and CAFOD and Christian Aid – Wales (£300 each); and Churches Together in England – Women (£65).
FINANCES *Year* 2008 *Income* £486,691 *Grants* £148,276 *Assets* £289,608
TRUSTEES Mrs J Hackett; Mrs Emma Wilcock; Mrs M M Barton.
PUBLICATIONS Order of service for the Day of Prayer; children's service; Bible study notes on theme for year; annual booklet, *Together in Prayer*; meditation cards; prayer cards.
HOW TO APPLY In writing to the correspondent, before the end of June. Grants are made in November.
WHO TO APPLY TO Mrs Mary Judd, Administrator, Commercial Road, Tunbridge Wells, Kent TN1 2RR *Tel* 01892 541 411 *Fax* 01892 541745 *email* office@wwdp-natcomm.org *Website* www.wwdp-natcomm.org
CC NO 233242   **ESTABLISHED** 1932

■ The James Wood Bequest Fund

WHERE FUNDING CAN BE GIVEN Glasgow and the 'central belt of Scotland'.
WHO CAN BENEFIT Registered charities.
WHAT IS FUNDED General charitable purposes. Church of Scotland, historic buildings and other registered charities based in Scotland with preference being given to the central belt.
WHAT IS NOT FUNDED Registered charities only. Grants cannot be made to individuals.
TYPE OF GRANT Capital.
RANGE OF GRANTS £500–£4,000.
SAMPLE GRANTS Previous benficiaries included: Society of Friends of Glasgow Cathedral, Scottish Brass Band Association, Shelter Scotland, Children 1st, Princess Royal Trust for Carers, Erskine Hospital and Scottish Spina

Bifida Association; Glasgow and West of Scotland Society for the Blind, Mental Health Foundation, Aberlour Child Care Trust, RSPB Scotland, Hopscotch Theatre Company, Reality at Work in Scotland and Sense Scotland.
FINANCES *Year* 2008 *Income* £79,025
TRUSTEES Eric H Webster; David A R Ballantine; Alistair James Campbell.
HOW TO APPLY In writing to the correspondent, including if possible a copy of the latest accounts, a budget for the project, sources of funding received and other relevant financial information. Trustees meet in January, April, July and October. Applications should be received by the preceding month.
WHO TO APPLY TO David A R Ballantine, Trustee, Mitchells Roberton Solicitors, George House, 36 North Hanover Street, Glasgow G1 2AD *Tel* 0141 552 3422 *Fax* 0141 552 2935 *email* darb@mitchells-roberton.co.uk
SC NO SC000459   **ESTABLISHED** 1932

■ The Wood Family Trust

WHERE FUNDING CAN BE GIVEN UK, with a preference for Scotland; developing countries.
WHO CAN BENEFIT Organisations and individuals.
WHAT IS FUNDED The Wood Family Trust has three clear areas of investment focus: (1) Making Markets Work for the Poor Sub Saharan Africa (anticipated to be 75% of the overall investment); (2) Volunteering Overseas and Global Citizenship (anticipated to be 12.5% of the overall investment); (3) Developing Young People in Scotland(anticipated to be 12.5% of the overall investment).
FINANCES *Year* 2007–08 *Income* £18,757,597 *Grants* £674,708
TRUSTEES Sir Ian Wood, Chair; Lady Helen Wood; Garreth Wood; Graham Good.
OTHER INFORMATION This trust became operational in September 2007.
HOW TO APPLY 'The trust is proactive by nature and will only accept applications through our Volunteering Overseas investment programme.' Please contact the trust for further information on how to make an application.
WHO TO APPLY TO Jo Mackie, Chief Executive, John Wood House, Greenwell Road, Aberdeen AB12 3AX *email* info@woodfamilytrust.org.uk *Website* www.woodfamilytrust.org.uk
SC NO SC037957   **ESTABLISHED** 2007

■ The Woodcock Charitable Trust

WHERE FUNDING CAN BE GIVEN UK.
WHO CAN BENEFIT Charitable organisations.
WHAT IS FUNDED General charitable purposes and children's charities.
SAMPLE GRANTS Egmont Trust (£140,000); Kids Company (£127,000); the Cambridge Foundation (£25,000); Forever Angels (£11,000); and Magdalene College Cambridge (£10,000).
FINANCES *Year* 2007–08 *Income* £260,735 *Grants* £315,250 *Assets* £137,150
TRUSTEES M N Woodcock; S M Woodcock.
HOW TO APPLY In writing to the correspondent.
WHO TO APPLY TO The Trustees, Harcus Sinclair, 40 Victoria Embankment, London EC4Y 0BA
CC NO 1110896   **ESTABLISHED** 2005

Think carefully about every application. Is it justified?

959

■ The F Glenister Woodger Trust

WHERE FUNDING CAN BE GIVEN West Wittering.

WHO CAN BENEFIT Charities and other community organisations.

WHAT IS FUNDED General charitable purposes in West Wittering and surrounding areas.

SAMPLE GRANTS Chichester Cathedral Restoration and Development Trust (£525,000); Chichester Boys Club (£100,000); Donnington House (£70,000); St Wilfrid's Hospice (South Coast) Limited (£50,000); New Park Community and Arts Association and West Wittering Sailing Club (£40,000 each); Christian Care/Stone Pillow (£30,000); Birdham Primary School (£22,000); Witterings and District Bowls Club (£10,000); Friends Health Centre (£5,000); Wittering and District 1st Responders (£2,500); and National Talking Newspapers (£500).

FINANCES *Year* 2008–09 *Income* £1,386,632 *Grants* £977,110 *Assets* £28,193,822

TRUSTEES R C Shrubb, Chair; Mrs R Champ; W H Craven; S F Dobbin; Miss M Thompson; Mrs T Thompson; Revd J B Williams.

HOW TO APPLY In writing to the correspondent. Trustees meet quarterly.

WHO TO APPLY TO R C Shrubb, Chair, Wicks Farm Holiday Park, Redlands Lane, West Wittering, West Sussex PO20 8QE

CC NO 802642

■ Woodlands Foundation Limited

WHERE FUNDING CAN BE GIVEN UK and Israel.

WHO CAN BENEFIT Students studying in Jewish Talmudical colleges and relevant schools and institutions which teach the Orthodox Jewish religion.

WHAT IS FUNDED Jewish education.

SAMPLE GRANTS Previous beneficiaries have included Bais Menachem Charity, Chabud Community Centre, Labuvitch Community Centre, Lolev Charity and Parsha Ltd.

FINANCES *Year* 2007 *Income* £177,114 *Grants* £57,410 *Assets* £370,968

TRUSTEES M Taub, Chair; R Klopmann; M C Lehrfeld.

HOW TO APPLY In writing to the correspondent.

WHO TO APPLY TO The Trustees, c/o Martin and Heller, 5 North End Road, Golders Green, London NW11 7RJ

CC NO 1108132   **ESTABLISHED** 2004

■ Woodlands Green Ltd

WHERE FUNDING CAN BE GIVEN Worldwide.

WHO CAN BENEFIT Organisations benefiting Jewish people.

WHAT IS FUNDED Jewish charities performing educational projects.

WHAT IS NOT FUNDED No grants to individuals, or for expeditions or scholarships.

SAMPLE GRANTS Previous beneficiaries have included Achisomoch Aid Co, Beis Soro Schneirer, Friends of Beis Yisroel Trust, Friends of Mir, Friends of Seret Wiznitz, Friends of Toldos Avrohom Yitzchok, JET, Kahal Imrei Chaim, Oizer Dalim Trust, NWLCM, TYY Square and UTA.

FINANCES *Year* 2006–07 *Income* £248,462 *Grants* £178,541 *Assets* £1,282,443

TRUSTEES A Ost; E Ost; D J A Ost; J A Ost; A Hepner.

HOW TO APPLY In writing to the correspondent.

WHO TO APPLY TO J A Ost, Secretary, 19 Green Walk, London NW4 2AL

CC NO 277299   **ESTABLISHED** 1979

■ Woodlands Trust

WHERE FUNDING CAN BE GIVEN West Midlands, Warwickshire, London within the boundaries of the M25.

WHO CAN BENEFIT Organisations benefiting young adults and older people; at risk groups; carers; disabled people; people disadvantaged by poverty; ex-offenders and those at risk of offending; homeless people; people living in rural and urban areas; socially isolated people; refugees; victims of abuse, crime or domestic violence.

WHAT IS FUNDED Preference to charities which the trust has special interest in, knowledge of, or association with. Particularly charities working in the fields of hospice at home; respite care and care for carers; support and self-help groups; woodlands and horticulture.

WHAT IS NOT FUNDED No grant for the cost of buildings. No grants to individuals.

TYPE OF GRANT Core costs, one-off, project, research, running costs, recurring costs, salaries and start-up costs. Funding of up to three years will be considered.

RANGE OF GRANTS £1000–£10,000.

SAMPLE GRANTS The Birmingham Settlement (£12,000); Ryders Green Methodist Centre and Warwickshire Crimebeat (£5,000 each); the Where Next Association (£4,000); Karis Neighbour Scheme (£3,000); and Kenilworth Methodist Church (£1,200).

FINANCES *Year* 2006–07 *Income* £92,054 *Grants* £60,147 *Assets* £2,030,676

TRUSTEES Miss J M Steele; Mrs R M Bagshaw; Mrs J N Houston; T R W Steele.

HOW TO APPLY On a form available from the correspondent. The trustees meet to consider applications in April and October each year, and applications should be submitted in January and July.

WHO TO APPLY TO Jayne Day, Administrator, c/o PWW Solicitors, White Horse Court, North Street, Bishop's Stortford, Hertfordshire CM23 2LD *Tel* 01279 506421 *email* charities@ pwwsolicitors.co.uk *Website* www.pwwsolicitors. co.uk/charitable-applications

CC NO 259569   **ESTABLISHED** 1969

■ The Woodroffe Benton Foundation

WHERE FUNDING CAN BE GIVEN UK.

WHO CAN BENEFIT Registered charities only.

WHAT IS FUNDED Financial assistance in times of disaster on behalf of individuals in need within the UK through registered charitable bodies; accommodation and housing; promotion of education – especially through scholarships at Queen Elizabeth Grammar School in Ashbourne; conservation and environment; and community services and facilities.

WHAT IS NOT FUNDED Grants are not made outside the UK and are only made to registered charities. No grants to individuals. Branches of UK charities should not apply as grants, if made, would go to the charity's headquarters.

TYPE OF GRANT Starter finances, recurrent, research, project, one-off, core costs, feasibility studies and running costs. Funding is available for one year or less.

RANGE OF GRANTS The trust rarely donates more than £2,000 and does not normally make more than one grant to the same charity in a 12 month period.

SAMPLE GRANTS Queen Elizabeth's Grammar School (£17,000 in four grants); Ifield Park Care Home

(£15,000 in two grants); Community Links (£10,000); Friends United Network, Prisoners' Families and Friends Service, Soundaround, St Jude's Community Association and Young Peoples Trust for the Environment (£5,000 each); Charity Search (£4,000); and Disability Aid Fund (£1,000 in two grants).

FINANCES *Year* 2007–08 *Income* £246,642 *Grants* £257,188 *Assets* £4,788,680

TRUSTEES J J Hope, Chair: Mrs S E M Dickson; Mrs R A P G Foster; P M Miles; C G Russell.

HOW TO APPLY On a form available from the correspondent. Full guidance notes on completing the form and procedures for processing applications are sent with the form. Trustees meet quarterly.

WHO TO APPLY TO Alan King, Secretary, 16 Fernleigh Court, Harrow, London HA2 6NA *Tel* 020 8421 4120 *email* alan.king3@which.net

CC NO 1075272   **ESTABLISHED** 1988

....

■ The Geoffrey Woods Charitable Foundation

WHERE FUNDING CAN BE GIVEN UK and overseas.

WHO CAN BENEFIT Grants are now only given to charities nominated by members of the Girdler's Company who are involved with that charity and who make a donation to the foundation.

WHAT IS FUNDED The objects of the foundation are the advancement of education and religion and the relief of poverty.

TYPE OF GRANT One-off and capital grants. Special projects preferred.

FINANCES *Year* 2007–08 *Income* £77,386 *Grants* £131,300 *Assets* £825,475

TRUSTEES The Girdlers Company; N K Maitland; A J R Fairclough.

HOW TO APPLY 'Beneficiaries are nominated by members of the company and outside applications are no longer considered.'

WHO TO APPLY TO Brig. Ian Rees, Clerk to the Company, The Girdlers Company, Girdlers Hall, Basinghall Avenue, London EC2V 5DD

CC NO 248205   **ESTABLISHED** 1966

....

■ The Woodward Charitable Trust

WHERE FUNDING CAN BE GIVEN Unrestricted.

WHO CAN BENEFIT Registered charities.

WHAT IS FUNDED Arts, community and social welfare (including children's summer holiday schemes), disability, health, education, environment. Priority to a few charitable causes of which the trustees have personal knowledge, and smaller-scale, locally based initiatives.

WHAT IS NOT FUNDED Trustees will not normally fund: charities whose annual turnover exceeds £250,000; construction projects such as playgrounds, village halls, and disabled accesses; general school appeals including out of hours provision; hospices; medical research; parish facilities; playgroups and pre-school groups; requests for vehicles. Trustees will definitely not support: individuals in any capacity; educational fees.

TYPE OF GRANT Usually one-off.

RANGE OF GRANTS Usually between £1,000–£5,000.

SAMPLE GRANTS Deafness Research UK (£20,000); National Association of Reformed Offenders (£15,000); Gymnasian UK Limited (£12,300); Ideas Foundation (£8,000); Reach Inclusive Arts and Asylum Welcome (£5,000 each); Hull Lighthouse Project and Stourbridge Cyber Bus Project (£4,000 each); Relate Kent Consortium

(£3,000); St Peter's Community & Advice Centre (£2,000); and School-Aid UK (£1,000).

FINANCES *Year* 2008–09 *Income* £490,820 *Grants* £343,982 *Assets* £8,480,693

TRUSTEES Camilla Woodward; Rt Hon. Shaun A Woodward; Miss Judith Portrait.

OTHER INFORMATION The trust is one of the Sainsbury Family Charitable Trusts which share a common administration. An application to one is taken as an application to all.

HOW TO APPLY On simple application forms available from the trust, or via its website. Potential applicants are invited to telephone the administrator in advance to discuss the advisability of making an application. Main grants are allocated following trustees' meetings in January and July each year, with the exception of summer schemes, which are considered at the beginning of May each year. All application forms are assessed on arrival and if additional information is required you will be contacted further. Applicants must make sure the trust receives a project budget and audited accounts. The website has a useful diary of trustees' meetings and of the cut-off dates for applications.

WHO TO APPLY TO Karin Hooper, Administrator, Allington House, 1st Floor, 150 Victoria Street, London SW1E 5AE *Tel* 020 7410 0330 *Fax* 020 7410 0332 *email* contact@ woodwardcharitabletrust.org.uk *Website* www.woodwardcharitabletrust.org.uk

CC NO 299963   **ESTABLISHED** 1988

....

■ The A and R Woolf Charitable Trust

WHERE FUNDING CAN BE GIVEN Worldwide; UK, mainly in Hertfordshire.

WHO CAN BENEFIT Registered charities and voluntary organisations only.

WHAT IS FUNDED The trust supports a range of causes, including Jewish organisations, animal welfare and conservation causes, children and health and welfare charities.

WHAT IS NOT FUNDED No grants to individuals or non-registered charities unless schools, hospices and so on.

RANGE OF GRANTS £100–£5,000.

SAMPLE GRANTS The Central British Fund for World Jewish Relief (£10,000); the Peace Hospice (£8,500); United Nations International Children's Emergency Fund and University of Hertfordshire Charitable Trust (£5,000 each); Northwood and Pinner Liberal Synagogue (£1,300); RSPCA and WWF UK (£1,000 each); the Multiple Sclerosis Society (£500); Jewish Child's Day and Wellbeing for Women (£250 each); National Schizophrenia Fellowship (£200); International Primate Protection League UK (£150); the Hertfordshire and Middlesex Wildlife Trust (£130); and Senahasa Trust (£100).

FINANCES *Year* 2007–08 *Income* £68,867 *Grants* £37,658 *Assets* £2,388,155

TRUSTEES Mrs J D H Rose; C Rose; Dr G L Edmonds; S Rose; A Rose.

HOW TO APPLY Support is only given to projects/ organisations/causes personally known to the trustees. The trust does not respond to unsolicited applications.

WHO TO APPLY TO The Trustees, Aldbury House, Dower Mews, 108 High Street, Berkhamsted, Hertfordshire HP4 2BL

CC NO 273079   **ESTABLISHED** 1977

■ The Woolnoth Society Charitable Trust

WHERE FUNDING CAN BE GIVEN Greater London.

WHO CAN BENEFIT Local organisations and smaller charities benefiting children, at risk groups, and people who are disadvantaged by poverty, homeless or socially isolated.

WHAT IS FUNDED Welfare, housing, relief in need, community health groups, facilities for children in their local communities, transportation.

WHAT IS NOT FUNDED No grants for general funding or to large charities with significant administration resources.

TYPE OF GRANT Cash grants for specific purposes.

RANGE OF GRANTS £400–£5,000.

SAMPLE GRANTS Lord Mayor's Appeal (£5,000); Newham Carers Network (£3,000); the Sunday Club, Brick by Brick and Lighthouse Education Service (£2,000 each); Downside Fisher (£1,000); and People Care Association (£500).

FINANCES *Year* 2007 *Income* £37,762 *Grants* £35,068 *Assets* £38,383

TRUSTEES Dr D McMullan; H M D Woolley; J Ruzicka; R Parkinson; Ms J Enzmann.

HOW TO APPLY In writing to the correspondent.

WHO TO APPLY TO Dr D J McMullan, Trustee, c/o Bank of America, 5 Canada Square, London E14 5AQ *Tel* 020 7174 4282 *Fax* 020 7174 6444 *email* skip.mcmullan@bankofamerica.com *Website* www.woolnothsociety.org.uk

CC NO 274008   **ESTABLISHED** 1977

■ Worcester Municipal Charities (incorporating Worcester Consolidated Municipal Charity and Worcester Municipal Exhibitions Foundation)

WHERE FUNDING CAN BE GIVEN The city of Worcester.

WHO CAN BENEFIT Poorer people, individually or generally, in Worcester City.

WHAT IS FUNDED Grants to relieve need. Purchase of household equipment, clothes, food and so on, help with bills. Donations to organisations that help poorer people. Grants to poorer students.

WHAT IS NOT FUNDED No grants to organisations of over 49% of their annual income. No grants to individuals unless all statutory sources have been exhausted. Requests for furniture (except bunk beds) are referred to the 'Armchair Project'. Requests for clothes are referred to the 'Lydia Project'.

TYPE OF GRANT Cheque or purchase of item.

RANGE OF GRANTS £1,000–£35,000 for running costs; £100–£100,000 for capital costs; £50–£1,000 for individuals.

SAMPLE GRANTS Citizens Advice (£40,000); Black Pearl Credit Union (£35,000); Maggs Day Centre (£20,000); Worcester Play Council (£11,000).

FINANCES *Year* 2008 *Income* £761,675 *Grants* £293,565 *Assets* £11,169,264

TRUSTEES Paul Griffith, Chair; Philip Hytch; Roger Berry; P Denham; Michael Gardner; Gail Grinnell; Margaret Jones; Bob Kington; Cliff Lord; Susan McKenzie-Willliams; Stanley Markwell; G Hughes; Sue Osborne; Ms M Edmunds; Martyn Saunders; Brenda Sheridan; Dr David Tibbutt; Brian Whitmore.

OTHER INFORMATION £171,000 to organisations and £72,000 to individuals.

HOW TO APPLY In writing to the correspondent requesting an application form.

WHO TO APPLY TO Ian Pugh, Clerk to the Trustees, Hallmarks Solicitors, 3–5 Sansome Place, Worcester WR1 1UQ *Tel* 01905 726600 *Fax* 01905 743366 *email* mary.barker@ hallmarkhulme.co.uk

CC NO 205299   **ESTABLISHED** 1836

■ The Worcestershire and Dudley Historic Churches Trust

WHERE FUNDING CAN BE GIVEN The diocese and county of Worcester.

WHO CAN BENEFIT Christian churches.

WHAT IS FUNDED The trust gives grants for the preservation, repair and improvement of churches in the beneficial area and of the monuments, fittings and furniture etc., of such churches.

WHAT IS NOT FUNDED No grants for new building projects or bells.

TYPE OF GRANT £500–£5,000.

SAMPLE GRANTS St. John the Baptist – Suckley and St. James – Harvington (£3,000 each); St. Marys – Oldswinford and Quarter Meeting House – Bewdley (£2,000 each); St. Thomas – Stourbridge (£1,000); and St Peters – Astley (£500).

FINANCES *Year* 2008 *Income* £41,824 *Grants* £20,000 *Assets* £107,703

TRUSTEES T Bridges – Chair; J S Davies; J Crabbe; J S. Bailey; J Colley; S Driver White; R Foot; A Grant; A Leech; M J Wall; R J Slawson.

HOW TO APPLY In writing to the correspondent.

WHO TO APPLY TO John Davies, Secretary, Yarrington's, Alfrick, Worcestershire WR6 5EX *Tel* 01886 884336 *email* flora.donald@virgin. net *Website* www.worcestershirechurches. blogspot.com

CC NO 1035156   **ESTABLISHED** 1993

■ The Fred and Della Worms Charitable Trust

WHERE FUNDING CAN BE GIVEN UK.

WHO CAN BENEFIT Jewish organisations, education and the arts.

WHAT IS FUNDED General charitable purposes, but in practice almost all of the money goes to Jewish organisations.

WHAT IS NOT FUNDED No grants to individuals.

TYPE OF GRANT One-off grants.

SAMPLE GRANTS Joint Jewish Charitable Trust (£25,000); Maccabi Union (£18,000); Emunah (£6,100); Brai Birth Hillel Foundation and Jewish Care (£5,000 each); British Friends of the Art Museum of Israel (£3,100); Jewish Museum (£3,000); Jerusalem Foundation (£2,500); JNF Botanical Gardens (£1, 500); Royal National Theatre (£1,300); English National Opera Company (£1,200); and Aleph Society and Ben Uri Art Gallery (£1,000 each).

FINANCES *Year* 2007–08 *Income* £95,038 *Grants* £86,756 *Assets* £2,106,288

TRUSTEES Mrs D Worms; M D Paisner; F S Worms; A D Harverd.

HOW TO APPLY The trust has previously stated that its funds were fully committed.

WHO TO APPLY TO The Trustees, 23 Highpoint, North Hill, London N6 4BA

CC NO 200036   **ESTABLISHED** 1961

■ The Worwin UK Foundation

WHERE FUNDING CAN BE GIVEN UK and overseas, particularly Canada.

WHO CAN BENEFIT Registered charities.

WHAT IS FUNDED General charitable purposes, including the advancement of education, the promotion of the arts (particularly focused on young people from low-income backgrounds) and the prevention and relief of sickness.

RANGE OF GRANTS £500–£54,000.

SAMPLE GRANTS Excellence in Literacy Foundation (£54,000); Hospital for Sick Children – Clown Programme (£53,000); Heart and Stroke Foundation of Ontario (£49,000); Evergreen (£45,000); Theodora Children's Trust (£37,000); Toronto Symphony Orchestra (£34,000); National Arts Centre Foundation (£27,000); Operation Go Home (£19,000); Sleeping Children Around the World (£14,000); L'Arche – Ottawa (£7,300); Urbanarts Community Arts Council (£3,000); and Viscount Alexander Public School (£490).

FINANCES *Year* 2007–08 *Income* £2,627,872 *Grants* £1,291,821 *Assets* £1,718,606

TRUSTEES William Hancock; Brian Moore; Mark Musgrave; Nick Dunnell; John Ward.

HOW TO APPLY In writing to the correspondent.

WHO TO APPLY TO John Ward, Trustee, 6 New Street Square, London EC4A 3LX *Tel* 020 7427 6400

CC NO 1037981   **ESTABLISHED** 1994

■ The Wragge and Co. Charitable Trust

WHERE FUNDING CAN BE GIVEN Mainly West Midlands.

WHO CAN BENEFIT Local and national charities operating in the area.

WHAT IS FUNDED General charitable purposes, with an interest in health.

WHAT IS NOT FUNDED No grants to individuals or to organisations which are not charities.

RANGE OF GRANTS Generally £100/£500 each.

SAMPLE GRANTS Katherine House Hospice (£8,000); Birmingham Women's Aid (£7,000); University of Warwick Foundation (£6,000); Multiple Sclerosis Society (£2,500); the British Legion (£1,000); the Vine Trust (£500); and Worcester Porcelain Museum Endowment Fund (£250).

FINANCES *Year* 2007–08 *Income* £58,193 *Grants* £59,023 *Assets* £36,211

TRUSTEES Jeremy Q S Poole; Philip Clissitt; Lee Nuttall.

HOW TO APPLY In writing to the correspondent with a copy of the most recent accounts.

WHO TO APPLY TO Lee Nuttall, Trustee, Wragge and Co., 55 Colmore Row, Birmingham B3 2AS *Tel* 0121 233 1000 *Fax* 0870 904 1099

CC NO 803009   **ESTABLISHED** 1990

■ The Diana Edgson Wright Charitable Trust

WHERE FUNDING CAN BE GIVEN UK with some preference for Kent.

WHO CAN BENEFIT Registered charities.

WHAT IS FUNDED General charitable purposes and animal conservation and social welfare causes.

SAMPLE GRANTS Previous beneficiaries have included Age Concern – Hythe, British Red Cross, Caldecott Foundation, Campaign to Protect Rural England, Paula Carr Charitable Trust, Chernobyl Children's Project, Combat Stress, Dragon School Trust, Folkstone Rainbow Trust, Kent Air Ambulance, Marine Conservation Society, the National Trust, Royal British Legion, Sellinge Parish Church, St James' Church – Egerton, Sightsavers International, Sustain and Wildfowl and Wetlands Trust.

FINANCES *Year* 2008 *Income* £72,879

TRUSTEES R H V Moorhead; P Edgson Wright; H C D Moorhead.

HOW TO APPLY In writing to the correspondent.

WHO TO APPLY TO R H V Moorhead, Trustee, c/o 2 Stade Street, Hythe, Kent CT21 6BD

CC NO 327737   **ESTABLISHED** 1987

■ The Matthews Wrightson Charity Trust

WHERE FUNDING CAN BE GIVEN UK and some overseas.

WHO CAN BENEFIT Smaller charities and individuals.

WHAT IS FUNDED General charitable purposes. The trustees favour smaller charitable projects seeking to raise under £25,000. Grants are given in the following categories 'youth', 'third world', 'disabled', 'Christian causes', 'rehabilitation', 'arts', 'poor and homeless', 'medical' and 'elderly'. In 2008 youth causes received significant support (£43,000 in 52 grants).

WHAT IS NOT FUNDED 'The trustees would not normally support the maintenance of the fabric of churches, schools and village halls, and do not make donations to animal charities.'

TYPE OF GRANT One-off cash grants, on annual basis. Core costs are preferred to projects.

RANGE OF GRANTS The standard 'unit' donation for 2008 was £500, with a few larger grants made to regular beneficiaries.

SAMPLE GRANTS The Royal College of Art – hardship grants and awards (£18,000) and for a pilot programme in training students in business financial management (£3,000); Tools for Self-Reliance (£2,400); and the Butler Trust, Childhood First, the Daneford Trust, DEMAND, Help Tibet, Live Music Now! New Bridge and Practical Action (£1,200 each).

FINANCES *Year* 2008 *Income* £75,382 *Grants* £97,278 *Assets* £1,300,562

TRUSTEES Priscilla W Wrightson; Anthony H Isaacs; Guy D G Wrightson; Isabelle S White; Maria de Broe Ferguson.

OTHER INFORMATION In addition to donations to charitable bodies, the trust also gives to trainee doctors for medical elective expenses and to individuals taking 'gaps' abroad for personal development. The grants total in 2008 includes £9,270 donated to 23 individuals.

HOW TO APPLY In writing to the correspondent including a set of accounts. Applications received are considered by the trustees on a monthly basis. Applicants who wish to be advised of the outcome of their application must include an sae. Successful applicants are advised of the trustees' decision at the earliest opportunity.

WHO TO APPLY TO Jon Mills, Secretary and Administrator, The Old School House, Church Lane, Easton, Hampshire SO21 1 EH

CC NO 262109   **ESTABLISHED** 1970

■ Miss E B Wrightson's Charitable Settlement

WHERE FUNDING CAN BE GIVEN UK.

WHO CAN BENEFIT Organisations and individual young people with musical talent.

WHAT IS FUNDED The trust makes grants for general charitable purposes, with a preference for inshore rescue services, multiple sclerosis causes and young people with musical talent. It primarily supports individuals, but applications can also be made by groups and charities seeking funding for the advancement of music education and recreational charitable objects.

SAMPLE GRANTS CORDA (£5,000); and Chernobyl Children's Charity (£2,000).

FINANCES *Year* 2007–08 *Income* £42,315 *Grants* £26,347 *Assets* £1,365,185

TRUSTEES A Callard; Mrs E Clarke; P Dorkings.

OTHER INFORMATION There were 31 grants made in 2007–08, most of which went to individuals.

HOW TO APPLY In writing to the correspondent. Trustees meet regularly to consider applications and 'all properly completed applications are acknowledged'. Guidelines are provided by the trust for applications by individuals, but not organisations.

WHO TO APPLY TO Mrs N Hickman, Swangles Farm, Cold Christmas Lane, Thundridge, Ware SG12 7SP

CC NO 1002147   **ESTABLISHED** 1990

■ Wychdale Ltd

WHERE FUNDING CAN BE GIVEN UK and abroad.

WHO CAN BENEFIT Jewish people.

WHAT IS FUNDED Jewish educational institutions.

WHAT IS NOT FUNDED Non-Jewish organisations are not supported.

SAMPLE GRANTS Dajtrain Ltd (£28,000); United Ttalmudical Associates (£24,000); the Society of Friends of the Torah (£18,000); Chevras Mo'oz Ladol (£16,000); and Tomchei Sharei Zion (£10,000).

FINANCES *Year* 2007–08 *Income* £148,515 *Grants* £145,155 *Assets* £956,965

TRUSTEES C D Schlaff; J Schlaff; Mrs Z Schlaff.

HOW TO APPLY In writing to the correspondent.

WHO TO APPLY TO The Secretary, 89 Darenth Road, London N16 6EB

CC NO 267447   **ESTABLISHED** 1974

■ Wychville Ltd

WHERE FUNDING CAN BE GIVEN UK.

WHO CAN BENEFIT Organisations benefiting Jewish people.

WHAT IS FUNDED Jewish organisations and general charitable purposes.

FINANCES *Year* 2007–08 *Income* £370,976 *Grants* £358,365 *Assets* £78,127

TRUSTEES B Englander, Chair; Mrs S Englander; E Englander; Mrs B R Englander.

HOW TO APPLY In writing to the correspondent.

WHO TO APPLY TO Mrs S Englander, Secretary, 44 Leweston Place, London N16 6RH

CC NO 267584   **ESTABLISHED** 1973

■ The Wyndham Charitable Trust

WHERE FUNDING CAN BE GIVEN UK and developing countries.

WHO CAN BENEFIT Charitable organisations.

WHAT IS FUNDED General charitable purposes.

WHAT IS NOT FUNDED No grants to organisations not known to the trustees, or to any individuals.

RANGE OF GRANTS Up to £10,000.

SAMPLE GRANTS Anti-Slavery International (£11,000); Cancer Research UK (£2,500); The Royal College of Surgeons of England (£2,200); and Fight for Sight (£1,000). Other beneficiaries receiving less than £1,000 each included: International Children's Trust; Stand Up for Africa; Centrepoint; The Stroke Association; RNLI; Newbridge; Hope UK; and Hampshire and the Isle of Wight Air Ambulance.

FINANCES *Year* 2008–09 *Income* £101,646 *Grants* £48,414 *Assets* £720,725

TRUSTEES John Gaselee; Juliet Gaselee.

HOW TO APPLY In writing to the correspondent. The trust stated that unsolicited applications are unlikely to be supported and they do not encourage requests.

WHO TO APPLY TO John Gaselee, Trustee, 34a Westfield Road, Lymington, Hampshire SO41 3QA *email* wyndham_ct@yahoo.co.uk *Website* www.wyndham-ct.org

CC NO 259313   **ESTABLISHED** 1969

■ The Wyseliot Charitable Trust

WHERE FUNDING CAN BE GIVEN UK.

WHO CAN BENEFIT Registered charities only.

WHAT IS FUNDED Medical, especially cancer research and care; welfare; arts organisations, including music, visual arts and literature.

WHAT IS NOT FUNDED Local charities are not supported. No support for individuals; grants are only made to registered charities.

RANGE OF GRANTS Up to £5,000.

SAMPLE GRANTS Alzheimer's Trust, Cystic Fibrosis Trust, New Avenues Youth Project, Oxford Foundation, Royal Marsden Cancer Fund, St Mungo's Trust and Time and Talents Association (£5,000 each); Enham Trust, Cancer Relief Macmillan Fund and Trinity Hospice (£4,000 each); Brain Research Trust and Notting Hill Foundation (£3,500 each); Musicians Benevolent Fund, Vitalise and Vitiligo Society (£3,000 each); and Runnymede Trust (£2,000 each).

FINANCES *Year* 2007–08 *Income* £112,992 *Grants* £105,400 *Assets* £1,905,933

TRUSTEES Jonathan Rose; Emma Rose; Adam Raphael.

HOW TO APPLY In writing to the correspondent; however, note that the trust states that the same charities are supported each year, with perhaps one or two changes. It is unlikely new charities sending circular appeals will be supported and large UK charities are generally not supported.

WHO TO APPLY TO J H Rose, Trustee, 17 Chelsea Square, London SW3 6LF

CC NO 257219   **ESTABLISHED** 1968

■ The Xerox (UK) Trust

WHERE FUNDING CAN BE GIVEN UK.

WHO CAN BENEFIT Usually local or mid-sized organisations benefiting children, young adults, at risk groups, and people who are disabled, disadvantaged by poverty or socially isolated.

WHAT IS FUNDED The advancement of equality of opportunity, working with people who are disabled, disadvantaged or terminally ill; and young people.

WHAT IS NOT FUNDED No grants to individuals, religious or political organisations or national bodies.

TYPE OF GRANT One-off grants.

SAMPLE GRANTS Beating Bowel Cancer (£8,000); Ataxia-Telangiectasie Society and Disabled Online (£5,000 each); Hemel Hempstead Explorer Scouts and the Elizabeth Foundation (£1,000 each); Deafblind UK (£500); and MacMillan Cancer Support (£200).

FINANCES *Year* 2006–07 *Income* £61,355 *Grants* £62,731 *Assets* £803,293

TRUSTEES F J Mooney; Mrs J M Robertson; J Hopwood.

HOW TO APPLY In writing to the correspondent, preferably supported by a Xerox employee. Applications are considered in April and October, for payment in June and December respectively.

WHO TO APPLY TO John Barratt, Trust Adminstrator, Xerox Ltd, Bridge House, Oxford Road, Uxbridge UB8 1HS *Tel* 01895 251133

CC NO 284698   **ESTABLISHED** 1982

■ Yankov Charitable Trust

WHERE FUNDING CAN BE GIVEN Worldwide.

WHO CAN BENEFIT Jewish organisations.

WHAT IS FUNDED 'The advancement of the Jewish religion and culture among the Jewish community throughout the world.'

SAMPLE GRANTS European Yarchei Kalloh (£53,000); Keren Machzikei Torah (£23,000); Kollel Tiferes Chaim (£21,000); Agudas Israel Housing Association (£12,000); Ponovez Hachnosos Kalloh (£7,600); Freiman Appeal (£7,200); Beth Jacob Grammar School (£4,000); British Friends of Tiferes Chaim (£3,000); Yeshiva Tzemach Yisroel (£2,000); British Friends of Rinat Ahsron (£1,500); and Yeshivat Givat Shaul (£1,000).

FINANCES *Year* 2007–08 *Income* £196,280 *Grants* £160,377 *Assets* £149,806

TRUSTEES J Schonberg; Mrs B S Schonberg.

HOW TO APPLY In writing to the correspondent.

WHO TO APPLY TO The Trustees, 40 Wellington Avenue, London N15 6AS

CC NO 1106703   **ESTABLISHED** 2004

■ The Yapp Charitable Trust

WHERE FUNDING CAN BE GIVEN England and Wales.

WHO CAN BENEFIT It is the trustees' policy to focus their support on smaller charities (local rather than UK), and to offer grants only in situations where a small grant will make a significant difference. The trust therefore only considers applications from charities whose normal turnover is less than £60,000 in the year of application. Grants are only made to applicants who have charitable status. 'We concentrate on sustaining existing work rather than funding new work because many funders prefer new projects.'

WHAT IS FUNDED Older people; children and young people aged 5–25; people with disabilities or mental health problems; moral welfare, e.g. people trying to overcome life-limiting problems such as addiction, relationship difficulties, abuse or a history of offending; education and learning (including lifelong learning); and scientific or medical research. The trust gives priority to work that is unattractive to the general public or unpopular with other funders, particularly when it helps improve the lives of marginalised, disadvantaged or isolated people. Within these areas the trust gives preference to charities that can demonstrate the effective use of volunteers. Grant-making policies are kept under review – current priorities and exclusions are publicised on the trust's website.

WHAT IS NOT FUNDED 'We do not accept applications from: (i) Scotland and Northern Ireland – your charity must work in England or Wales; (ii) charities whose total annual expenditure is more than £60,000; (iii) charities that are not registered with the Charity Commission in England and Wales – you must have your own charity number or be excepted from registration (Industrial and Provident Societies and Community Interest Companies are not eligible to apply); (iv) branches of national charities – you must have your own charity number, not a shared national registration; (v) new

organisations – you must have been operating as a fully constituted charity for at least three years, even though you may have registered as a charity more recently. We do not make grants for: (i) new work – we provide continuation funding to sustain existing work that has been happening for at least a year (we do not offer grants to launch new or additional activities nor to put on special events); (ii) we do not offer funding to create new paid posts even if the work is now being done by volunteers; (iii) capital-type expenditure – equipment, buildings, renovations, furnishings, minibuses. (iv) work with under-5s; (v) childcare; (vi) holidays and holiday centres; (vii) core funding of general community organisations such as community associations, community centres and general advice services, because some of their work is outside our charitable objects: (viii) bereavement support: (ix) debt advice; (x) community safety initiatives; (xi) charities raising money to give to another organisation, such as schools, hospitals or other voluntary groups (xii) individuals – including charities raising funds to purchase equipment for or make grants to individuals.'

TYPE OF GRANT Running costs and salaries.

RANGE OF GRANTS Grants are normally for a maximum of £3,000 per year. Most grants are for more than one year because priority is given to ongoing needs.

FINANCES *Year* 2007–08 *Income* £329,917 *Grants* £500,570 *Assets* £5,022,919

TRUSTEES David Aeron-Thomas; Revd Timothy C Brooke; Annette Figueiredo; Peter G Murray; Stephanie Willats.

OTHER INFORMATION The Yapp Welfare Trust (two-thirds share) and The Yapp Education and Research Trust (one-third share) merged in September 1999 to become The Yapp Charitable Trust.

HOW TO APPLY 'We have a simple application form which we ask you to send in by post, together with a copy of your most recent annual report and accounts and any other information you wish to send. Applications are processed continuously. When we receive your application we will be in touch, usually within two weeks: to ask for more information; or to tell you the application will be going forward to the next stage of assessment and give an idea of when you can expect a decision; or to let you know we can't help. The time it takes to process an application and make a grant is usually between two months and six months. We always write to let you know the decision. We will accept an application only once each year and you can have only one grant at a time from us. Current grant-holders may make a new application when their grant is coming to an end. If we refused your last application you must wait a year before applying again. The application form and guidelines can be downloaded in Word or pdf format from the trust's website. Alternatively they can be obtained from the trust's administrator.'

WHO TO APPLY TO Mrs Margaret Thompson, Administrator, 47a Paris Road, Scholes, Holmfirth HD9 1SY *Tel* 01484 683403 *email* info@yappcharitabletrust.org.uk *Website* www.yappcharitabletrust.org.uk

CC NO 1076803   **ESTABLISHED** 1999

■ The Yardley Great Trust

WHERE FUNDING CAN BE GIVEN The ancient parish of Yardley now part of the County of West Midlands. This includes the wards of Yardley, Acocks Green, Fox Hollies, Billesley, Hall Green and parts of the wards of Hodge Hill, Shard End, Sheldon, Small Heath, Sparkhill, Moseley, Stechford, Sparkbrook and Brandwood. (A map is available on request.).

WHO CAN BENEFIT Individuals and organisations benefiting people of all ages in the ancient parish of Yardley in Birmingham.

WHAT IS FUNDED Individuals in need, hardship or distress. Projects which benefit the community, particularly charities working in the fields of support for voluntary and community organisations, community centres and village halls, community transport, day centres, holidays and outings, meals provision and play schemes.

TYPE OF GRANT Usually one-off. Buildings, capital, feasibility studies, project and start-up costs funded for one year or less will be considered.

RANGE OF GRANTS £100–£8,000.

SAMPLE GRANTS Holy Cross (£8,000); Springfield Project (£5,000); Gospel Oak (£3,000); Freshwinds (£1,000); Birmingham Volunteers (£500); and Greswold Gardens residents (£300).

FINANCES *Year* 2008 *Income* £1,641,630 *Grants* £81,520 *Assets* £5,277,907

TRUSTEES Mrs I Aylin, Chair; A Beach; A J Boden; Revd A Bullock; Mrs J Holt; Cllr Mrs B Jackson; C James; R B W Lowndes; Revd Dr J Ormoyajowo; Revd J Ray; Revd J Richards; K Rollins; Revd J Self; Revd D Senior.

OTHER INFORMATION In 2008 grants were also made to individuals of less than £600 each amounting to £2,400 and included £1,800 given as Christmas money to local residents.

HOW TO APPLY On a form available from the correspondent. Applications from individuals should be via a third party. Applications are considered on the second Thursday of each month.

WHO TO APPLY TO Mrs K L Grice, Clerk to the Trustees, Old Brookside, Yardley Fields Road, Stechford, Birmingham B33 8QL *Tel* 0121 784 7889 *Fax* 0121 785 1386 *email* enquiries@ygtrust.org.uk *Website* www.yardley-great-trust.org.uk

CC NO 216082   **ESTABLISHED** 1355

■ The Dennis Alan Yardy Charitable Trust

WHERE FUNDING CAN BE GIVEN Overseas and UK with a preference for the East Midlands.

WHO CAN BENEFIT Major UK and international charities.

WHAT IS FUNDED General charitable purposes.

WHAT IS NOT FUNDED No grants to individuals or non-registered charities.

FINANCES *Year* 2007–08 *Income* £35,758 *Grants* £33,250 *Assets* £567,373

TRUSTEES Dennis Alan Yardy, Chair; Mrs Christine Anne Yardy; Jeffrey Creek; Mrs Joanne Stoney.

HOW TO APPLY In writing to the correspondent.

WHO TO APPLY TO The Secretary, PO Box 5039, Spratton, Northampton NN6 8YH

CC NO 1039719   **ESTABLISHED** 1993

■ The W Wing Yip and Brothers Foundation

WHERE FUNDING CAN BE GIVEN Birmingham, Manchester, Croydon and Cricklewood.

WHO CAN BENEFIT Chinese organisations benefiting children, young adults, students and people disadvantaged by poverty.

WHAT IS FUNDED Chinese organisations especially those concerned with education, relief of poverty, Chinese students, and education of Chinese children living in the above stated areas.

TYPE OF GRANT One-off, project and start-up costs. Funding for up to two years will be considered.

SAMPLE GRANTS Heung Yee Kuk Foundation (£30,000); Churchill College Cambridge (£17,000); Birinus St Joseph's Community Project (£10,000); Overseas Chinese Association School (£3,000); Chinese Education Cultural Community Centre (£2,500); and South Wales Chinese School (£2,000).

FINANCES *Year* 2007–08 *Income* £145,669 *Grants* £172,340 *Assets* £1,235,403

TRUSTEES Robert A Brittain; Ms Jenny Loynton; Git Ying Yap; Hon Yuen Yap; Lee Sing Yap; Brian J Win Yip; Woon Wing Yip.

HOW TO APPLY In writing to the correspondent.

WHO TO APPLY TO Robert A Brittain, Trustee, W Wing Yip PLC, The Wing Yip Centre, 375 Nechells Park Road, Nechells, Birmingham B7 5NT *Tel* 0121 327 6618 *Fax* 0121 327 6612

CC NO 326999   **ESTABLISHED** 1986

■ York and North Yorkshire Community Foundation

WHERE FUNDING CAN BE GIVEN York and North Yorkshire.

WHO CAN BENEFIT Charities and community groups.

WHAT IS FUNDED Health and social welfare.

FINANCES *Year* 2007–08 *Income* £716,000 *Grants* £530,000

TRUSTEES Wendy Bundy, Chair; Colin Stroud; John Webster; Christine Bainton; Hon. Judge John Behrens; Michael Benson; Fred Brown; Geoffrey Brownlee; Lady Clarissa Collin; Michael Holford; Philip Ingham; Susan Winterburn.

HOW TO APPLY The foundation's website has details of the grant schemes currently being administered and how to apply.

WHO TO APPLY TO Jan Norton, Grants Manager, Primrose Hill, Buttercrambe Road, Stamford Bridge, York YO41 1AW *Tel* 01759 377400 *email* office@ynycf.org.uk *Website* www.ynycf.org.uk

CC NO 1084043   **ESTABLISHED** 2000

■ The York Children's Trust

WHERE FUNDING CAN BE GIVEN Within 20 miles of York City.

WHO CAN BENEFIT Individuals; group-based organisations; local groups and schools benefiting people under 25 years of age, parents and children; one-parent families; at risk groups; people with disabilities; people disadvantaged by poverty, and people fostering talents in music, drama and athletic activities.

WHAT IS FUNDED Voluntary groups helping in the care and development of young people through arts, culture and recreation, healthcare, education and community services; support of individuals with special needs.

Think carefully about every application. Is it justified?

967

WHAT IS NOT FUNDED The trust will not normally give grants for private education fees. Exceptions may be made where unforeseen circumstances, such as the death of a parent, would prevent a child completing the last year of a critical stage of education such as A-levels.

SAMPLE GRANTS City of York Council (£13,000); York Scout Joint Trust (£5,000); Yearsley Bridge Gateway Club (£1,500); and Henshaws Society for Blind People (£1,000).

FINANCES *Year* 2007 *Income* £98,683 *Grants* £38,897 *Assets* £2,346,464

TRUSTEES R W Miers, Chair; and fifteen others.

OTHER INFORMATION In addition, £26,000 was given in grants to 99 individuals.

HOW TO APPLY In writing to the correspondent.

WHO TO APPLY TO H G Sherriff, Secretary, 29 Whinney Lane, Harrogate, North Yorkshire HG2 9LS *Tel* 01423 524765 *email* yorkchildrenstrust@hotmail.co.uk

CC NO 222279   **ESTABLISHED** 1976

■ Yorkshire Agricultural Society

WHERE FUNDING CAN BE GIVEN Yorkshire and Humbershire; occasionally extending into Durham, Northumberland and the former county of Cleveland.

WHO CAN BENEFIT Primarily local activities and organisations, particularly those in farming and related industries, and those living in rural areas. Priority is given to charities in Yorkshire and former Cleveland, with some activities extending into Durham and Northumberland.

WHAT IS FUNDED (a) Promotion of agriculture and allied industries, related research and education. (b) Protection and safeguarding of the environment. (c) Holding of an annual agricultural show. (d) Appropriate charitable purposes. Environmental projects normally require relevance to agriculture to attract support. The trust will consider giving support to religious umbrella bodies, schools and colleges, and rural crime prevention schemes, all within the context of farming and the rural economy.

WHAT IS NOT FUNDED No support to students. Overseas projects are seldom supported.

TYPE OF GRANT Most usually once only or starter/pump priming finance. Buildings, capital, core costs, feasibility studies, projects, research, running costs, recurring costs and salaries will be considered. Funding may be given for up to three years.

RANGE OF GRANTS £200–£10,000, typical grant under £1,000.

SAMPLE GRANTS Farming Wildlife Advisory Group and Nuffield Scholarship (£8,000 each); Teeside University (£6,000); East Yorkshire Young Farmers (£3,000); Oxford Farming Conference (£2,500); and National Pony Society (£1,000).

FINANCES *Year* 2008 *Income* £6,340,376 *Grants* £48,510 *Assets* £21,625,238

TRUSTEES Mrs C Bromet; R W Twiddle; W M Cowling; J J E Brennan; S F O Theakson; J D M Stoddart-Scott; R E H Vyse.

PUBLICATIONS Quarterly newsletter.

OTHER INFORMATION Grants were also made to individuals totalling £55,750.

HOW TO APPLY In writing to the correspondent, to be considered quarterly. Applications should include accounts, proposed budget, details of confirmed and anticipated funding and ongoing management and costs.

WHO TO APPLY TO N Pulling, Chief Executive, Great Yorkshire Showground, Harrogate HG2 8PW *Tel* 01423 541000 *Fax* 01423 541414 *email* info@yas.co.uk *Website* www.yas.co.uk

CC NO 513238   **ESTABLISHED** 1837

■ Yorkshire Building Society Charitable Foundation

WHERE FUNDING CAN BE GIVEN UK, with a preference for grant making in branch localities.

WHO CAN BENEFIT Charitable organisations/good causes meeting foundation criteria.

WHAT IS FUNDED General charitable purposes/specific items to maximum donation of £2,000.

WHAT IS NOT FUNDED The foundation is unable to support: contributions towards large funds; expenses/fees/salaries, administration, research, sponsorship of individuals and events; advancement of religious/political activities including specific sectors of the community; mainstream schools and other local/government funded bodies.

TYPE OF GRANT Money for specific items.

RANGE OF GRANTS Maximum of £2,000.

SAMPLE GRANTS Whiz Kids (£90,000); Huddersfield and Calderdale Special Care Baby Unit (£10,000); the Butterfly Project (£3,000); Stick N Step (£2,500); Happy Wanderers Ambulance Organisation and Manorlands Hospice and Refuge (£2,000 each); and Christies NHS Foundation Trust and Bradford Toy Library (£1,500 each).

FINANCES *Year* 2008–09 *Income* £415,720 *Grants* £376,772 *Assets* £333,613

TRUSTEES C J Faulkner; Miss L S Will; Mrs S Wildon; Mrs J Lee; J Watson.

HOW TO APPLY Please contact the branch closest to you who will be able to help with an initial assessment of your application. Alternatively, if there isn't a local branch near you, details can be sent direct to head office for consideration. Application forms can be downloaded from the society's website.

WHO TO APPLY TO The Charitable Foundation Team, Yorkshire House, Yorkshire Drive, Bradford, West Yorkshire BD5 8LJ *Tel* 0845 1 200100 *Fax* 01274 472251 *email* charitable@ybs.co.uk *Website* www.ybs.co.uk

CC NO 1069082   **ESTABLISHED** 1998

■ The South Yorkshire Community Foundation

WHERE FUNDING CAN BE GIVEN South Yorkshire wide, with specific reference to Barnsley, Doncaster, Rotherham, Sheffield.

WHO CAN BENEFIT Community and voluntary organisations benefiting people disadvantaged by poverty children and young people.

WHAT IS FUNDED General charitable purposes, particularly social welfare.

WHAT IS NOT FUNDED Groups that have substantial unrestricted funds, national charities, activities promoting political or religious beliefs or where people are excluded on political or religious grounds, statutory bodies e.g. schools, local councils, colleges, projects outside of South Yorkshire, endowments, small contributions to large projects, projects for personal profit, minibuses or other vehicle purchases, projects that have already happened, animals, sponsorship and fundraising events.

TYPE OF GRANT The main grants programme is for amounts under £1,000. Capital and revenue costs. South Yorkshire Key Fund grants are for similar purposes for larger amounts.

RANGE OF GRANTS Generally up to £10,000.

SAMPLE GRANTS Monk Bretton Cricket Club (£103,000 in total); North Barnsley Partnership (£65,000 in total); Stainforth Community Partnership (£45,000); Friends of Thornhill School (£18,200 in total); Kiveton Park & Wales Community Development Fund (£16,200); Somali Special Needs Scheme (£12,000 in total); Roughwood Primary School (£11,000); Doncaster Rowing Club (£7,000); Carterknowle and Burngreave Youth Club Group (£6,000); Shiregreen Children & Families Project (£5,000); Owls Trust All Stars (£4,600); Sheffield Disabled Fishing Group (£3,000); Tinsley Parent and Children's Consortium (£2,000); and Beighton Welfare Recreation Ground (£1,500).

FINANCES *Year* 2007–08 *Income* £3,643,909 *Grants* £2,700,000 *Assets* £2,502,652

TRUSTEES Jonathan Hunt, Chair; David Moody; Sir Hugh Neill; Peter W Lee; Martin P W Lee; Peter Hollis; Isadora Aiken; Frank Carter; Jackie Drayton; Galen Ives; Christopher Jewitt; Michael Mallett; Sue Scholey; Maureen Shah; Allan Sherriff; Lady R Sykes; R J Giles Bloomer; Timothy M Greenacre; Allan Jackson; Jane Kemp; Jane Marshall.

HOW TO APPLY Applications are made by completing a simple form, available for download from the foundation's website.

WHO TO APPLY TO Pauline Grice, Chief Executive, Unit 3 – G1 Building, 6 Leeds Road, Attercliffe, Sheffield S9 3TY *Tel* 0114 242 4294 *Fax* 0114 242 4605 *email* grants@sycf.org.uk *Website* www.sycf.org.uk

CC NO 517714   **ESTABLISHED** 1986

■ The Yorkshire Dales Millennium Trust

WHERE FUNDING CAN BE GIVEN The Yorkshire Dales.

WHO CAN BENEFIT Voluntary organisations, community groups, farmers and other individuals, Yorkshire Dales National Park Authority, estates, National Trust, parish councils, district councils and English Nature.

WHAT IS FUNDED The conservation and regeneration of the natural and built heritage and community life of the Yorkshire Dales, for example, planting new and restoring old woods, the restoration of dry stone walls and field barns, conservation of historical features and community projects.

FINANCES *Year* 2007–08 *Income* £1,353,632 *Grants* £786,393 *Assets* £648,891

TRUSTEES Joseph Pearlman; Carl Lis; Brian Braithwaite-Exley; Colin Speakman; Dorothy Fairburn; Hazel Waters; David Sanders Rees-Jones; Jane Roberts; Peter Charlesworth; Steve Macaré David Joy; Thomas Wheelwright; Lesley Emin; Margaret Billing; Michael Ackrel; Andrew Campbell.

HOW TO APPLY In writing to the correspondent.

WHO TO APPLY TO David Sharrod, Director, The Old Post Office, Main Street, Clapham, Lancaster LA2 8DP *Tel* 01524 251002 *Fax* 01524 251150 *email* info@ydmt.org *Website* www.ydmt.org

CC NO 1061687   **ESTABLISHED** 1996

■ The Yorkshire Historic Churches Trust

WHERE FUNDING CAN BE GIVEN Yorkshire (the historic county of Yorkshire before local government reorganisation in 1974).

WHO CAN BENEFIT All Christian churches.

WHAT IS FUNDED The repair, restoration, preservation and maintenance of churches in the area stated above.

WHAT IS NOT FUNDED No grants for the reordering of churches or any other new work including provision of disabled facilities.

TYPE OF GRANT Capital building grants. Funding of up to three years will be considered.

RANGE OF GRANTS £750–£15,000.

SAMPLE GRANTS Selby Abbey (£28,000); Holy Trinity, Batley Carr (£18,000); All Saints, Normanton (£11,000); St John the Baptist, Carnaby (£5,000); St Paul Old Town, Barnsley (£4,000); Our Lady of Lourdes, Hessle (£1,700); and St Barnabas Alwoodley, Leeds (£500).

FINANCES *Year* 2007 *Income* £279,076 *Grants* £195,878 *Assets* £307,423

TRUSTEES C Clarkson; G Binfield; R J Carr-Archer; The Lord Crathorne; Mrs I Cunliffe; The Ven C J Hawthorn; Rt Revd Mgr D Hogan; W Legard; L Lennox; J G H Mackrell; D Quick; S Reynolds; B Smith; W J A Smith; The Very Revd H E C Stapleton; Miss S Weston; R Ogley; Ms C Otton-Goulder; Revd A Holmes.

HOW TO APPLY In writing to the correspondent to obtain an application form.

WHO TO APPLY TO Mrs J V Fotheringham, c/o Ferrey and Mennim, 48 Goodramgate, York YO1 7LF *Tel* 01904 620103 *Fax* 01904 626983 *email* jvf@ferreyandmennim.co.uk

CC NO 700639   **ESTABLISHED** 1988

■ The John Young Charitable Settlement

WHERE FUNDING CAN BE GIVEN UK and overseas.

WHO CAN BENEFIT Charitable organisations.

WHAT IS FUNDED General charitable purposes.

RANGE OF GRANTS £120–£10,000.

SAMPLE GRANTS Caius House (£13,000); the Boulase Smart, Médecins du Monde, Pancreatic Cancer Research Fund, RSBP and St Barnabas Hospice Trust (£5,000 each); Chichester Harbour Trust (£2,000); and Action Aid (£250).

FINANCES *Year* 2007–08 *Income* £453,950 *Grants* £42,550 *Assets* £1,142,911

TRUSTEES J M Young; D P H Burgess.

HOW TO APPLY In writing to the correspondent.

WHO TO APPLY TO The Trustees, c/o Lee Associates, 5 Southampton Place, London WC1A 2DA

CC NO 283254   **ESTABLISHED** 1981

■ The William Allen Young Charitable Trust

WHERE FUNDING CAN BE GIVEN UK, with a preference for south London.

WHO CAN BENEFIT Registered charities.

WHAT IS FUNDED General charitable purposes, with a preference for health and social welfare.

SAMPLE GRANTS Fly Navy Heritage Trust (£40,000); British Benevolent Fund of Madrid (£15,000); Southwark Cathedral (£11,000); Queen Alexandra Home (£7,000); Anti-Slavery International, the Ness Foundation and St Margaret's Yeovil Hospice (£5,000 each); the Ebbisham Association (£3,500); Shaftesbury Young People (£2,000); Association of

Children's Hospices, Battersea Dogs and Cats Home and Lowe Syndrome Trust (£1,000 each); and Diabetes UK (£500).

FINANCES *Year* 2007–08 *Income* £364,115 *Grants* £416,660 *Assets* £16,158,758

TRUSTEES T F B Young; J G A Young; T Sligo-Young.

HOW TO APPLY The trust has stressed that all funds are committed and consequently unsolicited applications will not be supported.

WHO TO APPLY TO Torquil Sligo-Young, Trustee, Young & Co.'s Brewery PLC, Riverside House, 26 Osiers Road, London SW18 1NH

CC NO 283102   **ESTABLISHED** 1978

■ The John K Young Endowment Fund

WHERE FUNDING CAN BE GIVEN Edinburgh.

WHO CAN BENEFIT Registered charities.

WHAT IS FUNDED Grants are given to support medical and surgical research and research in chemistry as an aid to UK industry. Also to fund charities which are concerned with the physical wellbeing of the young people of Edinburgh or with restoring people who are sick to health.

WHAT IS NOT FUNDED No grants to individuals or non-registered charities.

TYPE OF GRANT One-off grants are awarded. Funding is available for up to one year.

RANGE OF GRANTS £500–£2,000.

SAMPLE GRANTS Alzheimer's Scotland, Kidney Kids Scotland and Tommy's (£2,000 each); Alzheimer's Research Trust, British Institute for Brian Injured Children, Capability Scotland, Maggie's Cancer Caring Centres and Lee Smith Foundation (£1,000 each); Bethany Christian Trust and Fairbridge in Scotland (£1,500 each); and Guide Dogs for the Blind Association, PBC Foundation and Youth Scotland (£500 each).

FINANCES *Year* 2007–08 *Income* £39,030 *Grants* £34,000 *Assets* £1,064,206

TRUSTEES A J R Ferguson; R J S Morton; Mrs S F J Judson; D J Hamilton.

HOW TO APPLY In writing to the correspondent. Trustees meet to consider grants in the autumn.

WHO TO APPLY TO The Trust Administrator, Skene Edwards WS, 5 Albyn Place, Edinburgh EH2 4NJ

SC NO SC002264

■ The Young Foundation

WHERE FUNDING CAN BE GIVEN UK.

WHO CAN BENEFIT Charities, social enterprises, government funded initiatives and for-profit businesses.

WHAT IS FUNDED Innovative new ideas which meet the following objectives: the relief of needs arising from financial hardship, mental or physical illness, disability, or old age; the promotion of equality and diversity through research and the design and delivery of services that address exclusion; the promotion of health; and the promotion of research and education.

TYPE OF GRANT Start-up grants/investments; project funding.

RANGE OF GRANTS Up to £100,000.

SAMPLE GRANTS Healthy Incentives: Active Community Living; Neuroresponse; Plan My Care; Supportmyparent.com; Faking It; Teach Too; Studio Schools; and Arrival Education. No grant figures were available.

FINANCES *Year* 2007 *Income* £2,488,755 *Grants* £607,881 *Assets* £5,179,002

TRUSTEES Marcial Boo; Peter S W Wheeler; Dr Kate Gavron; Margaret K Tait; Kevin O'Sullivan;

Malcolm Dean; Edward M Mayo; Michele Giddens; Prof. Paul Dolan; Dalwardin Babu.

HOW TO APPLY Each programme has a separate application process and the foundation advises potential beneficiaries to read all the relevant guidelines before applying. Information on application deadlines is available on the foundation's website. The foundation expects to notify all applicants within two weeks of the deadline. Please note: the foundation states that it will only be able to provide feedback on applications which make it through to their initial shortlist.

WHO TO APPLY TO Andrew Brough, Launchpad Head of Fund Development, 18 Victoria Park Square, Bethnal Green, London E2 9PF *Tel* 020 8980 6263 *Fax* 020 8981 6719 *email* launchpad@ youngfoundation.org *Website* www. youngfoundation.org.uk

CC NO 274345   **ESTABLISHED** 1977

■ Youth Music

WHERE FUNDING CAN BE GIVEN England.

WHO CAN BENEFIT Music organisations, singing groups, nursery schools, nursery departments of large organisations, schools, after-school clubs, youth groups, recording studios, local authority departments and other organisations providing music-making opportunities to children and young people of any age up to 18.

WHAT IS FUNDED Funding programmes exist on a one-year cycle, targeting a specific element of youth music. Current programmes are: First Steps, which supports music-making activities for 0–5 year olds; Make It Sound, which focuses on music-making for 5–18 year olds who otherwise lack the chance to take part; and Vocalise!, which aims to encourage children and young people to sing, particularly those who would otherwise lack the chance to take part.

WHAT IS NOT FUNDED Funding is not available towards: instrument purchase; individual schools (although work between two or more schools can be supported); individuals; equipment purchases (unless as part of a project, in which case equipment purchases can constitute up to five per cent of the grant); one-off events, including trips; projects lasting less than three months; or work which is a continuation of an existing project rather than new work or a new approach to work already undertaken.

FINANCES *Year* 2007–08 *Income* £20,185,321 *Grants* £9,298,066

TRUSTEES Richard Stilgoe, Chair; David Carrington; Howard Goodall; Menna McGregor; Anthony Blackstock; George Caird; Kathleen Duncan; Tolga Kashif; Sally Osman; Caragh Merrick.

OTHER INFORMATION This trust is funded each year by a £10 million payment from the National Lottery, channelled through Arts Council England.

HOW TO APPLY On a form available from the correspondent, or downloadable from the website. Decisions on whether an application is successful will be made within three months of application, although they must be received by 31 March each year as each programme only has a one-year life span (although they can be continued into the following year). New programmes come into effect on 1 July each year, with information on what can be funded announced on 29 April. The first decisions for each programme are announced on 1 October. It is recommended that potential applicants check the trust's website for up-to-date criteria, priorities and guidelines prior to application.

WHO TO APPLY TO Michael Jones, One America Street, London SE1 0NE *Tel* 020 7902 1060 *Fax* 020 7902 1061 *email* info@youthmusic. org.uk *Website* www.youthmusic.org.uk

CC NO 1075032   **ESTABLISHED** 1999

Elizabeth and Prince Zaiger Trust

WHERE FUNDING CAN BE GIVEN UK, some preference for Somerset, Dorset and the south west.

WHO CAN BENEFIT Registered charities benefiting people of all ages who are mentally and physically disabled and disadvantaged by poverty; registered charities providing care and protection for animals.

WHAT IS FUNDED Relief for older people and people with disabilities; advancement of education; care and protection for animals; relief of poverty and general charitable purposes.

TYPE OF GRANT One-off and recurrent.

RANGE OF GRANTS £1,000–£7,000.

SAMPLE GRANTS Variety Club of Great Britain and St Margaret's Somerset Hospice (£30,000 each); Centre 70 Community Association (£25,000); Brainwave (£20,000); Kids Company (£15,000); Home-Start Taunton Deane Ltd, Neuromuscular Centre and St David's Foundation (£10,000 each); Abbeyfield UK (£7,000); Design & Manufacture for Disability (£6,000); Action Medical Research, Mission Care and Well Being of Yeovil Community Association (£5,000 each); Marie Curie Cancer Care (£4,000); Spinal Injuries Association (£3,000) and Knight's Youth Centre and Woborns Almshouses (£2,000 each).

FINANCES *Year* 2007–08 *Income* £800,903 *Grants* £836,000 *Assets* £14,914,641

TRUSTEES David J Davidge; Peter J Harvey; Derek G Long; David W Parry.

HOW TO APPLY 'The only thing people need to know is that we do not respond to unsolicited applications and it is, therefore, useless and a waste of time and money to contact us.'

WHO TO APPLY TO David W Parry, Trustee, 6 Alleyn Road, Dulwich, London SE21 8AL

CC NO 282096   **ESTABLISHED** 1981

Zambia Paul Foundation

WHERE FUNDING CAN BE GIVEN UK and India.

WHO CAN BENEFIT Large organisations, registered charities, colleges and universities benefiting children, young adults and students.

WHAT IS FUNDED Main areas of interest are young people and education.

WHAT IS NOT FUNDED Applications from individuals, including students, are mainly ineligible. Funding for scholarships is made directly to colleges/universities, not to individuals. No expeditions.

RANGE OF GRANTS Usually £100–£3,000.

SAMPLE GRANTS University of Westminster (£300,000); Bloomsbury Books (£25,000); Chance to Shine (£5,000); CAP Foundation (£11,000); Cultural Centre in Kolkata (£5,500); the Shela Dispensary and Victoria and Albert Museum (£5,000 each); St Mary's Paddington Charitable Trust (£4,000); Coran Family (£1,500); World Punjabi Organisation (£1,000); Earth Restoration Service (£200); Victoria and Albert Museum (£100); and Prostate Cancer (£25).

FINANCES *Year* 2007–08 *Income* £885,036 *Grants* £384,623 *Assets* £6,749,036

TRUSTEES Lord Paul; Lady Paul; Hon. Angad Paul; Hon. Anjli Paul; Hon. Ambar Paul; Hon. Akash Paul.

HOW TO APPLY In writing to the trustees at the address above. Acknowledgements are sent if an sae is enclosed. However, the trust has no paid employees and the enormous number of requests it receives creates administrative difficulties.

WHO TO APPLY TO Lord Paul, Trustee, Caparo House, 103 Baker Street, London W1U 6LN

CC NO 276127   **ESTABLISHED** 1978

Zephyr Charitable Trust

WHERE FUNDING CAN BE GIVEN UK and worldwide.

WHO CAN BENEFIT Organisations.

WHAT IS FUNDED The trust's grants are particularly targeted towards three areas: enabling lower income communities to be self-sustaining; the protection and improvement of the environment; providing relief and support for those in need, particularly from medical conditions or social or financial disadvantage.

WHAT IS NOT FUNDED No grants to individuals, expeditions or scholarships.

TYPE OF GRANT Mainly annual 'subscriptions' decided by the trustees.

RANGE OF GRANTS £500–£3,000.

SAMPLE GRANTS Paddington Farm Trust (£10,000); UNICEF (£4,600); Friends of the Earth Trust (£3,000); Crisis and Survival International (£2,500 each); WOMANKIND (£2,100); Karuna Trust, Organic Research Centre – Elm Farm and Tools for Self Reliance (£2,000 each); Quaker Social Action Group (£1,700); and Mind – Brent and Missing People (£1,500 each).

FINANCES *Year* 2007–08 *Income* £87,179 *Grants* £62,000 *Assets* £1,488,917

TRUSTEES Elizabeth Breeze; Roger Harriman; David Baldock; Donald I Watson.

HOW TO APPLY In writing to the correspondent. The trustees usually meet to consider grants in July each year. Unsolicited applications are unlikely to be successful, since the trust makes annual donations to a list of beneficiaries. However, the trust stated that unsolicited applications are considered on a quarterly basis by the trustees and very occasional support is given. Telephone applications are not accepted.

WHO TO APPLY TO The Trust Administrator, Luminary Finance LLP, PO Box 135, Longfield, Kent DA3 8WF

CC NO 1003234   **ESTABLISHED** 1991

The Marjorie and Arnold Ziff Charitable Foundation

WHERE FUNDING CAN BE GIVEN UK, with a preference for Yorkshire, especially Leeds and Harrogate.

WHO CAN BENEFIT There are no restrictions regarding which organisations can benefit.

WHAT IS FUNDED This trust likes to support causes that will provide good value for the money donated by benefiting a large number of people, as well as encouraging others to make contributions to the work. This includes a wide variety of schemes that involve the community at many levels, including education, public places, the arts and helping people who are disadvantaged.

WHAT IS NOT FUNDED No grants to individuals.

TYPE OF GRANT Capital costs and building work are particularly favoured by the trustees.

SAMPLE GRANTS The University of Leeds (£350,000); United Jewish Israel Appeal (£90,000); United Synagogue Youth Charity (£60,000); Leeds Jewish Welfare Board (£36,000); the Chief Rabbinate Charitable Trust, Shabbaton Choir and Wellington College (£10,000 each); Jewish Care Scotland and World Jewish Relief (£5,000 each); Manchester Jewish Federation (£3,000); Footwear Benevolent Society (£2,500); British friends of Hatzolah Israel (£2,000); Benji Hillman Foundation, Jewish Care and Jewish Leadership Council (£1,000 each); Great Ormond Street Hospital (£500); Royal British Legion (£200); Cancer Research UK (£75); Au Israel (£30); and Foundation for the Study of Infant Deaths (£25).

FINANCES *Year* 2007–08 *Income* £1,809,892 *Grants* £664,343 *Assets* £9,589,154

TRUSTEES Mrs Marjorie E Ziff; Michael A Ziff; Edward M Ziff; Mrs Ann L Manning.

HOW TO APPLY In writing to the correspondent. Replies will only be given to a request accompanied by an sae. Please note that funds available from the trust are limited and requests not previously supported are unlikely to be successful. Initial telephone calls are welcome but please note the foregoing comments.

WHO TO APPLY TO Bryan Rouse, Secretary, Town Centre House, The Merrion Centre, Leeds LS2 8LY *Tel* 0113 222 1234

CC NO 249368　　　　**ESTABLISHED** 1964

....

■ Stephen Zimmerman Charitable Trust

WHERE FUNDING CAN BE GIVEN UK.

WHO CAN BENEFIT Jewish organisations.

WHAT IS FUNDED Jewish causes.

SAMPLE GRANTS Previous beneficiaries have included British ORT, Cancer Research, CIS Development Fund, London Youth, Jewish Association of Business Ethics, Jewish Care, Norwood Ltd, RNIB, United Jewish Israel Appeal and United Synagogue.

FINANCES *Year* 2007–08 *Income* £27,093 *Grants* £70,770

TRUSTEES Mrs L J Zimmerman; S Hauswirth; S Zimmerman.

HOW TO APPLY The trust does not respond to unsolicited applications.

WHO TO APPLY TO S Zimmerman, Trustee, 35 Stormont Road, London N6 4NR

CC NO 1038310　　　　**ESTABLISHED** 1994

....

■ The Zochonis Charitable Trust

WHERE FUNDING CAN BE GIVEN UK, particularly Greater Manchester, and overseas, particularly Africa.

WHO CAN BENEFIT Registered charities only.

WHAT IS FUNDED General charitable purposes, with some preference for education and the welfare of children.

WHAT IS NOT FUNDED No grants for individuals.

TYPE OF GRANT One-off and recurrent.

RANGE OF GRANTS £2,500–£150,000.

SAMPLE GRANTS Cancer Research UK (£150,000); Christie Hospital NHS Foundation Trust (£100,000 each); Greater Manchester High Sheriffs Trust (£60,000); Big Issue in the North (£50,000); Manchester YMCA (£35,000); Smile Train (£25,000); Manchester Library Theatre Development Trust (£15,000 each); Concern Worldwide (£12,000); Child Victims of Crime (£10,000); Willow Wood Hospice (£3,000); and CHICKS (£2,500).

FINANCES *Year* 2007–08 *Income* £2,425,318 *Grants* £2,119,700 *Assets* £92,266,613

TRUSTEES Sir John Zochonis; Christopher Nigel Green; Archibald G Calder; Joseph J Swift.

HOW TO APPLY In writing to the correspondent.

WHO TO APPLY TO Ruth Barron, c/o Cobbetts LLP, 58 Mosley Street, Manchester M2 3HZ *Tel* 0845 165 5270 *Fax* 0845 166 6733 *email* ruth. barron@cobbetts.com

CC NO 274769　　　　**ESTABLISHED** 1977

....

■ Zurich Community Trust (UK) Limited

WHERE FUNDING CAN BE GIVEN UK and overseas. Mainly focused around the company's main office locations in Wiltshire, Hampshire and Gloucestershire. Other areas include Birmingham, Brighton, Cardiff, Glasgow, Leeds, London, Manchester, Nottingham, Reigate, Southampton, Sutton, Watford and Wilmslow.

WHO CAN BENEFIT Registered charities, voluntary organisations and non-governmental organisations that help people who are disadvantaged achieve a better quality of life by moving from dependence to independence.

WHAT IS FUNDED National programmes that create sustainable change, tackle issues in disadvantaged areas or work with disadvantaged groups of older people, such as those who are homeless or abused. Projects aiming to break the cycle of generational drug misuse by focussing on children and the family. Work with children under 18 years of age who are disadvantaged.

WHAT IS NOT FUNDED No grants made for: Statutory organisations (including mainstream schools and hospitals), unless exclusively for a special needs unit; Fundraising events including appeals or events for national charities; Expeditions, exchanges or study tours; Playgroups and mother and toddler groups, unless for special needs groups; Medical research, animal welfare charities, conservation or environmental projects; Sports clubs, village halls, political or religious organisations (including the upkeep and repair of places of worship); or Advertising or sponsorship connected with charitable events or appeals.

TYPE OF GRANT One-off, or partnership grants for three to five years; core costs; project costs; revenues; salaries; seed funding; capital.

RANGE OF GRANTS Local grants: £100–£10,000; partnership grants: £20,000–£100,000.

SAMPLE GRANTS Calvert Trust (£67,000); and NSPCC (Childline) and the Foundation for Conductive Education (£25,000 each).

FINANCES *Year* 2008 *Income* £3,560,000 *Grants* £2,062,000 *Assets* £5,083,000

TRUSTEES T P Culling; A C Gillies; D S Hall; E Hopkins; I N Lovett; A Moore; G Munnoch; D P Sims.

OTHER INFORMATION The trust also runs a programme called the Employee Involvement Programme.

HOW TO APPLY In the first instance, visit the trust's website and follow the links to check eligibility and download the guidelines and application forms.

WHO TO APPLY TO Pam Webb, Head of Zurich Community Trust (UK), PO Box 1288, Swindon, Wiltshire SN1 1FL *Tel* 01793 511227 *Fax* 01793 506982 *email* pam.webb@uk.zurich. com *Website* www.zurich.co.uk/zurichcares

CC NO 266983　　　　**ESTABLISHED** 1973